MW00845855

Programmable Logic Controllers:

An Emphasis on Design and Application

Kelvin T. Erickson

University of Missouri–Rolla

Dedicated to Fran, Esther, and David

This book was set in Times New Roman and printed on acid-free paper.

Printed in the United States of America

ISBN 0-9766259-0-3

Dogwood Valley Press, LLC
1604 Lincoln Lane
Rolla, MO 65401
1-573-426-3507

http://www.DogwoodValleyPress.com

10 9 8 7 6 5 4 3 2 1

CONTENTS

PREFACE

The field of automatic control has been undergoing a transformation over the past twenty years. Twenty years ago, the engineering undergraduate had a course in feedback control theory and those interested in control engineering secured a position in the aerospace or chemical industries. Due to various factors, the number of control engineering positions in the aerospace industry has been declining, but the number of control engineering positions in manufacturing has been dramatically increasing to the point that the majority of control engineering positions is now in manufacturing and involves PLCs.

This book presents the subject of programming industrial controllers, called programmable logic controllers (PLCs) with an emphasis on the design of the programs. Many texts teach one how to program the PLC in its languages, but little, if any, attention is paid to how does one attack the problem: "Given a set of operational specifications, how does one develop the PLC program?" This book develops the design process: the tasks involved, breaking the program into manageable pieces, standard code for the various parts, and handling the sequential parts of the problem. The emphasis is toward those who will be programming PLCs.

Because of its popularity (now and in the future), ladder logic is the language that is used for the majority of the text. The industry trend is toward using the IEC 61131-3 (formerly IEC 1131-3) standard, and so it is the primary language. However, IEC 61131-3 is only a voluntary standard and individual manufacturers have some freedom in the implementation. Therefore, the Allen-Bradley ControlLogix, Modicon, and Siemens S7 implementations of the 61131-3 standard are covered. Because of their large installed base, Allen-Bradley PLC-5/SLC-500 and GE Fanuc PLC languages are also covered.

Due to the limitations of ladder logic, the IEC 61131-3 standard defines four other languages: function block diagram, structured text, instruction list, and sequential function chart. These four languages will become more popular in the future. Therefore, this text also covers these languages.

Since a typical manufacturing plant may contain discrete, continuous, and batch processes, all of these applications are treated in this text, although the emphasis is on discrete and continuous processes. The emphasis is on a methodology that can be applied to any automation project, regardless of the size.

Throughout, the book contains example problems demonstrating good design practice. In addition, these problems are solved with each PLC covered in the book. The text culminates in two full-length case studies where the application of the design techniques to a large problem is illustrated.

This book takes a practical approach to the design of PLC control systems. Some mathematical theory is used to backup the presentation on PID controllers. However, the theory is not detailed and can be omitted.

Except for Chapters 1 and 13, every chapter begins with a scenario that reflects the experience of the author and his colleagues in the challenging world of factory automation.

These scenarios present a small problem and the solution and are intended to illustrate troubleshooting techniques.

Objectives

The main objectives of this text are to teach:

- PLC programming languages (with emphasis on IEC 61131-3)
- Approach to sequential problems
- Good program design practice
- Simple PID control tuning
- Introduction to sensors and actuators
- Factory communications
- Human-machine interface (HMI) concepts

Content Overview

The book starts by introducing programmable logic controllers (PLCs) and their distinguishing characteristics. Chapters 2 – 5 cover basic ladder logic programming: contact, timer, and counter instructions. As part of the basics, the memory structure of the five particular PLCs and installation topics are treated. Chapter 6 covers ladder logic program design for sequential applications, probably the most significant contribution of the text. Chapters 7 and 8 treat computation, comparison, and advanced ladder logic instructions. Alternate sequential implementations in ladder logic are covered in Chapter 9 and PID controller tuning is covered in Chapter 10. Chapters 11 – 14 cover the other four IEC programming languages: function block diagram, statement list, instruction list, and sequential function chart. PLC troubleshooting is covered in Chapter 15. Sensors and actuators appear in Chapter 16. Chapter 17 introduces factory communication networks. Operator interface, often called human-machine interface (HMI), issues are treated in Chapter 18. Control system security is addressed in Chapter 19 and PLC selection is introduced in Chapter 20. Chapter 21 presents the perspective of an entire automation project, bringing together the various pieces of PLC control design. Chapter 22 outlines two full-length project case studies. One case study is for a process that is primarily discrete and the other case study is for a process that is primarily continuous in nature. Details about number systems and drawing symbols are included as appendices, rather than interrupt the flow of the text material.

The Audience

This book primarily serves the academic market, at the junior or senior undergraduate electrical, mechanical, or industrial engineering or engineering technology level. This text is also suitable for the two-year technical school market. There is nothing in the material that requires a college degree, though the material will be more challenging than the typical PLC textbook for this level of student.

In addition, this text serves the professional market. Economic and regulatory pressures in the manufacturing, chemical, petrochemical, pharmaceutical, and food industries have forced control engineers to design new systems or retrofit existing control systems. Hence, there are many control engineers (primarily chemical and electrical) who need to rapidly educate themselves in an area of technology in which they are probably only somewhat familiar. This book is valuable to this audience.

Acknowledgements

The author wishes to acknowledge the beneficial suggestions and comments of many colleagues. Steve Ingracia provided the sample panel specification in Chapter 4. Bill Bichler, Dean Ford, and Esther Erickson reviewed drafts of this book and provided many suggestions and corrections to improve the final product. I especially thank Esther and Fran Erickson for correcting the entire manuscript for grammatical errors, and Fran for doing the initial typesetting.

Portions of this material were taught in industrial short courses and university courses and the students are acknowledged for their help in pointing out errors in the text and where the presentation was unclear.

Disclaimer

Information furnished herein is believed to be accurate and reliable; however no responsibility is assumed for any errors. The user assumes full responsibility for the accuracy and appropriateness of this information.

1 Introduction to PLCs

Chapter Topics:

- Control system categories
- History of PLCs
- PLC versus other technologies
- PLC architecture

OBJECTIVES

Upon completion of this chapter, you will be able to understand:

- Two ways to categorize a control system
- PLC history and developments
- The differences between PLC, relay and PC-based control
- Basic PLC architecture

1.1 INTRODUCTION

Programmable logic controllers (PLCs) are definitely the workhorses of modern manufacturing automation. Automatic control allows the production of a consistent product at reasonable cost and the PLC is the most prevalent control technology in manufacturing. In order to establish a context for PLCs, the need for automatic control in manufacturing is justified along with the major ways control systems are classified. The history of the PLC is outlined and placed in the context of the parallel development of computer control in the chemical industry. The use of the PLC in automation is compared with other automation technologies, with special attention to a comparison of PLC versus personal computer-based control. Finally, the architecture of the PLC is described and its place in the context of an automation system is shown.

1.2 AUTOMATIC CONTROL IN MANUFACTURING

There are many reasons automatic control is indispensable to manufacturing. The most important reasons are:

- To improve the quality and lower the cost of production.
- To attain optimal performance.
- To relieve the drudgery of many routine, repetitive manual operations.

Over the last three decades, manufacturing has been receiving more emphasis from the engineering community. To an enterprise, profitability usually depends on productivity and automation is a means towards greater productivity. Usually, the most important question is not, "Should we automate production?" but "What should be automated to increase productivity?"

As an example, throughout the 1950's and 1960's the American automakers were placing their emphasis on the power and style of their automobiles and not on producing a high quality product at the lowest possible cost. The gasoline shortages of the early 1970's forced many people to buy smaller automobiles and they discovered that the small automobiles produced by the Japanese automakers were of better quality and at a lower cost than the equivalent American automobiles. To remain competitive, the American automakers started placing more emphasis on manufacturing quality automobiles at the lowest possible cost and automation was the means toward their goal. This renewed emphasis on manufacturing extended to other industries and will not soon diminish.

The basic elements of an automatic control system are shown in Figure 1.1. A control system has three basic elements:

Input sensors:	Convert physical phenomena (for example, position) to electrical signal.
Programmable Logic Controller:	Using the measurements, calculate control actions.
Output actuators:	Convert electrical signal to a physical action (for example, motor rotation).

In this text, the PLC is the controller, which was initially developed out of the needs of the automotive industry. In the chemical industry, a distributed control system (DCS) is typically used in place of the PLC. As will be shown later, DCS and PLC systems are merging into one device called a programmable electronic system (PES).

1.3 CONTROL SYSTEM CLASSIFICATIONS

Control systems are commonly categorized two ways: (1) type of sensors/actuators, and (2) type of process. Either way is valid, but in certain contexts one is often preferred over the other. For example, many people choose whether to use a PLC versus a DCS based on the type of sensors/actuators.

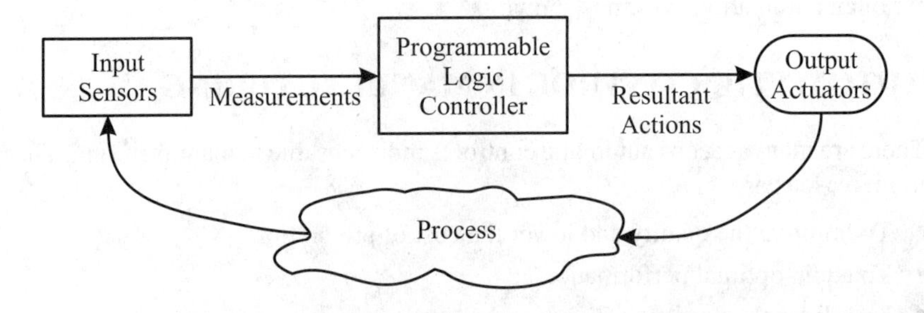

Figure 1.1. Basic elements of an automatic control system.

1.3.1 Type of Sensors/Actuators

When considering the sensor or actuator, there are two major types: (1) discrete, and (2) analog. A discrete control system has mainly discrete sensors and actuators. Similarly, an analog system has mainly analog sensors and actuators. A discrete sensor or actuator has one of two values, for example: on/off, open/closed, present/not present, running/stopped, or extended/retracted. An analog sensor or actuator theoretically has an infinite number of values. For example, an analog sensor value could represent position, velocity, acceleration, temperature, pressure, flow, or weight. An analog actuator value could represent valve position, motor speed (for motor controller), damper position, or strip-chart recorder value. Because an analog sensor or actuator value is converted to an integer value within the input/output (I/O) module, an analog value practically assumes a finite number of values. This point becomes more apparent when analog I/O modules are discussed in Chapter 4.

Bear in mind that most real programmable logic control systems are a combination of analog and discrete elements. For example, Figure 1.2 depicts some of the elements of a heating, ventilation and air conditioning (HVAC) system. The proximity switches that detect the presence of a person in a room are discrete sensors and the control valve for an air solenoid is a discrete actuator. As an example of the PLC operation, the damper is opened whenever anyone is present in the room and closed when no one is present for 15 minutes. The airflow sensor is an analog sensor and the fan motor speed command is an analog actuator signal. The PLC calculates the desired fan speed in order to maintain the airflow at a desired value.

1.3.2 Type of Process

A process is a sequence of chemical, physical, or biological activities for the conversion, transport, or storage of material or energy (ISA, 1995). Industrial manufacturing processes are generally classified as continuous, batch, or discrete-parts manufacturing. This classification stems from the way the output appears: as a continuous flow (continuous); in finite quantities of material (batch); or in finite quantities of parts (discrete-parts manufacturing).

Continuous Process. In a continuous process, material passes in a continuous stream through the processing equipment. Once the process has established a steady operating state, the nature of the process does not depend on the length of time the process is operating

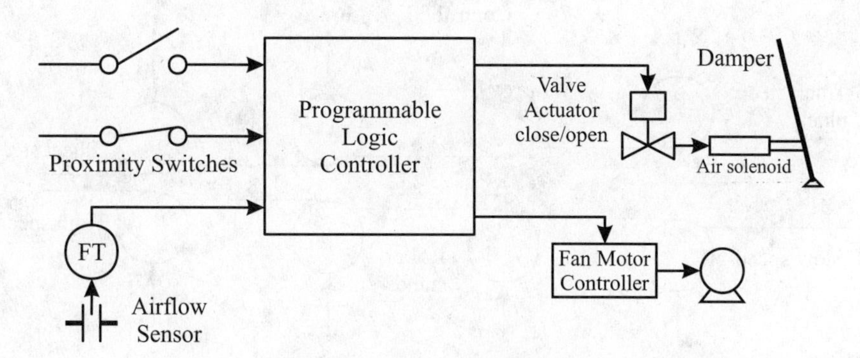

Figure 1.2. Control elements of HVAC system.

(ISA, 1995). Commodity chemical manufacturing typically falls into this category. A continuous steel rolling mill, simplified in Figure 1.3, is an example continuous process. The control system manipulates the force at each stand and the speed of each roller in order to control the thickness and speed of the steel sheet at the exit. As the thickness of the steel sheet is reduced by each roller stand, the speed of the sheet must be increased proportionally to maintain a constant steel mass flow rate. If the last roller stand rotates a little too slow, material will accumulate between the third and fourth stands and eventually cause a jam. If the last roller stand rotates a little too fast, the sheet will be torn. Either scenario is not desirable.

Batch Process. In a batch process, finite quantities (batches) of material are produced by subjecting quantities of input materials to a defined order of processing actions using one or more pieces of equipment. Batch processes are discontinuous processes from a material flow standpoint. Batch processes are neither discrete nor continuous, though they have characteristics of both (ISA, 1995). Food, beverage, pharmaceutical, and specialty chemical processes are usually encompassed by this category. An example of a small batch process is illustrated in Figure 1.4. In this process, ingredients A and B are measured into tanks. Ingredient A is heated to a desired temperature and then the two ingredients are pumped to a third vessel where a chemical reaction occurs. After a certain length of time, the resultant product is pumped through a filter and then on to storage.

Discrete-Parts Manufacturing Process. In a discrete-parts manufacturing process, a specified quantity of material moves as a unit (part or group of parts) between workstations, and each unit maintains its unique identity (ISA, 1995). At a workstation, a unit may be modified (drilled, machined, painted, etc.) or may be combined with one or more other parts (assembly). Packaging operations also fall into this category. An example of a discrete-parts workstation is shown in Figure 1.5. Incoming parts are received on the input conveyor, moved to the drilling station where a few holes are drilled, moved to the computer numerical control (CNC) station where the part is shaped, and then moved to the output conveyor. A simple packaging operation is shown in simplified form in Figure 1.6. An empty carton arrives on the incoming conveyor. When the loading area is clear, the carton is moved into position. The parts are marshaled to form a row and the row is pushed into the carton. The carton is indexed down and succeeding rows of parts are placed in the carton. When fully loaded, the carton is moved out to the next station where the flaps are sealed.

Processes are often primarily one of the three main types, though they often contain at least one of the other types. For example, the output of many batch processes is packaged in

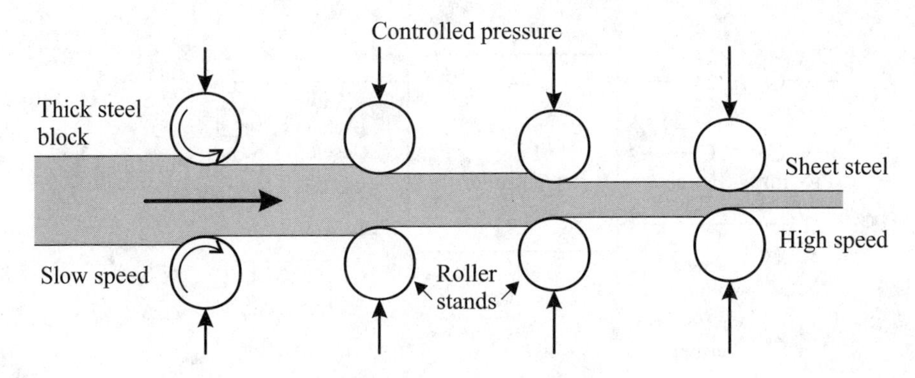

Figure 1.3. Continuous steel rolling mill.

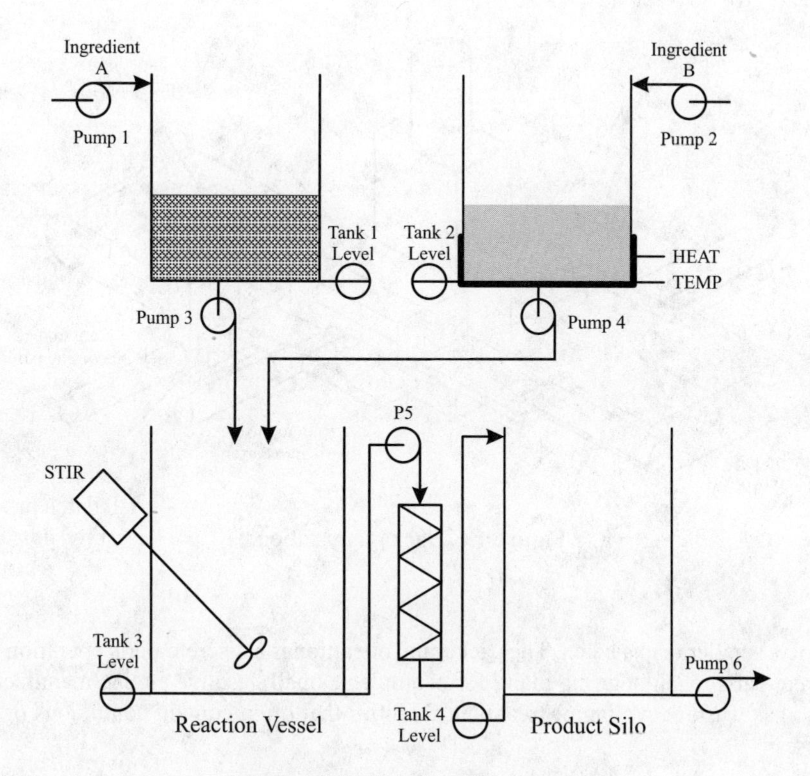

Figure 1.4. Small batch process.

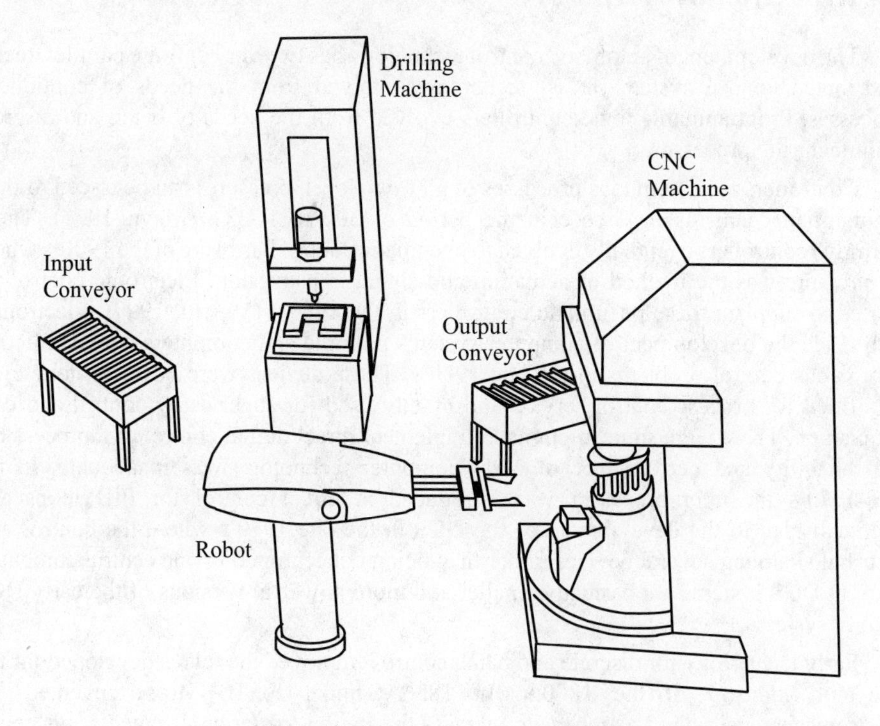

Figure 1.5. Discrete parts workcell.

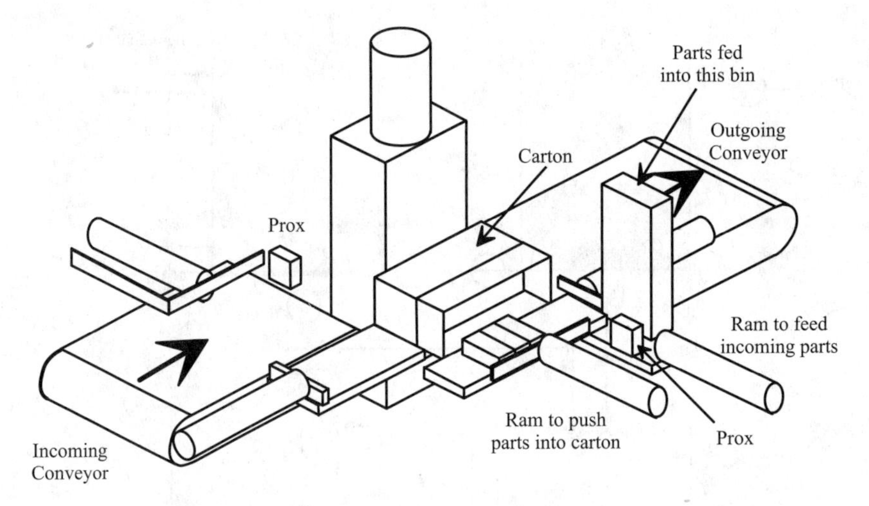

Figure 1.6. Packaging station.

containers smaller than a batch. The packaging operation is a discrete-parts operation. Even a discrete-parts manufacturing plant, for example, a small gasoline engine manufacturing facility, has waste recycling or treatment facilities that often contain continuous or batch processes.

1.4 HISTORY OF THE PLC

The development of automatic control technology has two very definite parallel tracks. Distributed control system (DCS) technology evolved from the needs of continuous processes. Programmable logic controllers evolved from the needs of batch and discrete manufacturing processes.

Controllers for continuous processes (e.g., flow, level, pressure) can be traced to float regulator mechanisms in Greece in the period of 300 to 1 B.C. (Mayr, 1971). These primitive controllers eventually evolved to pneumatic control hardware of the 1900's where air pressure was the method of actuation and signal transmission. Electronic controllers started to supplant these pneumatic controllers in the 1960's (Merritt, 1999). Electronics also made the development of computer systems possible and computers were applied to continuous control problems in the late 1950's. These devices were business computers retrofitted for process control service and mainly used for supervisory control and data acquisition. There were some attempts to implement direct digital control of a process but the reliability and performance of early computer technology was inadequate. In the mid-1970's the microprocessor was introduced in direct control for PID loops and eventually led to the development of the DCS in the late 1970's where the control was distributed among several devices rather than being concentrated in one central computer. Current DCS systems are basically smaller and more powerful versions of the early DCS control systems.

Early technology for discrete and batch control employed the relays developed for the telegraph industry of the 1800's. In 1836 Samuel F. B. Morse invented the electromechanical relay as a means to increase the station-to-station distance of his newly

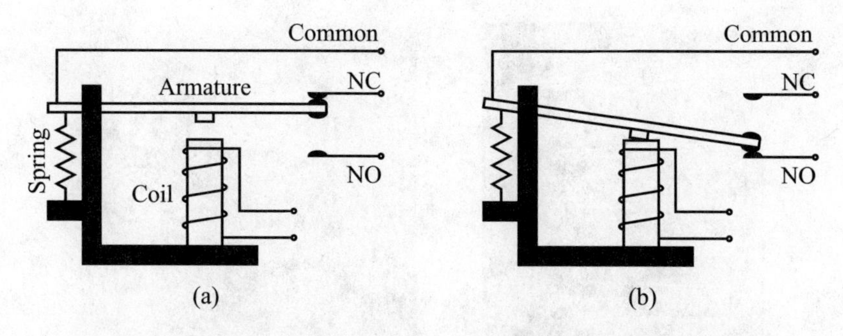

Figure 1.7. Electromechanical relay: *(a)* unenergized; *(b)* energized.

developed telegraph system, then limited to about 20 miles. This electromechanical device sensed the small telegraphic signal current and "relayed" or amplified this signal to carry the information to the next station or relay. An electromechanical relay consists of a coil of wire magnetically coupled to a moveable piece of iron, called an armature (Figure 1.7). A spring holds the armature in its resting position in which there is continuity between the "Common" and "NC" connections (Figure 1.7*a*). When a sufficient current passes through the coil, the armature is forced downward causing continuity to be established between the "Common" and the "NO" connections (Figure 1.7*b*). Eventually, interconnections of electromechanical relays were used to implement logic functions, as explained in Chapter 2.

In concert with electromechanical relays, drum sequencers were developed to control sequential processes, where the operation is expressed as a sequence of steps. An electromechanical drum sequencer (Figure 1.8) is a cylinder with pegs strategically placed to make or break contacts. When the contact is closed, power is applied to relay logic or a final control element. The drum advances one row at a time triggered by an external event. As the drum advances, it makes or breaks control circuits in a pattern prescribed by the position of each peg in a row.

Relay and sequencer technology remained relatively stagnant until the late 1960's. The only real change was the replacement of electromechanical relays with solid-state (electronic) relays in the 1960's. Computers were tried but were even less reliable than relay systems because of the harsh environment of the typical factory. A state-of-the-art manufacturing control system consisted of racks of relays (Figure 1.9*a*) whose wiring was documented by drawings called relay ladder logic diagrams (Figure 1.10). Relay systems

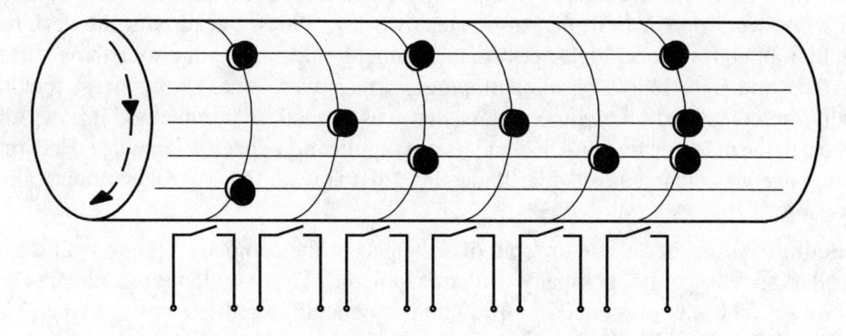

Figure 1.8. Electromechanical drum sequencer.

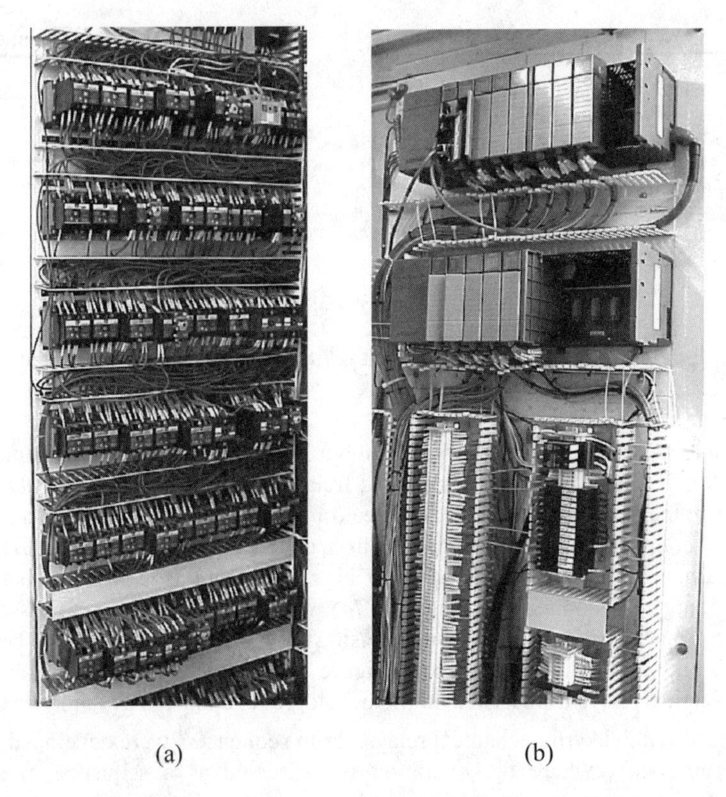

(a) (b)

Figure 1.9. Small control system: *(a)* relay rack; *(b)* PLC replacement.

were maintenance headaches: prone to failure and hard to troubleshoot. In addition, a change to the function of the control system meant a wiring change at a minimum and often meant additional relays.

The machine tool and automotive industries were large users of relay control systems. A simple machine tool would require six months to a year to completely debug (Morley, 2001). Every year, automotive manufacturing facilities would be shut down for two to three months in order to implement the changes due to the new automobile models. The lost production due to these changes was significant.

Richard Morley is credited with inventing the initial concept for the PLC in January, 1968 while working for Bedford Associates (Morley, 2001). Faced with the design of a machine tool control for a high-performance lathe, he decided to try something different from the solid-state relays or minicomputers which were state-of-the-art at that time. Initially, he conceived a machine or box that was rugged, that contained its own direct interface to the machine tool and that had its own application-specific language. Eventually, the language was changed to ladder logic since that is what the control engineers already knew.

Bedford Associates chose to "spin off" the part of the company dealing with this new controller as a separate company called Modicon. The Modicon (MOdular DIgital CONtroller) 084 was introduced in 1969 and is generally credited as the first PLC and proved the concept of the PLC.

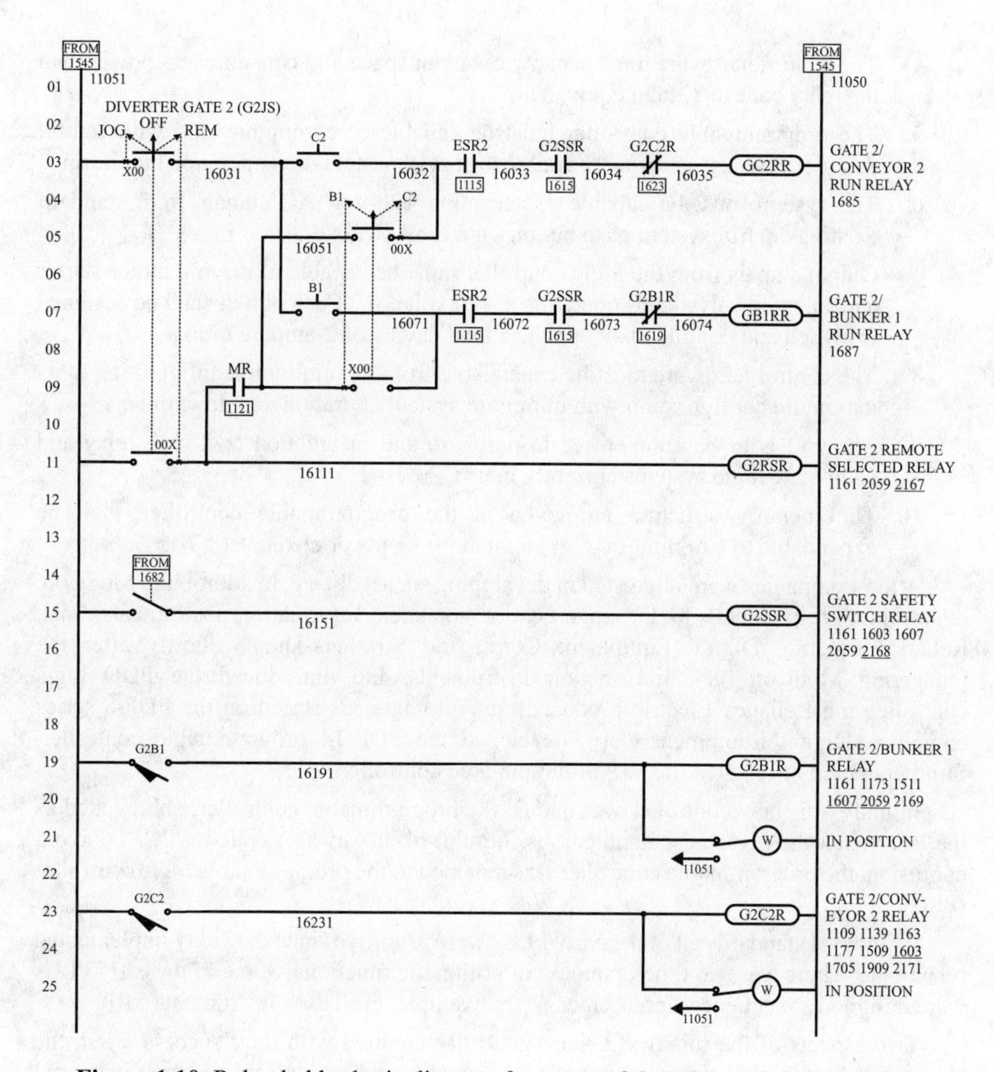

Figure 1.10. Relay ladder logic diagram for a part of the relay rack in Figure 1.9.

In parallel with the developments at Bedford Associates in 1968, a group of engineers at the Hydramatic Division of General Motors specified a controller with similar features (Stone et al, 1968). The GM specification requirements are summarized in the following categories:

1. The control hardware and/or device must be easily and quickly programmed and reprogrammed at the user's facility with a minimum of service interruption.
2. All system components must be capable of operation in industrial plants without special support equipment, hardware, or environments.
3. The system must be easily maintained and repaired. Status indicators and plug-in modularity should be designed into the system to facilitate troubleshooting and repairs with minimum downtime.

4. The control hardware must occupy less plant space and consume less power than the relay control system equivalent.
5. The programmable controller must be capable of communication with central data-collection systems for the purpose of system status and operation monitoring.
6. The system must be capable of accepting 120-volt AC signals from standard existing control system push buttons and limit switches.
7. Output signals from the logic controller must be capable of driving motor starter and solenoid valve loads operating at 120 volts AC. Each output shall be designed to switch and continuously operate a load device of 2-ampere rating.
8. The control hardware must be expandable from its minimum configuration to its maximum configuration with minimum system alteration and downtime.
9. The unit is to be competitive in purchase and installation cost with relay and solid-state logic systems currently in use.
10. The memory structure employed in the programmable controller shall be expandable to a minimum of 4000 memory words or elements.

A few companies were interested in developing such a device. In addition to Modicon, other initial respondents to the specification included Information Instruments, Inc., Reliance Electric, Digital Equipment Corp., and Struthers-Dunn. Shortly after the pioneering Modicon 084, Information Instruments, Inc. introduced the PDQ logic controller and Reliance Electric produced the Automate 33. Based on the PDP-8 series computer, Digital Equipment Corp. developed the PDP-14 programmable controller. Struthers-Dunn introduced the VIP programmable controller.

Initially, this new controller was named the programmable controller, abbreviated as the PC. When the personal computer was introduced, it was also called a PC. To avoid confusion, the programmable controller was renamed to the programmable *logic* controller (PLC).

By today's standards all of the early PLCs were primitive since they only implemented relay logic. There were no timer, counter, or arithmetic functions. Some of the early PLCs were designed as sequencer replacements (for example, the Texas Instruments 510).

Two aspects of the initial PLCs are generally credited with their success. First, the electronic circuits were designed to be highly reliable and to work in the harsh industrial environment. Dick Morley tells the following tale about the Modicon 084 (Morley, 2001):

> Landis [a machine tool company] decided to purchase the MODICON units and not use the PDP-14. When DIGITAL [*sic*] tried to get back into Landis, Landis wrapped a welder cable (operating) around the 084 and poured Coke over the unit. The 084 kept right on trucking. Digital retreated with grace.

Second, the programming language was based on standard electrical relay ladder logic drawings. Some earlier computer applications in manufacturing had failed because the plant technicians and engineers had difficulty learning the computer language. In contrast, most of them already knew relay ladder logic design and so could quickly learn PLC ladder logic.

Though adoption by industry was initially slow, other well-known electrical controls manufacturers began either developing their own PLCs, or reselling someone else's PLC. Of the original five PLC developers, only Digital Equipment Corp. and Struthers-Dunn no longer produce PLCs. Modicon is now a part of AEG Schneider Automation. Information

Instruments, Inc. was later purchased by Allen-Bradley, which is now part of Rockwell Automation. Reliance Electric was also purchased by Rockwell Automation. There are currently over 40 vendors of PLCs (Cleaveland, 1999).

Table 1.1 presents an abbreviated list of PLC developments. From the relatively primitive beginnings, the general trend has been toward more functions, larger memory, and more sophisticated communication.

The initial PLCs used bit-slice processors (e.g., Advanced Micro Devices 2901) to solve the logic. Microprocessors eventually assumed all of the processing functions of the PLC. However, due to the relative slowness of the microprocessor, bit-slice logic-solving co-processors were used on the larger PLCs until the late 1980's. The microprocessor spurred the development of intelligent I/O modules and ever physically smaller PLCs. Currently, the smallest PLC is no larger than a relay and has 6 I/O points.

Table 1.1 PLC Developments

Year	Nature of developments
1968	Initial concept developed
1969	Hardware CPU controller, with logic instructions, 1K of memory and 128 I/O points
1971	First application outside automotive industry
1972	Timing and counting instructions
1973	Arithmetic and data move instructions
	Computer-to-PLC communications
1974	Several processors within a PLC, 12K of memory, 1024 I/O points, CRT programming terminal
1975	PID control
1976	Remote input/output systems
1977	Microprocessor-based small PLC
1978	PLC-to-PLC communications
1980	Intelligent I/O modules
	Enhanced software features (e.g., documentation)
	Program with personal computers
1983	Large PLCs: 4M of memory, 8192 I/O points
1985	GM manufacturing automation protocol (MAP)
1986	Other languages (not ladder logic)
1993	Connection to Ethernet
	IEC 61131-3 standard languages
1994	Standard remote I/O protocols
1996	PC-based control as PLC alternative
2000	IEC 61158 communication networks

The ability of PLCs to communicate appeared in 1973 when Modicon introduced the Modbus communication network. Initially, Modbus was used for computer-to-PLC communication. Other manufacturers soon followed with their proprietary communication networks and also developed remote I/O communication networks. The lack of standardization made it very complicated for a PLC of one vendor to communicate with the PLC of another vendor. In the mid-1980's, General Motors attempted to resolve the situation with the development of GM MAP (manufacturing automation protocol). However, the connection cost of this network was relatively high and thus was never well accepted. Eventually, initial misgivings about using Ethernet in a manufacturing environment were overcome and Ethernet appeared as a communication option for the larger PLCs. Today, even the smallest PLCs can interface to Ethernet. During the 1990's, the Instrument Society of America (ISA) sponsored the development of two communication networks: one suitable for remote I/O and the other for PLC-to-PLC communication. Due to political pressures, this standard (IEC 61158) eventually included eight networks (Amos, 2000). Therefore, the convergence toward one or two standard networks may never happen. Often, the most complicated part of commissioning a system is getting the communication networks and connections properly configured.

Initially, PLC programming was done with a hand-held programmer and eventually with a dedicated CRT programming terminal, both supplied by the PLC vendor. With the advent of the personal computer (PC) in the 1980's, the PLC vendors developed PC-based programming software and operator interface stations. When graphical user interfaces (GUIs) were developed for personal computers, they were also applied to operator interface stations. Since most PLC systems had an operator interface, it seemed natural to also utilize the PC to replace the PLC processor. This type of control system is called PC-based control or a "soft" PLC. The differences between PLCs and PC-based control are considered in the next section.

Listings of the ladder logic program on the early PLCs consisted of the relay and function block symbols and the numbers for the I/O points and memory locations. A maintenance person would require a few months to learn the operation of a reasonably complicated program. In 1980, a small company introduced programming software for the Allen-Bradley PLCs where the user could attach symbols and descriptions to the numeric I/O and memory locations, include comments in the program, and print a cross-reference listing of the program. Today, these documentation features are standard for PLC programming software.

Incorporation of PID control and motion control into the PLC happened slowly. Control schemes for continuous processes utilized PID control and were generally implemented with distributed control systems (DCSs). Nevertheless, analog I/O modules were incorporated into PLC systems in order to read analog values and to output calculated values to the operator panel. Initially, PID control was handled as an intelligent I/O module and the PID control algorithm was executed by the microprocessor on the module. Eventually, PID control was implemented as a function block in the PLC processor. The incorporation of motion control into the PLC processor proceeded along the same lines as for PID control. Initially, it was handled only in separately programmed intelligent I/O modules. This weakness of the PLC-based motion control also spurred the development of PC-based motion control since the PC could handle the sophistication of motion control and were not constrained by the limitations of ladder logic. To counter this weakness, many newer PLCs have tightly coupled the motion module with the PLC processor so that the motion module is not separately programmed, but is a part of the program in the PLC processor.

The original PLC language was ladder logic. However, each PLC manufacturer did not implement ladder logic in the same fashion; therefore, programs could not be easily copied between PLC manufacturers. In addition, ladder logic is not very well suited to arithmetic calculations, PID control, or motion control. This need to incorporate other control languages and to copy programs among PLC vendors led to the development of the IEC 61131-3 (originally numbered 1131-3) standard (IEC, 1993). The industry trend is toward using the IEC 61131-3 standard, and thus it is the primary focus of this text. However, 61131-3 is only a voluntary standard and individual manufacturers have some freedom in the implementation.

The PLC evolved from its initial role as a "relay replacer" and the DCS evolved from its initial role as a "PID loop replacer". The distinction between PLC and DCS systems persisted throughout the 1990's. While both control technology types claimed to do some of the functions of the other type, it was not until the 61131-3 standard blended them that the distinction became obsolete. This merging of the PLC and DCS technology suggests a new term to describe control technology: *programmable electronic system (PES)*. This term is now used in many standards such as the ISA S84.01 (ISA, 1996) for safety-instrumented systems.

1.5 PLC VERSUS OTHER TECHNOLOGIES

As demonstrated by the history of the PLC, it is not the only technology available for implementing factory automation. Table 1.2 shows a comparison of available control system technologies. This table clearly shows why PLCs quickly supplanted relay systems.

Except for recovery from power failure, the PLC has a clear advantage over relay systems. Figure 1.9*b* shows the PLC replacement of the relay rack of Figure 1.9*a* and illustrates the smaller space required for the PLC system. Less clear are the advantages of PLCs over computers.

In many respects, the architecture of the PLC resembles a general-purpose computer. In fact, some of the early PLCs (e.g., PDP-14) were computer-based. However, there are some important characteristics of a PLC that distinguish it from a general-purpose or personal computer.

A PLC can be placed in an **industrial environment**. In contrast to the typical computer, a PLC can be placed in areas with substantial amount of:

Electrical noise
Electromagnetic interference
Mechanical vibration
Extreme temperatures (e.g., 140° F)
Non-condensing humidity (95%)

Most PLCs are placed in cabinets in order to protect them and the electrical wiring from dust and other airborne contaminants. However, some manufacturers offer PLC modules with a conformal coating that protects the electronics from dust and certain other airborne contaminants.

A PLC is **more reliable**. Manufacturing is often an unforgiving environment. General Motors estimates that production line downtime costs $15,000 a minute (Garber, 2001). In

Table 1.2. Comparison of Control System Hardware

Characteristic	Relay Systems	Computers	PLC Systems
Price per function	Moderate	Low	Low
Physical size	Bulky	Fairly compact	Compact
Operating speed	Slow	Fairly fast	Fast
Industrial environment	Excellent	Fair to good	Good
Design	Time-consuming	Usually simple	Simple
Complicated operations	No	Yes	Yes
Installation	Time-consuming	Simple to complex	Simple
Easy to change function	Difficult	Usually simple	Very simple
Ease of maintenance	Poor - many contacts	Good if std. I/O modules	Good - few std. cards
Power failure recovery	0 sec.	10 - 100 sec.	1 - 3 sec.

some processes, a millisecond mistiming can mean a multimillion-dollar loss or personnel casualties. The mean time between failure of most PLCs is measured in years whereas the mean time between failure of a Windows NT-based PC is on the order of a few days (in the author's experience). The PLC also does not have any inherently less-reliable mechanical components (e.g., disk drives).

A PLC is **easily maintained by plant technicians**. The hardware interfaces are standardized and are easily connected. The interface circuitry is modular and self-diagnosing to pinpoint malfunctions and allow easy replacement. The PLC is programmed using ladder logic, which was already established as the standard documentation tool for relay systems. In addition, ladder logic is easily learned.

The PLC **executes a single program in an orderly and sequential fashion**. However, most medium to large PLCs have instructions that allow subroutine calling, interrupt routines, and bypass of certain instructions. Also, many PLCs can have modules that implement higher-level languages (e.g., BASIC or C).

The PLC **recovers quickly from a power failure**. There are no boot-up procedures or a need to load programs on power-up. If the PLC is running when the power fails, when power is restored, it quickly runs some diagnostic self-tests and resumes running the program without operator intervention.

Currently, PC-based control (sometimes called "soft" PLC) is working to address these weaknesses. Typically, the I/O modules are the same as used by PLCs. So, the environmental, reliability, and maintenance aspects of these modules are retained. The reliability of the PC is partly addressed by using a proprietary operating system that is more reliable than Windows NT and does not access the disk drives after boot-up (Murray, 1998). According to Murray (1998) PC-based control systems must:

- Provide deterministic operation. Control must be the highest priority and ensure a predictable, repeatable process.
- Survive a Windows crash and continue to operate in a safe manner.
- Be isolated from poorly behaved Windows applications and drivers.
- Survive a hard disk crash.
- Be based on a proven, real-time engine. The control engine must have a proven track record in mission-critical applications.

The main advantages of PC-based control are the ability to use other programming languages when implementing sophisticated control and to include the operator interface with the control program. When PC-based control was first introduced in the mid-1980's, the demise of the PLC was predicted. This demise has not happened and probably will not happen. Both PC-based control and PLCs will coexist and find their application niches.

1.6 BASIC PLC ARCHITECTURE

The basic architecture of a PLC is shown in Figure 1.11. The main components are the processor module, the power supply and the input/output (I/O) modules. The processor module consists of the central processing unit (CPU) and memory. In addition to a

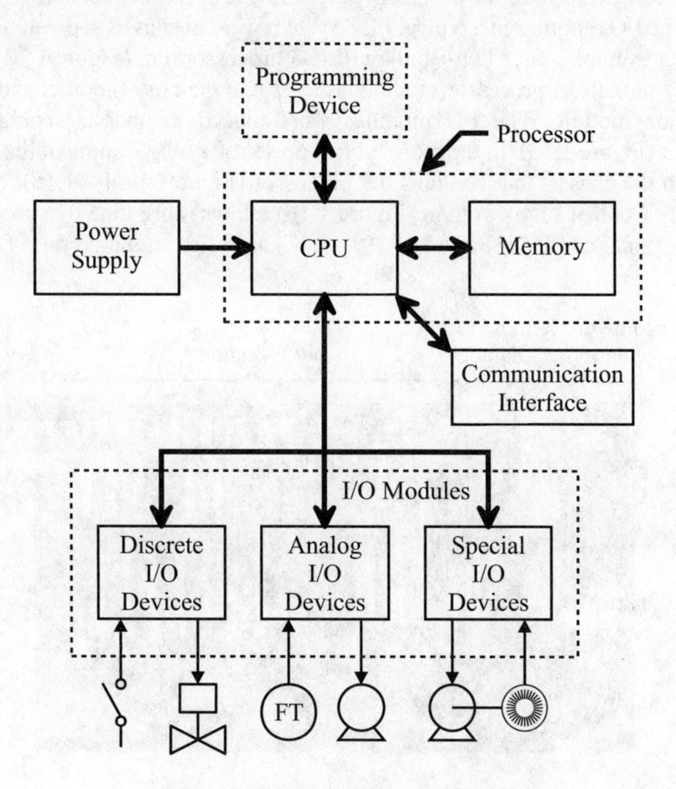

Figure 1.11. Basic PLC architecture.

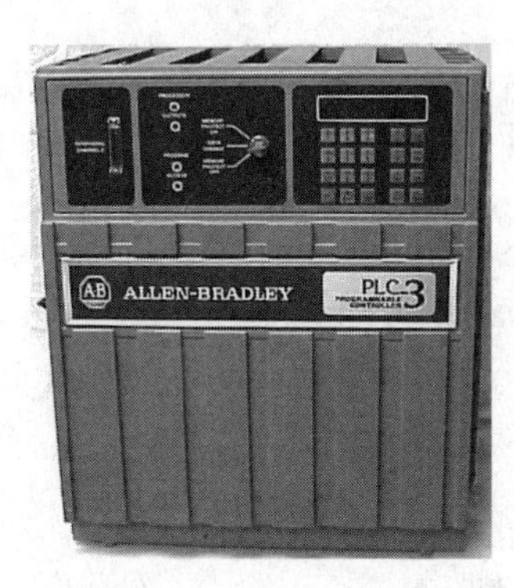

Figure 1.12. Allen-Bradley PLC-3 processor unit.

microprocessor, the CPU also contains at least an interface to a programming device and may contain interfaces to remote I/O and other communication networks. The power supply is usually a separate module and the I/O modules are separate from the processor. The types of I/O modules include discrete (on/off), analog (continuous variable), and special modules like motion control or high-speed counters. The field devices are connected to the I/O modules.

Depending on the amount of I/O and the particular PLC processor, the I/O modules may be in the same chassis as the processor and/or in one or more other chassis. Up until the late 1980's, the I/O modules in a typical PLC system were in chassis separate from the PLC processor. For example, the Allen-Bradley PLC-3 processor unit (Figure 1.12) contained a power supply module, a processor module, at least one memory module, and at least one communication module. The I/O modules were placed in chassis separate from the processor unit (Figure 1.13). In the more typical present-day PLC, some of the I/O modules are present in the chassis that contains the processor (Figures 1.14 – 1.18). Note that the Allen-Bradley Control Logix system (Figure 1.16) allows more than one processor in the same chassis. Smaller PLCs (Figures 1.19 – 1.21) are often mounted on a DIN rail. The

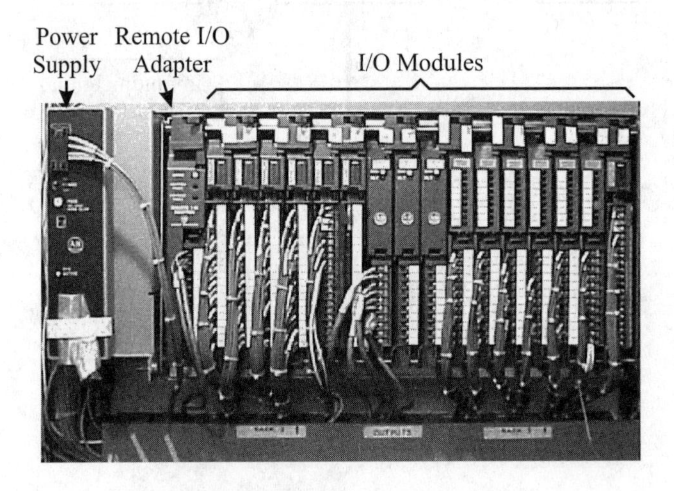

Figure 1.13. Remote I/O chassis.

Figure 1.14. Allen-Bradley PLC-5 chassis.

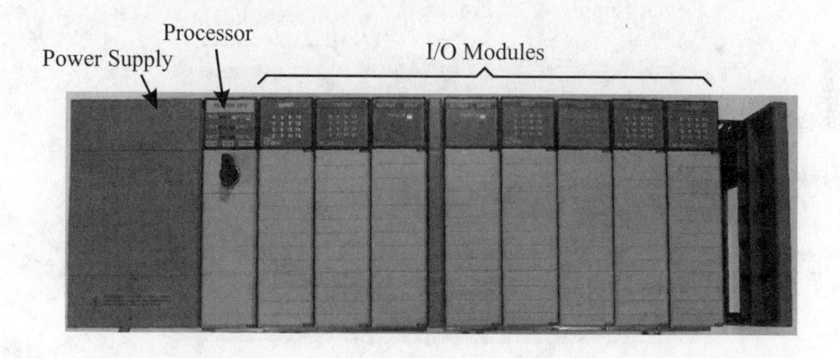

Figure 1.15. Allen-Bradley SLC-500 chassis.

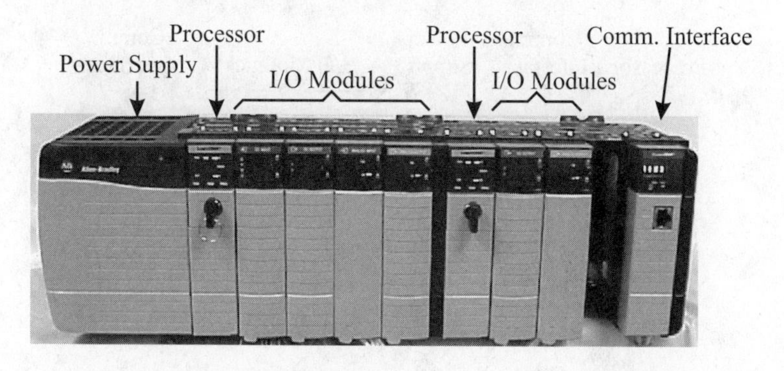

Figure 1.16. Allen-Bradley Control Logix chassis.

Figure 1.17. Modicon Quantum chassis.

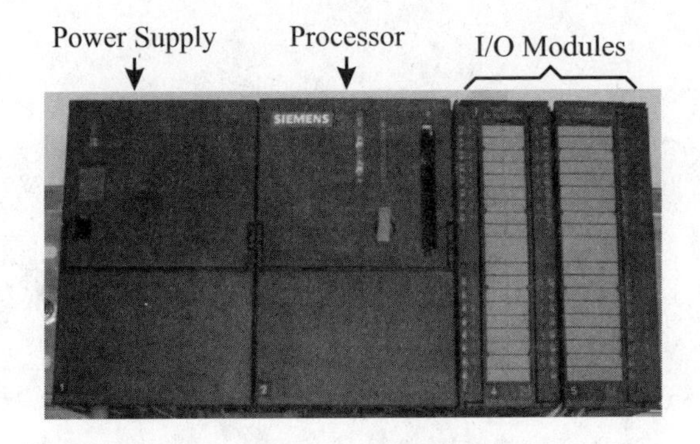

Figure 1.18. Siemens S7-300 chassis.

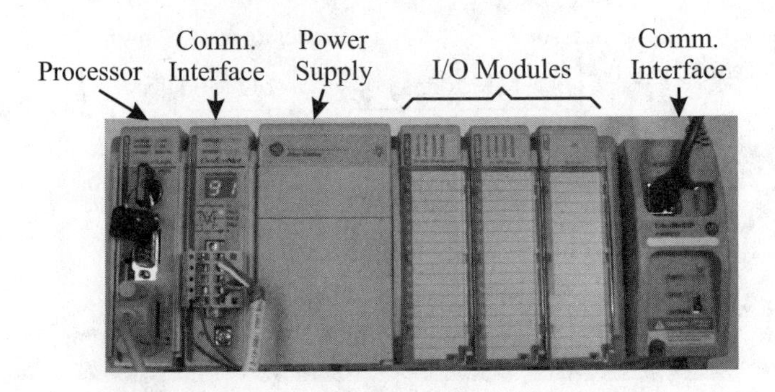

Figure 1.19. Allen-Bradley CompactLogix PLC.

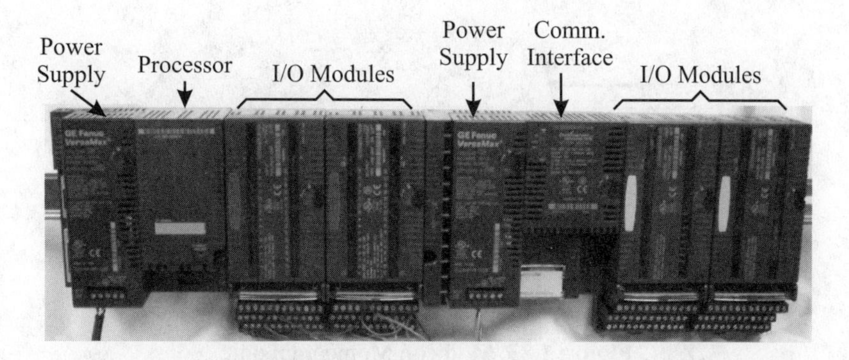

Figure 1.20. GE Fanuc VersaMax.

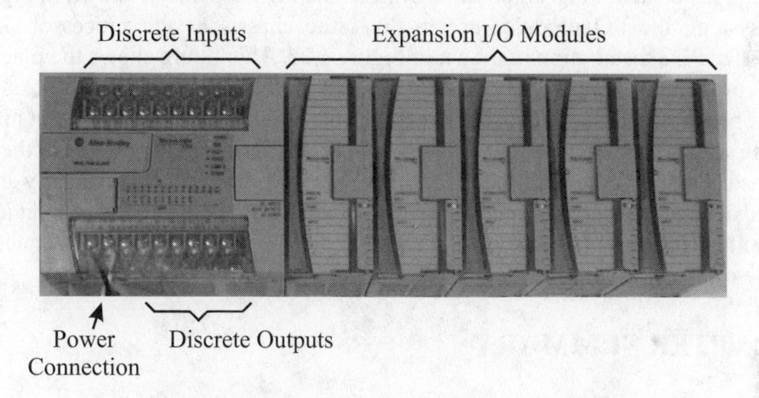

Figure 1.21. Allen-Bradley MicroLogix 1200 PLC.

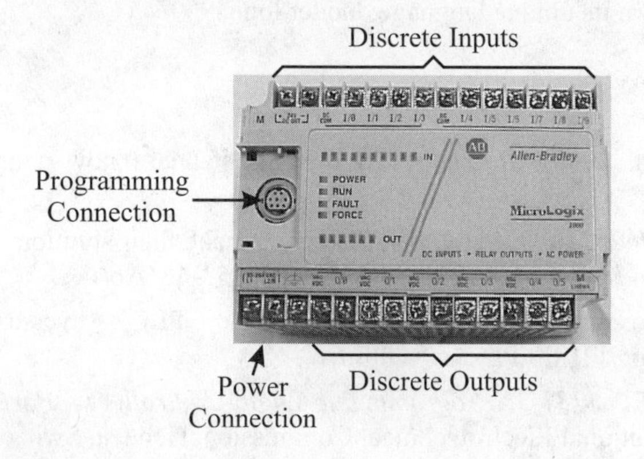

Figure 1.22. Allen-Bradley MicroLogix 1000 unit.

smallest PLCs (often called micro-PLCs or nano-PLCs) include the power supply, processor, and all of the I/O in one package (Figures 1.22 – 1.23). However, for many micro-PLCs, the amount of I/O is limited and not expandable.

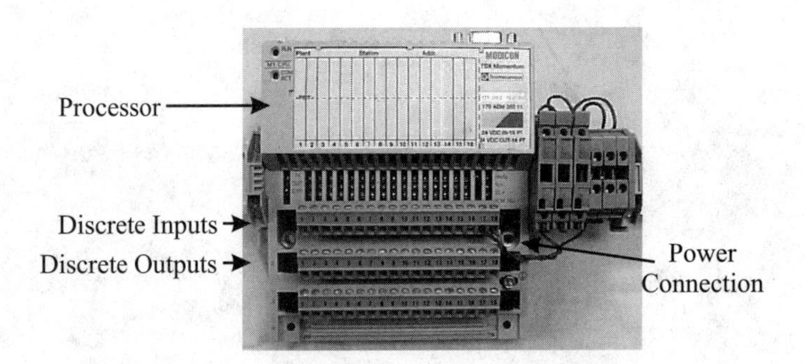

Figure 1.23. Modicon Momentum unit.

Within the context of an automation system, the PLC appears as shown in Figure 1.24. In this system, the I/O modules are in the same chassis as the processor. A typical medium-size PLC installation is shown in Figure 1.25. This figure shows the placement of the PLC processor, I/O modules, power supplies, and wiring terminal blocks within a cabinet. There are also fuses or circuit breakers, one or more per input or output module for protection of the I/O module circuitry. The I/O modules are wired to one side of the terminal blocks instead of being wired directly to the field devices. A cabinet is typically assembled and wired at a location away from the process. When ready to install, the cabinet is brought to the plant location and only the plant power and field devices need to be connected to the other side of the terminal blocks.

1.7 CHAPTER SUMMARY

This chapter introduced the programmable logic controller and placed it in the context of manufacturing automation. The evolution of the PLC was outlined and compared to other automation technologies, especially personal computers. With this basic PLC knowledge, one is ready to learn its unique language, ladder logic.

REFERENCES

Amos, Kenna, 2000. "IEC's 61158 fieldbus standard now a new spec," *InTech Magazine*, April.

Cleaveland, Peter, 1999. "PLC manufacturers make their solutions a lot more open," *Instrumentation and Control Systems Magazine*, pp. 53-62, April.

Garber, Joseph R., 2001. "The PLC versus the PC," http://www.barn.org/FILES/PLCvsPC.htm.

IEC, 1993. *IEC 1131-3: Programmable Logic Controllers - Part 3: Programming Languages*, International Electrotechnical Commission, Geneva, Switzerland.

ISA, 1995. *ISA-S88.01, Batch Control, Part 1: Models and Terminology*, Instrument Society of America, Research Triangle Park, NC.

ISA, 1996. *ISA-S84.01, Application of Safety Instrumented Systems for the Process Industries - 1996*, Instrument Society of America, Research Triangle Park, NC.

Mayr, Otto, 1971. *Feedback Mechanisms in the Historical Collections of the National Museum of History and Technology*, Smithsonian Institution Press, Washington, D.C.

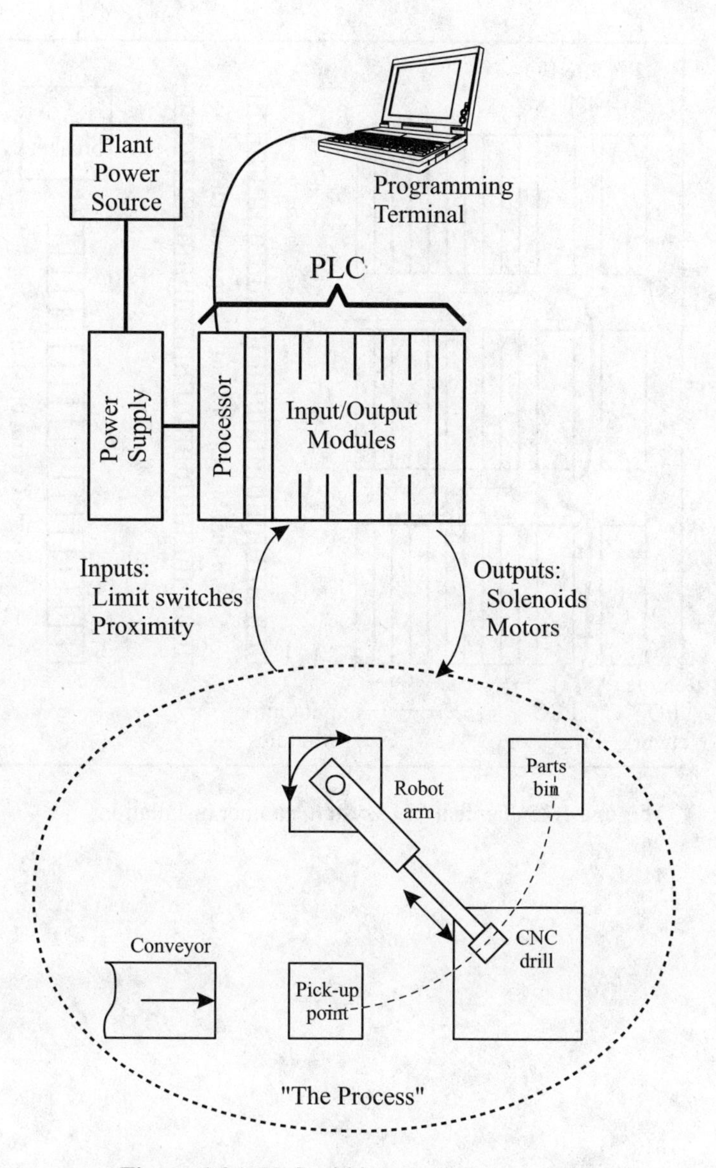

Figure 1.24. PLC within automation system.

Merritt, Rich, 1999. "The electronic age," *Control Magazine*, Dec.

Morley, Richard, 2001. "History of the PLC," R. Morley Incorporated.

Murray, Charles J., 1998. "PC vs. PLC: The lines blur", Special Supplement: Motion Control, *Design News*, March 23.

Stone, William S., David C. Emmett, Edward J. O'Connell, Leonard Radionoff, William Wegryn, and Clifford H. Wilford, "Standard Machine Controller," General Motors, June 6, 1968.

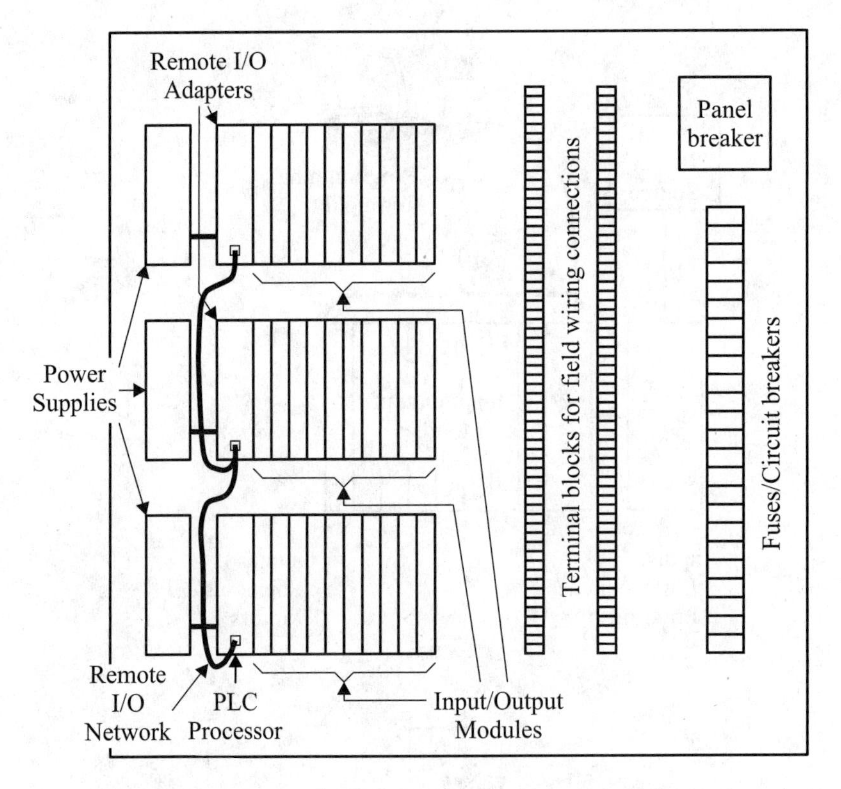

Figure 1.25. Typical PLC system cabinet installation.

2 Basic Ladder Logic Programming

Chapter Topics:

- Basic ladder logic symbols
- Ladder logic diagram
- Ladder logic evaluation
- Converting relay logic to ladder logic

OBJECTIVES

Upon completion of this chapter, you will be able to:

- Understand basic ladder logic symbols
- Write ladder logic for simple applications
- Translate relay ladder logic into PLC ladder logic

Scenario: A program with a long scan time may not detect short-duration events.

A manufacturer of small gasoline engines had an intermittent problem on the final assembly line. Sometimes, a defective engine would not be automatically removed from the line for repair at a "kick-out" station. If an operator noticed a problem with an engine, he/she inserted a bolt into a certain hole in the engine carrier. A proximity sensor before the kick-out station sensed the presence of the bolt, and the PLC activated a hydraulic solenoid to push the carrier (and engine) off the main conveyor and into the repair area. A view of this station is shown in Figure 2.1. Further investigation revealed that the duration of the **on** pulse of the proximity sensor was approximately 3/4 seconds. One PLC controlled all of the stations on the assembly line and its ladder logic program was quite large. As indicated in the PLC status, the time to scan the ladder logic program was slightly less than 1 second. Hence, it was very likely that a pulse from the proximity sensor could be undetected by the PLC processor. The proximity sensor could be **off** at the start of the ladder scan, generate an **on** pulse from a passing bolt in the carrier, and be **off** at the start of the next ladder scan.

Solution: Logic to examine the proximity sensor is placed in a ladder logic routine that is executed every ½ second. If the proximity sensor is detected to be on, an internal coil is turned on for at least 1.5 seconds. The main PLC program is changed to examine this internal coil to determine when to activate the hydraulic solenoid and push a carrier off the main conveyor.

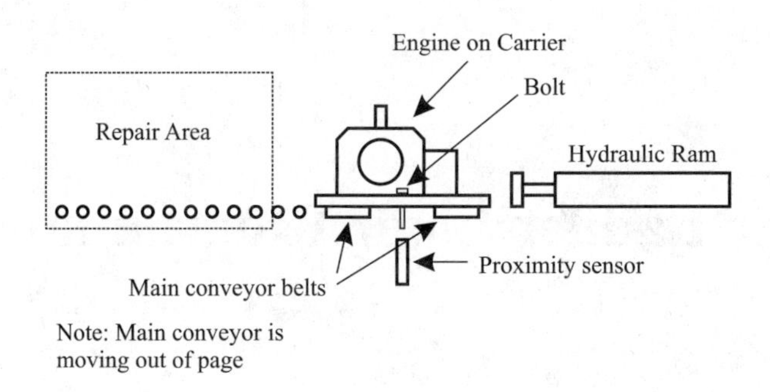

Figure 2.1. Kick-out station.

2.1 INTRODUCTION

Now that the PLC has been introduced, let us move on to programming the PLC. The first, and still most popular programming language, is ladder logic. Using examples, the language is developed from the electromechanical relay system-wiring diagram. After describing the basic symbols for the various processors covered by this text, they are combined into a ladder diagram. The subsequent section details the process of scanning a program and accessing the physical inputs and outputs. Programming with the normally closed contact is given particular attention because it is often misapplied by novice programmers. To solidify these concepts, the start/stop of a physical device is considered. Start/stop is a very common PLC application and occurs in many other contexts. An optional section on relay to PLC ladder logic conversion concludes the chapter.

2.2 SIMPLE LADDER LOGIC

Ladder logic is the primary programming language of programmable logic controllers. Since the PLC was developed to replace relay logic control systems, it was only natural that the initial language closely resembles the diagrams used to document the relay logic. By using this approach, the engineers and technicians using the early PLCs did not need retraining to understand the program. To introduce ladder logic programming simple switch circuits are converted to relay logic and then to PLC ladder logic.

In all of the ladder logic examples used in this chapter, tags (symbols) are used for all inputs, outputs, and internal memory in the examples to avoid having to deal with input/output addressing. This addressing, treated in Chapter 3, is generally different for each PLC manufacturer.

Example 2.1. OR Circuit. Two switches labeled A and B are wired in parallel controlling a lamp as shown in Figure 2.2*a*. Implement this function as PLC ladder logic where the two switches are separate inputs.

Solution. The switch circuit action is described as, "The lamp is **on** when switch A is **on** (closed) or switch B is **on** (closed)." All possible combinations of the two switches and the consequent lamp action is shown as a truth table in Figure 2.2*b*.

To implement this function using relays, the switches A and B are not connected to the lamp directly, but are connected to relay coils labeled AR and BR whose normally-open

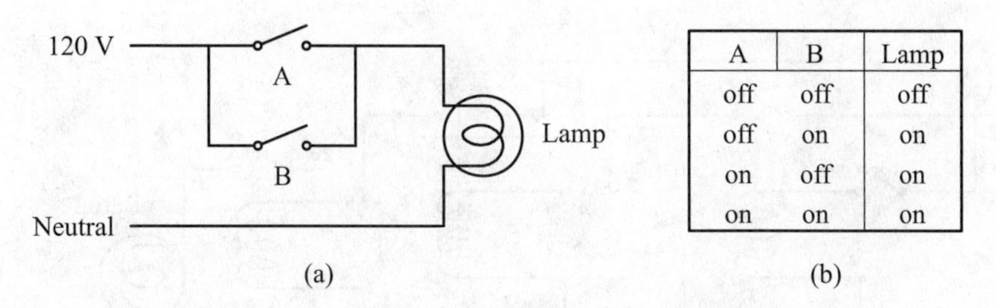

A	B	Lamp
off	off	off
off	on	on
on	off	on
on	on	on

Figure 2.2. Parallel switch circuit: *(a)* switch circuit; *(b)* truth table.

(NO) contacts control a relay coil, LR, whose contacts control the lamp, Figure 2.3*a*. The switches, A and B, are the inputs to the circuit. When either switch A or B is closed, the corresponding relay coil AR or BR is energized, closing a contact and supplying power to the LR relay coil. The LR coil is energized, closing its contact and supplying power to the lamp.

The output (lamp in this case) is driven by the LR relay to provide voltage isolation from the relays implementing the logic. The switches, A and B, control relay coils (AR and BR) to isolate the inputs from the logic. Also, with this arrangement, the one switch connection to an input relay can be used multiple times in the logic. A typical industrial control relay can have up to 12 poles, or sets of contacts, per coil. For example, if the AR relay has six poles (only one shown in Figure 2.3*a*), then the other five poles are available for use in the relay logic without requiring five other connections to switch A.

Before the PLC was developed, engineers had already developed a graphical electrical circuit shorthand notation for the relay circuit of Figure 2.3*a*. This notation was called a *relay ladder logic diagram*, shown in Figure 2.3*b*. The switches are shown as their usual symbol, the circles indicate the relay coils, and the NO relay contacts are shown as the vertical parallel bars.

The *PLC ladder logic* notation (Figure 2.3*c*) is shortened from the relay wiring diagram to show only the third line, the relay contacts and the coil of the output relay. The PLC ladder logic notation assumes that the inputs (switches in this example) are connected to discrete input channels (equivalent to the relay coils AR and BR in Figure 2.3*b*). Also, the actual output (lamp) is connected to a discrete output channel (equivalent to the normally open contacts of LR in Figure 2.3*b*) controlled by the coil. The label shown above a contact symbol is not the contact label, but the control for the coil that drives the contact. Also, the output for the rung occurs on the extreme right side of the rung and power is assumed to flow from left to right. The PLC ladder logic rung is interpreted as: "When input (switch) A is **on** OR input (switch) B is **on** then the lamp is **on**," which is the same as the statement describing the switch circuit in Figure 2.2*a*.

Notice that the original description of the switch circuit in Figure 2.2*a*,

The lamp is **on** when switch A is **on** <u>or</u> switch B is **on**.

translates into a relay circuit described as

A <u>parallel</u> connection of **normally-open contacts**,

which describes the PLC ladder logic in Figure 2.3*c*.

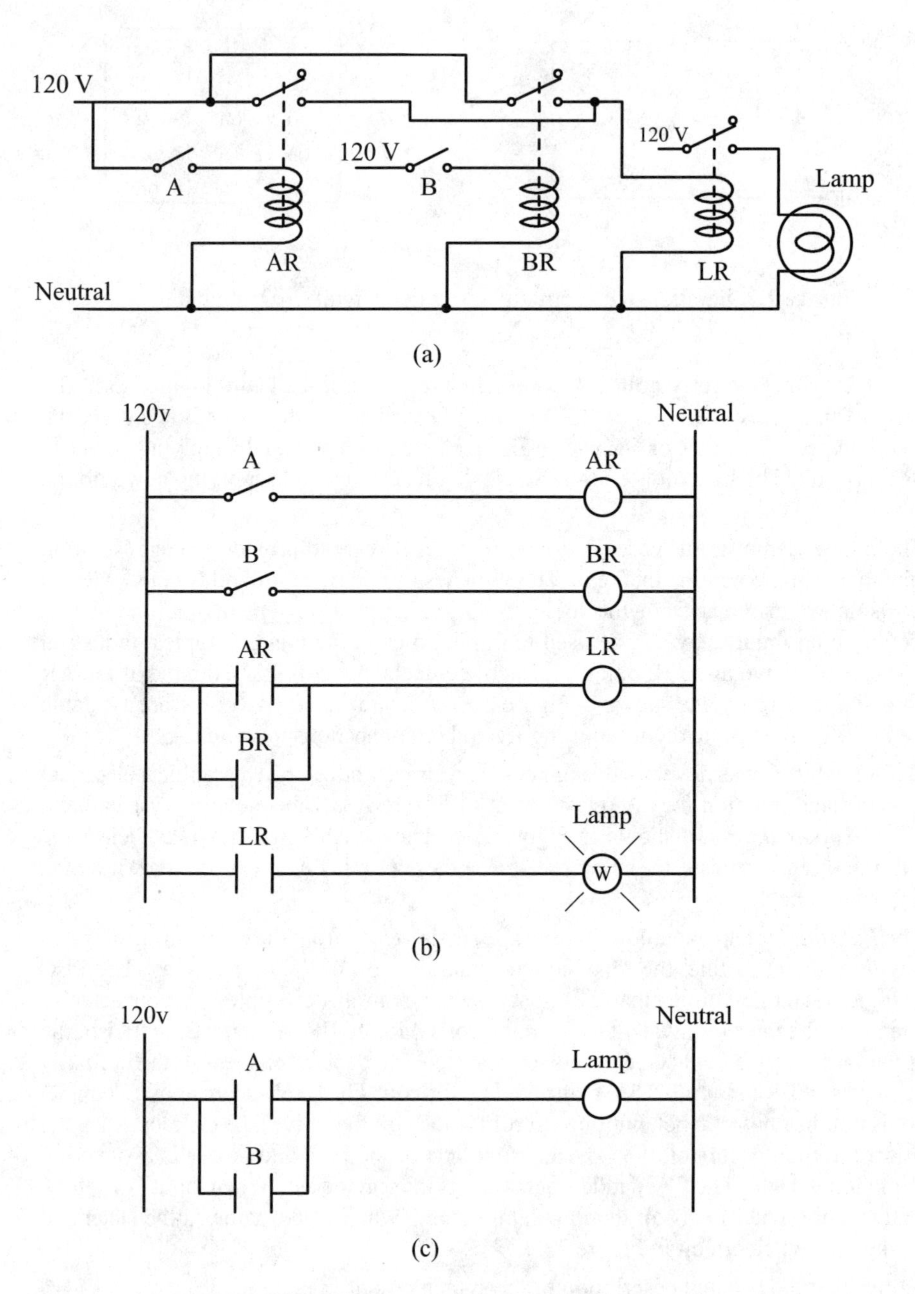

Figure 2.3. Parallel switch relay and ladder logic circuits: *(a)* equivalent relay circuit; *(b)* equivalent relay ladder logic circuit; *(c)* equivalent PLC ladder logic.

Example 2.2. AND Circuit. Two switches labeled A and B are wired in series controlling a lamp as shown in Figure 2.4*a*. Implement this function as PLC ladder logic where the two switches are separate inputs.

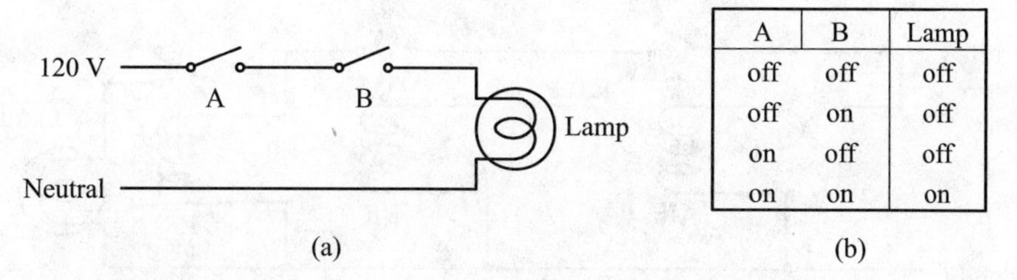

A	B	Lamp
off	off	off
off	on	off
on	off	off
on	on	on

Figure 2.4. Series switch circuit: *(a)* switch circuit; *(b)* truth table.

Solution. The switch circuit action is described as, "The lamp is **on** when switch A is **on** (closed) and switch B is **on** (closed)." All possible combinations of the two switches and the consequent lamp action is shown as a truth table in Figure 2.4*b*. To implement this function using relays, the only change from Example 2.1 is to wire the normally-open contacts of control relays AR and BR in series to control the light, Figure 2.5*a*. The wiring of switches A and B and the wiring of the lamp do not change. The relay circuit diagram, shown in Figure 2.5*b* is different from Figure 2.3*b* only in the third line. As for example 2.1, the PLC ladder logic notation (Figure 2.5*c*) is shortened from the relay wiring diagram to show only the third line, the relay contacts and the coil of the output relay. The PLC ladder logic rung is interpreted as: "When input (switch) A is **on** AND input (switch) B is **on** then the lamp is **on**."

Notice that the original description of the switch circuit in Figure 2.4*a*,

The lamp is **on** when switch A is **on** and switch B is **on**.

translates into a relay circuit described as

A series connection of **normally-open contacts**,

which describes the PLC ladder logic in Figure 2.5*c*.

Example 2.3. As a third example, consider the implementation of a logical NOT function. Suppose a lamp needs to be turned **on** when switch A is **on** (closed) and switch B is **off** (open). Implement this function as PLC ladder logic where the two switches are separate inputs.

Solution. Figure 2.6 shows the truth table, relay implementation and ladder logic for this example. The only difference between the relay implementation in Figure 2.6*b* and Figure 2.5*a* is the wiring of the relay BR contacts. The logical NOT for switch B is accomplished with the normally closed (NC) contact of relay BR. The PLC ladder logic rung in Figure 2.6*c* is different from Figure 2.5*c* only in the second contact symbol. The PLC ladder logic is interpreted as: "When input (switch) A is **on** (closed) and input (switch) B is **off** (open) then the lamp is **on**." This particular example is impossible to implement with a combination of only two normally open switches and no relays.

Notice that the original description of the Example 2.3,

The lamp is **on** when switch A is **on** and switch B is **off**.

translates into a relay circuit described as

A series connection of a **normally-open contact** and a **normally-closed contact**,

which describes the PLC ladder logic in Figure 2.6*c*.

Summarizing these three examples, one should notice that key words in the description of the operation translate into certain aspects of the solution:

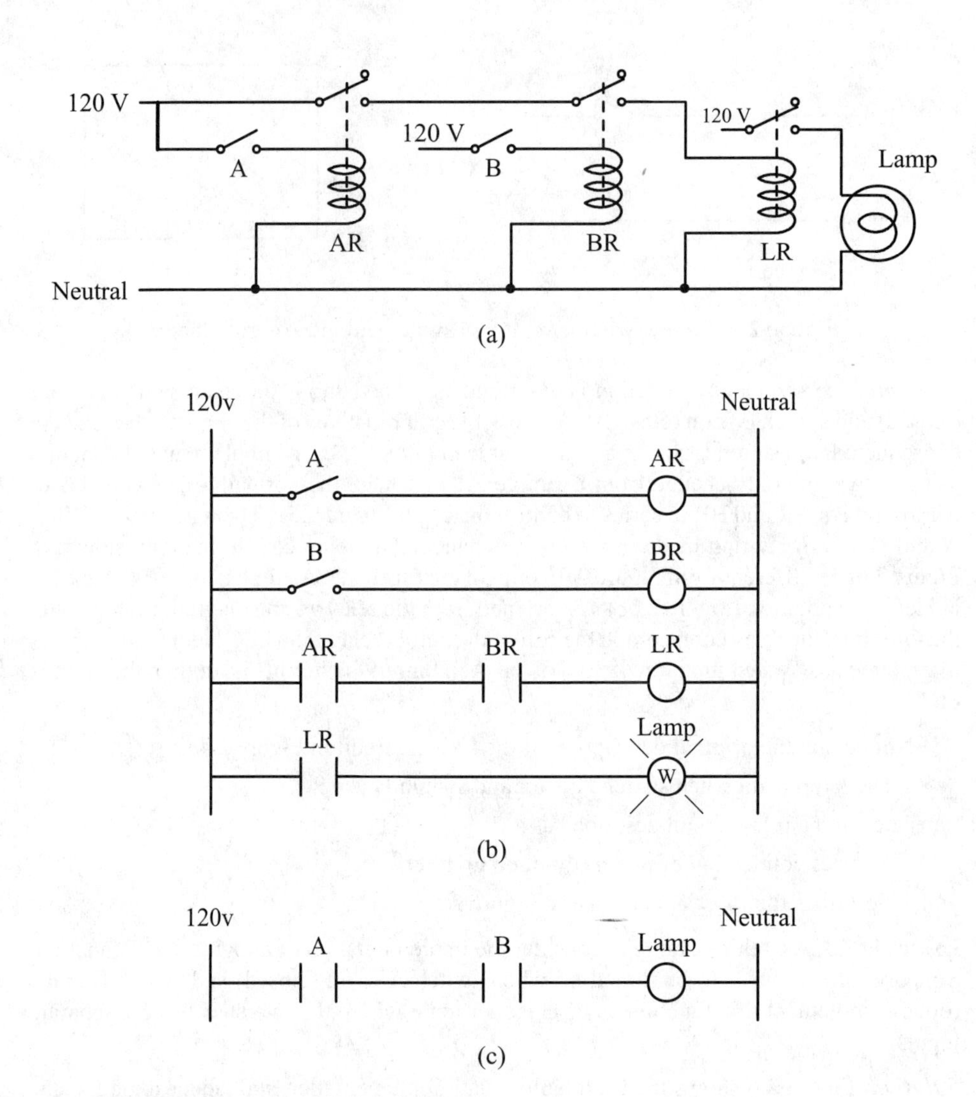

Figure 2.5. Series switch relay and ladder logic circuits: *(a)* equivalent relay circuit; *(b)* equivalent relay ladder logic circuit; *(c)* equivalent PLC ladder logic.

and	→	series connection of contacts
or	→	parallel connection of contacts
on	→	**normally-open** contact
off	→	**normally-closed** contact

These concepts are key to being able to understand and write ladder logic. To many people these concepts appear strange and foreign at first. However, they will become more natural as one works problems. Ladder logic is a very visual and graphical language. It is very different from textual languages like C++, Fortran, Basic, and Java. In contrast, one can become proficient at ladder logic much quicker than with textual languages.

A	B	Lamp
off	off	off
off	on	off
on	off	on
on	on	off

(a)

120 V
120 V
120 V
A
B
AR
BR
LR
Lamp
Neutral

(b)

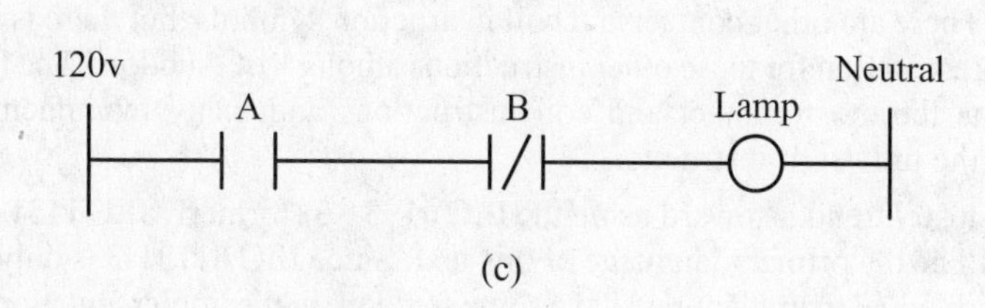

(c)

Figure 2.6. NOT function ladder logic circuits; *(a)* truth table; *(b)* equivalent relay circuit; *(c)* equivalent PLC ladder logic.

NAND and NOR logic functions are left as exercises for the interested reader. More information about the conversion between relay ladder logic and PLC ladder logic appears in section 2.8.

2.3 BASIC LADDER LOGIC SYMBOLS

At this point, one should start interpreting ladder logic directly and not think of its implementation with relays. As introduced by the examples in the previous section, the basic ladder logic symbols are

—| |— *Normally open (NO) contact.* Passes power (**on**) if coil driving the contact is **on** (closed).

—|/|— *Normally closed (NC) contact.* Passes power (**on**) if coil driving the contact is **off** (open).

—○— Output or *coil*. If any left-to-right path of contacts passes power, the output is energized. If there is no continuous left-to-right path of contacts passing power, the output is de-energized.

These symbols are ladder logic instructions that are scanned (executed) by the PLC. In order to avoid confusion, the contact symbols should be equated with certain concepts as follows:

–| |– = **on** = Closed = True = 1

–|/|– = **off** = Open = False = 0

This crucial point will be repeated later when the use of the NC contact is clarified. Figure 2.7 is an example ladder logic diagram with the basic instructions. The first line (also called a *rung*) that determines output labeled Out1 is interpreted as follows: Out1 is **on** if inputs A, B, and C are all **on**, or if inputs A and C are **on** and input D is **off**. Notice that for Out1 to be **on** there must be a continuous electrical path through the contacts.

Every PLC manufacturer uses the instruction symbols shown in the previous paragraph. There are other contact and coil instruction symbols, but there is no universal graphic representation for these other instructions among PLC vendors. The IEC 61131-3 standard has the most contact and coil instructions and many manufacturers do not implement the full set of instructions.

The industry trend is toward using the IEC 61131-3 (formerly IEC 1131-3) standard, and so it will be the primary language of this text. Since IEC 61131-3 is only a voluntary standard, individual manufacturers have some freedom in the implementation. Therefore, the Allen-Bradley ControlLogix, Modicon, and Siemens S7 implementations of the 61131-3 standard are covered. Because of their widespread use, Allen-Bradley PLC-5/SLC-500 and GE Fanuc PLC languages are also covered.

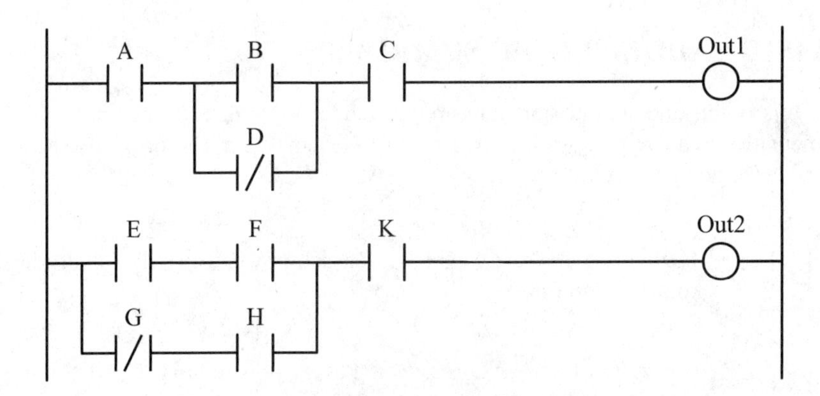

Figure 2.7. Ladder logic diagram with basic instructions.

For the remainder of the book, the languages will be presented in the following order:

IEC 61131-3 standard
Modicon Concept (IEC compliant)
Allen-Bradley ControlLogix (IEC compliant)
Allen-Bradley PLC-5/SLC-500 (not IEC compliant)
Siemens S7 (IEC compliant)
GE Fanuc (not IEC compliant)

The Modicon Concept ladder logic is presented first because it is closest to the IEC 61131-3 standard. The Allen-Bradley processors are presented next because of their widespread use in North America.

2.3.1 IEC 61131-3

The basic ladder logic contact symbols are

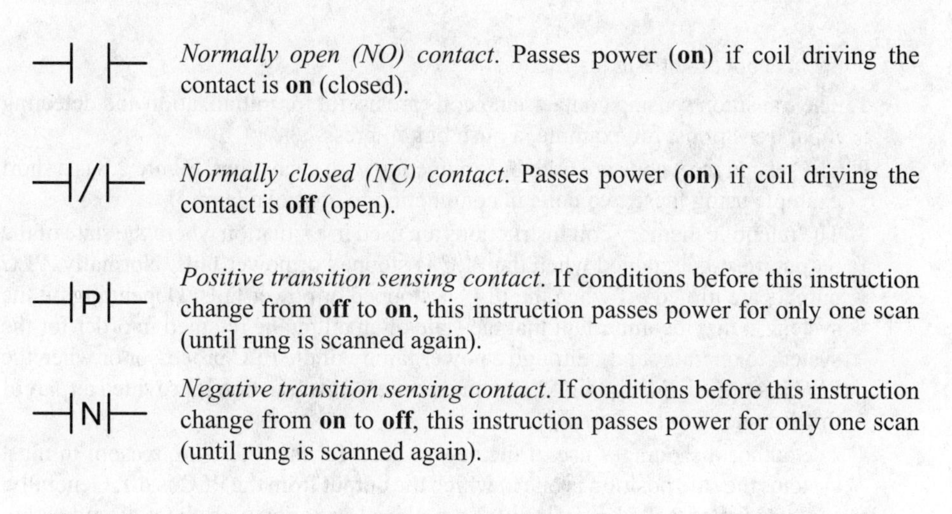

Normally open (NO) contact. Passes power (**on**) if coil driving the contact is **on** (closed).

Normally closed (NC) contact. Passes power (**on**) if coil driving the contact is **off** (open).

Positive transition sensing contact. If conditions before this instruction change from **off** to **on**, this instruction passes power for only one scan (until rung is scanned again).

Negative transition sensing contact. If conditions before this instruction change from **on** to **off**, this instruction passes power for only one scan (until rung is scanned again).

The basic ladder logic coil (output) symbols are

—( )— Output or *coil*. If any left-to-right path of instructions passes power, the output is energized. If there is no continuous left-to-right path of instructions passing power, the output is de-energized.

—(/)— *Negated coil.* If any left-to-right path of inputs passes power, the output is de-energized. If there is no continuous left-to-right path of instructions passing power, the output is energized.

—(S)— *Set coil.* If any rung path passes power, output is energized and remains energized, even when no rung path passes power.

—(R)— *Reset coil.* If any rung path passes power, output is de-energized and remains de-energized, even when no rung path passes power.

—(P)— *Positive transition sensing coil.* If conditions before this instruction change from **off** to **on**, coil is turned **on** for one scan.

—(N)— *Negative transition sensing coil.* If conditions before this instruction change from **on** to **off**, coil is turned **on** for one scan.

—(M)— *Retentive memory coil.* Like the ordinary coil, except the value of the output is retained even when the PLC is stopped or power fails.

—(SM)— *Set retentive memory coil.* Like the set coil, except the value of the output is retained even when the PLC is stopped or power fails.

—(RM)— *Reset retentive memory coil.* Like the reset coil, except the value of the output is retained even when the PLC is stopped or power fails.

Comments about the basic instructions

1. The transition sensing contacts and coils are useful for initialization and detecting input transitions, for example, a push button press.
2. The set and reset coils are used in conjunction with each other. Figure 2.8 is a short example using these two coils in conjunction to control a lamp.
3. The retentive memory coil instructions are used in a situation where the state of the output must be retained when the PLC is stopped or power fails. Normally, PLC outputs are turned **off** when the PLC is stopped or power fails. Depending on the system, it may be important that the state of an output be retained in order for the system to operate safely through a power failure of the PLC processor or when the PLC is stopped. For certain PLC manufacturers, this function is provided as part of the discrete output module.
4. The author discourages use of the negated coil for the following reason. In most systems the safe position is one in which the output from the PLC is **off**. Generally, contacts (often called permissives) are placed in series with the coil, indicating multiple conditions must be satisfied before the output is allowed to be energized. With the negated coil the rung conditions must be satisfied to turn **off** the output which is opposite to most safety concepts.

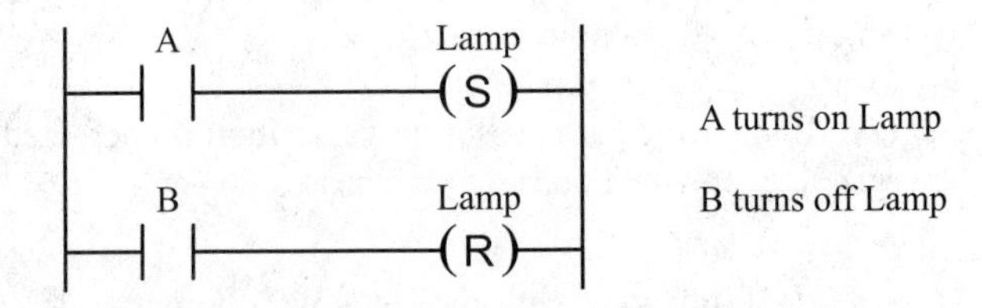

Figure 2.8. Set and reset coil example.

2.3.2 Modicon Quantum/Momentum

Using the Concept programming software, the Modicon Quantum and Momentum PLC processors may be programmed in ladder logic compatible with the older 984-series processors, or with IEC 61131-3 compliant ladder logic. The IEC 61131-3 compliant ladder logic instructions are described here. The Modicon IEC basic ladder logic contact symbols are the same as described in section 2.3.1.

The Modicon IEC basic ladder logic coil symbols are similar to those described in section 2.3.1, except that Modicon does not support the following:

Retentive memory coil

Set retentive memory coil

Reset retentive memory coil

The instructions are:

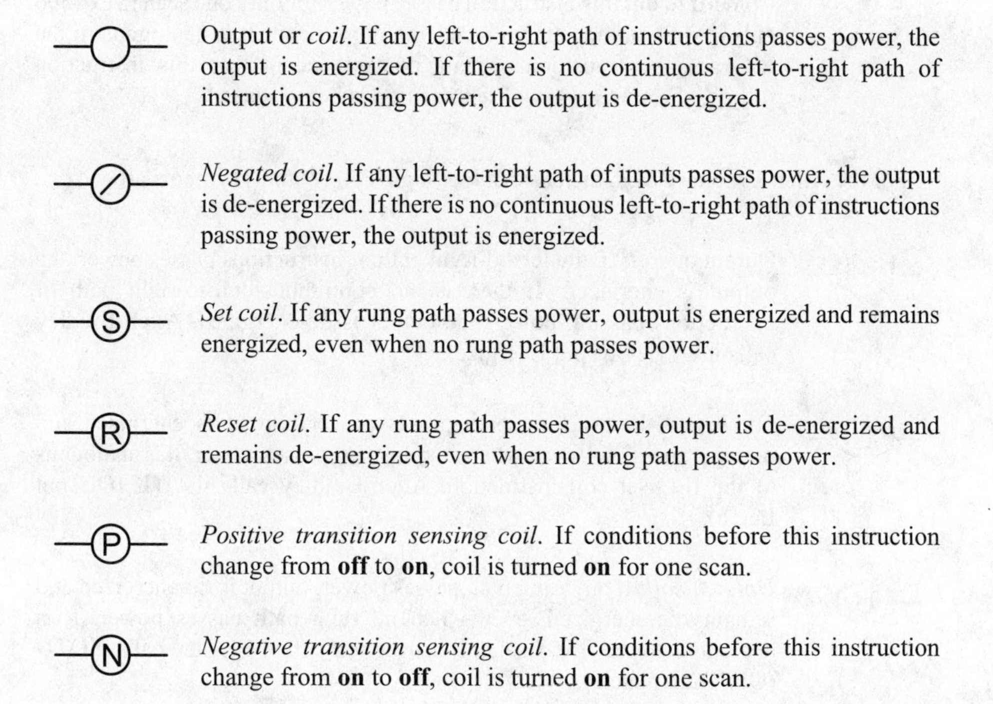

Output or *coil*. If any left-to-right path of instructions passes power, the output is energized. If there is no continuous left-to-right path of instructions passing power, the output is de-energized.

Negated coil. If any left-to-right path of inputs passes power, the output is de-energized. If there is no continuous left-to-right path of instructions passing power, the output is energized.

Set coil. If any rung path passes power, output is energized and remains energized, even when no rung path passes power.

Reset coil. If any rung path passes power, output is de-energized and remains de-energized, even when no rung path passes power.

Positive transition sensing coil. If conditions before this instruction change from **off** to **on**, coil is turned **on** for one scan.

Negative transition sensing coil. If conditions before this instruction change from **on** to **off**, coil is turned **on** for one scan.

2.3.3 Allen-Bradley ControlLogix and PLC-5/SLC-500

The Allen-Bradley PLC basic instructions are not as numerous as for the IEC 61131-3 basic instructions. In addition, for many of the instructions, a different symbol is used, though the function is the same as an IEC 61131-3 instruction. The Allen-Bradley basic ladder logic contact symbols are

Normally open (NO) contact. Passes power (**on**) if coil driving the contact is **on** (closed). Allen-Bradley calls it XIC (eXamine If Closed).

Normally closed (NC) contact. Passes power (**on**) if coil driving the contact is **off** (open). Allen-Bradley calls it XIO (eXamine If Open).

ONS

One-shot contact. If conditions before this instruction change from **off** to **on**, this instruction passes power for only one scan (ControlLogix and PLC-5 only). It is analogous to the IEC positive transition sensing contact except that this instruction follows the contact(s) whose transition is being sensed.

OSR

One-shot rising contact. If conditions before this instruction change from **off** to **on**, this instruction passes power for only one scan (SLC-500 only). Must immediately precede an output coil. It is analogous to the IEC positive transition sensing contact except that this instruction follows the contact(s) whose transition is being sensed.

For the Allen-Bradley PLCs, the basic ladder logic coil (output) symbols are

Output or *coil.* If any left-to-right path of instructions passes power, the output is energized. If there is no continuous left-to-right path of instructions passing power, the output is de-energized. Allen-Bradley calls it OTE (OuTput Energize).

L

Latch coil. If any rung path passes power, output is energized and remains energized, even when no rung path passes power. It is analogous to the IEC set coil instruction. Allen-Bradley calls it OTL (OuTput Latch).

U

Unlatch coil. If any rung path passes power, output is de-energized and remains de-energized, even when no rung path passes power. It is analogous to the IEC reset coil instruction. Allen-Bradley calls it OTU (OuTput Unlatch).

OSR
One Shot Rising (OB)
Bit Address B3/25 (SB)
Source Bit 2
Dest O:11

One shot rising output. If conditions before this instruction change from **off** to **on**, the specified bit is turned **on** for one scan (ControlLogix and enhanced PLC-5 only). This is more appropriately a function block instruction because of its appearance. It is analogous to the IEC positive transition sensing coil instruction.

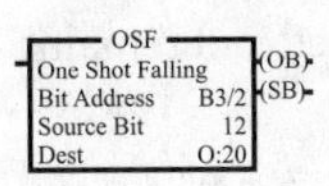

One shot falling output. If conditions before this instruction change from **on** to **off**, the specified bit is turned **on** for one scan (ControlLogix and enhanced PLC-5 only). This is more appropriately a function block instruction because of its appearance. It is analogous to the IEC negative transition sensing coil instruction.

There are no retentive memory coil instructions. The retentive function is handled in the discrete output modules.

2.3.4 Siemens S7

The three types of S7 processors (S7-200, S7-300, and S7-400) have the same basic instructions. The only exception is the midline output coil that is not valid for the S7-200 processors. The basic ladder logic contact symbols are

—| |— *Normally open (NO) contact*. Passes power (**on**) if coil driving the contact is **on** (closed).

—|/|— *Normally closed (NC) contact*. Passes power (**on**) if coil driving the contact is **off** (open).

—(P)— *Positive transition sensing contact*. If conditions before this instruction change from **off** to **on**, this instruction passes power for only one scan (until rung is scanned again). For the S7-200 processors, this contact uses vertical bars, rather than parentheses.

—(N)— *Negative transition sensing contact*. If conditions before this instruction change from **on** to **off**, this instruction passes power for only one scan (until rung is scanned again). For the S7-200 processors, this contact uses vertical bars, rather than parentheses.

—|NOT|— *Invert power flow*. If any left-to-right path of inputs before this contact passes power, the power flow to succeeding elements is interrupted (turned **off**). If no left-to-right path of inputs before this contact passes power, the power flow to succeeding elements is turned **on**.

The basic ladder logic coil (output) symbols are

—( )—| Output or *coil*. If any left-to-right path of instructions passes power, the output is energized. If there is no continuous left-to-right path of instructions passing power, the output is de-energized.

—(#)— *Midline output coil*. Output coil in middle of rung. Other logic can occur to the right of this coil. Not valid for the S7-200 processors.

-(S)- *Set coil.* If any rung path passes power, output is energized and remains energized, even when no rung path passes power.

-(R)- *Reset coil.* If any rung path passes power, output is de-energized and remains de-energized, even when no rung path passes power.

2.3.5 GE Fanuc

For the GE Fanuc PLCs, the basic ladder logic contact symbols are

-| |- *Normally open (NO) contact.* Passes power (**on**) if coil driving the contact is **on** (closed).

-|/|- *Normally closed (NC) contact.* Passes power (**on**) if coil driving the contact is **off** (open).

-|↑|- *Positive transition sensing contact.* If conditions before this contact change from **off** to **on**, power is passed for one scan (until rung is scanned again). Valid for 90-70 processors only.

-|↓|- *Negative transition sensing contact.* If conditions before this contact change from **on** to **off**, power is passed for one scan (until rung is scanned again). Valid for 90-70 processors only.

The basic ladder logic coil (output) symbols are

-( )- Output or *coil.* If any left-to-right path of instructions passes power, the output is energized. If there is no continuous left-to-right path of instructions passing power, the output is de-energized.

-(/)- *Negated coil.* If any left-to-right path of inputs passes power, the output is de-energized. If there is no continuous left-to-right path of instructions passing power, the output is energized.

-(S)- *Set coil.* If any rung path passes power, output is energized and remains energized, even when no rung path passes power.

-(R)- *Reset coil.* If any rung path passes power, output is de-energized and remains de-energized, even when no rung path passes power.

—(↑)— *Positive transition sensing coil.* If conditions before this instruction change from **off** to **on**, coil is turned **on** for one scan.

—(↓)— *Negative transition sensing coil.* If conditions before this instruction change from **on** to **off**, coil is turned **on** for one scan.

—(M)— *Retentive memory coil.* Like the ordinary coil, except the value of the output is retained even when the PLC is stopped or power fails.

—(/M)— *Negated retentive memory coil.* Like the negated coil, except the value of the output is retained even when the PLC is stopped or power fails.

—(SM)— *Set retentive memory coil.* Like the set coil, except the value of the output is retained even when the PLC is stopped or power fails.

—(RM)— *Reset retentive memory coil.* Like the reset coil, except the value of the output is retained even when the PLC is stopped or power fails.

A continuation coil and contact are used to handle ladder rungs with more than 10 columns:

—(+)— *Continuation coil.* If any left-to-right path of instructions passes power, the next continuation contact is turned **on**. If there is no continuous left-to-right path of instructions passing power, the next continuation contact is turned **off**.

—|+|— *Continuation contact.* Passes power (**on**) if preceding continuation coil is **on**.

2.4 LADDER LOGIC DIAGRAM

An example PLC ladder logic diagram appears in Figure 2.9. The vertical lines on the left and right are called the power rails. The contacts are arranged horizontally between the power rails, hence the term *rung*. The ladder diagram in Figure 2.9 has three rungs. The arrangement is similar to a ladder one uses to climb onto a roof. In addition, Figure 2.9 shows an example diagram like one would see if monitoring the running program in the PLC. The thick lines indicate continuity and the state (**on**/**off**) of the inputs and outputs is shown next to the tag. Regardless of the contact symbol, if the contact is closed (continuity through it), it is shown as thick lines. If the contact is open, it is shown as thin lines. In a relay ladder diagram, power flows from left to right. In PLC ladder logic, there is no real power flow, but there still must be a continuous path through closed contacts in order to energize an output. In Figure 2.9 the output on the first rung is **off** because the contact for C is open, blocking continuity through the D and E contacts. Also notice that the E input is **off**,

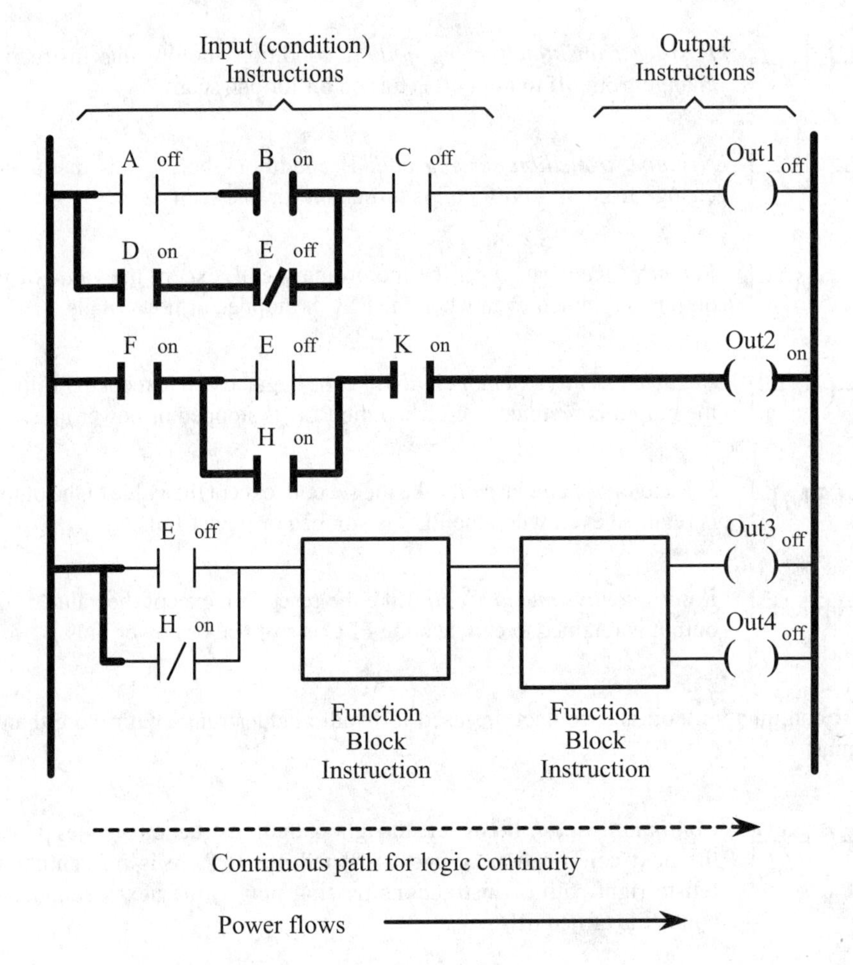

Figure 2.9. Sample ladder logic diagram.

which means the NC contact in the first rung is closed and the NO contact in the second rung is open.

Figure 2.9 also introduces the concept of *function block instructions*. Any instruction that is not contact or a coil is called a function block instruction because of its appearance in the ladder diagram. The most common function block instructions are timer, counter, comparison, and computation operations. More advanced function block instructions include sequencer, shift register, and first-in first-out operations.

Some manufacturers group the instructions into two classes: input instructions and output instructions. This distinction was made because in relay ladder logic, outputs were never connected in series and always occurred on the extreme right hand side of the rung. Contacts always appeared on the left side of coils and never on the right side. To turn on multiple outputs simultaneously, coils are connected in parallel. This restriction was relaxed in IEC 61131-3 and outputs may be connected in series. Also, contacts can occur on the right side of a coil as long as a coil is the last element in the rung. Of the ladder logic languages covered by this text, only the IEC 61131-3, Modicon Concept, and Allen-Bradley ControlLogix allow coil instructions to be connected in series.

This text avoids using a series connection of coils for two reasons:

1. most PLCs do not allow it, and
2. it is counterintuitive to maintenance personnel who often interpret ladder logic in the context of an electrical diagram.

Also, in IEC 61131-3, all function block instructions are input instructions because the only output instructions are the coils. The Allen-Bradley PLC-5 and SLC-500 have function block output instructions (e.g., timer, counter, and computation) which must be remembered when constructing ladder logic programs for these PLCs.

Example 2.4. Draw a ladder diagram that will cause the output, pilot light PL2, to be **on** when selector switch SS2 is **closed**, push-button PB4 is **closed** and limit switch LS3 is **open**. (Note: no I/O addresses yet.)

***Solution*.** The first question to answer is "What is the output?" The output is PL2, so the coil labeled as PL2 is put on the right side of the rung. Secondly, consider the type of connection of contacts to use. Since **all** three switches must be in a certain position to turn on the pilot light, a <u>series</u> connection is needed. Thirdly, the type of contact is determined by the switch position to turn on the pilot light:

SS2 closed → ┤ ├

PB4 closed → ┤ ├

LS3 open → ┤/├

Putting all the pieces together, only one rung of ladder logic is needed, as shown in Figure 2.10.

Design Tip

The concept of placing the output on the rung first and then "looking back" to determine the input conditions is very important. Because of the way the diagram is configured, one has a tendency to consider the input conditions first and then position the output coil as the last step. As will be shown later, the coil or negated coil instruction referring to a particular output must only occur <u>**once**</u> in a ladder program. Considering the output coil first and the conditions for which it is active (on) will avoid repeating coils.

Example 2.5. Draw a ladder diagram that is equivalent to the digital logic diagram in Figure 2.11, which is the same as the following descriptions.

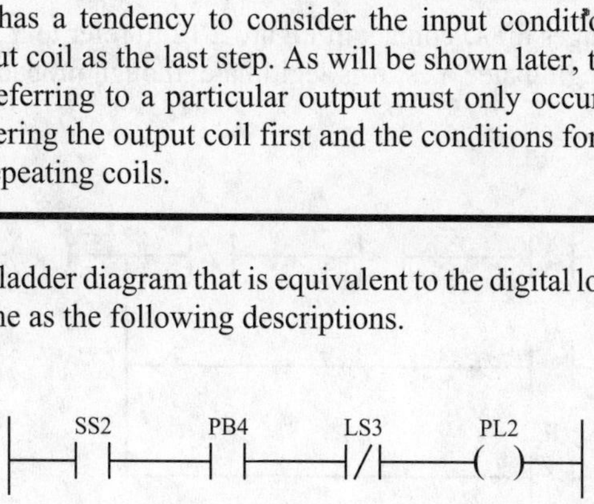

SS2 PB4 LS3 PL2

Figure 2.10. Solution to Example 2.4.

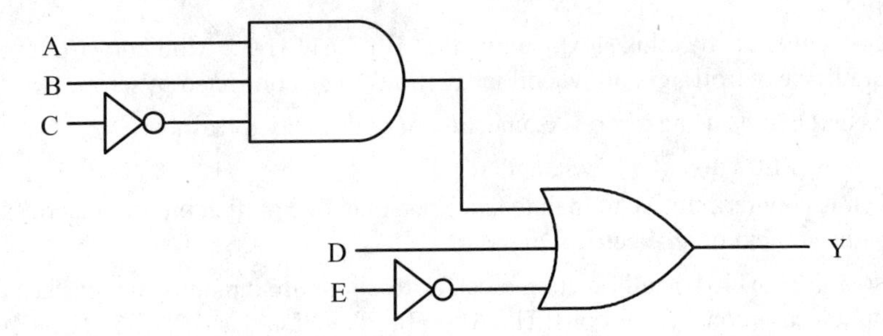

Figure 2.11. Digital logic for Example 2.5.

In words:

Y is **on** when (A is **on** and B is **on** and C is **off**) or D is **on** or E is **off**.

Boolean logic equation:

$$Y = AB\overline{C} + D + \overline{E}$$

Solution. First, answer, "What is the output?" The output is Y, so the coil labeled as Y is put on the right side of the rung. Secondly, consider the type of connection of contacts to use. For this problem, there is more than one type of connection. The three inputs within the parentheses (the AND gate in Figure 2.11) are connected with "and," so a series connection is required for these three contacts. The other two inputs (D and E) are connected with the three series contacts by "or" (the OR gate inputs), so a parallel connection is required. Thirdly, the type of contact is determined by the input state that turns **on** the output, Y:

A **on**	→	┤├	D **on**	→	┤├
B **on**	→	┤├	E **off**	→	┤/├
C **off**	→	┤/├			

Putting all the parts together, only one rung of ladder logic is needed, as shown in Figure 2.12.

Suppose one changes the D contact in Figure 2.12 to refer to Y, the output (shown as Figure 2.13). Is this legitimate? Yes, it is legitimate, though probably not something one

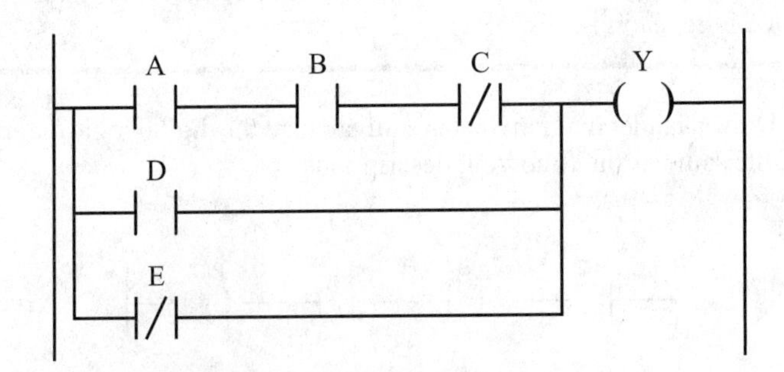

Figure 2.12. Solution to Example 2.5.

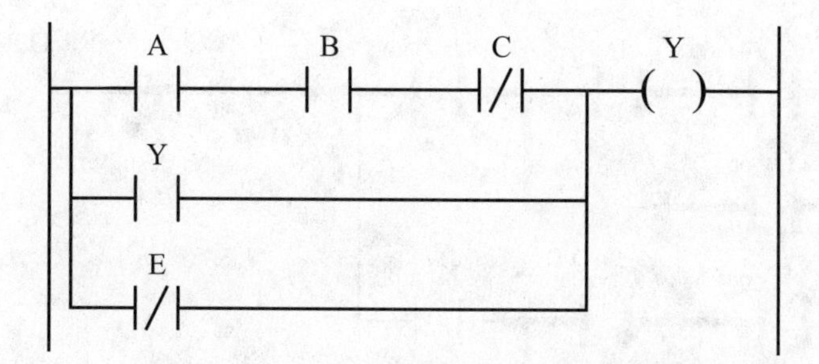

Figure 2.13. Output that appears as an input.

would want to do for this example. Even in relay ladder logic, it is legal and there is no wiring short because the coil for relay Y and its NO contact are not connected. This concept is called *sealing* or latching an output without using the set (or latch) coil instruction. In this example, it is not a good idea because once Y is sealed **on**, there is no provision to turn it off. Why?

There are some precautions to observe when programming in ladder logic:

1. **DO NOT** repeat normal output coils or negated coils that refer to the same tag. To illustrate what happens when this is done, consider the ladder logic diagram in Figure 2.14. This is the ladder of Figure 2.9, modified for this illustration. Note that the coils for both the first and second rung refer to Out1. When the first rung of the ladder is scanned, Out1 is turned **on**. However, when the second rung is scanned, Out1 is turned **off**, overriding the logic in the first rung. If all of these conditions are needed to turn on Out1, then they all should be placed in parallel, as in Figure 2.15. In this illustration, it was obvious there is a problem. Normally,

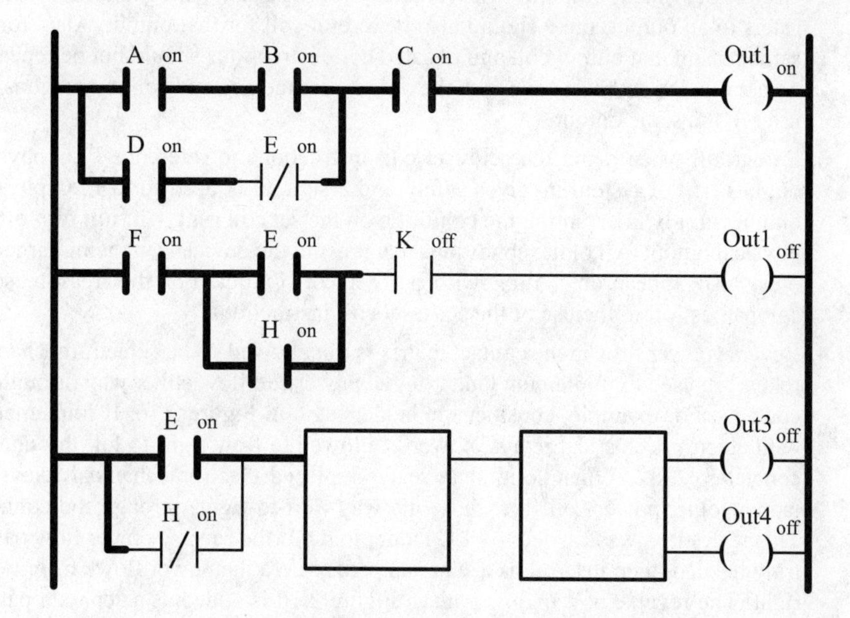

Figure 2.14. Ladder with repeated output.

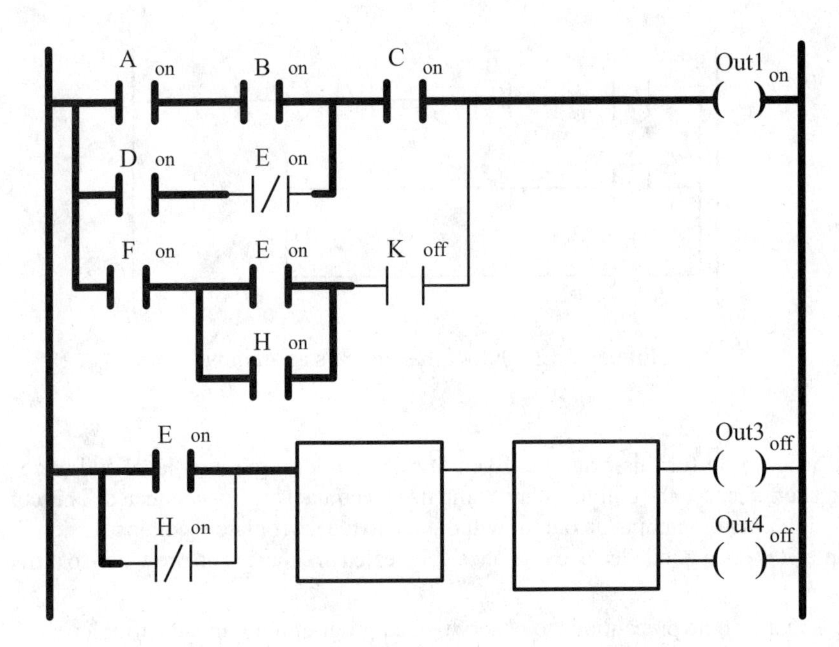

Figure 2.15. Repeated output corrected.

when this problem occurs, the rungs are not adjacent, and it is not so obvious. Compounding the problem, not all PLC programming software checks for this situation. Therefore, the best way to prevent this problem is to consider the output coil **first** and then consider all of the conditions that drive that output.

2. Use the set (latch) coil and reset (unlatch) coil instructions together. If a set coil refers to an output, there should also be a reset coil for that output. Also, for the same reason that output coil and negated coil instructions should not be repeated, do not mix the set/reset coils with the output coil and negated coil instructions that refer to the same output.
3. Be careful when using the set/reset coil instructions to reference PLC physical outputs. If the system involves safety and a set coil is used for a PLC physical output, simply interrupting the condition on the set coil rung **will not** turn off the physical output. All of the conditions that prevent the device from being turned on must also appear on a rung with a reset coil output. For this reason, some companies forbid the use of the set/reset coil instructions.
4. Reverse power flow in the contact matrix is **not** allowed. When electromechanical relays are used to implement ladder logic, power can flow either way through the contacts. For example, consider the ladder logic in Figure 2.16. If implemented with electromechanical relays, power is allowed to flow right-to-left through the contact for SS2. When solid state relays replaced electromechanical relays for ladder logic, power can flow only one way (left-to-right) through the contacts. This restriction was carried to PLC ladder logic. If the reverse power flow path is truly needed, then insert it as a separate path, where the power flows from left to right. The reverse power flow path in Figure 2.16 is added as a separate path in Figure 2.17.

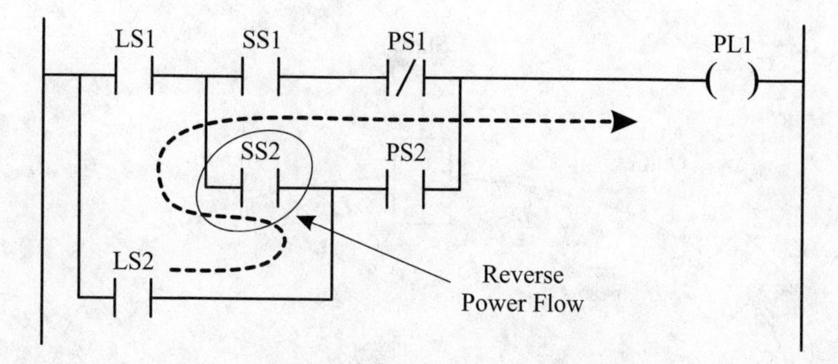

Figure 2.16. Reverse power flow in ladder logic.

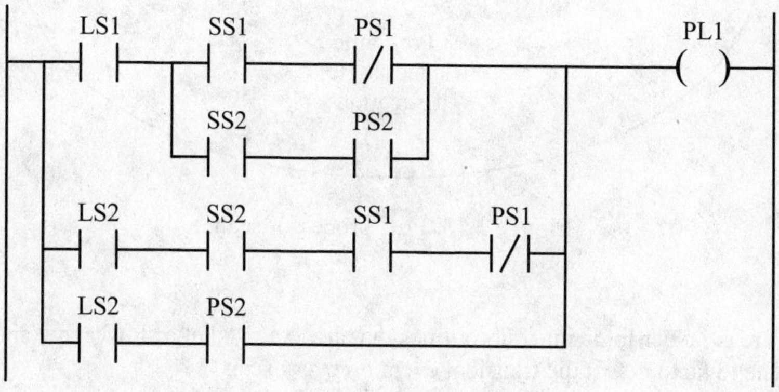

Figure 2.17. Reverse power flow in ladder logic corrected.

2.5 PLC PROCCESSOR SCAN

Previously, the process that the PLC uses to scan the ladder logic has only been implied. Now it will be discussed in detail. In addition to scanning the ladder logic, the PLC processor must also read the state of its physical inputs and set the state of the physical outputs. These three major tasks in a PLC processor scan are executed in the following order:

Read the physical inputs

Scan the ladder logic program

Write the physical outputs

The processor repeats these tasks as long as it is running, as shown pictorially in Figure 2.18. The time required to complete these three tasks is defined as the *scan time* and is typically 1 - 200 milliseconds, depending on the length of the ladder logic program. For very large ladder logic programs, the scan time can be more than one second. When this happens, the PLC program may miss transient events, especially if they are shorter than one second. In this situation, the possible solutions are:

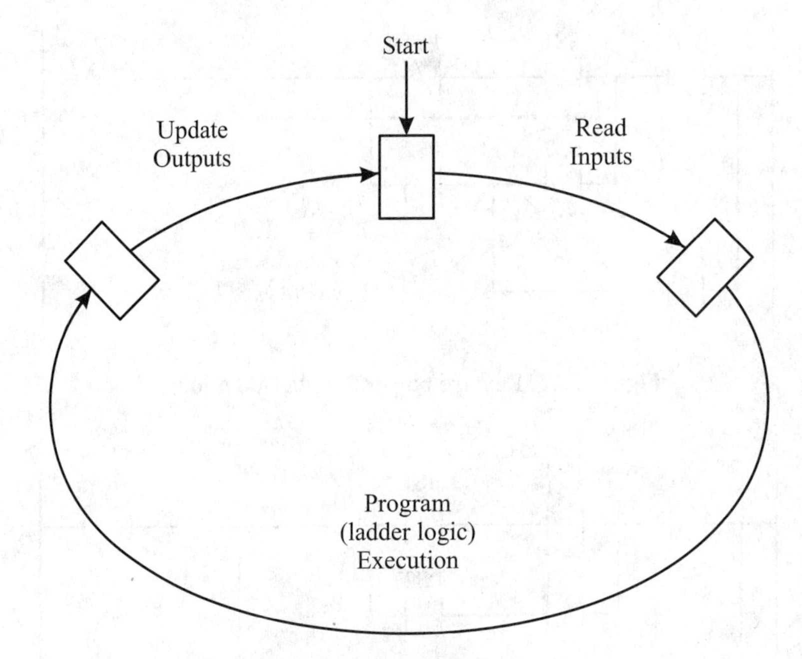

Figure 2.18. PLC processor scan.

1. Break ladder logic into subroutines that are executed at a slower rate and execute the logic to detect the transient event on every scan.
2. Lengthen the time of the transient event so that it is at least twice the maximum scan time.
3. Place the logic examining the transient in a ladder logic routine that is executed at a fixed time interval, smaller than one-half the length of the transient event.

Depending on the PLC processor, one or more of these solutions may be unavailable.

Normally, during the ladder logic program scan, changes in physical inputs cannot be sensed, nor can physical outputs be changed at the output module terminals. However, some PLC processors have an instruction that can read the current state of a physical input and another instruction that can immediately set the current state of a physical output, as shown in Figure 2.19. However, using the immediate input/output instruction incurs a severe time penalty on the program scan. For example, to scan one contact in the ladder logic typically requires less than one microsecond. The time to execute an immediate input/output instruction typically requires 200 to 300 microseconds. Consequently, these instructions are used sparingly.

Another way to view the processor scan is shown in Figure 2.20. In this figure the state of the actual physical inputs is copied to a portion of the PLC memory, commonly called the *input image table*. When the ladder logic is scanned, it examines the input image table to read the state of a physical input. When the ladder logic determines the state of a physical output, it writes to a portion of the PLC memory commonly called the *output image table*. The output image may also be examined during the ladder logic scan. To update the physical outputs, the output image table contents are copied to the physical outputs **after** the ladder logic is scanned.

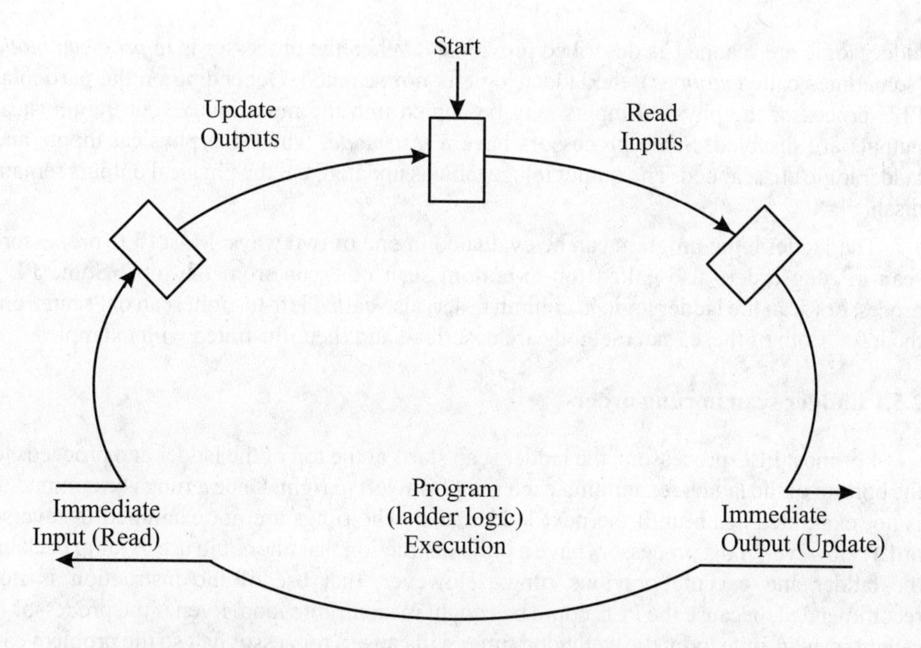

Figure 2.19. PLC processor scan with immediate input/output.

An actual PLC processor executes other tasks than the three listed above. At a minimum, it communicates with other devices and checks its own hardware for faults. These other tasks occur in the background and have some influence on the scan time but are generally not considered part of the scan time.

Most PLC processors have a *watchdog timer* that monitors the scan time. If the processor scan time exceeds the watchdog timer time-out value, the processor halts ladder program execution and signals a fault. This type of fault usually indicates the presence of an infinite loop in the ladder program or too many interrupts to the ladder scan.

In the Allen-Bradley ControlLogix, the PLC processor scan is not synchronized to the reading of the inputs and the update of the outputs. More details are contained in Chapter 3.

The overall execution of the PLC processor scan is controlled by the processor *mode*. When the PLC processor is in the *run mode*, the physical inputs, physical outputs, and

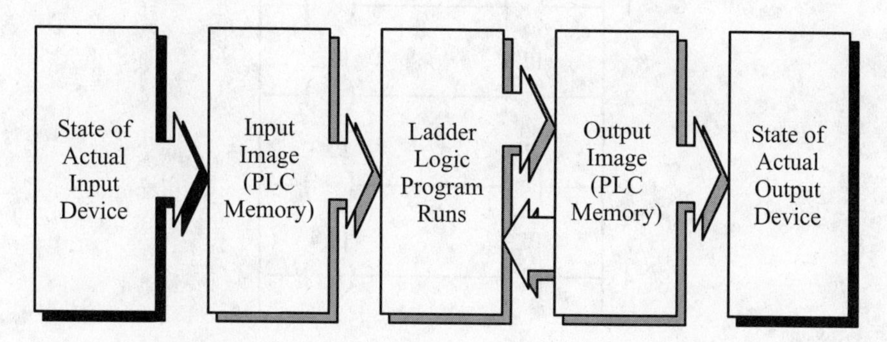

Figure 2.20. Alternate view of PLC processor scan.

ladder logic are scanned as described previously. When the processor is in *program mode* (sometimes called *stopped*), the ladder logic is **not** scanned. Depending on the particular PLC processor the physical inputs may be copied into the input image, but the physical outputs are disabled. Some processors have a *test mode*, where the physical inputs and ladder logic are scanned. The output image table is updated, but the physical outputs remain disabled.

The ladder logic program can be evaluated in one of two ways. Most PLC processors scan in rung order, also called top-to-bottom scan or "scan from the top". Some PLC processors scan the ladder logic in column order, also called left-to-right scan or "scan from the left." Both of these scan methods are described and then illustrated with examples.

2.5.1 Ladder scan in rung order

For most PLC processors, the ladder scan starts at the top of the ladder and proceeds to the bottom of the ladder, examining each rung from left to right. Once a rung is examined, it is not examined again until the next ladder scan. The rungs are not examined in reverse order. However, most processors have a jump instruction that one could use to jump back up the ladder and execute previous rungs. However, that use of the instruction is **not** recommended, because the PLC could be caught in an infinite loop. Even if the processor is caught in an infinite loop, the watchdog timer will cause a processor halt so the problem can be corrected.

Example 2.6. Show the scan timing for the ladder diagram in Figure 2.21 when it is scanned by rungs. The only physical input is PB, a push button. The physical outputs are PL1, PL2, PL3, and PL4.

Solution. When constructing a diagram showing scan timing, remember that the ladder scan uses the input and output image tables, the input image is updated before the ladder is scanned and the physical outputs are updated after the ladder is scanned. The timing diagram is shown in Figure 2.22. The widely spaced dashed vertical lines indicate the start of the processor scans. The solid lines indicate the state of the physical input or output at the module terminal. The dashed lines indicate the state of the PLC image memory corresponding to the physical input or output. Assume everything starts **off** (a value of 0).

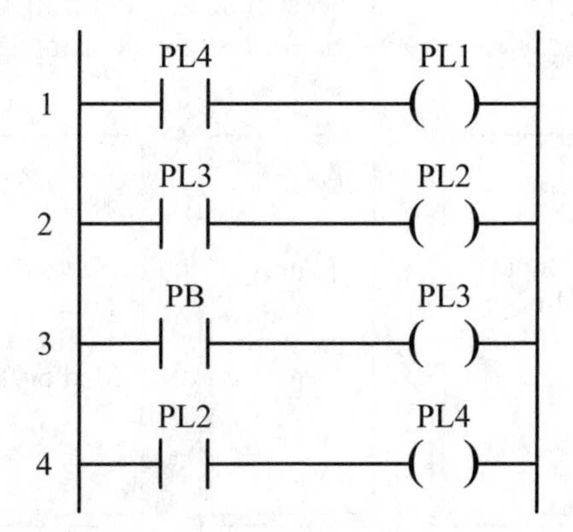

Figure 2.21. Ladder logic for Example 2.6.

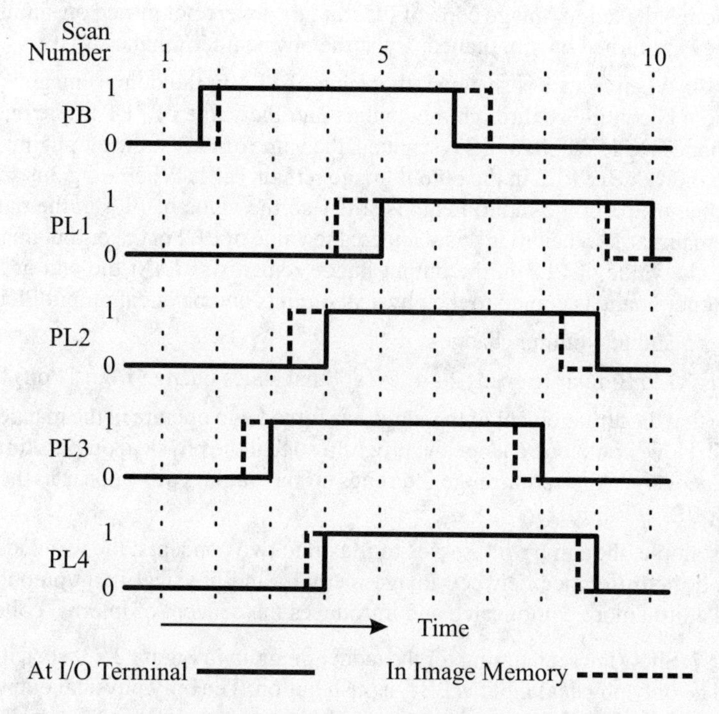

Figure 2.22. Timing diagram for Figure 2.21.

The **on** state is indicated by a value of 1. The ladder logic rungs are scanned in this order: 1, 2, 3, and 4. The actions happening during each scan are as follows:

Scan 1: Nothing happens even though physical input PB changes during the ladder scan. The new state of PB is not copied into the PLC input image until the start of the next scan.

Scan 2: The new state of PB is copied into the PLC input image before the ladder logic is scanned. When rungs 1 and 2 are scanned, the values of PL1 and PL2 in the output image remain at 0 (**off**) because the values of PL4 and PL3 are 0 in the output image. When rung 3 is scanned, the value of PB in the input image is now 1 (**on**), so there is continuity through the contact and the value of PL3 in the output image changes to 1 (**on**). When rung 4 is scanned, the value of PL4 in the output image remains at 0. At the end of scan 2, the output image is copied to the physical outputs, and the physical output PL3 turns **on**.

Scan 3: When rung 1 is scanned, the value of PL4 in the output image is 0, so the value of PL1 in the output image remains at 0. When rung 2 is scanned, the value of PL3 in the output image is now 1 so there is continuity through the contact and the value of PL2 in the output image changes to 1. When rung 3 is scanned, the value of PB in the input image is still 1, so the value of PL3 in the output image remains at 1. When rung 4 is scanned, the value of PL2 in the output image is now 1, so there is continuity through the contact and the value of PL4 in the output image changes to 1. At the end of scan 3, the output image is copied to the physical outputs and physical outputs PL2 and PL4 turn **on** simultaneously. So, even though the output image copy of PL2 and PL4 were not turned on simultaneously, they are turned on simultaneously at the physical terminal.

Scan 4: When rung 1 is scanned, the value of PL4 in the output image is now 1, so there is continuity through the contact and the value of PL1 in the output image changes to 1. When rung 2 is scanned, the value of PL3 in the output image is still 1 so the value of PL2 in the output image remains at 1. When rung 3 is scanned, the value of PB in the input image is still 1 so the value of PL3 in the output image remains at 1. When rung 4 is scanned, the value of PL2 in the output image is still 1 so the value of PL4 in the output image remains at 1. At the end of scan 3, the output image is copied to the physical outputs and physical output PL1 turns **on**.

Scans 5 and 6: Nothing changes.

Scans 7 - 9: Similar to scans 2 - 4, except that states change from 1 (**on**) to 0 (**off**).

Notice that the arrangement of the rungs has forced it to operate in the manner shown in Figure 2.22. How would one change the program so that the physical outputs turned **on** and **off** simultaneously? Answer: arrange the rungs so the output coils appear in the following order: PL3, PL2, PL4, PL1.

This example, though trivial, serves to illustrate two concepts: the way ladder logic is scanned and the difference between image memory and physical input/output. The next example is a little more complicated and introduces the concept of internal coils.

Example 2.7. Show the scan timing for the ladder diagram in Figure 2.23 when it is scanned by rungs. The only physical input is PB1, a push button. The only physical output is PL1, a pilot lamp. Int1, Int2, and Int3 are internal one-bit memory locations, often called *internal coils*. They are not attached to any physical outputs. What does this ladder logic program do?

Solution. The scan timing diagram is shown in Figure 2.24 and has the same representation as in the previous example. Assume everything starts **off** (a value of 0). The ladder logic rungs are scanned in this order: 1, 2, 3, and 4. The actions happening during each scan are as follows:

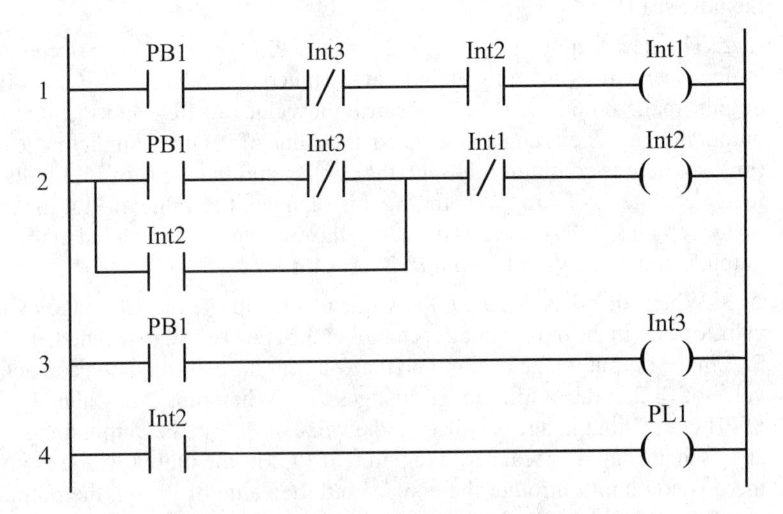

Figure 2.23. Ladder logic for Example 2.7.

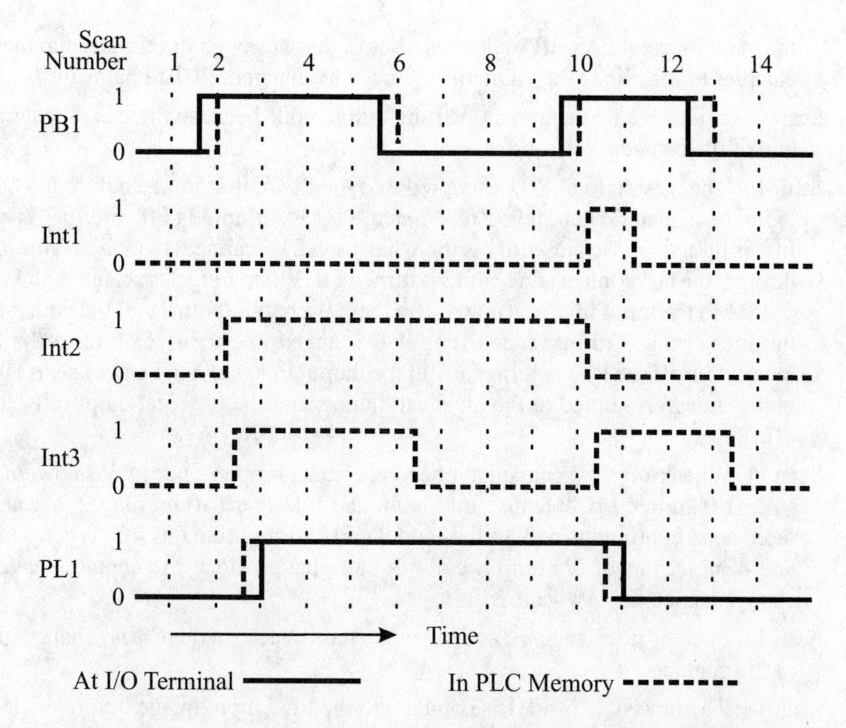

Figure 2.24. Scan timing diagram for Figure 2.23 (scan in rung order).

Scan 1: Nothing happens even though physical input PB1 changes during the ladder scan. The new state of PB1 is not copied into the PLC input image until the start of the next scan.

Scan 2: The new state of PB1 is copied into the PLC input image before the ladder logic is scanned. When rung 1 is scanned, PB1 is **on**, and Int3 is **off**, so the first two contacts pass power, but Int2 is off. So, Int1 remains **off**. When rung 2 is scanned, there is continuity along the top path, so Int2 is turned **on**. When rung 3 is scanned, the value of PB1 in the input image is now **on**, so there is continuity through the contact and the Int3 changes to **on**. Note that this change in Int3 will not be sensed by the first two rungs until the next scan. When rung 4 is scanned, the value of Int2 in the PLC memory is **on**, so PL1 is turned **on** in the output image. At the end of scan 2, the output image is copied to the physical outputs and the physical output PL1 turns **on**.

Scan 3: There is no change in the rung output coils, though some of the contacts in the first two rungs have changed since last scanned. When rung 1 is scanned, there is now continuity through the first and third contact, but not through the second (Int3 is **off**). When rung 2 is scanned, there is no continuity through the top branch, but there is continuity through the bottom branch, and so Int2 remains **on**.

Scans 4-5: There is no change in the rung output coils because there is no change in any of the contacts.

Scan 6: The new state of PB1 is copied into the PLC input image before the ladder logic is scanned. When rungs 1 and 2 are scanned, there is no change in the output coils even though PB1 has changed. When rung 3 is scanned, the value of PB1 in the input image is now **off** so there is no continuity through the contact and the Int3 changes to **off**. Since the value of Int2 has not changed, PL1 remains **on**.

Scans 7-9: There is no change in the rung output coils because there is no change in any of the contacts.

Scan 10: The new state of PB1 is copied into the PLC input image before the ladder logic is scanned. When rung 1 is scanned, PB1 is **on**, Int3 is **off**, and Int2 is **on** so Int1 is turned **on**. Because Int1 is **on**, when rung 2 is scanned, there is no continuity through the last contact and so Int2 is turned **off**. When rung 3 is scanned, the value of PB1 in the input image is now **on** so there is continuity through the contact and the Int3 changes to **on**. When rung 4 is scanned, the value of Int2 in the PLC memory is **off**, so PL1 is turned **off** in the output image. At the end of scan 10, the output image is copied to the physical outputs and the physical output PL1 turns **off**.

Scan 11: When rung 1 is scanned, the second contact is open since Int3 is now **on**, and so Int1 is turned **off**. Because Int3 is **on** and Int2 is **off** when rung 2 is scanned, there is no continuous path to the output coil and Int2 remains **off**. When rungs 3 and 4 are scanned, the output coils do not change since the contacts have not changed since the last scan.

Scan 12: There is no change in the rung output coils because there is no change in any of the contacts.

Scan 13: The new state of PB1 is copied into the PLC input image before the ladder logic is scanned. When rungs 1 and 2 are scanned, there is no change in the output coils even though PB1 has changed. When rung 3 is scanned, the value of PB1 in the input image is now **off** so there is no continuity through the contact and the Int3 changes to **off**. Since the value of Int2 has not changed, PL1 remains **off**.

What does this ladder program do? This is called a "toggle" or "push-to-start, push-to-stop" circuit. Every time the push button PB1 is pushed (turned **on**), PL1 changes its state.

2.5.2 Ladder scan by columns

Some PLC processors, most notable the Modicon x84 PLCs, scan the ladder by columns. A pictorial representation of this method of ladder scan is shown in Figure 2.25. Rather than scan all of the columns in the entire ladder, the ladder is divided into networks of 7 rows and 11 columns. The first 10 columns may have contacts or coils; the last column may only have coils. The first (leftmost) column of contacts is scanned from top to bottom and then the next column to the right is scanned in the same way. When a coil is encountered, its value is based on the value of the logic in the cell immediately left of the coil. Each column is examined and lastly the column of outputs is scanned, setting or resetting them.

Example 2.8. Show the scan timing for the ladder diagram in Figure 2.23 when it is scanned by columns. The only physical input is PB1, a push button. The only physical output is PL1, a pilot lamp. As for Example 2.7, Int1, Int2, and Int3 are internal one-bit memory locations.

Solution. The scan timing diagram is shown in Figure 2.26 and has the same representation as in the previous example. Assume everything starts **off** (a value of 0). The entire ladder logic is contained in one network using 5 rows (the second rung occupies 2 rows) and 4

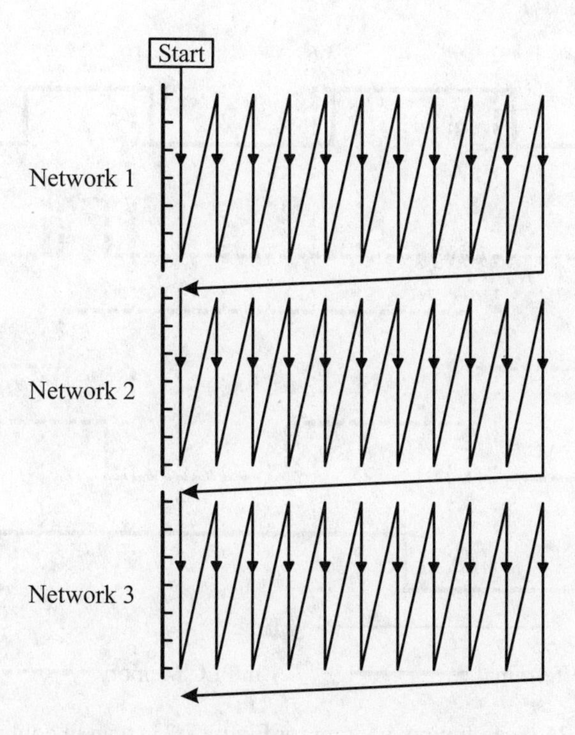

Figure 2.25. Scanning ladder by columns.

columns numbered from the left as 1, 2, 3, and 4. The actions happening during each scan are as follows:

Scan 1: Nothing happens even though physical input PB1 changes during the ladder scan. The new state of PB1 is not copied into the PLC input image until the start of the next scan.

Scan 2: The new state of PB1 is copied into the PLC input image before the ladder logic is scanned. When a column is scanned, the current status (**off** or **on**) of the row element is the combination of the current contact and the status of the row elements to the immediate left. A horizontal wire row element is interpreted as an always-closed contact. When column 1 is scanned, the row statuses (from the top) are determined by the current contact continuity: **on**, **on**, **off**, **on**, **off**. When column 2 is scanned, the row statuses (from the top) are determined by the status of the previous column and the contact continuity: **on, on, off, on, off**. When column 3 is scanned, the row statuses are: **off, on,** —, **on, off**. When column 4 is scanned, the coils are set to the row statuses from the previous column: **off, on,** —, **on, off**. So, as a result of this scan, Int2 and Int3 are turned **on**.

Scan 3: When column 1 is scanned, the row statuses (from the top) are determined by the current contact continuity: **on, on, on, on, on**. When column 2 is scanned, the row statuses are: **off** (Int3 is **on**), **off, on, on, on**. When column 3 is scanned, the row statuses are: **off, on,** —, **on, on**. When column 4 is scanned, the coils are set to the row statuses from the previous column: **off, on,** —, **on, on**. So, as a result of

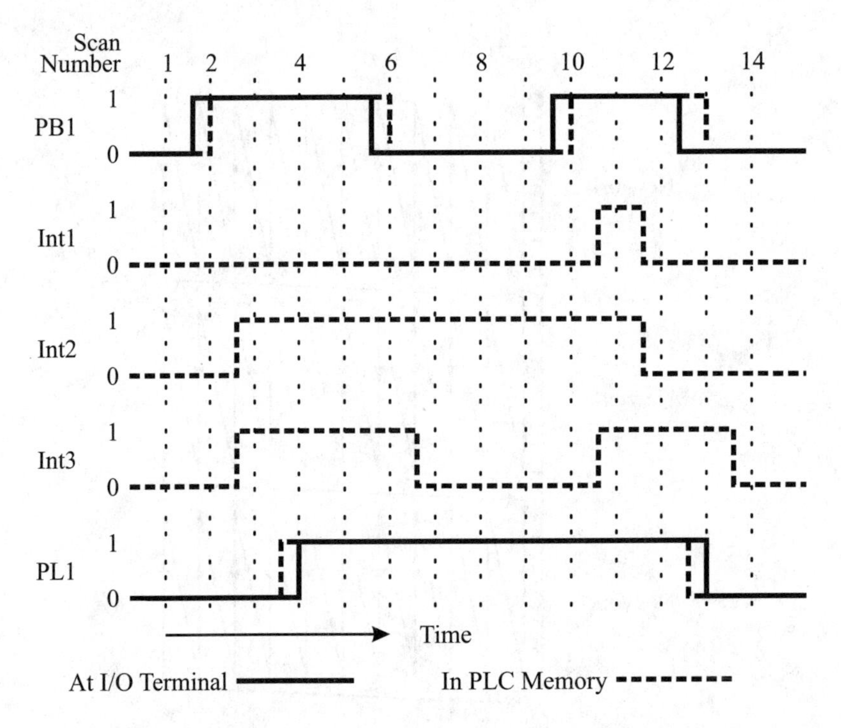

Figure 2.26. Scan timing diagram for Figure 2.23 (scan in column order).

this scan, PL1 is turned **on** in the output image. At the end of scan 3, the output image is copied to the physical outputs, and the physical output PL1 turns **on**.

Scans 4-5: There is no change in the rung output coils because there is no change in any of the contacts.

Scan 6: When column 1 is scanned, the row statuses (from the top) are: **off, off, on, off, on**. When column 2 is scanned, the row statuses are: **off, off, on, off, on**. When column 3 is scanned, the row statuses are: **off, on**, —, **off, on**. When column 4 is scanned, the coils are set to the row statuses from the previous column: **off, on**, —, **off, on**. So, as a result of this scan Int3 is turned **off**.

Scans 7-9: There is no change in the rung output coils because there is no change in any of the contacts.

Scan 10: The new state of PB1 is copied into the PLC input image before the ladder logic is scanned. When column 1 is scanned, the row statuses (from the top) are: **on, on, on, on, on**. When column 2 is scanned, the row statuses are: **on, on, on, on, on**. When column 3 is scanned, the row statuses are: **on, on**, —, **on, on**. When column 4 is scanned, the coils are set to the row statuses from the previous column: **on, on**, —, **on, on**. So, as a result of this scan, Int1 and Int3 are turned **on**.

Scan 11: When column 1 is scanned, the row statuses (from the top) are: **on, on, on, on, on**. When column 2 is scanned, the row statuses are: **off, off, on, on, on**. When column 3 is scanned, the row statuses are: **off, off**, —, **on, on**. When column 4 is scanned, the coils are set to the row statuses from the previous column: **off, off**, —, **on, on**. So, as a result of this scan, Int1 and Int2 are turned **off**.

Scan 12: When column 1 is scanned, the row statuses (from the top) are: **on**, **on**, **off**, **on**, **off**. When column 2 is scanned, the row statuses are: **off**, **off**, **off**, **on**, **off**. When column 3 is scanned, the row statuses are: **off**, **off**, —, **on**, **off**. When column 4 is scanned, the coils are set to the row statuses from the previous column: **off**, **off**, —, **on**, **off**. So, as a result of this scan, PL1 is turned **off** in the output image. At the end of this scan, the output image is copied to the physical outputs, and the physical output PL1 turns **off**.

Scan 13: The new state of PB1 is copied into the PLC input image before the ladder logic is scanned. As a result of this scan, Int3 changes to **off** when the fourth column is scanned.

If the scan timing diagram in Figure 2.26 (scan by column) is compared with the scan timing diagram of Figure 2.24 (scan by rung), the only major difference is that one or two extra scans are required to resolve the logic after PB1 changes state. However, PB1 does not need to be **on** for at least two scans in order for the logic to resolve correctly. Why?

If it is important that the logic be resolved on the scan after PB1 is pressed, the ladder logic of Figure 2.22 can be modified in one of two ways:

1. Move the contact for Int2 on the fifth row (last rung) from the first column to the fourth column and move the coil for PL1 to the fifth column of the fifth row. This change guarantees that PL1 is set to the same value as Int2 on the same scan.
2. Delete the fifth row and move the coil for PL1 to be in parallel with the coil for Int2.

2.6 PROGRAMMING WITH NC CONTACT

Many novice PLC ladder logic programmers tend to use the same type of contact (NO or NC) in the ladder that corresponds to the type of field switch (or sensor) wired to the discrete input channel. While this is true in many cases, this is not the best way to think of the concept.

A NO switch does not require a ─┤ ├─ **in the ladder logic.**

A NC switch does not require a ─┤/├─ **in the ladder logic.**

The PLC only knows one thing about the discrete input: whether it is **on** (closed) or **off** (open). The PLC knows nothing about how the switch is wired in the field; whether it is NO held open, NO held closed, NC held open, or any other combination.

For example, safety switches are generally NC switches, but the contact in the ladder logic that refers to the safety switch is generally a NO contact. The reason for this type of safety switch will be explained in the next section.

Regardless of the type of switch in the field, the principle to remember is

If one wants "action" (turn ON) when the switch is closed, use ─┤ ├─

If one wants "action" (turn ON) when the switch is open, use ─┤/├─

As explained earlier in this chapter, think of the contact as a symbol

—| |— = **on** = Closed = True = 1

—|/|— = **off** = Open = False = 0

An alternative view of this concept is to consider the contact symbol in the ladder as the unenergized state of the discrete input:

has no continuity (**off**, or false) when the discrete input is **off**. Consequently, when the discrete input is **on**, the contact has continuity (**on**, or true).

has continuity (**on**, or true) when the discrete input is **off**. Consequently, when the discrete input is **on**, the contact has no continuity (**off**, or false).

To illustrate this concept, consider the system in Figure 2.27*a* that is a simple water level control system. S1 is a NC safety switch and FS1 is a NO float switch. The water inlet valve V1 should be **on** (fill tank) when S1 is **closed** and FS1 is **open**. The ladder logic rung to accomplish this operation is shown in Figure 2.27*b*. Notice that for both switches, the contact used in the ladder is the opposite of the type of field switch. The type of field switch is irrelevant to the PLC ladder logic. The type of contact in the PLC ladder logic is determined by the operation description

V1 is **on** when S1 is **closed** and FS1 is **open**.

S1 closed → —| |—

FS1 open → —|/|—

Design Tip

The type of contact (NO, NC) in the field is determined by safety or fail-safe factors, but **these factors are not relevant to the PLC ladder logic**. The PLC is concerned only about the current state of the discrete input (open or closed).

2.7 START/STOP

The concept described in the previous section will be reinforced when we consider the problem of starting and stopping a motor with momentary switches. The motor is representative of any device that must run continuously but started and stopped with momentary switches.

This problem is handled in two parts: starting and stopping. How do I start a motor and keep it running with a momentary normally open push button switch? The switch closes to start the motor and when it is released (opened) the motor should continue to run. Obviously, one needs to add a contact in parallel with the start switch contact that maintains continuity when the start switch is opened. One way is to use the PLC output that drives the motor to seal around the start switch contact, as shown in Figure 2.28. Note that the MOTOR output does not directly control the motor (the PLC output cannot handle high currents) but represents the input to a motor contactor or motor controller.

The second part of the problem is to add a stop switch. The stop switch is a normally closed push button switch, (push) open to stop, closed to run. A contact for this stop switch needs to be added in series with the motor coil, as shown in Figure 2.29. Notice that the

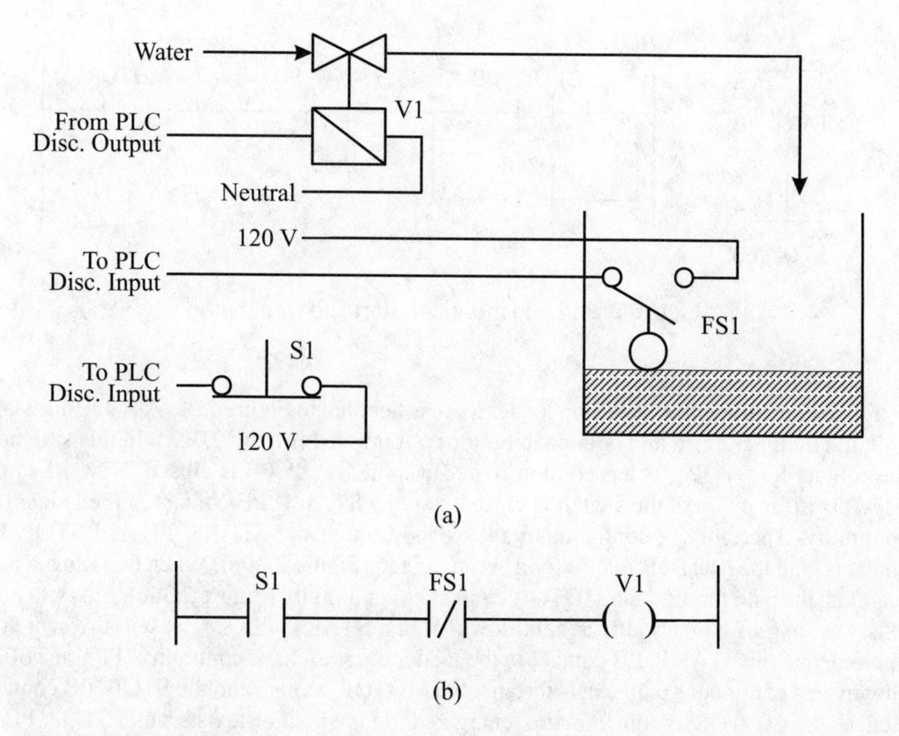

Figure 2.27. Example showing differences in field switch and ladder logic contact: *(a)* simple level control system; *(b)* PLC ladder logic.

contact in the ladder logic is a NO contact, which is not the same as the NC push button stop switch. This is a common situation where the novice PLC programmer makes a mistake. Many people do not resolve the issue for themselves until they actually program it the wrong way (use a NC contact for the stop switch) and then understand the correct concept.

> ## Design Tip
>
> In PLC ladder logic, use the NO contact instruction for physical stop switches. This is not universal, but any physical stop switch that is not closed to run probably should be replaced for safety reasons.

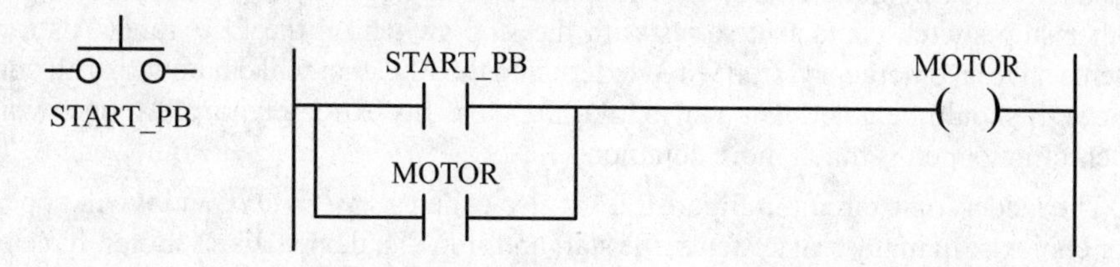

Figure 2.28. Ladder logic to start motor with momentary switch.

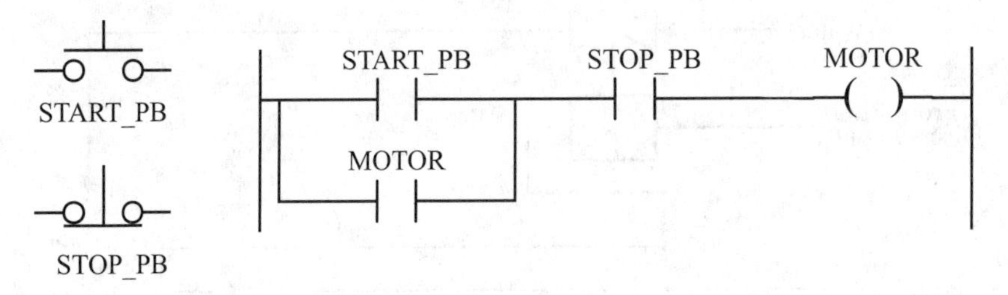

Figure 2.29. Ladder logic to start and stop motor.

The operation of the start/stop ladder logic is detailed in Figure 2.30. Assume one starts with the motor stopped and both push buttons not pressed (Figure 2.30*a*). In this situation, the contact for STOP_PB has continuity because the STOP_PB is **closed**. Now when the START_PB is pressed, the switch is **closed**, and the START_PB contact in the ladder has continuity. Therefore, a continuous path exists through the START_PB and STOP_PB contacts, and the MOTOR output (coil) is energized (Figure 2.30*b*). When this rung is next scanned, the path through the MOTOR contact has continuity (Figure 2.30*c*). This situation exists as long as START_PB is held down. When START_PB is released, the switch is **opened**, and the START_PB contact in the ladder does not have continuity (Figure 2.30*d*). However, a continuous path exists through the MOTOR contact and the STOP_PB contact. Hence, the MOTOR output remains energized. This situation exists until STOP_PB is pressed. When STOP_PB is pressed, the switch is **opened**, and the STOP_PB contact in the ladder does not have continuity (Figure 2.30*e*). Thus, there is no continuous path to the MOTOR output, and it is de-energized, which stops the motor. Now the system is in the same state as when the description of its operation commenced.

The questions arise: "Why are the switches wired this way?"; "Why not use normally open push button switches for the start switch and the stop switch?"; "Why not use normally closed switches for both?" The switches are wired this way for safety reasons. If any part of the system fails (switch or wiring), the motor will go to a safe state. If the start switch wiring is faulty (open wire), then the motor cannot be started because the PLC will not sense a closed start switch. If the stop switch wiring is faulty (open wire), then the motor will immediately stop if it is running. Also, the motor cannot be started with an open wire to the stop switch. Since the operator has lost control over stopping the motor, the safe state is one in which the motor is stopped.

However, these types of switches do not automatically handle all failures. If the start switch fails so that its contact is always closed, the stop push button must be held in to prevent the motor from starting. In this case, the circuit breaker at the motor controller must be opened to stop the motor. If the stop push button fails so that the contact is always closed, the ladder logic cannot de-energize the motor. To handle this situation, many systems have another stop switch contact in series with the stop switch on the PLC rung. Also, most systems have an emergency-stop wired external to the PLC that will cut power to all control devices. It should be noted that a switch failing closed is extremely rare. An open wire or switch failing open is much more common.

The ladder logic circuit in Figure 2.29 is also called a *seal circuit*, and it will appear in other contexts. In many real systems, the start and stop of a device, like a motor, have more conditions that must be satisfied in order for the motor to run. These conditions are referred to as *permissives*, *permits*, *lockouts*, *inhibits*, or *restrictions*. These conditions appear on the

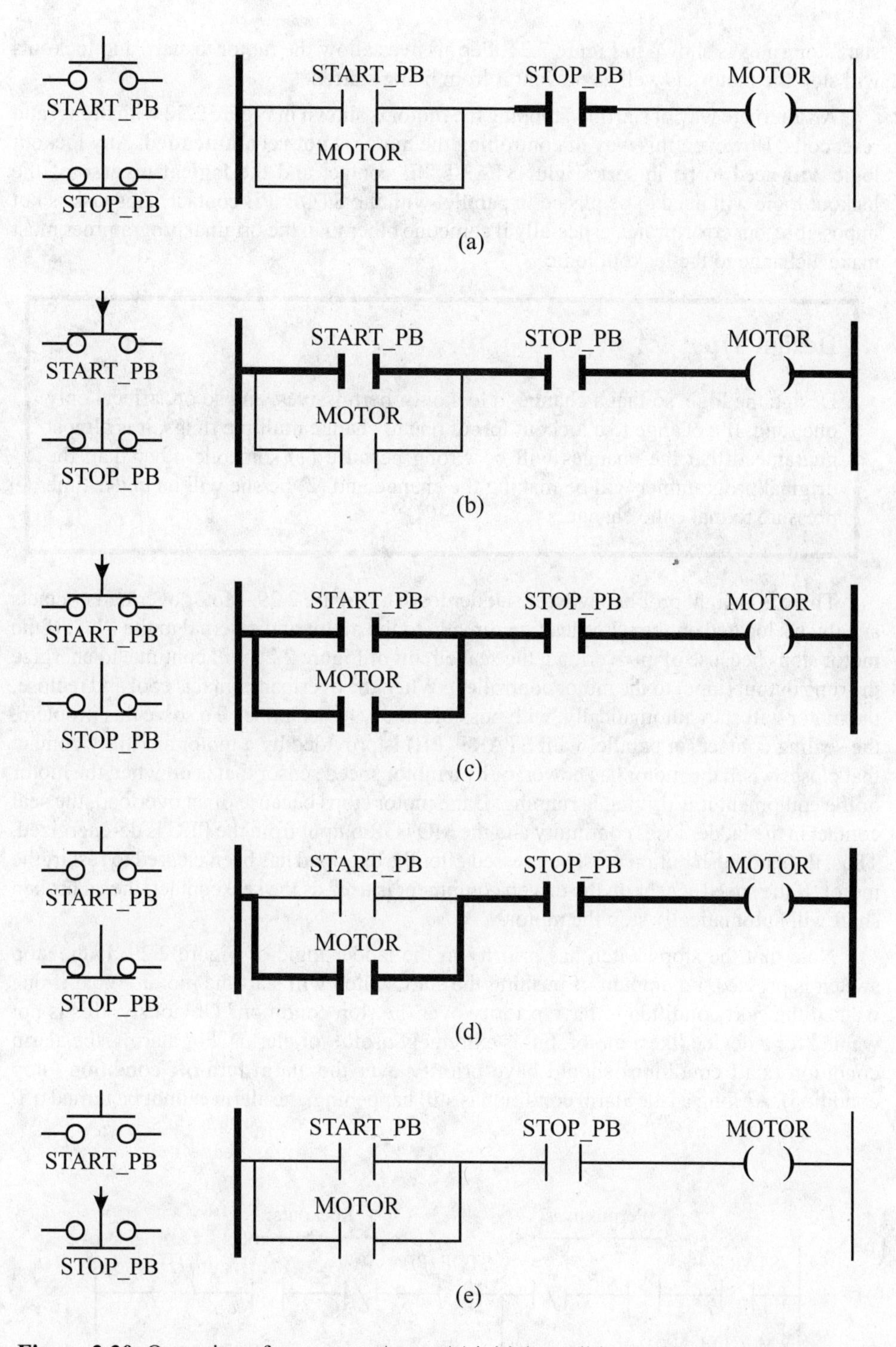

Figure 2.30. Operation of motor start/stop: *(a)* initial conditions; *(b)* start switch pressed; *(c)* scan after start switch pressed; *(d)* start switch released; *(e)* stop switch pressed.

start/stop rung as shown in Figure 2.31. Permissives allow the motor to start, and lockouts will stop the motor, as well as prevent it from being started.

An alternate way of starting/stopping the motor is shown in Figure 2.32 with the set and reset coils. However, this way of controlling the motor is **not recommended**. Any lockout logic will need to be in series with START_PB contact and the **logical inverse** of the lockout logic will need to be placed in parallel with the STOP_PB contact. This task is not impossible, but error-prone, especially if someone other than the original programmer must make a change to the lockout logic.

Design Tip

Design the logic so that a change to lockouts, permissives, and so on, affects only one rung. If a change to a lockout forces one to change multiple rungs, it is almost guaranteed that the changes will be wrong because (1) someone other than the original programmer will be making the change and (2) he/she will be under time pressure to make the change.

There is a slight problem with the ladder logic of Figure 2.29. Motor overload contacts are always located on the wires leading directly to the motor and external to the PLC. If the motor stops because of an overload, the seal circuit of Figure 2.29 will continue to energize the rung output (input to the motor controller). When the overload contacts cool and reclose, the motor will start automatically, with possible injury to personnel. To solve this problem, the sealing contact (in parallel with START_PB) is provided by a motor auxiliary contact that closes when the motor has power, or by a motor speed sensor that is **on** when the motor or the equipment it is driving is running. If the motor stops because of an overload, the seal contact in the ladder loses continuity and the MOTOR output from the PLC is de-energized. Thus, the start push button must be pressed after the overload has been cleared to restart the motor. If the speed sensor on the driven equipment is used as the seal contact, then a broken shaft will automatically stop the motor.

Note that the stop switch has priority in the ladder logic of Figure 2.29. If the stop switch is pressed, no amount of pushing the start switch will start the motor. What if one wanted the start condition to have priority over the stop condition? Obviously, this is not wanted for a device like a motor, but is extremely useful for alarms. For alarms, the alarm condition (start condition) should have priority over the alarm turn-off condition (stop condition). As long as the alarm condition is still happening, the alarm cannot be turned off.

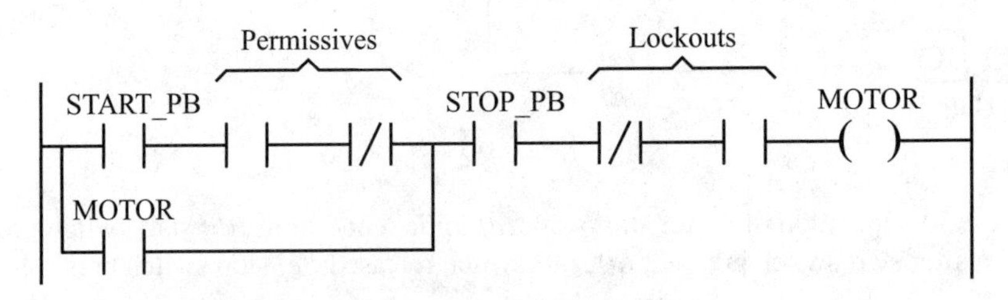

Figure 2.31. Start/stop with permissives and lockouts.

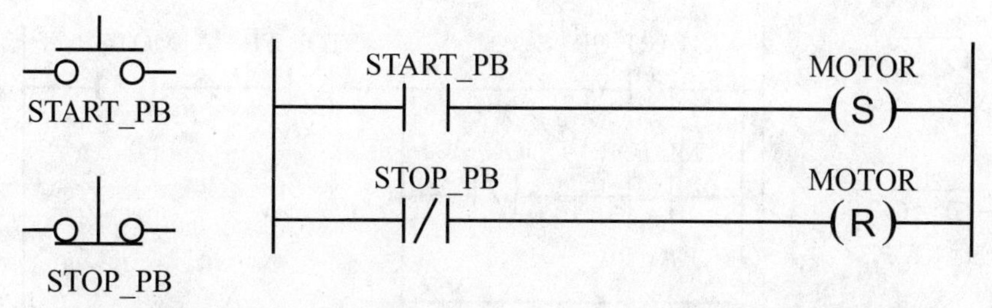

Figure 2.32. Start/stop with set and reset coils (**not recommended**).

This type of start/stop ladder is shown in Figure 2.33. Note that Alarm_Off is **on** to turn off the alarm (as long as Alarm_Condition is **off**).

Example 2.9. Add a jog switch to the motor start/stop ladder logic of Figure 2.29. The jog switch is a normally open push button switch that when pressed (closed) runs the motor as long as it is held in. If the stop push button switch is pressed, the motor should immediately stop if the jog or start switches are closed. The jog switch should have no effect if the motor is already running.

Solution. One may be tempted to just place the JOG_PB contact in parallel with the START_PB contact, but then the jog switch functions as another start switch. When it is released, the motor will still be running. So the seal circuit will need to drive an internal coil INT_MOTOR instead of the motor coil directly. The INT_MOTOR internal coil, in parallel with the jog and stop switches, drives the motor coil. This ladder logic is shown in Figure 2.34.

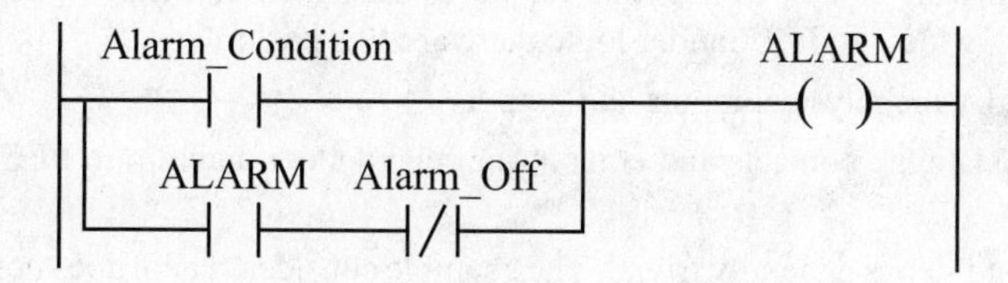

Figure 2.33. Start/stop with start priority.

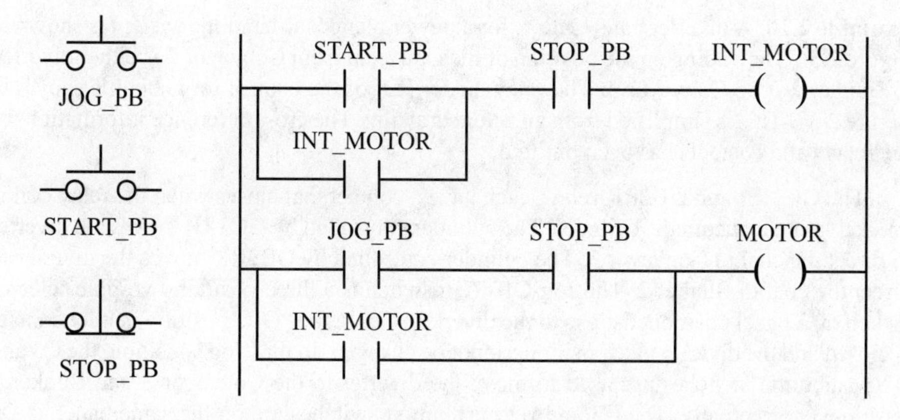

Figure 2.34. Start/stop/jog motor control.

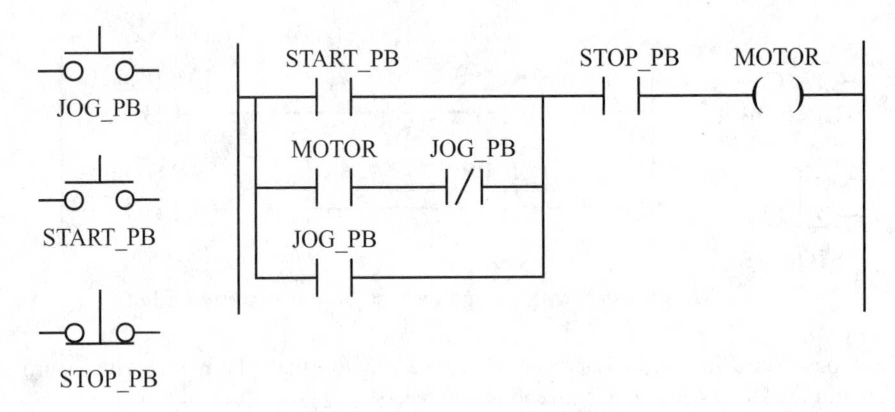

Figure 2.35. Incorrect start/stop/jog motor control.

Figure 2.35 shows one incorrect solution to this problem. At first glance, it seems correct because the motor is not sealed when the JOG_PB contact is pressed. However, when the JOG_PB is released, there is continuity through the middle branch because at that instant MOTOR is **on** and JOG_PB is **off**, and so MOTOR remains **on**.

2.8 CONVERTING RELAY LOGIC TO LADDER LOGIC

Even though relay logic systems are largely obsolete, one occasionally needs to replace a relay system with a PLC. Hence, this subject is examined in a little more detail. When converting relay logic to PLC ladder logic there are two basic steps:

1. Identify the physical inputs and outputs.
2. Translate the contacts and coils in the relay ladder diagram to PLC contacts and coils.

The second step is generally trivial. The example considered here does not consider any emergency switches controlling power to the physical equipment. This installation issue is treated in Chapter 4. Also, the particular example in this section has no delays or timers, which are treated in Chapter 5.

Example 2.10. A diverter gate, Gate 4, for a power plant coal-handling system is shown in Figure 2.36. Depending on the position of the gate, coal from Conveyor 2 is either diverted to Bunker 2 or to Conveyor 3. The relay ladder part of the control for Gate 4 is shown in Figure 2.37. This is simplified from an actual drawing. The cross-reference information for the relays and contacts has been omitted.

The GC3RR and GB2RR relays each have a contact that closes when the relay coil is on, activating a pneumatic cylinder. The cylinder controlled by GC3RR moves the diverter to direct the coal to Conveyor 3. The cylinder controlled by GB2RR moves the diverter to direct the coal to Bunker 2. The Jog-Off-Rem switch is a three-position two-pole selector switch on a panel positioned close to the diverter gate. In the "Off" position neither contact is closed and the diverter gate position cannot be changed. In the "Jog" position, the C3 and B2 pushbutton switches are used to move the diverter to the Conveyor 3 and Bunker 2 positions, respectively. The C3 and B2 pushbutton switches are on the same panel as the Jog-Off-Rem switch. When the Jog-Off-Rem switch is in the "Rem" position, the diverter

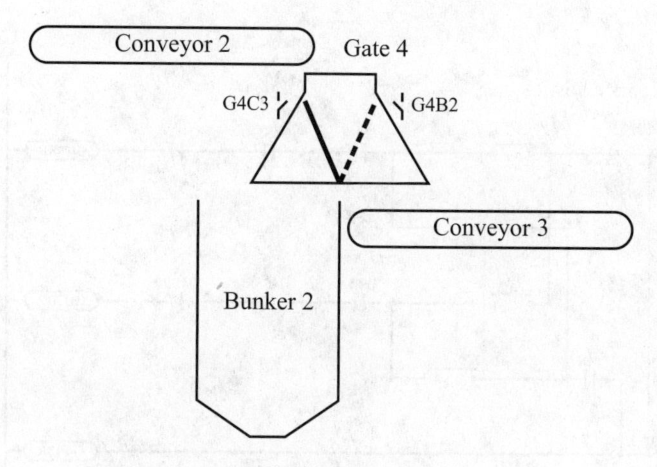

Figure 2.36. Coal handling diverter, Gate 4.

is controlled by the B2-C3 selector switch, mounted on a panel in the control room, some distance from the diverter. There is safety switch, G4SS, which must be closed for the diverter to operate. There are also limit switches, G4C3 and G4B2, that indicate when the diverter is in proper position to divert coal to Conveyor 3 or Bunker 2. Convert this relay ladder to PLC ladder logic.

Solution. The first step is to identify the physical inputs and outputs. Dashed circles in Figure 2.38 show the physical inputs that must be retained. The outputs that must be retained are shown by dashed rectangles. The two outputs driving the pneumatic cylinder valves must be relay contacts to be compatible with the existing equipment. Also, power must be supplied to both poles of the B2-C3 selector switch so that their closure can be detected by the PLC. The input and output wiring is shown in Figure 2.39. Note that a connection from L1 (line) to both poles of the B2-C3 selector switch has been added. An exact translation to ladder logic is shown in Figure 2.40. However, notice that the internal relays G4RSR, G4SSR, G4B2R, and G4C3R are merely copies of physical inputs, so they can be replaced by references to the physical inputs. Also, since the GC3RR and GB2RR relays only drive the G4C3_SOL and G4B2_SOL physical outputs, they can be replaced by the physical outputs. This PLC ladder is shown in Figure 2.41. However, in this application the GC3RR, GB2RR, G4RSR, G4B2R, and G4C3R internal coils are referenced in other parts of the ladder logic. Consequently, any reference to these coils must be replaced by the appropriate reference in other parts of the ladder. For a large project, it may be deemed simpler to utilize the exact translation and not worry about removing the duplicates, especially if the relay logic drawings do not cross-reference the coils with the their use as contacts.

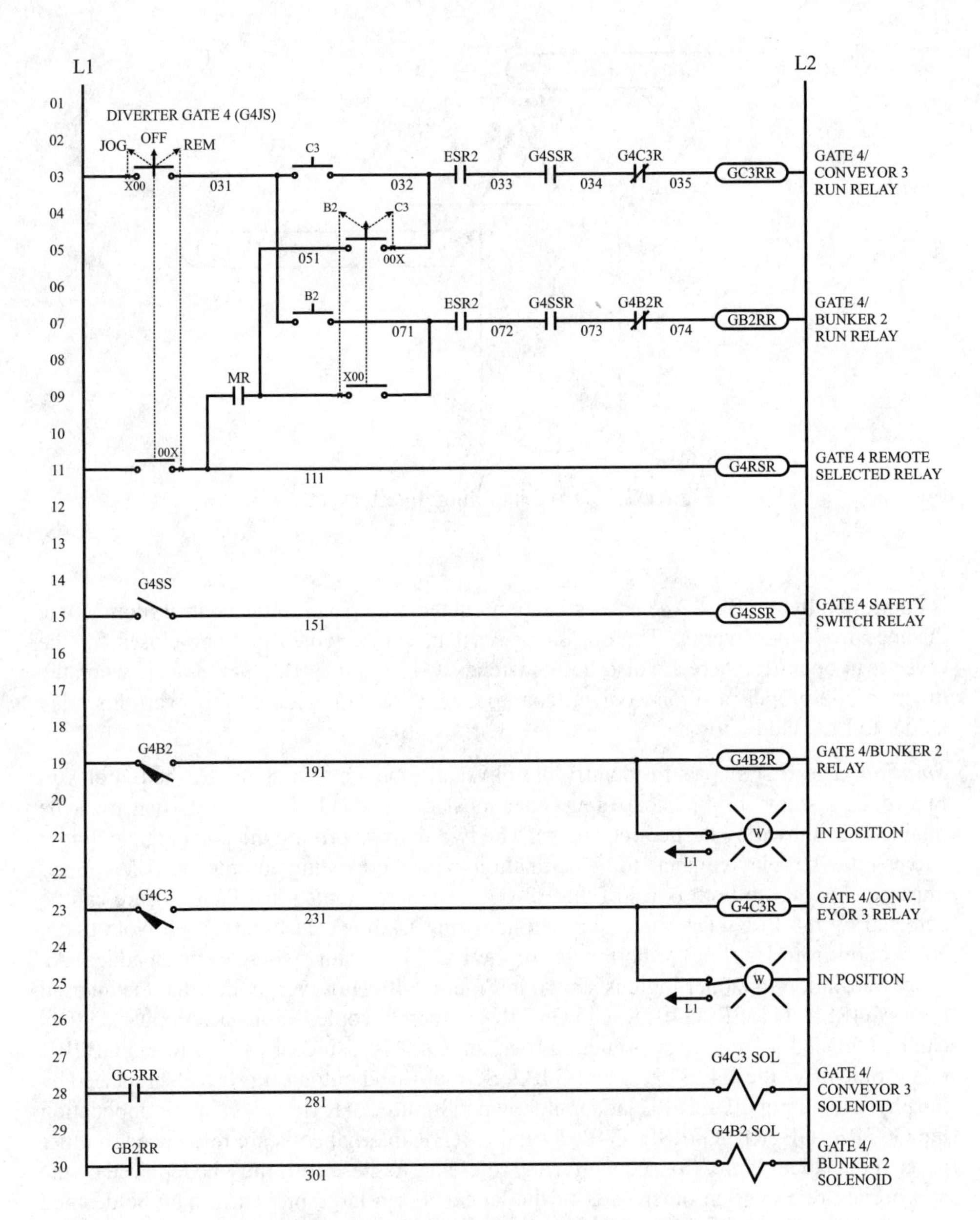

Figure 2.37. Relay ladder control for Gate 4.

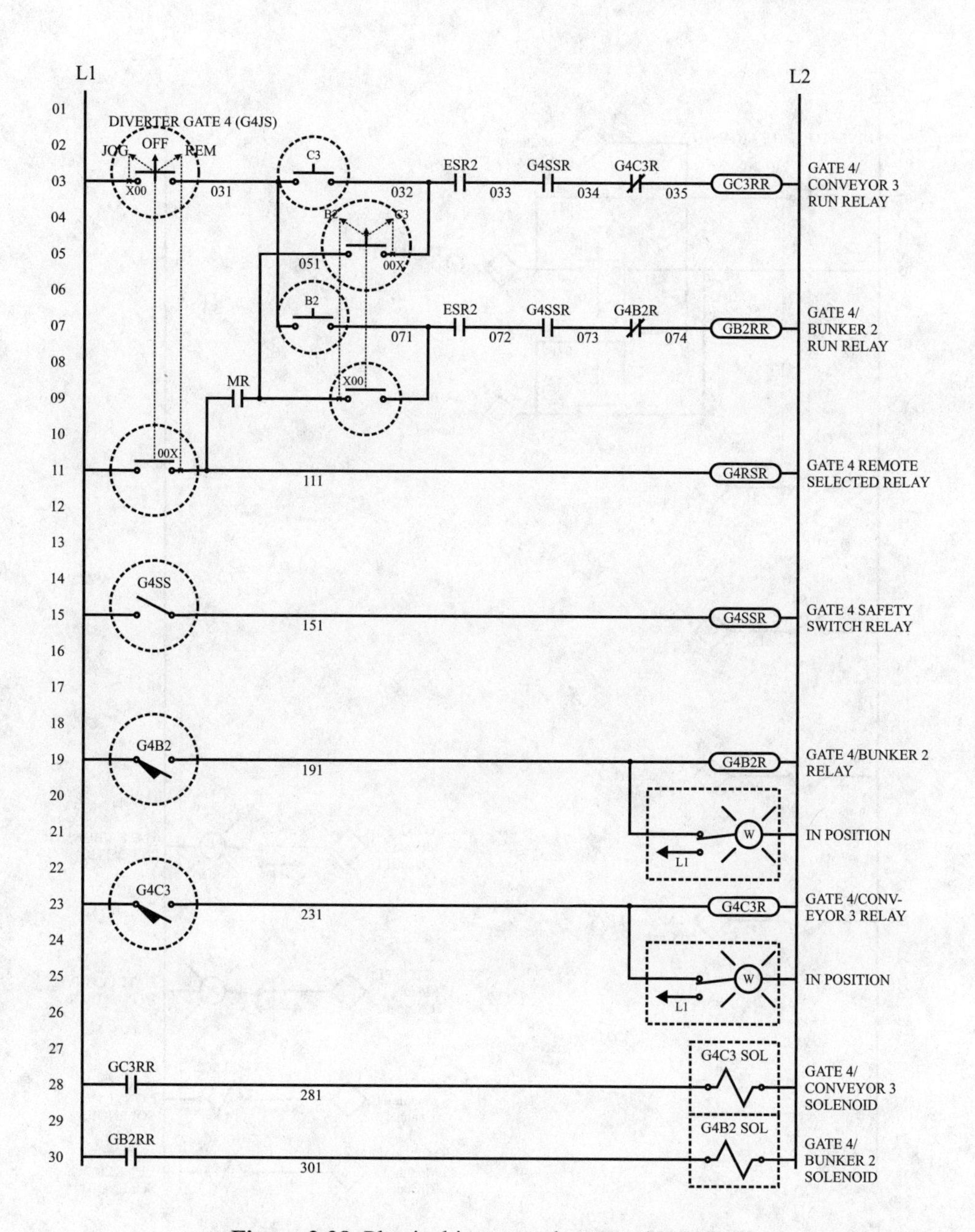

Figure 2.38. Physical inputs and outputs identified.

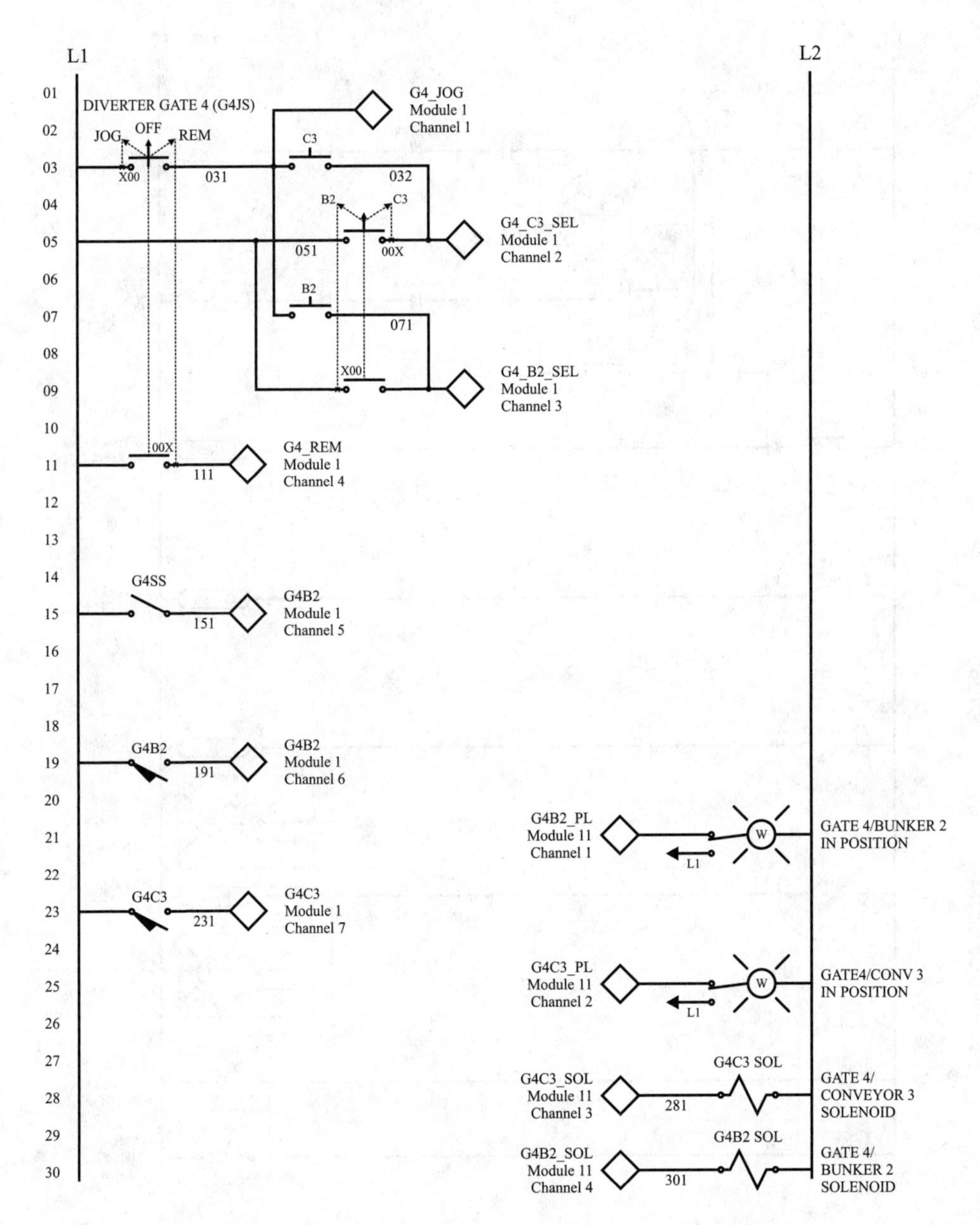

Figure 2.39. PLC input and output wiring for Gate 4 control.

2.9 CHAPTER SUMMARY

This chapter introduced the basics of PLC ladder logic: the contacts, coils, and their assemblage into a ladder logic program. The process of scanning a program and the use of the NC contact received special attention. For those interested, the chapter concludes with more information on the relay to PLC ladder logic conversion. For the most part, this chapter has used the IEC 61131-3 ladder logic language to take a generic approach to ladder logic and

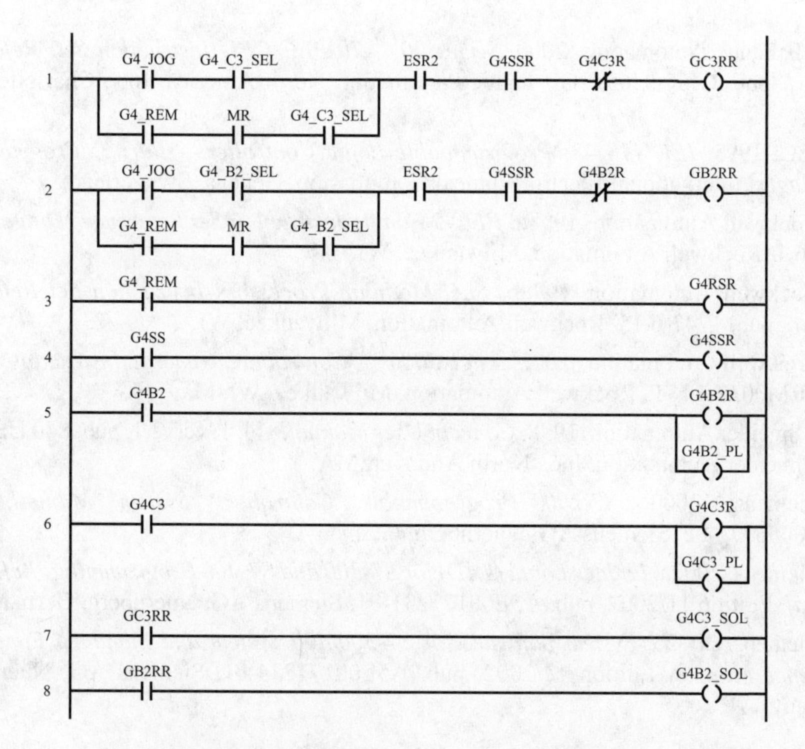

Figure 2.40. PLC ladder logic exactly translated.

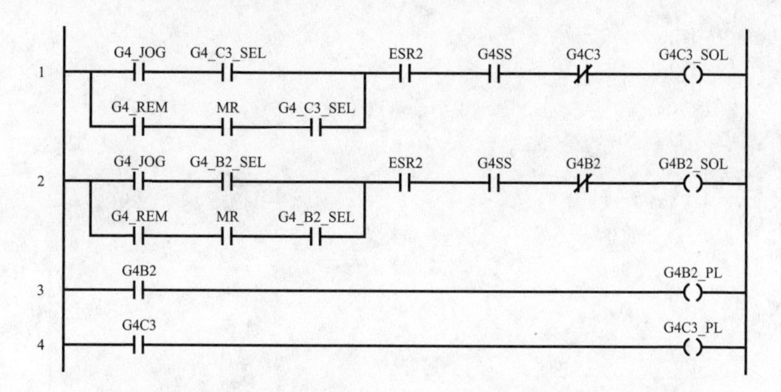

Figure 2.41. Simplified PLC ladder logic for Gate 4 control.

avoided treating the memory addressing details specific to each PLC vendor or PLC model. This topic cannot be ignored any further and is the subject of the next chapter, before timer and counter instructions are examined.

REFERENCES

GE Fanuc Automation, 1999. *Series 90^{TM}-30/20/Micro PLC CPU Instruction Set: Reference Manual,* pub. GFK-0467L, GE Fanuc Automation North America, Inc., Charlottesville, VA.

GE Fanuc Automation, 2000. *Series 90^{TM}-70 PLC CPU Instruction Set: Reference Manual,* pub. GFK-0265J, GE Fanuc Automation North America, Inc., Charlottesville, VA.

IEC, 1993. *IEC 1131-3: Programmable Logic Controllers - Part 3: Programming Languages*, International Electrotechnical Commission, Geneva, Switzerland.

Rockwell Automation, 1998a. *PLC-5 Family Instruction Set Reference Manual*, pub. 1785-6.1, Rockwell Automation, Milwaukee, WI.

Rockwell Automation, 1998b. *SLC Modular Processors Instruction Set Reference Manual*, pub. 1747-6.15, Rockwell Automation, Milwaukee, WI.

Rockwell Automation, 2002. *Logix5000^{TM} Controllers General Instructions*, pub. 1756-RM003F-EN-P, Rockwell Automation, Milwaukee, WI, May.

Schneider Automation, 1998. *Concept User Manual,* vol. 1, ver. 2.1, pub. 840 USE 461 00, Schneider Automation, Inc., North Andover, MA.

Siemens, 2000. *S7-200 Programmable Controller: System Manual,* pub. A5E00066097-02, Siemens AG, Nuernberg, Germany.

Siemens, 2002a. *Ladder Logic (LAD) for S7-300 and S7-400 Programming: Reference Manual,* Edition 11/2002, pub. A5E00171231-01, Siemens AG, Nuernberg, Germany.

Siemens, 2002b. *System Software for S7-300/400 System and Standard Functions: Reference Manual,* Edition 12/2002, pub. A5E00171234-01, Siemens AG, Nuernberg, Germany.

PROBLEMS

P2-1. Implement the digital logic diagram in Figure P2.1 in PLC ladder logic. The symbols starting with "In" are physical inputs. Do not use any internal coils. The equations of the outputs are:

$$\text{Out1} = \overline{\text{In1}} + \text{In2} + \text{In3}$$
$$\text{Out2} = \overline{\text{Out1}} \bullet \text{In4} \bullet \text{In5}$$

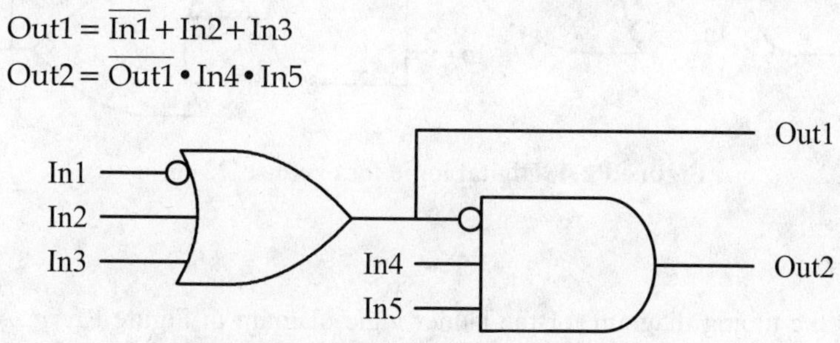

Figure P2.1. Digital logic for exercise P2-3.

P2-2. Implement the digital logic gate circuit in Figure P2.2 in PLC ladder logic. The symbols starting with "In" are physical inputs. You may use a maximum of one internal coil.

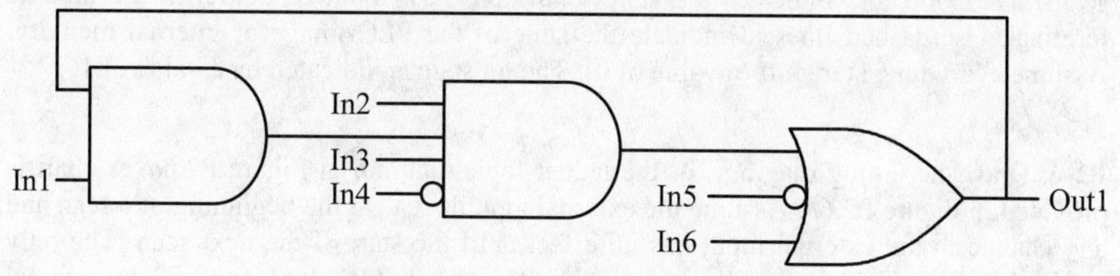

Figure P2.2. Digital logic for exercise P2-4.

P2-3. Implement the digital logic gate circuit in Figure P2.3 in PLC ladder logic. The symbols starting with "In" are physical inputs. Do not use any internal coils.

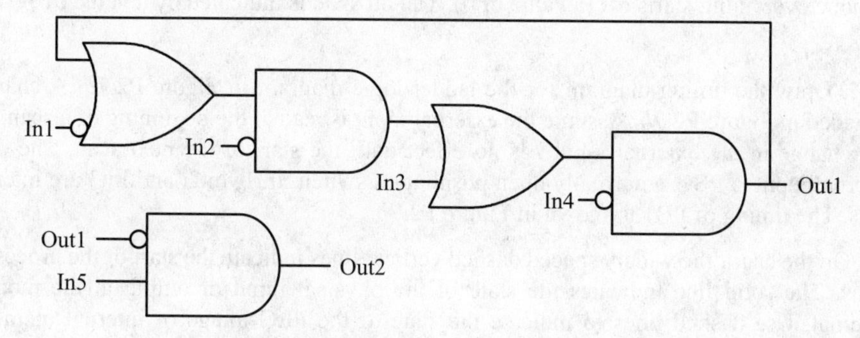

Figure P2.3. Digital logic for exercise P2-5.

P2-4. Implement the digital logic gate circuit in Figure P2.4 in PLC ladder logic. The symbols starting with "In" are physical inputs. Use a maximum of one internal coil. Note that the rightmost gate is an exclusive-or gate.

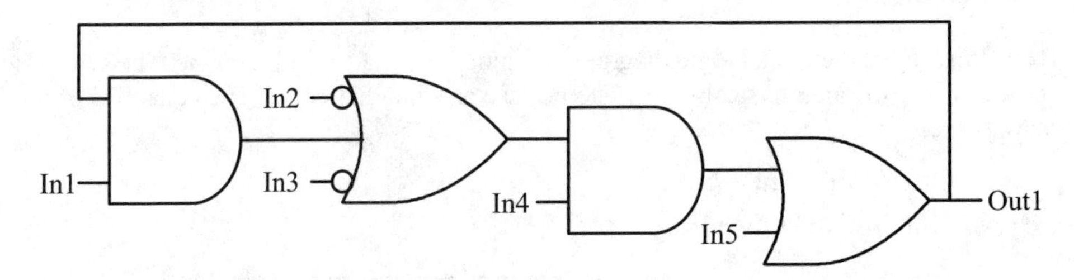

Figure P2.4. Digital logic for exercise P2-6.

P2-5. Draw the timing diagram for the ladder logic diagram in Figure P2.5*a*. A chart is provided in Figure P2.5*b*. Assume the external input is read at the beginning of a scan and any change in the external input has no effect until the start of the next scan. The only external input is PB1, a normally open pushbutton switch. Int1, Int2, and Int3 are internal coils. The timing of PB1 is shown in Figure P2.5*b*.

On the chart, the widely spaced dashed vertical lines indicate the start of the processor scans. The solid line indicates the state of the physical input or output at the module terminal. Use dashed lines to indicate the state of the PLC image or internal memory. Assume everything starts **off** (a value of 0). The **on** state is indicated by a value of 1.

P2-6. Draw the timing diagram for the ladder logic diagram in Figure P2.6*a*. A chart is provided in Figure P2.6*b*. Assume the external input is read at the beginning of a scan and any change in the external input has no effect until the start of the next scan. The only external input is PB1, a normally open pushbutton switch. Int1, Int2, and Int3 are internal coils. The timing of PB1 is shown in Figure P2.6*b*.

On the chart, the widely spaced dashed vertical lines indicate the start of the processor scans. The solid line indicates the state of the physical input or output at the module terminal. Use dashed lines to indicate the state of the PLC image or internal memory. Assume everything starts **off** (a value of 0). The **on** state is indicated by a value of 1.

P2-7. Draw the timing diagram for the ladder logic diagram in Figure P2.7*a*. A chart is provided in Figure P2.7*b*. Assume the external input is read at the beginning of a scan and any change in the external input has no effect until the start of the next scan. The only external input is PB1, a normally open pushbutton switch. Int1, Int2, and Int3 are internal coils. The timing of PB1 is shown in Figure P2.7*b*.

On the chart, the widely spaced dashed vertical lines indicate the start of the processor scans. The solid line indicates the state of the physical input or output at the module terminal. Use dashed lines to indicate the state of the PLC image or internal memory. Assume everything starts **off** (a value of 0). The **on** state is indicated by a value of 1.

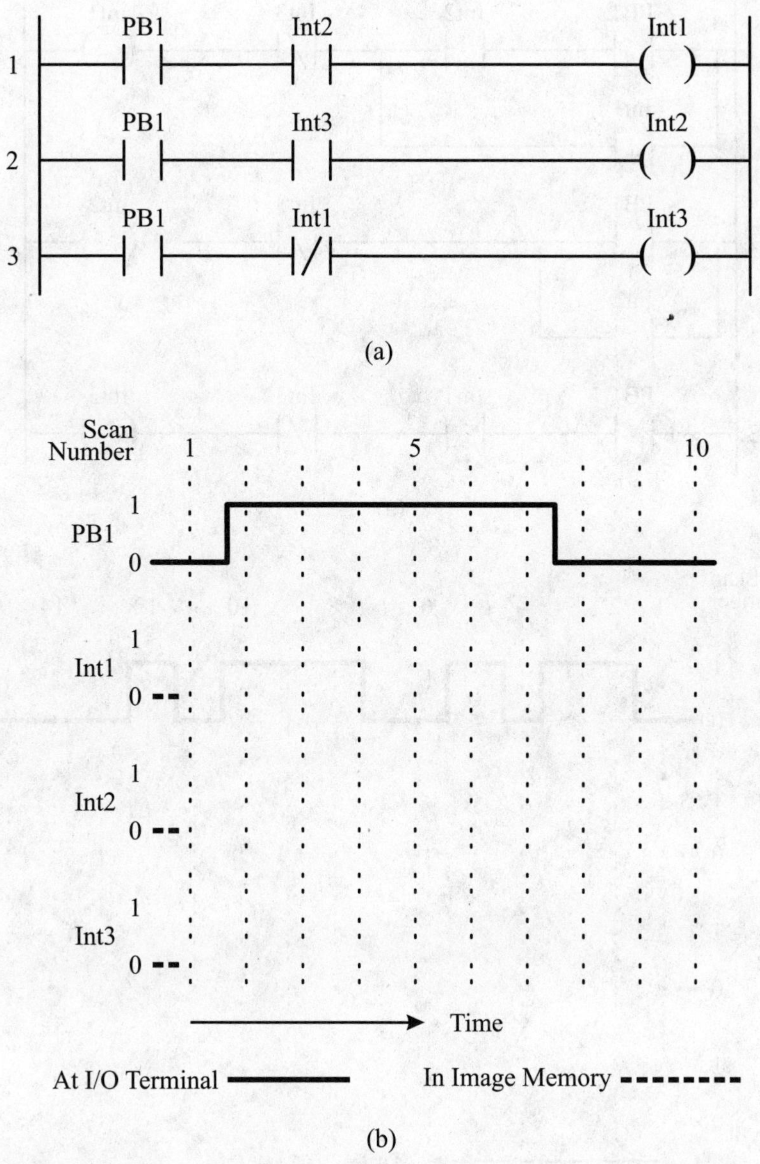

Figure P2.5. Ladder logic and timing diagram for exercise P2-5: *(a)* ladder logic; *(b)*timing diagram.

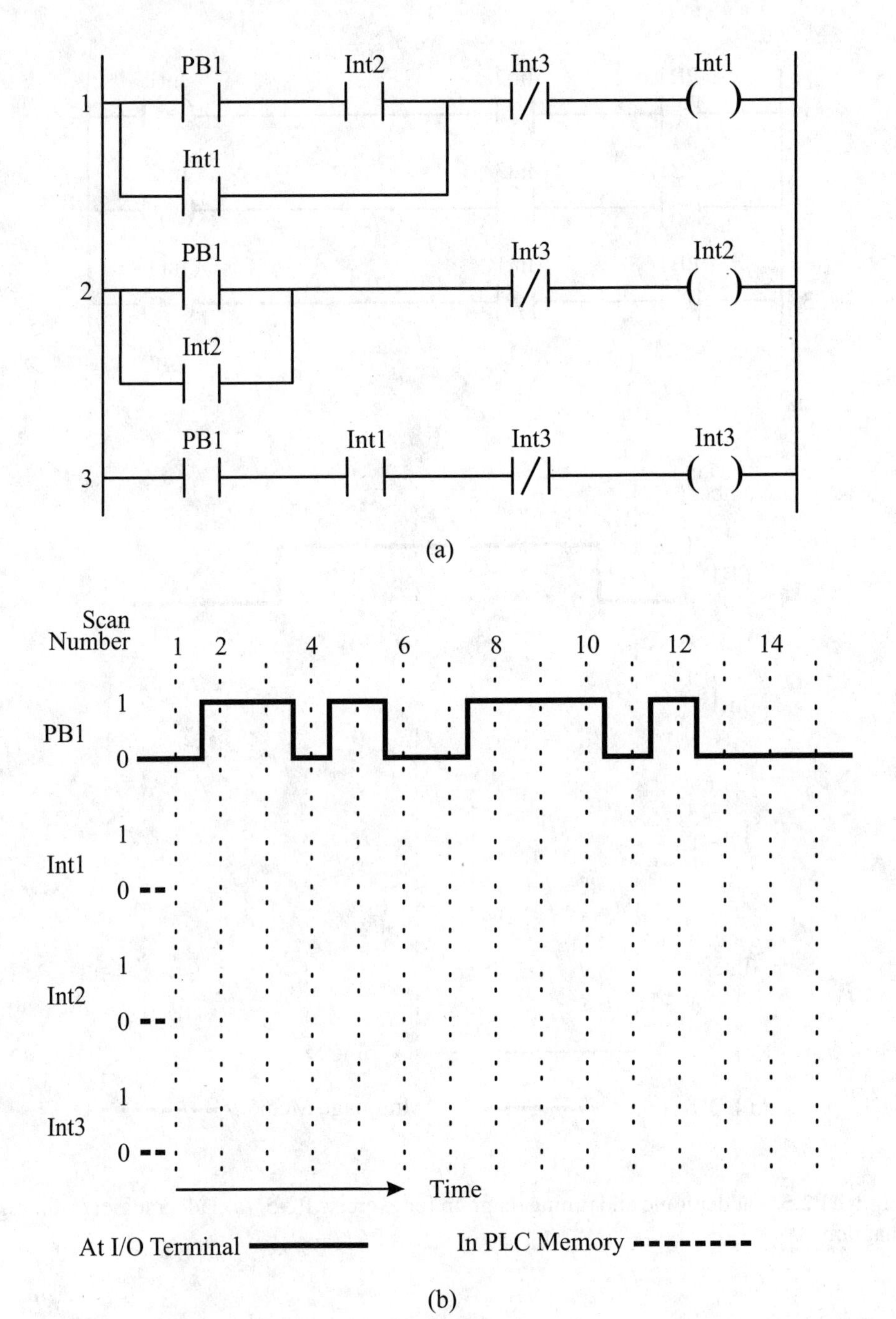

Figure P2.6. Ladder logic and timing diagram for exercise P2-6: *(a)* ladder logic; *(b)* timing diagram.

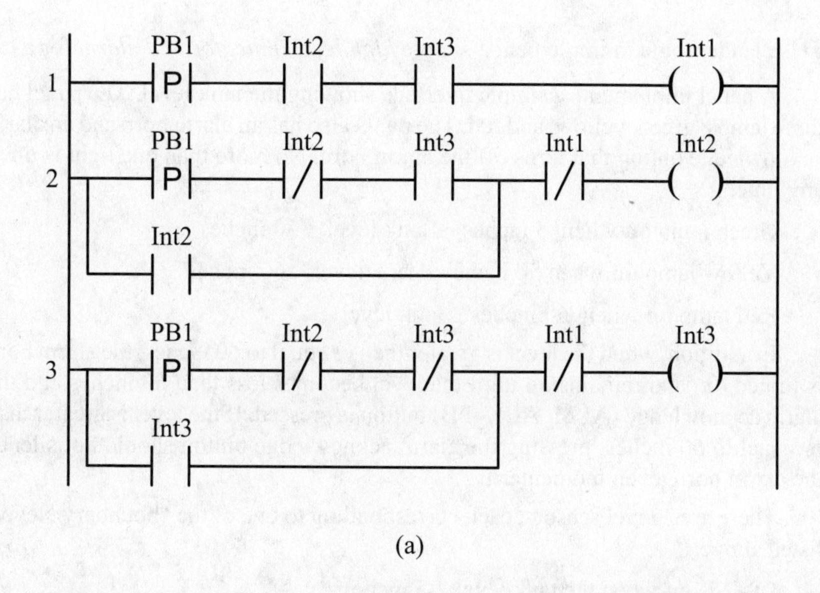

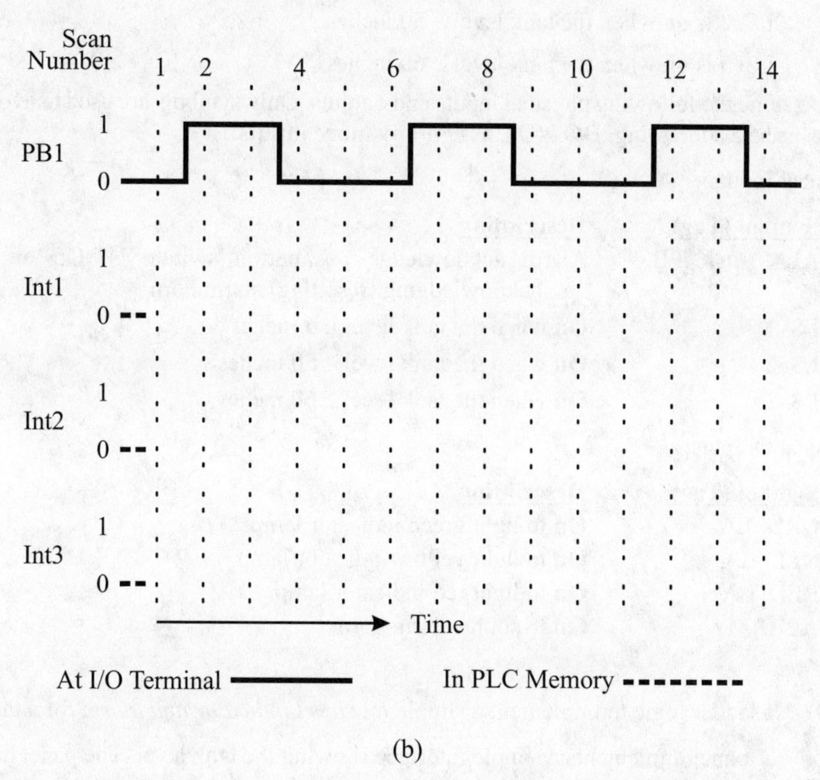

Figure P2.7. Ladder logic and timing diagram for exercise P2-7: *(a)* ladder logic; *(b)*timing diagram.

P2-8. Use ladder logic to implement a simple *high level indicator and alarm* for a tank.

A panel implements a simple interface showing the tank level. The panel has three lamps: green, yellow, and red. The panel also has an alarm horn and an alarm acknowledge button that turns off the alarm horn. No more than one light is **on** at any time:

Green lamp **on** when 5 inches ≤ tank level < 50 inches

Yellow lamp **on** when 50 inches ≤ tank level < 60 inches

Red lamp **on** when 60 inches ≤ tank level

In addition, when the level is greater than or equal to 60 inches, the alarm horn is turned **on**, and remains **on** until the level becomes less than 60 inches and the alarm acknowledge (ALM_ACK_PB) button is pressed. If the level is greater than or equal to 60 inches, pressing the alarm acknowledge button should not silence the alarm horn, even momentarily.

There are 3 level sensors, each corresponding to one of the "boundary" levels listed above:

LS–1 is **on** when the tank level ≥ 5 inches

LS–2 is **on** when the tank level ≥ 50 inches

LS–3 is **on** when the tank level ≥ 60 inches

Assume the following physical inputs and outputs. Only symbols are used to avoid any PLC-specific addressing. **DO NOT assign any more inputs!!**

Physical Inputs:

Symbol (Tag)	Description
ALM_ACK_PB	Alarm acknowledge pushbutton switch, N. O., **on** when acknowledging (resetting) alarm horn
LS–1	**On** when the tank level ≥ 5 inches
LS–2	**On** when the tank level ≥ 50 inches
LS–3	**On** when the tank level ≥ 60 inches

Physical Outputs:

Symbol (Tag)	Description
GRN_LA	**On** to light green indicator lamp
YEL_LA	**On** to light yellow indicator lamp
RED_LA	**On** to light red indicator lamp
ALARM	**On** to sound alarm horn

P2-9. Use ladder logic to implement a simple *low level indicator and alarm* for a tank.

A panel implements a simple interface showing the tank level. The panel has three lamps: green, yellow, and red. The panel also has an alarm horn and an alarm acknowledge button that turns off the alarm horn. No more than one light is **on** at any time:

Green lamp **on** when 7 inches ≤ tank level < 50 inches

Yellow lamp **on** when 5 inches ≤ tank level < 7 inches

Red lamp **on** when tank level < 5 inches

In addition, when the level is less than 5 inches, the alarm horn is turned **on**, and remains **on** until the level becomes greater than or equal to 5 inches and the alarm acknowledge (ALM_ACK_PB) button is pressed. If the level is less than 5 inches, pressing the alarm acknowledge button should not silence the alarm horn, even momentarily.

There are 3 level sensors, each corresponding to one of the "boundary" levels listed above:

LS–1 is **on** when the tank level ≥ 5 inches

LS–2 is **on** when the tank level ≥ 7 inches

LS–3 is **on** when the tank level ≥ 50 inches

Assume the following physical inputs and outputs. Only symbols are used to avoid any PLC-specific addressing. **DO NOT assign any more inputs!!**

Physical Inputs:

Symbol (Tag)	Description
ALM_ACK_PB	Alarm acknowledge pushbutton switch, N. O., **on** when acknowledging (resetting) alarm horn
LS–1	**On** when the tank level ≥ 5 inches
LS–2	**On** when the tank level ≥ 7 inches
LS–3	**On** when the tank level ≥ 50 inches

Physical Outputs:

Symbol (Tag)	Description
GRN_LA	**On** to light green indicator lamp
YEL_LA	**On** to light yellow indicator lamp
RED_LA	**On** to light red indicator lamp
ALARM	**On** to sound alarm horn

P2-10. Use ladder logic to implement a *first failure annunciator* for the tank shown in Figure P2.10.

A first failure annunciator is a circuit that informs system operators which input device(s) gave a warning signal that resulted in the alarm. The tank has 3 monitoring devices: liquid level, pressure, and temperature. If an unsafe condition should occur, certain combinations of these devices should cause an alarm. The three conditions that are considered to be unsafe and thus activate an alarm are:

High level with high temperature

High level with high pressure

High level with high temperature and high pressure

In addition, once the alarm occurs, lights will indicate the condition(s) that cause the alarm to sound. Once an alarm condition is detected, the alarm sounds until the ALM_ACK_PB button is pressed (and the condition that caused the alarm must also return to normal). Also, when the alarm is acknowledged (and the condition that caused the alarm returns to normal), any lights that are **on** should be

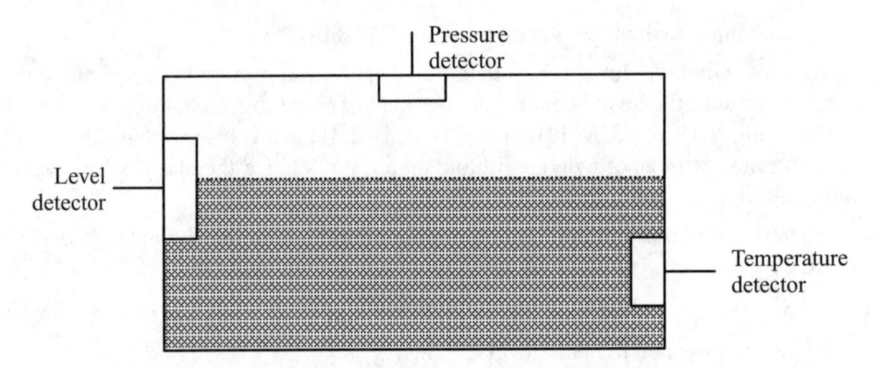

Figure P2.10. Tank sensors for problem P2-12.

turned **off**. The ALM_ACK_PB should not turn **off** any lights for an alarm condition if the condition still persists. For example, if a high level and high pressure triggered the alarm, the lights should remain **on** if the level and pressure are high when the ALM_ACK_PB is pressed.

The three monitoring devices produce an **on** signal when the physical quantity is in the high state and an **off** signal when the physical quantity is in the low (normal) state.

Only when the alarm sounds does the ladder logic turn on any of the three lights that indicate the problem that caused the alarm. For example, the HIGH_LEVEL_LA is **off** when the high level detect input is **on** and the alarm is **off** (because a high level, by itself, does not trigger an alarm).

Assume the following physical inputs and outputs. Only symbols are used to avoid any PLC-specific addressing. **DO NOT assign any more inputs!!**

Physical Inputs:

Symbol (Tag)	Description
ALM_ACK_PB	Alarm acknowledge pushbutton switch, N. O., **on** when acknowledging (resetting) alarm horn
LVL_HIGH_SENS	**On** when high level is detected
PRS_HIGH_SENS	**On** when high pressure is detected
TMP_HIGH_SENS	**On** when high temperature is detected

Physical Outputs:

Symbol (Tag)	Description
ALARM	**On** to sound alarm
LEVEL_LA	**On** when high level is one of conditions that triggered alarm
PRESS_LA	**On** when high pressure is one of conditions that triggered alarm
TEMPER_LA	**On** when high temperature is one of conditions that triggered alarm

P2-11. Design a ladder logic program to provide the intrusion interlock for a machine work cell shown in Figure P2.11*a*.

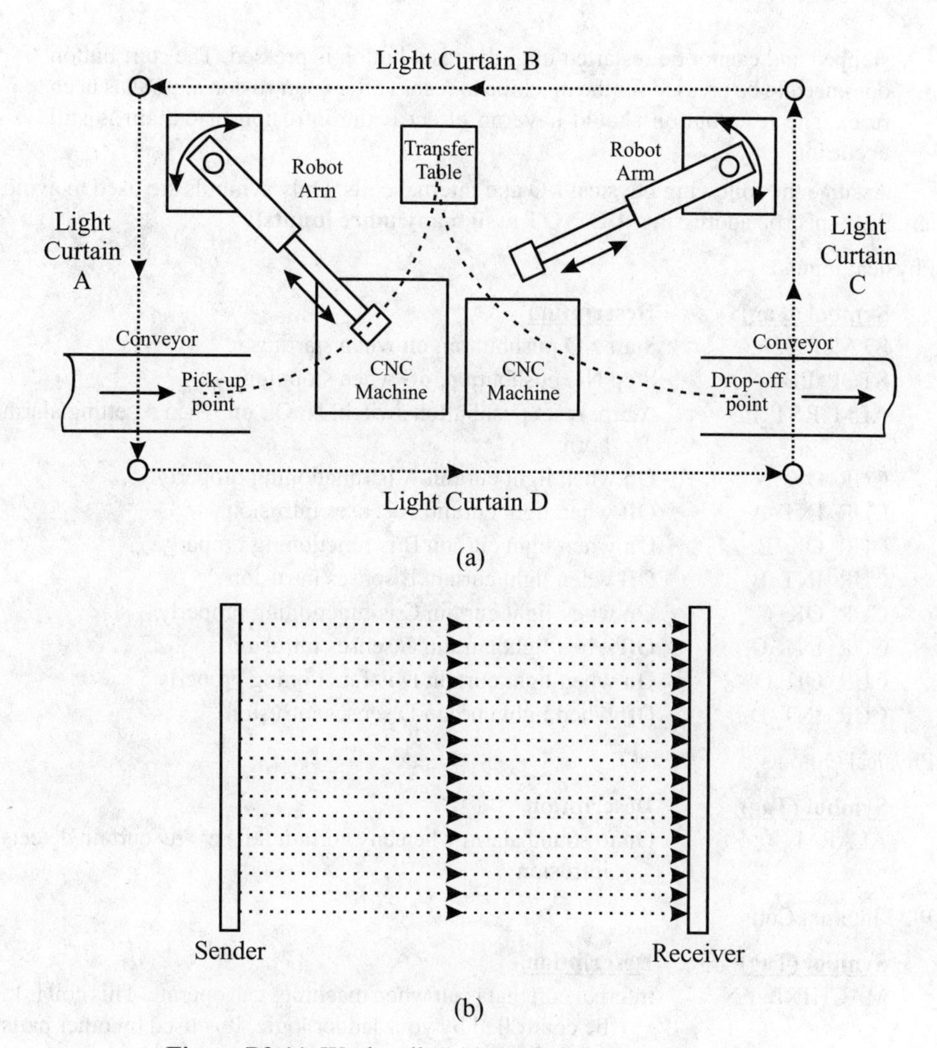

Figure P2.11. Work cell: *(a)* boundaries; *(b)* light curtain.

The work cell is bounded by an array of four light curtains to detect the presence of people or objects entering the work area. When any light curtain sensor is tripped, the motion of all machines in the work cell must stop and an alarm must be sounded. This action ensures that no injury or damage to the "intruder" occurs. To allow the process to continue all sensors must signal "no intrusion" and a reset button must be pressed.

A light curtain sensor detects the presence of an intruder by using a series of light beams (Figure P2.11*b*) where any broken beam = intrusion. The sensors are self-diagnosing and detect when they are not functioning properly. Therefore, the process must be halted whenever any light curtain malfunctions or when any light curtain senses an intrusion. Design the PLC control program so that the machines will be halted if any light curtain malfunctions or senses an "intrusion".

The machine start and stop push buttons are used to start and stop the work cell operation. If an intrusion or curtain malfunction occurs, the machine is stopped and cannot be restarted until the reset button is pressed. The start button does need to be pressed for the machine to restart after an intrusion alarm has been reset. The reset button should have no effect if the intrusion or curtain is still occurring.

Assume the following physical I/O and internal coils. Only symbols are used to avoid any PLC-specific addressing. **DO NOT assign any more inputs!!**

Physical Inputs:

Symbol (Tag)	Description
START_PB	Start NO pushbutton, **on** when starting
STOP_PB	Stop NC pushbutton, **off** when stopping
ALM_RST_PB	Alarm reset pushbutton switch, N. O., **on** when resetting alarm horn
CUR_OK_A	**On** when light curtain A is functioning properly
CUR_INT_A	**Off** when light curtain A senses intrusion
CUR_OK_B	**On** when light curtain B is functioning properly
CUR_INT_B	**Off** when light curtain B senses intrusion
CUR_OK_C	**On** when light curtain C is functioning properly
CUR_INT_C	**Off** when light curtain C senses intrusion
CUR_OK_D	**On** when light curtain D is functioning properly
CUR_INT_D	**Off** when light curtain D senses intrusion

Physical Outputs:

Symbol (Tag)	Description
ALARM	**On** to sound alarm when any curtain fails or any curtain detects intrusion

PLC Internal Coils:

Symbol (Tag)	Description
MACHINE_EN	Internal coil that is **on** when machines can operate. This coil is to be controlled by your ladder logic. It is used by other parts of the ladder logic.

3 Memory Organization and Addressing

Chapter Topics:

- PLC memory organization
- PLC memory addressing

OBJECTIVES

Upon completion of this chapter, you will be able to understand how the memory is organized and addressed for the following PLCs:

- IEC 61131-3
- Modicon Quantum/Momentum
- Allen-Bradley ControlLogix
- Allen-Bradley PLC-5/SLC-500
- Siemens S7
- GE Fanuc

Scenario: Every control engineer's nightmare.

The phone call came at 2 a.m. The shift supervisor is on the line. "We're having trouble with the A2438 agitator. It keeps faulting out. The maintenance electrician has traced it to a faulty vibration sensor. It is occasionally turning on, even when there isn't any noticeable vibration, causing the batch procedure to go to hold. This problem started occurring this afternoon, but now it seems to happen every 10 minutes. We do not have a spare sensor in stock. The earliest we can get one is in two days." You then remember the particular batch system was recently commissioned and the contractor who installed it left a week ago. The operator breaks into your thoughts. "Is there anything you can do in the PLC? I don't have a spare operator who can restart the batch procedure every 10 minutes." In your half-awake state you cannot recall exactly what the supervisor says next. Something about losing $10,000 if the batch procedure does not run to completion in 3 hours. You mumble something in reply and then hang up the phone to hurriedly dress and drive to the plant.

While driving to the plant, you think of some possible temporary solutions. You could force the vibration sensor discrete input off, but then if a vibration is truly occurring equipment could be damaged, forcing costly downtime and repairs. The best solution would be to add a 2-second time delay to the sensor signal. The vibration sensor signal would have to remain on for 2 seconds before it would cause a fault and put the batch procedure in hold.

"At least it's a PLC-5," you think to yourself. "I can make online changes to the ladder logic while the PLC is in run mode." When you arrive at the control room, you discuss these solutions with the shift supervisor and he okays the additional delay on the sensor. "The contractor should have added this delay for the sensor anyway," you add. The supervisor agrees.

With the engineering workstation you connect to the PLC and find the discrete input address. You check the cross-reference and find that the discrete input is used in only two places in the program. "This will be easy," you think to yourself. "I need to find a spare timer, replace the references to the sensor with the timer done bit, drive the timer with the sensor, and I can go home."

When you check the data files, the only file of timers is the default, T4. You check the usage table and discover that every timer is being used. There are no spare timers. You must put the PLC in program mode in order to expand the timer data file. However, the plant rules dictate that you obtain the shift supervisor's permission since operations could be disrupted when the PLC is put in program mode. When you ask the supervisor for permission to take the PLC to program mode for 1 minute in order to add a few timers, he asks, "Will it turn anything off?" "I don't know," you reply. "It depends on the jumper position on the discrete output modules." The supervisor responds, "Then you may not. The PLC also controls your steam generator unit. If the PLC causes the steam generator to shut down, it takes a minimum of an hour to get it back on-line and so your batch will certainly be ruined." You sigh, tell him that you will force the vibration sensor off and request a radio so that you can inform the operator if the agitator starts vibrating. You get a radio and a chair and post yourself by the agitator, ready to radio the control room if a vibration occurs. It is a long night.

Solution: The programmer should have left spare timers in the data files to handle these situations. As a rule, one should ALWAYS put spare timers, counters, internal coils, and so on, to allow code corrections without requiring the PLC to be taken out of run mode. In this situation, there was another mistake made by the programmer who originally programmed the PLC. Every sensor that can cause a fault should be delayed in the PLC. In other words, the sensor signal should persist for at least a second before the PLC turns on an alarm and causes some other action. Frequently, fault sensors are plagued with intermittent false readings. The addition of the timer will prevent false alarms.

3.1 INTRODUCTION

This chapter summarizes the organization and addressing of the memory for the PLCs covered by this text. Each of the sections is written as stand-alone. That is, only the section(s) pertaining to the PLC(s) of interest need to be studied. Since the Modicon Quantum/Momentum and the Allen-Bradley ControlLogix PLCs are IEC-compliant, the IEC 61131-3 memory model is introduced. Since IEC 61131-3 is a voluntary standard, only the overall memory and program model is described and the details are described within the Modicon and Allen-Bradley implementations of the standard.

3.2 IEC 61131-3 MEMORY MODEL

The IEC 61131-3 standard defines a memory and program model that is very much like modern software engineering concepts. This model incorporates such features as top-down design, structured programming, hierarchical organization, formal software interfaces, and program encapsulation. If fully implemented, the model is reasonably complicated. Currently, no one has fully implemented the model. The downside of the model is that it is reasonably complicated and is not fully appreciated by the novice programmer. One of the reasons that PLCs have become well established is because of their simplicity. One does not require extensive training in software engineering techniques in order to become a proficient programmer.

Since IEC 61131-3 is a voluntary standard that no vendor implements entirely, only the overall memory and program model is described. The details are described within the various implementations of the standard.

The IEC 61131-3 memory model (what the standard calls the software model) is presented in Figure 3.1. The model is layered; that is, each layer hides many of the features of the layers beneath. Each of the main elements is now described.

The **configuration** is the entire body of software (program and data) that corresponds to a PLC system. Generally, a configuration equates with the program and data for one PLC. In large complex systems that require multiple cooperating PLCs, each PLC has a separate configuration. Unfortunately, the choice of the term *configuration* conflicts with the historic use of this term in the controls industry. Generally, *configuration* refers to the process of specifying items such as the PLC processor model, communication interfaces, remote I/O connections, memory allocation, and so on. Therefore, the vendors producing

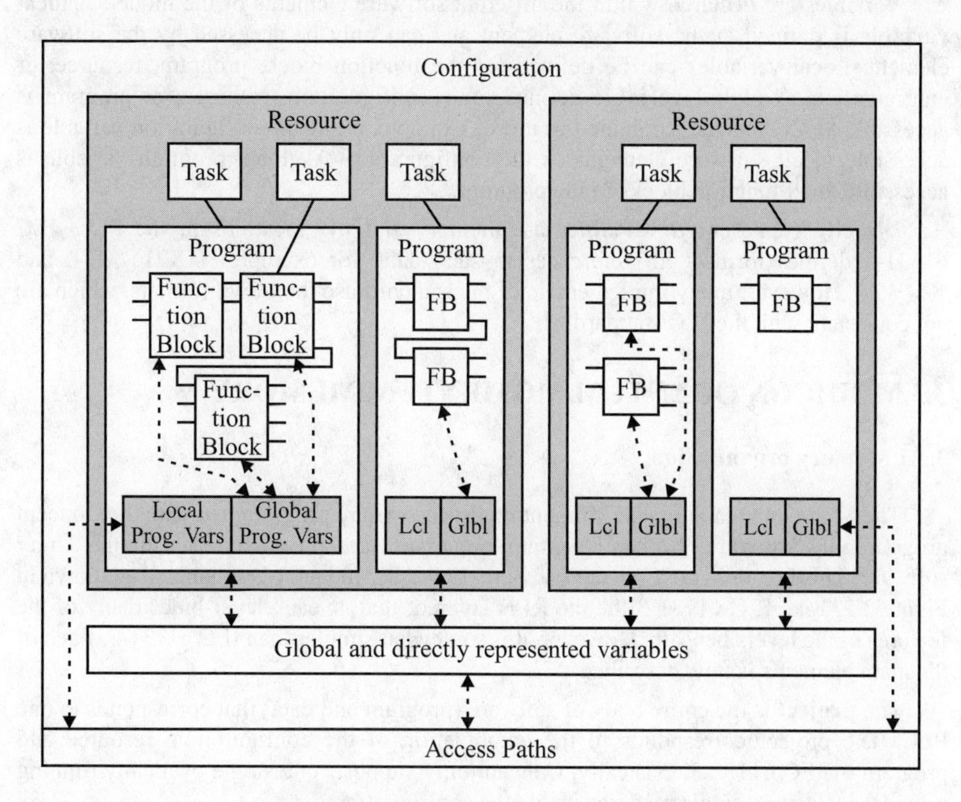

Figure 3.1. IEC 61131-3 memory model.

IEC-compliant PLCs that use the term *configuration* in the historic sense refer to the entire body of software with some other term.

A **resource** provides the support functions for the execution of programs. A configuration is composed of one or more resources. Normally a resource exists within a PLC, but it may exist within a personal computer to support program testing. One of the main functions of a resource is to provide an interface between a program and the physical I/O of the PLC.

A **program** generally consists of an interconnection of **function blocks**, each of which may be written in any of the IEC languages. A function block or program is also called a *program organization unit* (POU). In addition to the function blocks, the program contains declarations of physical inputs/outputs and any variables local to the program. A program can read and write to I/O channels, global variables, and communicate with other programs. A mechanism called access paths provides the means to transfer information between configurations. Tasks control the execution of the program or parts of a program.

A **task** is set up to control one or more programs and/or function blocks to execute periodically or to execute upon the occurrence of a specified trigger. The execution of a program implies that all of the function blocks in the program are processed once. The execution of a function block implies that all of the software elements of the function block are processed once. There are no implied mechanisms for program execution. In order for a program to be executed, it must be assigned to a task and the task must be configured to execute periodically or with a trigger.

Variables are declared within the different software elements of the model. A **local variable** is defined at the software element and can only be accessed by the software element. Local variables can be defined for the function block, program, resource, or configuration. A **global variable** defined for a configuration, resource, or program is accessible to all elements contained in it. For example, a global configuration variable is accessible to all software elements in the configuration. A global program variable is accessible to all function blocks in the program.

Directly represented variables are memory and I/O locations in the PLC. IEC 61131-3 defines formats for references to such data, for example %IX21, %Q4, and %MW24. However, many implementers of the standard use their own formats, which are not consistent with the IEC standard.

3.3 MODICON QUANTUM/MOMENTUM MEMORY

3.3.1 Memory organization

The Modicon Quantum and Momentum processors are programmed with the Concept programming software. Newer Quantum processors are programmed with the Unity software. This text uses the Concept software. Processor memory is organized as shown in Figure 3.2. Like IEC 61131-3 the model is layered; that is, each layer hides many of the features of the layers beneath. However, it is somewhat simpler than IEC 61131-3. Each of the main elements is now described.

The **project** is the entire body of software (program and data) that corresponds to one PLC. The project corresponds to the combination of the configuration, resource and program of IEC 61131-3. Basically, Concept only supports one single cyclically running program inside one single resource inside the configuration.

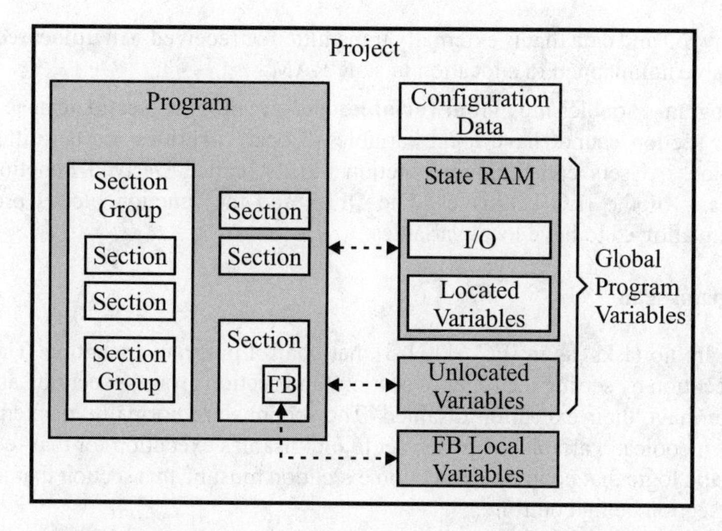

Figure 3.2. Modicon Quantum/Momentum memory model.

In Concept, the **configuration data** contains such items as the PLC processor model, I/O map, communication interfaces, remote I/O connections, and data memory allocation. Configuration data is not accessible to the program.

A **program** generally consists of **sections**, each of which may be written in any one of the following languages:

Ladder Diagram (LD)

Sequential Function Chart (SFC)

Function Block Diagram (FBD)

Structured Text (ST)

Instruction List (IL)

984 Ladder Logic (LL984)

Note that the LL984 section allows legacy software to be incorporated into the new processors. Pre-Quantum processors (e.g., 984, 884, 584) can only be programmed in ladder logic that is not necessarily backward compatible among the models. The Momentum processors do not allow 984 ladder logic to co-exist with the other IEC languages. The processor can be configured to execute 984 ladder logic sections or to execute IEC sections, but not both.

Sections can be combined into a **section group**. All sections of a program can read and write to the state RAM (which includes I/O) and communicate with other programs. Communication-related function blocks provide the means to transfer data (state RAM) between PLCs. A section or section group is roughly equivalent to the IEC function block.

The **state RAM** is the location for all directly represented variables. The state RAM is formatted like the 984 (and previous Modicon PLCs) and its specific structure and format of the addresses are shown later in this book section. A LL984 section can only access state RAM. Any program **located variables** are mapped to locations in the state RAM that includes any I/O and data that is externally transmitted or received. An **unlocated variable** is any variable not mapped to a location in state RAM.

All program variables are **global variables** and any program section can access them. A program section cannot have local variables. **Local variables** are permitted only in function blocks. Users can program function blocks (called Derived Function Blocks, DFBs) in any of the IEC languages. The DFBs and the function blocks provided by Modicon are allowed to have local variables.

3.3.2 Program scan

There are no tasks, as in IEC 61131-3, that control program execution. The user can control execution by setting the order of section (and section group) execution and specific sections can have their execution disabled. The sections are normally enabled, but each section has a boolean variable that when set to **on**, disables execution for that section. Any programmatic logic that controls the section execution must be in a section that is executed before the section being controlled.

Pictorially, a Quantum/Momentum program is executed as shown in Figure 3.3. The execution is basically the same as introduced in Chapter 2. The physical inputs are read, the program is scanned, and the physical outputs are written. Within the program, any LL984 sections are scanned first and scanned in the manner that the 984 PLC scans its program. The LL984 section is organized into segments; each local or remote I/O network is assigned

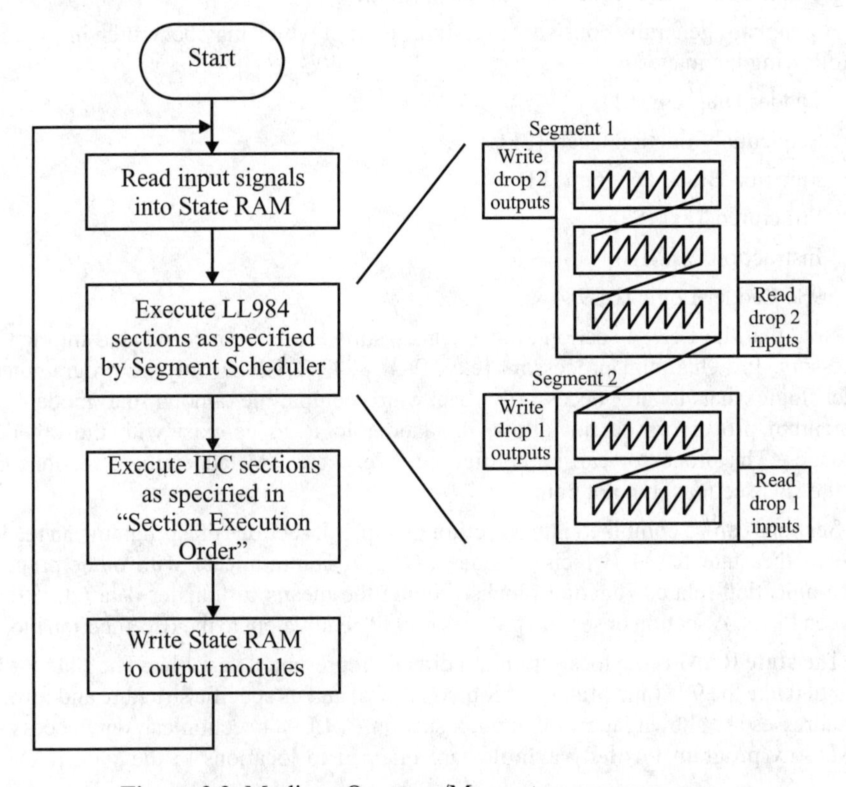

Figure 3.3. Modicon Quantum/Momentum program scan.

a segment. Each segment consists of ladder logic networks where each network has a maximum of 7 rows and 11 columns. Within a segment, the networks are examined from first to last. Within a network, the ladder logic is scanned by columns (section 2.5.2). At the start of a segment scan, the physical outputs from the previously executed segment are written, and at the end of a segment scan, the physical inputs for the next segment are read. After any LL984 sections are scanned, then the other sections (and section groups) are scanned in the specified order.

3.3.3 Variables and data types

The symbolic name (identifier) of a variable can be any string of letters, digits, and underlines up to 32 characters long provided that:

1. The first character is not a digit.
2. There are not two or more consecutive underlines.

These rules comply with the IEC 61131-3 naming convention. However, Modicon does allow the first rule to be relaxed by specifying that identifiers can have leading digits in the IEC extensions part of the options menu. The symbolic name must be unique throughout the entire project; there is no distinction between upper and lower case. A symbolic name must exist only once as a variable, step name or instance name.

When a variable is declared, it must be assigned a data type. The **elementary data types** are as follows:

Name	Description	Range of values
BOOL	1-bit Boolean	0=cleared, 1=set
BYTE	8-bit	0 to FF hexadecimal
WORD	16-bit	0 to FFFF hexadecimal
INT	2-byte integer	-32,768 to 32,767
UINT	2-byte integer	0 to 65,535
DINT	4-byte integer	-2^{31} to $2^{31}-1$ (-2,147,483,648 to 2,147,483,647)
UDINT	4-byte integer	0 to $2^{32}-1$
REAL	4-byte float. pt.	$\pm 8.43\times 10^{37}$ to $\pm 3.36\times 10^{+38}$
TIME	4-byte	0 to $2^{32}-1$ milliseconds (>49 days)

The ability to examine a bit in an integer variable is provided by a function block and only for the BYTE and WORD data types. Though the WORD and INT data types are both 16 bits, the WORD data type is generally used for logical operations (for example, OR) and the INT data type is used for arithmetic operations (for example, addition).

Literals are used to directly provide values for inputs of function blocks, transition conditions, and so on. These values cannot be overwritten by the program logic. Literals are also used to assign a value to a constant or an initial value to a variable.

The BOOL (Boolean) data type has the literals FALSE (or 0) and TRUE (or 1). Literals for the integer data types (including BYTE and WORD) can be expressed as an integer literal, base 2 literal (binary), base 8 literal (octal), or base 16 (hexadecimal) literal. The formats are as follows:

Literal type	Examples
integer	-12, 0, +23, 14_639
base-2	2#111 (7 decimal)
	2#1011_0011 (179 decimal)
base-8	8#177 (127 decimal)
	8#2001 (1025 decimal)
base-16	16#FFFF (65,535 decimal)
	16#AA (170 decimal)

The underline character may be inserted into numeric literals to aid readability; otherwise it has no significance. Literals for the REAL type may be expressed as normal decimal numbers,

5.341, +14_639.7, -0.0041

or with "E" or "e" indicating the tens' exponential value,

7.45e-12, 1.27E+4, 1.27E4.

Literals for the TIME type (called duration literals) are specified in days (D), hours (H), minutes (M), seconds (S), and milliseconds (MS), or combinations thereof. The duration must be identified by the prefix t#, T#, time# or TIME#. The "overflow" of the most significant unit is allowed; e.g. the entry T#25H15M is allowed. Also, the last field of a duration literal may be given in the decimal format. Some examples are:

T#10MS	10 milliseconds
T#3.5s	3 seconds, 500 milliseconds
Time#18m	18 minutes
TIME#5d14h12m	5 days, 14 hours, 12 minutes

For the Quantum processors, one may define a table of ASCII messages for communication with certain message display modules. The configuration of these messages is not part of the normal variable definitions. In addition, these messages can only be accessed in a LL984 section.

Concept also allows one to define new data types from the elementary data types. IEC 61131-3 allows one to alias, or redefine a data type, for example, all position values could be placed in variables whose data type called POSITION which is based on the REAL data type. Concept does not allow this kind of derived data type. Concept allows one to define structured data types and array data types. A **structured data type** is a collection of data elements, generally with different data types (elementary data types and/or other derived data types) framed by STRUCT and END_STRUCT. For example, one could define the following MACHINE_INFO data type:

```
TYPE MACHINE_INFO:
    STRUCT
            Serial_Num:     UDINT;
            Location:       LOC_TYPE;
            Oper_Time:      TIME;
            Shift_Faults:   UINT;
            Last_Fault:     INT;
    END_STRUCT;
END_TYPE
```

If variable Mach23 is defined as type MACHINE_INFO, then to access its serial number, the reference is Mach23.Serial_Num. There are predefined structured data types that are parameters for function blocks, for example, the Para_PID data type is the structure of the parameters for the PID function block.

Array data types are defined in a similar manner, except that the keyword is ARRAY. For example, the definition of an array of position information could be defined as

```
TYPE Position_Array:
    ARRAY [1..20] OF REAL;
END_TYPE
```

Only one dimension can be defined in the square brackets. To get more than one dimension, the type of the array elements needs to be an array. As an example, a two-dimension array of part position data could be defined as

```
TYPE Position_Data:
    ARRAY [1..20] OF REAL;
END_TYPE
TYPE Position_Data_2D:
    ARRAY [1..20] OF Position_Data;
END_TYPE
```

If the variable Part76 is defined as data type Position_Data_2D, then one element is referenced as Part76[14][3]. It is also possible to define an array of a structured data type. There are some predefined arrays, for example, IntArray12 and WordArray128.

In Concept, all derived data types must be defined within a *.DTY file. The Data Type editor is used to edit and check a *.DTY file.

3.3.4 State RAM

The state RAM is the location for all I/O addresses and other directly represented variables. The state RAM is formatted like the 984 (and previous Modicon *x*84 PLCs) and its addresses are all numbers where the prefix is most important. Figure 3.4 shows the valid addresses. For example, the memory address 40202 refers to the 202nd word in the 4*x* register memory. An address can be referenced/displayed one of three ways:

Standard:	400010
Separator:	4:00010
Compact:	4:10

The maximum amount of available of 0*x*, 1*x*, 3*x*, 4*x*, and 6*x* memory depends on the processor model. In addition, the specific amount of these memory types is part of the project configuration. Those that are astute will notice that 2*x* and 5*x* are missing from Figure 3.4. The 2*x* memory type was used for sequencer instructions in the Modicon 484 and 884 processors. For the 884 processor, 5*x* memory referred to double-precision arithmetic registers. In the 184 and 384 processors, 5*x* memory was privileged registers and accessed like the 6*x* memory. The 2*x* and 5*x* memory types are not valid for Quantum and Momentum processors.

When shown on a program listing, the state RAM addresses are prefixed with a "%" in accordance with IEC 61131-3. When programmed with the graphical (LD, SFC, or FBD)

	Address	Type	Meaning
0*x*	000001 ⋮ 0*nnnnn*	Discrete Output or Internal Coil	Drives a real output if mapped to a discrete output module. Otherwise, it is an internal coil
1*x*	100001 ⋮ 1*nnnnn*	Discrete Input	Mapped to discrete input modules
3*x*	300001 ⋮ 3*nnnnn*	Input Register	Mapped to word input modules (e.g., analog input, high-speed counter)
4*x*	400001 ⋮ 4*nnnnn*	Output Register or Word Storage	Drives a word output if mapped to a word output module (e.g., analog output) otherwise it is an internal word..
6*x*	600001 ⋮ 6*nnnnn*	Extended Memory Register	Only available for PLC's with 24-bit CPU, e.g., Quantum

Figure 3.4. Modicon state RAM address types.

languages, the user can type the address with or without the "%" prefix. For the remainder of the text the state RAM addresses are referenced in the text without the "%" prefix, but the ladder logic listings properly show the prefix. Except for the addressing examples in this chapter, the remainder of the text shows the symbolic representation of a variable in the graphical listings.

The **0*x* memory** holds the value of physical discrete outputs (Booleans). The specific addresses are mapped to discrete output modules and this mapping is demonstrated in the next book section. Any 0*x* addresses not mapped to a discrete output module may be used as internal coils or to locate variables (information to/from HMI or other PLCs). Note that the leading "0" must be entered in order to be a valid 0*x* address. An address of "113" is interpreted as "100013" and not as "000113."

The **1*x* memory** holds the value of the physical discrete inputs. All of the 1*x* addresses are mapped to discrete input modules. Any 1*x* address not mapped to a discrete input module is not accessible.

The **3*x* memory** holds the values of any I/O modules that generate register or integer-type data. For example, analog input modules and high-speed counter modules generate register data. The actual number of 3*x* words and the format of the data will vary with the specific module. All of the 3*x* addresses are mapped to register I/O modules. Any 3*x* address not mapped to a register I/O module is not accessible.

The **4*x* memory** holds the values of any I/O modules that receive register or integer-type data. For example, analog output modules receive register data. The actual number of 4*x* words and the format of the data will vary with the specific module. Any 4*x* addresses not mapped to register I/O modules may be used to locate variables (information to/from HMI or other PLCs) and can be any of the IEC data types. However, most current HMI packages only recognize INT and UINT data types.

The **6*x* memory** holds tables of integer-type data. This type of memory is only available for certain Quantum processors and only accessible from a LL984 section. The 6*x* memory is referenced only by instructions that move blocks of data between 4*x* and 6*x* memory. The 6x memory is primarily used to save tabular data, for example, a set of motion commands to produce a part, and then copy this table to 4*x* memory when needed. This method of data storage frees up 4*x* memory for frequently accessed data.

The structure of state RAM is shown in Figure 3.5 and it shows some of the other information stored in state RAM. The 0*x* and 1*x* history table stores the values of the discrete I/O at the end of the last scan and is used to detect transitions for the transitional contacts. The up/down counter history table stores the value of each counter count input at the end of the last scan to detect transitions on the count input. This table is used only for LL984 sections. The counter function blocks for the IEC sections have an internal variable to detect these transitions. The 0*x* DISABLE bits are used to override the logic that drives the discrete output or internal coil (Chapter 15). The 1*x* DISABLE bits are used to override the status of the field input devices (Chapter 15).

3.3.5 I/O Addressing

For Modicon PLCs the physical I/O channels are associated with a state RAM address through the **I/O map**. This I/O map is part of the configuration data and includes information for the I/O modules in the same chassis as the processor and for I/O modules on the remote I/O network. Information exchanged on other networks (e.g., Modbus+, Ethernet) is configured to use 3*x* and 4*x* memory only.

To illustrate the process for discrete I/O, a sample hardwired circuit is shown in Figure 3.6. A Modicon PLC implementation of the previous circuit might appear as in Figure 3.7. The switches are connected to channels 1 through 4 of a discrete input module and the lights, solenoid, and motor are connected to channels 1 through 4 of a discrete output module. The address of the input channel is shown with the contact in the ladder. Normally, one would use located variables for the I/O and the address would not appear on the listing. However, for the purpose of this example the addresses are shown. The address %100019 means the contact is controlled by (discrete input) address 100019, which is channel 3 on the module in slot 4 (where channel 1 has been mapped to address 100017). The mapping of the physical I/O to the 1*x* number is specified as part of the I/O map. The user specifies

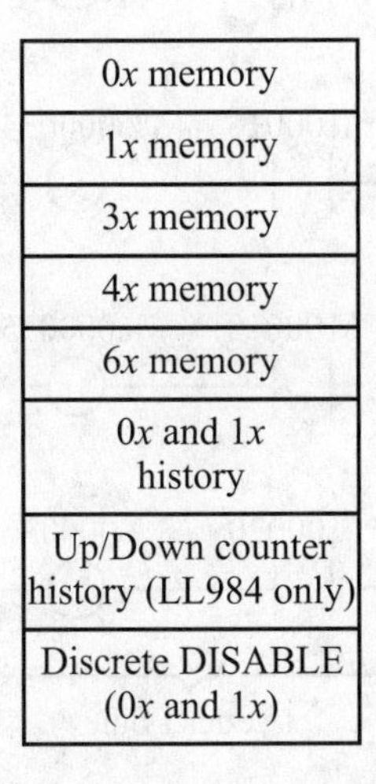

Figure 3.5. Structure of Modicon state RAM.

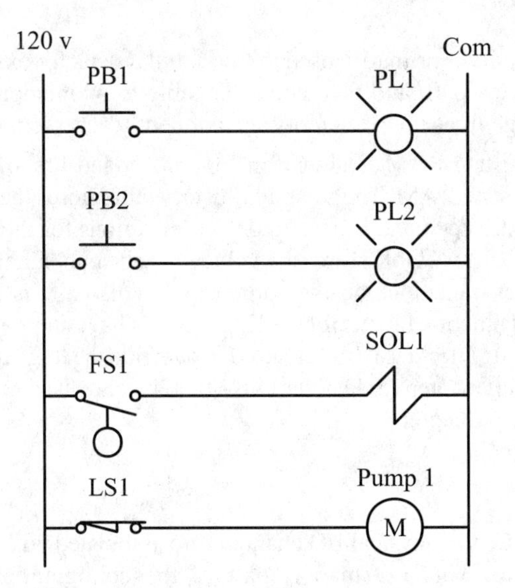

Figure 3.6. Sample hard-wired circuit.

which number maps to the starting number on the I/O module. The numbers are in decimal. Similarly, address %000036 means the discrete output (coil) is channel 4 on the module in slot 9 (where channel 1 has been mapped to address 000033).

When configuring the I/O Map, one specifies the type of module in a slot and specifies the starting address of the input reference (1*x* or 3*x*) and/or the starting address of the output reference (0*x* or 4*x*). A discrete input module needs only the starting 1*x* address. Similarly, a

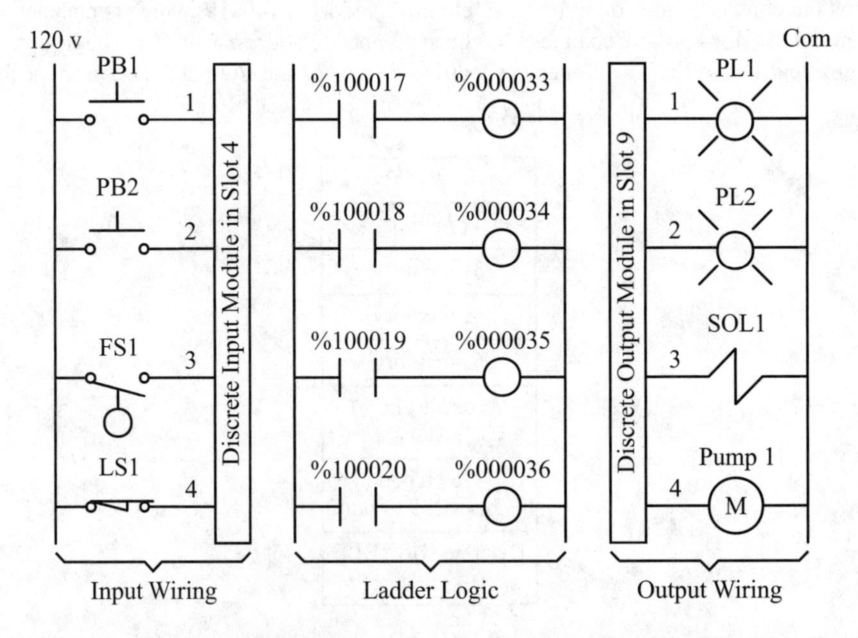

Figure 3.7. Modicon PLC implementation for Figure 3.6 showing I/O addressing.

discrete output module requires only the starting 0x address. A module that has both discrete input and discrete output channels requires a starting 1x and a starting 0x address. An analog input module needs only the starting 3x address. An analog output module requires only the starting 4x address. A module having both analog input and analog output channels or an intelligent module, such as a high-speed counter or a motion module, needs a starting 3x and a starting 4x address.

For discrete and analog modules, the address for a particular channel is related to the channel number as:

(Address for channel #) = (Channel #) - 1 + (Channel 1 address)

Figure 3.8 illustrates the I/O addressing in one chassis.

Analog I/O and intelligent modules generally use more 3x and/or 4x memory than is required for just the data. For example, the I/O map for a PLC chassis could appear as follows:

Slot	Module Type	In Ref.	In End	Out Ref.	Out End
1	Power supply				
2	CPU				
3	32 Ch. Disc. In.	100001	100032		
4	32 Ch. Disc. Out			000001	000032
5	Din/Dout 16/8	100033	100048	000033	000040
6	Ana In/Out 4/2	300001	300005	400001	400002
7	HS Ctr, 5 ch.	300006	300017	400003	400015
8	RTD in, 8 ch.	300018	300026		
9	32 Ch. Disc. In.	100049	100080		
10	32 Ch. Disc. Out			000041	000072

Note that the analog input module in slot 8 needs 9 words of 3x memory even though there are only 8 analog input channels. The other word contains status information about the module channels, such as open circuit or range violation indications.

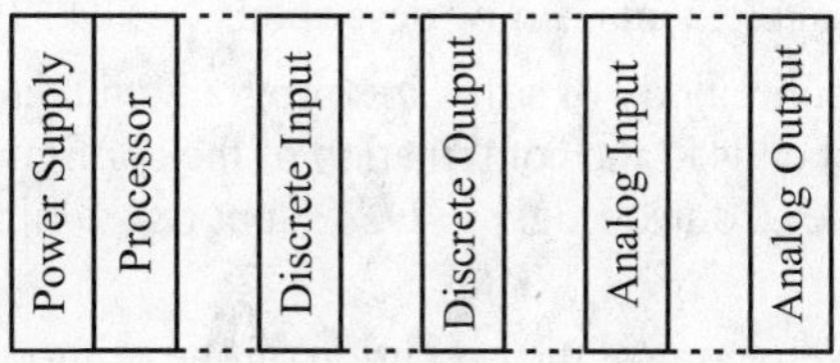

Power Supply
Processor
Discrete Input
Discrete Output
Analog Input
Analog Output

	Discrete Input	Discrete Output	Analog Input	Analog Output
Module Start Address	100001	000033	300009	400017
Chan. 1	100001	000033	300009	400017
Chan. 2	100002	000034	300010	400018
Chan. 3	100003	000035	300011	400019
Chan. 16	100016	000048	300024	400032

Figure 3.8. Example Modicon I/O addressing.

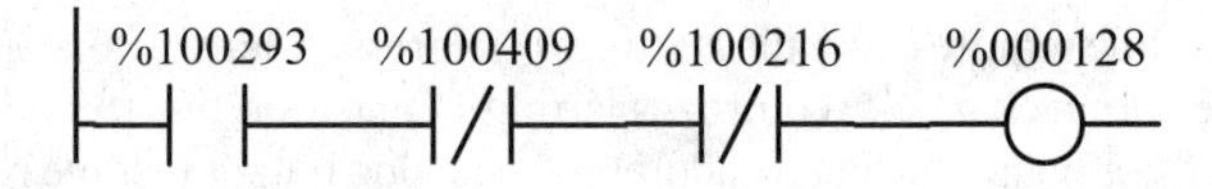

Figure 3.9. Solution to Example 3.1.

Example 3.1. Draw a Modicon ladder diagram that will cause the output, pilot light PL2, to be **on** when selector switch SS1 is closed, push button switch PB5 is open, and limit switch LS7 is open. Show the I/O addressing in the logic. The input/output devices are wired to the following locations:

PL2: Output module, local rack, I/O slot 8, channel 16
channel 1 is output address 000113

SS1: Input module, remote drop 1, I/O slot 3, channel 5
channel 1 is input address 100289

PB5: Input module, remote drop 2, I/O slot 2, channel 9
channel 1 is input address 100401

LS7: Input module, local rack, I/O slot 6, channel 8
channel 1 is input address 100209

Solution. First, determine the addresses of the devices. Applying the formula above,

Address for PL2 (channel 16) = 16 - 1 + 000113 = 000128
Address for SS1 (channel 5) = 5 - 1 + 100289 = 100293
Address for PB5 (channel 9) = 9 - 1 + 100401 = 100409
Address for LS7 (channel 8) = 8 - 1 + 100209 = 100216

The ladder logic is shown in Figure 3.9. The addresses are shown above the contact and coil symbols.

3.4 A-B CONTROLLOGIX MEMORY

3.4.1 Memory Organization

The Allen-Bradley ControlLogix PLC memory model is presented in Figure 3.10. The model is similar in many respects to the IEC 61131-3 memory model, but is somewhat simpler. Each of the main elements is now described.

The **project** is the entire body of software (program and data) that corresponds to one PLC. The project corresponds to the combination of the configuration and resource of IEC 61131-3. Basically, the ControlLogix PLC supports a single resource inside the configuration.

A **task** is configured to control the execution of one or more programs, similar to IEC 61131-3. There is a maximum of 32 tasks. No more than one task can be continuously executed. The other tasks are periodic, executed at a fixed time interval. Priority may be assigned to the periodic tasks and so a periodic task may be interrupted by a higher-priority periodic task. A task can contain up to 32 programs, executed in the specified order. Each task also contains status information and a watchdog timer to detect if the task does not finish execution within a specified interval.

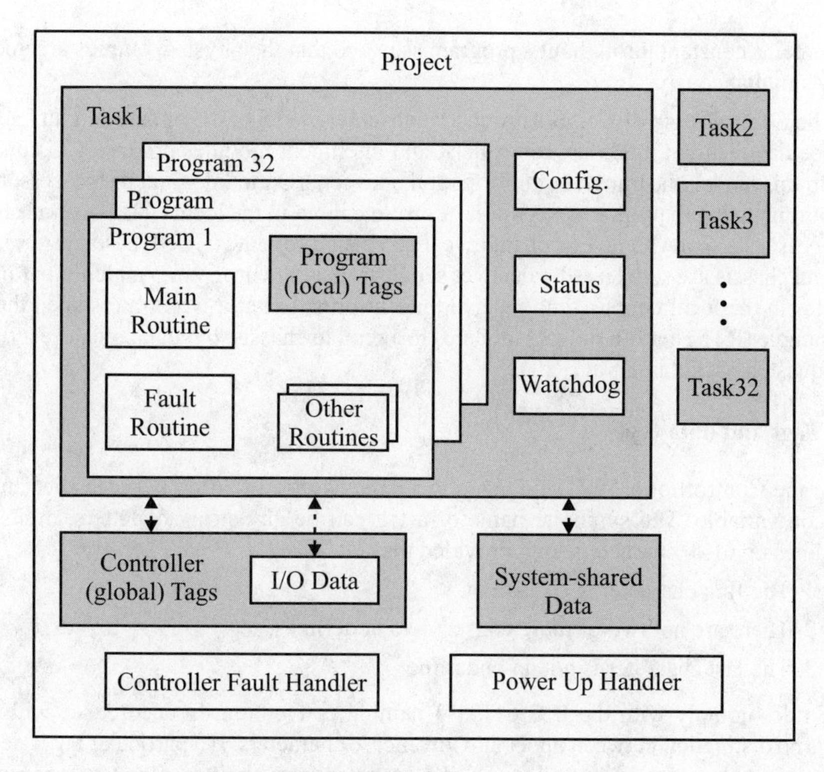

Figure 3.10. ControlLogix memory model.

A **program** consists of **routines**. The main routine, called "MainRoutine" is always executed first and must call the other routines (with a Jump to Subroutine instruction). The "FaultRoutine" is executed if a program fault is encountered when executing any of the routines in the program. Currently, the main and fault routines must be written in ladder logic. The other routines may be written in either ladder logic, function block diagram, sequential function chart, or structured text. Each routine can be coded in a single programming language. Each program has an area of local memory called **program tags**. Only the program for which they are defined can access program tags. Every routine in the program can access the program tags.

The **controller tags** are the global controller memory. The I/O data is considered part of the controller tags.

3.4.2 Program scan

In the ControlLogix PLC, the program execution is not coordinated with the scan of the I/O modules, as described in section 2.5. The programs in the continuous task are continuously scanned and data is transferred to/from the I/O modules any time during the logic scan. In order to duplicate the historic PLC scan process, a copy of the input data must be made at the beginning of the first program and used throughout the scan. Additionally, any writes to physical outputs are made to a copy of the output data and the copy is transferred to the physical outputs at the end of the scan. These two changes ensure the input data remains constant throughout a program scan and that the physical outputs are updated nearly simultaneously.

The ControlLogix PLC uses a producer/consumer model of I/O updates. Input modules produce data. Output modules, controllers, and intelligent modules produce and consume data. In this model, the transfer of information between I/O modules and the processor(s) is not coordinated with program execution. A discrete input in the local chassis (same chassis as processor) is sent whenever it changes, called change-of-state (COS). Discrete outputs in the local chassis are set/cleared whenever set/cleared by the program. Analog input/output modules in the local chassis send/receive their information at a fixed rate, called the real time sample (RTS) period. For I/O modules in a remote chassis, I/O data is sent/received at the requested packet interval (RPI).

3.4.3 Tags and data types

In the ControlLogix PLC, the tag is the same as the IEC 61131-3 identifier and the Modicon variable. The symbolic name of a tag can be any string of letters, digits, and underlines up to 40 characters long provided that:

1. The first character is not a digit.
2. There are not two or more consecutive underlines.
3. The last character is not an underline.

These rules comply with the IEC 61131-3 naming convention. In accordance with IEC, there is no distinction between upper and lower case characters. If a particular tag is defined as a program tag and a controller tag, the program uses the program tag, and not the controller tag. In order to avoid potential problems, there should not be a controller tag with the same name as any program tag.

When a tag is declared, it must be assigned a data type. The **simple data types** are as follows:

Name	Description	Range of values
BOOL	1-bit Boolean	0=cleared, 1=set
SINT	1-byte integer	-128 to 127
INT	2-byte integer	-32,768 to 32,767
DINT	4-byte integer	-2^{31} to $2^{31}-1$ (-2,147,483,648 to 2,147,483,647)
REAL	4-byte float. pt.	8.43×10^{37} to $3.36\times10^{+38}$

To identify a bit in an integer tag use "." between the tag name and the bit number, for example,

"MyInt.2" identifies bit 2 in "MyInt"(MyInt can be SINT, INT, DINT)

Some useful predefined controller tags that represent control status information are:

S:FS	First scan of program
S:C	Carry
S:N	Negative sign
S:V	Overflow
S:Z	Zero

Literals are used to directly provide values for inputs of function blocks, transition conditions, and so on. These values cannot be overwritten by the program logic. Literals are also used to assign a value to a constant or an initial value to a variable.

The BOOL (Boolean) data type has the literals 0 and 1. Literals for the integer data types can be expressed as an integer literal, base 2 literal (binary), base 8 literal (octal), or base 16 (hexadecimal) literal. The formats are as follows:

Literal type	Examples
integer	-12, 0, +23, 14_639
base-2	2#111 (7 decimal)
	2#1011_0011 (179 decimal)
base-8	8#177 (127 decimal)
	8#2001 (1025 decimal)
base-16	16#FFFF (65,535 decimal)
	16#AA (170 decimal)

The underline character may be inserted into numeric literals to aid readability; otherwise it has no significance. Literals for the REAL type may be expressed as normal decimal numbers,

5.341, +14_639.7, -0.0041

or with "E" or "e" indicating the tens' exponential value,

7.45e-12, 1.27E+4, 1.27E4.

One can define new data types from the simple data types. IEC 61131-3 allows one to alias, or redefine a data type, for example, all position values could be placed in variables whose data type called POSITION which is based on the REAL data type. This kind of derived data type is allowed in the ControlLogix PLC. In addition, one can define structured data types and array data types. A **structured data type** is generally a collection of data elements. Some of the more common predefined structured data types are the following:

Data Type	Use
AXIS	axis in motion instructions
CONTROL	bit shift, sequencer, array (file) instructions
COUNTER	counter instructions
MESSAGE	MSG instruction
MOTION_GROUP	one per controller (if doing motion)
MOTION_INSTRUCTION	motion instructions
PID	PID instruction
TIMER	timer instructions

The CONTROL, COUNTER and TIMER data types are constructed from 3 DINT's and are shown in Figure 3.11.

A user-defined data type allows one to define a new structured data type from the elementary and complex data types. After creating the user-defined data type, one can use it multiple times. For example, one could define the following Machine_Info data type:

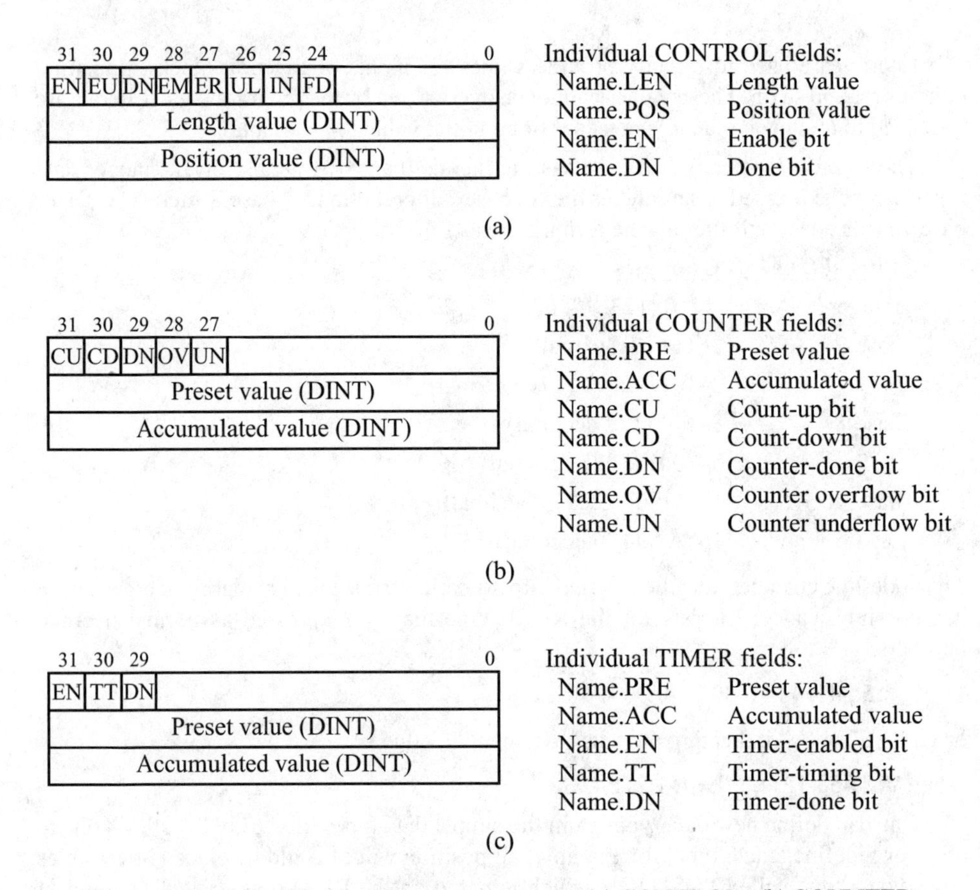

Figure 3.11. ControlLogix data type structures: *(a)* CONTROL; *(b)* COUNTER; *(c)* TIMER.

Data type Name: MACHINE_INFO

Member Name	Data Type
Serial_Num	DINT
Location	LOC_TYPE
Oper_Time	DINT
Shift_Faults	INT
Last_Fault	INT

Array data types are defined in a manner similar to the structured data types. Up to three dimensions can be defined. For example,

one dimension	array_name[subscript_0]
two dimensions	array_name[subscript_0, subscript_1]
three dimensions	array_name[subscript_0, subscript_1, subscript_2]

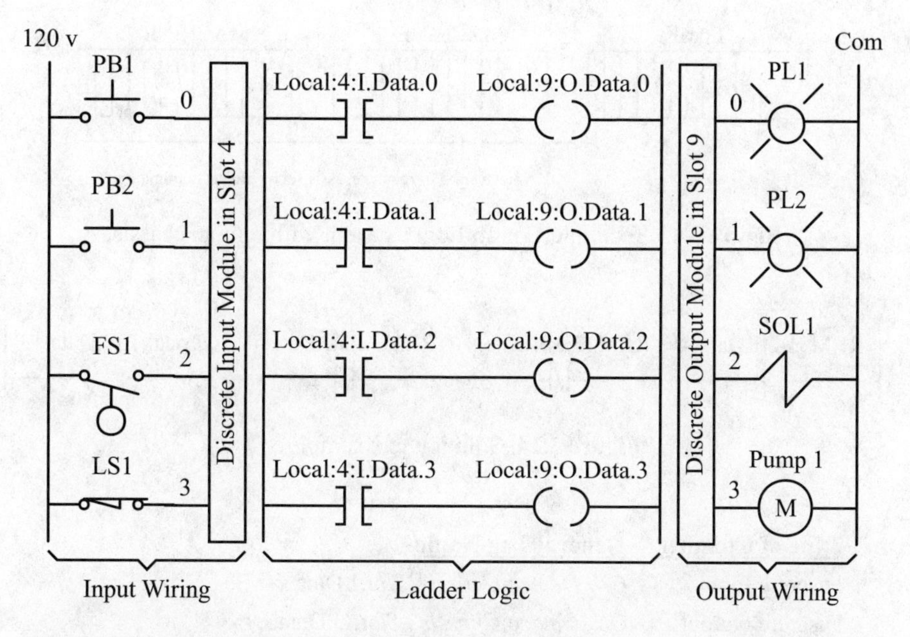

Figure 3.12. ControlLogix PLC implementation for Figure 3.6 showing I/O tags.

When used in instructions, the subscript can be a constant, tag, or expression (the latter 2 are similar to PLC-5 indirect addressing). One can make arrays of structures, except for the AXIS, MESSAGE, and MOTION_GROUP data types.

3.4.4 Input/Output Tags

For the ControlLogix PLC the physical I/O channels are addressed directly and have pre-defined tags. There is no need to construct an I/O map, as in the Modicon PLCs. The user does need to specify the location and type of each I/O module that will be used by the processor.

A ControlLogix PLC implementation of the hardwired circuit of Figure 3.6 might appear as in Figure 3.12. The switches are connected to channels 0 through 3 of a discrete input module and the lights, solenoid, and motor are connected to channels 0 through 3 of a discrete output module. The tag of the input channel is shown with the contact in the ladder. Normally, one would define a symbolic tag that refers to the I/O tag (called an alias tag) and the I/O tag would not appear on the listing. However, for the purpose of this example the addresses are shown. The tag "Local:4:I.Data.2" means the contact is controlled by the discrete input point (channel) 2, in slot 4 of the local chassis. In general, the tag for a discrete input channel is

CN_Device:*Chassis_Slot*:I.Data.*x*

where *CN_Device* is the name of the chassis, which is "Local" for inputs in the same chassis as the processor, *Chassis_Slot* is the chassis slot in which the module resides, and *x* is replaced by the channel number. Similarly, the tag "Local:9:O.Data.3" means the output (coil) is connected to output channel 3, in slot 9 of the local chassis. The most common I/O tags are:

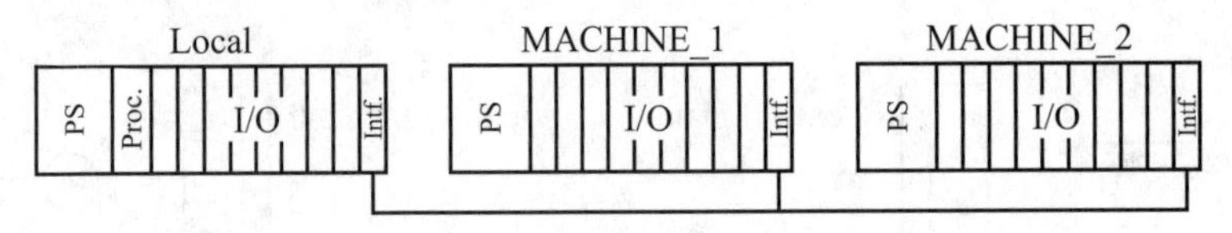

Figure 3.13. Example ControlLogix system with remote chassis.

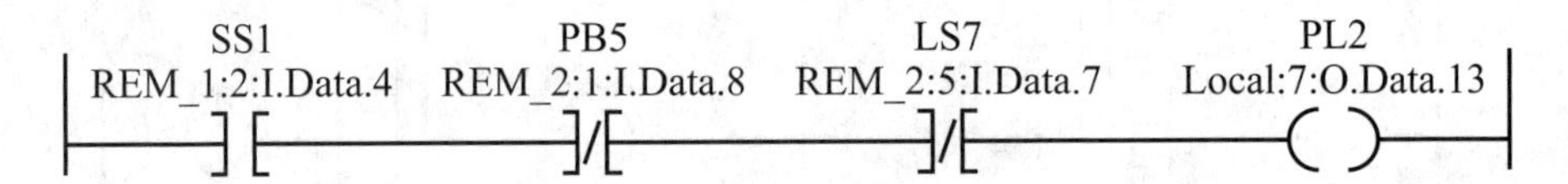

Figure 3.14. Solution to Example 3.2.

Type of Channel	General Tag Name
Discrete Input	*CN_Device*:*Chassis_Slot*:I.Data.*x*
Discrete Output	*CN_Device*:*Chassis _Slot*:O.Data.*x*
Analog Input	*CN_Device*:*Chassis _Slot*:I.Ch*x*Data
Analog Output	*CN_Device*:*Chassis _Slot*:O.Ch*x*Data

where

CN_Device is the name of the chassis, which is "Local" for inputs in the same chassis as the processor,

Chassis_Slot is the chassis slot in which the module resides, and

x is replaced by the channel number.

The chassis slots and module channels are numbered in decimal. An example ControlLogix system with two remote chassis is shown in Figure 3.13. Each I/O module has information other than just the channel data (e.g., channel errors). Consult the module documentation for information about the other pre-defined tags for that module.

Example 3.2. Draw a ControlLogix ladder diagram that will cause the output, pilot light PL2, to be **on** when selector switch SS1 is closed, push button switch PB5 is open, and limit switch LS7 is open. Show the I/O tags in the logic. The input/output devices are wired to the following locations:

PL2:	Output module, local chassis, slot 7, channel 13
SS1:	Input module, chassis 'REM_1', slot 2, channel 4
PB5:	Input module, chassis 'REM_2', slot 1, channel 8
LS7:	Input module, chassis 'REM_2', slot 5, channel 7

Solution. The tags are predefined, so there is no need to map channels to addresses. The tags are,

PL2:	Local:7:O.Data.13
SS1:	REM_1:2:I.Data.4
PB5:	REM_2:1:I.Data.8
LS7:	REM_2:5:I.Data.7

The ladder logic is shown in Figure 3.14. The tags are shown above the contact and coil instructions.

3.5 A-B PLC-5 AND SLC-500 MEMORY

The memory organization of the PLC-5 and the SLC-500 are very similar. The only major differences are:

- different I/O addressing, and
- the SLC-500 does not support as many program and data files, and
- the SLC-500 does not support the A and D data file types.

The majority of the material is presented from the standpoint of the PLC-5 and the limitations of the SLC-500 are mentioned in the appropriate places. The I/O addressing of the PLC-5 and the SLC-500 are described separately.

3.5.1 Memory Organization

The memory model of the Allen-Bradley PLC-5 and SLC-500 PLC processors is presented in Figure 3.15. The model is simpler than the IEC 61131-3 memory model, and represents the most structured form of pre-IEC 61131-3 PLCs. When the PLC-5 memory model was developed and later adopted by the SLC-500, it was the most sophisticated memory model and is suited to projects with large programs and large amounts of data. Each of the main elements of the memory is now described.

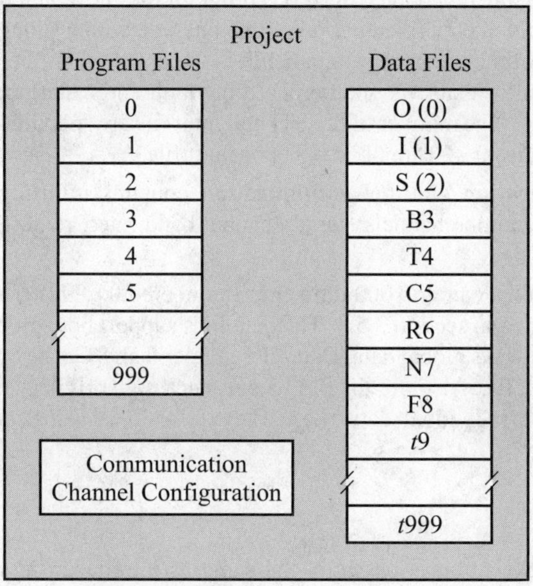

Project

Program Files: 0, 1, 2, 3, 4, 5, …, 999

Data Files: O (0), I (1), S (2), B3, T4, C5, R6, N7, F8, *t*9, …, *t*999

Communication Channel Configuration

Note: For SLC processors, the last program and data file number is 255

Figure 3.15. PLC-5/SLC-500 memory model.

The **project** memory is divided into 4 major parts: program files, data files, communication channel configuration, and unused memory. Technically, the project is more than the program, data files, and configuration that reside in the PLC. The project also includes program documentation that resides in the programming device only.

The **program files** contain controller information, the main program(s), and any subroutine programs. With some restrictions, a program file can contain ladder logic, a sequential function chart, or structured text. The purpose of the program files is as follows:

File Number	Use
0	Password and program identification
1	Sequential function chart, SFC (if supported by processor)
2	Main ladder logic program
3-999	Subroutine files
2-999	Ladder logic programs for SFC (if used)

The original PLC-5 processors (5/10, 5/12, 5/15, 5/25, 5/VME) have only one main ladder file and no more than one SFC (in file 1). The processor starts executing the first program file that is defined as a ladder file and ignores the other program files, unless those files are called by ladder logic in the first ladder file (such as a subroutine call). For enhanced PLC-5 processors (5/11, 5/20, 5/30 and above), one can define more than one main ladder file and more than one SFC file. Later revisions of the enhanced processors also allow more than 1000 program files. For the SLC-500, the maximum file number is 255 and program file 1 cannot be used because the SLC-500 does not support the SFC language.

The PLC-5 processors and the SLC-5/02 and later processors also support the definition of a selectable timed interrupt (STI) program file and a fault program file. An STI program file is executed on a fixed periodic time interval, which should be longer than the main program scan time. A fault program file is executed when the processor detects a major fault. The fault file allows one to record the fault and restart the processor without operator intervention. The number of the STI and fault file are specified as part of the status data file. Program files 0 - 2 cannot be a STI or fault file.

The **communication channel configuration** contains information specific to the processor communication channels: serial channel baud rates, remote I/O addresses, and channel protocols.

The PLC-5 can have up to 1000 **data files** (numbered 0 - 999). The address format of these files is explained in section 3.5.3. The data files support both global and local access. Data files 0 - 8 are always global data. Data files greater than 8 can be configured to be local data for one program file. Also, for the PLC-5 one can assign privilege classes and use them to restrict access to individual data files. The SLC-500 is restricted to 256 data files (numbered 0 - 255).

3.5.2 Program scan

The program execution is basically the same as introduced in section 2.5. For the PLC-5, the physical discrete inputs are read, the program is scanned from top to bottom, and the physical discrete outputs are written. The PLC-5 does not address analog I/O directly, which is explained in section 3.5.7.2. In contrast, the SLC-500 addresses analog I/O directly

Number of Elements	Data File	File Type	File Number	Words per Element	Addressed As
32 - 192	Discrete Output Image	O	0	1	O:*rrg*/*cc*
32 - 192	Discrete Input Image	I	1	1	I:*rrg*/*cc*
32 or 128	Status	S	2	1	S:*n* or S:*n*/*m*
1-1000	Bit	B	3	1	B3/*n* or B3:*n*/*m*
1-1000	Timer	T	4	3	T4:*n*
1-1000	Counter	C	5	3	C5:*n*
1-1000	(File) Control	R	6	3	R6:*n*
1-1000	Integer	N	7	1	N7:*n*
1-1000	Floating Point	F	8	2	F8:*n*
1-1000	Binary Coded Decimal (BCD)	D	9-999	1	D*x*:*n*
1-1000	ASCII Message	A	9-999	1	A*x*:*n*
1-1000	Any Type (except O, I, S)	any (not O, I, S)	9-999	varies	

Figure 3.16. PLC-5/SLC-500 data file organization.

and in other regards scans the program and I/O like the PLC-5. For both the PLC-5 and SLC-500, immediate input and output instructions are supported.

3.5.3 Data files

The organization of the data files is shown in Figure 3.16. Except for the first three files, every data file is designated by a letter and a number. Within a project, the letter/number combination is unique. For example, once data file 12 is designated as a timer file (T12), then an instruction cannot reference it as an integer file (N12). The first three data files are only designated by their letter (O, I, or S) since these types cannot be assigned to any other data files.

Data files 0 - 8 are the default data files that are defined for a new project. The type for data files 0 - 2 cannot be changed and their length depends on the processor model. It is possible to redefine the file types for files 3 - 8, but it is not recommended since those are the file types most people expect to find on any PLC-5. Data files 9 - 999 can be defined as any of the possible types and can be created as needed.

Except for the O, I, and S files, the length of a data file can be from 1 to 1000 elements (addressed as 0 - 999), subject to the available processor memory. When programming offline, the lengths of the data files are increased as needed. For example, if the counter file C5 contains 24 elements (last address is C5:23) and a counter instruction is programmed to refer to C5:24, the C5 file length is increased by one. Typically, one does not size the data files in this manner. Normally, the data files are manually created and sized before the program is entered. After the programming is complete, the data file sizes should be increased to accommodate online editing changes.

Data files 9-999 may be assigned any file type (except O, I, or S), as needed by the program. These data files are often used to organize the data files by process area or function. For example,

Separate bit/timer/counter/integer files for each process section or machine.

Integer file for PID controller storage.

Integer file for analog input block transfers.

The format of each data file type is now explained. The format of the output and input image files are explained in section 3.5.7 (PLC-5) and section 3.5.8 (SLC-500).

The **status** file contains detailed information regarding the processor status and the specific information varies by the processor. Some of the status file addresses that are common to many of the PLC-5 processors:

Address	Description
S:0	arithmetic flags, such as carry, sign, and zero
S:1	processor mode and force flags
S:1/15	"first pass" flag, set if processor is executing ladder for first time
S:2	other processor status, such as the data highway station number, type of slot addressing, etc.
S:3-S:6	table of bits indicating which stations on the data highway are active

A **bit** data file is internal one-bit memory used for internal coils and bit-shift instructions. For the default bit file, individual bits (coils) are addressed as

B3/*n*

where *n* is the bit number, 0-15999. A bit file can be addressed as words

B3:*n*

where *n* is the word number, 0-999. One can address individual bits in a word as

B3:*n*/*m*

where *n* is the word number and *m* is the bit number, 0-15. The bits within a word are numbered as shown in Figure 3.17. Other data files (>8) can also be bit files. For example, if data file 9 is a bit file, each coil in that file is addressed as B9/*n*.

The relationship between the two ways to address bits in a bit file is shown in Figure 3.18. For example, B3:2/5 addresses the same bit as B3/37 and B3:10/11 and B3/171

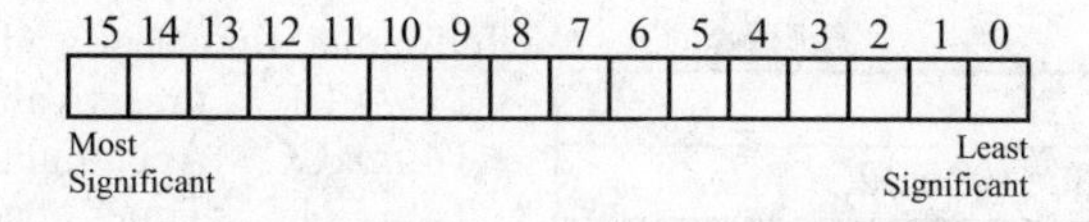

Figure 3.17. Bit numbering within bit file word or integer.

Bit number in word

15	14	13	12	11	10	9	8	7	6	5	4	3	2	1	0	
15	14	13	12	11	10	9	8	7	6	5	4	3	2	1	0	B3:0
31	30	29	28	27	26	25	24	23	22	21	20	19	18	17	16	B3:1
47	46	45	44	43	42	41	40	39	38	37	36	35	34	33	32	B3:2
⋮															⋮	⋮
159	158	157	156	155	154	153	152	151	150	149	148	147	146	145	144	B3:9
175	174	173	172	171	170	169	168	167	166	165	164	163	162	161	160	B3:10

Figure 3.18. Relationship between bit and word addressing in bit file type.

address the same bit. The programming software can be configured to display bit addresses in either format.

A **timer** file consists of timer elements whose structure appears in Figure 3.19*a*. For the default timer file, each individual timer is addressed as

T4:*n*

where *n* is the timer number, 0-999. The individual parts of each timer element can be addressed as shown in Figure 3.19*a*. The "/" can be used in place of the "." For example, the addresses T4:14.DN and T4:14/DN are equivalent. Other data files (>8) can also be timer files. For example, if data file 10 is a timer file, each timer in that file is addressed as T10:*n*.

A **counter** file consists of counter elements whose structure is shown in Figure 3.19*b*. For the default counter file, each individual counter is addressed as

C5:*n*

where *n* is the counter number, 0-999. The individual parts of each counter element can be addressed as shown in Figure 3.19*b*. The "/" can be used in place of the "." Other data files (>8) can also be counter files. For example, if data file 14 is a counter file, each counter in that file is addressed as C14:*n*.

A **file control** data file element (Figure 3.19*c*) is used to store information for block transfers and various other instructions, such as file arithmetic, shift register, and sequencer. For the default control file, each individual element is addressed as

R6:*n*

where *n* is the element number, 0-999. The individual parts of each file control element can be addressed as shown in Figure 3.19*c*. Other data files (>8) can also be file control data files.

An **integer** data file stores integer data values, with a range from -32,768 through 32,767. Individual integers are addressed as

N7:*n*

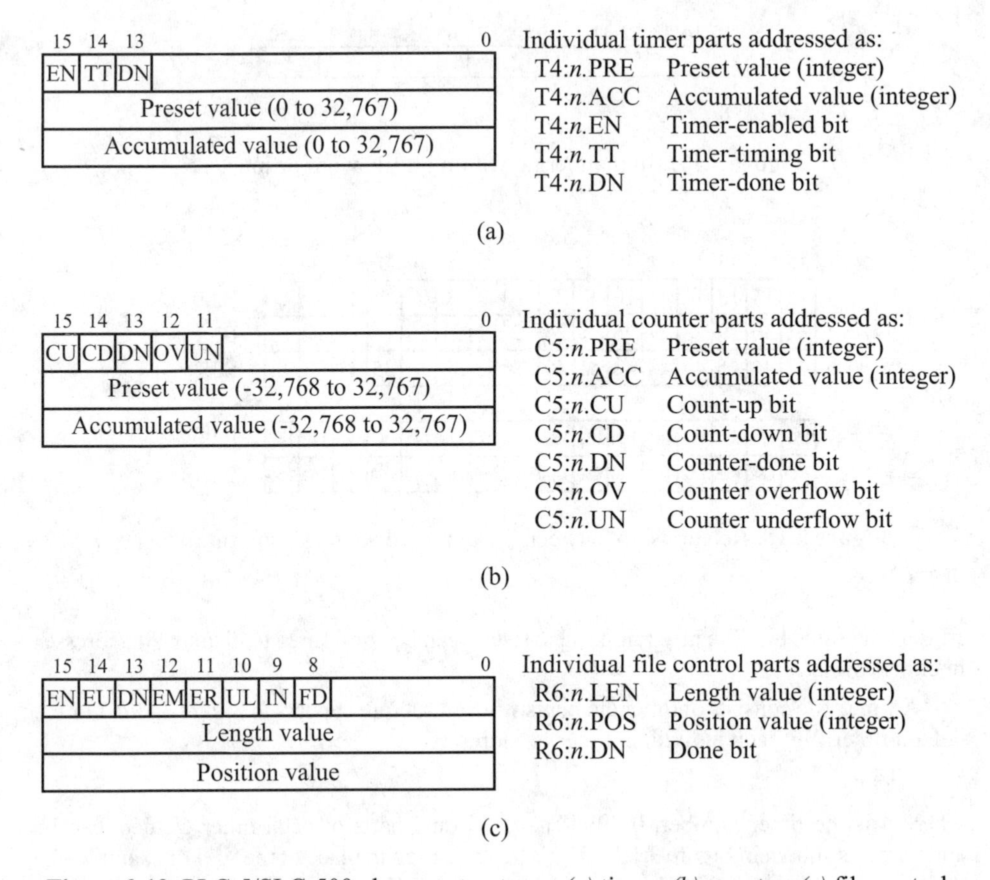

Figure 3.19. PLC-5/SLC-500 element structures: *(a)* timer; *(b)* counter; *(c)* file control.

where *n* is the elcment number, 0-999. One can address individual bits within the integer as

N7:*n*/*m*

where *n* is the word number and *m* is the bit number, 0-15. The bits within a word are numbered in the same manner as for the words in a bit file (Figure 3.17). Other data files (>8) can also be integer files. For example, if data file 21 is an integer file, each integer in that file is addressed as N21:*n*.

A **floating-point** data file stores floating-point values, with a range from $\pm 1.1755\times 10^{-38}$ through $\pm 6.8056\times 10^{+38}$. Individual floating-point numbers are addressed as

F8:*n*

where *n* is the element number, 0-999. Each floating-point number occupies 2 words, but individual words or bits cannot be addressed within the floating-point file. To access the individual words or bits, the COP instruction must be used to copy the floating-point number to a bit or integer file.

A **BCD** (binary coded decimal) data file is used mainly for display of numbers and for certain types of inputs (e.g., thumbwheel switches). Individual BCD numbers are addressed as

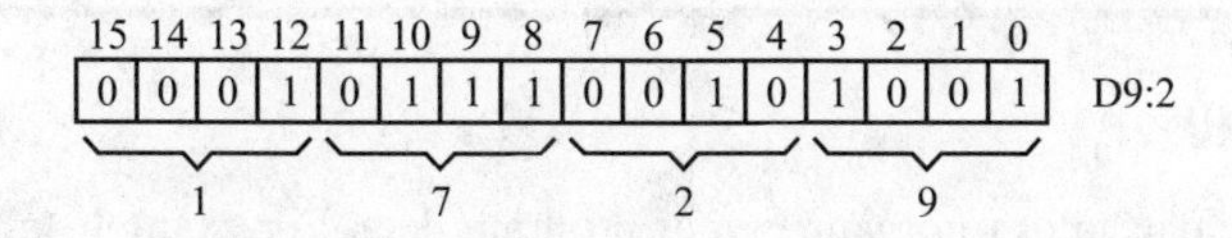

Figure 3.20. Example storage of BCD number.

D*x*:*n*

where *x* is the file number (9-999) and *n* is word number, 0-999. In a BCD number, each group of 4 bits in the word is the binary representation of a decimal digit. For example, Figure 3.20 shows the binary pattern of decimal 1729. Note that each group of 4 bits represents one of the decimal digits. If this word is moved to an integer location, the bit pattern is interpreted as 5929 (decimal). The SLC-500 does not support the BCD data file type and stores BCD numbers in integer addresses.

An **ASCII** data file is used mainly for the storage of messages. Each word in an ASCII data file contains two ASCII characters, but only words can be addressed as

A*x*:*n*

where *x* is the file number (9-999) and *n* is the word number, 0-999. Figure 3.21 shows how the message "PLC" is stored starting at address A15:10. This data file type can be used to store messages for communication with certain display modules. Message-type data can be received from certain devices (for example, bar-code readers) and stored in this file type. The SLC-500 does not support this data file type.

The enhanced PLC-5 processors have some additional files types, which can be used for data files 9-999:

Letter	Meaning	Use	Max. elements
BT	Block transfer	BTR/BTW instructions	1000
MG	Message	MSG instruction	585
PD	PID	PID instruction	399
SC	SFC status	SFC files	1000
ST	ASCII string	Data for ASCII instr.	780

In addition, the ControlNet PLC-5 processors have an additional data file type, CT, used for the ControlNet messages.

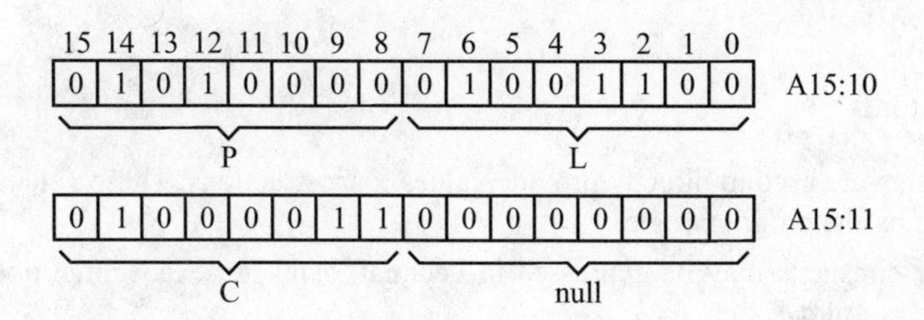

Figure 3.21. Representation of "PLC" in ASCII data file.

Design Tip

Use the data files to organize your program data. For example, a PLC-5 that controls multiple assembly machines could have data files organized in blocks of 10 files as:

B10	Machine 1 bits
T11	Machine 1 timers
C12	Machine 1 counters
R13	Machine 1 file control
N14	Machine 1 integers
F15	Machine 1 floating-point
A16	Machine 1 messages
B20	Machine 2 bits
T21	Machine 2 timers
C22	Machine 2 counters

and so on.

3.5.4 Indirect and Indexed Addressing

In order to aid in structuring and accessing large amounts of data, the PLC-5 and SLC-500 support indirect and indexed addressing.

In **indirect addressing**, an address may substitute for the numerical part of an address. Indirect addressing is identified by square brackets around the address supplying the number. Indirect addressing is useful for accessing arrays of elements (bits, integers, etc.). For example, in the address B3/[N7:3], the N7:3 address determines the bit number in B3 that will be accessed. The programmer must ensure that the value of N7:3 does not cause a reference beyond the number of words in B3, or the processor will fault.

As another application of indirect addressing, the data file number can be supplied by an integer address. For example, in the address N[N7:4]:10, the value in N7:4 determines which integer file is accessed to get the word 10 value. This type of indirect addressing could be used in a batch control application where there are a series of integer files, each holding a separate batch recipe. An integer location specifies the particular integer file, and thus the current recipe.

In **indexed addressing**, the value of the index register (S:24) is added to the address to obtain a new address. Indexed addressing is identified by a "#" character in front of an address reference. For example, an address of #N30:4 means the actual address is obtained by the index register as an offset to N30:4. If the value of S:24 is 9, then the actual address is N30:13 (N30:4+9).

3.5.5 Constants

Constants are used to directly provide values for instructions. These values cannot be overwritten by the program logic.

Integer constants may be expressed in decimal, octal or hexadecimal notation. The formats are as follows:

Type	Examples
integer	-12, 0, 23D, 14639
octal	177O (127 decimal)
	2001O (1025 decimal)
hexadecimal	FFFFH (65,535 decimal)
	AAH (170 decimal)

Floating-point constants may be expressed as normal decimal numbers,

5.341, +1439.7, -0.0041

or with "E" indicating the tens' exponential value,

7.45E-12, 1.27E+4, 1.27E4.

3.5.6 Symbols

The variables in a PLC-5 and SLC-500 program are basically address-based. In other words, only addresses are needed to construct a program, though a program constructed in such a manner would be difficult to understand. Therefore, symbols are associated with each address used in a program. The database of symbols and descriptions for each address is maintained separately on the programming device and it does not reside in the controller. Therefore, when connecting to a PLC-5/SLC-500 in order to examine the online operation of the program, the connecting computer must also have the project file in order to display the symbols with the program addresses.

The symbol associated with an address can be any string of letters, digits, and underlines up to 20 characters long. The symbol must have at least one letter and must not end in one or more digits followed by the single letter D, O, H, or E, because it is interpreted as a value.

3.5.7 PLC-5 Input/Output Addressing

In the PLC-5, the discrete I/O is handled differently from the analog I/O. The discrete I/O appears as part of the data files. Analog I/O must use block transfer instructions to move data between the modules and the processor memory.

3.5.7.1 Discrete Input/Output

In the PLC-5, the O data file contains the discrete output image, which is transferred to the physical output modules at the end of a program scan. The I data file contains the discrete input image, which is read from the physical input modules at the beginning of a scan.

A PLC-5 implementation of the hardwired circuit of Figure 3.6 might appear as in Figure 3.22. The switches are connected to channels 0 through 3 of a discrete input module and the lights, solenoid, and motor are connected to channels 0 through 3 of a discrete output module. The address of the input channel is shown with the contact in the ladder. Normally, one defines a symbol that refers to the I/O address and both the address and its symbol appears on the listing. However, for the purpose of this example only the addresses are shown. The address format shown in Figure 3.22 is called the "single line" format. The

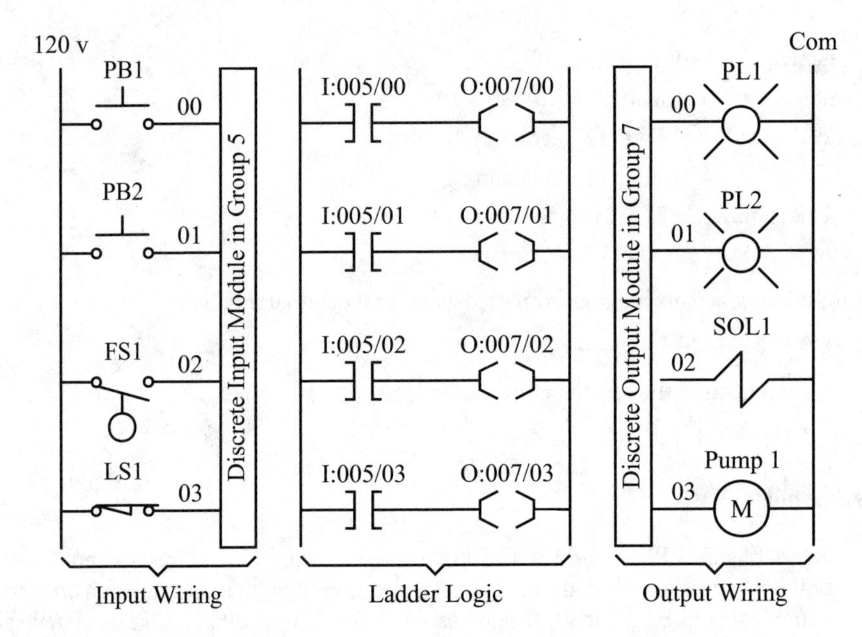

Figure 3.22. PLC-5 implementation for Figure 3.6 showing I/O addressing.

address "I:005/02" means the contact is controlled by the discrete input channel 02, in group 5 of the local chassis. In general, the address for a discrete input channel is

I:*rrg*/*cc*

where *rr* is the rack number, *g* is the group number in which the module resides, and *cc* is the channel number. The PLC-5 processor resides in rack 0, also called the local chassis. Similarly, the address "O:007/01" means the output (coil) is connected to output channel 01, in group 7 of the local chassis. All of the numbers in an I/O address are octal.

The alternate format of the discrete I/O address display is called the "split line" format. In this format, the bit (discrete channel) is shown below the contact or coil instruction.

Summarizing, the PLC-5 discrete I/O addresses are:

Type of Channel	General Address
Discrete Input	I:*rrg*/*cc*
Discrete Output	O:*rrg*/*cc*

where

rr is the rack number (octal),

g is the group number (0 - 7, octal), and

cc is the channel number (0 - 17, octal).

The allowable maximum number of racks depends on the particular PLC-5 processor. In contrast to all of the other address formats of the PLC-5 data, the discrete I/O is numbered in octal. Therefore, addresses like I:025/08 and O:195/12 are ILLEGAL.

The terms rack and group have a definite meaning for the PLC-5. They are defined as follows:

I/O Group - addressing unit corresponding to an input-image word and an output-image word. An I/O group can contain up to 16 input channels and 16 output channels and can occupy two, one, or one-half slots in the chassis.

I/O Rack - 8 I/O groups. Depending on I/O chassis size and I/O group size (2, 1, or 1/2 slots), an I/O rack can occupy a fraction of an I/O chassis, a full I/O chassis, or multiple I/O chassis.

In order to accommodate legacy I/O modules, fit them into the definition of no more than 16 channels in a group, and to use the I/O address space efficiently, the addressing scheme for the PLC-5 is rather complicated. There are 3 addressing schemes: two-slot, one-slot, and half-slot, which corresponds to the number of slots assigned to a group. In simple terms, two-slot addressing allows two 8-point discrete modules to occupy one group, one-slot addressing allows one 16-point discrete module to occupy one group, and half-slot addressing allows one 32-point discrete module to occupy two groups. However, each addressing scheme allows more complicated configurations and permits efficient use of the available addresses. Additionally, a concept called complementary I/O can be used for even greater efficiency.

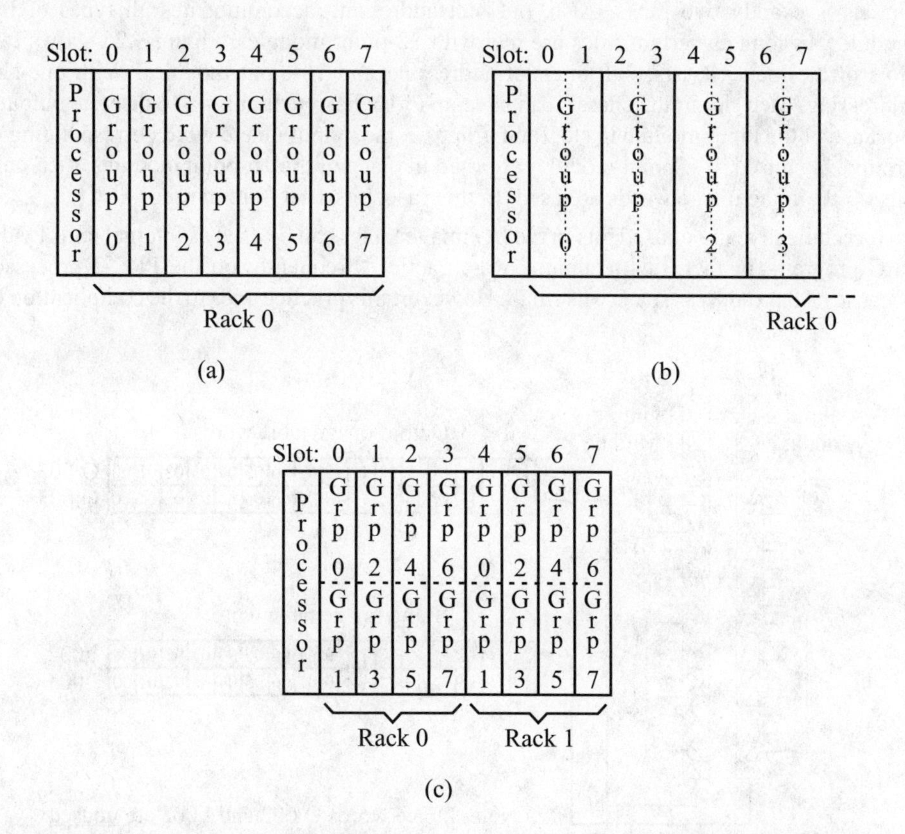

Figure 3.23. Comparison of slot addressing methods: *(a)* one-slot addressing; *(b)* two-slot addressing; *(c)* half-slot addressing.

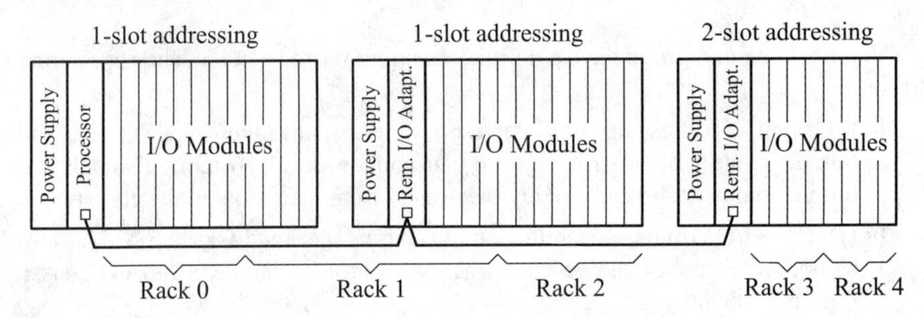

Figure 3.24. PLC-5 racks for system with remote I/O.

The number of slots actually occupied by a rack depends on the number of slots per group. Figure 3.23 shows the number of racks in an 8-slot chassis when the various addressing schemes are used. When two-slot addressing is used with an 8-slot chassis, the other half of the rack must reside in another chassis. Rack assignment for an example PLC-5 system with remote I/O and differing chassis slot addressing schemes is shown in Figure 3.24.

One-Slot Addressing. One-slot addressing is the easiest to understand because the slot numbers correspond to group numbers. An 8-slot chassis is exactly one rack and a 16-slot chassis is exactly two racks. Also, one-slot addressing accommodates all types of I/O modules, as long as certain rules are met with 32-point modules. Figure 3.25 shows two slots of the local chassis with one-slot addressing and 16-point modules. With one-slot addressing, each slot in the chassis can have up to 16 discrete inputs or 16 discrete outputs. Because of the input module in slot (and group) 2, the output image word corresponding to group 2 is unused. If 8-point modules are used in place of the 16-point modules, then only bits 00-07 in the image words are used. In this case, bits 10-17 are unused.

Technically, any unused bits in the I/O image tables can be used as internal coils by the PLC program. In fact, this technique was practiced frequently on the PLC-2 processor because its data address space was small. However, this practice adds to the complication of

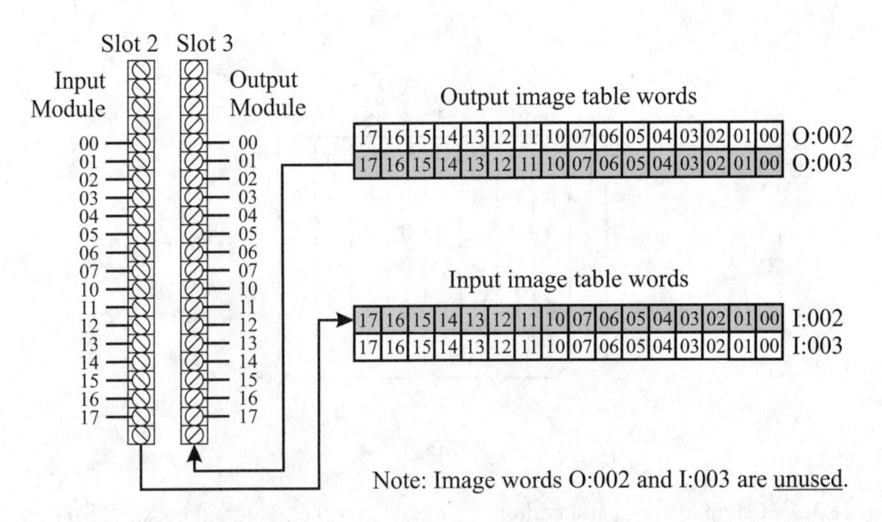

Figure 3.25. One-slot addressing with 16-point modules.

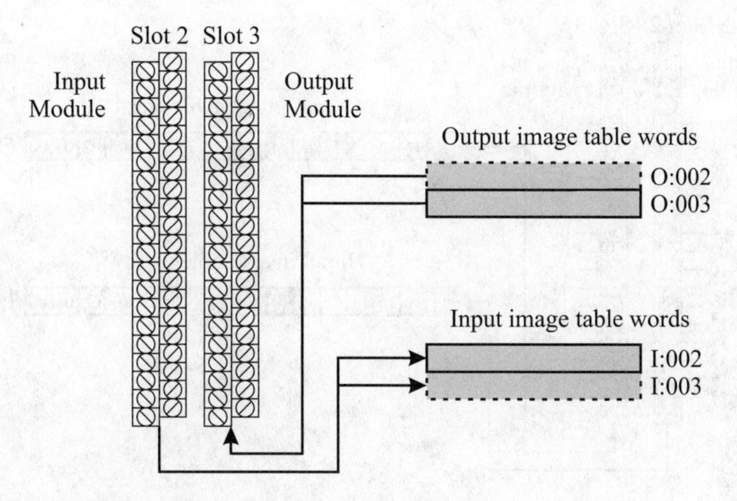

Figure 3.26. One-slot addressing with 32-point modules.

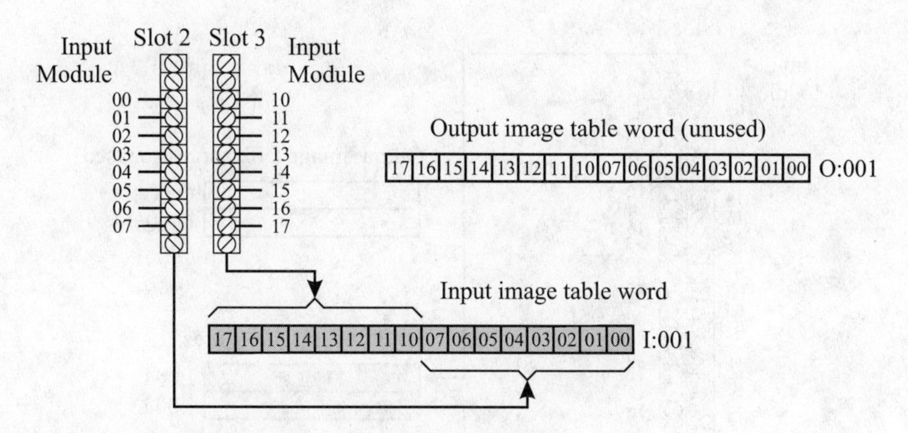

Figure 3.27. Two-slot addressing with 8-point modules.

converting the PLC-2 code to PLC-5 code. The practice of assigning unused I/O bits as internal coils is not necessary on the PLC-5 since its memory space is not as limited.

When using 32-point discrete I/O modules with one-slot addressing, a 32-point input module and a 32-point output module must be in adjacent slots (Figure 3.26). This is the most efficient way to use one-slot addressing.

Two-Slot Addressing. In two-slot addressing, two I/O slots in the chassis make up a group of 16 discrete channels. Figure 3.27 shows two slots of the local chassis with two-slot addressing and 8-point modules. Together, slots 2 and 3 compose group 1. If an output module is in slot 3 of Figure 3.27, then bits 10-17 in input image word 1 (I:001) would be always 0, and bits 10-17 for the output module would come from bits 10-17 in output image word 1 (O:001).

When using 16-point discrete I/O modules with two-slot addressing, a 16-point input module and a 16-point output module must be in adjacent slots (Figure 3.28). This is the

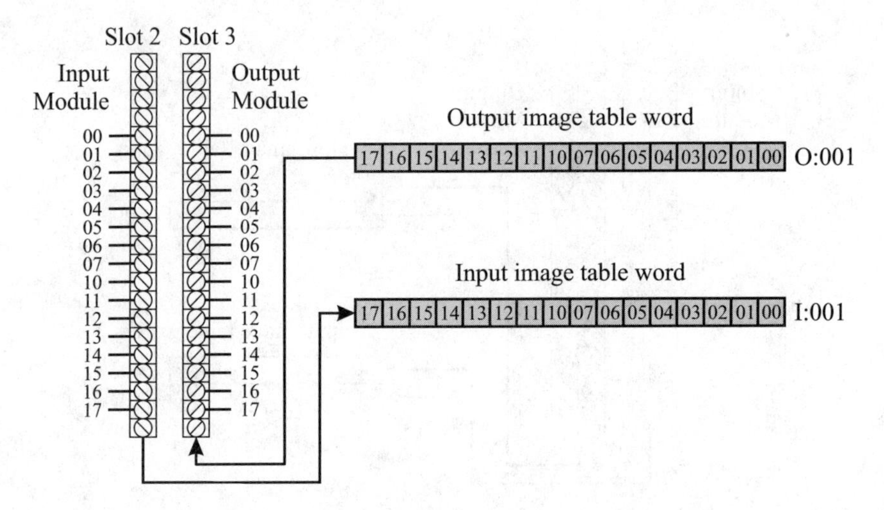

Figure 3.28. Two-slot addressing with 16-point modules.

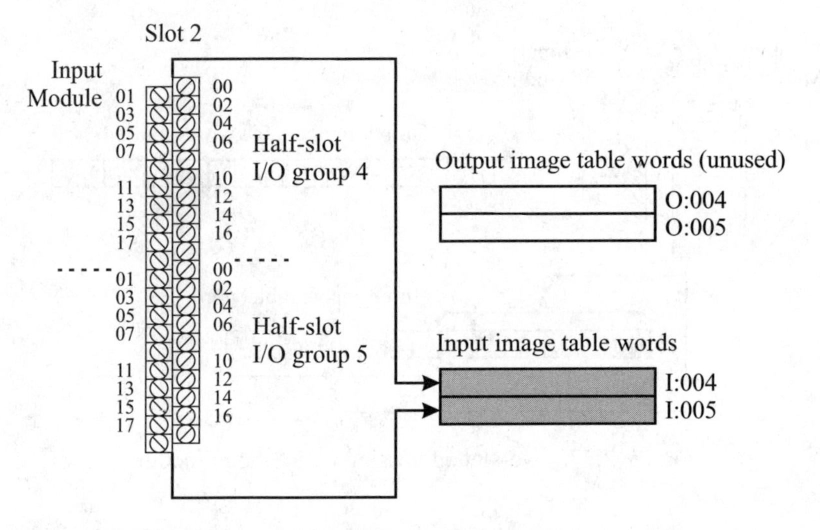

Figure 3.29. Half-slot addressing with 32-point modules.

most efficient way to use two-slot addressing because both input and output image words are used.

Half-Slot Addressing. In half-slot addressing, each chassis slot is assigned two groups. This method of addressing is primarily for 32-point I/O modules. Figure 3.29 shows how the group numbers relate to slot 2 in the local chassis. Since an input module is in this slot, the output image words are unused. With half-slot addressing 8-, 16- and 32-point modules can be installed in any order in the chassis, but many of the bits in the input and output image words, especially for those I/O groups having 8- and 16-point modules, will be wasted. This approach could be a problem with the PLC-5 processors that do not have much I/O space.

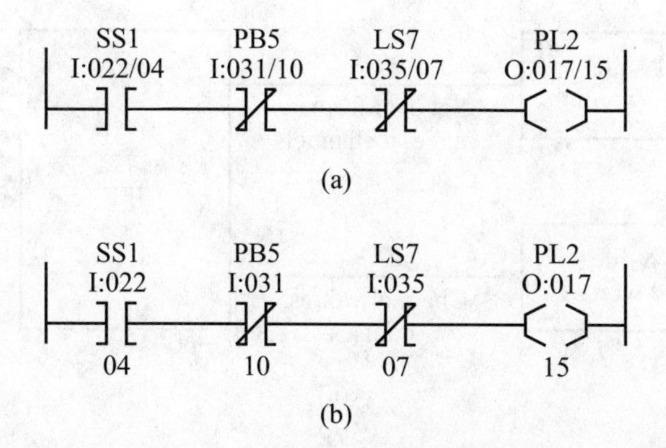

Figure 3.30. Solution to Example 3.3: *(a)* single line address format; *(b)* split line address format.

Complementary I/O. In a complementary I/O configuration, two chassis are assigned the same rack number, but the discrete modules are complements of each other. That is, if one rack has all input modules, then the complement rack has all output modules. This scheme is similar to two-slot addressing with 16-channel modules (Figure 3.28) in that all words of the input and output image can be used with the proper selection of modules. All three slot-addressing schemes may be used with complementary I/O, except that 32-channel modules cannot be used with one-slot addressing and 16-channel modules cannot be used with two-slot addressing.

Example 3.3. Draw a PLC-5 ladder diagram that will cause the output, pilot light PL2, to be **on** when selector switch SS1 is closed, push button switch PB5 is open, and limit switch LS7 is open. Show the I/O tags in the logic. The input/output devices are wired to the following locations (rack, group, and channel numbers in octal):

PL2:	Output module, rack 01, I/O group 7, channel 15
SS1:	Input module, rack 02, I/O group 2, channel 04
PB5:	Input module, rack 03, I/O group 1, channel 10
LS7:	Input module, rack 03, I/O group 5, channel 07

Solution. The addresses are predefined, so there is no need to map channels to addresses. The addresses are,

PL2:	O:017/15
SS1:	I:022/04
PB5:	I:031/10
LS7:	I:035/07

The ladder logic is shown in Figure 3.30. The addresses are shown above the contact and coil instructions and the symbols are shown above the addresses. The addresses are shown in the single line format in Figure 3.30*a* and in the split line format in Figure 3.30*b*.

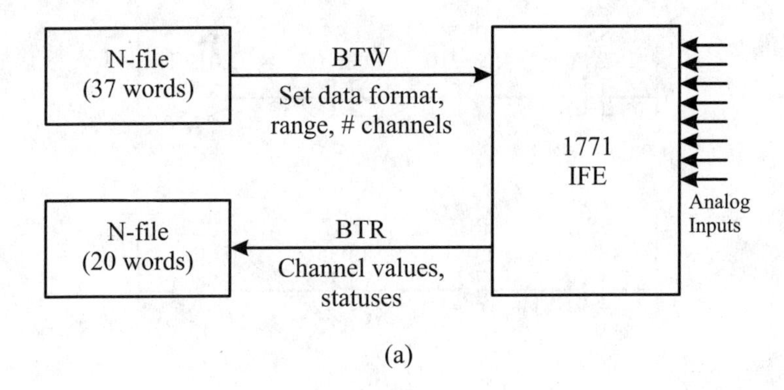

(a)

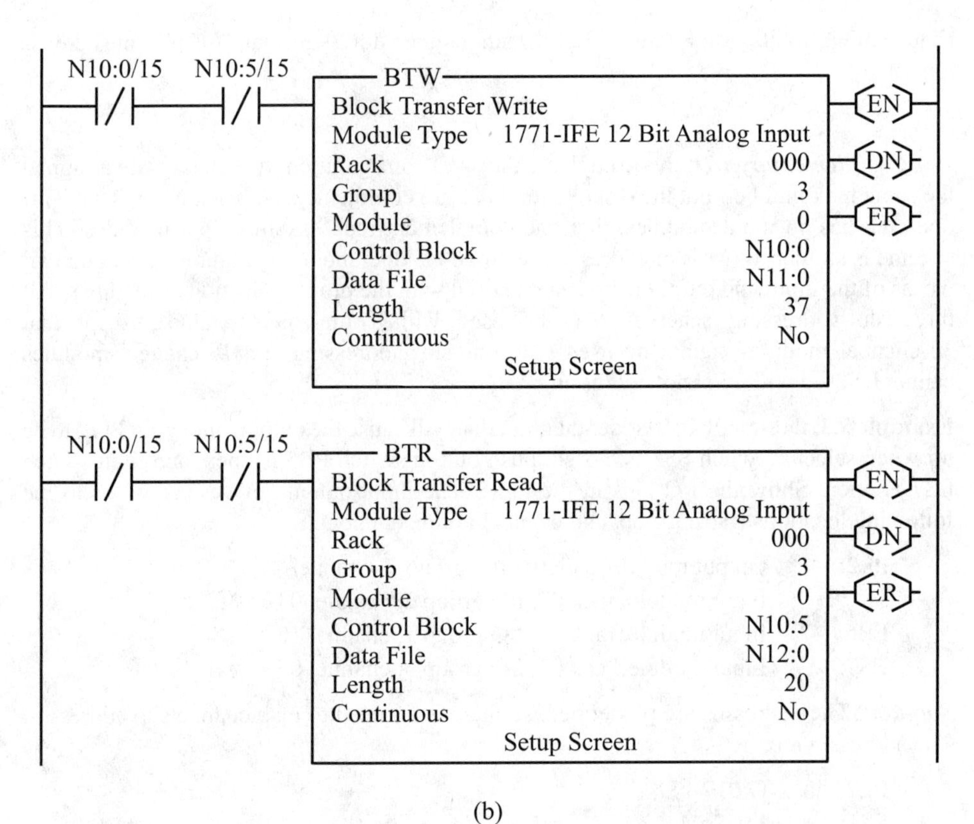

(b)

Figure 3.31. Example PLC-5 block transfers for analog input module: *(a)* transfers; *(b)* ladder logic.

3.5.7.2 Analog Input/Output

In a PLC-5 system, the analog I/O channel values do not appear in the I/O image data files. Block transfer instructions move data between the modules and the processor memory, usually integer data files.

Figure 3.31 shows the block transfers required to interface with a 1771-IFE 16-channel analog input module. Figure 3.31*a* conceptually shows the transfers that must occur. A block transfer write (BTW) is needed to configure the module with the number of channels to read, the data format, and other configuration information. A block transfer read (BTR) is required to read the channel values and status information.

The ladder logic code to implement these two transfers is shown in Figure 3.31*b*. The two block transfers are set up to alternate. The control blocks are set up in an integer file, which is required when using the BTR/BTW in an original PLC-5. The N10:0/15 bit is **on** when the write-transfer is enabled and in progress. The N10:5/15 bit is **on** when the read-transfer is enabled and in progress. When these two rungs are scanned for the first time, both N10:0/15 and N10:5/15 bits are **off**, which means the BTW is started. The BTR is not started until the N10:0/15 bit is turned **off** at the conclusion of the write-transfer. The BTW is not started until the N10:5/15 bit is turned **off** at the end of the read-transfer. The actual analog channel values are in the 20-word integer block starting with N12:0 and the value of the first channel is in N12:4. When the program is scanned for the first time, the BTW is always executed first in order to configure the module. One could set up the BTW to only execute once, on the first scan of the program. However, if the BTW is set up to only execute once, then if the module is ever replaced due to a faulty channel, the new module will not be properly configured. Forcing the processor into program mode and then back to run mode in order to configure the new analog input module is generally not acceptable in most systems. Alternating the block transfers solves this potential problem.

Figure 3.32 shows the block transfers required to interface with a 1771-OFE 4-channel analog output module. Figure 3.32*a* conceptually shows the transfers that must take place. A block transfer write (BTW) is needed to configure the module and to write the channel values. A block transfer read (BTR) is required to read the channel status information. The ladder logic code to implement these two transfers is shown in Figure 3.32*b*. As for the analog input transfers, the two block transfers are set up to alternate. This example uses the BT file type for the control block. The BT15:*n*/EN bit is on when the transfer is enabled and in progress. The actual analog channel values are part of the 13-word integer block starting with N13:0. The value of the first channel is in N13:0.

The parameters of the BTR/BTW instructions are as follows. The rack, group, and module specify the module address. The module parameter is only applicable if two-slot addressing is being used; module 0 is the left slot in the group and module 1 is the right slot in the group. The control block is the starting address of a 5-word integer block or a BT file element. The data file is the starting address of the integer data to be transferred to or from the module. The value of the length parameter depends on the particular module. If continuous operation is enabled, then when the rung condition changes to true, the block transfer happens every scan until an error is encountered. If an error occurs, the block transfer halts and will not restart until the processor is either forced into program mode and back into run mode, or the instruction is edited online to disable continuous operation. For this reason, the continuous operation is rarely used. If non-continuous operation is enabled, then when the rung condition transitions from **off** to **on**, the block transfer happens only once.

In operation, the BTR/BTW does not happen as soon as the rung condition turns **on**. It is placed into a queue and each block transfer is executed, in order. Block transfers happen in the background while the other ladder rungs are scanned. One must examine the "done" or "enable" bits to determine when the block transfer is finished. The block transfer "done" bit is bit 13 of the first word in an integer control block, or addressed as BT*x*:*n*/DN if using a BT data file for the control block.

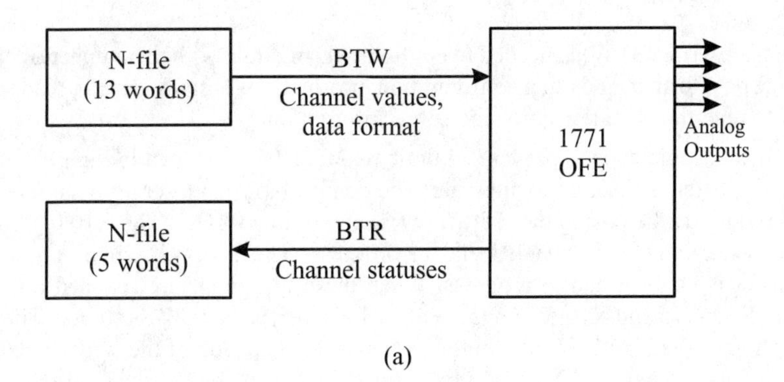

(a)

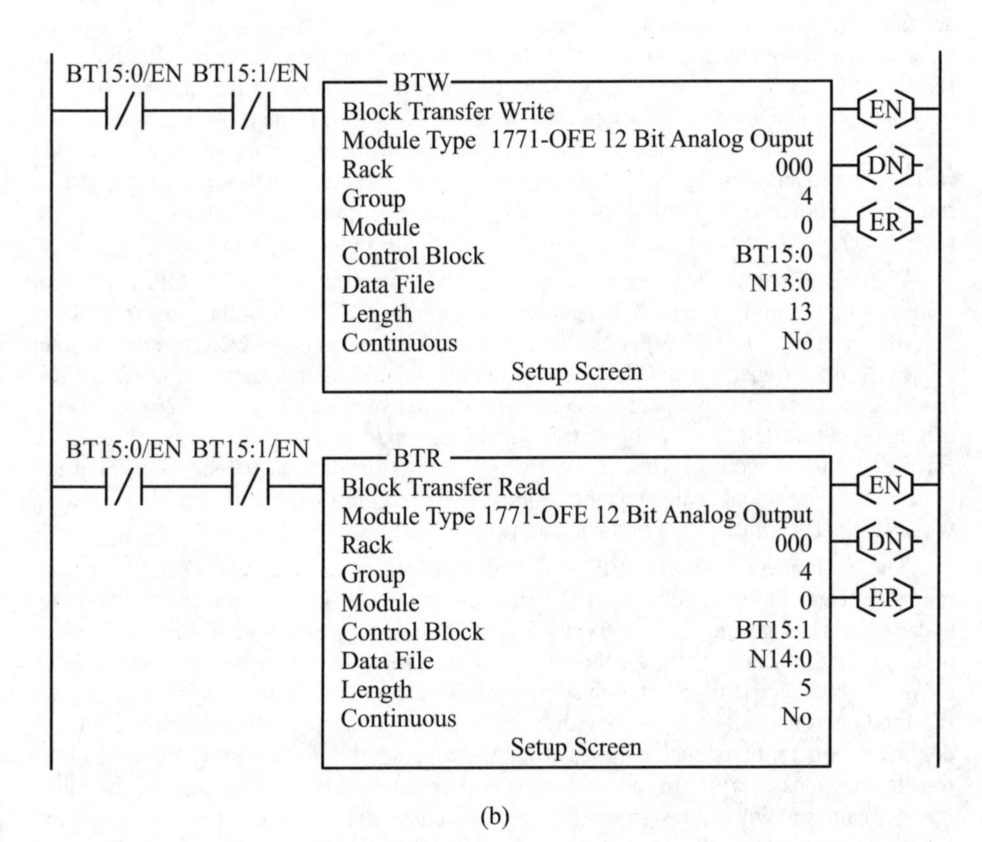

(b)

Figure 3.32. Example PLC-5 block transfers for analog output module: *(a)* transfers; *(b)* ladder logic.

3.5.8 SLC-500 Input/Output Addressing

In the SLC-500, the discrete I/O and the analog I/O are part of the I/O image. The O data file contains the image for all output channels, which is transferred to the physical

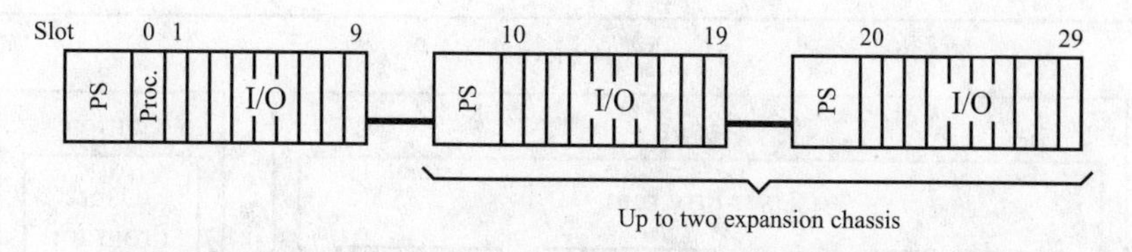

Figure 3.33. Local and expansion I/O for SLC-500 processors.

output modules at the end of a program scan. The I data file contains the image of all input channels, which is read from the physical input modules at the beginning of a scan.

The format is very similar to the format for PLC-5 discrete I/O addresses. The only real differences are that the rack and group is replaced by the slot number and the channels are numbered in decimal instead of octal. Summarizing, the SLC-5 I/O addresses are:

Type of Channel	General Address
Discrete Input	I:*ss*/*cc*
Discrete Output	O:*ss*/*cc*
Analog Input	I:*ss.cc*
Analog Output	O:*ss.cc*

where

ss is the slot number (1 - 30),

cc is the channel number (0 - 16).

The allowable maximum number of slots depends on the particular SLC-500 processor. The numbering of slots for an example SLC-500 system with expansion chassis is shown in Figure 3.33.

3.6 SIEMENS S7 MEMORY

There are three types of S7 processors: (1) S7-200, (2) S7-300, and (3) S7-400. From a programming viewpoint, the S7-300 and S7-400 differ only in the default I/O module slot addresses. The S7-200 processors differ significantly from the S7-300/400 processors. However, the memory model is basically a restricted version of the S7-300/400 processors. Therefore, this section presents the memory organization of the S7-300/400 processors and the restrictions and differences of the S7-200 processors are noted in the appropriate places.

3.6.1 Memory Organization

The Siemens S7 processors are programmed with the STEP 7 programming software and the S7-300/400 processor memory is organized as shown in Figure 3.34. Like IEC 61131-3 the model is layered and structured. However, it is somewhat different than IEC 61131-3. Each of the main elements is now described.

The **project** is the entire body of software (program and data) that corresponds to a PLC system that has one or more PLC processors. Each **station** is a PLC processor. The project corresponds to the configuration of IEC 61131-3 and the station corresponds to a resource.

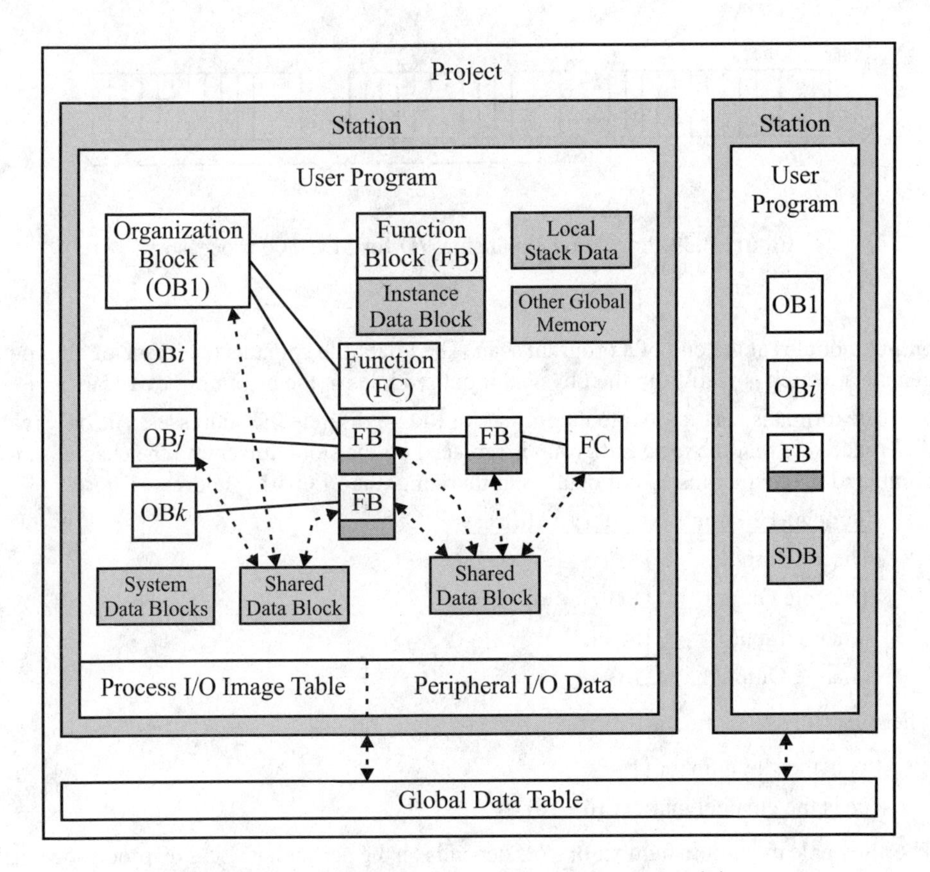

Figure 3.34. Siemens S7-300/400 memory model.

The **system data blocks** (SDBs) contain such items as the PLC processor model, I/O map, communication interfaces, remote I/O connections, and data memory allocation. This data is not accessible to the program.

A **station** consists of one **user program** which has organization blocks (OBs) as the main program entities. An **organization block** is basically a combination of one IEC 61131-3 task and program. The program in organization block OB1 executes once for each program scan. Organization blocks OB10 to OB122 are provided for non-cyclic types of program execution such as:

Fixed periodic interval
Process interrupt occurrence
Diagnostic interrupt occurrence
Synchronous and asynchronous error processing
Different types of startup processing
Multicomputing interrupt occurrence
Background program

The available organization blocks are specific to a particular processor. More detailed information is in Siemens (1996).

Each organization block, function, and function block (called logic blocks) has access to some temporary memory, called **local stack data memory**. Whenever a logic block is first executed, temporary data is allocated from the local data stack. This temporary data is released when the logic block finishes execution.

The program in an organization block can call function blocks or functions. A **function block** (FB) has local variables contained in an **instance data block**. A **function** (FC) does not have any local storage. A **shared data block** can be accessed by any of the program units (OB, FB, or FC). Built-in functions and function blocks are called system functions (SFC) and system function blocks (SFB).The **process I/O image table** contains the image of the physical input and output modules. The **peripheral I/O data** contains the same information as the process I/O image table, but it resides in the input and output modules.

The **global data table** is data that is shared between processors. Once configured, the transfer of information between processors is transparent to the user program.

An organization block may be written in any one of the following languages:

Ladder Diagram (LAD)
Function Block Diagram (FBD)
Statement List (STL, like IEC instruction list)
Structured Control Language (SCL, like IEC structured text)

A function block or function may be written in the three languages listed above, plus the following languages:

S7-Graph (like IEC sequential function chart)
S7-HiGraph (a state-transition language)
Continuous Function Chart (CFC)

The continuous function chart and S7-HiGraph languages are not covered by this text.

The S7-300/400 processors divide the processor memory into the **load memory** and the **work memory**. The load memory contains the complete user program (OBs, FCs, FBs, SDBs, etc.) without the symbol table and comments. Depending on the processor, the load memory can be RAM (random-access memory), EPROM, (erasable programmable read-only memory), or EEPROM (electrically erasable programmable read-only memory). The work memory is RAM, optimized for high-speed access. At startup, the parts of the program relevant for program execution are copied from the load memory to the work memory. The program is executed from the work memory.

The memory model of the S7-200 processors differs from the S7-300/400 model in the following aspects:

- Only one organization block (OB1).
- Subroutines instead of user-defined functions and function blocks.
- No shared data blocks.

In addition, the S7-200 processors only support the LAD, FBD, and STL languages.

3.6.2 Program Scan

Each organization block is a task. The program in organization block OB1 executes once for each program scan. Except for the background organization block (OB90), the main program OB1 has the lowest priority. While OB1 is executing, it can be interrupted by a higher-priority organization block. There are up to 28 priority levels in the S7 processor. The background organization block OB90 is executed if the actual program scan time is shorter than the specified minimum scan time. In this text, OB1 is assumed to contain the entire program or to call function blocks.

The OB1 program execution is basically the same as introduced in section 2.5. The physical inputs are read, the program is scanned from top to bottom, and the physical outputs are written. The current values in the I/O modules can be directly accessed as peripheral I/O data. With some S7-300/400 processors, one can create and update up to eight sections of the I/O image tables, independent of the cyclic updating of the I/O image. The UPDAT_PI or UPDAT_PO system function blocks (SFBs) are used to programmatically update a section of the input or output image, respectively. The SET and RSET SFBs set or clear, respectively, individual bits in the output image.

3.6.3 Addressable data memory

In the S7 processor, data may be addressed as a symbol or as an absolute address. Though only absolute addresses are required to construct a program, it is not recommended. Therefore, a symbol is associated with each absolute address in a program. The format of the absolute addresses is explained after first describing the symbols and the various data types.

The symbolic name of an absolute address can be any string of letters, digits, and underlines up to 24 characters long provided that there are not two or more consecutive underlines. STEP 7 relaxes the IEC61131-3 naming convention by allowing leading digits in the name. There is no distinction between upper and lower case (though STEP 7 versions prior to 4.02 allowed a distinction between upper and lower case symbols). Generally, a symbolic name should exist only once as a memory, function block or instance name. However, a symbol local to an organization block can be identical to a shared symbol.

Shared and local symbols are distinguished in a program in the following manner:

- Shared symbols (in the symbol table) are enclosed in quotation marks "..".
- Local symbols (in the block variable declaration table) are preceded by the "#" character.

The quotation marks or the "#" are normally added by STEP 7 when entering the program. However, if the symbol name is defined as a shared symbol and a local symbol exists, then the local symbol name is assumed. The quotation marks must be added if the shared symbol is desired.

The symbol and description for each address is maintained separately on the programming device and this symbol table does not reside in the controller. Therefore, when connecting to a S7 processor in order to examine the online operation of the program, the connecting computer must also have the project file in order to display the symbols with the program addresses.

When a symbol is declared, it must be assigned a data type. The **elementary data types** are as follows:

Name	**Description**	**Range of values**
BOOL	1-bit Boolean	0=cleared, 1=set
BYTE	8-bit	0 to FF hexadecimal
WORD	16-bit	0 to FFFF hexadecimal or -999 to 999 BCD
DWORD	32-bit	0 to FFFFFFFF hexadecimal
INT	2-byte integer	-32,768 to 32,767
DINT	4-byte integer	-2^{31} to $2^{31}-1$ (-2,147,483,648 to 2,147,483,647)
REAL	4-byte float. pt.	1.17510^{38} to 3.40310^{+38}
TIME	4-byte	-2^{31} to $2^{31}-1$ milliseconds (<-24 to >24 days)
DATE	2-byte	Jan. 1, 1990 to Dec. 31, 2168
TIME_OF_DAY	4-byte	0:0:0.0 to 23:59:59.999
CHAR	8-bit	ASCII characters
S5TIME	2-byte	0 to 999 BCD format with 0.01-, 0.1-, 1.0-, or 10-sec units

The TIME_OF_DAY and S5TIME data types are extensions to the IEC-61131-3 standard data types. The TIME, DATE, TIME_OF_DAY, CHAR, and S5TIME data types are not valid for the S7-200 processors.

Constants are used to directly provide values for inputs of function blocks, transition conditions, and so on. These values cannot be overwritten by the program logic. Constants are also used to assign a value to a constant or an initial value to a variable.

The BOOL (boolean) data type has the constants FALSE (or 0) and TRUE (or 1). Constants for the BYTE, WORD, and DWORD data types can be expressed in various formats:

Data Type	**Format**	**Example**
BYTE	Hex:	B#16#0 (0 decimal)
	Hex:	B#16#4C (76 decimal)
WORD	Binary:	2#111 (7 decimal)
	Binary:	2#1011_0011 (179 decimal)
	Hex:	W#16#7F (127 decimal)
	BCD:	C#271 (271 BCD)
	Decimal-byte:	B#(23,255) (17FF hexadecimal)
DWORD	Binary:	2#0000_1111_0111 (247 decimal)
	Hex:	DW#16#7F (127 decimal)
	Decimal-byte:	B#(0,0,23,255) (17FF hexadecimal)

Constants for the BYTE data type can only be expressed as hexadecimal numbers, identified by the B#16# prefix. The WORD data constants can be expressed in the binary, hexadecimal, BCD, or decimal-byte formats and each format has its separate prefix. In the decimal-byte format, each 8-bit byte is specified as a decimal number, starting with the most significant byte and finishing with the least significant byte. Constants for the DWORD data type can be expressed in the binary, hexadecimal, or decimal-byte formats.

The underline character may be inserted into binary constants to aid readability; otherwise it has no significance. Constants for the INT data type are expressed as normal integers without commas,

23, 18929, -32000

The DINT data types are expressed as a normal integer, prefixed by "L#" without commas,

L#23, L#645100, L#-2147483600

Constants for the REAL type may be expressed as normal decimal numbers,

5.341, +14_639.7, -0.0041

or with "E" or "e" indicating the tens' exponential value,

7.45e-12, 1.27E+4, 1.27E4.

Constants for the TIME type (called duration constants) are specified in days (D), hours (H), minutes (M), seconds (S), and milliseconds (MS), or combinations thereof. The duration must be identified by the prefix T# or TIME#. The "overflow" of the most significant unit is not allowed; e.g. the entry T#25H15M is changed into T#1D1H15M. Also, any decimal part of the duration constant is converted to its integer representation. For example, if one typed T#2.5S, it is converted into T#2S500MS. Some examples are:

T#10MS	10 milliseconds
T#3.5s	3 seconds, 500 milliseconds
TIME#18M	18 minutes
TIME#5D_14H_12M	5 days, 14 hours, 12 minutes

Constants for the DATE type are specified as the 4-digit year, month, and day of month prefixed by D# or DATE#. Some examples are:

D#1996-4-5	April 5, 1996
DATE#2005-12-4	December 4, 2005

Constants for the TIME_OF_DAY type are specified as the time in hours, minutes, seconds and thousandths of a second. The time must be identified by the prefix TOD# or TIME_OF_DAY#.Some examples are:

TOD#8:1:1.2	1.2 seconds past 8:01 AM
TOD#16:12:45.572	45.572 seconds past 4:12 PM

The S5TIME type is provided for backward compatibility with S5 processors and is not IEC-compliant. Constants for the S5TIME type follow the same format as for the TIME type except that days are not possible and the prefix is S5T# or S5TIME#. The value must be consistent with the timer resolution (0.01-, 0.1-, 1.0-, or 10-sec units) and be no more than 999 resolution units. Some examples are:

S5t#10MS	10 milliseconds
S5TIME#18M	18 minutes
S5TIME#1H_2M	1 hour, 2 minutes (372 10-sec units)

Constants for the CHAR type are single ASCII characters (letters, numbers, and symbols) enclosed in single quote marks. Some examples are:

'A'	Letter "A"
'x'	Letter "x"

The S7-300/400 processors also allow **complex data types**. Complex data types define groups of data larger than 32 bits or consisting of other data types. The complex data types are as follows:

Name	Description
DATE_AND_TIME	8-byte BCD
STRING	1 to 254 bytes of ASCII characters
ARRAY	multi-dimensional group of one data type
STRUCT	user-defined structured data group
POINTER	6-byte identification of a memory location
ANY	undefined data type for function block parameter
UDT	user-defined data type

The DATE_AND_TIME data type is an 8-byte structure that contains the year, month, day, hour, minute, seconds, milliseconds, and weekday stored as a set of BCD values. A DATE_AND_TIME constant is preceded by DT#. Some examples are

DT#2001-2-15-8-12-50-300-5

DT#1999-11-2-14-1-43-0-3

A STRING data type is an array of CHAR elements. The array consists of a two-byte header followed by the CHAR data (Figure 3.35). The first byte in the header contains the number of memory bytes reserved for the string (including the header) and the second byte holds the string length, the number of bytes actually containing data. The default and maximum size of a STRING is 256 bytes, though shorter strings can be specified, for example,

STRING[12]

which can contain a maximum of 10 characters (2 bytes reserved for the header). A string constant is a series of ASCII characters enclosed in single-quotation marks, for example,

'Sample'

An ARRAY data type is a multi-dimensional grouping of one data type (elementary or complex). One can define up to six dimensions. For example,

one dimension	ARRAY[1..31] OF TIME
two dimensions	ARRAY[-3..3, 0..25] OF INT
three dimensions	ARRAY[1..10, 1..10, 1..10] OF REAL

To access an element an array, the indices are enclosed in square brackets, for example, "[4,5]."

A structure is a collection of data elements, generally with different data types (elementary data types and/or complex data types) framed by STRUCT and END_STRUCT. For example, one could define the following structure (and symbols):

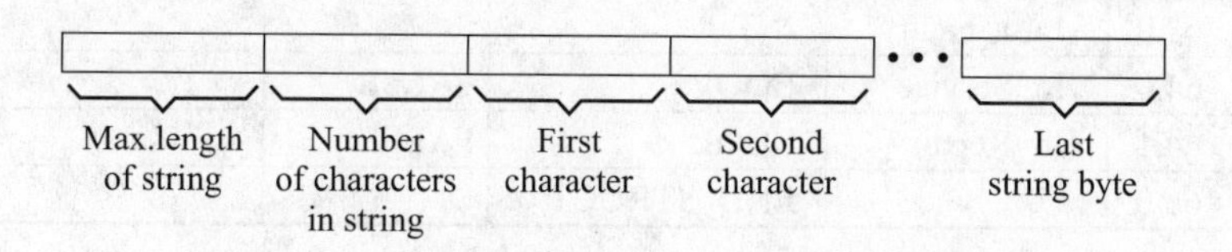

Figure 3.35. Structure of S7 STRING data type.

```
STRUCT
        Serial_Num      DINT
        Name            STRING[50]
        Oper_Time       TIME
        Shift_Faults    INT
        Last_Fault      INT
        In_Service      BOOL
        In_Repair       BOOL
END_STRUCT
```

A POINTER identifies the address of a memory location, rather than its value. It is often used to pass the address of a complex data structure to a function block rather than pass the contents of the structure. Often, a pointer is identified with a "P#" preceding the bit-level memory address. However, all parameters passed to a FC (function) are all pointers, even if "P#" does not precede the address. The POINTER data type occupies 6 bytes of memory. Since a pointer may only be modified and used within an OB, FB, or FC written in the instruction list language, it is described in Chapter 13.

The ANY data type is used for function block parameters when the data type of the parameter is unknown or when any date type is permitted. The data type of the parameter is declared as ANY when the block parameters are defined. This data type occupies 10 bytes of memory. More information about the use of the ANY data type is contained in Chapter 12, when structured control language programming is discussed.

A user-defined data type (UDT) allows one to define a new data type from the elementary and complex data types. After creating the UDT and assigning a name to it, one can use it multiple times. Figure 3.36 illustrates the structure of a UDT named Machine_Info consisting of a double integer, a string, a time, two integers and two booleans. The address column shows the offset from the start of the structure, as a byte and the starting bit number.

The memory of the S7 processors is divided into address areas identified by one or more letters followed by a number (Table 3.1). Note that the possible types vary with the processor type. For the S7-300/400 processors, the general memory, counter, and timer address areas are accessible by all logic blocks and are intended for temporary program storage. Most of the program data should be contained in shared data blocks or instance data

Address	Name	Type	Init. Value	Comment
0.0		STRUCT		
+0.0	Serial_Num	DINT	L#0	
+4.0	Nam	STRING[50]	''	
+56.0	Oper_Time	TIME	T#0MS	
+60.0	Shift_Faults	INT	0	
+62.0	Last_Fault	INT	0	
+64.0	In_Service	BOOL	FALSE	
+64.1	In_Repair	BOOL	FALSE	
=66.0		END_STRUCT		

Figure 3.36. Example "Machine_Info" user-defined data type.

Table 3.1 S7 Addressable Data Types.

Memory Type	Bit Address	Byte Address	Word Address	Dbl. Word Address
Common To All S7 Processors				
General Memory	M*n.m*	MB*n*	MW*n*	MD*n*
Timer	T*n*		T*n*	
Counter	C*n*		C*n*	
Local (stack) data	L*n.m*	LB*n*	LW*n*	LD*n*
Input Image	I*n.m*	IB*n*	IW*n*	ID*n*
Output Image	Q*n.m*	QB*n*	QW*n*	QD*n*
S7-300/400 Processors Only				
Status			STW	
Shared Data Block (DB*n*)	DBX*n.m*	DBB*n*	DBW*n*	DBD*n*
Instance Data Block (DB*n*)	DIX*n.m*	DIB*n*	DIW*n*	DID*n*
Peripheral Input Data		PIB*n*	PIW*n*	PID*n*
Peripheral Output Data		PQB*n*	PQW*n*	PQD*n*
S7-200 Processors Only				
Variable	V*n.m*	VB*n*	VW*n*	VD*n*
Special	SM*n.m*	SMB*n*	SMW*n*	SMD*n*
Sequence	S*n.m*	SB*n*	SW*n*	SD*n*
Accumulator		AC*n*	AC*n*	AC*n*
High Speed Counter				HC*n*
Analog In			AIW*n*	
Analog Out			AQW*n*	

blocks. For the S7-200 processors, most of the data should be contained in the variable memory. For all processors, the available amount of any type of memory depends on the specific processor.

For the S7-300/400 processors, one can declare a certain number of general memory, timers, counters, and shared data blocks as retentive, that is, the values are retained when the program is restarted. The values of data contained in instance data blocks are retained when the program is restarted. The amount of default and available retentive memory depends on the particular processor. Within limits, the amount of default retentive memory can be changed. For the S7-200 processors, one can define up to six ranges of M, C, T, and V memory to be retentive.

The format of each type of address is now explained. The format of the input and output data addresses are explained in section 3.6.4.

The general **memory** area may be accessed as bits, bytes, words, or double words. Individual bits (coils) are addressed as

M*n.m*

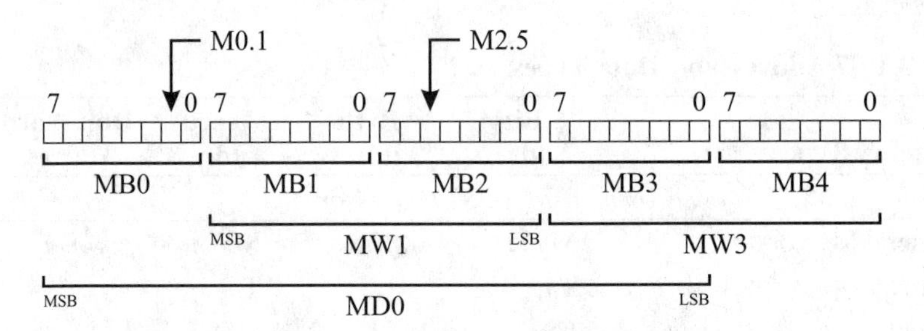

Figure 3.37. Relationship between general memory addressing.

where *n* is the byte number and *m* is the bit number, 0-7. The general memory area can be addressed as bytes, words, or double words as follows

MB*n* Byte *n*

MW*n* Word starting at byte *n*

MD*n* Double word starting at byte *n*

The relationship between the ways to address the general memory area is shown in Figure 3.37. Note that the MW1 address overlaps both MB1 and MB2. The least-significant bit of a byte, word, or double word is the right-most bit. In the same manner, MB2 is the least-significant byte of MW1.

The **timer** area contains the data for the timer function blocks. Though addressed the same, the S7-300/400 timers and S7-200 timers have different formats. For the S7-300/400 processors, the value of the S5-compatible 10-bit timer remaining time is addressed as

T*n*

where *n* is the timer number. For the S7-200 processors, the 16-bit integer value of the accumulator (elapsed time) is addressed in the same manner. For all S7 processors, the timer status bit (**on** when timer running) is addressed in the same way. The program determines which value to use (integer or Boolean) by the type of the instruction that uses the address. For the S7-300/400 processors, the IEC 61131-3 timer function blocks do not use the timer area, but store the values in an instance data block.

The **counter** area contains the data for the counter function blocks. As for the timers, the S7-300/400 counters and S7-200 counters have different formats. For the S7-300/400 processors, the value of the S5-compatible 10-bit accumulator is addressed as

C*n*

where *n* is the counter number. For the S7-200 processors, the 16-bit integer value of the accumulator is addressed in the same manner. For all processors, the counter status bit is addressed in the same way. The program determines which value to use by the type of the instruction that uses the address. For the S7-300/400 processors, the IEC 61131-3 counter function blocks do not use the counter area, but store the values in an instance data block.

The **local (stack) data** stores temporary program data. Each program unit (OB, FB, and FC, subroutine) is allocated some space on the stack that is used as long as the unit is executing. When programming a program unit one declares the temporary variables that are allocated on the local stack. The size of the local data stack is dependent on the particular processor and is generally not very large. Some S7-200 processors do not support L memory. For the S7-300/400 processors, the space in the local data stack is normally divided up equally among the priority classes. Thus every priority class has its own local data area, ensuring that the higher priority classes and their organization blocks have some local data space.

Normally, the local data is defined symbolically, though when addressed as an absolute memory location; it may be accessed as bits, bytes, words, or double words similarly to M memory except with an "L" prefix. If a symbol is defined for a particular local data element, the programming software will not display the absolute address, but will always use the symbol prefixed with a "#."

For S7-300/400 processors, the **status** word contains the status information about logical and arithmetic operations. The entire word can be addressed as STW (but only by an instruction list program). The more important individual bits in the status word are:

RLO	Result of previous logic operation
OV	Overflow
CC0	Negative result
CC1	Positive result
BR	Binary result (built-in block executed correctly)

For S7-300/400 processors, **shared data blocks** are the preferred way of storing data values that must be accessed by various program function blocks. An **instance data block** is associated with a programmed function block and is introduced in Chapter 5 as part of the IEC timers and counters. Chapter 11 (function block programming) provides more detailed information. When a shared or instance data block is created, it is given an address "DB*n*" where *n* is a number. A symbolic name can also be associated with the data block. A shared data block may be opened with the OPN coil or instruction (Figure 3.38). Only one shared data block can be open, so opening a shared data block automatically closes any currently open shared data block. Opening a shared data block is not required to access the data block, it only shortens the address.

A sample data block declaration is shown in Figure 3.39. It appears similar to a user-defined data type. When addressing the individual elements, the information in the "Address" column shows the offset from the start of the data block, as a byte and the starting bit number. If Figure 3.39 defines DB1, then absolute addresses for some of the elementary data types are:

DB1.DBX0.0	Run
DB1.DBX1.0	Step_6
DB1.DBW2	Des_Torque

If DB1 was opened as a shared data block (with OPN), the "DB1." in the above addresses is not necessary. The individual elements of the Machine_Info data type (defined as in Figure 3.36) can be accessed symbolically by specifying the symbol of the structure instance

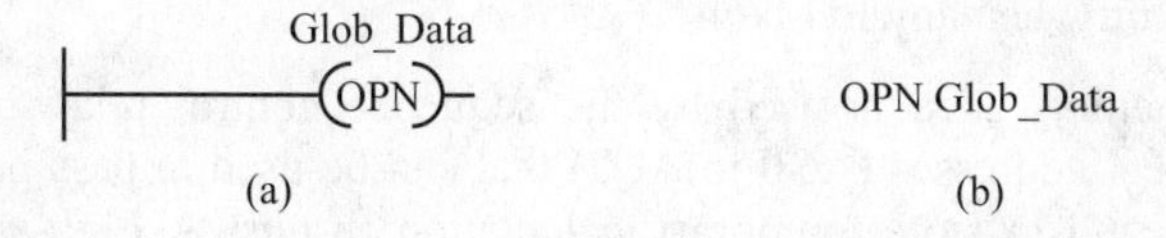

Figure 3.38. Opening a S7 shared data block: *(a)* ladder logic; *(b)* instruction list.

Address	Name	Type	Init. Value	Comment
0.0		STRUCT		
+0.0	Run	BOOL	FALSE	
+0.1	First_Start	BOOL	FALSE	
+0.2	Int_Reset	BOOL	FALSE	
+0.3	Step_1	BOOL	FALSE	
+0.4	Step_2	BOOL	FALSE	
+0.5	Step_3	BOOL	FALSE	
+0.6	Step_4	BOOL	FALSE	
+0.7	Step_5	BOOL	FALSE	
+1.0	Step_6	BOOL	FALSE	
+1.1	Step_7	BOOL	FALSE	
+2.0	Des_Torque	REAL	10.5	
+6.0	Machine	"Machine_Info"		
=70.0		END_STRUCT		

Figure 3.39. Example shared data block definition.

(Machine in this example) followed by a decimal point and then the symbol of the structure element. For example, if the symbolic name of DB1 is "Mach423," the following are valid:

"Mach423".Machine.Serial_Num
"Mach423".Machine.Shift_Faults
"Mach423".Machine.In_Repair

To absolutely address the individual elements of the Machine structure in Figure 3.39, the element offset must be added to the starting structure address to obtain the absolute address. For example,

DB1.DBD6	Machine.Serial_Num
DB1.DBW64	Machine.Shift_Faults
DB1.DBX68.1	Machine.In_Repair

For S7-200 processors, the **variable** memory area is larger than the general (M) memory area. It may be accessed as bits, bytes, words, or double words similarly to M memory except with a "V" prefix. The **special** memory area contains detailed information about the processor status (Siemens, 2000). Some of the common status addresses are:

Address	Description
SM0.0	always **on**
SM0.1	"first scan" flag, set if processor is executing ladder for first time
SM0.5	1.0 sec. timer contact
SM5.0	**on** when any I/O fault

The **sequence** memory area is used by the sequence control relay instructions. The **accumulators** are 4 addresses (AC0 to AC3) that can be used to pass parameters to and from subroutines and to store temporary calculation results. A **high-speed counter** is addressed only as a double word and is read-only.

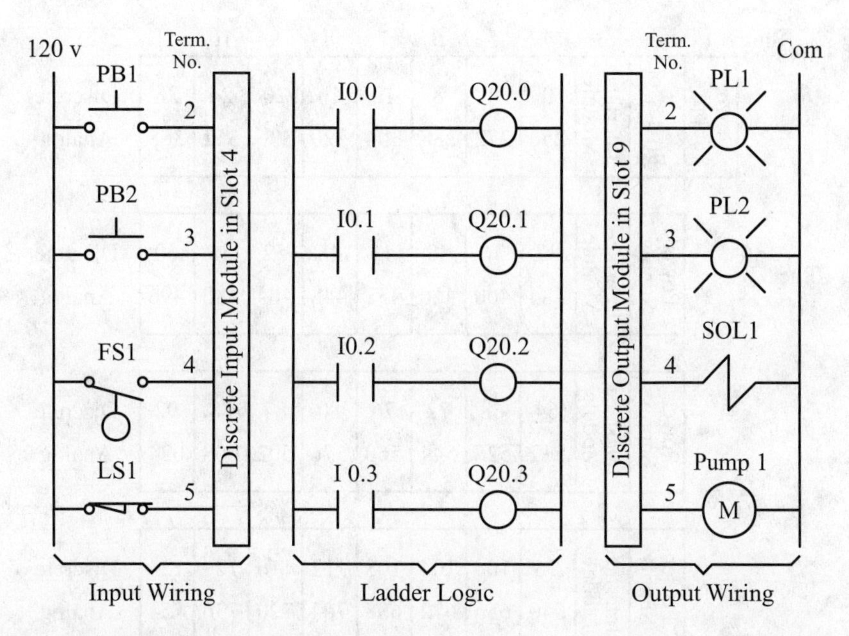

Figure 3.40. S7-300/400 implementation of Figure 3.6 showing I/O addressing.

3.6.4 Input/Output Addressing

For the S7-300/400 PLC, the physical I/O channels have default addresses based on the module placement. The default addresses can be changed by the user. The input image may be accessed as bits, bytes, words, or double words, depending on the particular module. In contrast, the S7-200 processors have a certain amount of discrete I/O built-in to the processor. In this case, the input and output image addresses are fixed. Certain S7-200 processors support expansion I/O modules. In this case, the addresses of the physical I/O channels depend on the module placement and on the types of modules installed to the left of a given module.

A S7-300/400 implementation of the hardwired circuit of Figure 3.6 might appear as in Figure 3.40. The switches are connected to channels 0 through 3 of a discrete input module and the lights, solenoid, and motor are connected to channels 0 through 3 of a discrete output module. The address of the input channel is shown with the contact in the ladder. Normally, one defines a symbol that refers to the I/O address and its symbol appears enclosed in quotation marks on the listing. However, for the purpose of this example the addresses are shown. The address "I0.2" means the contact is controlled by the discrete input channel 2, in the module whose byte address is zero. In general, discrete input channels are addressed as

I*n*.*m*

where *n* is the module byte address and *m* is the bit number, 0-7. Similarly, the address "Q20.1" means the output (coil) is connected to output channel 1, in the module whose byte address is 20. In general, discrete output channels are addressed as

Q*n*.*m*

where *n* is the module byte address and *m* is the bit number, 0-7.

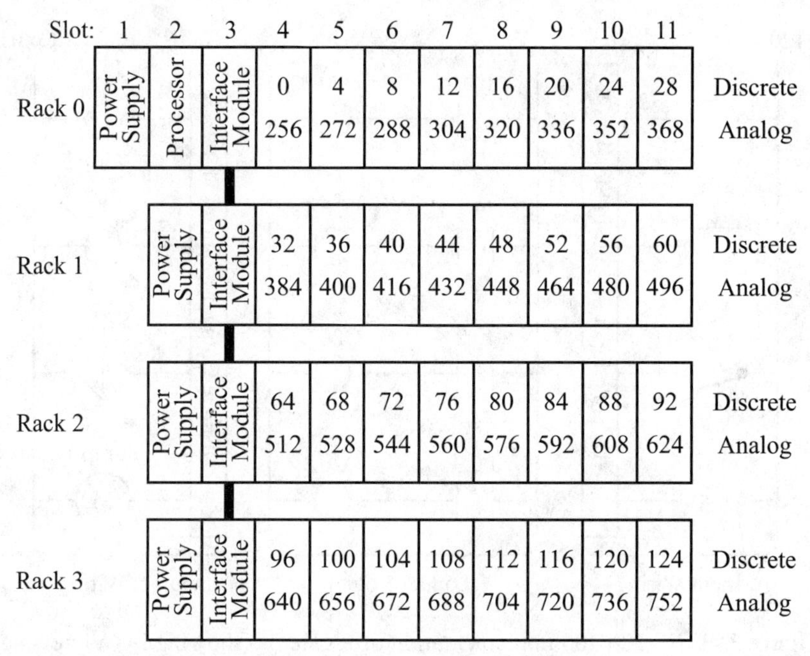

Notes: Rack 0 only valid rack for CPU 312 IFM and CPU 313
Rack 3, slot 11 note valid for CPU 314 IFM

Figure 3.41. S7-300 default I/O addressing.

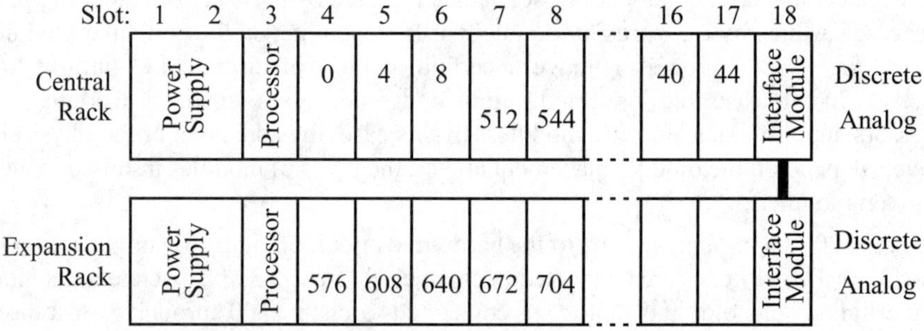

Slot:	1	2	3	4	5	6	7	8	...	16	17	18	
Central Rack	Power Supply		Processor	0	4	8				40	44	Interface Module	Discrete
							512	544					Analog
Expansion Rack	Power Supply		Processor									Interface Module	Discrete
				576	608	640	672	704					Analog

Figure 3.42. Example S7-400 I/O addressing.

The module starting byte address is allocated depending on its position in the chassis (Figures 3.41 and 3.42). The number of valid addresses for a module depends on the number of channels on the module. For example, an 8-channel discrete input module in slot 8 of rack 0 of a S7-300 system is addressed with I16.0 to I16.7. A 32-channel discrete input module in slot 6 of rack 2 is addressed with I72.0 to I75.7.

For S7-300/400 processors, analog (and other non-discrete) input modules may be addressed as bytes, words, or double words as follows

IB*n* Byte *n*
IW*n* Word starting at address *n*
ID*n* Double word starting at address *n*

As for the discrete input modules, the analog module starting address depends on its position in the chassis (Figure 3.41). Actually, discrete input modules can also be addressed as bytes, words, or double words (depending on the number of discrete channels). For S7-200 processors, analog input module channels are addressed as words with the format "AIW*n*" where *n* is the starting byte number.

For S7-300/400 processors, analog and other types of non-discrete output modules may be addressed as bytes, words, or double words as follows

QB*n* Byte *n*
QW*n* Word starting at address *n*
QD*n* Double word starting at address *n*

For S7-200 processors, analog output module channels are addressed as words with the format "AQW*n*" where *n* is the starting byte number.

For S7-300/400 processors, the information in the input and output modules can be directly accessed as **peripheral I/O data**. Peripheral input data may be addressed as bytes, words, or double words as follows

PIB*n* Byte *n*
PIW*n* Word starting at address *n*
PID*n* Double word starting at address *n*

The module starting address is determined in the same manner as for the I/O image data. Peripheral input data reflects the current input status and not the status as it was at the beginning of the program scan cycle. Peripheral output data may be addressed as bytes, words, or double words as follows

PQB*n* Byte *n*
PQW*n* Word starting at address *n*
PQD*n* Double word starting at address *n*

Addressing outputs as peripheral data allows one to immediately change the current output state instead of waiting until the end of the program scan cycle.

The S7-300 and S7-400 processors have slightly different default slot addresses. For the S7-300 processors, the default address extends to the expansion chassis (Figure 3.41). For the S7-400 processors, there is no default addressing. Each discrete module is allocated four bytes and the first discrete module is assigned a starting address of zero. Each analog module is allocated 32 bytes and the first analog module is assigned a starting address of 512. An example addressing scheme for S7-400 processor with an expansion chassis is shown in Figure 3.42.

Discrete input and discrete output module channels are addressed in groups of 8 channels. Each group is the offset from the module start address. For example, a discrete output module having 16 channels has two groups of 8 channels (Figure 3.43*a*). If the module starting address is 32, group 0 channels are addressed as Q32.0 through Q32.7. The group 1 channels are addressed as Q33.0 through Q33.7. As another example, a discrete input module having 32 channels has four groups of 8 channels (Figures 3.43*b* and 3.42*c*). If

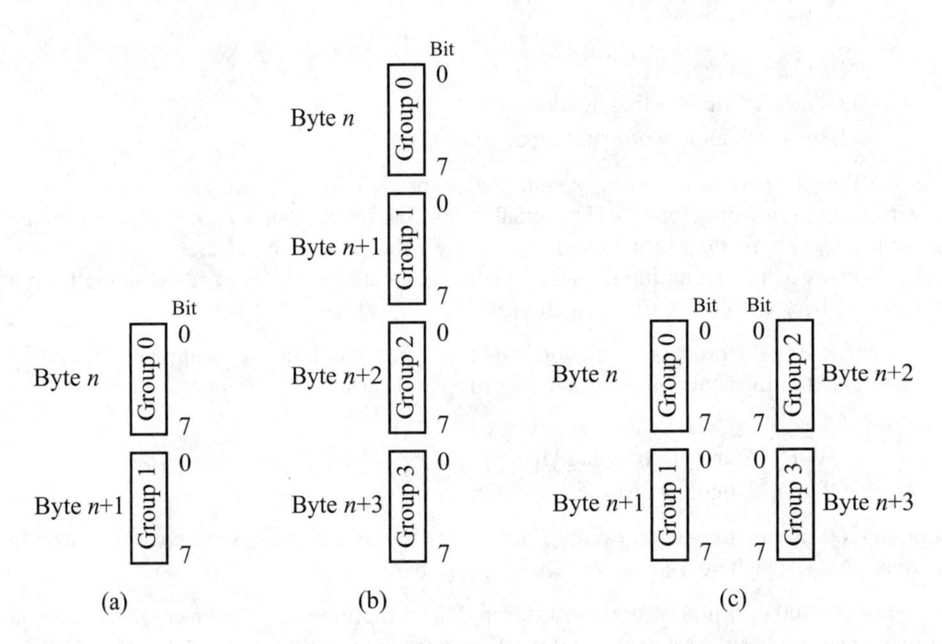

Figure 3.43. Discrete module bytes: *(a)* 16 channels; *(b)* S7-400 32 channels; *(c)* S7-300 32 channels.

the module starting address is 36, group 0 channels are addressed as I36.0 through I36.7. The group 3 channels are addressed as I39.0 through I39.7.

Analog input and analog output module channels are addressed as words. The address for a particular channel is related to the channel number as:

(Address for channel #) = 2×(Channel #) + (Module start address)

For example, if the module start address for an analog input module is 288, the value for channel 0 is addressed as IW288 and the value for channel 7 is addressed as IW302.

Example 3.4. Draw a S7 ladder diagram that will cause the output, pilot light PL2, to be **on** when selector switch SS1 is closed, push button switch PB5 is open, and limit switch LS7 is open. Show the I/O addresses in the logic. The input/output devices are wired to the following locations:

PL2: Output module, central rack slot 8, group 1, channel 7
module start address is 16

SS1: Input module, expansion rack slot 7, group 0, channel 5
module start address is 44

PB5: Input module, expansion rack slot 5, group 1, channel 1
module start address is 68

LS7: Input module, local rack slot 6, group 1, channel 0
module start address is 8

Solution. The addresses are,

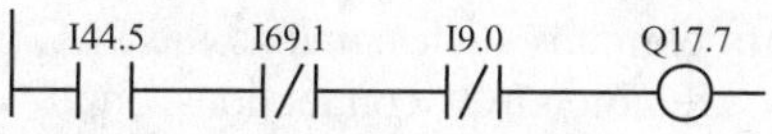

I44.5 I69.1 I9.0 Q17.7

Figure 3.44. Solution to Example 3.4.

PL2:	Q17.7	Byte addr. = 16 + (group) 1 = 17
SS1:	I44.5	Byte addr. = 44 + (group) 0 = 44
PB5:	I69.1	Byte addr. = 68 + (group) 1 = 69
LS7:	I9.0	Byte addr. = 8 + (group) 1 = 9

The ladder logic is shown in Figure 3.44. The addresses are shown above the contact and coil instructions.

3.7 GE FANUC MEMORY

3.7.1 Memory Organization

The memory of GE Fanuc Series 90 (90-70, 90-30, Micro) and VersaMax processors is organized as shown in Figure 3.45. The model is much simpler than the IEC 61131-3 memory model. Each of the main elements is now described.

The **project** is the entire body of software (program and data) that corresponds to one PLC. The project corresponds to the combination of the configuration, resource and program of IEC 61131-3. Basically, GE Fanuc PLCs support one single cyclically running program inside one single resource inside the configuration.

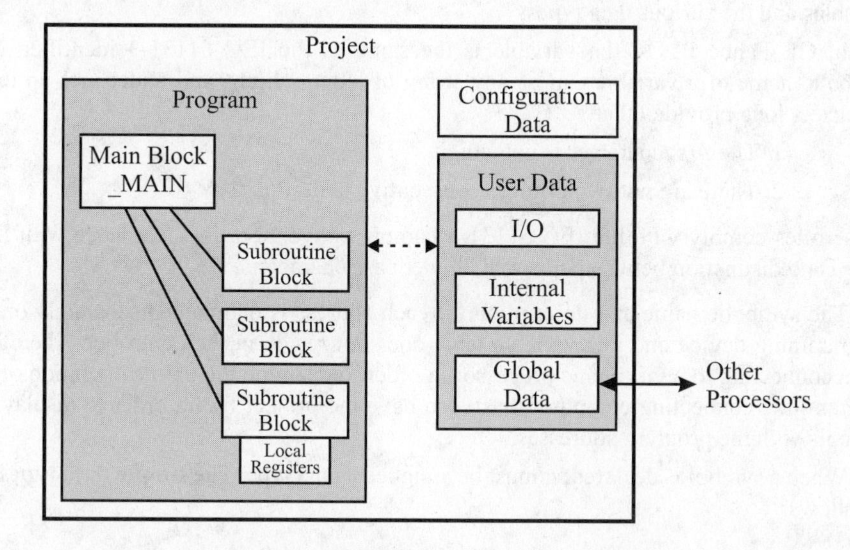

Figure 3.45. GE Fanuc memory model.

The **configuration data** contains such items as the PLC processor model, I/O map, communication interfaces, remote I/O connections, and data memory allocation. Configuration data is not accessible to the program.

A **program** generally consists of one main block (named _MAIN). The main block can call other program blocks, which are subroutines. Each block (including _MAIN) may be written in any one of the following languages:

Ladder Diagram (LD)

Instruction List (IL)

The state transition and C programming languages may also be used, but are not covered by this text.

The **user data** is the location for all variables and can be accessed by any program block. For the 90-70 processors, one can define **local** registers that are accessible only to a subroutine block. **Global data** references are used to access data in other processors.

3.7.2 Program scan

The _MAIN block program execution is basically the same as introduced in section 2.5. The physical inputs are read, the program is scanned from top to bottom, and the physical outputs are written. Normally, the program scan executes as quickly as possible, which means it typically varies. The processor can be configured to initiate the scan at a constant time interval, but this interval should be longer than the maximum program scan time to prevent a processor oversweep fault.

3.7.3 User data memory

In the GE Fanuc processor, data may be addressed as a symbolic variable or as an absolute address. Though only absolute addresses are required to construct a program, it is not recommended. Therefore, a variable symbol is associated with each absolute address in a program. The format of the absolute addresses is explained after first describing the variables and the various data types.

In GE Fanuc PLCs, the variable is the same as the IEC 61131-3 identifier. The symbolic name of a variable can be any string of letters, digits, and underlines up to 32 characters long provided that:

1. The first character is not a digit.
2. There are not two or more consecutive underlines.

These rules comply with the IEC 61131-3 naming convention. In accordance with IEC, there is no distinction between upper and lower case characters.

The symbolic name and description for each address is maintained separately on the programming device and this variable table does not reside in the controller. Therefore, when connecting to a GE Fanuc processor in order to examine the online operation of the program, the connecting computer must also have the project file in order to display the symbols with the program addresses.

When a symbol is declared, it must be assigned a data type. The **simple data types** are as follows:

Name	Description	Range of values
BOOL	1-bit Boolean	0=cleared, 1=set
BYTE	8-bit	0 to FF hexadecimal
WORD	16-bit	0 to FFFF hexadecimal or -999 to 999 BCD
DWORD	32-bit	0 to FFFFFFFF hexadecimal
INT	16-bit integer	-32,768 to 32,767
DINT	32-bit integer	-2^{31} to $2^{31}-1$ (-2,147,483,648 to 2,147,483,647)
UINT	16-bit integer	0 to 65,535
REAL	32-bit float. pt.	1.17510^{38} to 3.40310^{+38}
STRING	ASCII text	up to 82 characters
BCD-4	4-digit BCD	0 to 9999
BCD-8	8-digit BCD	0 to 99,999,999

The REAL data type is valid only for processors that support floating-point operations.The BCD-8 data type is valid only for the 90-70 processor. The ability to examine a bit in an integer is provided as a standard function block.

Constants are used to directly provide values for inputs of function blocks, transition conditions, and so on. These values cannot be overwritten by the program logic. Constants are also used to assign an initial value to a variable.

The BOOL (boolean) data type has the constants 0 (false) and 1 (true). Constants for the integer data types can be expressed as an integer constant, base 2 constant (binary), base 8 constant (octal), or base 16 (hexadecimal) constant. The formats are as follows:

Constant	Examples
integer	-12, 0, +23, 14_639
base-2	2#111 (7 decimal)
	2#1011_0011 (179 decimal)
base-8	8#177 (127 decimal)
	8#2001 (1025 decimal)
base-16	16#FFFF (65,535 decimal)
	16#AA (170 decimal)

Constants for the REAL type may be expressed as normal decimal numbers,

5.341, +14_639.7, -0.0041

or with "E" indicating the tens' exponential value,

7.45E-12, 1.27E+04, 1.27E04.

A STRING data type is an array of ASCII characters. A string is stored in 16-bit registers, two characters in each register (Figure 3.46). The maximum size of a STRING is 82 characters. In the GE Fanuc processors, strings are merely stored for use by an HMI since there are no ladder logic instructions that manipulate string variables.

The memory of the GE Fanuc processors is divided into address areas identified by one or more letters followed by a number (Table 3.2). All areas except for the local areas are accessible by all program blocks. The amount of available memory areas depends on the specific processor.

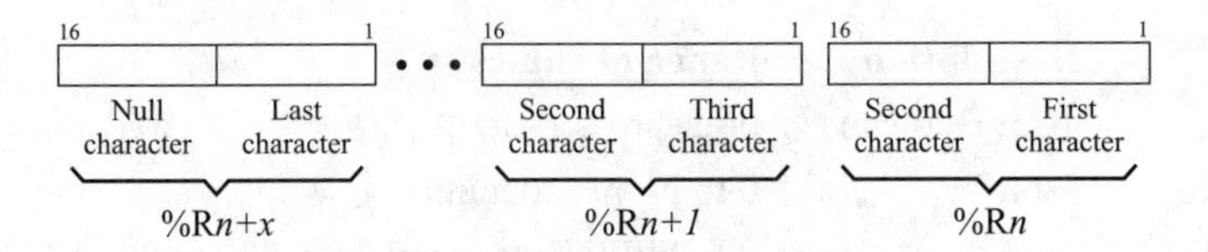

Figure 3.46. Structure of GE Fanuc STRING data type.

Table 3.2 GE Fanuc Addresses.

Memory Type		Letter Notation	Addressed As
General Memory	Bit	M	%M*n*
	Temporary bit	T	%T*n*
	Register (word)	R	%R*n*
Program	Register (word)	P*	%P*n*
Local	Register (word)	L*	%L*n*
Global		G	%G*n*
		GA*	%GA*n*
		GB*	%GB*n*
		GC*	%GC*n*
		GD*	%GD*n*
		GE*	%GE*n*
Status		S	%S*n*
		SA	%SA*n*
		SB	%SB*n*
		SC	%SC*n*
Input Image	Bit	I	%I*n*
	Analog (word)	AI	%AI*n*
Output Image	Bit	Q	%Q*n*
	Analog (word)	AQ	%AQ*n*

*Only available for 90-70 processors

The format of each type of address is now explained. The format of the input and output data addresses are explained in section 3.7.5.

Individual **bits** (coils) in general memory are addressed as

%M*n*

where *n* is the bit number. **Temporary bits** (coils) are addressed as

%T*n*

where *n* is the bit number. Temporary bits are never checked for repeated coil references and thus can be used many times in the same program. These bits are useful when cutting and pasting groups of rungs so that repeated coil conflicts are not a problem. However, temporary bits make troubleshooting more difficult. Temporary bits are never retained

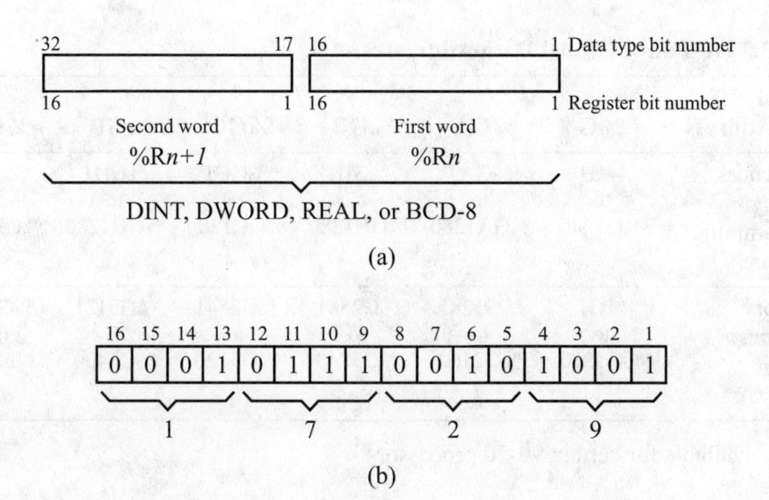

Figure 3.47. GE Fanuc register storage: *(a)* 32-bit data types; *(b)* BCD-4 number.

through power loss or Run-to-Stop-to-Run transitions and cannot be used with retentive coils.

The **register** (word) memory area is addressed as

%R*n*

where *n* is the word number. The maximum word number depends on the processor. The 32-bit DINT, DWORD, REAL and BCD-8 data types occupy two consecutive register addresses as shown in Figure 3.47*a*. For these data types, only the first register address is specified. The second register address is assumed. For this reason, one needs to ensure that 32-bit values do not overlap. For example, if a REAL value has address %R234, then %R235 should not be used by any other variable. A BCD-4 binary-coded decimal number is stored in a register as shown in Figure 3.47*b*.

Program registers store program data from the _MAIN block and are addressed as

%P*n*

where *n* is the word number. Program registers can be accessed from all program blocks. Program register addresses are valid only for the 90-70 processors.

Local registers store program data unique to a block and are addressed as

%L*n*

where *n* is the register (word) number. Local registers are accessible only from within the program block where they are defined. Local register addresses are valid only for the 90-70 processors.

Global data references are used to access data shared among several processors and are accessed as %G, %GA, %GB, %GC, %GD, or %GE. For the 90-70 processors, the global data is 7680 bits in length. This space is subdivided into six 1280-bit arrays (Table 3.3), with each space designated by a separate letter designation. For the other GE Fanuc processors, only %G1 through %G1280 are valid global data addresses. Other address types may also be shared among processors.

Table 3.3 GE Fanuc Global Data Addresses.

Global Data Address	%G	%GA*	%GB*	%GC*	%GD*	%GE*
References used by programming software	%G1 to %G1280	%GA1 to %GA1280	%GB1 to %GB1280	%GC1 to %GC1280	%GD1 to %GD1280	%GE1 to %GE1280
Memory locations used in processor	%G1 to %G1280	%G1281 to %G2560	%G2561 to %G3840	%G3841 to %G5120	%G5121 to %G6400	%G6401 to %G7680

*Only available for certain 90-70 processors

The **status** addresses contain detailed information about the processor status and the specific information varies by the processor. Some of the common status addresses are:

Address	Symbol	Description
%S0001	FST_SCN	"first scan" flag, set if processor is executing ladder for first time
%S0005	T_SEC	1.0 sec. timer contact
%S0007	ALW_ON	always **on**
%S0008	ALW_OFF	always **off**
%SA0011	LOW_BAT	low battery fault
%SC0011	IO_FLT	**on** when any I/O fault

The %S addresses may only be addressed as contacts. The %SA, %SB, and %SC addresses may be referenced by set or reset coils.

Retentive data is saved by the processor when it is stopped. In the GE Fanuc processors the following data is retentive:

Register data (%R, %P, %L, %AI, %AQ),

Bit data (%I, %SC, %G), and

%Q and %M addresses when used with retentive coils

When used with non-retentive coils, %Q and %M addresses are non-retentive and are cleared when the processor switches from the stop mode to the run mode. Temporary (%T) addresses are also non-retentive. The retentive and non-retentive coils are described in section 2.3.5.

The 8-bit, 16-bit, and 32-bit data types can also be assigned to bit memory (%G, %M, %Q, and %T). In order to treat bit memory as a register, the bit number must be on 8-bit boundaries, that is, the bit number must be one plus a multiple of eight (at 00001, 00009, 00017, 00025, 00033, etc.), as illustrated in Figure 3.48. Though the ability to examine a bit in an integer is provided as a standard function block, none of the GE Fanuc processors support addressing of individual register bits for the contact symbols. Many users find it useful to store the result of an integer operation in bit memory and then access the individual

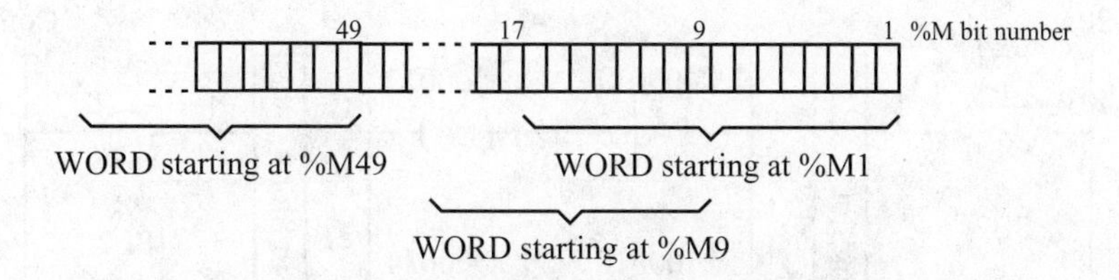

Figure 3.48. Addressing bit memory as words.

bits using contacts. In like manner, individual bits in the integer can be set or reset with coils.

3.7.4 Indirect References

In **indirect referencing**, the address for a particular location is contained in a register. Indirect referencing is valid for all register addresses (%R, %AI, %AQ, %P, and %L) on 90-70 processors. Indirect addressing is identified by "@" in place of the "%" character. Indirect referencing is useful for accessing arrays of registers. For example, in the indirect address reference @R00102, the contents of register %R102 is the offset in the %R memory that will be actually referenced. If %R102 contains 2010, then a data reference of @R00102 will direct the processor to use the register %R2010. The programmer must ensure that the content of %R102 does not cause a reference beyond the number of valid registers, or the processor will record this fault in the fault table.

3.7.5 Input/Output Addressing

For GE Fanuc PLCs the physical I/O channels are associated with an address through the **I/O map**. This I/O map is part of the configuration data and includes information for the I/O modules in the same chassis as the processor and for I/O modules on the remote I/O or other network.

A GE Fanuc PLC implementation of the hardwired circuit of Figure 3.6 might appear as in Figure 3.49. The switches are connected to channels 1 through 4 of a discrete input module and the lights, solenoid, and motor are connected to channels 1 through 4 of a discrete output module. The address of the input channel is shown with the contact in the ladder. Normally, one would use symbols for the I/O and the address would not appear on the listing. However, for the purpose of this example the addresses are shown. The address %I00019 means the contact is controlled by (discrete input) address 00019, which is channel 3 on the module in slot 4 (where channel 1 has been mapped to address %I00017). The mapping of the physical I/O to the %I*x* number is specified as part of the I/O map. The user specifies which number maps to the starting number on the I/O module. The numbers are in decimal. Similarly, address %Q00036 means the discrete output (coil) is channel 4 on the module in slot 9 (where channel 1 has been mapped to address %Q00033).

When configuring the I/O Map, one specifies the type of module in a slot and specifies the starting address of the input reference (%I*x* or %AI*x*) and/or the starting address of the output reference (%Q*x* or %AQ*x*). A discrete input module needs only the starting I*x* address. Similarly, a discrete output module requires only the starting Q*x* address. A module that has both discrete input and discrete output channels requires a starting I*x* and a starting Q*x* address. An analog input module needs only the starting AI*x* address. An analog output

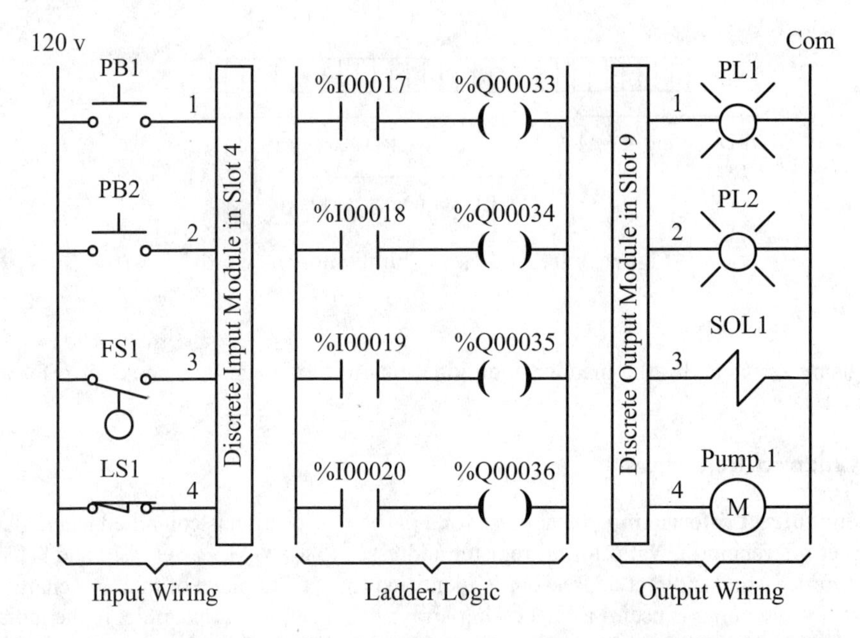

Figure 3.49. GE Fanuc implementation for Figure 3.6 showing I/O addressing.

module requires only the starting AQ*x* address. A module having both analog input and analog output channels or an intelligent module, such as a high-speed counter or a motion module, needs a starting AI*x* and a starting AQ*x* address.

For input/ouput modules, the address for a particular channel is related to the channel number as:

(Address for channel #) = (Channel #) - 1 + (Channel 1 address)

Figure 3.50 illustrates the I/O addressing in one chassis. Analog I/O and intelligent modules generally use more AI and/or AQ memory than is required for just the data. For example, the I/O map for a PLC chassis could appear as follows:

Slot	Module Type	Disc. In	Disc. Out	Ana. In	Ana. Out
	Power supply				
1	CPU				
2	32 Ch. Disc. In.	%I00001			
3	32 Ch. Disc. In.	%I00033			
4	32 Ch. Disc. Out		%Q00001		
5	32 Ch. Disc. Out		%Q00033		
6	Din/Dout 16/8	%I00065	%Q00065		
7	Ana In/Out 4/2	%I00081		%AI00001	%AQ00001
8	HS Ctr, 4 ch.	%I00089	%Q00073	%AI00005	
9	Ana In, 16 ch.	%I00105		%AI00020	
10	Ana In, 16 ch.	%I00145		%AI00036	

	Power Supply	Processor	Discrete Input	Discrete Output	Analog Input	Analog Output
Module Start Address			%I00001	%Q00033	%AI00009	%AQ00017
Chan. 1			%I00001	%Q00033	%AI00009	%AQ00017
Chan. 2			%I00002	%Q00034	%AI00010	%AQ00018
Chan. 3			%I00003	%Q00035	%AI00011	%AQ00019
Chan. 16			%I00016	%Q00048	%AI00024	%AQ00032

Figure 3.50. Example GE Fanuc I/O addressing.

Note that the analog input modules in slots 9 and 10 need 40 bits of %I memory for status information. The status information contains the status of the module and channel range violation indications.

Example 3.5. Draw a GE Fanuc ladder diagram that will cause the output, pilot light PL2, to be **on** when selector switch SS1 is closed, push button switch PB5 is open, and limit switch LS7 is open. Show the I/O addressing in the logic. The input/output devices are wired to the following locations:

PL2: Output module, CPU baseplate, I/O slot 8, channel 16
channel 1 is reference address %Q00113

SS1: Input module; expansion baseplate 1, I/O slot 3, channel 5
channel 1 is reference address %I00289

PB5: Input module, expansion baseplate 2, I/O slot 2, channel 9
channel 1 is reference address %I00401

LS7: Input module, CPU baseplate, I/O slot 6, channel 8
channel 1 is reference address %I00209

Solution. First, determine the addresses of the devices. Applying the formula above,

Address for PL2 (channel 16) = 16 - 1 + %Q00113 = %Q00128

Address for SS1 (channel 5) = 5 - 1 + %I00289 = %I00293

Address for PB5 (channel 9) = 9 - 1 + %I00401 = %I00409

Address for LS7 (channel 8) = 8 - 1 + %I00209 = %I00216

The ladder logic is shown in Figure 3.51. The addresses are shown above the contact and coil symbols.

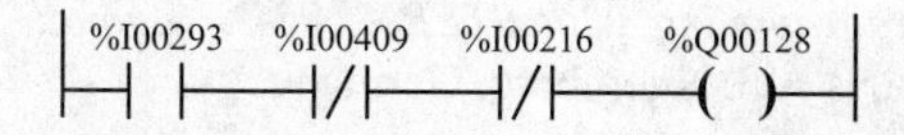

Figure 3.51. Solution to Example 3.5.

3.8 CHAPTER SUMMARY

This chapter summarized the organization and addressing of the memory and I/O for the PLCs covered by this text. With the basic PLC knowledge from Chapter 2 and the knowledge about the internal organization of the PLC, one is ready to tackle timers and counters, the most common block instructions.

REFERENCES

Allen-Bradley, 1995. *Classic 1785 PLC-5 Family Programmable Controllers: Hardware Installation Manual*, pub. 1785-6.6.1, Allen-Bradley, Milwaukee, WI.

Allen-Bradley, 1998. *Classic SLC 500™ Modular Hardware Style: Installation and Operation Manual*, pub. 1747-6.2, Allen-Bradley, Milwaukee, WI.

GE Fanuc Automation, 1999. *Series 90™-30/20/Micro PLC CPU Instruction Set: Reference Manual,* pub. GFK-0467L, GE Fanuc Automation North America, Inc., Charlottesville, VA.

GE Fanuc Automation, 2000. *Series 90™-70 PLC CPU Instruction Set: Reference Manual,* pub. GFK-0265J, GE Fanuc Automation North America, Inc, Charlottesville, VA.

IEC, 1993. *IEC 1131-3: Programmable Logic Controllers - Part 3: Programming Languages*, International Electrotechnical Commission, Geneva, Switzerland.

Rockwell Automation, 1998a. *Enhanced and Ethernet PLC-5 Programmable Controllers: User Manual*, pub. 1785-6.5.12, Rockwell Automation, Milwaukee, WI.

Rockwell Automation, 1998b. *Logix5550 Controller: User Manual*, pub. 1756-6.5.12, Rockwell Automation, Milwaukee, WI.

Rockwell Automation, 1998c. *PLC-5 Family Instruction Set Reference Manual*, pub. 1785-6.1, Rockwell Automation, Milwaukee, WI.

Schneider Automation, 1998. *Concept User Manual,* vol. 1, ver. 2.1, pub. 840 USE 461 00, Schneider Automation, Inc., North Andover, MA.

Siemens, 1996. *System Software for S7-300 and S7-400 Program Design: Programming Manual,* pub. C79000-G7076-C506-01, Siemens AG, Nürnberg, Germany.

Siemens, 1998. *S7-300 Programmable Controller Hardware and Installation: Manual,* Edition 2, 10/99, pub. EWA 4NEB 710 6084-02 01, Siemens AG, Nürnberg, Germany.

Siemens, 1999. *S7-400 and M7-400 Programmable Controllers Hardware and Installation: Manual,* Release 01, 7/99, pub. C79000-G7076-C424, Siemens AG, Nürnberg, Germany.

Siemens, 2000. *S7-200 Programmable Controller: System Manual,* pub. A5E00066097-02, Siemens AG, Nuernberg, Germany.

Siemens, 2002a. *Configuring Hardware and Communication Connections STEP 7 V5.2: Manual,* Edition 12/2002, pub. A5E00171229-01, Siemens AG, Nuernberg, Germany.

Siemens, 2002b *Programming with STEP 7 V5.2: Manual,* Edition 12/2002, pub. A5E00171230-01, Siemens AG, Nuernberg, Germany.

Siemens, 2002c *Working with STEP 7 V5.2: Getting Started,* Edition 12/2002, pub. A5E00171228-03, Siemens AG, Nuernberg, Germany.

PROBLEMS

P3-1. Draw a ladder diagram that will cause the output, solenoid SOL2, to be ON when push button switch PB1 is closed (pushed), and either limit switch LS2 or limit switch LS3 is closed. Do this problem for the Modicon Quantum, ControlLogix, PLC-5, SLC-500, S7, and/or GE Fanuc PLCs. Show only the I/O address with the ladder contacts/coils.

a) For a Modicon Quantum, the input/output devices are wired to the following locations:

SOL2:	Output module, rack 1, I/O slot 7, channel 11, channel 1 is address 000113
PB1:	Input module, rack 2, I/O slot 2, channel 1 channel 1 is address 100065
LS2:	Input module, drop 1, I/O slot 2, channel 9 channel 1 is address 100257
LS3:	Input module, drop 1, I/O slot 2, channel 10 channel 1 is address 100257

b) For an Allen-Bradley ControlLogix, the input/output devices are wired to the following locations:

PSOL2:	Output module, chassis 'REM_2', slot 6, channel 10
PB1:	Input module, local chassis, slot 0, channel 0
LS2:	Input module, chassis 'REM_1', slot 2, channel 8
LS3:	Input module, chassis 'REM_1', slot 2, channel 9

c) For an Allen-Bradley PLC-5, the input/output devices are wired to the following locations (use the single-line format). All numbers are octal.

SOL2:	Output module, rack 2, I/O group 6, channel 12
PB1:	Input module, rack 0, I/O group 1, channel 01
LS2:	Input module, rack 1, I/O group 2, channel 10
LS3:	Input module, rack 1, I/O group 2, channel 11

d) For an Allen-Bradley SLC-500, the input/output devices are wired to the following locations (use the single-line format):

PSOL2:	Output module, slot 27, channel 10
PB1:	Input module, slot 2, channel 0
LS2:	Input module, slot 13, channel 8
LS3:	Input module, slot 13, channel 9

e) For a S7-300/400 system, the input/output devices are wired to the following locations:

SOL2:	Output module, central rack slot 7, channel 11, channel 1 is address 112
PB1:	Input module, expansion rack slot 2, channel 1 channel 1 is address 64
LS2:	Input module, central rack slot 2, channel 9 channel 1 is address 256
LS3:	Input module, central rack slot 2, channel 10 channel 1 is address 256

f) For a GE Fanuc system, the input/output devices are wired to the following locations:

SOL2: Output module, CPU baseplate slot 7, channel 11,
channel 1 is address 113

PB1: Input module, expansion baseplate slot 2, channel 1
channel 1 is address 65

LS2: Input module, CPU baseplate slot 2, channel 9
channel 1 is address 257

LS3: Input module, CPU baseplate slot 2, channel 10
channel 1 is address 257

P3-2. Draw a ladder diagram that will cause the output, pneumatic solenoid PS4250, to be ON when both push button switches PB4251 is open and PB4252 is closed, and either limit switch LS4112 is open or limit switch LS4479 is closed. Do this problem for the Modicon Quantum, ControlLogix, PLC-5, SLC-500, S7, and/or GE Fanuc PLCs. Show only the I/O address with the ladder contacts/coils.

a) For a Modicon Quantum, the input/output devices are wired to the following locations:

PS4250: Output module, drop 2, I/O slot 5, channel 13,
channel 1 is address 000097

PB4251: Input module, drop 1, I/O slot 6, channel 3
channel 1 is address 100081

PB4252: Input module, drop 1, I/O slot 6, channel 4
channel 1 is address 100081

LS4112: Input module, drop 5, I/O slot 8, channel 3
channel 1 is address 100369

LS4479: Input module, drop 3, I/O slot 1, channel 9
channel 1 is address 100129

b) For an Allen-Bradley ControlLogix, the input/output devices are wired to the following locations:

PS4250: Output module, chassis 'REM_1', slot 5, channel 12
PB4251: Input module, local chassis, slot 6, channel 2
PB4252: Input module, local chassis, slot 6, channel 3
LS4112: Input module, chassis 'REM_4', slot 8, channel 2
LS4479: Input module, chassis 'REM_2', slot 1, channel 8

c) For an Allen-Bradley PLC-5, the input/output devices are wired to the following locations (use the single-line format). All numbers are octal.

PS4250: Output module, rack 1, I/O group 5, channel 14
PB4251: Input module, rack 0, I/O group 6, channel 02
PB4252: Input module, rack 0, I/O group 6, channel 03
LS4112: Input module, rack 4, I/O group 8, channel 02
LS4479: Input module, rack 2, I/O group 1, channel 10

d) For an Allen-Bradley SLC-500, the input/output devices are wired to the following locations (use the single-line format):

PS4250: Output module, slot 14, channel 12
PB4251: Input module, slot 7, channel 2
PB4252: Input module, slot 7, channel 3
LS4112: Input module, slot 28, channel 2
LS4479: Input module, slot 17, channel 8

e) For a S7-300/400 system, the input/output devices are wired to the following locations:

PS4250: Output module, expansion rack slot 5, channel 13,
channel 1 is address 96
PB4251: Input module, central rack slot 6, channel 3
channel 1 is address 80
PB4252: Input module, central rack slot 6, channel 4
channel 1 is address 80
LS4112: Input module, expansion rack slot 8, channel 3
channel 1 is address 368
LS4479: Input module, expansion rack slot 1, channel 9
channel 1 is address 128

f) For a GE Fanuc system, the input/output devices are wired to the following locations:

PS4250: Output module, expansion baseplate slot 5, channel 13,
channel 1 is address 97
PB4251: Input module, CPU baseplate slot 6, channel 3
channel 1 is address 81
PB4252: Input module, CPU baseplate slot 6, channel 4
channel 1 is address 81
LS4112: Input module, expansion baseplate slot 8, channel 3
channel 1 is address 369
LS4479: Input module, expansion baseplate slot 1, channel 9
channel 1 is address 129

P3-3. Draw a ladder diagram that will cause the output, pneumatic solenoid PS6124, to be ON when both push button switches PB6121 and PB6122 are closed (pushed), and either limit switch LS6123 is open or limit switch LS6125 is closed. Do this problem for the Modicon Quantum, ControlLogix, PLC-5, SLC-500, S7, and/or GE Fanuc PLCs. Show only the I/O address with the ladder contacts/coils.

a) For a Modicon Quantum, the input/output devices are wired to the following locations:

PS6124: Output module, drop 3, I/O slot 6, channel 12
channel 1 is address 000081
PB6121: Input module, drop 2, I/O slot 1, channel 8
channel 1 is address 100033
PB6122: Input module, drop 2, I/O slot 1, channel 9
channel 1 is address 100033
LS6123: Input module, drop 3, I/O slot 3, channel 6

channel 1 is address 100289

LS6125: Input module, drop 4, I/O slot 6, channel 3
channel 1 is address 100369

b) For an Allen-Bradley ControlLogix, the input/output devices are wired to the following locations:

PS6124: Output module, chassis 'REM_2', slot 5, channel 12
PB6121: Input module, local chassis, slot 0, channel 7
PB6122: Input module, local chassis, slot 0, channel 8
LS6123: Input module, chassis 'REM_2', slot 4, channel 5
LS6125: Input module, chassis 'REM_3', slot 7, channel 0

c) For an Allen-Bradley PLC-5, the input/output devices are wired to the following locations (use the single-line format). All numbers are octal.

PS6124: Output module, rack 2, I/O group 5, channel 14
PB6121: Input module, rack 1, I/O group 0, channel 07
PB6122: Input module, rack 1, I/O group 0, channel 10
LS6123: Input module, rack 2, I/O group 4, channel 05
LS6125: Input module, rack 3, I/O group 7, channel 00

d) For an Allen-Bradley SLC-500, the input/output devices are wired to the following locations (use the single-line format):

PS6124: Output module, slot 26, channel 15
PB6121: Input module, slot 11, channel 7
PB6122: Input module, slot 11, channel 8
LS6123: Input module, slot 23, channel 12
LS6125: Input module, slot 30, channel 0

e) For a S7-300/400 system, the input/output devices are wired to the following locations:

PS6124: Output module, expansion rack slot 6, channel 12
channel 1 is address 80

PB6121: Input module, expansion rack slot 1, channel 8
channel 1 is address 32

PB6122: Input module, expansion rack slot 1, channel 9
channel 1 is address 32

LS6123: Input module, expansion rack slot 3, channel 6
channel 1 is address 288

LS6125: Input module, expansion rack slot 6, channel 3
channel 1 is address 368

f) For a GE Fanuc system, the input/output devices are wired to the following locations:

PS6124: Output module, expansion baseplate slot 6, channel 12
channel 1 is address 81

PB6121: Input module, expansion baseplate slot 1, channel 8
channel 1 is address 33

PB6122: Input module, expansion baseplate slot 1, channel 9
channel 1 is address 33

LS6123: Input module, expansion baseplate slot 3, channel 6
channel 1 is address 289

LS6125: Input module, expansion baseplate slot 6, channel 3
channel 1 is address 369

P3-4. Draw a ladder diagram that will cause the output, pneumatic solenoid PSOL2, to be ON when both push button switches PB1 and PB2 are closed (pushed), and either limit switch LS20 is closed or limit switch LS101 is open. Do this problem for the Modicon Quantum, ControlLogix, PLC-5, SLC-500, S7, and/or GE Fanuc PLCs. Show only the I/O address with the ladder contacts/coils.

a) For a Modicon Quantum, the input/output devices are wired to the following locations:

PSOL2: Output module, drop 2, I/O slot 7, channel 11,
channel 1 is address 000129

PB1: Input module, drop 1, I/O slot 4, channel 7
channel 1 is address 100065

PB2: Input module, drop 1, I/O slot 4, channel 8
channel 1 is address 100065

LS20: Input module, drop 2, I/O slot 2, channel 2
channel 1 is address 100225

LS101: Input module, drop 3, I/O slot 5, channel 16
channel 1 is address 100497

b) For an Allen-Bradley ControlLogix, the input/output devices are wired to the following locations:

PSOL2: Output module, chassis 'REM_1', slot 5, channel 10
PB1: Input module, local chassis, slot 4, channel 6
PB2: Input module, local chassis, slot 4, channel 7
LS20: Input module, chassis 'REM_1', slot 2, channel 2
LS101: Input module, chassis 'REM_2', slot 5, channel 15

c) For an Allen-Bradley PLC-5, the input/output devices are wired to the following locations (use the single-line format). All numbers are octal.

PSOL2: Output module, rack 3, I/O group 5, channel 12
PB1: Input module, rack 2, I/O group 0, channel 07
PB2: Input module, rack 2, I/O group 0, channel 10
LS20: Input module, rack 3, I/O group 4, channel 01
LS101: Input module, rack 4, I/O group 7, channel 17

d) For an Allen-Bradley SLC-500, the input/output devices are wired to the following locations (use the single-line format):

PSOL2: Output module, slot 7, channel 10
PB1: Input module, slot 21, channel 7
PB2: Input module, slot 21, channel 8
LS20: Input module, slot 14, channel 1
LS101: Input module, slot 17, channel 15

e) For a S7-300/400 system, the input/output devices are wired to the following locations:

PSOL2: Output module, expansion rack slot 7, channel 11, channel 1 is address 128

PB1: Input module, central rack slot 4, channel 7 channel 1 is address 64

PB2: Input module, central rack slot 4, channel 8 channel 1 is address 64

LS20: Input module, expansion rack slot 2, channel 2 channel 1 is address 224

LS101: Input module, expansion rack slot 5, channel 16 channel 1 is address 496

f) For a GE Fanuc system, the input/output devices are wired to the following locations:

PSOL2: Output module, expansion baseplate slot 7, channel 11, channel 1 is address 129

PB1: Input module, CPU baseplate slot 4, channel 7 channel 1 is address 65

PB2: Input module, CPU baseplate slot 4, channel 8 channel 1 is address 65

LS20: Input module, expansion baseplate slot 2, channel 2 channel 1 is address 225

LS101: Input module, expansion baseplate slot 5, channel 16 channel 1 is address 497

4 Input/Output Modules and Installation

Chapter Topics:

- Discrete input and output modules
- Analog input and output modules
- Specialized modules
- Installation wiring

OBJECTIVES

Upon completion of this chapter, you will be able to understand:

- Wiring of typical sensors and actuators to PLC I/O modules
- Surge protection for certain types of devices
- Typical control cabinet layout
- Typical installation wiring

Scenario: Plug-chute switch problem.

In a power plant coal-handling system, a plug-chute switch is placed at the end of conveyor belt and detects when coal is "piling up" and plugging the system. Obviously, when a plug is detected, the conveyor should be immediately stopped.

A simplified diagram of the system is shown in Figure 4.1. The plug-chute switch is a normally-closed contact that opens as the coal presses against a diaphragm. The switch wire eventually reaches a terminal block in the control cabinet where it is wired to a PLC AC discrete input module and to a time-delay relay. The PLC replaces a relay control system, and the relay system is being dismantled but is still connected to many of the field sensors. In the PLC program, the plug-chute switch is the input to a timer. The timer protects against intermittent pieces of coal hitting the diaphragm and shutting down the system. The switch must be open for 2 seconds before the conveyor is shut off.

Yesterday, one of the workers discovered a pile of coal around the end of the conveyor and the chamber at the end of the conveyor was completely full of coal. Apparently, the plug-chute switch had not stopped the conveyor.

Solution: After cleaning out the coal, the conveyors are run without coal. The PLC properly senses the closed plug-chute switch (or else the conveyor would not run). However, pushing the diaphragm on the plug-chute switch does not stop the conveyor. The plug-chute switch is replaced with a known good switch, and it still does not stop the conveyor when pressed.

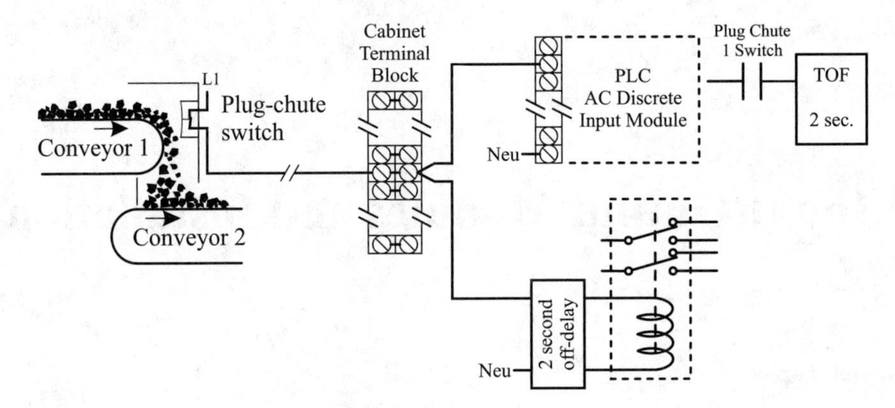

Figure 4.1. Plug-chute switch wiring.

A broomstick is wedged in to constantly press the diaphragm. The PLC program operation is then observed. The plug-chute input intermittently flashes off but does not stay off longer than 0.01 second. The intensity of the channel indicator lamp on the discrete input module is about half of other discrete inputs that are on. At this point the problem is in one of three places: the PLC module, the time-delay relay, or the wiring between the PLC and the switch. Disconnecting the time-delay relay is the easiest thing to try, and so it is tried first. When the time-delay relay is disconnected, the PLC correctly senses the open plug-chute switch. Since the time-delay relay is no longer used, it is left disconnected.

4.1 INTRODUCTION

In order for a PLC to be functional, it must connect to the "real world," involving wiring to discrete, analog, and specialized field devices. This chapter describes these connections and covers other installation issues such as power distribution and control panel layout.

The input and output (I/O) modules provide the physical interface between the PLC processor and the field devices, such as switches, lamps, and valves. There are various types of modules to handle the different types of sensors and actuators. Regardless of the type of module, there are some common features: removable terminal blocks, isolation, and diagnostic indicators.

All wiring to the I/O module is connected to a removable terminal block, and the terminal block is plugged onto the module. If the module must be replaced, the terminal block is removed, the old module is removed, the new module is inserted, and the terminal block is plugged onto the new module. This process of changing the module requires less than a minute and does not involve rewiring the module, an important maintenance consideration.

The I/O modules provide isolation between the field wiring and PLC internal circuitry. Figure 4.2 shows this isolation barrier in both the input and output module. Optical isolators provide the isolation barrier, shown in the circuit diagrams in the succeeding sections. This isolation is important since the field wiring is generally powered from a different circuit and/or voltage level than the PLC processor. The PLC power supply provides low-voltage power to the right side of the input module and the left side of the output module. In addition

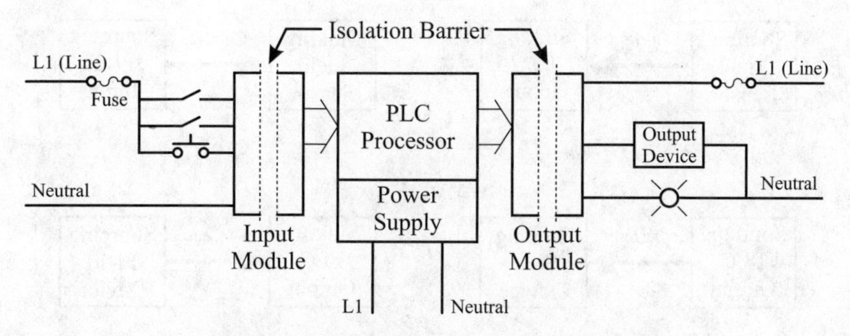

Figure 4.2. Isolation between I/O devices and PLC.

Active	
0	8
1	9
2	10
3	11
4	12
5	13
6	14
7	15

(a)

Active	
0	8
1	9
2	10
3	11
4	12
5	13
6	14
7	15
Fuse	

(b)

Active			
0	8	F0	F8
1	9	F1	F9
2	10	F2	F10
3	11	F3	F11
4	12	F4	F12
5	13	F5	F13
6	14	F6	F14
7	15	F7	F15

(c)

Figure 4.3. Example module indicators: *(a)* discrete input; *(b)* discrete output; *(c)* discrete output with individual fuse indicators.

to providing the interface between the field and PLC voltage levels, the isolation prevents ground loops and noisy electrical signals from interfering with the PLC operation. Typically, there are also differences in the earth (ground) potential between the field wiring circuits and the PLC power wiring. Also, during an abnormal event, such as a near lightning strike, circuit commons that are normally at the same potential may have a short-term (< 1 second) potential difference. The isolation prevents damage to the PLC even if a surge damages the module. For example, a wiring fault that causes 440-volt AC to be imposed on a 24-volt DC input channel would only damage the input module. The PLC itself and the other modules in the system will not be affected.

I/O modules have indicators useful for troubleshooting. For example, discrete input modules have one indicator for every channel that is **on** when its corresponding input channel is **on** (Figure 4.3*a*). Similarly, discrete output modules have one indicator for each channel that is **on** when the corresponding output channel is being commanded to turn **on** (Figure 4.3*b*). A blown (open) fuse indicator on an output module may be turned on if any output fuse is open ("Fuse" in Figure 4.3*b*) or they may be an indication for each fuse ("Fx" in Figure 4.3*c*). Modules may have indicators that turn **on** when the module is functioning properly. For example, in Figure 4.3*a*, the "Active" indicator on a discrete input module lights when the module is properly communicating with the processor. For a discrete output module, the "Active" indicator may also indicate that the processor is in the run mode.

One aspect of PLC I/O modules that is often confusing is the designation of a device connection as being *sinking* or *sourcing*. Sinking and sourcing refer to the flow of current (power) when the device is active. An output is called sourcing if current flows **out** when the output is active. An output is called sinking if current flows **in** when the output is active. An

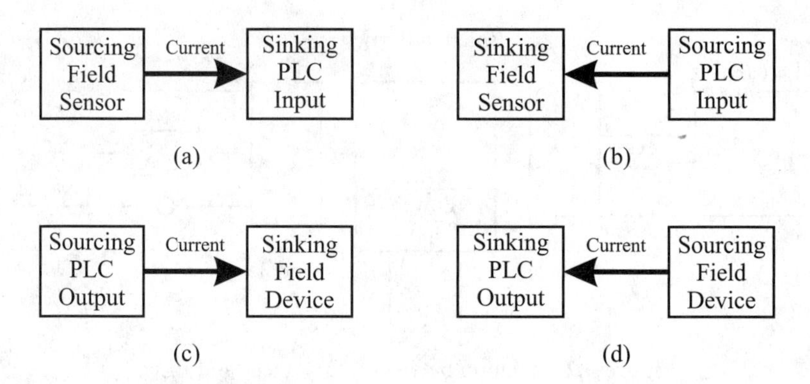

Figure 4.4. Sourcing and sinking connections: *(a)* sinking PLC input; *(b)* sourcing PLC input; *(c)* sourcing PLC output; *(d)* sinking PLC output.

input is called sourcing if current flows **out** when the input is active. An input is called sinking if current flows **in** when the input is active. Normally, a sourcing field sensor is connected to a sinking PLC input (Figure 4.4*a*) and a sinking field sensor is connected to a sourcing PLC input (Figure 4.4*b*). Similarly, a sourcing PLC output is connected to a sinking field output device (Figure 4.4*c*) and a sinking PLC output is connected to a sourcing field output device (Figure 4.4*d*). For DC devices, the arrows in Figure 4.4 indicate the direction of current flow when the field sensor or PLC output is active (**on**). For AC devices, the arrows indicate the direction of power flow.

Only the basic operation of the modules is described. Many older I/O modules have switches and/or jumpers that set up, or configure, the module to operate as desired. Most newer I/O modules have an included microprocessor and so the configuration parameters are set up with the PLC programming software. For discrete modules, the configuration information consists of such items as channel filter time constants, on-to-off transition delay times, and off-to-on transition delay times. For analog modules, the configuration information consists of such items as number of channels, type of channel (single-ended or differential, current or voltage), data format (binary or BCD), voltage/current range, and integer range.

Also, the process of configuring the PLC processor for the actual I/O modules is not presented. Some processors require the user to set switches that determine the modules in each chassis position. For other processors, the user configures the types of modules that are expected in each chassis slot as part of the PLC software set up. In this case, when the PLC is placed in run mode, the processor verifies that the expected modules are present and functioning before commencing the program scan. Other processors automatically identify the I/O modules that are present and adjust the I/O scan accordingly.

Finally, the connection diagrams in this chapter are typical and are not specific to a particular manufacturer. One should always refer to the manufacturer's documentation for details.

4.2 DISCRETE MODULES

Since PLCs were originally developed to solve discrete sequential control problems, discrete modules remain the largest number of modules in a PLC system. Even though

PLCs are capable of performing continuous control functions, their mainstay is still discrete control.

There is a limited set of standard discrete voltage levels handled by discrete input and output modules:

120 volt AC or DC	10 - 30 volt DC
220 volt AC or DC	20 - 60 volt DC
10 - 30 volt AC or DC	5 v digital logic

Historically, most discrete input/output signals in non-chemical control applications were nominally 120 volts. Due to safety considerations, most chemical control applications used 24-volt signals. However, recent safe electrical work practices (National Fire Protection Association, 2000) require protective clothing for electricians working on exposed wiring having voltages higher than 50 volts. Because of these regulations, newer systems use 24-volt control signals, and many older systems are being converted to 24-volt signals.

4.2.1 Discrete Input Modules

A discrete input module senses the status of a device that has only two states, on/off, open/closed, running/stopped, and so on. The most common discrete devices sensed by a PLC module are some kind of a switch, for example,

Pushbutton	Level	Starter auxiliary
Selector	Pressure	Relay contact
Limit	Position	Zero-speed
Proximity	Thumbwheel	

The block diagram of a typical discrete input is shown in Figure 4.5. The optical isolator provides electrical isolation between the field wiring and the PLC internal circuitry. The electronic circuitry to the left of the optical isolator is powered from the field, and the circuitry to the right of the optical isolator is powered from the internal PLC voltage source.

Each discrete input module has a threshold detector that senses when the input device is on. Threshold sensing is different for sinking and sourcing modules. For sinking input modules, the device is sensed **on** when the voltage produced by the input device is above a minimum voltage, commonly called the "minimum on-state voltage." If the input device produces a voltage below the "maximum off-state voltage," then the device is sensed to be **off**. The maximum off-state voltage is less than the minimum on-state voltage. For example, a 120-volt AC/DC sinking input module may have a minimum on-state voltage of 80 volts AC/DC and a maximum off-state voltage of 45 volts AC/DC. A 24-volt DC sinking module may have a minimum on-state voltage of 10 volts and a maximum off-state voltage of 6 volts. Obviously, module operation is not guaranteed if the device produces a voltage between the maximum off-state and minimum on-state voltages. For sourcing input

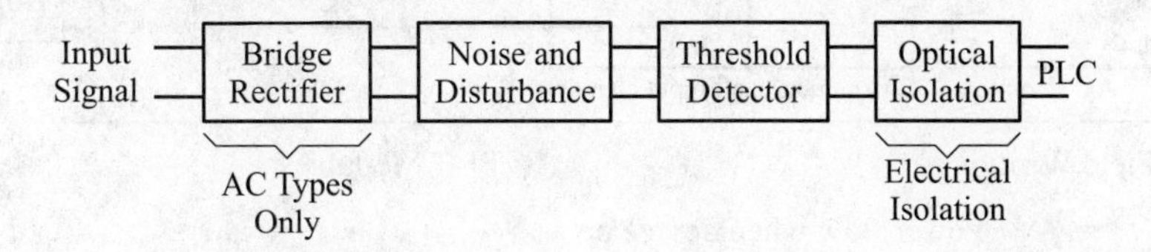

Figure 4.5. Discrete input module block diagram.

modules, the device is sensed **on** when the voltage produced by the input device is below a maximum voltage, commonly called the "maximum on-state voltage." If the input device produces a voltage above the "minimum off-state voltage", then the device is sensed to be **off**. For example, a 24-volt DC sourcing module may have a maximum on-state voltage of 14 volts and a minimum off-state voltage of 20 volts.

The circuitry of a typical AC discrete input module, along with connections to typical input devices, is shown in Figure 4.6. The capacitor and resistors R_1 and R_2 form a simple noise filter. The bridge rectifier converts the AC to full-wave rectified DC. The resistor R_3 and the zener diode (D_Z) form the threshold detection. An optoisolator, consisting of a light-emitting diode and a photoelectric transistor, provides electrical isolation between the field wiring and the PLC internal circuitry. When a switch is closed, producing an input voltage of sufficient magnitude, current flows through the light-emitting diode in the optoisolator, generating light and triggering current flow through the photoelectric transistor which is sensed by the PLC digital logic. For fault diagnosis, an input state indication is **on** when the input switch is **closed**. This indicator may be on the field wiring side of the optoisolator or may be on the PLC side of the optoisolator. Input modules that handle AC signals are typically *sinking* modules, that is, power flows **into** the module when the field device is **on**. This module can also handle DC voltages.

The module shown in Figure 4.6 has one common connection for all channels. This common is the return path for all of the input devices. Some modules provide multiple commons, for example, one common for every four input channels. Other modules provide isolated channels, that is, the common of each channel is separated from the other channel commons. Isolated channels or multiple commons are needed when

1. Mixing voltages on the same module.
2. Mixing different AC phases on the same module. This is especially needed when the 3-phase plant wiring is in a delta configuration.
3. Mixing AC and DC circuits on the same module.

There may be a problem when connecting a solid-state sensor with a triac-type output to an AC discrete input module. This sensor produces a small leakage current even when the device is off. Unfortunately, this leakage current may be large enough to trigger the input

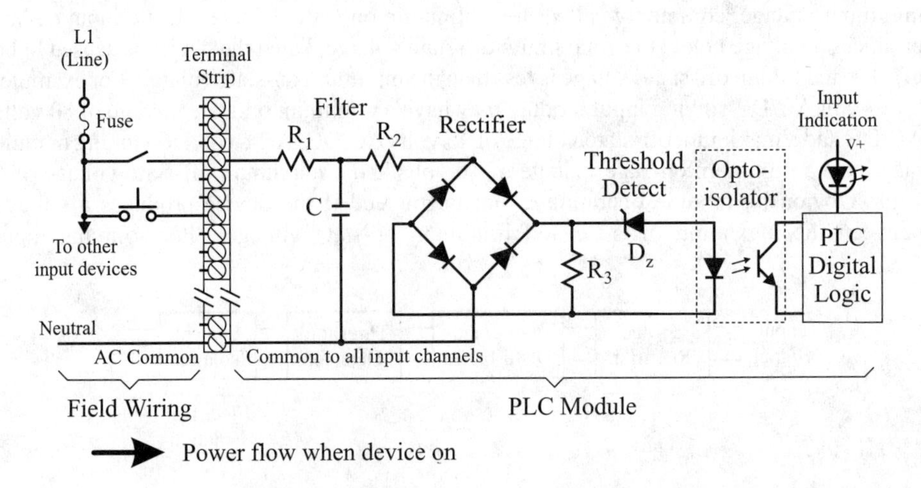

Figure 4.6. Typical AC discrete input channel.

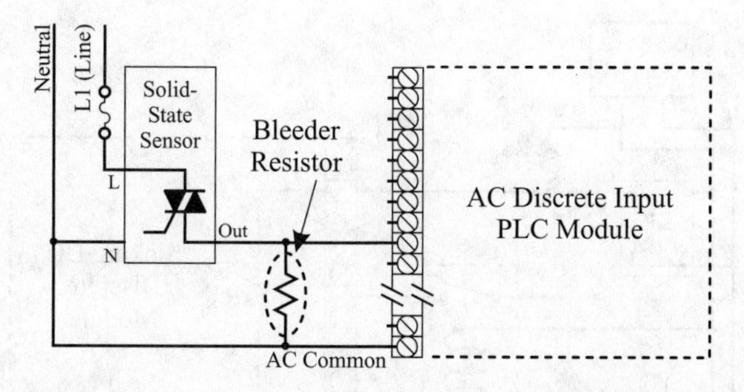

Figure 4.7. Using bleeder resistor with solid-state sensor.

module channel. In this case, a bleeder resistor is added as shown in Figure 4.7 to "bleed" the leakage current to the AC common. The bleeder resistor assures that the PLC input channel senses the **on** state of the device only when the device is truly **on**.

Figure 4.8 shows circuitry of a typical *sinking* DC discrete input module channel. Connections to typical switches and a 3-wire sensor are also illustrated. The two resistors form a simple threshold detector, and the capacitor is a simple noise filter. The diode D_1 provides protection for the optoisolator in case the DC power supply polarity is accidentally reversed. When a switch is closed, current flows through the optoisolator LED and is sensed by the PLC digital logic. The 3-wire sensor (having a PNP transistor output) is a sourcing device. When active, the PNP output transistor conducts, causing current to flow into the discrete input channel and then be sensed by the PLC logic. The module shown in Figure 4.8 has one DC common connection for all channels. Some modules may provide one DC common connection for a group of channels, for example, four or eight channels. Isolated channels may also be used and are discussed below.

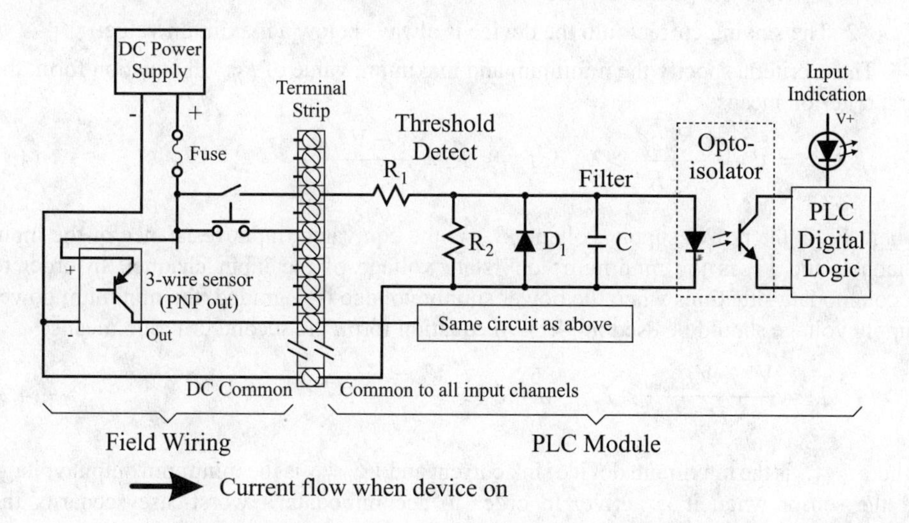

Figure 4.8. Typical sinking DC discrete input channel.

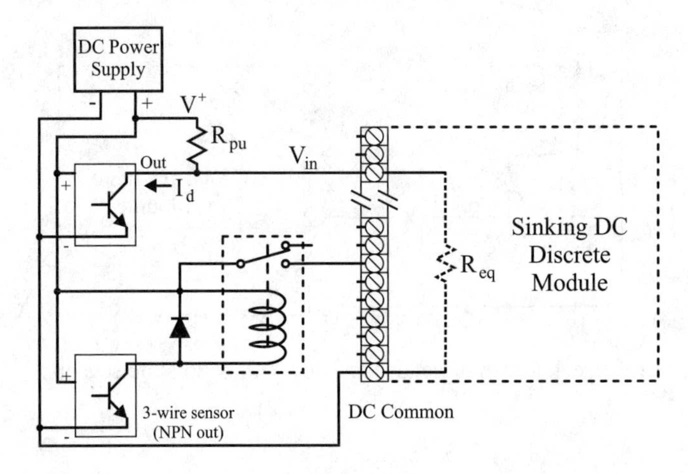

Figure 4.9. Connect a sinking sensor to a sinking DC discrete input channel.

It is possible to connect a sinking field input to a sinking DC discrete input channel with a pull-up resistor or interposing relay, as shown in Figure 4.9. The interposing relay is less reliable and introduces an additional delay that may be unacceptable for a rapidly switching discrete device. A pull-up resistor is less expensive, but may not be possible if there is no resistor that satifies the criteria below. The pull-up resistor (R_{pu}) in Figure 4.9 ensures the voltage sensed by the input channel is sufficiently high when the device is **off**. When using the pull-up resistor, the PLC state of the input is opposite to the input sensor state. When the sensor is **on**, the PLC detects it as **off** since the voltage at the discrete input channel is below the threshold for detection of the **on** state. When the sensor is **off**, the PLC detects it as **on** since the pull-up resistor ensures the voltage at the input channel is above the threshold voltage. When specifying the value of R_{pu}, it must be selected so

1. The voltage at the PLC discrete input is above the minimum **on** voltage when the device is **off** (inactive), and
2. The sinking current into the device is always below a maximum value.

These criteria specify the minimum and maximum value of R_{pu}. In equation form, the first criterion means

$$V_{in} = V^{+} \frac{R_{eq}}{R_{pu} + R_{eq}} > V_{th} \text{ or } R_{pu} < R_{eq} \frac{V^{+} - V_{th}}{V_{th}} \tag{4.1}$$

where V^{+} is the power supply voltage, R_{eq} is the equivalent input resistance of the input channel, and V_{th} is the minimum "on" state voltage of the input channel. In order to accommodate situations when the power supply voltage is degraded, the minimum power supply voltage should be used in (4.1). In equation form, the second criterion means

$$I_{d} = \frac{V^{+} - V_{out,\min}}{R_{pu}} < I_{d,\max} \text{ or } R_{pu} > \frac{V^{+} - V_{out,\min}}{I_{d,\max}} \tag{4.2}$$

where $I_{d,\max}$ is the maximum device sink current and $V_{out,\min}$ is the minimum output voltage of the sensor when it is active. In order to accommodate a worst-case scenario, the maximum power supply voltage should be used in (4.2). Combining equations 4.1 and 4.2 to specify the acceptable range of the pull-up resistor,

$$\frac{V^{+}_{\max} - V_{out,\min}}{I_{d,\max}} < R_{pu} < R_{eq}\frac{V^{+}_{\min} - V_{th}}{V_{th}} \tag{4.3}$$

where $V^{+}_{\min}$ and $V^{+}_{\max}$ are the minimum and maximum power supply voltages, respectively. In general, the largest acceptable resistance will be the best since it will require the smallest power rating.

Example 4.1. Specify an acceptable value and power rating of a pull-up resistor to be used to connect a sinking sensor device to a PLC sinking discrete input channel. The power supply is nominally 24 volts, but can range between 23 and 25 volts, depending on the current draw. The minimum "on" state voltage of the discrete input channel is 10 volts, and the equivalent input resistance is 2500 ohms. The maximum device sink current is 20 mA, and the minimum device output voltage is 0.3 volts.

Solution. The values to be used in equation 4.3 are:

$$V^{+}_{\max} = 25 \qquad R_{eq} = 2500 \qquad I_{d,\max} = 0.02$$
$$V^{+}_{\min} = 23 \qquad V_{th} = 10 \qquad V_{out,\min} = 0.3$$

Substituting into (4.3),

$$\frac{25-0.3}{0.02} < R_{pu} < 2500\frac{23-10}{10}$$
$$1235 < R_{pu} < 3250$$

If the standard 5% tolerance resistor of 3000 ohms is selected, its range of 2850 to 3150 ohms is acceptable. The required power rating is determined by squaring the maximum voltage across the resistor and dividing it by the minimum possible resistance,

$$P_{pu} = \frac{(25-0.3)^2}{2850} = 0.214 \text{ watts}$$

Therefore, a 3000 ohm resistor with a 1/4-watt power rating must be used.

The circuit for a typical *sourcing* DC discrete input channel is shown in Figure 4.10. Note that when a switch is closed, current flows **out** of the discrete input module. The two resistors form a simple threshold detector, and the capacitor is a simple noise filter. The diode D_1 provides protection for the optoisolator in case the DC power supply polarity is accidentally reversed. When a switch is closed, current flows through the optoisolator LED and is sensed by the PLC digital logic. The 3-wire sensor (having a NPN transistor output) is a sinking device. When active, the NPN output transistor conducts, causing current to flow into NPN collector (and out of the discrete input channel). The fuse shown internal to the module may or may not be present. If an internal fuse is not provided, one should be provided external to the module. The module shown in Figure 4.10 has one DC power supply connection for all channels. Some modules may provide one power supply connection for a group of channels, for example, four or eight channels. Isolated channels may also be used and are discussed below.

It is possible to connect a sourcing field sensor to a sourcing DC discrete input channel. In this case, an interposing NPN transistor or relay is added as shown in Figure 4.11. When using a transistor, the NPN transistor Q_1 conducts when the device is **on**, causing current to

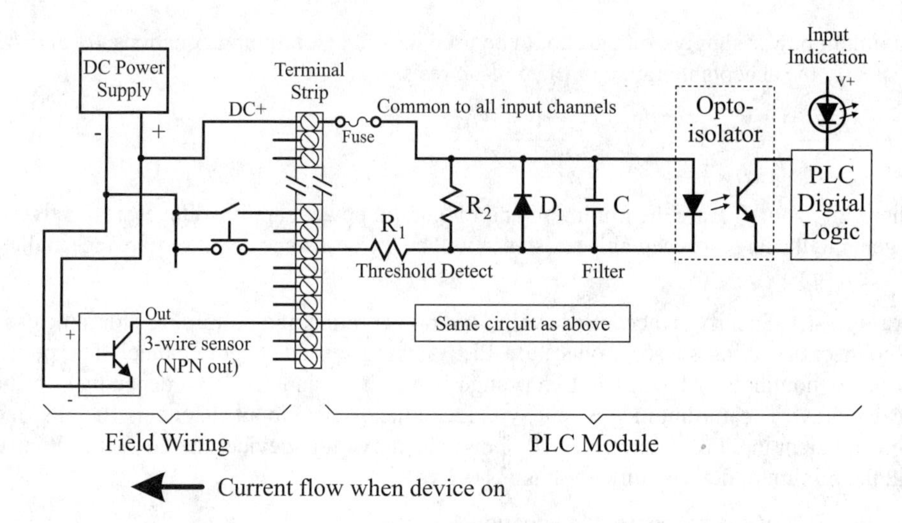

Figure 4.10. Typical sourcing DC discrete input channel.

flow **out** of the discrete input channel. This approach is not recommended because (1) many maintenance electricians will have trouble diagnosing device and/or PLC channel problems and (2) a replacement transistor may not be readily available. An interposing relay is a better approach from the maintenance standpoint. However, the interposing relay introduces an additional delay that may be unacceptable if the output changes rapidly. An even better approach is to use isolated discrete input modules if both sourcing and sinking input devices must be connected to the same discrete input module.

Isolated discrete input modules are most useful when sourcing and sinking input devices must be connected to the same discrete input module. As shown in Figure 4.12, isolated DC discrete input channels may be wired for either sinking or sourcing operation. The channels do not share either DC power or DC common.

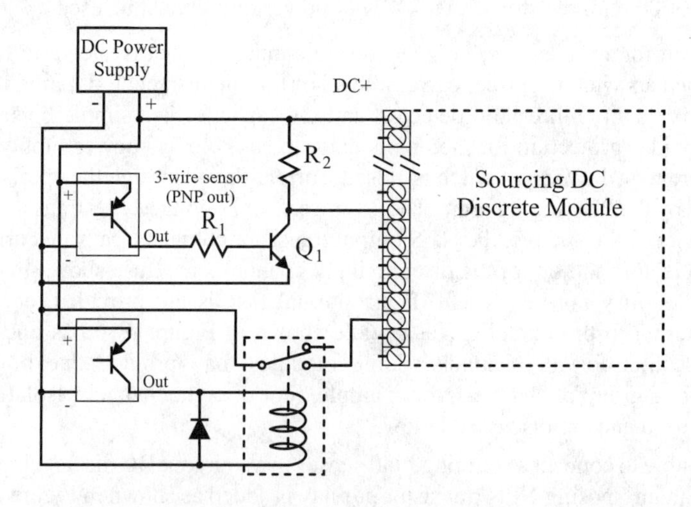

Figure 4.11. Connecting a sourcing sensor to sourcing DC discrete input channel.

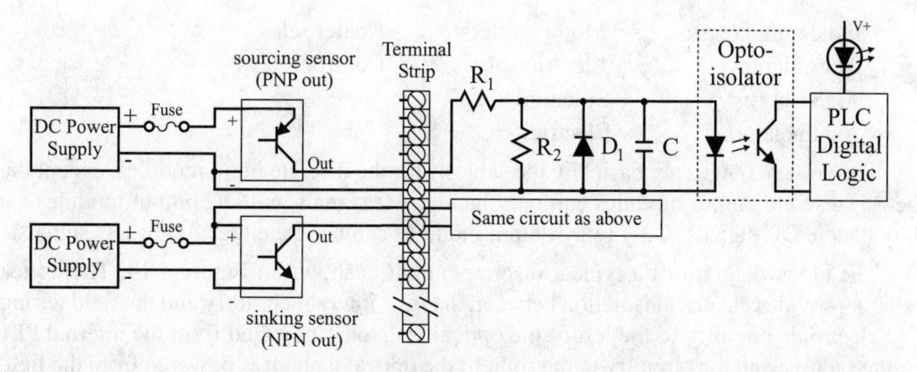

Figure 4.12. Isolated DC discrete input module for mixture of sinking and sourcing input devices.

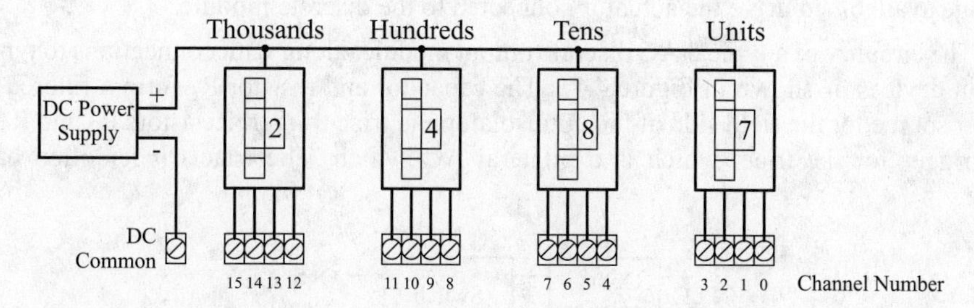

Figure 4.13. Thumbwheel switches connected to DC discrete input module.

Thumbwheel switches can be connected to multiple DC discrete input channels to allow inexpensive operator input of numerical values. Figure 4.13 shows four thumbwheel switches, each with four connections to a discrete input module. A sinking DC discrete input module is shown, but a sourcing module can be used by connecting the DC- power supply connection as the common to the thumbwheel switches and connecting the DC+ power supply to the DC+ terminal of the module. In either case, the 16-bit discrete input is read as a 4-digit binary-coded decimal (BCD) value. Some manufacturers have special modules that have multiplexing and handle three or four groups of four thumbwheel switches. In this case, each group of four digits is handled in a manner similar to analog input cards. That is, each group of digits is a BCD number.

Most PLC vendors also provide a discrete input module that handles 5-volt TTL (transistor-transistor logic) devices. This type of module is generally used for discrete sensors that produce TTL-level signals. This module is often required to receive numerical output from specialized equipment. For example, the thickness reading from a high-precision thickness-measuring device could be presented as 32 TTL signals, representing 8 BCD digits.

4.2.2 Discrete Output Modules

A discrete output module switches a device that has only two states, on/off, open/closed, and so on. Common discrete devices controlled by a PLC are,

Indicating lamps	Motor starters	Heater relay
Alarm lamps	Electric valves	Control relays
Alarm horns	Solenoid valves	
Annunciators	Electric fans	

The voltage ranges are basically the same as for the discrete input modules, except that the AC discrete output modules can only handle AC signals and DC output modules can only handle DC signals. Only relay output modules can handle either AC or DC signals.

The block diagram of a typical discrete output is shown in Figure 4.14. The optical isolator provides electrical isolation between the PLC internal circuitry and the field wiring. The electronic circuitry to the left of the optical isolator is powered from the internal PLC voltage source and the circuitry to the right of the optical isolator is powered from the field. In the case of a relay output module, the optical isolation is not needed since the isolation is provided by the relay. Except for relay output modules, the switch on all other discrete output modules is not perfect and introduces a voltage drop. Depending on the actual circuitry, this voltage drop will range from 0.3 to 2 volts. This voltage drop reduces the voltage available to drive the actuator connected to the discrete module.

The circuitry of a typical AC discrete output module, along with connections to typical output devices, is shown in Figure 4.15. The capacitor and resistor R_1 form a filtered DC power source for the field side of the optoisolator and triac trigger. Resistors R_2 and R_3 are the trigger for the triac, which is a bilateral AC switch. The triac trigger often has a

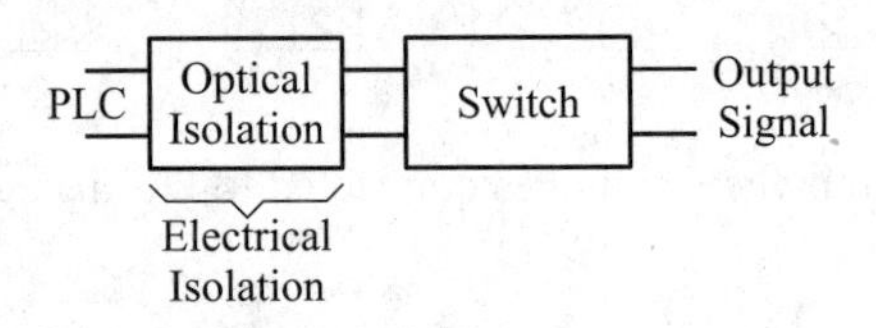

Figure 4.14. Discrete output module block diagram.

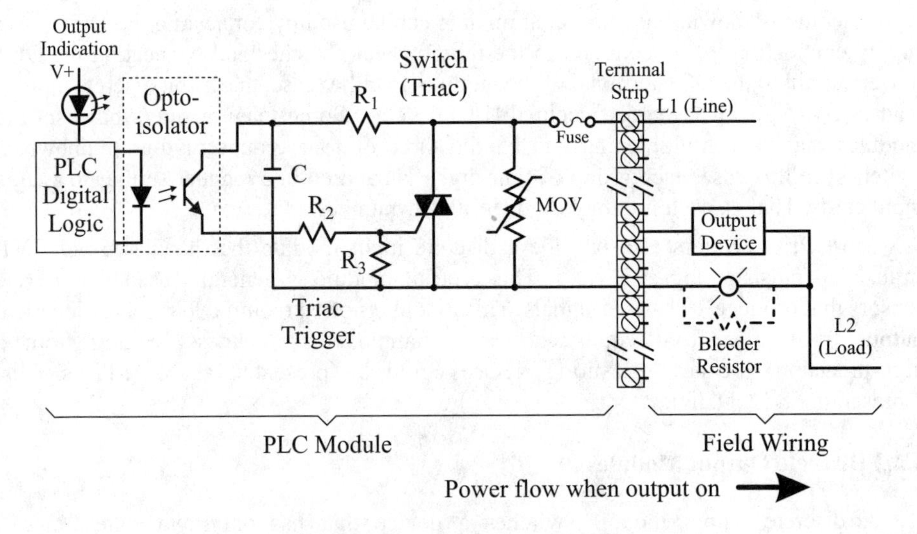

Figure 4.15. Typical AC discrete output channel.

zero-crossing detector so that the triac is switched on when the AC waveform is close to zero. This feature prolongs the life of the triac. The MOV (metal-oxide varistor) suppresses high-voltage transients from the AC source. When the PLC logic turns on the light-emitting diode in the optoisolator, current flows through the photoelectric transistor and triggers the triac. When the triac is triggered, it conducts AC current in either direction. After it is triggered, the triac will continue to conduct current until the next zero crossing of the AC source. A triac cannot be used to switch a DC signal since the triac continues to conduct current until the DC power source is turned off. For fault diagnosis, an output state indication is **on** when the PLC is commanding the output switch (triac) to conduct power to the output channel. This indicator may be on the field wiring side of the optoisolator or may be on the PLC side of the optoisolator. Output modules that handle AC signals are *sourcing* modules, that is, power flows **out of** the module when the triac is **on**.

Figure 4.15 shows an optional bleeder resistor in parallel with the indicator lamp. A triac-type output produces a small leakage current even when the triac is off. Unfortunately, this leakage current may be large enough to trigger the output device. For example, this leakage current causes neon indicator lamps to glow. The bleeder resistor "bleeds" the leakage current to the AC common and assures that the output device senses the on state of the output channel only when the PLC logic is turning it on.

If the load has a rectifying diode in series with a resistor or inductor (Figure 4.16*a*), a shunt resistor should be added to allow proper operation of the PLC output channel. If the shunt resistor is absent from Figure 4.16*a*, the circuit operation is described as follows. When L1 is positive with respect to L2, the capacitor is charged. When L2 is positive with respect to L1, the diode prevents the capacitor from discharging. Therefore, the zero-crossing detector will not detect a zero voltage due to the charged capacitor and the triac will not be triggered when the PLC logic attempts to turn on the output. Reversing the polarity of the load diode only changes the polarity of the charged capacitor voltage. The

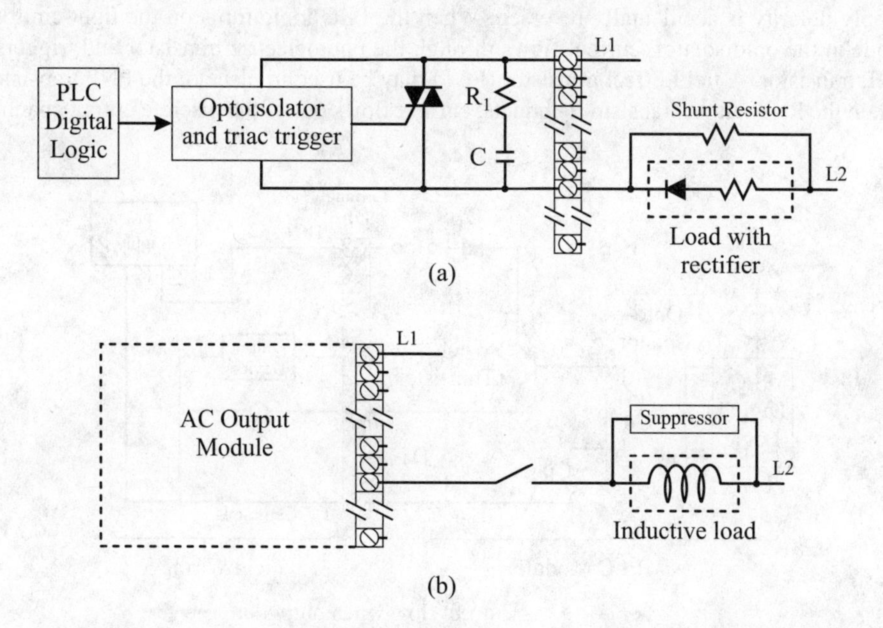

Figure 4.16. AC discrete output channel suppression devices: *(a)* rectifier in load; *(b)* driving contact in series with inductive load.

shunt resistor allows the capacitor voltage to bleed off, ensuring proper operation of the zero-crossing detector.

If the output device is primarily inductive (for example, a relay coil or a pilot light with step-down transformer) and is in series with or parallel to a "hard contact" such as a push button or selector switch, a suppression device (or snubber) should be added in parallel with the coil (Figure 4.16*b*). The suppressor prevents arcing across the switch contact, prolonging contact life.

The module may have a fuse for every output channel, or one fuse for a group of channels. Even if a fuse is provided for every channel, the maximum current that the module can handle is generally less than the sum of the individual channel maximum currents. For example, each channel of a certain 16-output module can handle a maximum of 2 amperes, but the module can handle a maximum of 8 amperes. It is generally up to the user to ensure the module current limits are met. The module may not have any built-in current limit protection. In this case, violating the module current limit often causes the module to overheat. Normally, the outputs will not each draw the maximum channel current, not will all outputs be on simultaneously. Nevertheless, the user should consider the worst case when choosing the output module.

There is a very definite reason why discrete outputs are typically sourcing: safety. When the PLC is not in run mode or commanding the output to be **off**, there is no power at the field device. This is the same reason that in residential or commercial wiring the switch to control an overhead lamp is placed in the line (L1) wire, not the neutral wire. When the switch is in the off position, the lamp may be safely changed because the socket is completely unpowered.

The circuit for a typical *sourcing* DC discrete output channel, including devices, is shown in Figure 4.17. The optoisolator transistor switches a PNP power transistor to control the output device. The diode D_1 provides protection for the circuit in case the DC power supply polarity is accidentally reversed. When the PLC logic turns on the light-emitting diode in the optoisolator, current flows through the photoelectric transistor and triggers a PNP transistor. A field-effect transistor (FET) may be used in place of the PNP transistor. When the PNP output transistor conducts, current flows out of the discrete output channel.

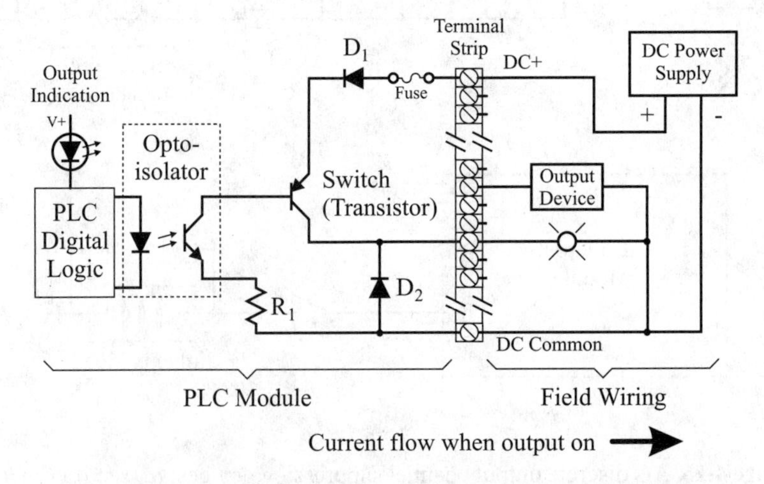

Figure 4.17. Typical sourcing DC discrete output channel.

Diode D_2 suppresses the negative voltage spike that inductive loads produce when they are turned off. The fuse shown internal to the module may be common to all channels, or there may be one fuse per channel. The module shown in Figure 4.17 has one DC power supply connection for all channels. Some modules may provide one power supply connection for a group of channels, for example, four or eight channels. Isolated channels may also be used and are discussed below.

A sourcing DC discrete output module is normally used with sinking output devices. However, a sourcing discrete output module can drive a sourcing output device by interposing a transistor circuit or a relay, similar to that shown in Figure 4.11.

The circuit for a typical *sinking* DC discrete output channel and associated devices, is shown in Figure 4.18. The only basic difference with the sourcing output module is that the output switch is a NPN power transistor. A FET may be used in place of the NPN transistor. Diode D_1 protects the circuit in case the DC power supply polarity is accidentally reversed. When the NPN output transistor conducts, current flows into the discrete output channel. Diode D_2 suppresses the positive voltage spike that inductive loads produce when they are turned off. As for the DC sourcing discrete output module, the fuse shown internal to the module may be common to all channels, or there may be one fuse per channel.

A sinking DC discrete output module is normally used with sourcing output devices. However, a sinking discrete output module can drive a sinking output device by using a pull-up resistor or interposing relay, similar to that shown in Figure 4.9. The pull-up resistor value is determined in the same manner as when connecting a sinking sensor device with a sinking discrete input channel.

Isolated discrete output modules are most useful when sourcing and sinking output devices must be connected to the same discrete output module. As shown in Figure 4.19, isolated DC discrete output channels may be wired for either sinking or sourcing operation. A transformer provides the isolation so that power can be transferred across the barrier to provide a positive gate voltage to the FET and thus allow current to flow from the drain to the source. The channels do not share either DC power or DC common. An alternate way to provide an isolated output with either a sourcing or sinking discrete module is to use an output channel to drive a relay. The relay contacts provide an isolated output.

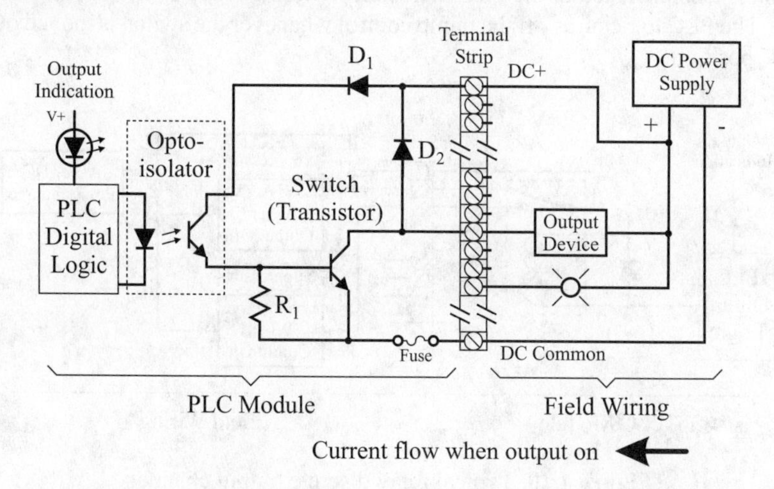

Figure 4.18. Typical sinking DC discrete output channel.

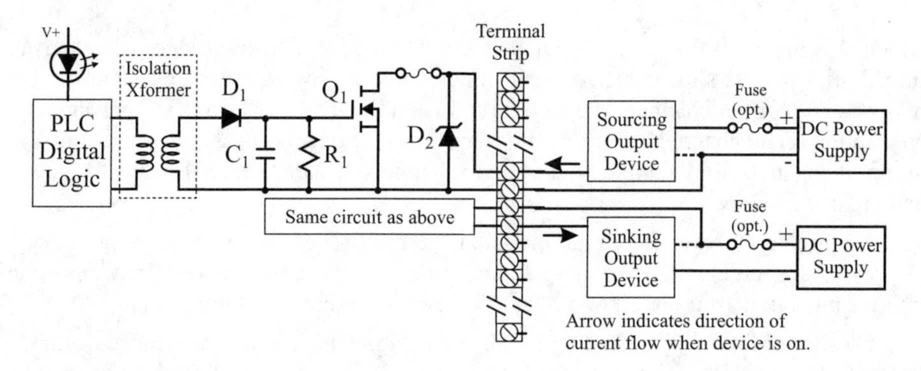

Figure 4.19. Isolated DC discrete output module for mixture of sinking and sourcing output devices.

The circuitry for a relay discrete output module is shown in Figure 4.20. In contrast to the other types of discrete output modules, there is no optoisolator. The lack of an electrical connection between the coil and contacts provides the electrical isolation. Relay outputs are used for output devices that have a power source isolated from the PLC. A typical example is a motor control center (MCC) where each motor starter has a separate 120-volt supply derived from the 440-volt bus, shown in Figure 4.21. If the output device is an inductive load, then a suppressor device should be placed in parallel with the inductive load to protect the relay contacts. Figure 4.22 shows typical suppression devices for an inductive load powered by AC and DC sources (GE Fanuc, 2000).

Most systems also provide some capability to manually operate a device in conjunction with the PLC control. A typical device is called a Hand-Off-Auto (HOA) switch, illustrated in Figure 4.23. The "HAND" and "OFF" positions override the state of the PLC output. When the switch is in the "HAND" position, the P-101 pump runs, regardless of the state of the PLC output. In the "OFF" position, the pump stops, regardless of the state of the PLC output. When the HOA switch is in the "AUTO" position, the PLC controls the pump. An indication is also provided to the PLC that is **on** when the HOA switch is in the "AUTO" position. The PLC logic turns off the pump control whenever the switch is moved out of the "AUTO" position.

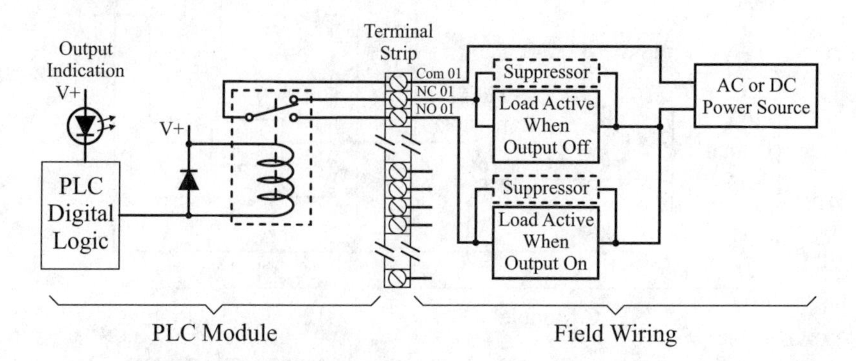

Figure 4.20. Typical relay discrete output channel.

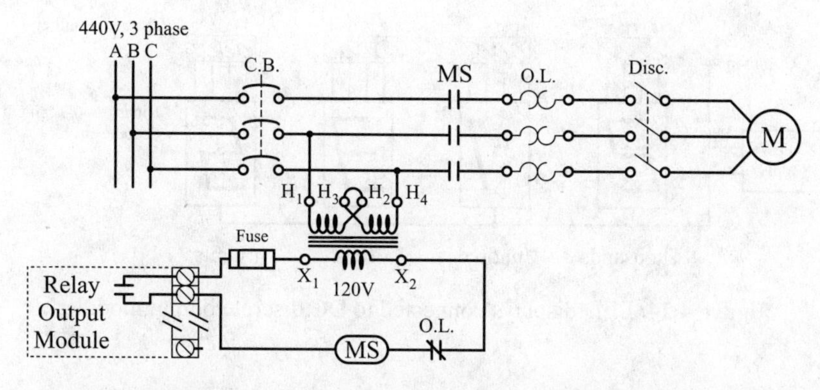

Figure 4.21. Relay discrete output channel controlling a MCC.

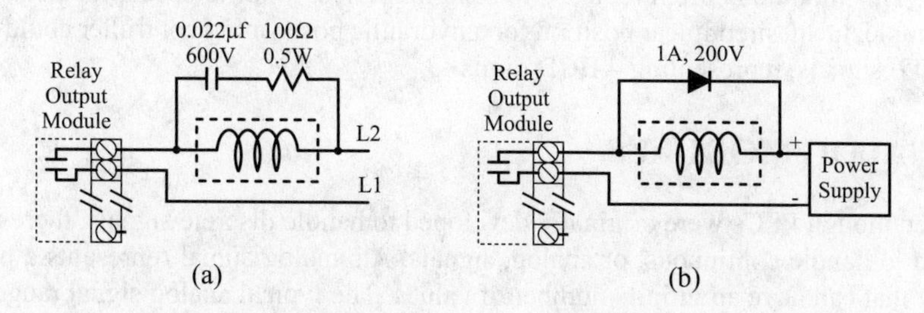

Figure 4.22. Relay output suppression devices: *(a)* AC powered load; *(b)* DC powered load.

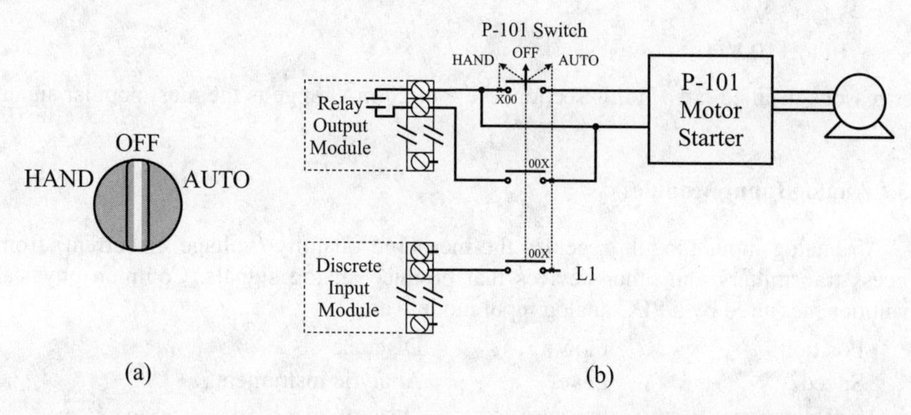

Figure 4.23. Hand-Off-Auto switch between PLC output and MCC: *(a)* HOA switch; *(b)* switch wiring.

Multiple DC discrete output channels can be connected to LED 7-segment displays to provide inexpensive operator display of numerical values. Figure 4.24 shows four LED 7-segment displays, each with four connections to a discrete output module. A sinking DC discrete output module is shown since most of these modules have a TTL (sourcing) input. In either case, the 16-bit discrete output must be formatted as a 4-digit BCD value.

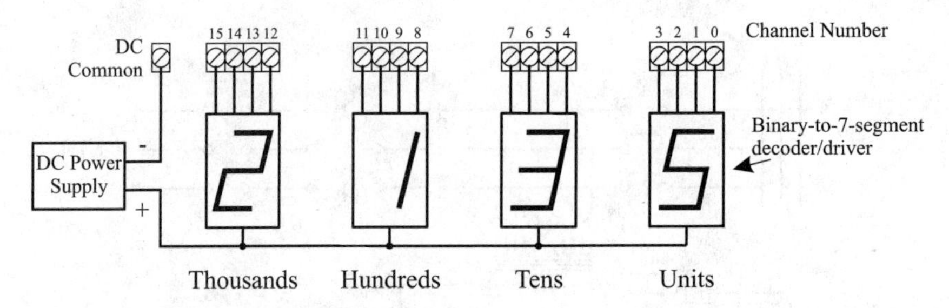

Figure 4.24. LED displays connected to DC discrete output module.

Most PLC vendors provide a discrete output module that interfaces to 5-volt TTL devices. This module is often required to send numerical input to specialized equipment. For example, the desired linear position for a hydraulic positioning controller could be sent as 16 TTL signals, representing 4 BCD digits.

4.3 ANALOG MODULES

Even though PLCs were originally developed to handle discrete signals, there is often the need to handle continuous, or analog, signals. An analog signal represents a physical quantity that can have an infinite number of values. The typical analog signal ranges are:

1 to 5 V	4 to 20 mA
0 to 5 V	0 to 20 mA
0 to 10 V	–20 to 20 mA
–5 to +5 V	
–10 to +10 V	

For reasons detailed later in this section, the 4 to 20 mA range is the most popular signal range.

4.3.1 Analog Input Modules

An analog input module receives the measured quantity (voltage or current) from process transmitters and other devices that produce analog signals. Common physical quantities measured by a PLC analog input module are:

Position	Flow	Distance
Speed	Level	Analytic instruments
Acceleration	Pressure	Opacity
Weight	Temperature	

The block diagram of a typical analog input is shown in Figure 4.25. The optical isolator provides electrical isolation between the field wiring and the PLC internal circuitry. The electronic circuitry to the left of the optical isolator is typically powered from the internal PLC, but through an isolated power supply to maintain isolation between the field wiring and the PLC voltage source. The sensor may be powered by an external power supply or by the PLC isolated power supply. The analog signal is filtered to remove noise. The actual field signal may be a single-ended voltage, single-ended current, differential

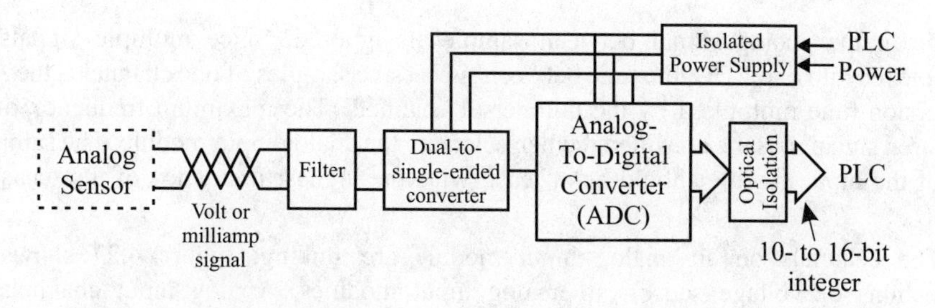

Figure 4.25. Analog input module block diagram.

voltage, or differential current. In all cases, the analog signal is converted into a single-ended voltage for the analog-to-digital converter (ADC). There is generally only one ADC per module, regardless of the number of input channels. The individual channel voltages are multiplexed into the ADC input.

The ADC converts the analog voltage into an integer number, which has a finite resolution. The most common ADC outputs a 12-bit integer, which means the output integer ranges from 0 to 4095. The relationship between the analog input voltage and the ADC output integer is illustrated in Figure 4.26. In this example, the output integer is assumed to be 4 bits, which means the output integer value ranges from 0 to 15. If the conversion were perfect for this example, the ADC output would be three times the input voltage. The actual relationship between the input voltage and the output integer resembles "stair steps" (Figure 4.26*b*). For example, an input voltage between 0.833 volts and 1.166 volts is read as the integer 3. The *resolution* of an analog input channel is the smallest change that can be sensed and corresponds to the width of each step in Figure 4.26*b*. The resolution is calculated as the maximum span of the signal divided by the integer range of the ADC output. For example, a 12-bit ADC with a signal range of 5 volts has a resolution of 5/4095 = 1.22 mV.

The ADC requires a finite time to perform the analog-to-digital conversion, so the analog signal is sampled repeatedly and the conversion is performed on each sample. Any

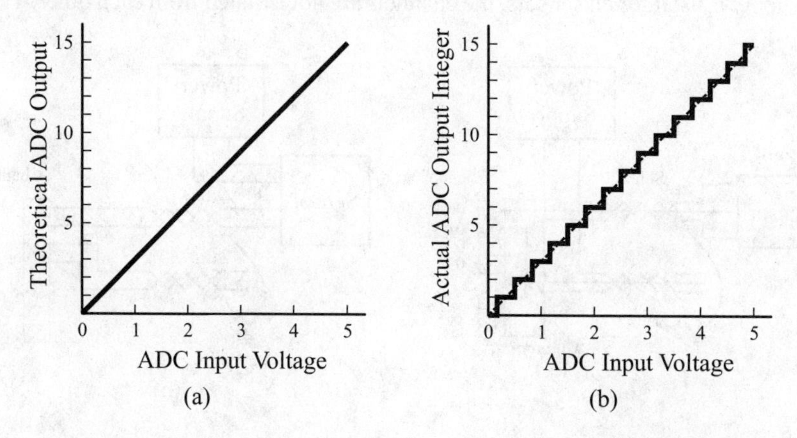

Figure 4.26. ADC input/output relationship: *(a)* theoretical output; *(b)* actual output integer.

change in the analog signal between samples is ignored. Since multiple signals are multiplexed into one ADC, the time between successive samples of one channel is the ADC conversion time multiplied by the number of channels. The maximum frequency of the measured signal must be considered when selecting the analog input module. The sampling rate of the input module should be at least twice the highest frequency of the measured signal.

The channels on an analog input module are sinking. Figure 4.27 shows the connections of voltage sensors to analog input modules. Analog input channels are generally configured as single-ended (Figure 4.27*a*) or differential (Figure 4.27*b*). Single-ended channels share a common connection that may also be the common of the sensor power supply. In contrast, differential channels do not share a common connection and are isolated from each other and from the sensor power supply. In either case, the signals are shielded to attenuate electromagnetic noise. The shield is connected to earth ground on only one end of the cable, preferably close to the point where the measured signal is connected to earth ground (Morrison, 1986) usually at the source (sensor) end. If the shield cannot be grounded at the sensor, then it should be connected to an earth ground at the PLC module.

There are two disadvantages to using voltage to represent the analog signal:

1. Even with careful shielding, the signals easily pick up electromagnetic noise.
2. The signal cannot be transmitted long distances. The wire resistance causes a significant voltage drop for long cables. For example, the resistance of 18-gauge wire is 0.0064 ohms per foot. If the cable length is 2000 feet, the combined resistance of the signal and common is 12.8 ohms. If the current through the differential signal loop is 0.1 mA, the resulting voltage drop is 1.28 mV, which is larger than the resolution of a 12-bit ADC when the maximum signal is 5 volts.

The solution to the disadvantages of voltage signals is to use current to transmit the signal, as shown in Figure 4.28. As for the voltage sensors, the input channels are generally connected as single-ended (Figure 4.28*a*) or differential (Figure 4.28*b*). Single-ended channels share a common connection that is also the common of the loop (and sensor) power supply. In contrast, differential channels do not share a common connection in the analog input module. However, the power supply is still part of the loop, and if the same power supply is used for all sensors, the channels are not isolated from each other. The loop

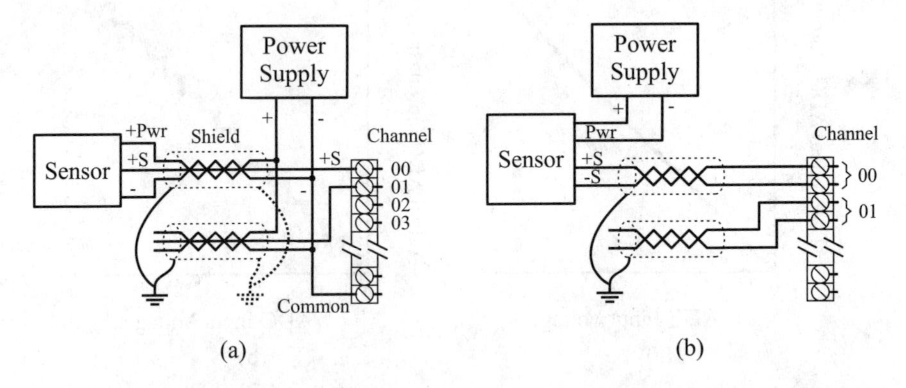

Figure 4.27. Connection of sensors to voltage-input analog input module: *(a)* single-ended; *(b)* differential.

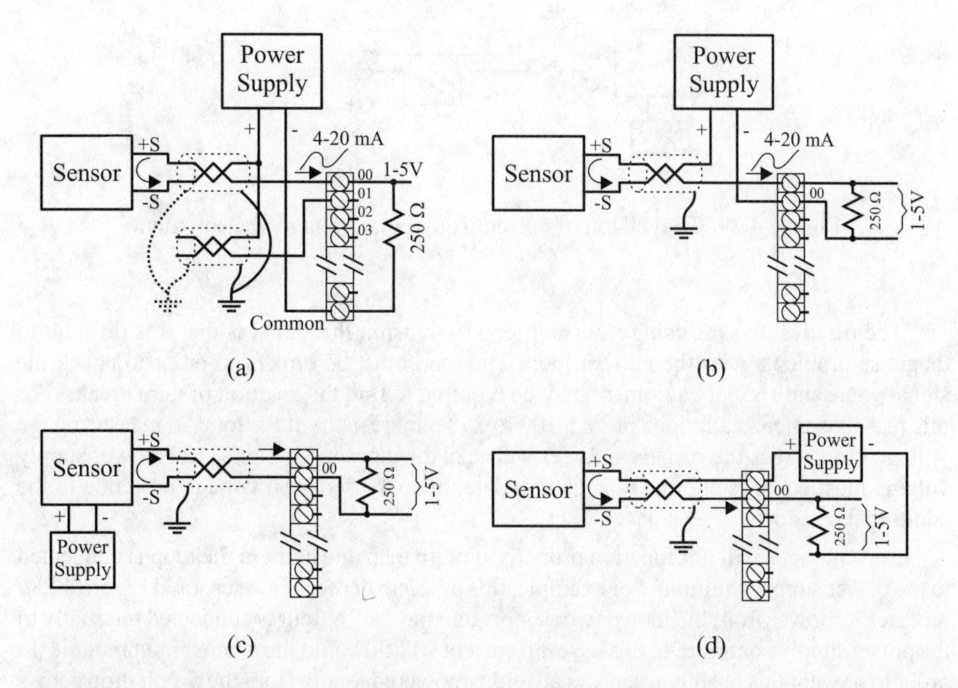

Figure 4.28. Connection of sensors to current-input analog input module: *(a)* single-ended; *(b)* differential; *(c)* separate sensor power supply; *(d)* module-supplied power.

power may be supplied by the sensor (Figure 4.28*c*) or may be provided by the analog output module (Figure 4.28*d*). In all cases, the signals are shielded, and the shield is grounded to attenuate electromagnetic noise.

The advantages to using current to transmit the signal are:

1. Current signals are less susceptible to electromagnetic interference.
2. The signal can be transmitted long distances (thousands of feet) limited only by power supply voltage and wire resistance. For long wire runs, the power supply voltage is increased to be at least 2 volts higher than the maximum voltage drop (wire resistance times 20 mA) plus the minimum sensor voltage drop plus the 5-volt drop at the analog input channel. For the circuit in Figure 4.28*a*, if the minimum sensor voltage drop is 5 volts and the sensor wiring run is 5000 feet of 18-gauge wire, the minimum power supply voltage is

   $$V_{min} = 2 + (10000 \text{ ft.}) \times (0.0064 \text{ ohms/ft.}) \times (0.020 \text{ amps}) + 5 + 5 = 13.28 \text{ volts}$$

3. Power and signal are carried by two wires.
4. A broken loop (wire) is indicated by zero mA, assuming the normal range of the signal is 4 to 20 mA.

A current signal can easily be converted to a voltage signal by installing a resistor across the voltage input terminals, as shown in Figure 4.29. This method is often used for sensors that produce non-standard current signal ranges. For example, if a sensor outputs a 0 to 1 mA signal, a resistor value of 5000 ohms in Figure 4.29 converts the current signal into a 0 to 5 volt signal to be measured by the analog input module.

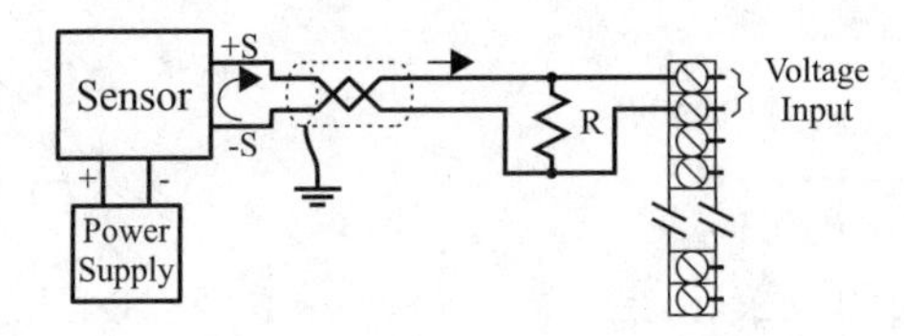

Figure 4.29. Conversion of current signal into voltage measurement.

The disadvantage of using a current loop to transmit the signal is that it is difficult to diagnose problems with the current loop. The loop must be broken in order to check the signal value and special equipment may be required to find the location of wire breaks. For this reason, some installations place a 100 to 250 ohm resistor in the loop so measuring the voltage drop across the resistor indirectly checks the current. Of course, the power supply voltage must be large enough to accommodate the increased loop voltage drop due to the additional resistor.

Current loops will not function properly if more than one point in the loop is connected to the power supply common. For example, this problem occurs if the sensor in Figure 4.28*a* receives its power from the loop power supply and the "S-" output is connected internally to the power supply common. In this case, no current will flow into the analog input module. In order to prevent this problem, sensors are either powered totally from the 5-volt drop across the output terminals or from a power supply completely isolated from the loop power supply.

A separate visual indicator may be part of the wiring of the sensor to the PLC (Figure 4.30). This indicator provides inexpensive local display of the sensor value and is often useful for diagnostics. For a sensor that provides a voltage signal, this indicator is connected in parallel to the PLC channel wiring, as shown in Figure 4.30*a*. For a current signal, the indicator is placed in series with the current loop wiring, as in Figure 4.30*b*. Indicators that measure current may be completely powered by the current loop and not require a separate power supply. If a current indicator uses a separate power supply, one should verify that there is no internal connection between the indicator power supply and the sensing inputs. This internal connection may cause more than one point in the loop to be connected to the common of the analog input module.

Thermocouple and resistance temperature device (RTD) sensors are generally connected to specialized analog input modules. Figure 4.31 shows typical connections. A

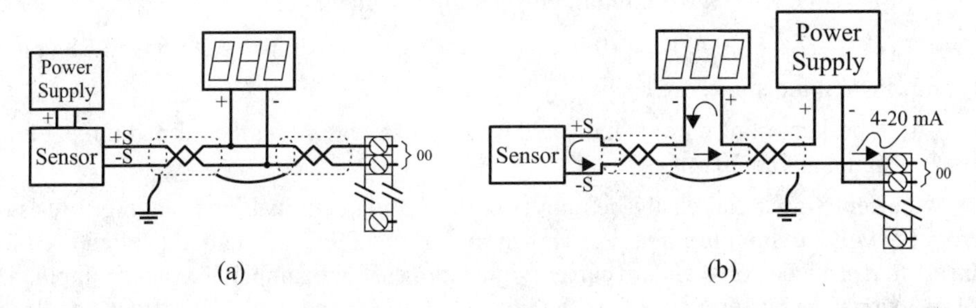

Figure 4.30. Connection of indicator to analog input signal: *(a)* voltage sensor; *(b)* current sensor.

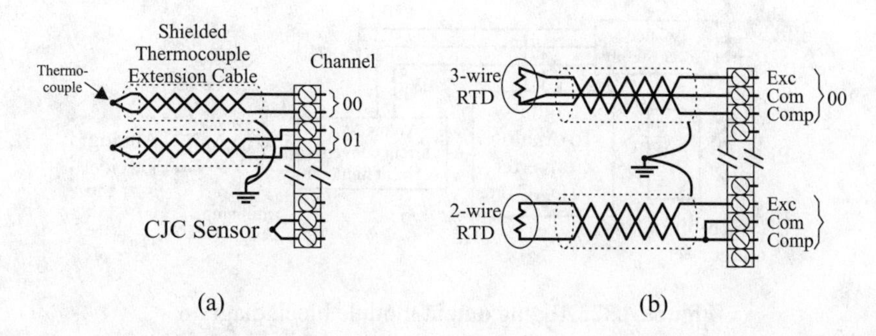

Figure 4.31. Connection of temperature sensors: *(a)* thermocouples; *(b)* RTD sensors.

thermocouple generates a small voltage (-10 to 80 mV) and so requires a high-gain amplifier. Proper voltage-to-temperature conversion requires cold-junction compensation (CJC), provided by a separate sensor measuring the terminal block temperature. A RTD is basically a temperature-sensitive resistor. The most common conversion of RTD resistance to temperature places the RTD in a Wheatstone bridge circuit before amplification. A three-wire RTD provides compensation for the resistance of the cable wires. Chapter 16 contains more information about these temperature sensors.

4.3.2 Analog Output Modules

An analog output module generates a voltage or current signal that drives another device to manipulate a physical quantity. Common devices controlled by a PLC analog output module are:

Variable-speed motor drive (speed)
Current-to-pneumatic converter (pneumatic regulating valve position)
Electronic valve (valve position)
Analog meter
Chart recorder

The block diagram of a typical analog output module is shown in Figure 4.32. A digital-to-analog converter (DAC) converts the integer number from the PLC into a single-ended voltage. If the output signal is a current, then the DAC output voltage must be converted into a current signal. Like the analog input modules, the actual field signal may be a single-ended voltage, single-ended current, differential voltage, or differential current. There is generally a separate DAC for each channel. The optical isolator provides electrical isolation between the field wiring and the PLC internal circuitry. The electronic circuitry to the right of the optical isolator is typically powered from the internal PLC, but through an isolated power supply to maintain isolation between the field wiring and the PLC voltage source. The field device may be powered by an external power supply or by the PLC isolated power supply.

The channels on an analog output module are sourcing. Figure 4.33 shows the connections of voltage and current devices to analog output modules. Analog output channels are generally configured as single-ended (Figure 4.33*a*,*c*) or differential (Figure 4.33*b*,*d*). Single-ended channels share a common connection. In contrast, differential channels do not share a common connection and are isolated from each other. As for the

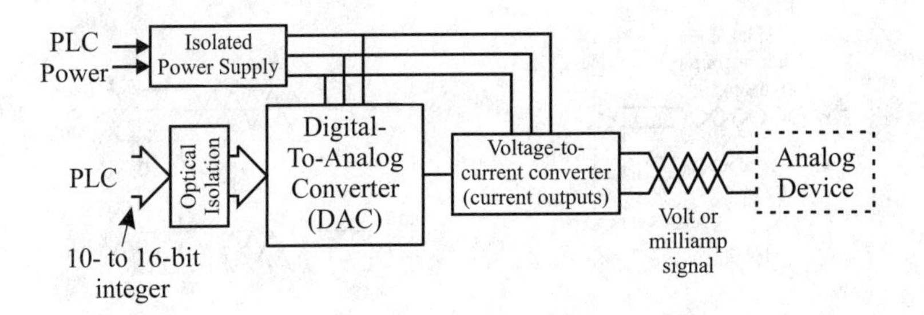

Figure 4.32. Analog output module block diagram.

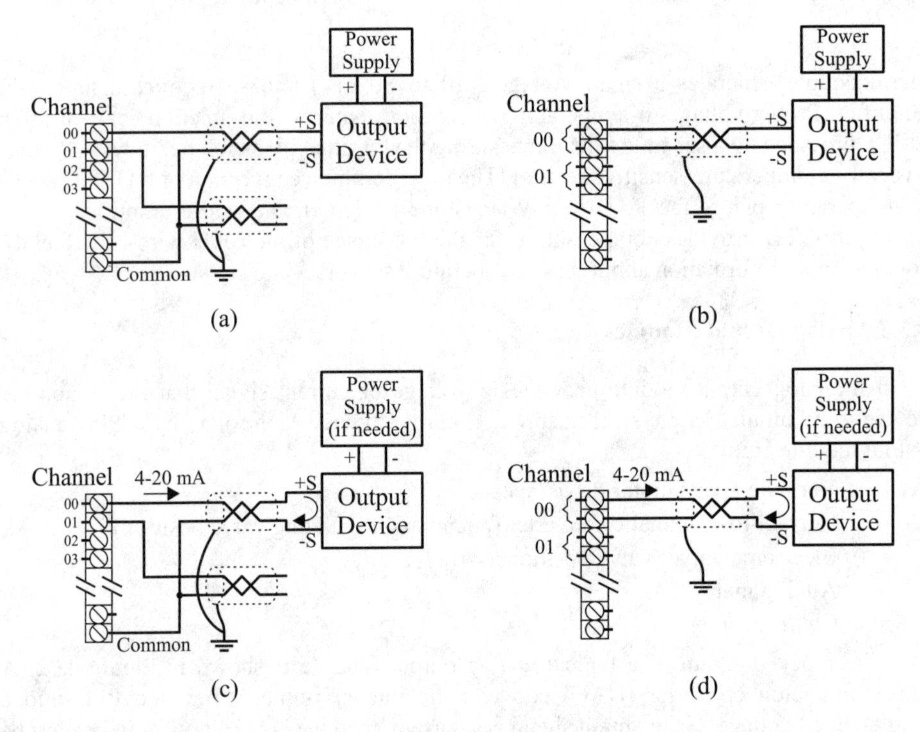

Figure 4.33. Connection of devices to analog output module: *(a)* single-ended voltage; *(b)* differential voltage; *(c)* single-ended current; *(d)* differential current.

analog inputs, the signals are shielded, and the shield is connected to earth ground at the source (module) end.

Some systems also provide the capability to manually operate an analog output device in conjunction with the PLC control. A typical device is called an auto/manual station, illustrated in Figure 4.34. When the switch is in the "MAN" position, the P-101 pump speed is set by the potentiometer, regardless of the value of the PLC output. When the switch is in the "AUTO" position, the PLC analog output controls the pump speed setting. The panel also shows the pump speed. The actual pump speed setting and an indication of the switch position is also provided to the PLC. When the selector switch is not in the "AUTO"

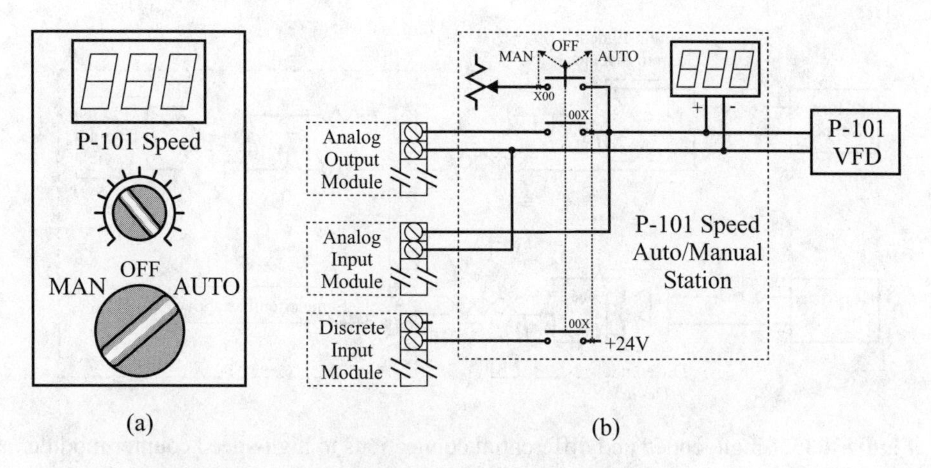

Figure 4.34. Analog output bypass station: *(a)* panel; *(b)* wiring.

position, the PLC logic disables any automatic control of the pump and adjusts the PLC analog output to match the operator setting.

4.4 SPECIALIZED MODULES

Many control systems need special-purpose I/O modules. For many systems, these modules are a minority of the total number of modules in the system but are essential for certain applications. Among specialized I/O modules, the high-speed counter and motion control modules are probably the most popular.

4.4.1 High-speed counter

A high-speed counter module provides a means to count pulses and time events independent of the program or I/O scan. A high-speed counter module is generally used as an interface for position encoders and positive-displacement flow meters. If a normal discrete input channel is used to count pulses, the highest pulse frequency is limited by the program scan time. For example, if the maximum program scan time is 1 ms, the minimum pulse width that can be reliably sensed is 2 ms (twice the maximum program scan time). Thus the maximum frequency that can be reliably sensed is 250 Hz (the reciprocal of twice the minimum pulse width). Many position encoder signals operate at 20 kHz and higher. Therefore, a normal discrete input channel is inadequate to count position encoder pulses. In addition, a high-speed counter module provides a differential input interface required by many encoders.

Figure 4.35 shows the connections of typical devices to a high-speed counter module used in simple counting applications. The connection to a single-ended device is similar to a sourcing discrete input device (Figure 4.8). Whenever possible, differential devices are preferred since the differential signal provides the best immunity to electrical noise. Many high-speed counter modules provide options to set the signal voltage level and signal filtering.

In most motion applications, a position encoder generates two-phase quadrature signals, shown in Figure 4.36*a* connected to a high-speed counter module. The relative

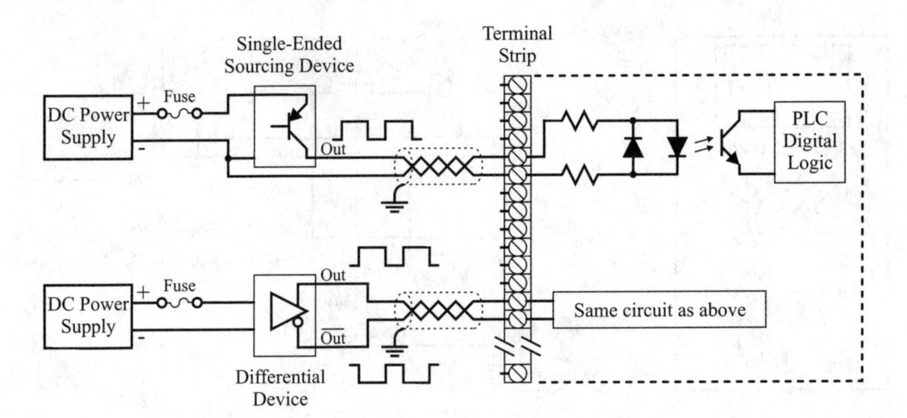

Figure 4.35. Single-ended and differential connections to high-speed counter module.

phasing of the A and B signals indicate the direction of encoder rotation. If the positive edge of A leads the positive edge of B, the encoder is rotating clockwise (Figure 4.36*b*). For counterclockwise rotation, the positive edge of A lags the positive edge of B (Figure 4.36*c*). The Z signal is the index pulse, which pulses once for each encoder revolution.

Many high-speed counter modules can also be programmed for operations more complex than simple counting. For example, many modules can calculate the frequency of

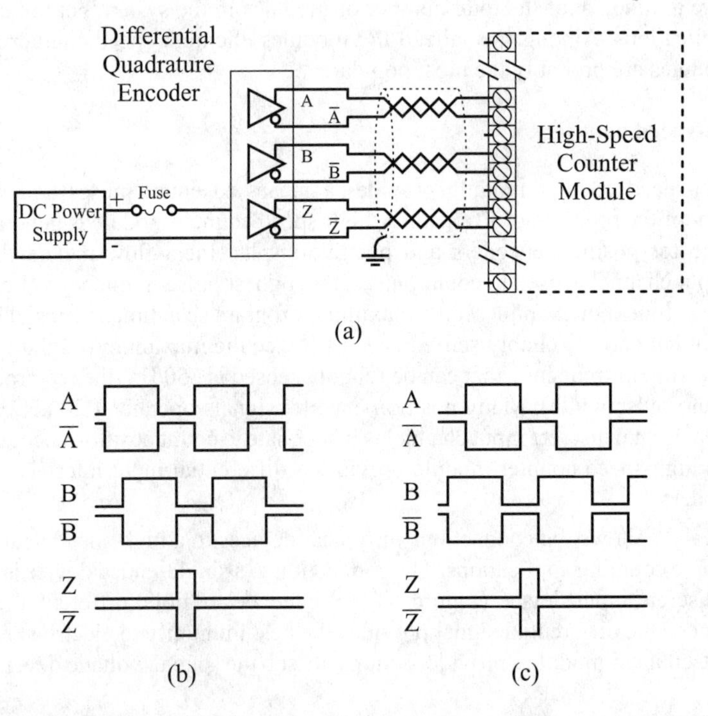

Figure 4.36. Quadrature encoder connections: *(a)* wiring to high-speed counter module; *(b)* timing for clockwise rotation; *(c)* timing for counterclockwise rotation.

the pulses by measuring the pulse period (averaged over a specified number of pulses) or by counting the number of pulses during a fixed interval.

4.4.2 Motion control

Motion control modules meet the needs of accurate, high-speed machining, packaging, and other types of production machinery. There are two types of motors used in motion control systems: servomotors and stepper motors. Generally, servomotors are used in applications that require high torque or power and stepper motors are used in low-torque, low-power applications. Both types of motors require a ***drive***, which contains the power electronics that translate the signals from the PLC motion module into the signals required by the motor. The drive for a stepper motor is usually less expensive than the drive for a servomotor.

A servomotor is a specially-designed brushed DC motor or brushless AC motor. The traditional servomotor is a brushed DC motor, where the coil is wound on the armature and the stator is a permanent magnet. In this motor, accurate speed control is obtained by manipulating the armature current while keeping the field current constant. By manipulating the field current with a constant armature current, the torque of the servomotor can be controlled. In a brushless AC motor, the rotor is a permanent magnet, and the coils are wound on the stator. A brushless servomotor requires complicated stator drive signals, and hence its drive is more complicated. Chapter 16 contains more details about the differences between brushed and brushless servomotors. Regardless of the type of servomotor, the speed and/or position is typically measured and fed back to the motion module, and the motor speed is adjusted accordingly. Figure 4.37 shows typical connections from the PLC servo motion module to the servo drive and to the servomotor when the servo is used in positioning control. In the example shown, an encoder is used for feedback, but a tachometer or a resolver could be used in place of the encoder. Also shown is a brake, which prevents motion when the motor is not powered. A brake is especially needed in certain vertical motion applications to hold a load at a certain position when motor power is removed. The over-travel limit switches cut off the motor power when the device moves too far in either direction.

The electrical connections in Figure 4.37 are sensitive to electrical noise and cannot be located very far away (Rockwell Automation, 2001e). In order to alleviate these electrical problems in motion control systems, many recent systems use the SERCOS (SErial Real-time COmmunication System) fiber optic communication medium (IEC, 1995), as

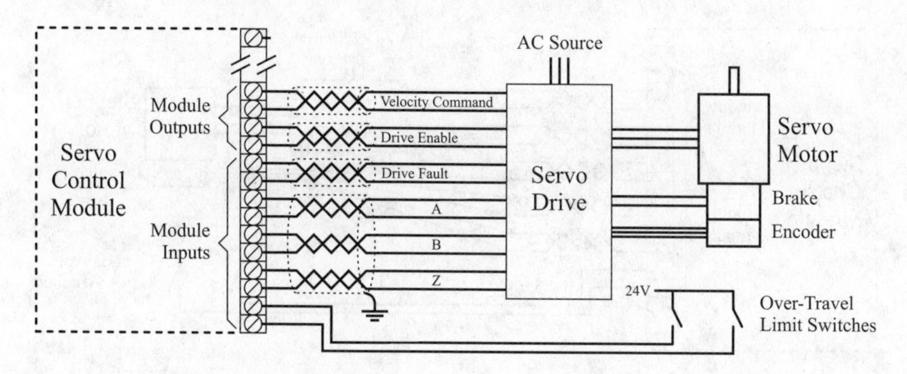

Figure 4.37. Typical servo-motor control module wiring.

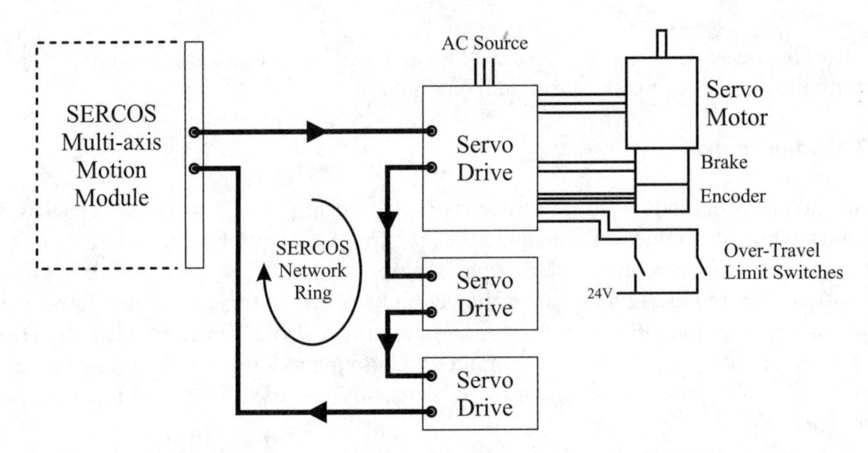

Figure 4.38. Typical SERCOS multi-axis motion module connections.

shown in Figure 4.38. The fiber optic medium assures reliable high-speed data transmission with excellent noise immunity and eliminates the interconnection wiring. A typical SERCOS system has one master control module communicating with multiple drives. The network is a ring topology, and any break in the fiber optic ring disables the entire network.

A stepper motor is a brushless permanent-magnet type motor that translates incoming pulses into mechanical motion. Because the stepper motor makes a fixed angular motion in response to the pulses, stepper motors are often used in an open-loop configuration. In this case, the motion is controlled by generating the proper pulses to the motor, and encoders are not used. Figure 4.39 shows typical connections from the PLC stepper control module to the stepper drive and to the stepper motor. This figure also shows the optional encoder connections. Note that a brake may not be needed, since the signals from the drive to the stepper will hold the stepper motor shaft in a fixed position. However, when the power to the drive is removed, the motor is free to spin. In vertical applications, a brake will hold a load at a certain position when power to the stepper drive is lost.

Stepper motors have two disadvantages. First, if the stepper motor encounters a torque load higher than its rating, the motor "cogs" and does not move. For this reason, encoders are utilized in high-performance motion applications. Second, one must be careful when using encoders in a stepper motor application. Because the motor is driven with pulses, the

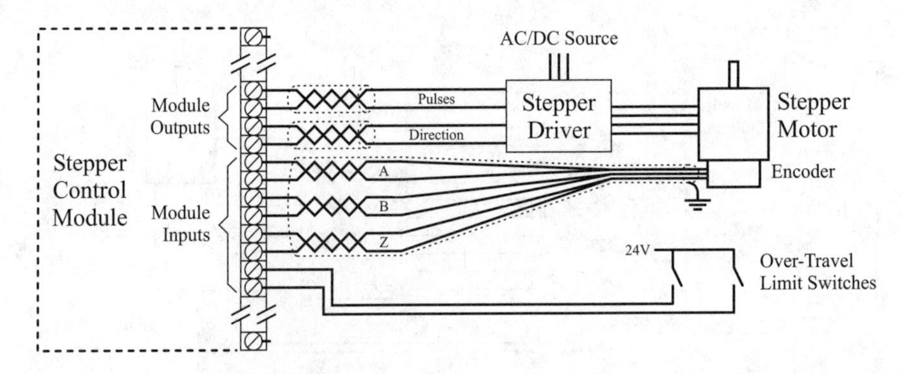

Figure 4.39. Typical stepper motor control module wiring.

actual shaft rotational motion is also "pulsed" and not smooth as for a servomotor. If the stepper motor is driving a flexible belt, the pulsed shaft motion is magnified and will cause false encoder pulses to be generated. For this reason, servomotors are a better choice when driving a flexible belt.

4.4.3 Other specialized devices

Other types of specialized I/O devices include bar code readers, vision systems, message displays, and operator terminals. These types of devices generally do not have a separate PLC I/O module, and the PLC provides communication interface modules to handle these types of devices. The simplest type of connection is a RS-232 serial port. Figure 4.40*a* shows a bar code reader, a vision system, and an operator terminal connected to RS-232 serial ports provided by the PLC. These serial ports may be on the PLC processor or may be provided by a separate module. Each specialized device generally requires a PLC serial port, though for some vendors, a *serial multiplexer*, can multiplex multiple serial connections into one PLC serial port, as shown for the bar code reader and the operator terminal in Figure 4.40*a*. As an alternative to serial port connections to each device, a multi-drop communication network may be used to connect the devices to the PLC, as shown in Figure 4.40*b*. Modbus and RS-485 are two popular simple multi-drop communications networks. Communication networks are discussed in Chapter 17.

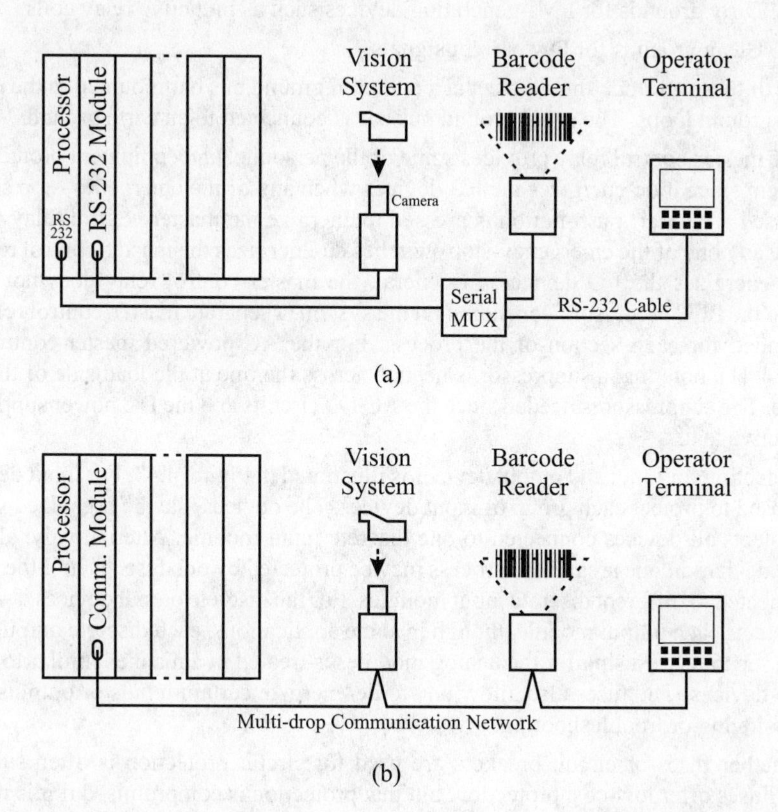

Figure 4.40. Connections to other intelligent devices: *(a)* serial communications; *(b)* communication network.

4.5 INSTALLATION WIRING

This section outlines general guidelines for the wiring required to install a PLC-based control system. It covers power distribution, control cabinet and control panel layout. Consult any vendor documentation and the appropriate standards (e.g., NFPA 70E and NFPA 79) for specific information.

4.5.1 Power distribution

If the control system power supply source is 120 AC volts, a typical distribution of power is shown in Figure 4.41. A step-down transformer decreases the higher voltage for the motor starters (typically 440 volts) to the 120 volts for the controller power supplies and DC power supplies. The power supplies for the PLC processor and all chassis that contain I/O modules are powered directly from the 120-volt source, protected by a fuse (or circuit breaker). The DC power supply in this configuration is used only to supply power to the I/O circuitry. For a system where DC powers the PLC processor and I/O modules, a typical power distribution is shown in Figure 4.42.

For safety and reliability in both AC and DC power distribution systems, all equipment must be properly grounded. There are typically three types of circuit grounds:

1. Safety grounds for chassis, panels, and junction boxes
2. Dirty grounds for EMI-generating devices such as inductive relay coils
3. Clean grounds for low current signals.

All of these grounds should meet at a common ground bus bar mounted in the panel to prevent ground loops. The panel ground bus bar is connected to an earth ground.

The master-control relay provides some of the personnel and equipment protection for the system since it de-energizes the I/O devices when any of the emergency-stop switches are pressed. The Start push-button is pressed to energize the master-control relay (MCR). Pressing any one of the emergency-stop switches de-energizes the master-control relay and thus de-energizes the I/O devices. In general, the master-control relay does not control power to the PLC processor. Depending on the system, a separate master-control relay may be provided for each section of the process. For the AC-powered master-control relay (Figure 4.41), note that a suppressor is needed across the line at the load side of the MCR contacts. The suppressor is needed since the AC I/O circuits and the DC power supply form an inductive load.

Protection for input and output devices is illustrated in Figure 4.43. For input devices, a fuse is used to protect each group of input devices. The devices may be organized so that a fuse protects all devices connected to one discrete input module. Alternatively, all of the discrete devices in one area of the process may be protected by one fuse, even if the devices are connected to different discrete input modules. For the discrete output devices, a separate fuse protects each output module, though in some applications, each discrete output device is fused separately. Fusing for the analog modules is treated in a manner similar to the DC discrete devices. The fuses also allow one to de-energize certain inputs or outputs during commissioning or troubleshooting.

Whether fuses or circuit breakers are used for circuit protection is often subject to debate. Fuses offer low-cost protection, but that protection is compromised if it is replaced with a higher-rated fuse when maintenance personnel tire of frequent blown fuses. Circuit breakers are often more convenient since a trip does not necessitate a trip to the storeroom

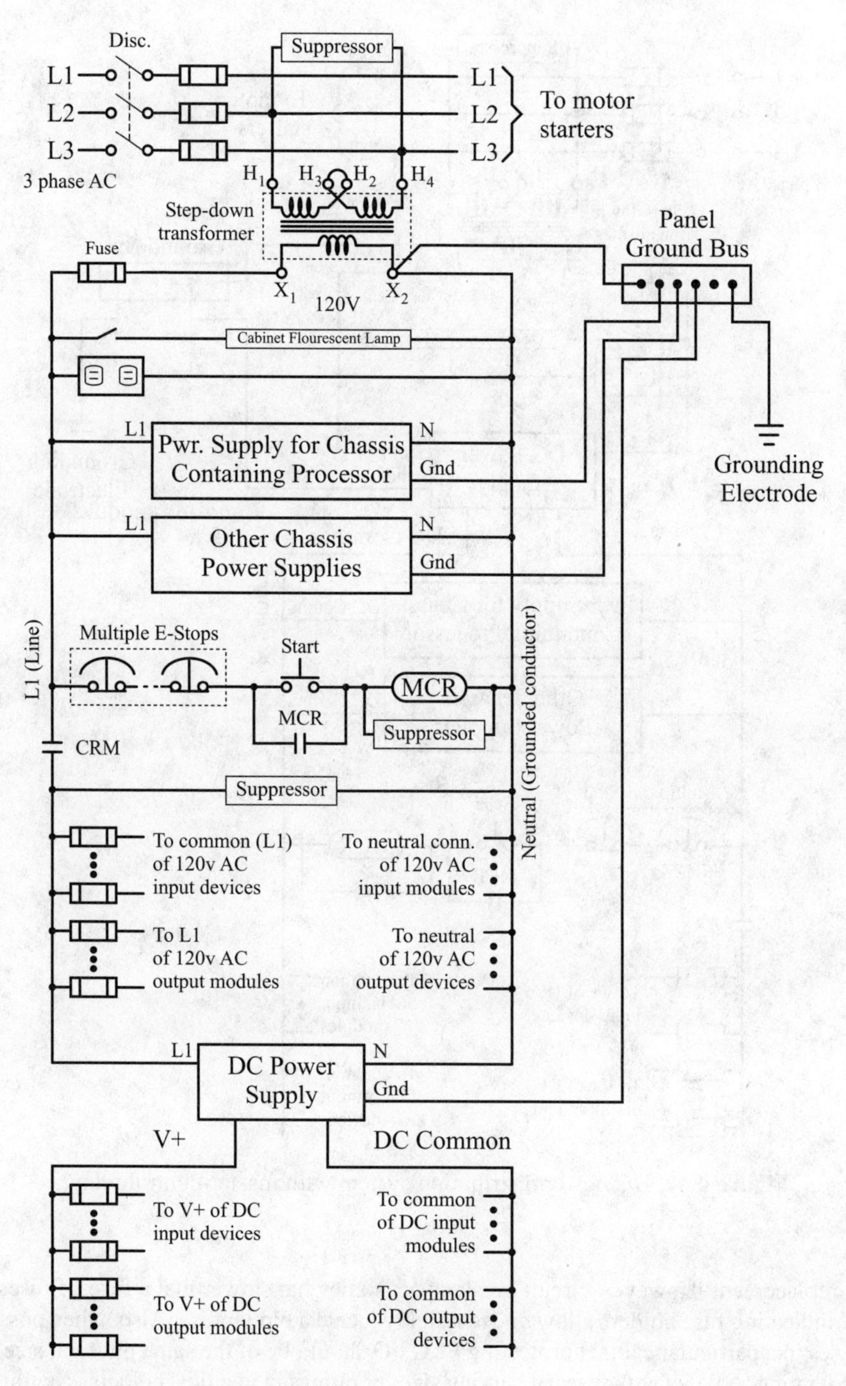

Figure 4.41. AC power distribution system with master-control relay.

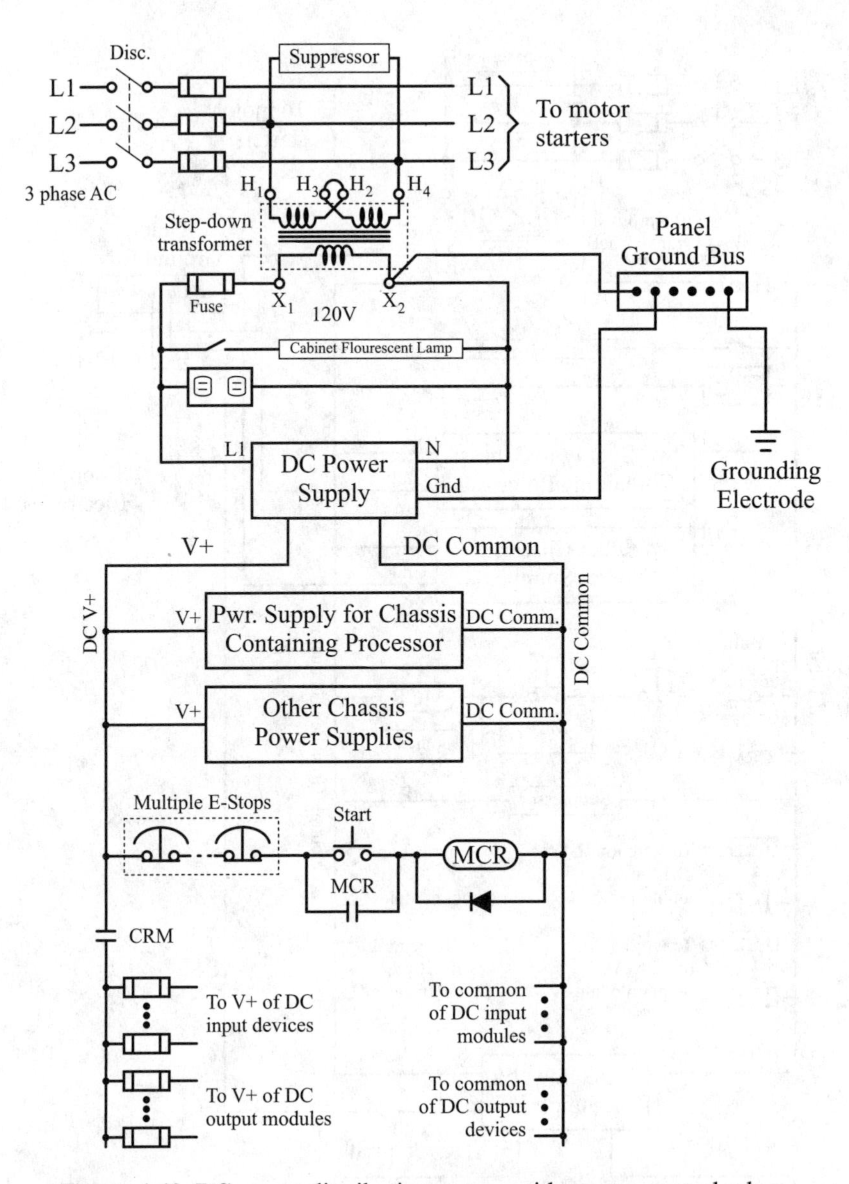

Figure 4.42. DC power distribution system with master-control relay.

for a replacement. However, circuit breakers act somewhat slower that a fuse. If fuses are used, indicating fuse holders allow one to quickly locate a blown fuse. Also, when possible all fuses in a particular cabinet protecting PLC I/O should be of the same physical size and current rating. A panel with fuses of varying sizes or ratings in identical holders is confusing to maintenance personnel.

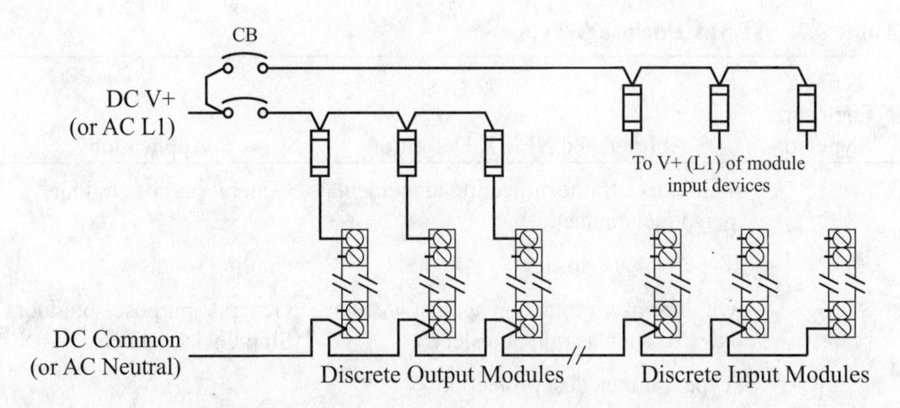

Figure 4.43. Protection of input and output devices.

4.5.2 Enclosure types

Even though PLCs are designed to operate in harsh industrial environments, most are installed in a metal enclosure, also called a control panel. The panel protects the components from atmospheric contaminants such as dust, moisture, oil and corrosive vapors. The panel also deters tampering and protects operating personnel from dangerous voltages. Finally, a panel reduces the effect of electromagnetic radiation generated by other electrical equipment, especially welders.

All enclosures installed in industrial applications must meet certain standards. In the United States, the types of enclosures are often described by the NEMA type number (NEMA, 1997). Table 4.1 summarizes the definitions of the various NEMA type numbers and their common applications. The most common types for industrial applications are types 12 and 4X. The IEC enclosure designation (IEC, 2001) consists of the letters "IP" followed by two digits and is summarized in Table 4.2. The first digit indicates the degree of protection against persons and solid objects entering the enclosure. The second digit indicates the degree of protection against water ingress. Common ratings are IP11, IP21, IP22, IP44, IP54, and IP55.

The IEC enclosure classifications (IEC, 2001) specify the degrees of protection against solid bodies and liquids. The IEC classifications do not specify protection against mechanical damage, risk of explosion, condensation, or corrosive vapors. The NEMA enclosure type numbers (NEMA, 1997) consider environmental conditions such as rust, corrosion, icing, and oil. Because of these differences, the IEC and NEMA enclosure classifications cannot be exactly equated. However, the replacement NEMA enclosure for certain IEC IP classifications can be designated as in Table 4.3. In general, the NEMA type numbers meet or exceed the associated IEC IP classification. For example, a NEMA type 12 enclosure can be used where an IEC IP52 classification is specified. However, an IEC IP52 enclosure cannot be used where a NEMA 12 enclosure is specified, since IP52 does not specify enclosure rust resistance.

4.5.3 Control Panel Design

A well-designed control panel interior and exterior is simple to understand and easily installed and maintained. Example layouts are shown in Figure 4.44 – 4.46. A panel where

Table 4.1. NEMA Enclosure Types

NEMA Enclosure Type no.	Abbreviated NEMA Definition	Application
1	Indoor use. Some protection to incidental personnel contact.	General purpose indoors
2	Type 1 plus drip-tight	Cooling rooms
3	Outdoor use. Protection against weather hazards such as rain and sleet.	General purpose outdoors Ship docks, tunnels
3R	Type 3 minus dust protection	
3S	Type 3 plus external mechanisms remain operable when ice laden	
4	Watertight. Protection against wash-down	Food processing
4X	Type 4 plus corrosion protection	Food processing
5	Indoor use. Dust-tight	Cement, powder blending
6	Submersible	Mines, quarries
6P	Prolonged submersible	Mines, quarries
7	Hazardous. Indoor use in NEC Class I, Groups A, B, C, D (certain gases and vapors which may be explosive)	Petrochemical plants
8	Hazardous. Type 7 plus outdoors	Petrochemical plants
9	Hazardous. Indoor/outdoor use in NEC Class II, Groups E, F, G (combustible dust	Petrochemical plants
10	Meets requirements of the Mine Safety and Health Administration, 10 CFR, Part 18 (1978)	Mines
12	Type 1 plus dust-tight, drip-tight, protection against lint and fibers	Industrial indoors
12X	Type 12 with knockouts	
13	Type 12 plus protection against spraying water, oil, noncorrosive coolant	Metal machining

the field I/O connections and high-volt AC enter from the top is shown in Figure 4.44. This panel also includes a transformer and a disconnect. Figure 4.45 shows the layout of a panel where the field I/O wiring enters from the bottom. A vertical mounting of a PLC chassis is shown in Figure 4.46. The more important recommendations are outlined below and then followed by a typical control panel specification.

Table 4.2. IEC Ingress Protection (IP) Ratings

First No.	Protection against:
0	No protection
1	Solid objects more than 50 mm (e.g., hands)
2	Solid objects more than 12 mm (e.g., fingers)
3	Solid objects more than 2.5 mm (e.g., tools)
4	Solid objects more than 1 mm
5	Totally enclosed. Dust may enter but not in harmful quantities
6	Totally dust-tight
Second No.	**Protection against:**
0	No protection
1	Vertically falling drops of water
2	Falling liquid up to 15° from vertical
3	Falling liquid up to 60° from vertical
4	Splashing from any direction. Limited ingress permitted
5	Strong jets of water. Limited ingress permitted
6	Occasional immersion. Water must not enter
7	Permanent submersion up to 1 meter
8	Permanent submersion up to specified depth and pressure

Table 4.3. Conversion of NEMA Enclosure Type Numbers to IEC Classification Designations (NEMA, 1997).

NEMA Enclosure Type Number	Meets or Exceeds IEC Enclosure Classification
1	IP10
2	IP11
3	IP54
3R	IP14
3S	IP54
4 and 4X	IP56
5	IP52
6 and 6P	IP67
12 and 12K	IP52
13	IP54

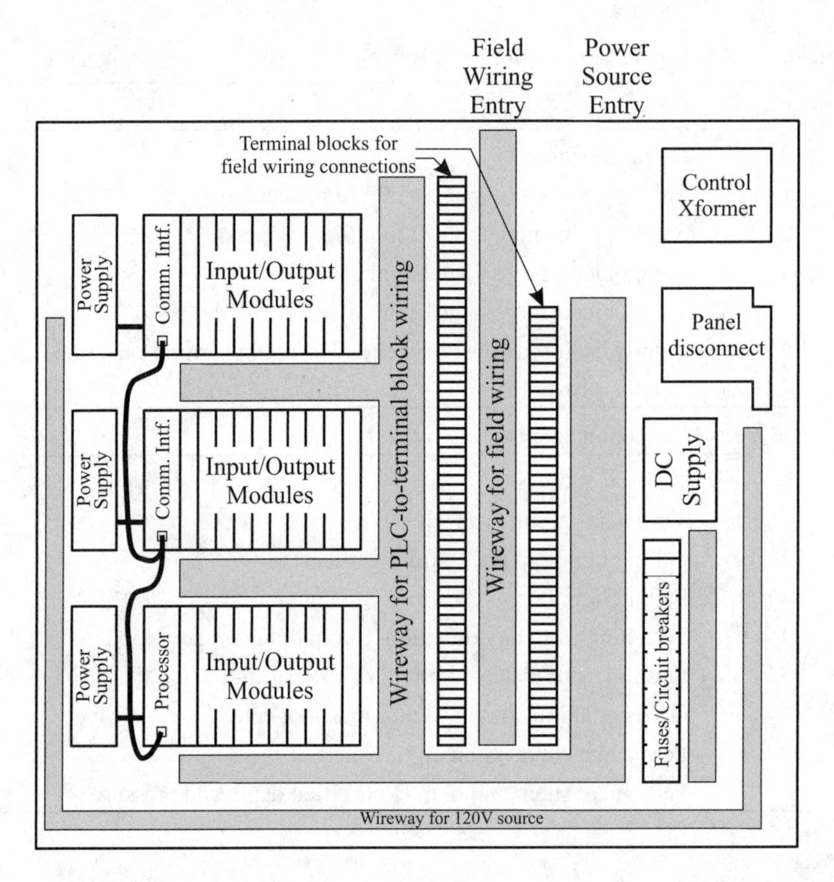

Figure 4.44. Typical panel layout that includes transformer and disconnect.

General. Some general aspects of the physical particulars of a PLC enclosure are:

- The enclosure should be located so that the doors can be fully opened.
- The enclosure depth should provide adequate clearance between the enclosed equipment, including cables and the closed door of the enclosure. If switches and/or indicators are mounted on the door or the door contains a drawing pocket, then these items should also factor into the depth requirements.
- The enclosure should contain lighting and convenience outlets to be used for troubleshooting and maintenance.
- All components should be mounted on a removable back panel.
- An emergency disconnect switch should be provided. If the enclosure contains a voltage greater than 120 volts, then the panel should have a through-the-door disconnect switch.

Environmental. The effects of temperature, humidity, electrical noise, and vibration are important when designing the panel layout. In particular:

- The temperature inside the enclosure must not exceed the maximum temperature allowed by the electronic equipment (typically 55 – 60 °C or 130 – 140 °F).

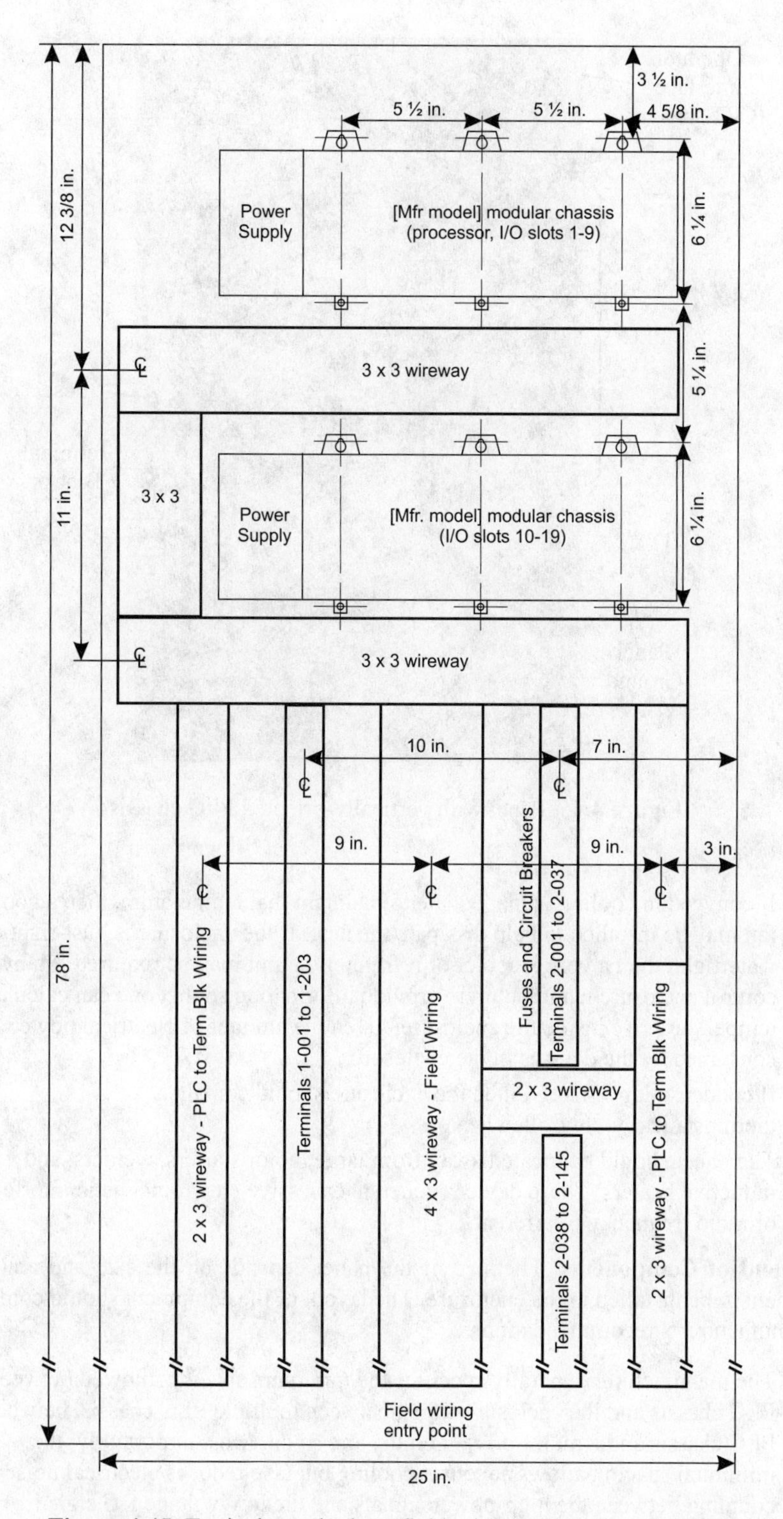

Figure 4.45. Typical panel where field wiring enters from bottom.

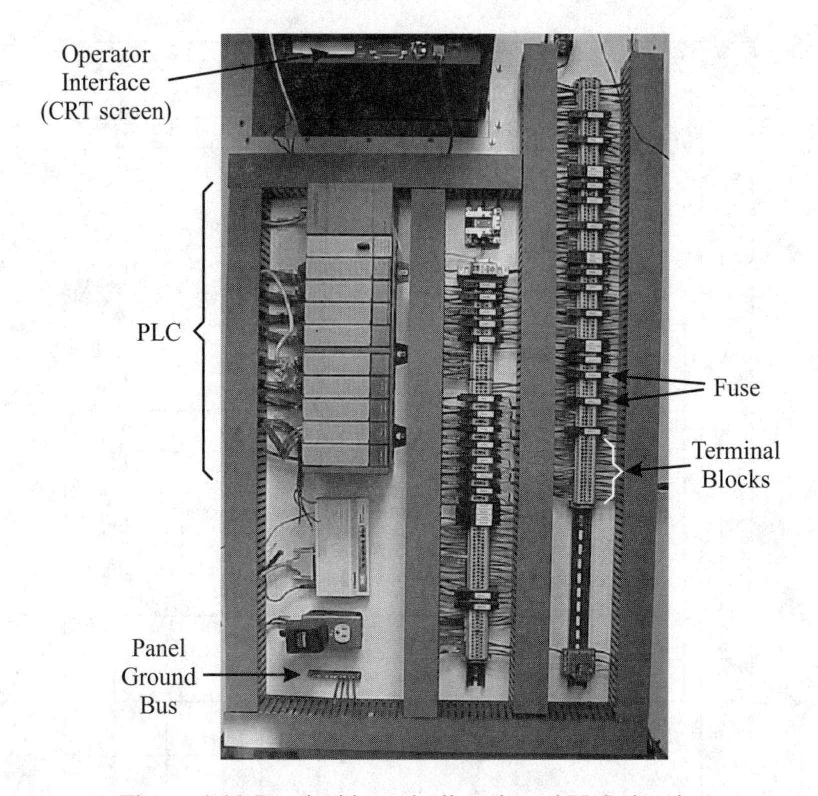

Figure 4.46. Panel with vertically-oriented PLC chassis.

- If convection cooling is inadequate to maintain that temperature, then a cooling fan may be installed to help dissipate the heat. If the enclosure is dust-tight or watertight, then a vortex cooler or refrigeration unit may be required. Many control enclosure manufacturers provide information so that one can calculate the temperature rise inside the enclosure, given the amount of electrical power consumed by the devices in the enclosure.
- If condensation is likely, then the enclosure should contain a thermostatically-controlled heater.
- The panel should be located away from large motor starters, welders, and inductive heaters. These devices generate excessive electromagnetic interference or radio frequency interference.

Placement of Components. The size of the panel depends on the size and amount of equipment to be installed in the enclosure. The layout of the equipment should conform to the manufacturer's recommendations.

- The manufacturer generally specifies the minimum spacing allowed between a PLC chassis and the enclosure walls, between multiple PLC chassis, between a PLC chassis and a motor drive module, and so on. Most importantly, the minimum spacing allows adequate cooling but also reduces electrical noise coupling between the high-power signals and the low-voltage DC signals.

- System components should be mounted in a position that allows effective convective cooling. For example, any cooling fins should be oriented vertically. Even though the layout in Figure 4.46 is not optimal in this regard, the chassis is oriented so the power supply is at the top.
- Incoming line devices, such as constant voltage transformers and local power disconnects should be mounted close to the top of the enclosure, which is a common entry point for power.
- Power supplies generate heat and so are mounted toward the top of the panel and close to the incoming line devices.
- The PLC processor and I/O modules should be mounted close to eye level, either adjacent to or below the power supply.
- Motor contactors, relays and other electromechanical components should be mounted in an area well away from the PLC components, typically toward the top of the cabinet.
- Motor drives should also be located well away from the PLC components. Large drives should be in a separate cabinet.
- The I/O modules should be grouped according to the voltage level. Whenever possible, the 120-volt AC discrete input or output modules should be segregated from the DC discrete input or output modules. The analog modules should be separated from the AC or DC discrete modules.
- If possible, all I/O modules in a chassis should be the same general type (AC discrete, DC discrete, or analog). If general types must be mixed, then they should be grouped together in the chassis, and any unused slots should be allocated between the groups.

Wireway and Wiring Layout. Wires within a cabinet are routed in wireways that organize the wiring and give a neat appearance to the panel. All wires should be organized into the three categories in Table 4.4 (IEEE, 1982). In order to guard against coupling noise from

Table 4.4. Conductor categories (IEEE, 1982).

Category	Description	Examples
1	Control and AC power	AC power lines for I/O circuits and power supplies High-power digital AC I/O lines High-power digital DC I/O lines (typically connection to relays)
2	Signal and communication	Analog I/O lines and DC power for analog circuits Low-power digital DC I/O lines Communication cables (Ethernet, ControlNet, remote I/O, etc.)
3	Intra-enclosure	Low-voltage DC power wires (power modules in cabinet) Communication cables

Table 4.5. Wire routing guidelines to reduce noise coupling (IEEE, 1982).

Category	Routing Guidelines
1	Can be routed in the same cable tray or raceway with machine power conductors of up to 600V AC (feeding up to 100HP devices).
2	If it must cross power feed lines, it should do so at a right angle. Route at least 5 ft. from high-voltage enclosures or sources of RF/microwave radiation. Properly shield (where applicable) and route in a wireway separate from category-1 conductors. If **not in a contiguous metallic wireway or conduit**, route at least 0.15m (6 in.) from category-1 conductors of less than 20A; 0.3m (1 ft.) from AC power lines of 20A or more, but only up to 100 kVA; 0.6m (2 ft.) from AC power lines of greater than 100 kVA. If **in a contiguous metallic wireway or conduit**, route at least 0.08m (3 in.) from category-1 conductors of less than 20A; 0.15m (6 in.) from AC power lines of 20A or more, but only up to 100 kVA; 0.3m (1 ft.) from AC power lines of greater than 100 kVA.
3	Route conductors external to all wireways in the enclosure or in a wireway separate from any category-1 conductors with the same spacing listed from category-2 conductors, where possible.

one conductor to another, follow the routing guidelines in Table 4.5. Some other considerations are:

- Analog I/O signals should be shielded and routed separate from the discrete signals. A foil shield is preferable to a braided shield. When possible, the shield on shielded cable should be grounded at the signal source. When a shielded cable passes through intermediate junction boxes, shield continuity must be maintained.
- I/O rack interconnection cables (not the same as remote I/O cables) should be in a wireway separate from other wiring. If this is not practical, then they should be routed external to all wireways and fastened directly to the panel.
- The field devices are generally not wired directly to the I/O modules. Instead, the field devices are wired to interposing terminal blocks. The connections between the I/O module to the interposing terminal blocks can be done with individual wires to terminal blocks (Figure 4.47*a*) or with a prewired cable between the I/O module and a prefabricated termination module (Figure 4.47*b*).
- There should be at least 1 inch between wireways and terminals to allow for wiring room and to show the wire labels.
- All wires should be clearly labeled with the same designation on both ends. Wire labels should be easily matched to the control panel drawings. All labels in a PLC-based system should be labeled in such a way that relates to the PLC addressing, that is, the label should indicate the chassis, module, and channel.
- Color-code wires according to their function in order to aid troubleshooting. NFPA 79 (NFPA, 2002) defines the following colors:

Green/yellow stripe	Equipment grounding conductor.
Black	Ungrounded line, load, control conductors at line voltage.
Red	Ungrounded AC control conductors at less than line voltage.
Blue	Ungrounded DC control conductors.
Yellow	Ungrounded control circuit conductors that remain energized when the main disconnect switch is in the OFF position.
White or gray	Grounded circuit conductor.
White/blue stripe	Grounded (current-carrying) DC circuit conductor.
White/yellow stripe	Grounded (current-carrying) AC control circuit conductor that remains energized when the main disconnect switch is in the OFF position.

Others define colors differently and add colors for analog signals.

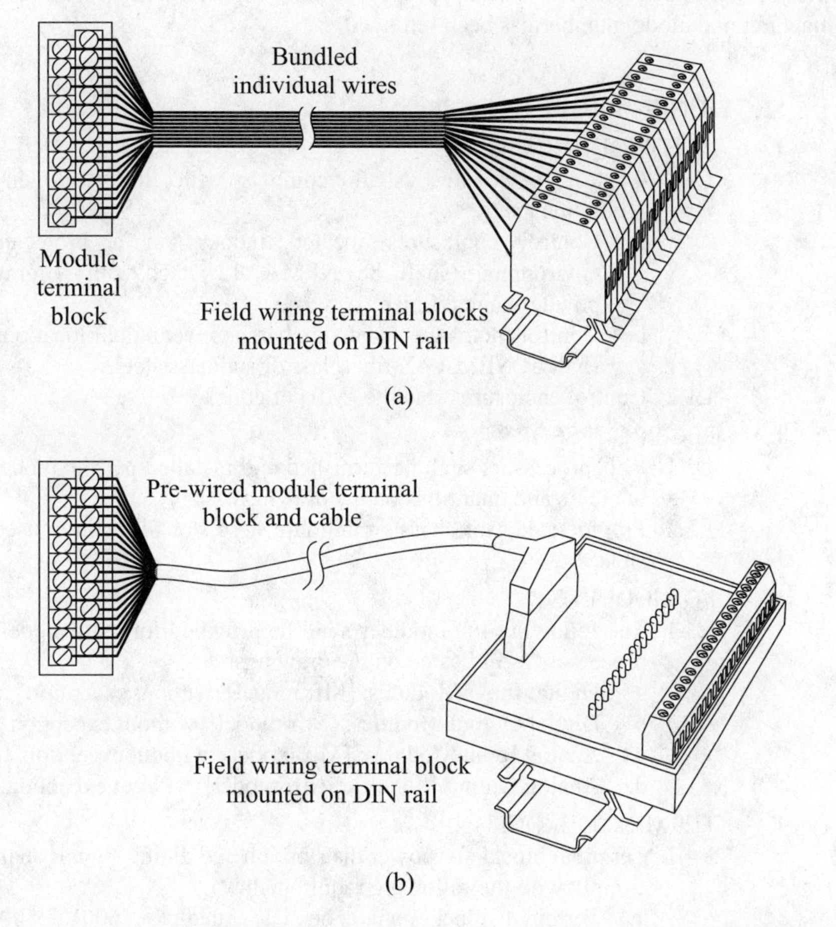

Figure 4.47. Interconnection between I/O module and field-wiring terminal blocks: *(a)* individual wires; *(b)* prefabricated termination module.

Operator Control Station Layout. If the panel door has operator controls or indications, then it should be organized for ease of understanding and use. Considerations (Lawrence, 1998):

- Locate controls at a comfortable height for viewing and operating. Indicators, alarm pilot lights, and meters should be at eye level, generally 62" to 67" from the floor. Push-button and selector switches should be about 48" to 60" from the floor.
- Group operator control devices into master, manual, and automatic functions. Within these groups, arrange the controls into a logical order to initiate machine functions in the proper sequence.
- Remember to check for the presence of a door stiffener or rib when placing the indicators and controls, since they cannot be placed there.
- The legend plates should clearly describe the action to occur and the mechanism's direction of movement.
- Do not abbreviate a word on the legend plate unless necessary.

Sample Panel Specification. A sample specification follows. Any reference to a manufacturer and model number has been removed.

SECTION 1 – PRODUCTS

1.1 CONTROL ENCLOSURES

1.1.1 Control enclosures shall comply with the following requirements:

a. Control enclosures located indoors in a protected environment shall be NEMA 12 steel with a gray powder-coated finish.

b. Control enclosures located in harsh or wet indoor locations shall be NEMA 4X fiberglass or stainless steel.

1.1.2 Control enclosures shall be [Mfr] or equal.

1.2 PLC PROCESSORS

1.2.1 PLC processors shall be furnished and installed per the model numbers and quantities on the drawings.

1.2.2 Provide a 13-slot chassis minimum. Use slot fillers in unused slots.

1.3 I/O MODULES

1.3.1 The following I/O modules shall be provided for [Mfr model] processors as indicated on the drawings:

a. Digital Input Modules: [Mfr model], without exception.

b. Digital Output Modules: [Mfr model], without exception.

c. Analog Input Modules: [Mfr model], without exception.

d. Analog Output Modules: [Mfr model], without exception.

1.4 TERMINAL BLOCKS

1.4.1 Terminal blocks for power distribution and digital signals shall comply with the following requirements:

a. Terminal blocks shall be UL rated for 600V, 30A minimum.

b. Terminal blocks shall have a compression-style screw clamp connection.
c. Terminal blocks shall be capable of accepting two #12 AWG wires.

1.4.2 Terminal blocks for analog signals shall comply with the following requirements:
a. Terminal blocks shall be UL rated for 300V, 20A minimum.
b. Terminal blocks shall have a compression-style screw clamp connection.
c. Terminal blocks shall be capable of accepting two #16 AWG wires.
d. Terminal blocks shall be three level sensor blocks for termination of signal positive, negative, and shield.

1.4.3 Fuse blocks shall comply with the following requirements:
a. Fuse blocks shall be UL rated for 600V, 10A minimum.
b. Fuse blocks shall incorporate a hinged lever that accepts 5x20 mm fuses.
c. Fuse blocks shall have a compression-style screw clamp connection.
d. Fuse blocks shall be capable of accepting two #12 AWG wires.
e. Fuse blocks shall contain blown-fuse indication through the use of a neon lamp or an LED.

1.4.4 All terminal blocks and fuse blocks shall be designed for DIN rail mounting. Extra deep 25 mm DIN rail shall be used.

1.4.5 Contractor shall provide terminal block end sections and end stops as necessary for a complete installation.

1.4.6 Terminal blocks and fuse blocks shall be provided with snap-on label strips. Label shall be consistent with Contractor's control panel drawings.

1.4.7 Terminal blocks and fuse blocks shall be [Mfr] or equal.

1.5 CIRCUIT BREAKERS

1.5.1 Circuit Breakers shall comply with the following requirements:
a. Single pole circuit breakers shall be [Mfr model] series or approved equal.
b. Double and triple pole circuit breakers shall be [Mfr model] series or approved equal.

1.6 RELAYS

1.6.1 Relays shall comply with the following requirements:
a. Relays shall be plug-in style with a DIN-rail mountable base.
b. Relays shall have on/off indication.
c. Relays shall have a manual operator.

1.6.2. Relays shall be [Mfr model] or equal.

1.7 PUSHBUTTONS AND SELECTOR SWITCHES

1.7.1 Pushbuttons and selector switches shall comply with the following requirements:

a. Pushbuttons and selector switches shall be suitable for a 30.5 mm mounting hole.
b. Pushbuttons and selector switches shall be NEMA type 4/13.
c. Pushbuttons used for non-emergency service shall be black flush-head.
d. Pushbuttons used for emergency stop service shall be red mushroom-head.
e. Pushbuttons and selector switches shall be provided with engraved legend plates indicating their function.
f. Pushbuttons and selector switches shall be provided with normally-open and normally-closed contact blocks as necessary. For pushbuttons, a minimum of 1 normally-open contact block and 1 normally-closed contact block shall be provided. For selector switches, a minimum of 1 normally-open contact block and 1 normally-closed contact block shall be provided in each position other than the "off" position.

1.7.2 Pushbuttons and selector switches shall be [Mfr model] or equal.

1.8 INDICATORS

1.8.1 Indicators shall comply with the following requirements:

a. Indicators shall be full-voltage incandescent.
b. Indicators shall be suitable for a 30.5 mm mounting hole.
c. Indicators shall be NEMA type 4/13.
d. Indicators shall be provided with engraved legend plates indicating their meaning.

1.8.2. Indicators shall be [Mfr model] or equal.

1.9 CONTROL PANEL FUSED DISCONNECT SWITCHES

1.9.1 Fused disconnect switches for use in control panels shall comply with the following requirements:

a. Disconnect switches shall be rated for 600V service.
b. Disconnect switches shall incorporate a blown fuse indication.
c. Disconnect switches shall have an option for handles that can be through-the-door mounted or direct mounted.

1.9.1 Control panels containing voltages in excess of 120V shall have a through-the-door disconnect switch. Control panels containing voltages of 120V or less shall have a disconnect switch with a direct-mounted handle that does not penetrate the enclosure.

1.9.2 Control panel disconnect switches shall be [Mfr model] or equal.

1.10 INSTRUMENT POWER SUPPLIES

1.10.1 Instrument power supplies shall comply with the following requirements:

a. Power supplies that feed voltage to DC devices or PLC inputs at DC voltage levels shall be either linear or switching.

b. Power supplies that feed analog voltage inputs or analog current loops shall be linear.

1.10.2 Instrument power supplies shall be [Mfr] or equal.

SECTION 2 – EXECUTION

2.1 CONTROL PANEL CONSTRUCTION

2.1.1 The Contractor shall size the control panels to allow sufficient space for all interior mounted equipment and wiring. Control panels shall be sized for ease of maintenance.

2.1.2 All control panels shall have 10% spare terminal blocks and fuse blocks, with a minimum of 10 spare terminal blocks and 2 spare fuse blocks.

2.1.3 All I/O including spare shall be wired out to terminal blocks.

2.1.4 All major panel equipment including PLC power supply, I/O chassis power supply, 24VDC power supply and power to each I/O module shall be sub-fused.

2.1.5 A minimum of two 120-VAC 60-Hz utility outlets should be installed in the panel.

2.1.6 An internal fluorescent light with a conveniently located on/off switch shall be installed in the panel.

2.2 I/O MODULE WIRING

2.2.1 Connections from the control panel to field devices shall only be made from interposing terminal blocks, not directly from the PLC I/O modules. Provide the following interposing methods:

a. For digital input or digital output modules provide prefabricated termination module, [Mfr model].

b. For analog input modules wire each channel to terminal blocks per requirements of section 1.4.2. Provide minimum of 4 terminal block connections per channel for (1) power, (2) signal +, (3) signal -, and (4) shield. Distribute 24VDC power for each channel. Tie all shield blocks together and wire to enclosure ground.

c. For analog output modules, wire each channel to terminal blocks per requirements of section 1.4.2. Provide a minimum of 3 terminal block connections per channel for (1) signal +, (2) signal -, and (3) shield. Configure analog output module to provide 24VDC power from the module. Tie all shield blocks together and wire to enclosure ground.

2.3 CONTROL PANEL WIRING PRACTICES

2.3.1 All internal control panel wiring shall be a minimum of #16 AWG. Power distribution wiring shall be stranded copper with MTW insulation, rated 600V. Digital input/output wiring shall be stranded copper UL 1061, rated 300V.

2.3.2 As an exception to the previous paragraph, analog input/output wiring shall be stranded copper, twisted, shielded pair, #24 AWG minimum, rated 300V, [Mfr model] or equal.

2.3.3 Every effort shall be made to segregate analog signals from power distribution and digital signal wiring. Where analog wiring must cross other wiring, it shall cross at right (90 degree) angles.

2.3.4 Use the following wire colors:

Green	Equipment grounding conductor.
White	Neutral (grounded) 120 VAC circuit conductor.
Black	Line (120 VAC) control conductor.
Red	AC Discrete output control conductor.
Orange	AC Discrete input conductor.
Brown	DC positive voltage control conductor
White/blue stripe	DC negative (common) voltage control conductor.
Blue	DC Discrete output control conductor.
Violet	DC Discrete input

2.3.5 All wiring shall be firmly supported inside the control panel. A wireway system such as [Mfr model] shall be utilized in each control panel. Wire ties shall be used as needed to support cabling and to provide a clean installation. The Contractor shall size the wireways to allow ample space for both internal control panel wiring and field wiring.

2.3.6 All wiring in each control panel shall be clearly labeled with the same designation on both ends. Wire labels shall be easily matched to the control panel drawings. Wire labels shall be [Mfr model] heat-shrink or equivalent.

2.3.7 All wiring shall be in compliance with the National Electrical Code and other applicable state and local building codes.

4.6 CHAPTER SUMMARY

This chapter describes the wiring of PLC I/O modules to discrete, analog, and specialized field devices. In addition, other installation issues such as power distribution and control panel layout is covered.

REFERENCES

Allen-Bradley, 1986. *DC (5V) Multiplexer Input Module: User Manual*, pub. 1771-6.5.10, Allen-Bradley Company, Inc, Milwaukee, WI.

Allen-Bradley, 1992. *1771 Discrete I/O DC Input and Output Modules*, pub. 1771-2.180, Allen-Bradley Company, Inc, Milwaukee, WI.

Allen-Bradley, 1993. *Very High Speed Counter Module: User Manual*, pub. 1771-6.5.74, Allen-Bradley Company, Inc, Milwaukee, WI.

Allen-Bradley, 1996a. *1771 Discrete I/O AC Input and Output Modules*, pub. 1771-2.182, Allen-Bradley Company, Inc, Milwaukee, WI.

Allen-Bradley, 1996b. *High Speed Counter Module: User Manual*, pub. 1746-6.5, Allen-Bradley Company, Inc, Milwaukee, WI.

Allen-Bradley, 1996c. *SLC 500 TM Analog I/O Modules: User Manual*, pub. 1746-6.4, Allen-Bradley Company, Inc, Milwaukee, WI.

Allen-Bradley, 1996d. *SLC 500 TM Thermocouple/mV Input Module: User Manual*, pub. 1746-6.6.1, Allen-Bradley Company, Inc, Milwaukee, WI.

Allen-Bradley, 1996e. *Stepper Controller Module: User's Manual*, pub. 1746-999-121, Allen-Bradley Company, Inc., Milwaukee, WI.

Allen-Bradley, 1998a. *Analog Output Module: User Manual*, pub. 1771-6.5.30, Allen-Bradley Company, Inc, Milwaukee, WI.

Allen-Bradley, 1998b. *Discrete Input and Output Modules: Product Data*, pub. 1746-2.35, Allen-Bradley Company, Inc, Milwaukee, WI.

Allen-Bradley, 1998c. *SLC 500 TM RTD/Resistance Input Module: User Manual*, pub. 1746-6.7, Allen-Bradley Company, Inc, Milwaukee, WI.

Allen-Bradley, 1999a. *Analog Input Module: User Manual*, pub. 1771-6.5.115, Allen-Bradley Company, Inc, Milwaukee, WI.

Allen-Bradley, 1999b. *High Resolution Isolated Analog Modules: User Manual*, pub. 1771-6.5.127, Allen-Bradley Company, Inc, Milwaukee, WI.

GE Fanuc Automation, 1999. *Series 90TM-70 Programmable Controller: Data Sheet Manual,* pub. GFK-0600F, GE Fanuc Automation North America, Inc., Charlottesville, VA.

GE Fanuc Automation, 2000. *Series 90TM-30 PLC I/O Module Sepcifications,* pub. GFK-0898F, GE Fanuc Automation North America, Inc., Charlottesville, VA.

GE Fanuc Automation, 2003. *VersaMax® Modules, Power Supplies, Carriers: User Manual,* pub. GFK-1504K, GE Fanuc Automation North America, Inc., Charlottesville, VA.

Institute of Electrical and Electronic Engineers, 1982. *IEEE Guide for the Installation of Electrical Equipment to Minimize Electrical Noise Inputs to Controllers from External Sources,* (IEEE Std. 518-1982), IEEE, New York, NY.

Institute of Electrical and Electronic Engineers, 2001. *IEEE Recommended Practice for Protection and Coordination of Industrial and Commercial Power Systems – IEEE Buff BookTM*, (IEEE Std. 242-2001), IEEE, New York, NY.

International Electrotechnical Commission, 1995. *IEC 61491: Electrical Equipment of Industrial Machines – Serial Data Link for Real-time Communication Between Controls and Drives*, International Electrotechnical Commission, Geneva, Switzerland.

International Electrotechnical Commission, 2001. *IEC 60529: Classification of Degrees of Protection Provided by Enclosures (IP Code)*, International Electrotechnical Commission, Geneva, Switzerland.

Lawrence, Ken, 1998. "Successful Control Panel Design", *The Dynamic Engineer*, Dynamic Engineering, Inc.

Morrison, Ralph, 1986. *Grounding and Shielding Techniques in Instrumentation*, 3rd Ed., John Wiley & Sons, 1986.

National Fire Protection Association, 2000. *NFPA 70E – Standard for Electrical Safety Requirements for Employee Workplaces*, National Fire Protection Association, Quincy, MA.

National Fire Protection Association, 2002. *NFPA 79 – Electrical Standard for Industrial Machinery*, 2002 Edition, National Fire Protection Association, Quincy, MA.

NEMA, 1997. *Enclosures for Electrical Equipment (1000 Volts Maximum)*, pub. 250-1997, National Electrical Manufacturers Association, Rosslyn, VA.

Rockwell Automation, 1998a. *Industrial Automation Wiring and Grounding Guidelines*, pub. 1770-4.1, Rockwell Automation, Inc., Milwaukee, WI.

Rockwell Automation, 1998b. *Logix5550 Controller: User Manual*, pub. 1756-6.5.12, Rockwell Automation, Inc., Milwaukee, WI.

Rockwell Automation, 1998c. *ControlLogix Analog I/O Modules: User Manual*, pub. 1756-6.5.9, Rockwell Automation, Inc., Milwaukee, WI.

Rockwell Automation, 2000. *ControlLogix High Speed Counter Module: User Manual*, pub. 1756-UM007A-EN-P, Rockwell Automation, Inc., Milwaukee, WI.

Rockwell Automation, 2001a. *1394 SERCOS Interface Multi-Axis Motion Control System: Integration Manual*, pub. 1394-IN024A-EN-P, Rockwell Automation, Milwaukee, WI.

Rockwell Automation, 2001b. *8 Axis SERCOS Interface Module: Installation Instructions*, pub. 1756-IN572B-EN-P, Rockwell Automation, Inc., Milwaukee, WI.

Rockwell Automation, 2001c. *ControlLogix Configurable Flowmeter Module: User Manual*, pub. 1756-UM010A-EN-P, Rockwell Automation, Inc., Milwaukee, WI.

Rockwell Automation, 2001d. *ControlLogix Digital I/O Modules: User Manual*, pub. 1756-UM058C-EN-P, Rockwell Automation, Inc., Milwaukee, WI.

Rockwell Automation, 2001e. *System Design for Control of Electrical Noise*, pub. GMC-RM001A-EN-P, Rockwell Automation, Inc., Milwaukee, WI.

Schneider Automation, 1998. *Quantum SERCOS Multi-Axis Motion Controller User Guide*, pub. 890 USE 116 00, Schneider Automation, Inc., North Andover, MA.

Siemens, 1998. *S7-300 and M7-300 Programmable Controllers Module Specifications: Reference manual,* pub. EWA 4NEB 710 6067-02 01, Siemens AG, Nürnberg, Germany.

Siemens, 2000. *S7-400 and M7-400 Programmable Controllers Module Specifications: Reference manual,* July, 2000 edition, pub. A5E00069467-03, Siemens AG, Nürnberg, Germany.

PROBLEMS

P4-1. Specify an acceptable value and power rating of a pull-up resistor, R_{pu}, to be used to connect a sinking sensor device to a PLC sinking discrete input channel (Figure P4.1). The power supply is nominally 24 volts but can range between 23 and 25 volts, depending on the current draw. The minimum "on" state voltage of the discrete input channel is 10 volts, and the equivalent input resistance is 2200 ohms. The maximum device sink current is 50 mA, and the minimum device output voltage is 2.0 volts.

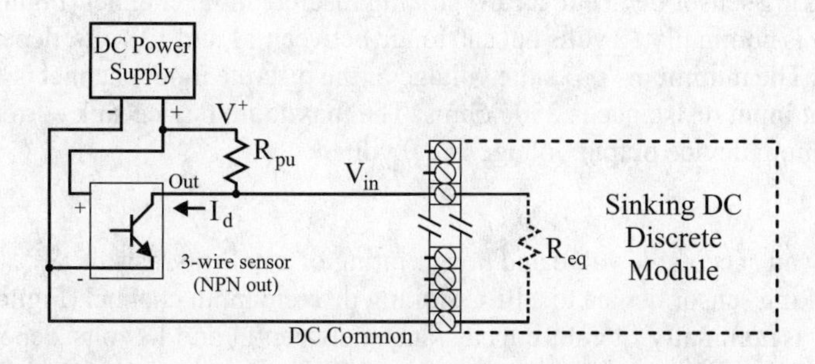

Figure P4.1. Sinking sensor connected to sinking DC discrete input channel.

P4-2. Specify an acceptable value and power rating of a pull-up resistor, R_{pu}, to be used to connect a sinking sensor device to a PLC sinking discrete input channel (Figure P4.1). The power supply is nominally 24 volts but can range between 22 and 25 volts, depending on the current draw. The minimum "on" state voltage of the discrete input channel is 20 volts, and the equivalent input resistance is 10,000 ohms. The maximum device sink current is 50 mA, and the minimum device output voltage is 0.7 volts.

P4-3. Specify an acceptable value and power rating of a pull-up resistor, R_{pu}, to be used to connect a sinking sensor device to a PLC sinking discrete input channel (Figure P4.1). The power supply is nominally 24 volts but can range between 23 and 25 volts, depending on the current draw. The minimum "on" state voltage of the discrete input channel is 10 volts, and the equivalent input resistance is 1000 ohms. The maximum device sink current is 100 mA, and the minimum device output voltage is 2.0 volts.

P4-4. Specify an acceptable value and power rating of a pull-up resistor, R_{pu}, to be used to connect a sinking sensor device to a PLC sinking discrete input channel (Figure P4.1). The power supply is nominally 24 volts but can range between 23 and 25 volts, depending on the current draw. The minimum "on" state voltage of the discrete input channel is 13 volts, and the equivalent input resistance is 2200 ohms. The maximum device sink current is 200 mA, and the minimum device output voltage is 2.0 volts.

P4-5. Specify an acceptable value and power rating of a pull-up resistor, R_{pu}, to be used to connect a sinking sensor device to a PLC sinking discrete input channel (Figure P4.1). The power supply is nominally 24 volts but can range between 23 and 25 volts, depending on the current draw. The minimum "on" state voltage of the discrete input channel is 20 volts, and the equivalent input resistance is 10,000 ohms. The maximum device sink current is 10 mA, and the minimum device output voltage is 2.0 volts.

P4-6. Specify an acceptable value and power rating of a pull-up resistor, R_{pu}, to be used to connect a sinking sensor device to a PLC sinking discrete input channel (Figure P4.1). The power supply is nominally 12 volts but can range between 11 and 13 volts, depending on the current draw. The minimum "on" state voltage of the discrete input channel is 10 volts, and the equivalent input resistance is 2500 ohms. The maximum device sink current is 50 mA, and the minimum device output voltage is 2.0 volts.

P4-7. Specify an acceptable value and power rating of a pull-up resistor, R_{pu}, to be used to connect a sinking sensor device to a PLC sinking discrete input channel (Figure P4.1). The power supply is nominally 12 volts but can range between 11 and 13 volts, depending on the current draw. The minimum "on" state voltage of the discrete input channel is 10 volts, and the equivalent input resistance is 2200 ohms. The maximum device sink current is 50 mA, and the minimum device output voltage is 2.0 volts.

P4-8. Specify an acceptable value and power rating of a pull-up resistor, , to be used to connect a sinking sensor device to a PLC sinking discrete input channel (Figure P4.1). The power supply is nominally 12 volts but can range between 11 and 13 volts, depending on the current draw. The minimum "on" state voltage of the discrete input channel is 10 volts, and the equivalent input resistance is 2200 ohms. The maximum device sink current is 100 mA, and the minimum device output voltage is 2.0 volts.

5 Timers and Counters

Chapter Topics:

- PLC timers
- PLC counters
- Timing and counting applications

OBJECTIVES

Upon completion of this chapter, you will be able to:

- Describe the function of the timers and counters of the PLCs covered by this text
- Describe the major types of industrial timing and counting applications
- Apply PLC timers and counters to industrial situations

Scenario: Conversion of a Modicon 884 PLC to a 984 PLC on a freeze-drier control.

You are called in to help out on a project to convert a freeze drier control from a Modicon 884 PLC to a 984 PLC. Beyond the replacement of the processor, there are no significant hardware changes. All of the I/O modules and their wiring remain intact. The software is a different story. The 884 PLC program cannot be simply copied to the 984. The freeze drier control used many of the 884 sequencer instructions and the 984 does not have the equivalent to the 884 sequencer instruction and the freeze drier control uses many of these sequencers. The Modicon distributor has an 884-to-984 conversion program and did the initial conversion. Another engineer in the consulting firm for which you work has been working on debugging the converted program. He has been working on it for three days and thinks he has found all the problems. Unfortunately, he has been called to work on a more urgent project and you have been assigned to monitor the system while they start it up and do any further debugging. He explains how each 884 counter-based sequencer has been converted to a counter-based index into a bit array, preserving the functionality. He also reviews the changes he has made to the program. The conversion was only supposed to take a week and the week is finished. The biological research firm needs the freeze drier working because it is starting to impact their research schedule. The freeze drier starts up as usual and goes through the operation steps normally. After about two hours, the operator informs you that the operation appears to be "stuck" in one step and not advancing to the next one. You find the particular counter that controls this sequence (for example, Figure 5.1*a*) and one of the parallel contacts connected to the counter input (top UCTR connection) is closed,

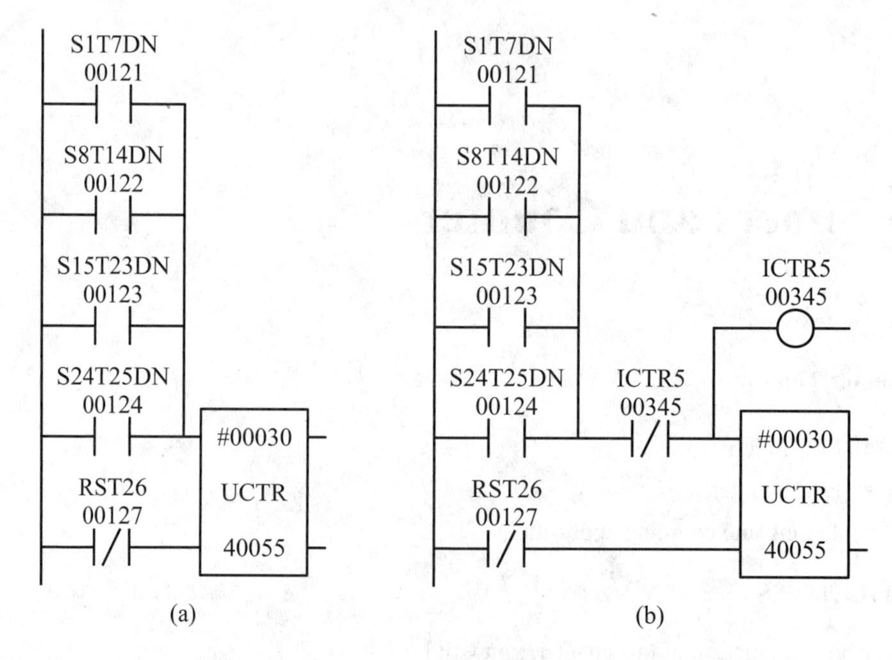

Figure 5.1. Counter scenario: *(a)* 884 code; *(b)* correct 984 code.

indicating that the counter should increment to the next step. Why did the counter not increment?

Solution: Thinking that the behavior was a chance event, you manually change the counter accumulator and the operation continues, as it should. However, about three hours later, the same thing happens. This time, it is not the same counter as before, but the symptoms are the same. One of the parallel conditions to advance the counter is **on**, indicating that the counter should increment its accumulator, yet that is not happening. You manually change this counter accumulator and now know it is not a fluke. You dig through the program operation manuals, but find no clues. You strongly suspect the problem lies with the counter. On a hunch, you locate a document describing the 884 ladder logic instructions and compare the description of its UCTR with that of the 984 UCTR instruction. Aha! The 884 UCTR instruction is level-sensitive, that is, the counter increments if its input is **on**. The 984 UCTR is edge-sensitive, that is, the counter increments if its input changes from **off** to **on**. If the counter input does not turn **off** between steps then the counter does not increment. Upon further investigation, you find that on the two times where you found a "stuck" counter, the previous step had zero duration. The conditions to transition out of the step were already satisfied when the step was initiated. Therefore, the counter input condition did not change from one program scan to the next. The 884 UCTR would increment under this condition. The 984 UCTR would not. The fix is to simply force the counter input condition off whenever the counter input condition turns on. The change is shown in Figure 5.1*b*. The addition of the NC contact and coil forces the counter input to be **off** during the next scan after the counter input turns **on**. When you change all of the sequencer counters, the freeze drier runs as it should and in fact, that is the last problem with the program and you spend the next day just sitting while the process runs.

5.1 INTRODUCTION

After coils and contacts, timers and counters are the next most commonly used ladder logic instruction. This chapter describes the timer and counter function blocks for the PLCs covered by this text. As for Chapter 3, the timer and counter function blocks for a particular PLC are described in separate sections. That is, only the section(s) pertaining to the PLC(s) of interest need to be studied. Following these timer and counter descriptions, common timer and counter situations are described and illustrated with industrial examples.

There are two basic types of timers: on-delay and off-delay. The off-delay timer is often confusing to PLC programmers. The on-delay timer basically delays the turn-on of a discrete signal and the off-delay timer basically delays the turn-off of a discrete signal. This difference is illustrated in Figure 5.2. The PROX_1 discrete input is the input to an on-delay timer and an off-delay timer. The output of the on-delay timer delays the off-to-on transition of PROX_1, but does not delay the on-to-off transition. The output of the off-delay timer delays the on-to-off transition of PROX_1, but does not delay the off-to-on transition. Which type is appropriate? It depends on the application. For example, if an action needs to be initiated *x* seconds after PROX_1 turns on, then an on-delay timer is appropriate. If an action needs to be stopped *x* seconds after PROX_1 turns off, then an off-delay timer is appropriate.

There are three basic types of counters: up-counter, down-counter, and up/down counter. The three types are largely self-explanatory and their operation is explained in the following sections.

5.2 IEC TIMERS AND COUNTERS

The IEC 61131-3 timers and counters are function block instructions. The standard defines three timer function blocks and three counter function blocks. As described in the standard, the operation of each of these function blocks is identical to a Modicon function block of the same name. The names and description of these function blocks are:

IEC Function Block	Description
TON	On-delay timer
TOF	Off-delay timer
TP	Pulse timer
CTU	Up counter
CTD	Down counter
CTUD	Up/down counter

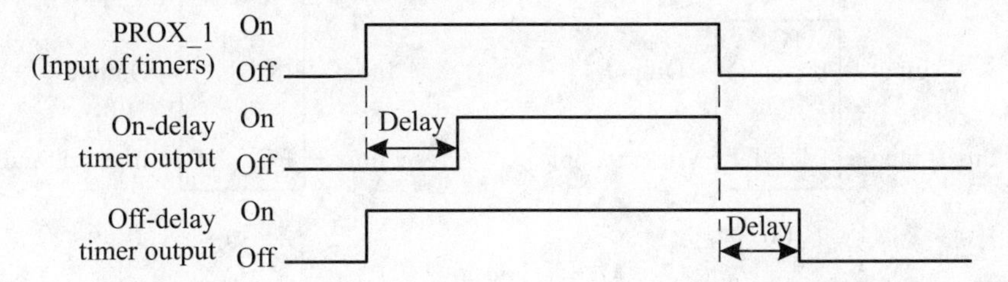

Figure 5.2. Comparison of on-delay and off-delay timers.

The next section details the operation and use of these function blocks.

5.3 MODICON TIMERS AND COUNTERS

The Modicon Concept programming software for the Quantum and Momentum processors defines three basic timer function blocks and three basic counter function blocks. The names and description of these function blocks are as follows:

Modicon Function Block	Description
TON	On-delay timer
TOF	Off-delay timer
TP	Pulse timer
CTU	Up counter
CTD	Down counter
CTUD	Up/down counter

In addition, the three counter function block names can be suffixed with an integer data type, an extension of the IEC 61131-3 standard. The operation of each of these function blocks is described and illustrated. The section is concluded with an implementation of the retentive timer function which is not a standard function block.

5.3.1 TON On-Delay Timer

The TON on-delay timer is shown in Figure 5.3. There are two versions of this function block: without the EN/ENO connections (Figure 5.3*a*) and with the EN/ENO connections (Figure 5.3*b*). If the EN/ENO are configured for the block, the EN input must be **on** for the block to execute. The ENO output echoes the EN input and is **on** if EN is **on** and the block executes without error. If the EN/ENO connections are not configured, the block executes every scan.

The TON timer basically delays the turn-on of a signal and does not delay the turn-off. When the IN input turns **on**, the internal time (ET) increases. When ET equals the preset time (PT), the timer is "timed out" and the Q output turns **on**. If IN turns **off** during the timing interval, Q remains **off**, ET is set to zero, and timing recommences when the IN turns **on**. The ET output can be connected to a variable (of type TIME) in order to monitor the internal time. The instance name of the timer appears above the block.

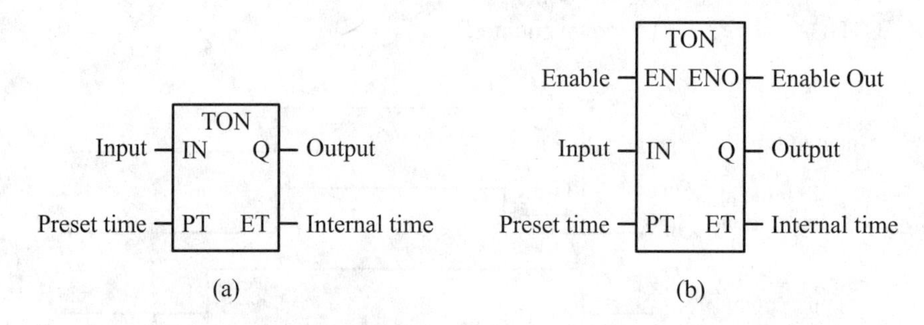

Figure 5.3. Modicon TON timer: *(a)* without EN/ENO; *(b)* with EN/ENO.

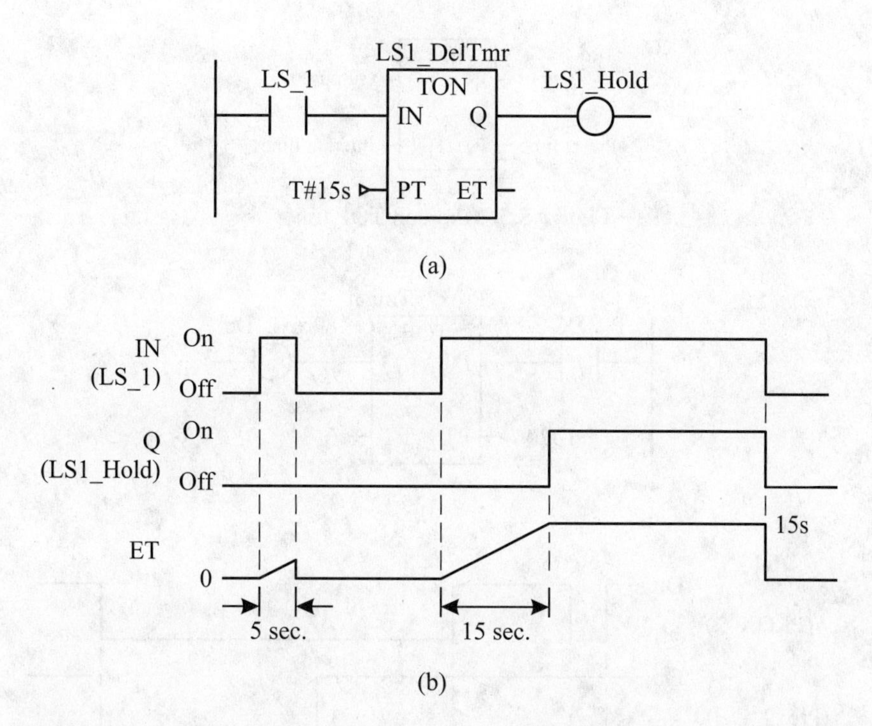

Figure 5.4. Example Modicon TON timer: *(a)* ladder logic; *(b)* timing diagram.

Preset time can be a variable, or a literal of type TIME:

t#2d4h45m12s450ms

The prefix must be TIME#, T#, time#, or t#. The time is specified in days (D), hours (H), minutes (M), seconds (S), and milliseconds (MS). The accuracy is 1 millisecond.

An example application of the TON instruction is shown in Figure 5.4*a* and its associated timing diagram is shown in Figure 5.4*b*. The LS_1 discrete input must remain **on** for at least 15 seconds before the LS1_Hold coil is turned **on**. When LS_1 is turned **off** after 5 seconds, ET is set to zero time and the LS1_Hold coil remains **off**.

The Modicon TON function block is nearly identical to the S7 TON function block and similar to the Allen-Bradley TON function block and the GE Fanuc TMR function block.

5.3.2 TOF Off-Delay Timer

The TOF off-delay timer is shown in Figure 5.5. As with the TON function block, the EN/ENO connections are optionally configured. In Figure 5.5, they are not configured.

Looking at the IN and Q connections, the TOF timer operates exactly opposite of the TON timer. The TOF timer basically delays the turn-off of a signal and does not delay the turn-on. When the IN input turns **off**, the internal time (ET) increases. When ET equals the preset time (PT), the timer is "timed out" and the Q output turns **off**. If IN turns **on** during the timing interval, Q remains **on**, ET is set to zero, and timing recommences when the IN turns **off**. The preset time is specified in the same manner as for TON. The ET output can be connected to a variable (of type TIME) in order to monitor the internal time.

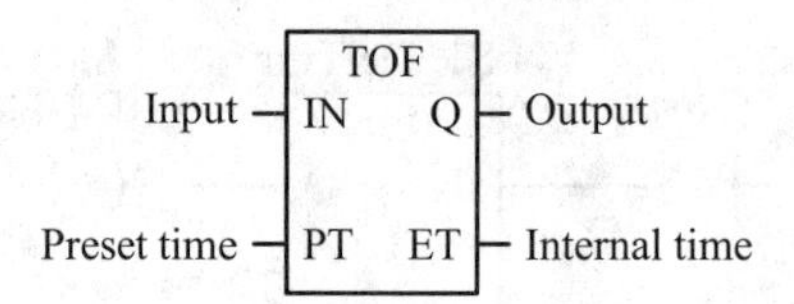

Figure 5.5. Modicon TOF timer.

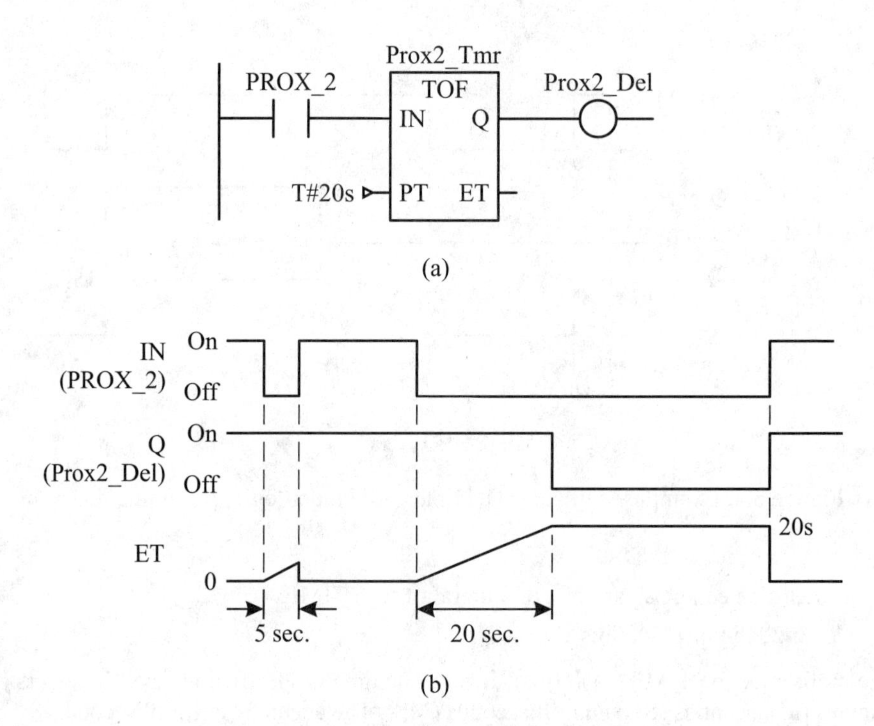

Figure 5.6. Example Modicon TOF timer: *(a)* ladder logic; *(b)* timing diagram.

An example application of the TOF instruction is shown in Figure 5.6*a* and its associated timing diagram is shown in Figure 5.6*b*. The PROX_2 discrete input must remain **off** for at least 20 seconds before the Prox2_Del coil is turned **off**. When PROX_2 is turned **on** after 5 seconds, ET is set to zero time and the Prox2_Del coil remains **on**.

The Modicon TOF function block is nearly identical to the S7 TOF function block and similar to the Allen-Bradley TOF function block and the GE Fanuc OFDT function block.

5.3.3 TP Pulse Timer

The TP pulse timer function block is shown in Figure 5.7. As with the other timer function blocks, the EN/ENO connections are optionally configured.

The TP timer generates a pulse at the Q output with duration of the preset time (PT) when the IN input transitions from **off** to **on**. When IN changes from **off** to **on**, Q is turned **on** and ET starts increasing. When ET equals PT, Q turns **off**. The internal time is set to zero only if ET equals PT and IN is **off**. While the ET is increasing toward PT, any transitions on IN are ignored. The preset time is specified in the same manner as for TON or TOF.

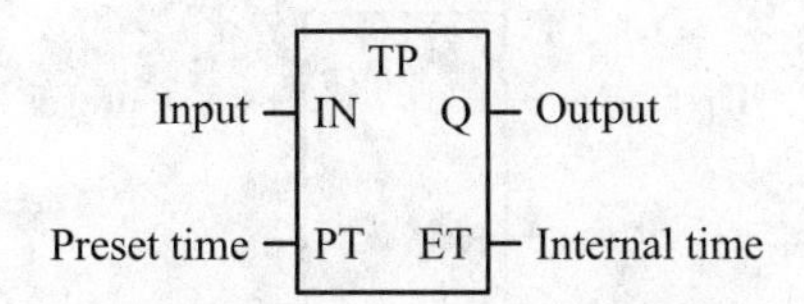

Figure 5.7. Modicon TP timer.

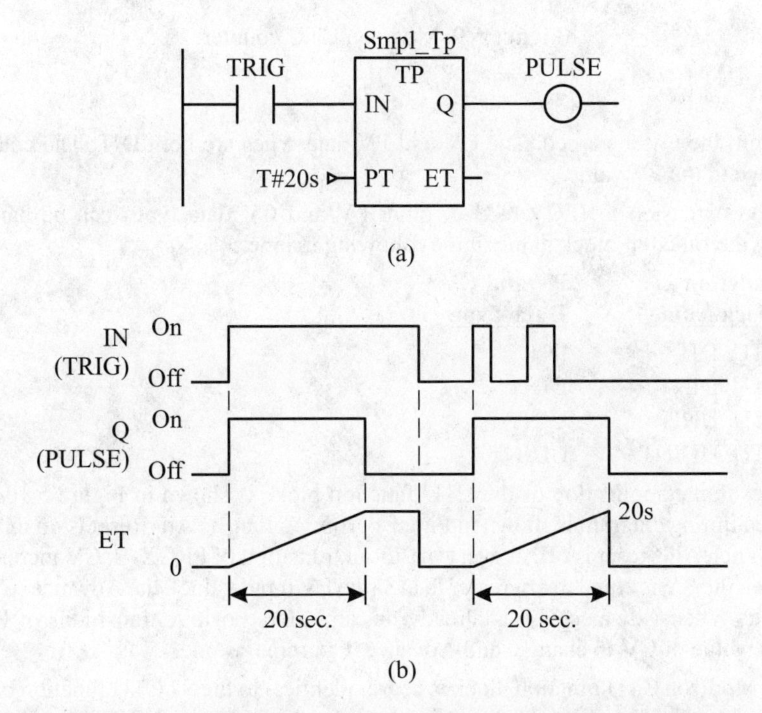

Figure 5.8. Example Modicon TP timer: *(a)* ladder logic; *(b)* timing diagram.

An example application of the TP instruction is shown in Figure 5.8*a* and its associated timing diagram is shown in Figure 5.8*b*. When the ET is zero, an **off** to **on** transition of TRIG causes the PULSE output to be turned **on** for 20 seconds. Keeping TRIG on longer than 20 seconds does not alter the duration of PULSE, it only prevents ET from being set to zero at the end of the 20-second duration. Changes in TRIG during the 20-second pulse duration are ignored.

The Modicon TP function block is nearly identical to the S7 TP function block. There is no equivalent for the Allen-Bradley and GE Fanuc PLCs.

5.3.4 CTU Up Counter

The CTU up counter function block is shown in Figure 5.9. As with the timer function blocks, the EN/ENO connections are optionally configured (not shown in Figure 5.9).

The counter accumulator (CV) increments by one for every **off**-to-**on** transition of the count up (CU) input. When the CV ≥ PV, then the Q output is turned **on**. When the reset (R)

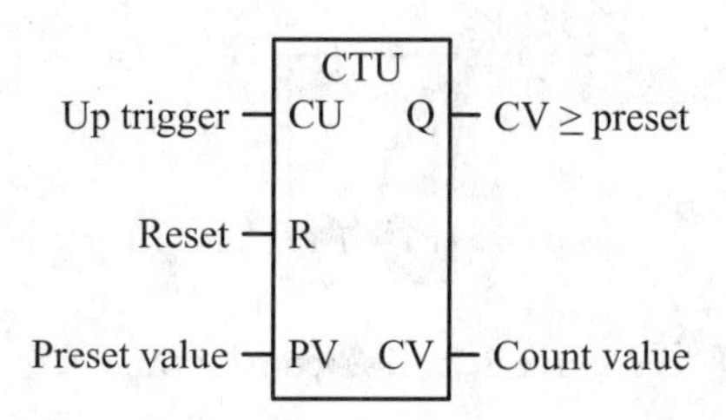

Figure 5.9. Modicon CTU counter.

input is **on**, the CV is zeroed. The CV and PV data types are both INT. The counter can count beyond the PV value.

As an extension to IEC 61131-3, other PV and CV data types can be handled by suffixing the function block name in the following manner:

Function Block Name	PV and CV Data Type
CTU_INT	INT
CTU_DINT	DINT
CTU_UNIT	UINT
CTU_UDINT	UDINT

An example application of the CTU function block is shown in Figure 5.10*a* and its associated timing diagram is shown in Figure 5.10*b*. As long as All_Reset is **on**, CV is held at zero. When All_Reset is **off**, at every **off**-to-**on** transition of PROX_2, CV increments by one. When the CV is equal to or greater than 3 (the PV input value), the Advance_Cyl coil is turned **on**. When Advance_Cyl is already **on**, any more positive transitions of PROX_2 cause the value of CV to change, and Advance_Cyl remains **on**.

The Modicon CTU function block is nearly identical to the S7 CTU function block and similar to the Allen-Bradley CTU function block and the GE Fanuc UPCTR function block.

5.3.5 CTD Down Counter

The CTD up counter function block is shown in Figure 5.11. The counter accumulator (CV) decrements by one for every **off**-to-**on** transition of the count down (CD) input. When the CV ≤ 0, then the Q output is turned **on**. When the load (LD) input is **on**, the CV is set to the PV value. The CV and PV data types are both INT. The counter can count below zero.

As an extension to IEC 61131-3, other PV and CV data types can be handled by suffixing the function block name in the same manner as for the CTU function block.

An example application of the CTD function block is shown in Figure 5.12*a* and its associated timing diagram is shown in Figure 5.12*b*. When Prox3_CtLd is **on**, the CV is loaded with the PV (4). When Prox3_CtLd is **off**, at every **off**-to-**on** transition of PROX_3, PV decrements by one. When the CV is equal to or less than 0, the Prox3_Zero coil is turned **on**. When Prox3_Zero is already **on**, any more positive transitions of PROX_3 cause the value of CV to change, and Prox3_Zero remains **on**.

The Modicon CTD function block is nearly identical to the S7 CTD function block and similar to the Allen-Bradley CTD function block and the GE Fanuc DNCTR function block.

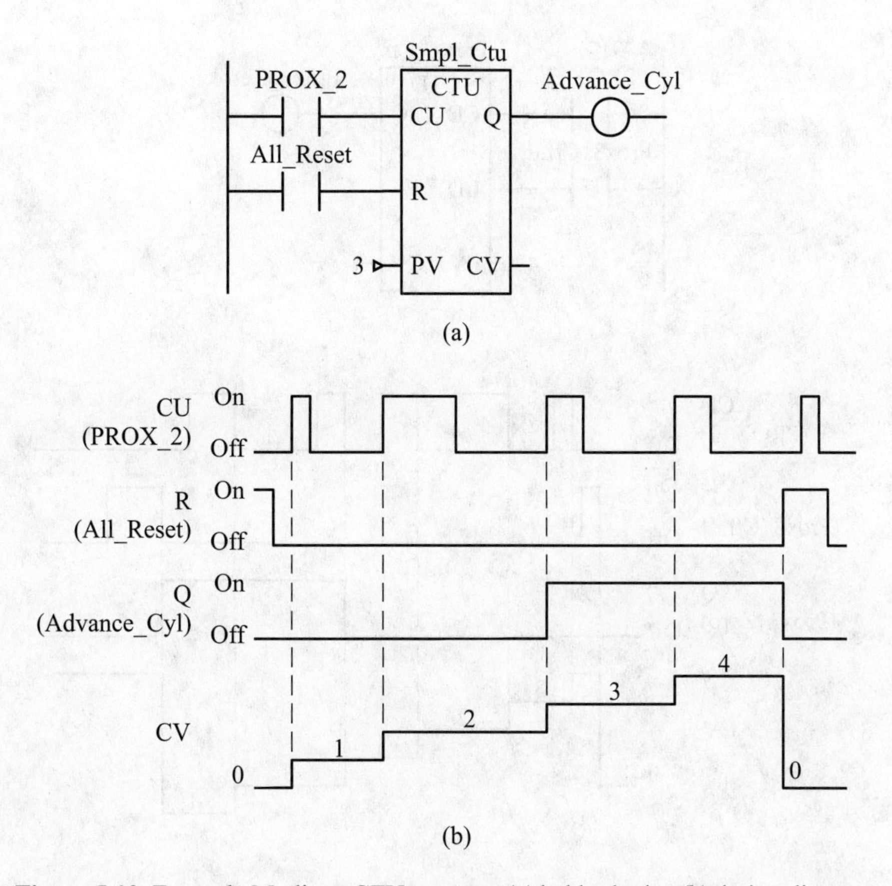

Figure 5.10. Example Modicon CTU counter: *(a)* ladder logic; *(b)* timing diagram.

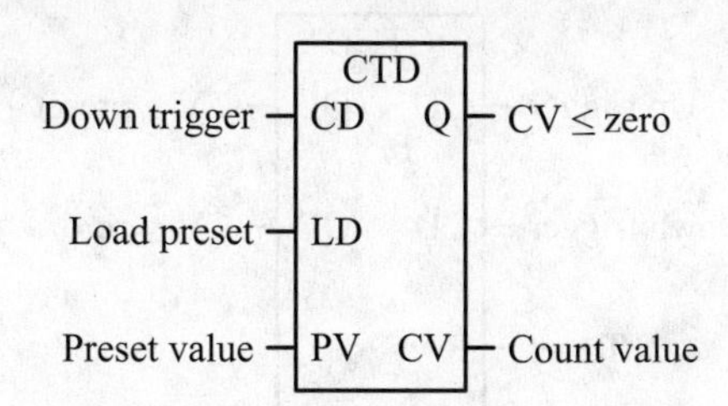

Figure 5.11. Modicon CTD counter.

5.3.6 CTUD Up/Down Counter

The CTUD up/down counter function block is shown in Figure 5.13. It is basically a combination of the CTU and CTD function blocks. The counter accumulator (CV) increments by one for every **off**-to-**on** transition of the count up (CU) input. The counter accumulator (CV) decrements by one for every **off**-to-**on** transition of the count down (CD) input. When the CV ≥ PV, then the QU output is turned **on**. When the CV ≤ 0, then the QD output is turned **on**. When the reset (R) input is **on**, the CV is zeroed. When the load (LD)

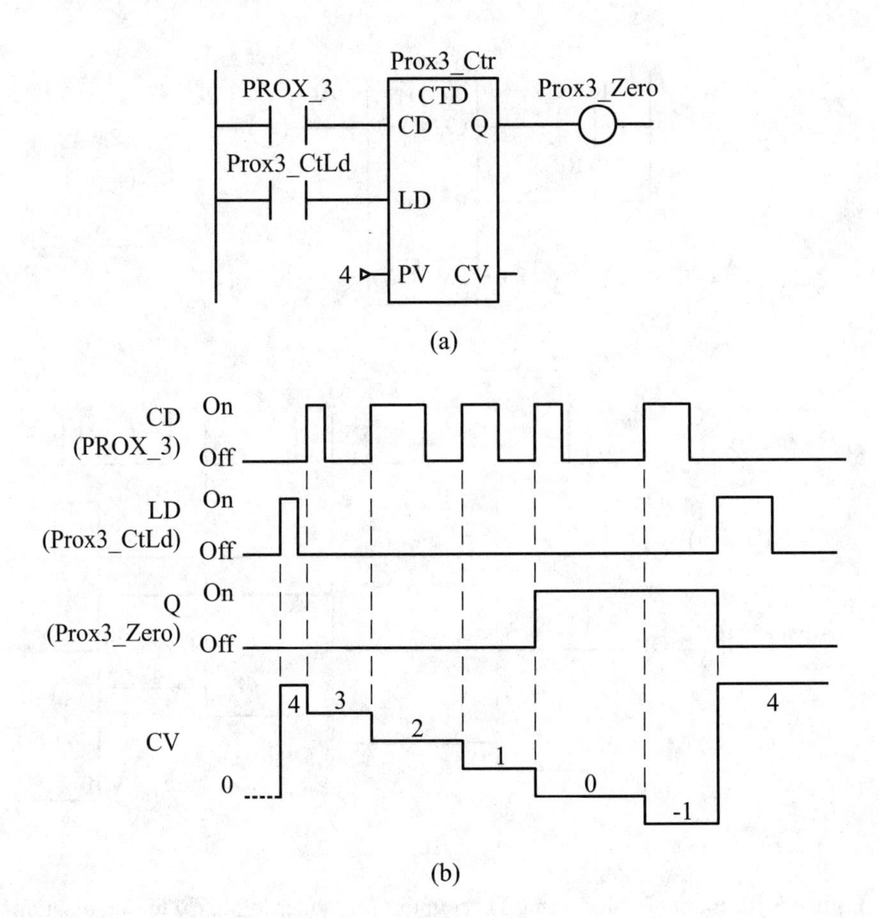

Figure 5.12. Example Modicon CTD counter: *(a)* ladder logic; *(b)* timing diagram.

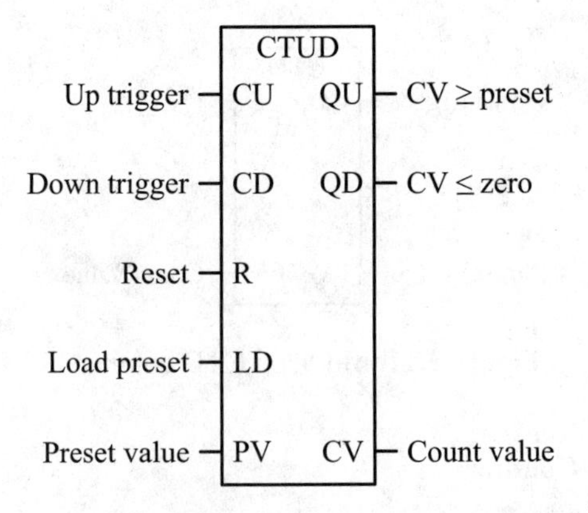

Figure 5.13. Modicon CTUD counter.

input is **on**, the CV is set to the PV value. If both R and LD are on simultaneously, the R input has precedence and sets the CV to zero. The CV and PV data types are both INT. The counter can count above the preset value and below zero. As an extension to IEC 61131-3, other PV and CV data types can be handled by suffixing the function block name in the same manner as for the CTU function block.

An example application of the CTUD function block is shown in Figure 5.14*a* and its associated timing diagram is shown in Figure 5.14*b*. When both All_Reset and Boxes_Ld are **off**, at every **off**-to-**on** transition of Box_In, PV increments by one. When both All_Reset and Boxes_Ld are **off**, at every **off**-to-**on** transition of Box_Out, PV decrements

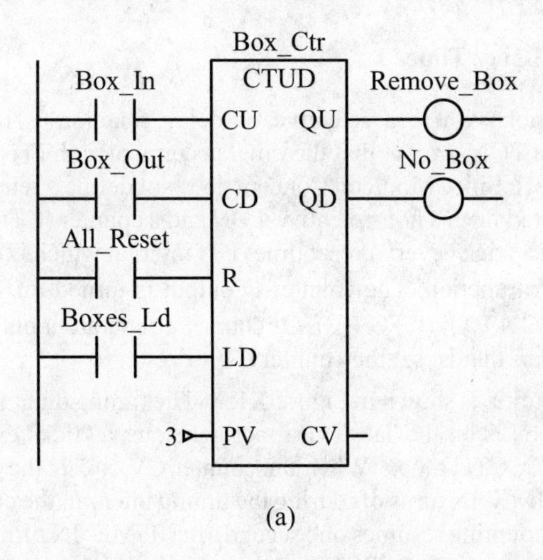

(a)

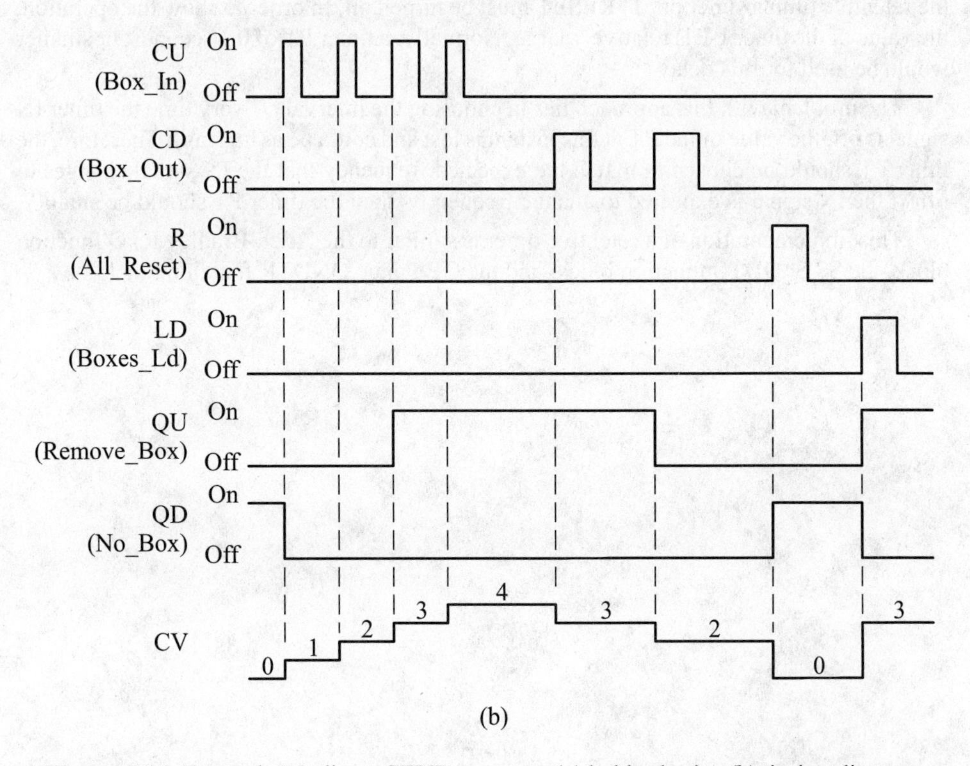

(b)

Figure 5.14. Example Modicon CTUD counter: *(a)* ladder logic; *(b)* timing diagram.

by one. When the CV is equal to or greater than 3 (the PV input value), the Remove_Box coil is turned **on**. When the CV is equal to or less than 0, the No_Box coil is turned **on**. When All_Reset is **on**, CV is loaded with zero. When Boxes_Ld is **on**, the CV is loaded with the PV (3).

The Modicon CTUD function block is nearly identical to the S7 CTUD function block and similar to the combination of the Allen-Bradley CTU and CTD function blocks. It is also similar to the combination of the GE Fanuc UPCTR and DNCTR blocks..

5.3.7 Retentive On-Delay Timer

There are situations where a retentive on-delay function is required. A retentive on-delay works like a TON, except that the timer accumulator (ET) is not set to zero every time the IN signal is **off**. Since Modicon Concept does not define a retentive on-delay timer, one must be constructed from a non-retentive TON and a counter (CTU). The non-retentive TON timer generates a "tick" every preset time (PT) interval which is counted. The counter provides the retentive function. The counter Q output is turned **on** when CV ≥ PV. The delay time is then (TON PT)×(CTU PV). Of course, a separate input must be provided in order to reset the timer, that is, set the counter CV to zero.

One possible solution is shown in Figure 5.15*a*. The timing diagram is shown in Figure 5.15*b*. When TIME_IN is **on** the Tic_Tmr timer generates a "tick" every second which is counted by the Tic_Ctr CTU block. When the counter CV equals the PV (3) the TOT_DN coil is turned **on**. If TIME_IN turns **off** during the timing interval, the counter CV remains at its current value and counting resumes one second after TIME_IN turns **on**. In order to reset the retentive timing function, T_RESET must be turned **on**. In order to show the operation, the value of the timer PT is relatively large. Normally, a timer PT of 0.1 seconds, or smaller would be used for this delay.

The problem with this approach lies in choosing the interval t. Every time the timer IN signal is **off**, the value of the ET at this instant is lost and could be as high as t. Therefore, the timer PT should be chosen to match the expected frequency that the IN signal changes to **off**. If the IN signal is expected to change frequently, then the timer PT should be small.

This implementation of a retentive timer is similar to the Allen-Bradley RTO function block, the S7 S_ODTS function block, and the GE Fanuc ONDTR function block.

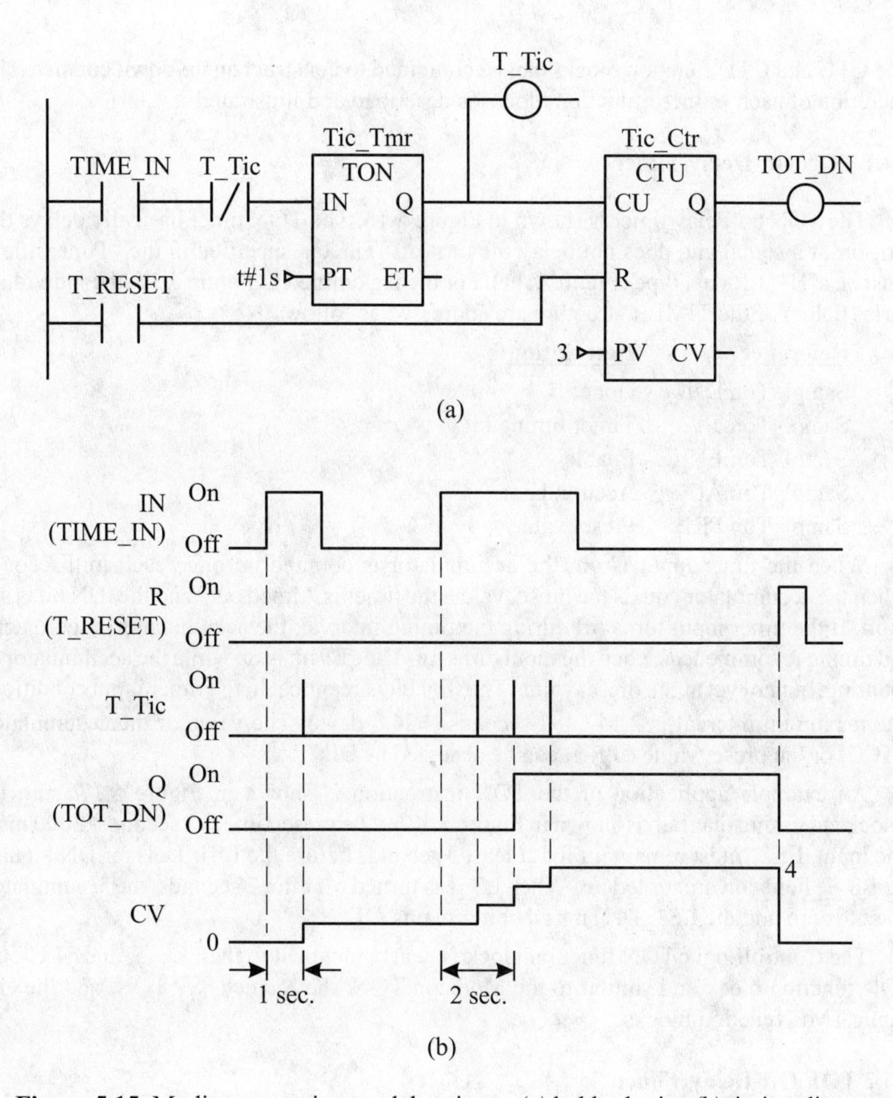

Figure 5.15. Modicon retentive on-delay timer: *(a)* ladder logic; *(b)* timing diagram.

5.4 A-B CONTROLLOGIX TIMERS AND COUNTERS

The Allen-Bradley ControlLogix processor has three timer function blocks and two counter function blocks. The names and description of these function blocks are as follows:

ControlLogix Function Block	**Description**
TON	On-delay timer
TOF	Off-delay timer
RTO	Retentive on-delay timer
CTU	Up counter
CTD	Down counter

The CTU and CTD function blocks can be combined to construct an up/down counter. The operation of each of these function blocks is described and illustrated.

5.4.1 TON On-Delay Timer

The TON on-delay timer is shown in Figure 5.16. The TON timer basically delays the turn-on of a signal and does not delay the turn-off. The tag specified in the "Timer" field must be a TIMER data type (Figure 3.11). For the tag defined in Figure 5.16, the individual parts (fields) of the TIMER structure are addressed as follows:

Reference	Description
Sampl_Ton.DN	Done
Sampl_Ton.TT	Timer timing bit
Sampl_Ton.EN	Enable
Sampl_Ton.ACC	Accumulator
Sampl_Ton.PRE	Preset value

When the timer input is **on**, the accumulator is counted up once each millisecond. When the accumulator equals the preset value, the timer is "timed out" and the .DN bit is set to **on**. If the timer input turns **off** during the timing interval, the accumulator is set to zero and timing recommences when the input turns **on**. The .TT bit is on while the accumulator is counting, but not yet at the preset value. The .EN bit is identical to the timer input condition. The maximum interval is 2,147,483 seconds (≈24.8 days). The value of the accumulator (.ACC) or the preset value (.PRE) can be accessed as DINT.

An example application of the TON instruction is shown in Figure 5.17*a* and its associated timing diagram is shown in Figure 5.17*b*. The preset time is 3 seconds (3000 ms). The input, LS_1 must remain **on** for at least 3 seconds before the LS1_DelTmr.DN bit and the LS_1_hold coil are turned **on**. When LS_1 is turned **off** after 2 seconds, the accumulator is set to zero and the LS1_DelTmr.DN bit remains **off**.

The ControlLogix TON function block is nearly identical to the PLC-5, and SLC-500 TON function block and similar to the Modicon TON, the Siemens S7 TON, and the GE Fanuc TMR function blocks.

5.4.2 TOF Off-Delay Timer

The TOF off-delay timer is shown in Figure 5.18. Looking at the timer input and the .DN bit, the TOF timer operates exactly opposite of the TON timer. The TOF timer basically delays the turn-off of a signal and does not delay the turn-on. The descriptions of the function block fields and the tag references are the same as for the TON function block.

When the timer input is **off**, the accumulator is counted up once each millisecond. When the accumulator equals the preset value, the timer is "timed out" and the .DN bit is

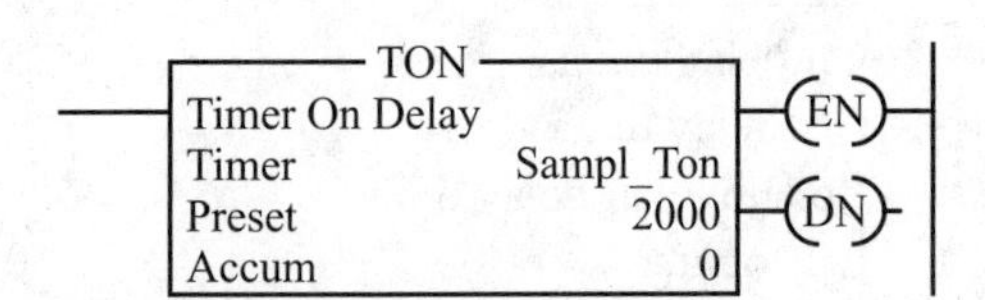

Figure 5.16. ControlLogix TON timer.

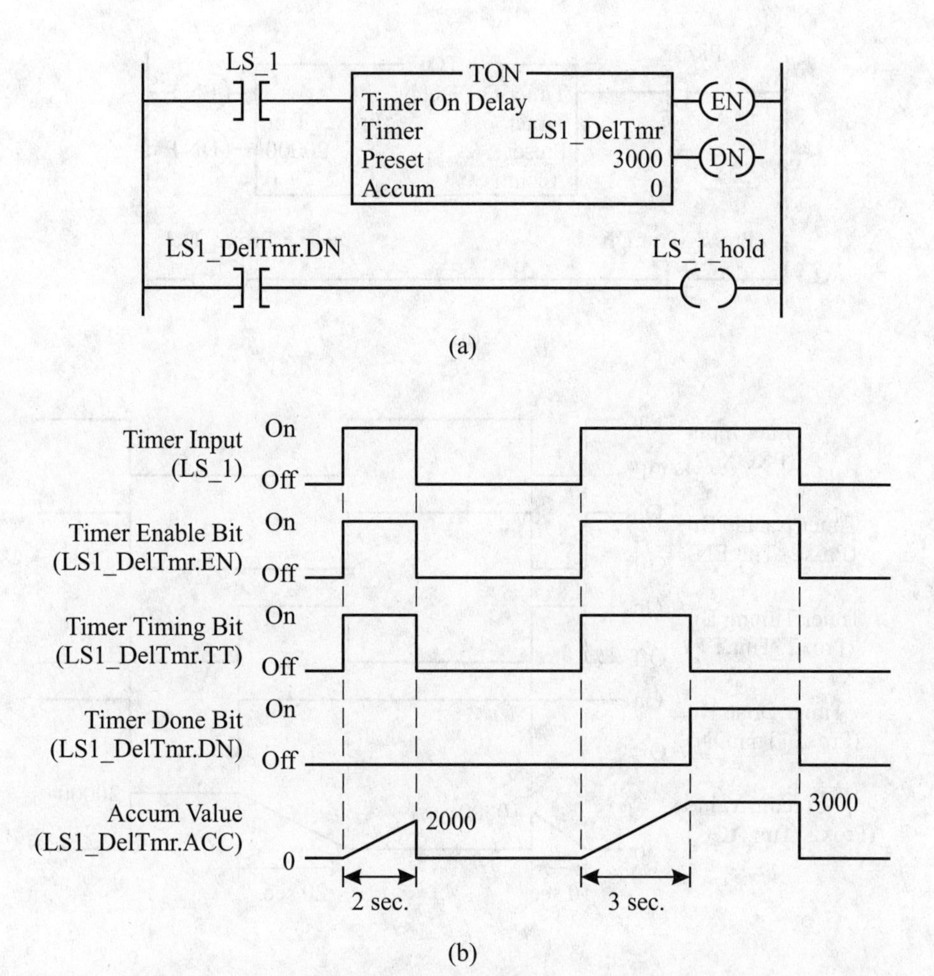

Figure 5.17. Example ControlLogix TON timer: *(a)* ladder logic; *(b)* timing diagram.

turned **off**. If the timer input turns **on** anytime, the accumulator is set to zero and timing recommences when the input turns **off**. The operation of the .EN and .TT bits is the same as for the TON timer instruction.

An example application of the TOF instruction is shown in Figure 5.19*a* and its associated timing diagram is shown in Figure 5.19*b*. The preset time is 20 seconds (20,000 ms). The input, PROX_2 must remain **off** for at least 20 seconds before the Prox2_Tmr.DN

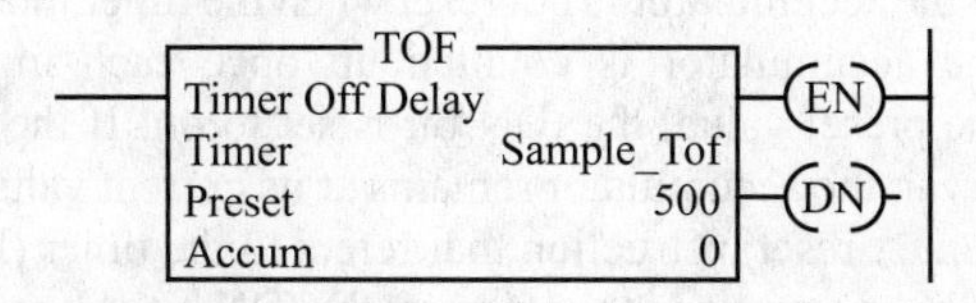

Figure 5.18. ControlLogix TOF timer.

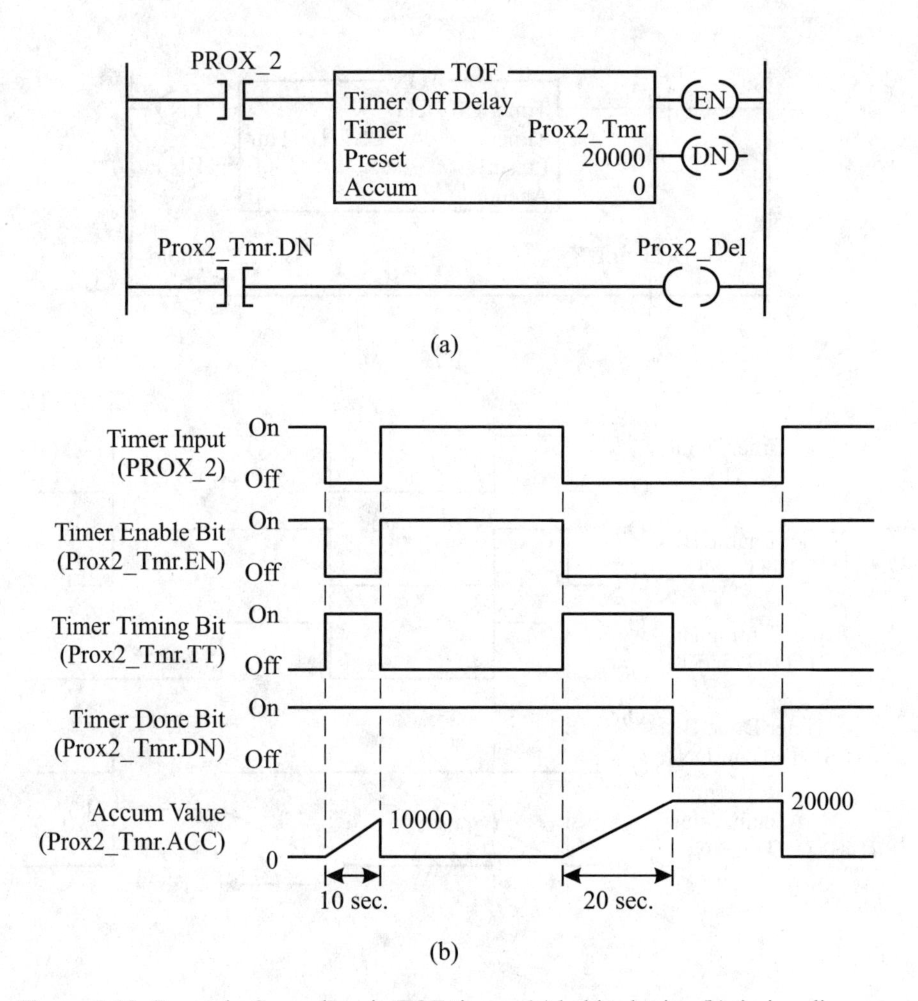

Figure 5.19. Example ControlLogix TOF timer: *(a)* ladder logic; *(b)* timing diagram.

bit and the Prox2_Del coil are turned **off**. When PROX_2 is turned **on** after 10 seconds, the accumulator is set to zero and the Prox2_Tmr.DN bit remains **on**.

The ControlLogix TOF function block is nearly identical to the PLC-5, and SLC-500 TOF function block and similar to the Modicon TOF, the Siemens S7 TOF, and GE Fanuc OFDT function blocks.

5.4.3 RTO Retentive On-Delay Timer

The RTO retentive on-delay timer is shown in Figure 5.20*a*. The RTO timer is like the TON timer except that the accumulator is not reset when the timer input turns **off**. When the timer input is **on**, the accumulator is counted up once each millisecond. When the accumulator equals the preset value, the .DN bit is set to **on**. If the timer input turns **off** during the timing interval, the accumulator remains at its current value and timing resumes when the input turns **on**. A reset instruction that refers to the timer (Figure 5.20*b*) may be used to set the accumulator to zero and thus turn **off** the .DN bit. Alternatively, one can use a

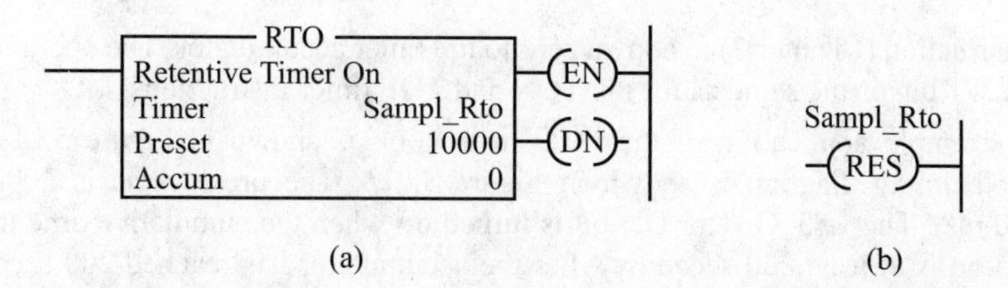

Figure 5.20. ControlLogix RTO timer: *(a)* RTO instruction; *(b)* RES coil to reset RTO.

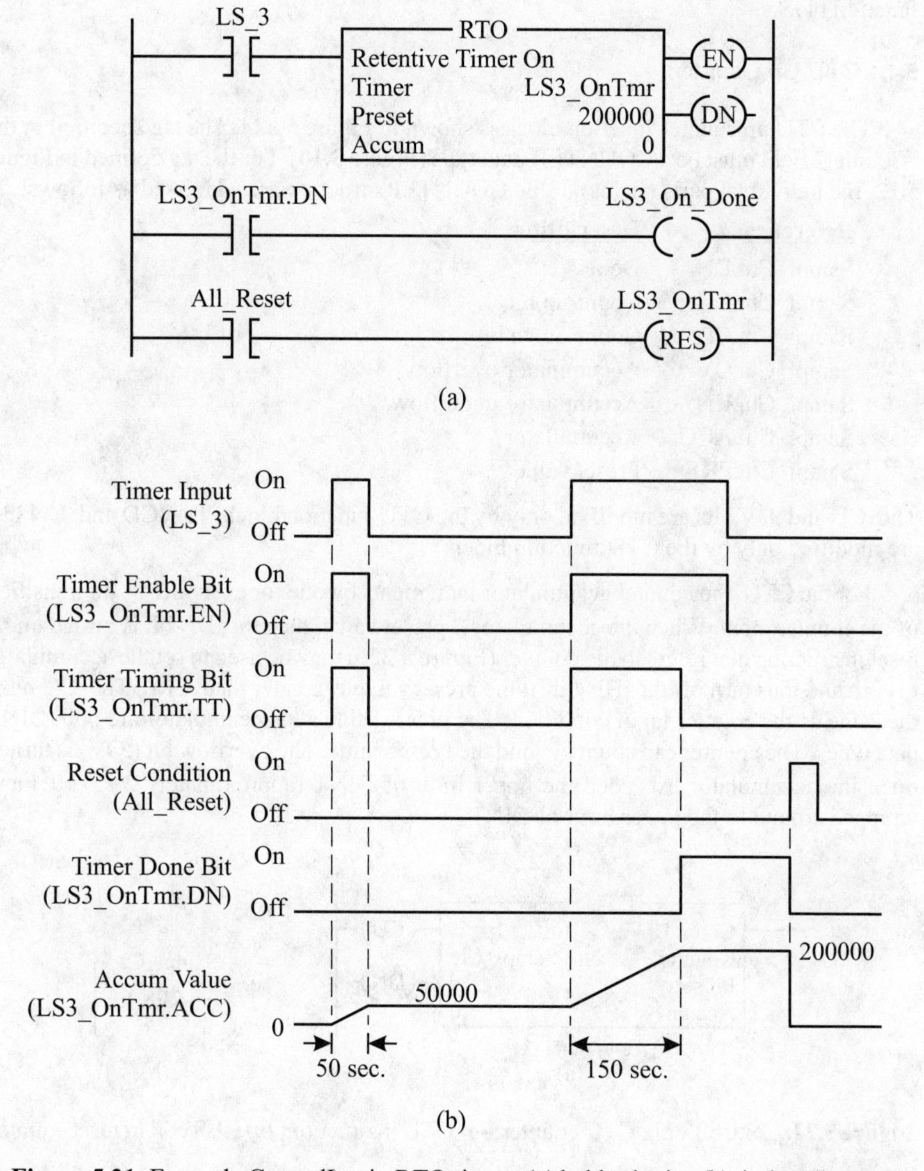

Figure 5.21. Example ControlLogix RTO timer: *(a)* ladder logic; *(b)* timing diagram.

MOV instruction (Chapter 7) to copy a zero to the timer accumulator. The operation of the .EN and .TT bits is the same as for the TON and TOF timer instructions.

An example application of the RTO instruction is shown in Figure 5.21*a* and its associated timing diagram is shown in Figure 5.21*b*. The preset time is 200 seconds (200,000 ms). The LS3_OnTmr.DN bit is turned **on** when the cumulative time that LS_3 has been **on** is at least 200 seconds. After the accumulator has reached 200 seconds, the LS3_OnTmr.DN bit remains **on** even after LS_3 turns **off**. The All_Reset must be turned **on** to reset the timer.

The ControlLogix RTO function block is nearly identical to the PLC-5, and SLC-500 RTO function block and similar to the GE Fanuc ONDTR and Siemens S7 S_ODTS function blocks.

5.4.4 CTU Up Counter

The CTU up counter function block is shown in Figure 5.22*a*. The tag specified in the "Counter" field must be a COUNTER data type (Figure 3.10). For the tag defined in Figure 5.22, the individual parts (fields) of the COUNTER structure are addressed as follows:

Reference	Description
Sampl_Ctu.DN	Done
Sampl_Ctu.CU	Count-up bit
Sampl_Ctu.CD	Count-down bit
Sampl_Ctu.OV	Accumulator overflow
Sampl_Ctu.UN	Accumulator underflow
Sampl_Ctu.ACC	Accumulator
Sampl_Ctu.PRE	Preset value

The .CU and .OV bits are modified only by the CTU function block. The .CD and .UN bits are modified only by the CTD function block.

For the CTU, the counter accumulator increments by one for every **off**-to-**on** transition of the counter input. When the accumulator ≥ preset value, then the .DN bit is turned **on**. A reset instruction that refers to the counter (Figure 5.22*b*) may be used to set the accumulator to zero and thus turn **off** the .DN bit (if the preset value is greater than zero). The .CU bit is the same as the counter input condition. The preset value and accumulator are both DINT data types. The counter can count beyond the Preset value. The overflow bit (.OV) is turned **on** if the accumulator exceeded the upper limit of DINT (approximately $2.15{\times}10^9$) and wrapped around to the lower limit of DINT.

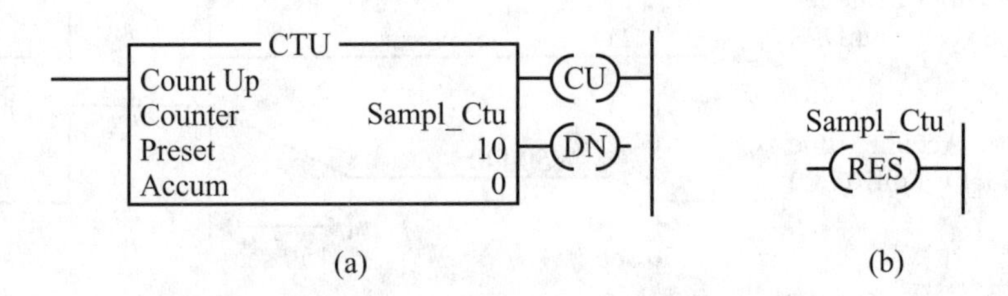

Figure 5.22. ControlLogix CTU counter: *(a)* CTU instruction; *(b)* RES coil to reset counter.

An example application of the CTU function block is shown in Figure 5.23*a* and its associated timing diagram is shown in Figure 5.23*b*. As long as All_Reset is **on**, the accumulator is held at zero. When All_Reset is **off**, at every **off**-to-**on** transition of PROX_2, the accumulator, Prox2_Ctr.ACC, increases by one. When the accumulator is equal to or greater than 3 (the preset value), the Prox2_Ctr.DN bit is turned **on**. When Prox2_Ctr.DN is already **on**, any more positive transitions of PROX_2 cause the value of Prox2_Ctr.ACC to change, and Prox2_Ctr.DN remains **on**.

The ControlLogix CTU function block is nearly identical to the PLC-5, and SLC-500 CTU function block and similar to the Modicon CTU, the Siemens S7 CTU, and GE Fanuc UPCTR function blocks.

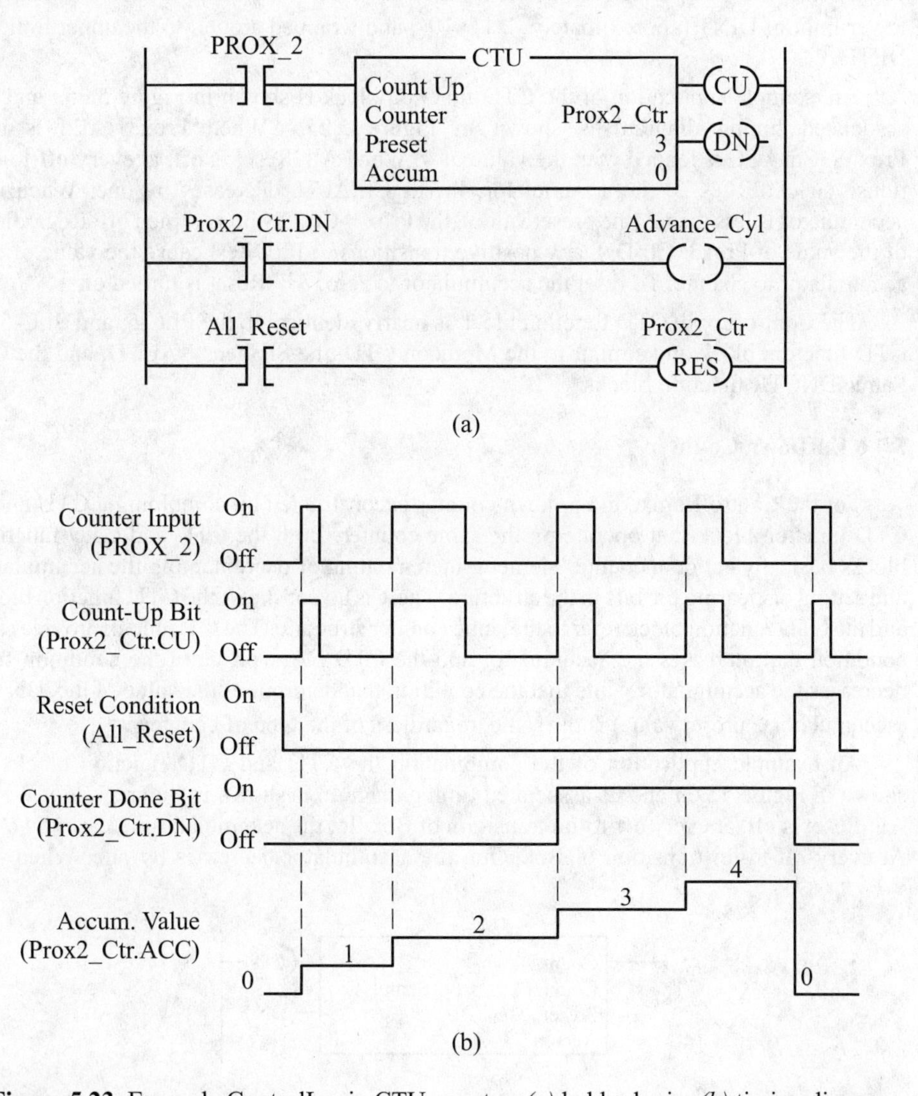

Figure 5.23. Example ControlLogix CTU counter: *(a)* ladder logic; *(b)* timing diagram.

5.4.5 CTD Down Counter

The CTD down counter function block is shown in Figure 5.24. The descriptions of the function block fields and the tag references are the same as described with the CTU function block.

For the CTD function block, the counter accumulator decrements by one for every **off**-to-**on** transition of the counter input. When the accumulator ≥ preset value, then the .DN bit is turned **on**, which is the same behavior as for CTU. A reset instruction that refers to the counter (Figure 5.22*b*) may be used to set the accumulator to zero and thus turn **off** the .DN bit (if the preset value is greater than zero). A MOV instruction (Chapter 7) must be used to set the accumulator to a nonzero value. The .CD bit is the same as the counter input condition. The preset value and accumulator are both DINT data types. The counter can count below zero. The underflow bit (.UN) is turned **on** if the accumulator went below the lower limit of DINT (approximately -2.15×10^9) and wrapped around to the upper limit of DINT.

An example application of the CTD function block is shown in Figure 5.25*a* and its associated timing diagram is shown in Figure 5.25*b*. When Prox3_CtLd is **on**, Prox_3_Ctr.ACC is loaded with the value of 4. When All_Reset is **off**, at every **off**-to-**on** transition of PROX_3, the accumulator, Prox3_Ctr.ACC, decreases by one. When the accumulator is less than 2 (the preset value), the Prox3_Ctr.DN bit is turned **off**. Regardless of the value of Prox3_Ctr.DN, any positive transitions of PROX_3 cause the value of the accumulator to change. To reset the accumulator to zero, All_Reset is turned **on**.

The ControlLogix CTD function block is nearly identical to the PLC-5, and SLC-500 CTD function block and similar to the Modicon CTD, the Siemens S7 CTD, and the GE Fanuc DNCTR function blocks.

5.4.6 Up/Down Counter

For the ControlLogix, an up/down counter is constructed by combining a CTU and a CTD function block that operate on the same counter. Both the CTU and CTD function blocks basically act on a counter element, incrementing or decrementing the accumulator and setting or clearing the bits in the structure. There is no conflict if the CTU function block and the CTD function block refer to the same counter structure. The CTU block provides the condition that increases the accumulator and the CTD block provides the condition that decreases the accumulator. Note that the condition that determines the value of the .DN bit (accumulator ≥ preset value) is the same, regardless of the type of counter.

An example application of the combination the CTU and CTD function blocks is shown in Figure 5.26*a* and its associated timing diagram is shown in Figure 5.26*b*. When All_Reset is **off**, at every **off**-to-**on** transition of Box_In, the accumulator increases by one. At every **off**-to-**on** transition of Box_Out, the accumulator decreases by one. When the

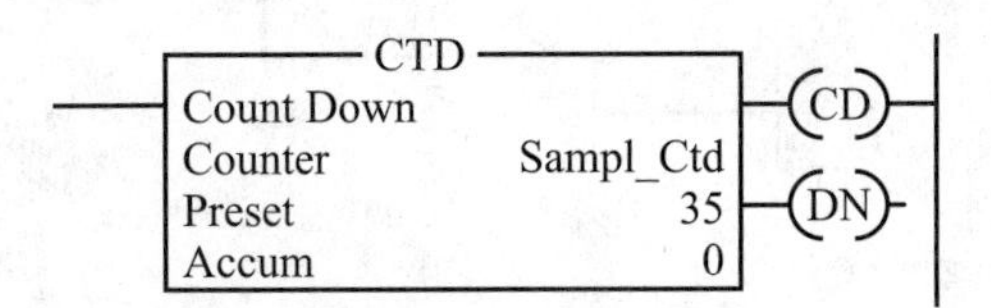

Figure 5.24. ControlLogix CTD counter.

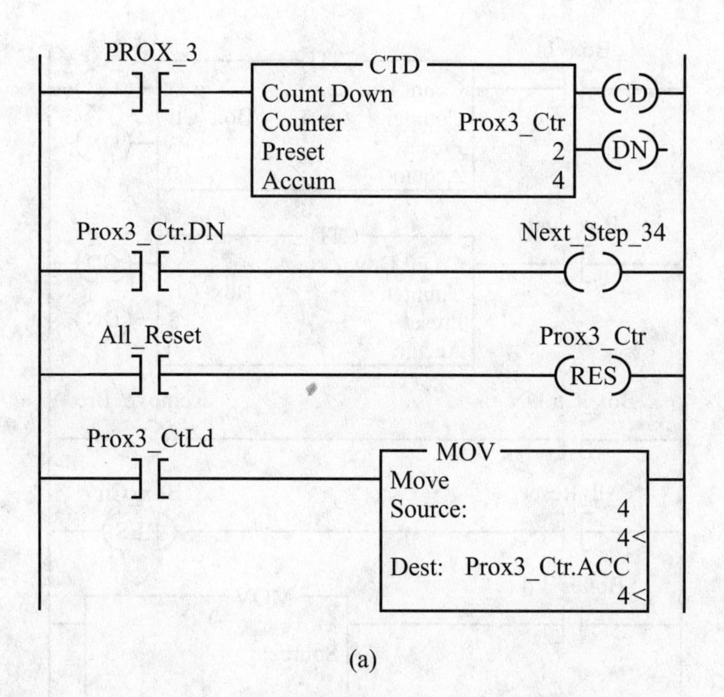

(a)

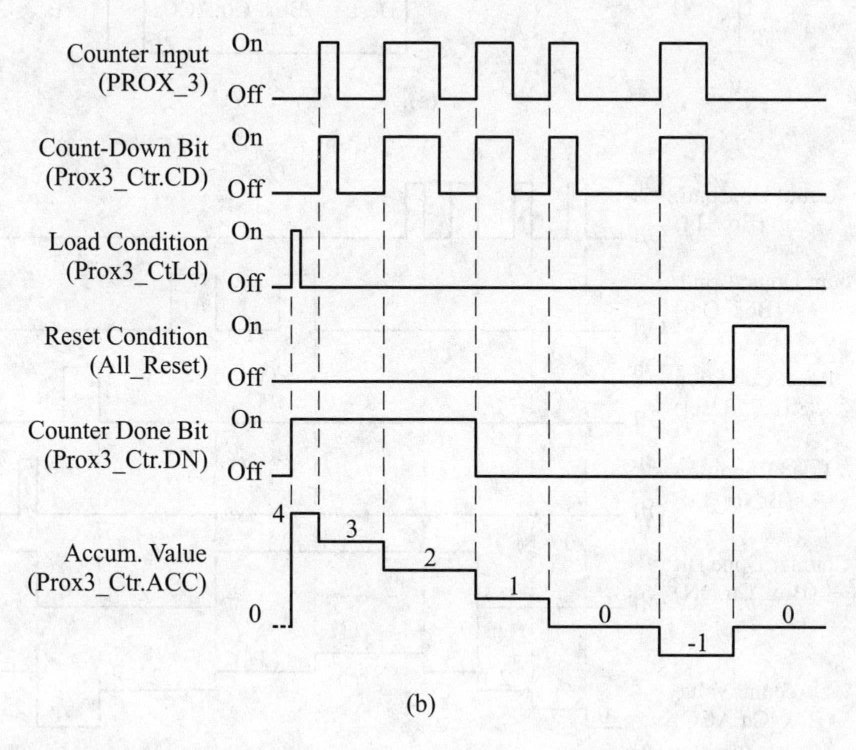

(b)

Figure 5.25. Example ControlLogix CTD counter: *(a)* ladder logic; *(b)* timing diagram.

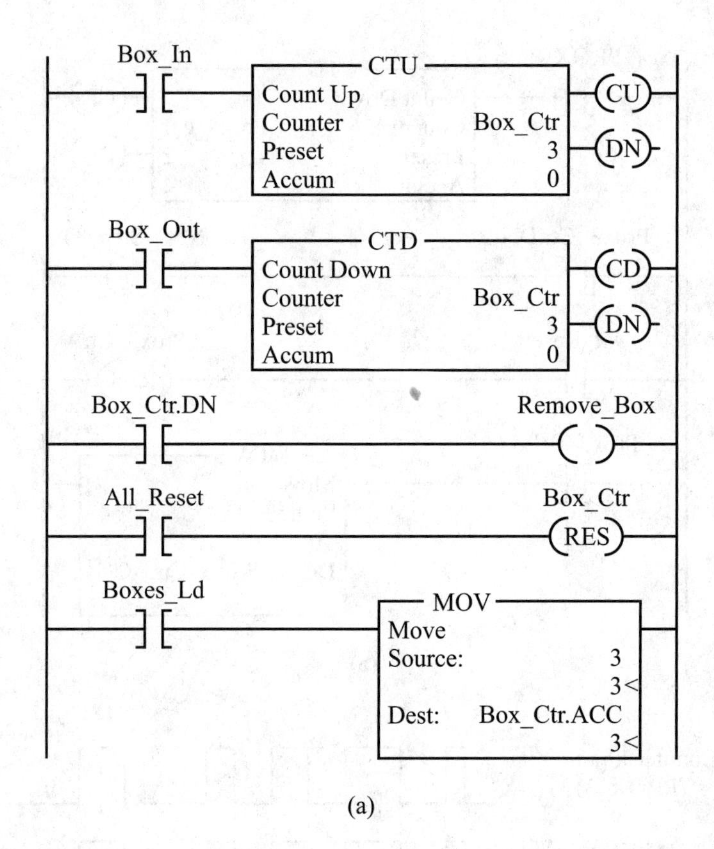

(a)

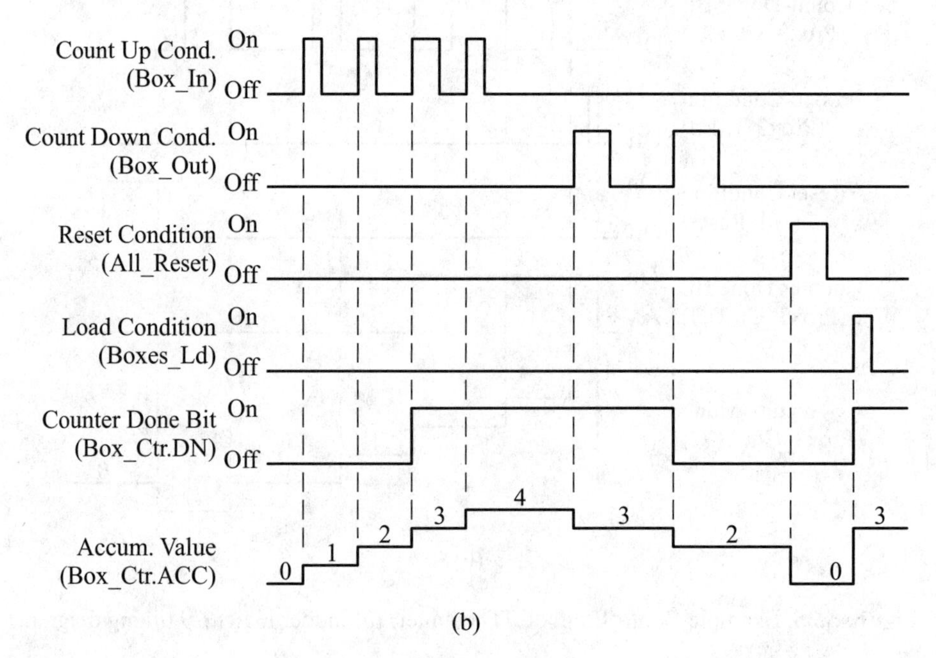

(b)

Figure 5.26. Example ControlLogix up/down counter: *(a)* ladder logic; *(b)* timing diagram.

accumulator is equal to or greater than 3 (the preset value), the Box_Ctr.DN bit and the Remove_Box coil are turned **on**. When All_Reset is **on**, the accumulator is cleared. When Boxes_Ld is **on**, the accumulator is set to 3.

The ControlLogix CTU/CTD combination is nearly identical to the same PLC-5, and SLC-500 function blocks and similar to the Modicon CTUD and the Siemens S7 CTUD function blocks.

5.5 A-B PLC-5/SLC-500 TIMERS AND COUNTERS

The Allen-Bradley PLC-5 and SLC-500 processors have three timer function blocks and two counter function blocks. The names and description of these function blocks are as follows:

PLC-5/SLC-500 Function Block	Description
TON	On-delay timer
TOF	Off-delay timer
RTO	Retentive on-delay timer
CTU	Up counter
CTD	Down counter

As for the ControlLogix PLC, the CTU and CTD function blocks can be combined to construct an up/down counter.

The PLC-5 and SLC-500 timers and counters function blocks are nearly identical to the ControlLogix function blocks of the same name. The major difference is that the PLC-5/SLC-500 timers and counters are output instructions, meaning they must always occur at the right side of the rung. Other differences are as follows:

	ControlLogix	PLC-5/SLC-500
Timer accumulator	DINT	INT
Timer time base	1 ms	.01 or 1 sec.
Counter preset	DINT	INT
Counter accumulator	DINT	INT

Therefore, the approach in this section will be to show the function block and describe the operation of each one, but only the operation of the TON and CTU function blocks is illustrated.

5.5.1 TON On-Delay Timer

The TON on-delay timer is shown in Figure 5.27. The TON timer basically delays the turn-on of a signal and does not delay the turn-off. The address specified in the "Timer" field must be an element of a timer (T*x*) data file (Figure 3.18). For the symbol and address defined in Figure 5.27, the individual parts (fields) of the timer data type are referenced as follows:

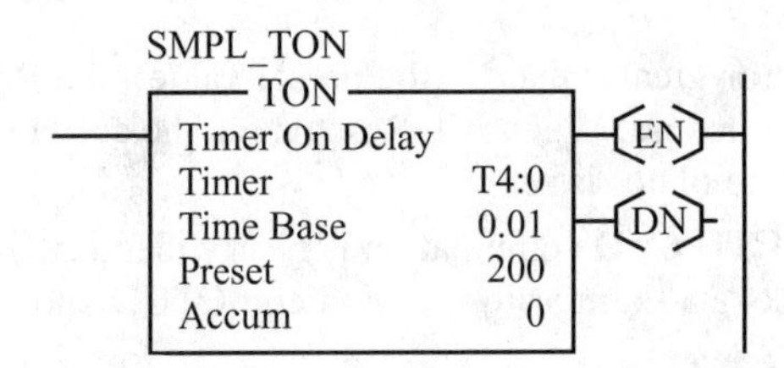

Figure 5.27. PLC-5/SLC-500 TON timer.

Symbol Reference	Address Reference	Description
SMPL_TON/DN	T4:0/DN	Done
SMPL_TON/TT	T4:0/TT	Timer timing bit
SMPL_TON/EN	T4:0/EN	Enable
SMPL_TON.ACC	T4:0.ACC	Accumulator
SMPL_TON.PRE	T4:0.PRE	Preset value

When entering the reference into an instruction, a "/" or "." can be used to separate the symbol or address from the field name, but the above table shows how they are displayed.

When the timer input is **on**, the accumulator is counted up once for each time base interval (1 or 0.01 seconds). When the accumulator equals the preset value, the timer is "timed out" and the /DN bit is set to **on**. If the timer input turns **off** during the timing interval, the accumulator is set to zero and timing restarts when the input turns **on**. The /TT bit is on while the accumulator is counting, but not yet at the preset value. The /EN bit is the same as the timer input condition. The maximum interval is 32,767 seconds (with a 1 second time base). The value of the accumulator (.ACC) or the preset value (.PRE) can be accessed as integers.

The accuracy of the timer is basically ±1 time base interval. If the time base is 0.01 second, the timer could finish as much as 0.01 second before desired interval or as much as 0.01 second after the desired interval. For a one second time base, the timer could finish as much as one second earlier or one second later than the desired interval. This behavior also means that a timer with a preset value of one may have **no** delay.

An example application of the TON instruction is shown in Figure 5.28*a* and its associated timing diagram is shown in Figure 5.28*b*. The preset time is 3 seconds (300×0.01 sec.). The input, LS_1 must remain **on** for at least 3 seconds before the LS1_DELTMR/DN bit and the LS_1_HOLD coil are turned **on**. When LS_1 is turned **off** after 2 seconds, the accumulator is set to zero and the LS1_DELTMR/DN bit remains **off**. Note that the symbol, LS1_DELTMR, associated with the timer address, T4:0, is shown above the TON function block.

The PLC-5/SLC-500 TON function block is nearly identical to the ControlLogix TON function block and similar to the Modicon TON, the Siemens S7 TON, and the GE Fanuc TMR function blocks.

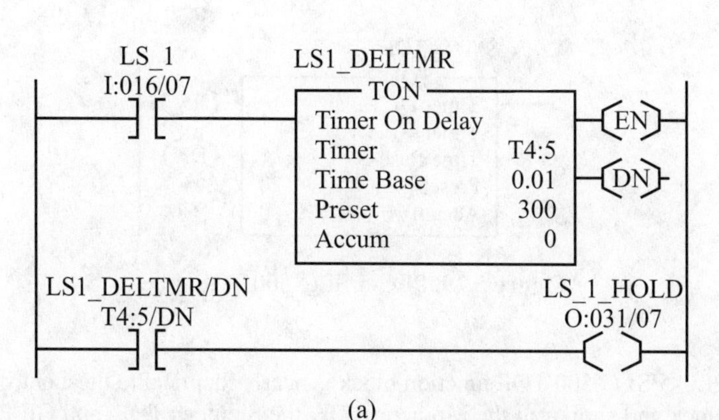

(a)

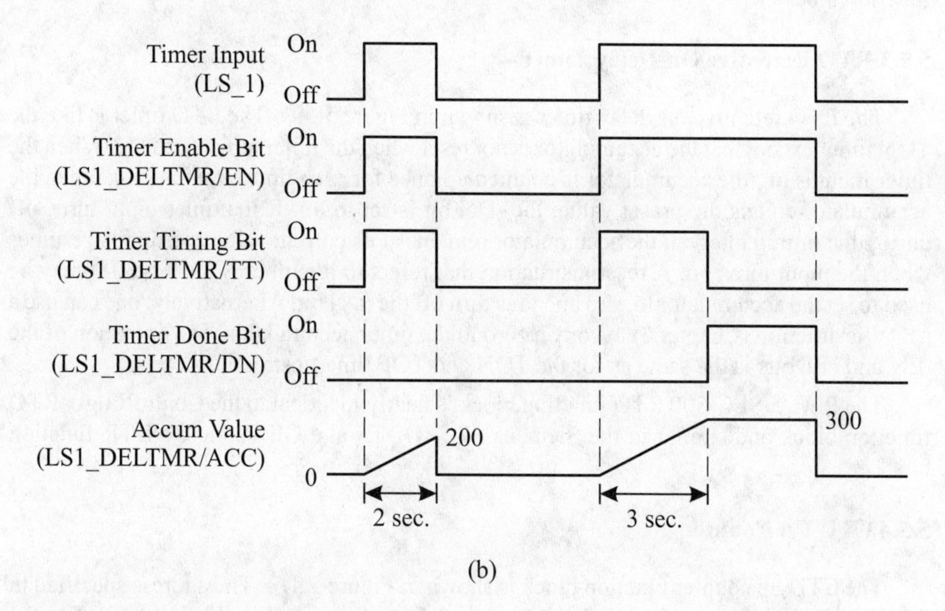

(b)

Figure 5.28. Example PLC-5/SLC-500 TON timer: *(a)* ladder logic; *(b)* timing diagram.

5.5.2 TOF Off-Delay Timer

The TOF off-delay timer is shown in Figure 5.29. Looking at the timer input and the /DN bit, the TOF timer operates exactly opposite of the TON timer. The TOF timer basically delays the turn-off of a signal and does not delay the turn-on. The descriptions of the function block fields and the symbol/address references are the same as for the TON function block.

When the timer input is **off**, the accumulator is counted up once for each time base interval (1 or 0.01 seconds). When the accumulator equals the preset value, the timer is "timed out" and the /DN bit is turned **off**. If the timer input turns **on** anytime, the accumulator is set to zero and timing recommences when the input turns **off**. The operation of the /EN and /TT bits is the same as for the TON timer instruction.

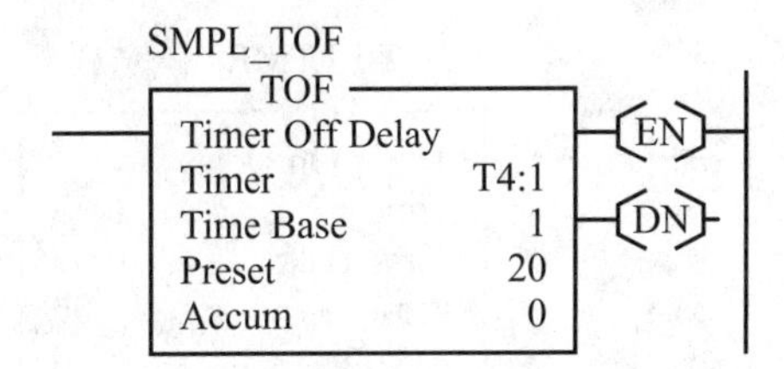

Figure 5.29. PLC-5/SLC-500 TOF timer.

The PLC-5/SLC-500 TOF function block is nearly identical to the ControlLogix TOF function block and similar to the Modicon TOF, the Siemens TOF, and GE Fanuc OFDT function blocks.

5.5.3 RTO Retentive On-Delay Timer

The RTO retentive on-delay timer is shown in Figure 5.30*a*. The RTO timer is like the TON timer except that the accumulator is not reset when the timer input turns **off**. When the timer input is **on**, the accumulator is counted up once for each time base interval.When the accumulator equals the preset value, the /DN bit is set to **on**. If the timer input turns **off** during the timing interval, the accumulator remains at its current value and timing resumes when the input turns **on**. A reset instruction that refers to the timer (Figure 5.30*b*) may be used to set the accumulator to zero and thus turn **off** the /DN bit. Alternatively, one can use a MOV instruction (Chapter 7) to copy a zero to the timer accumulator. The operation of the /EN and /TT bits is the same as for the TON and TOF timer instructions.

The PLC-5/SLC-500 RTO function block is nearly identical to the ControlLogix RTO function block and similar to the Siemens S7 S_ODTS and GE Fanuc ONDTR function blocks.

5.5.4 CTU Up Counter

The CTU up counter function block is shown in Figure 5.31*a*. The address specified in the "Counter" field must be an element of a counter (C*x*) data file (Figure 3.19). For the symbol defined in Figure 5.31, the individual parts (fields) of the COUNTER structure are addressed as follows:

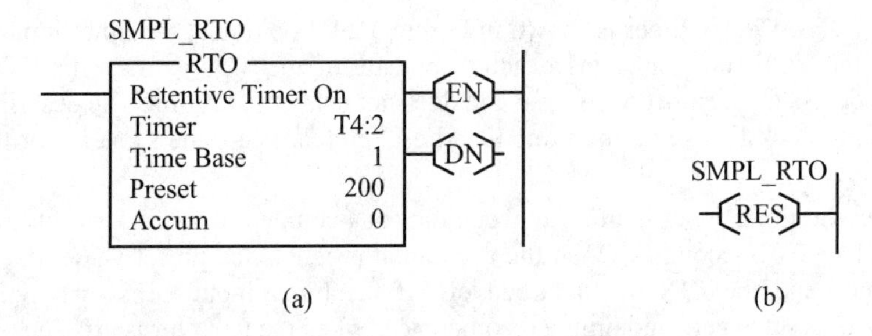

Figure 5.30. PLC-5/SLC-500 RTO timer: *(a)* RTO instruction; *(b)* RES coil to reset RTO.

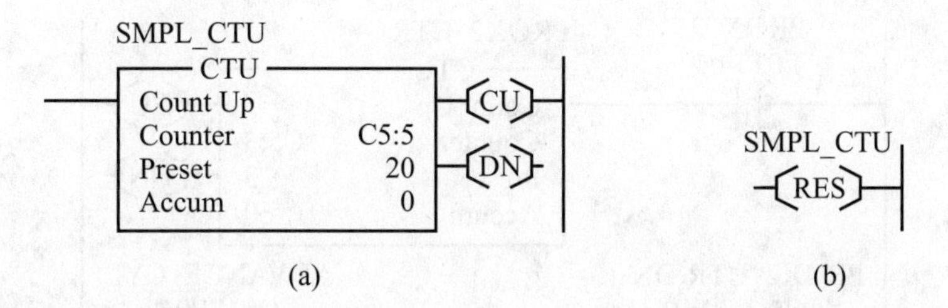

Figure 5.31. PLC-5/SLC-500 CTU counter: *(a)* CTU instruction; *(b)* RES coil to reset counter.

Symbol Reference	Address Reference	Description
SMPL_CTU/DN	C5:5/DN	Done
SMPL_CTU/CU	C5:5/CU	Count-up bit
SMPL_CTU/CD	C5:5/CD	Count-down bit
SMPL_CTU/OV	C5:5/OV	Accumulator overflow
SMPL_CTU/UN	C5:5/UN	Accumulator underflow
SMPL_CTU.ACC	C5:5.ACC	Accumulator
SMPL_CTU.PRE	C5:5.PRE	Preset value

The /CU and /OV bits are modified only by the CTU function block. The /CD and /UN bits are modified only by the CTD function block. When entering the reference into an instruction, a "/" or "." can be used to separate the symbol or address from the field name, but the above table shows how they are displayed.

For the CTU function block, the counter accumulator increments by one for every **off**-to-**on** transition of the counter input. When the accumulator ≥ preset value, then the /DN bit is turned **on**. A reset instruction that refers to the counter (Figure 5.31*b*) may be used to set the accumulator to zero and thus turn **off** the /DN bit. The /CU bit is the same as the counter input condition. The preset value and accumulator are both integer data types. The counter can count beyond the preset value. The overflow bit (/OV) is turned **on** if the accumulator exceeded the upper limit of 32,767 and wrapped around to –32,768.

An example application of the CTU function block is shown in Figure 5.32*a* and its associated timing diagram is shown in Figure 5.32*b*. As long as All_Reset is **on**, the accumulator is held at zero. When All_Reset is **off**, at every **off**-to-**on** transition of PROX_2, the accumulator, PROX2_CTR.ACC, increases by one. When the accumulator is equal to or greater than 3 (the preset value), the PROX2_CTR/DN bit is turned **on**. When PROX2_CTR/DN is already **on**, any more positive transitions of PROX_2 cause the value of PROX2_CTR.ACC to change, and PROX2_CTR/DN remains **on**.

The PLC-5/SLC-500 CTU function block is nearly identical to the ControlLogix CTU function block and similar to the Modicon CTU, the Siemens S7 CTU, and the GE Fanuc UPCTR function blocks.

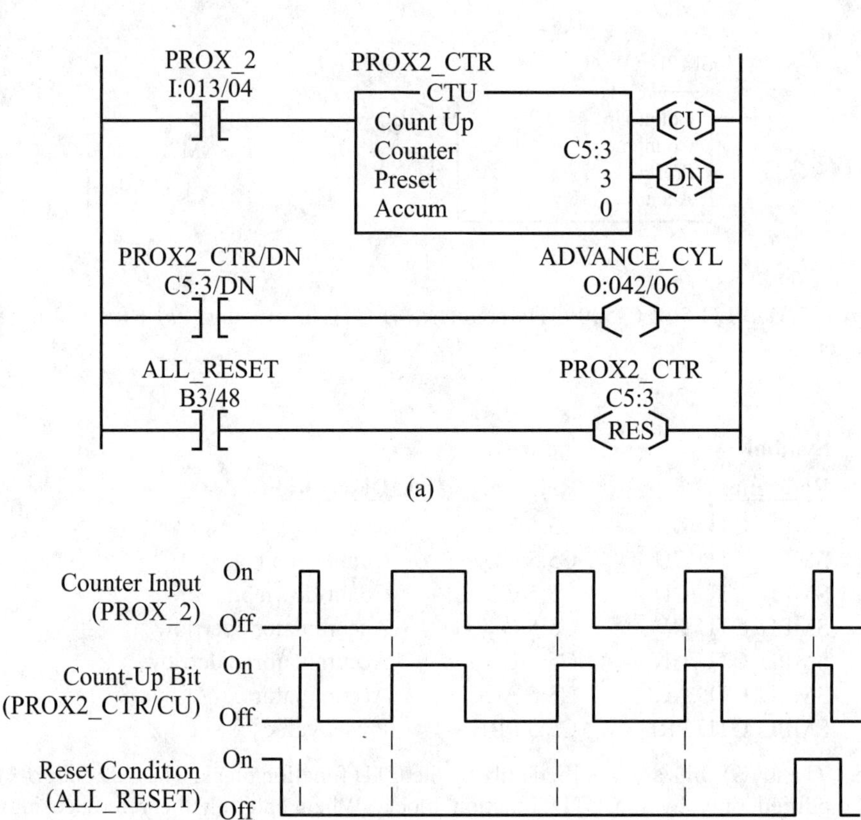

Figure 5.32. Example PLC-5/SLC-500 CTU counter: *(a)* ladder logic; *(b)* timing diagram.

5.5.5 CTD Down Counter

The CTD down counter function block is shown in Figure 5.33. The function block fields and the symbol/address references are described with the CTU function block.

The counter accumulator decrements by one for every **off**-to-**on** transition of the counter input. When the accumulator ≥ preset value, then the /DN bit is turned **on**, which is the same behavior as for CTU. A reset instruction that refers to the counter (Figure 5.31*b*) may be used to set the accumulator to zero and thus turn **off** the /DN bit. The /CD bit is the same as the counter input condition. The preset value and accumulator are both integer data

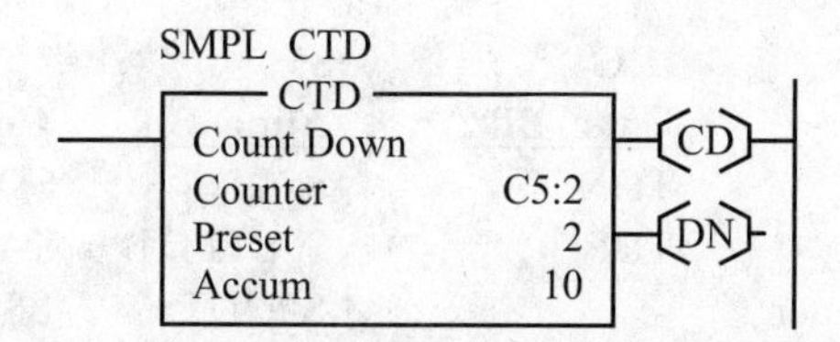

Figure 5.33. PLC-5/SLC-500 CTD counter.

types. The counter can count below zero. The underflow bit (/UN) is turned **on** if the accumulator went below –32,768 and wrapped around to 32,767.

The PLC-5/SLC-500 CTD function block is nearly identical to the ControlLogix CTD function block and similar to the Modicon CTD, the Siemens S7 CTD, and the GE Fanuc DNCTR function blocks.

5.5.6 Up/Down Counter

For the PLC-5 and SLC-500, an up/down counter is constructed by combining a CTU and a CTD function block that operate on the same counter. Both the CTU and CTD function blocks basically affect a counter element, incrementing or decrementing the accumulator and setting or clearing the bits in the structure. There is no conflict if the CTU function block and the CTD function block refer to the same counter structure. The CTU block provides the condition that increases the accumulator and the CTD block provides the condition that decreases the accumulator. Note that the condition that determines the value of the .DN bit (accumulator ≥ preset value) is the same, regardless of the type of counter.

An example application of the combination the CTU and CTD function blocks is shown in Figure 5.26 for the ControlLogix PLC. The only difference is that for the PLC-5/SLC-500 the counter address is shown in the function block and the symbol appears above the function block

The PLC-5, and SLC-500 CTU/CTD combination is nearly identical to the same ControlLogix function blocks and similar to the Modicon and Siemens S7 CTUD function blocks.

5.6 SIEMENS S7 TIMERS AND COUNTERS

The timers and counters for the Siemens S7-300 and S7-400 processors are identical to each other and this section describes them in detail. The S7-200 timers and counters, though somewhat different, operate in the same manner, and are described in a separate sub-section.

The Siemens S7-300/400 processors have three sets of timer and counter ladder logic instructions: IEC function blocks, S5-compatible function blocks, and S5-compatible coils. The descriptions and names of the timers and counters are as follows:

Description	IEC Func. Blk.	S5 Func. Blk.	Coil
On-delay timer	TON	S_ODT	SD
Off-delay timer	TOF	S_OFFDT	SA
Ret. on-delay timer		S_ODTS	SS
Pulse timer	TP	S_PULSE	SP
Ext. pulse timer		S_PEXT	SE
Up counter	CTU	S_CU	CU
Down counter	CTD	S_CD	CD
Up/down counter	CTUD	S_CUD	

This text favors the IEC-compatible timers and counters. Though the operation of all timer and counter instructions is explained, the IEC-compatible timers and counters, with one exception, are used in the application examples.

The IEC timer and counter function blocks are system function blocks (SFBs). Each timer and counter must have an instance data block that holds the timer/counter accumulator. The status and accumulator values may be accessed through the data block name and the name of the connection. For example, the "Q" output of a TON timer whose data block is named "Timer1" may be accessed as "Timer1".Q in addition to the normal output connection. The IEC timers and counters have the EN and ENO connections as specified in the 61131-3 standard. The EN input must be **on** for the block to execute. The ENO output echoes the EN input and is **on** if EN is **on** and the block executes without error. In addition, the S7 IEC timer and counter function blocks have some limitations. Except for the ENO output, the outputs of these SFBs must be connected to a variable. The boolean outputs cannot be connected to contacts or coils like the Modicon implementation of the IEC 61131-3 standard. The ENO output can be connected to a contact, coil, or to the EN input of another block. Ladder logic contacts can be connected to the boolean input connections, but only to the first timer or counter in a network. If timers or counters are cascaded, then all connections to the second timer/counter other than EN/ENO must be connected to a variable.

Design Tip

If the EN input is not directly connected to the power rail, the behavior of the function block outputs must be considered when EN is **off**. If the EN input is turned **off**, the block outputs remain at their last value, which may mean the timer/counter status remains **on**.

Design Tip

Because the IEC timer and counter function blocks are SFBs, an open shared data block must be re-opened after the timer and counter function block.

In contrast, the S5-compatible timer/counter function blocks and coils use the timer/counter memory areas to store the accumulator. The connections to the S5-compatible timer/counter function blocks do not have the limitations of the IEC-compatible timers and counters. Contacts and coils can be connected to all boolean output connections and the blocks can be cascaded. For the timer and counter coils, the value of the timer/counter accumulator and status is available by directly addressing the particular timer/counter.

The preset time for the S5-compatible timer function blocks and coils may be specified as a constant in the hexadecimal word or S5TIME format (Siemens, 2000). Only the S5TIME format is used in this text. The general format for a S5TIME constant is:

S5T#*aa*H_*bb*M_*cc*S_*dd*MS

The time is specified in hours (H), minutes (M), seconds (S), and milliseconds (MS) and *aa*, *bb*, *cc*, and *dd* are appropriate numbers. The underlines are optional and the prefix can be S5T#, s5t#, S5TIME#, or s5time#. Four time bases are available: 0.01-, 0.1-, 1.0-, or 10-seconds. The actual time base is selected automatically, depending on the specified time:

Time range	Time base
10MS to 9S_990MS	0.01 second
10S to 1M_39S_900MS	0.1 second
1M_40S to 16M_39S	1 second
16M_40S to 2H_46M_30S	10 second

The maximum value is 2 hours, 46 minutes, and 30 seconds. The constant must be consistent with the timer resolution (0.01-, 0.1-, 1.0-, or 10-second units) and be no more than 999 time base units. A constant whose resolution is inconsistent with the time base is truncated to a constant consistent with the time base. For example, if one enters "S5T#1H_15S_50MS", the programming software changes the value to "S5T#1H_10S" since that is consistent with the 10-second time base required by the constant.

One drawback of the S5 timers is their update. The update of the timer accumulator and status is synchronized to the processor clock and is not synchronized to the program scan. Therefore, it is possible that a constant reference to a timer can be **off** in one network and be **on** in a later network. In contrast, the timer status for the IEC timers is updated only when the block is scanned.

5.6.1 On-Delay Timers

An on-delay timer can be implemented one of three ways, shown in Figure 5.34. The TON and S_ODT function blocks and the SD coil basically delay the turn-on of a signal and do not delay the turn-off. The IEC on-delay timer, TON, has EN/ENO connections (Figure 5.34*a*). The EN input must be **on** for the block to execute. The ENO output echoes the EN input and is **on** if EN is **on** and the block executes without error.

The TON block is shown in Figure 5.34*a*. When the IN input turns **on**, the internal time (ET) increases. When ET equals the preset time (PT), the timer is "timed out" and the Q output turns **on**. If IN turns **off** during the timing interval, Q remains **off**, ET is set to zero, and timing recommences when IN turns **on**. The ET output can be connected to a variable (of type TIME) in order to monitor the internal time. The preset time can be a variable, or a constant of type TIME. The accuracy is 1 millisecond. The name or address of the instance data block for the timer is shown above the block.

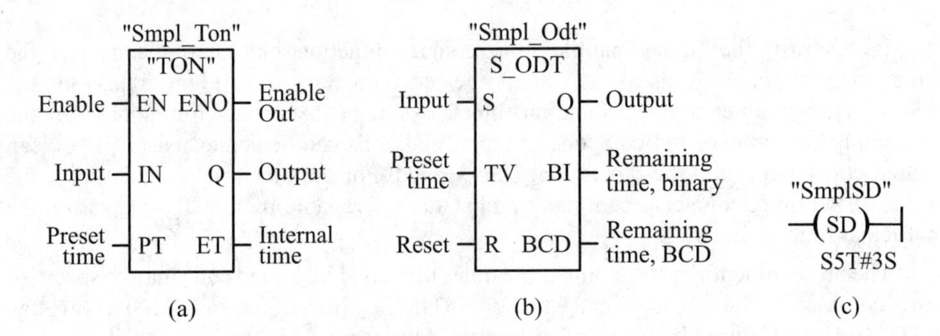

Figure 5.34. S7-300 on-delay timers: *(a)* TON block; *(b)* S_ODT block; *(c)* SD coil.

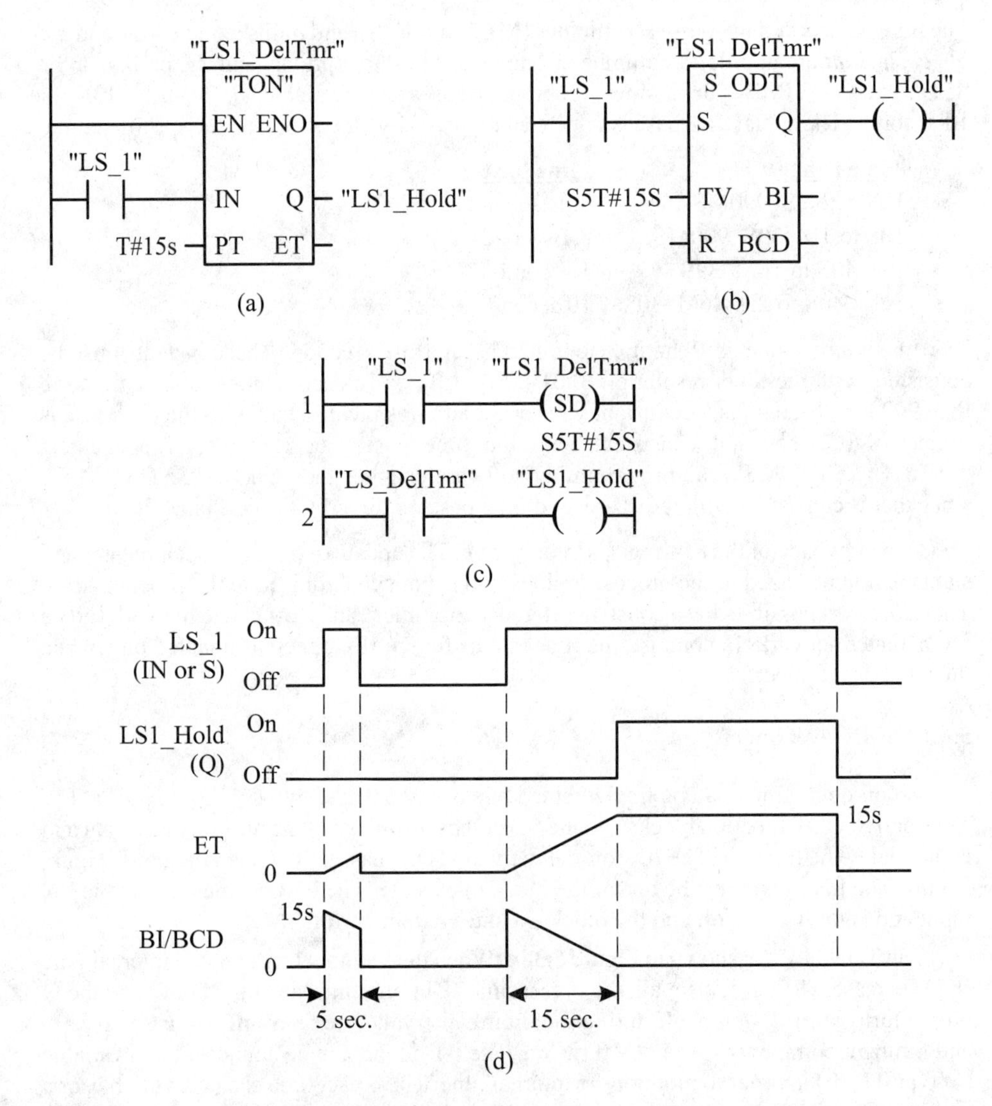

Figure 5.35. Example S7 on-delay timers: *(a)* TON; *(b)* S_ODT; *(c)* SD coil; *(d)* timing diagram.

The S_ODT S5-compatible timer is shown in Figure 5.34*b*. When the S input is **on**, the accumulator starts at the preset time value (TV) and decrements once for each time base interval. When the accumulator equals zero, the timer is "timed out" and the Q output turns **on**. If S turns **off** during the timing interval, Q remains **off**, and timing recommences when S turns **on**. The R input is the timer reset. If R is **on** while the timer is running (S input is **on**) the Q output remains **off**. The BI output is the remaining time, in time base units, and the BCD output is the remaining time in the S5TIME format. The preset time, TV, can be a variable or a constant of type S5TIME. The name or address of the timer is shown above the block.

As a coil, the S5-compatible timer is shown in Figure 5.34*c*. When the SD coil input is **on**, the accumulator is set to the preset time value shown below the coil and decrements as for the S_ODT block. When the accumulator equals zero, the timer is "timed out" and the contact reference to the timer turns **on**. If the coil input turns **off** during the timing interval, the timer contact remains **off**, and timing recommences when the coil turns **on**. The preset time can be a variable, or a constant of type S5TIME. The name or address of the timer is shown above the coil. To reset a SD coil timer, turn **on** a reset coil that refers to the timer.

An example application implemented with each type of on-delay timer is shown in Figures 5.35*a-c* and the associated timing diagram is shown in Figure 5.35*d*. The LS_1 discrete input must remain **on** for at least 15 seconds before the LS1_Hold coil is turned **on**. When LS_1 is turned **off** after 5 seconds, internal times are set to zero and the LS1_Hold coil remains **off**.

The S7 on-delay timer function blocks are similar to the Modicon TON, the Allen-Bradley TON, and the GE Fanuc TMR function blocks.

5.6.2 Off-Delay Timers

The off-delay timer can be implemented in any one of three ways shown in Figure 5.36. The TOF and S_OFFDT function blocks and the SA coil basically delay the turn-off of a signal and do not delay the turn-on.

The TOF block is shown in Figure 5.36*a*. When the IN input turns **off**, the ET increases. When ET equals PT, the timer is "timed out" and the Q output turns **off**. If IN turns **on** during the timing interval, Q remains **on**, ET is set to zero, and timing recommences when IN turns **off**.

The S_OFFDT S5-compatible timer is shown in Figure 5.36*b*. When the S input is **off**, the accumulator starts at TV and decrements once for each time base interval. When the accumulator equals zero, the timer is "timed out" and the Q output turns **off**. If S turns **on** during the timing interval, Q remains **on**, and timing recommences when S turns **off**. The R input is the timer reset. If R is **on** while the timer is running (S input is **off**) the Q output remains **on**.

As a coil, the S5-compatible timer is shown in Figure 5.36*c*. When the SA coil input is **off**, the accumulator starts at the preset time value shown below the coil and decrements as for the SD coil. When the accumulator equals zero, the timer is "timed out" and the contact reference to the timer turns **off**. If the coil input turns **on** during the timing interval, the timer contact remains **on**, and timing recommences when the coil turns **off**. As for the SD coil timer, a SA coil timer is reset by turning **on** a reset coil referring to the timer.

An example application implemented with each type of off-delay timer is shown in Figures 5.37*a-c* and the associated timing diagram is shown in Figure 5.37*d*. The PROX_2

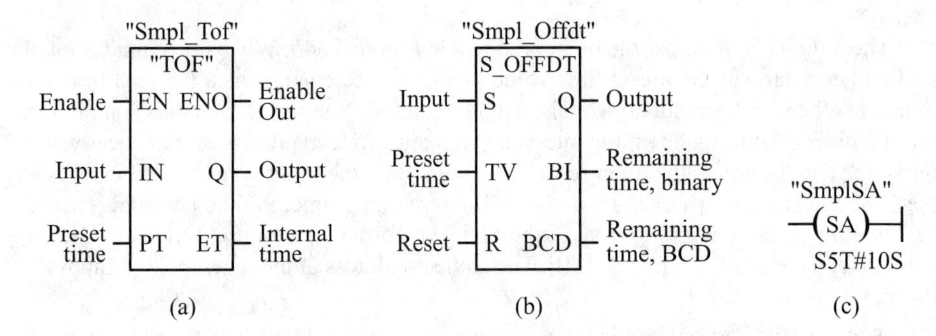

Figure 5.36. S7-300 off-delay timers: *(a)* TOF block; *(b)* S_OFFDT block; *(c)* SA coil.

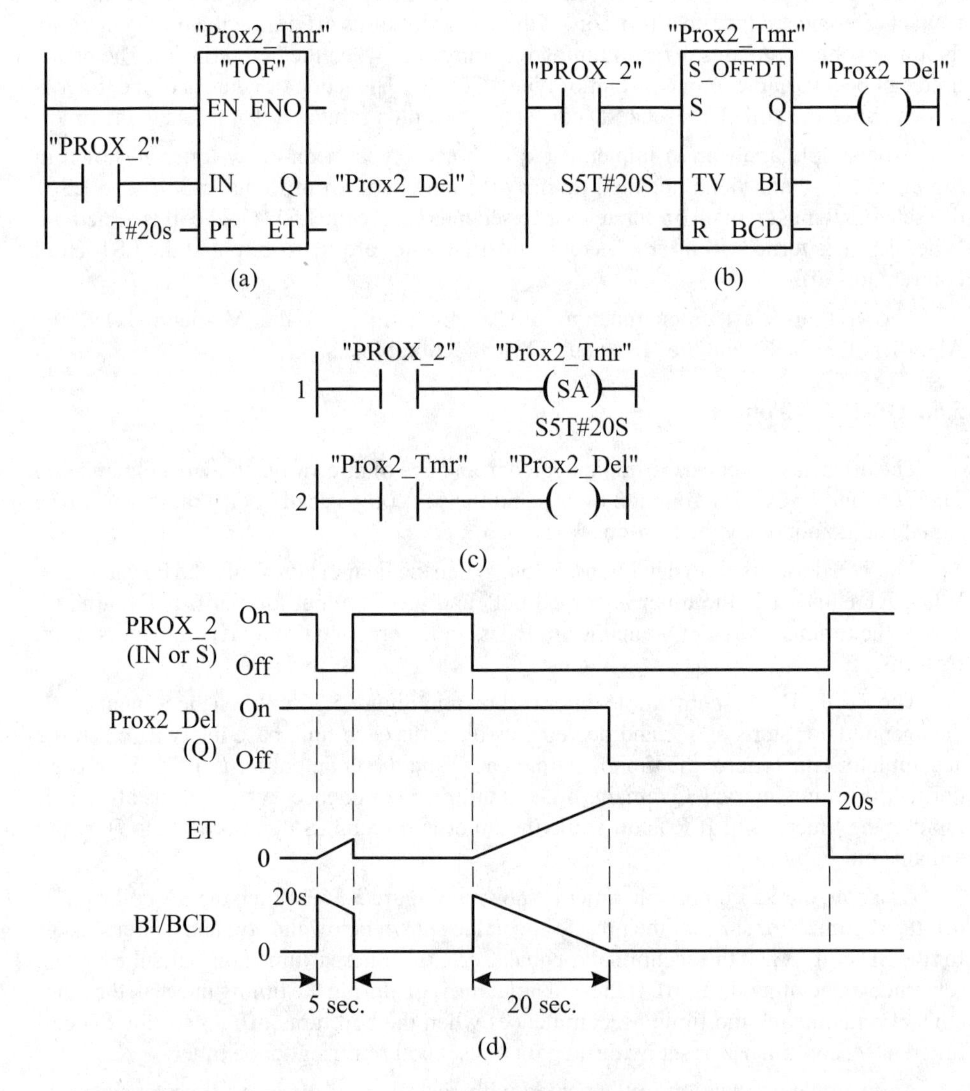

Figure 5.37. Example S7 off-delay timers: *(a)* TOF; *(b)* S_OFFDT; *(c)* SA coil; *(d)* timing diagram.

discrete input must remain **off** for at least 20 seconds before the Prox2_Del coil is turned **off**. When PROX_2 is turned **on** after 5 seconds, internal times are set to zero and the Prox2_Del coil remains **on**.

The S7 off-delay timer function blocks are similar to the Modicon TOF, the Allen-Bradley TOF, and the GE Fanuc OFDT function blocks.

5.6.3 Retentive On-Delay Timers

A retentive on-delay timer can be implemented one of two ways, shown in Figure 5.38. There is no IEC-compatible retentive on-delay timer. An IEC-compatible retentive on-delay can be implemented as shown in Figure 5.15 for the Modicon PLC. The S_ODTS function block and the SS coil function like the on-delay timers except the accumulator is not reset when the timer input turns **off**.

The S_ODTS S5-compatible timer is shown in Figure 5.38*a*. When the S input is **on**, the accumulator is set to TV and decrements as for the S_ODT block. When the accumulator equals zero, the timer is "timed out" and the Q output turns **on**. If S turns **off** during the timing interval, the accumulator remains at its current value and timing resumes when the S input turns **on**. The R input is the timer reset. Anytime R is **on** the accumulator is zeroed and the Q output remains **off**.

As a coil, the S5-compatible timer is shown in Figure 5.38*b*. When the coil input is **on**, the accumulator is set to the preset time value shown below the coil and decrements as for the SD coil. When the accumulator equals zero, the timer is "timed out" and the contact reference to the timer turns **on**. If the coil input turns **off** during the timing interval, the accumulator remains at its current value and timing resumes when the coil turns **on**. As for other coil timers, a SS coil timer is reset by turning **on** a reset coil referring to the timer.

An example application implemented with each type of retentive on-delay timer is shown in Figures 5.39*a,b* and the associated timing diagram is shown in Figure 5.39*c*. The preset time is 200 seconds (3 minutes, 20 seconds). The LS3_On_Dn bit is turned **on** when the cumulative time that LS_3 has been **on** is at least 200 seconds. After the accumulator has reached 200 seconds, the LS3_On_Dn bit remains **on** even after LS_3 turns **off**. The All_Reset must be turned **on** to reset the timer.

The S7 S_ODTS retentive on-delay timer function block is similar to the Allen-Bradley RTO and the GE Fanuc ONDTR function blocks.

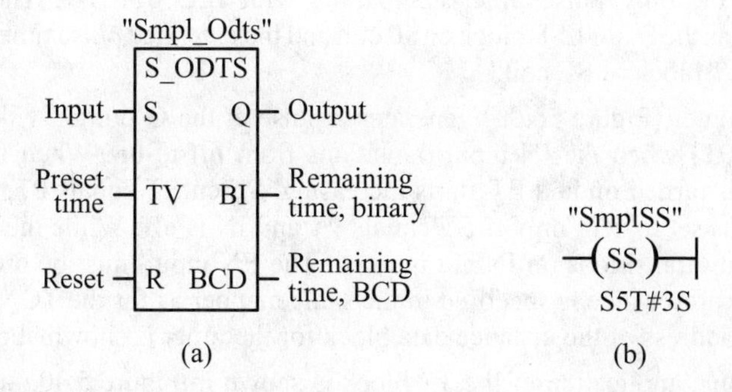

Figure 5.38. S7-300 retentive on-delay timers: *(a)* S_ODT block; *(b)* SD coil.

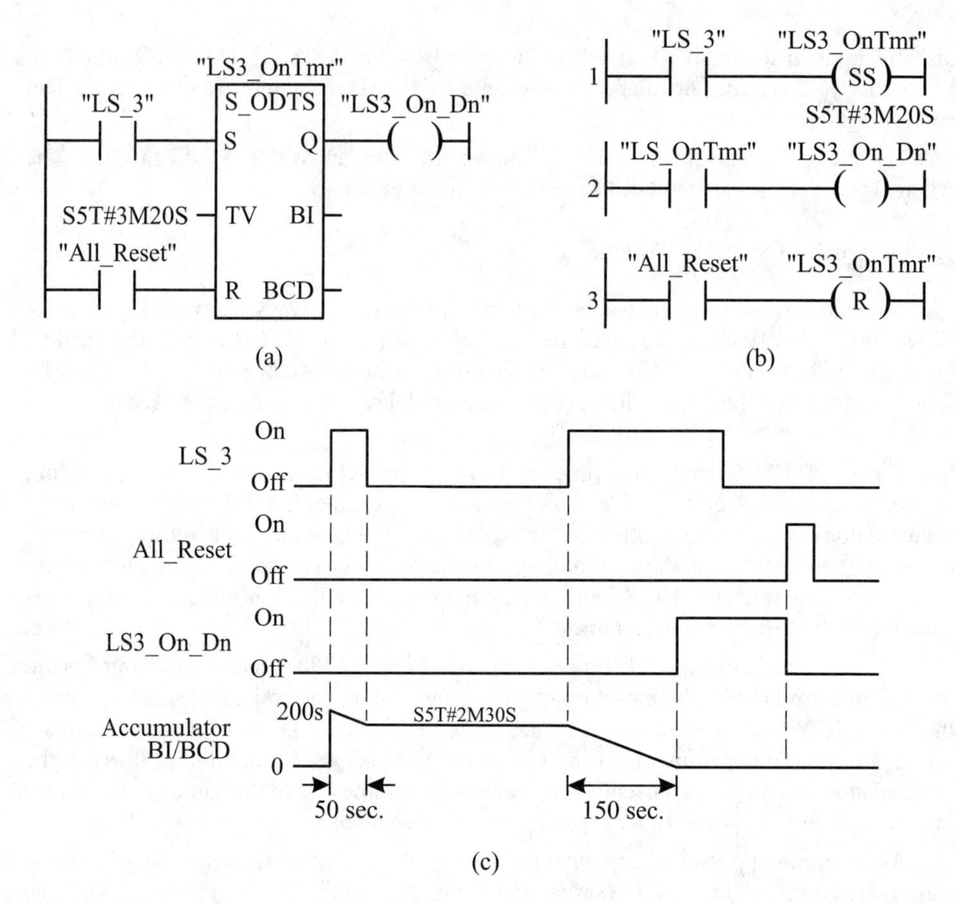

Figure 5.39. Example S7 retentive on-delay timers: *(a)* S_ODTS; *(b)* SS coil; *(c)* timing diagram.

5.6.4 Pulse Timers

There are three different types of pulse timers for the S7 processors: (1) IEC-compatible TP block, (2) pulse timer, and (3) extended re-triggerable pulse timer. The TP block is the only pulse timer compatible with IEC 61131-3. The pulse timer is implemented as the S_PULSE block or SP coil and the extended pulse timer is implemented as the S_PEXT block or SE coil.

The TP timer (Figure 5.40*a*) generates a pulse at the Q output with duration of the preset time (PT) when the IN input transitions from **off**-to-**on**. When IN changes from **off**-to-**on**, Q is turned **on** and ET starts increasing. When ET equals PT, Q turns **off**. The internal time is set to zero only if ET equals PT and IN is **off**. While the ET is increasing toward PT, any transitions on IN are ignored. The EN input must be **on** for the timer to function. The preset time is specified in the same manner as for the TON and TOF SFBs. The name or address of the instance data block for the timer is shown above the block.

An example application of the TP block is shown in Figure 5.40*a* and its associated timing diagram is shown in Figure 5.40*b*. An **off**-to-**on** transition of TRIG causes the

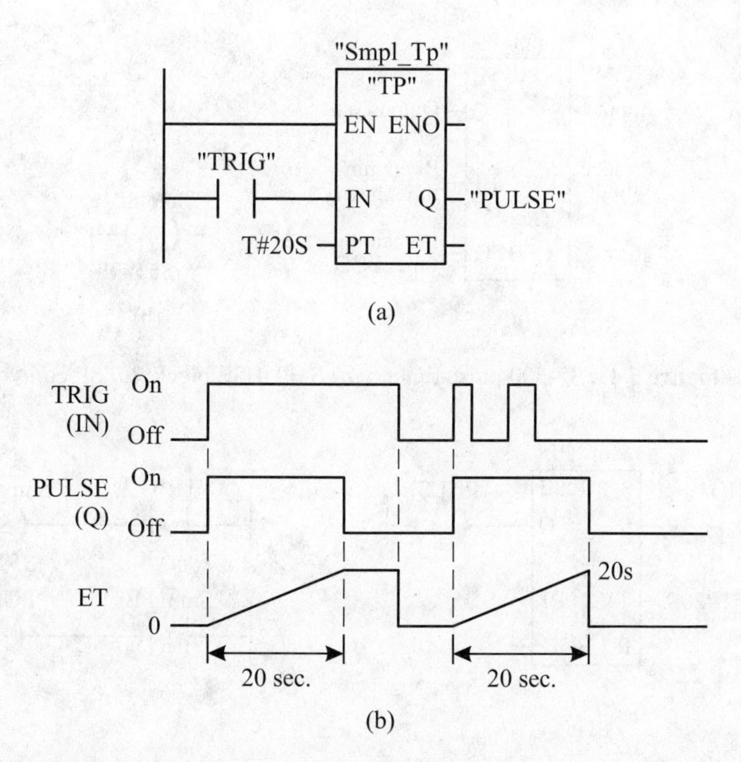

Figure 5.40. Example S7-300 TP pulse timer: *(a)* TP example; *(b)* timing diagram.

PULSE output to be turned **on** for 20 seconds. Keeping TRIG on longer than 20 seconds does not alter the duration of PULSE, it only prevents ET from being set to zero at the end of the 20-second duration. Changes in TRIG during the 20-second pulse duration are ignored.

The S7 and Modicon TP function blocks operate in a similar manner. There is no standard function block that implements a pulse for the Allen-Bradley and the GE Fanuc PLCs.

The S_PULSE function block and the SP coil basically generate a pulse whose **maximum** duration is specified by the preset time. The S_PEXT function block and the SE coil basically generate a pulse whose **minimum** duration is specified by the preset time. The extended pulse timer can be retriggered to extend the pulse width.

The S_PULSE S5-compatible pulse timer is shown in Figure 5.41*a*. An **off**-to-**on** transition of the S input causes the Q output to turn **on**, the accumulator starts at TV, and the accumulator decrements once for each time base interval. When the accumulator equals zero, the timer is "timed out" and the Q output turns **off**. If S turns **off** during the timing interval, the accumulator is reset and the Q output turns **off**. The R input is the timer reset. Anytime R is **on** the accumulator is zeroed and the Q output remains **off**.

As a coil, the S5-compatible pulse timer is shown in Figure 5.41*b*. An **off**-to-**on** transition at the coil input causes the contact reference to the timer to turn **on** and the accumulator acts in the same manner as for the S_PULSE block. When the accumulator equals zero, the timer is "timed out" and the contact reference to the timer turns **off**. If the coil input turns **off** during the timing interval, the accumulator is reset and the contact

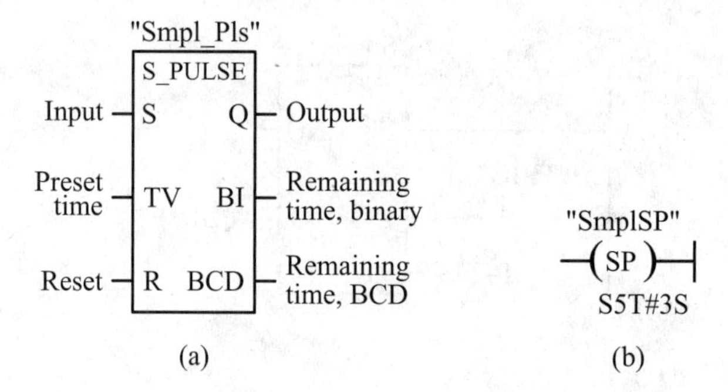

Figure 5.41. S7-300 pulse timers: *(a)* S_PULSE block; *(b)* SP coil.

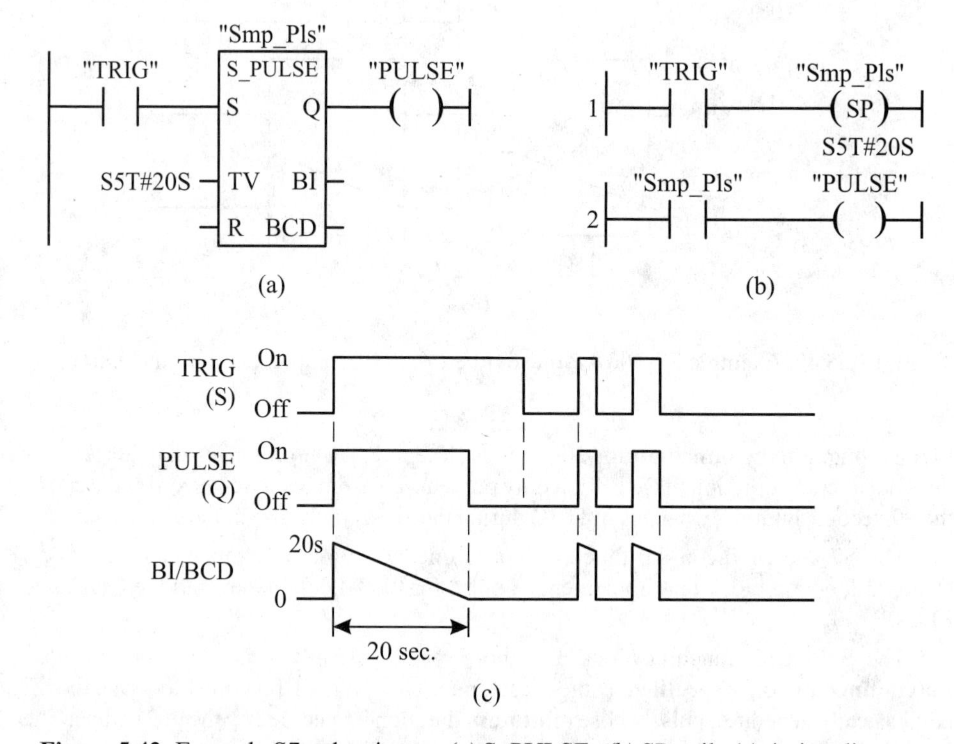

Figure 5.42. Example S7 pulse timers: *(a)* S_PULSE; *(b)* SP coil; *(c)* timing diagram.

reference to the timer remains **off**. A SP coil timer is reset by turning **on** a reset coil referring to the timer.

An example application implemented with the S_PULSE block and the SP coil is shown in Figure 5.42*a* and Figure 5.42*b*, respectively. The associated timing diagram is shown in Figure 5.42*c*. An **off**-to-**on** transition of TRIG causes the PULSE output to be turned **on** for 20 seconds (as long as TRIG remains **on**). If TRIG turns **off** within the 20-second duration, the timer is reset. Keeping TRIG on longer than 20 seconds does not alter the duration of PULSE.

The S_PEXT S5-compatible extended pulse timer is shown in Figure 5.43*a*. There are two differences with the S_PULSE block: (1) if S turns **off** during the timing interval, the accumulator continues to decrement; and (2) if the S input has an **off**-to-**on** transition during the Q output pulse, the accumulator is set to TV, restarting the timing interval.

As a coil, the S5-compatible extended pulse timer is shown in Figure 5.43*b*.The SE coil operates like the SP coil except: (1) if the coil input turns **off** during the timing interval, the accumulator continues to decrement; and (2) if the coil input has an **off**-to-**on** transition during the output pulse, the accumulator is set to TV, restarting the timing interval.

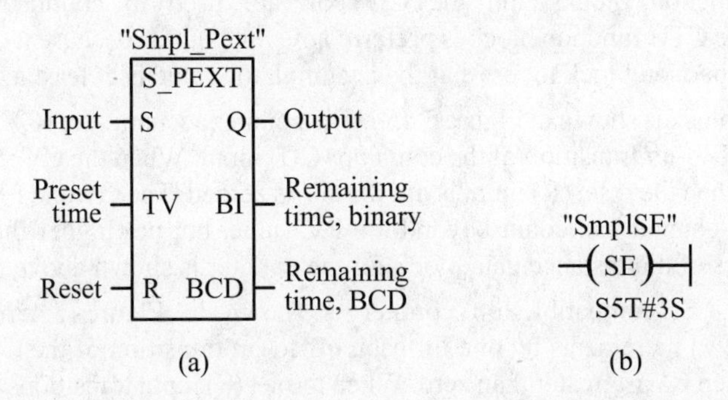

Figure 5.43. S7-300 extended pulse timers: *(a)* S_PEXT block; *(b)* SE coil.

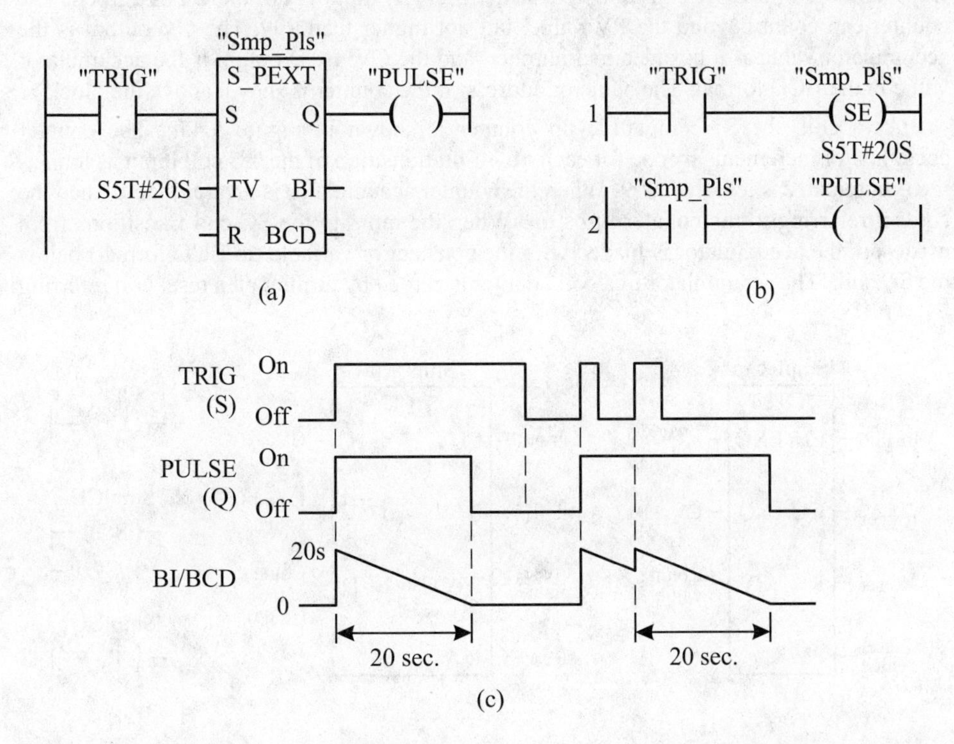

Figure 5.44. Example S7 extended pulse timers: *(a)* S_PEXT; *(b)* SE coil; *(c)* timing diagram.

An example application implemented with the S_PEXT block and the SE coil is shown in Figure 5.44*a* and Figure 5.44*b*, respectively. The associated timing diagram is shown in Figure 5.44*c*. An **off**-to-**on** transition of TRIG causes the PULSE output to be turned **on** for 20 seconds. If TRIG has an **off**-to-**on** transition within the 20-second duration, the pulse timing is restarted. Keeping TRIG on longer than 20 seconds does not alter the duration of PULSE.

5.6.5 Up Counters

An up counter can be implemented one of three ways, shown in Figure 5.45. The CTU and S_CU function blocks and the CU coil are used to count transitions. The IEC-compatible CTU function block is preferred over the others because it does not require a separate comparison block to test that the accumulator value is at least a certain value.

The CTU block is shown in Figure 5.45*a*. The counter accumulator (CV) increments by one for each **off**-to-**on** transition of the count up (CU) input. When the CV = PV, then the Q output is **on**. When the reset (R) input is **on**, the CV is zeroed. The CV and PV data types are both INT. The counter can count beyond the PV value, but not higher than 32,767. The name or address of the instance data block for the counter is shown above the block.

The S_CU S5-compatible up counter is shown in Figure 5.45*b*. The counter accumulator (CV) increments by one for each **off**-to-**on** transition of the CU input. The Q output is **on** when CV is greater than zero. When the set (S) input transitions from **off**-to-**on**, the CV is loaded with the value at the preset value (PV) input. The preset value can be a word variable or a BCD constant. When the reset (R) input is **on**, the CV is zeroed. The counter can count beyond the PV value, but not higher than 999. The CV output is the accumulator value as a hexadecimal number, and the CV_BCD output is the accumulator value in the BCD format. The name or address of the counter is shown above the block.

As a coil, the S5-compatible up counter is shown in Figure 5.45*c*. The counter accumulator increments by one for each **off**-to-**on** transition of the CU coil input as long as the accumulator is less than 999. When the counter accumulator is greater than 0, then the contact referring to the counter turns **on**. When the input to the SC coil transitions from **off**-to-**on**, the accumulator is loaded with the constant or variable (in BCD format) below the SC coil. The accumulator of a coil counter is zeroed by turning **on** a reset coil referring

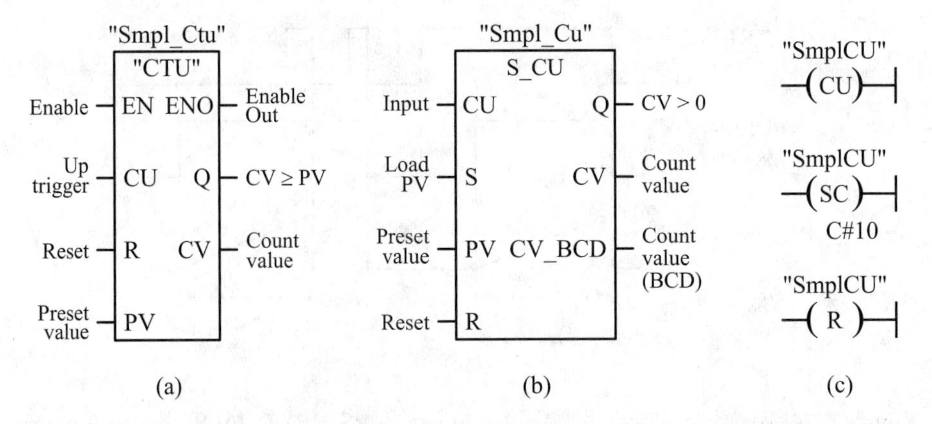

Figure 5.45. S7-300 up counters: *(a)* CTU block; *(b)* S_CU block; *(c)* CU and SC coils.

to the counter. The counter accumulator value is accessed as a hexadecimal number and must be moved to a word location before it can be examined.

An example application implemented with each type of up counter is shown in Figure 5.46 and the associated timing diagram is shown in Figure 5.47. As long as All_Reset is **on**, the counter accumulator is held at zero. When All_Reset is **off**, at every **off**-to-**on** transition of PROX_2, the counter accumulator increments by one. When the accumulator is equal to or greater than 3, the Advance_Cyl coil is turned **on**. When Advance_Cyl is already **on**, any more positive transitions of PROX_2 cause the value of the accumulator to change, and Advance_Cyl remains **on**. Note that for the S5-compatible function block (Figure 5.46*b*), a

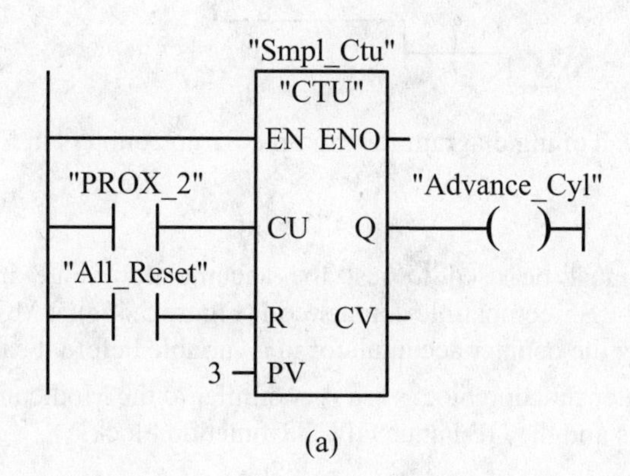

(a)

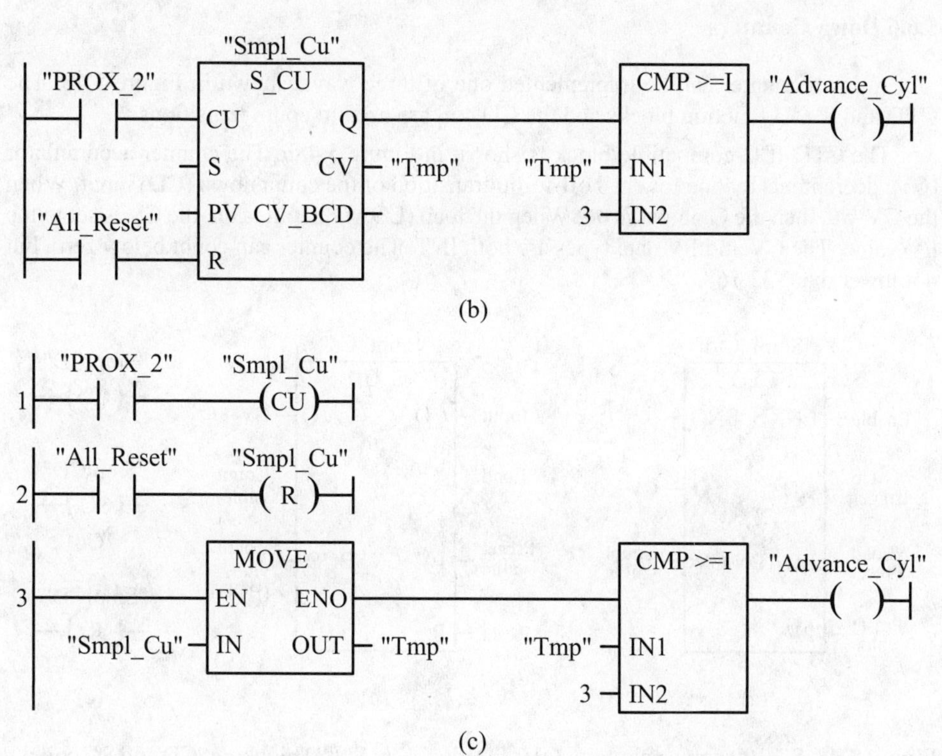

Figure 5.46. Example S7 up counters: *(a)* CTU; *(b)* S_CU *(c)* SC coil.

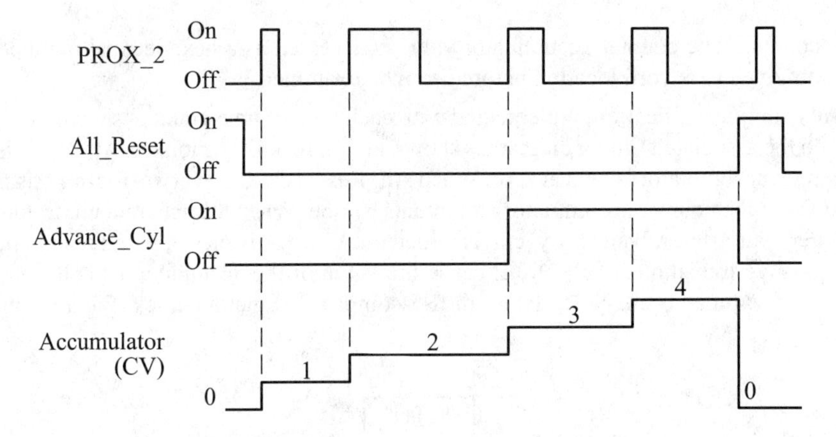

Figure 5.47. Timing diagram for example S7 up counters in Figure 5.46.

comparison block must be used to test the accumulator value in order to control Advance_Cyl. For the S5-compatible counter coil (Figure 5.46*c*), a MOVE function block must be used to copy the counter accumulator to a variable before it can be tested.

The S7 up-counter function blocks are very similar to the Modicon and Allen-Bradley CTU function blocks and the GE Fanuc UPCTR function block.

5.6.6 Down Counters

A down counter can be implemented one of three ways, shown in Figure 5.48. The CTD and S_CD function blocks and the CD coil are used to count transitions.

The CTD IEC-compatible block is shown in Figure 5.48*a*. The counter accumulator (CV) decrements by one for each **off**-to-**on** transition of the count down (CD) input. When the CV = 0, then the Q output is **on**. When the load (LOAD) input is **on**, the CV is set to the PV value. The CV and PV data types are both INT. The counter can count below zero, but not lower than -32,768.

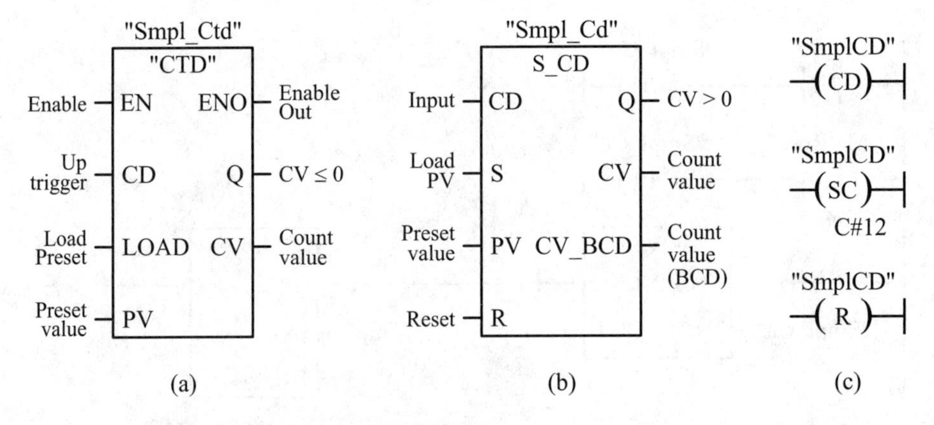

Figure 5.48. S7-300 down counters: *(a)* CTD block; *(b)* S_CD block; *(c)* CD and SC coils.

The S_CD S5-compatible down counter is shown in Figure 5.48*b*. The counter accumulator (CV) decrements by one for each **off**-to-**on** transition of the CD input. The Q output is **on** when CV is greater than zero. When the set (S) input transitions from **off**-to-**on**,

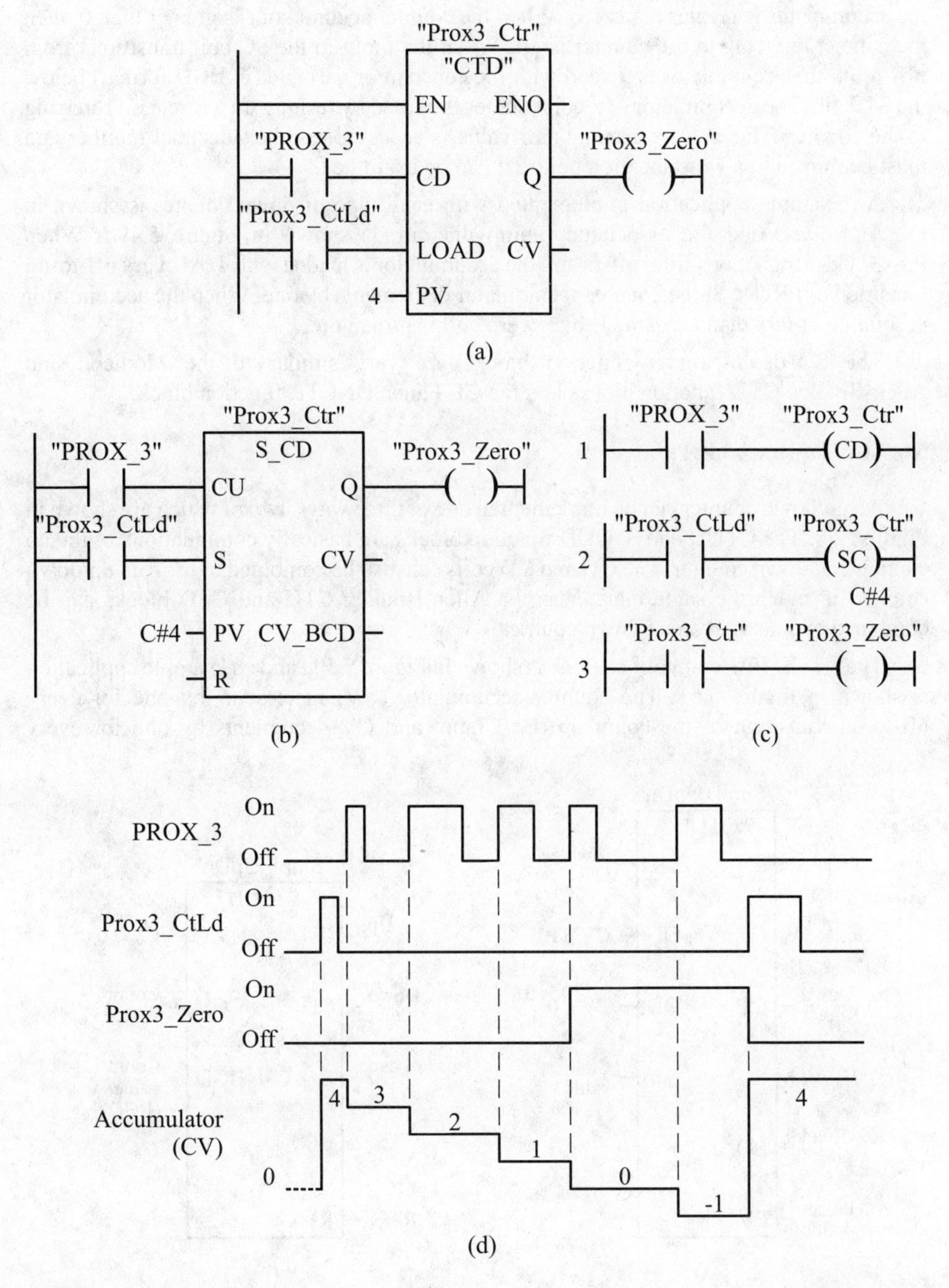

Figure 5.49. Example S7 down counters: *(a)* CTD; *(b)* S_CD *(c)* CD coil; *(d)* timing diagram.

the CV is loaded with the value at the preset value (PV) input. When the reset (R) input is **on**, the CV is zeroed. The counter can count no lower than zero.

As a coil, the S5-compatible down counter is shown in Figure 5.48*c*. The counter accumulator decrements by one for each **off**-to-**on** transition of the CU coil input as long as the accumulator is greater than zero. When the counter accumulator is greater than 0, then the contact referring to the counter is **on**. When the input to the SC coil transitions from **off**-to-**on**, the accumulator is loaded with the constant or variable (in BCD format) below the SC coil. The accumulator of a coil counter is zeroed by turning **on** a reset coil referring to the counter. The counter accumulator value is accessed as a hexadecimal number and must be moved to a word location before it can be examined.

An example application implemented with each type of down counter is shown in Figure 5.49*a-c* and the associated timing diagram is shown in Figure 5.49*d*. When Prox3_CtLd transitions from **off**-to-**on**, the accumulator is loaded with 4. At every **off**-to-**on** transition of PROX_3, the counter accumulator decrements by one. When the accumulator is equal to or less than zero, the Prox3_Zero coil is turned **on**.

The S7 down-counter function blocks are very similar to the Modicon and Allen-Bradley CTD function blocks and the GE Fanuc DNCTR function block.

5.6.7 Up/Down Counters

An up/down counter can be implemented one of three ways, two of which are shown in Figure 5.50. The CTUD and S_CUD function blocks are basically combinations of the up counter and down counter. The CU and CD coils can also be combined to form an up/down counter, in much the same manner as the Allen-Bradley CTU and CTD blocks can be combined to construct an up/down counter.

The CTUD IEC-compatible block is shown in Figure 5.50*a* and an example application is shown in Figure 5.51. The counter accumulator (CV) increments by one for every **off**-to-**on** transition of the count up (CU) input and CV decrements by one for every

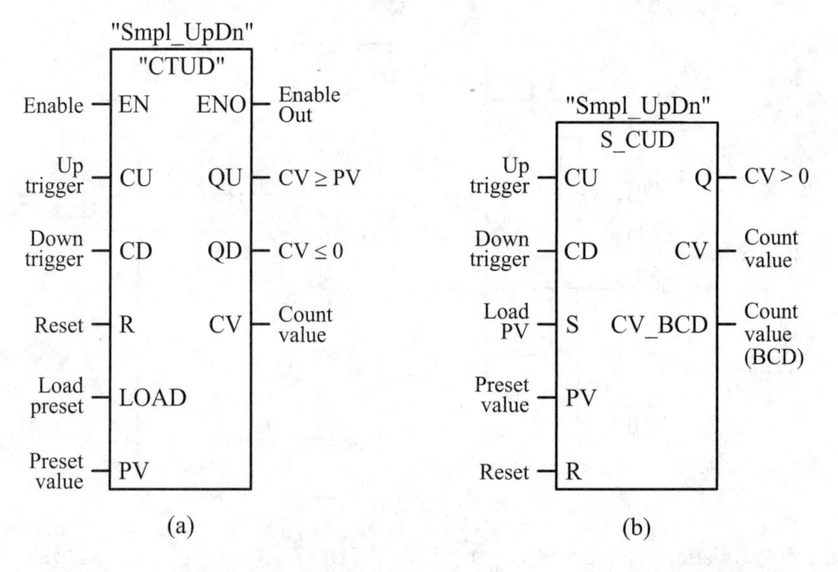

Figure 5.50. S7-300 up/down counters: *(a)* CTUD block; *(b)* S_CUD block.

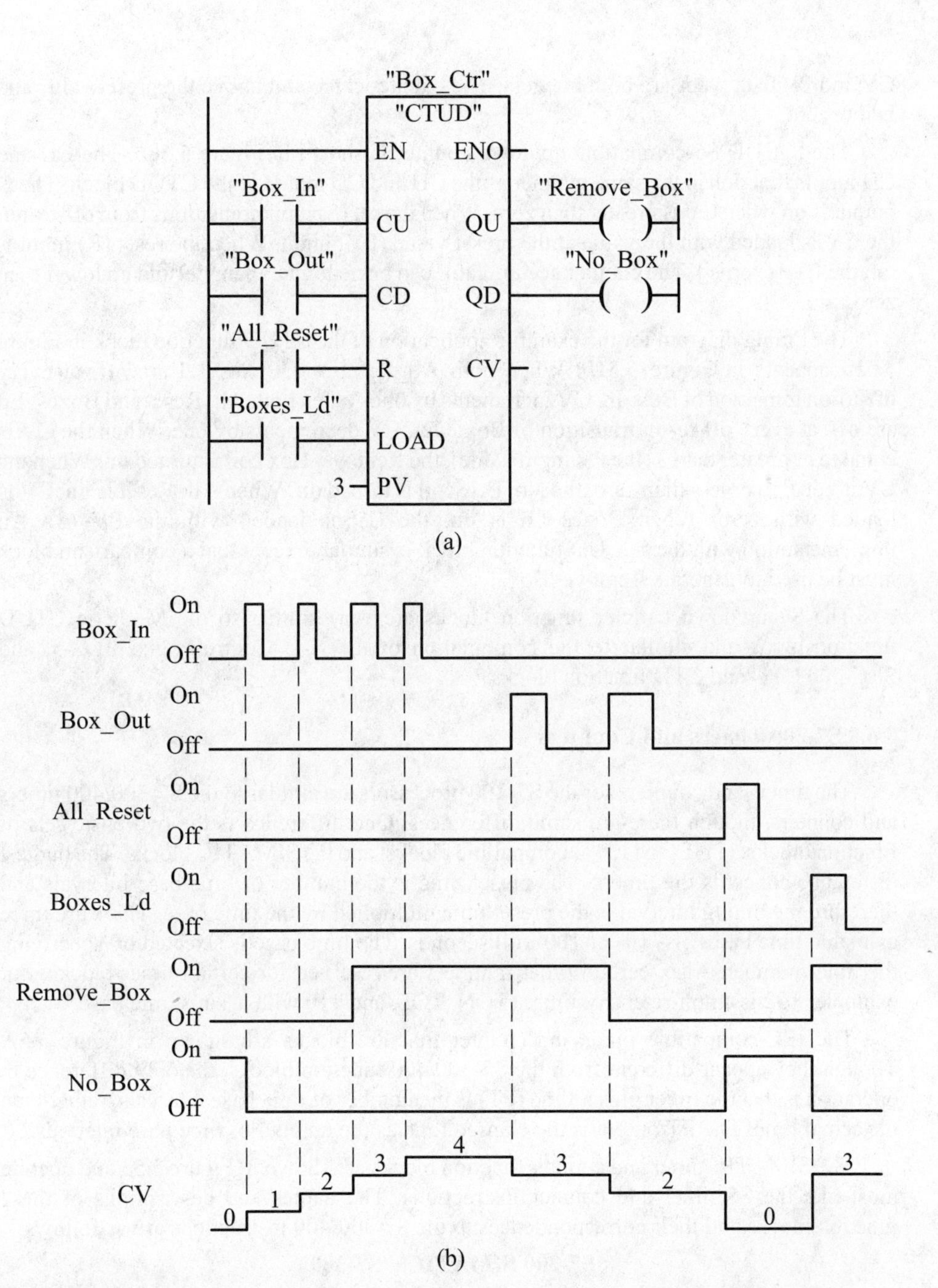

Figure 5.51. Example S7 CTUD counter: *(a)* ladder logic; *(b)* timing diagram.

off-to-**on** transition of the count down (CD) input. When the CV PV, then the QU output is turned **on**. When the CV 0, then the QD output is turned **on**. When the reset (R) input is **on**, the CV is zeroed. When the load (LOAD) input is **on**, the CV is set to the PV value. If both R and LOAD are on simultaneously, the R input has precedence and sets the CV to zero. The

CV and PV data types are both integers. The counter can count above the preset value and below zero.

The S_CUD S5-compatible up/down counter is shown in Figure 5.50*b*. The CU and CD inputs function in the same manner as the CU and CD inputs of the CTUD block. The Q output is **on** when CV is greater than zero. When the set (S) input transitions from **off**-to-**on**, the CV is loaded with the value at the preset value (PV) input. When the reset (R) input is **on**, the CV is zeroed. The counter accumulator can be no higher than 999 and no lower than zero.

The timing diagram for the example application of the CTUD function block in Figure 5.51*a* appears in Figure 5.51*b*. When both All_Reset and Boxes_Ld are **off**, at every **off**-to-**on** transition of Box_In, CV increments by one. When both All_Reset and Boxes_Ld are **off**, at every **off**-to-**on** transition of Box_Out, CV decrements by one. When the CV is equal to or greater than 3 (the PV input value), the Remove_Box coil is turned **on**. When the CV is equal to or less than zero, the No_Box coil is turned **on**. When All_Reset is **on**, CV is loaded with zero. When Boxes_Ld is **on**, the CV is loaded with the PV (3). An implementation with the S_CUD function block is similar, except that a comparison block must be used to generate Remove_Box.

The S7 up/down counter function blocks are very similar to the Modicon CTUD function block and similar to the combination of the A-B ControlLogix, PLC-5, and SLC-500 CTU and CTD function blocks.

5.6.8 S7-200 Timers and Counters

The timers and counters for the S7-200 processors are similar to the S7-300/400 timers and counters, though there are some differences. One difference is the two basic sets of function blocks: (1) IEC 61131-3 compatible blocks; and (2) SIMATIC blocks. The biggest difference concerns the timers. The preset time is the number of time base intervals and therefore the timing interval is the preset time multiplied by the time base. There are three available time bases: 1-, 10- or 100-milliseconds. The time base is selected by specifying the timer number. Also, certain timer numbers are reserved for certain timer blocks. For example, T32 is a non-retentive timer (TON, TOF, and TP) with a 1-ms time base.

The IEC-compatible timer and counter function blocks are shown in Figure 5.52. Though they appear different from the S7-300/400 function blocks, the only difference in operation is that the timer preset time (PT) is the number of time base intervals, rather than the actual time. The ET output is the elapsed time as the number of time base intervals.

The SIMATIC timer and counter function blocks are shown in Figure 5.53 and operate most like the S5 timer and counter instructions. The names and descriptions of these function blocks and their correspondences to the S7-300/400 instructions are as follows:

Description	S7-200 SIMATIC Function Block	S7-300 Instruction
On-delay timer	TON	SD coil
Off-delay timer	TOF	SA coil
Ret. on-delay timer	TONR	SS coil
Up counter	CTU	S_CU block
Down counter	CTD	S_CD block
Up/down counter	CTUD	CTUD block

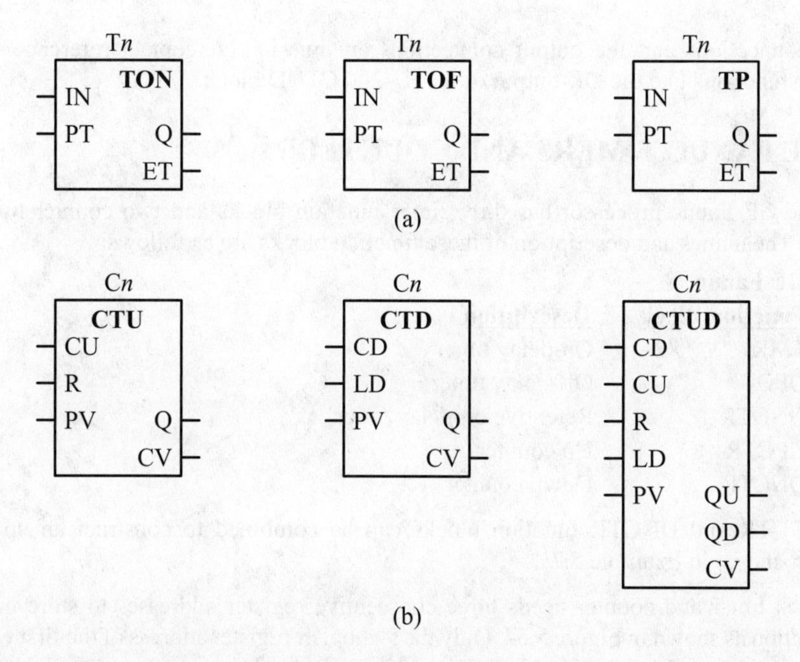

Figure 5.52. S7-200 IEC function blocks: *(a)* timers; *(b)* counters.

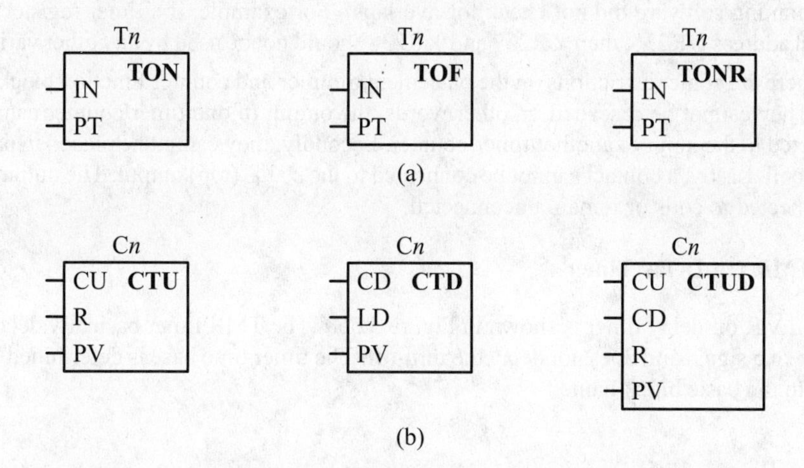

Figure 5.53. S7-200 SIMATIC function blocks: *(a)* timers; *(b)* counters.

For the SIMATIC timers (Figure 5.53*a*), the preset time is the PT input to the block rather than shown as a time interval below the S5 timer coil. As for the S5 coils, the status of the timer is accessed by a contact reference to the timer. The SIMATIC CTU block functions like the S7-300 S_CU block, minus the output connections. A contact reference to the counter functions like the Q output of the S_CU block. In a similar manner, the SIMATIC CTD block operates like the S_CD block of the S7-300 processor. The SIMATIC CTUD block functions like the S7-300 block of the same name except the LOAD input connections and the output connections are missing. A contact reference to the counter functions like the QU output of the S7-300 CTUD block.

5.7 GE FANUC TIMERS AND COUNTERS

The GE Fanuc processor has three timer function blocks and two counter function blocks. The names and description of these function blocks are as follows:

GE Fanuc Function Block	Description
TMR	On-delay timer
OFDT	Off-delay timer
ONDTR	Retentive on-delay timer
UPCTR	Up counter
DNCTR	Down counter

The UPCTR and DNCTR function blocks can be combined to construct an up/down counter, shown in Example 5.7.

Each timer and counter needs three consecutive register addresses to store internal information as shown in Figure 5.54. Only the symbol or register address of the first word is specified as part of the function block. The other register addresses are assumed. Note that when accessed with a symbol, the timer/counter registers are treated as an array of integers. The three-register block should not overlap with other data (earlier versions of the programming software did not check for overlaps). For example, if a timer register block starts at address %R236, then %R237 and %R238 should not be used by any other variables.

There are some restrictions on the placement of timer and counter function blocks on a rung. They cannot be cascaded, in other words, the output of one timer/counter cannot be connected to the input of another timer/counter. Secondly, they cannot be placed in parallel with a coil. Lastly, a contact cannot be connected to the status (top) output. The output must be connected to coils or remain unconnected.

5.7.1 TMR On-Delay Timer

A TMR on-delay timer is shown in Figure 5.55*a*. The TMR timer basically delays the turn-on of a signal and does not delay the turn-off. The timer time base is determined by the suffix to the basic block name:

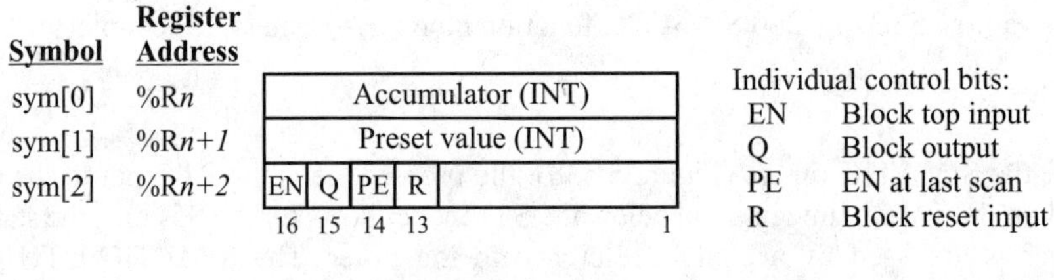

Symbol	Register Address	
sym[0]	%R*n*	Accumulator (INT)
sym[1]	%R*n+1*	Preset value (INT)
sym[2]	%R*n*+2	EN (16) | Q (15) | PE (14) | R (13) | … (1)

Individual control bits:

EN	Block top input
Q	Block output
PE	EN at last scan
R	Block reset input

Figure 5.54. GE Fanuc timer/counter registers.

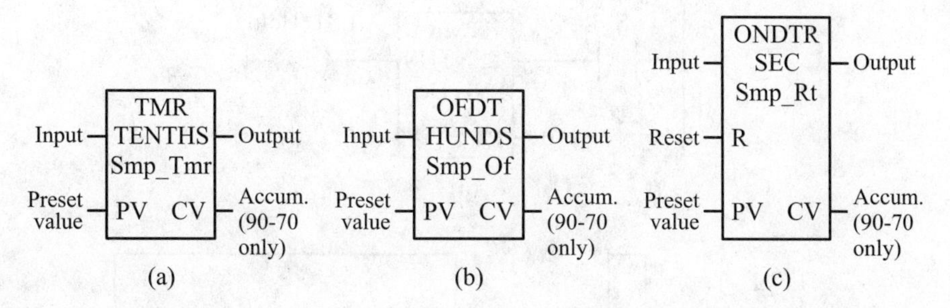

Figure 5.55. GE Fanuc timers: *(a)* TMR on-delay; *(b)* OFDT off-delay; *(c)* ONDTR retentive on-delay.

Block Name	Time Base
TMR_THOUS	0.001 seconds
TMR_HUNDS	0.01 seconds
TMR_TENTHS	0.1 seconds
TMR_SEC	1.0 seconds (only valid for 90-70)

The time-base suffix is shown by the second text line within the block. The symbol or starting address of the three registers storing the internal information (Figure 5.54) is displayed below the timer suffix.

When the top timer input is **on**, the accumulator is counted up once for each time base interval. When the accumulator equals the preset value (PV), the timer is "timed out" and the output is set to **on**. The accumulator continues to increment as long as the input is **on**. If the timer input turns **off**, the accumulator is set to zero and timing restarts when the input turns **on**. The PV may be a constant or the symbol/address of an integer. The timing interval is the preset time multiplied by the time base. The maximum interval is 32,767 seconds (with a 1 second time base). The value of the accumulator or the preset value can be accessed as integers (through the three timer registers). For the 90-70 processors, the CV output can be connected to an integer in order to monitor the accumulator.

An example application of the TON instruction is shown in Figure 5.56*a* and its associated timing diagram is shown in Figure 5.56*b*. The preset time is 15 seconds (1500.1 sec.). The input, LS_1 must remain **on** for at least 15 seconds before the timer output and the LS_1_Hold coil is turned **on**. When LS_1 is turned **off** after 5 seconds, the accumulator is set to zero and the timer output remains **off**. The timer registers are accessed with the "LS1_DelTmr" symbol, which is truncated in the TMR block display.

The GE Fanuc TMR function block is similar to the Modicon TON, the Allen-Bradley TON, and the Siemens on-delay timer function blocks.

5.7.2 OFDT Off-Delay Timer 5.57

An OFDT off-delay timer is shown in Figure 5.55*b* and an example application is in Figure 5.57. The OFDT timer basically delays the turn-off of a signal and does not delay the turn-on. As for the TMR block, the timer time base is determined by the suffix to the basic block name.

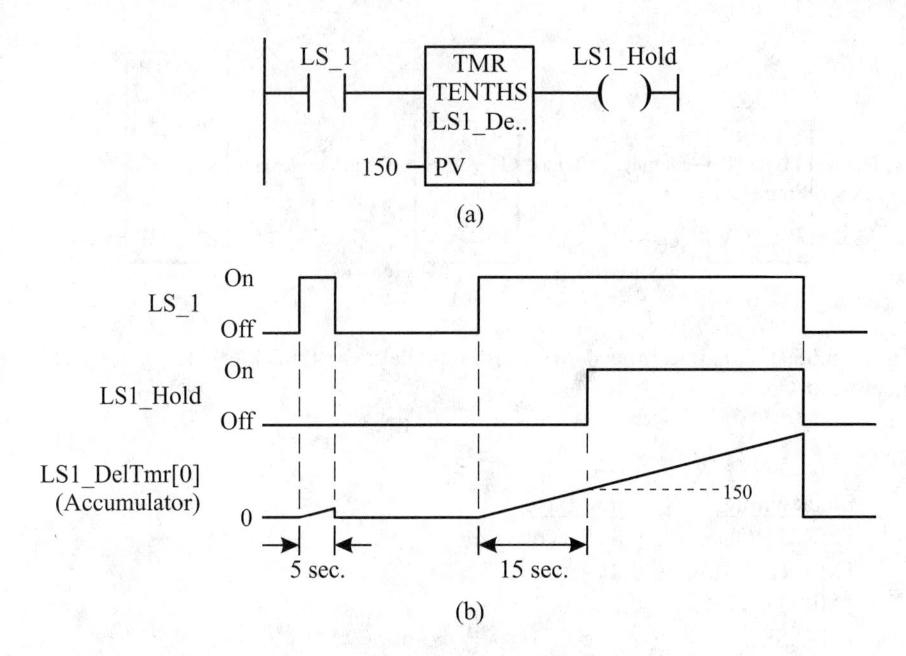

Figure 5.56. Example GE Fanuc TMR timer: *(a)* ladder logic; *(b)* timing diagram.

Looking at the top input and output connections, the OFDT timer operates exactly opposite of the TMR timer. When the top input turns **off**, the accumulator is counted up once for each time base interval. When accumulator equals the preset value (PV), the timer

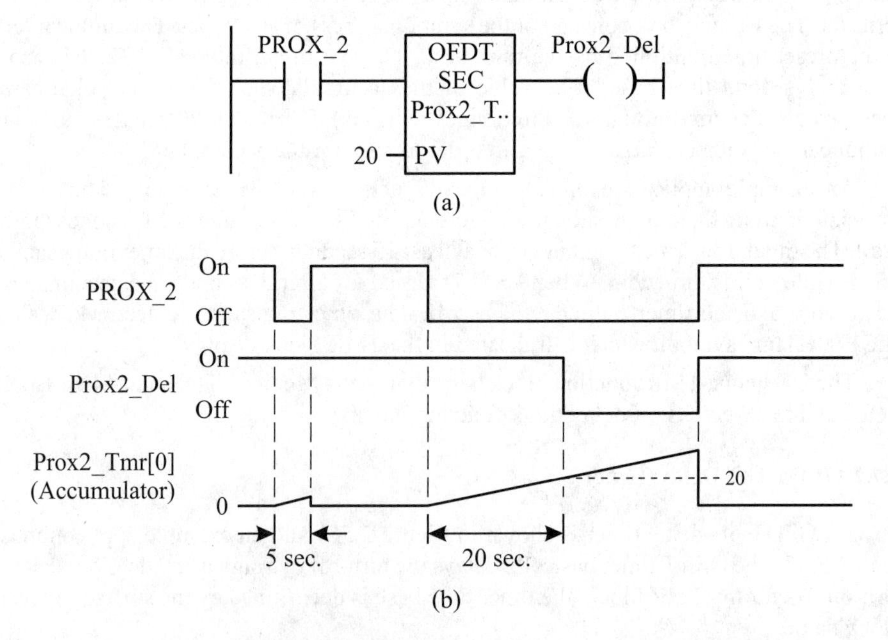

Figure 5.57. Example GE Fanuc OFDT timer: *(a)* ladder logic; *(b)* timing diagram.

is "timed out" and the output turns **off**. The accumulator continues to increment as long as the input is **off**. If the timer input turns **on**, the output remains **on**, the accumulator is set to zero, and timing recommences when the input turns **off**. The preset value is specified in the same manner as for TMR.

An example application of the OFDT instruction is shown in Figure 5.57*a* and its associated timing diagram is shown in Figure 5.57*b*. The PROX_2 discrete input must remain **off** for at least 20 seconds before the Prox2_Del coil is turned **off**. When PROX_2 is turned **on** after 5 seconds, the accumulator is reset and the Prox2_Del coil remains **on**. The symbol, Prox2_Tmr, accesses the timer registers.

The GE Fanuc OFDT function block is similar to the Modicon TOF, the Allen-Bradley TOF, and the Siemens off-delay timer function blocks.

5.7.3 ONDTR Retentive On-Delay Timer

The ONDTR retentive on-delay timer is shown in Figure 5.55*c* and an application is shown in Figure 5.58. The ONDTR timer is like the TMR timer except that the accumulator is not reset when the timer input turns **off**. As for the TMR block, the timer time base is determined by the suffix to the basic block name.

When the timer input is **on**, the accumulator is counted up once for each time base interval. When the accumulator equals the preset value, the output is set to **on**. If the timer input turns **off**, the accumulator remains at its current value and timing resumes when the

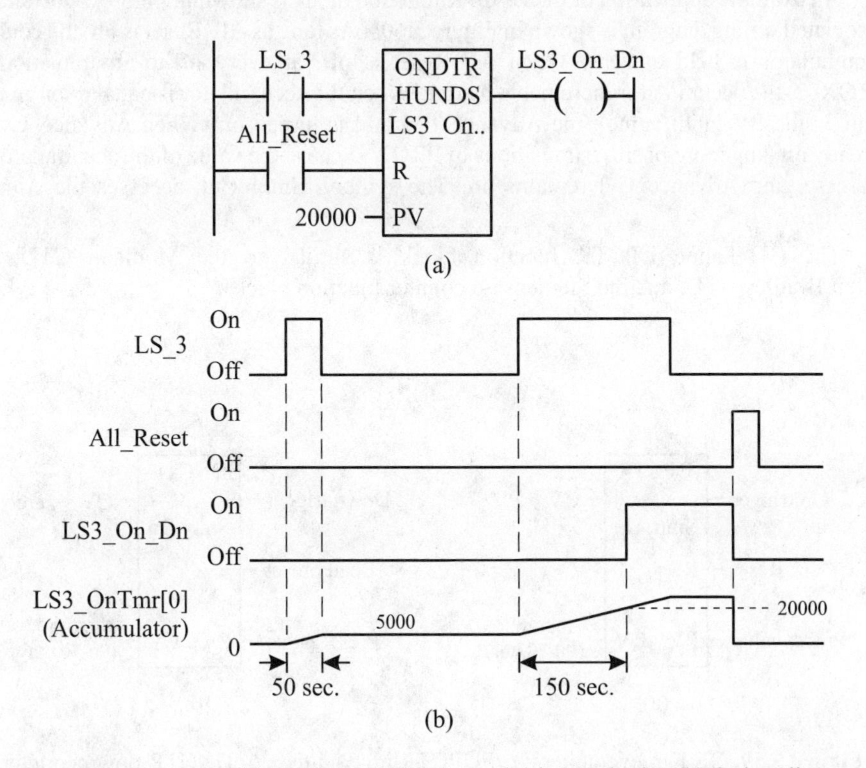

Figure 5.58. Example GE Fanuc ONDTR timer: *(a)* ladder logic; *(b)* timing diagram

input turns **on**. The R input is the timer reset. Anytime R is **on** the accumulator is zeroed and the block output remains **off**.

An example application of the ONDTR block is shown in Figure 5.58*a* and its associated timing diagram is shown in Figure 5.58*b*. The preset time is 200 seconds. The LS3_On_Dn bit is turned **on** when the cumulative time that LS_3 has been **on** is at least 200 seconds. After the accumulator has reached 200 seconds, LS3_On_Dn remains **on** even after LS_3 turns **off**. The All_Reset must be turned **on** to reset the timer. The LS3_OnTmr symbol accesses the timer registers.

The GE Fanuc ONDTR function block is similar to the Allen-Bradley RTO and the Siemens retentive on-delay timer function blocks.

5.7.4 UPCTR Up Counter

An UPCTR up counter is shown in Figure 5.59*a*. The symbol or starting address of the three registers storing the internal information (Figure 5.54) is displayed below the block name.

The counter accumulator increments by one for every **off**-to-**on** transition of the top input. When the accumulator is equal to or greater than the preset value (PV), the counter output is set to **on**. When the reset (R) input is **on**, the accumulator is set to zero. The PV may be a constant or the symbol/address of an integer. The maximum accumulator or preset value is 32,767. The accumulator can count beyond the PV. The accumulator or the preset value can be accessed as integers.

An example application of the UPCTR function block is shown in Figure 5.60*a* and its associated timing diagram is shown in Figure 5.60*b*. As long as All_Reset is **on**, the counter accumulator is held at zero. When All_Reset is **off**, at every **off**-to-**on** transition of PROX_2, the accumulator increments by one. When the accumulator is equal to or greater than 3 (the PV input value), the Advance_Cyl coil is turned **on**. When Advance_Cyl is already **on**, any more positive transitions of PROX_2 cause the value of the accumulator to increase, and Advance_Cyl remains **on**. The symbol, Smpl_Ctu, accesses the counter registers.

The GE Fanuc UPCTR function block is similar to the Modicon CTU, the Allen-Bradley CTU, and the Siemens up counter function blocks.

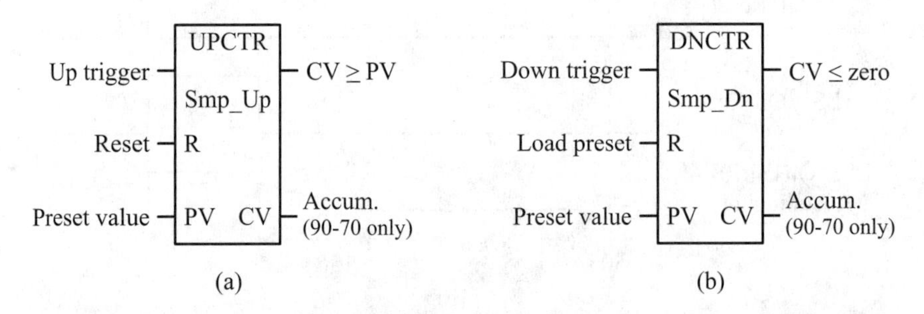

Figure 5.59. GE Fanuc counters: *(a)* UPCTR up counter; *(b)* DNCTR down counter.

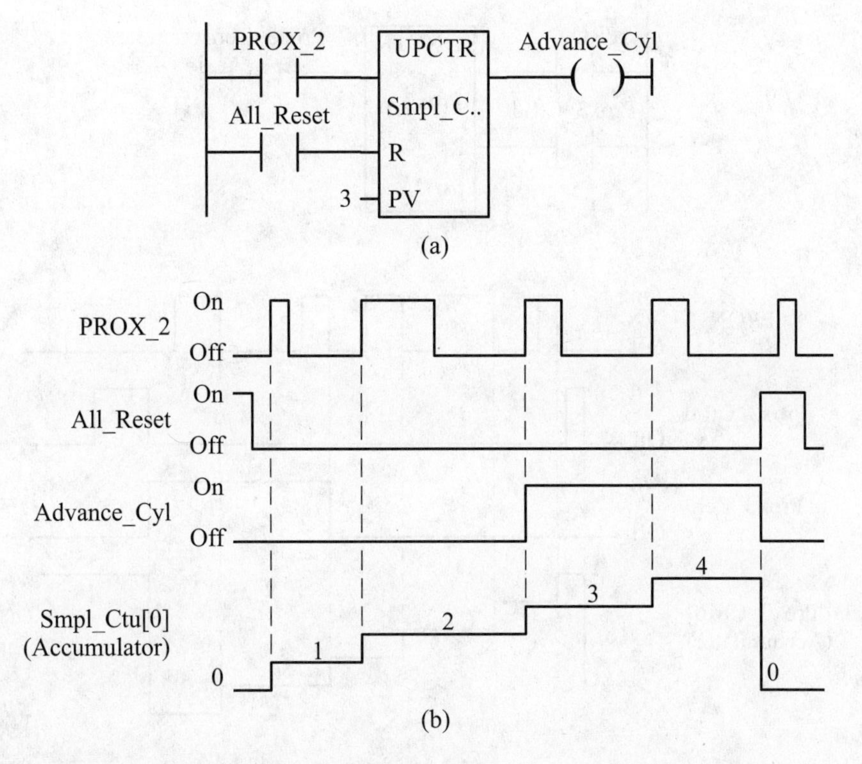

Figure 5.60. Example GE Fanuc UPCTR counter: *(a)* ladder logic; *(b)* timing diagram.

5.7.5 DNCTR Down Counter

A DNCTR down counter is shown in Figure 5.59*b*. The counter accumulator decrements by one for every **off**-to-**on** transition of the top input. When the accumulator is less than or equal to zero, the counter output is set to **on**. When the R input is **on**, the accumulator is set to the PV input. The PV may be a constant or the symbol/address of an integer. The preset value minimum is zero and its maximum is 32,767. The accumulator can count lower than zero to a minimum of -32,768. The accumulator or the preset value can be accessed as integers.

An example application of the DNCTR function block is shown in Figure 5.61*a* and its associated timing diagram is shown in Figure 5.61*b*. When Prox3_CtLd is **on**, the accumulator is loaded with the PV (4). When Prox3_CtLd is **off**, at every **off**-to-**on** transition of Prox_3, the accumulator decrements by one. When the CV is equal to or less than 0, the Prox3_Zero coil is turned **on**. When Prox3_Zero is already **on**, any more positive transitions of PROX_3 cause the value of the accumulator to descrease, and Prox3_Zero remains **on**. The Prox3_Ctr symbol accesses the counter registers.

The GE Fanuc DNCTR function block is similar to the Modicon CTD, the Allen-Bradley CTD, and the Siemens down counter function blocks.

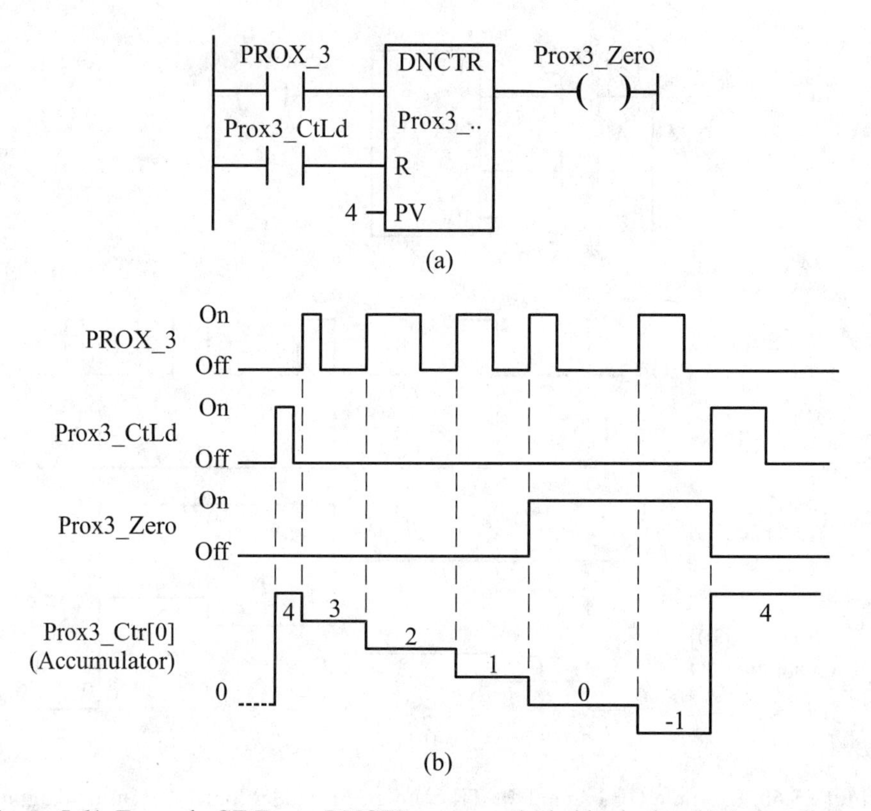

Figure 5.61. Example GE Fanuc DNCTR counter: *(a)* ladder logic; *(b)* timing diagram.

5.8 GENERAL TIMER AND COUNTER SITUATIONS

When formulating the ladder logic for an application involving timers, some general questions are:

What is being delayed?

Is it an on-delay or an off-delay?

The appropriate timer most often depends on whether an action is started or stopped after the delay. An on-delay timer is appropriate if an action is started after a delay. If an action needs to be stopped after a delay, then an off-delay timer is usually appropriate. However, since many find the off-delay timer confusing, many programmers avoid the off-delay timer entirely.

When formulating the ladder logic for an application involving counters, some general questions are:

What is being counted?

Is the count up, down, or both?

What are the reset conditions for each counter?

The counter reset conditions are important, but often overlooked by the novice programmer.

Common timer situations are the following:

1. *On delay*. B turns **on** at a specified time after A turns **on**. Both turn **off** simultaneously.
2. *Cascaded on delay*. A is turned **on**. After a specified time, B turns **on**. After a specified time, C turns **on**. The process is repeated as necessary. All turn **off** simultaneously. An example application: turning on multiple devices (e.g., motors) that would cause voltage sag if turned on simultaneously.
3. *Off delay*. Both A and B are turned **on** simultaneously. When A is turned **off**, B remains **on** for a specified time and then turns **off**.
4. *Cascaded off delay*. All devices turn on simultaneously. A is turned **off** and all others remain **on**. After a specified time, B is turned **off**. After a specified time, C is turned **off**. The process is repeated as necessary. An example application: turning off the transfer devices in a conveyor (or other material handling) system. The feeding device is turned off immediately and successive conveyors are turned off as material clears them.
5. *Timed clock "ticks."* A is **on** for one scan at a periodic interval. An example application: generate an enable signal to execute a PID controller or send a message to another PLC.
6. *One-shot*. A is **on** for a specified time after a trigger goes **on**. A stays **on** for the specified interval even if the trigger turns **off** during the interval. An example application: control a pneumatic cylinder to eject a bad part from a conveyor.
7. *Alternate cycling*. Also know as "flashing lights." A and B alternate being **on**. The "on" time of A and B can be the same or different. An example application: alarm lamps or alarm horn.
8. *Delayed one-shot*. A specified time after a trigger turns **on**, A stays **on** for a specified interval. The initial delay and duration that A stays **on** do not change even if the trigger turns **off** before the end of the duration that A stays **on**. Example application: Marking a part on a moving assembly line where the part-sensing device is some distance before the marking device.
9. *Monitor cumulative time*. Determine the total time that A has been **on**. Often used with a counter for long durations. Example application: determine the "run" time for a pump motor and generate a message for maintenance when it has a total run time of 2000 hours.

Common counter situations are the following:

1. *Straight counting*. Counter output turns **on** after a specified number of pulses at the counter input.
2. *Cascaded counters*. The output of one counter serves as the input to another counter. An example application: determine the number of items in a lot when the total number will overflow the accumulator.
3. *Difference between two counts*. Example application: determine the number of parts on a conveyor system by finding the difference between the count of parts going in and coming out of a conveyor system.
4. *Sum of multiple counts*. Count multiple events with the same counter. Example application: determine the sum of parts on multiple conveyors where each conveyor has its own part sensor.

5. *Determine rate*. Count pulses within a certain time interval. This type of application uses a timer and a counter. Example application: determine the number of parts per hour being produced by a machine.

5.9 EXAMPLES

Of the timer situations listed in the previous section, #1 and #3 are handled with the examples given with the timer function block descriptions. Situations #6 and #7 are relegated to the problems. The others will be demonstrated by the following examples:

Example 5.1 Turn on three pumps (timer situation #2)
Example 5.2 Turn off two conveyors (timer situation #4)
Example 5.3 Message send tick (timer situation #5)
Example 5.4 Marking defective parts (timer situation #8)
Example 5.5 Monitor pump run time (timer situation #9)

Of the counter situations listed in the previous section, #1 is handled with the description of the up counter function block. The others will be demonstrated with the following examples:

Example 5.6 Clock (counter situation #2)
Example 5.7 Determine amount of work in progress (counter situation #3)
Example 5.8 Sum total of pieces on two conveyors (counter situation #4)
Example 5.9 Determine number of parts per hour produced (counter situation #5)

All of the examples are worked for the Modicon Quantum/Momentum and the Allen-Bradley PLC-5/SLC-500. The ControlLogix solutions are nearly identical to the PLC-5 solutions. The solutions for the Siemens S7 and GE Fanuc PLCs are similar to the Modicon Quantum and are only shown for certain examples.

Example 5.1. Control three pumps (timer situation #2). Design a ladder logic program to sequentially start three pump motors. When the start button is pressed, Pump 1 should be started by turning **on** (closing) its run contact. After a delay of at least 5 seconds, Pump 2 should be started. After a delay of at least another 5 seconds, Pump 3 should be started. When the stop button is pressed, all three pumps should be stopped by turning **off** (opening) all three pump run contacts.

Assume the following physical input and physical output assignments:

Variable	Description
PSTRT_PB	Start push button, N. O., **on** when starting
PSTOP_PB	Stop push button, N. C., **off** when stopping
PUMP_1	Pump 1 run contact, **on** to close and start pump
PUMP_2	Pump 2 run contact, **on** to close and start pump
PUMP_3	Pump 3 run contact, **on** to close and start pump

The addresses associated with the physical inputs and outputs are:

Variable	Modicon	PLC-5	ControlLogix	Siemens	GE Fanuc
PSTRT_PB	100001	I:0/00	Local:1:I.Data.0	I0.0	%I1
PSTOP_PB	100002	I:0/01	Local:1:I.Data.1	I0.1	%I2
PUMP_1	000001	O:1/00	Local:2:O.Data.0	Q4.0	%Q1

PUMP_2	000002	O:1/01	Local:2:O.Data.1	Q4.1	%Q2
PUMP_3	000003	O:1/02	Local:2:O.Data.2	Q4.2	%Q3

Solution. Basically, the solution needs two on-delay timers: one to delay between Pump 1 started and Pump 2 started, and one to delay between Pump 2 started and Pump 3 started. The start/stop buttons only directly control Pump 1. The addresses or data types associated with the internal variables:

Variable	Modicon Data Type	PLC-5 Addr.	ControlLogix Data Type	Siemens Addr.	GE Fanuc Addr.
P2_Delay	n/a	T4:0	TIMER	DB1	%R104
P3_Delay	n/a	T4:1	TIMER	DB2	%R107

The Modicon code is shown in Figure 5.62. Since the timers are function blocks, there is no conflict to use the output of one timer to drive the input to another timer.

The Allen-Bradley PLC-5 code is shown in Figure 5.63. Since the PLC-5 timers are output instructions, the timers cannot be placed in series on a rung. Also note that the /DN bit must be referenced with a contact in order to control a pump control. Since the timer is an output instruction, it can be placed in parallel with another output coil, as the P3_DELAY timer is placed in parallel with the PUMP_2 coil. For a ControlLogix implementation, the only difference is that the timers have no time base and the preset value is 10 times the preset value of the PLC-5 timers shown.

The Siemens S7 and GE Fanuc ladder logic is shown in Figure 5.64 and Figure 5.65, respectively. Because of the EN inputs, the S7 timers must be placed in a separate network. If the P2_Delay timer is placed in parallel with the PUMP_1 coil, when PUMP_1 is stopped, the other pumps will continue to run because the EN input to P2_Delay is turned **off** preserving the last state of the timer output (which is **on**).

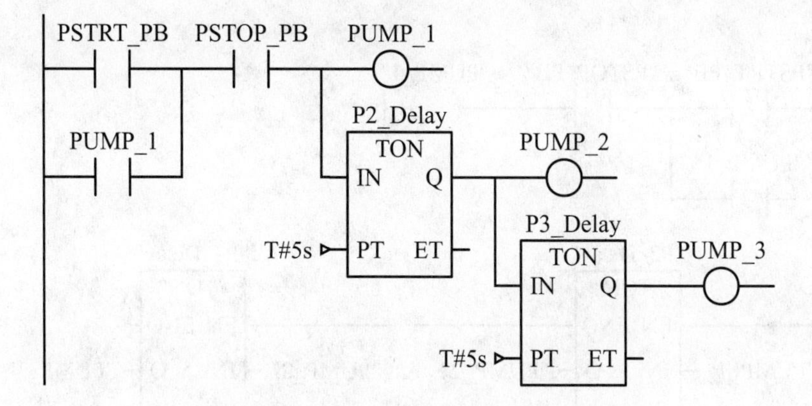

Figure 5.62. Modicon solution to Example 5.1.

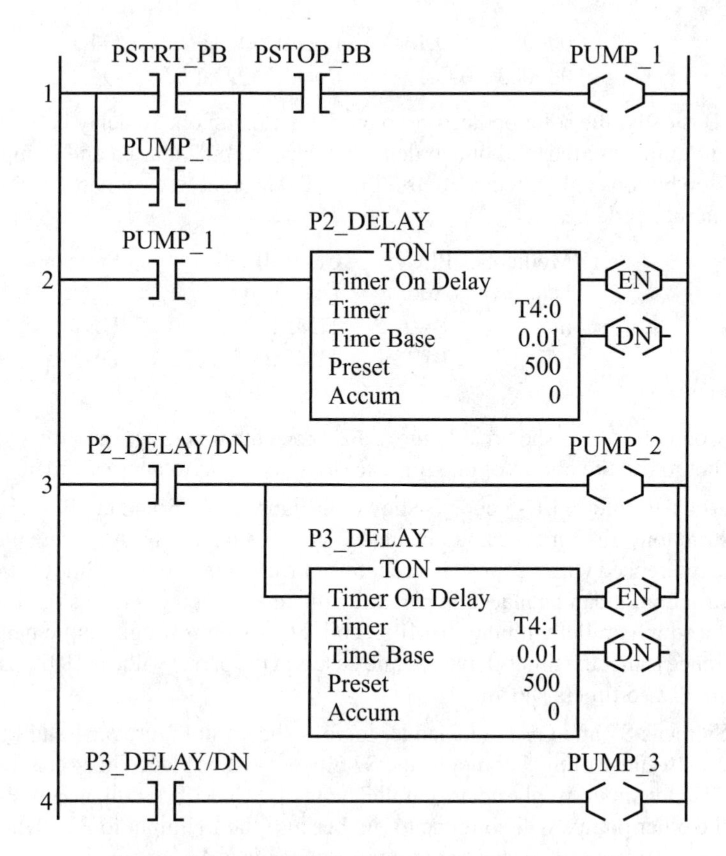

Figure 5.63. A-B PLC-5 solution to Example 5.1.

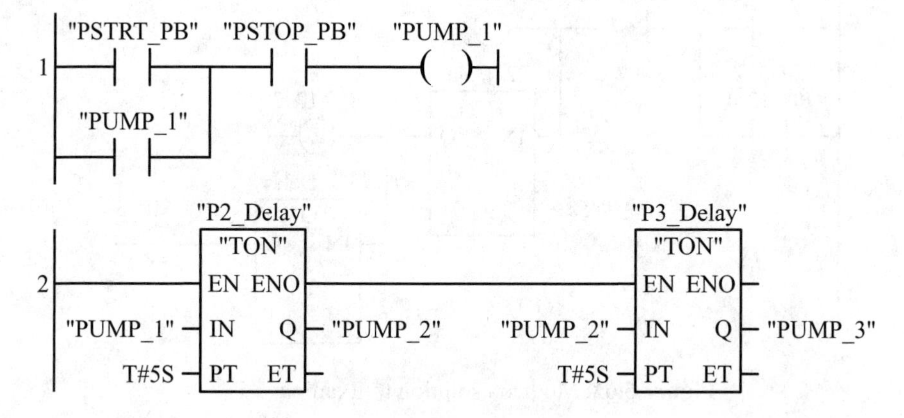

Figure 5.64. Siemens S7-300 solution to Example 5.1.

```
   PSTRT_PB   PSTOP_PB                         PUMP_1
1 ---| |---+----| |------------------------------( )---
           |
   PUMP_1  |
  ---| |---+

   PUMP_1      +---------+                     PUMP_2
2 ---| |-------| TMR     |------------------------( )---
               | TENTHS  |
               |P2_Delay |
          50 --| PV      |
               +---------+

   PUMP_2      +---------+                     PUMP_3
3 ---| |-------| TMR     |------------------------( )---
               | TENTHS  |
               |P3_Delay |
          50 --| PV      |
               +---------+
```

Figure 5.65. GE Fanuc solution to Example 5.1.

Example 5.2. Control conveyors (timer situation #4). Design a ladder logic program to sequentially stop an airlock motor and two conveyor motors, shown in Figure 5.66. When the start button is pressed, the airlock motor and the two conveyor motors are started. When the stop button is pressed, the airlock motor, L-4100, should stop immediately. After a delay of at least 45 seconds (to allow material to be completely removed from the conveyor), conveyor motor C-4100 should be stopped. After a delay of at least another 60 seconds (to allow material to be completely removed from the conveyor), conveyor motor C-4101 should be stopped.

Assume the following physical input and physical output assignments:

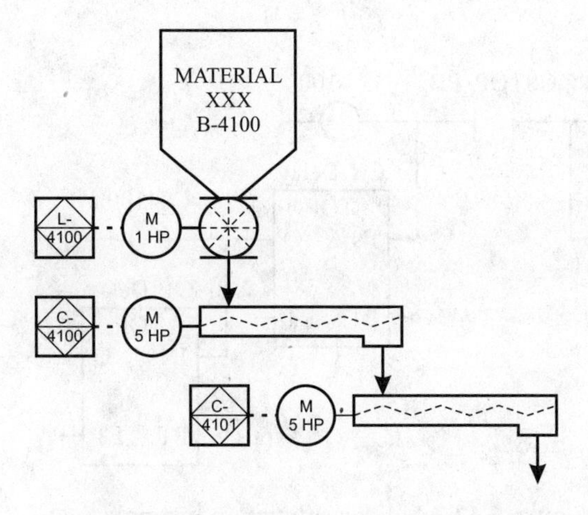

Figure 5.66. Bin and conveyor system.

Variable	Description
CSTRT_PB	Start push button, N. O., **on** when starting
CSTOP_PB	Stop push button, N. C., **off** when stopping
L_4100	L-4100 airlock motor run contact, **on** to close and start motor
C_4100	C-4100 conveyor motor run contact, **on** to close and start motor
C_4101	C-4101 conveyor motor run contact, **on** to close and start motor

The addresses associated with the physical inputs and outputs are:

Variable	Modicon	PLC-5	ControlLogix	Siemens	GE Fanuc
CSTRT_PB	100003	I:0/02	Local:1:I.Data.2	I0.2	%I3
CSTOP_PB	100004	I:0/03	Local:1:I.Data.3	I0.3	%I4
L_4100	000004	O:1/03	Local:2:O.Data.3	Q4.3	%Q4
C_4100	000005	O:1/04	Local:2:O.Data.4	Q4.4	%Q5
C_4101	000006	O:1/05	Local:2:O.Data.5	Q4.5	%Q6

Solution. Basically, the solution needs two off-delay timers: one to delay between the airlock stopped and conveyor C-4100 stopped, and one to delay between C-4100 stopped and C-4101 stopped. The start/stop buttons only directly control the airlock motor. The addresses or data types associated with the internal variables:

Variable	Modicon Data Type	PLC-5 Addr.	ControlLogix Data Type	Siemens Addr.	GE Fanuc Addr.
C0_Delay	n/a	T4:2	TIMER	DB3	%R110
C1_Delay	n/a	T4:3	TIMER	DB4	%R113

The Modicon code is shown in Figure 5.67. The Allen-Bradley PLC-5 code is shown in Figure 5.68. Note that the delay timers are placed in parallel with the motor controls. Also note that the timer preset times are 1 second longer than needed since the accuracy of the timers is ±1 second and since the specification specifies a minimum time, then 1 second is added to the specified delay time. For a ControlLogix implementation, the only difference is that the timers have no time base and the preset values are 45000 and 60000. The Siemens S7 and GE Fanuc implementations are similar to the Modicon imlementation.

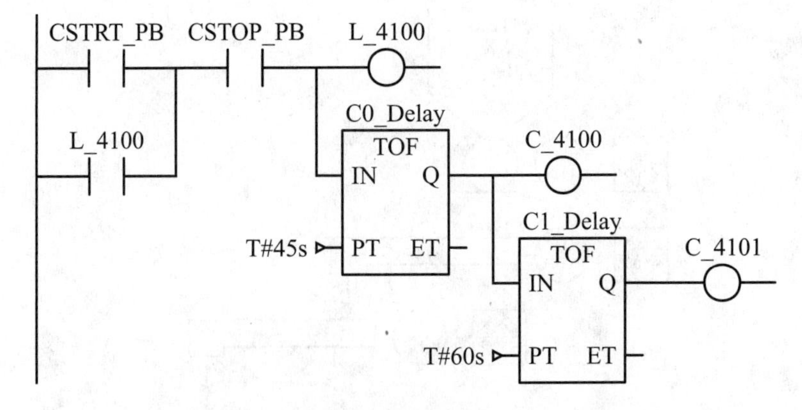

Figure 5.67. Modicon solution to Example 5.2.

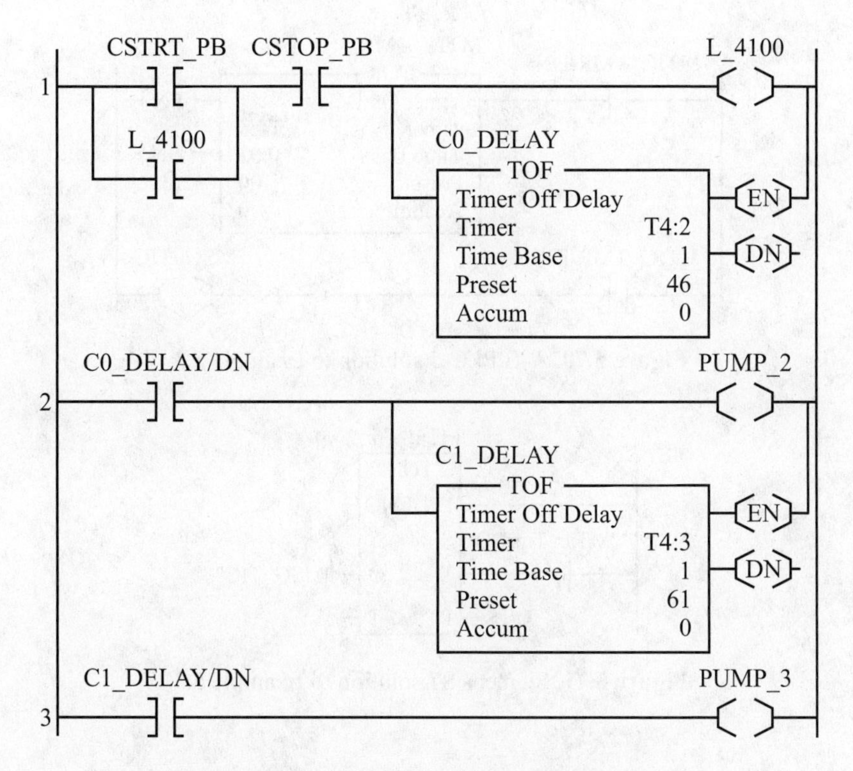

Figure 5.68. A-B PLC-5 solution to Example 5.2.

Example 5.3. Message send tick (timer situation #5). Design a ladder logic program to generate a 1-second "tick", called MSG_TIC, that will be used to send a message to another PLC. The tick should only be one scan in duration.

Solution. The solution needs one on-delay timer and MSG_TIC is its output. When MSG_TIC turns **on**, it is used to reset the timer on the next scan, which also turns MSG_TIC off. The Modicon code is shown in Figure 5.69 and the A-B PLC-5 code is shown in Figure 5.70. The Siemens S7 code appears in Figure 5.71. Note the use of "MTic_Tmr.Q" to refer to the timer output. The addresses or data types associated with the internal variables:

Variable	Modicon Data Type	PLC-5 Addr.	ControlLogix Data Type	Siemens Addr.	GE Fanuc Addr.
MSG_TIC	BOOL	B3/163	BOOL	M10.3	%M163
MTic_Tmr	n/a	T4:4	TIMER	DB5	%R116

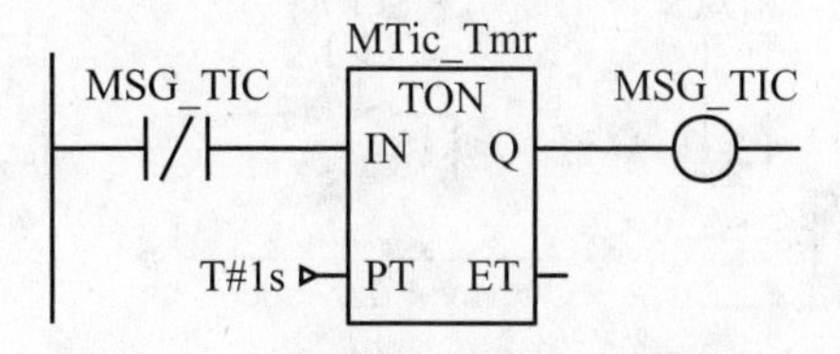

Figure 5.69. Modicon solution to Example 5.3.

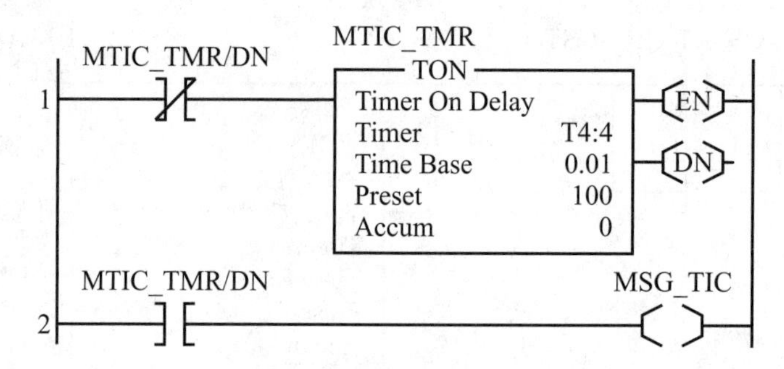

Figure 5.70. A-B PLC-5 solution to Example 5.3.

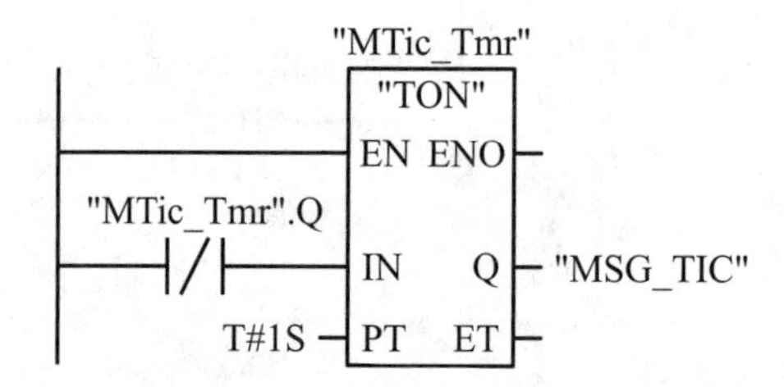

Figure 5.71. Siemens S7 solution to Example 5.3.

Example 5.4. Marking defective parts (timer situation #8). Design a ladder logic program to mark defective parts for removal from the assembly line. A simplified diagram of the station is shown in Figure 5.72. If the PDEFECT internal coil is **on** when the part passes the PROX5 proximity sensor, then the part must be marked with a 1-second pulse of spray paint. The spray head is 5.5 seconds after the PROX5 sensor, so there must be a 5.5-second delay before the sprayer is activated. The PROX5 input turns **off** when a part passes. Make no assumption about the off-time duration of PROX5 except that it is at least one program scan. Also, assume that the PDEFECT internal coil is **on** at least as long as PROX5 senses the part.

Assume the following physical input, physical output, and internal variable assignments:

Variable	Description
PROX5	Senses part on conveyor, **off** when part is present
SPRAY	Paint sprayer control valve, **on** to spray
PDEFECT	Defective part internal coil, if **on** when part is sensed, then the part needs to be marked

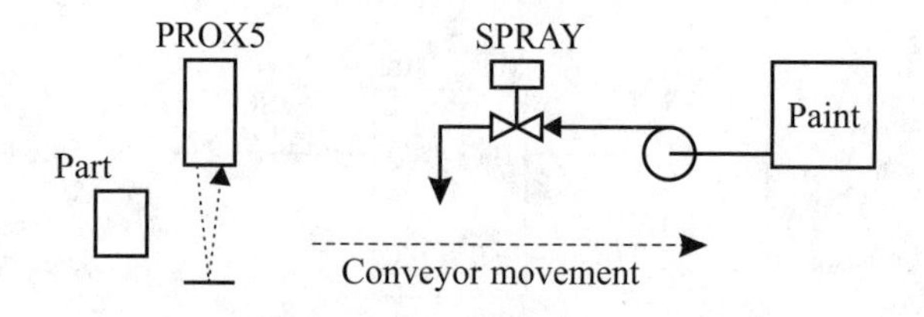

Figure 5.72. Defective part marking system.

The addresses and/or data types associated with the physical I/O and internal variables are:

Variable	Modicon	PLC-5	ControlLogix	Siemens	GE Fanuc
PROX5	100005	I:0/04	Local:1:I.Data.4	I0.4	%I5
SPRAY	000007	O:1/06	Local:2:O.Data.6	Q4.6	%Q7
PDEFECT	BOOL	B3/102	BOOL	M12.0	%M102

Solution. The Modicon code is shown in Figure 5.73, the A-B PLC-5 code is shown in Figure 5.74, and the Siemens S7 code appears in Figure 5.75. The GE Fanuc solution is similar to the Modicon solution.

Since the trigger is only momentary, the first part of the code is a start/stop rung. The timing cycle is triggered (start condition) when a defect is detected and a part is detected at the proximity sensor. For Modicon (Figure 5.73), the internal coil P_Seal is turned **on** and

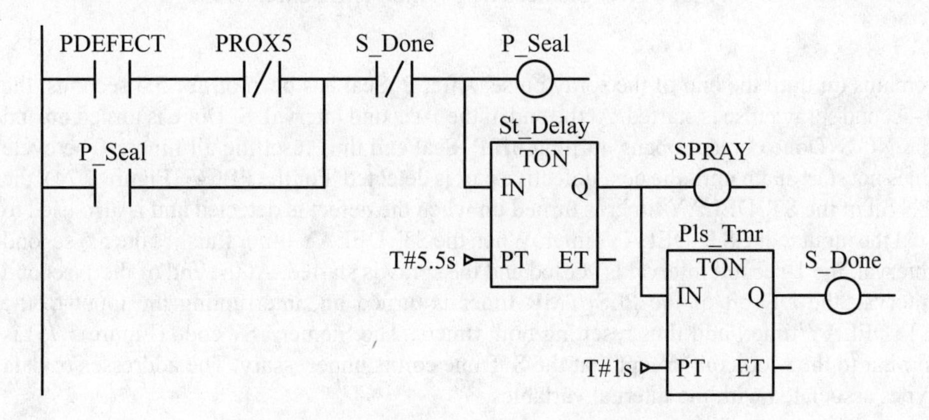

Figure 5.73. Modicon solution to Example 5.4.

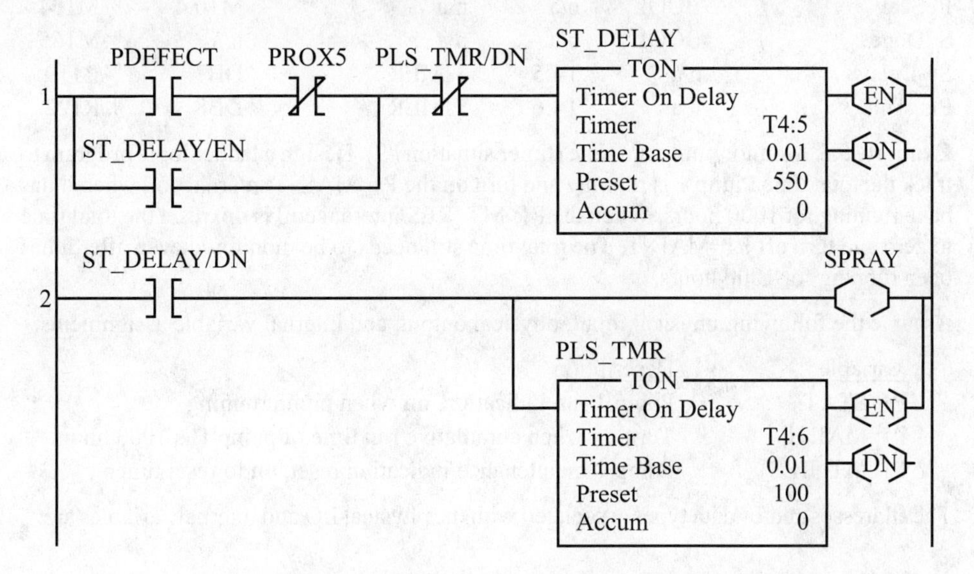

Figure 5.74. A-B PLC-5 solution to Example 5.4.

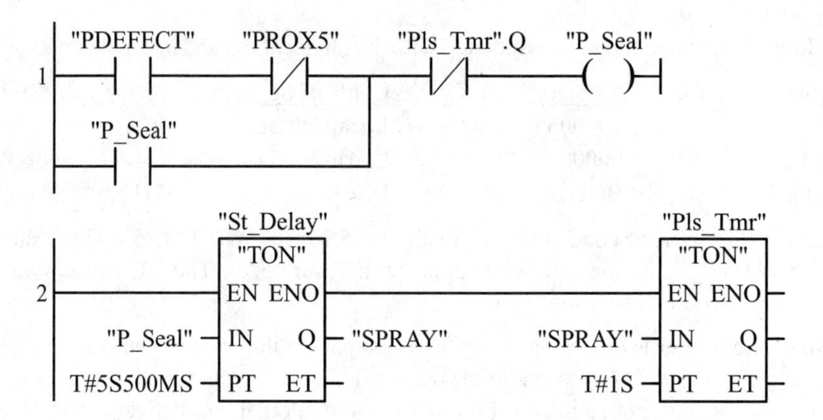

Figure 5.75. Siemens S7 solution to Example 5.4.

remains **on** until the end of the spray pulse. After P_Seal has been **on** for 5.5 seconds, the 1-second spray pulse is started. At the end of the 1-second interval, S_Done is turned **on** and the NC S_Done contact opens, turning **off** P_Seal and thus resetting all timers. The cycle does not start again until the next defective part is detected. For the PLC-5 (Figure 5.74), the EN bit of the ST_DELAY timer is turned **on** when the defect is detected and is also used to seal the input to the ST_DELAY timer. When the ST_DELAY timer finishes the 5.5 second interval, the 1-second interval is started and the spray is started. At the end of the 1-second interval, the DN bit of the PLS_TMR timer is turned **on**, interrupting the input to the ST_DELAY timer, and thus resetting both timers. The Siemens S7 code (Figure 5.75) is similar to the Modicon, except that the S_Done coil is unnecessary. The addresses or data types associated with the internal variables:

Variable	Modicon Data Type	PLC-5 Addr.	ControlLogix Data Type	Siemens Addr.	GE Fanuc Addr.
P_Seal	BOOL	n/a	n/a	M10.4	%M164
S_Done	BOOL	n/a	n/a	n/a	%M165
St_Delay	n/a	T4:5	TIMER	DB7	%R119
Pls_Tmr	n/a	T4:6	TIMER	DB8	%R122

Example 5.5. Monitor pump run time (timer situation #9). Design a ladder logic program to track the total time Pump 1 is running and turn **on** the P1_MAINT internal coil when it has been running for 1000 hours. When the P1_MT_RES internal coil is **on**, reset the total time to zero and turn **off** P1_MAINT. The total time still needs to be monitored even after it has been running for 1000 hours.

Assume the following physical input, physical output, and internal variable assignments:

Variable	Description
P1_STAT	Pump 1 run indication, **on** when pump running
P1_MAINT	Turn **on** when cumulative run time of pump 1 is 1000 hours
P1_MT_RES	Pump 1 maintenance indication reset, **on** to reset timer

The addresses and/or data types associated with the physical I/O and internal variables are:

Variable	Modicon	PLC-5	ControlLogix	Siemens	GE Fanuc
P1_STAT	100011	I:0/12	Local:1:I.Data.10	I1.2	%I11
P1_MAINT	BOOL	B3/103	BOOL	M12.1	%M103
P1_MT_RES	BOOL	B3/104	BOOL	M12.2	%M104

Solution. The Modicon code is shown in Figure 5.76. Rung 1 implements a one-hour retentive timer as explained in section 5.3.7. The P1_Hr_Tic counter generates a one-scan "tick" that increments the P1_Th_Ctr counter and resets the P1_Hr_Tic counter for the next hour. When the P1_Th_Ctr accumulator (CV) reaches 1000, the P1_MAINT coil is turned **on** and remains **on** until reset by P1_MT_RES.

The PLC-5, S7, and GE Fanuc code is shown in Figures 5.77 – 5.79. As in the Modicon code, a retentive timer generates a "tick" every hour, which increments a counter and resets itself. When the P1_TH_CTR accumulator reaches 1000, the P1_MAINT internal coil is turned **on**. The S7 implementation uses the S5-compatible S_ODTS block for the retentive timer. For all PLCs, the P1_MT_RES internal coil resets the counting and the retentive timing functions. The addresses or data types associated with the internal variables:

Variable	Modicon Data Type	PLC-5 Addr.	ControlLogix Data Type	Siemens Addr.	GE Fanuc Addr.
T_Tic	BOOL	n/a	n/a	M10.6	%M166
P1_Hr_TDn	BOOL	n/a	n/a	M10.7	%M167
P1_Hr_Tic	n/a	T4:7	TIMER	DB9	%R125
P1_Th_Ctr	n/a	C5:0	COUNTER	DB10	%R128

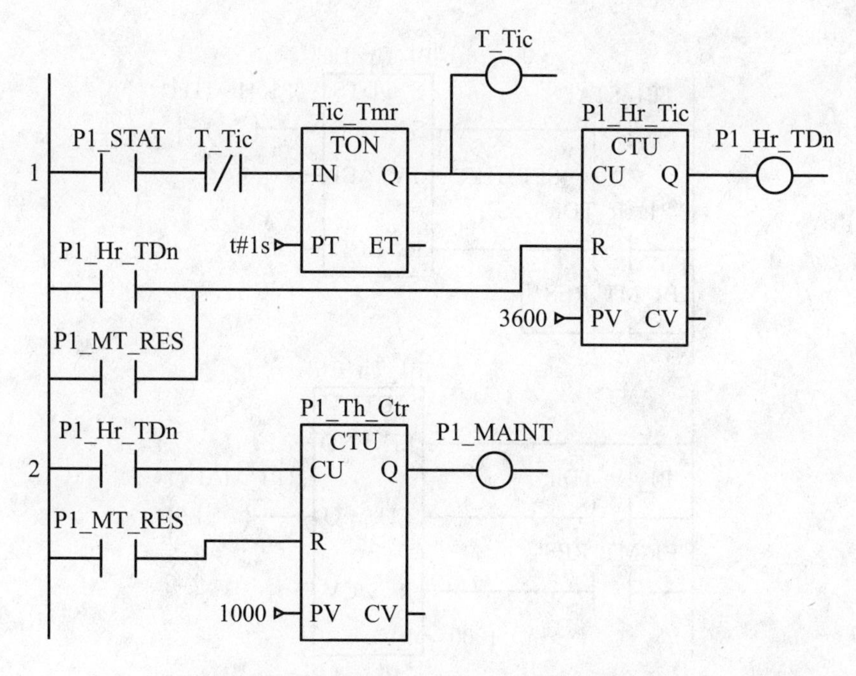

Figure 5.76. Modicon solution to Example 5.5.

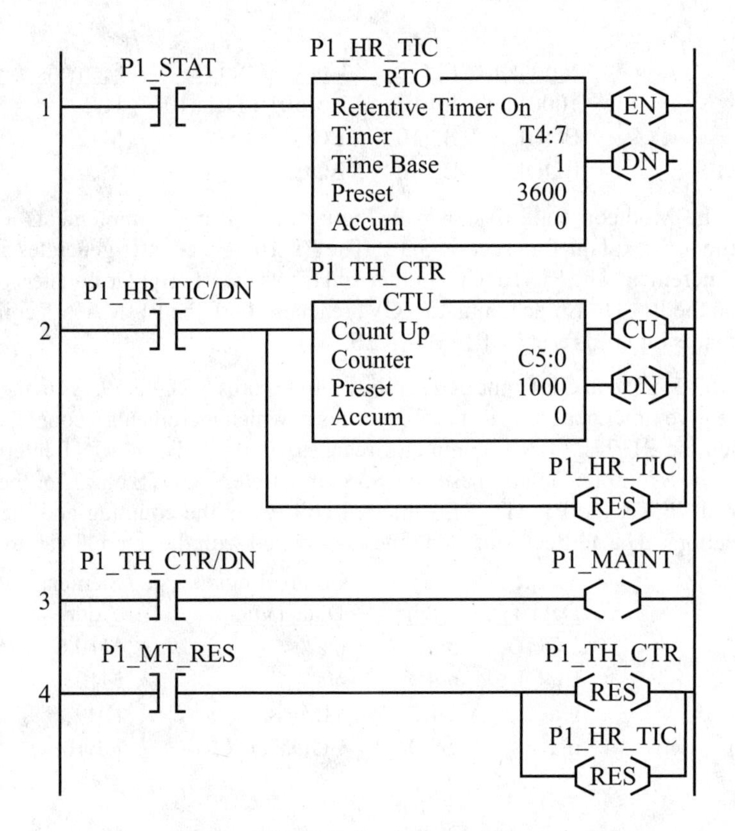

Figure 5.77. A-B PLC-5 solution to Example 5.5.

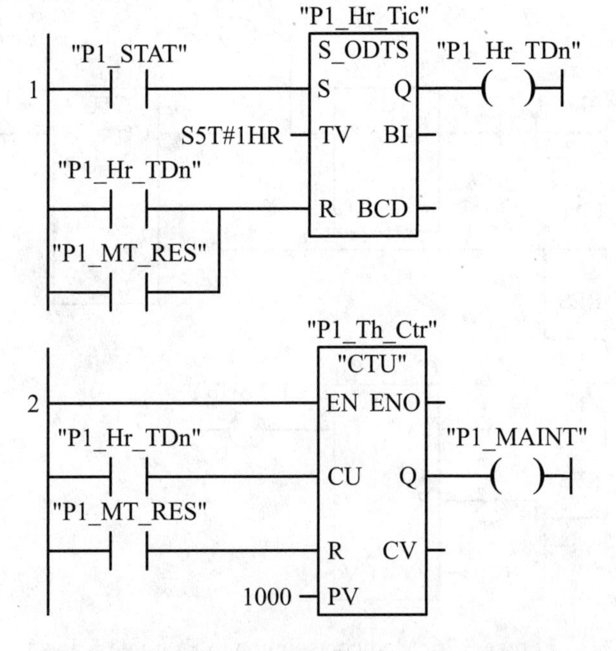

Figure 5.78. Siemens S7 solution to Example 5.5.

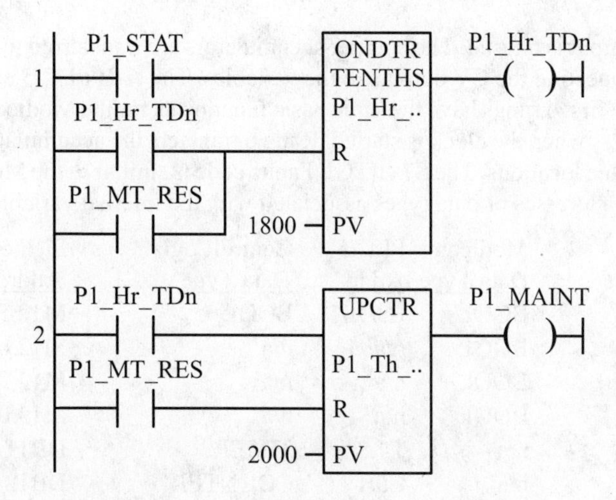

Figure 5.79. GE Fanuc solution to Example 5.5.

Example 5.6. Clock (counter situation #2). Design a ladder logic program to keep track of the age of the material in tank T-28 in days, hours, and minutes. There are only two controls for this clock: T28_CLK_STT starts the clock by resetting it and then allowing it to run; and T28_CLK_STP stops the clock and holds the current time (does not change). The days, hours, and minutes are retained in T28_DAY, T28_HR, and T28_MIN, respectively.

Assume the following internal variable assignments:

Variable	Description
T28_CLK_STT	T-28 age clock start command. Transition to **on** resets the current hours, minutes, and seconds and starts the clock running.
T28_CLK_STP	T-28 age clock stop command. Transition to **on** stops the clock at its current time, but does not reset the time. The time remains constant until the start command is turned **on**.
T28_MIN	Age of tank T-28 in minutes
T28_HR	Age of tank T-28 in hours
T28_DAY	Age of tank T-28 in days

The addresses and/or data types associated with the internal variables are:

Variable	Modicon	PLC-5	ControlLogix	Siemens	GE Fanuc
T28_CLK_STT	BOOL	B3/105	BOOL	M12.3	%M105
T28_CLK_STP	BOOL	B3/106	BOOL	M12.4	%M106
T28_MIN	INT	N7:45	INT	MW46	%R134
T28_HR	INT	N7:46	INT	MW47	%R137
T28_DAY	INT	N7:47	INT	MW48	%R140

Solution. The Modicon code is shown in Figure 5.80. Rung 1 has the clock start/stop and generates a one-minute tick. Rung 2 has the counter that maintains the clock minute value. Rungs 3 and 4 are the hour and day counters, respectively. The minute and hour counters are reset when they have reached their preset value or when the clock is started. The day counter is reset only when the clock is started. Note that the PV for the day counter is irrelevant since the counter Q output is unused. The counter accumulators are transferred to the appropriate variables by connecting the CV outputs to the variables. The A-B PLC-5 code is shown in Figure 5.81. The first 4 rungs have the same basic function as for the Modicon code. Rung 5 resets the counters when the clock is started. Rung 6 transfers the accumulator values to the correct clock value locations. The S7 and GE Fanuc code is similar to the Modicon and thus not shown. The addresses or data types associated with the internal variables:

Variable	Modicon Data Type	PLC-5 Addr.	ControlLogix Data Type	Siemens Addr.	GE Fanuc Addr.
T28_Clk_Run	BOOL	B3/107	BOOL	M12.5	%M107
T_Tic	BOOL	n/a	n/a	M12.6	%M108
T28_Mn_Dn	BOOL	n/a	n/a	M12.7	%M109
T28_Hr_Dn	BOOL	n/a	n/a	M13.0	%M110
Tic_Tmr	n/a	T4:8	TIMER	DB11	%R131
T28_Mn_Ctr	n/a	C5:1	COUNTER	DB12	%R134
T28_Hr_Ctr	n/a	C5:2	COUNTER	DB13	%R137
T28_Dy_Ctr	n/a	C5:3	COUNTER	DB14	%R140

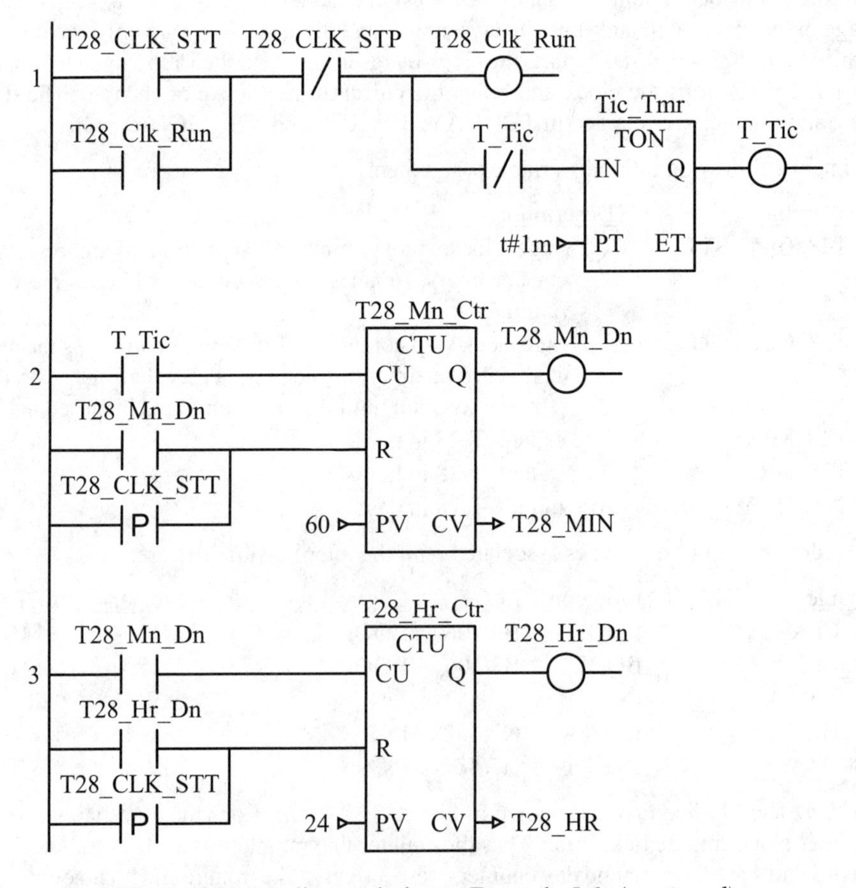

Figure 5.80. Modicon solution to Example 5.6. *(continued)*

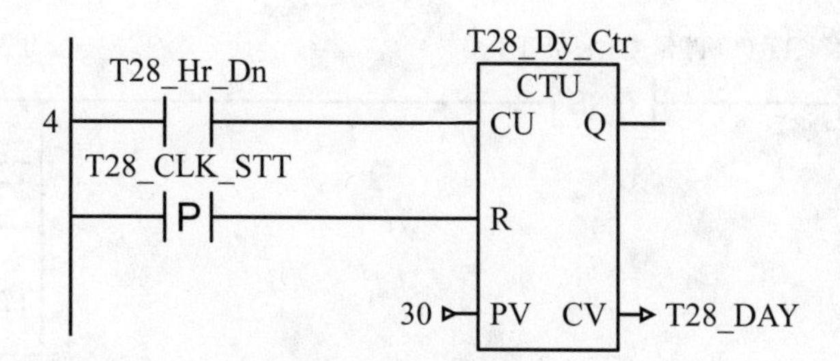

Figure 5.80. *(continued)*

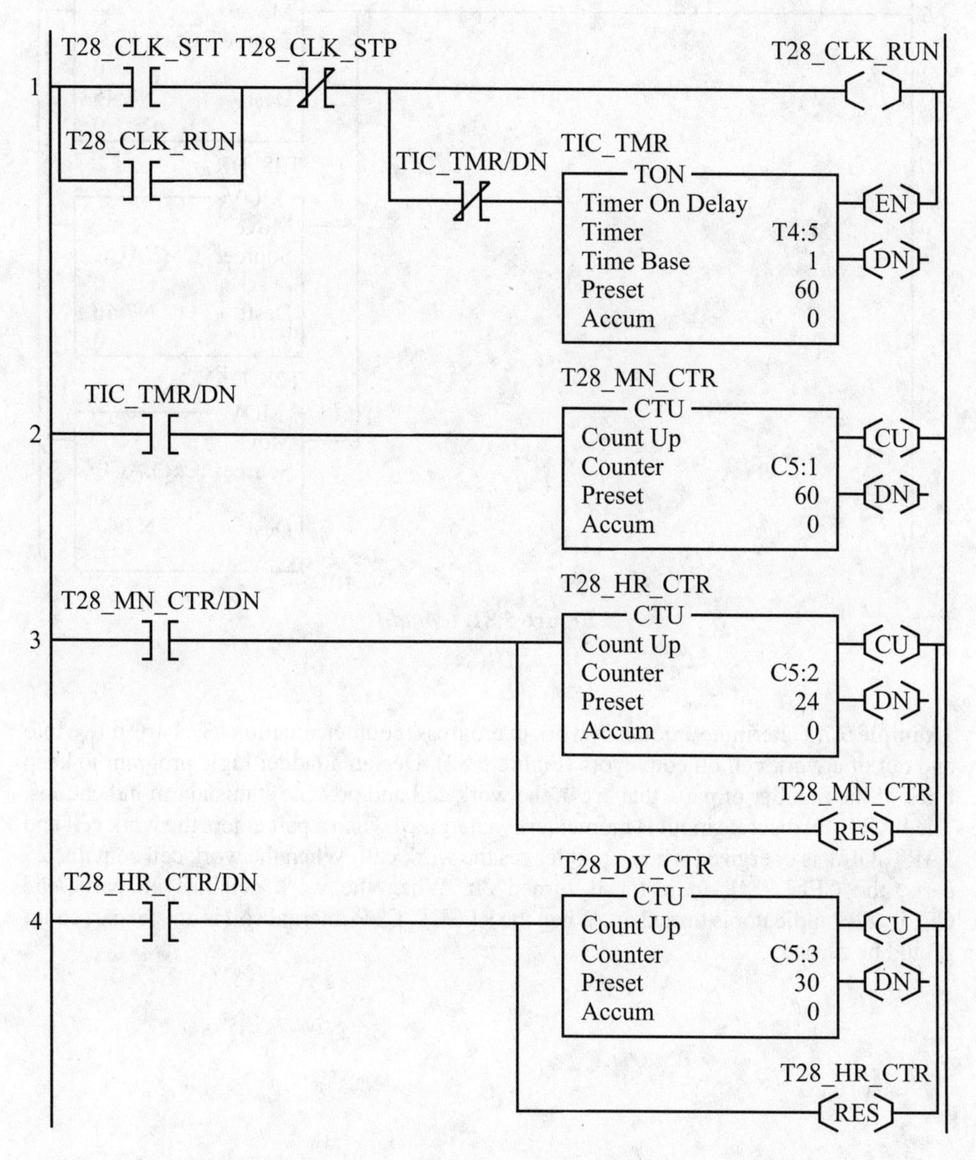

Figure 5.81. A-B PLC-5 solution to Example 5.6. *(contd.)*

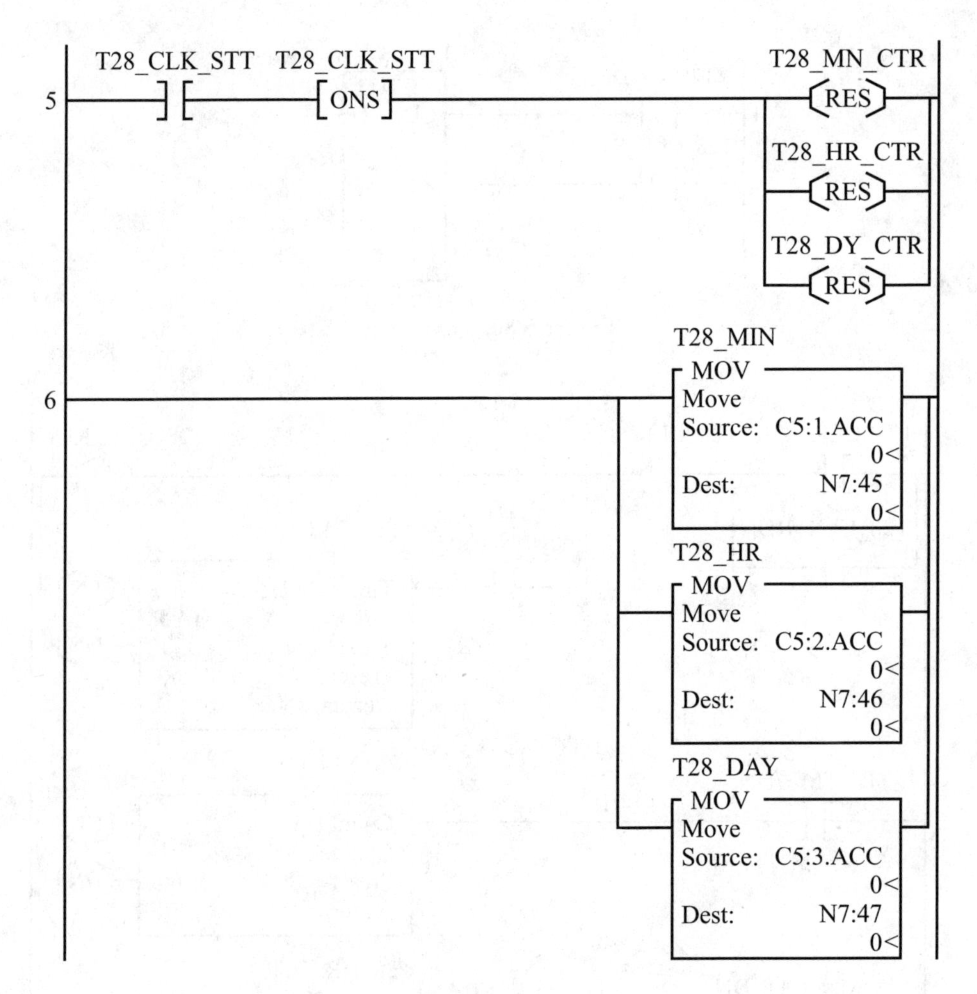

Figure 5.81. *(contd.)*

Example 5.7. Determine amount of work in progress (counter situation #3). Parts move into and out of a work cell on conveyors (Figure 5.82). Design a ladder logic program to keep track of the number of parts that are in the work cell and provide status/alarm indications. The PART_IN discrete input is momentarily energized when a part enters the work cell and PART_OUT is energized when a part leaves the work cell. When the work cell contains 25 parts, the CELL_25P indicator is turned on. When the work cell has no parts, the CELL_ZRP indicator is turned on. When the RESET_CTR internal coil is on, the part count should be zeroed.

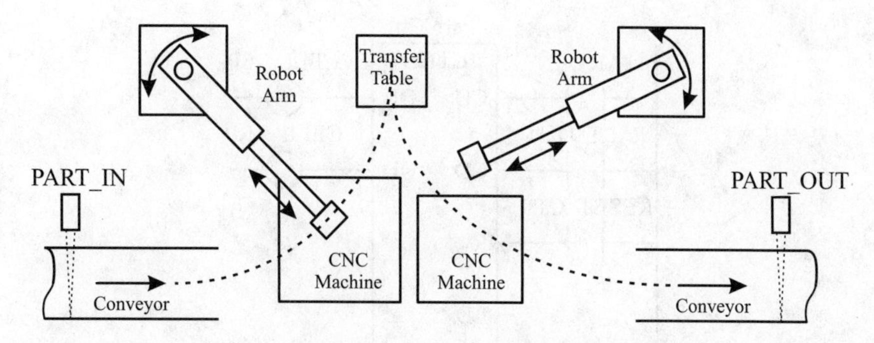

Figure 5.82. Work cell for Example 5.7.

Assume the following physical input, physical output, and internal variable assignments:

Variable	Description
PART_IN	Senses part entering work cell, energized (**on**) and then de-energized as part enters work cell.
PART_OUT	Senses part exiting work cell, energized (**on**) and then de-energized as part exits work cell.
RESET_CTR	**On** to clear part count.
CELL_25P	**On** when at least 25 parts are in work cell.
CELL_ZRP	**On** when no parts are in work cell.

The addresses and/or data types associated with the physical I/O and internal variables are:

Variable	Modicon	PLC-5	ControlLogix	Siemens	GE Fanuc
PART_IN	100012	I:0/13	Local:1:I.Data.11	I1.3	%I12
PART_OUT	100013	I:0/14	Local:1:I.Data.12	I1.4	%I13
RESET_CTR	BOOL	B3/111	BOOL	M13.1	%M111
CELL_25P	000009	O:1/10	Local:2:O.Data.8	Q5.0	%Q9
CELL_ZRP	000010	O:1/11	Local:2:O.Data.9	Q5.1	%Q10

Solution. The Modicon code is shown in Figure 5.83. This solution is a straightforward application of the up/down counter. There is no connection to the LD input. The A-B PLC-5 code is shown in Figure 5.84. The first four rungs implement a basic up/down counter. The last rung generates the indication that no parts are present by checking if the counter accumulator is zero. The CMP instruction is explained in Chapter 7. The S7 solution is nearly identical to Figure 5.83. The GE Fanuc solution in Figure 5.85 uses the UPCTR and DNCTR blocks. Basically, when one counter accumulator is changed, it is also copied to the other counter. The addresses or data types associated with the internal variables:

Variable	Modicon Data Type	PLC-5 Addr.	ControlLogix Data Type	Siemens Addr.	GE Fanuc Addr.
Part_Ctr	n/a	C5:4	COUNTER	DB14	%R143
Part_Ctd	n/a	n/a	n/a	n/a	%R146

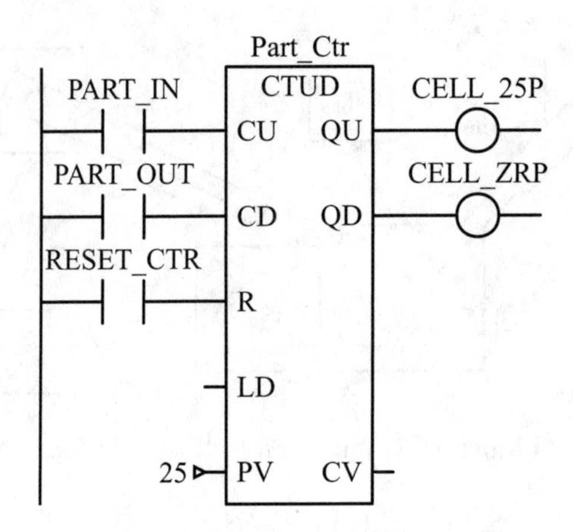

Figure 5.83. Modicon solution to Example 5.7.

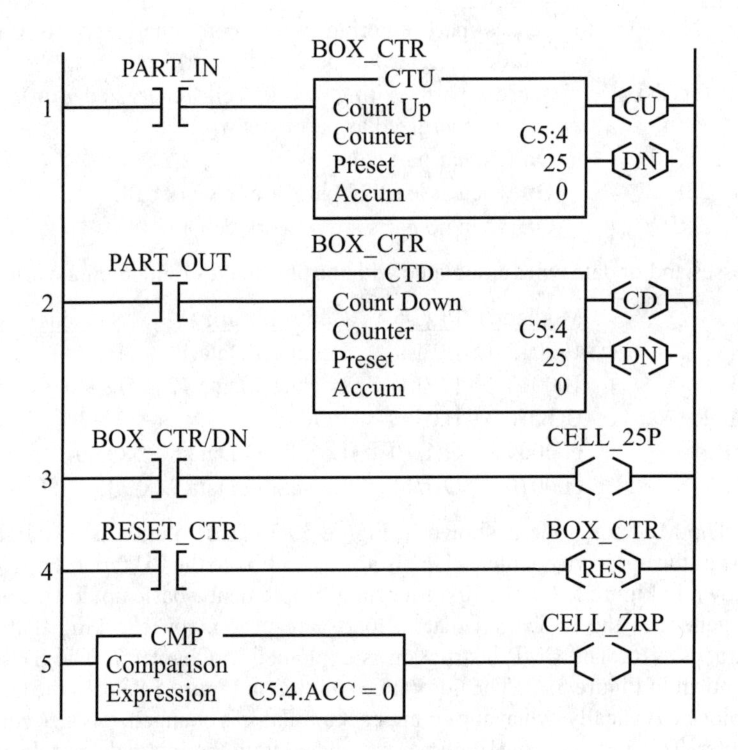

Figure 5.84. A-B PLC-5 solution to Example 5.7.

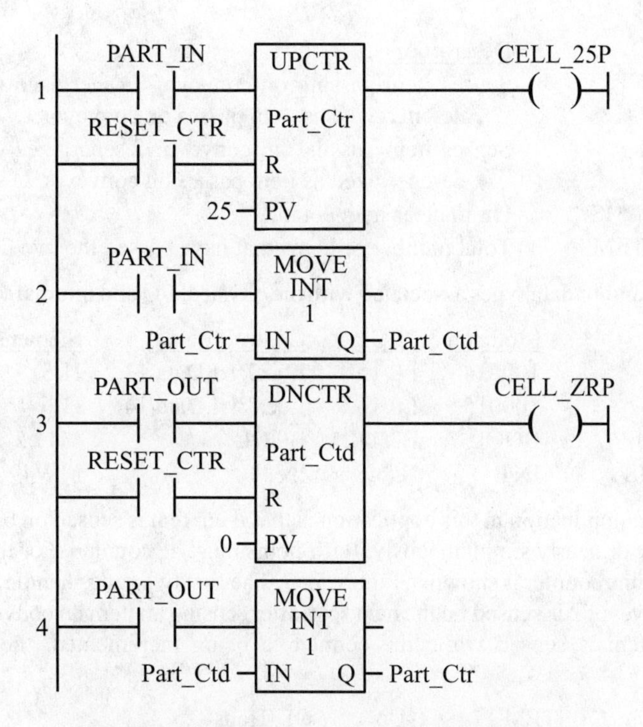

Figure 5.85. GE Fanuc solution to Example 5.7.

Example 5.8. Sum total of pieces on two conveyors (counter situation #4). Design a ladder logic program to count the total number of items traveling down two conveyors (Figure 5.86). It is not necessary to generate a count of the items on each conveyor. The C1_ITEM and C2_ITEM discrete inputs are momentarily energized (but more than one scan) when an item passes the detector. The integer, NUM_CITEMS, contains the total number of items that have passed the two detectors. When the RST_CITEMS internal coil is on, the item count should be zeroed.

Assume the following physical input, physical output, and internal variable assignments:

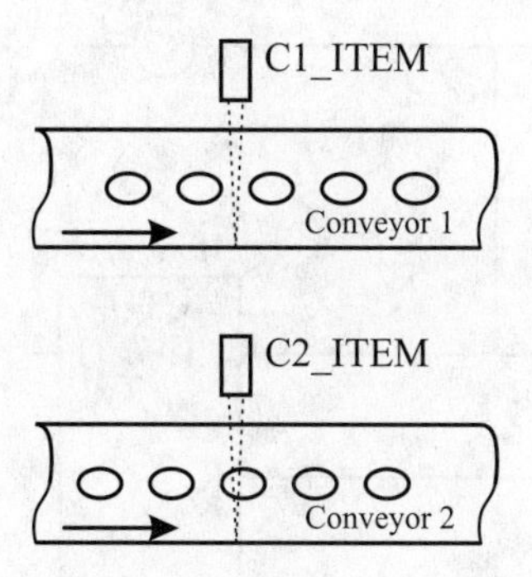

Figure 5.86. Two conveyors for Example 5.8.

Variable	Description
C1_ITEM	Senses item passing on conveyor 1, energized (**on**) and then de-energized as item passes on conveyor 1.
C2_ITEM	Senses item passing on conveyor 2, energized (**on**) and then de-energized as item passes on conveyor 2.
RST_CITEMS	**On** to clear item count.
NUM_CITEMS	Total number of items that have passed the two detectors.

The addresses and/or data types associated with the physical I/O and internal variables are:

Variable	Modicon	PLC-5	ControlLogix	Siemens	GE Fanuc
C1_ITEM	100014	I:0/15	Local:1:I.Data.13	I1.5	%I14
C2_ITEM	100015	I:0/16	Local:1:I.Data.14	I1.6	%I15
RST_CITEMS	BOOL	B3/112	BOOL	M13.2	%M112
NUM_CITEMS	INT	N7:48	INT	MW49	%R150

Solution. The complication in this application is that if an item is sensed on both conveyors simultaneously or nearly simultaneously, **both** items must be counted. For the Modicon, a solution using one counter is shown in Figure 5.87. The first two rungs handle the case when an item on conveyor 2 is sensed on the next scan after sensing an item on conveyor 1, or vice versa. If an item is sensed while the counter is being incremented, the transition to

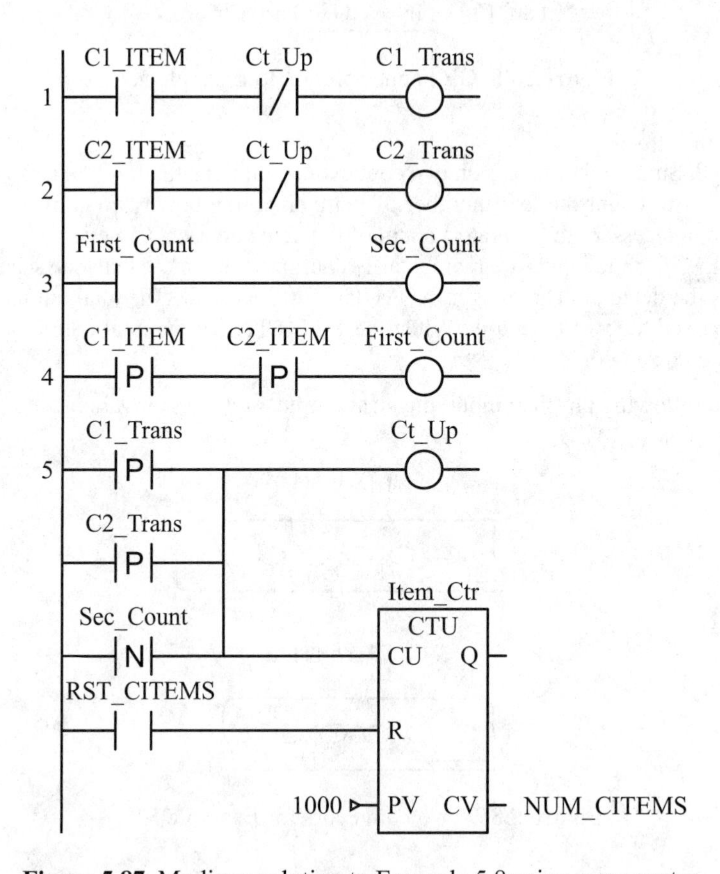

Figure 5.87. Modicon solution to Example 5.8 using one counter.

increment the counter is delayed until the counter input is turned **off**. Rungs 3 and 4 handle the case when both items are sensed simultaneously. The Sec_Count coil is turned **on** during the scan **after** both items are sensed simultaneously. The negative transition of Sec_Count increments the counter on the second scan after they are sensed simultaneously, which allows the counter input to change to **off** before incrementing it again. The counter requires an **off-to-on** transition at the input in order to increment. A more straightforward solution uses two counters, as shown in Figure 5.88, and adds the accumulators to produce the final count. The ADD function block is explained in Chapter 7. This approach is also more easily extended to more than two conveyors.

The A-B PLC-5 code is shown in Figure 5.89. In this case, only one counter is needed, but it is incremented by two CTU blocks. The CU bit stores the status of the counter input in order to detect transitions. By unlatching the CU bit, an item on the other conveyor can be sensed on the current scan or the next scan. The last rung moves the counter accumulator to the location specified in the problem statement. The MOV instruction is explained in Chapter 7.

The Siemens S7 and GE Fanuc implementation of the one counter and two counter solutions are similar to the Modicon solutions. The GE Fanuc VersaMax and 90-30 PLCs do not have a transitional contact, and the transitional contacts of Figure 5.87 will need to be replaced by ordinary contacts referring to transitional coils.

In order to handle false indications from the item sensors, a better solution to this problem would place on-delay timers after each of the item sensors. If the problem is modified so that items on each conveyor must be separately counted, then there should be a

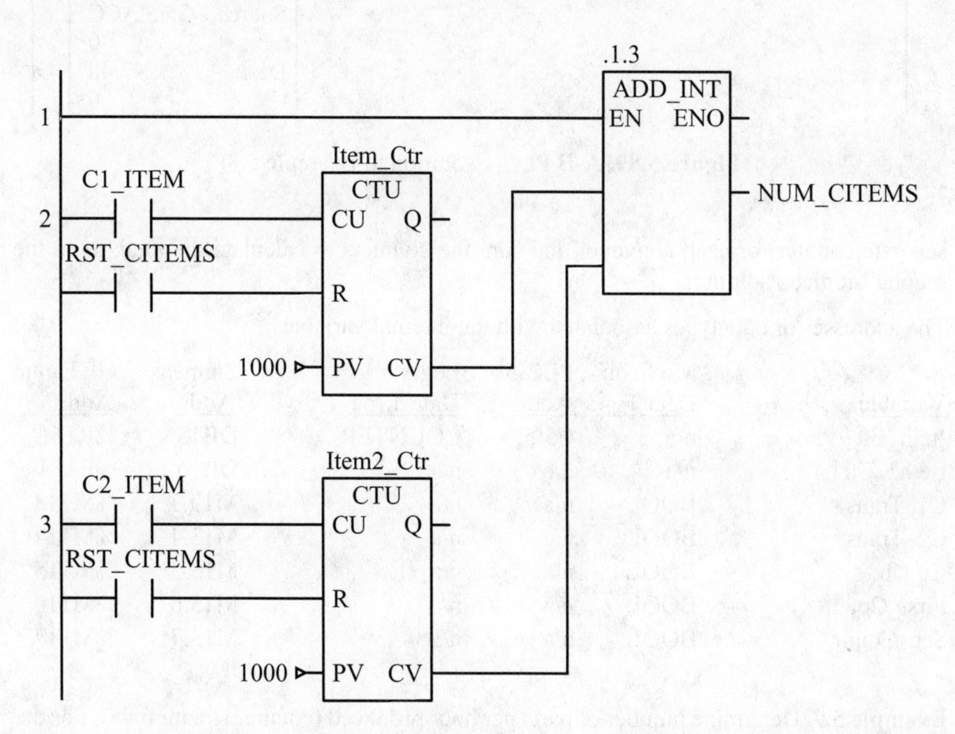

Figure 5.88. Modicon solution to Example 5.8 using two counters.

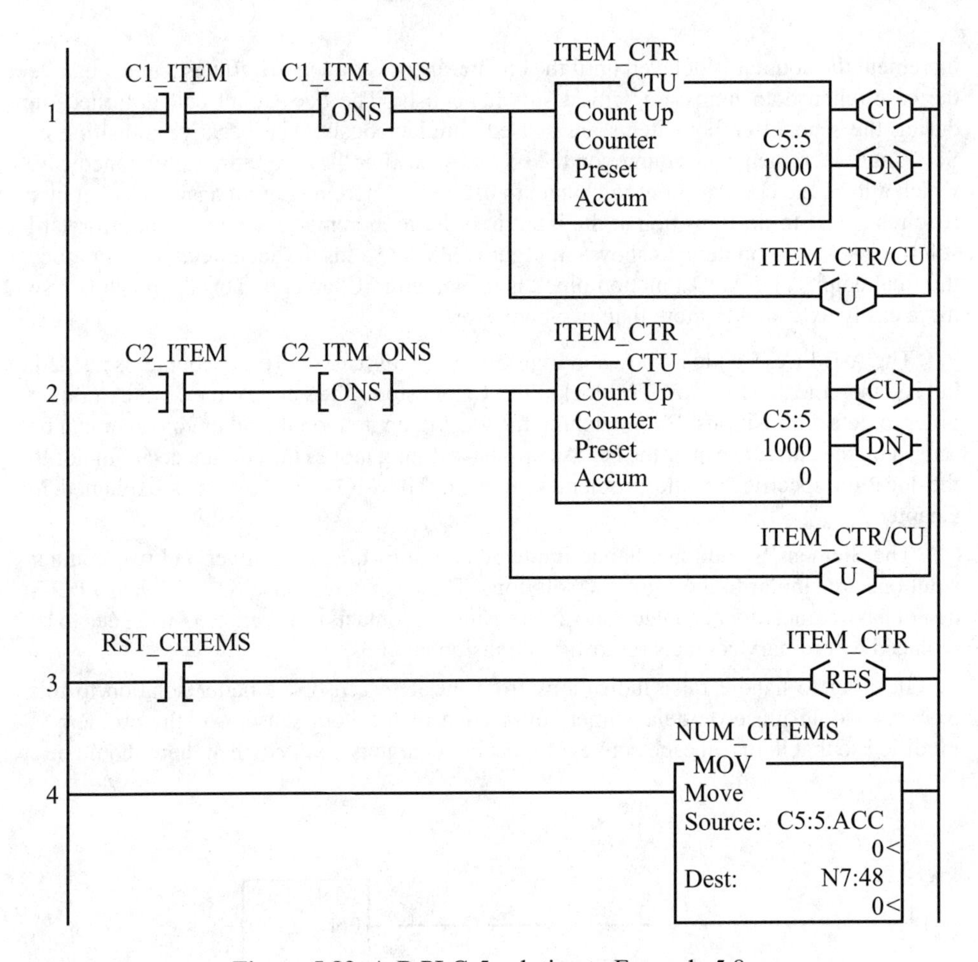

Figure 5.89. A-B PLC-5 solution to Example 5.8.

separate counter for each conveyor and sum the counters to calculate the total, as in the second Modicon solution.

The addresses or data types associated with the internal variables:

Variable	Modicon Data Type	PLC-5 Addr.	Logix Data Type	Siemens Addr.	GE Fanuc Addr.
Item_Ctr	n/a	C5:5	COUNTER	DB15	%R151
Item2_Ctr	n/a	n/a	n/a	DB16	%R154
C1_Trans	BOOL	n/a	n/a	M13.3	%M113
C2_Trans	BOOL	n/a	n/a	M13.4	%M114
Ct_Up	BOOL	n/a	n/a	M13.5	%M115
First_Count	BOOL	n/a	n/a	M13.6	%M116
Sec_Count	BOOL	n/a	n/a	M13.7	%M117

Example 5.9. Determine number of parts per hour produced (counter situation #5). For the work cell depicted in Figure 5.82, determine the production rate in parts per hour.

Assume the following physical input, physical output, and internal variable assignments:

Variable	Description
PART_OUT	Senses part exiting work cell, energized (**on**) and then de-energized as part exits work cell.
CELL_PRATE	Cell production rate, in parts per hour.

The addresses and/or data types associated with the physical I/O and internal variables are:

Variable	Modicon	PLC-5	ControlLogix	Siemens	GE Fanuc
PART_OUT	100013	I:0/14	Local:1:I.Data.12	I1.4	%I13
CELL_PRATE	INT	N7:50	INT	MW50	%R160

Solution. Basically, in order to determine the production rate, one must count the number of parts produced in a certain time interval and then translate that number into parts per hour. To keep the solution simple, the time interval is one hour and at the end of each hour, the counter accumulator is transferred to the appropriate location and then reset. The Modicon solution is shown in Figure 5.90. The MOVE instruction is explained in Chapter 7. The A-B PLC-5 code is shown in Figure 5.91. The Siemens S7 and GE Fanuc solutions are nearly identical to the Modicon solution except that the MOVE block must be on a separate rung.

The addresses or data types associated with the internal variables:

Variable	Modicon Data Type	PLC-5 Addr.	Logix Data Type	Siemens Addr.	GE Fanuc Addr.
CHr_Tmr	n/a	T4:10	TIMER	DB17	%R170
Cell_PRate_Ctr	n/a	C5:6	COUNTER	DB18	%R173
Hr_Done	BOOL	n/a	n/a	M13.4	%M114
Part_Cnt	INT	n/a	n/a	MW14	%R176

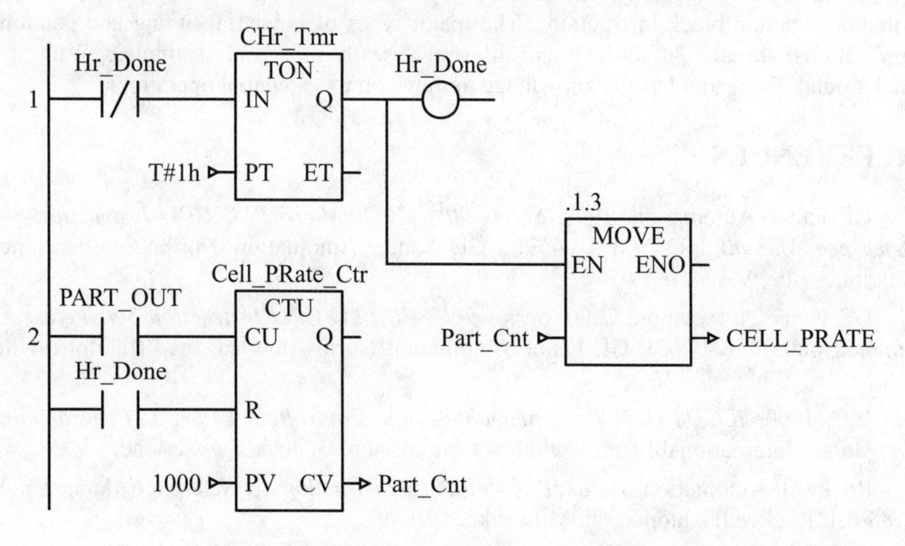

Figure 5.90. Modicon solution to Example 5.9.

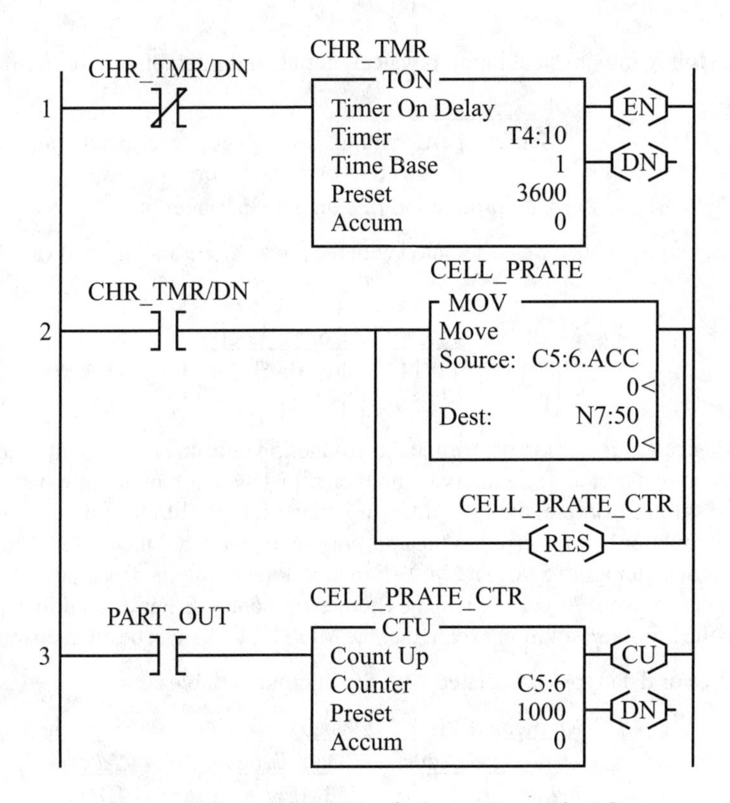

Figure 5.91. A-B PLC-5 solution to Example 5.9.

5.10 CHAPTER SUMMARY

For the PLCs covered by this text, this chapter described timers and counters, the most common function block instructions. The major types of industrial timing and counting applications are also described and illustrated with industrial examples. With this background, the reader has the knowledge to move on to sequential operations.

REFERENCES

GE Fanuc Automation, 1999. *Series 90™-30/20/Micro PLC CPU Instruction Set: Reference Manual,* pub. GFK-0467L, GE Fanuc Automation North America, Inc., Charlottesville, VA.

GE Fanuc Automation, 2000. *Series 90™-70 PLC CPU Instruction Set: Reference Manual,* pub. GFK-0265J, GE Fanuc Automation North America, Inc., Charlottesville, VA.

IEC, 1993. *IEC 1131-3: Programmable Logic Controllers - Part 3: Programming Languages*, International Electrotechnical Commission, Geneva, Switzerland.

Rockwell Automation, 1998a. *PLC-5 Family Instruction Set Reference Manual*, pub. 1785-6.1, Rockwell Automation, Milwaukee, WI.

Rockwell Automation, 1998b. *SLC Modular Processors Instruction Set Reference Manual*, pub. 1747-6.15, Rockwell Automation, Milwaukee, WI.

Rockwell Automation, 2002. *Logix5000^{TM} Controllers General Instructions*, pub. 1756-RM003F-EN-P, Rockwell Automation, Milwaukee, WI, May.

Schneider Automation, 1998. *Concept Block Library IEC,* vol. 1, ver. 2.1, pub. 840 USE 462 00, Schneider Automation, Inc., North Andover, MA.

Siemens, 2000. *S7-200 Programmable Controller: System Manual,* pub. A5E00066097-02, Siemens AG, Nuernberg, Germany.

Siemens, 2002a. *Ladder Logic (LAD) for S7-300 and S7-400 Programming: Reference Manual,* Edition 11/2002, pub. A5E00171231-01, Siemens AG, Nuernberg, Germany.

Siemens, 2002b. *System Software for S7-300/400 System and Standard Functions: Reference Manual,* Edition 12/2002, pub. A5E00171234-01, Siemens AG, Nuernberg, Germany.

General instructions for the problems:

Write a ladder logic program for the application and implement it for one or more of the following PLC ladder logic languages:

Modicon Concept, **or**
Allen-Bradley PLC-5/SLC-500, **or**
Allen-Bradley ControlLogix, **or**
Siemens S7-300/400, **or** S7-200, **or**
GE Fanuc

If any part of the operation is ambiguous, write down your additional assumptions.

The physical inputs, physical outputs, and internal variables for each problem are given in the problem. **DO NOT** assign any more physical inputs!

Your solution should include the following:

1. Specify the PLC processor used.
2. Ladder logic diagram (with comments). For consistency among the different PLCs, use only variables/symbols/tags in the ladder logic. Use instructions consistent with the PLC processor.
3. Table listing additional internal memory (variables/symbols/tags) used and a brief description of their use. For the Allen-Bradley ControlLogix and the Modicon Quantum/Momentum processors, list the internal variables/tags and the data type. For the other processors, list the internal variables/symbols and the associated memory address.

PROBLEMS

P5-1. Develop a ladder logic program that will turn **on** air cylinder CYL101 0.7 seconds after proximity switch PROX101 is turned **on**. Air cylinder CYL102 should turn **on** 2.5 seconds after CYL101 is turned **on**. Pilot light PL105 should turn **on** 3.0 seconds after CYL102 is turned **on**. Activating (turning **on**) limit switch LS110 will reset all timers and turn off all cylinders and the pilot light. The program must ensure that turning **on** LS110 is ignored if PL105 is **off**. Assume that PROX101 is **on** for at least one scan, but no longer than 1 second. Use no more than two internal coils.

Assume the following input and output assignments:

Variable	Description
PROX101	Proximity switch, **on** when closed.
LS110	Limit switch, **on** when closed.
CYL101	Air cylinder control, **on** to extend cylinder
CYL102	Air cylinder control, **on** to extend cylinder
PL105	Pilot light

The addresses associated with the physical I/O are:

Variable	Modicon	PLC-5	ControlLogix	Siemens	GE Fanuc
PROX101	100065	I:02/00	Local:2:I.Data.0	I8.0	%I95
LS110	100066	I:02/01	Local:2:I.Data.1	I8.1	%I96
CYL101	000033	O:04/00	Local:4:O.Data.0	Q16.0	%Q33

CYL102	000034	O:04/01	Local:4:O.Data.1	Q16.1	%Q34
PL105	000035	O:04/02	Local:4:O.Data.2	Q16.2	%Q35

P5-2. Develop a ladder logic program that will turn **on** pilot light PL202 5 seconds after pressure switch PS201 is turned **on**. Valve XV203 should be opened (turned **on**) 6 seconds after PL202 turns **on**. Pilot light PL204 should turn **on** 8 seconds after XV203 is opened. Pressing PB205 will reset all timers and turn **off** the valve and all pilot lights. The operation of PB205 is allowed only when PL204 is **on**. Assume that PS201 is **on** for at least 6 seconds. After 6 seconds, PS201 may be **on** or **off**. In either case, the operation is not triggered until PS201 turns **on** again after PL204 has been turned **off**.

Timers must be accurate to the nearest 0.01 second.

Assume the following input and output assignments:

Variable	Description
PS201	Pressure switch, **on** when closed.
PB205	Push button switch, **on** when pressed.
PL202	Pilot light
PL204	Pilot light
XV203	Air valve, **on** to open valve.

The addresses associated with the physical I/O are:

Variable	Modicon	PLC-5	ControlLogix	Siemens	GE Fanuc
PS201	100033	I:01/00	Local:1:I.Data.0	I4.0	%I85
PB205	100037	I:01/04	Local:1:I.Data.4	I4.4	%I87
PL202	000035	O:03/02	Local:3:O.Data.2	Q12.2	%Q35
XV203	000036	O:03/03	Local:3:O.Data.3	Q12.3	%Q36
PL204	000038	O:03/05	Local:3:O.Data.5	Q12.5	%Q38

P5-3. Develop a ladder logic program that will extend (turn **on**) air cylinder CYL312 10 seconds after limit switch LS311 is turned **on**. Valve XV313 should be opened (turned **on**) 5 seconds after CYL312 turns **on**. Pilot light PL314 should turn **on** 8 seconds after XV313 is opened. Pressing PB315 will reset all timers and turn **off** the cylinder, valve and pilot light. The operation of PB315 is allowed only when PL314 is **on**. Assume that LS311 is **on** for no longer than one second.

Timers must be accurate to the nearest 0.01 second.

Assume the following input and output assignments:

Variable	Description
LS311	Limit switch, **on** when closed.
PB315	Push button switch, **on** when pressed.
CYL312	Air cylinder control, **on** to extend cylinder
XV313	Air valve, **on** to open valve.
PL314	Pilot light

The addresses associated with the physical I/O are:

Variable	Modicon	PLC-5	ControlLogix	Siemens	GE Fanuc
LS311	100038	I:01/05	Local:1:I.Data.5	I4.5	%I88
PB315	100039	I:01/06	Local:1:I.Data.6	I4.6	%I89
CYL312	000039	O:03/06	Local:3:O.Data.6	Q12.6	%Q39
XV313	000040	O:03/07	Local:3:O.Data.7	Q12.7	%Q40
PL314	000041	O:03/10	Local:3:O.Data.8	Q13.0	%Q41

P5-4. Develop a ladder logic program that will turn **on** pump motor P1441 1.2 seconds after limit switch LS1444 is closed. Pump motor P1442 should turn **on** 4.5 seconds after P1441 is turned **on**. Pilot light PL1443 should turn **on** 8.0 seconds after P1442 is turned **on**. Activating (turning **on**) limit switch LS1445 should reset all timers and turn off all motors and the pilot light. The program must ensure that turning **on** LS1445 is ignored if PL1443 is **off**. Assume that LS1444 is **on** only momentarily (for only one scan). Use no more than two internal coils.

Timers must be accurate to the nearest 0.01 second.

Assume the following physical inputs and outputs:

Variable	Description
LS1444	Limit switch, **on** when closed
LS1445	Limit switch, **on** when closed
P1441	Pump motor contacter, **on** to run motor
P1442	Pump motor contacter, **on** to run motor
PL1443	Pilot light

The addresses associated with the physical I/O are:

Variable	Modicon	PLC-5	ControlLogix	Siemens	GE Fanuc
LS1444	100001	I:01/00	Local:1:I.Data.0	I4.0	%I81
LS1445	100002	I:01/01	Local:1:I.Data.1	I4.1	%I82
P1441	000001	O:03/00	Local:3:O.Data.0	Q12.0	%Q1
P1442	000002	O:03/01	Local:3:O.Data.1	Q12.1	%Q2
PL1443	000003	O:03/02	Local:3:O.Data.2	Q12.2	%Q3

P5-5. Develop a ladder logic program to produce a 20-second one-shot pulse. When the START_PB is pressed, the LA1 lamp should light for 20±0.1 seconds and then turn **off**. Pressing START_PB should have no effect when the lamp is **on** (the light should not go out, nor should the light remain on any longer). When the lamp turns **off**, another press of START_PB should start the pulse over. If START_PB is held down, the lamp should light for ten seconds and turn **off**. The lamp should not turn **on** until the start switch is released and pressed again. Use only one timer.

Assume the following input and output assignments:

Variable	Description
START_PB	Start push button switch, **on** when pressed.
LA1	Pilot light

The addresses associated with the physical I/O are:

Variable	Modicon	PLC-5	ControlLogix	Siemens	GE Fanuc
START_PB	100040	I:01/07	Local:1:I.Data.7	I4.7	%I120
LA1	000042	O:03/11	Local:3:O.Data.9	Q13.1	%Q42

P5-6. Develop a ladder logic program using two timers to make the two lamps flash (LA101 and LA102) alternately. Lamp LA101 should be **on** for one second and LA102 should be **on** for one second, as shown in Figure P5.6. The FLASH switch input controls the flashing lamps. When FLASH is **on**, the lamps flash. When FLASH is **off**, both lamps should be **off**.

Assume the following input and output assignments:

Variable	Description
FLASH	Flashing lights enable, **on** to cause lamps to alternatively flash, **off** turns both lamps **off**.
LA101	Pilot light
LA102	Pilot light

The addresses associated with the physical I/O are:

Variable	Modicon	PLC-5	ControlLogix	Siemens	GE Fanuc
FLASH	100041	I:01/10	Local:1:I.Data.8	I5.0	%I121
LA101	000043	O:03/12	Local:3:O.Data.10	Q13.2	%Q43
LA102	000044	O:03/13	Local:3:O.Data.11	Q13.3	%Q44

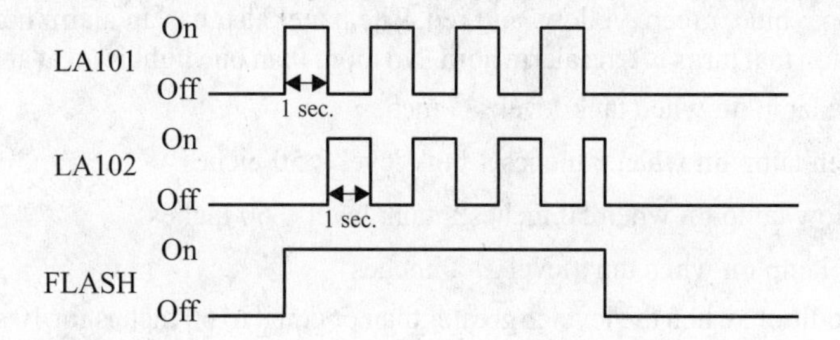

Figure P5.6. Timing diagram for alternating flashing lamps.

P5-7. Develop a ladder logic program to make lamp LA103 to flash. Lamp LA103 should be **on** for one-half second and **off** for one second, as shown in Figure P5.7. The ALARM internal coil controls the flashing lamp. When FLASH is **on**, the lamp flashes. When FLASH is **off**, the lamp should be **off**. When ALARM turns on, LA103 should immediately start its **on** period, as shown in Figure P5.7. Timers must be accurate to the nearest 0.01 second.

Hint: this problem is another variation on the flashing lamps of P5-6.

Assume the following input and output assignments:

Variable	Description
ALARM	Flashing lamp enable; **on** to cause lamp to flash, **off** turns lamp **off**.
LA103	Pilot light

The addresses associated with the physical I/O are:

Variable	Modicon	PLC-5	ControlLogix	Siemens	GE Fanuc
ALARM	100042	I:01/11	Local:1:I.Data.9	I5.1	%I82
LA103	000045	O:03/14	Local:3:O.Data.12	Q13.4	%Q45

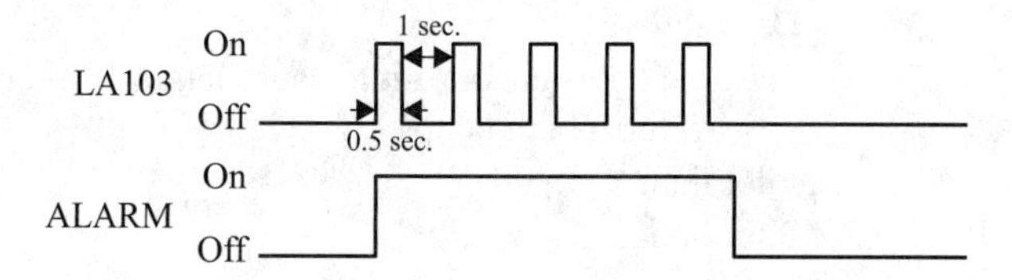

Figure P5.7. Timing diagram for flashing lamp.

P5-8. Use ladder logic to implement a simple *level indicator and alarm* for a tank.

A panel implements a simple interface showing the tank level. The panel has four lamps: blue, green, yellow, and red. The panel also has an alarm horn and a reset button that turns **off** the alarm horn. No more than one light is **on** at any time:

Blue lamp **on** when tank level < 5 inches

Green lamp **on** when 5 inches ≤ tank level < 50 inches

Yellow lamp **on** when 50 inches ≤ tank level < 60 inches

Red lamp **on** when tank level ≥ 60 inches

In addition, when the level is greater than or equal to 60 inches for 10 seconds, the alarm horn is turned **on**, and remains **on** until the RESET_PB button is pressed. In addition, the red lamp flashes at 1 Hz (0.5 sec **on**, 0.5 sec **off**) when the alarm is **on**. Pressing the RESET_PB button should silence the alarm horn, even if the level is still greater than or equal to 60 inches. The level must drop below 60 inches and then increase to 60 inches before the alarm is re-activated.

There are 3 level sensors, each corresponding to one of the "boundary" levels listed above:

LS_1 is **on** when the tank level ≥ 5 inches

LS_2 is **on** when the tank level ≥ 50 inches

LS_3 is **on** when the tank level ≥ 60 inches

Assume the following physical input and output assignments:

Variable	Description
RESET_PB	Push button switch, N. O., **on** when resetting alarm
LS_1	Level switch, **on** when the tank level ≥ 5 inches

LS_2	Level switch, **on** when the tank level ≥ 50 inches
LS_3	Level switch, **on** when the tank level ≥ 60 inches
BLUE	**On** to light blue indicator lamp
GREEN	**On** to light green indicator lamp
YELLOW	**On** to light yellow indicator lamp
RED	**On** to light red indicator lamp
ALARM_HRN	**On** to sound alarm horn

The addresses associated with the physical I/O are:

Variable	Modicon	PLC-5	ControlLogix	Siemens	GE Fanuc
RESET_PB	100065	I:04/00	Local:4:I.Data.0	I16.0	%I105
LS_1	100066	I:04/01	Local:4:I.Data.1	I16.1	%I106
LS_2	100067	I:04/02	Local:4:I.Data.2	I16.2	%I107
LS_3	100068	I:04/03	Local:4:I.Data.3	I16.3	%I108
BLUE	000017	O:06/00	Local:6:O.Data.0	Q24.0	%Q17
GREEN	000018	O:06/01	Local:6:O.Data.1	Q24.1	%Q18
YELLOW	000019	O:06/02	Local:6:O.Data.2	Q24.2	%Q19
RED	000020	O:06/03	Local:6:O.Data.3	Q24.3	%Q20
ALARM_HORN	000021	O:06/04	Local:6:O.Data.4	Q24.4	%Q21

P5-9. Implement the relay logic of Figure P5.9*a* in ladder logic. The description of the operation is below. The connections to the PLC are shown in Figure P5.9*b*.

For safety reasons, an operator is required to actuate two pushbuttons in order to close a stamping press. The intention is to ensure that both of the operator's hands are out of the press when it closes. The press is equipped with the relay logic circuit shown in Figure P5.9*a*, which incorporates timing relays that prevent the operator from taping one pushbutton down and making the press faster but unsafe to operate.

The normally-closed timing relay contacts labeled HP3TR1[1 s] and HP3TR2[1 s] in Figure P5.9*a* open 1 second after the relay coil is energized. These contacts close immediately when the coil is de-energized. The normally-open contacts labeled HP3TR1 and HP3TR2 close and open immediately. A solenoid labeled HP3SOL is used to actuate the hydraulic press. The pushbuttons are HP3PB1 and HP3PB2. The numbers beneath the lines are the wire numbers used in the installation.

The relay logic operates as follows. Assume both pushbuttons are open and HP3PB1 is pressed first.

1. An operator presses (closes) HP3PB1, power flows through the HP3TR2[1 s] contact and energizes the HP3TR1 coil.
2. The HP3TR1 contact on the first rung closes, sealing the HP3TR1 coil **on** as long as HP3PB1 is held down.
3. One second after HP3TR1 is energized, the HP3TR1[1 s] contact on the second rung opens.
4. If HP3PB2 is pressed within one second after HP3PB1 is pressed, power flows through the HP3TR1[1 s] contact, energizing the HP3TR2 coil.

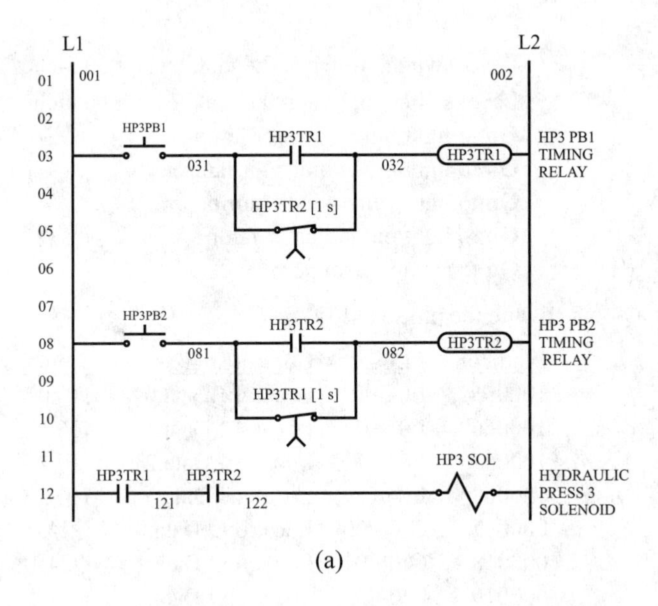

(a)

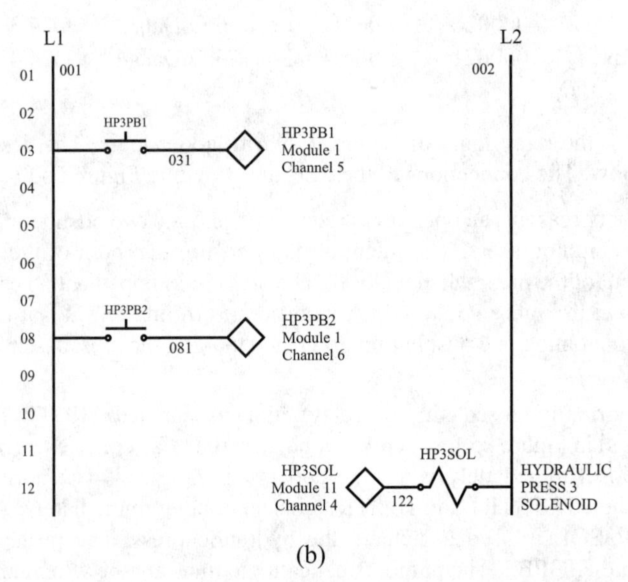

(b)

Figure P5.9. Press operator safety push buttons: *(a)* relay ladder logic;

5. When both HP3TR1 and HP3TR2 relay coils are energized, both contacts on the third rung close, energizing the HP3SOL solenoid.
6. If HP3PB2 is pressed more than one second after HP3PB1 is pressed, then the HP3TR2 coil is **not** energized because the HP3TR1[1 s] contact has opened, blocking power flow to the HP3TR2 coil. In this case, the second contact on the third rung remains open and the solenoid does not turn **on**.

Assume the following physical input and output assignments:

Variable	Description
HP3PB1	N.O. push button
HP3PB2	N.O. push button
HP3SOL	Press solenoid; **on** to run press

The addresses associated with the physical I/O are:

Variable	Modicon	PLC-5	ControlLogix	Siemens	GE Fanuc
HP3PB1	100005	I:01/04	Local:1:I.Data.4	I4.4	%I85
HP3PB2	100006	I:01/05	Local:1:I.Data.5	I4.5	%I86
HP3SOL	000020	O:06/03	Local:6:O.Data.3	Q24.3	%Q20

P5-10. Develop a ladder logic program to handle a low bunker alarm for a coal-fired power plant coal bunker. The devices are shown in Figure P5.10. Normal sequence of events:

Coal bunker 2 becomes low for 3 seconds (BUNK2_LLEV turns off for 3 sec.) which causes

- BUNK2_LLMP starts flashing (1 sec. on, 1 sec. off)
- ALARM_HORN sounds (turns on).

Operator hears horn and/or sees lamp and presses the ALARM_ACK button which causes

- ALARM_HORN is silenced
- BUNK2_LLMP constantly on

Operator activates the conveyor(s) to cause bunker 2 to be filled with coal. When coal level is high enough to make the BUNK2_LLEV sensor to turn on for 5 seconds, then the BUNK2_LLMP turns off.

Other specifications:

- The BUNK2_LLMP is extinguished only when BUNK2_LLEV turns on and the alarm has been acknowledged (operator has pressed ALARM_ACK). If

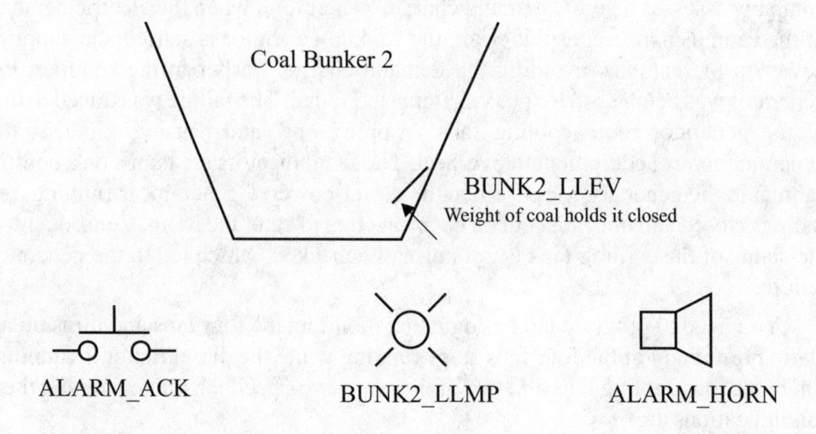

Figure P5.10. Coal bunker devices associated with low level alarm.

the level becomes high enough to turn on BUNK2_LLEV, but the operator has not pressed ALARM_ACK, the lamp remains flashing.

- The alarm horn must stay on until ALARM_ACK is pressed. If the level becomes high enough to turn **on** BUNK2_LLEV but the operator has not pressed ALARM_ACK, the horn must remain **on**.
- If BUNK2_LLEV has been **on** for 5 seconds while the alarm is unacknowledged, the BUNK2_LLMP should turn **off** immediately when the ALARM_ACK button is pressed.
- All timing intervals must be accurate to ± 0.1 seconds.

Assume the following physical input and output assignments:

Variable	Description
ALARM_ACK	Alarm acknowledge; N.O. push button, **on** to acknowledge alarm
BUNK2_LLEV	Bunker 2 low level indication; **off** indicates low level
ALARM_HORN	Alarm horn; **on** to sound alarm
BUNK2_LLMP	Bunker 2 low level indicator; **on** when bunker 2 level is low

The addresses associated with the physical I/O are:

Variable	Modicon	PLC-5	ControlLogix	Siemens	GE Fanuc
ALARM_ACK	100066	I:04/01	Local:4:I.Data.1	I16.1	%I106
BUNK2_LLEV	100010	I:00/11	Local:0:I.Data.9	I0.7	%I90
ALARM_HORN	000008	O:05/07	Local:5:O.Data.7	Q20.7	%Q8
BUNK2_LLMP	000012	O:05/13	Local:5:O.Data.11	Q21.3	%Q12

P5-11. Implement an alarm for the generator room cooling fans.

The university power plant basically generates steam for the campus. But, it has a 1 MW backup diesel-powered generator to supply electric power to run the motors and other steam boiler equipment when the normal electric feed into the plant fails. In the summer, the backup generator is also used to “shave” the campus peak electric demand. If the campus demand goes above a certain value, the utility company assesses a hefty “demand charge.” Therefore, when the electric demand of the campus approaches this peak, the backup generator is started and supplies power to the campus, avoiding the demand charge. Earlier in the summer, the generator was being used for peak shaving and failed. The failure was traced to one of the generator room cooling fans “tripping out” and causing some of the generator control equipment to overheat. The fan indicators are lamps on a control cabinet in the generator room. When the diesel-powered generator is running, the room is closed and one must put on ear protectors to enter the room. Consequently, the status of the cooling fans is not normally checked, which led to the generator failure.

You need to program ladder logic that monitors the four fans and turns **on** an alarm horn if any of the four fans stops running while the diesel motor is running. There are four cooling fans and two of these are two-speed fans. The fans and their run indications are:

Supply (two-speed)	SUP_HI and SUP_LO
Exhaust (two-speed)	EXH_HI and EXH_LO
Cooling #1	COOL_1
Cooling #2	COOL_2

The program needs to monitor these six indications. The GEN3_RUN input is **on** when the diesel is running. The ALARM physical output controls the alarm horn.

(a) If the diesel is running and any of the four fans is **off** for 2 seconds, the ALARM output is 2 seconds **on** and then 2 seconds **off**, in a repeating cycle. There is no separate reset button. The alarm continues to sound as long as at least one of the four fans is not running. When the diesel is not running or the diesel is running and all four fans are on, the ALARM output should be **off**.

(b) The alarm is to be fail-safe, that is the alarm sounds if the PLC fails or one of the fans stops running. To sound the alarm when the PLC fails, the ALARM physical output connection to the alarm horn is modified from part (a). Now, the ALARM output drives a relay whose NC contact drives the alarm horn. When ALARM is **on**, the relay coil is energized, which causes the NC contact to stay open and the alarm does not sound. If the PLC fails, then the PLC output turns **off** and the NC relay contact closes, causing the alarm horn to sound steadily. Modify your program from (a) to invert the ALARM output. If the diesel is running and any of the four fans is **off** for 2 seconds, the ALARM output is 2 seconds **off** and then 2 seconds **on**, in a repeating cycle. When the diesel is not running or the diesel is running and all four fans are on, the ALARM output should be **on**.

Assume the following physical input and output assignments:

Variable	Description
SUP_HI	Supply fan high-speed indication, **on** when supply fan is running on high speed.
SUP_LO	Supply fan low-speed indication, **on** when supply fan is running on low speed.
EXH_HI	Exhaust fan high-speed indication, **on** when exhaust fan is running on high speed.
EXH_LO	Exhaust fan low-speed indication, **on** when exhaust fan is running on low speed.
COOL_1	Cooling fan #1 run indication, **on** when cooling fan #1 is running.
COOL_2	Cooling fan #2 run indication, **on** when cooling fan #2 is running.
GEN3_RUN	Diesel running indication; **on** indicates diesel is running, **off** indicates diesel is not running.
ALARM	Alarm horn; operation described above.

The addresses associated with the physical I/O are:

Variable	Modicon	PLC-5	ControlLogix	Siemens	GE Fanuc
SUP_HI	100001	I:00/00	Local:0:I.Data.0	I0.0	%I81
SUP_LO	100002	I:00/01	Local:0:I.Data.1	I0.1	%I82

EXH_HI	100003	I:00/02	Local:0:I.Data.2	I0.2	%I83
EXH_LO	100004	I:00/03	Local:0:I.Data.3	I0.3	%I84
COOL_1	100005	I:00/04	Local:0:I.Data.4	I0.4	%I85
COOL_2	100006	I:00/05	Local:0:I.Data.5	I0.5	%I86
GEN3_RUN	100007	I:00/06	Local:0:I.Data.6	I0.6	%I87
ALARM	000004	O:01/04	Local:1:O.Data.4	Q4.4	%Q4

P5-12. Develop a ladder logic program that will latch **on** an output, CYL410, after a proximity switch, PROX412, indicates that 100 parts have passed. When the count of 100 is reached, the logic should reset the counter. Push button PB421 is pressed to unlatch CYL410. The counter should be allowed to count while CYL410 is **on** (but not yet unlatched).

Assume the following input and output assignments:

Variable	Description
PROX412	Proximity switch, **on** when part passes
PB421	Push button switch that is **on** when pressed
CYL410	Pneumatic cylinder control

The addresses associated with the physical I/O are:

Variable	Modicon	PLC-5	ControlLogix	Siemens	GE Fanuc
PROX412	100004	I:01/03	Local:1:I.Data.3	I4.3	%I84
PB421	100006	I:01/05	Local:1:I.Data.5	I4.5	%I86
CYL410	000008	O:02/07	Local:2:O.Data.7	Q8.7	%Q8

P5-13. Develop a ladder logic program that provides an indication when a certain push button has been pressed 20 times. Latch **on** an output, PL612, after an input, PB151, has been pressed 20 times. When the count of 20 is reached, the logic should reset the counter. Pushbutton PB613 is pressed to unlatch PL612. The counter should be allowed to count while PL612 is **on** (but not yet unlatched).

Assume the following input and output assignments:

Variable	Description
PB151	Push button switch that is **on** when pressed.
PB613	Push button switch that is **on** when pressed.
PL612	Pilot light

The addresses associated with the physical I/O are:

Variable	Modicon	PLC-5	ControlLogix	Siemens	GE Fanuc
PB151	100005	I:01/04	Local:1:I.Data.4	I4.4	%I85
PB613	100035	I:06/02	Local:6:I.Data.2	I24.2	%I105
PL612	000035	O:07/02	Local:7:O.Data.2	Q28.2	%Q35

P5-14. Use ladder logic to implement a *classifier* station that checks the length of bars that are coming down a conveyor and increments a counter for the appropriate length.

Figure P5.14 shows the layout of the station that check the length of bars and classifies them according to length. A counter is incremented for the appropriate length. The counter accumulators indicate the numbers of bars in three size ranges and provide diagnostics for an upstream bar-cutting machine.

The station uses two proximity sensors (LEN_NORM and LEN_LONG) to determine the length range of bars coming down the conveyor. The bars do not stop and so the check can only be made on the rising edge of the PROX sensor signal. Develop a program that will increment the appropriate counter, indicating that a bar passed in the appropriate size range:

CNT_SHORT	Length < 95.5 inches
CNT_NORM	95.5 inches ≤ Length < 96.5 inches
CNT_LONG	96.5 inches ≤ Length

The addresses of the three counters are specified below. The two proximity sensors correspond to the boundary lengths:

LEN_NORM	95.5 inches ≤ Length
LEN_LONG	96.5 inches ≤ Length

In addition to incrementing the appropriate counter depending on the length, an alarm is sounded (ALARM_HORN) if there is an illegal combination of the two boundary proximity sensors. The alarm must be turned **on** when an illegal combination is detected, and only turned **off** when a reset button (RESET_PB) is pressed. Bars should continue to be counted even when ALARM_HORN is **on**.

Any counter presets must be set so that the counter can count up to its maximum possible value. You do not need to handle overflow. A CNT_RESET internal coil is provided, that when **on**, resets all counter accumulators to zero. Assume that another part of the ladder controls the CNT_RESET.

Assume the following physical I/O and internal variable assignments:

Variable Description

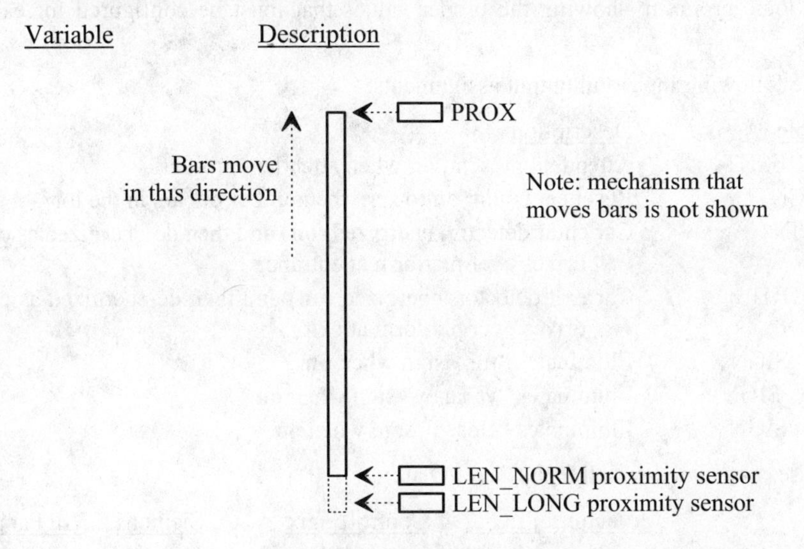

Figure P5.14. Bar classifier station.

PROX	Proximity sensor; check length of bar on rising edge
LEN_NORM	Normal length proximity, **on** when Length ≥ 95.5 inches
LEN_LONG	Long length proximity, **on** when Length ≥ 96.5 inches
RESET_PB	Reset push button switch, N. O., **on** to reset alarm horn
CNT_RESET	Counter reset, **on** to reset counters
ALARM_HORN	Alarm horn; **on** to sound alarm
CNT_SHORT	Number of bars whose length < 95.5 inches
CNT_NORM	Number of bars whose length < 96.5 inches and length ≥ 95.5 inches
CNT_LONG	Number of bars whose length ≥ 96.5 inches

The addresses and data types associated with the physical I/O and internal variables are:

Variable	Modicon	PLC-5	ControlLogix	Siemens	GE Fanuc
PROX	100051	I:03/03	Local:3:I.Data.3	I12.3	%I101
LEN_NORM	100052	I:03/04	Local:3:I.Data.4	I12.4	%I102
LEN_LONG	100053	I:03/05	Local:3:I.Data.5	I12.5	%I103
RESET_PB	100055	I:03/07	Local:3:I.Data.7	I12.7	%I105
CNT_RESET	BOOL	B3/26	BOOL	M1.7	%M26
ALARM_HORN	000017	O:04/01	Local:4:O.Data.1	Q16.1	%Q17
CNT_SHORT	INT	C5:31	COUNTER	MW51	%R120
CNT_NORM	INT	C5:32	COUNTER	MW53	%R123
CNT_LONG	INT	C5:33	COUNTER	MW55	%R126

P5-15. A parking lot has a capacity of 2000 cars. A FULL sign is **on** when the parking lot is full, and a VACANCY sign is **on** when parking space is available. Also, a CLOSED sign is **on** (and the other two signs are **off**) when no attendant is on duty. When the attendant leaves, there may be cars in the parking lot. To handle imperfect sensing of the automobiles, the attendant presses the RST_CNT push button **only if** the lot is empty when s/he leaves. Draw the ladder logic program, showing the proper values that must be configured for each instruction.

Assume the following input and output assignments:

Variable	Description
AT_PRESNT	Attendant present, **on** when attendant present
RST_CNT	Reset car count, **on** to zero the number of cars in the lot
CAR_IN	Car enter detector, energized (**on**) and then de-energized as car drives over platform at entrance
CAR_OUT	Car exit detector, energized (**on**) and then de-energized as car drives over platform at exit
FULL_SIGN	Illuminates "full" sign when **on**.
VACY_SIGN	Illuminates "vacancy" sign when **on**
CLOS_SIGN	Illuminates "closed" sign when **on**

The addresses associated with the physical I/O are:

Variable	Modicon	PLC-5	ControlLogix	Siemens	GE Fanuc
AT_PRESNT	100001	I:01/00	Local:1:I.Data.0	I4.0	%I81

CAR_IN	100002	I:01/01	Local:1:I.Data.1	I4.1	%I82
CAR_OUT	100003	I:01/02	Local:1:I.Data.2	I4.2	%I83
RST_CNT	100004	I:01/03	Local:1:I.Data.3	I4.3	%I84
FULL_SIGN	000001	O:02/00	Local:2:O.Data.0	Q8.0	%Q1
VACY_SIGN	000002	O:02/01	Local:2:O.Data.1	Q8.1	%Q2
CLOS_SIGN	000003	O:02/02	Local:2:O.Data.2	Q8.2	%Q3

P5-16. Building security needs a means of determining if there is anyone present in a particular office building. Each person entering the building passes though a turnstile that trips the PERSON_IN detector. Also, each person exiting the building passes through another turnstile that trips the PERSON_OUT detector. Develop a ladder logic program that will track the number of persons in the building and provides two indicators: OCCUPIED is **on** when anyone is in the building and VACANT is **on** when there are no people in the building. These indicators are visible from outside the building and so one does not need to enter the building to view these indicators. A guard checks the building late at night and makes sure the building is unoccupied. To handle the situation where there is a miscount, the guard always resets the occupancy count by pressing the RESET button when s/he leaves. The guard than has 30 seconds to actually leave the building before the occupancy count is zeroed. The guard does check that the EMPTY indicator is **on** at the end of the 30 seconds (after exiting the building). Assume that there can be no more than 450 people in the building. Develop a ladder logic program to handle this occupancy system.

Assume the following input and output assignments:

Variable	Description
PERSON_IN	Person enter detector, **on** for about 0.5 second when person passes through entrance turnstile
PERSON_OUT	Person exit detector, **on** for about 0.5 second when person passes through exit turnstile
RESET	Reset button switch, **on** to reset occupancy count in 30 seconds
OCCUPIED	Illuminates when there is anyone in the building
VACANT	Illuminates when there is no one in the building

The addresses and data types associated with the physical I/O and internal variables are:

Variable	Modicon	PLC-5	ControlLogix	Siemens	GE Fanuc
PERSON_IN	100001	I:01/00	Local:1:I.Data.0	I4.0	%I81
PERSON_OUT	100002	I:01/01	Local:1:I.Data.1	I4.1	%I82
RESET	100003	I:01/02	Local:1:I.Data.2	I4.2	%I83
OCCUPIED	000005	O:02/04	Local:2:O.Data.4	Q8.4	%Q5
VACANT	000006	O:02/05	Local:2:O.Data.5	Q8.5	%Q6

P5-17. Use ladder logic to implement a simple *tank volume alarm system* for the tank shown in Figure P5.17 described as:

> This particular problem is one part of a production process where a fluid is transferred from one place to another. You have no control over IN_VALVE or OUT_VALVE. Assume another part of the ladder logic controls these valves. The only valve you control is DRAIN_VALVE.

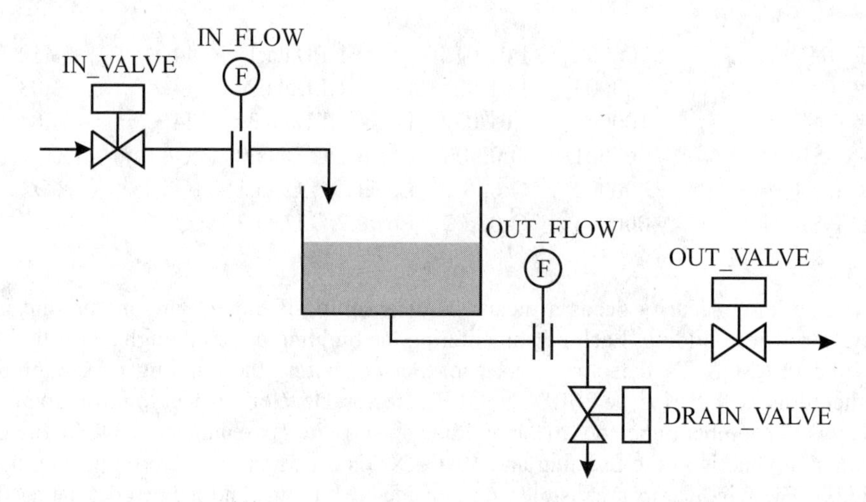

Figure P5.17. Tank system.

The volume of fluid in the tank is determined by monitoring the inlet flow meter, IN_FLOW and outlet flow meter, OUT_FLOW. These particular flow meters output a pulse for every 0.1 gallon of fluid that passes through the meter. The pulse is read as a discrete input and is normally **off**. When 0.1 gallons passes through the meter, the meter output turns **on** for about 0.1 seconds, and then turns **off**. In other words, whenever, IN_FLOW is **on**, the volume in the tank has just increased by 0.1 gallons. Whenever OUT_FLOW is **on**, the volume in the tank has just decreased by 0.1 gallons.

When the tank contains at least 2000 gallons, an alarm horn (ALARM_HORN) is sounded. When the alarm sounds, assume that something else in the process immediately shuts the inlet flow and there is no chance that an additional 0.1 gallons can go into the tank. When the tank volume goes below 2000 gallons, the alarm should be silenced.

A RESET internal coil is provided that when **on**, should cause the tank to be completely drained by opening DRAIN_VALVE. The RESET internal coil is controlled by another part of the ladder. During the draining process, the DRAIN_LAMP must be **on**. When the tank is empty, the DRAIN_LAMP must be turned **off** and the DRAIN_VALVE closed. You may assume a perfect measurement of inlet and outlet flow and no leaks in the tank. This assumption guarantees that the tank volume will reach zero when the tank is being drained (which may not be true for a real process). The DRAIN_LAMP may only be **on** during the reset process. During normal operation, it is **off**. Also, assume that the RESET internal coil is only **on** momentarily, that is, it is **on** for only one scan of the ladder.

An ENABLE internal coil is provided that when **on**, allows the tank volume alarm system to operate. When it is off, you may assume that no fluid is in the tank. The ENABLE coil is controlled by another part of the ladder.

Assume the following physical I/O and internal variable assignments:

Variable	Description
IN_FLOW	Inlet flow meter, **on** for 0.1 sec. when 0.1 gal flows through meter (into tank).
OUT_FLOW	Outlet flow meter, **on** for 0.1 sec. when 0.1 gal flows through meter (out of tank).
ENABLE	Alarm enable, when **on** allows the tank volume alarm system to operate.
RESET	System reset, when **on**, see description above.
ALARM_HORN	Alarm horn; **on** to sound alarm.
DRAIN_VALVE	Tank drain valve, **on** to open drain to tank.
DRAIN_LAMP	Tank drain indication, **on** when tank is draining.

The addresses and data types associated with the physical I/O and internal variables are:

Variable	Modicon	PLC-5	ControlLogix	Siemens	GE Fanuc
IN_FLOW	100001	I:01/00	Local:1:I.Data.0	I4.0	%I81
OUT_FLOW	100002	I:01/01	Local:1:I.Data.1	I4.1	%I82
ENABLE	BOOL	B3/101	BOOL	M6.5	%M101
RESET	BOOL	B3/102	BOOL	M6.6	%M102
ALARM_HORN	000001	O:02/00	Local:2:O.Data.0	Q8.0	%Q1
DRAIN_VALVE	000002	O:02/01	Local:2:O.Data.1	Q8.1	%Q2
DRAIN_LAMP	000003	O:02/02	Local:2:O.Data.2	Q8.2	%Q3

P5-18. Modify the solution to problem P5-17 to remove the assumption that the inlet and outlet flows are measured perfectly and that there are no tank leaks. Therefore, the tank volume will probably not reach zero when the tank is being drained. So, an alternative way of automatically determining when the tank is actually empty must be provided. Your solution should not:

1. Involve the operator (for example, require the operator to look in the tank), and
2. Require any more physical I/O channels.

Also, the drain valve must be closed no longer than 2 minutes after the tank is empty. Hint: the solution involves a timer.

P5-19. Use ladder logic to implement a simple *warning indicator* described below:

Flash a lamp, PL5, 10 times after LS2 has been turned on. For each on-off period, the lamp should be **on** for 1±0.1 second, and **off** for 1±0.1 second. After PL5 has flashed **on** 10 times, it remains **off** until LS2 is turned **on**. Assume LS2 will remain **on** for at least one scan, but no longer than 18.9 seconds. Once LS2 turns **off**, it will not turn **on** until after PL5 has flashed 10 times.

When LS2 turns **on**, PL5 should start flashing immediately. There should not be a one second delay between LS2 turning **on** and PL5 turning **on** for the first time.

The ladder logic does not require a separate reset switch. Anything that should be reset at the end of the 10 flashes should be handled automatically.

The addresses associated with the physical I/O are:

Variable	Modicon	PLC-5	ControlLogix	Siemens	GE Fanuc
LS2	100001	I:01/00	Local:1:I.Data.0	I4.0	%I81
PL5	000001	O:02/00	Local:2:O.Data.0	Q8.0	%Q1

P5-20. Use ladder logic to implement the following simple tank level control.

Figure P5.20 shows the schematic diagram of a tank with level sensor that is supplied by a pump, T100_PUMP. There is only one level sensor, T100_LEVEL. Currently, the pump is controlled directly by the level sensor. When the RUN switch is **on** and the level sensor is **off**, the pump is **on**. However, the pump motor wears out quickly due to excessive cycling (short on, short off periods). You need to do a fair job of level control, and yet not wear out the motor. Therefore, the pump motor control is to be changed to the following:

When the RUN switch is **on** and the level sensor is **off** for 1 minute, turn **on** the pump motor. When the level sensor is **on** for 2 minutes, or the RUN switch is turned **off**, turn **off** the pump motor.

In addition, as an aid for maintenance personnel, the number of pump cycles is counted, and P_CYC_ALM is turned **on** at the beginning of the 1001st cycle. A cycle is defined as pump **on** and pump **off**. A reset switch, PCYC_RESET, is provided to reset (turn **off** P_CYC_ALM and reset the counter. The counter should not be reset unless the P_CYC_ALM is already **on**.

Assume the following physical I/O assignments.

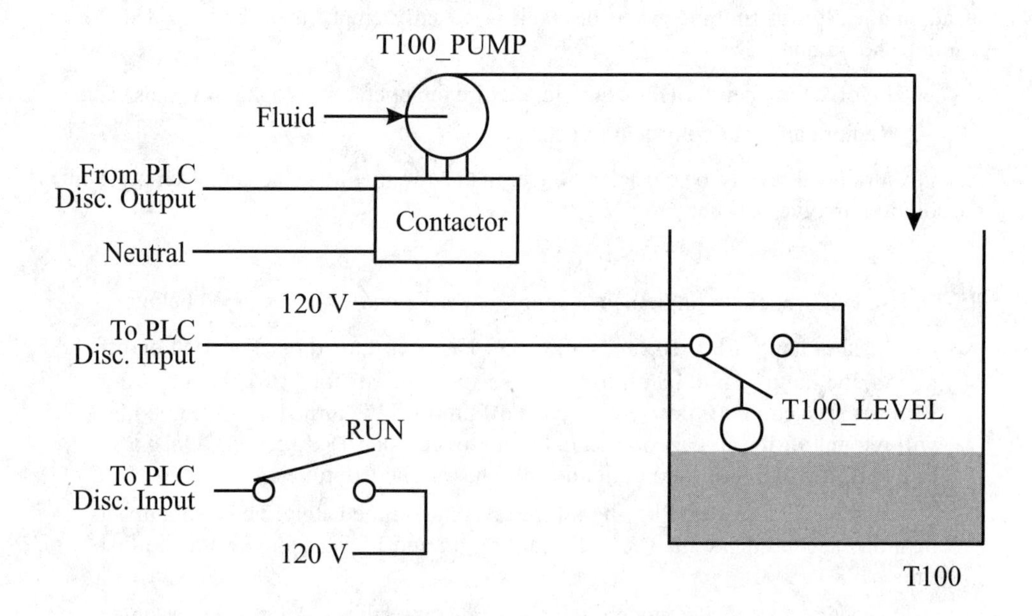

Figure P5.20. Simple tank level control.

Variable	Description
RUN	Pump run toggle switch, **on** to run, **off** to stop.
T100_LEVEL	Level switch, N. O., **on** when fluid at or above proper level, **off** when fluid below proper level.
PCYC_RESET	Reset for pump cycle alarm, **on** to reset alarm and reset counter (see above).
T100_PUMP	Pump motor, **on** to run, **off** to stop.
P_CYC_ALM	Pump cycle alarm, on to indicate 1000 cycles have run (see above).

The addresses associated with the physical I/O are:

Variable	Modicon	PLC-5	ControlLogix	Siemens	GE Fanuc
RUN	100033	I:03/00	Local:3:I.Data.0	I12.0	%I103
T100_LEVEL	100034	I:03/01	Local:3:I.Data.1	I12.1	%I104
PCYC_RESET	100036	I:03/03	Local:3:I.Data.3	I12.3	%I106
T100_PUMP	000065	O:04/00	Local:4:O.Data.0	Q16.0	%Q65
P_CYC_ALM	000067	O:04/02	Local:4:O.Data.2	Q16.2	%Q67

P5-21. Develop a ladder logic program for an automatic plant waterer (Figure P5.21) with the following specifications:

1. Every 8 hours, water is added to the container, by turning on P103, up to the desired level (LS102 closes). When the desired level is reached, P103 should be shut off. At the end of the 8-hour interval, the 8-hour clock should be reset.
2. If LS102 is still closed at the end of the 8-hour interval, assume the level switch is stuck on, and turn on the AH104 alarm. Do not add any water, but still reset the 8-hour clock.
3. If P103 remains on for 25 seconds and LS102 has not turned on, then assume either LS102 is stuck off or the reservoir is empty and turn on the AH104 alarm.
4. When the alarm is on, the pump will be shut off and the 8-hour timer is paused.
5. SW101 must be on for the waterer to operate. If SW101 is off, the 8-hour timer must be paused (but not reset).
6. OVERRIDE is an override/reset switch. When this switch is pressed, the action of the program is as if the end of the 8-hour interval is reached (attempt to fill container and reset 8-hour timer). Also, the OVERRIDE switch turns off the alarm. Holding down the override switch should not change its operation, even if held down for more than 8 hours.
7. The OVERRIDE switch is the only item that can turn off the AH104 alarm.
8. As part of your program construct an 8-hour clock that keeps track of seconds, minutes, and hours. Do not use a timer with an 8-hour preset time.

Assume the following physical input and output assignments:

Variable	Description
SW101	Toggle switch, **on** (closed) when enabling plant waterer.
LS102	Level switch, N.O., closed when water at correct level.

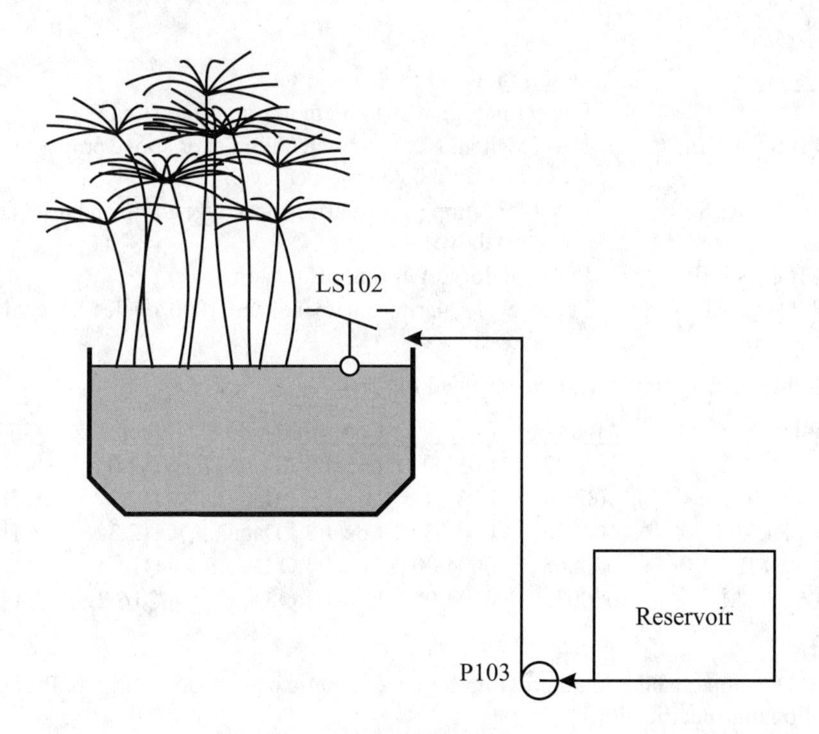

Figure P5.21. Plant waterer.

OVERRIDE	Override push button, **on** to override the timer operation (described above).
P103	Pump, **on** to pump water into plant container.
AH104	Alarm horn; **on** to sound alarm.

The addresses associated with the physical I/O are:

Variable	Modicon	PLC-5	ControlLogix	Siemens	GE Fanuc
SW101	100001	I:01/00	Local:1:I.Data.0	I4.0	%I81
LS102	100002	I:01/01	Local:1:I.Data.1	I4.1	%I82
OVERRIDE	100003	I:01/02	Local:1:I.Data.2	I4.2	%I83
P103	000001	O:02/00	Local:2:O.Data.0	Q8.0	%Q1
AH104	000002	O:02/01	Local:2:O.Data.1	Q8.1	%Q2

6 Sequential Applications

Chapter Topics:

- Function charts
- Simple ladder logic implementation of function charts
- Parallel operations

OBJECTIVES

Upon completion of this chapter, you will be able to:

- Draw a function chart, given the operational description of a sequential process
- Translate the function chart to ladder logic
- Handle pause and reset of the sequential operation

Scenario: Using a proximity sensor to detect material moving into and out of a station.

Commonly, only one sensor is used to detect the presence of material as it moves into a station, is processed, and moves out of the station. As an example, consider the problem of applying a label to each box as it travels on a conveyor, shown in Figure 6.1. A retro-reflective proximity sensor (PROX) is used to detect the presence of the box. Assume PROX turns **on** when the box is in the proper position to have the label applied. When the labeling station is started, the presence of a box must be detected, the label is applied (involving multiple steps), and then the operation is repeated. A chart of the steps of this process is shown in Figure 6.2. The process starts waiting for a box to be detected. When PROX turns **on**, then the machinery applies the label (multiple steps). When the labeling steps are finished, then the station waits for the next box. However, as depicted in Figure 6.2, the operation **does not work!** After applying the label, PROX remains **on**, (box still in

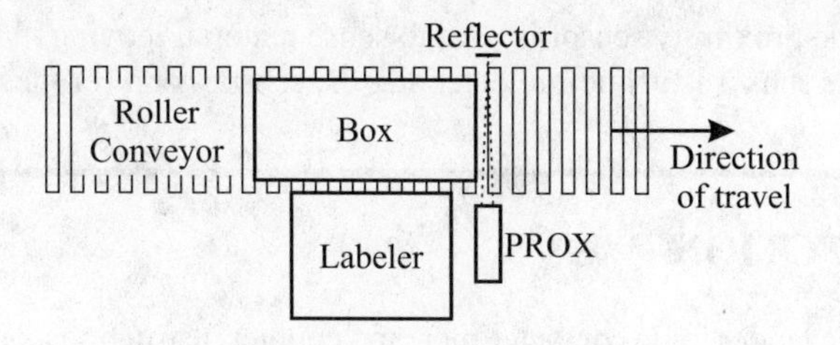

Figure 6.1. Labeling station.

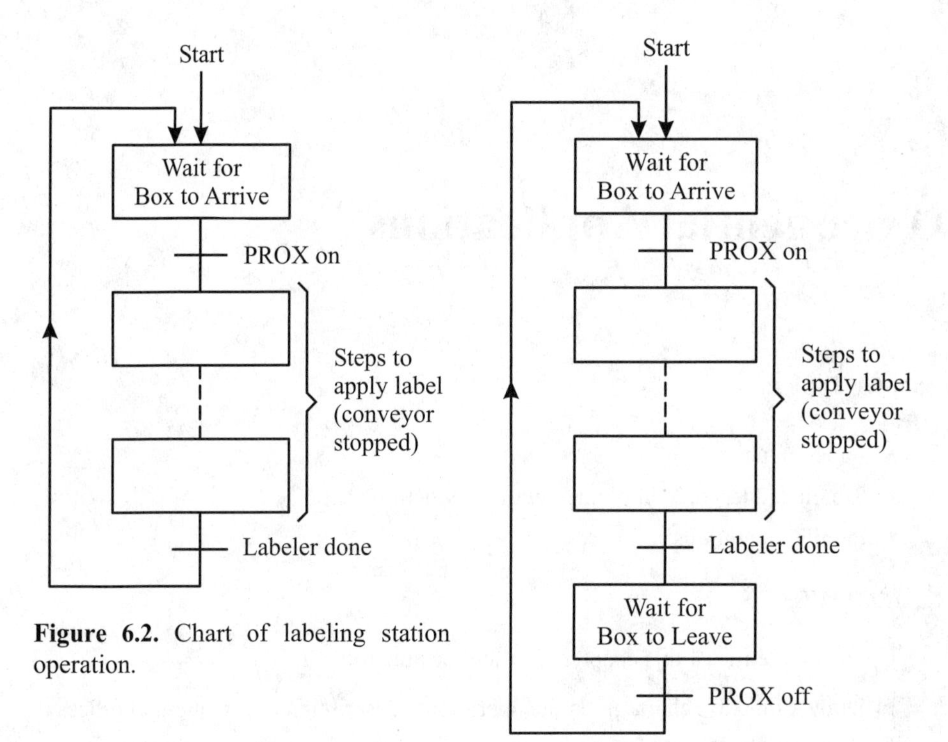

Figure 6.2. Chart of labeling station operation.

Figure 6.3. Corrected chart of labeling station operation.

station) and so the condition that indicates a new box (PROX **on**) is true. Therefore, a new label is applied to the box before it leaves the station. If left to run unattended, this station will continue to apply multiple labels to the first box that enters the station!

Solution: The station must detect that a labeled box has exited the station before detecting that a new box has entered. Therefore, a step must be added to wait for the box to leave the station, detecting PROX is **off**. The correct chart of this process is shown in Figure 6.3. The moral of this scenario is to remember that one must detect that a proximity sensor is first **off** before it can be detected to be **on**.

Design Tip

When one proximity sensor is used to sense material moving in/out , one must detect that the sensor is **off** before detecting the sensor is **on** (or vice versa).

6.1 INTRODUCTION

With the basic ladder logic contact, timer, and counter instructions, one is able to tackle more significant problems. This chapter introduces ladder logic program design for sequential applications, a significant contribution of the text. More advanced techniques for sequential control are treated in Chapter 9.

The sequential design technique is based on describing the operation as a function chart and then translating the function chart to ladder logic code. The ladder logic primarily uses the basic contact and coil instructions. Timers and counters are used only when explicitly needed by the operation. The ability to pause and reset an operation is added to the basic sequential design. Operations with parallel steps and machine control involving manual and single-step modes are also considered. Since the design technique uses the set/reset instructions, the last section presents an alternate implementation using only the ordinary output coil that may be used for PLCs that do not have the set/reset coil instructions.

6.2 FUNCTION CHART

The basic tool used to design sequential control applications is the function chart. This method of describing sequential operations is described in the IEC 848 standard (IEC, 1988) and incorporated as one of the IEC 61131-3 languages (IEC, 1993). The form of the function chart described in this chapter is a simplified version of the IEC 61131-3 SFC (sequential function chart) language. The full IEC sequential function chart language is described in Chapter 14.

The general form of the function chart is shown in Figure 6.4. The function chart has the following major parts:

Steps of the sequential operation,

Transition conditions to move to next step

Actions of each step

The **initial step** is indicated by the double-line rectangle. The initial step is the initial state of the ladder logic when the PLC is first powered up or when the operator resets the operation. The **steps** of the operation are shown as rectangles on the left side of the diagram. Unless shown by an arrow, the progression of the steps proceeds from top to bottom. Each step rectangle contains a short description of what is happening during the step. To the left of the step rectangle is the variable/symbol/tag name of the step-in-progress coil (or bit) that is **on** when that step is active. The **transition condition** is shown as a horizontal bar between steps. If a step is active and the transition condition below that step becomes true, the step becomes inactive, and the next step becomes active. The stepwise flow continues until the bottom of the diagram. At the bottom, the sequencing may end, as indicated by a filled black circle within another circle, or it may repeat by going back to the first step. The **actions** associated with a step are shown in the rectangle to the right of the step. The actions are output(s) that are **on** when a step is active. Any outputs not listed are assumed to be **off**. However, the set/reset of outputs may be indicated. Any timer or counter active during a particular step is also listed as an action.

The function chart is prepared from the operational description of the system. Often, the hardest part about formulating the function chart is making a distinction between the transitions and the steps. Also, one must remember that physical outputs are actions associated with a step. In order to help in the recognition of the steps and transitions within an operational description, use the following definitions:

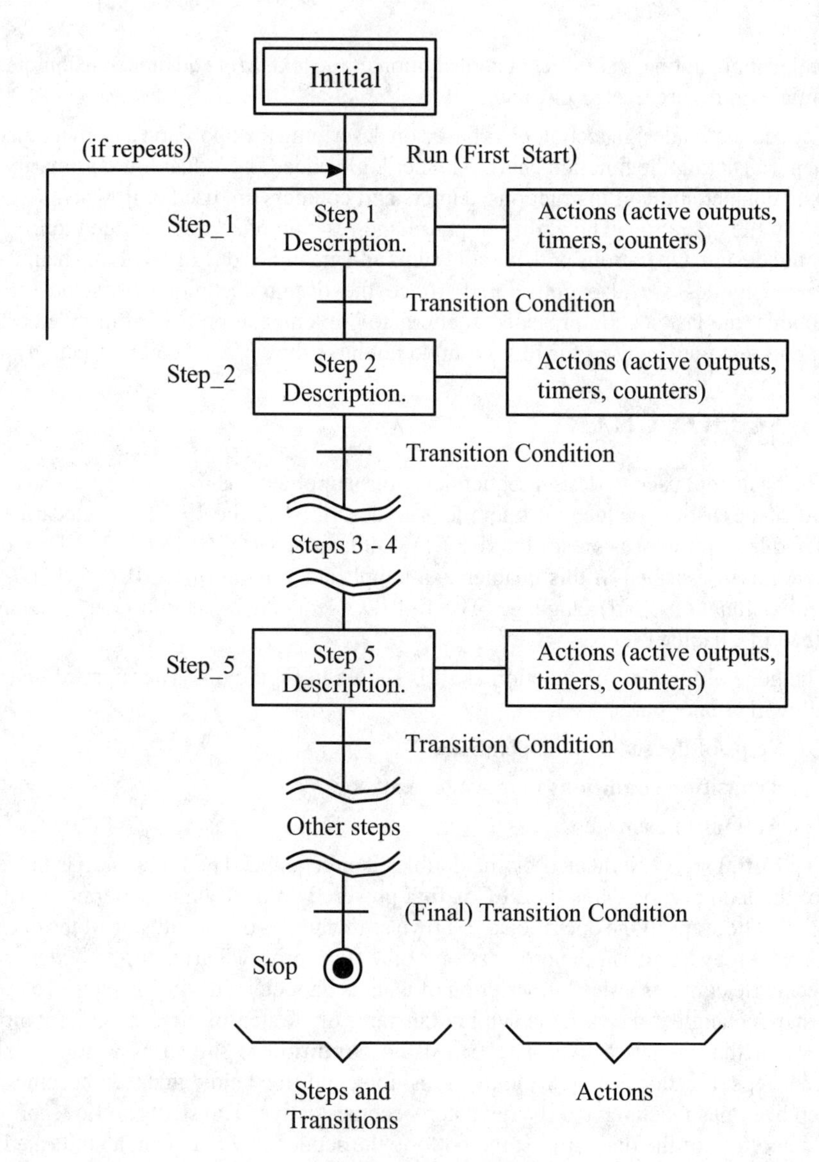

Figure 6.4. General function chart.

Step:

Operation spanning a length of time (however long or short).
The time period may be defined or undefined.

Transition:

Physical input device or internal coil turning **on** or **off**

— or —

Physical input device or internal coil being turned **on** or **off**

A transition condition is recognized when the narrative describes a physical input device or internal coil turning **on** or **off**. Alternatively, the end of a defined time period also signals a transition to the next step. If the narrative describes a physical output being turned on/off, that is not a transition. A physical output is considered a step action and the turning on/off of a physical output is handled by a change in the active step. For example, if "Output1" is being turned on as the active step is changed from "Step1" to "Step2," it is accomplished by **not** listing "Output1" as a "Step1" action and by listing it as a "Step2" action. Output1 is **not** a transition condition. The change in Output1 does not cause a change in the active step, but is a consequence of the change in the active step.

Design Tip

When constructing the function chart, remember that physical outputs **never** occur as part of the transition condition. Also, physical inputs are **never** an action.

These concepts are illustrated by the following example.

Example 6.1. Metal Shear Control. Design the function chart of the program to control the metal shear shown in Figure 6.5 and whose operation is described as:

> The shear cuts a continuous length of steel strip. Two conveyors (driven by CONV1_MTR and CONV2_MTR) move the strip into position. Inductive proximity sensor PROX turns **on** to indicate that the strip is in position to be sheared. When the strip is in position, both conveyors should stop. A hydraulic cylinder (controlled by SHEAR_CYL_RET) is then retracted to move the shear down to cut the material. Limit switch DOWN_LS closes (turns **on**) when the shear is fully down. The cylinder is then extended to move the shear blade up. Limit switch UP_LS closes when the shear blade is fully up. Conveyor 2 (controlled by CONV2_MTR) is now turned **on** to move the cut sheet out of the station. The proximity sensor PROX turns **off** when the sheet has been moved out of the station. Both conveyors are now operated to move the strip into position, and the operation repeats.
>
> Your program is not controlling conveyor 3, so assume it is always running.
>
> The shear is controlled by SHEAR_CYL_RET, a single action linear hydraulic cylinder. Once SHEAR_CYL_RET is energized, the shear blade moves down to cut the material until a mechanical stop is reached and remains in the "down" position as long as power is applied (turned **on**). The shear blade moves up when power is removed (turned **off**).
>
> Upon initial startup, no material is in the shear and the conveyors operate to bring the material into the shearing position (PROX turns **on**). The start switch should have no effect if the process is already running. If the stop switch is pressed at any time, the station operation should pause, except when the shear blade is moving. If the stop switch is pressed when the shear blade is moving, the blade movement must complete. When the start switch is pressed while the operation is paused, the station should resume the suspended step. When the station is paused, the conveyor drive motors should be shut off.

Assume the following physical input and physical outputs:

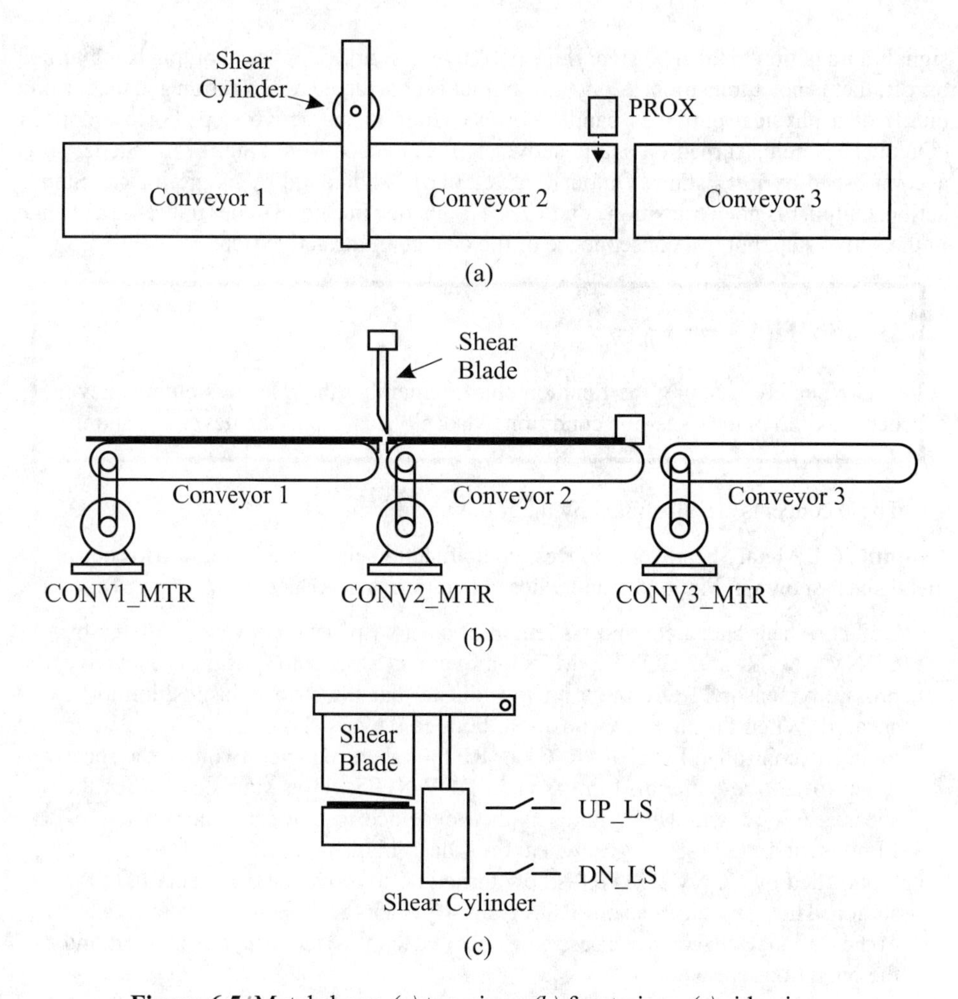

Figure 6.5. Metal shear: *(a)* top view; *(b)* front view; *(c)* side view.

Variable	Description
START_PB	Start push button, N. O., **on** when starting
STOP_PB	Stop push button, N. C., **off** when stopping
PROX	Proximity sensor, **on** when strip in shearing position
DOWN_LS	Limit switch, N. O., **on** (closed) when blade fully down
UP_LS	Limit switch, N. O., **on** (closed) when blade fully up
CONV1_MTR	Conveyor 1 control, **on** to move material on conveyor 1
CONV2_MTR	Conveyor 2 control, **on** to move material on conveyor 2
SHEAR_CYL_RET	Shear cylinder control, **on** to retract cylinder and move blade down

Solution. There are two main steps to develop the function chart:

1. Identify the steps and transition conditions.
2. Add step actions.

To identify the steps and transitions, the first paragraph of the process description is repeated, with the steps identified by the underlined phrases and the transition conditions identified by the *italicized phrases*. Often, it is easier to identify the first transition condition (signaled by an input sensor change) and then recognize the step before and the step after the transition condition. Also, many times the steps and transition conditions alternate during the narrative.

> The shear cuts a continuous length of steel strip. Two conveyors (driven by CONV1_MTR and CONV2_MTR) move the strip into position. Inductive proximity sensor *PROX turns **on*** to indicate that the strip is in position to be sheared. When the strip is in position, both conveyors should stop. A hydraulic cylinder (controlled by SHEAR_CYL_RET) is then retracted to move the shear down to cut the material. Limit switch *DOWN_LS closes (turns **on**)* when the shear is fully down. The cylinder is then extended to move the shear blade up. Limit switch *UP_LS closes* when the shear blade is fully up. Conveyor 2 (controlled by CONV2_MTR) is now turned **on** to move the cut sheet out of the station. The proximity sensor *PROX turns **off*** when the sheet has been moved out of the station. Both conveyors are now be operated to move the strip into position, and the operation repeats.

Notice that the phrase "... both conveyors should stop." is not marked as a transition condition. This phrase describes a physical output being turned on/off and that will be handled by a change in the active step.

So, the steps and the transition conditions that indicate the end of each step are:

Step	Transition Condition (out of step)
Move strip into position	PROX on
Move shear down	DOWN_LS on
Move shear up	UP_LS on
Move cut sheet out	PROX off

These steps and the transition conditions between them are shown in Figure 6.6. The "off" state of PROX that signals the end of the fourth step is shown with the "/" in front of the variable name. The variable name of the step-in-progress bit for each step is also shown beside the step box. This particular operation repeats, indicated by the line from the fourth step back to the first step.

The next part of the function chart development is to add the actions to each step. Reading back through the metal shear narrative, the process actions for each step are:

Step	Action
Move strip into position	CONV1_MTR and CONV2_MTR
Move shear down	SHEAR_CYL_RET
Move shear up	
Move cut sheet out	CONV2_MTR

These actions are added to the steps and the transition conditions to form the function chart shown in Figure 6.7.

The part of the narrative that describes the operation pause is handled in the ladder logic code and is considered in the following section.

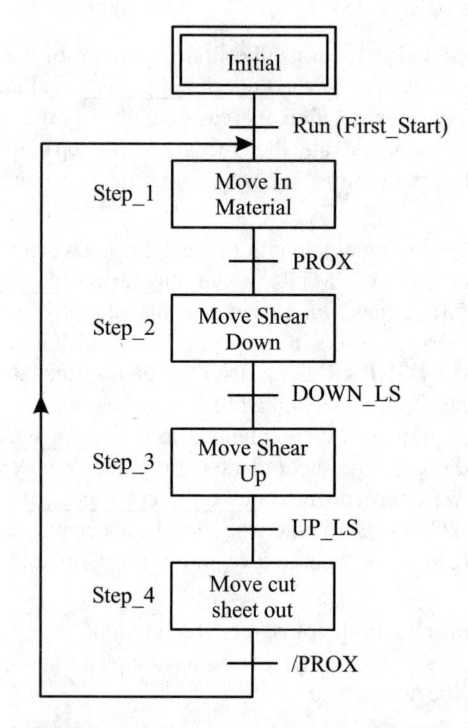

Figure 6.6. Steps and transitions for metal shear.

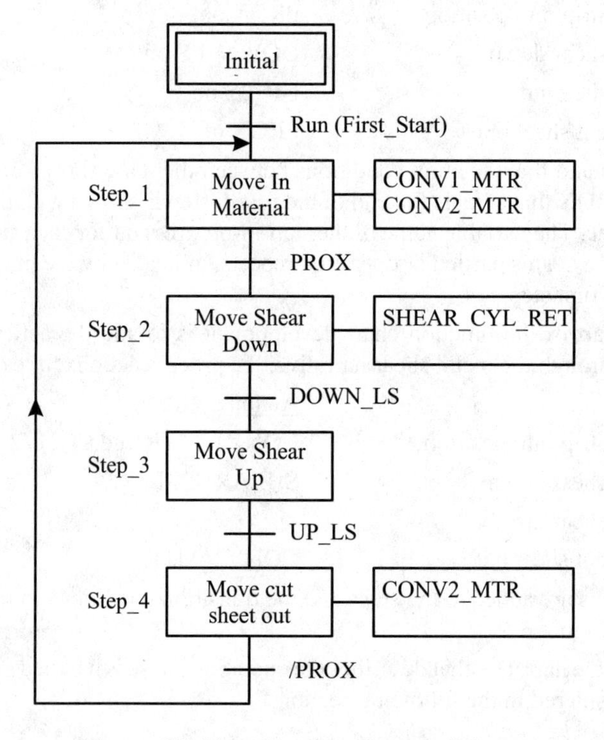

Figure 6.7. Function chart for metal shear.

6.3 IMPLEMENTING FUNCTION CHART IN LADDER LOGIC

Once a function chart has been developed, it needs to be implemented in ladder logic. There are multiple ways to accomplish this task. The design technique described in this chapter utilizes only the basic ladder logic instructions to implement the step and transition logic. Other methods are shown in Chapter 9.

The author calls this method the "cookie cutter" or "template-based" approach because the form of the ladder logic code is the same, regardless of the application. Also, this approach aids in debugging because the logic that handles the transitions and the logic that handles the step actions are distinct. The latter advantage is apparent when comparing this approach to the ad-hoc approach of section 9.5.

The code is broken into the following sections:

Start/stop/pause of overall operation

First start

Transitions between steps

Step actions

Each of these code templates is covered in detail and then applied to the metal shear of Example 6.1.

The start/stop/pause of the overall operation is handled as the rung in Figure 6.8, which is the same general format as the start/stop rung shown in section 2.7. An internal coil (variable) named Run controls the overall operation of the function chart. It will be used to turn **off** physical outputs that need to be **off** when pausing the operation. Occasionally, the Run may be used as part of a transition condition. The optional permissive conditions must be satisfied to allow the operation to be started or restarted after an abnormal condition. The optional lockout conditions cause the operation to pause or stop in addition to preventing a restart.

The "first start" transition condition causes the operation to be initiated when no steps are currently active. The ladder logic to generate First_Start is shown in Figure 6.9*a*. When the Run internal coil is turned **on** (start push button pressed) and no steps are active (Step_N is the last step), the First_Start internal coil is turned **on** and will be used as a transition condition into the first step. Alternatively, the first step (Step_1) can be set (latched) to start the operation (Figure 6.9*b*). START_PB could be used in place of Run in Figure 6.9, but if the run rung has permissive and/or lockout conditions, these conditions should also be repeated on the rung that starts the operation for the first time. As explained in section 2.7, a change to lockouts and permissives should affect only one rung.

Transitions between steps are handled as shown in Figure 6.10. The logic implements the transition condition below the step in the function chart, which is the transition condition

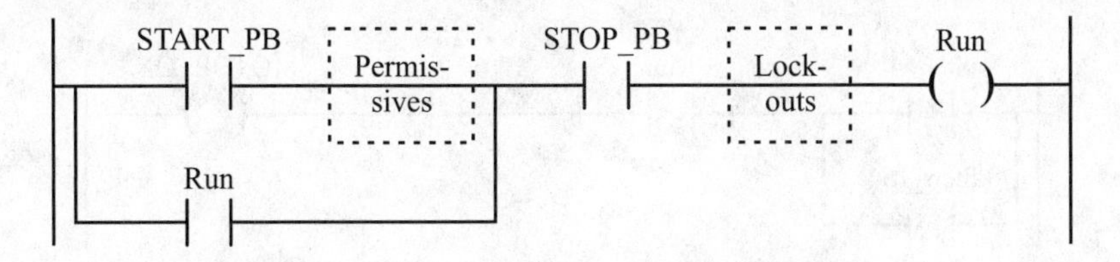

Figure 6.8. General start/stop/pause rung.

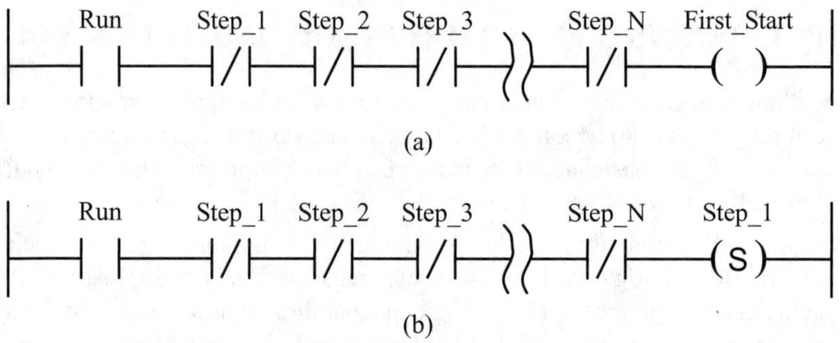

(a)

(b)

Figure 6.9. General first start rung: *(a)* First_Start internal coil; *(b)* set first step.

out of a step. When the current step is active (Current_Step is **on**) and the transition condition is true, then the step-in-progress bit of the next step is set and the step-in-progress-bit of the current step is reset. Thus, the next step becomes active and the current step becomes inactive.

If the PLC does not have set/reset or latch/unlatch instructions (e.g., Modicon 984 and Siemens TI-5x5) then an alternative approach must be used, as detailed in section 6.8.

The step-in-progress internal coils are used to control the step actions. The appropriate step-in-progress bits turn **on** the outputs and timers that are the step actions. The Run internal coil is also used as part of the condition for those actions that must be **off** when the operation is paused. For example, if the MOTOR_ON output should be **on** in steps 4 and 15 of the function chart (represented by Step_4 and Step_15), then the logic driving MOTOR_ON appears as shown in Figure 6.11. The Run internal coil turns **off** MOTOR_ON if step 4 or step 15 is active and the stop push button is pressed to pause the operation. When the operation is resumed (by pressing the start push button), then MOTOR_ON is reactivated. If the Run internal coil is omitted from the rung in Figure 6.11, then MOTOR_ON will remain **on** when the operation is paused when in step 4 or step 15.

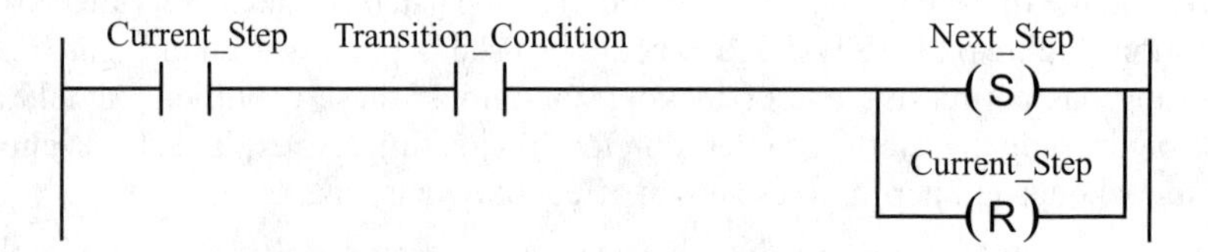

Figure 6.10. General transition between steps.

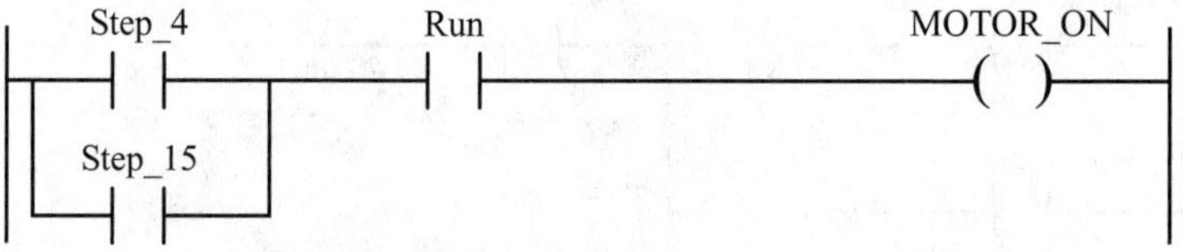

Figure 6.11. Example step action.

Note that in Figure 6.11, the Step_4 and Step_15 step-in-progress bits are in parallel, meaning that MOTOR_ON is an action in steps 4 and 15. The MOTOR_ON output is **off** for any other steps.

If the action associated with a step is a set/reset of an output, then the output coil of Figure 6.11 is replaced by a set or reset coil.

Design Tip

Repeating outputs is a common mistake when implementing a function chart where a particular output is the action for more than one step. Consider the output first and then the steps for which it is **on** to avoid repeating output instructions.

Example 6.2. Metal Shear Control. Use ladder logic to implement the metal shear operation described in Example 6.1.

The physical inputs and physical outputs are:

Variable	Description
START_PB	Start push button, N. O., **on** when starting
STOP_PB	Stop push button, N. C., **off** when stopping
PROX	Proximity sensor, **on** when strip in shearing position
DOWN_LS	Limit switch, N. O., **on** (closed) when blade fully down
UP_LS	Limit switch, N. O., **on** (closed) when blade fully up
CONV1_MTR	Conveyor 1 control, **on** to move material on conveyor 1
CONV2_MTR	Conveyor 2 control, **on** to move material on conveyor 2
SHEAR_CYL_RET	Shear cylinder control, **on** to retract cylinder and move blade down

The addresses associated with the variables:

Variable	Modicon	PLC-5	ControlLogix	Siemens	GE Fanuc
START_PB	100001	I:0/00	Local:1:I.Data.0	I0.0	%I1
STOP_PB	100002	I:0/01	Local:1:I.Data.1	I0.1	%I2
PROX	100003	I:0/02	Local:1:I.Data.2	I0.2	%I3
DOWN_LS	100004	I:0/03	Local:1:I.Data.3	I0.3	%I4
UP_LS	100005	I:0/04	Local:1:I.Data.4	I0.4	%I5
CONV1_MTR	000001	O:1/00	Local:2:O.Data.0	Q4.0	%Q1
CONV2_MTR	000002	O:1/01	Local:2:O.Data.1	Q4.1	%Q2
SHEAR_CYL_RET	000003	O:1/02	Local:2:O.Data.2	Q4.2	%Q3

Solution. The function chart for the shear operation is shown in Figure 6.7. Before developing the ladder logic code, the internal variables should be identified:

Variable	Description
Run	Indicates operation running
Step_1 to Step_4	Step-in-progress bits for steps

The addresses or data types associated with the variables:

Variable	Modicon Data Type	PLC-5 Addr.	ControlLogix Data Type	Siemens Addr.	GE Fanuc Addr.
Run	BOOL	B3/0	BOOL	M0.0	%M0
Step_1 to	BOOL	B20/1	BOOL	M50.1	%M51
Step_4	BOOL	B20/4	BOOL	M50.4	%M54

The ladder logic code is broken into the following sections:

Start/stop/pause of overall operation

First start

Transitions between steps

Step actions

The IEC 61131-3 code for the metal shear, shown in Figure 6.12, is developed using the code templates shown in Figures 6.8 - 6.11. A rung comment is shown within a rectangle above the rung. The function of each rung is as follows:

1. Start/stop/pause of overall operation
2. First start (starting the operation for the very first time)
3. Transition from step 1 to step 2
4. Transition from step 2 to step 3
5. Transition from step 3 to step 4
6. Transition from step 4 to step 1
7. Control of conveyor 1 (an action for step 1)
8. Control of conveyor 2 (an action for steps 1 and 4)
9. Control of shear cylinder (an action for step 2)

The initial start of the operation is handled like Figure 6.9*b*. Note the use of the Run in rungs 7 and 8 to turn **off** the conveyors when the station is paused. Since the shear cylinder operation should not stop if the stop push button is pressed while it is moving, Run is not used as a condition in rung 9.

The CONV2_MTR output is an action for 2 steps, as shown in rung 8 of Figure 6.12. Note that if a particular output is an action for multiple steps, then the step-in-progress bits of each step are placed in parallel. When a particular output is the action for more than one step, novice programmers often repeat the outputs. If one did not consider the output first

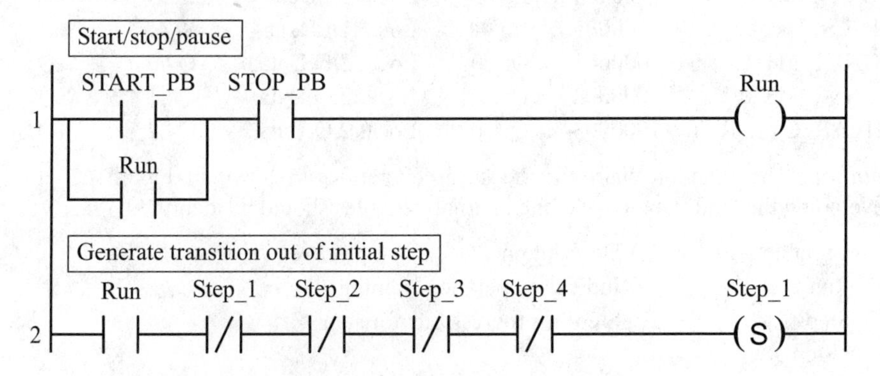

Figure 6.12. IEC ladder logic for metal shear. *(continued)*

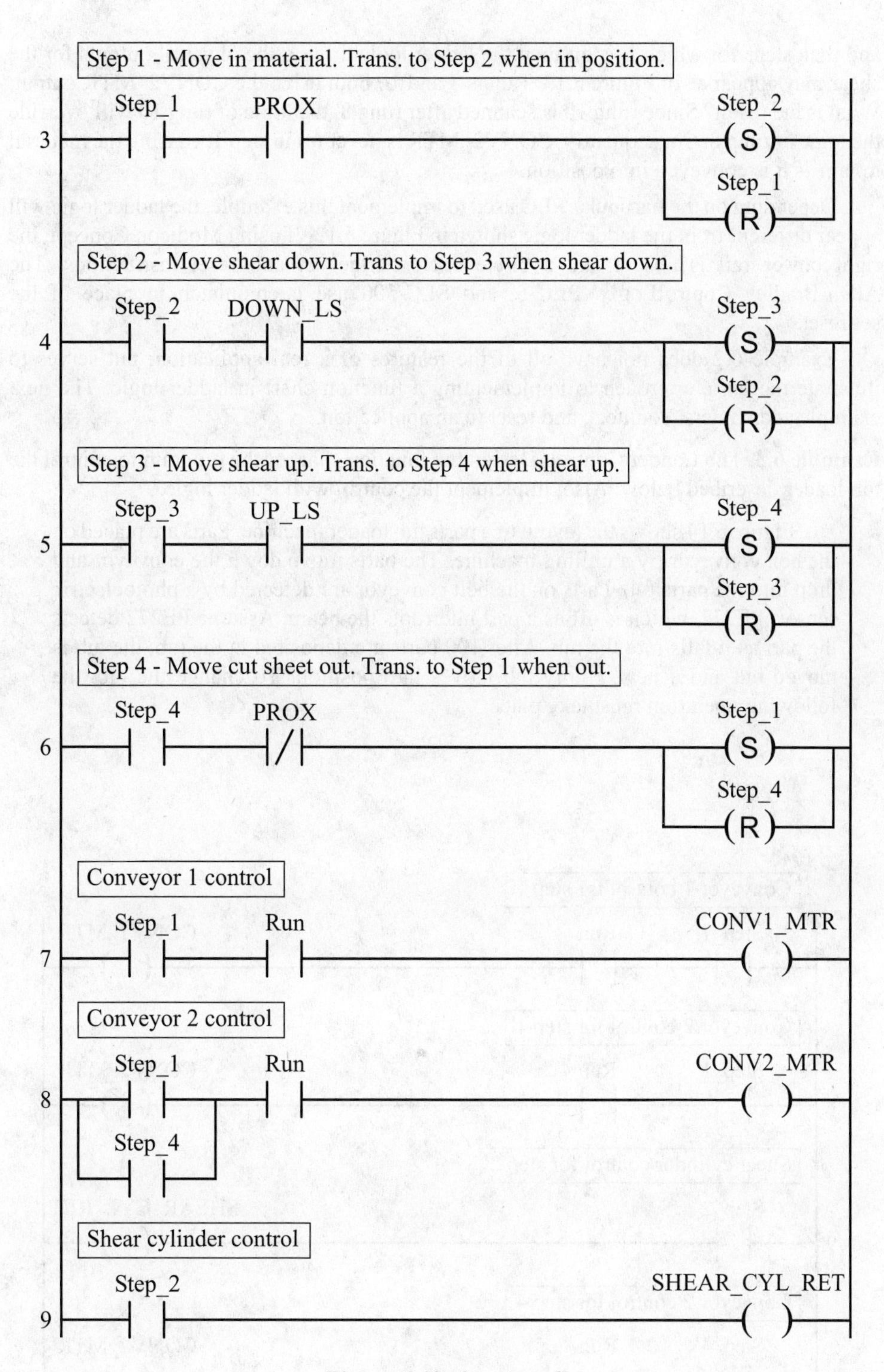

Figure 6.12. *(continued)*

and then steps for which it is **on** then the ladder logic driving the physical outputs for the shear may appear as in Figure 6.13. Rungs 8 and 10 both drive the CONV2_MTR output. What is the result? Since rung 10 is scanned after rung 8, the logic of rung 10 will override the logic of rung 8. Consequently, CONV2_MTR is never **on** in step 1, causing the material to jam as it is conveyed into position.

Depending on the particular PLC used to implement this example, the ladder logic will appear different from the ladder logic shown in Figure 6.12. If using Modicon Concept, the right power rail is absent and a circle encloses the set and reset instructions. The Allen-Bradley ControlLogix, PLC-5, and SLC-500 use latch/unlatch in place of the set/reset.

Example 6.2 does not have all of the features of a real application, but serves to illustrate the basic approach to implementing a function chart in ladder logic. The next example adds timers, counters, and reset to an application.

Example 6.3. Tub Loader Control. Design the function chart of the program to control the tub loader described below. Also, implement the control with ladder logic.

> Figure 6.14 shows the layout of a parts tub loader machine. Parts are placed on the belt conveyor by a milling machine. The parts move down the conveyor and drop into the parts tub. Parts on the belt conveyor are detected by a photoelectric sensor, PE272, which is **off** as a part interrupts the beam. Assume PE272 detects the part as it falls into the tub. After 100 parts are deposited in the tub, the tub is moved out and a new, empty tub moves into position. To change the tub, the following operation must take place:

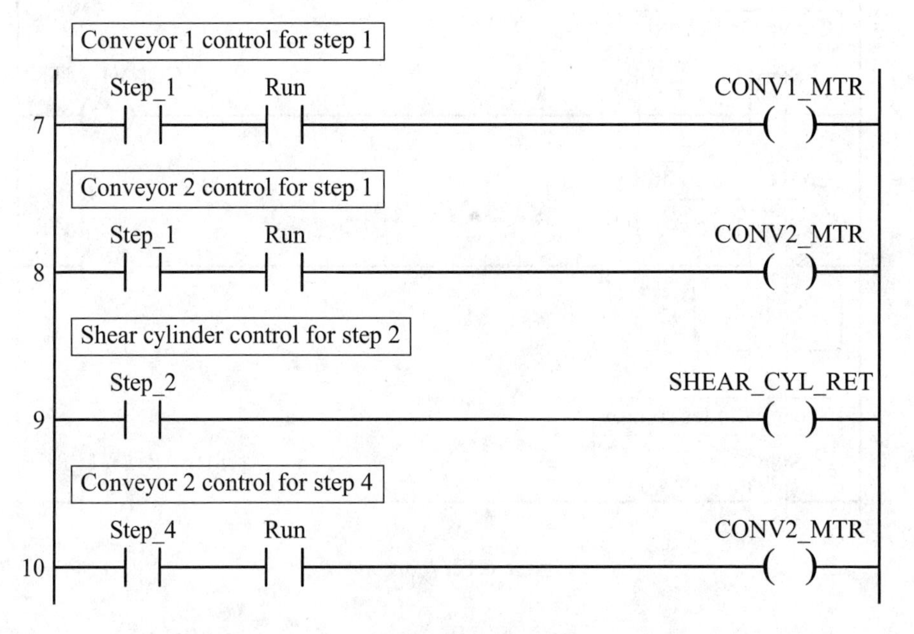

Figure 6.13. Incorrect output logic for metal shear.

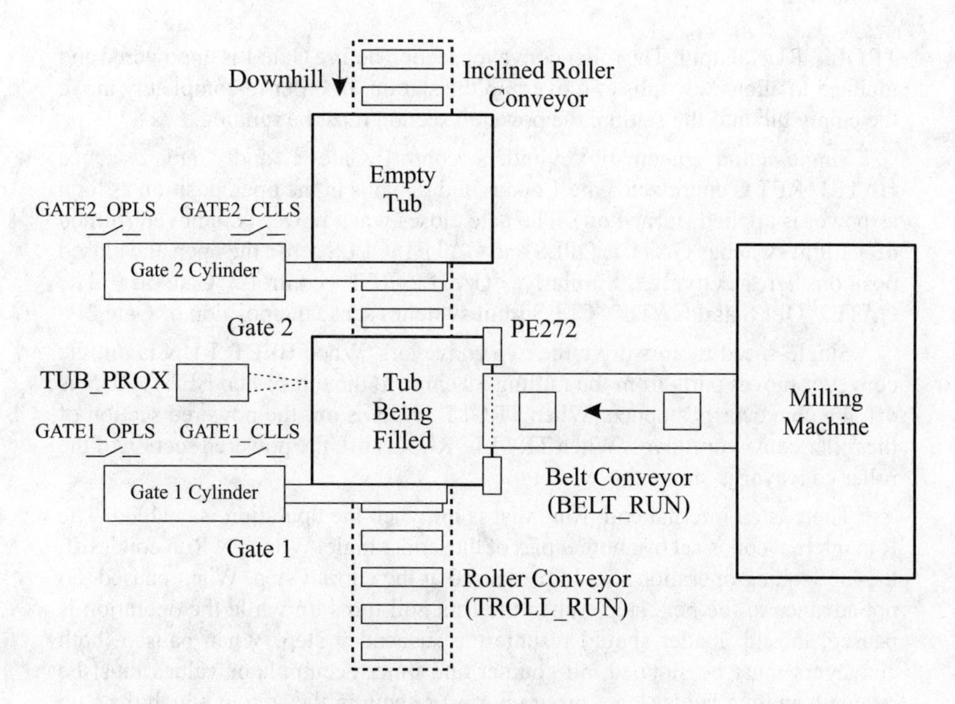

Figure 6.14. Parts tub loading station.

Open Gate 1 (GATE1_OPLS senses when open).

Hold Gate 1 open and wait for TUB_PROX to be **off** for 3 seconds to allow the full tub to be moved out of the loading station. Run the tub roller conveyor to move out the full tub.

Gate 1 is closed (GATE1_CLLS senses when closed).

Gate 2 is opened (GATE2_OPLS senses when open).

Hold Gate 2 open to allow an empty tub to move down a slight incline into the loading station. When the tub contacts the tub roller conveyor, the tub roller conveyor moves the tub into position. When TUB_PROX is **on** for 5 seconds, the tub is in position (front resting on Gate 1).

Gate 2 is closed (GATE2_CLLS senses when closed).

The TUB_PROX proximity sensor is **on** when the tub is present, though not necessarily in position. Hence, the delays ensure the empty tub has moved in and the full one has moved out.

While the tub is being changed, the belt conveyor motor must be stopped (BELT_RUN **off**) and an internal coil, Tub_Permissive, must be turned **off**. After a new tub is in position, BELT_RUN is turned **on**, the Tub_Permissive coil is turned **on**, and the counting of parts is resumed. The Tub_Permissive is used by the milling machine ladder logic. When Tub_Permissive is **on**, the machine produces parts.

The roller conveyor for the tubs has two sections. The section between the two gates and extending out of the station is powered and controlled by the

TROLL_RUN output. The roller conveyor section before Gate 1 is unpowered and inclined to allow new tubs to move into the station. In order to completely move the empty tub into the station, the powered section must be running.

Single-action pneumatic cylinders control Gate 1 and Gate 2. Once GATE1_RET is energized, gate 1 opens and remains in the open position as long as power is applied (turned **on**). The gate closes when power is removed (turned **off**). Limit switches GATE1_OPLS and GATE1_CLLS sense the open and closed positions, respectively. Similarly, GATE2_RET controls Gate 2. The GATE2_OPLS and GATE2_CLLS limit switches sense the position of Gate 2.

Single-speed motors drive the two conveyors. When BELT_RUN is **on**, the conveyor moves parts from the milling machine to the tub. When BELT_RUN is **off**, the conveyor is stopped. When TROLL_RUN is **on**, the powered section of the roller conveyor moves. When TROLL_RUN is **off**, the powered section of the roller conveyor is stopped.

There is an internal coil, Run, that is **on** when the operation is enabled. The Run internal coil is set by another part of the ladder logic. When the Run coil is **off**, the tub loading operation should be paused at the current step. When paused, do not advance to the next step. When the Run coil turns **on** while the operation is paused, the tub loader should resume the suspended step. When paused, both conveyors must be stopped, all counter and timer accumulator values must be retained, and the ladder logic program must remain in the step in which the Run coil changed from **on** to **off**. If the Run coil turns **off** when changing tubs, the pneumatic cylinder controls must continue to be activated, holding the gate open (otherwise, a tub may be damaged).

There is another internal coil, Reset, that when **on**, restarts the operation. The Reset internal coil is set by another part of the ladder logic. When Reset is **on**, internal counters and timers are reset and the internal state is set so that the ladder logic program assumes an empty tub is in position. The Reset internal coil must be ignored while Run is **on**.

Assume the following physical input, physical output, and internal coil assignments:

Variable	Description
PE272	Photoelectric sensor, **off** when part passes.
TUB_PROX	Proximity sensor, **on** (closed) when tub is present, though not necessarily in position to receive parts.
GATE1_OPLS	Limit switch, **on** (closed) when Gate 1 is open.
GATE1_CLLS	Limit switch, **on** (closed) when Gate 1 is closed.
GATE2_OPLS	Limit switch, **on** (closed) when Gate 2 is open.
GATE2_CLLS	Limit switch, **on** (closed) when Gate 2 is closed.
BELT_RUN	Belt conveyor control, **on** to run conveyor to move parts from milling machine to the parts tub.
TROLL_RUN	Powered roller conveyor control, **on** to run conveyor to move parts tub.
GATE1_RET	Gate 1 cylinder control, **on** to retract cylinder and open gate; **off** closes gate.
GATE2_RET	Gate 2 cylinder control, **on** to retract cylinder and open gate; **off** closes gate.

Run	Internal coil, **on** when loading enabled to operate (controlled by another part of the ladder logic).
Reset	Internal coil, **on** to reset tub loader operation (controlled by another part of the ladder logic).
Tub_Permissive	Internal coil, **on** when milling machine is permitted to run (controlled by this part of the ladder logic).

The addresses associated with the physical inputs and outputs are:

Variable	Modicon	PLC-5	ControlLogix	Siemens	GE Fanuc
PE272	100003	I:0/02	Local:1:I.Data.2	I0.2	%I3
TUB_PROX	100004	I:0/03	Local:1:I.Data.3	I0.3	%I4
GATE1_OPLS	100005	I:0/04	Local:1:I.Data.4	I0.4	%I5
GATE1_CLLS	100006	I:0/05	Local:1:I.Data.5	I0.5	%I6
GATE2_OPLS	100007	I:0/06	Local:1:I.Data.6	I0.6	%I7
GATE2_CLLS	100008	I:0/07	Local:1:I.Data.7	I0.7	%I8
BELT_RUN	000001	O:1/00	Local:2:O.Data.0	Q4.0	%Q1
TROLL_RUN	000002	O:1/01	Local:2:O.Data.1	Q4.1	%Q2
GATE1_RET	000003	O:1/02	Local:2:O.Data.2	Q4.2	%Q3
GATE2_RET	000004	O:1/03	Local:2:O.Data.3	Q4.3	%Q4

The addresses/data types associated with the internal variables are:

	Modicon	PLC-5	ControlLogix	Siemens	GE Fanuc
Variable	Data Type	Addr.	Data Type	Addr.	Addr.
Run	BOOL	B3/100	BOOL	M62.0	%M100
Reset	BOOL	B3/101	BOOL	M62.1	%M101
Tub_Permissive	BOOL	B3/102	BOOL	M62.2	%M102

Solution. This example introduces the following aspects of sequential problems:

Using timers

Using counters

Using Run as part of the transition condition

Reset of the operation

As illustrated in Example 6.1, there are two main steps to develop the function chart:

1. Identify the steps and transition conditions.
2. Add step actions.

To identify the steps and transitions, the first paragraph of the process description is repeated, with the steps identified by the underlined phrases and the transition conditions identified by the *italicized phrases*. As in example 6.1, many times it is easier to identify the first transition condition (signaled by an input sensor change) and then recognize the step before and the step after the transition condition. Often, the steps and transition conditions alternate during the narrative.

> Figure 6.14 shows the layout of a parts tub loader machine. Parts are placed on the belt conveyor by a milling machine. The parts move down the conveyor and drop into the parts tub. Parts on the belt conveyor are detected by a photoelectric sensor, PE272, which is **off** as a part interrupts the beam. Assume PE272 detects the part as it falls into the tub. After *100 parts are deposited* in the tub, the tub is

moved out and a new, empty tub moves into position. To change the tub, the following operation must take place:

Open Gate 1 (*GATE1_OPLS senses* when open).

Hold Gate 1 open and wait for *TUB_PROX to be* ***off*** *for 3 seconds* to allow the full tub to be moved out of the loading station. Run the tub roller conveyor to move out the full tub.

Gate 1 is closed (*GATE1_CLLS senses* when closed).

Gate 2 is opened (*GATE2_OPLS senses* when open).

Hold Gate 2 open to allow an empty tub to move down a slight incline into the loading station. When the tub contacts the tub roller conveyor, the tub roller conveyor moves the tub into position. When *TUB_PROX is* ***on*** *for 5 seconds*, the tub is in position (front resting on Gate 1).

Gate 2 is closed (*GATE2_CLLS senses* when closed).

Since the timer accumulator values must be retained when paused, retentive timers must be used for the time delays. Also, the Run coil must be one of the conditions that controls the timer.

The sentence, "When paused, do not advance to the next step." normally means that the internal Run coil is part of the transition condition. However, since retentive timers are used for the transition out of the steps holding the gates open, the Run coil is not needed for these steps. One could argue that the Run coil is not needed for the transitions out of the other steps since the conveyors are stopped when paused, but for the purposes of the example, the Run coil is used.

So, the steps and the transition conditions that indicate the end of each step are:

Step	Transition Condition (out of step)
Parts into tub	Part_Ctr done (100 parts detected) and Run
Open Gate 1	GATE1_OPLS on and Run
Hold Gate 1 open	G1_Hold_Tmr done (TUB_PROX off for 3 sec.)
Close Gate 1	GATE1_CLLS on and Run
Open Gate 2	GATE2_OPLS on and Run
Hold Gate 2 open	G2_Hold_Tmr done (TUB_PROX on for 5 sec.)
Close Gate 2	GATE2_CLLS on and Run

The next part of the function chart development is to add the actions to each step. Reading back through the tub loader narrative, the process actions for each step are:

Step	Actions
Parts into tub	BELT_RUN and Tub_Permissive and Part_Ctr (counts 100 parts with /PE272)
Open Gate 1	GATE1_RET
Hold Gate 1 open	GATE1_RET and TROLL_RUN and G1_Hold_Tmr (3 sec.)
Close Gate 1	
Open Gate 2	GATE2_RET
Hold Gate 2 open	GATE2_RET and TROLL_RUN and G2_Hold_Tmr (5 sec.)
Close Gate 2	

The function chart for the tub loader is shown in Figure 6.15. This particular operation repeats, indicated by a line from the last step back to the first step. Before developing the ladder logic code, the internal variables should be identified:

The addresses or data types associated with the variables:

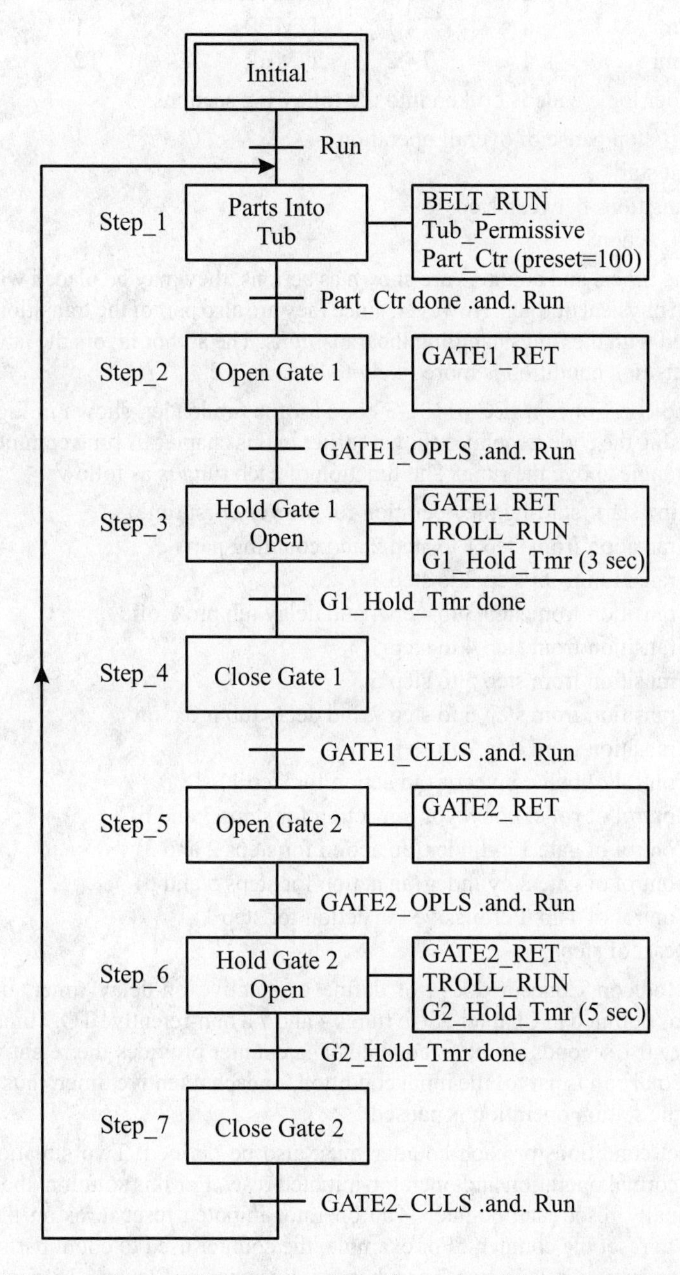

Figure 6.15. Function chart for parts tub loader.

Variable	Modicon Data Type	PLC-5 Addr.	ControlLogix Data Type	Siemens Data Type	GE Fanuc Addr.
Step_1 to	BOOL	B20/1	BOOL	M50.1	%M51
Step_7	BOOL	B20/7	BOOL	M50.7	%M57
Int_Reset	BOOL	B20/8	BOOL	M51.0	%M58
Ctr_Done	n/a	n/a	n/a	n/a	%M59
Part_Ctr	n/a	C5:1	COUNTER	DB2	%R101
G1_Hold_Tmr	n/a	T4:1	TIMER	T1	%R104
G2_Hold_Tmr	n/a	T4:2	TIMER	T2	%R107

The ladder logic code is broken into the following sections:

Start/stop/pause of overall operation
First start
Transitions between steps
Step actions

Since the timers and counters are shown as actions, they may be placed with the rungs that drive the physical outputs. However, since they are also part of the transitions, they may also be placed with the rungs handling the transitions. The author favors the latter approach since the transition condition is more likely to be changed.

The Modicon Concept IEC 61131-3 code for the tub loader, shown in Figure 6.16, is developed using the code templates shown earlier in this chapter. A rung comment is shown within a rectangle above the rung. The function of each rung is as follows:

1. First start (starting the operation for the very first time)
2. Transition from step 1 to step 2 and counting parts
3. Transition from step 2 to step 3
4. Transition from step 3 to step 4 and delay tub prox. off
5. Transition from step 4 to step 5
6. Transition from step 5 to step 6
7. Transition from step 6 to step 7 and delay tub prox. on
8. Transition from step 7 to step 1
9. Control of belt conveyor (an action for step 1)
10. Control of roller conveyor (an action for steps 3 and 6)
11. Control of gate 1 cylinder (an action for steps 2 and 3)
12. Control of gate 2 cylinder (an action for steps 5 and 6)
13. Control of Tub_Permissive (an action for step 1)
14. Reset of steps

Since Modicon Concept does not define a retentive on-delay timer, one must be constructed as outlined in Chapter 5. On rungs 4 and 7 a non-retentive TON timer generates a "tick" every 0.1 seconds which is counted. The counter provides the retentive function. The Run internal coil is part of the input condition for each retentive timer, thus pausing the timer when the station operation is paused.

The reset condition for each counter must also be defined. Two situations must be considered: normal operation and operator-initiated reset. For this solution, the next step is used to normally reset each counter. The operator-initiated reset turns on the Int_Reset internal coil to reset the counters. For example, the counter used to count parts in step 1 is reset when the operation is in step 2 or when Int_Reset is on (Figure 6.16, rung 2).

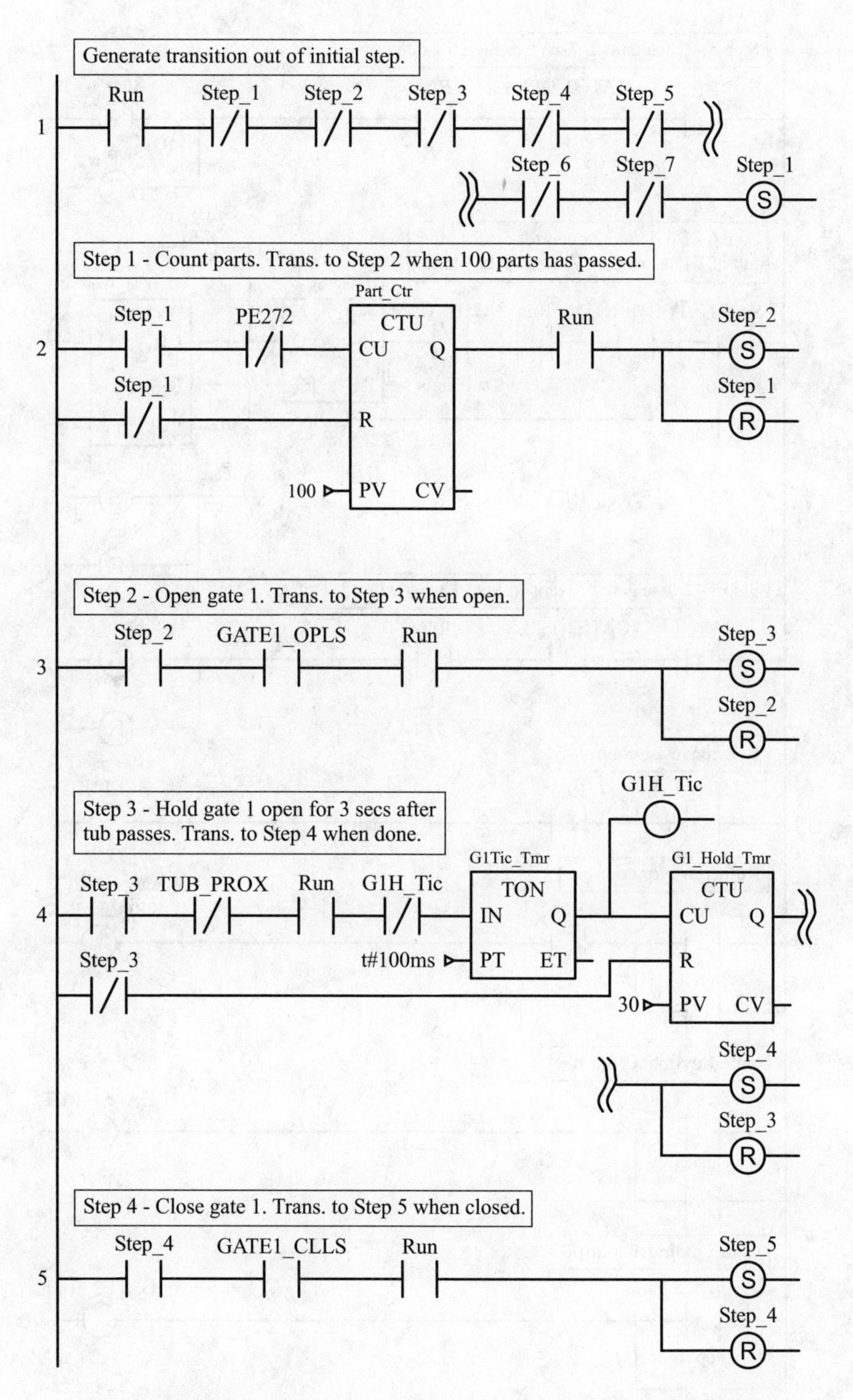

Figure 6.16. Modicon Concept ladder logic for tub loader. *(continued)*

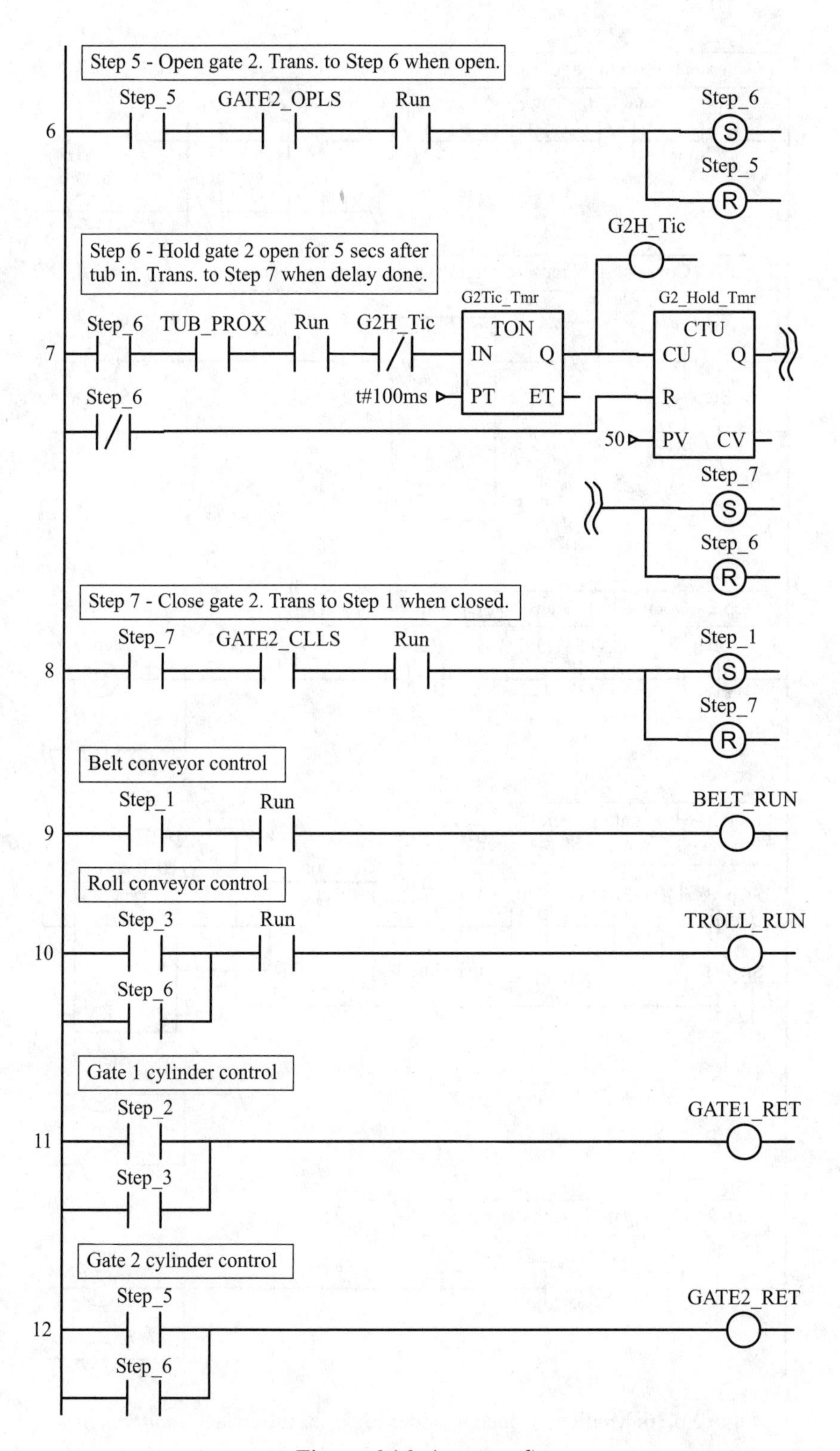

Figure 6.16. *(continued)*

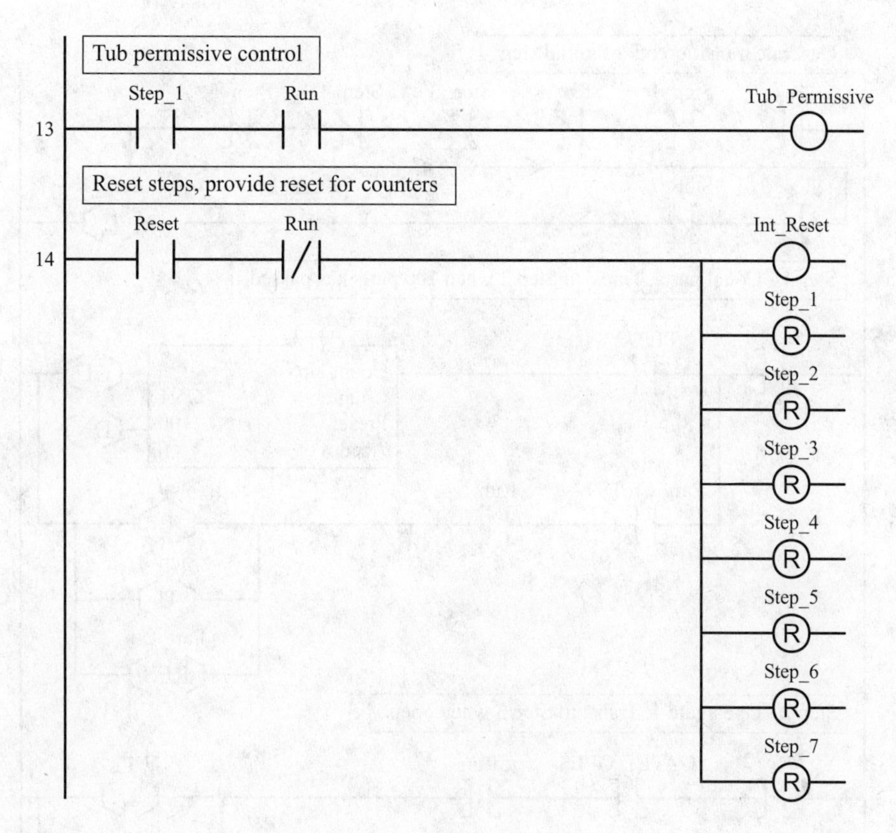

Figure 6.16. *(continued)*

When the reset push button is pressed while the station is paused, the Int_Reset coil is turned on (to reset the counters) and all step-in-progress coils are reset. This action effectively places the station operation in the initial state.

The Allen-Bradley PLC-5 code for the tub loader appears in Figure 6.17. Besides the use of latch/unlatch in place of set/reset, the only real difference is in the timers and counters. Timers and counters are output instructions, and so no logic can appear in series to the right of these instructions. Therefore, a parallel branch is used to handle the transition to the next step (Figure 6.17, rungs 2, 4, and 7). These parallel branches can be programmed as two rungs. However, in keeping with the convention that timers and counters remain with the transition condition, they are combined on a single rung. As with the IEC 61131-3 code, the Run internal coil is part of the input condition for each retentive timer, thus pausing the timer when the station operation is paused.

The counters and retentive timers are normally reset during the transition to the next step. For example, the Part_Ctr counter used in step 1 to count parts is reset during the transition from step 1 to step 2 (Figure 6.17, rung 3). The reset of retentive timers and counters as a result of an operator-initiated reset is handled on the same rung as the reset of all step-in-progress coils (Figure 6.17, rung 14).

The Allen-Bradley ControlLogix ladder logic code is nearly identical to the PLC-5 code in Figure 6.17. The only differences are:

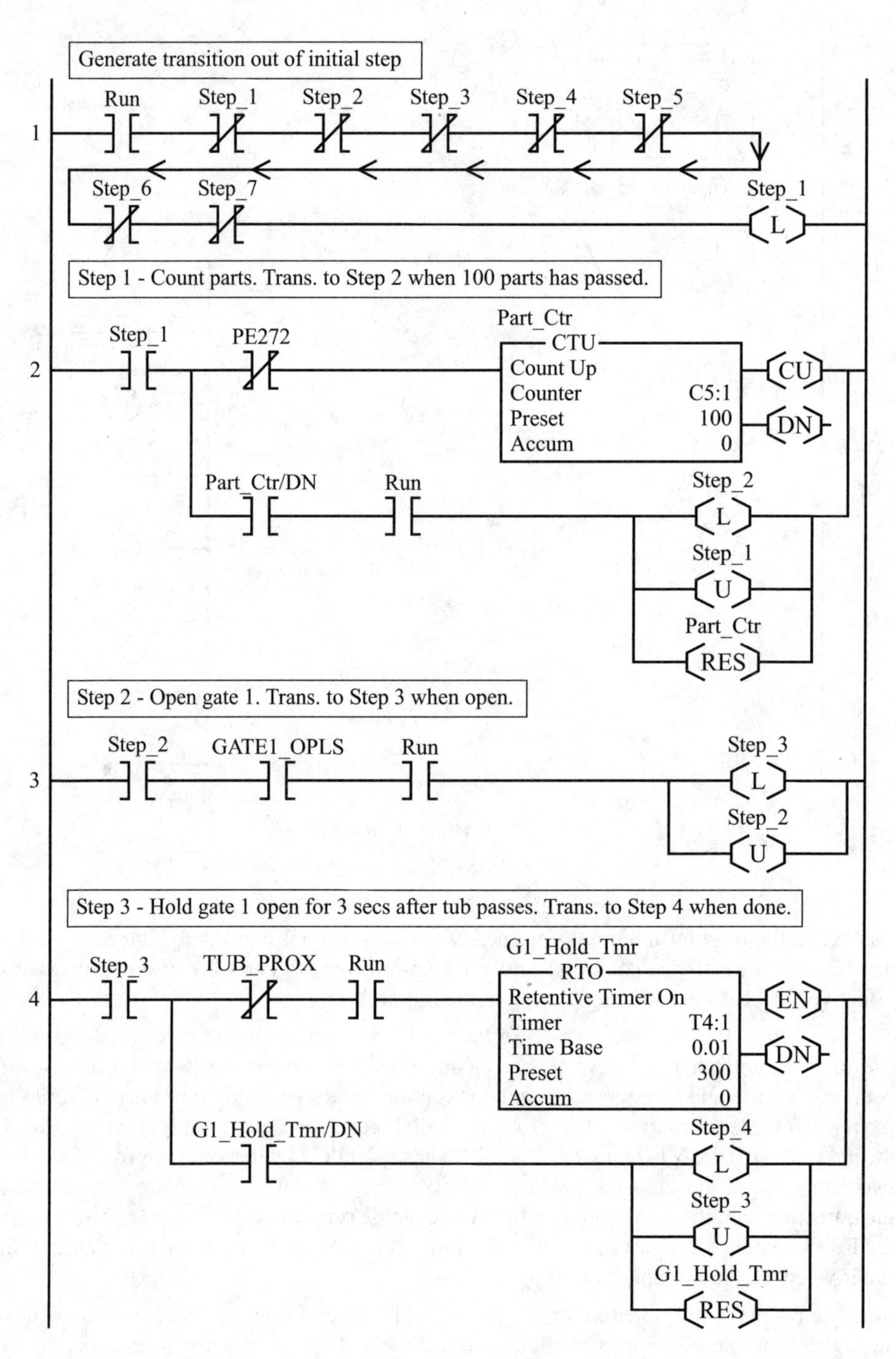

Figure 6.17. Allen-Bradley PLC-5 ladder logic for tub loader. *(continued)*

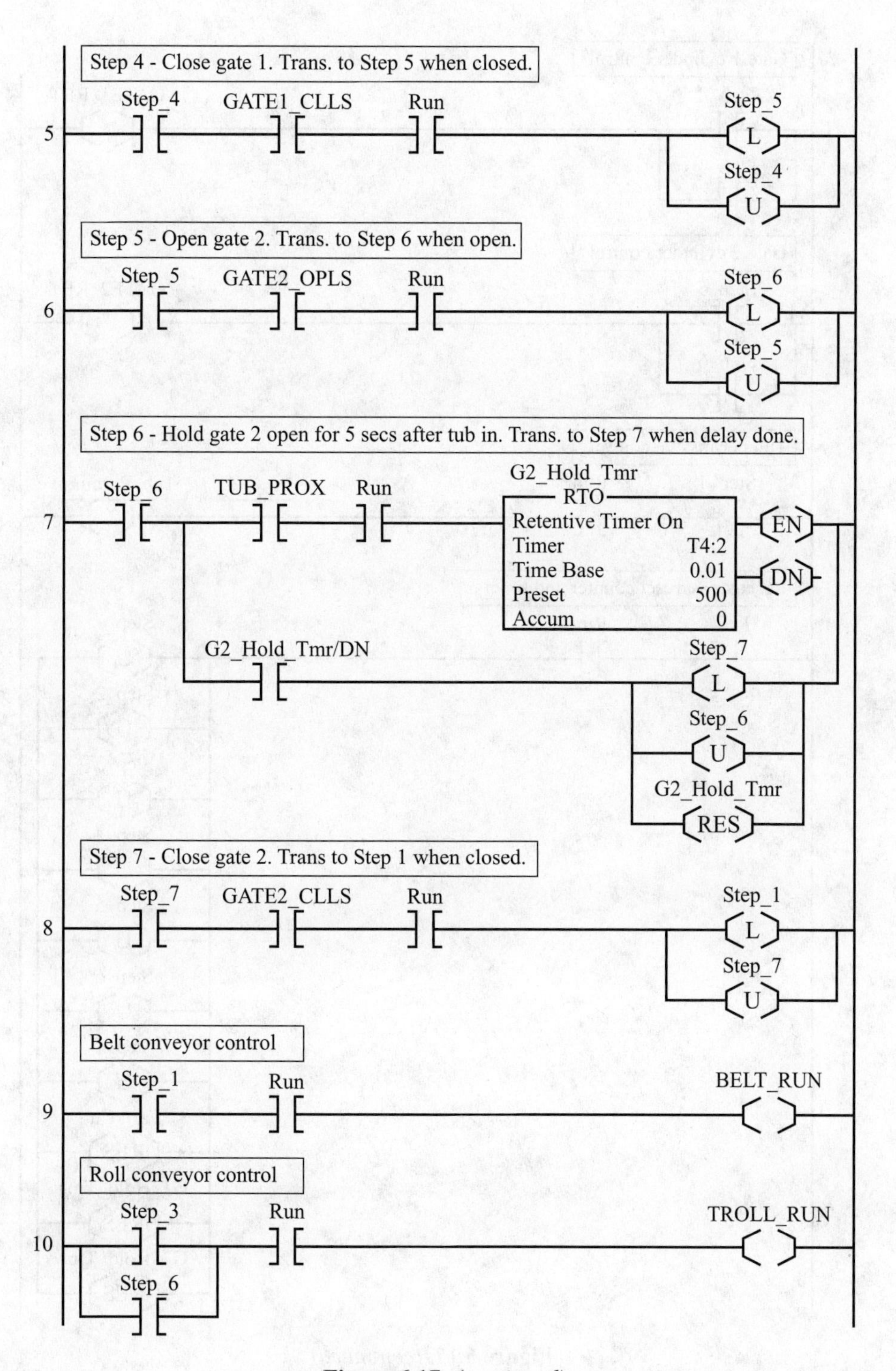

Figure 6.17. *(continued)*

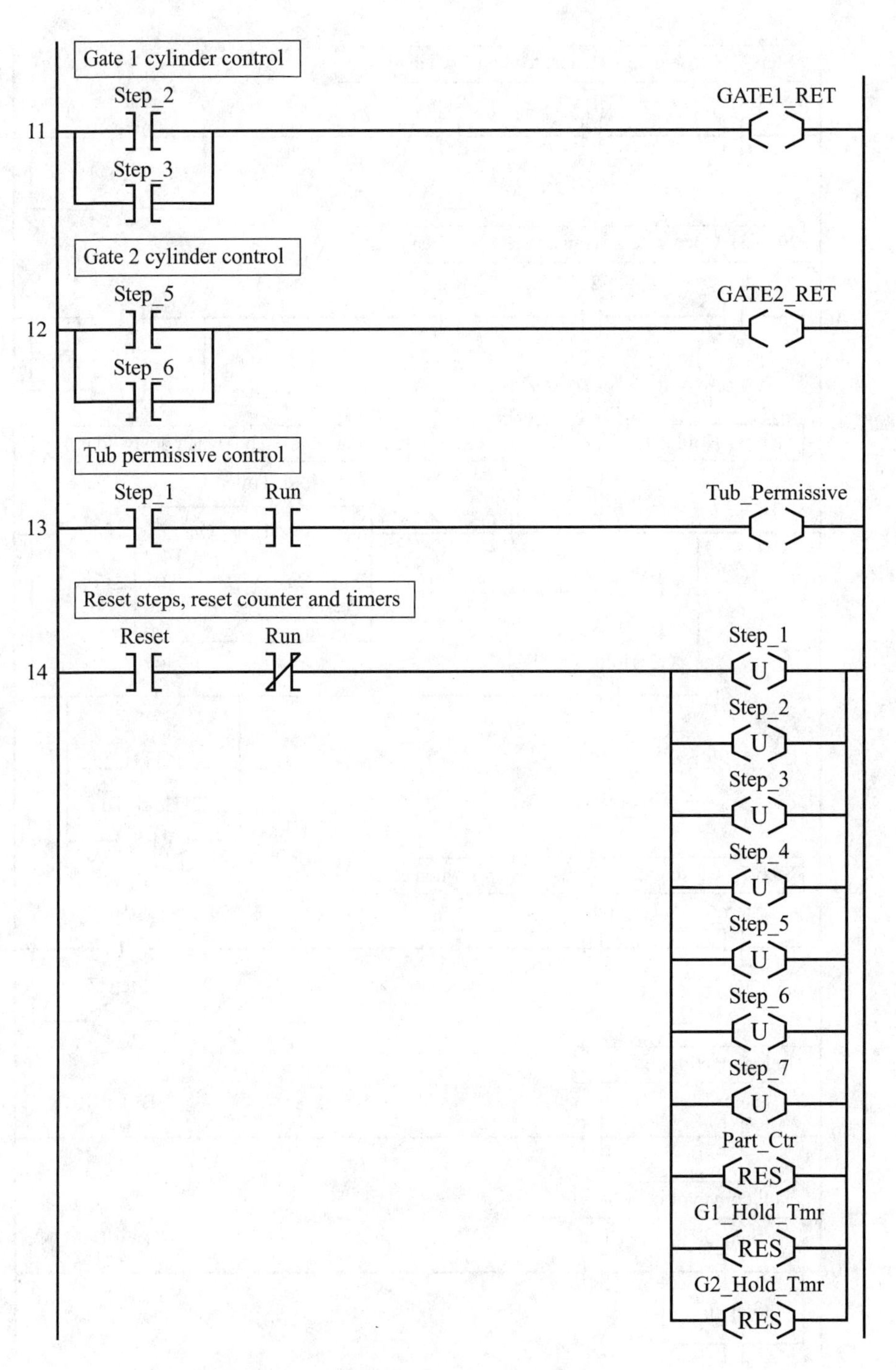

Figure 6.17. *(continued)*

1. The "Part_Ctr" tag appears in the Counter field of the CTU instruction in rung 3, replacing the address in the PLC-5 CTU instruction.
2. For the timers (rungs 5 and 8), the "Time Base" field is absent and the Preset value is multiplied by 10 (ControlLogix time base is 1 ms). Also, the timer tag appears in the Timer field of the RTO instruction, replacing the address in the PLC-5 RTO instruction.

The Siemens S7 ladder logic code (Figure 6.18) looks most similar to the Modicon PLC. The only differences are in the retentive timers and the counter. The S_ODTS retentive on-delay timer block is used in place of an IEC-compatible TON and CTU as in the Modicon PLC. Also note the use of the "Part_Ctr".Q contact on the ENO output of the counter. Since the CTU block Q ouput can only connect to a variable, this method allows one to place the "Run" contact in series with the Q output and to control the set and reset coils without starting a new network.

The GE Fanuc ladder logic is shown in Figure 6.19 and is similar to the Modicon and S7 ladder logic. Since the output of the counter in rung 3 cannot connect to a contact, an extra internal coil and rung must be added to accommodate the specification that the operation cannot advance to the next step when paused.

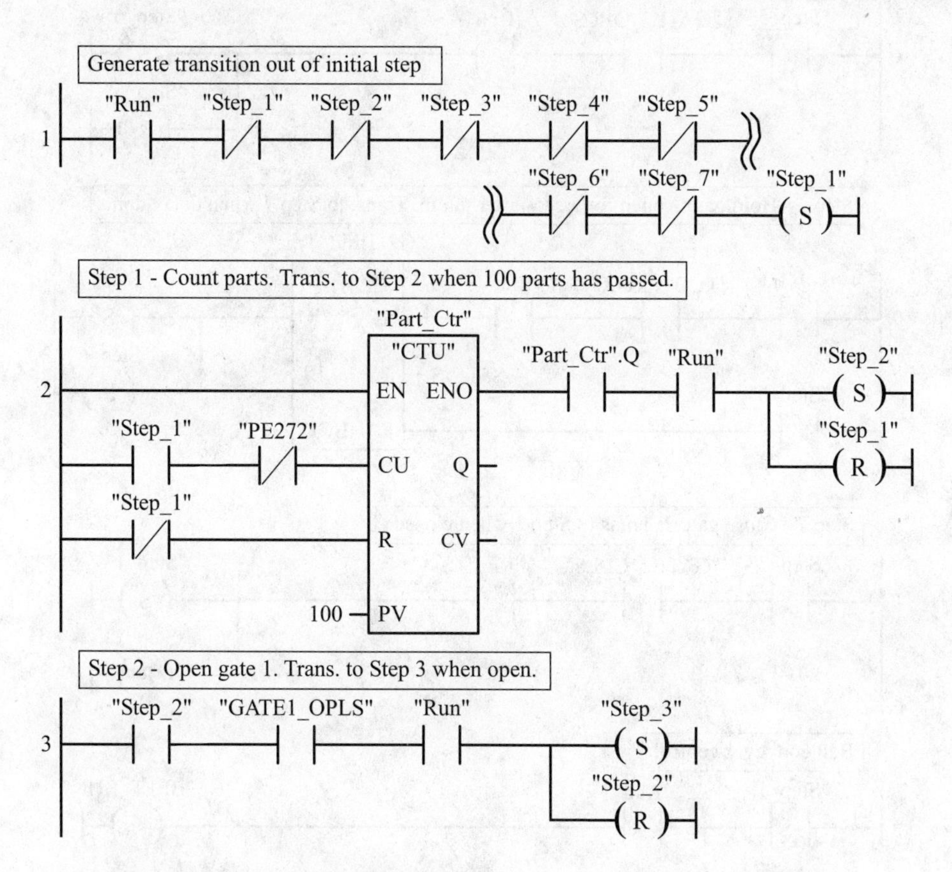

Figure 6.18. Siemens S7 ladder logic code for tub loader. *(continued)*

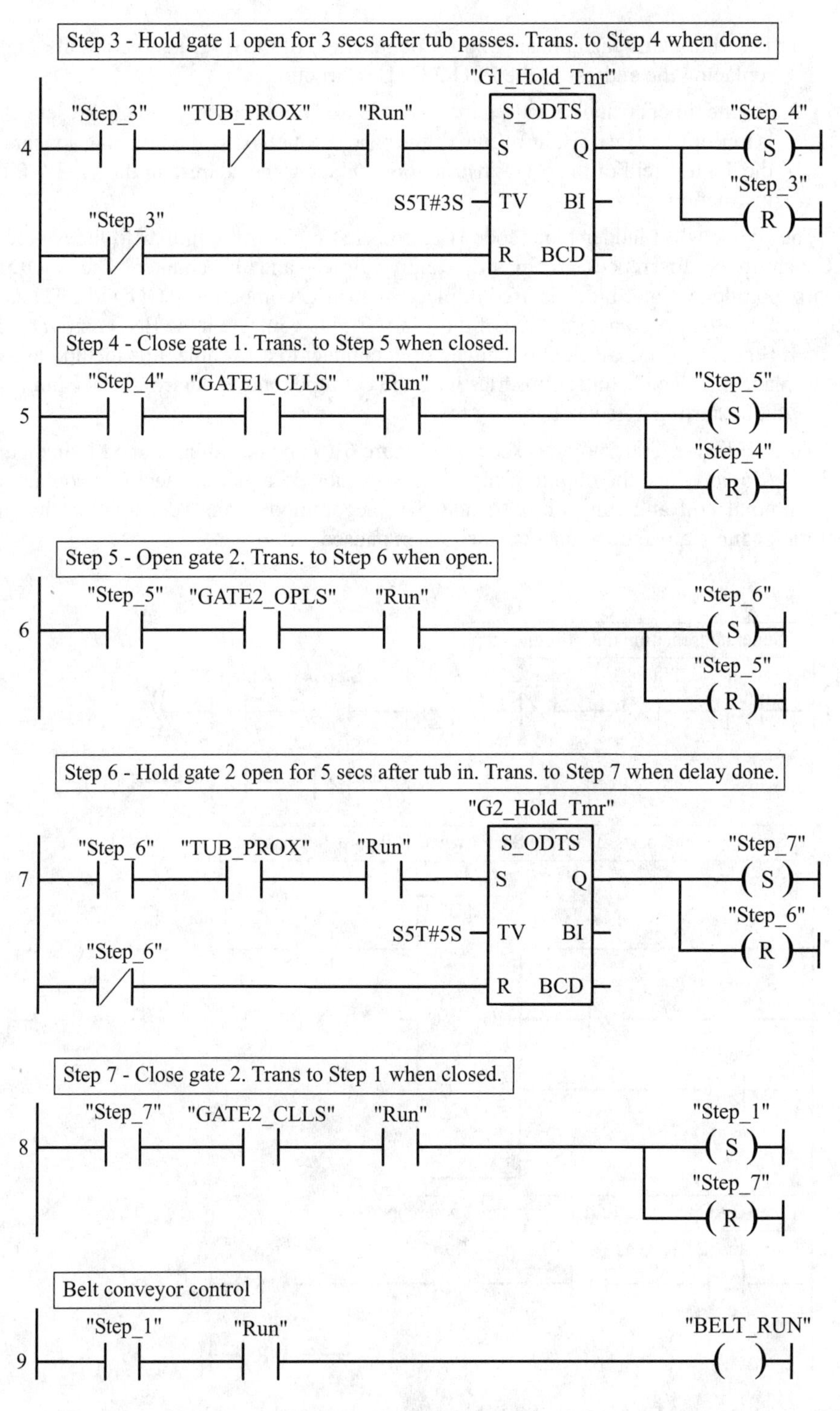

Figure 6.18. *(continued)*

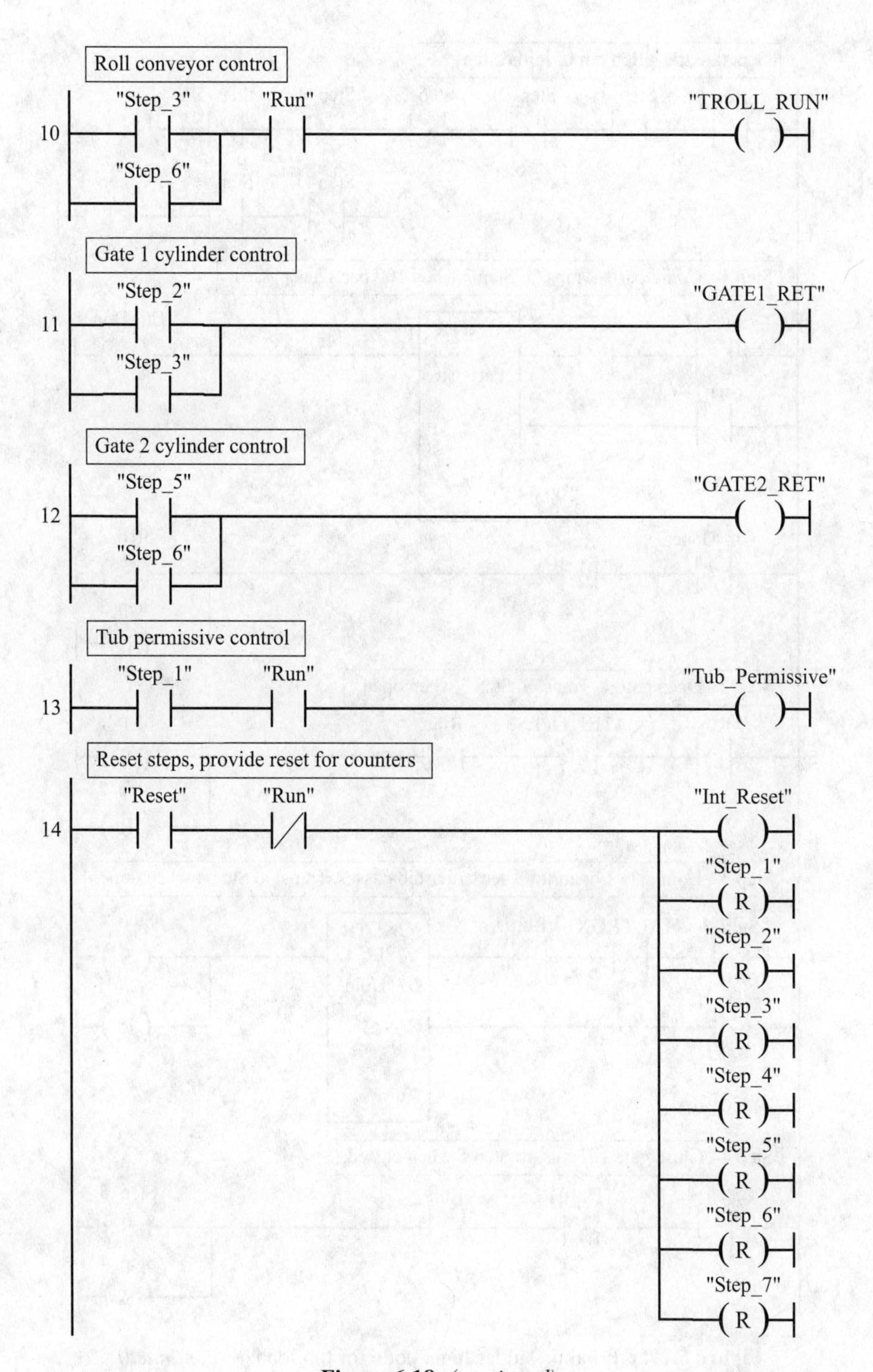

Figure 6.18. *(continued)*

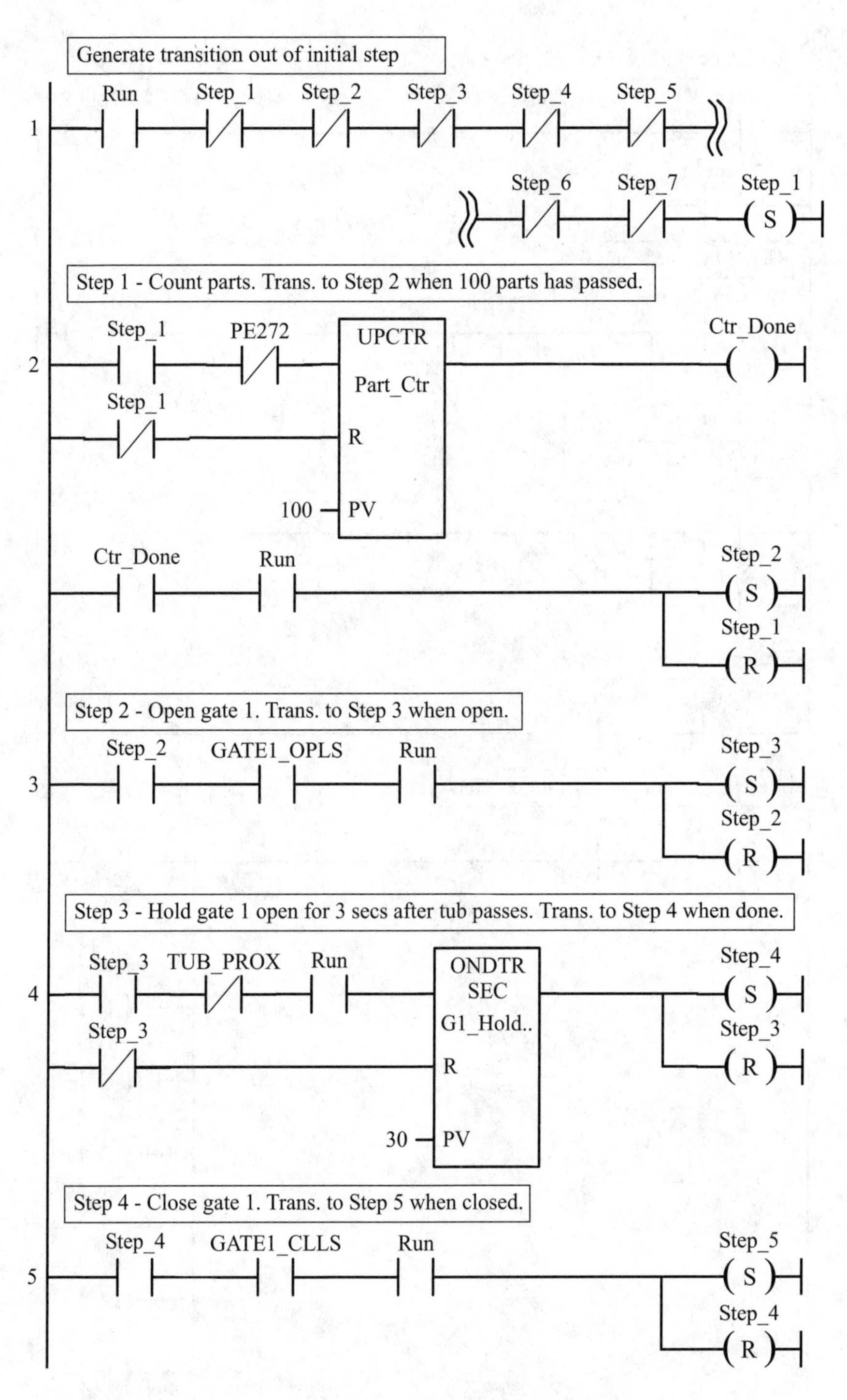

Figure 6.19. GE Fanuc ladder logic code for tub loader. *(continued)*

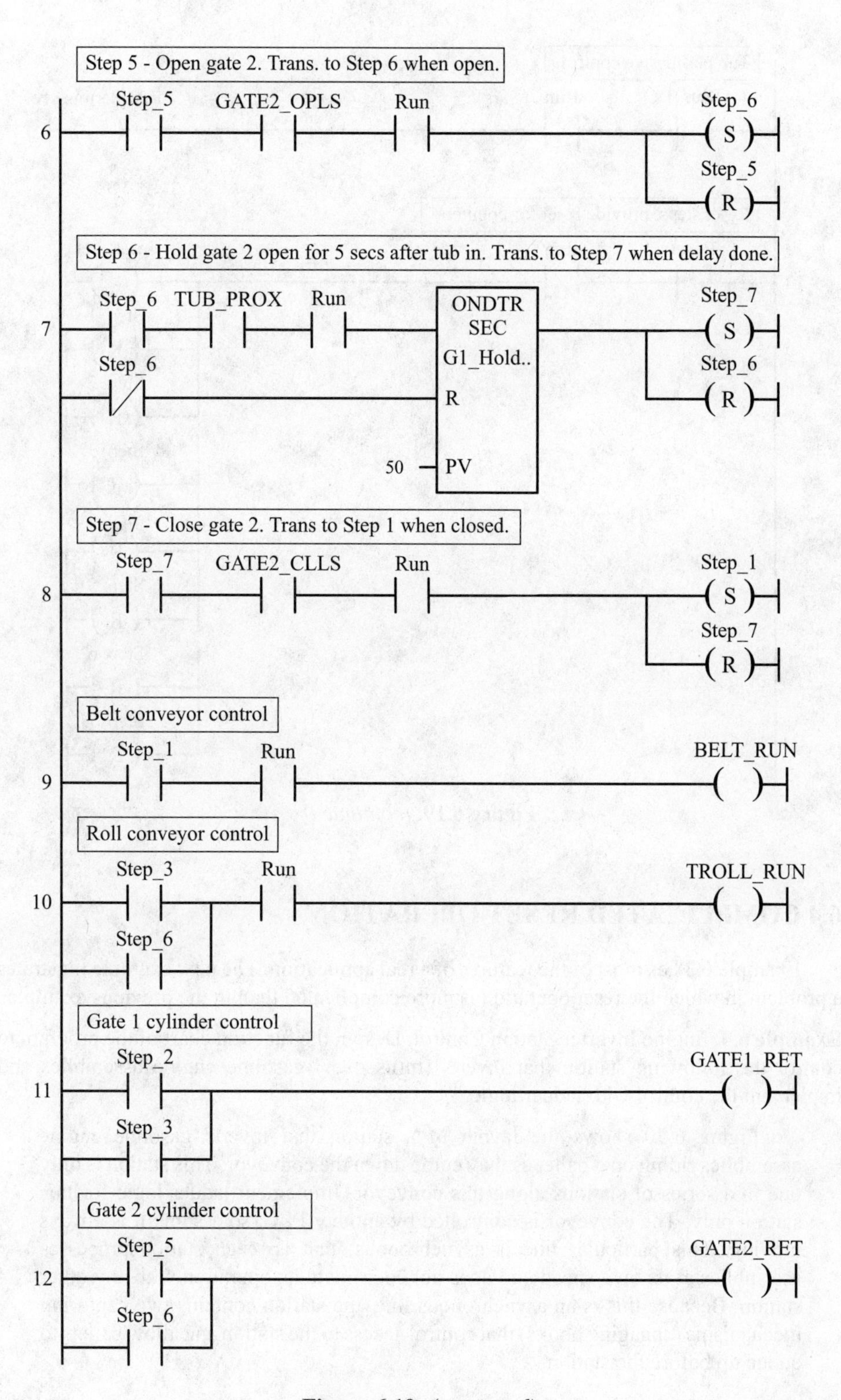

Figure 6.19. *(continued)*

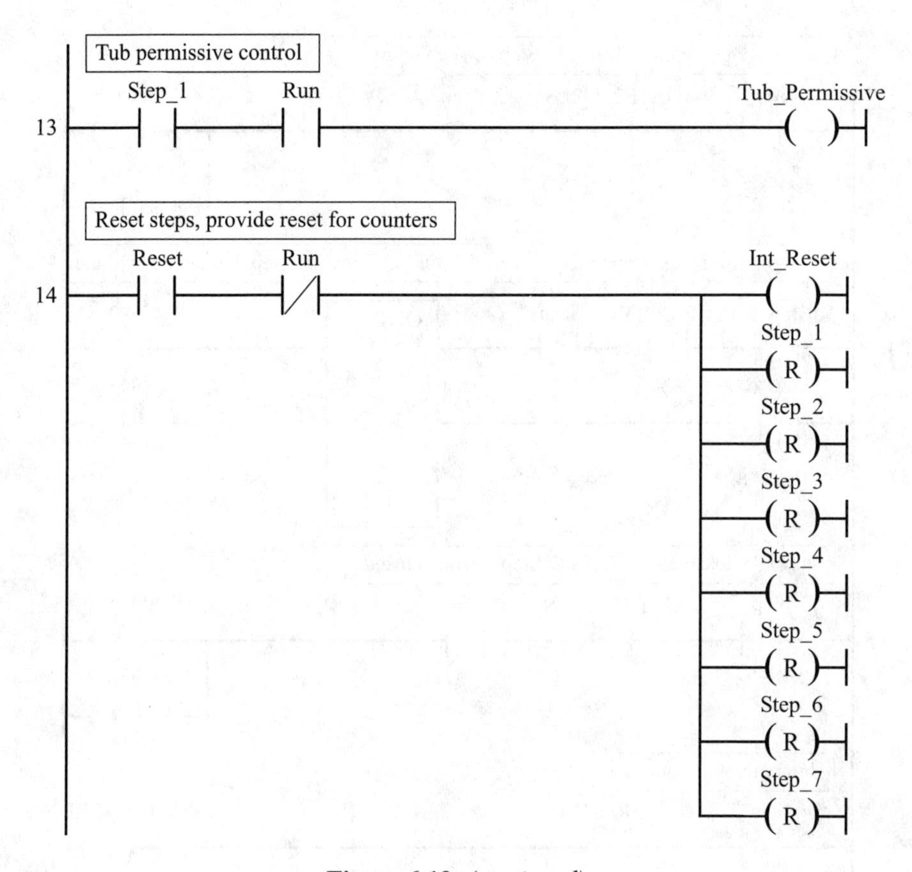

Figure 6.19. *(continued)*

6.4 COMPLICATED RESET OPERATION

Example 6.3 has most of the features of a real application. The next example illustrates a problem in which the reset operation is more complicated than in the previous example.

Example 6.4. Engine Inverter Station Control. Design the function chart of the program to control the following station that inverts (turns over) gasoline engine assemblies and implement the control with ladder logic.

> Figure 6.20 shows the layout of a station that inverts gasoline engine assemblies riding on a pallet as they come down the conveyor. This station is only one in a series of stations along this conveyor. Implement ladder logic for this station only. The conveyor is controlled by another PLC, so assume it is always moving. This particular line is asynchronous, that is, each station processes assemblies at its own speed and does not coordinate its operation with any other station. Because this is an asynchronous line, the station contains two capturing mechanisms (engaging hooks) that control access to the station and allow pallets to queue up before the station.

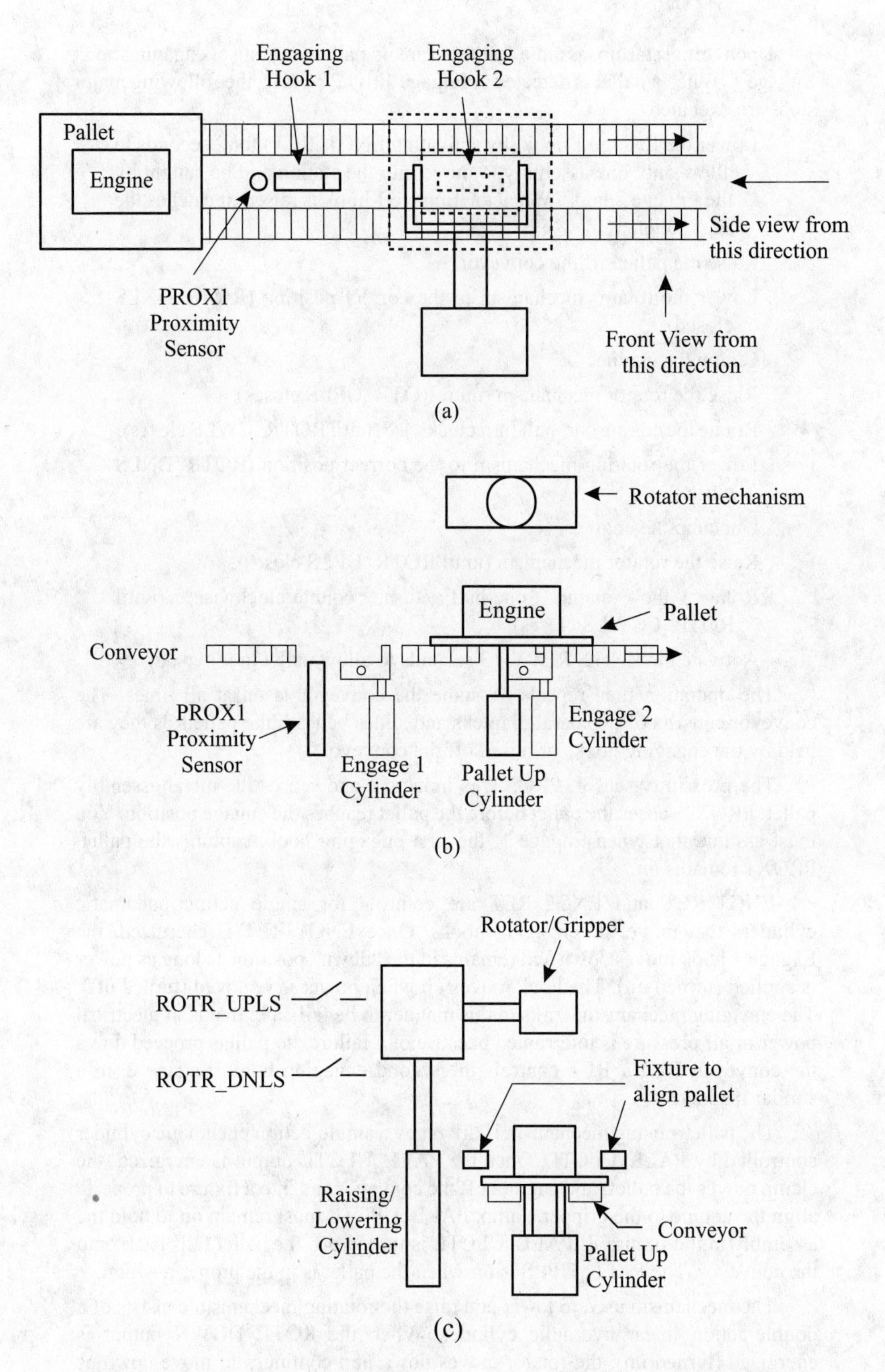

Figure 6.20. Engine inverter station: *(a)* top view; *(b)* front view; *(c)* side view.

Upon initial startup, assume that there are no pallets waiting at engaging hook Engage 1. When a pallet is detected at Engage 1 (by PROX1), the following major steps are executed:

Lower the Engage 1 hook (by activating ENG1_RET) for 2 seconds to allow only one assembly to move into the station and be caught by the Engage 2 hook. When the Engage 1 hook is raised, it catches the next pallet.

Raise the pallet off the conveyor.

Lower the rotator mechanism to the correct position (ROTR_DNLS closed).

Clamp the engine.

Raise the rotator mechanism (until ROTR_UPLS closes).

Rotate the engine one-half turn clockwise (until ROTR_CWLS closes).

Lower the rotating mechanism to the correct position (ROTR_DNLS closed).

Unclamp the engine.

Raise the rotator mechanism (until ROTR_UPLS closes).

Rotate the clamp one-half turn counterclockwise (until ROTR_CCWLS closes).

Activate the ENG2_RET for 3 seconds to allow pallet to move out.

The operation then repeats. Assume the conveyor is on at all times. The conveyor consists of two parallel tracks and slides beneath the pallets as they are held by the engaging hooks or raised off the conveyor.

The proximity sensor, PROX1, is inductive and senses the metal assembly pallet. PROX1 senses the pallet before the pallet reaches the engage position. You must assume that when Engage 1, the first engaging hook, captures the pallet, PROX1 remains **on**.

ENG1_RET and ENG2_RET are controls for single action pneumatic cylinders that move the engaging hooks. Once ENG1_RET is energized, the Engage 1 hook moves down and remains in the "down" position as long as power is applied (turned **on**). The hook moves up when power is removed (turned **off**). The engaging mechanism works in this manner to be fail-safe, that is, if electrical power or air pressure is interrupted because of a failure, no pallets proceed down the conveyor. ENG2_RET controls the second engaging hook, Engage 2, in a similar manner.

The pallet-raising mechanism is driven by a single-action pneumatic cylinder controlled by PALL_UPCTL. Once the PALL_UPCTL output is energized, the clamp moves the pallet (and engine) off the conveyor and into a fixture to properly align the engine to the gripper clamp. PALL_UPCTL must remain **on** to hold the assembly in the fixture. If PALL_UPCTL is turned **off**, the pallet falls back onto the conveyor. The PALL_UPLS is **on** when the pallet is in the proper position.

The mechanism used to lower and raise the rotating mechanism consists of a double-action linear hydraulic cylinder. When the ROTR_DOWN output is energized (turned **on**), the rotator moves down and continues to move down as long as it is energized and a mechanical stop is not reached. When the ROTR_UP output is energized, the rotator moves up and continues to move up as long as it is energized and a mechanical stop is not reached. The mechanism stops if neither output is **on**, or if they are energized simultaneously. ROTR_UPLS is **on** when the rotator is in the "up" position. ROTR_DNLS is **on** when the rotator is in the "down" position.

The gripper is powered by a single-action pneumatic cylinder. When the GRIP_CLOS output is energized, the gripper jaws close to clamp the engine and hold it in place as long as power is applied (turned **on**). GRIP_CLOS must remain **on** to hold the engine in the gripper. If GRIP_CLOS is turned **off**, the engine is released. There are no limit switches indicating the gripper is open or closed. Allow 1.5 seconds for the gripper to clamp (close) and 1.0 seconds for the gripper to unclamp (open).

A double-action pneumatic rotary cylinder controls the rotation action of the gripper. When the ROTAT_CW output is energized, the gripper rotates clockwise as long as power is applied (turned **on**) and the CW mechanical stop has not been reached. When the ROTAT_CCW output is energized, the gripper rotates counterclockwise as long as power is applied (turned **on**) and the CCW mechanical stop has not been reached. The rotation stops at its current position when power is removed (turned **off**). The rotation will not move if both opposing directions are energized simultaneously (e.g., CW and CCW). ROTR_CWLS is **on** when the gripper is fully clockwise. ROTR_CCWLS is **on** when the gripper is fully counterclockwise.

The start/stop switches are only for the station. They do not control any other stations or the conveyor. Upon initial startup, assume there are no pallets present in either of the engaging hooks. If the stop switch is pressed at any time, the station operation should pause, except when either engaging hook is activated. If the operation is paused when ENG1_RET is activated the station may contain two pallets with no space in between. When the start switch is pressed while the operation is paused, the station should resume the suspended step. When paused, do not advance to the next step. When the station is paused, the raise/lower and rotating cylinder controls should be turned off. The engine clamping gripper and the pallet raising cylinders must remain **on** when paused (or the engine may be dropped).

A separate reset switch is provided that when pressed, the clamp gripper is released, the rotating mechanism is raised, then rotated counterclockwise, and the process step is set as if the process is waiting for the next pallet. When the start switch is next pressed, no items are assumed present at the first engage position. The reset switch should have no effect unless the operation is already paused.

Assume the tolerance on all timer values is ±0.1 seconds.

Assume the following physical input and physical output assignments.

Variable	Description
START_PB	Start push button, N. O., **on** when starting.
STOP_PB	Stop push button, N. C., **off** when stopping.
RESET_PB	Reset push button, N. O., **on** when restoring station to initial state.

PROX1	Proximity sensor, **on** (closed) when pallet is either approaching or at the Engage 1 hook position.
PALL_UPLS	Limit switch, **on** when the pallet is lifted off conveyor and in the proper position.
ROTR_UPLS	Limit switch, **on** (closed) when rotating mechanism is up.
ROTR_DNLS	Limit switch, **on** (closed) when rotating mechanism is down (can clamp/unclamp engine).
ROTR_CWLS	Limit switch, **on** (closed) when rotary solenoid is clockwise.
ROTR_CCWLS	Limit switch, **on** (closed) when rotary solenoid is counterclockwise.
ENG1_RET	Engage hook 1 cylinder retract control, **on** to lower hook, **off** raises hook.
ENG2_RET	Engage hook 2 cylinder retract control, **on** to lower hook, **off** raises hook.
ROTR_UP	Rotating mechanism raise cylinder control, **on** to raise.
ROTR_DOWN	Rotating mechanism lower cylinder control, **on** to lower.
ROTAT_CW	Clockwise rotary cylinder control, **on** to rotate clockwise.
ROTAT_CCW	Counterclockwise rotary cylinder control, **on** to rotate counterclockwise.
GRIP_CLOS	Gripper cylinder control, **on** closes jaws, **off** opens jaws.
PALL_UPCTL	Pallet retainer cylinder control, **on** to move pallet up and off the conveyor and retain it there, **off** lowers pallet back onto conveyor.

The addresses associated with the physical inputs and outputs are:

Variable	Modicon	PLC-5	ControlLogix	Siemens	GE Fanuc
START_PB	100001	I:01/00	Local:1:I.Data.0	I0.0	%I81
STOP_PB	100002	I:01/01	Local:1:I.Data.1	I0.1	%I82
RESET_PB	100003	I:01/02	Local:1:I.Data.2	I0.2	%I83
PROX1	100004	I:01/03	Local:1:I.Data.3	I0.3	%I84
PALL_UPLS	100005	I:01/04	Local:1:I.Data.4	I0.4	%I85
ROTR_UPLS	100006	I:01/05	Local:1:I.Data.5	I0.5	%I86
ROTR_DNLS	100007	I:01/06	Local:1:I.Data.6	I0.6	%I87
ROTR_CWLS	100008	I:01/07	Local:1:I.Data.7	I0.7	%I88
ROTR_CCWLS	100009	I:01/10	Local:1:I.Data.8	I1.0	%I89
ENG1_RET	000001	O:02/00	Local:2:O.Data.0	Q4.0	%Q1
ENG2_RET	000002	O:02/01	Local:2:O.Data.1	Q4.1	%Q2
ROTR_UP	000003	O:02/02	Local:2:O.Data.2	Q4.2	%Q3
ROTR_DOWN	000004	O:02/03	Local:2:O.Data.3	Q4.3	%Q4
ROTAT_CW	000005	O:02/04	Local:2:O.Data.4	Q4.4	%Q5
ROTAT_CCW	000006	O:02/05	Local:2:O.Data.5	Q4.5	%Q6
GRIP_CLOS	000007	O:02/06	Local:2:O.Data.6	Q4.6	%Q7
PALL_UPCTL	000008	O:02/07	Local:2:O.Data.7	Q4.7	%Q8

Solution. The function chart for the station is shown in Figure 6.21. Run is not really needed as a transition condition out of steps 3, 4, 6, 7, 8, 10, and 11 since the motion ceases when paused. One could argue that Run is not needed as part of the transition condition out of steps 5 and 9 since advancing to the next step does not actually turn on any physical outputs (since they will remain off as long as the station is paused). Non-retentive timers are acceptable for steps 5 and 9 since the clamping/unclamping will still occur since the gripper continues to function when the operation is paused. Likewise, non-retentive timers are acceptable for steps 2 and 13 since the operation cannot be paused in these steps.

For this problem, the operator-initiated reset is not merely resetting all counters, retentive timers and step-in-progress bits. A sequential operation must restore the mechanical parts of the system to the initial state (clamp open, rotating mechanism in up and counterclockwise positions). The function chart of the reset operation is shown in Figure 6.22. Note that the last step exists only to reset the Int_Reset internal coil, that indicates the reset operation is in progress and prevents the station from restarting.

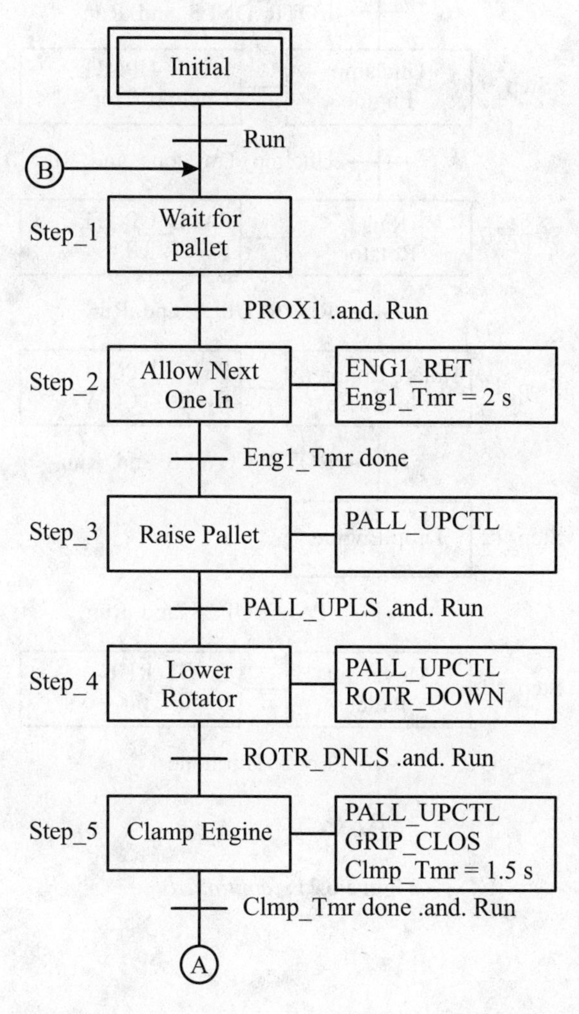

Figure 6.21. Function chart for engine inverter station. *(continued)*

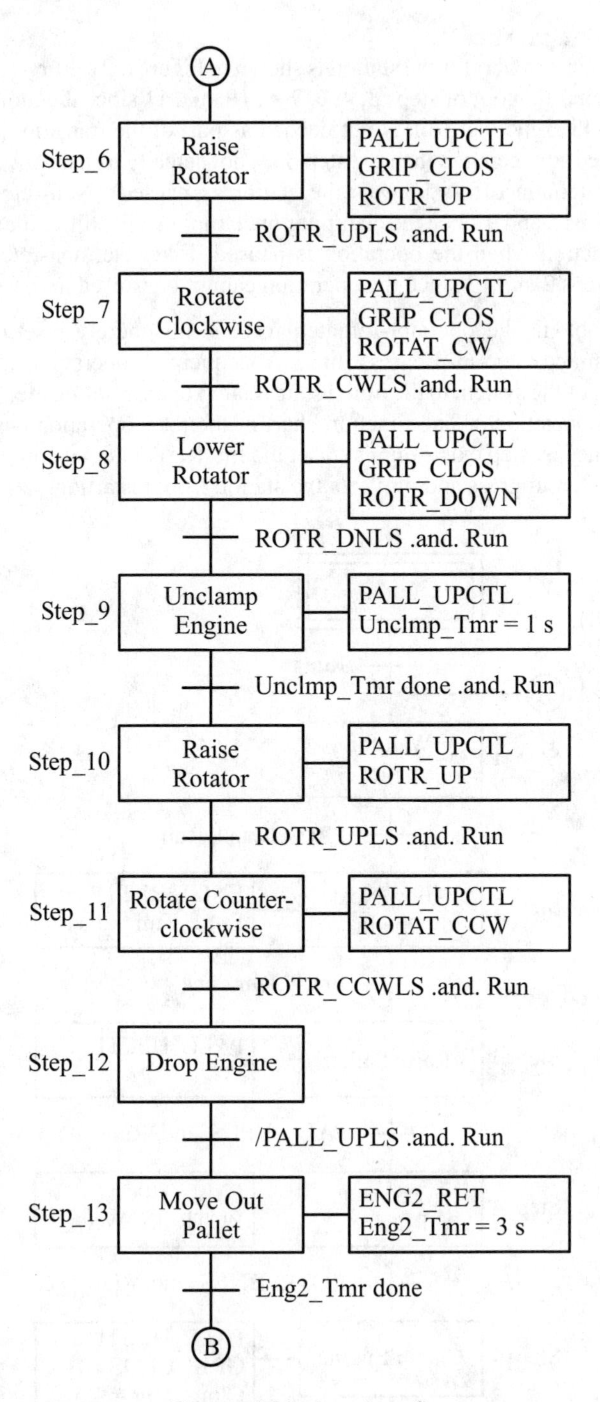

Figure 6.21. *(continued)*

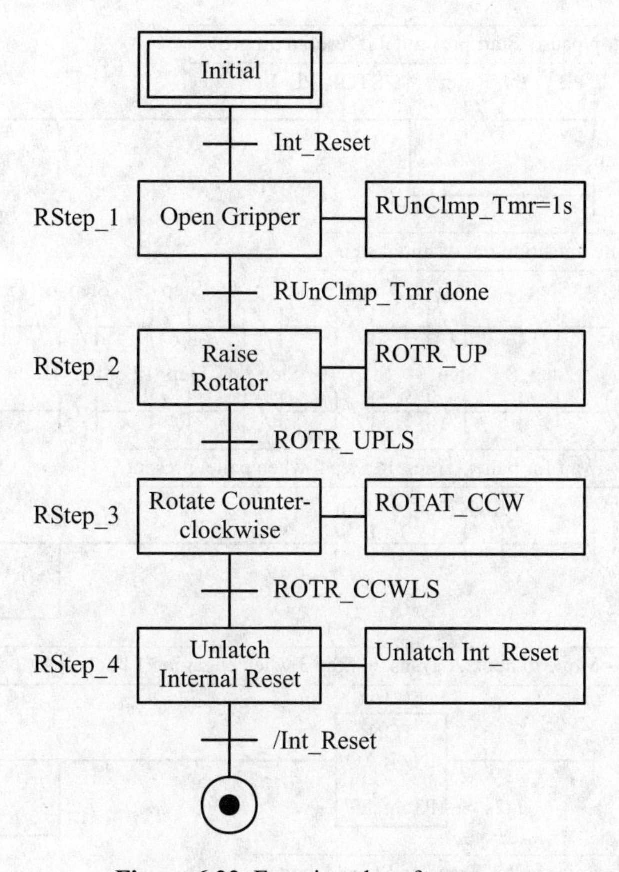

Figure 6.22. Function chart for reset.

Before developing the ladder logic code, the internal variable addresses or data types should be identified:

Variable	Modicon Data Type	PLC-5 Addr.	ControlLogix Data Type	Siemens Addr.	GE Fanuc Addr.
Step_1 to	BOOL	B20/1	BOOL	M50.1	%M1
Step_13	BOOL	B20/13	BOOL	M51.5	%M13
RStep_1 to	BOOL	B20/41	BOOL	M52.1	%M41
RStep_4	BOOL	B20/44	BOOL	M52.4	%M44
Run	BOOL	B20/0	BOOL	M0.0	%M39
Int_Reset	BOOL	B20/40	BOOL	M0.1	%M40
Eng1_Tmr	n/a	T4:1	TIMER	DB1	%R1
Eng2_Tmr	n/a	T4:2	TIMER	DB2	%R4
Clmp_Tmr	n/a	T4:3	TIMER	DB3	%R7
UnClmp_Tmr	n/a	T4:4	TIMER	DB4	%R10
RUnClmp_Tmr	n/a	T4:5	TIMER	DB5	%R13

The Modicon Concept code is shown in Figure 6.23. The Allen-Bradley PLC-5 code is shown in Figure 6.24. The ladder logic code is broken into the following sections:

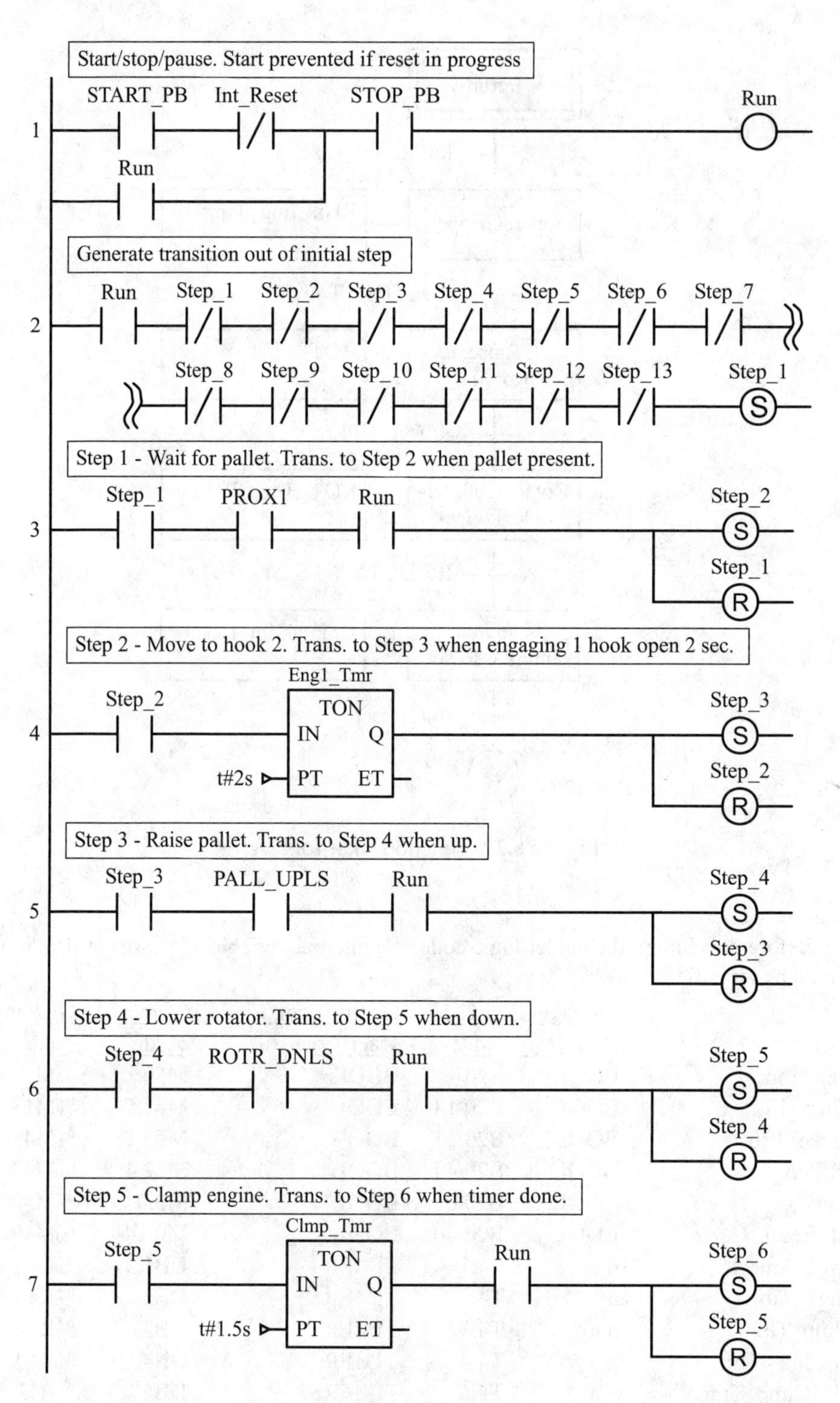

Figure 6.23. Modicon ladder logic for engine inverter station. *(continued)*

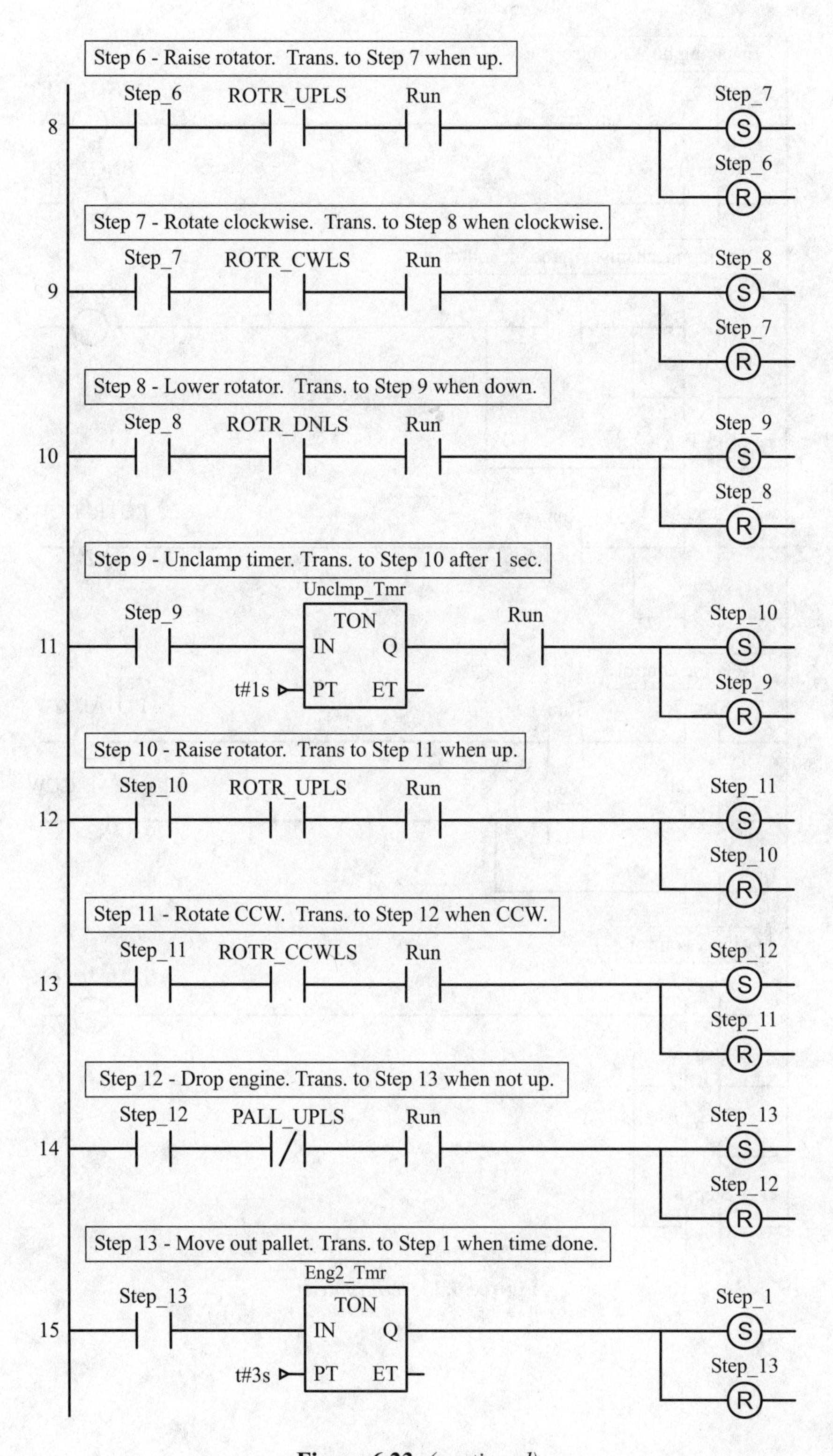

Figure 6.23. *(continued)*

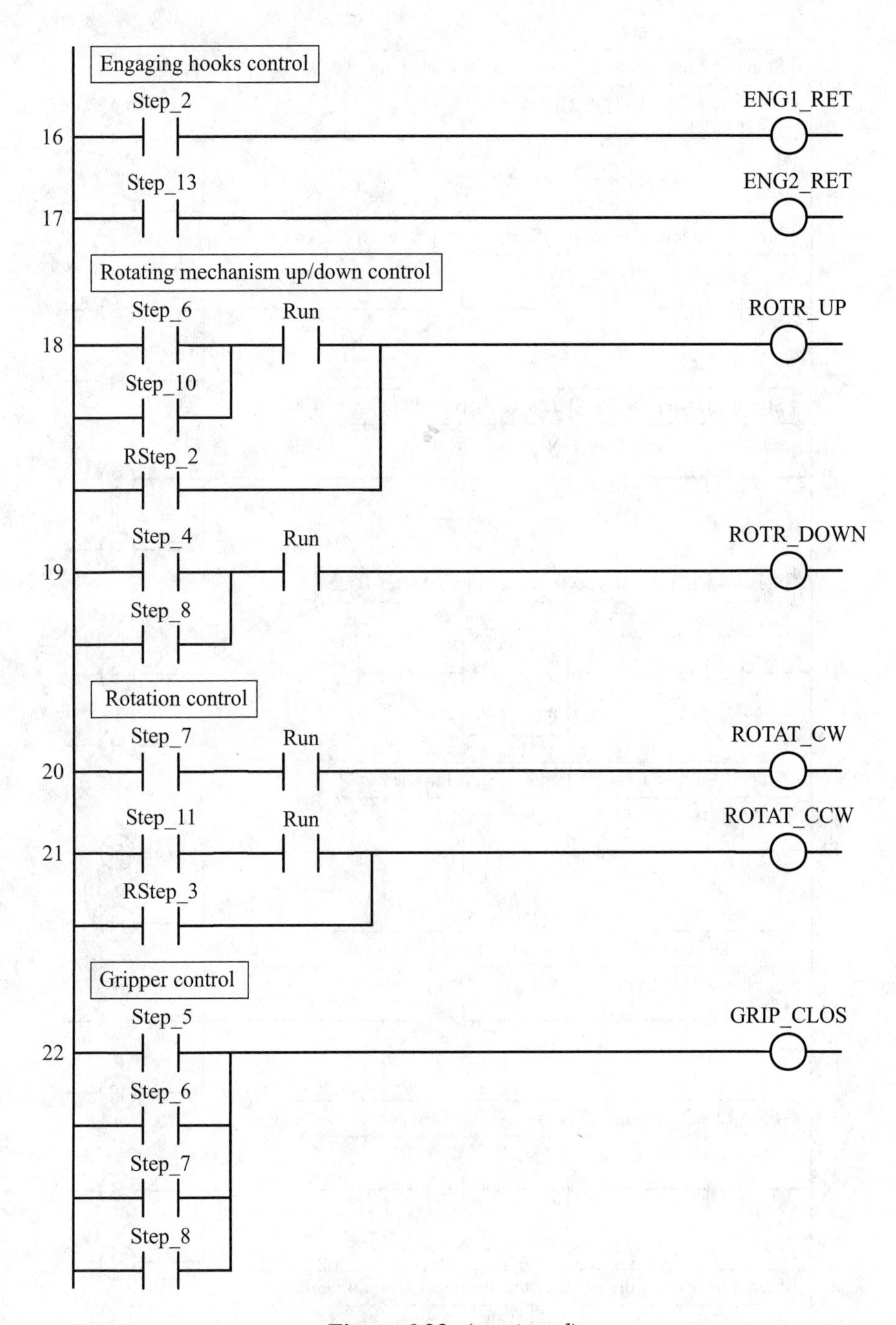

Figure 6.23. *(continued)*

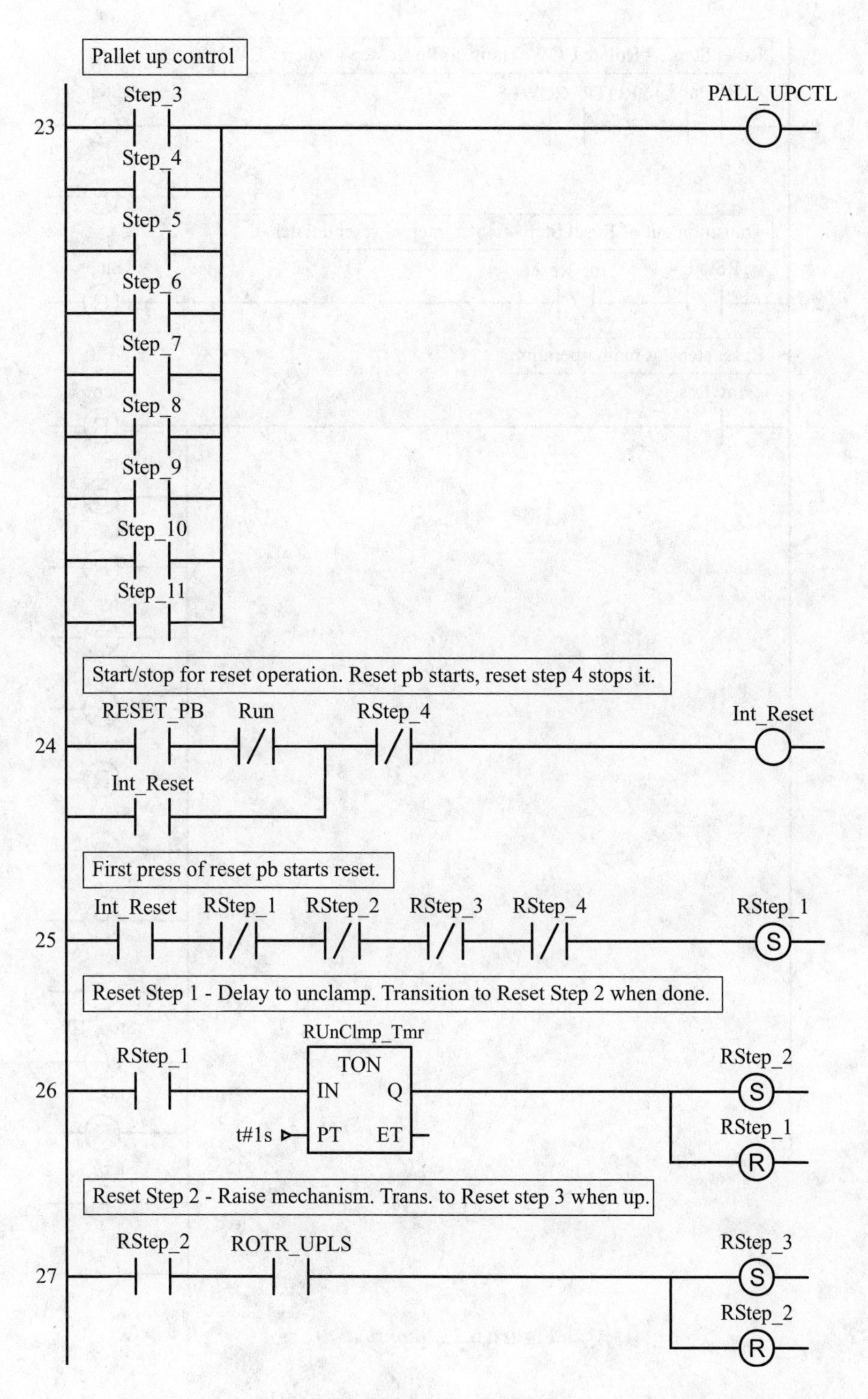

Figure 6.23. *(continued)*

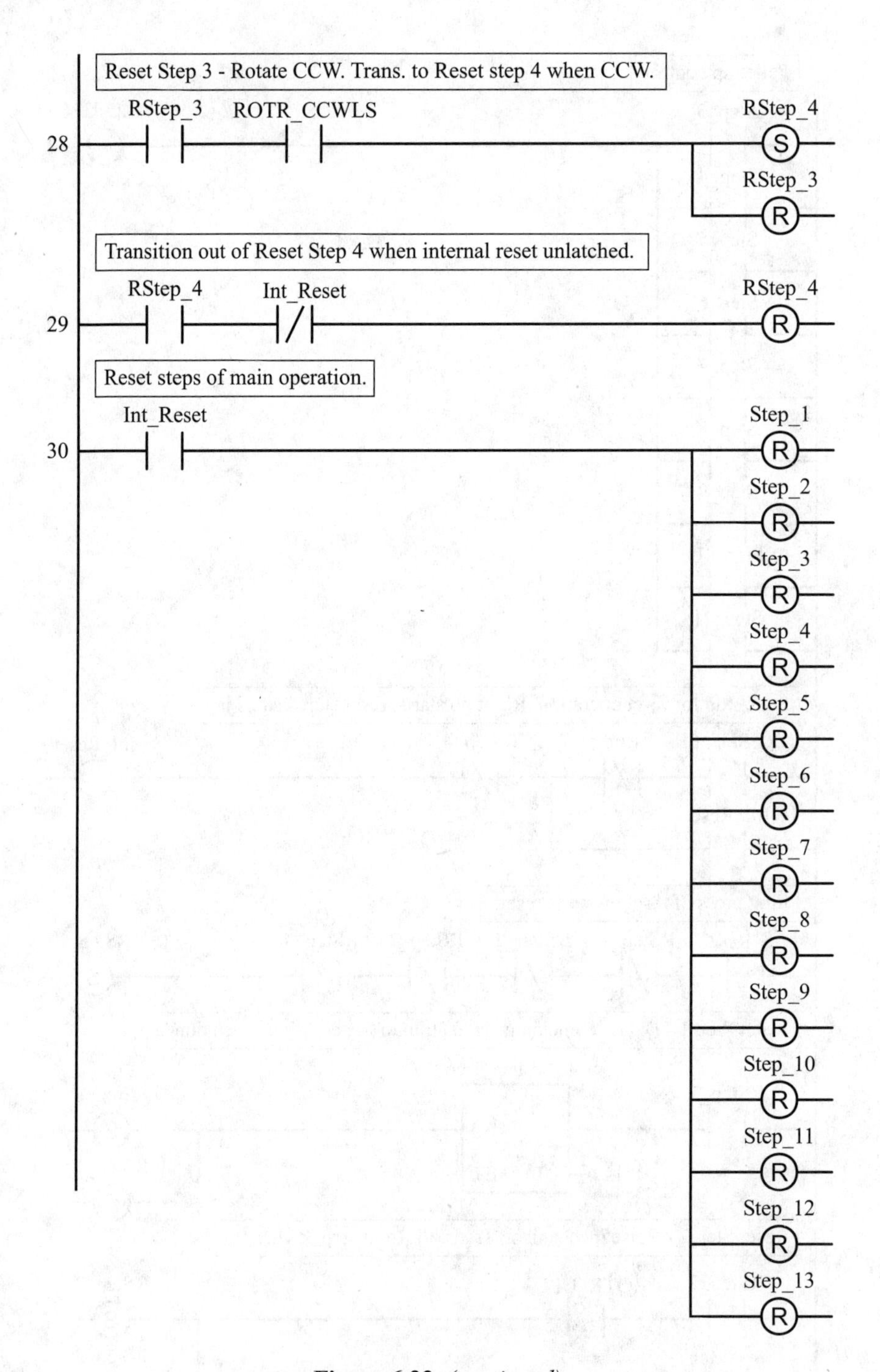

Figure 6.23. *(continued)*

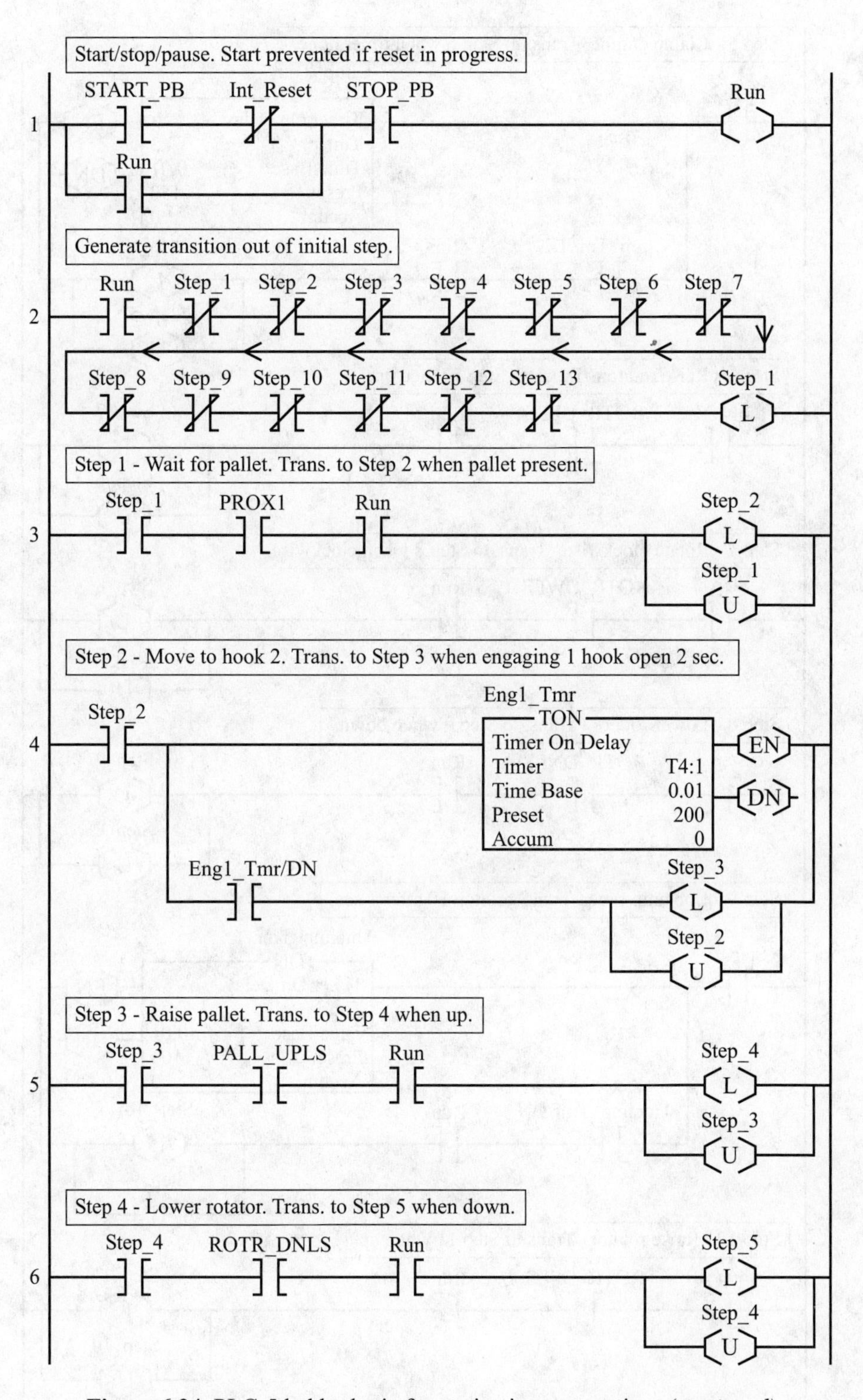

Figure 6.24. PLC-5 ladder logic for engine inverter station. *(continued)*

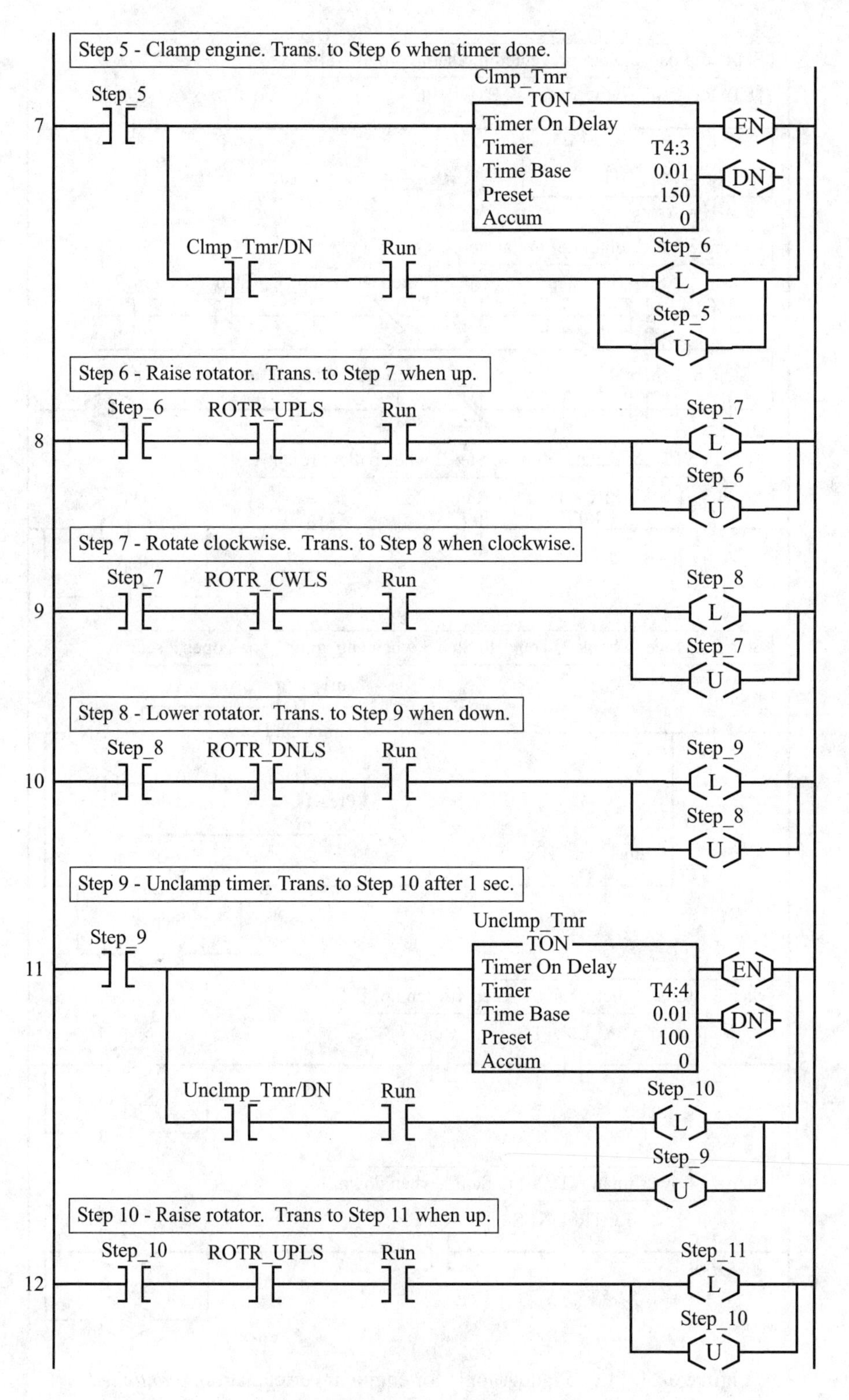

Figure 6.24. *(continued)*

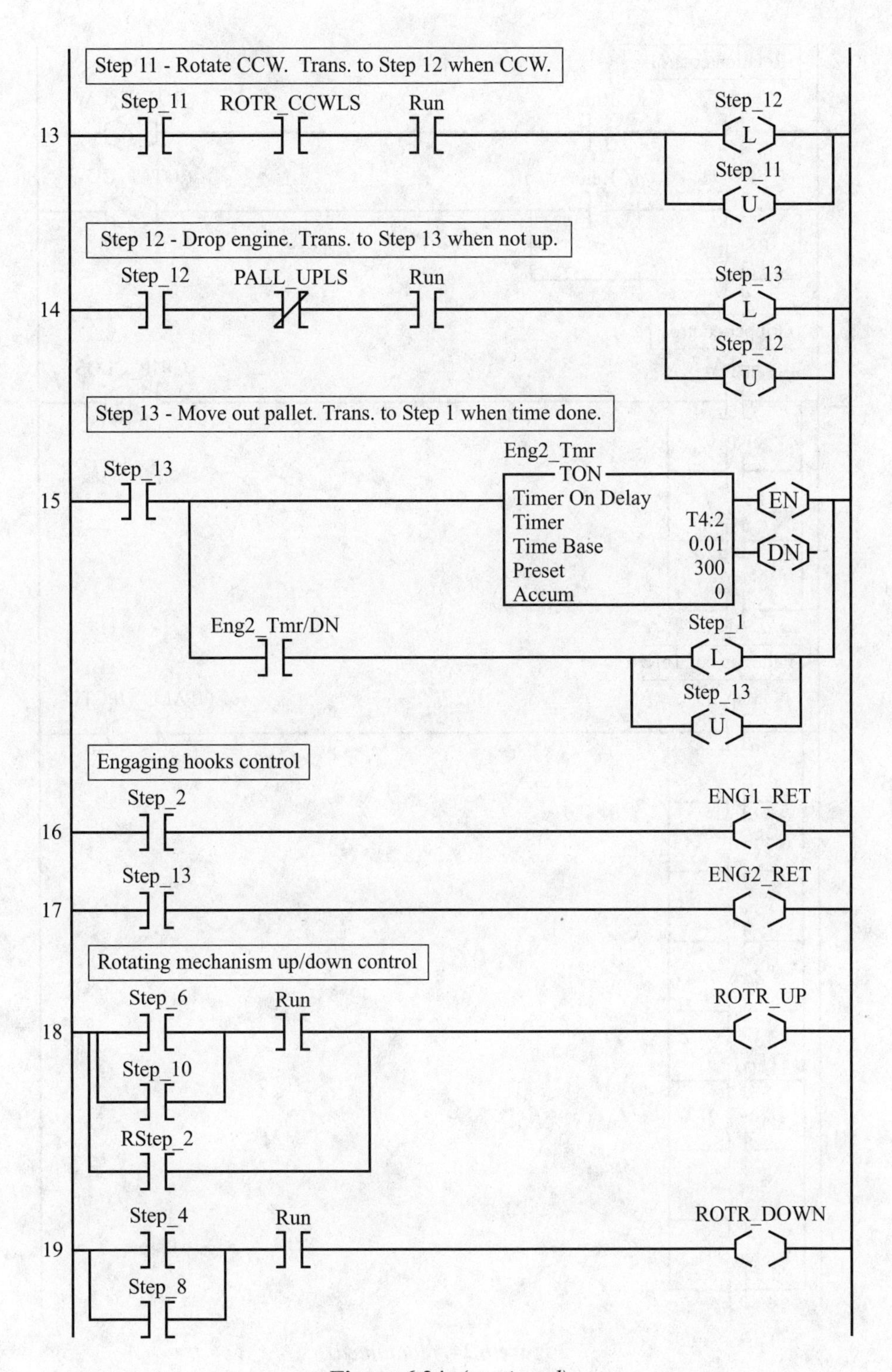

Figure 6.24. *(continued)*

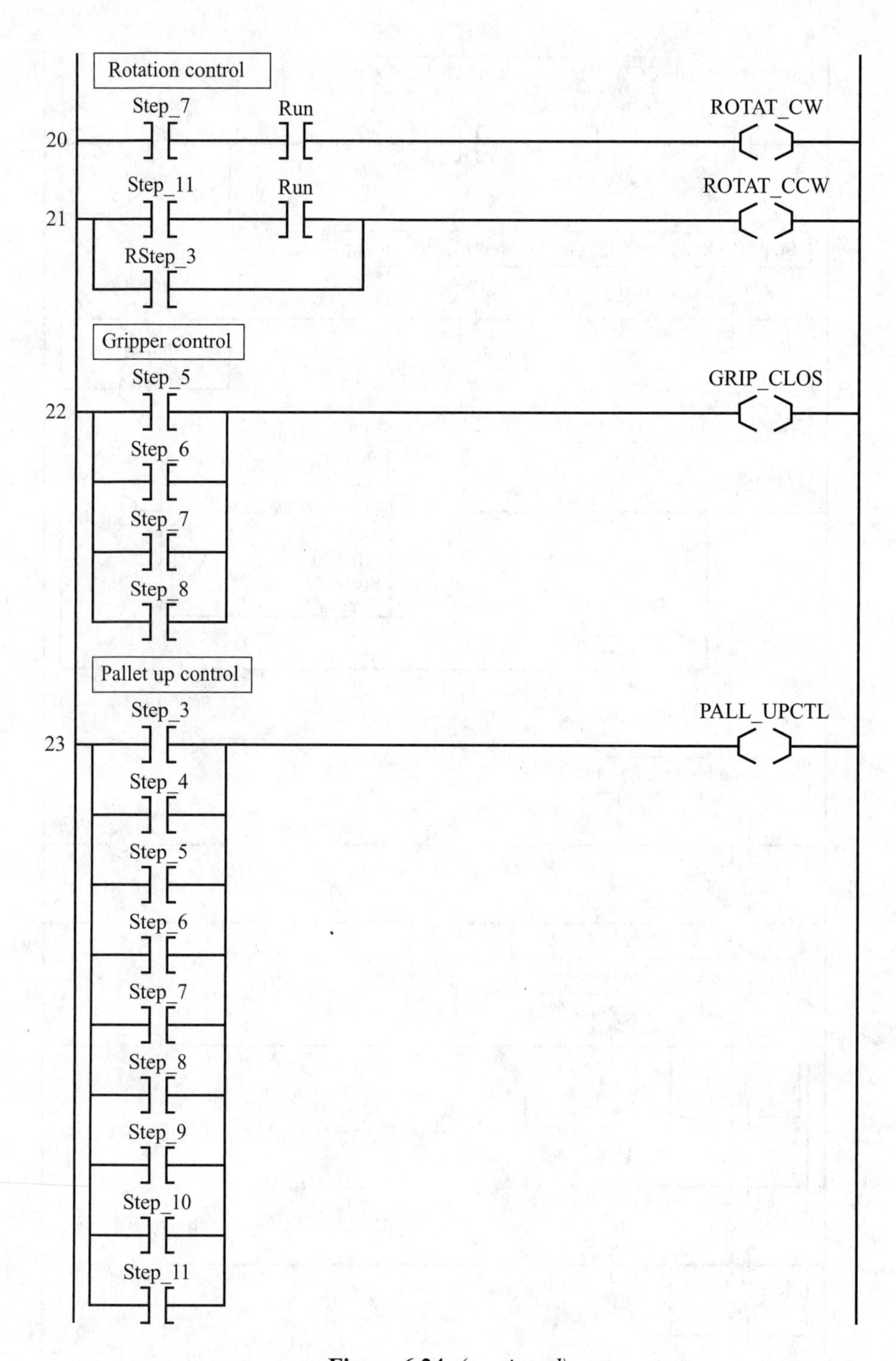

Figure 6.24. *(continued)*

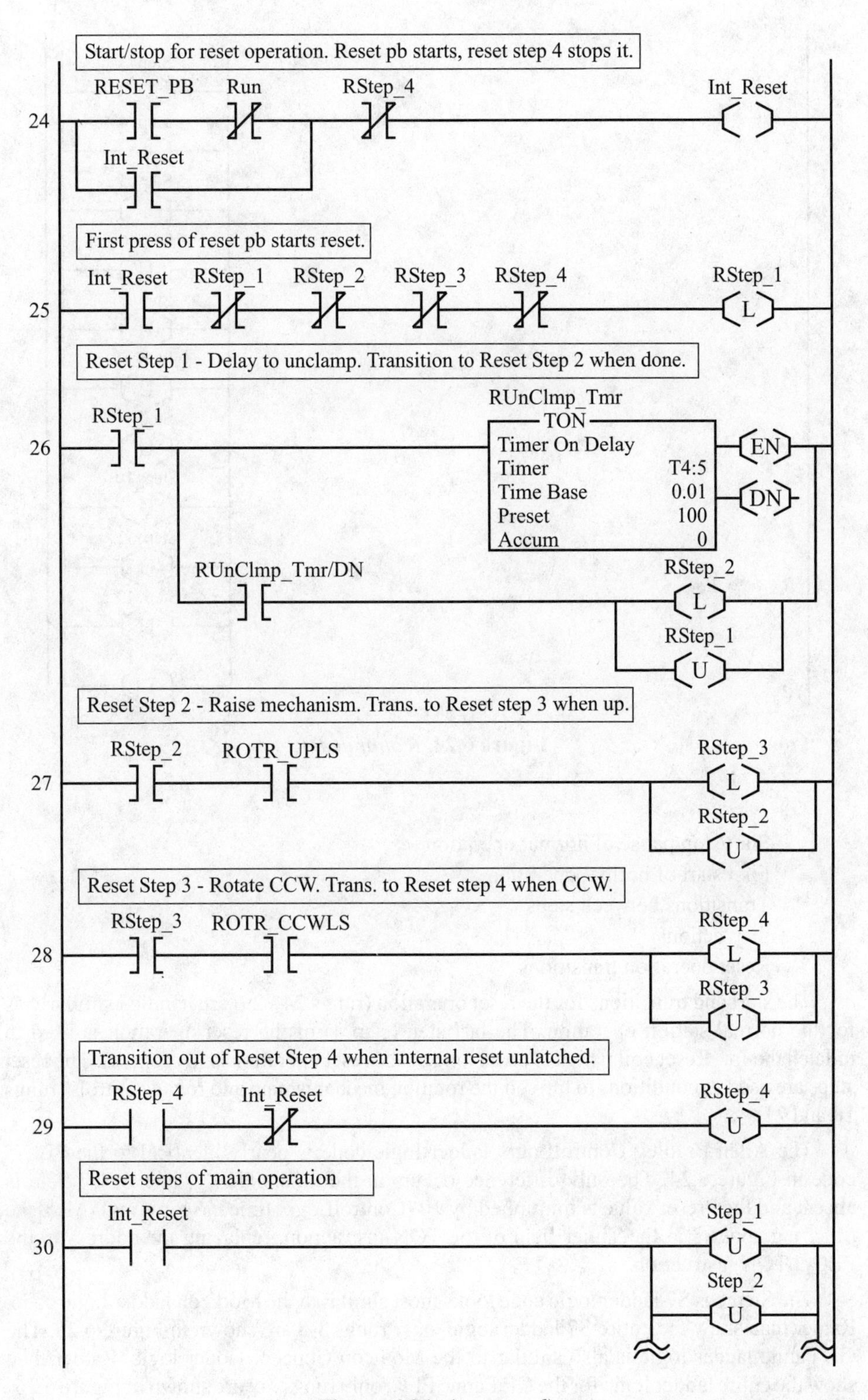

Figure 6.24. *(continued)*

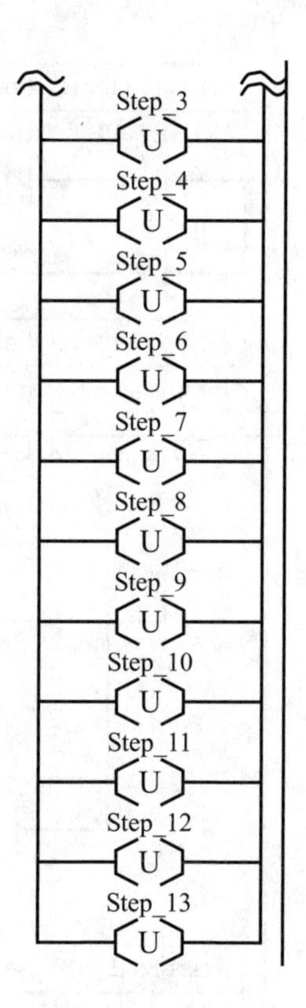

Figure 6.24. *(continued)*

Start/stop/pause of normal operation
First start of normal operation
Transitions between steps
Step actions
Reset operation transitions

The start and transitions for the reset operation (rungs 24 - 29) are handled similarly as for the normal station operation. The last step (step 4) of the reset operation is used to unlatch the Int_Reset coil which is **on** as long as the reset operation is in progress. The reset steps are used as conditions to turn on the rotation mechanism up and rotate controls (rungs 18 and 21).

The Allen-Bradley ControlLogix ladder logic code is nearly identical to the PLC-5 code in Figure 6.24. The only difference occurs in the timers. The "Time Base" field is absent and the Preset value is multiplied by 10 (ControlLogix time base is 1 ms). Also, the timer tag appears in the Timer field of the TON instruction, replacing the address in the PLC-5 TON instruction.

The Siemens S7 ladder logic code looks most similar to the Modicon ladder logic code. Rather than show the entire S7 ladder logic, only rungs 3-8 are shown in Figure 6.25. The GE Fanuc ladder logic is also similar to the Modicon Concept ladder logic. Rather than show the entire ladder logic for the GE Fanuc PLC, only rungs 3-9 are shown in Figure 6.26.

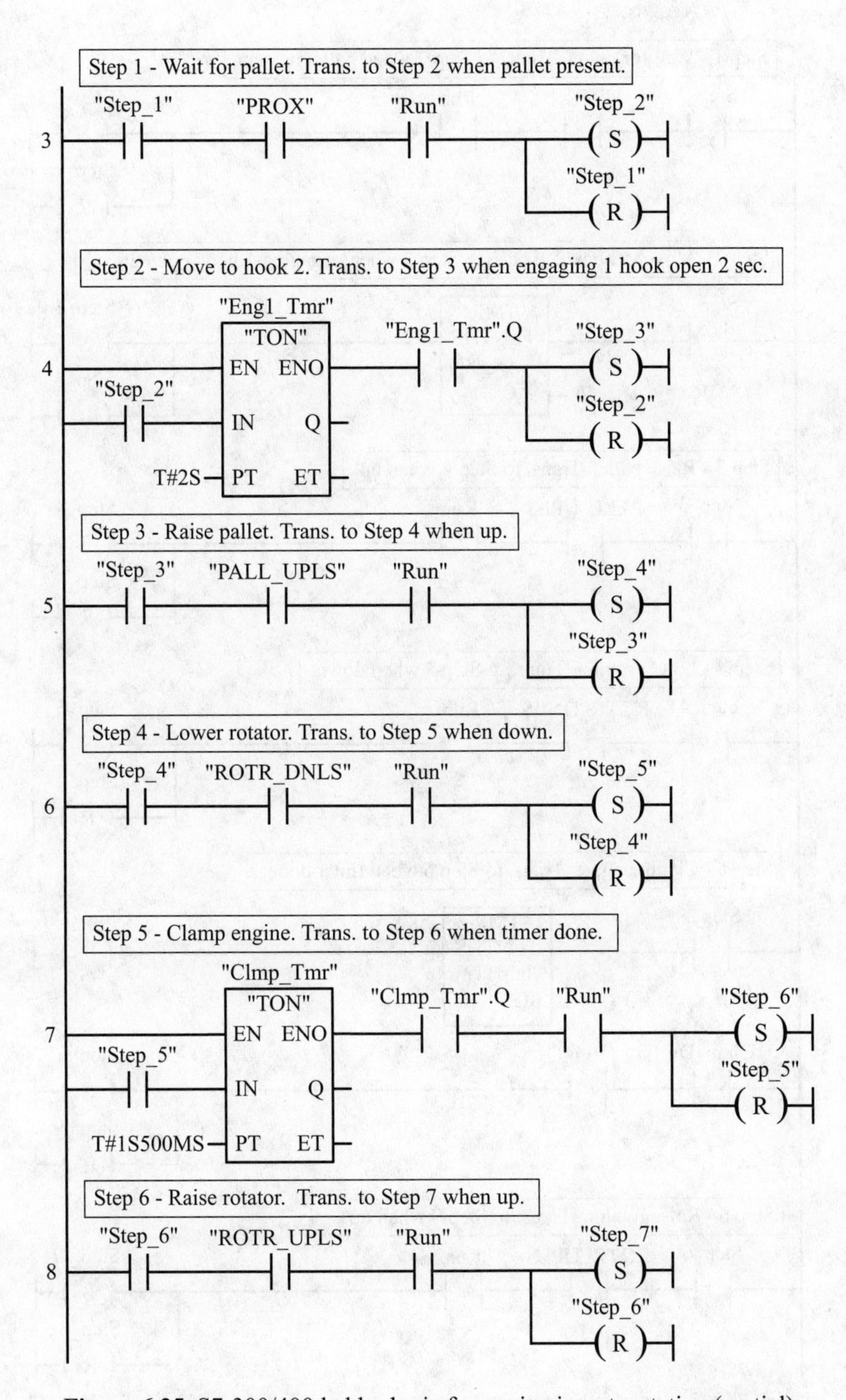

Figure 6.25. S7-300/400 ladder logic for engine inverter station (partial).

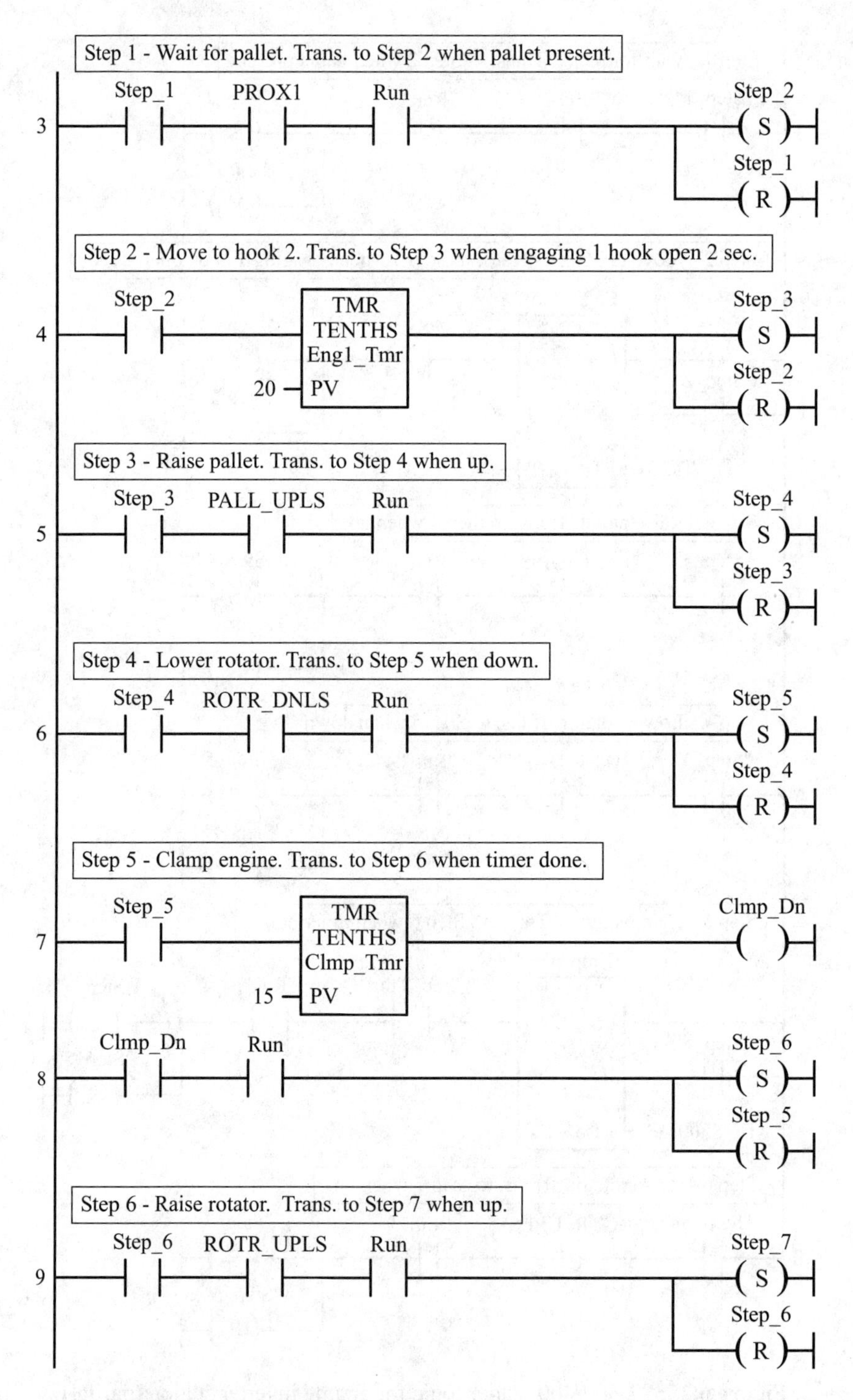

Figure 6.26. GE Fanuc ladder logic for engine inverter station (partial).

6.5 PARALLEL OPERATIONS

Suppose the gasoline engine manufacturer wants to increase the throughput of the assembly line. Therefore, the cycle time of each station must be decreased. One way to meet this requirement for the engine inverter station is to allow certain steps to happen simultaneously. For example, the raising of the pallet (step 2) and the lowering of the rotator (step 3) steps can occur simultaneously. The first part of this revised function chart (without the actions) is shown in Figure 6.27. The double horizontal line indicates that both paths are executed simultaneously.

On a function chart, two kinds of branching are allowed. If the transition out of a step causes more than one step to be activated simultaneously, called ***simultaneous divergence*** or ***AND branching***, these simultaneous sequences are represented as in Figure 6.28. The double horizontal lines distinguish this type of branching. Also, only one common transition condition is permitted above the top double horizontal line, and no transitions are permitted below the upper double horizontal line. When step 11 is active and the condition "XV110 Closed" is true, then step 11 becomes inactive and steps 12,14, and 16 become active simultaneously. The sequences converge with a double horizontal line having a common transition symbol under the double horizontal line. Step 18 will become the active step only when all the steps above the double horizontal line are active and the transition condition "XV201A Closed .and. XV202A Closed .and. XV203A Closed" is true. For some systems, especially those that involve mechanical motion, the simultaneous steps do not finish at the same time. In this situation, an extra step must be added before the branch convergence (lower double horizontal line). This step serves to stop the motion and to wait for the other parallel steps to finish. This issue is considered in Example 6.5.

A selection of one sequence out of more than one sequence is called ***exclusive divergence*** or ***OR branching*** and is represented by multiple transitions below the single horizontal line, as shown in the upper part of Figure 6.29. Each possible sequence path contains a transition condition. No common transition condition is permitted above the horizontal line. The exclusive divergence is differentiated from the simultaneous

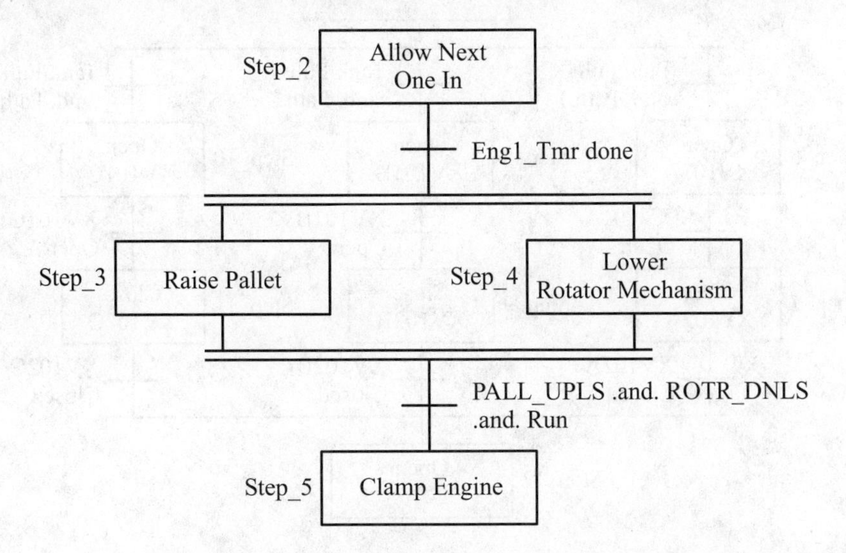

Figure 6.27. Example parallel steps.

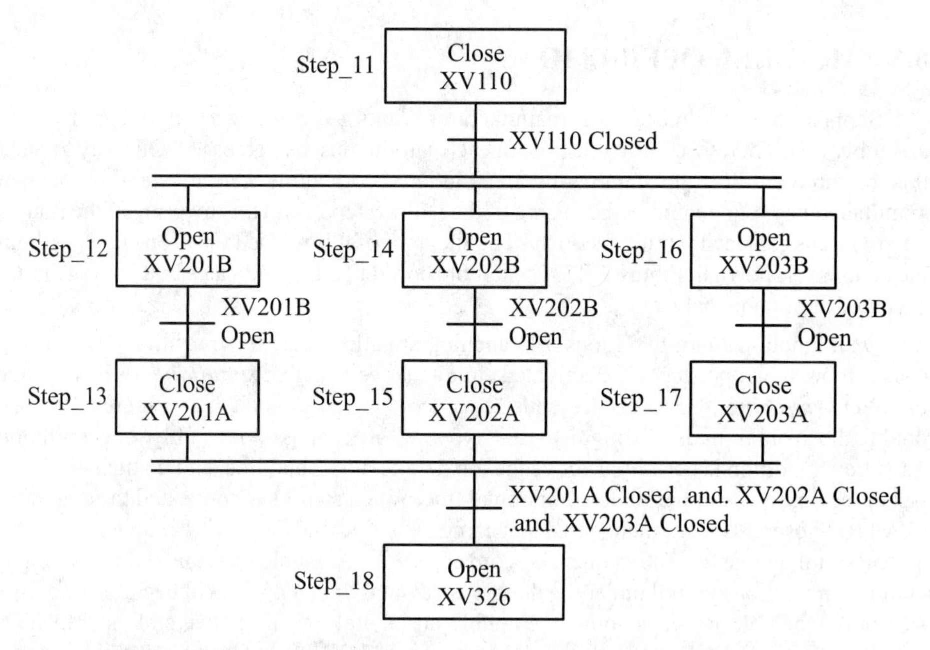

Figure 6.28. Example of simultaneous divergence (AND branching).

divergence by the single horizontal line. If step 5 is active and the tank is full, then there are three possible transition conditions. If the "Path 1" condition is true, then the logic advances to step 6. Otherwise, if "Path 2" is true, then the logic advances to step 8, or if "Path 3" is true, the logic advances to step 10. In order to select only one succeeding step, the transition

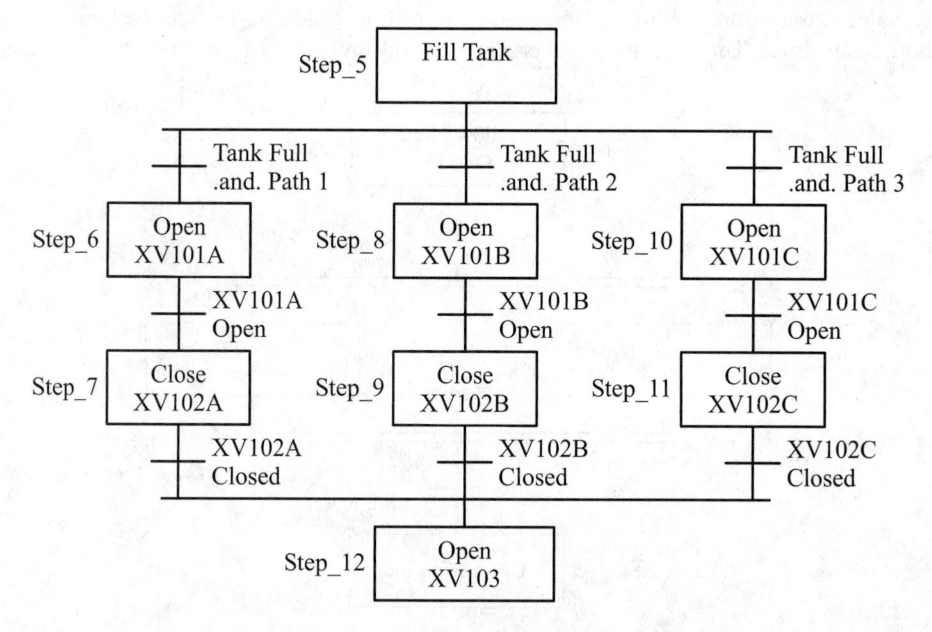

Figure 6.29. Example of exclusive divergence (OR branching).

conditions must be mutually exclusive. The several sequences must also converge to a common sequence, as in the lower part of Figure 6.29. There must be as many transitions above the horizontal line as sequences to be re-grouped. No common transition condition is permitted below the lower horizontal line. If step 7 is active and "XV102A Closed" is true, or if step 9 is active and "XV102B Closed" is true, or if step 11 is active and "XV102C Closed" is true, then step 12 becomes the active step.

Both types of branching can be combined on the same function chart as shown in Figure 6.30. Note that the beginning and ending of each branch must correspond. A simultaneous divergence (double horizontal line) cannot be finished with an exclusive divergence (single horizontal line).

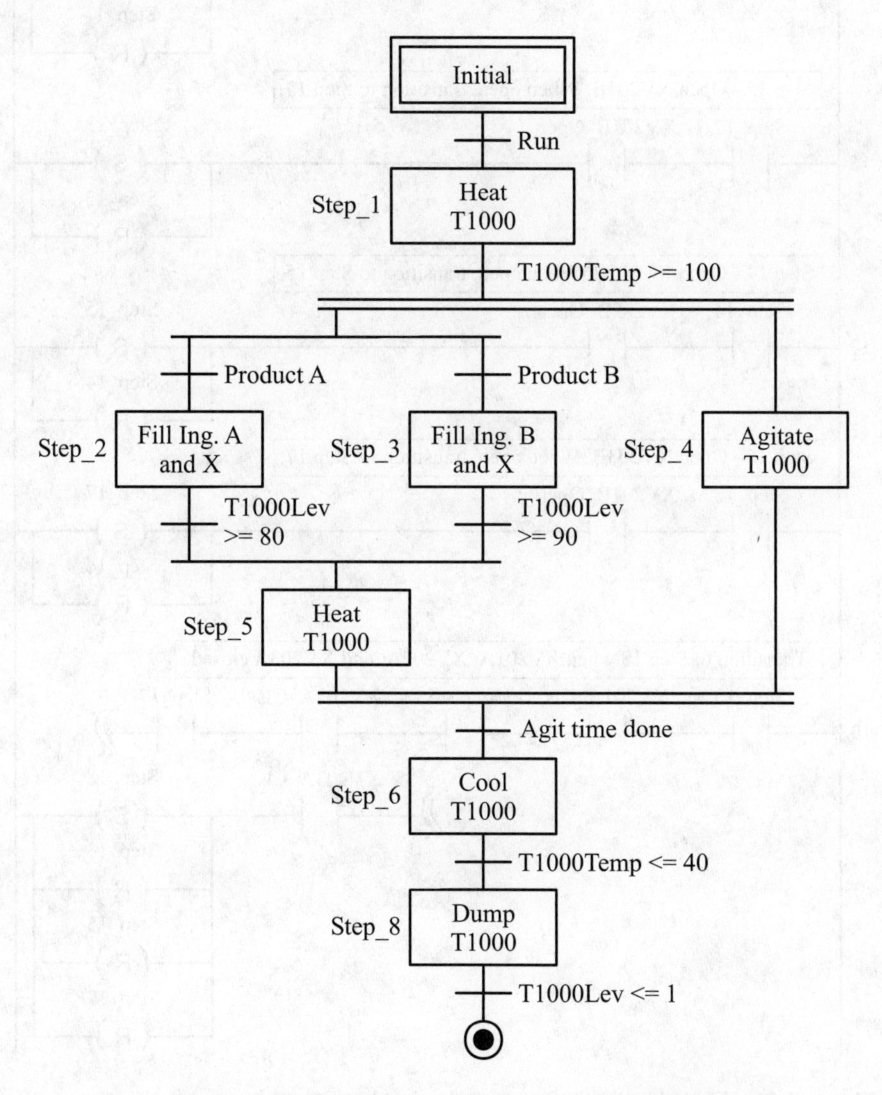

Figure 6.30. Example combined types of branching.

The code to handle the transitions for the simultaneous divergence in Figure 6.28 is shown in Figure 6.31. The exclusive divergence of Figure 6.29 is handled in ladder logic code as shown in Figure 6.32.

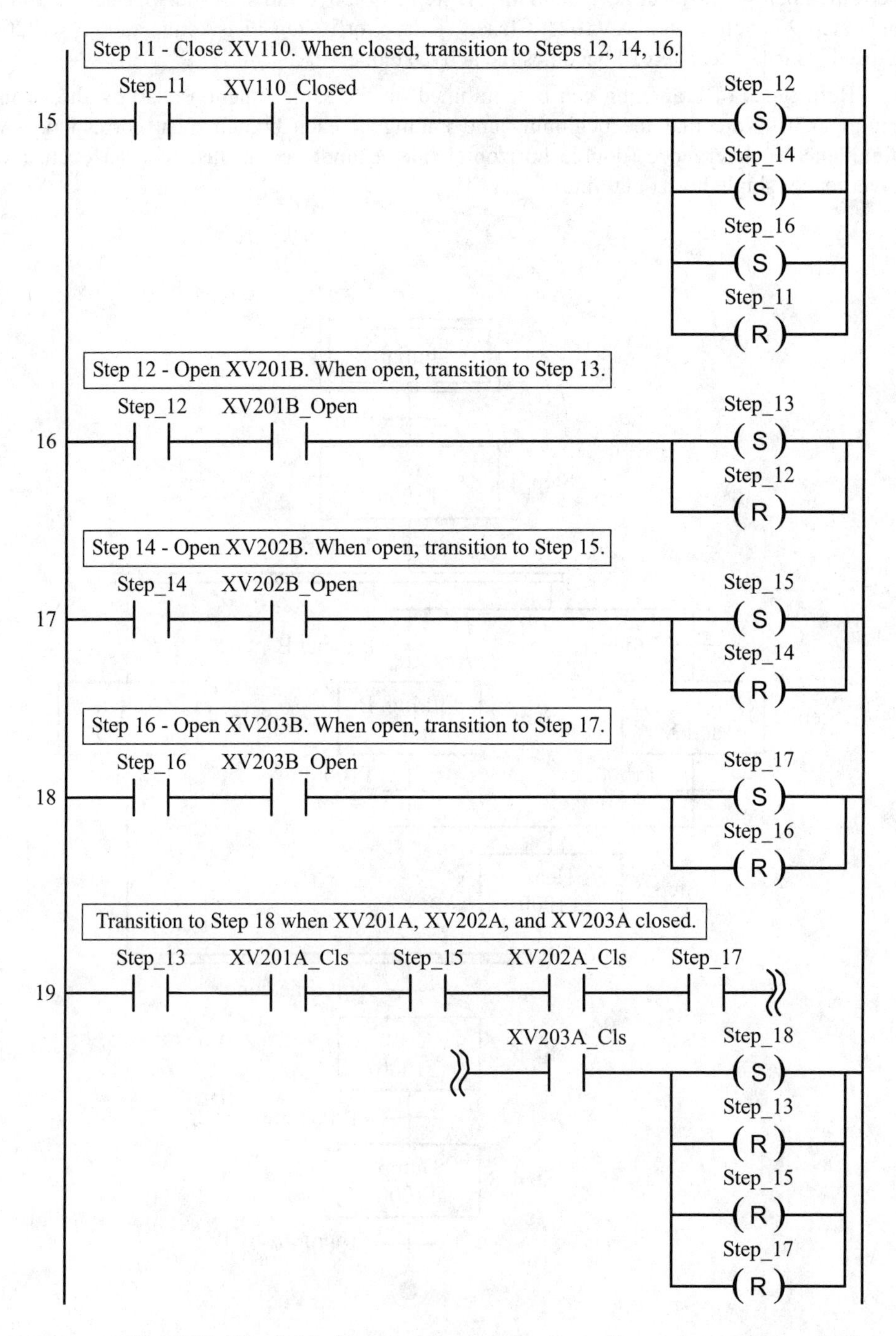

Figure 6.31. IEC ladder logic for example simultaneous divergence of Figure 6.28.

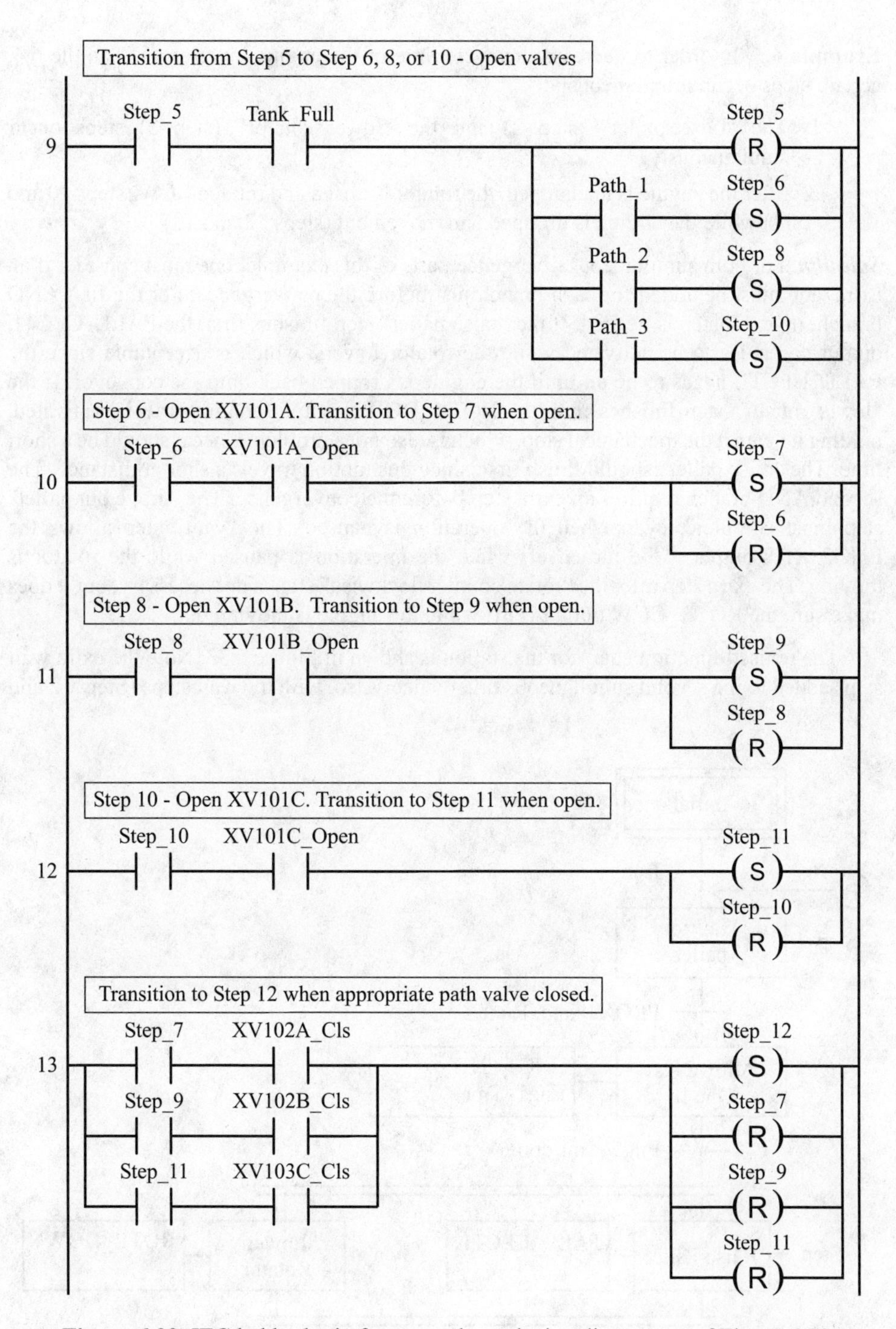

Figure 6.32. IEC ladder logic for example exclusive divergence of Figure 6.29.

Example 6.5. In order to decrease the cycle time of the engine inverter of Example 6.4, certain steps occur simultaneously:

1. The "raise pallet" (step 2) and the "lower rotator" (step 3) steps occur simultaneously.
2. After the engine is unclamped, the rotator is raised and rotated CCW (steps 10 and 11) while the engine is dropped and moved out (steps 12 and 13).

Solution. For both simultaneous divergence parts of this example, one must consider if an extra step must be added for each branch just before the convergence. For the first AND branch, no extra step is needed. If the "raise pallet" step finishes first, the PALL_UPCTL output continues to be activated while the rotator lowers, which is acceptable since the PALL_UPCTL needs to be **on** until the engine is dropped back onto the conveyor. If the "lower rotator" step finishes first, the ROTR_DOWN output continues to be activated, holding it against the mechanical stop, which is also not a problem since it should be a short time. The "raise pallet" should finish first, since this motion travels a shorter distance. The second AND branch requires an extra step before the convergence. The "move out pallet" step must complete, even when the operation is paused. The "wait" step allows the ENG2_RET output to be turned **off** when the operation is paused while the rotator is moving. The extra step after the "rotate counterclockwise" step is not necessary, but it does make sure the ROTR_CCW output is **off** while the engine is moving out.

The revised function chart for the station is shown in Figure 6.33. Note the extra wait steps added to the second simultaneous divergence. Also, with the wait steps (Step_12 and

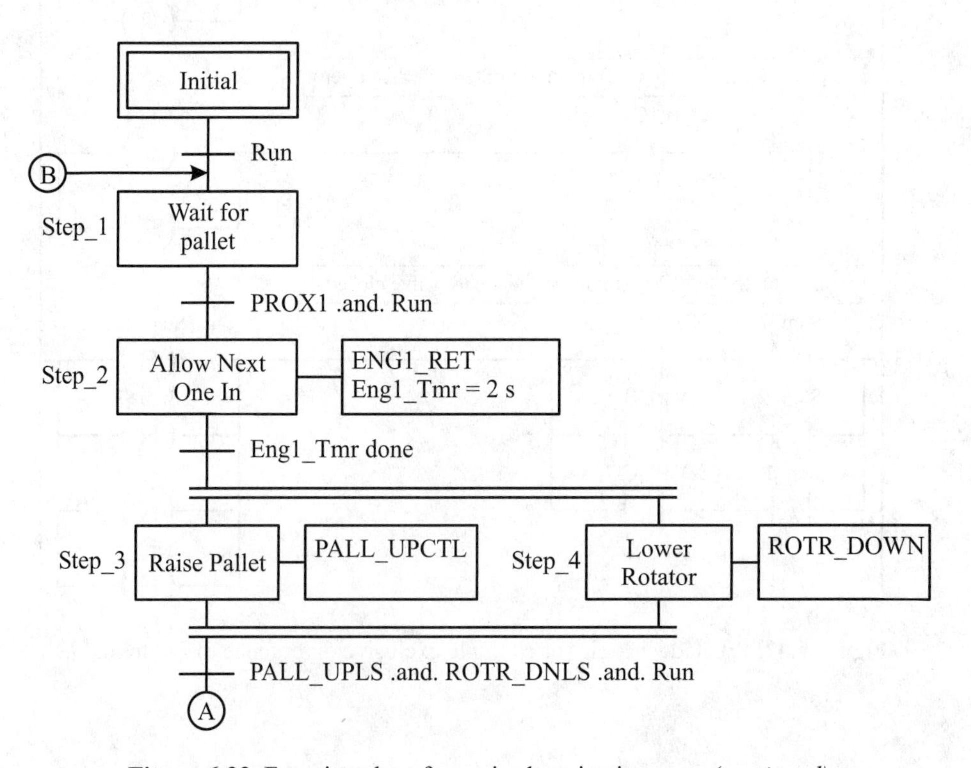

Figure 6.33. Function chart for revised engine inverter. *(continued)*

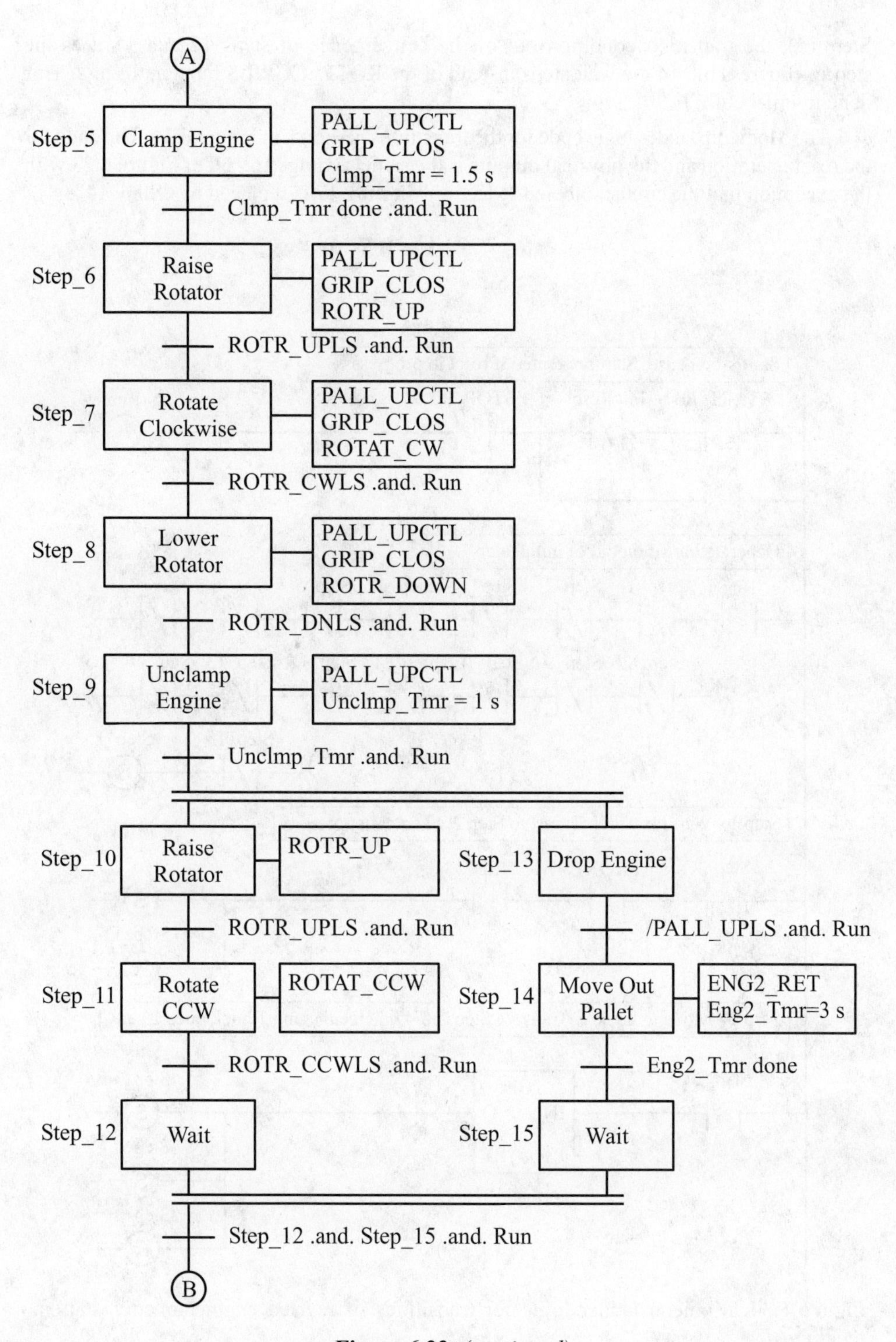

Figure 6.33. *(continued)*

Step_15), the transition condition out of the convergence of steps 12 and 15 uses the step-in-progress bits of the wait steps instead of the ROTR_CCWLS input and Eng2_Tmr done internal coil.

The Modicon ladder logic code for the transitions is shown in Figure 6.34. The code for the reset operation and the physical outputs is the same as rungs 16 - 30 of Figure 6.23 with the exception that the contact labeled "Step_13" in rung 17 is replaced by "Step_14".

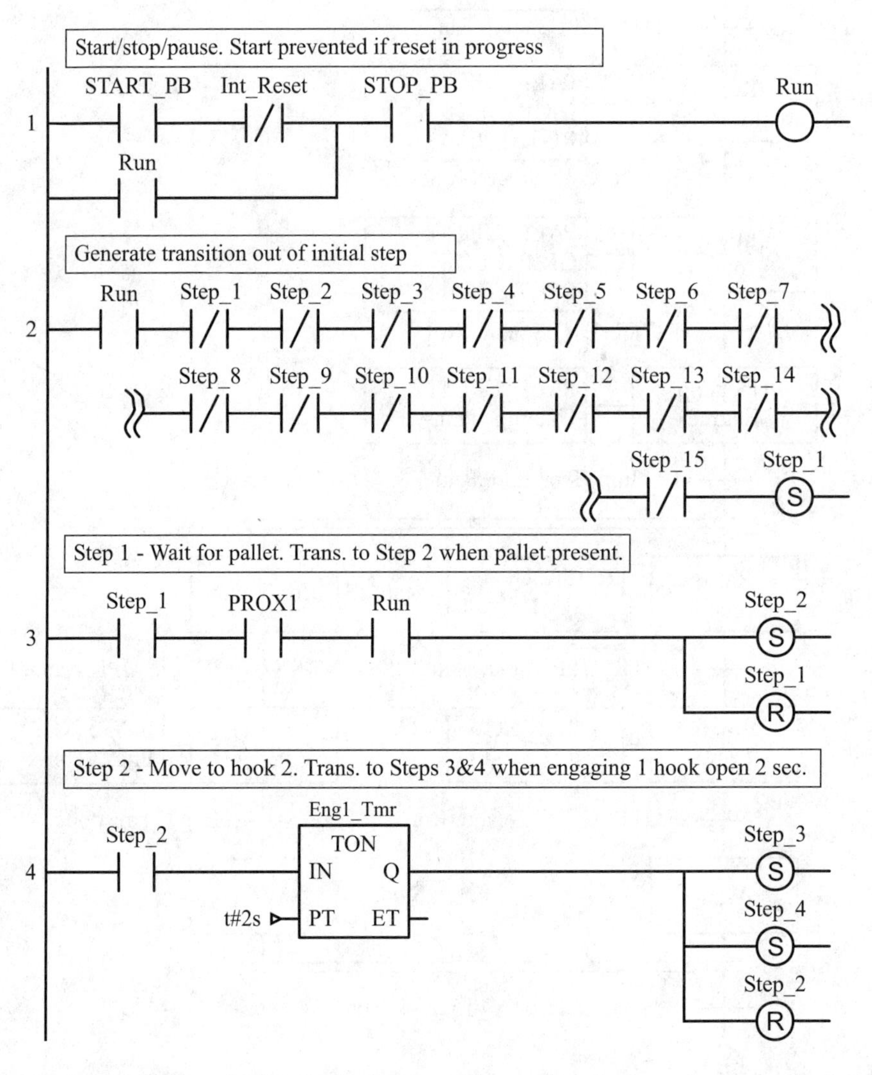

Figure 6.34. Modicon ladder logic for transitions of revised engine inverter station. *(continued)*

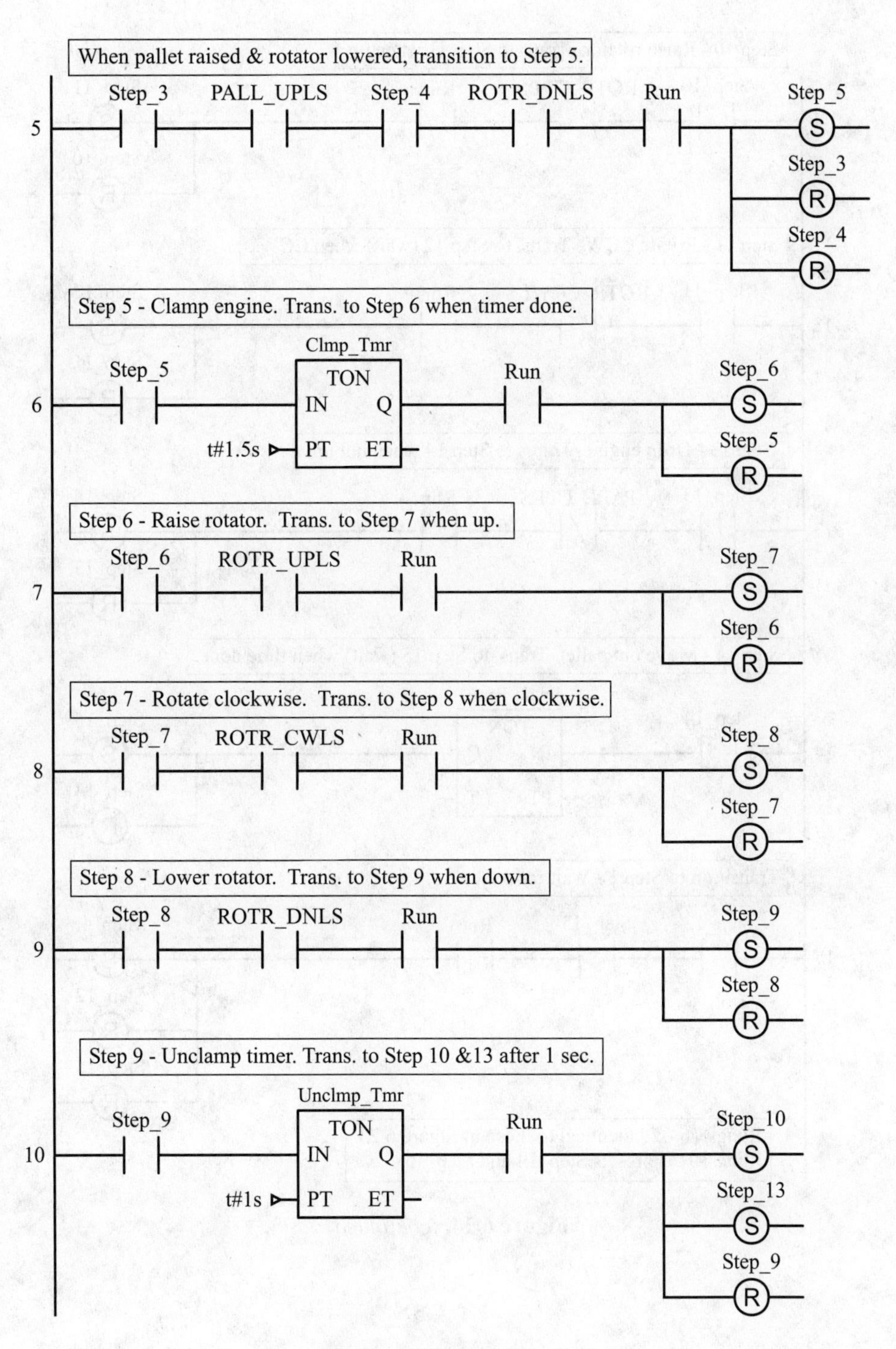

Figure 6.34. *(continued)*

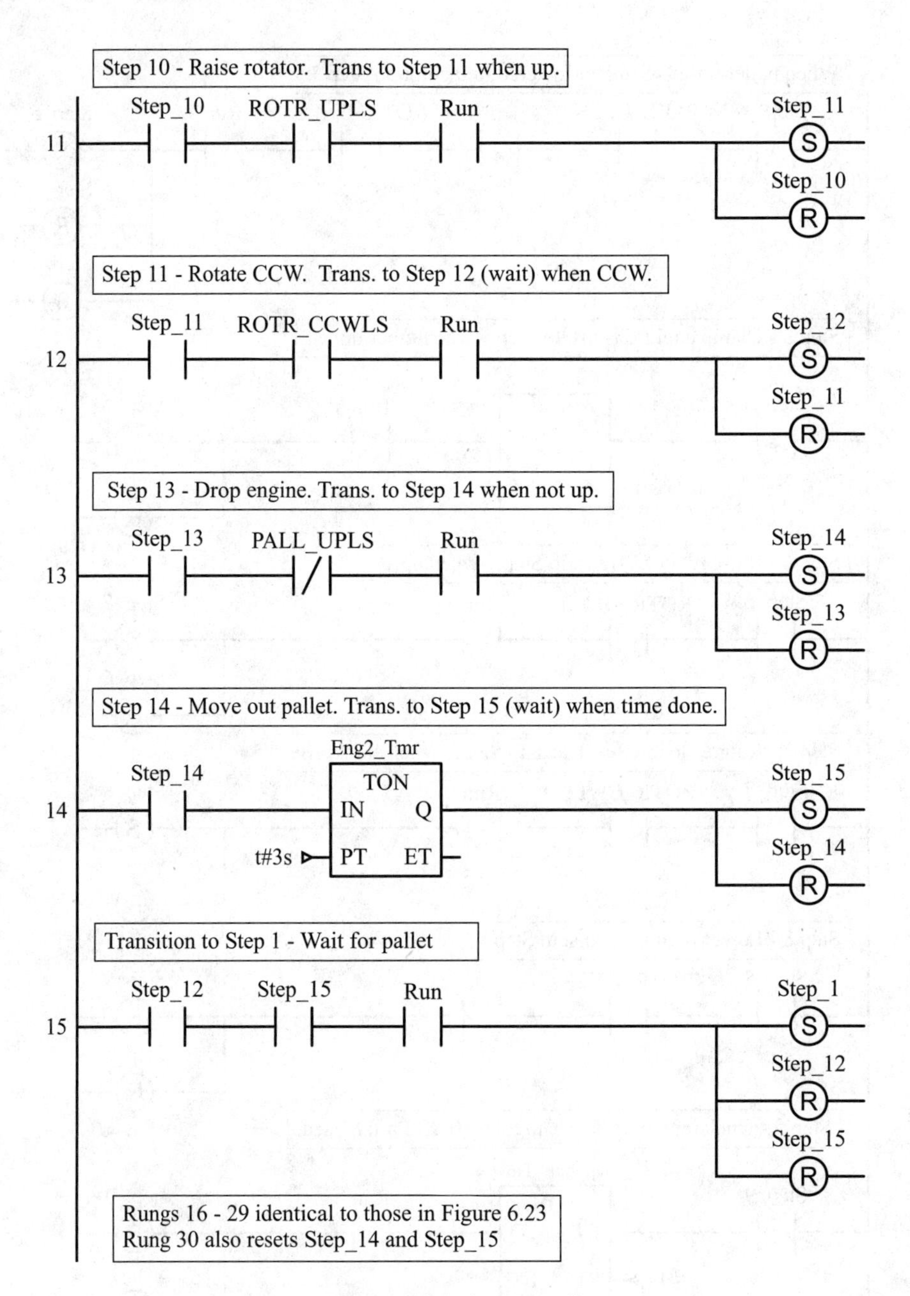

Figure 6.34. *(continued)*

6.6 KEY QUESTIONS IN THE SEQUENTIAL DESIGN PROCESS

The examples in this chapter illustrate a simple method of programming sequential operations. The major part of the method is to develop a function chart of the operation:

1. Identify the steps and transition conditions.
2. Add step actions.

After the first draft of the function chart is developed, other key questions to ask:

Does the operation repeat?

If it does not repeat, then the last step may need to reset (unlatch) the operation run status.

How is stop/pause handled?

Identify those physical outputs that must be off when paused.

Identify the timers that must retain their accumulator value.

Does pause prevent transitions?

Ignored in certain steps?

Does stop cause reset (or emergency stop)?

How is reset handled?

Reset only allowed when already paused?

Is there another sequential operation that must occur when the system is reset, to bring it back to an initial state?

6.7 MANUAL AND SINGLE-STEP SEQUENTIAL OPERATION

Up to this point, the control of a sequential machine has assumed mostly continuous operation. The operator can start and stop/pause the operation and reset it to the first step. This mode of operation typically called the auto mode. However, when devices malfunction, there are two other modes of operation that are also useful. The first is the ability to single-step the operation. When in the single-step mode and the conditions to the next step are met, the program waits for the operator to press a "Continue" button in order for the operation to advance to the next step. The single-step mode allows personnel to monitor the operation of each step individually. The second mode that is useful is completely manual operation. In this mode, the operator may individually manipulate the physical outputs. Of course, a push button must be provided for each manipulated physical output.

The operator panel for this *three-mode* control of the machine operation is shown in Figure 6.35. The mode switch is a three-position selector switch. The other switches are all push button switches. The switches required for manual manipulation of the physical outputs are not shown.

In the single-step mode, the start/stop push buttons function the same as in the auto mode. When in the single-step mode, pressing the stop button pauses the operation. When paused, the start button must be pressed before pressing the continue button.

The transitions between modes are handled as follows:

Auto to Single-step: Operation completes the current step and then pauses, waiting for the "Continue" button to be pressed. The state of the Run coil does not change.

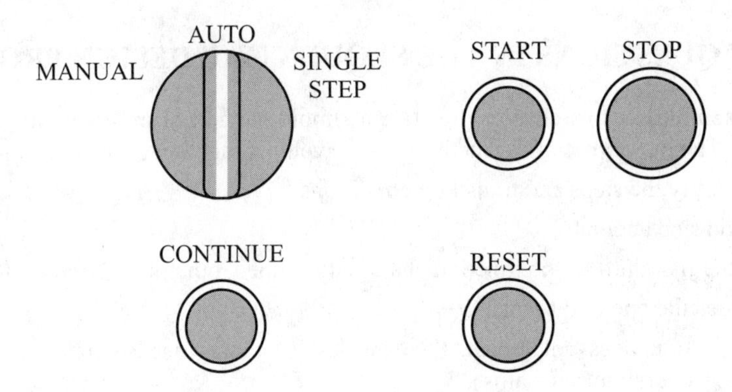

Figure 6.35. Operator panel for three-mode control.

Single-step to Auto: Operation will resume from the current step. The state of the Run coil does not change.

Auto to Manual: Operation pauses at the current step (like the stop switch was pressed). The Run coil is turned off.

Manual to Auto: Operator must also press the Start button to resume automatic operation at the step from which it was switched to Manual. If the operation must resume from the first step, the Reset button must be pressed before the Start button is pressed.

The single-step and manual modes are easily added to the sequential operation. The ladder logic is modified as follows:

1. The start/stop rung is modified to disable the Run coil when in manual mode.
2. Auto and single-step mode logic is added in series with the step transition logic.
3. Manual mode logic is added in parallel to the conditions driving the physical outputs.

When adding the single-step and manual logic to the ladder logic, particular attention must be paid to those physical outputs that must be turned off when some physical limit is reached. For example, the command to extend a double-acting pneumatic cylinder may need to be turned off when the cylinder is fully extended, even while the operator is still pressing the "Extend" button in manual mode or before the "Continue" button is pressed when in single-step mode.

Example 6.6. Add three-mode control to the engine inverter of Example 6.4. Four additional physical inputs are required:

Variable	Description
AUTO	Mode selector switch in "Auto" position.
MANUAL	Mode selector switch in "Manual" position.
SSTEP	Mode selector switch in "Single Step" position.
CONTINU	Single-step mode continue push button, N. O., **on** transition causes transition to the next step when other transition conditions met and in single-step mode.

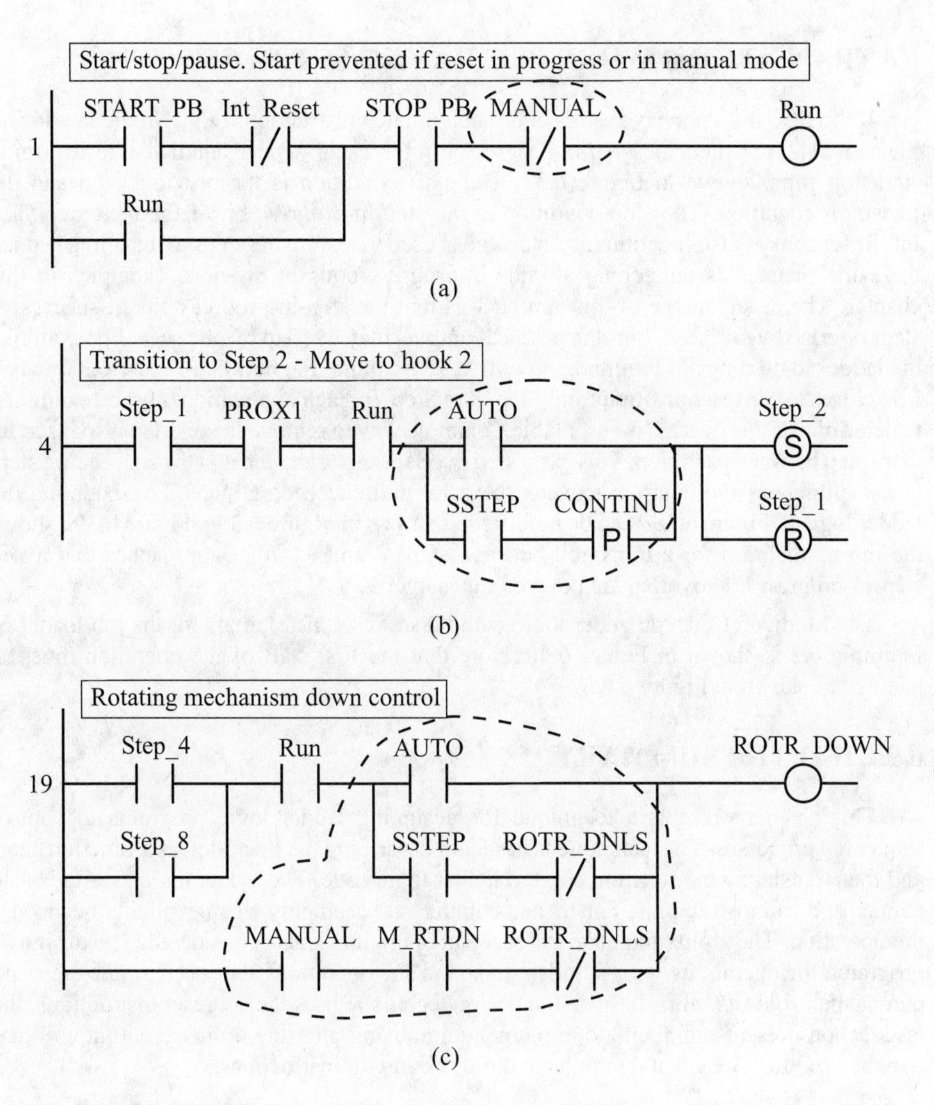

Figure 6.36. IEC (Modicon) ladder logic changes for three-mode control (partial): *(a)* start/stop rung; *(b)* transition to step 2; *(c)* ROTR_DOWN control.

Solution. Rather than giving a complete solution to this problem, the following changes to the ladder logic of Figure 6.23 are shown in Figure 6.36:

Start/stop, rung 1 (Figure 6.36*a*)

Transition to step 2, rung 4 (Figure 6.36*b*)

Rotating mechanism down control, rung 19 (Figure 6.36*c*)

The dashed lines indicate the changes to the original ladder logic.

In rung 19, M_RTDN is an operator manual push button to move the mechanism. Also note that for both the single-step and manual modes, the control to move the mechanism down is turned off as soon as the ROTR_DNLS limit switch turns on.

6.8 TRANSITIONS WHEN PLC HAS NO SET/RESET

If the PLC does not have set/reset or latch/unlatch instructions (e.g., Modicon x84 and Siemens TI-5x5) then the step-in-progress bit for each step is handled like a normal start/stop rung, shown in Figure 6.37. The start condition is the previous step and the transition condition. The stop condition is the step-in-progress bit of the next step. The Int_Reset contact also functions as a stop and is used to restore the steps to the initial state in the same manner as unlatching all step-in-progress coils in previous examples in this chapter. The disadvantage of this approach is that the step-in-progress bits of successive steps overlap by one scan, thus the physical outputs may overlap by one scan. For example, the ladder logic rungs in Figure 6.38*a* will have a timing diagram like Figure 6.38*b* when LS2 closes to cause a transition from Step_8 to Step_9. Each application must be examined to determine if this overlap is acceptable. A simple way to remove the overlap is to insert an extra step between each step. This extra step overlaps the prior step and the succeeding step, and it eliminates the overlap between the prior and succeeding steps. For example, the ladder logic in Figure 6.38*a* can be modified as shown in Figure 6.39*a*. Figure 6.39*b* shows the timing diagram for a transition between steps 8 and 9. Other approaches that avoid step-in-progress coil overlap are covered in Chapter 9.

The Modicon Concept ladder logic without set/reset instructions for the tub loader of Example 6.2 is shown in Figure 6.40. Note that the first start of the operation must be handled as shown in Figure 6.9*a*.

6.9 CHAPTER SUMMARY

This chapter presents a technique for designing ladder logic programs to control sequential processes. The technique is based on describing the operation as a function chart and then translating the function chart to ladder logic code. The ladder logic uses the basic contact and coil instructions. Timers and counters are used only when explicitly needed by the operation. The ability to pause and reset an operation is also considered. The design of programs for operations with parallel steps and for operations that need single-step and manual control is examined. Since the design technique uses the set/reset instructions, the last section presents an alternate implementation using only the ordinary output coil that may be used for PLCs that do not have the set/reset coil instructions.

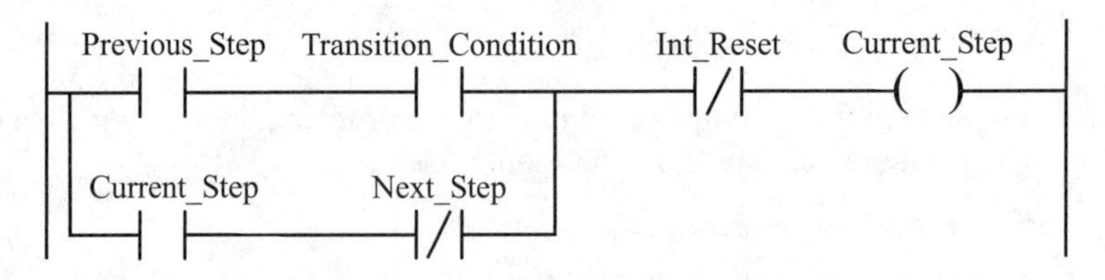

Figure 6.37. Non-latching step.

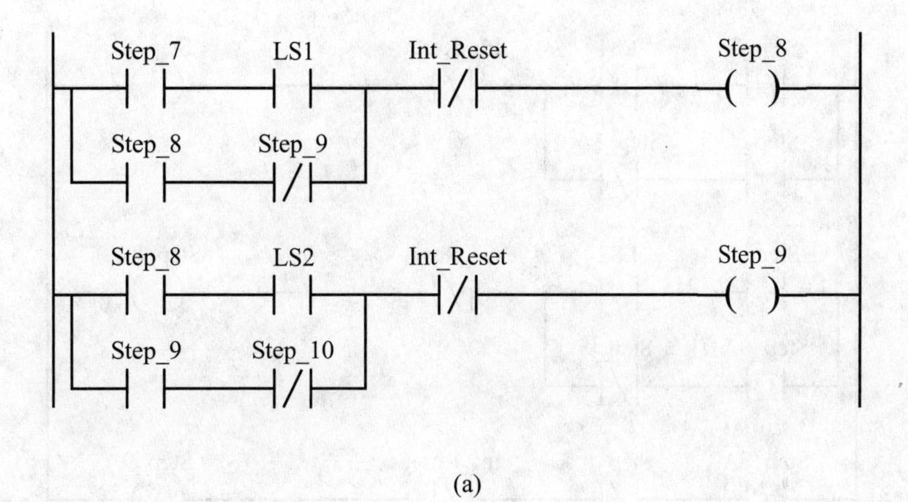

(a)

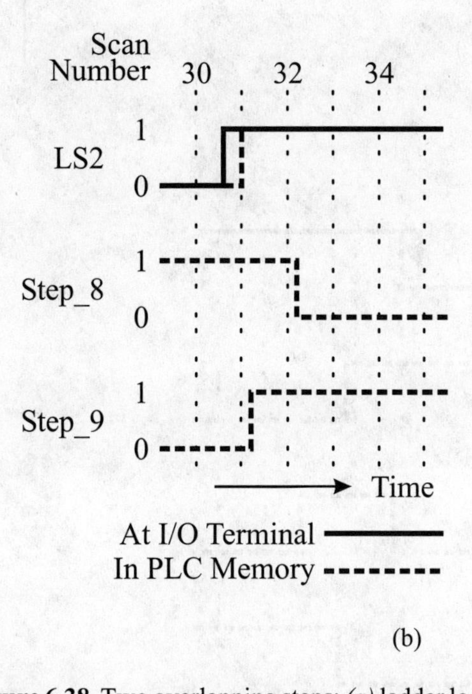

(b)

Figure 6.38. Two overlapping steps: *(a)* ladder logic; *(b)* transition from Step_8 to Step_9.

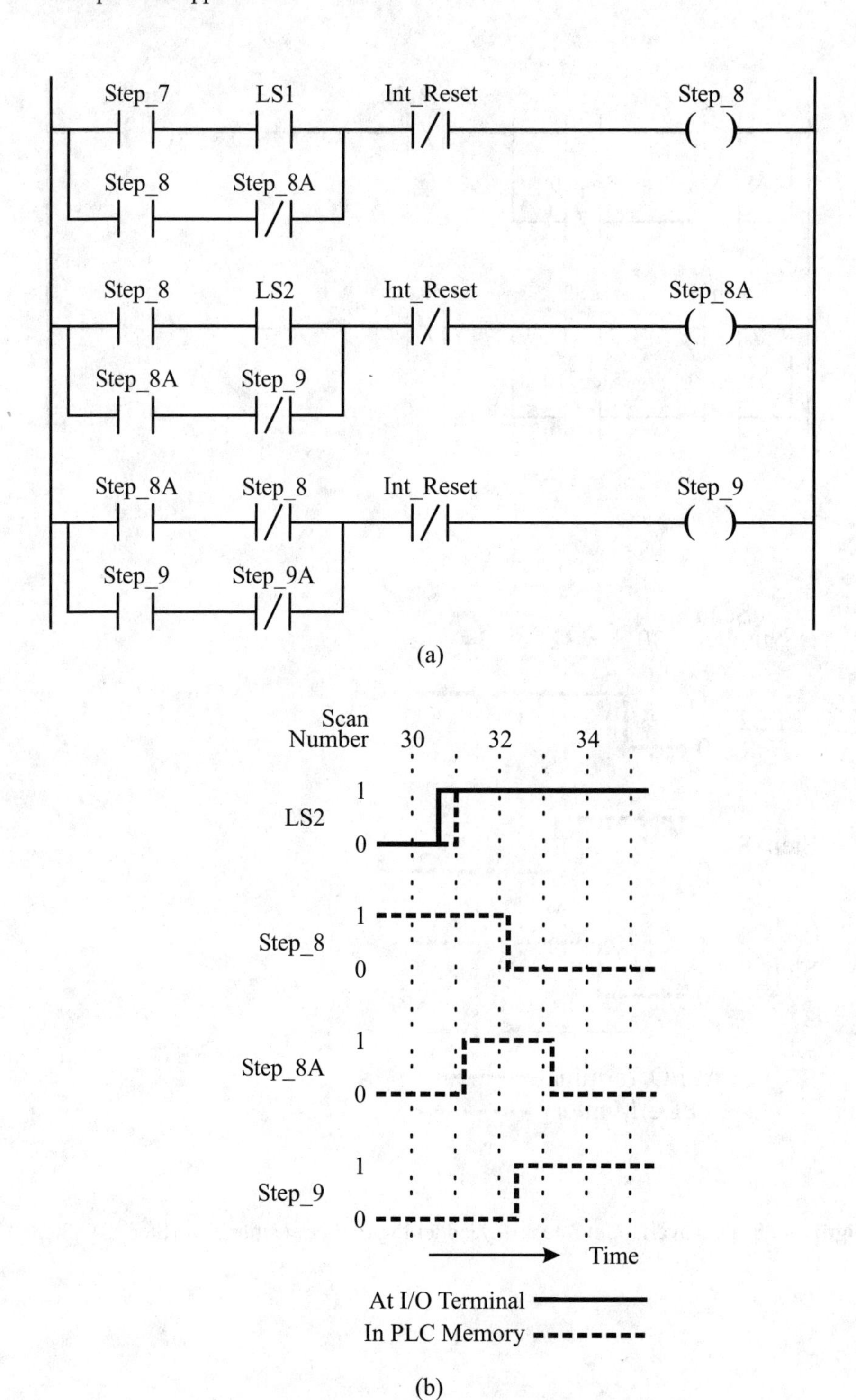

Figure 6.39. Extra step to eliminate overlap in steps: *(a)* ladder logic; *(b)* transition from Step_8 to Step_9.

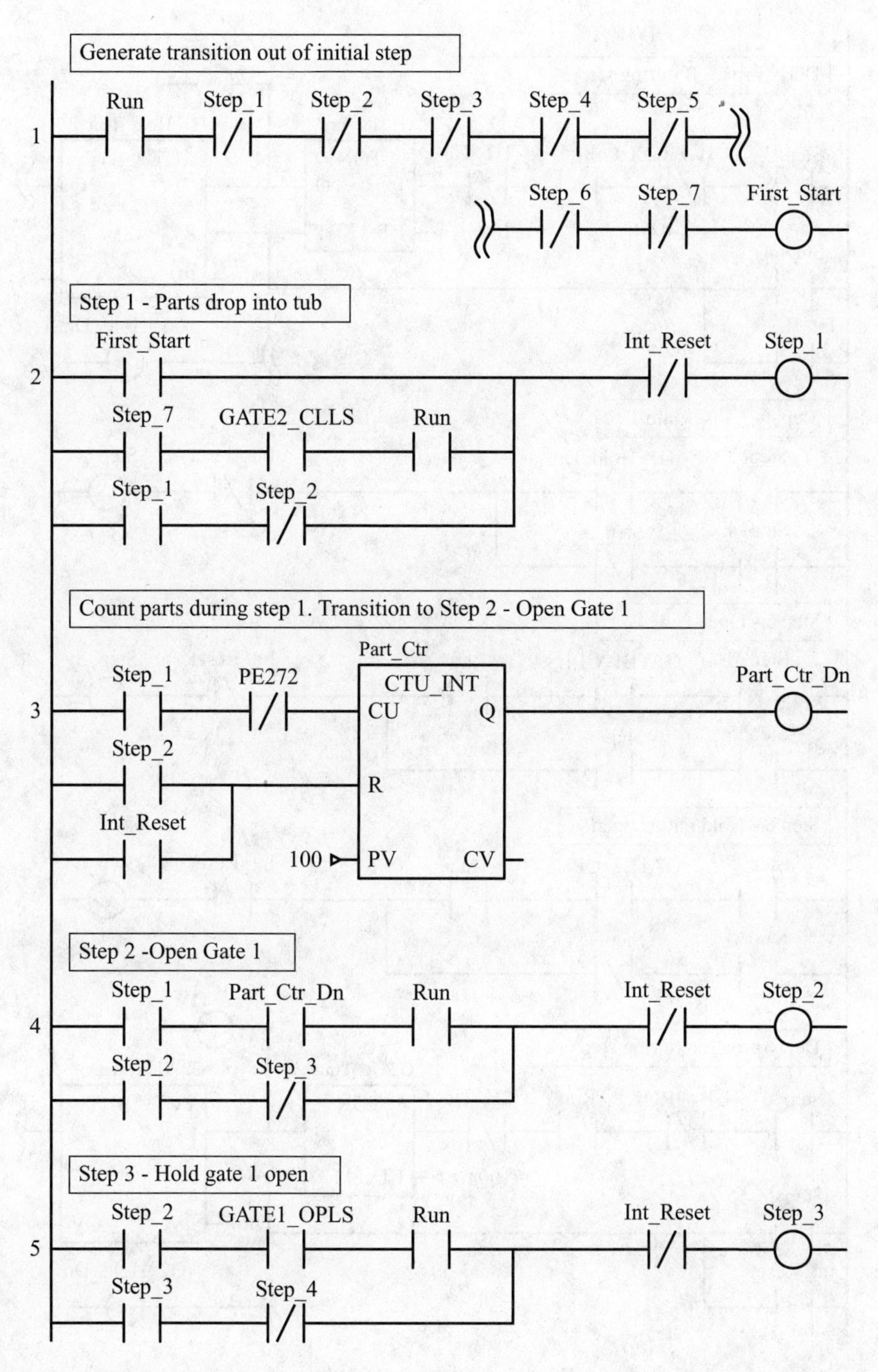

Figure 6.40. Modicon ladder logic for transitions for tub loader with no set/reset output instructions. *(continued)*

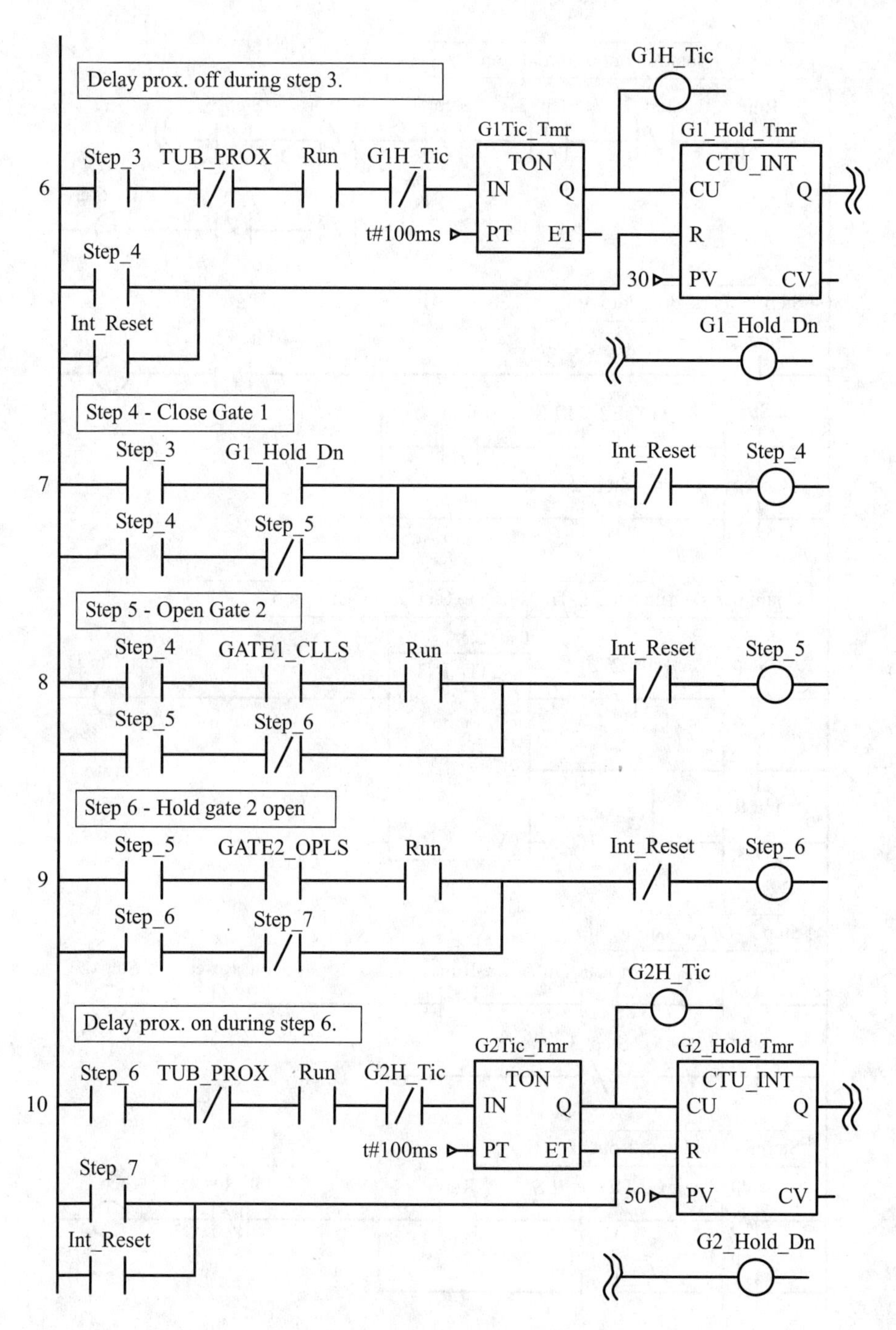

Figure 6.40. *(continued)*

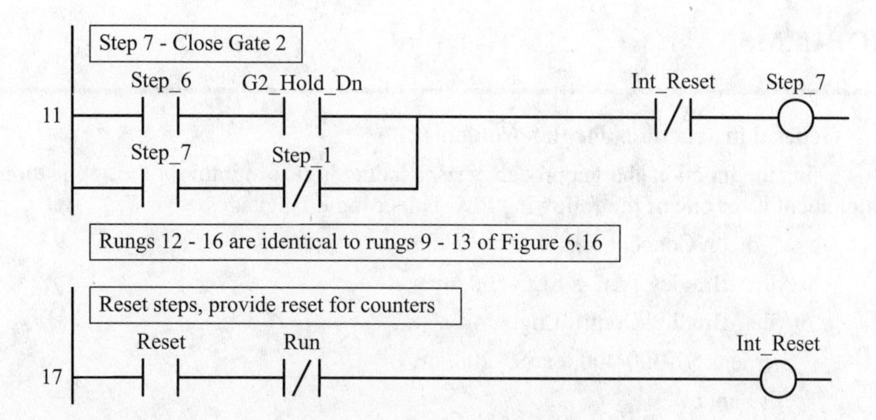

Figure 6.40. *(continued)*

REFERENCES

GE Fanuc, 1999. *Series 90™-30/20/Micro PLC CPU Instruction Set: Reference Manual,* pub. GFK-0467L, GE Fanuc Automation North America, Inc., Charlottesville, VA.

IEC, 1988. *IEC 848: Preparation of Function Charts for Control Systems*, International Electrotechnical Commission.

IEC, 1993. *IEC 1131-3: Programmable Logic Controllers - Part 3: Programming Languages*, International Electrotechnical Commission.

Rockwell Automation, 1998. *PLC-5 Family Instruction Set Reference Manual*, pub. 1785-6.1, Rockwell Automation, Milwaukee, WI.

Rockwell Automation, 2002. *Logix5000™ Controllers General Instructions*, pub. 1756-RM003F-EN-P, Rockwell Automation, Milwaukee, WI, May.

Schneider Automation, 1988. *Concept Block Library IEC,* vol. 1, ver. 2.1, pub. 840 USE 462 00, Schneider Automation, Inc., North Andover, MA.

Siemens, 2002a. *Ladder Logic (LAD) for S7-300 and S7-400 Programming: Reference Manual,* Edition 11/2002, pub. A5E00171231-01, Siemens AG, Nuernberg, Germany.

Siemens, 2002b. *System Software for S7-300/400 System and Standard Functions: Reference Manual,* Edition 12/2002, pub. A5E00171234-01, Siemens AG, Nuernberg, Germany.

PROBLEMS

General instructions for the problems:

Using the function chart approach, write a ladder logic program for the application. Implement it for one of the following PLC ladder logic languages

Modicon Concept, **or**

Allen-Bradley PLC-5/SLC-500, **or**

Allen-Bradley ControlLogix, **or**

Siemens S7-300/400, **or** S7-200, **or**

GE Fanuc

If any part of the operation is ambiguous, write down your additional assumptions.

The physical inputs, physical outputs, and internal variables for each problem are given in the problem. **DO NOT** assign any more physical inputs!

Your solution should include the following:

1. Function chart of the process, showing the transitions between steps and the outputs active (or **on**) during each step.
2. Specify the PLC processor used.
3. Ladder logic diagram (with comments). For consistency among the different PLCs, use only variables/symbols/tags in the ladder logic. Use instructions consistent with the PLC processor.
4. Table listing additional internal memory (variables/symbols/tags) used and a brief description of their use. For the Allen-Bradley ControlLogix and the Modicon Concept processors, list the internal variables/tags and the data type. For the other processors, list the internal variables/symbols and the associated memory address.

Note to instructor: Break each problem into two assignments. For the first assignment, the students draw the function chart. The second assignment implements the ladder logic. For the second assignment, the students are allowed to use the correct function chart or their function chart if it is close to the correct solution. This approach will save the instructor from needing to grade many different ladder logic solutions.

P6-1. Carton Sealer Control. Implement the program for the following station that folds and seals a corrugated cardboard box.

Figure P6.1 shows two views of a station that folds and glues a corrugated cardboard box. Assume the open boxes are already filled with product. Upon startup, the conveyor motor is **on** until the photoelectric eye senses a box in the station. When a box is in the station, the conveyor is stopped, and the box is closed and sealed by the following procedure. Two pneumatic rams (FRONT and BACK) are extended to push the two end flaps down, a glue sprayer is activated for 1 second, and then two more pneumatic rams (LEFT and RIGHT) are extended to push the two side flaps down. After a 5 second wait, all of the pneumatic rams are

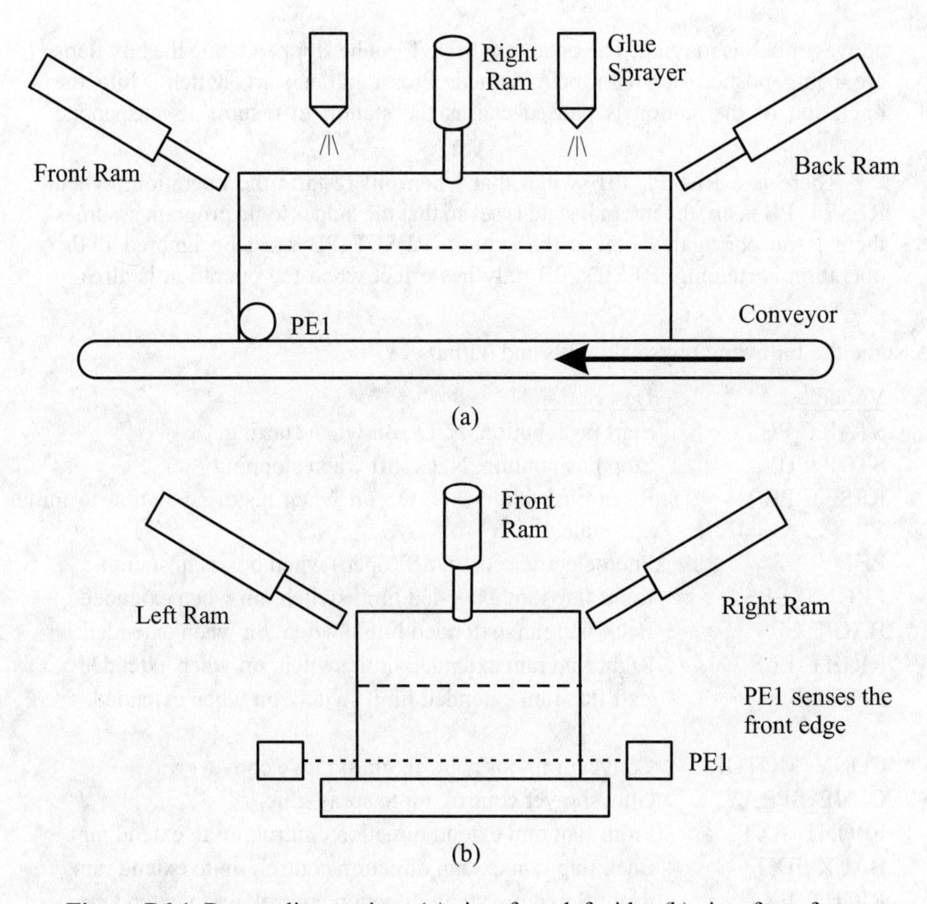

Figure P6.1. Box sealing station; *(a)* view from left side; *(b)* view from front.

retracted, and the conveyor motor is turned **on**. The sealed box is moved out of the station, and the conveyor continues to run until a new box moves into the station. Thus, the operation repeats. Assume there is a gap between the boxes, so that the photoelectric eye will also sense that there is no box in the station after the sealed box is moved out.

Each ram is a single-action linear pneumatic cylinder controlled by one output. Once an output is energized, the ram extends and keeps moving as long as power is applied (turned **on**) or a mechanical stop is reached. The ram retracts when power is removed (turned **off**). Each ram has a limit switch to detect when a ram is fully extended (out). There is no limit switch to detect when a ram is retracted. Assume that 2 seconds is sufficient time to retract a ram when its control is turned **off**.

When the start switch is pressed (turned **on**) for the first time only, the station assumes there is no box in the station, and waits for the photoelectric eye to detect the first box and perform the operation cycle continuously. Pressing the start switch when the mechanism is already running must have no effect. When the stop switch is pressed (turned **off**), the operation should stop (pause), but only when the conveyor belt is moving. The operation MUST not be stopped while the box flaps are being pushed down or being glued. Pressing the start switch while the operation of the station is paused causes the station to resume its suspended operation.

There is a RESET_PB switch that when **on**, restarts the operation. When RESET_PB is **on**, the internal state is set so that the ladder logic program assumes there is no corrugated box at the station. RESET_PB must be ignored if the operation is running. RESET_PB only has effect when the operation is already paused.

Assume the following physical inputs and outputs.

Variable	Description
START_PB	Start push button, N. O., **on** when starting.
STOP_PB	Stop push button, N. C., **off** when stopping.
RESET_PB	Reset push button, N. O., **on** when restoring station to initial state.
PE1	Photoelectric sensor, **off** (open) when box is in station.
FRONT_ELS	Front flap ram extended limit switch, **on** when extended.
BACK_ELS	Back flap ram extended limit switch, **on** when extended.
RIGHT_ELS	Right flap ram extended limit switch, **on** when extended.
LEFT_ELS	Left flap ram extended limit switch, **on** when extended.
CONV_MOTOR	Conveyor motor control, **on** to move conveyor.
GLUE_SPRAY	Glue sprayer control, **on** to spray glue.
FRONT_EXT	Front flap ram extend direction control, **on** to extend ram.
BACK_EXT	Back flap ram extend direction control, **on** to extend ram.
RIGHT_EXT	Right flap ram extend direction control, **on** to extend ram.
LEFT_EXT	Left flap ram extend direction control, **on** to extend ram.

The addresses associated with the physical inputs and outputs are:

Variable	Modicon	PLC-5	ControlLogix	Siemens	GE Fanuc
START_PB	100001	I:01/00	Local:1:I.Data.0	I4.0	%I81
STOP_PB	100002	I:01/01	Local:1:I.Data.1	I4.1	%I82
RESET_PB	100003	I:01/02	Local:1:I.Data.2	I4.2	%I83
PE1	100004	I:01/03	Local:1:I.Data.3	I4.3	%I84
FRONT_ELS	100005	I:01/04	Local:1:I.Data.4	I4.4	%I85
BACK_ELS	100006	I:01/05	Local:1:I.Data.5	I4.5	%I86
RIGHT_ELS	100007	I:01/06	Local:1:I.Data.6	I4.6	%I87
LEFT_ELS	100008	I:01/07	Local:1:I.Data.7	I4.7	%I88
CONV_MOTOR	000001	O:02/00	Local:2:O.Data.0	Q8.0	%Q1
GLUE_SPRAY	000002	O:02/01	Local:2:O.Data.1	Q8.1	%Q2
FRONT_EXT	000003	O:02/02	Local:2:O.Data.2	Q8.2	%Q3
BACK_EXT	000004	O:02/03	Local:2:O.Data.3	Q8.3	%Q4
RIGHT_EXT	000005	O:02/04	Local:2:O.Data.4	Q8.4	%Q5
LEFT_EXT	000006	O:02/05	Local:2:O.Data.5	Q9.5	%Q6

P6-2. Batch Process Control. Implement the program for the following batch process that mixes two chemicals.

A diagram of the equipment is shown in Figure P6.2. When the start switch is pressed (turned **on**) for the first time to start the operation, the tank is filled with Ingredient A up to Level A. After a 2 second wait, the tank is filled with Ingredient B up to Level B. Assume Level B is higher than Level A. After another 2 second wait, the stirrer motor is turned **on** for 10 minutes. Then the tank is emptied. The TANK_EMPTY sensor must be continuously **on** for 1 minute to ensure that the tank is completely empty. After the tank is empty, the process operation is finished and does not start again until the start push button is pressed. The operation does not repeat.

Pressing the start switch when the operation is already running must have no effect. When the stop switch is pressed (turned **off**) the operation should pause at the current step and all outputs must be **off**. All timer values must be retained during pause. Pressing the start switch while the operation of the station is paused causes the station to resume its suspended step.

A separate override switch is provided to drain the remainder of the material in the tank if the operation has been paused. The override switch should be ignored if the operation is not already paused. When the override switch is pressed to

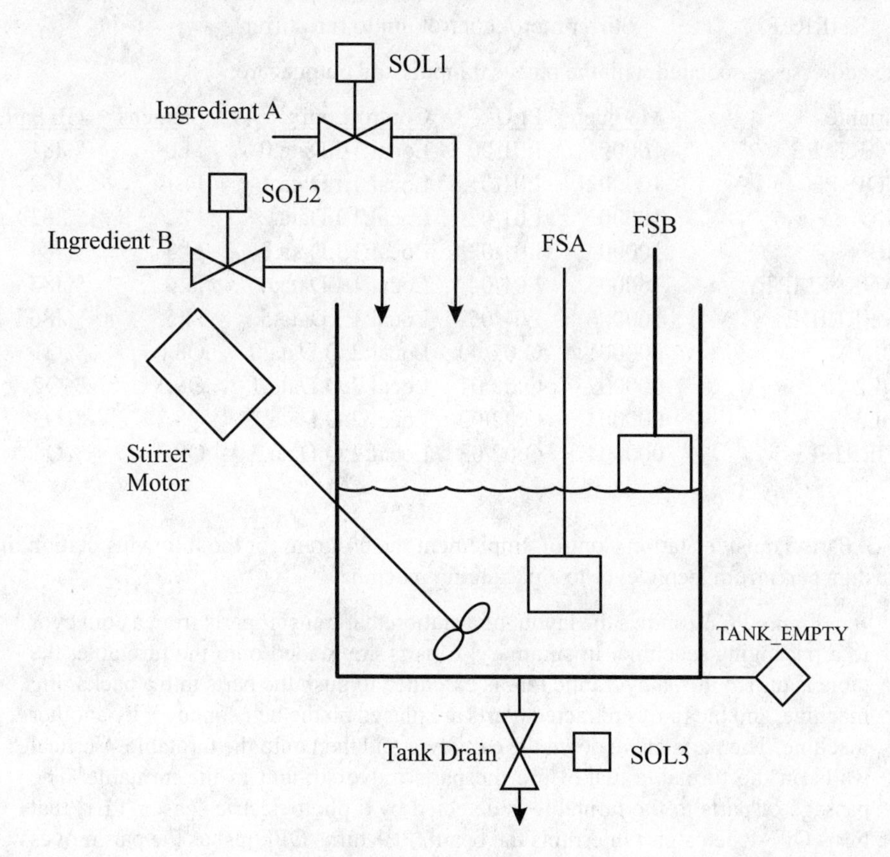

Figure P6.2. Batch process.

empty the tank, the emptying operation should continue until the TANK_EMPTY sensor is **on** for 1 minute to ensure that the tank is completely empty. The operation cannot be restarted until the tank emptying is complete.

Assume the following physical inputs and outputs.

Variable	Description
START_PB	Start push button, N. O., **on** when starting.
STOP_PB	Stop push button, N. C., **off** when stopping.
FSA	Float level A sensor, N. O., **on** (closed) when level of material in tank is at least level A.
FSB	Float level B sensor, N. O., **on** (closed) when level of material in tank is at least level B.
TANK_EMPTY	Tank empty sensor, **on** (closed) when tank is empty.
OVERRIDE	Outlet override, N. O., **on** (closed) to start tank draining.
SOL1	Ingredient A fill solenoid, **on** to allow ingredient A to flow into tank.
SOL2	Ingredient B fill solenoid, **on** to allow ingredient B to flow into tank.
SOL3	Tank outlet solenoid, **on** to empty tank.
STIRRER	Stirrer motor control, **on** to run stirrer.

The addresses associated with the physical inputs and outputs are:

Variable	Modicon	PLC-5	ControlLogix	Siemens	GE Fanuc
START_PB	100001	I:01/00	Local:1:I.Data.0	I4.0	%I81
STOP_PB	100002	I:01/01	Local:1:I.Data.1	I4.1	%I82
FSA	100003	I:01/02	Local:1:I.Data.2	I4.2	%I83
FSB	100004	I:01/03	Local:1:I.Data.3	I4.3	%I84
TANK_EMPTY	100005	I:01/04	Local:1:I.Data.4	I4.4	%I85
OVERRIDE	100006	I:01/05	Local:1:I.Data.5	I4.5	%I86
SOL1	000001	O:02/00	Local:2:O.Data.0	Q8.0	%Q1
SOL2	000002	O:02/01	Local:2:O.Data.1	Q8.1	%Q2
SOL3	000003	O:02/02	Local:2:O.Data.2	Q8.2	%Q3
STIRRER	000004	O:02/03	Local:2:O.Data.3	Q8.3	%Q4

P6-3. Parts Transfer Station Control. Implement the program for the following station that transfers parts from a conveyor to a packaging machine.

Figure P6.3*a* shows the layout of a station that transfer parts from a conveyor to a packaging machine. In summary, 6 parts are loaded onto the turntable, the table is turned 90°, a hydraulic ram is extended to push the parts into a packaging machine, and the ram is retracted. Parts are placed on the belt conveyor by another machine. The parts move down the conveyor and then onto the turntable. Vertical walls on the turntable make sure the parts move straight in the turntable. The passage of parts to the turntable is detected by a photoelectric sensor, PE1, that turns OFF when a part interrupts the beam. PE1 turns OFF just as the part moves on to the turntable. After 6 parts are on the turntable, the turntable is rotated

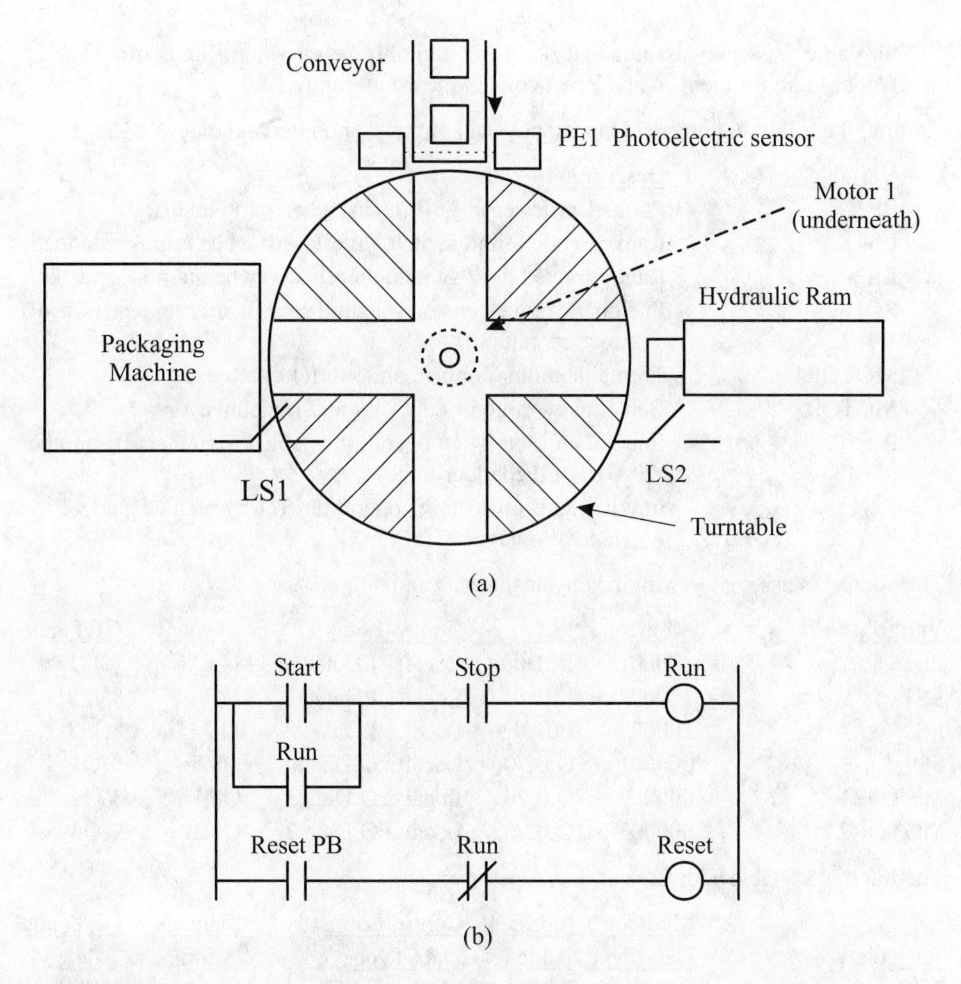

Figure P6.3. Parts transfer station; *(a)* equipment; *(b)* ladder logic for Run and Reset.

counterclockwise 90° by activating the turntable motor, MOTOR1, for 1 second. After the table is rotated, the hydraulic ram is extended by turning on SOL1 until limit switch LS1 closes. This operation pushes the parts into the packing machine. The ram is then retracted, by turning off SOL1, until limit switch LS2 closes. While the turntable is being rotated and the ram is moving, the belt conveyor motor, MOTOR2, must be stopped.

There is an internal coil, Run, that is **on** when the operation is enabled. The Run internal coil is set by another part of the ladder logic. When the Run coil is **off**, all counter values must be retained, and the ladder logic program must remain in the state in which the Run coil changed from **on** to **off**. If the Run coil becomes **off** when moving the turntable, MOTOR1 must continue to run and transition to the next step when the time is complete. There is another internal coil, Reset, that when **on**, restarts the operation. The Run internal coil is set by another part of the ladder logic. When Reset is **on**, internal counters and timers are reset, and the internal state is set so that the ladder logic program assumes no parts are on the turntable. You may assume that the Reset can only be **on** when Run is **off**. The ladder logic for the Run and Reset coils is shown in Figure P6.3*b*.

Assume the following physical inputs, physical outputs, and internal coils.

Variable	Description
PE1	Photoelectric sensor, **off** (open) when part passes.
LS1	Ram extended limit switch, **on** (closed) when ram is extended
LS2	Ram retracted limit switch, **on** (closed) when ram is retracted
SOL1	Pneumatic ram extension solenoid control, **on** to extend ram, **off** retracts ram.
MOTOR1	Turntable motor control, **on** to turn turntable
MOTOR2	Belt conveyor motor control, **on** to run conveyor
Run	Internal coil, **on** when operation enabled to run (set by another part of the ladder logic)
Reset	Internal coil, **on** to reset operation (set by another part of the ladder logic)

The addresses associated with the physical inputs and outputs are:

Variable	Modicon	PLC-5	ControlLogix	Siemens	GE Fanuc
PE1	100001	I:01/00	Local:1:I.Data.0	I4.0	%I81
LS1	100002	I:01/01	Local:1:I.Data.1	I4.1	%I82
LS2	100003	I:01/02	Local:1:I.Data.2	I4.2	%I83
SOL1	000001	O:02/00	Local:2:O.Data.0	Q8.0	%Q1
MOTOR1	000002	O:02/01	Local:2:O.Data.1	Q8.1	%Q2
MOTOR2	000003	O:02/02	Local:2:O.Data.2	Q8.2	%Q3

The internal variable addresses or data types are:

	Modicon	PLC-5	ControlLogix	Siemens	GE Fanuc
Variable	Data Type	Addr.	Data Type	Addr.	Addr.
Run	BOOL	B3/1	BOOL	M3.1	%M39
Reset	BOOL	B3/2	BOOL	M3.2	%M40

P6-4. Bag Sealing Station Control. Implement the program for the following station that seals plastic bags.

Figure P6.4 shows the layout of a station that seals plastic bags. Assume the bags are already filled with product. Upon startup, the conveyor motor is ON until the photoelectric "eye" senses a bag in the station. When a bag is in the station, the conveyor is stopped, and the bag is sealed by the following steps:

A mechanism using air cylinders is used to push two heated bars together (one bar on each side of the bag),

The bars are held together for 1 second, and

The bars are moved apart.

The mechanism used to move the heated bars is driven by a double-action linear pneumatic cylinder controlled by two outputs. Once a direction output is energized, the mechanism moves and keeps moving as long as power is applied

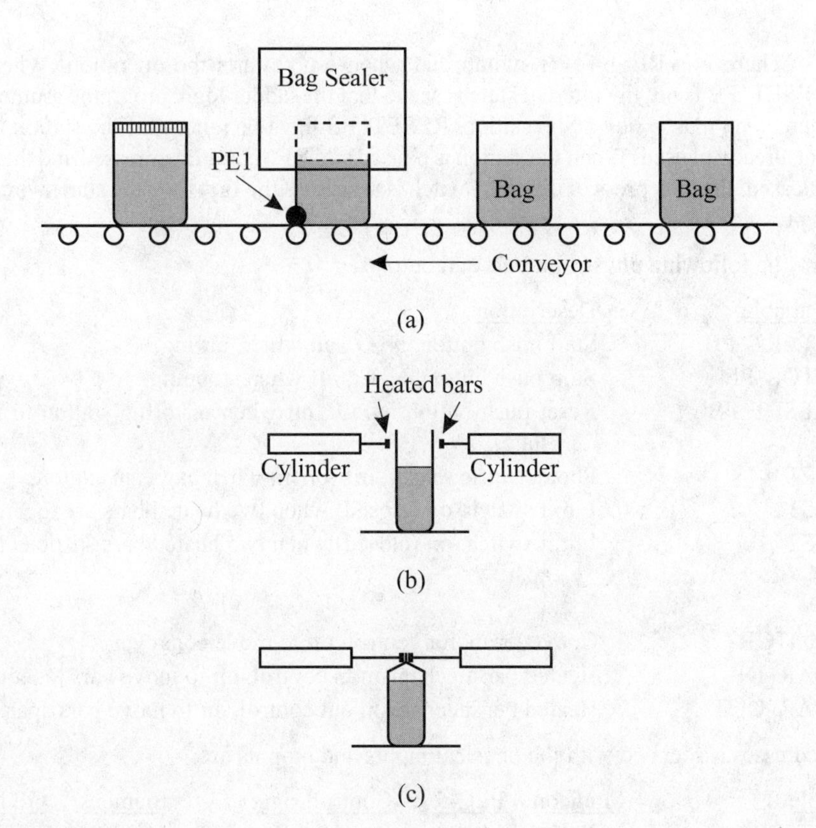

Figure P6.4. Bag sealing station; *(a)* front view; *(b)* view from side, bars apart; *(c)* view from side, bars together.

(turned **on**). The mechanism stops at its current position when power is removed (turned **off**). The mechanism will not move if both opposing directions are energized simultaneously (e.g., out and in). Limit switch LS1 is **on** when the two heated bars are together. Limit switch LS2 is **on** when the bars have been moved sufficiently far apart. When the bag-sealing operation is complete (bars have been moved apart), the conveyor motor is turned **on**. The sealed bag is moved out of the station, and the conveyor continues to run until a new bag moves into the station. Thus, the operation repeats. Assume there is a gap between the bags, so that the photoelectric "eye" will also sense that there is no bag in the station after the sealed bag is moved out.

When the start switch is pressed (turned **on**) for the first time only, the station assumes there is no bag in the station, and waits for the photoelectric "eye" to detect the first bag and perform the operation cycle continuously. Pressing the start switch when the mechanism is already running must have no effect. When the stop switch is pressed (turned **off**), the operation should stop (pause), but only when the conveyor belt is moving. The operation MUST not be stopped while the bars are being held together or when they are being moved. Pressing the start switch while the operation of the station is paused causes the station to resume its suspended operation.

There is a RESET_PB switch that when **on**, restarts the operation. When RESET_PB is **on**, the internal state is set so that the ladder logic program assumes there is no plastic bag at the station. RESET_PB must be ignored if the station is not already paused. When the station is paused and RESET_PB is pressed and then released, the next press of the start switch is treated as the first time the start switch is pressed.

Assume the following physical inputs and outputs.

Variable	Description
START_PB	Start push button, N. O., **on** when starting.
STOP_PB	Stop push button, N. C., **off** when stopping.
RESET_PB	Reset push button, N. O., **on** when restoring station to initial state.
PE1	Photoelectric sensor, **off** (open) when bag is in station.
LS1	Limit switch, **on** (closed) when two heated bars are together
LS2	Limit switch, **on** (closed) when two heated bars sufficiently far apart
MOTOR	Conveyor motor control, **on** to move conveyor
BAR_IN	Heated bar mechanism in control, **on** to move bars together
BAR_OUT	Heated bar mechanism out control, **on** to move bars apart

The addresses associated with the physical inputs and outputs are:

Variable	Modicon	PLC-5	ControlLogix	Siemens	GE Fanuc
START_PB	100001	I:01/00	Local:1:I.Data.0	I4.0	%I81
STOP_PB	100002	I:01/01	Local:1:I.Data.1	I4.1	%I82
RESET_PB	100003	I:01/02	Local:1:I.Data.2	I4.2	%I83
PE1	100004	I:01/03	Local:1:I.Data.3	I4.3	%I84
LS1	100005	I:01/04	Local:1:I.Data.4	I4.4	%I85
LS2	100006	I:01/05	Local:1:I.Data.5	I4.5	%I86
MOTOR	000033	O:03/11	Local:3:O.Data.9	Q13.1	%Q1
BAR_IN	000035	O:03/13	Local:3:O.Data.11	Q13.3	%Q2
BAR_OUT	000036	O:03/14	Local:3:O.Data.12	Q13.4	%Q3

P6-5. Erbia Elevator Control. Using the function chart approach, implement the program for the following elevator that moves cans of erbia (a metal) powder from the first floor to the second floor of the factory.

The memo below describes the operation of the erbia elevator. A simplified drawing of the elevator is shown in Figure P6.5.

To: A. Doe

From: B. Smith

Subject: Controls for Erbia Elevators

We need to design an elevator to move cans of erbia from the first floor to the second floor. Refer to the drawing of the elevators for switch reference numbers. The general operation is described as follows:

1. The platform is at the lower position so that LS_1 is actuated.
2. Press PB_1 switch. The motor starts in forward and drives the elevator to the up position where LS_2 is actuated. The motor stops.
3. AIR_CYL_1 is actuated and drives out for a limited time. Then it reverses to the retracted position.
4. PS_1 (off) indicates that the elevator is clear.
5. The motor starts in reverse to lower the platform to the bottom to activate LS_1. The motor stops.
6. The jog buttons drive the motor up or down between the limit switches, but not when in automatic control. These switches are intended for moving the elevator after an emergency stop and for drive troubleshooting. They should be ignored if the motor is under automatic control.

Notes to operation memo:

1. The two motor controls (MOTOR_UP and MOTOR_DOWN) connect to a motor controller that drives the motor.
2. Only one output, AIR CYL_1, is used to control the pneumatic cylinder (ram) that pushes the can off the elevator. When it is **on**, the ram moves out to its fully extended position and remains there (as long as AIR CYL_1 stays **on**). When **off**, the ram moves to the retracted position, if not already there. There are no switches to detect when the ram is fully extended or retracted. Assume that 10 seconds are required to fully extend the ram and 15 seconds will assure that it is fully retracted when AIR CYL_1 is turned OFF.
3. Pressing the JOG_UP switch should have no effect if the platform is in the upper position (top) or when the JOG_DOWN switch is already pressed. Also, pressing the JOG_DOWN switch should have no effect if the platform is in the lower position (bottom) or when the JOG_UP switch is already pressed. Both switches should have no effect if the elevator is moving between floors because the operator pressed the PB_1 switch.
4. Since the gate closed switch and the two emergency stop switches are wired in series to one PLC input, the ladder logic can only see them as one switch, E-STOP. When either E-stop switch is pressed (E_STOP input is **off**), the elevator should immediately stop, and the JOG_UP and JOG_DOWN switches must be used to move the elevator. When the E_STOP input is **off**, the JOG_UP and JOG_DOWN switches should be ignored.
5. Do not be concerned with how the cans are placed on the platform when it is in the lower position.

Assume the following physical inputs and outputs.

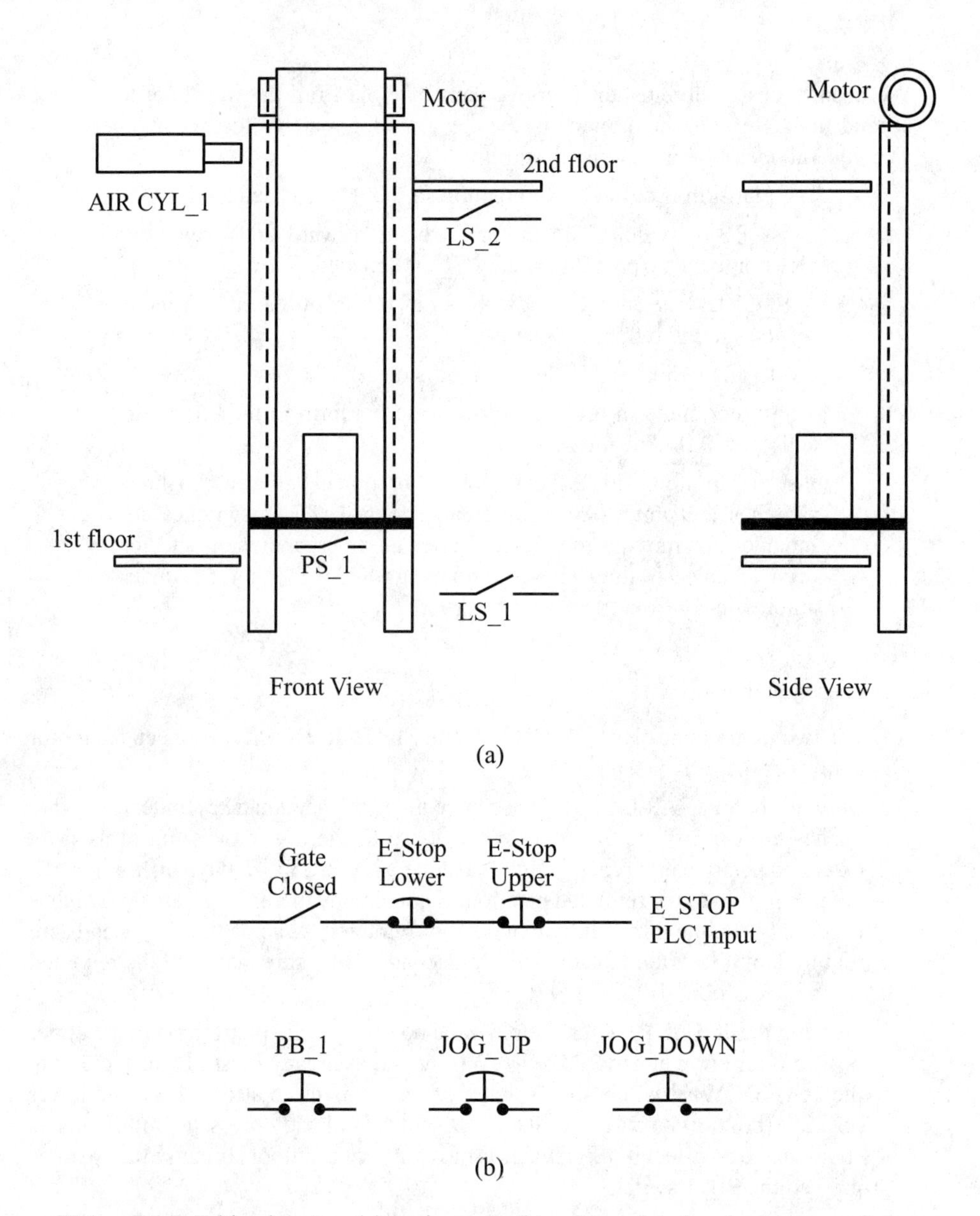

Figure P6.5. Erbia elevator: *(a)* equipment; *(b)* safety-related and operator switches.

Variable	Description
LS_1	Limit switch that closes (**on**) when elevator platform is in the lower position
LS_2	Limit switch that closes (**on**) when elevator platform is in the upper position
PS_1	Limit switch that closes (**on**) when a can is on the elevator platform
PB_1	N. O. push button, **on** when starting the elevator operation.

E_STOP	N. C. push button, **off** when stopping.
JOG_UP	N. O. push button, **on** to jog (manually move) platform up
JOG_DOWN	N. O. push button, **on** to jog move platform down
AIR_CYL_1	Pneumatic ram extension solenoid, **on** to extend ram, **off** causes ram to retract
MOTOR_UP	Elevator motor control, **on** to cause elevator platform to move up, **off** has no effect on platform position
MOTOR_DOWN	Elevator motor control, **on** to cause elevator platform to move down, **off** has no effect on platform position

The addresses associated with the physical inputs and outputs are:

Variable	Modicon	PLC-5	ControlLogix	Siemens	GE Fanuc
LS_1	100001	I:01/00	Local:1:I.Data.0	I4.0	%I81
LS_2	100002	I:01/01	Local:1:I.Data.1	I4.1	%I82
PS_1	100003	I:01/02	Local:1:I.Data.2	I4.2	%I83
PB_1	100004	I:01/03	Local:1:I.Data.3	I4.3	%I84
E_STOP	100017	I:02/00	Local:2:I.Data.0	I8.0	%I97
JOG_UP	100018	I:02/01	Local:2:I.Data.1	I8.1	%I98
JOG_DOWN	100019	I:02/02	Local:2:I.Data.2	I8.2	%I99
AIR_CYL_1	000033	O:03/00	Local:3:O.Data.0	Q12.0	%Q3
MOTOR_UP	000034	O:03/01	Local:3:O.Data.1	Q12.1	%Q4
MOTOR_DOWN	000035	O:03/02	Local:3:O.Data.2	Q12.2	%Q5

P6-6. Transfer Station Control. Using the function chart approach, implement the program for the following station that groups and transfers parts from one conveyor to another conveyor.

Figure P6.6 shows the layout of a station that transfers items from one conveyor to another. The items are long and actually hang over the sides of the conveyor so that they can be easily picked up and transferred to the other conveyor. In summary, four items are collected at the end of the inbound conveyor, and a mechanism executes the following moves to transfer the items to the outbound conveyor:

Move up 5 seconds (to lift group of items),
Move right to the right position,
Move down to the lower position (to put items on outbound conveyor),
Move left to the left position.

The directions assume a person is looking up the inbound conveyor and down the outbound conveyor. In the lower position, the arms can move horizontally without interference (crashing into the conveyors). The operation repeats.

Photoelectric sensor PE1 is used to detect the items as they near the end of the inbound conveyor. PE1 turns **off** as each part passes. There is a bar above the conveyor against which the items collect before they are transferred to the other conveyor. PE1 detects the fourth item (PE1 turns **off**) just before the item hits the

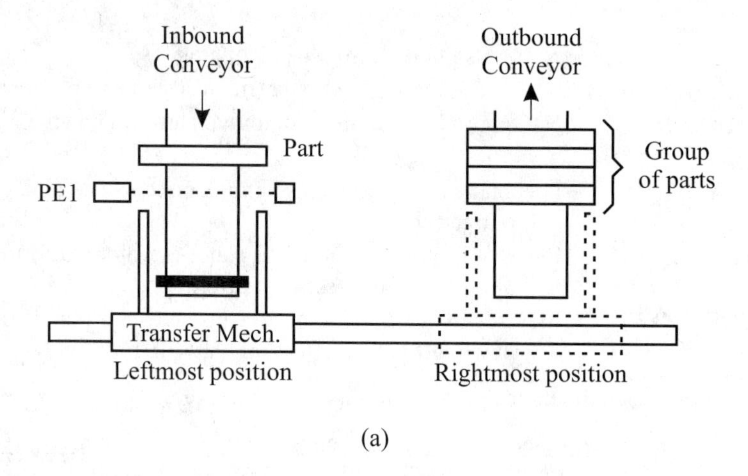

(a)

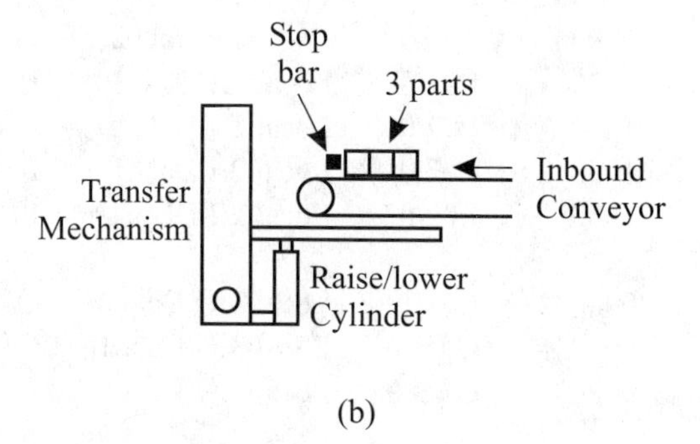

(b)

Figure P6.6. Transfer station: *(a)* top view; *(b)* side view.

three already stopped, and does not turn back **on** until the group of items has been moved off the inbound conveyor.

Limit switches LSRT and LSLT indicate the right and left positions, respectively, of the transfer mechanism. Limit switch LSDN indicates the lower (down) position of the transfer mechanism. There is no limit switch that indicates the upper position of the transfer mechanism.

The horizontal and vertical movements of the transfer mechanism are each driven by a double-action linear pneumatic cylinder — a raising/lowering unit and a rightward/leftward unit. Each cylinder is controlled by two outputs. Once a direction output is energized, the mechanism moves and keeps moving as long as power is applied (turned **on**). The mechanism stops at its current position when power is removed (turned **off**). The mechanism will not move if both opposing directions are energized simultaneously (e.g., left and right).

The inbound conveyor motor control, IN_MOTOR must be **on** whenever the station is running. The inbound conveyor is not turned off while the transfer mechanism is moving. Assume the items are spaced far enough that the transfer mechanism returns to the inbound conveyor before the next item comes down the conveyor. Your ladder has no control over the outbound conveyor motor.

Upon initial startup, assume there are no items present at the end of the inbound conveyor. If the stop switch is pressed at any time, the station operation should pause, except when the transfer mechanism is being lowered to place the items on the outbound conveyor. The operation **must not** pause when the mechanism is being lowered (otherwise the parts may not remain as a group if the conveyor catches one that is just barely touching the conveyor). When the start switch is pressed while the operation is paused, the station should resume the suspended step. When the station is paused, all active outputs are turned off.

A separate reset switch is provided which resets any internal states so that when the start switch is pressed, no items are assumed present at the collection bar. The reset switch should be ignored if the station is running. The operator is responsible for using the four jog switches to move the transfer mechanism back to the starting position. The operator must hold down the reset push button (station paused) while manipulating the jog switches.

Assume the tolerance on all timer values is ±0.1 seconds.

Assume the following physical inputs and outputs.

Variable	Description
START_PB	Start push button, N. O., **on** when starting.
STOP_PB	Stop push button, N. C., **off** when stopping.
RESET_PB	Reset push button, N. O., **on** when restoring station to initial state.
PE1	Photoelectric sensor, **off** (open) as item passes (see above).
LSDN	Limit switch that closes (**on**) when transfer mechanism is in the lower position
LSRT	Limit switch that closes (**on**) when transfer mechanism is in the rightmost position
LSLT	Limit switch that closes (**on**) when transfer mechanism is in the leftmost position
JOG_UP	Jog up button, N. O., **on** to move mechanism up when reset.
JOG_DN	Jog down button, N. O., **on** to move mechanism down on reset.
JOG_LT	Jog left button, N. O., **on** to move mechanism left when reset.
JOG_RT	Jog right button, N. O., **on** to move mechanism right when reset.
UP_CYL	Raising control, **on** to raise mechanism, **off** has no effect.
DN_CYL	Lowering control, **on** to lower mechanism, **off** has no effect.
LT_CYL	Left motion control, **on** to move mechanism left, **off** has no effect.
RT_CYL	Right motion control, **on** to move mechanism right, **off** has no effect.
IN_MOTOR	Inbound conveyor motor control, **on** to move conveyor.

The addresses associated with the physical inputs and outputs are:

Variable	Modicon	PLC-5	ControlLogix	Siemens	GE Fanuc
START_PB	100017	I:02/00	Local:2:I.Data.0	I8.0	%I87
STOP_PB	100018	I:02/01	Local:2:I.Data.1	I8.1	%I88
RESET_PB	100019	I:02/02	Local:2:I.Data.2	I8.2	%I89

PE1	100020	I:02/03	Local:2:I.Data.3	I8.3	%I90
LSDN	100021	I:02/04	Local:2:I.Data.4	I8.4	%I91
LSRT	100022	I:02/05	Local:2:I.Data.5	I8.5	%I92
LSLT	100023	I:02/06	Local:2:I.Data.6	I8.6	%I93
JOG_UP	100024	I:02/07	Local:2:I.Data.7	I8.7	%I94
JOG_DN	100025	I:02/10	Local:2:I.Data.8	I9.0	%I95
JOG_LT	100026	I:02/11	Local:2:I.Data.9	I9.1	%I96
JOG_RT	100027	I:02/12	Local:2:I.Data.10	I9.2	%I97
UP_CYL	000033	O:03/00	Local:3:O.Data.0	Q12.0	%Q13
DN_CYL	000034	O:03/01	Local:3:O.Data.1	Q12.1	%Q14
LT_CYL	000035	O:03/02	Local:3:O.Data.2	Q12.2	%Q15
RT_CYL	000036	O:03/03	Local:3:O.Data.3	Q12.3	%Q16
IN_MOTOR	000037	O:03/04	Local:3:O.Data.4	Q12.4	%Q17

P6-7. Conveyor Transfer Station Control. Using the function chart approach, implement the program for the following station that transfers boxes from one conveyor to another.

Figure P6.7 shows the layout of a station that transfer boxes from one conveyor to another. The inbound conveyor consists of rollers and has boxes placed upon it by other machines. The outbound conveyor is a belt and moves the boxes up to an overhead conveyor system. In summary, each box is individually pushed to the outbound conveyor. Of course, the next box is not moved until the station is ready to move it.

Upon initial start-up, the station waits for a box to arrive at the gate (indicated by BOX_PRESENT photoelectric sensor being **on**). The gate ensures that boxes are transferred one at a time. When a box is present, GATE_SOL is activated to hold down the gate so the box can move in front of the ram. When the box has passed the gate, BOX_PRESENT becomes **off** and then GATE_SOL is turned **off**, raising the gate and preventing the next box from entering until the first box is moved to the outbound conveyor. Assume that the box is moved past the gate faster than the box behind moves down the inbound conveyor, so that there is definitely a gap between boxes, if there is more than one box at the gate when it is moved down. After the box has passed the gate, there is a minimum 2 second delay to ensure that the box travels to the end of the conveyor where it is stopped by a fence. After the 2 second delay, a pneumatic ram is extended (using EXTEND_SOL) until LS2 operates (turns **on**). This action by the ram pushes the box onto the outbound conveyor. The ram is then retracted (using RETRACT_SOL) until LS1 operates (turns **on**), signaling that it is fully retracted. One cycle of the station operation is thus completed, and then it waits for the next box on the inbound conveyor.

The gate is moved with a single-action pneumatic cylinder, controlled by the GATE_SOL output. The pneumatic ram is a double-acting pneumatic cylinder controlled by the EXTEND_SOL and RETRACT_SOL outputs.

Both conveyor motor controls, MOTOR1 and MOTOR2 must be **on** whenever the station is running.

Upon initial startup, assume there are no boxes present at the gate. If the stop switch is pressed at any time, the station operation should pause, except when the

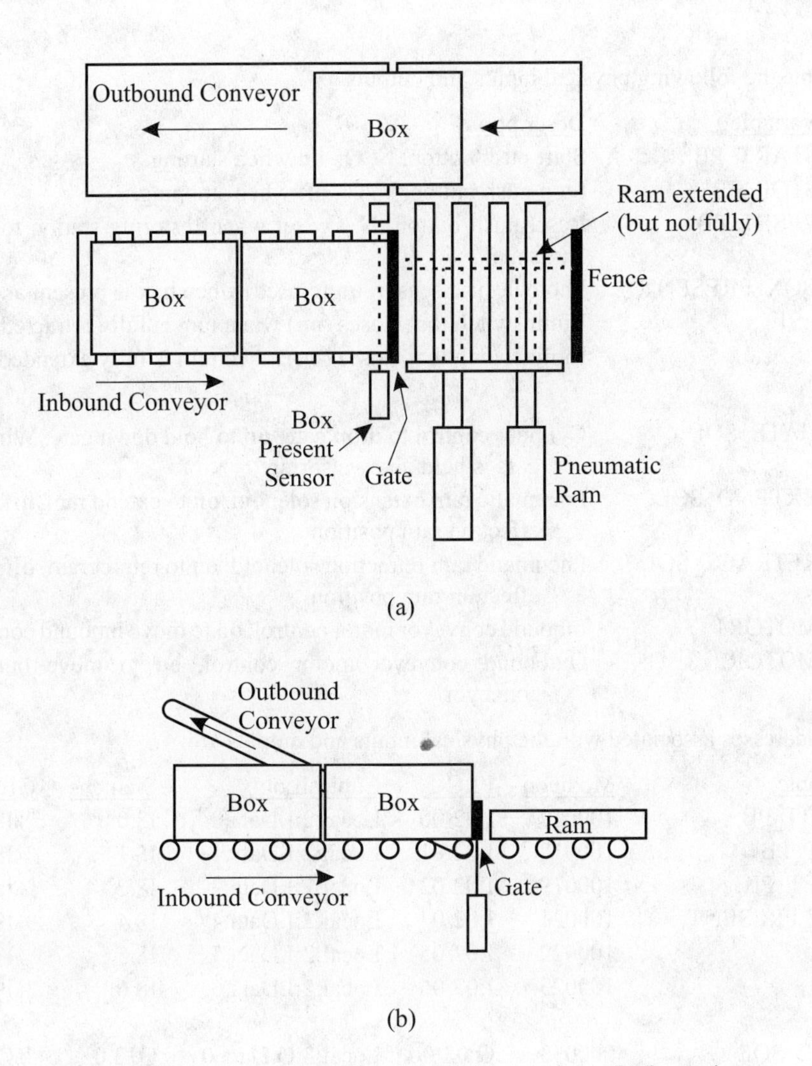

Figure P6.7. Conveyor transfer station: *(a)* top view; *(b)* front view.

gate is being held down. The operation **must not** pause when the gate is down (otherwise a box may be "flipped" when the gate solenoid is turned **off** upon reset.) If the stop pushbutton is pressed while the gate is down, the inbound conveyor should continue to run in order to move the box. After the gate is raised, the operation should pause. When the start switch is pressed while the operation is paused, the station should resume the suspended step. When the station is paused, all active outputs are turned **off** and timers paused (or reset). A separate reset switch is provided which retracts the ram and resets any internal steps so that when the start switch is pressed, no boxes are assumed present at the gate. The reset switch should be ignored when the gate is down and when the station is running. The start pushbutton should be ignored during reset (reset switch held down or ram retracting).

Assume the tolerance on all timer values is ±0.1 seconds.

Assume the following physical inputs and outputs.

Variable	Description
START_PB	Start push button, N. O., **on** when starting.
STOP_PB	Stop push button, N. C., **off** when stopping.
RESET_PB	Reset push button, N. O., **on** when restoring station to initial state.
BOX_PRESENT	Photoelectric sensor, **on** (closed) when box is present at gate.
LS1	Limit switch that closes (**on**) when ram is fully retracted
LS2	Limit switch that closes (**on**) when ram is fully extended
GATE_SOL	Cylinder control to drop gate, **on** to hold down gate. When **off**, gate is held up by a spring.
EXTEND_SOL	Pneumatic ram extension solenoid, **on** to extend ram, **off** has no effect on ram position
RETRACT_SOL	Pneumatic ram retraction solenoid, **on** to retract ram, **off** has no effect on ram position
MOTOR1	Inbound conveyor motor control, **on** to move inbound conveyor
MOTOR2	Outbound conveyor motor control, **on** to move outbound conveyor

The addresses associated with the physical inputs and outputs are:

Variable	Modicon	PLC-5	ControlLogix	Siemens	GE Fanuc
START_PB	100017	I:02/00	Local:2:I.Data.0	I8.0	%I87
STOP_PB	100018	I:02/01	Local:2:I.Data.1	I8.1	%I88
RESET_PB	100019	I:02/02	Local:2:I.Data.2	I8.2	%I89
BOX_PRESENT	100021	I:02/04	Local:2:I.Data.4	I8.4	%I91
LS1	100022	I:02/05	Local:2:I.Data.5	I8.5	%I92
LS2	100023	I:02/06	Local:2:I.Data.6	I8.6	%I93
GATE_SOL	000033	O:03/00	Local:3:O.Data.0	Q12.0	%Q13
EXTEND_SOL	000034	O:03/01	Local:3:O.Data.1	Q12.1	%Q14
RETRACT_SOL	000035	O:03/02	Local:3:O.Data.2	Q12.2	%Q15
MOTOR1	000036	O:03/03	Local:3:O.Data.3	Q12.3	%Q16
MOTOR2	000037	O:03/04	Local:3:O.Data.4	Q12.4	%Q17

P6-8. Hole Drilling Station 1 Control. Using the function chart approach, implement the program for the following station that drills a hole in each part on a conveyor.

Figure P6.8 shows the layout of a station that drills a hole in each part that comes down the conveyor. The part completely fills the area enclosed in the dashed lines. This station is only one is a series of stations along this conveyor. You are implementing ladder logic for this station only. You have no control over the conveyor, so assume it is always moving. This particular line is asynchronous, that is, each station processes parts at its own speed and does not coordinate its operation with any other station. Because this is an asynchronous line, each station

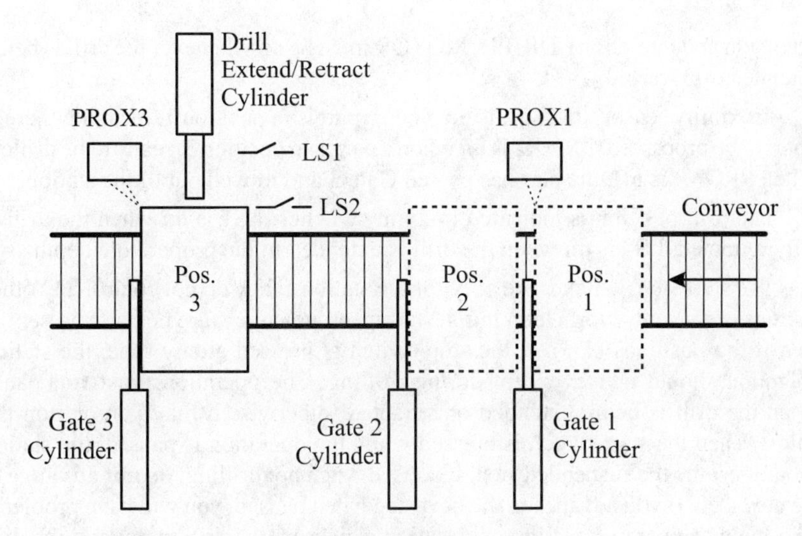

Figure P6.8. Drilling station.

contains a series of two gates that control access to the station and allow parts to queue up before the station.

Upon initial startup, assume that there are no parts waiting at gate 1. When a part is detected at Gate 1 (by PROX1), the following major steps are executed:

Sequence Gate 1 and Gate 2 to allow only one part to move into the drilling position (against Gate 3).

Drill is turned and is extended (moves out) to the correct depth,

Drill is retracted,

Open Gate 3 to allow drilled part to move out.

The operation then repeats. Assume the conveyor is on at all times. The conveyor slides beneath the parts as they are held against a gate or being drilled.

To move only one part into the station, Gates 1 and 2 are sequenced as follows (assume both gates are closed at the start): Gate 1 is opened to allow a part to move into position 2 (sensed by PROX2). Then Gate 1 is closed and Gate 2 is opened. As far as your ladder logic is concerned, assume that Gate 1 is closed and Gate 2 is opened at the same time. Physically, Gate 1 closes much faster than Gate 2 opens, so any part in position 1 is prevented from moving when Gate 2 is open enough to allow the part to move from position 2 to position 3. Gate 2 is closed when the part is in position 3 (sensed by PROX3).

A single-action air cylinder drives each gate. Once a cylinder control is energized, the gate is opened and remains open as long as power is applied (turned **on**). The gate closes when power is removed (turned **off**).

The drill extension/retraction is driven by a double-action air cylinder with two direction controls. Once a direction control is energized, the drill mechanism moves and keeps moving as long as power is applied (turned **on**). The mechanism stops at its current position when power is removed (turned **off**). The mechanism will not move if both opposing directions are energized simultaneously (e.g., extension and retraction). DRILL_MOTOR must be **on** whenever the drill is being extended or retracted.

Proximity sensor, PROX1, is **on** when a part is in position 1, meaning there is a part to be processed. PROX3 is **on** when a part is in position 3, ready to be drilled. When PROX3 is **off**, the part has passed Gate 3 and moved out of the station.

The drill position is indicated by limit switches. LS1 is **on** when the drill is fully retracted. LS2 is **on** when the drill is extended to the proper hole depth.

The start/stop switches are only for the station. They do not control any other stations or the conveyor. Upon initial startup, assume there are no parts present in any of the positions (1-3). If the stop switch is pressed at any time, the station operation should pause, except during drilling. The operation **must not** pause when the drill is being extended or retracted (otherwise it may jam or ruin the hole). When the start switch is pressed while the operation is paused, the station should resume the suspended step. If paused when not drilling, **do not advance** to the next step. If you advance to the next step when paused, you will have problems with the gate operations. When the station is paused, the drill motor and the drill extension/retraction solenoids should not be affected. Any open gates must not be closed when paused (or parts may be knocked off).

A separate reset switch is provided that when pressed, a drill not fully retracted is retracted, and the process step is set as if the process is waiting for the next part. Note that the drill motor must remain **on** while a drill is retracting. When the start switch is pressed, no items are assumed present at position 1. To keep the problem simple, do not implement a function chart for reset; just retract the drill (motor **on**) until finished. The reset switch should have no effect unless the operation is already paused.

Assume the tolerance on all timer values is ±0.1 seconds.

Assume the following physical inputs and outputs.

Variable	Description
START_PB	Start push button, N. O., **on** when starting.
STOP_PB	Stop push button, N. C., **off** when stopping.
RESET_PB	Reset push button, N. O., **on** when restoring station to initial state.
PROX1	Proximity sensor, **on** when part in position 1
PROX3	Proximity sensor, **on** when part in position 3
LS1	Limit switch that closes (**on**) drill is fully retracted
LS2	Limit switch that closes (**on**) when the drill is extended to the proper hole depth.
GATE_1	Gate 1 cylinder control, **on** to open gate 1, **off** closes gate.
GATE_2	Gate 2 cylinder control, **on** to open gate 2, **off** closes gate.
GATE_3	Gate 3 cylinder control, **on** to open gate 3, **off** closes gate.
DRILL_EXTEND	Drill extension cylinder control, **on** to extend drill.
DRILL_RETRACT	Drill retraction cylinder control, **on** to retract drill
DRILL_MOTOR	Drill motor control, **on** to cause drill to rotate.

The addresses associated with the physical inputs and outputs are:

Variable	Modicon	PLC-5	ControlLogix	Siemens	GE Fanuc
START_PB	100017	I:01/00	Local:1:I.Data.0	I4.0	%I97
STOP_PB	100018	I:01/01	Local:1:I.Data.1	I4.1	%I98
RESET_PB	100019	I:01/02	Local:1:I.Data.2	I4.2	%I99
PROX1	100021	I:01/04	Local:1:I.Data.4	I4.4	%I101
PROX3	100022	I:01/05	Local:1:I.Data.5	I4.5	%I102
LS1	100023	I:01/06	Local:1:I.Data.6	I4.6	%I103
LS2	100024	I:01/07	Local:1:I.Data.7	I4.7	%I104
GATE_1	000001	O:02/00	Local:2:O.Data.0	Q8.0	%Q1
GATE_2	000002	O:02/01	Local:2:O.Data.1	Q8.1	%Q2
GATE_3	000003	O:02/02	Local:2:O.Data.2	Q8.2	%Q3
DRILL_EXTEND	000004	O:02/03	Local:2:O.Data.3	Q8.3	%Q4
DRILL_RETRACT	000005	O:02/04	Local:2:O.Data.4	Q8.4	%Q5
DRILL_MOTOR	000006	O:02/05	Local:2:O.Data.5	Q8.5	%Q6

P6-9. Part Oiler Station Control. Using the function chart approach, implement the program for the following station that squirts oil onto each part that passes on a conveyor.

Figure P6.9 shows the layout of a station that squirts oil onto every part that comes down the conveyor. The station is only one in a series of stations along this conveyor. You are implementing ladder logic for this station only. You have no control over the conveyor, so assume it is always moving. This particular line is asynchronous, that is, each station processes parts at its own speed and does not coordinate its operation with any other station. Assume that the parts are spaced far enough apart that this operation can complete before the next part comes down the conveyor.

The conveyor consists of two parallel tracks. The part sensing and capturing mechanism is located between the two tracks. The part actually is attached to and rides upon an aluminum platform.

Upon initial startup, assume there are no parts in the station. When a part is detected by the proximity detector, PROX, the following steps are executed:

Capture part by activating ENGAGE_SOL and waiting for 4±0.1 seconds.

The oiler tip is lowered into position.

Open the oiler valve (OIL_VALVE) for 0.5±0.01 seconds, which squirts oil onto a certain place on the part.

The oiler is raised.

The ENGAGE_SOL is released and the part moves out of the station.

The operation then repeats.

The proximity sensor is inductive. PROX senses the platform before the platform reaches the engage position. You must assume that when the part is captured by the engaging mechanism, PROX remains **on**.

The engaging mechanism is driven by a single-action pneumatic cylinder, controlled by ENGAGE_SOL. When ENGAGE_SOL is energized, the "hook"

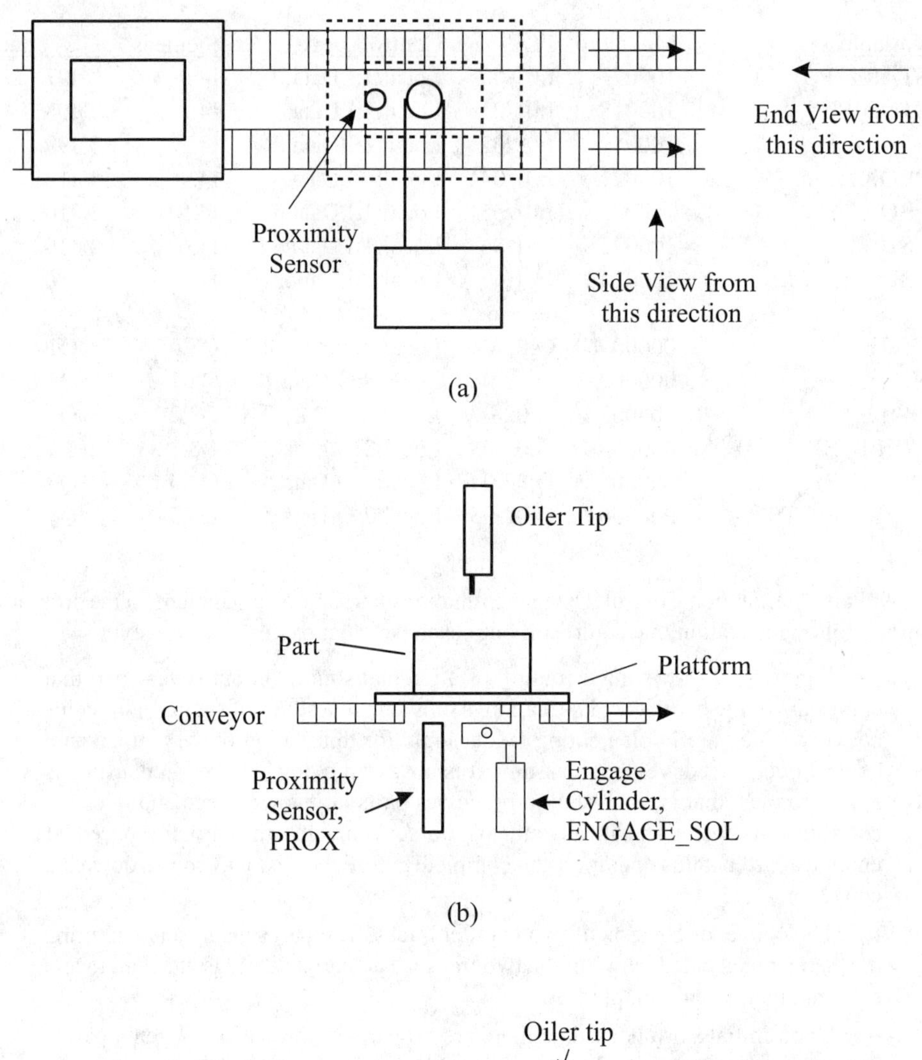

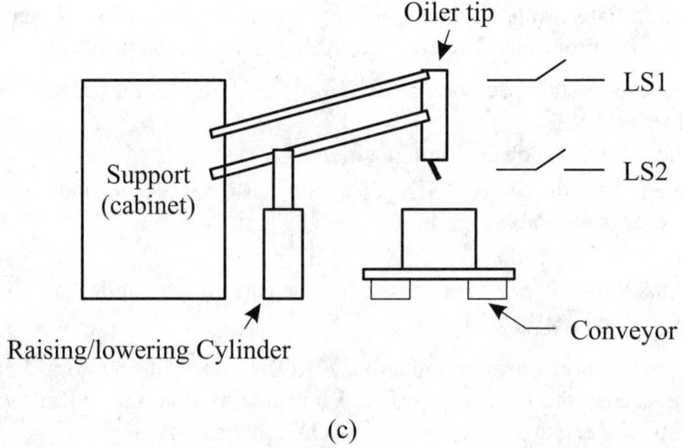

(c)

Figure P6.9. Oiler station: *(a)* top view; *(b)* side view; *(c)* end view.

moves up and remains in the "up" position as long as power is applied (turned **on**). The "hook" moves down when power is removed (turned **off**).

The mechanism used to lower and raise the oiler tip is driven by a double-acting pneumatic cylinder. When the OILER_DOWN output is energized, the oiler tip moves down and continues to move down as long as power is applied (turned **on**). When the OILER_UP output is energized, the oiler tip moves up and continues to move up as long as power is applied (turned **on**). The mechanism stops if neither output is **on** or if they are energized simultaneously. LS1 is **on** when the oiler tip is in the fully "up" position. LS2 is **on** when the oiler tip is in the fully "down" position.

When the start switch is pressed (turned **on**) for the first time only, the station assumes there is no part in the station and waits for the first part to arrive. When the stop switch is pressed (turned **off**), the operation should pause **except** when the oiler valve is opened to squirt the oil. If STOP_PB is pressed during the time the oil is being squirted, the step should be completed before pausing. Do not ignore STOP_PB during the step when oil is being squirted. When the operation is paused all outputs (except ENGAGE_SOL and OIL_VALVE) must be turned **off**. Pressing the start switch while the operation of the station is paused causes the station to resume its suspended operation.

If a timed step is paused, you need to determine if it is permissible to advance to the next step. It is permissible to advance to the next step if the timing interval has expired and no equipment will be damaged as a result of advancing to the next step.

There is a RESET_PB switch that when **on**, restarts the operation. When RESET_PB is **on**, the oiler is raised (if not in the "up" position), and the internal step is set so that the ladder logic program waits for the next part (but does not actually turn any outputs **on**). After a reset, START_PB must be pressed to actually restart the station. In other words, after RESET_PB is pressed and then released, the next press of the start switch is treated as the first time the start switch is pressed. However, the reset operation must be completed (oiler raised) before pressing START_PB has any effect. The RESET_PB switch must have no effect unless the operation is already paused.

Assume the following physical inputs and outputs.

Variable	Description
START_PB	Start push button, N. O., **on** when starting.
STOP_PB	Stop push button, N. C., **off** when stopping.
RESET_PB	Reset push button, N. O., **on** to restore station to initial state.
PROX	Proximity switch, **on** when platform is in station.
LS1	Limit switch, **on** (closed) when oiler tip is in raised position.
LS2	Limit switch, **on** (closed) when oiler tip is in lowered position.
ENGAGE_SOL	**On** to move up hook to engage platform in station, **off** releases platform to move down conveyor.
OILER_DOWN	**On** to lower oiler tip, **off** has no effect.
OILER_UP	**On** to raise oiler tip, **off** has no effect.
OIL_VALVE	**On** to open valve and squirt oil.

The addresses associated with the physical inputs and outputs are:

Variable	Modicon	PLC-5	ControlLogix	Siemens	GE Fanuc
START_PB	100001	I:01/00	Local:1:I.Data.0	I4.0	%I81
STOP_PB	100002	I:01/01	Local:1:I.Data.1	I4.1	%I82
RESET_PB	100003	I:01/02	Local:1:I.Data.2	I4.2	%I83
PROX	100017	I:02/00	Local:2:I.Data.0	I8.0	%I97
LS1	100018	I:02/01	Local:2:I.Data.1	I8.1	%I98
LS2	100019	I:02/02	Local:2:I.Data.2	I8.2	%I99
ENGAGE_SOL	000010	O:03/11	Local:3:O.Data.9	Q13.1	%Q10
OILER_DOWN	000011	O:03/12	Local:3:O.Data.10	Q13.2	%Q11
OILER_UP	000012	O:03/13	Local:3:O.Data.11	Q13.3	%Q12
OIL_VALVE	000013	O:03/14	Local:3:O.Data.12	Q13.4	%Q13

P6-10. Pressing Station Control. Using the function chart approach, implement the program for the following station that presses a pattern into each wood piece that passes on a conveyor.

Figure P6.10 shows the layout of a station that presses a pattern into each wood piece that passes on the conveyor. The station is only one in a series of stations along this conveyor. You are implementing ladder logic for this station only. You have control over the infeed conveyor. However, you have no control over the outfeed conveyor, so assume it is always moving. This particular line is asynchronous; that is, each station processes woods pieces at its own speed and does not coordinate its operation with any other station. Assume that the pieces are spaced far enough apart that this operation can complete before the next piece comes down the conveyor.

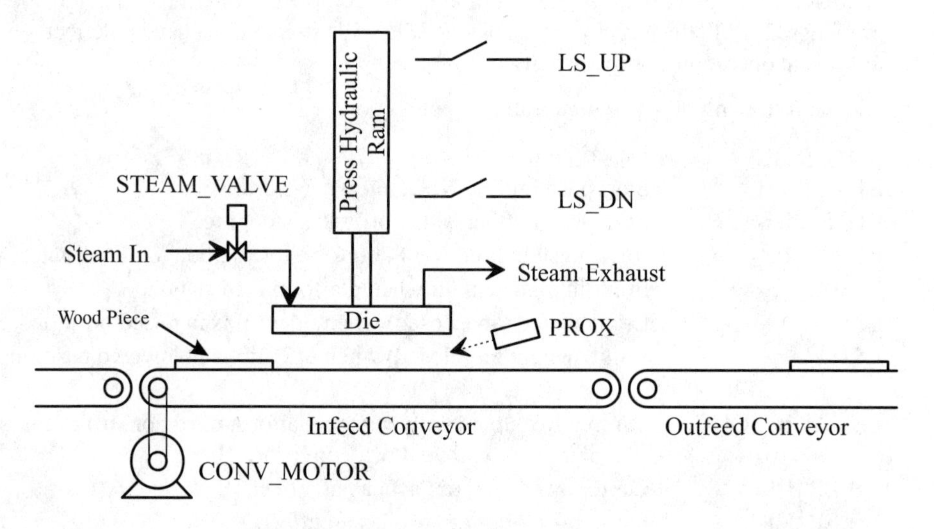

Figure P6.10. Pressing station (side view).

Upon initial pressing of the START_PB, assume there are no pieces in the station. So the infeed conveyor must be turned on to bring in a new wood piece. When a piece is detected by the proximity detector, PROX, the following happens:

The conveyor is stopped.

The hydraulic press (with the die) is lowered into position.

Press the piece for 30.5±0.1 seconds. During this time, the steam valve STEAM_VALVE) is opened to provide heat and moisture to the die.

The hydraulic press is raised.

Allow the part to cool for 45±1 seconds. Cooling cannot be started until the hydraulic press is completely raised.

Activate the conveyor to bring a new piece into the station (and move out the piece just pressed).

The operation then repeats.

The infeed conveyor (controlled by CONV_MTR) must be run in order to bring a piece into the station or move it out of the station. The conveyor must be off during all other steps.

The proximity sensor is a reflective infrared sensor. PROX senses the leading edge of the piece just before the proper position. The time required to stop the conveyor will place the piece into the correct position. You must assume that PROX remains **on** during the pressing and cooling steps.

The mechanism used to lower and raise the press consists of a single action hydraulic solenoid. When the PRESS_DOWN output is energized, the press moves down and continues to move down as long as power is applied (turned **on**). When the PRESS_DOWN output is de-energized, the press moves up and continues to move up as long as the output is de-energized. There is a mechanical stop for the fully up position. Limit switch LS_UP is **on** when the press is in the fully "up" position. LS_DN is **on** when the press is in the fully "down" (pressing) position.

When the start switch is pressed (turned **on**) for the first time only, the station assumes there is no piece in the station and waits for the first piece to arrive. When the stop switch is pressed (turned **off**), the operation should pause except when the board is being pressed. If STOP_PB is pressed during the time the piece is being pressed, the step should be completed (and advanced to the next step) before pausing. Do not ignore STOP_PB during the pressing step. When the operation is paused all outputs must be turned **off**. Pressing the start switch while the operation of the station is paused causes the station to resume its suspended step.

If a timed step is paused, you need to determine if it is permissible to advance to the next step. While paused, it is permissible to advance to the next step if the timing interval has expired and no equipment will be damaged as a result of advancing to the next step.

Do not add any more timed steps to those explicitly stated in the problem. In other words, do not put a timer in a step unless it is stated that the step duration is a specific time.

There is a RESET_PB switch that when **on**, restarts the operation. When RESET_PB is **on**, the press is raised (if not in the "up" position) and the internal step is set so that the ladder logic program waits for the next piece (but does not actually turn any outputs **on**). Assume there are no pieces in the station when RESET_PB is pressed. After a reset, START_PB must be pressed to actually restart the station. In other words, after RESET_PB is pressed and then released, the next press of the start switch is treated as the first time the start switch is pressed. However, the reset operation must be completed (press raised) before pressing START_PB has any effect. The RESET_PB switch must have no effect unless the operation is already paused.

Assume the following physical inputs and outputs.

Variable	Description
START_PB	Start push button, N. O., **on** when starting.
STOP_PB	Stop push button, N. C., **off** when stopping.
RESET_PB	Reset push button, N. O., **on** when restoring station to initial state.
PROX	Proximity switch, **on** when piece is in station.
LS_UP	Limit switch, **on** (closed) when press is in the fully raised position.
LS_DN	Limit switch, **on** (closed) when press is in the fully lowered position.
CONV_MTR	Infeed conveyor motor control, **on** run conveyor motor to move pieces into/out of station.
PRESS_DOWN	Press cylinder control, **on** to lower press, **off** raises press.
STEAM_VALVE	**On** to open valve that directs steam into die.

The addresses associated with the physical inputs and outputs are:

Variable	Modicon	PLC-5	ControlLogix	Siemens	GE Fanuc
START_PB	100017	I:01/00	Local:1:I.Data.0	I4.0	%I87
STOP_PB	100018	I:01/01	Local:1:I.Data.1	I4.1	%I88
RESET_PB	100019	I:01/02	Local:1:I.Data.2	I4.2	%I89
PROX	100033	I:03/00	Local:3:I.Data.0	I12.0	%I103
LS_UP	100034	I:03/01	Local:3:I.Data.1	I12.1	%I104
LS_DN	100035	I:03/02	Local:3:I.Data.2	I12.2	%I105
CONV_MTR	000024	O:04/07	Local:4:O.Data.7	Q16.7	%Q24
PRESS_DOWN	000025	O:04/10	Local:4:O.Data.8	Q17.0	%Q25
STEAM_VALVE	000026	O:04/11	Local:4:O.Data.9	Q17.1	%Q26

P6-11. Case Erector Control. Using the function chart approach, implement the program for the following case erector station that unfolds a corrugated cardboard carton blank and positions the flaps for the taping head after this station that tapes the bottom of the carton.

Figure P6.11 shows the layout of a station called a case erector. A case erector unfolds a corrugated cardboard carton blank and positions the flaps for the taping head. The taping head is after this station and tapes the bottom of a carton as it passes. The taping head is purely mechanical and so is not controlled by the PLC. In order to simplify this problem, you will not be concerned about the details how a

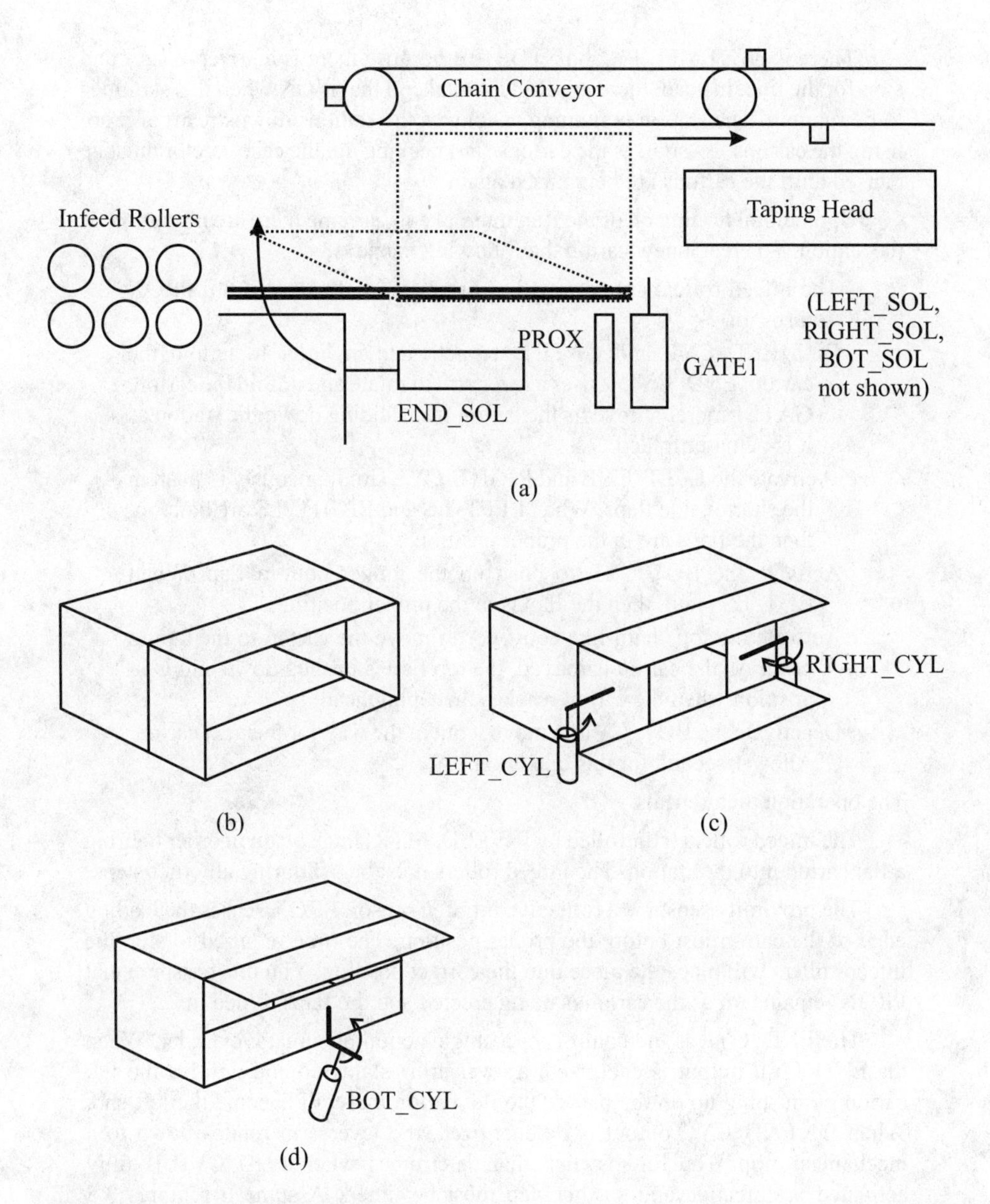

Figure P6.11. Carton erecting station: *(a)* side view; *(b)* view of erected carton; *(c)* side flaps folded; *(d)* bottom flap folded.

flat carton is fed off a stack of flat cartons. You only need to activate the appropriate output to feed one in. The station is the first in a series of stations along this conveyor. The other stations fill the carton, put on labels, tape it, etc. You are implementing ladder logic for this station only. You have control over the mechanism that feeds cartons through this station. You have no control over the outfeed conveyor, so assume it is always moving.

There is no START_PB and STOP_PB because there is an overall start and stop for the line. Instead, there is a Run internal coil that is ON when this station is to be running. The station is running as long as the stations downstream of it are using the cartons. As soon as the cartons start backing up, the case erector must be paused until the cartons are being used again.

Upon initial turning on of the Run internal coil, assume there are no cartons in the station. To erect a new carton the following happens:

The infeed rollers are activated to bring in a flat carton (until PROX turns **on**).

Both END_CYL and GATE1 are activated in order to unfold the carton. END_CYL causes a lever arm to rotate and unfold the carton. GATE1 merely prevents the carton from sliding down the station as it is being unfolded.

Activate the LEFT_CYL and RIGHT_CYL simultaneously to push in the shorter side flaps. When LEFT_LS and RIGHT_LS are both **on**, then the flaps are in the proper position.

Activate the BOT_CYL to push up the longer bottom flap. When BOT_LS is **on**, then the flap is in the proper position.

Activate the top chain-like conveyor to move the carton to the taping head. As the carton is moved, the top flap is pushed down and is in position when the carton reaches the taping head.

Deactivate the BOT_CYL to move it out of the way for the next carton. Allow 1 second for this operation.

The operation then repeats.

The infeed rollers (controlled by INFEED_MTR) must be **on** in order to bring a flat carton into the station. The infeed rollers must be **off** during all other steps.

The proximity sensor is a reflective infrared sensor. PROX senses the leading edge of the carton just before the proper position. The time required to stop the infeed rollers will place the piece into the correct position. You must assume that PROX remains **on** as the carton is being erected and the flaps folded in.

The END_CYL is the control for a single action pneumatic cylinder. When the END_CYL output is energized, a lever arm rotates up and unfolds the flat carton by pushing up on the part of the flat carton that will become the left end. When the END_CYL output is de-energized, the lever arm rotates down to a mechanical stop. The limit switch that determines when END_CYL is fully activated is defective and so this step must be timed. Assume it requires 3.5 seconds to fully activate END_CYL and erect the carton. While END_CYL is **on**, GATE1 must also be **on** to prevent the carton from sliding down the station as it is being unfolded. When activated, GATE1 moves very fast and so is fully extended by the time END_CYL has started to erect the carton.

Both LEFT_CYL and RIGHT_CYL are controls for single action pneumatic cylinders. When the LEFT_CYL output is energized, a lever arm rotates sideways and pushes (folds) the left flap inward. When LEFT_LS is energized, the left flap has been folded properly. When the RIGHT_CYL output is energized, a lever arm rotates sideways and pushes (folds) the right flap inward. When RIGHT_LS is energized, the right flap has been folded properly. Before the bottom flap may be pushed up, both LEFT_LS and RIGHT_LS must be **on**. You can make no assumptions about which flap (left or right) is folded in position last. Do not consider the case when one of these limit switches never turns on.

BOT_CYL is the control for a single action pneumatic cylinder. When the BOT_CYL output is energized, a lever arm rotates upwards and pushes (folds) the bottom flap inward. When BOT_LS is energized, the bottom flap has been folded properly and can now hold the shorter side flaps in position. When the BOT_CYL output is turned **off**, assume it requires 1 second to move out of the way before another flat carton may be moved in.

Both END_CYL and GATE1 must remain **on** as the shorter side flaps are being pushed and must be **off** while the long bottom flap is being pushed, the folded carton is being moved out, and while a new flat carton is being moved in. Both LEFT_CYL and RIGHT_CYL must remain **on** as the longer bottom flap is being pushed, and must be **off** while the folded carton is being moved out, while a new flat carton is being moved in, and while the carton is being erected.

The BOT_CYL must remain **on** while that the folded carton is being moved out, and must be **off** while a new flat carton is being moved in, while the carton is being erected, and while the shorter flaps are being pushed.

To move the carton out of the erector and into the taping head, activate CHAIN_CONV, which drives two overhead chains with a connecting bar between the chains that pushes the carton. The driving wheel on this chain conveyor has an encoder that generates pulses, ENC_PULSE, as it rotates. When ENC_PULSE has transitioned from **off** to **on** 500 times, the conveyor has moved the proper distance, and CHAIN_CONV must be shut **off**.

When the Run internal coil is turned **on** for the first time only, the station assumes there are no cartons in the station and immediately starts to feed in a flat carton. When the Run internal coil is turned **off** the operation should pause at its current step. If the Run is turned **off** while the carton is being erected or flaps being pushed, the step must run to completion, but you may not advance to the next step. When the operation is paused, only INFEED_MTR and CHAIN_CONV must be turned **off**. All other outputs (single action solenoids) must remain **on** if paused in a step where they should be **on**. If Run is turned on while the operation of the station is paused, the station should resume its suspended step.

Do not add any more timed steps to those explicitly stated in the problem. In other words, do not put a timer in a step unless it is stated that the step duration is a specific time.

There is a Reset internal coil that when **on**, restarts the operation. When Reset is **on**, the internal step is set so that the ladder logic program waits to feed in a new carton (but does not actually turn any outputs **on**). After a reset, Run must be turned **on** to actually restart the station. In other words, after Reset is turned **on** and then back **off**, the next time Run turns **on**, it is treated as the first time Run turns **on**. The Reset coil must have no effect unless the operation is already paused.

Assume the tolerance on all timer values is ±0.1 seconds.

Assume the following physical inputs, physical outputs, and internal coils.

Variable	Description
PROX	Proximity sensor, **on** when flat carton in position to be erected.
LEFT_LS	Limit switch, closes (**on**) when left flap is folded in position.

RIGHT_LS	Limit switch, closes (**on**) when right flap is folded in position.
BOT_LS	Limit switch, closes (**on**) when bottom flap is folded in position.
ENC_PULSE	Pulses to count for position of chain conveyor used to move erected carton out.
INFEED_MTR	Infeed rollers, **on** to move in flat carton.
END_CYL	End cylinder control. When **on**, a lever arm rotates up and unfolds the flat carton by pushing up on the part of the flat carton that will become the left end. When **off**, lever arm rotates down and out of the way.
LEFT_CYL	Left cylinder control. When **on**, a lever arm rotates sideways and pushes (folds) the left flap inward. When **off**, retracts.
RIGHT_CYL	Right cylinder control. When **on**, a lever arm rotates sideways and pushes (folds) the right flap inward. When **off**, retracts.
BOT_CYL	Bottom cylinder control. When **on**, a lever arm rotates upwards and pushes (folds) the bottom flap inward. When **off**, retracts.
GATE1	Gate cylinder control. **On** to prevent the carton from sliding down the station as it is being unfolded. When **off**, retracts allowing carton to move out of station.
CHAIN_CONV	Chain conveyor motor control When **on**, drives chain conveyor to move carton out of station.
Run	When **on**, allow case erector station to run. When **off**, pause (explained above)
Reset	When **on** resets operation of station (explained above).

The addresses associated with the physical inputs and outputs are:

Variable	Modicon	PLC-5	ControlLogix	Siemens	GE Fanuc
PROX	100033	I:04/00	Local:4:I.Data.0	I16.0	%I93
LEFT_LS	100034	I:04/01	Local:4:I.Data.1	I16.1	%I94
RIGHT_LS	100035	I:04/02	Local:4:I.Data.2	I16.2	%I95
BOT_LS	100036	I:04/03	Local:4:I.Data.3	I16.3	%I96
ENC_PULSE	100037	I:04/04	Local:4:I.Data.4	I16.4	%I97
INFEED_MTR	000017	O:05/00	Local:5:O.Data.0	Q20.0	%Q17
END_CYL	000018	O:05/01	Local:5:O.Data.1	Q20.1	%Q18
LEFT_CYL	000019	O:05/02	Local:5:O.Data.2	Q20.2	%Q19
RIGHT_CYL	000020	O:05/03	Local:5:O.Data.3	Q20.3	%Q20
BOT_CYL	000021	O:05/04	Local:5:O.Data.4	Q20.4	%Q21
GATE1	000022	O:05/05	Local:5:O.Data.5	Q20.5	%Q22
CHAIN_CONV	000023	O:05/06	Local:5:O.Data.6	Q20.6	%Q23

The internal variable addresses or data types are:

Variable	Modicon Data Type	PLC-5 Addr.	ControlLogix Data Type	Siemens Addr.	GE Fanuc Addr.
Run	BOOL	B35/22	BOOL	M110.0	%M1023
Reset	BOOL	B35/25	BOOL	M100.1	%M1024

P6-12. Batch Control. Using the function chart approach, implement the program for the following batch control system.

The process shown in Figure P6.12 consists of four tanks with pumps to transfer the liquid contents through the system. Each tank is fitted with sensors to detect empty and full conditions. In addition, tank 2 has an integral heating element with associated temperature sensor. Tank 3 is equipped with a stirrer to mix the two constituent liquids when they are pumped from tanks 1 and 2. The lower tanks, 3 and 4, have twice the capacity of tanks 1 and 2, and will therefore be filled by the contents of tanks 1 and 2 (alkali plus polymer).

The normal operation is described as follows. Tanks 1 and 2 are to be filled simultaneously from supply reservoirs of alkali and polymer respectively, via pumps 1 and 2. Pumps 1 and 2 should turn off as each tank-full sensor operates. The heating element in tank 2 is activated, raising the polymer temperature up to

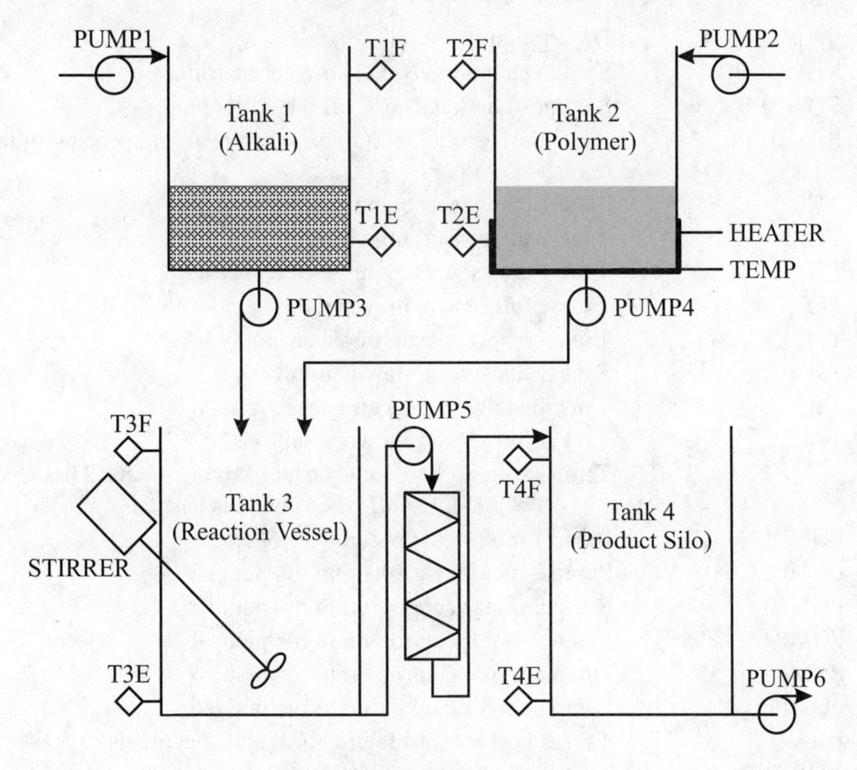

Figure P6.12. Batch process.

60°C, when the temperature sensor closes. This action should turn off the heater and turn on pumps 3 and 4 to transfer the liquids into the reaction vessel, tank 3. The stirrer must also run when tank 3 has anything in it. Once tank 3 is full or tank 1 is empty, pump 3 is stopped. In the same manner, pump 4 is stopped once tank 3 is full or tank 2 is empty. After pumps 3 and 4 have stopped, the stirrer remains **on** for an additional 90 seconds. Then pump 5 is turned **on** to transfer the mixture to tank 4 (the product silo) via a filter unit. Pump 5 is stopped once tank 4 is full or tank 3 is empty. Finally, the product is run off into storage using pump 6. The cycle is not repeated and must be restarted by the operator.

When the start switch is pressed (turned **on**) for the first time only, the process starts its operation as described above. When the stop switch is pressed (turned **off**) the operation should pause. When the operation is paused all outputs except STIRRER and HEATER must be turned **off**. The stirrer and heater must be allowed to operate while paused. Also, all timer values should be retained. Pressing the start switch while the operation of the station is paused causes the station to resume its suspended step.

There is a reset push button that when **on**, resets the operation. When RESET_PB is **on**, the internal step is set so that the ladder logic program waits for the operator to start a new cycle. Assume that if reset in the middle of a batch operation, the process has manually-operated valves to drain all tanks. After a reset, the operator must press the start push button to actually restart the station. The reset push button must have no effect unless the operation is already paused.

Assume the following physical inputs and outputs.

Variable	Description
START_PB	Start push button, N. O., **on** when starting.
STOP_PB	Stop push button, N. C., **off** when stopping.
RESET_PB	Reset push button, N. O., **on** when restoring process to initial state.
T1E	Tank 1 empty sensor, **on** when empty
T1F	Tank 1 full sensor, **on** when full
T2E	Tank 2 empty sensor, **on** when empty
T2F	Tank 2 full sensor, **on** when full
T3E	Tank 3 empty sensor, **on** when empty
T3F	Tank 3 full sensor, **on** when full
T4E	Tank 4 empty sensor, **on** when empty
T4F	Tank 4 full sensor, **on** when full
TEMP	Temperature sensor, **on** when temperature of tank 2 has reached 60°C, but turns **off** when tank 2 is half-empty.
PUMP1	Pump 1 motor control, **on** to run pump 1
PUMP2	Pump 2 motor control, **on** to run pump 2
PUMP3	Pump 3 motor control, **on** to run pump 3
PUMP4	Pump 4 motor control, **on** to run pump 4
PUMP5	Pump 5 motor control, **on** to run pump 5
PUMP6	Pump 6 motor control, **on** to run pump 6
HEATER	Tank 2 heater control, **on** to heat tank 2 contents
STIRRER	Tank 3 stirrer motor control, **on** to stir tank 3 contents

The addresses associated with the physical inputs and outputs are:

Variable	Modicon	PLC-5	ControlLogix	Siemens	GE Fanuc
START_PB	100001	I:01/00	Local:1:I.Data.0	I4.0	%I1
STOP_PB	100002	I:01/01	Local:1:I.Data.1	I4.1	%I2
RESET_PB	100003	I:01/02	Local:1:I.Data.2	I4.2	%I3
T1E	100004	I:01/03	Local:1:I.Data.3	I4.3	%I4
T1F	100005	I:01/04	Local:1:I.Data.4	I4.4	%I5
T2E	100006	I:01/05	Local:1:I.Data.5	I4.5	%I6
T2F	100007	I:01/06	Local:1:I.Data.6	I4.6	%I7
T3E	100008	I:01/07	Local:1:I.Data.7	I4.7	%I8
T3F	100009	I:01/10	Local:1:I.Data.8	I5.0	%I9
T4E	100010	I:01/11	Local:1:I.Data.9	I5.1	%I10
T4F	100011	I:01/12	Local:1:I.Data.10	I5.2	%I11
TEMP	100012	I:01/13	Local:1:I.Data.11	I5.3	%I12
PUMP1	000001	O:02/00	Local:2:O.Data.0	Q8.0	%Q1
PUMP2	000002	O:02/01	Local:2:O.Data.1	Q8.1	%Q2
PUMP3	000003	O:02/02	Local:2:O.Data.2	Q8.2	%Q3
PUMP4	000004	O:02/03	Local:2:O.Data.3	Q8.3	%Q4
PUMP5	000005	O:02/04	Local:2:O.Data.4	Q8.4	%Q5
PUMP6	000006	O:02/05	Local:2:O.Data.5	Q8.5	%Q6
HEATER	000007	O:02/06	Local:2:O.Data.6	Q8.6	%Q7
STIRRER	000008	O:02/07	Local:2:O.Data.7	Q8.7	%Q8

P6-13. Washing Machine Controller. Using the function chart approach, implement the program for the following washing machine controller.

When the controller receives a start signal, it fills the washer with the correct temperature of water (soap added by user) and agitates for 30 minutes. Warm water is obtained by mixing hot and cold water. Then, it empties the soapy water and fills the washer with the correct temperature of rinse water and agitates again for 10 minutes. Finally, it spins the clothes dry for 10 minutes after emptying the rinse water. The pump should also run during the spin step. If the user stops the washer in mid-cycle, the step of the washing machine and all timer values must be retained so that if the washer is subsequently restarted, it completes the washing operation.

The inputs TMP1, TMP2, and TMP3 determine the wash and rinse water temperature:

TMP1	TMP2	TMP3	Wash	Rinse
1	1	1	Hot	Warm
1	1	0	Hot	Cold
1	0	1	Warm	Warm
1	0	0	Warm	Cold
0	0	0	Cold	Cold

where “0” means **off** and “1” means **on**.

Assume the following physical inputs and outputs.

Variable	Description
RUN	Push/pull switch, **on** to start, **off** to stop, even in mid-cycle
FULL	Tub full indicator, **on** when washer full of water
EMPTY	Tub empty indicator, **on** when washer completely empty of water
TMP1	Desired wash and rinse water temperature (see above)
TMP2	Desired wash and rinse water temperature (see above)
TMP3	Desired wash and rinse water temperature (see above)
HOT_IN	Hot water inlet valve control, when **on**, allows hot water into washer
COLD_IN	Cold water inlet valve control, when **on**, allows cold water into washer
PUMP	Pump motor control, when **on**, pumps water out of washer
AGIT	Agitator control, when **on**, agitates wash
SPIN	Spin control, when **on**, spins wash

The addresses associated with the physical inputs and outputs are:

Variable	Modicon	PLC-5	ControlLogix	Siemens	GE Fanuc
RUN	100001	I:01/00	Local:1:I.Data.0	I4.0	%I1
FULL	100002	I:01/01	Local:1:I.Data.1	I4.1	%I2
EMPTY	100003	I:01/02	Local:1:I.Data.2	I4.2	%I3
TMP1	100004	I:01/03	Local:1:I.Data.3	I4.3	%I4
TMP2	100005	I:01/04	Local:1:I.Data.4	I4.4	%I5
TMP3	100006	I:01/05	Local:1:I.Data.5	I4.5	%I6
HOT_IN	000001	O:02/00	Local:2:O.Data.0	Q8.0	%Q1
COLD_IN	000002	O:02/01	Local:2:O.Data.1	Q8.1	%Q2
PUMP	000003	O:02/02	Local:2:O.Data.2	Q8.2	%Q3
AGIT	000004	O:02/03	Local:2:O.Data.3	Q8.3	%Q4
SPIN	000005	O:02/04	Local:2:O.Data.4	Q8.4	%Q5

P6-14. Packing Carton Changer Control. Using the function chart approach, implement the program for the following station that changes packing cartons that are receiving items as they are being produced.

Figure P6.14 shows the general layout of a station that allows 144 items to fall into a carton and then changes the full carton for an empty carton. In summary, 144 items fall off the conveyor. When the 144th item falls into the carton, it is pushed onto a roller conveyor (that moves it to a carton sealer), and the next empty carton is moved in. While the cartons are being moved, a "clam-shell" catcher is closed to contain the items while the cartons are being changed. The operation is described in the following manner:

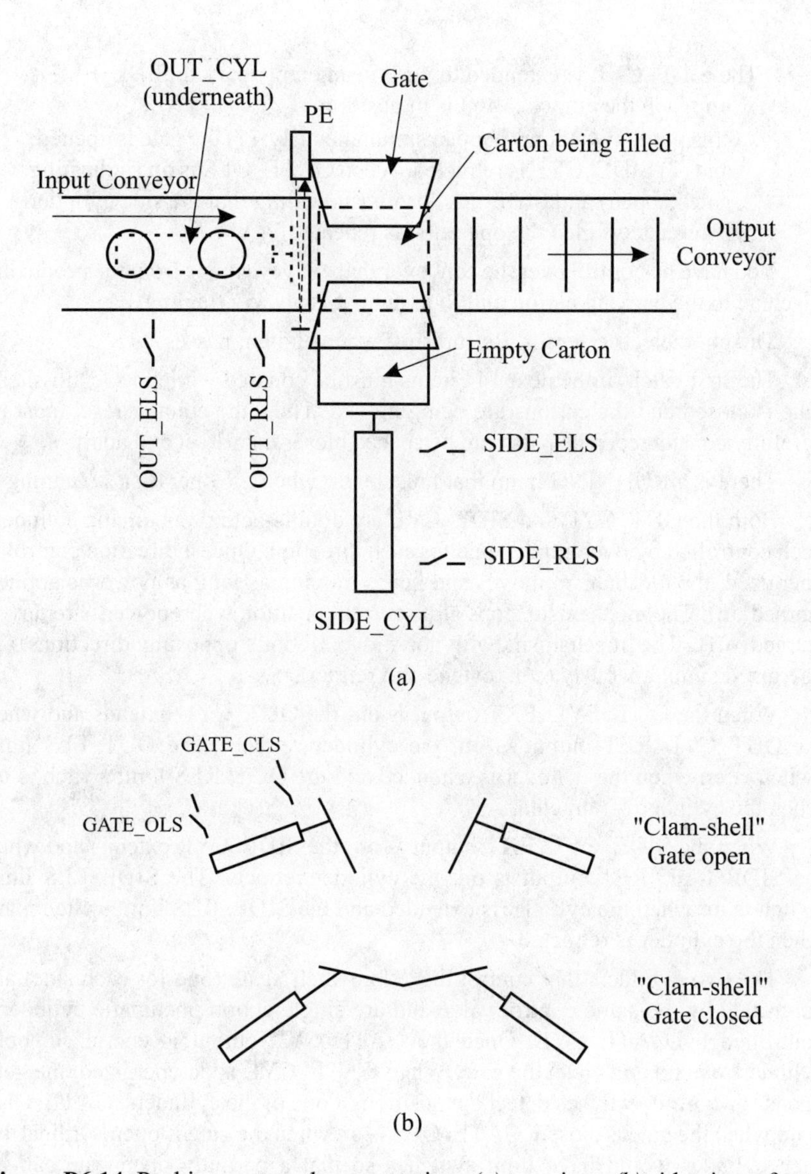

Figure P6.14. Packing carton changer station: *(a)* top view; *(b)* side view of gate.

Items coming off a conveyor are detected by PE, a retro-reflective proximity sensor.

When the carton contains 144 items, wait 1 second for the last item to fall off the end of the conveyor.

The GATE_CYL is activated to close a “clam-shell” gate. GATE_CLS is **on** when the gate is closed.

The OUT_CYL is extended to push the full carton onto a roller conveyor. OUT_ELS is **on** when the carton is pushed onto the roller conveyor.

The OUT_CYL is retracted (sensed by OUT_RLS).

The SIDE_CYL is extended to push in an empty carton. SIDE_ELS is **on** when the empty carton is in position.

At this point, two things happen simultaneously: (1) the gate is opened; and (2) SIDE_CYL is retracted. When GATE_OLS is **on** (indicating gate is open) and SIDE_RLS is **on** (indicating that the side cylinder is retracted), then the operation is repeated.

You have no control over the conveyor that conveys items from the producing machine to the packing carton and so assume it is always running.

The photoelectric sensor, PE turns **off** when an item passes.

The first batch of the next 144 items must be counted while the "clam-shell" gate is closed and the cartons are being moved. Thus, the counter reset must be carefully considered. The parts can be spaced closer than 1 second apart.

There is a RUNNING lamp that must be **on** when the operation is running.

Both the OUT_CYL and SIDE_CYL are double-acting pneumatic cylinders each controlled by two outputs, one for each direction. Once a direction control is energized, the mechanism moves and keeps moving as long as power is applied (turned **on**). The mechanism stops at its current position when power is removed (turned **off**). The mechanism will not move if both opposing directions are energized simultaneously (e.g., extend and retract).

When the OUT_CYL_EXT output is **on**, the OUT_CYL extends and when the OUT_CYL_RET output is **on**, the cylinder retracts. The OUT_ELS limit switch is **on** when the cylinder is extended and the OUT_RLS limit switch is **on** when the cylinder is retracted.

When the SIDE_CYL_EXT output is **on**, the SIDE_CYL extends and when the SIDE_CYL_RET output is **on**, the cylinder retracts. The SIDE_ELS limit switch is **on** when the cylinder is extended and the SIDE_RLS limit switch is **on** when the cylinder is retracted.

The two cylinders that control the "clam-shell" gate (one for each side) are controlled by the same control valve and are single-action pneumatic cylinders, controlled by GATE_CYL. Once the GATE_CYL output is energized, both cylinders extend and close the gate. When GATE_CYL is de-energized, the gate opens. Two limit switches detect the position of one of the cylinders. GATE_CLS is **on** when the gate is closed. GATE_OLS is **on** when the gate is open. Ordinarily, each cylinder would have limit switches so that a partially open gate can be detected, but this problem is simplified and so only one pair of limit switches exists.

Assume the input conveyor is always **on**. Your part of the program **does not** control the conveyor.

You are not concerned about how empty cartons are placed at the side, in order to be pushed into position. You are also not controlling the roller conveyor that moves the full cartons into the case sealer. So, assume it is always running.

When the start switch is pressed (turned **on**) for the first time only, the station assumes there is an empty carton in the station, ready to receive items. In general, when the stop switch is pressed (turned **off**) the operation should pause. However, if the stop switch is pressed during the one-second delay or while the gate is being closed, these steps should complete. Except for the two exceptions, **do not**

advance to the next step when paused. When paused, all outputs **except** for the GATE_CYL control must be turned **off**. When paused, GATE_CYL must remain **on** in those steps where the gate must be closed. While paused, the items must continue to be counted. Pressing the start switch while the operation of the station is paused causes the station to resume its suspended step. If the operation is still paused when 144 items have been counted, the operation does not change cartons, but waits for the start switch to be pressed to resume the operation. The carton will, of course, have more than 144 items.

A separate reset switch, RESET_PB, is provided which resets any internal states so that when the start switch is pressed, an empty carton is assumed present in the station, waiting to receive items. Obviously, the operator must put in an empty carton before resuming operation after a reset operation. Also, the reset operation should cause all cylinders to retract and the reset operation is not complete until all cylinders are retracted. Make no assumption about which cylinder requires the longest time to retract. The reset switch should be ignored if the station is running. The start switch should be ignored when the reset operation is in progress. If the station is paused and RESET_PB is **on**, the operator must release the RESET_PB before the start pushbutton switch can be used to restart the station.

Assume the tolerance on all timer values is ±0.1 seconds.

Assume the following physical inputs and outputs.

Variable	Description
START_PB	Start push button, N. O., **on** when starting.
STOP_PB	Stop push button, N. C., **off** when stopping.
RESET_PB	Reset push button, N. O., **on** when restoring station to initial state.
GATE_OLS	Limit switch that closes (**on**) when the "clam shell" gate is open.
GATE_CLS	Limit switch that closes (**on**) when the "clam shell" gate is closed.
OUT_ELS	Limit switch that closes (**on**) when OUT_CYL is extended (carton pushed onto roller conveyor).
OUT_RLS	Limit switch that closes (**on**) when OUT_CYL is retracted.
SIDE_ELS	Limit switch that closes (**on**) when SIDE_CYL is extended (empty carton pushed into position).
SIDE_RLS	Limit switch that closes (**on**) when SIDE_CYL is retracted.
PE	Photoelectric sensor, **off** (open) when the item passes the end of the conveyor.
GATE_CYL	"Clam shell" gate cylinder control, **on** to close gate, **off** causes gate to open.
OUT_CYL_EXT	OUT_CYL cylinder extend control, **on** to extend ram, **off** has no effect on cylinder position.
OUT_CYL_RET	OUT_CYL cylinder retract control, **on** to retract ram, **off** has no effect on cylinder position.
SIDE_CYL_EXT	SIDE_CYL cylinder extend control, **on** to extend ram, **off** has no effect on cylinder position.

SIDE_CYL_RET SIDE_CYL cylinder retract control, **on** to retract ram, **off** has no effect on cylinder position.

RUNNING Indicator lamp that must be **on** when the station is running.

The addresses associated with the physical inputs and outputs are:

Variable	Modicon	PLC-5	ControlLogix	Siemens	GE Fanuc
START_PB	100001	I:01/00	Local:1:I.Data.0	I4.0	%I1
STOP_PB	100002	I:01/01	Local:1:I.Data.1	I4.1	%I2
RESET_PB	100003	I:01/02	Local:1:I.Data.2	I4.2	%I3
GATE_OLS	100004	I:01/03	Local:1:I.Data.3	I4.3	%I4
GATE_CLS	100005	I:01/04	Local:1:I.Data.4	I4.4	%I5
OUT_ELS	100006	I:01/05	Local:1:I.Data.5	I4.5	%I6
OUT_RLS	100007	I:01/06	Local:1:I.Data.6	I4.6	%I7
SIDE_ELS	100008	I:01/07	Local:1:I.Data.7	I4.7	%I8
SIDE_RLS	100009	I:01/10	Local:1:I.Data.8	I5.0	%I9
PE	100010	I:01/11	Local:1:I.Data.9	I5.1	%I10
GATE_CYL	000001	O:02/00	Local:2:O.Data.0	Q8.0	%Q1
OUT_CYL_EXT	000002	O:02/01	Local:2:O.Data.1	Q8.1	%Q2
OUT_CYL_RET	000003	O:02/02	Local:2:O.Data.2	Q8.2	%Q3
SIDE_CYL_EXT	000004	O:02/03	Local:2:O.Data.3	Q8.3	%Q4
SIDE_CYL_RET	000005	O:02/04	Local:2:O.Data.4	Q8.4	%Q5
RUNNING	000006	O:02/05	Local:2:O.Data.5	Q8.5	%Q6

P6-15. Erbia Can Tipper/Rotator Control. Using the function chart approach, implement the program for the following process, which tips and rotates cans of erbia (a metal) powder.

The memo below describes the operation of the erbia tipper/rotator. A simplified drawing of the elevator is shown in Figure P6.15.

To: A. Doe

From: B. Smith

Subject: Controls for Erbia Line Tipper/Rotator

Following is the proposed controls for the machine to tip and rotate the erbia cans for mixing. Each can is tipped so the axis of rotation is horizontal, thus "tumbling" the powder to provide a uniform mixture. Your comments would be appreciated as well as the detail design and purchase of electronics and controllers. Refer to the drawings of the tipper system for switch numbers:

LS_x is a limit switch,

PS_x is a photocell switch,

CYL_x is an air cylinder. Please note that the control will be to a solenoid operated 4-way valve. I have purchased these valves.

Sequence:

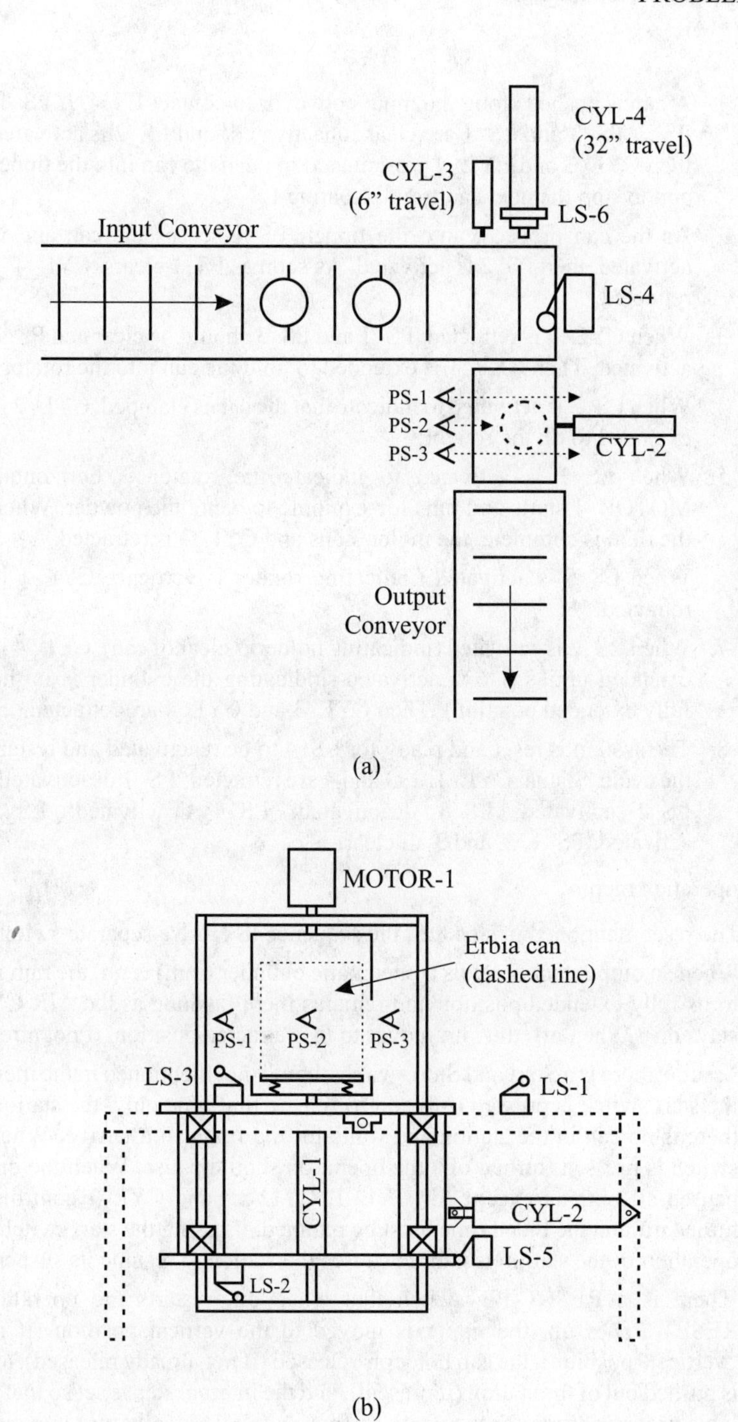

Figure P6.15. Erbia can tipper/rotator: *(a)* top view; *(b)* side view.

1. A can is pushed along the input conveyor to contact LS_4. If PS_1, PS_2, PS_3 and LS_1 are clear (unactivated) and LS_2 is activated then CYL_3 and CYL_4 are actuated to push the can into the tipper and to stop the next can from actuating LS_4.
2. As the can proceeds into the tipper, PS_1 senses the can and is activated, then PS_2 is activated. As soon as PS_1 clears, CYL_4 is retracted.
3. When CYL_4 is retracted, PS_1 and PS_3 should be clear and PS_2 activated. Then CYL_1 is extended to hold the can into the rotator.
4. When LS_3 is activated to indicate that the can is clamped, CYL_2 is extended to tip the rotator.
5. When LS_1 is activated to indicate the rotator is horizontal, MOTOR_1 starts and runs for 1 minute to blend the powder. When the time is complete, the motor stops and CYL_2 is retracted.
6. When LS_5 is activated (indicating rotator is vertical), CYL_1 is retracted.
7. When LS_2 is activated (indicating holder is clear of can), CYL_4 is extended until LS_6 is activated (indicating the cylinder is in the fully extended position). Then CYL_3 and CYL_4 are retracted.
8. The system is reset and ready for LS_4 to be reactivated and restart the cycle. Status: CYL_1, 2, 3 and 4 are retracted; LS_1 deactivated; LS_2 activated; LS_3 deactivated; LS_4 deactivated; LS_5 activated; PS_1, 2, and 3 all clear.

Notes to operation memo:

1. The reset mentioned in step 8 of the sequence IS NOT a separate switch.
2. When an output that controls a pneumatic cylinder (ram) is **on**, the ram moves out to its fully extended position and remains there (as long as the AIR CYL output stays **on**). When **off**, the ram moves to the retracted position, if not already there.
3. Assume there is a Start and Stop switch, though not mentioned in the memo. When the start switch is pressed (turned **on**) for the first time only, the station assumes there is no can in the station and waits for the first can to arrive. When the stop switch is pressed (turned **off**) the operation should pause. When the operation is paused all outputs **except** for CYL_1, CYL_2, and CYL_3 controls must be turned **off** and the blend time must be retained. Pressing the start switch while the operation of the station is paused causes the station to resume its suspended step.
4. There is a RESET_PB switch that when **on**, restarts the operation. When RESET_PB is **on**, the tipper is moved to the vertical position (if not in the "vertical" position), the can holder is released (if not already released), and the can is pushed out of the station (if present), and the internal step is set so that the ladder logic program waits for the next can (but does not actually turn any outputs **on**). After a reset, START_PB must be pressed to actually restart the station. In other words, after RESET_PB is pressed and then released, the next press of the start switch is treated as the first time the start switch is pressed. The RESET_PB switch must have no effect unless the operation is already paused.

5. Assume the input and output conveyors are always on when the station is running, even though not shown in your function chart.

Assume the following physical inputs and outputs.

Variable	Description
START_PB	Start push button, N. O., **on** when starting.
STOP_PB	Stop push button, N. C., **off** when stopping.
RESET_PB	Reset push button, N. O., **on** when restoring process to initial state.
LS_1	Horizontal position limit switch, **on** (closed) when rotator in horizontal position.
LS_2	Holder clear limit switch, **on** (closed) when holder is clear of can.
LS_3	Holder down limit switch, **on** (closed) when can is being held in rotator.
LS_4	Can present on input conveyor limit switch, **on** (closed) when can in position to be pushed into rotator.
LS_5	Vertical position limit switch, **on** (closed) when rotator in vertical position.
LS_6	Cylinder CYL_4 fully extended limit switch, **on** (closed) when cylinder is fully extended, pushing can out of rotator.
PS_1	Left can photoelectric switch, **on** (closed) when can moving into rotator.
PS_2	Middle can photoelectric switch, **on** (closed) when can moving into rotator and when in proper position to be rotated.
PS_3	Right can photoelectric switch, **on** (closed) when can moving out of rotator.
CYL_1	Can holder cylinder control, **on** to clamp can into rotator; **off** unclamps
CYL_2	Tipper cylinder control, **on** to tip rotator horizontal; **off** to restore vertical orientation of can.
CYL_3	Gate cylinder control, **on** to extend and prevent the next can from entering station; **off** to retract.
CYL_4	Can pusher cylinder control, **on** to push can into and out of rotator; **off** to retract.
MOTOR_1	Rotation motor control, **on** to rotate clamped can

The addresses associated with the physical inputs and outputs are:

Variable	Modicon	PLC-5	ControlLogix	Siemens	GE Fanuc
START_PB	100001	I:00/00	Local:1:I.Data.0	I0.0	%I1
STOP_PB	100002	I:00/01	Local:1:I.Data.1	I0.1	%I2
RESET_PB	100003	I:00/02	Local:1:I.Data.2	I0.2	%I3
LS_1	100004	I:00/03	Local:1:I.Data.3	I0.3	%I4
LS_2	100005	I:00/04	Local:1:I.Data.4	I0.4	%I5
LS_3	100006	I:00/05	Local:1:I.Data.5	I0.5	%I6
LS_4	100007	I:00/06	Local:1:I.Data.6	I0.6	%I7

LS_5	100008	I:00/07	Local:1:I.Data.7	I0.7	%I8
LS_6	100009	I:00/10	Local:1:I.Data.8	I1.0	%I9
PS_1	100010	I:00/11	Local:1:I.Data.9	I1.1	%I10
PS_2	100011	I:00/12	Local:1:I.Data.10	I1.2	%I11
PS_3	100012	I:00/13	Local:1:I.Data.11	I1.3	%I12
CYL_1	000001	O:01/00	Local:2:O.Data.0	Q4.0	%Q1
CYL_2	000002	O:01/01	Local:2:O.Data.1	Q4.1	%Q2
CYL_3	000003	O:01/02	Local:2:O.Data.2	Q4.2	%Q3
CYL_4	000004	O:01/03	Local:2:O.Data.3	Q4.3	%Q4
MOTOR_1	000005	O:01/04	Local:2:O.Data.4	Q4.4	%Q5

P6-16. Pick-and-place Machine Control. Using the function chart approach, implement the program for the following pick-and-place machine.

Figure P6.16 shows the layout of a "pick-and-place" machine, consisting of a horizontal/vertical mechanism which is used to transfer parts from the left-hand table to the right-hand table. The horizontal and vertical movements are each driven by a double-acting air cylinder — a raising/lowering cylinder and a leftward/rightward cylinder. Each cylinder is controlled by two outputs, one for each direction. Once a direction control is energized, the mechanism moves and keeps moving as long as power is applied (turned on). The mechanism stops at its current position when power is removed (turned off). The mechanism will not move if both opposing directions are energized simultaneously (e.g., left and right). The clamp/unclamp action is driven by a single-action air cylinder, which clamps the part into the mechanism when the control is **on** and releases it when the control is **off**. Power must continually be applied to the clamp to hold the part in the mechanism. Limit switches detect the position of the mechanism, and a photoelectric switch, for safety, checks for the presence of parts remaining on the right-hand table.

The basic sequence of operation is as follows: From the home position (signified by the upper and left limit switches both being ON), the machine waits for a part to be moved onto the left table (signified by the part-operation-in-progress switch being OFF). When the part is ready to be moved, the lowering cylinder is operated, moving the mechanism down until the lower limit switch operates (turns ON). This stops the lowering motion and activates the clamp. Wait 2.0 seconds for the clamp to grip the part. The mechanism now moves upward until the upper limit switch operates, causing the horizontal movement to start, taking the mechanism over to the right limit switch and initiating another downward path towards the right-hand table — providing no previous parts remain on the table (tested by the photoelectric switch). If a part remains on the right-hand table, then the mechanism remains in the upper right position until the part is removed. At the right table, the clamp is released (power is removed). Wait 2.4 seconds for the part to be released. The mechanism returns to the home position, where it waits for a new part to be moved off the left table. The circled numbers in the Figure P6.16 indicate the sequence of moves.

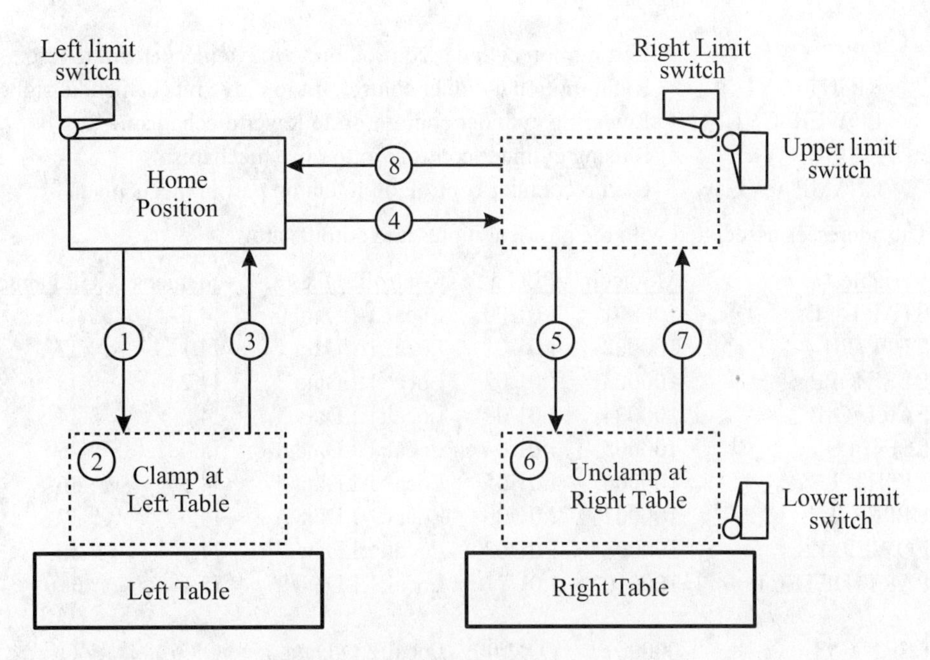

Figure P6.16. Pick-and-place machine.

When the start switch is pressed (turned **on**) for the first time only, the mechanism starts in the home position and performs the operation cycle continuously. Assume the mechanism is in the home position when the start switch is pressed for the first time. Pressing the start switch when the mechanism is already running must have no effect. When the stop switch is pressed (turned **off**) the mechanism should stop in its current position and in the middle of whatever operation it is doing. It must continue to clamp the part. Pressing the start switch causes the machine to resume its suspended operation.

When the reset switch is pressed, the mechanism should move to the top and then to the left. Also, the part should be released after reaching home. The reset switch should be ignored if the mechanism is not paused.

Assume the following physical inputs and outputs:

Variable	Description
START_PB	Start push button, N. O., **on** when starting.
STOP_PB	Stop push button, N. C., **off** when stopping.
RESET_PB	Reset push button, N. O., **on** to reset process.
PART_OIP	Part operation-in-progress switch, **on** (closed) when not ready to move part off of left table
LEFT_LS	Left limit switch, **on** when mechanism is over left table
RIGHT_LS	Right limit switch, **on** when mechanism is over right table
UPPER_LS	Upper limit switch, **on** when mechanism is raised
LOWER_LS	Lower limit switch, **on** when mechanism is lowered
PART_DETECT	Right table part detection switch, **on** when part is on right table

LEFT_CYL	Left motion cylinder control, **on** to move mechanism to left
RIGHT_CYL	Right motion cylinder control, **on** to move mechanism to right
LOWER_CYL	Lowering cylinder control, **on** to lower mechanism
RAISE_CYL	Raising cylinder control, **on** to raise mechanism
CLAMP_CYL	Clamp cylinder control, **on** to clamp part in mechanism

The addresses associated with the physical inputs and outputs are:

Variable	Modicon	PLC-5	ControlLogix	Siemens	GE Fanuc
START_PB	100001	I:01/00	Local:1:I.Data.0	I4.0	%I1
STOP_PB	100002	I:01/01	Local:1:I.Data.1	I4.1	%I2
RESET_PB	100003	I:01/02	Local:1:I.Data.2	I4.2	%I3
PART_OIP	100004	I:01/03	Local:1:I.Data.3	I4.3	%I4
LEFT_LS	100005	I:01/04	Local:1:I.Data.4	I4.4	%I5
RIGHT_LS	100006	I:01/05	Local:1:I.Data.5	I4.5	%I6
UPPER_LS	100007	I:01/06	Local:1:I.Data.6	I4.6	%I7
LOWER_LS	100008	I:01/07	Local:1:I.Data.7	I4.7	%I8
PART_DETECT	100010	I:01/11	Local:1:I.Data.9	I5.1	%I10
LEFT_CYL	000001	O:02/00	Local:2:O.Data.0	Q8.0	%Q1
RIGHT_CYL	000002	O:02/01	Local:2:O.Data.1	Q8.1	%Q2
LOWER_CYL	000003	O:02/02	Local:2:O.Data.2	Q8.2	%Q3
RAISE_CYL	000004	O:02/03	Local:2:O.Data.3	Q8.3	%Q4
CLAMP_CYL	000005	O:02/04	Local:2:O.Data.4	Q8.4	%Q5

P6-17. Bagging Machine Control. Using the function chart approach, implement the program for the following bagging machine.

Figure P6.17 shows the layout of a station that puts five items into a plastic bag. The items are skinny, e.g., rods or spark plugs. The major steps (but not necessarily all of the steps in your function chart) in the operation are:

Count and combine items,
Prepare bag for loading,
Load items into bag, and
Push the filled bag out where another part of the machine will finish sealing the bag.

One cycle of the station operation is thus completed, and the conveyor is started again and items are counted.

The items go down the item conveyor and are counted as they enter the marshaling area where they are pushed together. PE1 is used to count the items as they enter the marshaling area. When 5 items have been counted, wait 2 seconds for the last item to enter the marshaling area and pack into the other 4 items. The item conveyor is now turned **off**.

To prepare the plastic bag for loading, the bag conveyor is turned **on**, moving the printed plastic sheeting material into position. PE2, when **off**, indicates that the sheet is in position. A vacuum system is used to hold the plastic sheet to the conveyor. There are two vacuums that must be operated to hold down the sheet.

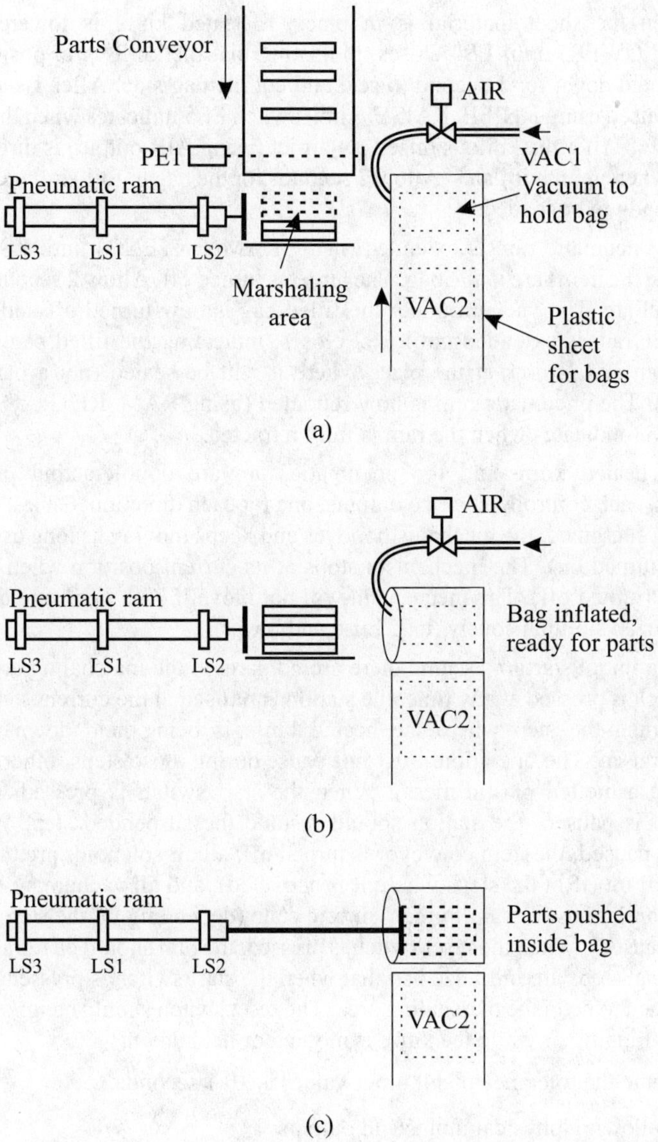

Parts Conveyor
AIR
PE1
VAC1
Pneumatic ram
Vacuum to hold bag
LS3 LS1 LS2
Marshaling area
VAC2
Plastic sheet for bags

(a)

AIR
Pneumatic ram
Bag inflated, ready for parts
LS3 LS1 LS2
VAC2

(b)

Pneumatic ram
Parts pushed inside bag
LS3 LS1 LS2
VAC2

(c)

Figure P6.17. Bagging station: *(a)* overall view; *(b)* bag inflated, ready for parts; *(c)* parts pushed inside bag.

One vacuum, controlled by VAC1, is directly under the place where the bag is loaded. VAC1 is turned on after the sheet is moved in to position and will be turned **off** when the bag is pushed off. The other vacuum, controlled by VAC2, is for the bag conveyor and is **on** all of the time the station is running. The plastic sheet material has already been folded over so that there is a top and bottom. The back edge is the fold.

When the sheet material is in place, a heated knife is lowered (using KNIFE_LOWER) until LS4 closes, indicating that the knife is in position. The knife is held down for 1 second to seal and cut the bag side. After 1 second, the knife is raised using KNIFE_RAISE. Limit switch LS5 indicates when the knife is fully raised. After the knife is raised, an air jet (using AIR output) is directed into the bag whereupon it inflates. Allow 2 seconds for the bag to fully inflate. The bag is now ready to be loaded.

The pneumatic ram is extended (using RAM_EXTEND) until LS1 closes, indicating the items are in the bag. The air jet is turned off. Allow 2 seconds for the bag to deflate. The vacuum under the filled bag is now turned **off** and then the pneumatic ram is extended until LS2 closes, indicating the filled bag has been pushed out and is now at the place where it will be sealed (not a part of this problem). The pneumatic ram is now retracted (using RAM_RETRACT). Limit switch LS3 indicates when the ram is fully retracted.

The heated knife and the pneumatic ram are double-acting pneumatic cylinders, each controlled by two outputs, one for each direction. Once a direction control is energized, the mechanism moves and keeps moving as long as power is applied (turned on). The mechanism stops at its current position when power is removed (turned off). The mechanism will not move if both opposing directions are energized simultaneously (e.g., raise and lower).

Upon initial startup, assume there are no parts in the marshaling area. If the stop switch is pressed at any time, the station is **paused** at the current step, except when timing the step where the heated knife is being held down or being lowered/raised. The operation **must not** pause during those steps (otherwise you will have a melted plastic mess). When the start switch is pressed while the operation is paused, the station should resume the suspended step. When the station is paused, the item conveyor is turned **off**, all air solenoids are turned **off**, AIR is left **on** (if in the steps where it is activated), and all vacuum systems and knife controls must remain in their current state (depending on the step at which you are paused). When the reset switch is pressed, the ram should be retracted, and any internal steps are initialized so that when the start switch is pressed, no parts are assumed to be in the marshaling area. The reset switch should be ignored if the station is running or while the knife is moving or held down.

Assume the tolerance on all timer values is ±0.1 seconds.

Assume the following physical inputs and outputs:

Variable	Description
START_PB	Start push button, N. O., **on** when starting.
STOP_PB	Stop push button, N. C., **off** when stopping.
RESET_PB	Reset push button, N. O., **on** to reset process.
PE1	Part photoelectric sensor, **off** (open) when part passes.
PE2	Plastic sheet photoelectric sensor, **off** (open) when plastic sheet in position to be cut and sealed.
LS1	Limit switch that closes (**on**) when ram is extended enough to push items into bag.
LS2	Limit switch that closes (**on**) when ram is extended enough to push filled bag out.

LS3	Limit switch that closes (**on**) when ram is retracted.
LS4	Limit switch that closes (**on**) when heated knife is down.
LS5	Limit switch that closes (**on**) when heated knife is up.
RAM_EXTEND	Pneumatic ram extension control, **on** to extend ram, **off** has no effect on ram position
RAM_RETRACT	Pneumatic ram retraction control, **on** to retract ram, **off** has no effect on ram position
KNIFE_LOWER	Pneumatic "knife down" control, **on** to move heated knife down, **off** has no effect on knife position
KNIFE_RAISE	Pneumatic "knife up" control, **on** to move heated knife up, **off** has no effect on knife position
MOTOR1	Item conveyor motor control, **on** to move item conveyor
MOTOR2	Bag conveyor motor control, **on** to move plastic sheet
AIR	Air stream solenoid control, **on** to turn on air stream to inflate plastic bag
VAC1	Control for vacuum that holds down bag when filling, **on** to turn on vacuum
VAC2	Control for vacuum that holds plastic sheet onto bag conveyor, **on** to turn on vacuum

The addresses associated with the physical inputs and outputs are:

Variable	Modicon	PLC-5	ControlLogix	Siemens	GE Fanuc
START_PB	100001	I:01/00	Local:1:I.Data.0	I4.0	%I1
STOP_PB	100002	I:01/01	Local:1:I.Data.1	I4.1	%I2
RESET_PB	100003	I:01/02	Local:1:I.Data.2	I4.2	%I3
PE1	100004	I:01/03	Local:1:I.Data.3	I4.3	%I4
PE2	100005	I:01/04	Local:1:I.Data.4	I4.4	%I5
LS1	100006	I:01/05	Local:1:I.Data.5	I4.5	%I6
LS2	100007	I:01/06	Local:1:I.Data.6	I4.6	%I7
LS3	100008	I:01/07	Local:1:I.Data.7	I4.7	%I8
LS4	100009	I:01/10	Local:1:I.Data.8	I5.0	%I9
LS5	100010	I:01/11	Local:1:I.Data.9	I5.1	%I10
RAM_EXTEND	000001	O:02/00	Local:2:O.Data.0	Q8.0	%Q1
RAM_RETRACT	000002	O:02/01	Local:2:O.Data.1	Q8.1	%Q2
KNIFE_LOWER	000003	O:02/02	Local:2:O.Data.2	Q8.2	%Q3
KNIFE_RAISE	000004	O:02/03	Local:2:O.Data.3	Q8.3	%Q4
MOTOR1	000005	O:02/04	Local:2:O.Data.4	Q8.4	%Q5
MOTOR2	000006	O:02/05	Local:2:O.Data.5	Q8.5	%Q6
AIR	000007	O:02/06	Local:2:O.Data.6	Q8.6	%Q7
VAC1	000008	O:02/07	Local:2:O.Data.7	Q8.7	%Q8
VAC2	000009	O:02/10	Local:2:O.Data.8	Q9.0	%Q9

P6-18. Drilling Station Control. Using the function chart approach, implement the program for the following station that drills two holes in each part that comes down the conveyor.

Figure P6.18 shows the layout of a station that drills two holes in each part that comes down the conveyor. This station is only one in a series of stations along this conveyor. You are implementing ladder logic for this station only. You have no control over the conveyor, so assume it is always moving. This particular line is asynchronous, that is, each station processes parts at its own speed and does not coordinate its operation with any other station. Because this is an asynchronous line, each station contains a series of two gates that control access to the station and allow parts to queue up before the station.

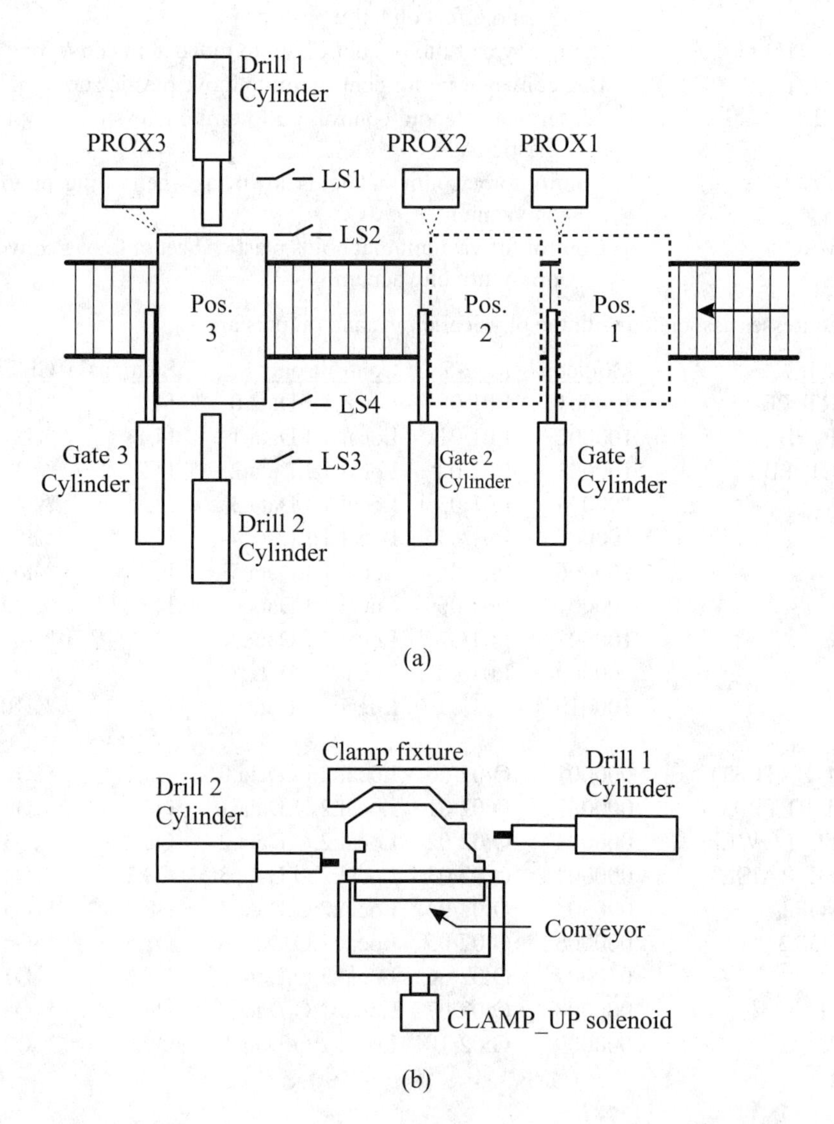

Figure P6.18. Drilling station: *(a)* top view; *(b)* view from right side.

Upon initial startup, assume that there are no parts waiting at gate 1. When a part is detected at Gate 1 (by PROX1), the following major steps are executed:

Sequence Gate 1 and Gate 2 to allow only one part to move into the drilling position (against Gate 3),
Clamp the part into position (and off of the conveyor),
Drill 1 is turned and is extended (moves out) to the correct depth,
Drill 1 is retracted,
Drill 2 is turned and is extended (moves out) to the correct depth,
Drill 2 is retracted,
Unclamp part,
Open Gate 3 to allow drilled part to move out.

The operation then repeats. Assume the conveyor is on at all times. The conveyor slides beneath the parts as they are held against a gate.

To move only one part into the station, Gates 1 and 2 are sequenced as follows (assume both gates are closed at the start): Gate 1 is opened to allow a part to move into position 2 (sensed by PROX2). Then, Gate 1 is closed, and Gate 2 is opened. As far as your ladder logic is concerned, assume that Gate 1 is closed and Gate 2 is opened at the same rate. Physically, Gate 1 closes much faster than Gate 2 opens, so any part in position 1 is prevented from moving when Gate 2 is open enough to allow the part to move from position 2 to position 3. Gate 2 is closed when the part is in position 3 (sensed by PROX3).

The gates are each driven by a single solenoid powered by an air cylinder. Once a solenoid is energized, the gate is opened and remains open as long as power is applied (turned **on**). The gate closes when power is removed (turned **off**).

The clamp is driven by a single-action pneumatic cylinder controlled by a solenoid. Once the CLAMP_UP solenoid is energized, the clamp moves the part up into a fixture to get the part in proper alignment to the drills. Limit switch LS5 indicates that the part is in the proper position. CLAMP_UP must remain **on** to hold the part in the fixture. If CLAMP_UP is turned **off**, the part falls back onto the conveyor. Allow 0.5 seconds for the part to unclamp and fall to the conveyor.

Each drill extension/retraction is driven by a double-action pneumatic cylinder with two controls. Once a direction control is energized, the drill mechanism is moved and keeps moving as long as power is applied (turned **on**). The mechanism stops at its current position when power is removed (turned **off**). The mechanism will not move if both opposing directions are energized simultaneously (e.g., extension and retraction). The drill motor must be **on** whenever the drill is being extended or retracted.

Proximity sensor, PROX1, is **on** when a part is in position 1, meaning there is a part to be processed. PROX2 is **on** when a part is in position 2. PROX3 is **on** when a part is in position 3, ready to be drilled. When PROX3 is **off**, the part has passed Gate 3 and moved out of the station.

The drill position is indicated by limit switches. LS1 is **on** when drill 1 is fully retracted and LS2 is **on** when drill 1 is extended to the proper hole depth. Similarly, LS3 and LS4 indicate the retracted and extended positions, respectively, for drill 2.

The start/stop switches are only for the station. They do not control any other stations, or the conveyor. Upon initial startup, assume there are no parts present in any of the positions (1-3). If the stop switch is pressed at any time, the station operation should **pause**, except when the drill is being extended or retracted. The operation **must not** pause when the drill is being moved (otherwise it may jam or ruin the hole). When the start switch is pressed while the operation is paused, the station should resume the suspended step. When paused, **do not advance** to the next step. If the operation advances to the next step when paused, there will be problems with the gate operations. When the station is paused, the drill motor and the drill cylinder retraction controls should remain **on**. Any open gates must not be closed when paused (or parts may be knocked off) and the CLAMP_UP solenoid must not be turned **off**. The stop push button switch cannot be ignored, even in those steps where the operation cannot be paused.

A separate reset switch is provided that when pressed, any drill not fully retracted is retracted, the part clamp is released, and the process step is set as if the process is waiting for the next part. Note that the part clamp must remain **on** while a drill is retracting. When the start switch is pressed, no items are assumed present at position 1. To keep the problem simple, do not try to implement a function chart for reset, just retract both drills (motor **on**) simultaneously until both limit switches are activated and then release the part. The reset switch should have no effect unless the operation is already paused.

Assume the tolerance on all timer values is ±0.1 seconds.

Assume the following physical inputs and outputs.

Variable	Description
START_PB	Start push button, N. O., **on** when starting.
STOP_PB	Stop push button, N. C., **off** when stopping.
RESET_PB	Reset push button, N. O., **on** when restoring process to initial state.
PROX1	Proximity sensor, **on** when part in position 1
PROX2	Proximity sensor, **on** when part in position 2
PROX3	Proximity sensor, **on** when part in position 3
LS1	Limit switch that closes (**on**) when drill 1 is fully retracted
LS2	Limit switch that closes (**on**) when drill 1 is extended to the proper hole depth
LS3	Limit switch that closes (**on**) when drill 2 is fully retracted
LS4	Limit switch that closes (**on**) when drill 2 is extended to the proper hole depth
LS5	Limit switch that closes (**on**) when part clamped in proper position
GATE_1	Gate 1 control, **on** to open gate 1, **off** closes gate.
GATE_2	Gate 2 control, **on** to open gate 2, **off** closes gate.
GATE_3	Gate 3 control, **on** to open gate 3, **off** closes gate.
DRILL1_EXTEND	Drill 1 extension control, **on** to extend drill 1.
DRILL1_RETRACT	Drill 1 retraction control, **on** to retract drill 1.
DRILL1_MOTOR	Drill 1 motor control, **on** to cause drill 1 to rotate.
DRILL2_EXTEND	Drill 2 extension control, **on** to extend drill 2.

DRILL2_RETRACT Drill 2 retraction control, **on** to retract drill 2.
DRILL2_MOTOR Drill 2 motor control, **on** to cause drill 2 to rotate.
CLAMP_UP Clamp control, **on** to move part up into fixture and retain it there.

The addresses associated with the physical inputs and outputs are:

Variable	Modicon	PLC-5	ControlLogix	Siemens	GE Fanuc
START_PB	100049	I:04/00	Local:4:I.Data.0	I16.0	%I49
STOP_PB	100050	I:04/01	Local:4:I.Data.1	I16.1	%I50
RESET_PB	100051	I:04/02	Local:4:I.Data.2	I16.2	%I51
PROX1	100052	I:04/03	Local:4:I.Data.3	I16.3	%I52
PROX2	100053	I:04/04	Local:4:I.Data.4	I16.4	%I53
PROX3	100054	I:04/05	Local:4:I.Data.5	I16.5	%I54
LS1	100055	I:04/06	Local:4:I.Data.6	I16.6	%I55
LS2	100056	I:04/07	Local:4:I.Data.7	I16.7	%I56
LS3	100057	I:04/10	Local:4:I.Data.8	I17.0	%I57
LS4	100058	I:04/11	Local:4:I.Data.9	I17.1	%I58
LS5	100059	I:04/12	Local:4:I.Data.10	I17.2	%I59
GATE_1	000001	O:05/00	Local:5:O.Data.0	Q20.0	%Q1
GATE_2	000002	O:05/01	Local:5:O.Data.1	Q20.1	%Q2
GATE_3	000003	O:05/02	Local:5:O.Data.2	Q20.2	%Q3
DRILL1_EXTEND	000004	O:05/03	Local:5:O.Data.3	Q20.3	%Q4
DRILL1_RETRACT	000005	O:05/04	Local:5:O.Data.4	Q20.4	%Q5
DRILL1_MOTOR	000006	O:05/05	Local:5:O.Data.5	Q20.5	%Q6
DRILL2_EXTEND	000007	O:05/06	Local:5:O.Data.6	Q20.6	%Q7
DRILL2_RETRACT	000008	O:05/07	Local:5:O.Data.7	Q20.7	%Q8
DRILL2_MOTOR	000009	O:05/10	Local:5:O.Data.8	Q21.0	%Q9
CLAMP_UP	000010	O:05/11	Local:5:O.Data.9	Q20.1	%Q10

P6-19. Bolt Driving Station Control. Using the function chart approach, implement the program for the following station that drives bolts in gasoline engine assemblies as they come down the conveyor. This is one of the stations on the final assembly line for the vertical shaft engines at a major manufacturer. The problem is simplified since the actual station drives six bolts.

Figure P6.19 shows the layout of a station that drives two bolts into gasoline engine assemblies riding on a pallet as they come down the conveyor. This station is only one in a series of stations along this conveyor. This solution implements ladder logic for this station only. Another PLC controls the conveyor, so assume it is always moving. This particular line is asynchronous, that is, each station processes assemblies at its own speed and does not coordinate its operation with any other station. Because this is an asynchronous line, each station contains two capturing mechanisms (engaging hooks) that control access to the station and allow assemblies to queue up before the station.

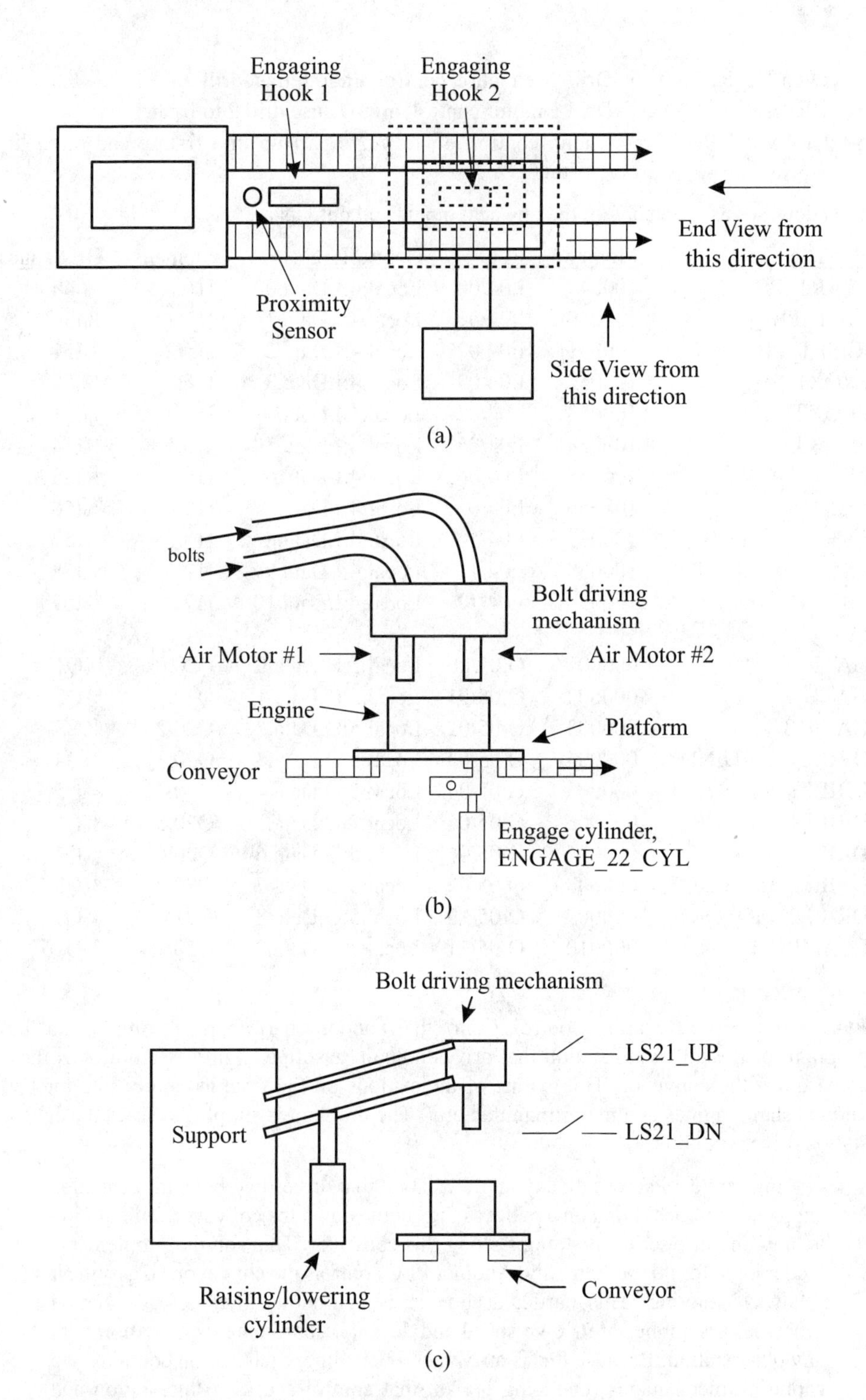

Figure P6.19. Bolt driving station: *(a)* top view; *(b)* side view; *(c)* end view; *(d)* top view of bolt conveying mechanism; *(e)* side view of bolt conveying. *(continued)*

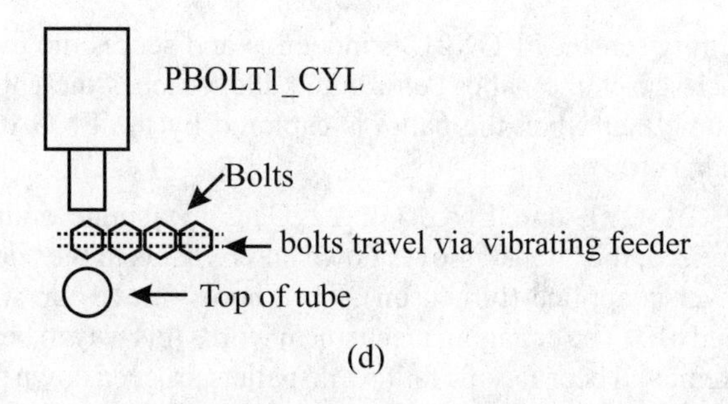

(d)

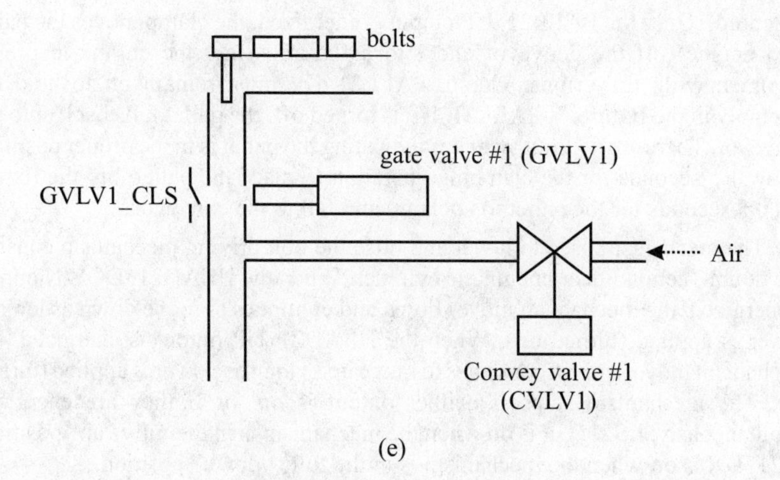

(e)

Figure P6.19. *(continued)*

Upon initial startup, assume that there are no pallets waiting at engaging hook, Engage 1. When a pallet is detected at Engage 1 (by PROX21), the following major steps are executed:

Activate the ENGAGE_21_CYL for 3 seconds to allow only one assembly to move into the station (when hook is raised, the next pallet is caught by the hook),

Raise the pallet off the conveyor,

Lower the bolt driving mechanism to the correct position (LS21_DN closes),

Activate appropriate solenoids and valves to convey the bolts into position (multiple steps),

Run air motors for 4 seconds to drive bolts,

Raise the bolt driving mechanism, until LS21_UP closes,

Lower pallet onto the conveyor,

Activate the ENGAGE_22_CYL for 3 seconds to allow pallet to move out.

The operation then repeats. Assume the conveyor is on at all times. The conveyor slides beneath the pallets as they are held by the engaging hooks or raised off the conveyor.

The proximity sensor, PROX21, is inductive and senses the metal assembly pallet. PROX21 senses the pallet before the pallet reaches the engage position. You must assume that when the pallet is captured by the ENGAGE_21_CYL, PROX21 remains **on**.

ENGAGE_21_CYL and ENGAGE_22_CYL are single action solenoids. Once it is energized, the "hook" moves down and remains in the "down" position as long as power is applied (turned **on**). The "hook" moves up when power is removed (turned **off**). The engaging mechanism works this way to be fail-safe, that is, if power is removed because of a failure, no pallets proceed down the conveyor.

The pallet-raising mechanism is driven by a single-action pneumatic cylinder (solenoid). Once the PALL21_UP output is energized, the clamp moves the pallet (and engine) off the conveyor and into a fixture to get the engine in proper alignment with the gripper clamp. PALL21_UP must remain **on** to hold the assembly in the fixture. If PALL21_UP is turned **off**, the pallet falls back onto the conveyor. There are no limit switches indicating the pallet is in the proper position. Allow 1.5 seconds for the clamping operation to place the pallet into the fixture and 0.5 seconds for the pallet to unclamp and fall to the conveyor.

The mechanism used to lower and raise the bolt driving mechanism consists of a double-action linear pneumatic cylinder. When the HEAD21_DOWN output is energized, the mechanism moves down and continues to move down as long as power is applied (turned **on**). When the HEAD21_UP output is energized, the mechanism moves up and continues to move up as long as power is applied (turned **on**). The mechanism stops if neither output is **on**, or if they are energized simultaneously. LS21_UP is **on** when the mechanism is in the fully "up" position. LS21_DN is **on** when the mechanism is in the fully "down" position.

The bolts are conveyed into position in the following manner. The bolts are marshaled by a vibrating feeder into a "line" so they are fed one at a time into the mechanism that places the bolt into a hose and is pneumatically conveyed to the bolt driver. Figures P6.19*d* and P6.19*e* show a more detailed view of this mechanism that conveys bolt #1 (the mechanism for bolt #2 is similar). Assume the two vibrating feeders (one for each bolt) are always on and thus are not a part of this problem. In order to convey bolt #1 and bolt #2 to the driving head, the following steps take place:

1. PBOLT1_CYL and PBOLT2_CYL are extended (turned **on**) to push the first bolt in each line into the open pneumatic tubes. These solenoids should only be activated for 1 second. They are single action solenoids and when PBOLT1_CYL (or PBOLT2_CYL) is turned **off**, the solenoid retracts, allowing the next bolt to become the first in line.
2. GVLV1 and GVLV2 are turned **on** to close gate valve #1 and #2 at the top of the pneumatic tube for bolt #1 and bolt #2. GVLV1_CLS limit switch indicates when gate valve #1 is closed and GVLV2_CLS indicates when gate valve #2 is closed. Both limit switches must be closed before continuing to the next step. Do not consider the case when one of these limit switches never turns **on**. There are no limit switches indicating that the valves are open. These

valves are controlled by single action solenoids and so gate valve #1 is opened when GVLV1 is turned **off**.

3. Open convey valve #1 (CVLV1 **on**) and convey valve #2 (CVLV2 **on**) to allow pressurized air to convey the bolts to the driving mechanism. At the head, each bolt enters a hollow tube whose sides are hexagonal and thus serve as the driver for the bolt. There are 2 proximity switches (PROXB1 and PROXB2) that indicate the presence of the bolt in the driving mechanism. Both proximity switches must be **on** before continuing to the next step. Do not consider the case when one of these proximity switches never turns **on**.

Note that gate valve #1 and gate valve #2 must be open for the first step above and closed for the second and third step. These valves are primarily used to seal the end of the pneumatic tube so that air can convey the bolt to the driving head. After the end of step 3, convey valve #1 and convey valve #2 should be closed.

The driving of the bolts is accomplished by two air motors. When AMOTOR1 is turned **on**, the tube that contains bolt #1 rotates and drives the bolt into the engine assembly. AMOTOR2 similarly drives bolt #2.

The start/stop switches are only for the station. They do not control any other stations, or the conveyor. Upon initial startup, assume there are no pallets present in either of the engaging hooks. If the stop switch is pressed at any time, the station operation should **pause**, except when the ENGAGE_21_CYL or ENGAGE_22_CYL engaging hook controls are activated. The operation **must not** pause when ENGAGE_21_CYL is activated (otherwise the station will contain two pallets with no space in between). If the stop switch is pressed when any engaging hook control is activated, the step should complete and the operation should advance to the next step. When the start switch is pressed while the operation is paused, the station should resume the suspended step. When paused, **do not advance** to the next step (exception noted earlier). When the station is paused, the raise/lower and air motor controls should be turned **off**. The pallet up solenoid PALL21_UP must not be turned **off** when paused (or the engine will be dropped onto the conveyor). Also, the engaging hook control, PBOLTx_CYL, and GVLVx **must not** be turned **off** when paused.

A separate reset switch is provided that when pressed, the bolt driving mechanism is raised, PBOLTx_CYL and GVLVx are turned **off**, convey valves closed, and the air motors turned **off**, and the process step is set as if the process is waiting for the next pallet. When the start switch is next pressed, no items are assumed present at the first engage position. To keep the problem simple, do not try to implement a function chart for reset; just activate the proper cylinder controls simultaneously until they are all finished. The reset switch should have no effect unless the operation is already paused.

Assume the tolerance on all timer values is ±0.1 seconds.

Assume the following physical inputs and outputs.

Variable	Description
START_PB	Start push button, N. O., **on** when starting.
STOP_PB	Stop push button, N. C., **off** when stopping.

RESET_PB	Reset push button, N. O., **on** when restoring process to initial state.
PROX21	Proximity sensor, **on** when pallet in position 1
LS21_UP	Limit switch that closes (**on**) when bolt driving mechanism is fully up
LS21_DN	Limit switch that closes (**on**) when bolt driving mechanism is fully down
GVLV1_CLS	Limit switch that closes (**on**) when gate valve #1 is fully closed.
GVLV2_CLS	Limit switch that closes (**on**) when gate valve #2 is fully closed.
PROXB1	Proximity switch that in **on** when bolt #1 is in position to be driven.
PROXB2	Proximity switch that in **on** when bolt #2 is in position to be driven.
ENGAGE_21_CYL	Engage hook 1 control, **on** to lower hook, **off** raises hook.
ENGAGE_22_CYL	Engage hook 2 control, **on** to lower hook, **off** raises hook.
HEAD21_UP	Bolt driving mechanism raise control, **on** to raise.
HEAD21_DOWN	Bolt driving mechanism lower control, **on** to lower.
PBOLT1_CYL	Pushes bolt #1 into pneumatic tube, **on** extends, **off** retracts.
PBOLT2_CYL	Pushes bolt #2 into pneumatic tube, **on** extends, **off** retracts.
GVLV1	Closes gate valve #1 to seal pneumatic tube, **on** to close, **off** to open.
GVLV2	Closes gate valve #2 to seal pneumatic tube, **on** to close, **off** to open.
CVLV1	Opens convey valve #1 to convey bolt #1 to driver, **on** to open valve, **off** to close.
CVLV2	Opens convey valve #2 to convey bolt #2 to driver, **on** to open valve, **off** to close.
AMOTOR1	Opens valve to air motor #1 to drive bolt #1, **on** to rotate bolt, **off** to stop rotation.
AMOTOR2	Opens valve to air motor #2 to drive bolt #2, **on** to rotate bolt, **off** to stop rotation.
PALL21_UP	Pallet up control, **on** to move pallet up and off the conveyor and clamp pallet in the proper position.

The addresses associated with the physical inputs and outputs are:

Variable	Modicon	PLC-5	ControlLogix	Siemens	GE Fanuc
START_PB	100033	I:04/00	Local:4:I.Data.0	I16.0	%I33
STOP_PB	100034	I:04/01	Local:4:I.Data.1	I16.1	%I34
RESET_PB	100035	I:04/02	Local:4:I.Data.2	I16.2	%I35
PROX21	100036	I:04/03	Local:4:I.Data.3	I16.3	%I36
LS21_UP	100039	I:04/06	Local:4:I.Data.6	I16.6	%I39
LS21_DN	100040	I:04/07	Local:4:I.Data.7	I16.7	%I40
GVLV1_CLS	100041	I:04/10	Local:4:I.Data.8	I17.0	%I41
GVLV2_CLS	100042	I:04/11	Local:4:I.Data.9	I17.1	%I42
PROXB1	100047	I:04/16	Local:4:I.Data.14	I17.6	%I47

PROXB2	100048	I:04/17	Local:4:I.Data.15	I17.7	%I48
ENGAGE_21_CYL	000017	O:06/00	Local:6:O.Data.0	Q24.0	%Q17
ENGAGE_22_CYL	000018	O:06/01	Local:6:O.Data.1	Q24.1	%Q18
HEAD21_UP	000019	O:06/02	Local:6:O.Data.2	Q24.2	%Q19
HEAD21_DOWN	000020	O:06/03	Local:6:O.Data.3	Q24.3	%Q20
PBOLT1_CYL	000021	O:06/04	Local:6:O.Data.4	Q24.4	%Q21
PBOLT2_CYL	000022	O:06/05	Local:6:O.Data.5	Q24.5	%Q22
GVLV1	000027	O:06/12	Local:6:O.Data.10	Q25.2	%Q27
GVLV2	000028	O:06/13	Local:6:O.Data.11	Q25.3	%Q28
CVLV1	000033	O:07/00	Local:7:O.Data.0	Q28.0	%Q33
CVLV2	000034	O:07/01	Local:7:O.Data.1	Q28.1	%Q34
AMOTOR1	000039	O:07/06	Local:7:O.Data.6	Q28.6	%Q39
AMOTOR2	000040	O:07/07	Local:7:O.Data.7	Q28.7	%Q40
PALL21_UP	000045	O:07/14	Local:7:O.Data.12	Q29.4	%Q45

P6-20. Palletizing Station Control. Using the function chart approach, implement the program for the following palletizing station.

Figure P6-20 shows the general layout of a station that palletizes bags. One conveyor feeds the bags to be palletized and another contains the empty pallets. A third conveyor receives the loaded pallets. In summary, an empty pallet is moved in, 5 bags are stacked on the pallet, and the full pallet is moved out. The operation is described in the following manner:

No pallet is assumed to be in the station upon initial startup.

To bring in an empty pallet, the pallet conveyor control, PALLET_CONV is turned **on** to bring in a new pallet into position (sensed by PALLET_PROX).

Then the PALLET_RAM cylinder control is energized to extend the ram that pushes an empty pallet from the empty pallet conveyor into the palletizing area. The ram is extended until the PALLET_ELS limit switch turns **on**, signaling that the pallet is in the station. The ram is retracted by turning the PALLET_RAM cylinder control **off**. The PALLET_RLS limit switch turns **on** when the pallet ram is retracted.

After the pallet ram is fully retracted, the infeed conveyor is turned **on** and the operation stacks 5 bags on the pallet. The passage of a bag is sensed by the BAG_PROX proximity sensor.

After 5 bags have passed, the infeed conveyor motor control (INFEED_CONV) is turned **off**, and the OUTFD_RAM control is energized to extend the ram that pushes the full pallet onto the outfeed conveyor. The ram is extended until the OUTFD_ELS limit switch turns **on**, signaling that the pallet is on the outfeed conveyor.

The ram is retracted by turning the OUTFD_RAM control off. The OUTFD_RLS limit switch turns **on** when the ram is fully retracted.

After the outfeed ram is fully retracted, the operation repeats by bringing in an empty pallet.

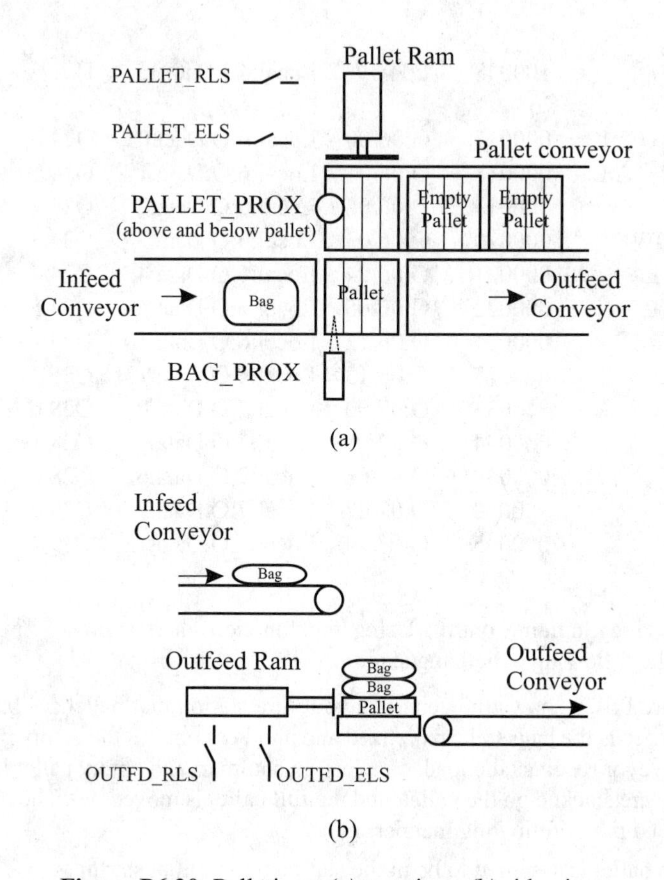

Figure P6.20. Palletizer: *(a)* top view; *(b)* side view.

All three conveyors are controlled by your PLC. The outfeed conveyor (controlled by OUTFEED_CONV) is **on** at all times that the palletizing station is running.

The pallet conveyor transports empty pallets in position to be pushed into the palletizer. The pallet conveyor motor control, PALLET_CONV must be **on** to move the empty pallet into position. PALLET _CONV must be **off** at all other times.

The infeed conveyor transports product bags into the palletizer. The infeed conveyor motor control, INFEED_CONV must be **on** to transport bags into the station. INFEED_CONV must be **off** whenever the full pallet is being moved out and an empty pallet is moved in.

Proximity sensor PALLET_PROX is a through sensor that turns **off** when the empty pallet is in position to be pushed into the palletizer. It turns **on** shortly after the ram pushes the pallet into the palletizer.

Proximity sensor BAG_PROX turns **on** as the bag falls to the pallet. It is **on** only momentarily (about 1 second) as the bag falls to the pallet. Assume the bag is detected as it falls onto the pallet. Assume that the product bags are spaced far enough apart so that BAG_PROX is **off** between bags.

The ram that pushes an empty pallet onto the palletizing area is a single-action hydraulic cylinder, controlled by PALLET_RAM. Once the PALLET_RAM output is energized, the ram extends and pushes the empty pallet into the palletizing area. Two limit switches detect the position of the ram. PALLET _ELS is **on** when the ram is extended (pallet in palletizing area). PALLET _RLS is **on** when the ram is retracted.

The ram that pushes the full pallet onto the outfeed conveyor is a single-action hydraulic cylinder, controlled by OUTFD_RAM. Once the OUTFD_RAM output is energized, the ram extends and pushes the pallet onto the outfeed conveyor. Two limit switches detect the position of the ram. OUTFD_ELS is **on** when the ram is extended (pallet on outfeed conveyor). OUTFD_RLS is **on** when the ram is retracted.

When the start switch is pressed (turned **on**) for the first time only, the station assumes that no pallet is in the station. When the stop switch is pressed (turned **off**) the operation should pause and all outputs must be turned **off**. Pressing the start switch while the operation of the station is paused causes the station to resume its suspended step. When paused, **do not advance** to the next step.

A separate reset switch, RESET_PB, is provided which resets any internal states so that when the start switch is pressed, no pallets are assumed present in the station. Obviously, the operator must clear everything out of the palletizing area before resuming operation after a reset operation. Also, the reset operation should cause the rams to retract and the reset operation is not complete until both rams are retracted. The reset switch should be ignored if the station is running. The start switch should be ignored when the reset operation is in progress. If the station is paused and RESET_PB is **on**, the operator must release the RESET_PB before the start pushbutton switch can be used to restart the palletizer.

Assume the tolerance on all timer values is ±0.1 seconds.

Assume the following physical inputs and outputs.

Variable	Description
START_PB	Start push button, N. O., **on** when starting.
STOP_PB	Stop push button, N. C., **off** when stopping.
RESET_PB	Reset push button, N. O., **on** when restoring station to initial state.
PALLET_PROX	Proximity sensor, turns **off** (open) when empty pallet in position to be pushed into palletizer; **on** as pallet is pushed into palletizer or when no pallet is present.
BAG_PROX	Proximity sensor, turns **on** (closed) momentarily as bag falls to pallet.
PALLET_ELS	Limit switch that closes (**on**) when empty pallet-pushing cylinder is extended (empty pallet in palletizer).
PALLET_RLS	Limit switch that closes (**on**) when empty pallet-pushing cylinder is retracted.
OUTFD_ELS	Limit switch that closes (**on**) when full pallet-pushing cylinder is extended (pallet on outfeed conveyor).
OUTFD_RLS	Limit switch that closes (**on**) when full pallet-pushing cylinder is retracted.

INFEED_CONV	Infeed conveyor motor control, **on** to move bags into station.
OUTFEED_CONV	Outfeed conveyor motor control, **on** to move full pallets to next station.
PALLET_CONV	Empty pallet conveyor motor control, **on** to move empty pallets into position to be pushed into palletizer.
PALLET_RAM	Empty pallet cylinder extend control, **on** to extend cylinder, **off** causes cylinder to retract.
OUTFD_RAM	Full pallet cylinder extend control, **on** to extend cylinder, **off** causes cylinder to retract.

The addresses associated with the physical inputs and outputs are:

Variable	Modicon	PLC-5	ControlLogix	Siemens	GE Fanuc
START_PB	100001	I:01/00	Local:1:I.Data.0	I4.0	%I1
STOP_PB	100002	I:01/01	Local:1:I.Data.1	I4.1	%I2
RESET_PB	100003	I:01/02	Local:1:I.Data.2	I4.2	%I3
PALLET_PROX	100004	I:01/03	Local:1:I.Data.3	I4.3	%I4
BAG_PROX	100005	I:01/04	Local:1:I.Data.4	I4.4	%I5
PALLET_ELS	100006	I:01/05	Local:1:I.Data.5	I4.5	%I6
PALLET_RLS	100007	I:01/06	Local:1:I.Data.6	I4.6	%I7
OUTFD_ELS	100008	I:01/07	Local:1:I.Data.7	I4.7	%I8
OUTFD_RLS	100009	I:01/10	Local:1:I.Data.8	I5.0	%I9
INFEED_CONV	000001	O:02/00	Local:2:O.Data.0	Q8.0	%Q1
OUTFEED_CONV	000002	O:02/01	Local:2:O.Data.1	Q8.1	%Q2
PALLET_CONV	000003	O:02/02	Local:2:O.Data.2	Q8.2	%Q3
PALLET_RAM	000004	O:02/03	Local:2:O.Data.3	Q8.3	%Q4
OUTFD_RAM	000005	O:02/04	Local:2:O.Data.4	Q8.4	%Q5

P6-21. Revised Parts Transfer Station Control. Using the function chart approach, implement the program for the following revision to a parts transfer station.

> Problem P6-3 describes a station that transfer parts from a conveyor to a packaging machine. The parts are now made faster and so the cycle time of the parts transfer station of problem P6-3 must be decreased. Specifically, the loading of the next 6 parts onto the turntable starts while the ram pushes parts into the packaging machine. Assume the time needed to extend and retract the ram is less than the time to accumulate 6 parts on the turntable.

P6-22. Revised Drilling Station Control. Using the function chart approach, implement the program for the following revisions to the drilling station.

> Rework the drilling station of problem P6-18, allowing certain operations to occur in parallel:
>
> 1. The extension/retraction of drill 1 and drill 2 occur simultaneously. However, make no assumption about which drilling operation finishes last.

2. Allow a new part to move into position 2 while the previous part is being drilled. However, a new part cannot move from position 2 to position 3 while a drilled part is moving out of position 3.

The assumption about initial startup does not change. Upon initial startup, assume that there are no parts waiting at gate 1 and that there are no parts in the station waiting to be drilled. DO NOT initiate a drilling operation while the first part moves into the station.

P6-23. Revised Bolt Driving Station Control. Using the function chart approach, implement the program for the following revisions to the bolt driving station of problem P6-19.

Rework the bolt driving station of P6-19, allowing certain operations to occur in parallel:

While the bolt driving mechanism is lowering to the correct position, convey all bolts into position. Make no assumption about which operation finishes last.

Also, the station now conveys and drives 6 bolts.

Assume the following additional physical inputs and outputs.

Variable	Description
GVLV3_CLS	Limit switch that closes (**on**) when gate valve #3 is fully closed.
GVLV4_CLS	Limit switch that closes (**on**) when gate valve #4 is fully closed.
GVLV5_CLS	Limit switch that closes (**on**) when gate valve #5 is fully closed.
GVLV6_CLS	Limit switch that closes (**on**) when gate valve #6 is fully closed.
PROXB3	Proximity switch that in **on** when bolt #3 is in position to be driven.
PROXB4	Proximity switch that in **on** when bolt #4 is in position to be driven.
PROXB5	Proximity switch that in **on** when bolt #5 is in position to be driven.
PROXB6	Proximity switch that in **on** when bolt #6 is in position to be driven.
PBOLT3_CYL	Pushes bolt #3 into pneumatic tube, **on** extend, **off** retracts.
PBOLT4_CYL	Pushes bolt #4 into pneumatic tube, **on** extend, **off** retracts.
PBOLT5_CYL	Pushes bolt #5 into pneumatic tube, **on** extend, **off** retracts.
PBOLT6_CYL	Pushes bolt #6 into pneumatic tube, **on** extend, **off** retracts.
GVLV3	Closes gate valve #3 to seal tube, **on** to close, **off** to open.
GVLV4	Closes gate valve #4 to seal tube, **on** to close, **off** to open.
GVLV5	Closes gate valve #5 to seal tube, **on** to close, **off** to open.
GVLV6	Closes gate valve #6 to seal tube, **on** to close, **off** to open.
CVLV3	Opens convey valve #3 to convey bolt #3 to driver, **on** to open valve, **off** to close.
CVLV4	Opens convey valve #4 to convey bolt #4 to driver, **on** to open valve, **off** to close.
CVLV5	Opens convey valve #5 to convey bolt #5 to driver, **on** to open valve, **off** to close.

CVLV6	Opens convey valve #6 to convey bolt #6 to driver, **on** to open valve, **off** to close.
AMOTOR3	Opens valve to air motor #3 to drive bolt #3, **on** to rotate bolt, **off** to not rotate.
AMOTOR4	Opens valve to air motor #4 to drive bolt #4, **on** to rotate bolt, **off** to not rotate.
AMOTOR5	Opens valve to air motor #5 to drive bolt #5, **on** to rotate bolt, **off** to not rotate.
AMOTOR6	Opens valve to air motor #6 to drive bolt #6, **on** to rotate bolt, **off** to not rotate.

The addresses associated with the additional physical inputs and outputs are:

Variable	Modicon	PLC-5	ControlLogix	Siemens	GE Fanuc
GVLV3_CLS	100043	I:04/12	Local:4:I.Data.10	I17.2	%I43
GVLV4_CLS	100044	I:04/13	Local:4:I.Data.11	I17.3	%I44
GVLV5_CLS	100045	I:04/14	Local:4:I.Data.12	I17.4	%I45
GVLV6_CLS	100046	I:04/15	Local:4:I.Data.13	I17.5	%I46
PROXB3	100049	I:05/00	Local:5:I.Data.0	I20.0	%I49
PROXB4	100050	I:05/01	Local:5:I.Data.1	I20.1	%I50
PROXB5	100051	I:05/02	Local:5:I.Data.2	I20.2	%I51
PROXB6	100052	I:05/03	Local:5:I.Data.3	I20.3	%I52
PBOLT3_CYL	000023	O:06/06	Local:6:O.Data.6	Q24.6	%Q23
PBOLT4_CYL	000024	O:06/07	Local:6:O.Data.7	Q24.7	%Q24
PBOLT5_CYL	000025	O:06/10	Local:6:O.Data.8	Q25.0	%Q25
PBOLT6_CYL	000026	O:06/11	Local:6:O.Data.9	Q25.1	%Q26
GVLV3	000029	O:06/14	Local:6:O.Data.12	Q25.4	%Q29
GVLV4	000030	O:06/15	Local:6:O.Data.13	Q25.5	%Q30
GVLV5	000031	O:06/16	Local:6:O.Data.14	Q25.6	%Q31
GVLV6	000032	O:06/17	Local:6:O.Data.15	Q25.7	%Q32
CVLV3	000035	O:07/02	Local:7:O.Data.2	Q28.2	%Q35
CVLV4	000036	O:07/03	Local:7:O.Data.3	Q28.3	%Q36
CVLV5	000037	O:07/04	Local:7:O.Data.4	Q28.4	%Q37
CVLV6	000038	O:07/05	Local:7:O.Data.5	Q28.5	%Q38
AMOTOR3	000041	O:07/10	Local:7:O.Data.8	Q29.0	%Q41
AMOTOR4	000042	O:07/11	Local:7:O.Data.9	Q29.1	%Q42
AMOTOR5	000043	O:07/12	Local:7:O.Data.10	Q29.2	%Q43
AMOTOR6	000044	O:07/13	Local:7:O.Data.11	Q29.3	%Q44

P6-24. Traffic Light Controller. Using the function chart approach, implement the program for the following traffic light controller.

A diagram of the intersection is shown in Figure P6.24. For simplicity, the traffic lights are red or green. There are no yellow lights.

The operation of the traffic light controller is broken up into cycles. During the north-south (NS) cycle, northbound (NB) and southbound (SB) straight traffic

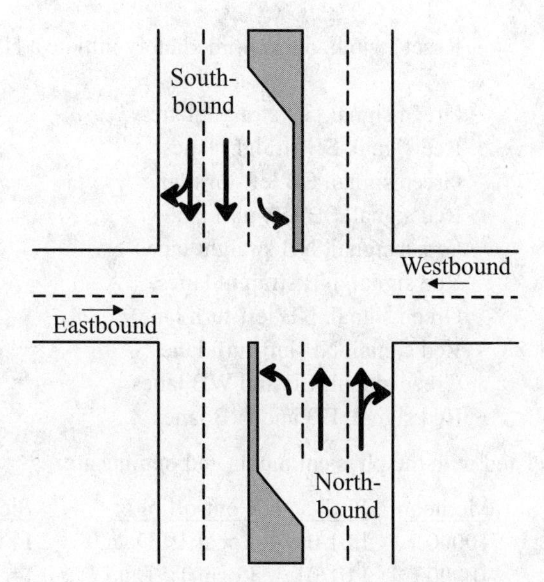

Figure P6.24. Street intersection.

has a green signal, and the signals for all other lanes are red. During an east-west (EW) cycle, eastbound (EB) and westbound (WB) traffic has a green signal and all other lanes have a red signal. The left turn (LT) cycle is activated whenever a NB or SB car is in its respective left-turn lane. During a LT cycle, the signals for the two left-turn lanes are green and the signals for the other lanes are red.

Northbound and southbound traffic is given priority, and the controller remains in the NS cycle as long as no cars are detected in the EB or WB lanes, and when no cars are in the NB and SB left-turn lanes. However, the NS cycle is no shorter than 30 seconds. If a car is present in the EB or WB lanes after the minimum 30 seconds in the NS cycle, an EW cycle is initiated. The EW cycle lasts for 20 seconds. At the end of the EW cycle, if any cars are present in either left-turn lane, the controller initiates an LT cycle. Otherwise, if no cars are present in either left-turn lane, the controller returns to the NS cycle. An LT cycle lasts for 10 seconds. At the end of an LT cycle, the controller returns to the NS cycle. If a car is present in either left turn lane after the minimum 30 seconds in the NS cycle, a LT cycle is initiated.

When the program initially runs, it should initiate a NS cycle. A reset switch is provided to initiate a NS cycle when the switch is **on**.

Assume the following physical inputs and outputs.

Variable	Description
SBS_PRES	**On** when SB car present in a straight-ahead lane
SBL_PRES	**On** when SB car present in left-turn lane
NBS_PRES	**On** when NB car present in a straight-ahead lane
NBL_PRES	**On** when NB car present in left-turn lane
EB_PRES	**On** when EB car present in lane
WB_PRES	**On** when WB car present in lane

RESET_PB	Reset switch, **on** to immediately initiate a NS cycle
SBS_GR	Green signal, SB straight lanes
SBS_RD	Red signal, SB straight lanes
SBL_GR	Green signal, SB left-turn lane
SBL_RD	Red signal, SB left-turn lane
NBS_GR	Green signal, NB straight lanes
NBS_RD	Red signal, NB straight lanes
NBL_GR	Green signal, NB left-turn lane
NBL_RD	Red signal, NB left-turn lane
EWB_GR	Green signal, EB and WB lanes
EWB_RD	Red signal, EB and WB lanes

The addresses associated with the physical inputs and outputs are:

Variable	Modicon	PLC-5	ControlLogix	Siemens	GE Fanuc
SBS_PRES	100001	I:01/00	Local:1:I.Data.0	I4.0	%I1
SBL_PRES	100002	I:01/01	Local:1:I.Data.1	I4.1	%I2
NBS_PRES	100003	I:01/02	Local:1:I.Data.2	I4.2	%I3
NBL_PRES	100004	I:01/03	Local:1:I.Data.3	I4.3	%I4
EB_PRES	100005	I:01/04	Local:1:I.Data.4	I4.4	%I5
WB_PRES	100006	I:01/05	Local:1:I.Data.5	I4.5	%I6
RESET_PB	100007	I:01/06	Local:1:I.Data.6	I4.6	%I7
SBS_GR	000001	O:02/00	Local:2:O.Data.0	Q8.0	%Q1
SBS_RD	000002	O:02/01	Local:2:O.Data.1	Q8.1	%Q2
SBL_GR	000003	O:02/02	Local:2:O.Data.2	Q8.2	%Q3
SBL_RD	000004	O:02/03	Local:2:O.Data.3	Q8.3	%Q4
NBS_GR	000005	O:02/04	Local:2:O.Data.4	Q8.4	%Q5
NBS_RD	000006	O:02/05	Local:2:O.Data.5	Q8.5	%Q6
NBL_GR	000007	O:02/06	Local:2:O.Data.6	Q8.6	%Q7
NBL_RD	000008	O:02/07	Local:2:O.Data.7	Q8.7	%Q8
EWB_GR	000009	O:02/10	Local:2:O.Data.8	Q9.0	%Q9
EWB_RD	000010	O:02/11	Local:2:O.Data.9	Q9.1	%Q10

7 Comparison and Computation

Chapter Topics:

- Comparison function blocks
- Computation function blocks
- Comparison and computation applications

OBJECTIVES

Upon completion of this chapter, you will be able to:

- Describe the operation of the comparison and computation function blocks of the PLCs covered by this text
- Apply comparison and computation to industrial situations

Scenario: Calibrating a differential pressure transmitter causes a major processor fault.

You are called by the power plant because they are having problems with the baghouse PLC. The baghouse (Figure 7.1) is essentially a filter for the boiler flue gas. It removes small particulates from the gas stream before it is released to the atmosphere. A technician has just recalibrated the differential pressure transmitter (PDT-016) and now the display on the operator panel shows "****" in place of the pressure reading and there is a message at

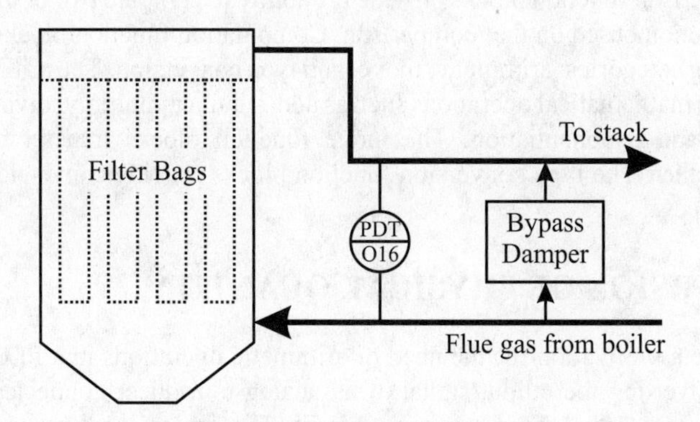

Figure 7.1. Power plant baghouse.

the top of the display that reads "PLC in Program Mode." They have opened the bypass damper so that the flue gases bypass the baghouse, but they will get in trouble with the regulatory agencies if the baghouse is not placed in service in a few minutes.

***Solution*:** When you arrive, you notice from the indicators on the SLC 5/03 processor module that the processor is faulted and not running. You connect your notebook computer to the processor and examine the processor status. The fault code is 20 and is described as "A minor error bit is set at end of the scan." The fault is located in rung 223 of program file 2, the last rung of the program, which is to be expected from the description of the fault. The math overflow trap bit is also set, indicating that a math overflow occurred as a result of the calibration process. Using the cross-reference, you find a SCL function block that scales the transmitter reading. Consulting the instruction set reference manual, you discover that an overflow in one part of this calculation causes the math overflow trap bit to be set. However, the code checks for the transmitter value within range before using the SCL function block. So the SCL is not the problem. The last reading of the analog input channel is 17,352. With the cross-reference, you find another place where this transmitter value is used. It is multiplied by 1.9 and copied to an analog output integer that is connected to a chart recorder. The constant 1.9 is the ratio of the maximum value of the analog output integer divided by the maximum value of the transmitter value (31208/16384). However, the last transmitter value (17,352) multiplied by 1.9 is 32,969, which is an overflow! To prevent the problem from happening, you limit the analog input integer to 16,384 before multiplying it by 1.9.

7.1 INTRODUCTION

Comparison and computation function blocks are used less frequently than timers and counters, but are still important. This chapter describes these types of function blocks for the PLCs covered by this text. As done in previous chapters, the comparison and computation function blocks for a particular PLC are described in separate sections. That is, only the section(s) pertaining to the PLC(s) of interest need to be studied. Following these descriptions, examples are used to illustrate their application. To illustrate the need for computation, the next section describes the conversion of a physical quantity, as measured by an analog input module, to a value in the PLC.

The comparison function blocks provide the ability to compare two or more values and initiate some action based on that comparison. Computation function blocks are classified in the following categories: arithmetic, move, and type conversion. The arithmetic function blocks perform mathematical operations such as add, subtract, multiply, divide, square root, trigonometry, and exponentiation. The move function blocks transfer data from one location to another. The type conversion function blocks provide conversion between the various data types.

7.2 CONVERSION OF PHYSICAL QUANTITY

To provide a motivation for the need of arithmetic operations in a PLC, consider the problem of converting the output signal of an analog transducer connected to an analog input module into a value in the appropriate units. The analog input module converts the transducer output signal into a digital value, usually an integer. However, in order to be

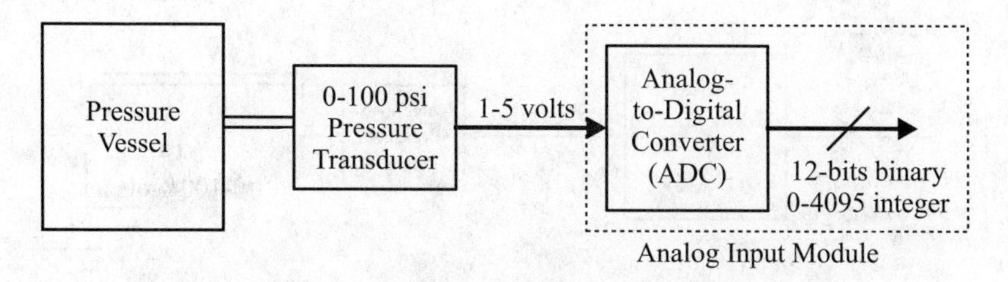

Figure 7.2. Pressure measurement example.

useful this integer should be converted into a value whose units are appropriate to the physical quantity being measured, for example, flow, level, or temperature. The following example illustrates this problem.

Example 7.1. A transducer measures pressure in the range of 0 to 100 pounds/square inch (psi) and transmits the pressure as a 1 to 5 volt signal to an analog input module having a 12-bit ADC whose output value is an integer in the range of 0 to 4095 (Figure 7.2). Find the transmitted voltage and ADC output value for pressures of 0, 25, 50, and 78 psi.

Solution. The table of signal voltages and ADC output values for the various pressures is shown below. Unless known otherwise, one assumes a linear relationship between the physical quantity being measured and the output signal of the transducer. So, when the pressure is zero (the low end of the range), the transducer voltage and therefore the ADC output are also at the low end of their respective ranges. A 50 psi pressure is in the middle of the measurement range and so the transducer voltage is also at the middle of its range (3 volts). The ADC output corresponding to 50 psi is also in the middle of its range, which is technically 2047.5, but must be rounded to the nearest integer, 2048. The values for 25 psi are basically halfway between the values corresponding to zero and 50 psi. A pressure of 78 psi is at 78% of the 0 to 100 psi range, so the transducer output is at 78% of its range, 1+0.78(5-1)=4.12. In a similar fashion, the ADC output is at 78% of its range, 0.78(4095-0)=3194.1 which rounds to 3194. The results are summarized as

Pressure	Transducer Voltage	ADC Output Value
0 psi	1.0 volt	0
25	2.0	1023.75 rounds to 1024
50	3.0	2047.5 rounds to 2048
78	4.12	3194.1 rounds to 3194

Example 7.1 also illustrates that a given physical quantity may be represented in a control system by more than one type of signal. The pressure was not only represented by an integer, but also by a voltage signal. In addition, the ranges of these two representations are not identical. As another example, Figure 7.3 depicts the analog output of a PLC used to control the position of a regulatory control valve. The PLC analog output is a signal in the range of 4 to 20 mA which is converted into a 3 to 15 psi pressure signal. The pressure signal drives the valve which converts the 3 to 15 psi into 0 to 100% open (0% is closed). The valve position of 0 to 100% is represented three other ways (integer, current, and pressure).

The need to represent a physical quantity with signals having different ranges is generalized as "percent of span." Even though a physical quantity takes on different signal representations, the percent of span remains the same. Expressing physical quantities as percent of span is commonly used in chemical process industries to avoid confusion and

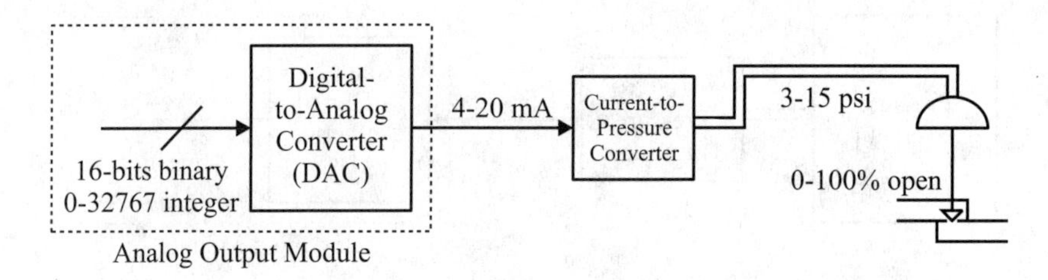

Figure 7.3. Valve position represented by multiple signals.

mistakes. Older, pneumatic control systems use a pressure signal with a range of 3 to 15 psi to transmit quantities between instruments. In electronic control systems, the common signal between instruments is a 4 to 20 mA current. Figure 7.4 illustrates the relationship between the values of a physical quantity, expressed in any units to percent of span. As an equation, the conversion of a value to percent of span is

$$\text{Percent of span} = \frac{\text{Value} - \text{Low}}{\text{High} - \text{Low}} \times 100$$

The conversion of percent of span to a value is expressed as

$$\text{Value} = \frac{\text{Percent of span}}{100} \times (\text{High} - \text{Low}) + \text{Low}$$

The high and low values are often called Engineering Units (E.U.):

E.U. Low = Lowest physical quantity measured by transducer

E.U. High = Highest physical quantity measured by transducer

E.U. Span = E.U. High - E.U. Low

For Example 7.1, the E.U. Low is 0 psi and the E.U. High is 100 psi.

In the PLC, one is only interested in obtaining a relationship between the integer output from the ADC to the value of the physical quantity. In this case, the value in % of span is not needed and the formula for the equation of a straight line between two points is used to find this relationship (Figure 7.5). Let

X = value of quantity in first units

X_1 = lowest value of first units (0%)

X_2 = highest value of first units (100%)

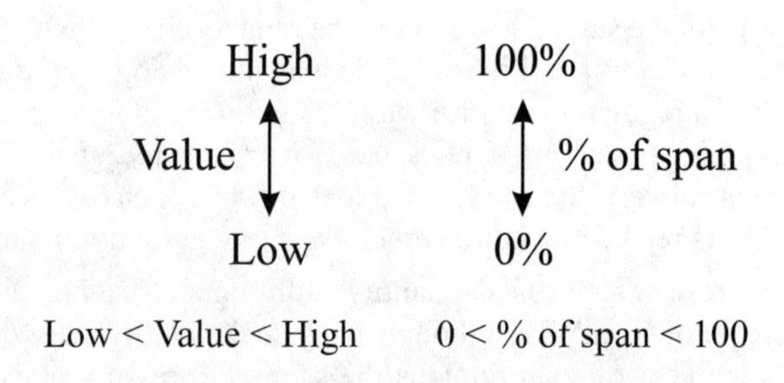

Figure 7.4. Relationship between value and % of span.

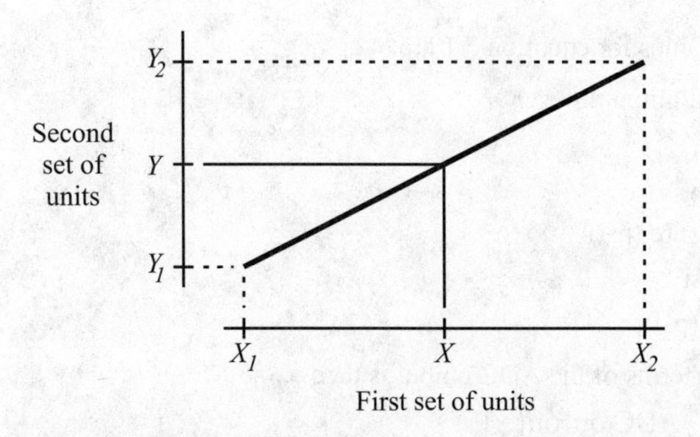

Figure 7.5. Linear relationship between two sets of units.

Y = value of quantity in second units

Y_1 = lowest value of second units (0%)

Y_2 = highest value of second units (100%)

To find the value of the quantity (Y) in the terms of the second units, given the value of the quantity (X) in terms of the first units,

$$Y = \frac{X - X_1}{X_2 - X_1} \times (Y_2 - Y_1) + Y_1 \tag{7.1}$$

The use of this formula is demonstrated by the following examples.

Example 7.2. For the situation of Example 7.1, (a) find the formula for the ADC output integer in terms of the pressure; (b) find the pressure (in psi), given the ADC output integer. The ranges of the values are:

Pressure transducer: 0 to 100 psi

ADC output integer: 0 to 4095

Solution. The formula given in (7.1) is applied for both of these situations. For (a) the variables for equation 7.1 are

X = Pressure (psi)

X_1 = 0 (psi)

X_2 = 100 (psi)

Y = ADC output integer

Y_1 = 0

Y_2 = 4095

The ADC output in terms of the pressure is then

$$\text{ADC output} = \frac{\text{Pressure} - 0}{100 - 0} \times (4095 - 0) + 0 \quad \text{rounded to nearest integer}$$

which simplifies to

ADC output = Pressure × 40.95 rounded to nearest integer

For (b) the variables for equation 7.1 are

X = ADC output integer

X_1 = 0

X_2 = 4095

Y = Pressure (psi)

Y_1 = 0 (psi)

Y_2 = 100 (psi)

The pressure in terms of the ADC output is then

$$\text{Pressure} = \frac{\text{ADC output} - 0}{4095 - 0} \times (100 - 0) + 0$$

which simplifies to

$$\text{Pressure} = \text{ADC output} \times 0.02442 \ \text{psi}$$

Part (b) of Example 7.2 is the usual situation that needs to be handled in the PLC. The ADC output integer is converted to the proper units in order to be displayed on an operator display or to be used with a comparison function block to provide an alarm indication.

Example 7.3. A transducer measures temperature in the range of 90 to 700 °C and is connected to an analog input module having a 16-bit ADC whose output value is an integer in the range of 0 to 32767. Find the formula to convert the ADC output integer to the temperature, in °C.

Solution. Equation (7.1) is used to find the conversion equation. The variables for equation 7.1 are

X = ADC output integer

X_1 = 0

X_2 = 32767

Y = Temperature (°C)

Y_1 = 90 (°C)

Y_2 = 700 (°C)

The temperature in terms of the ADC output is then

$$\text{Temperature} = \frac{\text{ADC output} - 0}{32767 - 0} \times (700 - 90) + 90$$

which simplifies to

$$\text{Temperature} = \text{ADC output} \times 0.01862 + 90 \ \ °\text{C}$$

7.3 IEC COMPARISON AND COMPUTATION

The IEC 61131-3 comparison and computation function blocks are very similar to the Modicon function blocks of the same name described in the next section. The only difference is that the name of most of the Modicon function blocks have a data type suffix appended to the IEC name. This naming convention is allowed in IEC 61131-3.

7.4 MODICON COMPARISON AND COMPUTATION

The Modicon comparison and computation function blocks are organized according to their function:

Category	Description
Comparison	Compare one or more values
Basic math	Basic arithmetic (+, -, ×, ÷)
Advanced math	Trigonometry and exponentiation
Logical	Bit-wise logical operators
Data type conversion	Convert value to another data type
Move	Copy data
Selection	Select one of a list of values

All of the comparison and computation function blocks have the EN and ENO connections as the topmost input and output, respectively (Figure 7.6). The EN input must be **on** ("1" or logical true) for the block to execute. The ENO output echoes the EN input and is **on** if EN is **on** and the block executes without error. If the EN input is **off** ("0" or logical false) the function block is **not** executed and all outputs remain with their old values, that is the value when the block was last executed. In this case, the value of ENO is automatically set to **off**.

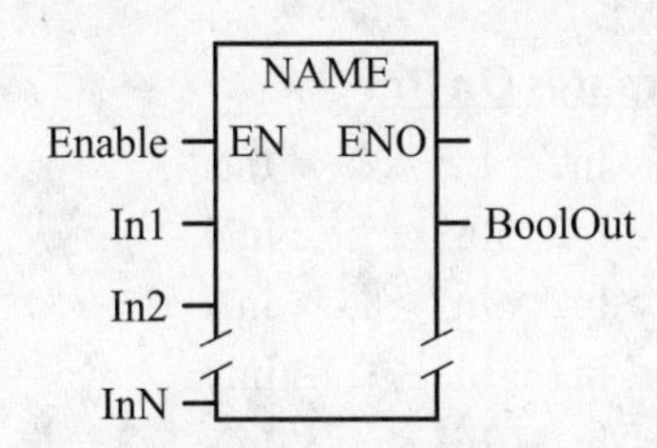

Figure 7.6. EN and ENO function block connections.

> **Design Tip**
>
> The behavior of the function block outputs when EN is off must be considered in the ladder logic code. If the EN input is off, the block outputs remain at their last value. This behavior may produce unexpected results.

7.4.1 Comparison Function Blocks

Example comparison function blocks are shown in Figure 7.7. The name of the comparison block consists of the comparison type (EQ, GE, GT, LE, LT, or NE) with a data

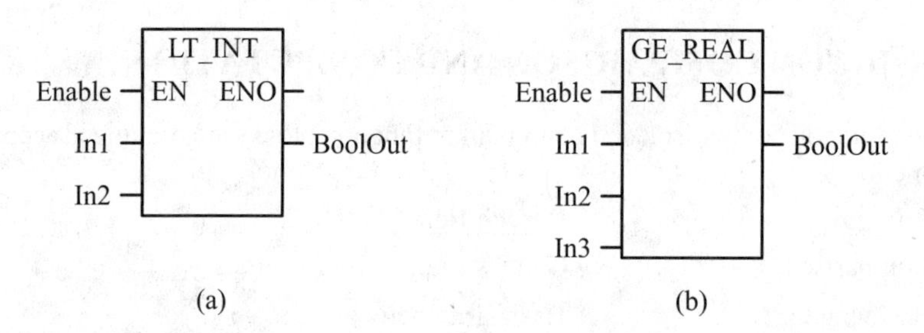

Figure 7.7. Example Modicon comparison function blocks: *(a)* less than; *(b)* greater than or equal.

type suffix. The suffix of the function block name determines the format of the data to be compared:

BOOL	INT	UDINT
BYTE	REAL	UINT
DINT	TIME	WORD

Each comparison function block has at least two inputs. Except for the not equal (NE) function block, the comparison blocks are extensible, that is, the number of inputs to the block may be increased up to 32. The result of the comparison (shown as BoolOut in Figure 7.6) is a Boolean. The possible comparison function blocks and the condition that turns on the BoolOut output are:

Block Name	Output is On if:
EQ_***	In1 = In2 = In3 = … = InN
GE_***	In1 ≥ In2 ≥ In3 ≥ … ≥ InN
GT_***	In1 > In2 > In3 > … > InN
LE_***	In1 ≤ In2 ≤ In3 ≤ … ≤ InN
LT_***	In1 < In2 < In3 < … < InN
NE_***	In1 ≠ In2 (only 2 inputs)

where *** is the data type suffix.

When cascading comparison blocks to implement complicated comparison operations, the behavior of the output must be considered when EN is off. It is entirely possible that the output of the second comparison is **on** when the output of the first comparison is **off**. For example, consider an implementation of a high level alarm for a tank. The alarm, LT1000_HIALM, is **on** when

90.0 ≤ LT1000 < 95.0

LT1000 is the tank level in whatever units are being used. An incorrect implementation of this comparison is shown in Figure 7.8*a*. If the tank level is greater than or equal to 90 and less than 95, the alarm is turned on. However, if the level later falls below 90, the alarm remains on. With the level below 90, the output of the GE_REAL block turns off, disabling the execution of the LT_REAL block. The value of the LT_REAL output remains on because that was the value on its last execution (the level is still below 95). Reversing the order of the function blocks as shown in Figure 7.8*b* will make the alarm operate properly when the level decreases below 90, however, the alarm will remain on when the level increases above 95. If the tank level is at least 95, then a high-high alarm indication is turned

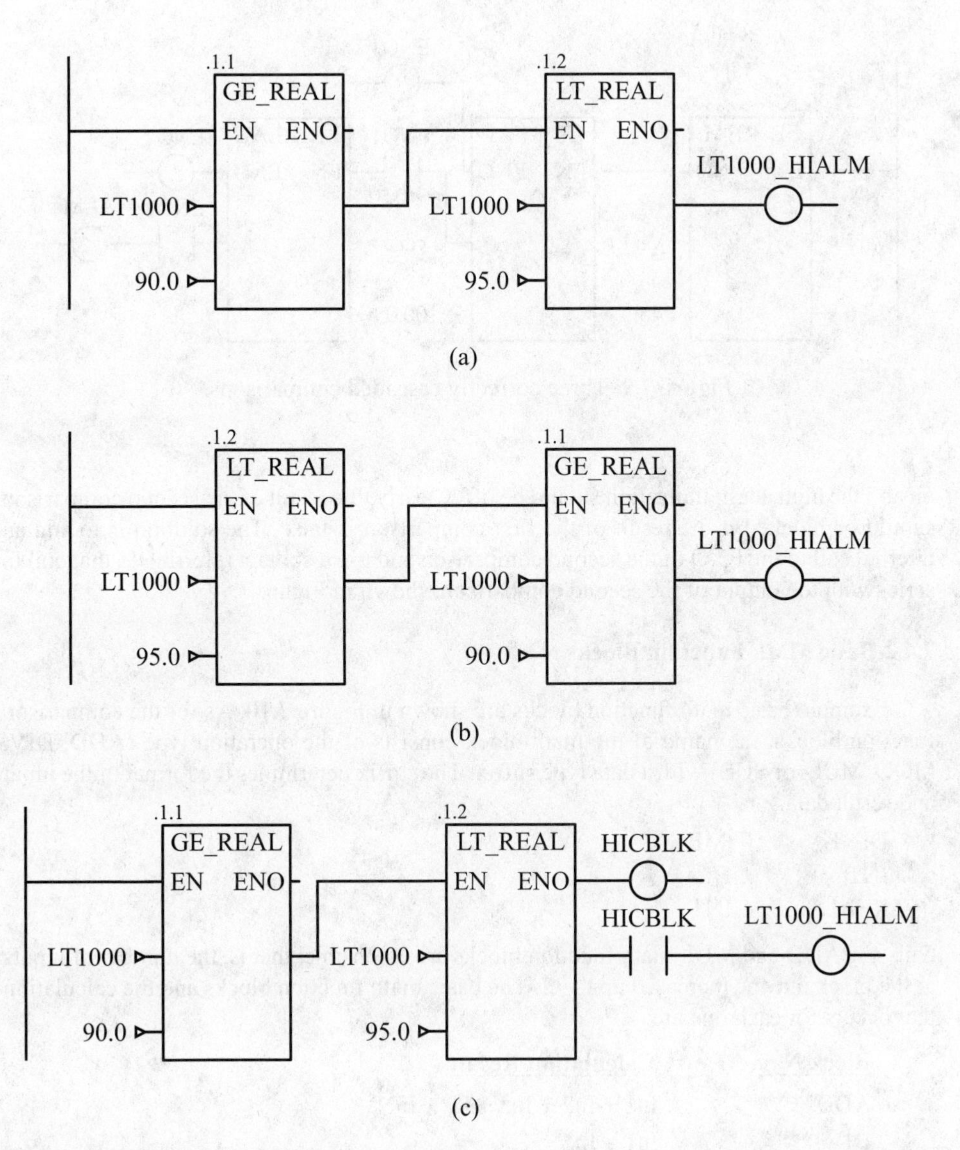

Figure 7.8. Cascaded Modicon comparison: *(a)* incorrect with GE first; *(b)* incorrect with LT first; *(c)* correct comparison.

Design Tip

When cascading comparison function blocks the output of every block but the first one may need a contact in series with its output. This contact should be **on** only when the ENO of that block is **on**. An example appears in Figure 7.9.

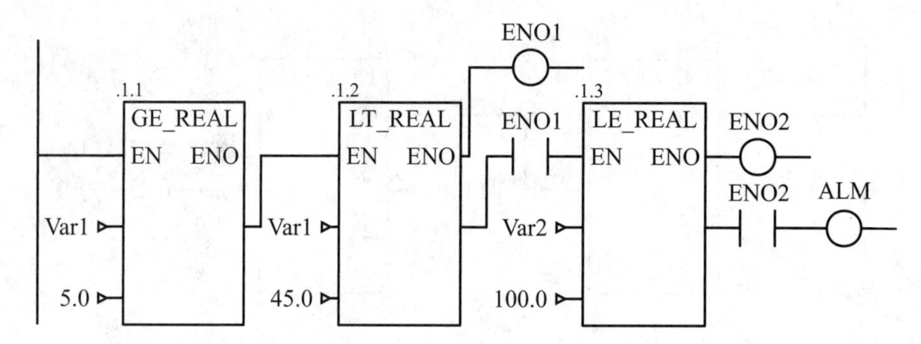

Figure 7.9. Three correctly cascaded comparisons.

on and the high alarm indication should be off. Clearly, the result of the second comparison should be blocked if the result of the first comparison is false. The solution is to add an internal coil to the ENO of the second comparison and use a contact referring to that coil in series with the output of the second comparison, shown in Figure 7.8*c*.

7.4.2 Basic Math Function Blocks

Example basic math function blocks are shown in Figure 7.10. As for the comparison function blocks, the name of the math block consists of the operation type (ADD, DIV, MOD, MUL, or SUB) with a data type suffix. The suffix determines the format of the input and result data:

DINT	TIME
INT	UDINT
REAL	UINT

Only the ADD and MUL math function blocks are extensible, that is, the number of inputs to the block may be increased up to 32. The basic math function blocks and the calculation that occurs for each one are:

Block Name	Calculation Result
ADD_***	In1 + In2 + In3 + … + InN
DIV_***	In1 ÷ In2
MOD_***	In1 modulo In2 = In1 – (In1/In2)×In2 (integer types only)
MUL_***	In1 × In2 × In3 × … × InN
SUB_***	In1 – In2
TIME_DIV_***	In1 ÷ In2 (In1 and Result are TIME type)
TIME_MUL_***	In1 × In2 (In1 and Result are TIME type)

where *** is the data type suffix. The MOD (modulo) function block is valid for integer types only (DINT, INT, UDINT, or UINT). The TIME data type is valid only for the ADD_*** and SUB_*** blocks listed in the above table. Division and multiplication of time is provided by the TIME_DIV and TIME_MUL function blocks, illustrated in Figure 7.11.

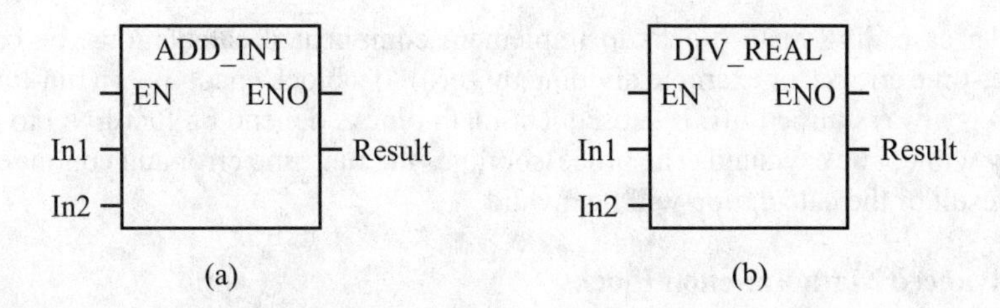

Figure 7.10. Example Modicon basic math function blocks: *(a)* addition; *(b)* divide.

If two integers are divided and the result contains a fraction, the fractional remainder is truncated. For example, if the two inputs to DIV_INT are 15 and 6, the output result is 2.

Similarly, if the result of TIME_DIV or TIME_MUL contains a fraction of a millisecond, the result is rounded to the nearest millisecond.

Note that the data type for the input and output connections to the math function blocks must match the suffix of the block name (except for TIME_DIV and TIME_MUL). Therefore, if dissimilar data types must be added, at least one of them will need to be converted with a data type conversion block.

The basic math function blocks that have only one input are shown in Figure 7.12 and are described as:

Block Name	Calculation Result
ABS_***	Absolute value of In1 (|In1|)
NEG_***	– In1

where *** is the data type suffix. Although the NEG_UDINT and NEG_UINT are provided, any execution of these two blocks will cause a run-time error. The NEG function block is an extension of IEC 61131-3.

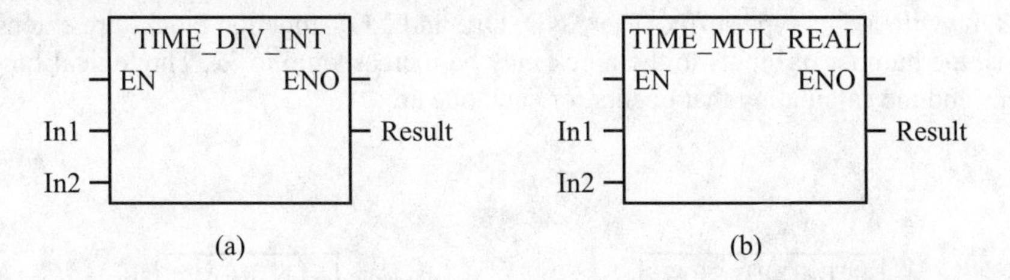

Figure 7.11. Time manipulation functions: *(a)* divide; *(b)* multiply.

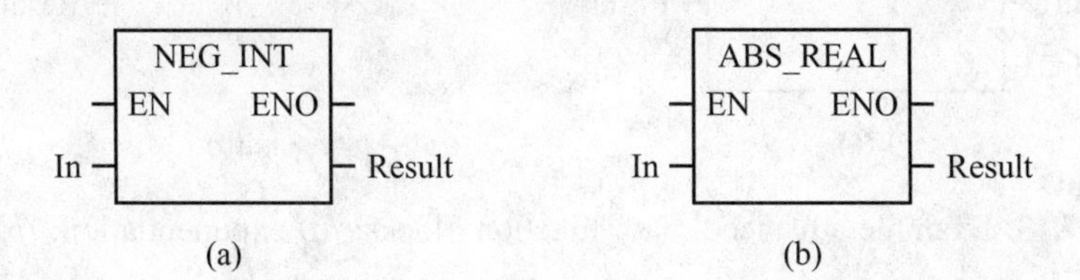

Figure 7.12. One-input basic math blocks: *(a)* absolute value; *(b)* negation.

When cascading math blocks to implement complicated calculations, be careful to avoid run-time errors (for example dividing by zero). If a block encounters a run-time error, the ENO is always turned off. If subsequent math blocks depend on that ENO to execute, then they will not be executed. The processor notes the run-time error and continues to run, but the result of the calculation will be invalid.

7.4.3 Advanced Math Function Blocks

There are a few advanced math function blocks whose output is a real data type. The names of these function blocks and the calculation that occurs for each one are:

Block Name	Calculation Result
***_EXPT_REAL	Raise a real number to a power $(\text{In1})^{\text{In2}}$
ACOS_REAL	Arc cosine of In1 (Result in radians)
ASIN_REAL	Arc sine of In1 (Result in radians)
ATAN_REAL	Arc tangent of In1 (Result in radians)
COS_REAL	Cosine of In1 (In1 in radians)
EXP_REAL	Raise *e* to exponent In1
LN_REAL	Natural logarithm of In1
LOG_REAL	Common logarithm of In1
SIN_REAL	Sine of In1 (In1 in radians)
SQRT_REAL	Square root of In1
TAN_REAL	Tangent of In1 (In1 in radians)

For the ***_EXPT_REAL function block, the *** is replaced by the data type of the exponent, In2. Two example blocks are shown in Figure 7.13.

7.4.4 Logical Function Blocks

The logical function blocks provide bit-wise logical operations for the bit data types (BOOL, BYTE, and WORD) and are shown in Figure 7.14. As for the other computation function blocks, the name of the math block consists of the operation type (AND, NOT, OR, or XOR) with a data type suffix. The AND, OR, and XOR function blocks are extensible, that is, the number of inputs to the block may be increased up to 32. The logical function blocks and the calculation that occurs for each one are:

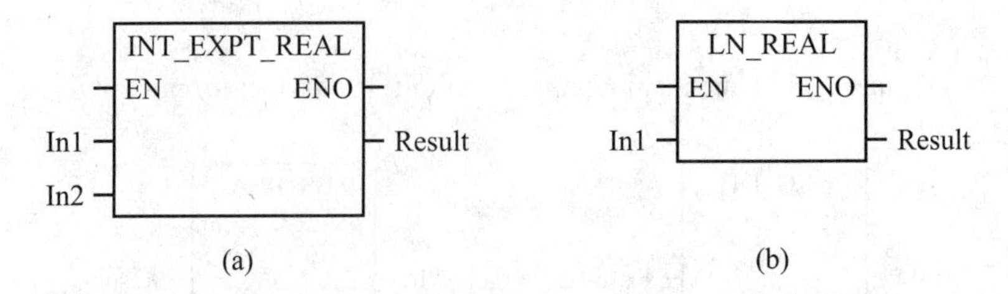

Figure 7.13. Example advanced math function blocks: *(a)* exponentiation; *(b)* natural logarithm.

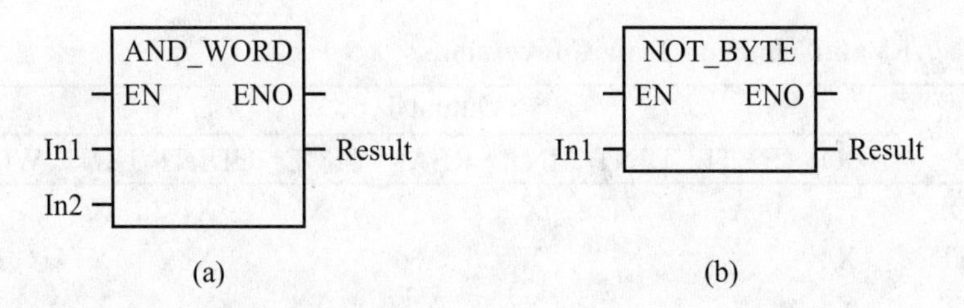

Figure 7.14. Example Modicon logical function blocks: *(a)* bit-wise AND; *(b)* bit-wise NOT.

Block Name	**Calculation Result**
AND_***	In1 AND In2 AND In3 AND … AND InN (bit-wise logical AND of 2 or more inputs)
NOT_***	Invert all bits
OR_***	In1 OR In2 OR In3 OR … OR InN (bit-wise logical OR of 2 or more inputs)
XOR_***	In1 XOR In2 XOR In3 XOR … XOR InN (bit-wise logical exclusive-OR of 2 or more inputs)

where *** is the data type suffix. The BOOL suffix is only valid for the XOR function block. The AND, NOT, and OR function blocks cannot be used with the data type BOOL because the same functionality can be realized with contacts and coils.

7.4.5 Data Type Conversion Function Blocks

Function blocks are provided to convert from one data type to another. The function blocks that are possible are:

Block Name	**Description**
BOOL_TO_***	Boolean to ...
BYTE_TO_***	Byte to ...
DINT_TO_***	Double integer to ...
INT_TO_***	Integer to ...
REAL_TO_***	Real to ...
REAL_TRUNC_***	Real to ..., truncate result
TIME_TO_***	Time to ...
UDINT_TO_***	Unsigned double integer to ...
UINT_TO_***	Unsigned integer to ...
WORD_TO_***	Word to ...

where *** is the data type of the result. Basically, a data type can be converted to any other data type. The exception is that the output of REAL_TRUNC can only be an integer type. However, not all possible conversions make sense. In addition, some conversions are incorrect. Valid conversions and possible pitfalls to avoid are shown in Table 7.1.

Table 7.1 Valid Modicon Type Conversions

Input Type	Output Type								
	BOOL	BYTE	DINT	INT	REAL	TIME[2]	UDINT	UINT	WORD
BOOL		X	X	X		X	X	X	X
BYTE	X^3		X	X		X	X	X	X
DINT	X^3	X^3		X^3	X^3	X^4	X^3	X^3	X^3
INT	X^3	X^3	X		X^3	X^4	X^3	X^3	X^3
REAL			X^3	X^3		X^4	X^3	X^3	
TIME[1]		X^3	X^3	X^3	X		X	X^3	X^3
UDINT	X^3	X^3	X^3	X^3	X	X		X^3	X^3
UINT	X^3	X^3	X	X^3	X	X	X		X^3
WORD	X^3	X^3	X	X		X	X	X	

Notes:
1. Output of function block is time in milliseconds
2. Input is interpreted as time in milliseconds
3. Run-time error if input value is outside valid range of output type
4. Run-time error if input value is negative

Conversions between REAL and the three bit types (BOOL, BYTE, and WORD) are handled as bit pattern transfers. For example if the input value of a WORD_TO_REAL block is 200, the output result is 7.17465×10^{-43}. To correctly convert a word value (for example, from a high-speed counter module) into a real number, the word must be converted into an integer before it is converted into a real number, as shown in Figure 7.15.

Design Tip

Do not convert directly between the REAL data type and the three bit data types (BOOL, BYTE, and WORD).

7.4.6 Move Function Blocks

The MOVE function block (Figure 7.16) transfers the value at the input to the output. The data types of the input and output must be identical. The name of this function block has

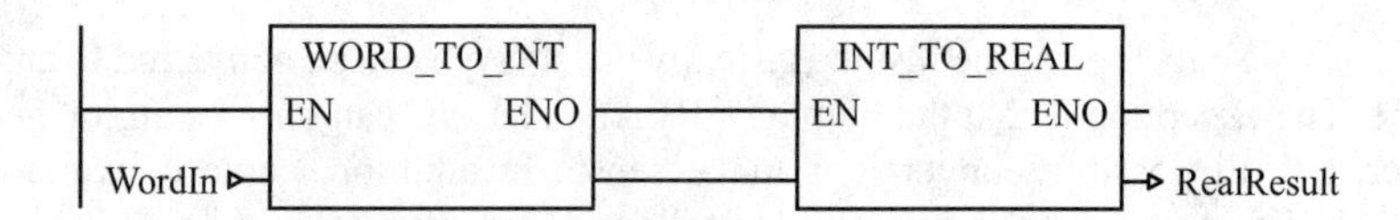

Figure 7.15. Correct conversion from WORD to REAL.

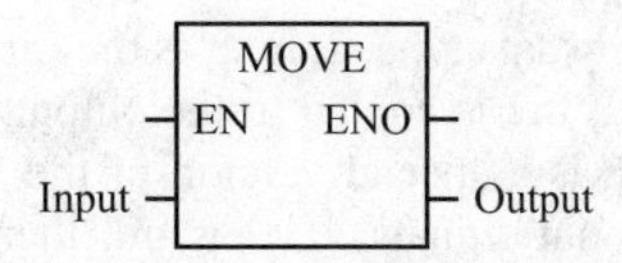

Figure 7.16. Modicon Move function block.

no data type suffix. However, this function cannot be used with the BOOL data type because the same functionality can be realized with a coil and a contact.

The following function blocks move bits into and out of words and bytes:

Block Name	**Description**
BIT_TO_BYTE	Copy 8 Boolean inputs to the appropriate bits in a byte
BIT_TO_WORD	Copy 16 Boolean inputs to the appropriate bits in a word
BYTE_TO_BIT	Copy the 8 bits in a byte to individual Boolean outputs
WORD_TO_BIT	Copy the 16 bits in a word to individual Boolean outputs

The BIT_TO_WORD and WORD_TO_BIT function blocks are shown in Figure 7.17.

7.4.7 Selection Function Blocks

The following function blocks allow one value to be selected from a given number of values:

Block Name	**Description**
MAX_***	Output is maximum value from up to 32 values.
MIN_***	Output is minimum value from up to 32 values.
MUX_***	Select nth value from a list of up to 32 values
SEL	Select one of two values

where *** is the data type suffix. For the MAX and MIN blocks, the data type suffix designates the type of the input values and output value (Figure 7.18*a*, *b*). For the MUX block, the data type suffix is one of the integer types (DINT, INT, UDINT, UINT) and designates the data type of the input (K) that selects the appropriate input signal (Figure

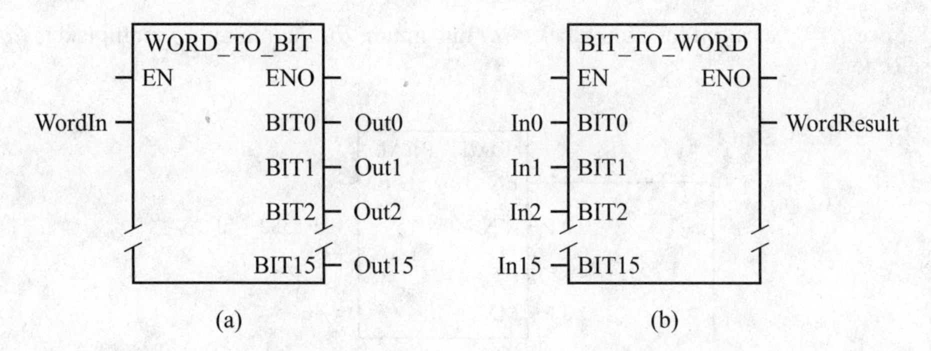

Figure 7.17. Bit move function blocks: *(a)* WORD_TO_BIT; *(b)* BIT_TO_WORD.

7.18*c*). The In*x* inputs can be any data type, as long as they are all the same type. If K=1, In1 is copied to the output; if K=2, In2 is copied to the output, and so on. The SEL function block, shown in Figure 7.18*d*, is a special version of the MUX block where a Boolean variable selects one of two input signals. If G is **on**, then In1 is copied to the output; otherwise, In0 is copied to the output.

The LIMIT function block, shown in the example of Figure 7.19, ensures a value is inside a specified range. The output of this block is determined as follows:

Output = IN if MN ≤ IN ≤ MX
Output = MN if IN < MN
Output = MX if IN > MX

For the example in Figure 7.19, the value of FT532_Val is limited to be between 0.0 and 103.0.

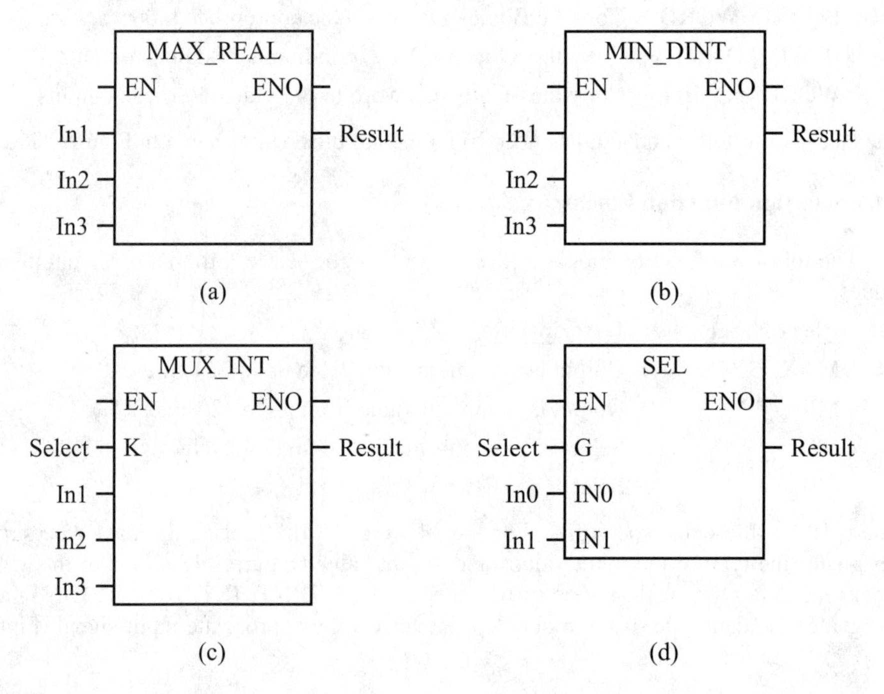

Figure 7.18. Selection function blocks: *(a)* maximum; *(b)* minimum; *(c)* multiplexer; *(d)* selection.

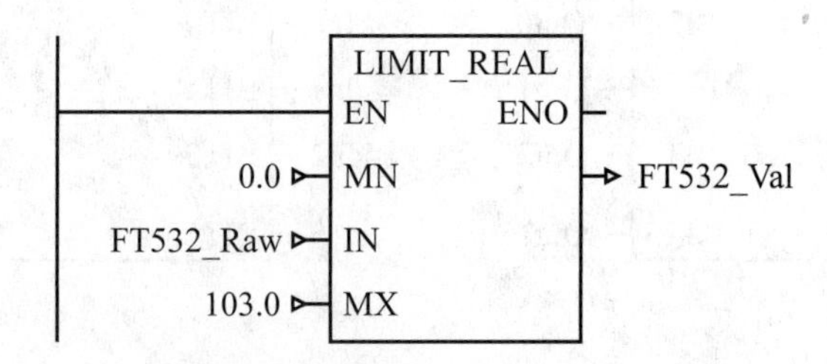

Figure 7.19. Example LIMIT function block.

7.5 A-B CONTROLLOGIX COMPARISION AND COMPUTATION

The ControlLogix comparison and computation function blocks are organized according to their function:

Category	Description
Comparison	Compare one or more values
Basic math	Basic arithmetic (+, -, ×, ÷)
Advanced math	Trigonometry and exponentiation
Format conversion	Integer/BCD and radian/degree
Logical	Bit-wise logical operators
Move	Copy data

The comparison function blocks are input instructions, that is, they can be placed anywhere on a rung, except at the rightmost position. All of the computation and move function blocks are output instructions, that is, they are normally placed on the rightmost position of the rung. As explained in section 2.4, this distinction is made because in relay ladder logic, outputs are never connected in series and always occur on the extreme right side of the rung. To activate multiple output function blocks simultaneously, the blocks are connected in parallel. This restriction is relaxed in the ControlLogix PLC and output function blocks may be placed in series. However, as explained in section 2.4, this text avoids placing output function blocks in series.

All of the comparison and computation function blocks have one input connection and one output connection. Multiple operands are handled as block parameters.

7.5.1 Comparison Function Blocks

For all of the comparison function blocks, integer and real data types may be mixed in the operands in the block. Any conversions between data types are handled automatically. Also, literals (constants) may be used in place of tags.

The most general comparison function block is CMP; an example is shown in Figure 7.20. The CMP block can evaluate any comparison operation, depending on the expression in the block. The output of the block is true (**on**) if the expression is true. The expression can contain only one comparison operation. The expression on either side of the comparison operation can include arithmetic operations. A table of valid expressions is in the instruction set reference (Rockwell Automation, 1999).

As an alternative to the CMP function block, there are individual comparison function blocks; examples are shown in Figure 7.21. The current value of a tag is shown below the tag. The possible comparison function blocks and the condition that turns on the output are:

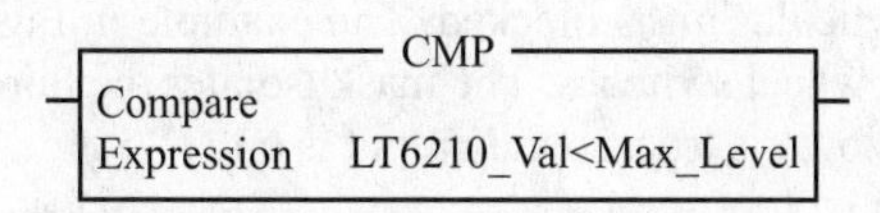

Figure 7.20. ControlLogix CMP comparison function block.

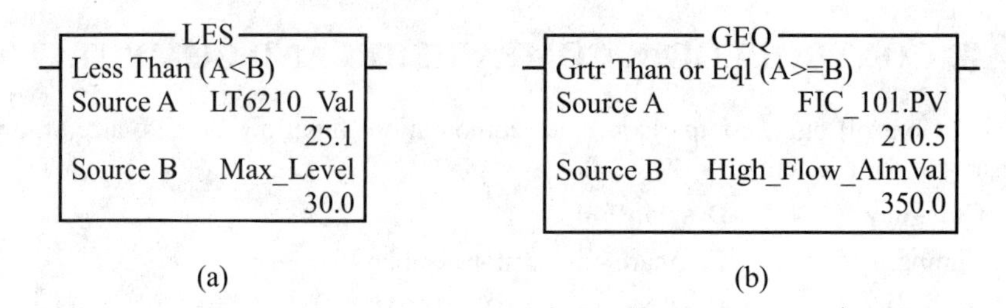

Figure 7.21. Example ControlLogix comparison blocks: *(a)* less than; *(b)* greater than or equal.

Block Name	Output is On if:
EQU	Source A = Source B
GEQ	Source A ≥ Source B
GRT	Source A > Source B
LEQ	Source A ≤ Source B
LES	Source A < Source B
LIM	Test value within Low Limit and High Limit
MEQ	Mask(Source A) = Mask(Source B)
NEQ	Source A ≠ Source B

The LIM and MEQ function blocks operate somewhat differently from the other comparison function blocks and are explained separately below.

At first glance, it would seem that the CMP block should always be used instead of the individual comparison function blocks. However, there are two important reasons that PLC programmers prefer the individual blocks for simple comparisons. Most importantly, the values of the two tags being compared are displayed when viewing the individual function block on-line. The CMP function block displays only the expression without showing any of the values. Often, when troubleshooting a program, one needs to easily see the two values and thus why a certain comparison is true or false. For example, one can easily see why the comparison is true in Figure 7.21*a* and false for Figure 7.21*b*. In Figure 7.20 there is no indication why the comparison is true or false. Secondly, the CMP block requires longer execution time and occupies more memory than the corresponding individual comparison blocks.

The MEQ is a masked equal comparison, an example is shown in Figure 7.22*a*. The MEQ block logically ANDs the Source and Compare values with the Mask value before comparing for equality. If the masked Source and Compare values are equal, the block output is turned on. The MEQ Source, Mask, and Compare operands must be integer data types (DINT, INT, SINT). A "1" in the mask means the particular bit is passed and a "0" in the mask means the particular bit is blocked. The example in Figure 7.22*a* compares the third digit of two thumbwheel switches. The mask isolates the third digit. The result of the MEQ with the values shown is true, so the output is on.

The LIM function block tests whether a value is either inside or outside of a specified range. An example LIM block is shown in Figure 7.22*b*. If Low Limit ≤ High Limit, then the block output functions as follows

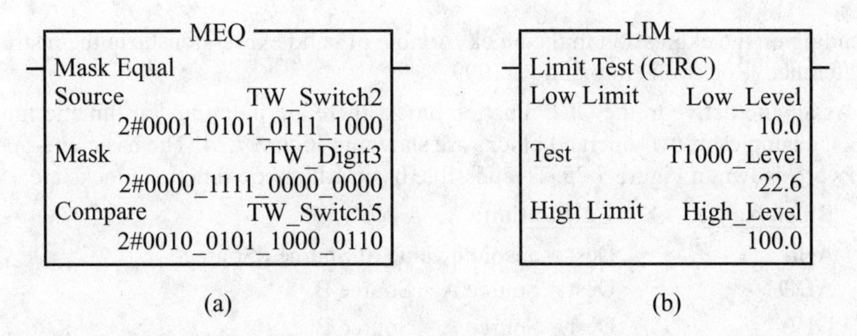

Figure 7.22. Advanced ControlLogix comparison blocks: *(a)* mask equal; *(b)* limit test.

Condition	Output
Low Limit ≤ Test ≤ High Limit	On
Test < Low Limit or Test > High Limit	Off

which means the block tests that a value is within the limits. For the example shown in Figure 7.22*b* the output is on. If the values of the limits are reversed such that Low Limit > High Limit, then the block output functions as follows

Condition	Output
Test > Low Limit or Test < High Limit	On
High Limit ≤ Test ≤ Low Limit	Off

which means the block tests that a value is outside the limits. If the low and high limit tags are reversed for the example in Figure 7.22*b* the output will be off.

7.5.2 Basic Math Function Blocks

For all of the computation and move function blocks, integer and real data types may be mixed in the operands. Any conversions between data types are handled automatically. However, when the result is an integer, values less than 0.5 are rounded to zero and values outside the valid range are truncated. The S:V status bit is set if the result is outside the valid range for the particular integer type. Also, literals (constants) may be used in place of source operand tags. If there are no contacts or other conditions attached to the block input, the function block will be executed on every scan.

The most general computation function block is CPT; an example is shown in Figure 7.23. The CPT block can evaluate any arithmetic, logical, conversion, and copy operation,

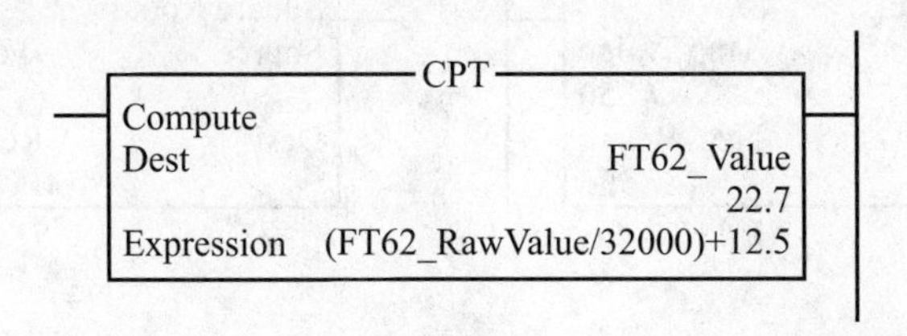

Figure 7.23. ControlLogix CPT compute function block.

depending on the expression in the block. A table of valid expressions is in the instruction set reference (Rockwell Automation, 1999).

As an alternative to the CPT function block, there are individual arithmetic function blocks; examples of two-operand blocks are shown in Figure 7.24. The basic one-operand blocks are shown in Figure 7.25. The possible basic arithmetic function blocks are:

Block Name	**Calculation:**
ABS	Dest = absolute value of Source (|Source|)
ADD	Dest = Source A + Source B
DIV	Dest = Source A ÷ Source B
MOD	Dest = Source A modulo Source B
MUL	Dest = Source A × Source B
NEG	Dest = – Source
SQR	Dest = square root of Source
SUB	Dest = Source A – Source B

Initially, it would seem that the CPT function block should always be used instead of the individual computation function blocks. As for the comparison blocks, there are two reasons that PLC programmers may prefer the individual function blocks for simple computations. Most importantly, the values of all two or three tags in the block are displayed when viewing the individual function block on-line. The CPT function block displays only the value of the result and does not show any of the values that lead to the result. Often, when troubleshooting a program, one needs to easily see source operands to verify the reasons behind incorrect calculations (for example, overflow or integer

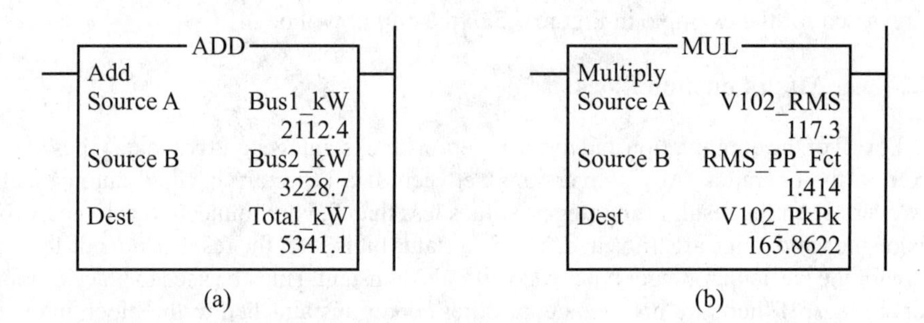

Figure 7.24. Example two-operand ControlLogix computation blocks: *(a)* addition; *(b)* multiply.

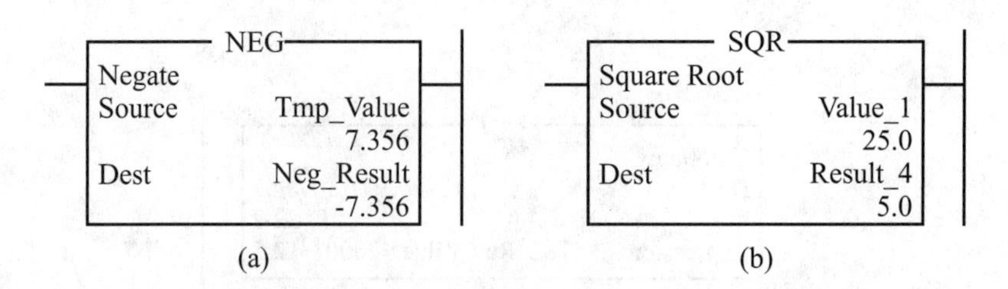

Figure 7.25. Example one-operand ControlLogix computation blocks:*(a)* negation; *(b)* square root.

truncation). Secondly, the CPT function block requires longer execution time and occupies more memory than the corresponding individual computation function blocks.

7.5.3 Advanced Math Function Blocks

The names of the advanced math function blocks and the calculation that occurs for each one are:

Block Name	Calculation Result
ACS	Dest = Arc cosine of Source (Dest in radians)
ASN	Dest = Arc sine of Source (Dest in radians)
ATN	Dest = Arctangent of Source (Dest in radians)
COS	Dest = Cosine of Source (Source in radians)
LN	Dest = Natural logarithm of Source
LOG	Dest = Common logarithm of Source
SIN	Dest = Sine of Source (Source in radians)
TAN	Dest = Tangent of Source (Source in radians)
XPY	$\text{Dest} = (\text{Source A})^{\text{Source B}}$

The XPY function block is a two-operand block, similar to the ones in Figure 7.24. The other advanced math function blocks are one-operand blocks, similar in format to the blocks in Figure 7.25. All of these function blocks are intended for use with REAL data types. Integer types may be used, but loss of accuracy and overflow may occur.

7.5.4 Logical Function Blocks

The logical function blocks provide bit-wise logical operations for the integer data types (SINT, INT, and DINT) and are shown in Figure 7.26. The logical function blocks and the calculation that occurs for each one are:

Block Name	Calculation Result
AND	Bitwise logical AND of Source A and Source B integers
NOT	Invert all bits of Source
OR	Bitwise logical OR of Source A and Source B integers
XOR	Bitwise logical exclusive-OR of Source A and Source A integers

If integer data types are mixed, the function block fills the upper bits of the smaller integer data types with zeros so that they are the same size as the largest data type.

7.5.5 Conversion Function Blocks

The names of the conversion function blocks and the conversion that occurs for each one are:

Block Name	Description
DEG	Convert source in radians to degrees.
RAD	Convert source in degrees to radians.
FRD	Convert source BCD (binary coded decimal) value to integer.
TOD	Convert source integer value to BCD.
TRN	Truncates (removes) fractional part of source.

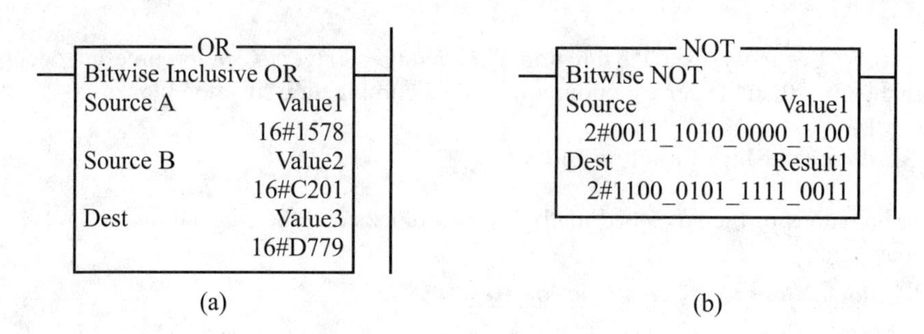

Figure 7.26. Example ControlLogix logical function blocks: *(a)* bit-wise OR; *(b)* bit-wise NOT.

The DEG and RAD function blocks are similar to the one-operand function blocks shown in Figure 7.25. An example FRD function block is shown in Figure 7.27. This example assumes that the bit pattern from two thumbwheel switches is transferred to the TW62 tag with a move type of function block. The FRD block converts a 2, 4, or 8-digit BCD value depending on the source type (SINT, INT, DINT) to a destination integer. An example TOD function block is shown in Figure 7.28. The integer in M32_Amp is converted into the BCD format and placed in DP532. A separate function block is assumed to transfer the BCD number contained in DP532 to discrete outputs that are attached to binary-to-7-segment decoder drivers.

7.5.6 Move Function Blocks

The move function blocks transfer data between tags. The names and descriptions of the move function blocks are:

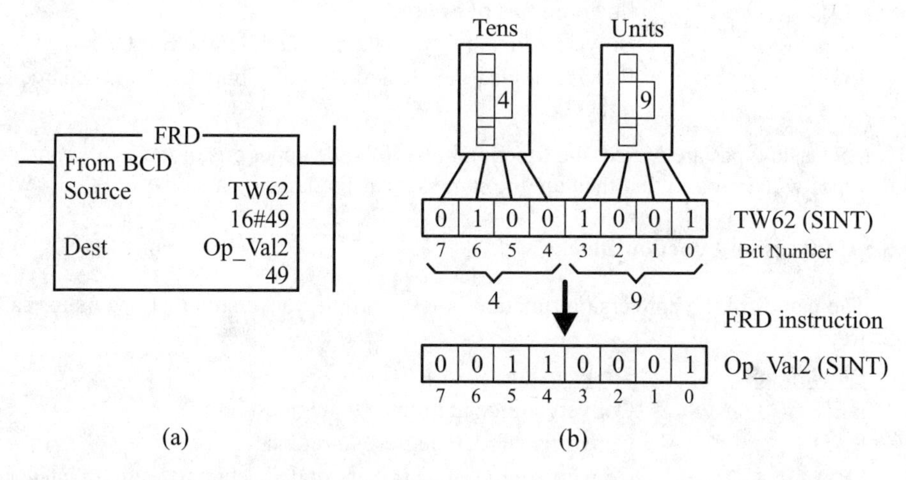

Figure 7.27. Example ControlLogix BCD-to-integer conversion: *(a)* function block; *(b)* operation.

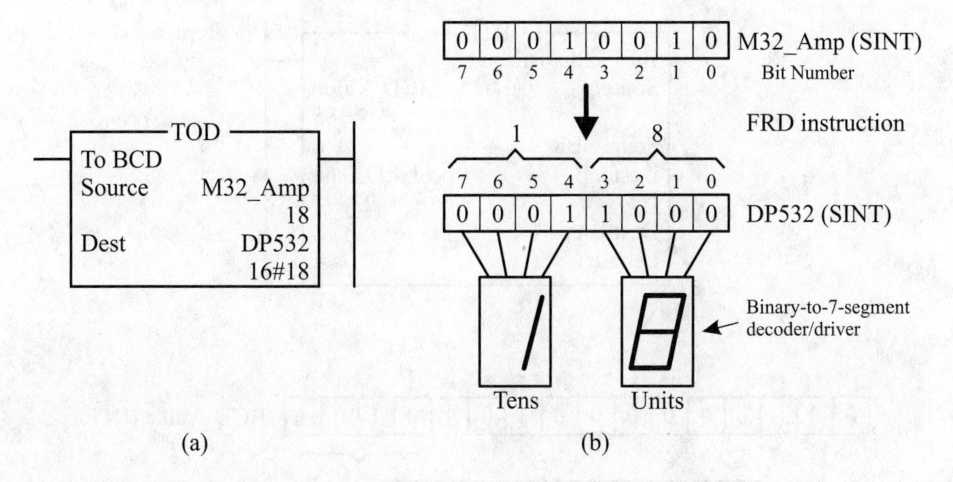

Figure 7.28. Example ControlLogix integer-to-BCD conversion: *(a)* function block; *(b)* operation.

Block Name	**Description**
BTD	Move bits within an integer or between integers
CLR	Clear tag
MOV	Copy source tag to destination tag
MVM	Copy source integer to destination integer, allowing portions of the integer to be masked

The MOV and MVM function blocks are shown in Figure 7.29. For the MOV function block, the data types of the source and destination do not need to be identical. Conversion between the integer and real data types are handled automatically. However, when moving a REAL tag to an integer tag, one should consider overflow. The MVM Source, Mask, and Dest operands must be integer data types (DINT, INT, SINT). A "1" in the mask means the particular bit is passed from the Source integer to the Dest integer and a "0" in the mask means the particular bit is blocked. A "0" in the mask also means that those bits in the destination integer are not modified. The example in Figure 7.29*b* transfers the third digit of a thumbwheel switch. The mask isolates the third digit. If integer data types are mixed, the function block fills the upper bits of the smaller integer data types with zeros so that they are the same size as the largest data type.

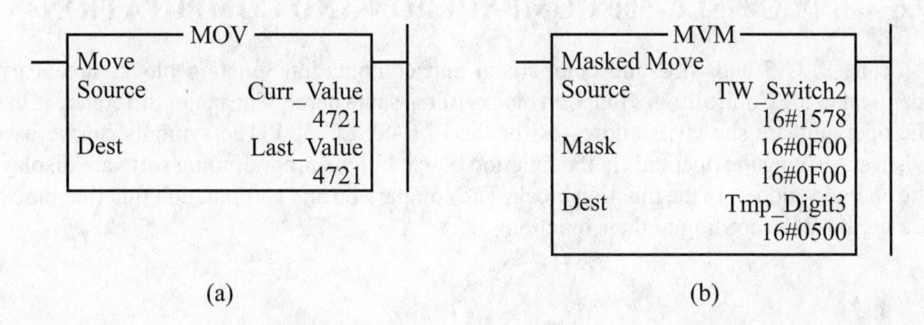

Figure 7.29. ControlLogix move function blocks: *(a)* move; *(b)* masked move.

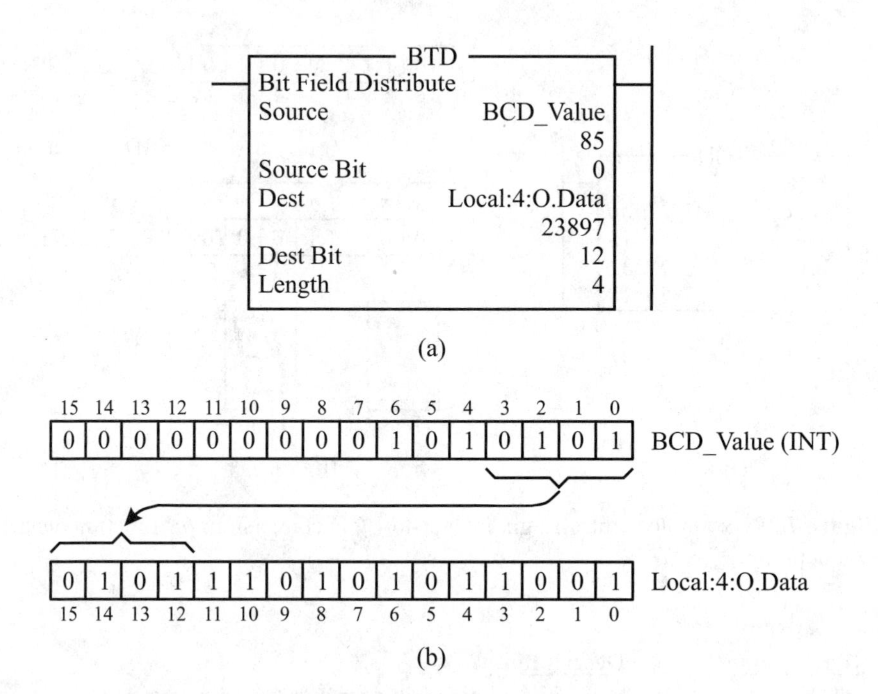

Figure 7.30. Example ControlLogix bit field distribute: *(a)* function block; *(b)* operation.

The BTD function block is useful for moving a group of bits. An example BTD function block is shown in Figure 7.30*a*. The Source Bit is the number of the least significant bit in the group of bits to be moved and the Length is the number of bits in the group. The group of bits are copied to the part of the Dest integer defined by the Dest Bit (the number of the least significant bit) and the Length. The other bits in the destination integer are not modified. The Source Bit and Dest Bit numbers must be in the valid range for the data types. If the length of the bit group extends beyond the destination most-significant bit, the extra bits are lost. The actual transfer for the BTD block in Figure 7.30*a* is illustrated in Figure 7.30*b*. The lower 4 bits of (BCD) BCD_Value are copied into bits 12 to 15 of output word Local:4:O.Data. The four outputs, 4:O.Data.12 to 4:O.Data.15, are connected to a 7 segment display that displays the (BCD) number represented by the 4 bits.

7.6 A-B PLC-5/SLC-500 COMPARISION AND COMPUTATION

The PLC-5 and SLC-500 comparison and computation function blocks are nearly identical to the ControlLogix function blocks of the same name. The major difference is that the operands are shown as addresses for the PLC-5/SLC-500. The symbols can be used when specifying the operands in the function block, but the programming software displays the operand address in the function block. The comparison and computation function blocks are organized according to their function:

Category	Description
Comparison	Compare one or more values
Basic math	Basic arithmetic (+, -, ×, ÷)
Advanced math	Trigonometry and exponentiation
Format conversion	Integer/BCD and radian/degree
Logical	Bit-wise logical operators
Move	Copy data

The comparison function blocks are input instructions, that is, they can be placed anywhere on a rung, except at the rightmost position. All of the computation and move function blocks are output instructions, that is, they are never connected in series and always occur on the extreme right side of the rung. To activate multiple output function blocks simultaneously, the blocks are connected in parallel.

All of the comparison and computation function blocks have one input connection and one output connection. Multiple operands are handled as block parameters.

The specific function blocks that are supported vary among the different PLC-5 and SLC-500 processors. All processors support the basic two-operand comparison, basic arithmetic (+, -, ×, ÷), integer/BCD conversion, logical, and basic move function blocks.

7.6.1 Comparison Function Blocks

For all of the comparison function blocks, integer and floating-point data types may be mixed in the operands in the block. Any conversions between data types are handled automatically. Also, literals (constants) may be used in place of tags. There is one caution concerning PLC-5/SLC-500 data types. If words from BCD or ASCII file types are used as operands in comparison function blocks, they will be treated as integer numbers. Therefore, comparison of BCD and integer values is **NOT RECOMMENDED**.

The most general comparison function block is CMP; an example is shown in Figure 7.31. The CMP block can evaluate any comparison operation, depending on the expression in the block. The output of the block is true (**on**) if the expression is true. The expression can contain only one comparison operation. For enhanced PLC-5 processors, the expression on either side of the comparison operation can include arithmetic operations. A table of valid expressions is in the instruction set reference (Rockwell Automation, 1998a). This function block is not available for the SLC-500 processors. The symbol of the first address in the expression is displayed above the function block.

As an alternative to the CMP function block, there are individual comparison function blocks; examples are shown in Figure 7.32. The possible comparison function blocks and the condition that turns on the output are:

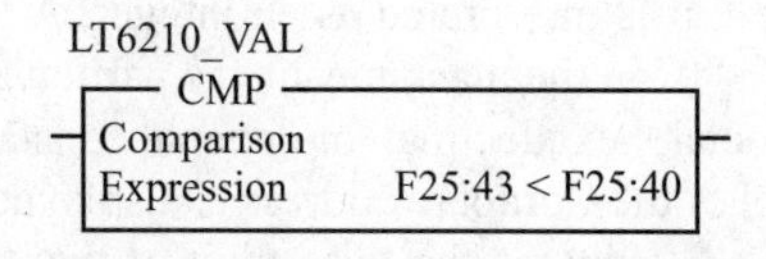

Figure 7.31. PLC-5 CMP comparison function block.

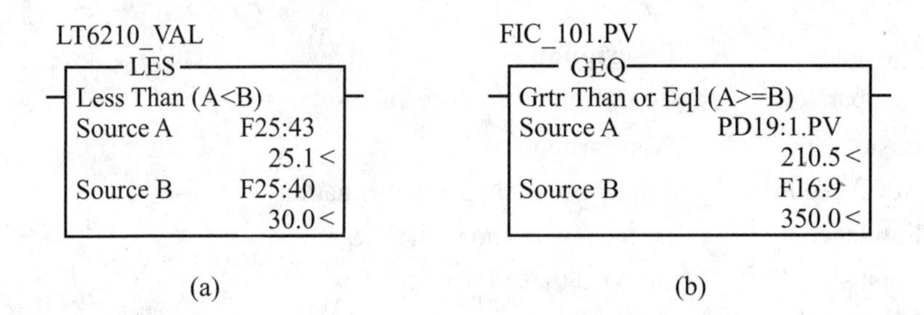

Figure 7.32. Example PLC-5/SLC-500 comparison blocks: *(a)* less than; *(b)* greater than or equal.

Block Name	Output is On if:
EQU	Source A = Source B
GEQ	Source A ≥ Source B
GRT	Source A > Source B
LEQ	Source A ≤ Source B
LES	Source A < Source B
LIM	Test value within Low Limit and High Limit
MEQ	Mask(Source A) = Mask(Source B)
NEQ	Source A ≠ Source B

The current value of an address is shown below the address and followed by a "<" symbol. Except for the LIM and MEQ blocks, the symbol of the Source A address is displayed above the function block. The LIM and MEQ function blocks operate somewhat differently from the other comparison function blocks and are explained separately below.

At the outset, it would seem that the CMP block should always be used instead of the individual comparison function blocks. However, there are two important reasons that PLC programmers prefer the individual blocks for simple comparisons. Most importantly, the values of the two addresses being compared are displayed when viewing the individual function block on-line. The CMP function block displays only the expression without showing any of the values. Often, when troubleshooting a program, one needs to easily see the two values and thus why a certain comparison is true or false. For example, one can easily see why the comparison is true in Figure 7.32*a* and false for Figure 7.32*b*. In Figure 7.31 there is no indication why the comparison is true or false. Secondly, the CMP block requires longer execution time and occupies more memory than the corresponding individual comparison blocks.

The MEQ is a masked equal comparison, an example is shown in Figure 7.33*a*. The MEQ block logically ANDs the Source and Compare values with the Mask value before comparing for equality. If the masked Source and Compare values are equal, the block output is turned on. The MEQ Source, Mask, and Compare operands must be integers. If a BCD or ASCII word is used, it is interpreted as an integer. A "1" in the mask means the particular bit is passed and a "0" in the mask means the particular bit is blocked. The mask can be entered as a binary, octal, hexadecimal, or decimal constant, but is always displayed as hexadecimal. The symbol of the Compare address is displayed above the function block. The example in Figure 7.33*a* compares the third digit of two thumbwheel switches. The

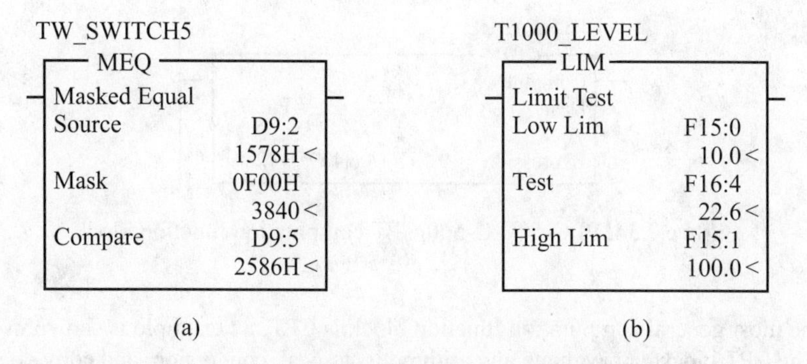

Figure 7.33. Advanced PLC-5/SLC-500 comparison blocks: *(a)* masked equal; *(b)* limit test.

mask isolates the third digit. The result of the MEQ with the values shown is true, so the output is on.

The LIM function block tests whether a value is either inside or outside of a specified range. An example LIM block is shown in Figure 7.33*b*. If Low Lim ≤ High Lim, then the block output functions as follows

Condition	Output
Low Lim ≤ Test ≤ High Lim	On
Test < Low Lim or Test > High Lim	Off

which means the block tests that a value is within the limits. For the example shown in Figure 7.33*b* the output is on. If the values of the limits are reversed such that Low Limit > High Limit, then the block output functions as follows

Condition	Output
Test > Low Lim or Test < High Lim	On
High Lim ≤ Test ≤ Low Lim	Off

which means the block tests that a value is outside the limits. If the low and high limit tags are reversed for the example in Figure 7.33*b* the output will be off. The symbol of the Test address is displayed above the function block.

7.6.2 Basic Math Function Blocks

For all of the computation and move function blocks, integer and floating-point data types may be mixed in the operands. Any conversions between data types are handled automatically. However, when the result is an integer, values less than 0.5 are rounded to zero and values outside the valid range are truncated. The S:0/01 (overflow) status bit is set if the result is outside the valid range for an integer. Also, literals (constants) may be used in place of source operand tags. As for the comparison function blocks, BCD or ASCII addresses are interpreted as integer numbers.

If there are no contacts or other conditions attached to the input of a computation or move function block, the function block will be executed on every scan. To execute the block only once, use an ONS contact (OSR for SLC-500) after any other conditions.

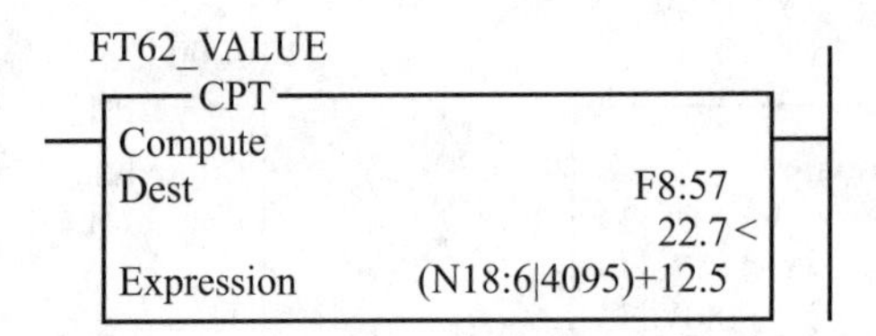

Figure 7.34. PLC-5/SLC-500 CPT computation function block.

The most general computation function block is CPT; an example is shown in Figure 7.34. The CPT block can evaluate any arithmetic, logical, conversion, and copy operation, depending on the expression in the function block. A table of valid expressions is in the instruction set reference (Rockwell Automation, 1998a, 1998b). The original PLC-5 processors limit the expression to one arithmetic operation or conversion. Enhanced PLC-5 processors can have complex expressions of up to 80 characters. For the SLC-500, the CPT block is only valid on the SLC-5/03 or later processors and the expression is limited to 255 characters. The symbol of the Dest address is displayed above the function block. The operator for division is a vertical bar. For example, to divide N7:0 by F8:3, the expression is: N7:0|F8:3.

Design Tip

If the destination of the CPT is an integer (address N*x*:*n*) and the expression contains constants, a decimal point in a constant forces the calculations to be done with floating point numbers, avoiding a possible overflow/rounding problem in an intermediate result.

As an alternative to the CPT function block, there are individual arithmetic function blocks; examples of two-operand blocks are shown in Figure 7.35. and one-operand blocks are shown in Figure 7.36. The possible basic arithmetic function blocks are:

Block Name	Calculation:
ABS	Dest = absolute value of Source (|Source|)
ADD	Dest = Source A + Source B
DDV	Dest = (S:14 and S:13) ÷ Source (SLC-500 only)
DIV	Dest = Source A ÷ Source B
MUL	Dest = Source A × Source B
NEG	Dest = – Source
SQR	Dest = square root of Source
SUB	Dest = Source A – Source B

The current value of an address is shown below the address and followed by a "<" symbol. The symbol of the Dest address is displayed above the function block. The SQR function block is not valid for the SLC-5/01 processor. The DDV function block is only valid for SLC-500 processors. For the DDV block, the 32-bit integer math register, consisting of words S:14 and S:13 is divided by the 16-bit source integer. The rounded result is placed in the Dest. The unrounded quotient is placed in S:14 and the remainder is placed in S:13.

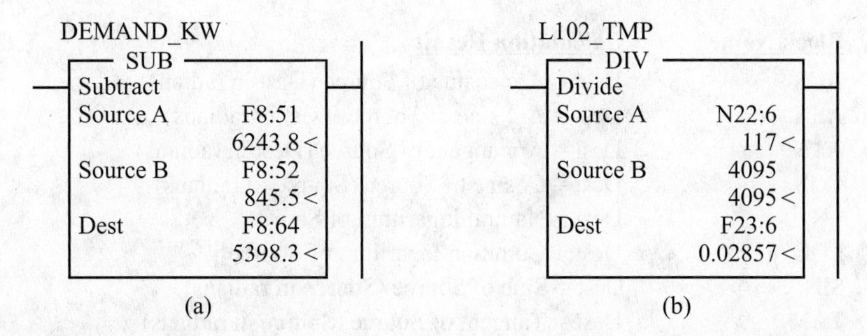

Figure 7.35. Example two-operand PLC-5/SLC-500 computation blocks: *(a)* subtract; *(b)* divide.

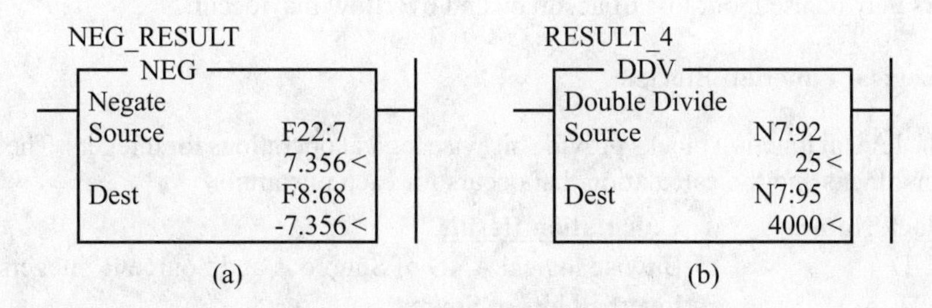

Figure 7.36. Example one-operand PLC-5/SLC-500 computation blocks: *(a)* negation; *(b)* double divide (SLC-500 only).

As for the comparison blocks, there are two reasons that one may prefer the individual function blocks for simple computations. Most importantly, the values of all two or three addresses in the block are displayed when viewing the individual function block on-line. The CPT function block displays only the value of the result and does not show any of the values that lead to the result. Often, when troubleshooting a program, one needs to easily see source operands to verify the reasons behind incorrect calculations (for example, overflow). Secondly, the CPT function block requires longer execution time and occupies more memory than the corresponding individual computation function blocks.

> **Design Tip**
>
> Individual computation blocks are more useful when troubleshooting calculations, since the source and destination values are easily seen.

7.6.3 Advanced Math Function Blocks

The advanced math function blocks are available for the enhanced PLC-5 processors only. Their names and the calculation that occurs for each one are:

Block Name	Calculation Result
ACS	Dest = Arc cosine of Source (Dest in radians)
ASN	Dest = Arc sine of Source (Dest in radians)
ATN	Dest = Arctangent of Source (Dest in radians)
COS	Dest = Cosine of Source (Source in radians)
LN	Dest = Natural logarithm of Source
LOG	Dest = Common logarithm of Source
SIN	Dest = Sine of Source (Source in radians)
TAN	Dest = Tangent of Source (Source in radians)
XPY	Dest = $(\text{Source A})^{\text{Source B}}$

The XPY function block is a two-operand block, similar to the ones in Figure 7.35. The other advanced math function blocks are one-operand blocks, similar in format to the blocks in Figure 7.36. All of these function blocks are intended for use with floating-point data. Integers may be used, but loss of accuracy and overflow may occur.

7.6.4 Logical Function Blocks

The logical function blocks provide bit-wise logical operations for integers. The logical function blocks and the calculation that occurs for each one are:

Block Name	Calculation Result
AND	Bitwise logical AND of Source A and Source B integers
NOT	Invert all bits of Source
OR	Bitwise logical OR of Source A and Source B integers
XOR	Bitwise logical exclusive-OR of Source A and Source A integers

Two example function blocks are shown in Figure 7.37.These function blocks may be used with BCD or ASCII data types, but the words are interpreted as if they are binary (integer) values.

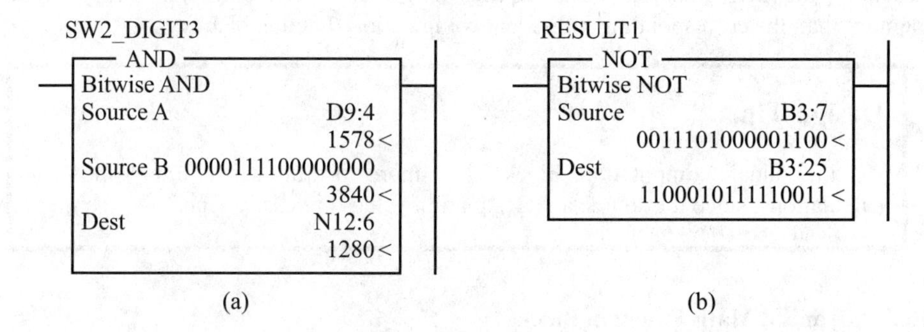

Figure 7.37. Example PLC-5/SLC-500 logical function blocks: *(a)* bit-wise AND; *(b)* bit-wise NOT.

7.6.5 Conversion Function Blocks

The names of the conversion function blocks and the conversion that occurs for each one are:

Block Name	Description
DEG	Convert source in radians to degrees.
RAD	Convert source in degrees to radians.
FRD	Convert source BCD (binary coded decimal) value to integer.
TOD	Convert source integer value to BCD.
SCL	Scale source integer value.

The DEG and RAD function blocks are similar to the one-operand function blocks shown in Figure 7.36. These two function blocks are not valid for the SLC-500 processors. The SCL function block is only valid for the SLC-5/02 and higher processors. The SCL function block is not valid for the PLC-5.

An example FRD function block is shown in Figure 7.38. This example assumes that the bit pattern from two thumbwheel switches is transferred to the lower 8 bits of D17:6 with a move type of function block. The FRD block converts the 4-digit BCD value to an integer and places the result in N7:75. An example TOD function block is shown in Figure 7.39. The integer in N10:5 is converted into the BCD format and placed in D9:5. A separate

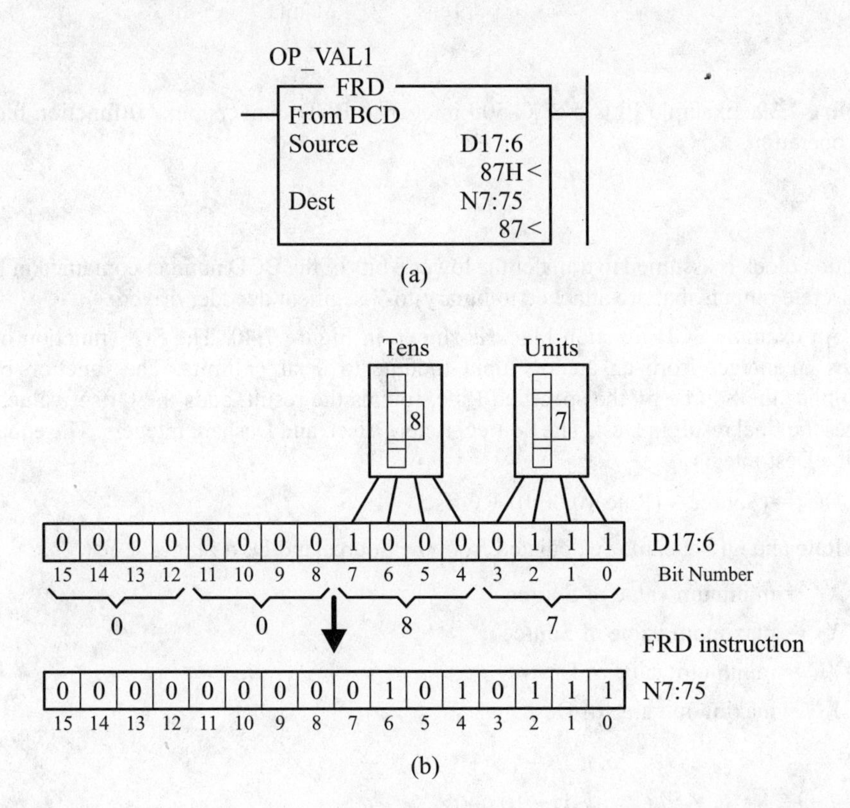

Figure 7.38. Example PLC-5/SLC-500 BCD-to-integer conversion: *(a)* function block; *(b)* operation.

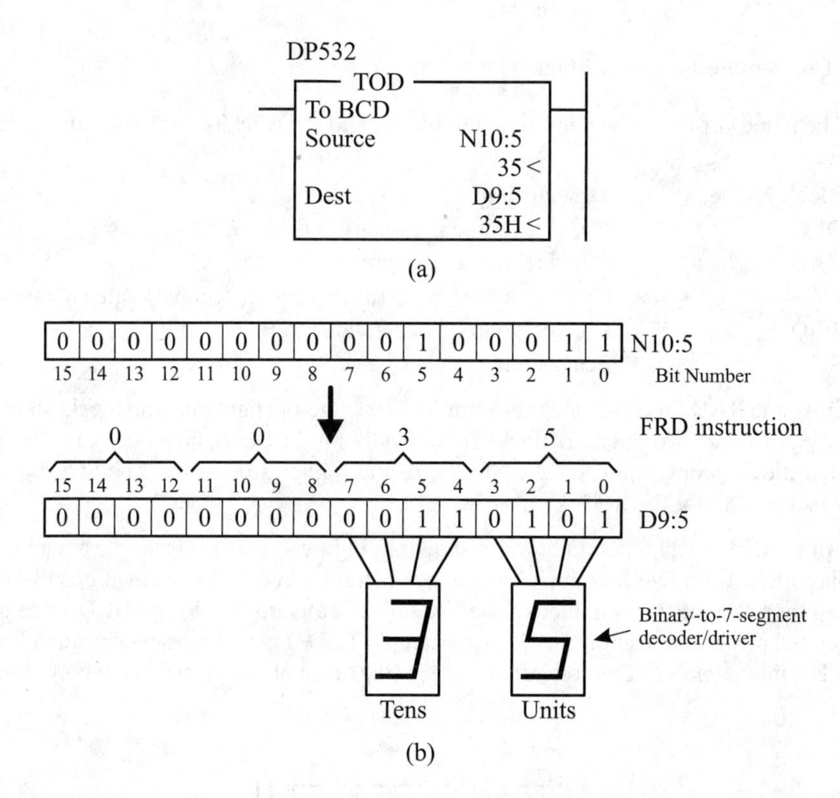

Figure 7.39. Example PLC-5/SLC-500 integer-to-BCD conversion: *(a)* function block; *(b)* operation.

function block is assumed to transfer the lower 8 bits of the BCD number contained in D9:5 to discrete outputs that are attached to binary-to-7-segment decoder drivers.

An example SCL function block is shown in Figure 7.40. The SCL function block scales an integer from an analog input module to desired limits. The function block multiplies the Source by the specified Rate, rounds the result, adds the Offset value, and places the final result in Dest. The Source, Rate, Offset, and Dest are integers. The equation for the Dest integer is:

$$\text{Dest} = (\text{Source} \times (\text{Rate}/10{,}000)) + \text{Offset}$$

The Rate and Offset can be calculated from the Source and Dest ranges. Let

X_1 = minimum value of Source

X_2 = maximum value of Source

Y_1 = minimum value of Dest

Y_2 = maximum value of Dest

then

$$\text{Rate} = ((Y_2 - Y_1) / (X_2 - X_1)) \times 10{,}000$$

$$\text{Offset} = Y_1 - (X_1 \times \text{Rate}/10{,}000)$$

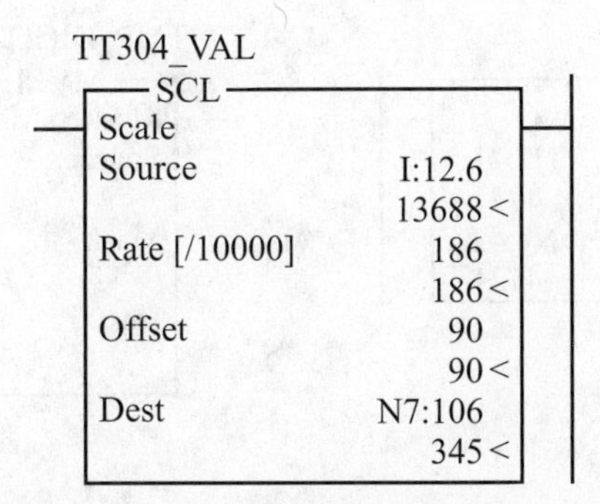

Figure 7.40. Example SLC-500 scale data function block.

The example SCL shown in Figure 7.40 performs the conversion in Example 7.3.

Design Tip

If the result of (Source × (Rate/10,000)) is greater than 32,767, the SCL function block overflows, setting the Overflow Trap Bit (S:5/0). The Overflow Trap Bit must be reset before the end of the scan, or the processor **will halt at the end of the program scan**.

7.6.6 Move Function Blocks

The move function blocks transfer data between addresses. The names and descriptions of the move function blocks are:

Block Name	**Description**
BTD	Move bits within an integer or between integers
CLR	Clear address
MOV	Copy source address to destination address
MVM	Copy source integer to destination integer, allowing portions of the integer to be masked

The MOV and MVM function blocks are shown in Figure 7.41. For the MOV function block, the data types of the source and destination do not need to be identical. Conversion between the integer and floating-point data types are handled automatically. However, when moving a floating-point value to an integer, one should consider overflow. The MVM Source, Mask, and Dest operands must be integers. If a BCD or ASCII word is used, it is interpreted as an integer. A "1" in the mask means the particular bit is passed from the Source integer to the Dest integer and a "0" in the mask means the particular bit is blocked. A "0" in the mask also means that those bits in the destination integer are not modified. The mask can be entered as a binary, octal, hexadecimal, or decimal constant, but is always displayed as hexadecimal. The symbol of the Compare address is displayed above the function block. The example in Figure 7.41*b* transfers the third digit of a thumbwheel switch. The mask isolates the third digit.

The BTD function block is valid only for the PLC-5 processors and is useful for moving a group of bits. An example BTD function block is shown in Figure 7.42*a*. The

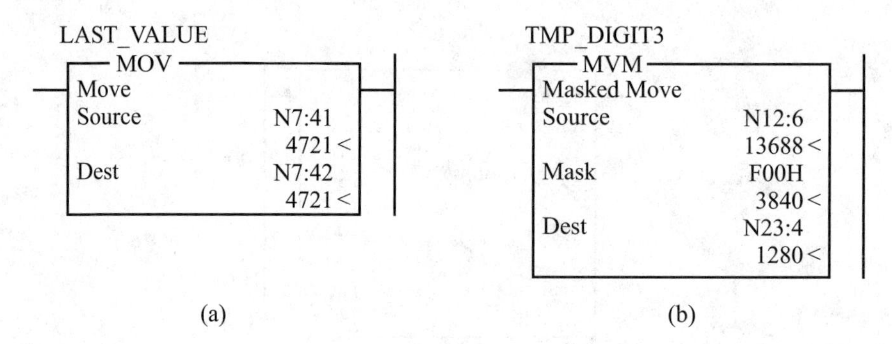

Figure 7.41. PLC-5/SLC-500 move function blocks: *(a)* move; *(b)* masked move.

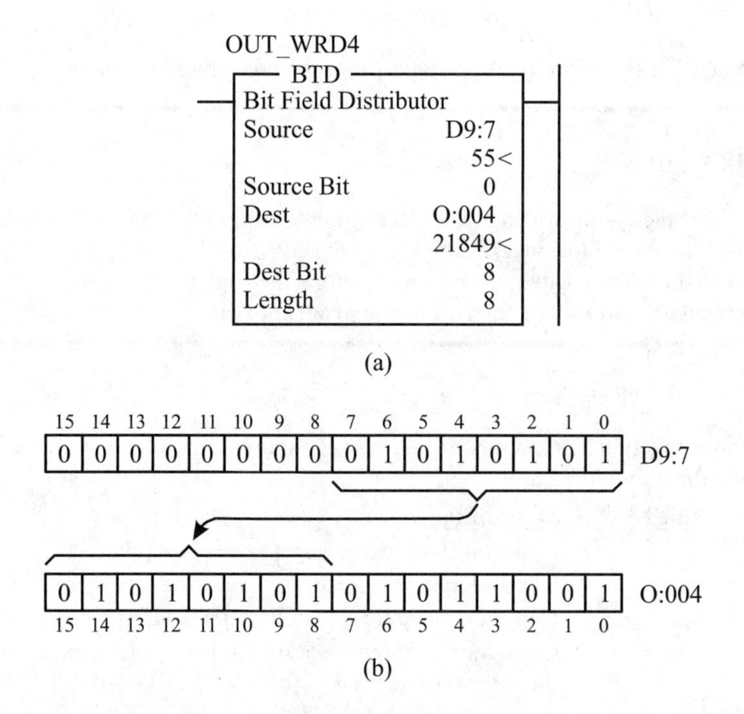

Figure 7.42. Example PLC-5 bit field distributor: *(a)* function block; *(b)* operation.

Source Bit is the number of the least significant bit in the group of bits to be moved and the Length is the number of bits in the group. The group of bits is copied to the part of the Dest address defined by the Dest Bit (the number of the least significant bit) and the Length. The other bits in the destination are not modified. The Source Bit and Dest Bit numbers must be between 0 and 15. If the length of the bit group extends beyond the destination most-significant bit, the extra bits are lost. The actual transfer for the BTD block in Figure 7.42*a* is illustrated in Figure 7.42*b*. The lower 8 bits of D9:7 are copied into bits 8 to 15 of output word O:004. The eight outputs, O:004/8 to O:004/15, are connected to 7-segment displays that show the BCD number represented by the 8 bits.

7.7 SIEMENS S7 COMPARISION AND COMPUTATION

The Siemens S7 comparison and computation function blocks are organized according to their function:

Category	Description
Comparison	Compare two values
Basic math	Basic arithmetic (+, -, ×, ÷)
Advanced math	Trigonometry and exponentiation
Logical	Bit-wise logical operators
Data type conversion	Convert value to another data type
Move	Copy data
Selection	Select one of a list of values
Date and time	Format conversions, add/subtract

The computation function blocks have the EN and ENO connections as the topmost input and output, respectively (Figure 7.6). The EN input must be **on** ("1" or logical true) for the block to execute. The ENO output echoes the EN input and is **on** if EN is **on** and the block executes without error. If the EN input is **off** ("0" or logical false) the function block is **not** executed and all outputs remain with their old values, that is the value when the block was last executed. In this case, the value of ENO is automatically set to **off**.

Design Tip

The behavior of the function block outputs when EN is off must be considered in the ladder logic code. If the EN input is off, the block outputs remain at their last value. This behavior may produce unexpected results.

Most of the functions described in this section are integrated with the processor. However, some of the functions described in this section are FC blocks, meaning they are not integrated with the processor and are loaded with the user program, if called by the user program.

7.7.1 Comparison Function Blocks

Example comparison functions are shown in Figure 7.43. The S7-300/400 and S7-200 processors have different names for the comparison functions, though their operation is the same. In addition, the S7-200 processors have comparison contacts, which are not covered by this text. Each comparison function block has two inputs. The result of the comparison (shown as BoolOut in Figure 7.43) is a Boolean. The possible comparison function blocks and the condition that turns on the BoolOut output are:

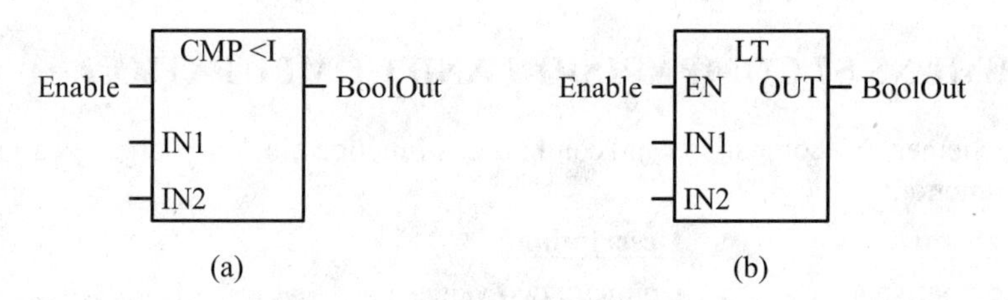

Figure 7.43. Example S7 less-than comparison function blocks: *(a)* S7-300/400; *(b)* S7-200.

S7-300/400 Block Name	**S7-200 Block Name**	**Output is *on* if top input is *on* and:**
CMP ==*	EQ	IN1 = IN2
CMP >=*	GE	IN1 ≥ IN2
CMP >*	GT	IN1 > IN2
CMP <=*	LE	IN1 ≤ IN2
CMP <*	LT	IN1 < IN2
CMP *	NE	IN1 ≠ IN2

where * is the data type suffix which is one of the following:

D - DINT
I - INT
R - REAL

The suffix of the S7-300/400 block name determines the format of the data to be compared. The S7-200 block names do not have a suffix, though the values being compared must be the same data type.

Comparison blocks can easily be cascaded to implement complicated comparison operations. The S7 comparison blocks do not have the EN/ENO problem that occurs with cascaded Modicon comparison blocks. For example, consider an implementation of a high level alarm for a tank. The alarm, LT1000_HIALM, is **on** when

90.0 ≤ LT1000 < 95.0

LT1000 is the tank level in whatever units are being used. An implementation of this comparison is shown in Figure 7.44. The comparisons can occur in either order.

On the S7-300/400 processors, comparison FC (function) blocks are provided for the DATE_AND_TIME and STRING variable types. Two sample comparison functions are shown in Figure 7.45. The possible comparisons are:

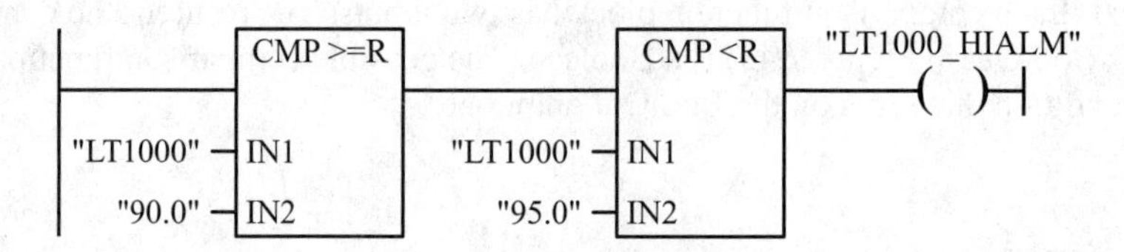

Figure 7.44. Cascaded S7-300/400 comparison.

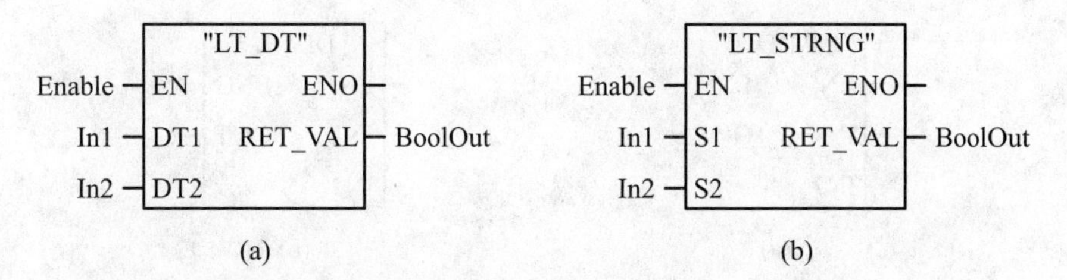

Figure 7.45. Example comparison function blocks for complex data types: *(a)* DATE_AND_TIME; *(b)* STRING.

Block Name	**RET_VAL is *on* if:**
EQ_***	In1 = In2
GE_***	In1 ≥ In2
GT_***	In1 > In2
LE_***	In1 ≤ In2
LT_***	In1 < In2
NE_***	In1 ≠ In2

where **** is "DT" for DATE_AND_TIME types or "STRNG" for STRING types. Only symbolic variables can be connected to the S1 and S2 (or DT1 and DT2) inputs. These functions do not report any errors with the input variables.

7.7.2 Basic Math Function Blocks

Example basic math function blocks are shown in Figure 7.46. As for the comparison function blocks, the name of the math block consists of the operation type (ADD, DIV, MOD, MUL, or SUB) with a data type suffix. The suffix determines the format of the input and result data. The basic math function blocks and the calculation that occurs for each one are:

Block Name	**OUT Value**
ADD_*	IN1 + IN2
DIV_*	IN1÷ IN2
MOD_*	IN1 modulo IN2 = IN1– (IN1/IN2)IN2 (DINT type only)
MUL_*	IN1× IN2
SUB_*	IN1 – IN2

where * is the data type suffix which is one of the following:

DI - DINT
I - INT
R - REAL

The MOD (modulo) function block is valid for the DINT data type only. The S7-200 IEC math function blocks do not have the suffix, but operate in the same manner as for the S7-300/400 blocks. For all blocks, the ENO output is **off** if the result of the calculation is outside the range of valid values for the data type.

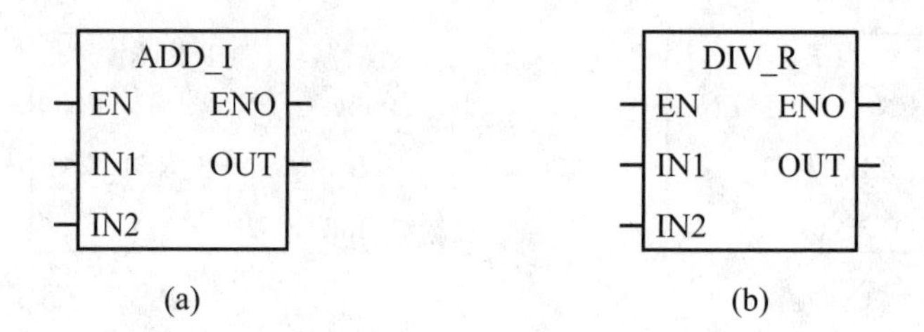

Figure 7.46. Example S7-300/400 basic math function blocks: *(a)* addition; *(b)* divide.

If two integers are divided and the result contains a fraction, the fractional remainder is truncated. For example, if the two inputs to DIV_I are 15 and 6, the output result is 2.

Note that the data type for the input and output connections to the math function blocks must match the suffix of the block name. Therefore, if dissimilar data types must be added, at least one of them will need to be converted with a data type conversion block.

The basic math function blocks that have only one input are shown in Figure 7.47 and are described as:

Block Name	OUT Value
ABS	Absolute value of IN1 (|IN1|)
NEG_*	– IN1

where * is the data type suffix. The ABS block is only valid for the REAL data type. These two blocks are not supported by the S7-200 processors.

When cascading math blocks to implement complicated calculations, be careful to avoid over-ranges and dividing by zero. If a block encounters an over-range or divide-by-zero, the ENO is always turned **off**. If subsequent math blocks depend on that ENO to execute, then they will not be executed and the result of the calculation will be invalid.

The result of a mathematical operation may be checked by examining the processor status bits. Specifically, one can check for overflow, underflow, invalid values, and the relationship of the result to zero (less than, equal to, etc.). Siemens (2000a, 2002a) document the effect of specific operations on the status bits.

For the S7-300/400 processors, the status bits are accessed by special contacts (both normally-open and normally-closed) that refer to the status bit. If the status bit is set, then the normally-open contact reference to that bit is **on** and if the status bit is clear, then the normally-open contact reference to that bit is **off**. If the status bit is set, then the

Figure 7.47. One-input S7-300/400 basic math blocks: *(a)* absolute value; *(b)* negation.

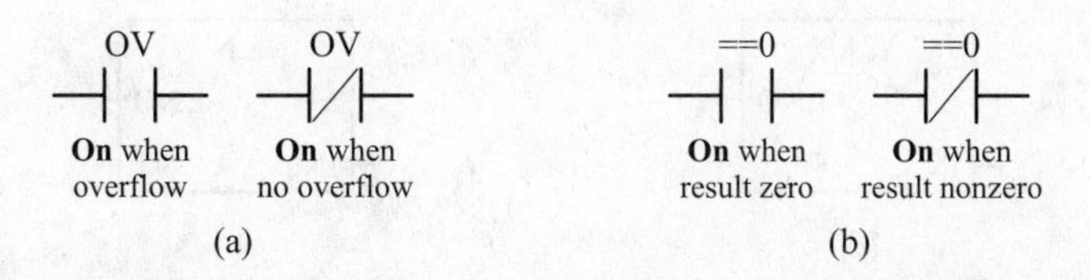

Figure 7.48. Status-bit contacts: *(a)* overflow; *(b)* result equal to zero.

normally-closed contact reference to that bit is **off** and if the status bit is clear, then the normally-closed contact reference to that bit is **on**. Sample status bit contacts are shown in Figure 7.48. The possible status bit contacts and their indication is as follows:

Name	Indication when *on*
BR	Binary result (BR) bit set
OS	Stored overflow
OV	Overflow
UO	Invalid floating-point number
==0	Result is equal to zero
0	Result is not zero
>=0	Result is greater than or equal to zero
>0	Result is greater than zero
<=0	Result is less than or equal to zero
<0	Result is less than zero

Note that there is no direct access to the CC0 and CC1 status bits, which determines the particular type of overflow when calculating real values. To access these bits, one must use a STW statement in an instruction list program.

For the S7-200 processors, the status bits are addressed directly as booleans, no special contacts are used. The status bit addresses and their indication is as follows:

Address	Indication when *on*
SM1.0	Result is zero
SM1.1	Overflow or illegal number
SM1.2	Result is negative
SM1.3	Division by zero attempted

Figure 7.49. Example S7 advanced math function blocks: *(a)* arctangant; *(b)* natural logarithm.

7.7.3 Advanced Math Function Blocks

There are a few advanced math function blocks that operate on REAL values. The names of these function blocks and the calculation that occurs for each one are:

Block Name	OUT Value
ACOS	Arc cosine of IN1 (Result in radians)
ASIN	Arc sine of IN1 (Result in radians)
ATAN	Arc tangent of IN1 (Result in radians)
COS	Cosine of IN1 (IN1 in radians)
EXP	Raise *e* to exponent IN1
LN	Natural logarithm of IN1
SIN	Sine of IN1 (IN1 in radians)
SQR	Square of IN1
SQRT	Square root of IN1
TAN	Tangent of IN1 (IN1 in radians)

Two example blocks are shown in Figure 7.49. The following blocks are not supported by the S7-200 processor: ACOS, ASIN, ATAN, and SQR.

7.7.4 Logical Function Blocks

The logical function blocks provide bit-wise logical operations for the WORD and DWORD data types and are shown in Figure 7.50. The logical function blocks and the calculation that occurs for each one are:

S7-300/400 Block Name	S7-200 IEC Block Name	OUT Value
WAND_*	AND	IN1 AND IN2 (bit-wise logical AND)
INV_I		Invert all bits in INT
INV_DI		Invert all bits in DINT
WOR_*	OR	IN1 OR IN2 (bit-wise logical OR)
WXOR_*	XOR	IN1 XOR IN2 (bit-wise logical exclusive-OR)

where * is the data type suffix: W for WORD; DW for DWORD. The suffix is not needed for the S7-200 IEC logical functions. The bit inversion is only available for the integer data types.

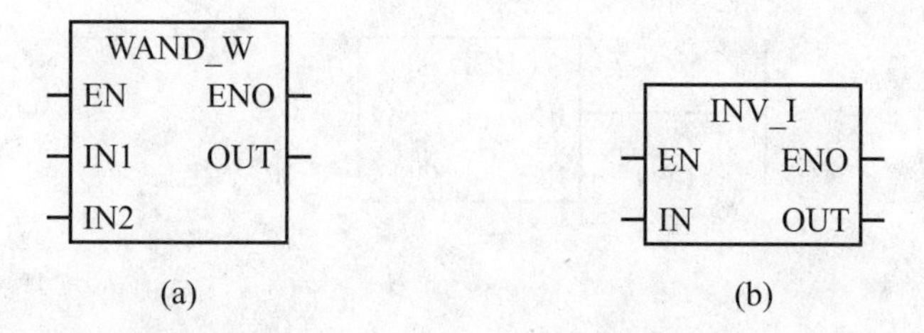

Figure 7.50. Example S7-300/400 logical function blocks: *(a)* bit-wise AND; *(b)* bit-wise inversion.

7.7.5 Conversion Function Blocks

Function blocks are provided to convert from one data type to another. These blocks appear similar to the advanced math block in Figure 7.49. The possible conversion function blocks are:

S7-300/400 Block Name	S7-200 IEC Block Name	Conversion Operation
	B_TO_I	BYTE to INT
BCD_I	BCD_TO_I	3- or 4-digit BCD (WORD) to INT
BCD_DI		7-digit BCD (DWORD) to DINT
DI_BCD		DINT to 7-digit BCD (DWORD)
	DI_TO_I	DINT to INT
DI_R	DI_TO_R	DINT to REAL
	I_TO_B	INT to BYTE
I_BCD	I_TO_BCD	INT to 3- or 4-digit BCD (WORD)
I_DI	I_TO_DI	INT to DINT
ROUND	R_TO_DI	REAL to DINT, rounding
TRUNC	TRUNC	REAL to DINT, truncation
CEIL		REAL to DINT, ceiling
FLOOR		REAL to DINT, floor
SCALE		Scale analog input to engineering units
UNSCALE		Scale engineering units to analog output

The ceiling function converts a real number to a double integer by "always rounding up" any fractional part of the real number. The floor function converts a real number to a double integer by "always rounding down" any fractional part of the real number. For example, the ceiling of 17.2 is 18 and the floor of 17.2 is 17. As another example, the ceiling of -17.2 is -17 and the floor of -17.2 is -18.

Note that the S7-300/400 processors have no standard block that will convert a DINT to an INT. This conversion can be done by using a MOVE block to copy a DINT to an INT variable. Also, there are no standard conversion blocks between the WORD and DWORD types to the INT and DINT types. Again, these conversions are done by using a MOVE block to copy between variables.

An example BCD_I function block for the S7-300/400 processors is shown in Figure 7.51. This example assumes that the bit pattern from the three thumbwheel switches is transferred to TW1. The BCD_I block converts the 3-digit-plus-sign BCD value to an

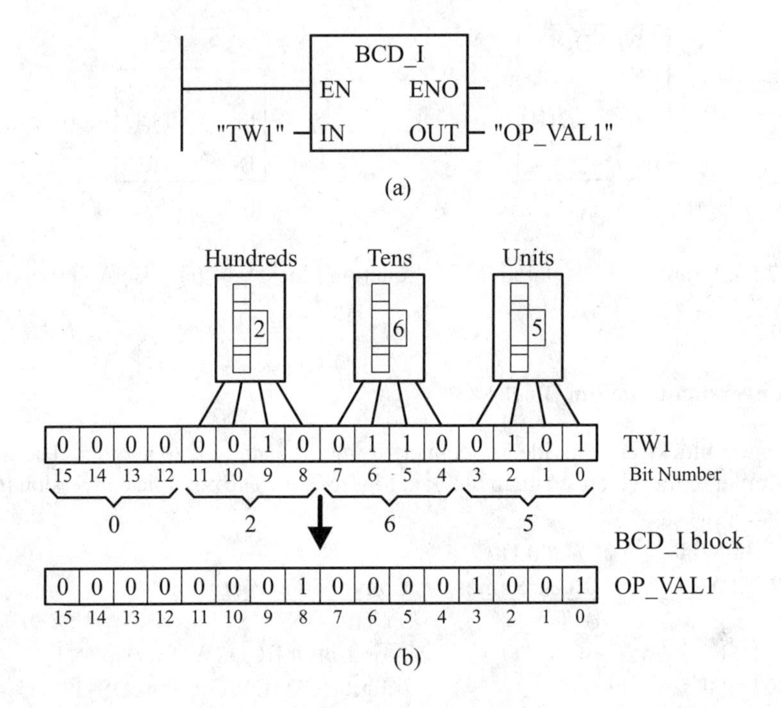

Figure 7.51. Example S7-300/400 BCD-to-integer conversion: *(a)* ladder logic; *(b)* operation.

integer, placing the result in OP_VAL1. For the S7-200 processors, the BCD value is an unsigned 4-digit number. If one needs to convert a 4-digit BCD number to an integer on the S7-300/400 processors, the BCD number needs to be transferred to the lower 16 bits of a DWORD and the BCD_DI function does the conversion.

An example I_BCD function block for the S7-300/400 processors appears in Figure 7.52. The integer in CUR_T is converted into a 3-digit-plus-sign BCD value and placed in DP532. Another function block is assumed to transfer the lower 12 bits of DP532 to the discrete outputs that are attached to binary-to-7-segment decoder drivers. If CUR_TEMP is negative, the upper 4 bits of DP532 are set to a hexadecimal "F". For the S7-200 processors, the BCD value is an unsigned 4-digit number. If one needs to convert an integer to a 4-digit BCD number on the S7-300/400 processors, the integer must be transferred to a DWORD, the DI_BCD function does the conversion, and the lower 16 bits of the result transferred to the destination.

An example SCALE function block is shown in Figure 7.53. The SCALE function block scales an integer from an analog input module to the desired engineering units. The IN integer input is scaled to the OUT real number. The scaling equation is the same as equation 7.1 where:

X = IN	Y = OUT
$X_1 = -27{,}648$ (BIPOLAR **on**)	Y_1 = LO_LIM
$X_1 = 0$ (BIPOLAR **off**)	Y_2 = HI_LIM
$X_2 = 27{,}648$	

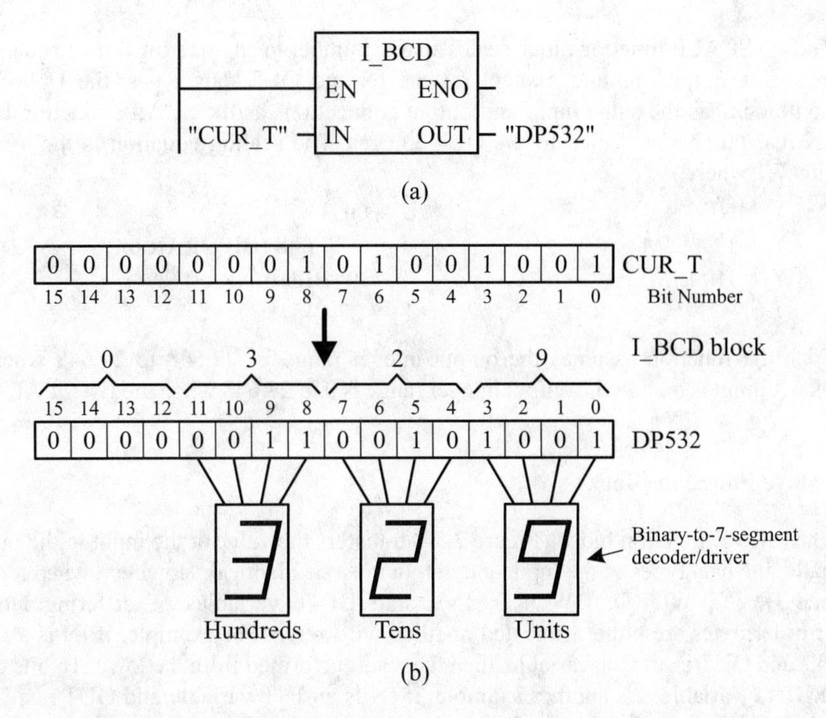

Figure 7.52. Example S7-300/400 integer-to-BCD conversion: *(a)* ladder logic; *(b)* operation.

Note that the function assumes the input integer range is -27,648 to 27,648 when the BIPOLAR input is **on** and the input integer range is 0 to 27,648 when the BIPOLAR input is **off**. The RET_VAL is zero if the function executed without error and contains an error code if the conversion had an error (Siemens, 2000).

The example SCALE shown in Figure 7.53 performs the conversion in Example 7.3 and assumes that the transmitter output range is 4 to 20 mA, but the analog input range is 0 to 20 mA. Therefore, one must artificially lower the LO_LIM by 25% of the normal range to account for the 4 mA low value of the transmitter corresponding to 90 °C. Hence, the LO_LIM of Figure 7.53 is 90 – (700–90)/4 = –62.5. With this change, when TT101_MEAS is 5530 (4 mA), TT101 is 90.

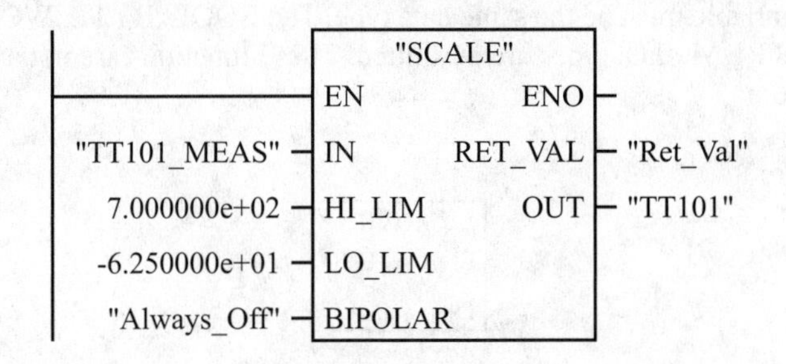

Figure 7.53. Example S7-300/400 SCALE function block.

The UNSCALE function block scales an real number in engineering units to an integer for an analog output module. Except for the IN and OUT data types, the UNSCALE function block has the same input and output connections as the SCALE function block. The IN real number is scaled to the OUT integer. The scaling equation is the same as equation 7.1 where:

X = IN	Y = OUT
X_1 = LO_LIM	Y_1 = –27,648 (BIPOLAR **on**)
X_2 = HI_LIM	Y_1 = 0 (BIPOLAR **off**)
	Y_2 = 27,648

Note that the function assumes the output integer range is -27,648 to 27,648 when the BIPOLAR input is **on** and the output integer range is 0 to 27,648 when the BIPOLAR input is **off**.

7.7.6 Move Function Block

The MOVE function block (Figure 7.54) transfers the value at the input to the output. Normally, the data types of the input and output must be identical. However, when moving between BYTE, WORD, DWORD, INT, and DINT variables of differing lengths, higher-order bytes are either truncated or filled with zeros. For example, if IN is a DINT variable and OUT is an INT variable, then the result is formed from the lower 16 bits of the 32-bit DINT variable. As another example, if IN is an INT variable and OUT is a DINT variable, then the result is formed by zeroing the upper 16 bits of the DINT variable and transferring the INT to the lower 16 bits of the DINT variable. Note that if an INT is negative, moving it to a DINT does not preserve the negative sign.

7.7.7 Selection Function Blocks

The following function blocks allow one value to be selected from a given number of values:

Block Name	Description
MAX	Output is maximum of three values.
MIN	Output is minimum of three values.
SEL	Select one of two values

For the MAX and MIN blocks (Figure 7.55*a*, *b*), IN1- IN3 may be INT, DINT, or REAL data types. All three inputs need to be the same data type. The SEL function block, shown in Figure 7.55*c*, uses a Boolean variable to select one of two input signals. If G is **on**, then IN1 is copied to the output; otherwise, IN0 is copied to the output. Both input variables and the output variable must be the same data type. The BOOL, BYTE, WORD, DWORD, INT, DINT, and REAL data types are permitted. These functions are not available for the S7-200 processors.

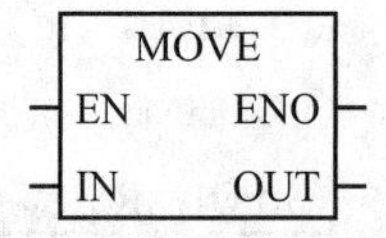

Figure 7.54. S7 move function block.

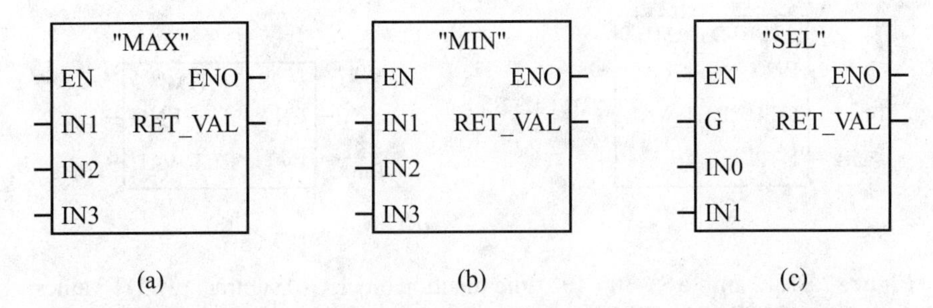

Figure 7.55. S7-300/400 selection function blocks: *(a)* maximum; *(b)* minimum; *(c)* selection.

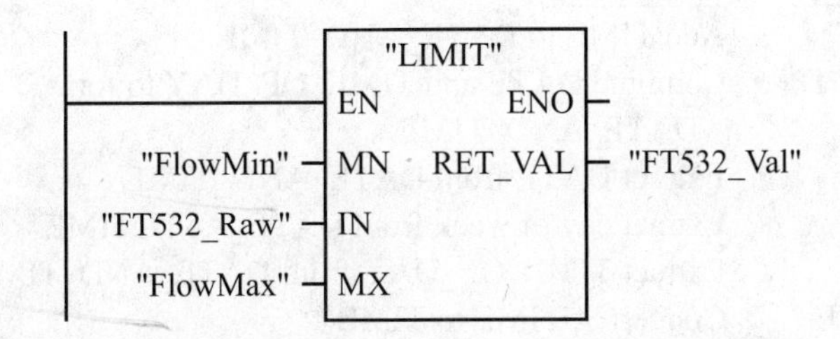

Figure 7.56. Example S7-300/400 LIMIT function block.

The LIMIT function block, shown in the example of Figure 7.56, ensures a value is inside a specified range. The output of this block is determined as follows:

RET_VAL = IN if MN ≤ IN ≤ MX
RET_VAL = MN if IN > MN
RET_VAL = MX if IN < MX

The MN, IN, MX, and RET_VAL signals must all be the same data type. The MN, IN, and MX inputs cannot be constants. For the example in Figure 7.56, the value of FT532_Val is limited to be between FlowMin and FlowMax.

For all the selection functions, if the inputs or result are invalid, the BR bit in the status is set **on**. All of these operations are FC blocks.

7.7.8 Date and Time Functions

The S7-300/400 processors have special function blocks to handle the conversion between time formats, to extract parts of the DATE_AND_TIME data type and to add/subtract time values. The available function blocks are:

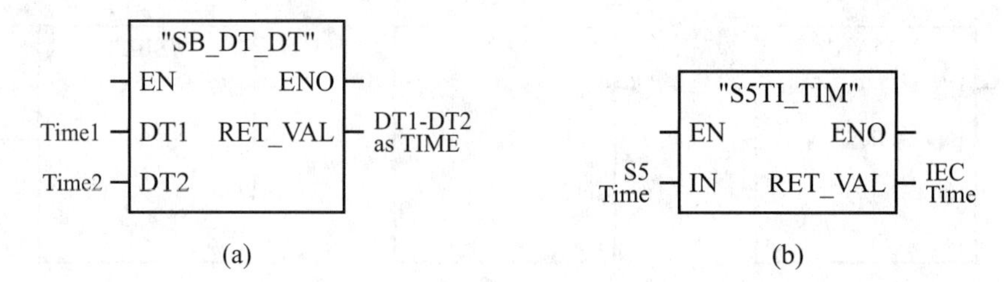

Figure 7.57. Example S7-300/400 time function blocks *(a)* subtract two DT values; *(b)* convert S5TIME to TIME.

Block Name	Description
AD_DT_TM	Add TIME to DATE_AND_TIME.
D_TOD_DT	Combine DATE and TIME_OF_DAY to form DATE_AND_TIME.
DT_DATE	Extract DATE from DATE_AND_TIME
DT_DAY	Extract day of week from DATE_AND_TIME
DT_TOD	Extract TIME_OF_DAY from DATE_AND_TIME
S5TI_TIME	Convert S5TIME to TIME
SB_DT_DT	Subtract two DATE_AND_TIME values as TIME
SB_DT_TM	Subtract TIME from DATE_AND_TIME
TIM_S5TI	Convert TIME to S5TIME

Two sample functions are shown in Figure 7.57. If the inputs or result are invalid, the BR bit in the status is set **on**. All of these operations are FC blocks.

7.8 GE FANUC COMPARISION AND COMPUTATION

The GE Fanuc comparison and computation function blocks are organized according to their function:

Category	Description
Comparison	Compare two values
Basic math	Basic arithmetic (+, -, ×, ÷)
Advanced math	Trigonometry and exponentiation
Logical	Bit-wise logical operators
Data type conversion	Convert value to another data type
Move	Copy data

The non-boolean input and output connections to comparison and computation function blocks are normally connected to a variable, address, or constant. However, for the Series 90-70 processors, a non-boolean output can be directly "wired" to a non-boolean input (called "data flow"). The data flow feature is especially useful for calculations where the result of one calculation function block is needed by the next calculation block. For compatibility among the various GE Fanuc processors, the examples presented in this text do not use data flow.

There are some restrictions on the placement of comparison and computation function blocks on a rung. They can be cascaded, in other words, the boolean output of one comparison/computation can be connected to the enable input of another comparison/computation. However, like the timers and counters, they cannot be placed in parallel with a coil. Also, a contact cannot be connected to the status (top) output. The output must be connected to a coil, be connected to another block enable, or remain unconnected.

There is some variation among the various GE Fanuc processors as to which specific computation and comparison blocks are supported. For the most part, these differences depend on the data type. With some exceptions, all GE Fanuc processors support operations on DINT and INT data types. Operations with REAL data types can be done only by processors that support floating-point operations. The UINT data type is supported by Series 90-70 processors only. Exceptions to these rules are indicated with the specific blocks. Specific information is contained in the instruction set manual (GE Fanuc Automation, 1999, 2000, 2001).

7.8.1 Comparison Function Blocks

Example comparison function blocks are shown in Figure 7.58. The name of a basic comparison block consists of the comparison type (EQ, GE, GT, LE, LT, or NE) with a data type suffix. The suffix of the function block name determines the format of the data to be compared:

DINT	REAL
INT	UINT

Each comparison function block has three inputs. The top input is an enable for the block. The result of the comparison is the Q Boolean output. The possible comparison function blocks and the condition that turns on the Q output are:

Block Name	Q is *on* if enable input is *on* and:
EQ_***	IN1 = IN2
GE_***	IN1 ≥ IN2
GT_***	IN1 > IN2
LE_***	IN1 ≤ IN2
LT_***	IN1 < IN2
NE_***	IN1 ≠ IN2

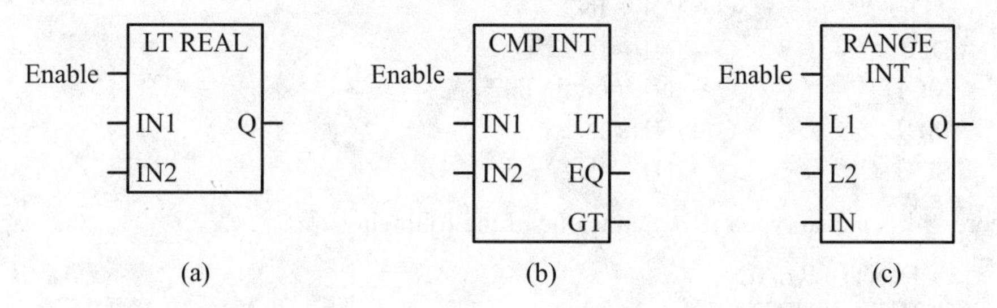

Figure 7.58. Example GE Fanuc comparison function blocks: *(a)* less-than; *(b)* generalized compare; *(c)* range check.

where *** is the data type suffix.

The basic comparison blocks can easily be cascaded to implement complicated comparison operations. The GE Fanuc comparison blocks do not have the EN/ENO problem that occurs with cascaded Modicon comparison blocks.

The Series 90-70 processors have a CMP block, illustrated in Figure 7.58*b*. This block has a data type suffix like the basic comparison blocks. However, only later 90-70 processors support the REAL data type. The outputs of the CMP block operate as follows:

Output	***On* if enable input is *on* and:**
LT	IN1 < IN2
EQ	IN1 = IN2
GT	IN1 > IN2

The RANGE function block tests whether a value is inside a specified range. An example RANGE block is shown in Figure 7.58*c*. This block has a data type suffix that is one of the following:

DINT	UINT
DWORD	WORD
INT	

The RANGE block basically checks that the IN input is in the range defined by the L1 and L2 inputs. Either L1 or L2 may be the "Low Limit" or the "High Limit" values. The block output, Q, functions as follows

Condition	**Q**
Low Limit ≤ IN ≤ High Limit	On
IN < Low Limit or IN > High Limit	Off

The RANGE block is only supported by recent Series 90-30 and 90-70 processors and by VersaMax processors . The DWORD and UINT data types are only supported by recent 90-70 processors.

7.8.2 Basic Math Function Blocks

Example basic arithmetic function blocks are shown in Figure 7.59. The possible basic arithmetic function blocks are:

Block Name	**Calculation:**
ABS_***	Q = absolute value of IN (|IN|)
ADD_***	Q = IN1 + IN2
DIV_***	Q = IN1 ÷ IN2
MOD_***	Q = IN1 modulo IN2
MUL_***	Q = IN1 × IN2
SUB_***	Q = IN1 – IN2

where *** is a data type suffix that is one of the following:

DINT	REAL
INT	UINT

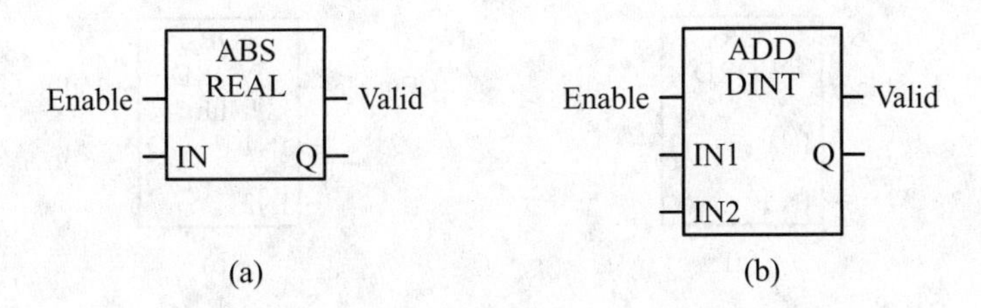

Figure 7.59. Example GE Fanuc calculation function blocks: *(a)* absolute value; *(b)* addition.

For recent Series 90-70 processors, the DIV and MUL blocks may have the MIXED suffix to accommodate certain mixed integer data types. For the DIV_MIXED block, IN1 is DINT, IN2 is INT and Q is INT. For the MUL_MIXED block, both IN1 and IN2 are INTs and Q is DINT. The ABS_*** block is valid for the Series 90-70 processors only and not for the UINT data type.

For all computation function blocks, the arithmetic operation is performed when the top input receives power. The top output is turned **on** if the calculation is performed and there are no errors (for example, over-range or divide-by-zero). If a block encounters an over-range or divide-by-zero, the top output is always turned **off**. When cascading math blocks to implement complicated calculations, one should be careful to avoid calculation errors. Subsequent math blocks will not execute if a prior block has a calculation error.

7.8.3 Advanced Math Function Blocks

The names of the advanced math function blocks and the calculation that occurs for each one are:

Block Name	Calculation Result
ACOS	Q = Arc cosine of IN (Q in radians)
ASIN	Q = Arc sine of IN (Q in radians)
ATAN	Q = Arctangent of IN (Q in radians)
COS	Q = Cosine of IN (IN in radians)
EXP	Q = *e* raised to exponent IN
EXPT	$Q = (IN1)^{IN2}$
LN	Q = Natural logarithm of IN
LOG	Q = Common logarithm of IN
SIN	Q = Sine of IN (IN in radians)
SQRT_***	Q = Square root of IN
TAN	Q = Tangent of IN (IN in radians)

The EXPT function block is a two-operand block, similar to the one in Figure 7.59*b*. The other advanced math function blocks are one-operand blocks, similar in format to the block in Figure 7.59*a*. Except for the SQRT_*** block, all of these function blocks are for REAL data types. For the SQRT, the valid suffixes are: DINT, INT, and REAL.

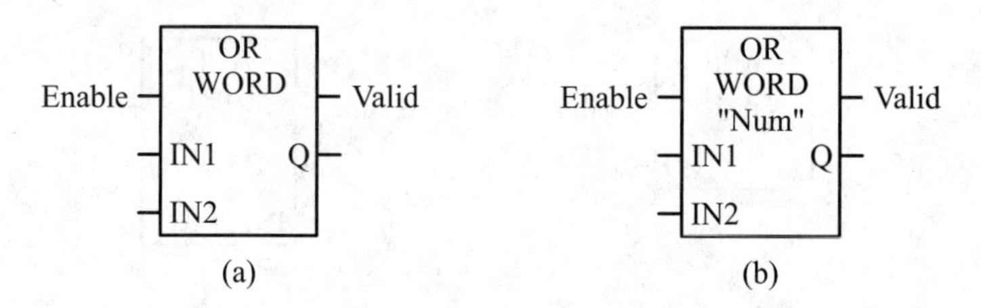

Figure 7.60. GE Fanuc logical or function block: *(a)* all but 90-70 processors; *(b)* 90-70 processors.

7.8.4 Logical Function Blocks

The logical function blocks provide bit-wise logical operations for the WORD and DWORD data types and examples are shown in Figure 7.60. The block executes when the top input turns **on**. The top output echoes the top input. The logical function blocks and the calculation that occurs for each one are:

Block Name	Q Value
AND_***	IN1 AND IN2 (bit-wise logical AND)
NOT_***	Invert all bits in IN
OR_***	IN1 OR IN2 (bit-wise logical OR)
XOR_***	IN1 XOR IN2 (bit-wise logical exclusive-OR)

where *** is the data type suffix: DWORD or WORD. The DWORD data type is supported for the Series 90-70 processors only. Also, the Series 90-70 processors allow one to operate on multi-word bit arrays. The "Num" field is a constant and it specifies the number of DWORDs or WORDs in the bit string (from 1 to 256). Bit arrays are detailed in Chapter 8.

7.8.5 Conversion Function Blocks

Function blocks are provided to convert from one data type to another. The function blocks that are possible are:

Block Name	Description
BCD4_TO_***	4-digit BCD to ...
BCD8_TO_***	8-digit BCD to ...
DINT_TO_***	Double integer to ...
INT_TO_***	Integer to ...
REAL_TO_***	Real to ...
TRUNC_TO_***	Real to ..., truncate result
UINT_TO_***	Unsigned integer to ...
WORD_TO_***	Word to ...

where *** is the data type of the result. However, a particular data type may not be converted to all other data types. In addition, many processors do not support all possible

Table 7.2 Valid GE Fanuc Type Conversions

Input Type	Output Type						
	BCD4	BCD8[1]	DINT	INT	REAL[2]	UINT[1]	WORD
BCD4				X	X	X	
BCD8[1]			X		X		
DINT		X		X[1]	X	X	
INT	X		X[1]		X	X	
REAL[2]			X	X		X	X[3]
TRUNC[2]			X	X			
UINT[1]	X		X	X	X		
WORD					X[3]		

Notes:

1. Series 90-70 processors version 3.0 or later
2. Floating-point processors
3. VersaMax and Series 90-30 floating-point processors.

conversions. Valid conversions and the processors that support them are shown in Table 7.2.

In appearance, the data type conversion blocks are similar to the single-input arithmetic blocks. The block executes when the top input turns **on**. The top output echoes the top input if the conversion does not result in an overflow.

An example BCD4_TO_INT function block is shown in Figure 7.61. This example assumes that the bit pattern from the two thumbwheel switches is transferred to TW62. The BCD4_TO_INT block converts the 4-digit BCD value to an INT, placing the result in OpVal2. An example INT_TO_BCD4 function block appears in Figure 7.62. The INT in

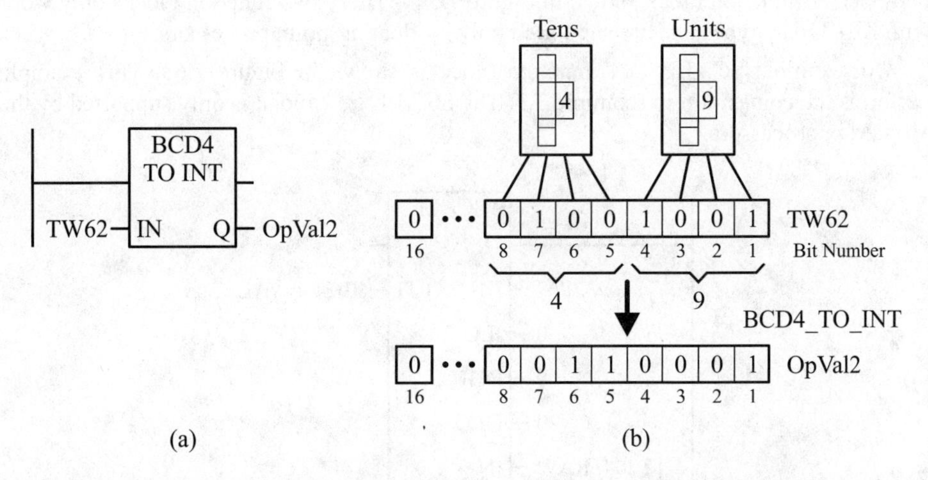

Figure 7.61. Example GE Fanuc BCD-to-integer conversion: *(a)* ladder logic; *(b)* operation.

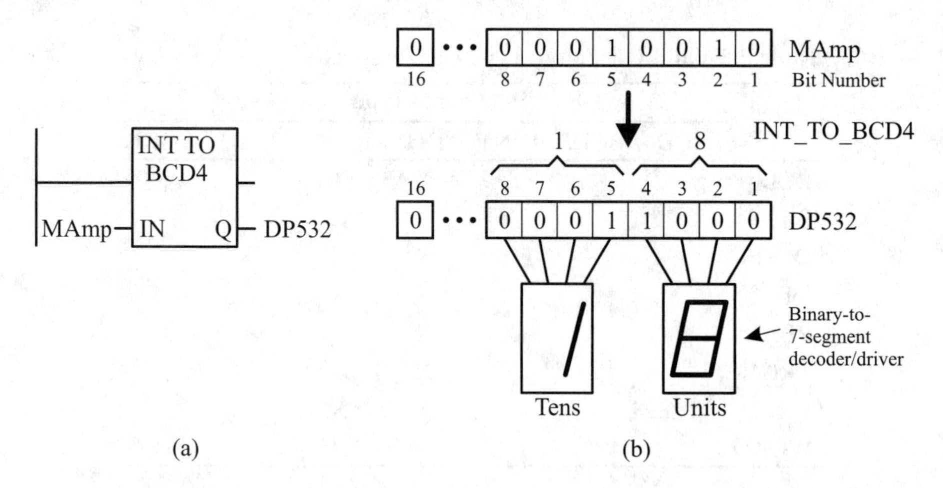

Figure 7.62. Example GE Fanuc integer-to-BCD conversion: *(a)* ladder logic; *(b)* operation.

MAmp is converted into a 4-digit BCD value and placed in DP532. Another function block is assumed to transfer the lower 8 bits of DP532 to the discrete outputs that are attached to binary-to-7-segment decoder drivers.

The names of miscellaneous conversion function blocks and the conversion that occurs for each one are:

Block Name	**Description**
DEG_TO_RAD	Convert IN in degrees to radians.
RAD_TO_DEG	Convert IN in radians to degrees.
SCALE_INT	Convert IN (INT) to another scale
SCALE_WORD	Convert IN (WORD) to another scale

The DEG_TO_RAD and RAD_TO_DEG function blocks are similar to the one-operand function block shown in Figure 7.59*b*. These two function blocks only work with REAL data types and are supported only by floating-point processors.

An example SCALE_INT function block is shown in Figure 7.63. This example performs the conversion in Example 7.3. The SCALE_*** block is only supported by the VersaMax processors.

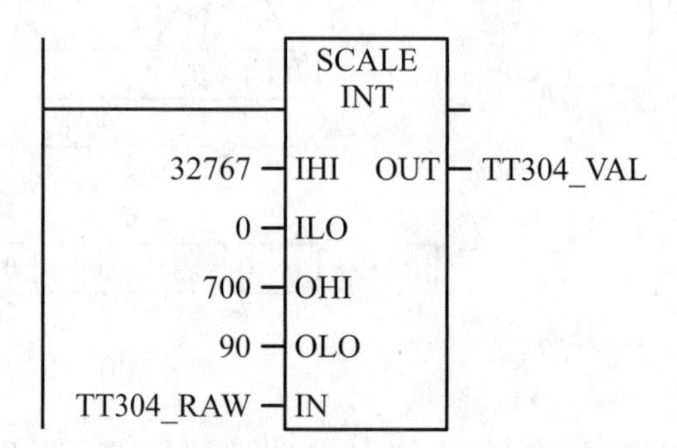

Figure 7.63. Example GE Fanuc SCALE_INT scale data function block.

7.8.6 Move Function Blocks

The move function blocks transfer data between addresses. The names and descriptions of the move function blocks are:

Block Name	Description
MOVE_BOOL	Copy bits
MOVE_DINT	Copy double integers (90-70 only)
MOVE_DWORD	Copy double words (90-70 only)
MOVE_INT	Copy integers
MOVE_REAL	Copy floating-point numbers
MOVE_UINT	Copy unsigned integers (90-70 only)
MOVE_WORD	Copy words
SWAP_DWORD	Exchange words within each DWORD
SWAP_WORD	Exchange bytes within each WORD

Example MOVE function blocks are shown in Figure 7.64*a*, *b*. The field below the block name is a constant and it specifies the number of Booleans, integers, and so on, that are copied. If IN is a constant, the constant is copied the specified number of times For the example in Figure 7.64*a*, the constant "50" is copied to the FIC101_SP register and the 4 registers that follow. More information about array operations is in section 8.7.3.

For all but MOVE_BOOL, the data types of the IN and Q need to be identical. When the top input of the MOVE_BOOL function is **on**, it copies the IN input to the Q output as bits. Therefore, the Q data type does not need to be the same as the IN data type. The MOVE_BOOL can thus be used in a similar manner as the Allen-Bradley BTD block. An example MOVE_BOOL is shown in Figure 7.64*b* and the transfer is illustrated in Figure 7.64*c*. The lower 8 bits of DP75 (of type BCD4) are copied into channels 9 to 16 of the output module whose starting address is %Q49. The eight outputs, %Q57 to %Q64, are connected to 7-segment displays that show the BCD number represented by the 8 bits.

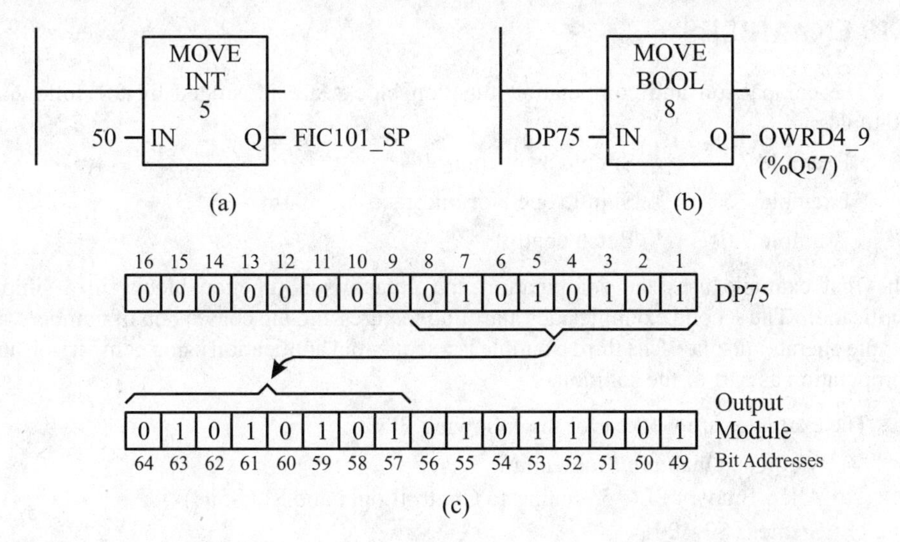

Figure 7.64. Example GE Fanuc move blocks: *(a)* MOVE_INT; *(b)* MOVE_BOOL; *(c)* operation of MOVE_BOOL.

The MOVE_INT and MOVE_WORD blocks are supported by all processors. The MOVE_BOOL block is supported by all processors except for early Series 90-30 and 90-70 processors.

7.9 APPLICATION CAVEATS

Regardless of the particular PLC processor, there are some details one should heed when using comparison and/or computation function blocks:

1. Do not use equality (=) with real or floating-point numbers. The comparison rarely, if ever, is true. A very small change in either number will make the comparison false. The ≥, >, ≤, or < comparisons are much better choices.
2. Do not use equality with any number that represents the value from a sensor. Just as for the previous rule, the comparison rarely, if ever, is true. Some types of sensor readings (for example, pressure and level) are rarely stable and will vary somewhat even when the system is apparently at rest. Even for other sensors, when the system is in a dynamic state a sensor reading may be below the desired threshold during one program scan and above the threshold during the next scan. Thus, the threshold will not be detected if equality is used to test for the threshold.
3. When dividing two integers to yield another integer, remember that any fractional part of the result is lost.
4. In any complex calculation that has a mixture of multiplication and division, do the division operation last, especially when the calculation involves integers. If the integer division is done first, the fractional part is lost, affecting the correctness of the final result.
5. When the result of a computation is an integer, watch out for overflow. On some SLC-500 processors, an overflow will cause the processor to halt at the end of a program scan.

7.10 EXAMPLES

The comparison and computation function blocks are illustrated by the following examples:

Example 7.4	Simple level control
Example 7.5	Simple operator interface and alarm
Example 7.6	Batch control

The first example uses the computation and comparison function blocks in a simple application. The second example adds alarming features and the conversion of numbers for simple operator display. The third example is a sequential application using comparison and computation as part of the solution.

The examples are worked for the following PLCs:

Modicon Quantum/Momentum
Allen-Bradley PLC-5 (similar to ControlLogix and SLC-500)
Siemens S7-300
GE Fanuc Series 90-30 (with floating point)

In addition, Example 7.4 is worked for ControlLogix and the different ways of doing calculations with the PLC-5 and SLC-500 processors. Also, only a portion of the solution to Example 7.6 is given.

Example 7.4. Simple tank level control. The PLC implements a simple level control for a tank (Figure 7.65). A level sensor (LT428) connected to an analog input channel measures the tank level. The PLC opens an inlet valve (XV427) to allow fluid to enter when the level is **below** a desired minimum and turns off the valve when the level is **above** a desired maximum. There is an internal coil, T428_CNTRL, which enables the level control operation. The desired minimum level, LT428_MIN, and the desired maximum level, LT428_MAX, are internal variables set by the operator.

The level transducer is calibrated to measure from 1.0 to 15.0 feet and is connected to an analog input module having an ADC whose output value (LT428_RAW) corresponds to the lowest and highest levels as:

Tank Level (ft.)	Modicon	PLC-5	ControlLogix	Siemens	GE Fanuc
1.0	0	0	1.0	5530	0
15.0	32,000	4095	15.0	27,648	32,000

The LT428_RAW value should be converted into a tank level, in feet (a real number) and placed in the LT428_VAL variable. In the case of the ControlLogix, the analog input is configured to scale the A/D converter output into the level in feet.

Assume the following physical input, physical output, and internal memory assignments:

Variable	Description
LT428_RAW	Level measurement from analog input ADC, see range above
XV427_OPEN	Inlet valve control; **on** to open valve, **off** to close valve
LT428_VAL	Level of tank, in feet
T428_MIN	Minimum tank level for control, in feet
T428_MAX	Maximum tank level for control, in feet
T428_CNTRL	Enables level control operation; **on** to run control, **off** keeps valve closed.

The addresses associated with the physical inputs and outputs are:

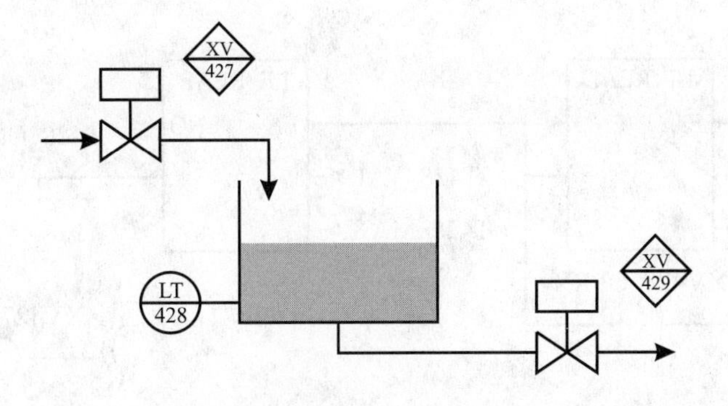

Figure 7.65. Tank level control.

Variable	Modicon	PLC-5	ControlLogix	Siemens	GE Fanuc
LT428_RAW	300002	N11:4	Local:4:I.Ch0Data	IW304	%AI1
XV427_OPEN	000001	O:2/00	Local:2:O.Data.0	Q4.0	%Q1

The addresses or data types associated with the internal variables:

Variable	Modicon Data Type	PLC-5 Addr.	Logix Data Type	Siemens Addr.	GE Fanuc Addr.
LT428_VAL	REAL	F8:20	REAL	MD40	%R120
T428_MIN	REAL	F8:21	REAL	MD44	%R122
T428_MAX	REAL	F8:22	REAL	MD48	%R124
T428_CNTRL	BOOL	B3/121	BOOL	M15.1	%M121

Solution. There are two parts to this problem: (1) conversion of analog input module reading into the level in feet; (2) control of XV428 valve. Because of the different ranges of the ADC output, the conversion equation for the first part will be different for each PLC. The second part will be very similar for all of the PLCs.

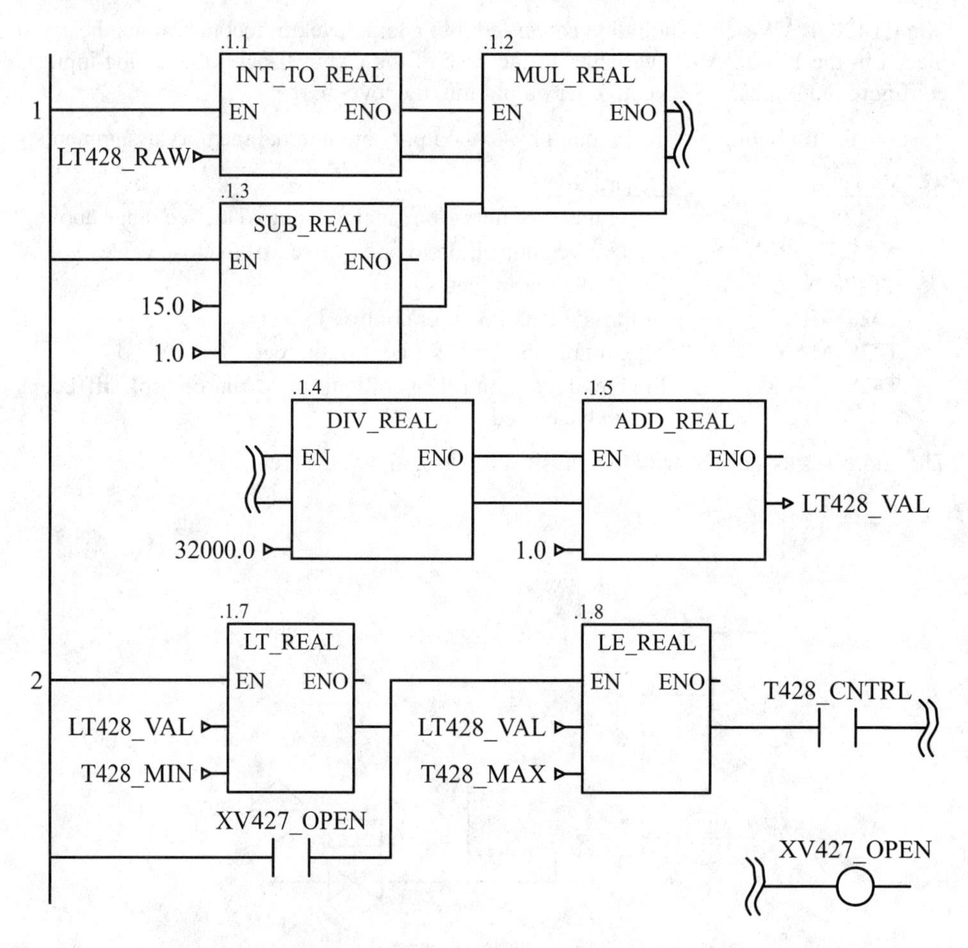

Figure 7.66. Modicon solution to Example 7.4, tank level control.

Using equation (7.1), the formula for converting the ADC output (LT428_RAW) into the level in feet (LT428_VAL) for the Modicon PLC is

$$LT428\_VAL = \frac{LT428\_RAW - 0}{32000 - 0} \times (15 - 1) + 1$$

The formula is not simplified so that if the transducer is recalibrated to a different maximum and/or minimum, one can easily find which constants in the ladder logic code need to be changed to accommodate the recalibration. The LT428_RAW value is a word data type and so must be converted to a real before using in the calculation. The conversion is rung 1 in Figure 7.66. The second rung is the control for the valve and is implemented as a start/stop rung. Assume that T428_CNTRL is on. The valve is opened when LT428_VAL < T428_MIN and the XV427_OPEN contact is used to seal the valve open. The valve remains open as long as LT428_VAL ≤ T428_MAX. When LT428_VAL > T428_MAX the second comparison becomes false, causing XV427_OPEN to turn off. The valve remains off until LT428_VAL < T428_MIN at which point, the valve is opened and the process is repeated. Whenever T428_CNTRL is off, the valve remains closed. If the tank level is below the minimum when T428_CNTRL turns on, the valve is opened.

The ladder logic for the ControlLogix solution for this example is shown in Figure 7.67. Since the analog input module scales the A/D converter output into the level in feet, LT428_RAW is simply copied to LT428_VAL (rung 1). As for the Modicon solution, the second rung is the control for the valve and is implemented as a start/stop rung.

For the PLC-5, the formula for converting the ADC output (LT428_RAW) into the level in feet (LT428_VAL) is

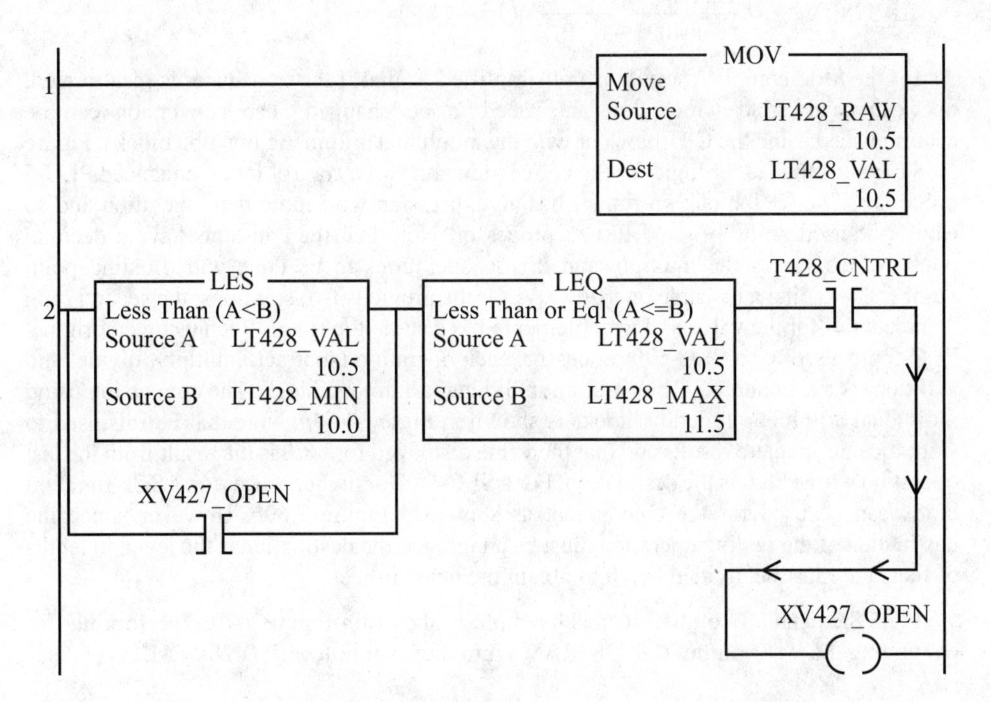

Figure 7.67. ControlLogix solution to Example 7.4, tank level control.

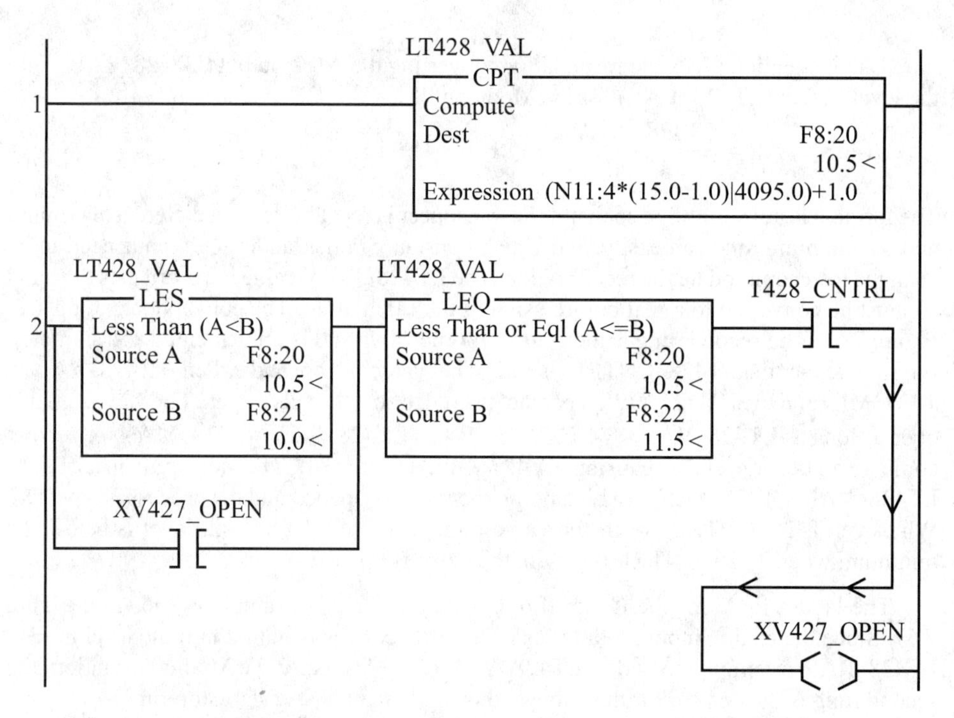

Figure 7.68. PLC-5 solution to Example 7.4, tank level control.

$$LT428\_VAL = \frac{LT428\_RAW - 0}{4095 - 0} \times (15 - 1) + 1$$

As for the Modicon, the formula is not simplified so that if the transducer is recalibrated, one can easily find which constants need to be changed. The conversion can be accomplished using the CPT block or with the individual arithmetic function blocks. Figure 7.68 contains the ladder logic for the conversion and valve control for an enhanced PLC-5 processor. The CPT block on rung 1 has an expression with more than operation and so cannot be used on an original PLC-5 processor. Note that the constants have a decimal point, which forces the multiply and divide operations to be done with floating point numbers, avoiding a possible overflow. As for the previous two solutions, the second rung is the control for the valve and is implemented as a start/stop rung. When using an original PLC-5 processor or a SLC-500 processor, each operation (subtract, multiply, divide, and addition) is a separate CPT block or an individual arithmetic block. The conversion using individual arithmetic function blocks is shown in Figure 7.69*a*. Note that F8:0 is used to store the intermediate results and that the value displayed for F8:0 is the result from the last operation where F8:0 is the destination. For a SLC-5/02 or higher processor, a SCL function block can be used for the conversion, as shown in Figure 7.69*b*. However, since the destination of the scaling operation must be an integer, the destination is the level, in tenths of feet, and must be divided by 10 to obtain the level, in feet.

The Siemens S7 solution to this example is shown in Figure 7.70. The formula for converting the ADC output (LT428_RAW) into the level in feet (LT428_VAL) is

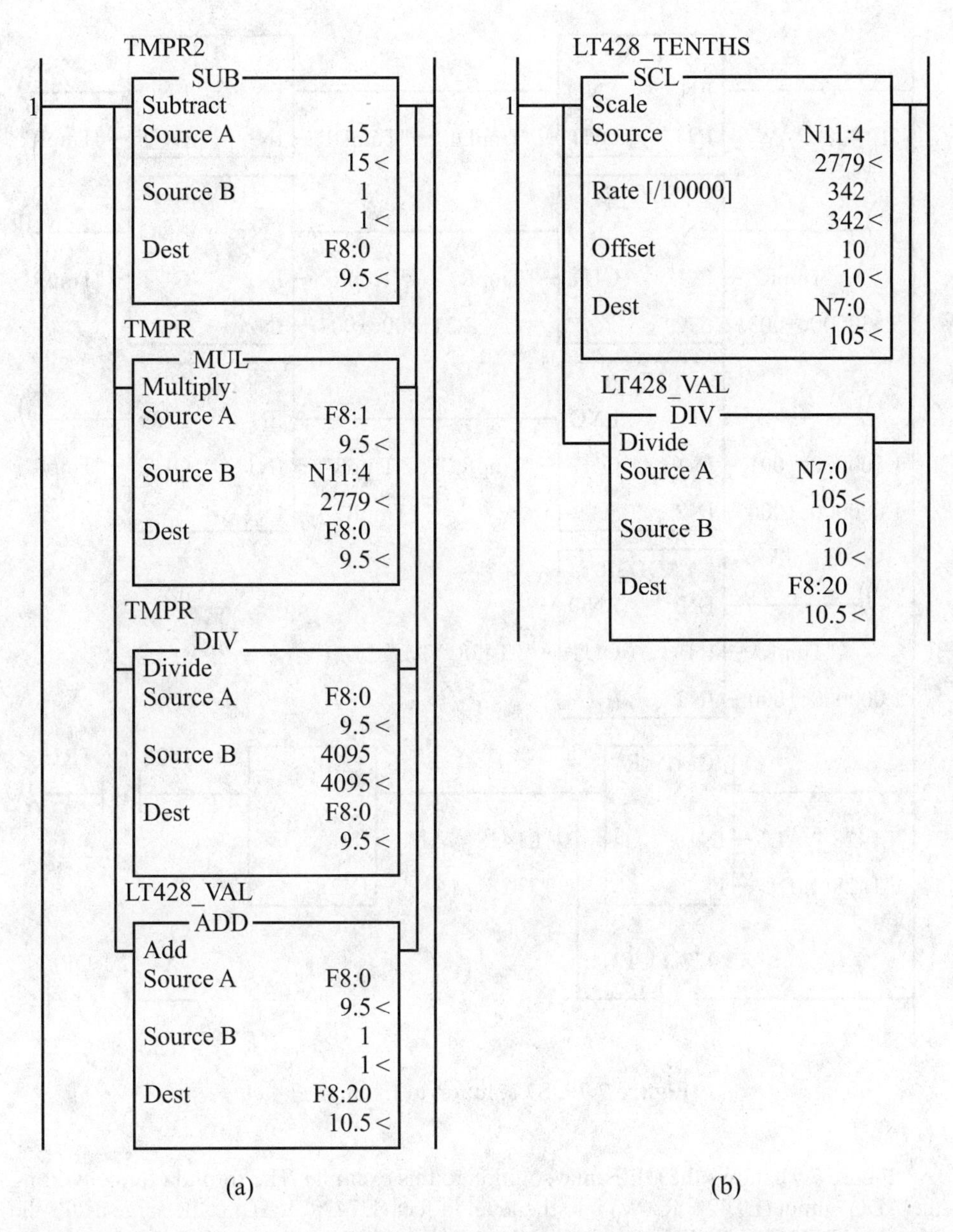

Figure 7.69. Alternate conversion rung: (a) PLC-5/SLC-500 with individual arithmetic function blocks; (b) SLC-500 SCL function block.

$$\text{LT428\_VAL} = \frac{\text{LT428\_RAW} - 5530}{27648 - 5530} \times (15 - 1) + 1$$

The individual arithmetic function blocks in network 1 implement the conversion. The SCALE block can also be used for the conversion. As for the previous solutions, the second rung is the control for the valve and is implemented as a start/stop rung.

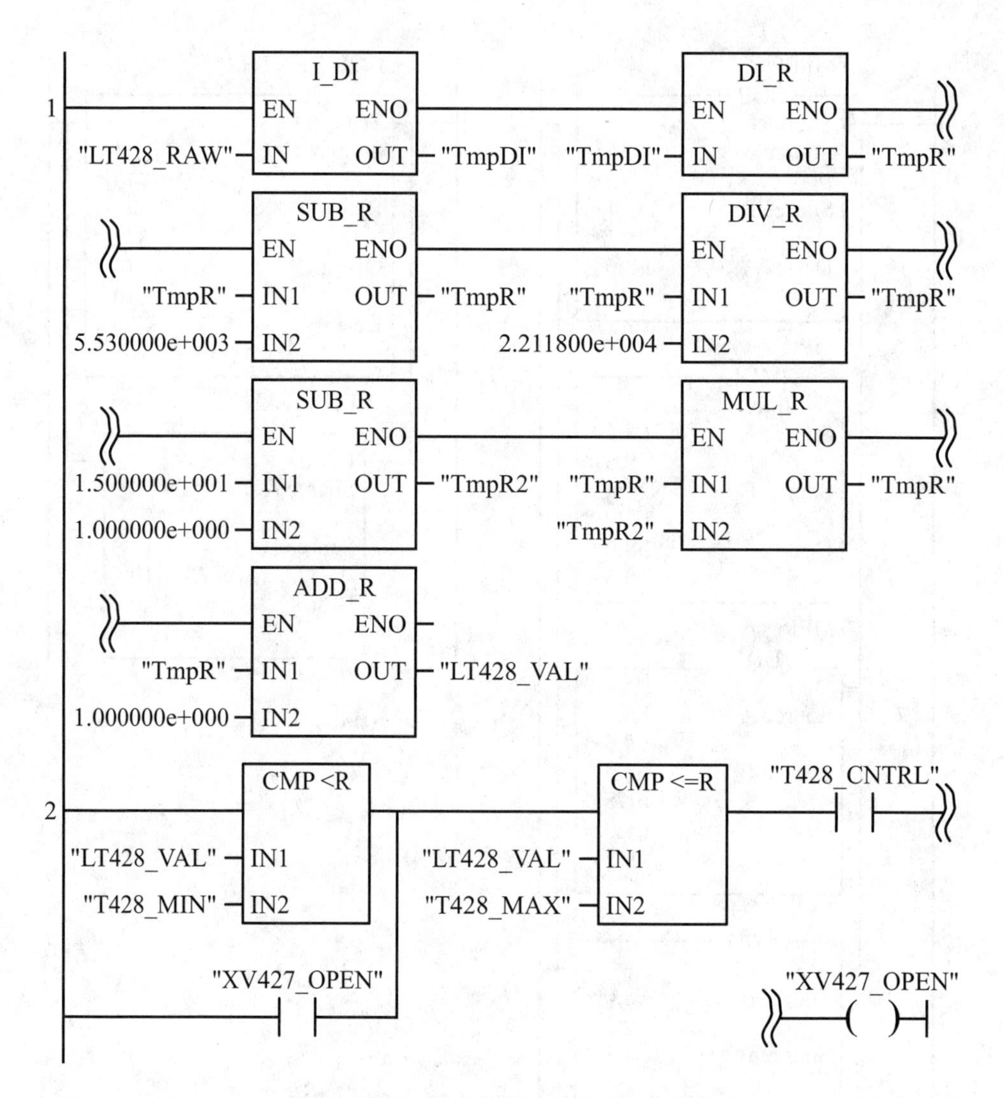

Figure 7.70. S7 solution to Example 7.4.

Figure 7.71 shows the GE Fanuc solution to this example. The formula for converting the ADC output (LT428_RAW) into the level in feet (LT428_VAL) is the same as for the Modicon PLC. The individual arithmetic function blocks in network 1 implement the conversion. Because contacts cannot follow comparison block outputs, the level comparisons are on individual rungs, rungs 2 and 3. The fourth rung is the control for the valve.

The addresses or data types associated with the internal variables are:

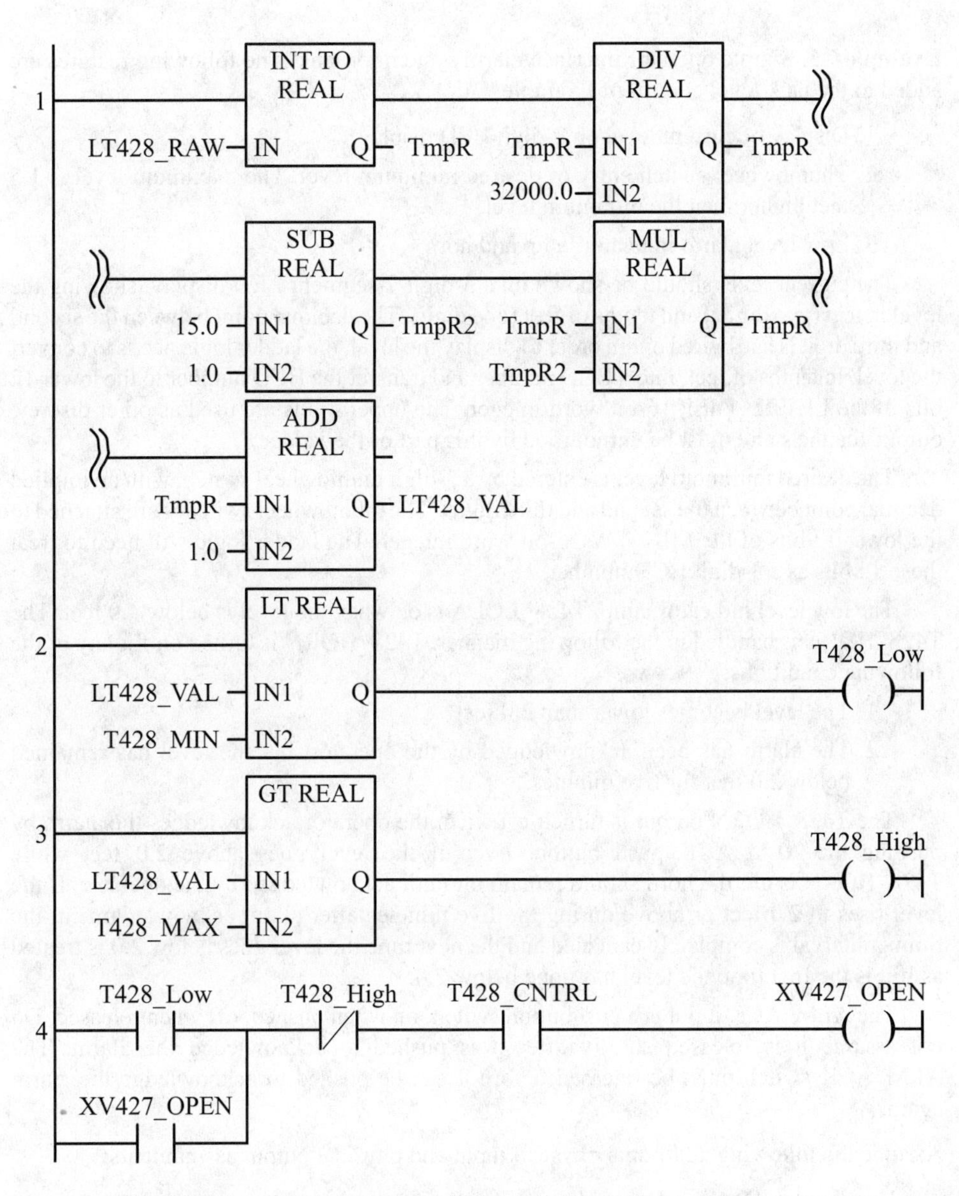

Figure 7.71. GE Fanuc 90-30 solution to Example 7.4.

Variable	Modicon Data Type	PLC-5 Addr.	Logix Data Type	Siemens Addr.	GE Fanuc Addr.
TmpI	n/a	n/a	n/a	MW100	n/a
TmpDI	n/a	n/a	n/a	MD102	n/a
TmpR	n/a	F8:0	n/a	MD106	%R194
TmpR2	n/a	F8:1	n/a	MW110	%R196
T428_Low	n/a	n/a	n/a	n/a	%M122
T428_High	n/a	n/a	n/a	n/a	%M123

Example 7.5. Simple operator interface/alarm system for tank. The following features are added to the tank level control of Example 7.4:

1. Display of current level on 3-digit LED display
2. Thumbwheel switch entry of desired minimum level. The maximum level is 1.5 feet higher than the minimum level.
3. Low level alarm indicator lamp and horn

The current level should be shown on a 3-digit 7-segment LED display, showing the level in feet (two digits) and tenths of feet (one digit). The decimal point between the second and third digit is hardwired on. In order to display the level, the ladder logic needs to convert the level, in tenths of feet, into a BCD number and transfer the BCD number to the lower 12 bits of the LEVEL_DISP 16-bit word/integer. The upper 4 bits are used as other discrete output channels and must be unmodified by this part of the ladder.

The desired minimum level is entered by a 3-digit thumbwheel switch, with an implied decimal point between the second and third digits. The thumbwheel switches are attached to the lower 12 bits of the MIN_TW 16-bit word/integer. The ladder logic will need to treat these 12 bits as a 3-digit BCD number.

The low level indicator lamp, T428_LOLA is on when the level is below 4.0 feet. The T428_HORN is handled in the following manner. T428_HORN is turned **on** for any of the following conditions:

1. The level becomes lower than 2.0 feet
2. The alarm has been acknowledged by the operator, but the level has remained below 2.0 feet for five minutes.

The T428_HORN output is turned **off** when the operator acknowledges the alarm by pushing the ALM_ACK push button. Even if the level goes above 2.0 feet while T428_HORN is **on**, the horn should remain **on** until acknowledged by the operator. If the level rises to 2.0 feet or above during the five minutes after alarm acknowledgment, the timing interval is completely canceled and the next time the level goes below 2.0 is treated as if it is the first time the level has gone below 2.0.

The ALM_ACK input is a pushbutton switch, **on** when pushed, **off** when released. Do not assume it is released shortly after it is pushed to acknowledge the alarm. The ALM_ACK switch must be released before it can be pushed to acknowledge the alarm again.

Assume the following additional physical input and physical output assignments:

Variable	Description
LEVEL_DISP	Current level in tenths of feet, 3 digits BCD connected to three 7-segment LED displays
MIN_TW	Minimum level thumbwheel switch reading in tenths of feet, 3 digits BCD
T428_LOLA	Low level indication; **on** when level < 4.0 feet
T428_HORN	Low level alarm horn, operation described above
ALM_ACK	Alarm acknowledge (pushbutton switch, **on** when pushed, **off** when released)

The addresses associated with the physical inputs and outputs are:

Variable	Modicon	PLC-5	ControlLogix	Siemens	GE Fanuc
LEVEL_DISP	400001	O:4	Local:4:O.Data	QW12	%AQ1
MIN_TW	300001	I:2	Local:2:O.Data.0	IW4	%AI5
T428_LOLA	000002	O:3/01	Local:3:O.Data.1	Q8.1	%Q2
T428_HORN	000003	O:3/02	Local:3:O.Data.2	Q8.2	%Q3
ALM_ACK	100001	I:1/00	Local:1:I.Data.0	I0.0	%I1

Solution. The ladder logic code is added to the ladder logic of Example 7.4. The Modicon code is shown in Figure 7.72. Rung 3 implements the first feature of the problem. The level is multiplied by 10 to convert into tenths of feet, converted into an integer, converted to a BCD word, and then the lower 12 bits of the BCD number are transferred to the lower 12 bits of LEVEL_DISP. The INT_BCD function block is not a standard Modicon function block, but is a derived function block (DFB), indicated by the double vertical lines. This particular DFB is written in the ST (structured text) language and explained in problem

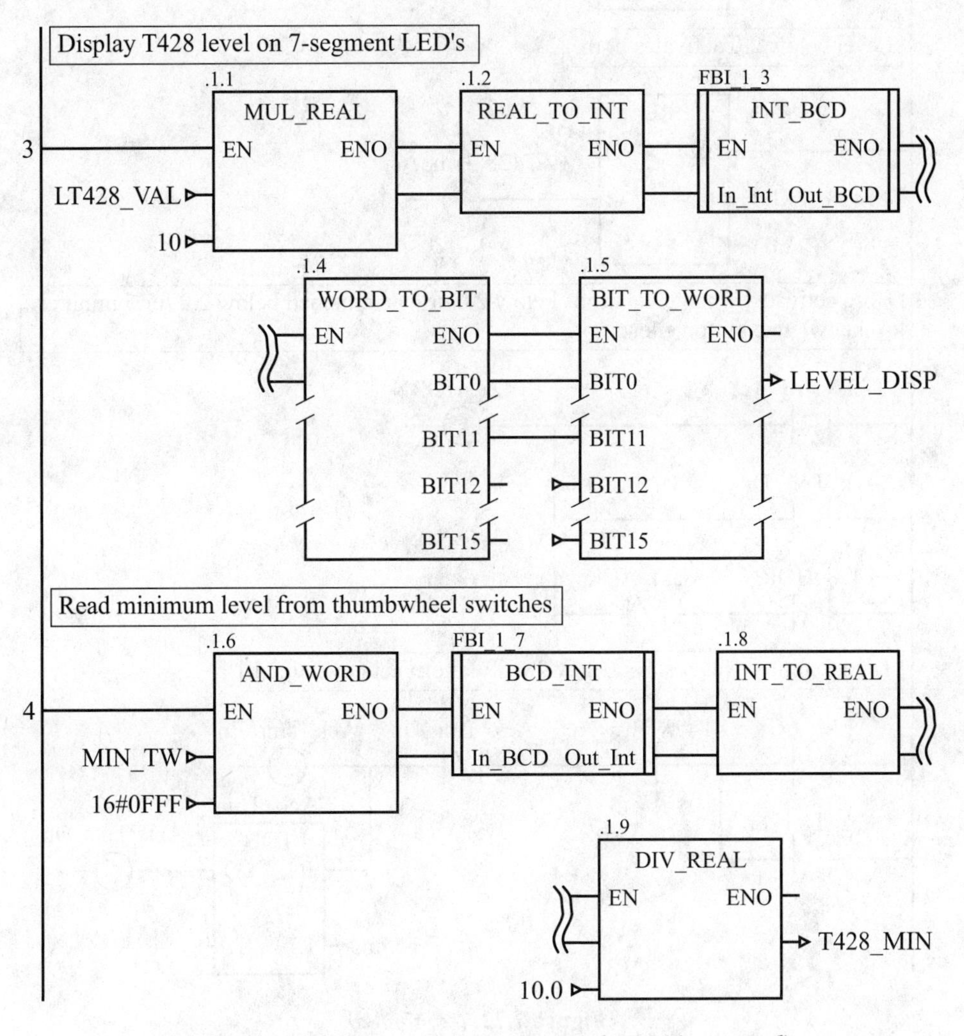

Figure 7.72. Modicon solution to Example 7.5. *(continued)*

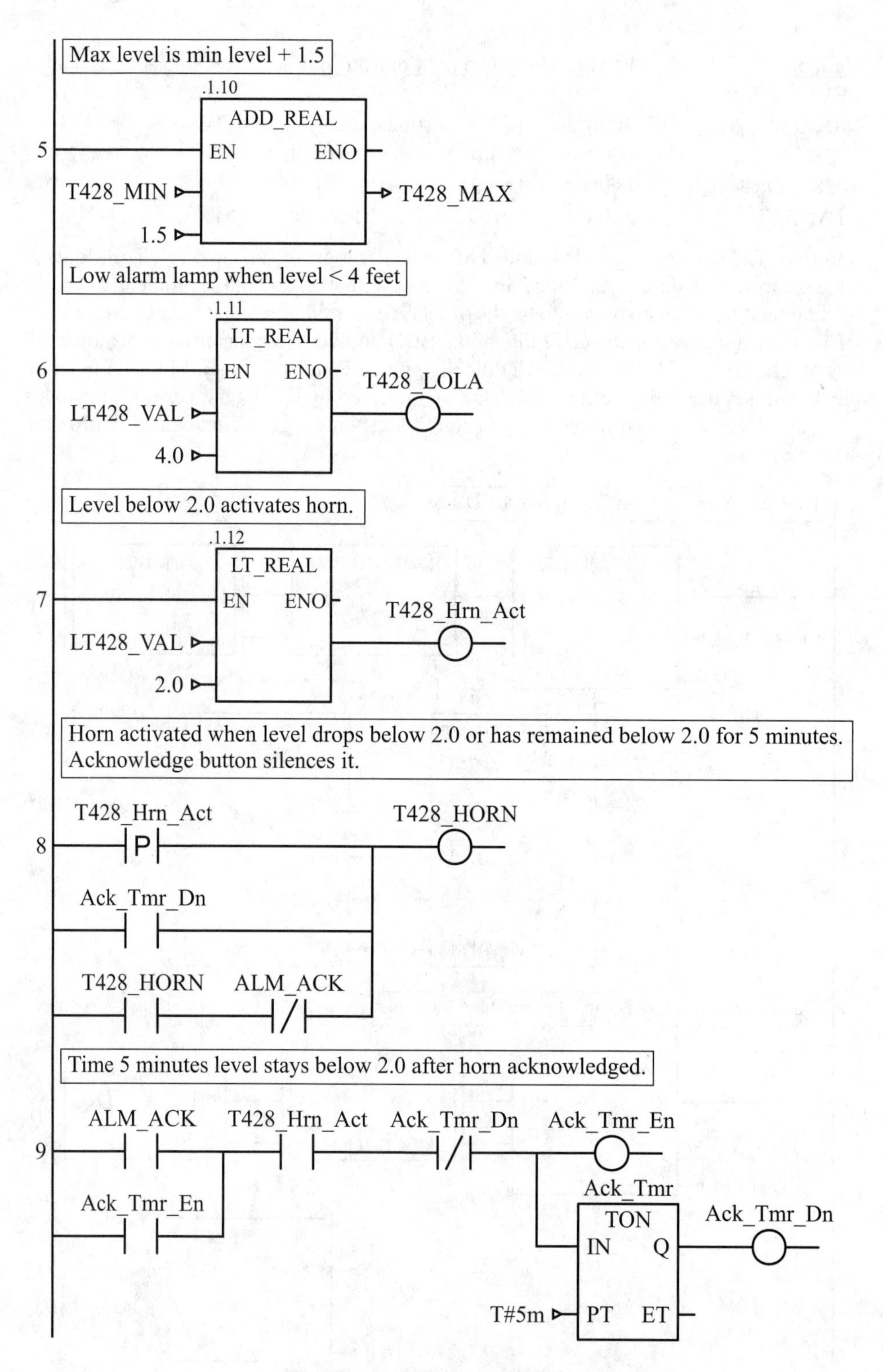

Figure 7.72. *(continued)*

P12-1. The second feature of the problem is implemented by rungs 4 and 5. The lower 12 bits of MIN_TW are converted from a BCD number into an integer, and then divided by 10 to calculate the minimum level, in feet. The maximum level is calculated by the function block in rung 5. Rungs 6 – 9 handle the third feature of the problem. The comparison function block in rung 6 drives the low level indicator lamp and the particular level that triggers the horn is determined by the LT_REAL block in rung 7. The horn is activated by the logic in rung 8. This is basically the start/stop rung of chapter 2, but with two starting conditions: (1) level falls below 2.0 feet, and (2) level has remained below 2.0 feet for 5 minutes after the acknowledge button has been pressed. The logic and timer to handle the second condition to turn on the horn are handled by rung 9. The ALM_ACK button starts the timer, which continues to run as long as the level stays below 2.0 feet. As soon as the timer finishes, it resets itself and generates a pulse (Ack_Tmr_Dn) that turns on the horn.

The PLC-5 code is shown in Figure 7.73. Rung 3 implements the first feature of the problem. The level is multiplied by 10 to convert into tenths of feet, converted into an integer, converted to a BCD word, and then the lower 12 bits of the BCD number are transferred to the lower 12 bits of LEVEL_DISP. For an enhanced PLC-5 and a ControlLogix processor, the multiplication and conversion into BCD could be handled by one CPT function block. The second feature of the problem is implemented by rungs 4 and 5. The lower 12 bits of MIN_TW are moved into a BCD location, converted into an integer, and then divided by 10 to calculate the minimum level, in feet. The maximum level is calculated by adding 1.5 to the minimum level. The logic in rungs 6 – 9 handles the indicator and alarm. The comparison function block in rung 6 drives the low level indicator lamp and the particular level that triggers the horn is determined by the LES block in rung 7. The horn is activated by the logic in rung 8. This is basically the start/stop rung of chapter 2, but with two starting conditions: (1) level falls below 2.0 feet, and (2) level has remained below 2.0 feet for 5 minutes after the acknowledge button has been pressed. The logic and timer to handle the second condition to turn on the horn are in rung 9. The ALM_ACK button starts

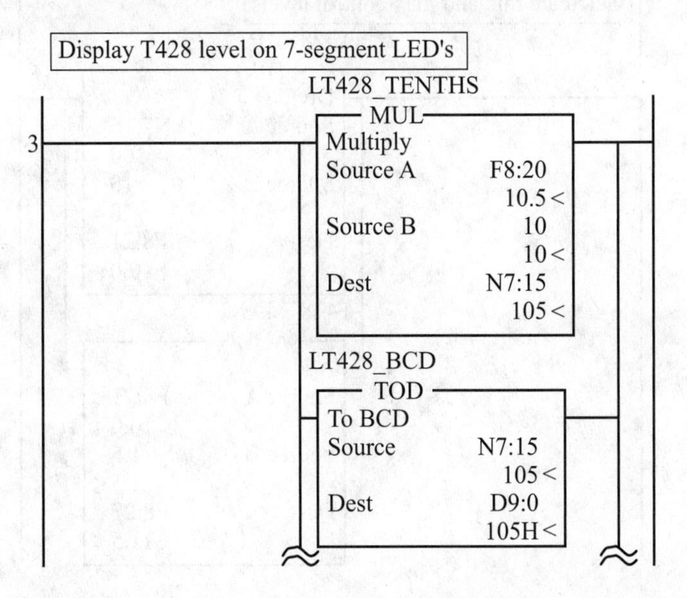

Figure 7.73. A-B PLC-5 solution to Example 7.5. *(continued)*

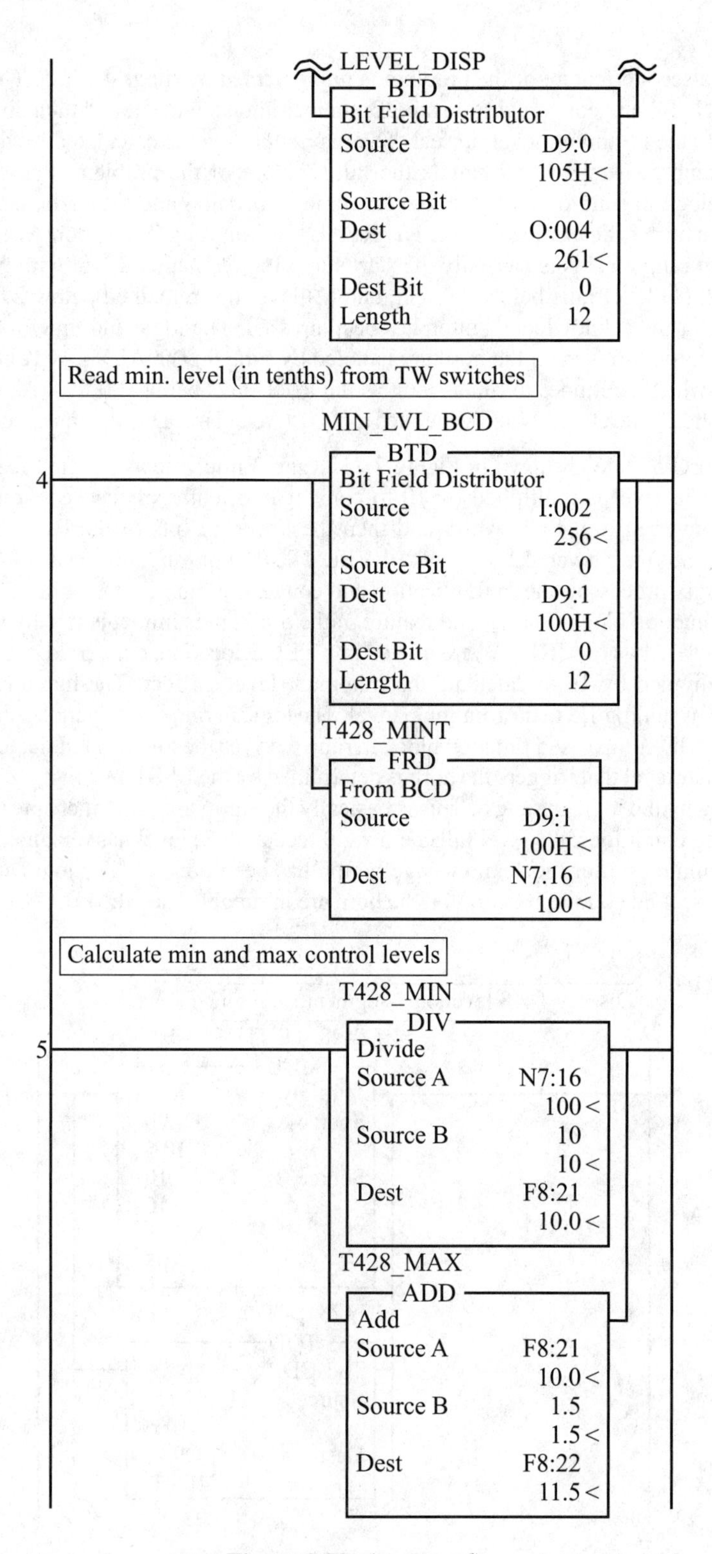

Figure 7.73. *(continued)*

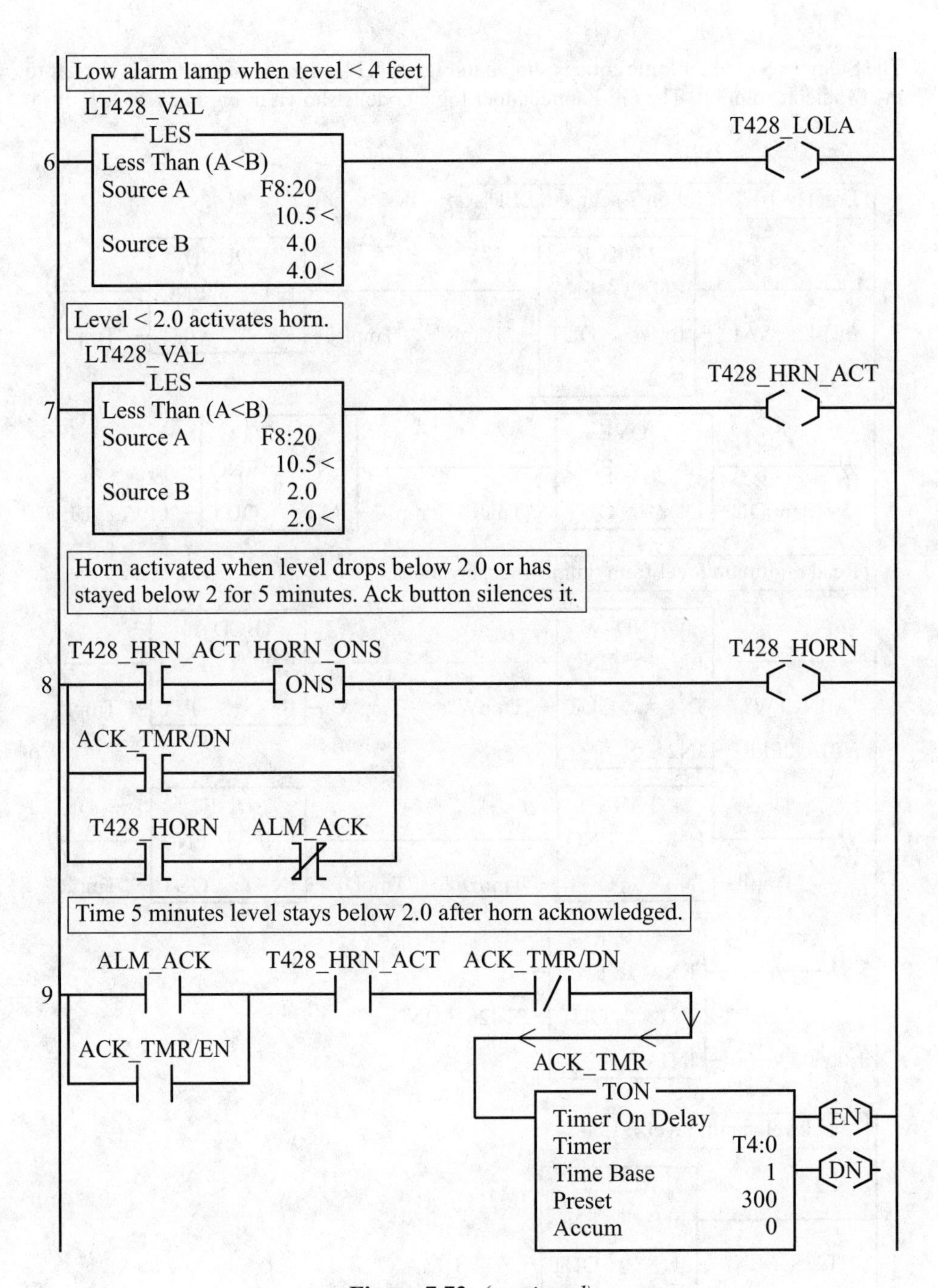

Figure 7.73. *(continued)*

the timer, which continues to run as long as the level stays below 2.0 feet. As soon as the timer finishes, it resets itself and generates a pulse (ACK_TMR/DN) that turns on the horn.

The Siemens S7 ladder logic code is shown in Figure 7.74. In many respects, it is similar to the Modicon solution. The GE Fanuc ladder logic code is shown in Figure. 7.75.

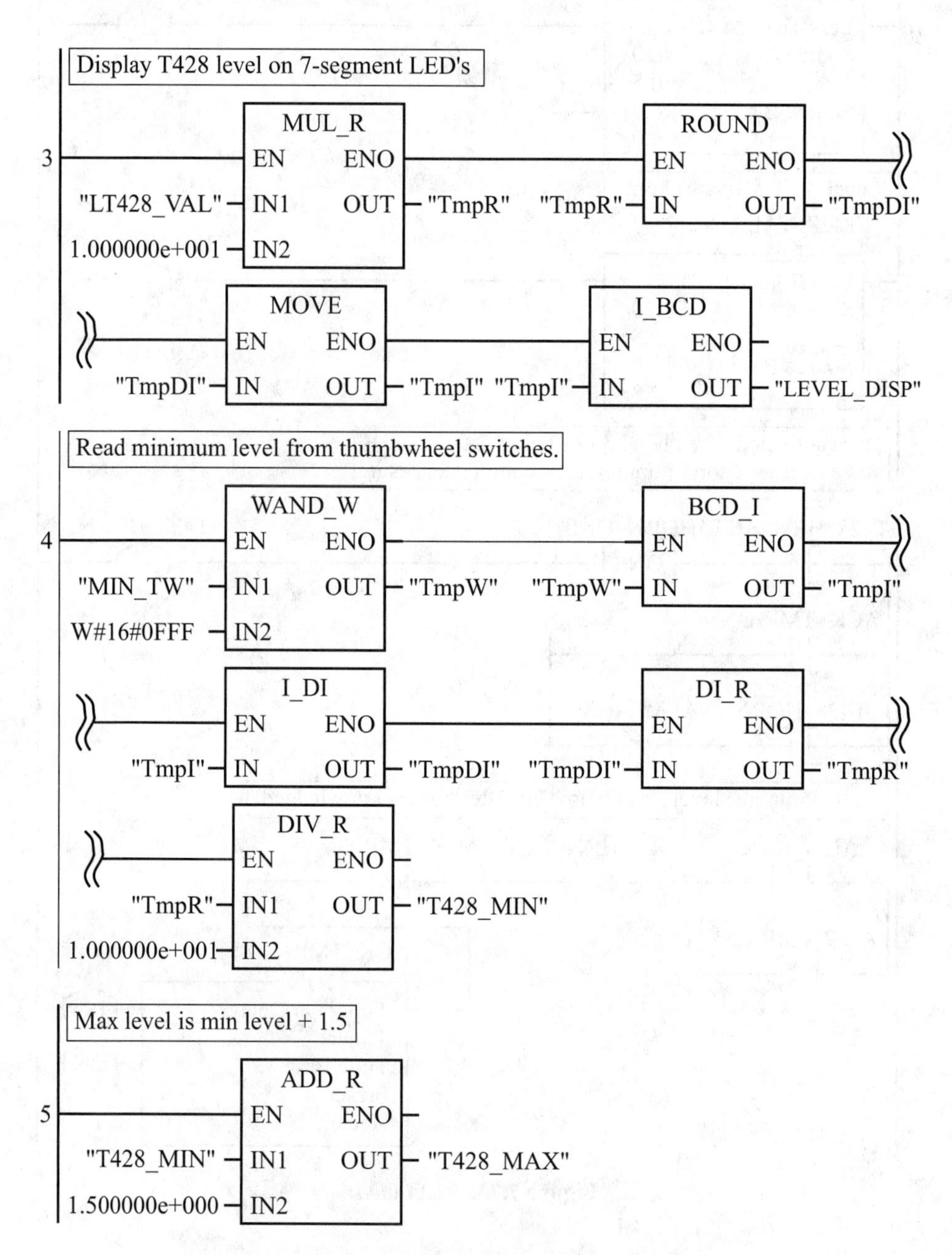

Figure 7.74. S7 solution to Example 7.5. *(continued)*

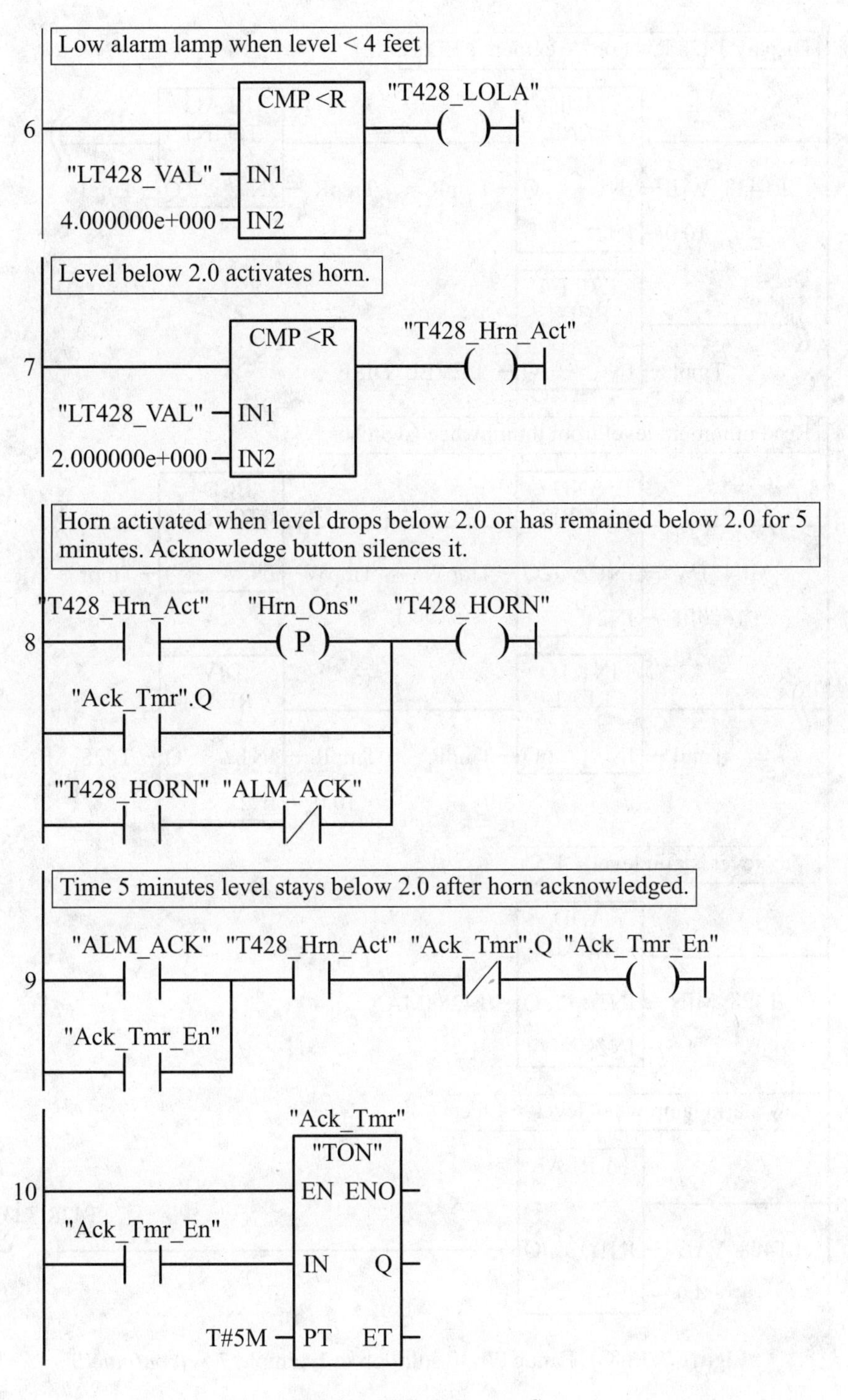

Figure 7.74. *(continued)*

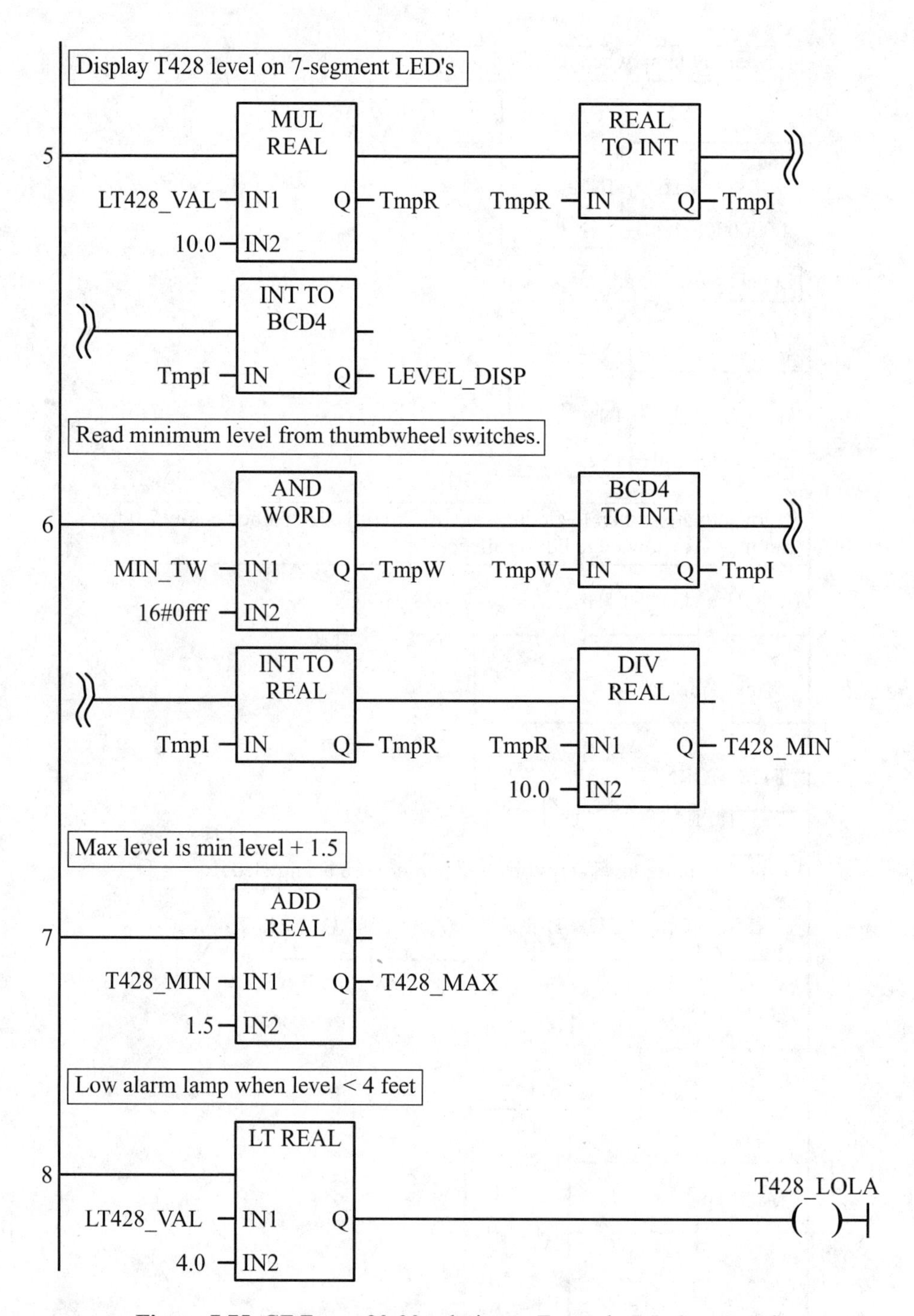

Figure 7.75. GE Fanuc 90-30 solution to Example 7.5. *(continued)*

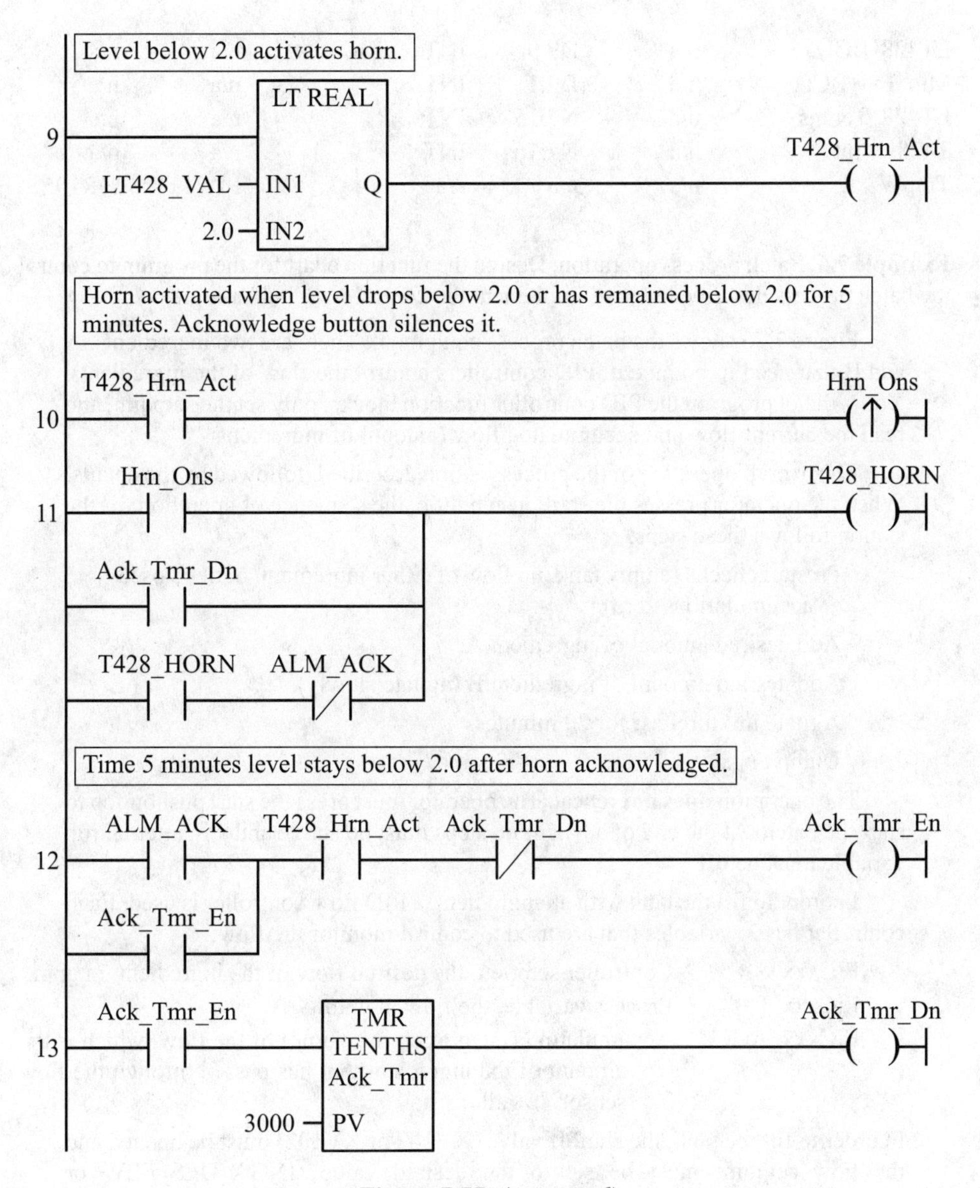

Figure 7.75. *(continued)*

The addresses or data types associated with the additional internal variables:

Variable	Modicon Data Type	PLC-5 Addr.	Logix Data Type	Siemens Addr.	GE Fanuc Addr.
T428_Hrn_Act	BOOL	B3/122	BOOL	M15.2	%M124
Hrn_Ons	n/a	B3/123	BOOL	M15.3	%M125
Ack_Tmr_Dn	BOOL	n/a	n/a	n/a	%M126
Ack_Tmr_En	BOOL	n/a	n/a	M15.4	%M127
Ack_Tmr	n/a	T4:0	TIMER	DB4	%R130

LT428_BCD	n/a	D9:0	INT	n/a	n/a
Min_Lvl_BCD	n/a	D9:1	INT	n/a	n/a
LT428_Tenths	n/a	N7:15	INT	n/a	n/a
T428_MInt	n/a	N7:16	INT	n/a	n/a
TmpW	n/a	n/a	n/a	MW114	%R105

Example 7.6. Batch process operation. Design the function chart for the program to control the batch process described below. Implement the control with ladder logic.

Figure 7.76 shows the batch process equipment. There are two ingredients, A and B that need to be mixed. PID controllers control the flow of the ingredients. You will not program the PID controller function blocks, only set the setpoint, and read the current flow and accumulated flow (amount of ingredient).

The overall operation of the process is first described, followed by the details. When the operator presses the start push button, the sequence of operation for the station follows these steps:

Prestart checks (empty tank, no flow of either ingredient, outlet closed, accumulations zero).

Add desired amount of ingredient A.

Add desired amount of ingredient B (agitate slowly).

Agitate mixture fast for 20 minutes.

Dump tank.

The operation **does not** repeat. The operator must press the start pushbutton to start the batch. At the end of a batch, **no** steps must be active and any internal run variable must be **off**.

In order to fill the tank with an ingredient, a PID flow controller is used. Each controller has 3 variables that are used to control/monitor the flow:

FICxxx_SP — Controller setpoint, the desired flow of the ingredient, in gpm.

FICxxx_PV — Process variable, the flow in gpm.

FICxxx_ACC — Accumulation (integration over time) of the flow, which is the amount of the ingredient that has passed through the flow sensor, in gallons.

In order to fill the tank, the shutoff valve (XV102 or XV102) must be opened and the flow setpoint must be set to the desired value (INGA_DES_FLW or INGB_DES_FLW). Then, the accumulation (FICxxx_ACC) must be monitored to determine when the desired amount of the ingredient (INGA_DES_AMT or INGB_DES_AMT) has been put in the tank. In order to turn off the flow of an ingredient, the shutoff valve must be closed, the flow setpoint must set to -2.0 gpm (ensures flow valve positively shut off) and then the flow must be monitored until it is < 0.1 gpm before going to the next step in the process.

Both accumulations (FIC101_ACC and FIC102_ACC) must be zeroed (write a zero into location) as part of the prestart. The batch operation must not proceed until both of the accumulations are zero.

The agitator is driven by a two-speed motor, whose controls are A105_SLOW and A105_FAST. The agitator must be run slowly when adding ingredient B or

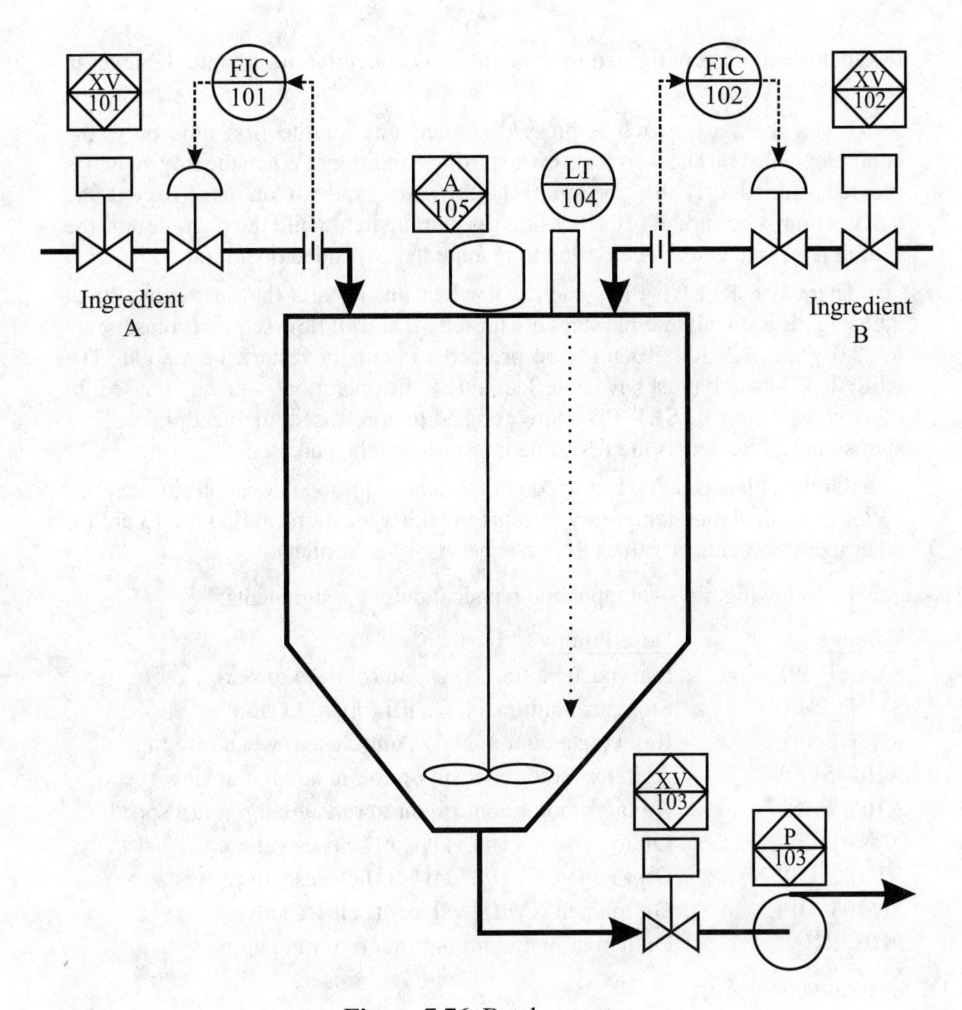

Figure 7.76. Batch process.

dumping the tank. The agitator is run fast for the specified time to mix after both ingredients have been added.

In order to dump the tank, the outlet valve, XV103, must be opened (with XV103_OPEN) and the outlet pump, controlled by P103_RUN, must be run. The tank is empty when the tank level is less than 0.1 feet. The level transducer is calibrated to measure from 0.0 to 15.0 feet and is connected to an analog input module having an ADC whose output value (LT104_RAW) corresponds to the lowest and highest levels as:

Tank Level (ft.)	Modicon	PLC-5	ControlLogix	Siemens	GE Fanuc
0.0 (empty)	0	0	0.0	5530	0
15.0 (full)	32,000	4095	15.0	27,648	32,000

The LT104_RAW value should be converted into a tank level, in feet (a real number) and placed in the LT104_VAL variable. In the case of the ControlLogix, the analog input is configured to scale the A/D converter output into the level in feet.

When the start switch is pressed (turned **on**) for the first time only, the equipment must be checked for proper starting conditions. When the stop switch is pressed (turned **off**) the operation should pause and all outputs (**except** the agitator) must be turned **off**. Pressing the start switch while the operation of the station is paused causes the station to resume its suspended operation.

There is a RESET_PB switch that when **on**, restarts the operation. When RESET_PB is **on**, all internal steps are turned **off** and all flow setpoints must be set to -2.0 gpm. START_PB must be pressed to actually restart the station. The RESET_PB switch must have no effect unless the operation is already paused. In other words, after RESET_PB is pressed and then released, the next press of the start switch is treated as the first time the start switch is pressed.

For the Allen-Bradley PLC-5, do not use any additional locations in files 10 - 13 for any calculation temporary results (any other locations in files 10-13 are for other measurements or values from a supervisory controller).

Assume the following physical input and physical output assignments:

Variable	Description
START_PB	Start push button, N. O., **on** (closed) to start
STOP_PB	Stop push button, N. C., **off** (open) to stop
RESET_PB	Reset push button, N. O., **on** (closed) when resetting
A105_SLOW	Agitator motor control, **on** to run agitator at slow speed.
A105_FAST	Agitator motor control, **on** to run agitator at fast speed.
XV101_OPEN	**On** to open XV101 valve, **off** closes valve.
XV102_OPEN	**On** to open XV102 valve, **off** closes valve.
XV103_OPEN	**On** to open XV103 valve, **off** closes valve.
P103_RUN	Outlet pump motor control, **on** to run pump.

The internal variables are:

LT104_RAW	Raw tank level measurement, represents 0-15 ft.; ranges listed above
INGA_DES_FLW	Desired flow rate setpoint (in gpm) for ingredient A flow (FIC101)
INGB_DES_FLW	Desired flow rate setpoint (in gpm) for ingredient B flow (FIC102)
INGA_DES_AMT	Desired amount of ingredient A (gallons) to put in tank.
INGB_DES_AMT	Desired amount of ingredient B (gallons) to put in tank.
FIC101_PV	Current value of ingredient A flow (gpm). Reading from FT101 flow transducer, converted to proper units.
FIC101_ACC	Accumulation for FIC101 PID loop. The amount of ingredient A that has passed through flow transducer FT101. Write a zero to this variable to reset it.
FIC102_PV	Current value of ingredient B flow (gpm). Reading from FT102 flow transducer, converted to proper units.

FIC102_ACC	Accumulation for FIC102 PID loop. The amount of ingredient A that has passed through flow transducer FT102. Write a zero to this variable to reset it.
FIC101_SP	Setpoint of FIC101, desired ingredient A flow (gpm).
FIC102_SP	Setpoint of FIC102, desired ingredient B flow (gpm).
LT104_VAL	Actual tank level, in feet
AGIT_TIME	Agitation time of step 6, in minutes.

The addresses associated with the physical inputs and outputs are:

Variable	Modicon	PLC-5	ControlLogix	Siemens	GE Fanuc
START_PB	100001	I:1/00	Local:1:I.Data.0	I0.0	%I1
STOP_PB	100002	I:1/01	Local:1:I.Data.1	I0.1	%I2
RESET_PB	100003	I:1/02	Local:1:I.Data.2	I0.2	%I3
A105_SLOW	000001	O:2/00	Local:2:O.Data.0	Q4.0	%Q1
A105_FAST	000002	O:2/01	Local:2:O.Data.1	Q4.1	%Q2
XV101_OPEN	000003	O:2/02	Local:2:O.Data.2	Q4.2	%Q3
XV102_OPEN	000004	O:2/03	Local:2:O.Data.3	Q4.3	%Q4
XV103_OPEN	000005	O:2/04	Local:2:O.Data.4	Q4.4	%Q5
P103_RUN	000006	O:2/05	Local:2:O.Data.5	Q4.5	%Q6
LT104_RAW	300001	N10:4	Local:3:I.Ch0Data	IW288	%AI1

The addresses or data types associated with the internal variables:

	Modicon	PLC-5	Logix	Siemens	GE Fanuc
Variable	Data Type	Addr.	Data Type	Addr.	Addr.
INGA_DES_FLW	REAL	F12:0	REAL	MD100	%R100
INGA_DES_AMT	REAL	F12:1	REAL	MD104	%R102
INGB_DES_FLW	REAL	F12:2	REAL	MD108	%R104
INGB_DES_AMT	REAL	F12:3	REAL	MD112	%R106
AGIT_TIME	REAL	F12:4	REAL	MD116	%R108
FIC101_PV	REAL	F12:5	REAL	MD120	%R110
FIC101_ACC	REAL	F12:6	REAL	MD124	%R112
FIC101_SP	REAL	F12:7	REAL	MD128	%R114
FIC102_PV	REAL	F12:8	REAL	MD132	%R116
FIC102_ACC	REAL	F12:9	REAL	MD136	%R118
FIC102_SP	REAL	F12:10	REAL	MD140	%R120
LT104_VAL	REAL	F13:5	REAL	MD210	%R210

Solution. The function chart for this batch process is shown in Figure 7.77. Rather than show a complete solution, only portions of the solution are shown.

The Modicon code for the start and the transitions into steps 2 and 3 are shown in Figure 7.78. Note that the "Step_*x*" contact must be placed **after** the comparisons used for transitions. Because of the way EN is handled, the output of the last comparison remains **on** even after EN turns **off**. The conversion of the level transducer reading, the initialization of the accumulators in step 1, and the handling of the FIC101 setpoint are shown in Figure 7.79. The ADD_REAL (or another arithmetic block) must be used when assigning a constant to a memory location. The MOVE block does not accept literals (constants) on an input connection. The use of the SEL block to move values into the setpoint avoids a

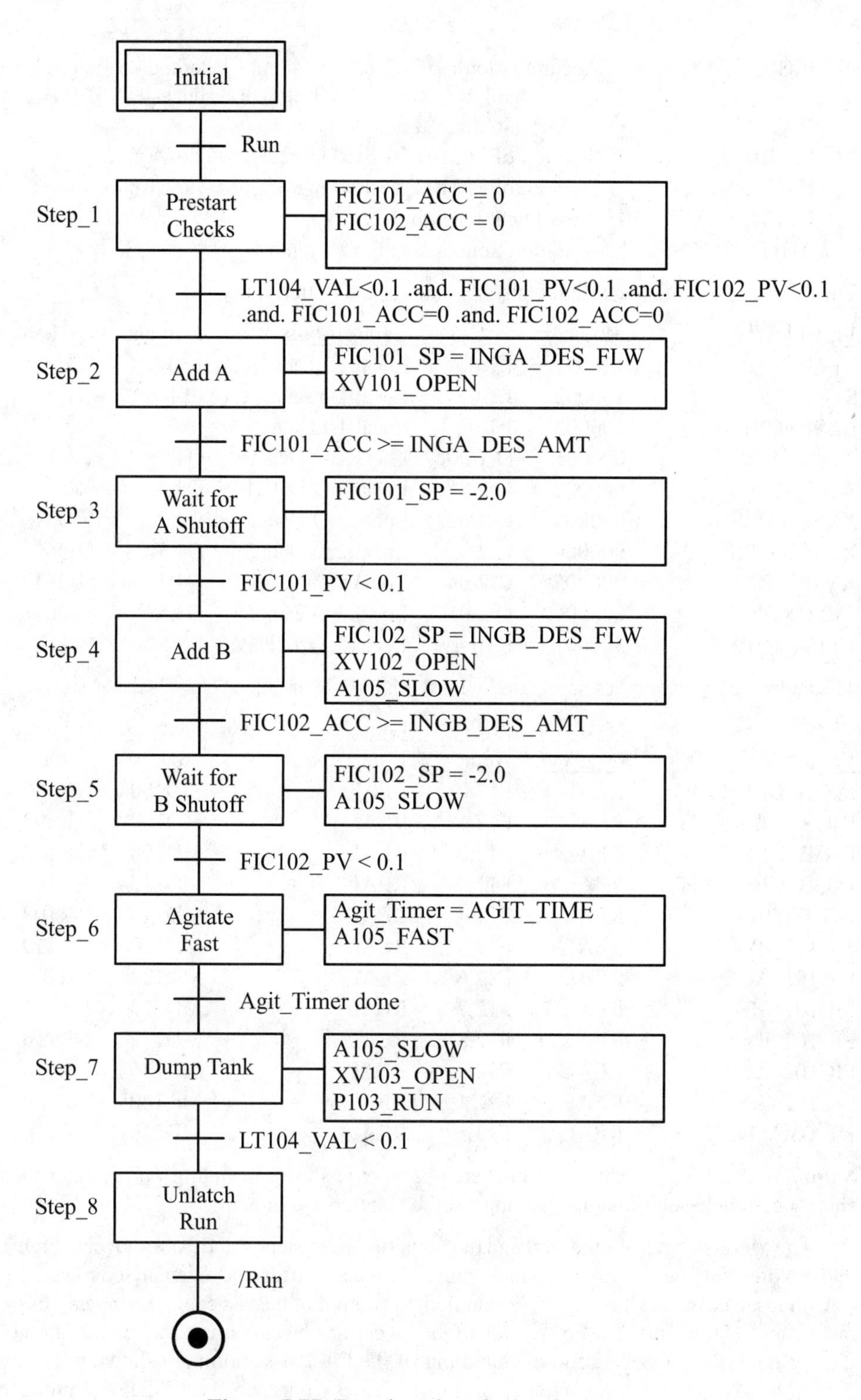

Figure 7.77. Function chart for batch process.

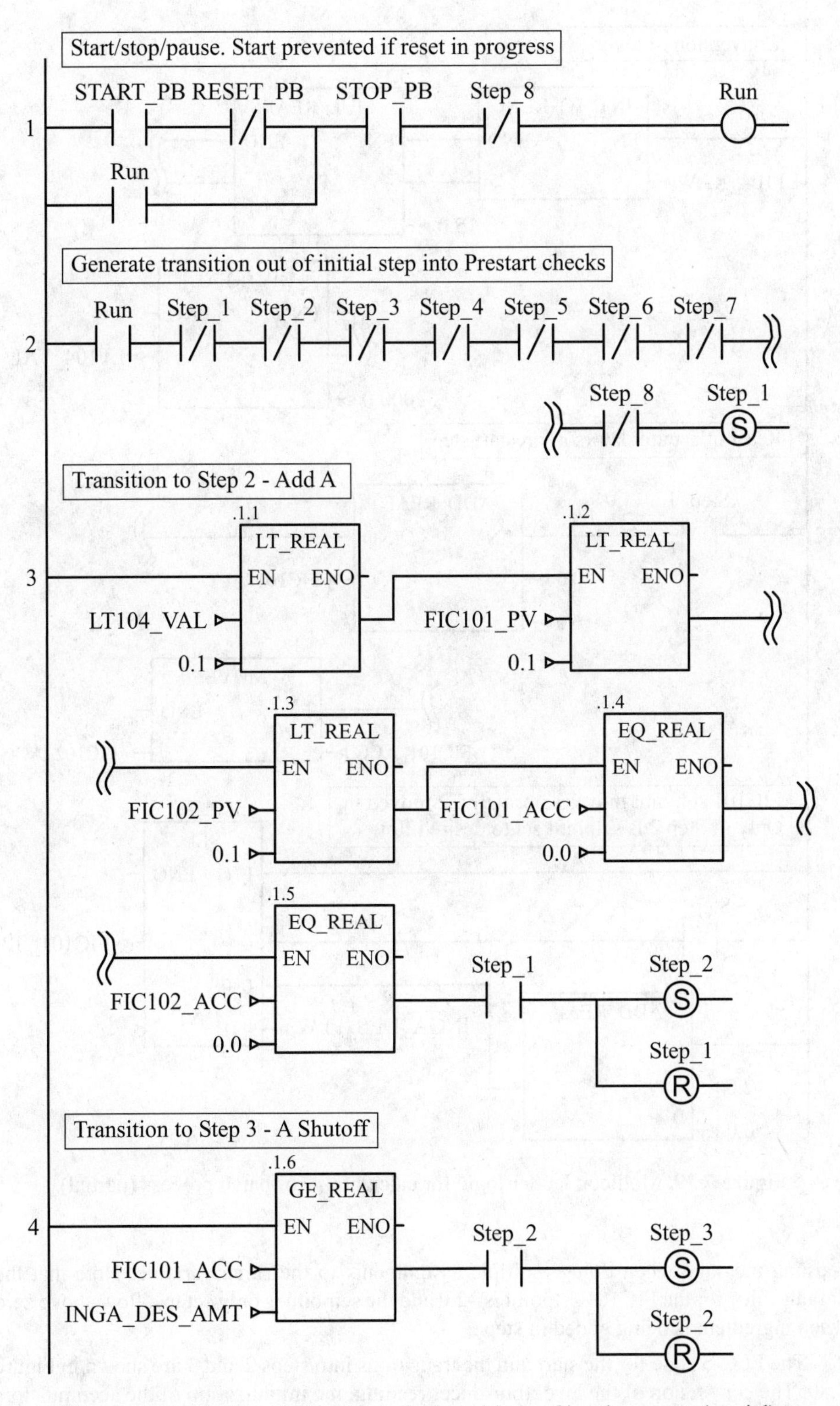

Figure 7.78. Modicon ladder logic for transitions of batch process (partial).

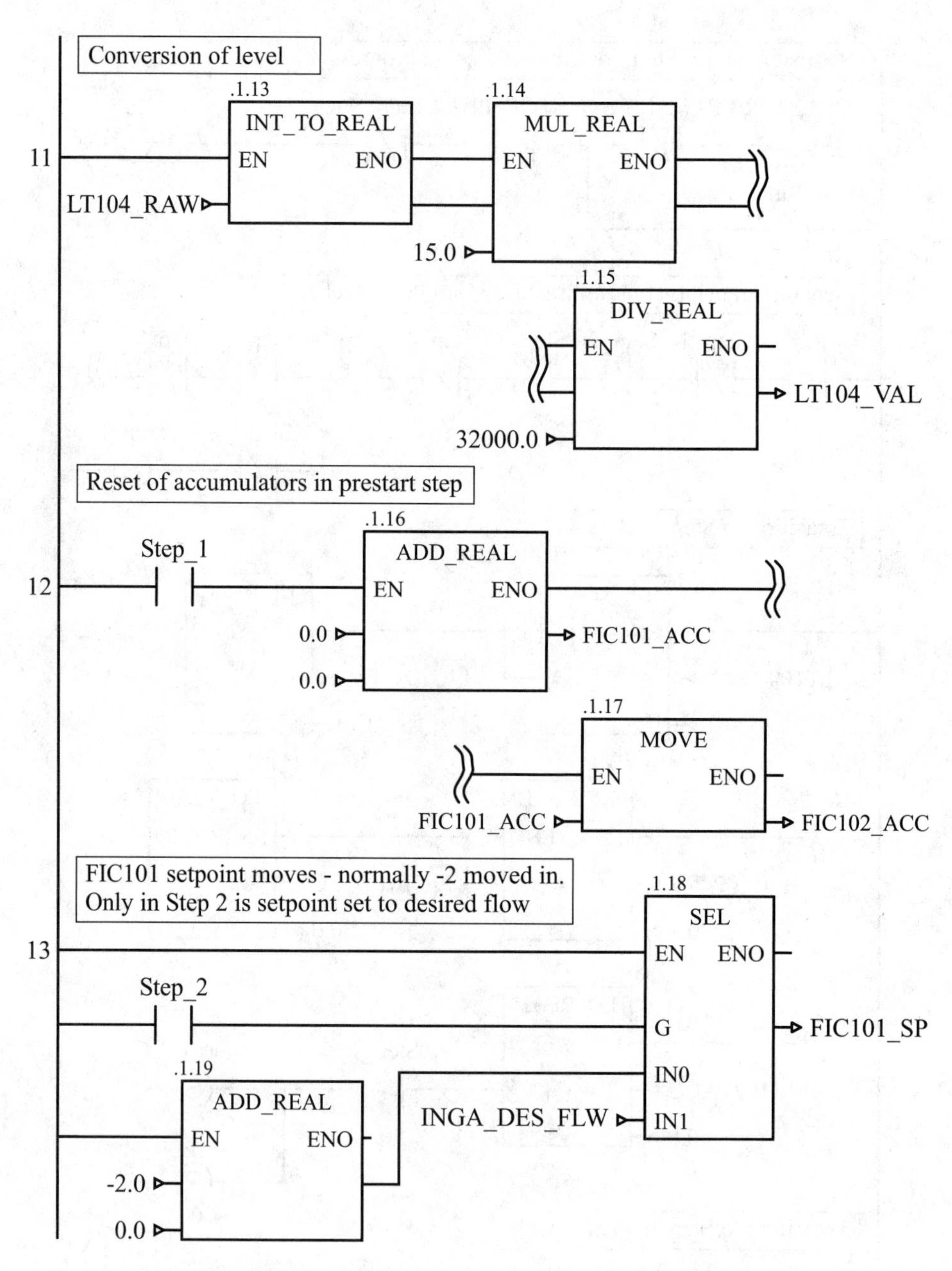

Figure 7.79. Modicon ladder logic for calculations of batch process (partial).

warning message when doing multiple assignments to the same variable. Note that the default value for the FIC101 setpoint is –2.0 and the setpoint is only set to a flow above zero when ingredient is being added in step 2.

The PLC-5 code for the start and the transitions into steps 2 and 3 are shown in Figure 7.80. The conversion of the level transducer reading, the initialization of the accumulators in step 1, and the handling of the FIC101 setpoint are shown in Figure 7.81. A CLR block

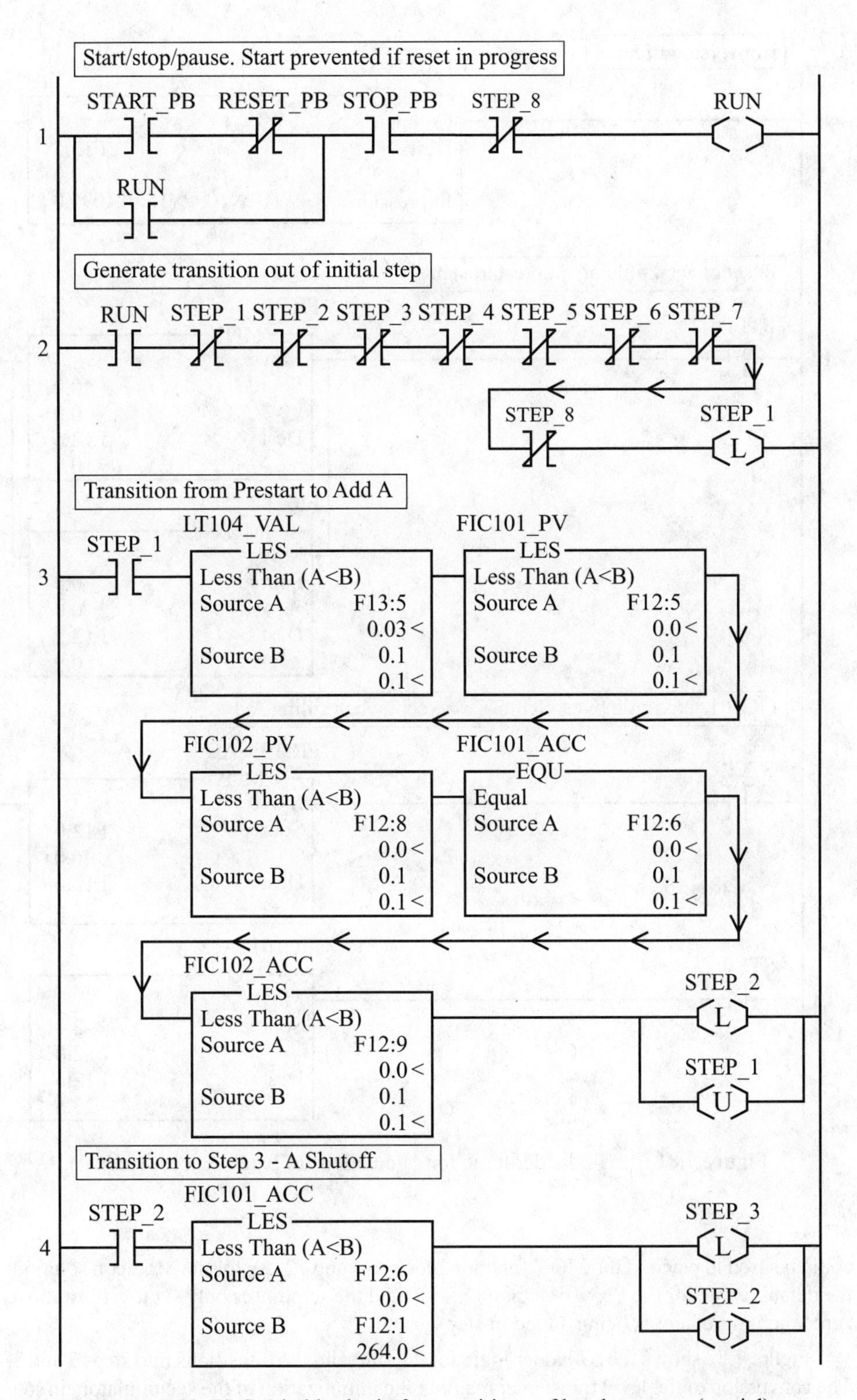

Figure 7.80. PLC-5 ladder logic for transitions of batch process (partial).

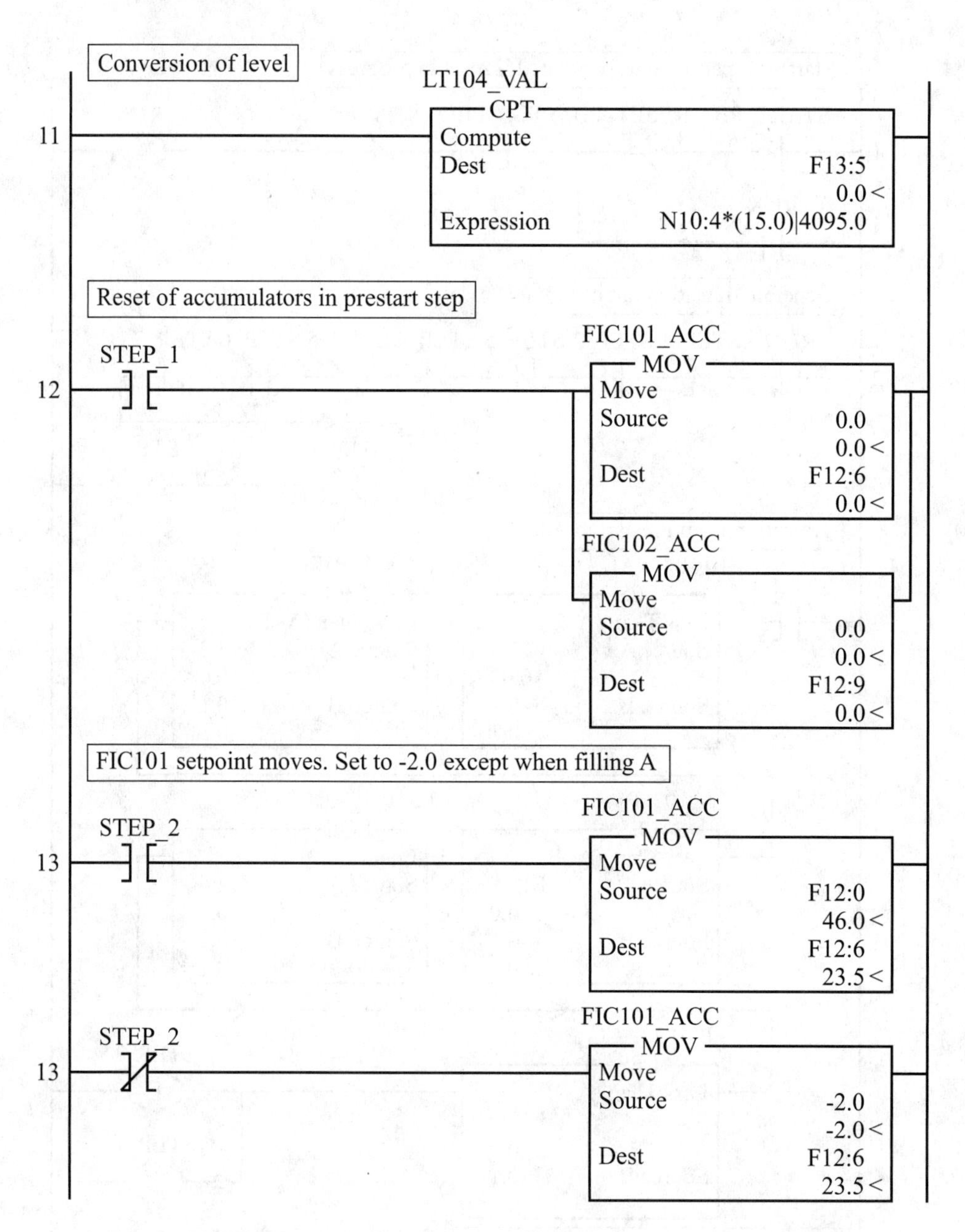

Figure 7.81. PLC-5 ladder logic for calculations of batch process (partial).

could be used in place of the MOV function blocks in rung 12. As for the Modicon solution, the default value for the FIC101 setpoint is –2.0 and the setpoint is only set to a flow above zero when ingredient is being added in step 2.

Figure 7.82 shows the S7 ladder logic for the start and the transitions into steps 2 and 3. The conversion of the level transducer reading, the initialization of the accumulators in step 1, and the handling of the FIC101 setpoint are shown in Figure 7.83. The SEL function can

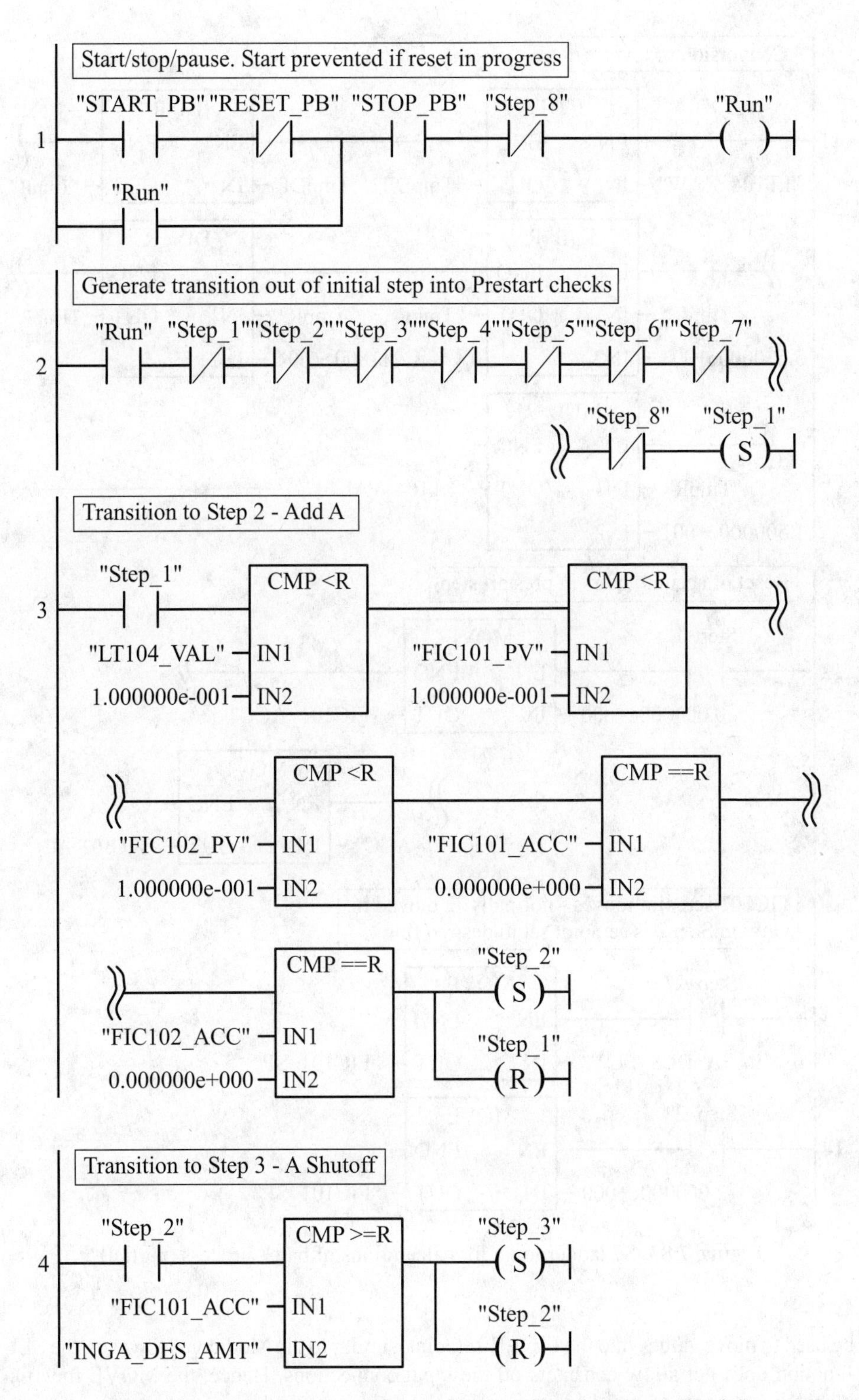

Figure 7.82. S7 ladder logic for transitions of batch process (partial).

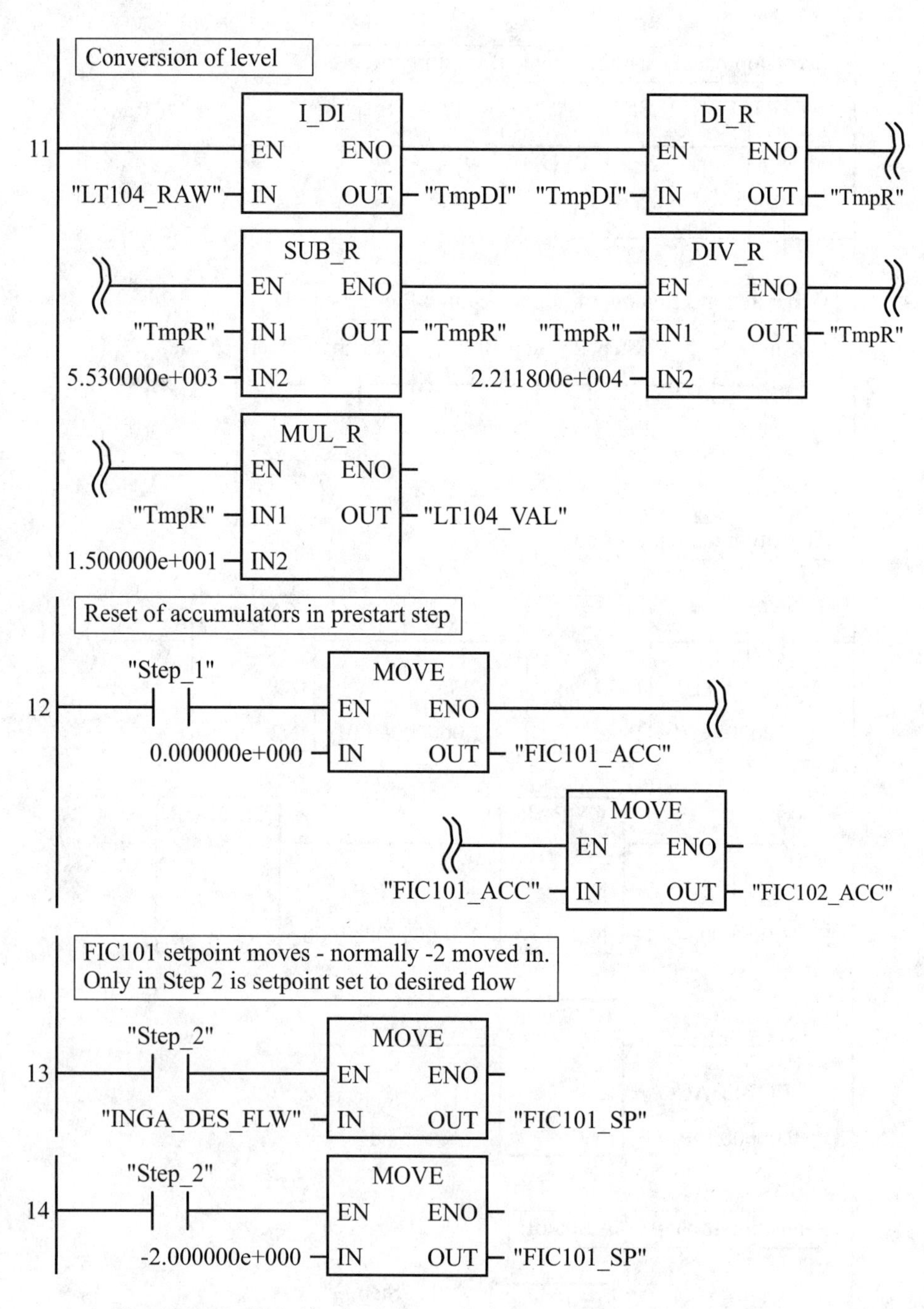

Figure 7.83. S7 ladder logic for calculations of batch process (partial).

be used to move values into the FIC101 setpoint, similar to the Modicon. However, the SEL function does not allow constants on the input connections. Hence, the MOVE function blocks in networks 13 and 14 is a simpler solution.

A partial GE Fanuc solution appears in Figures 7.84 and 7.85. The start and the transitions into steps 2 and 3 are shown in Figure 7.84. The conversion of the level transducer reading, the initialization of the accumulators in step 1, and the handling of the FIC101 setpoint are shown in Figure 7.85.

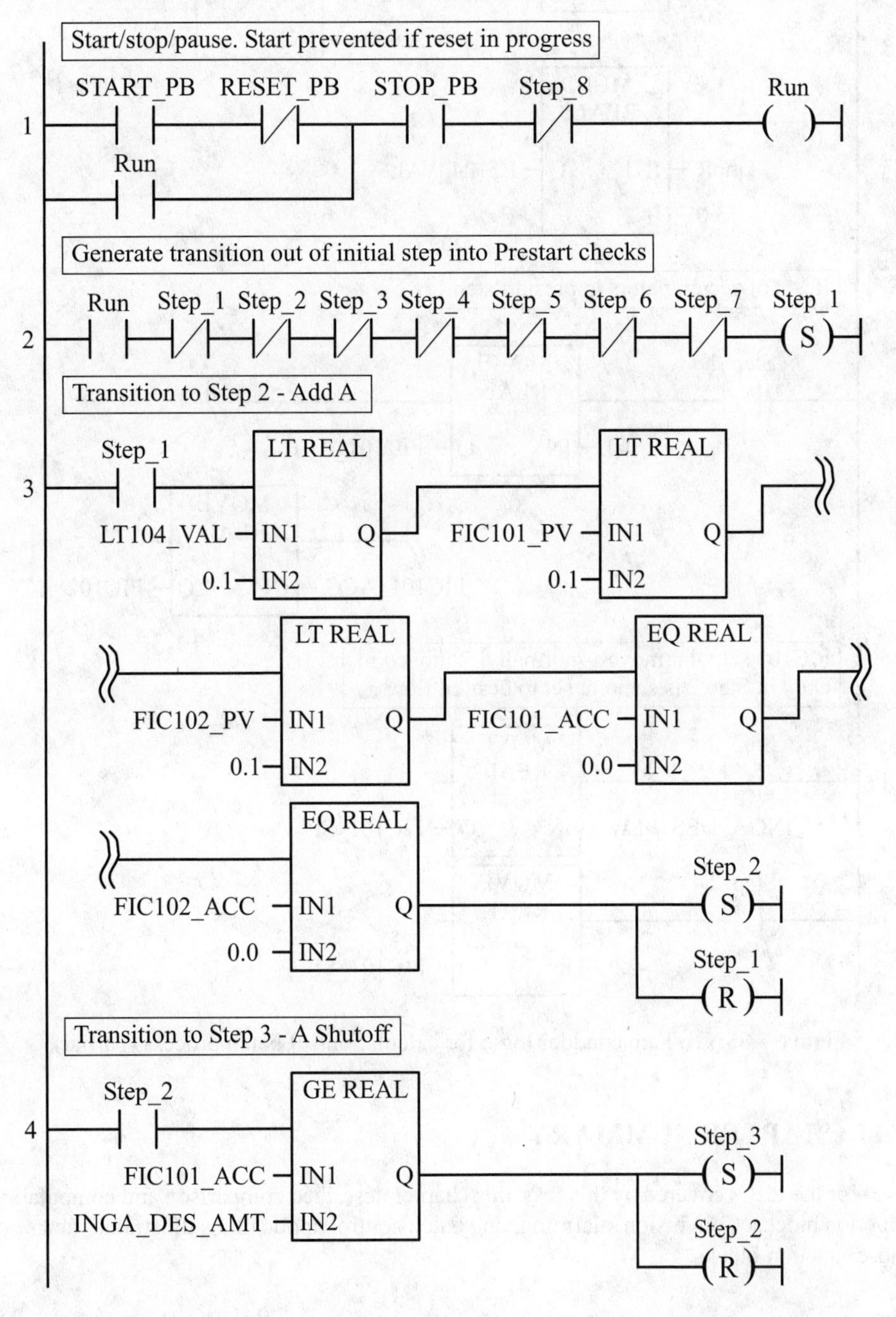

Figure 7.84. GE Fanuc ladder logic for transitions of batch process (partial).

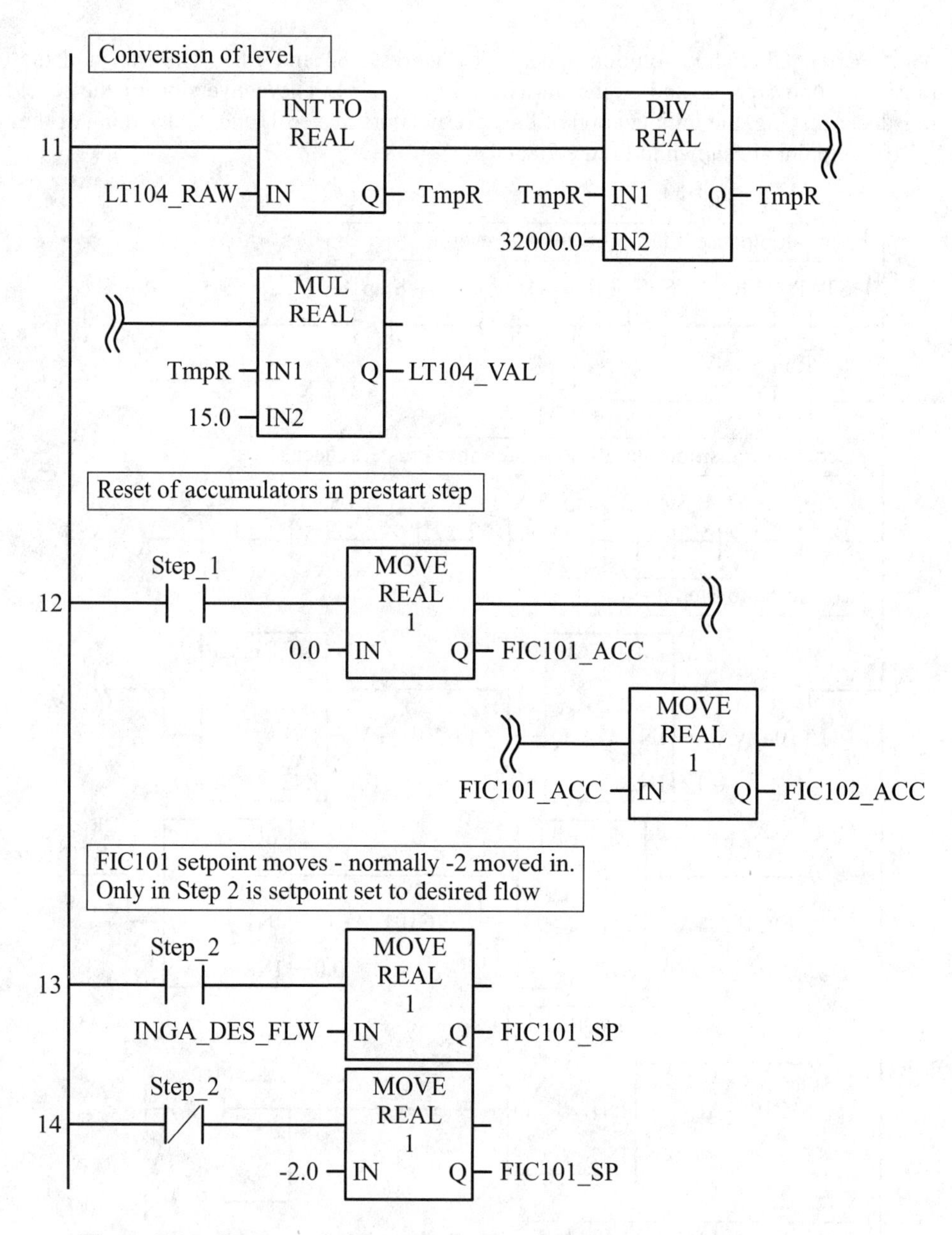

Figure 7.85. GE Fanuc ladder logic for calculations of batch process (partial).

7.11 CHAPTER SUMMARY

For the PLCs covered by this text, this chapter described comparison and computation function blocks. Conversion, alarming, and batch control applications illustrated the use of these function blocks.

REFERENCES

GE Fanuc Automation, 1999. *Series 90^{TM}-30/20/Micro PLC CPU Instruction Set: Reference Manual,* pub. GFK-0467L, GE Fanuc Automation North America, Inc., Charlottesville, VA.

GE Fanuc Automation, 2000. *Series 90^{TM}-70 PLC CPU Instruction Set: Reference Manual,* pub. GFK-0265J, GE Fanuc Automation North America, Inc., Charlottesville, VA.

GE Fanuc Automation, 2001. *VersaMax® PLC: User's Manual,* pub. GFK-1503C, GE Fanuc Automation North America, Inc., Charlottesville, VA.

IEC, 1993. *IEC 1131-3: Programmable Logic Controllers - Part 3: Programming Languages*, International Electrotechnical Commission, Geneva, Switzerland.

Rockwell Automation, 1998a. *PLC-5 Family Instruction Set Reference Manual*, pub. 1785-6.1, Rockwell Automation, Milwaukee, WI.

Rockwell Automation, 1998b. *SLC Modular Processors Instruction Set Reference Manual*, pub. 1747-6.15, Rockwell Automation, Milwaukee, WI.

Rockwell Automation, 2002. *Logix5000^{TM} Controllers General Instructions*, pub. 1756-RM003F-EN-P, Rockwell Automation, Milwaukee, WI, May.

Schneider Automation, 1998. *Concept Block Library IEC,* vol. 1, ver. 2.1, pub. 840 USE 462 00, Schneider Automation, Inc., North Andover, MA.

Siemens, 2000a. *S7-200 Programmable Controller: System Manual,* pub. A5E00066097-02, Siemens AG, Nuernberg, Germany.

Siemens, 2000b. *System Software for S7-300 and S7-400 System and Standard Functions Part 2: Reference Manual,* Edition 03, pub. A5E00066867-03, Siemens AG, Nuernberg, Germany.

Siemens, 2002a. *Ladder Logic (LAD) for S7-300 and S7-400 Programming: Reference Manual,* Edition 11/2002, pub. A5E00171231-01, Siemens AG, Nuernberg, Germany.

Siemens, 2002b. *System Software for S7-300/400 System and Standard Functions: Reference Manual,* Edition 12/2002, pub. A5E00171234-01, Siemens AG, Nuernberg, Germany.

PROBLEMS

P7-1. The Coriolis flow meter in Figure P7.1 is adjusted so that the electrical output signal span of 4 to 20 mA represents 0 to 15 liters/minute of flow. The 4 to 20 mA signal is connected to an analog input module having an ADC whose output integer value corresponds to the lowest and highest flows as:

Flow	Modicon	CLogix	PLC-5	SLC-500	Siemens	GE Fanuc
0.0	0	-20,030	0	3277	5530	0
15.0	32,000	30,920	4095	16,384	27,648	32,000

Find the equation that converts the ADC output integer into the flow, in liters/min., for

(a) Modicon
(b) ControlLogix
(c) PLC-5
(d) SLC-500
(e) Siemens S7
(f) GE Fanuc 90-30

P7-2. The LT143 level transmitter (Figure P7.2) measures water levels between 2 and 20 feet of water and converts the level into a 4 to 20 mA signal that is connected to an analog input module. The ADC output integer value corresponds to the lowest and highest levels as:

Level	Modicon	CLogix	PLC-5	SLC-500	Siemens	GE Fanuc
2.0	0	-20,030	0	3277	5530	0
20.0	32,000	30,920	4095	16,384	27,648	32,000

Find the equation that converts the ADC output integer into the level, in feet, for

(a) Modicon
(b) ControlLogix
(c) PLC-5
(d) SLC-500
(e) Siemens S7
(f) GE Fanuc 90-30

P7-3. A pressure sensor measures vessel pressures between 5 and 400 pounds per square inch (psi). The output of the pressure transmitter is a 1 to 5 volt signal that is connected to an

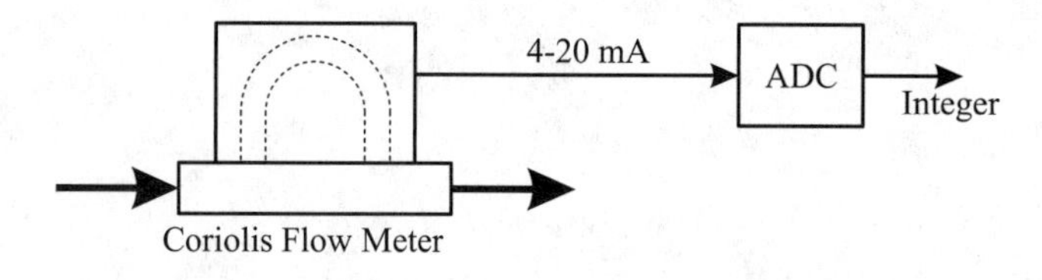

Figure P7.1. Coriolis flow measurement.

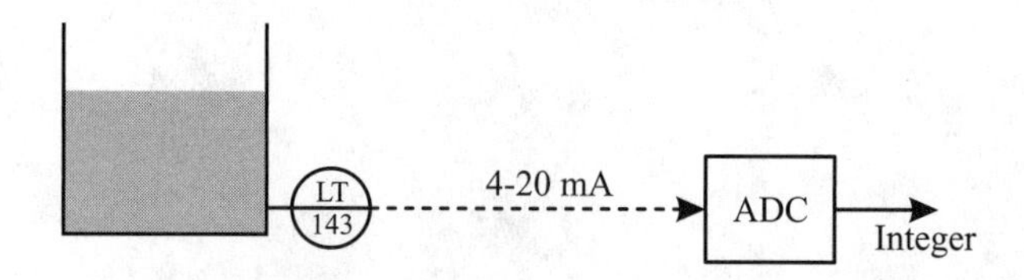

Figure P7.2. Level measurement.

analog input module having an ADC whose output integer value corresponds to the lowest and highest pressures as:

Pressure	Modicon	CLogix	PLC-5	SLC-500	Siemens	GE Fanuc
5.0	0	-20,030	0	3277	5530	0
400.0	32,000	30,920	4095	16,384	27,648	32,000

Find the equation that converts the ADC output integer into the pressure in psi, for

(a) Modicon (d) SLC-500
(b) ControlLogix (e) Siemens S7
(c) PLC-5 (f) GE Fanuc 90-30

P7-4. A load cell on a crane (Figure P7.4) measures the weight (10 - 500 pounds) of whatever is hanging from the crane. The output of the load cell is a 4 to 20 mA signal that is connected to an analog input module having an ADC whose output integer value corresponds to the lowest and highest weights as:

Weight	Modicon	CLogix	PLC-5	SLC-500	Siemens	GE Fanuc
10.0	0	-20,030	0	3277	5530	0
500.0	32,000	30,920	4095	16,384	27,648	32,000

Find the equation that converts the ADC output integer into the weight, in pounds, for

(a) Modicon (d) SLC-500
(b) ControlLogix (e) Siemens S7
(c) PLC-5 (f) GE Fanuc 90-30

P7-5. A pH probe measures the pH of the solution in a tank (Figure P7.5). The output of the pH transmitter, AT211, is a 4 to 20 mA signal that is connected to an analog input module having an ADC whose output integer value corresponds to the lowest and highest pH values as:

pH	Modicon	CLogix	PLC-5	SLC-500	Siemens	GE Fanuc
0.0	0	-20,030	0	3277	5530	0
14.0	32,000	30,920	4095	16,384	27,648	32,000

Find the equation that converts the ADC output integer into the pH for

(a) Modicon (d) SLC-500
(b) ControlLogix (e) Siemens S7
(c) PLC-5 (f) GE Fanuc 90-30

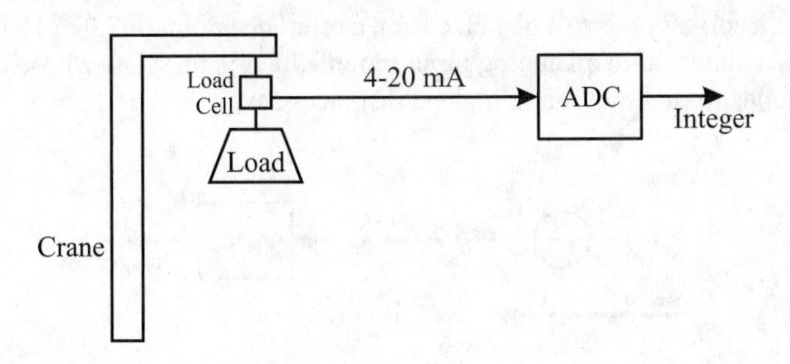

Figure P7.4. Weight measurement.

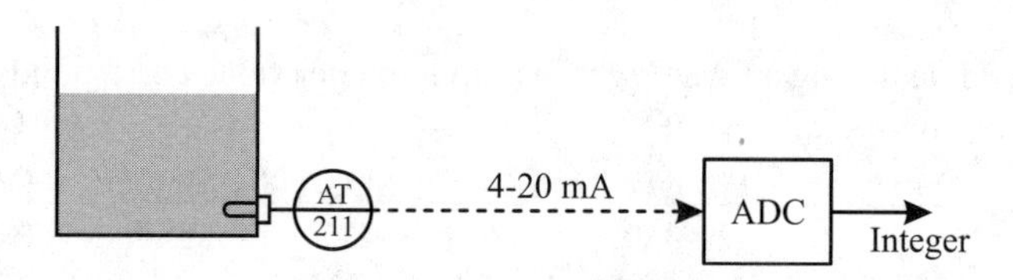

Figure P7.5. PH measurement.

P7-6. A type K thermocouple measures the temperature of a vessel. The thermocouple is connected to a transmitter whose output of 4 to 20 mA is calibrated to represent 40 to 800 °F. The transmitter output is connected to an analog input module having an ADC whose output integer value corresponds to the lowest and highest temperatures as:

Temper.	Modicon	CLogix	PLC-5	SLC-500	Siemens	GE Fanuc
40.0	0	-20,030	0	3277	5530	0
800.0	32,000	30,920	4095	16,384	27,648	32,000

Find the equation that converts the ADC output integer into the temperature, in °F, for

(a) Modicon (d) SLC-500
(b) ControlLogix (e) Siemens S7
(c) PLC-5 (f) GE Fanuc 90-30

P7-7. The transmitter of the FT104 orifice flow meter (Figure P7.7) is adjusted so that the electrical output signal span of 4 to 20 mA represents 10 to 300 pounds/hour of steam flow. The 4 to 20 mA signal is connected to an analog input module having an ADC whose output integer value corresponds to the lowest and highest flows as:

Flow	Modicon	CLogix	PLC-5	SLC-500	Siemens	GE Fanuc
10.0	0	-20,030	0	3277	5530	0
300.0	32,000	30,920	4095	16,384	27,648	32,000

Find the equation that converts the ADC output integer into the flow, in pounds/hour, for

(a) Modicon (d) SLC-500
(b) ControlLogix (e) Siemens S7
(c) PLC-5 (f) GE Fanuc 90-30

P7-8. A linear potentiometer is used to measure the position of a pneumatic actuator (Figure P7.8). The source voltage (V^+) is 5.0 volts and so the voltage range of the potentiometer is 0 to 5 volts, which corresponds to a distance from a reference point of 2.0 to 10.0 cm. The 0 to 5 volt signal is connected to an analog input module having an ADC whose output integer value corresponds to the lowest and highest distances as:

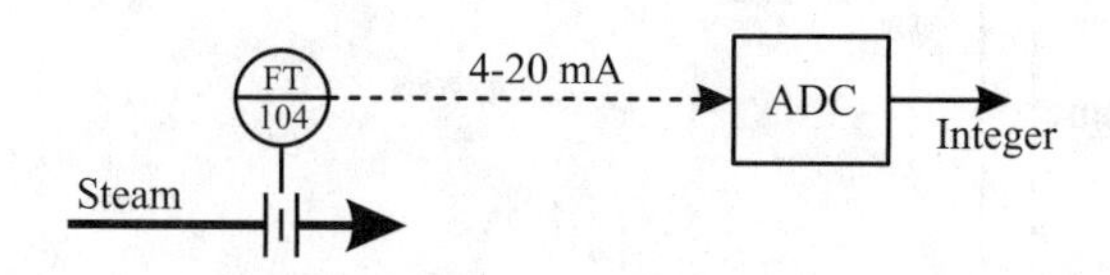

Figure P7.7. Orifice flow meter measurement.

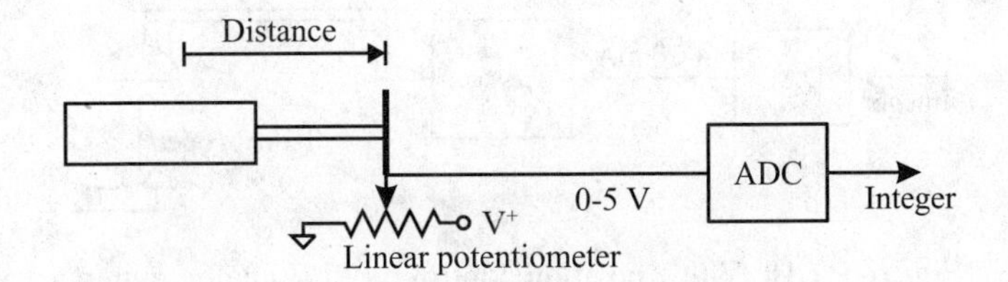

Figure P7.8. Position measurement.

Distance	Modicon	CLogix	PLC-5	SLC-500	Siemens	GE Fanuc
2.0	0	-20,030	0	3277	5530	0
10.0	32,000	30,920	4095	16,384	27,648	32,000

Find the equation that converts the ADC output integer into the distance, in centimeters, for

(a) Modicon (d) SLC-500
(b) ControlLogix (e) Siemens S7
(c) PLC-5 (f) GE Fanuc 90-30

P7-9. The ultrasonic level transmitter in Figure P7.9 measures the level of powder in a tank, in meters, and converts the level into a 4 to 20 mA signal that is connected to an analog input module. The ADC output integer value corresponds to the lowest and highest levels as:

Level	Modicon	CLogix	PLC-5	SLC-500	Siemens	GE Fanuc
45 ft.	0	-20,030	0	3277	5530	0
0	32,000	30,920	4095	16,384	27,648	32,000

Note that lower levels correspond to larger integer values. Find the equation that converts the ADC output integer into the level, in feet, for

(a) Modicon (d) SLC-500
(b) ControlLogix (e) Siemens S7
(c) PLC-5 (f) GE Fanuc 90-30

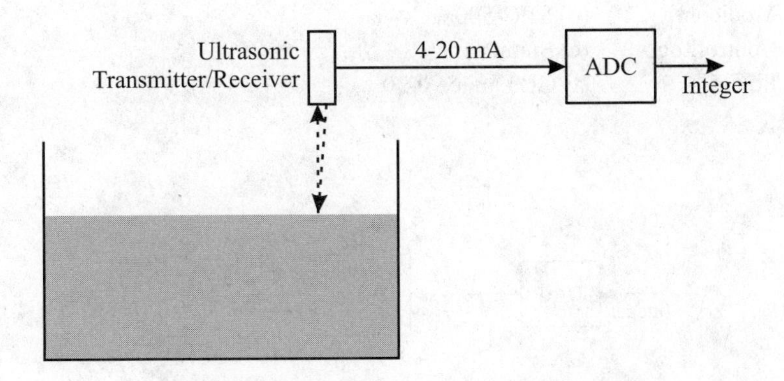

Figure P7.9. Ultrasonic level measurement.

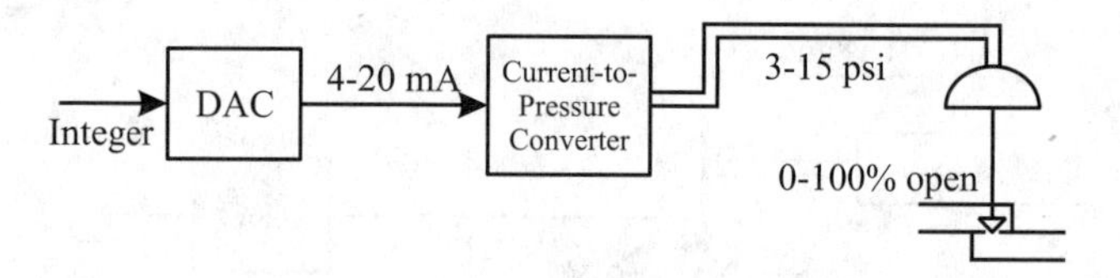

Figure P7.10. Valve position control by PLC analog output.

P7-10. Figure P7.10 depicts the analog output of a PLC used to control the position of a regulatory control valve. The PLC analog output is a signal in the range of 4 to 20 mA that is converted into a 3 to 15 psi pressure signal. The pressure signal drives the valve, which converts the 3 to 15 psi into 0 to 100% open (0% is closed). The input integer value to the DAC of the analog output module corresponds to the lowest and highest valve positions as:

Position	Modicon	CLogix	PLC-5	SLC-500	Siemens	GE Fanuc
100	0	-20,030	0	6242	5530	0
0	32,000	30,920	4095	31,208	27,648	32,000

This is a "fail-open" valve that opens when the air supply fails. Therefore, the lowest valve position corresponds to the higher analog output value. Find the equation that converts the desired position (0-100) into the DAC input integer for

(a) Modicon (d) SLC-500
(b) ControlLogix (e) Siemens S7
(c) PLC-5 (f) GE Fanuc 90-30

The range of the possible values of valve position is 0-100, **not** 0.01-1.00.

P7-11. The analog output of a PLC is used as the control signal to a variable speed drive (Figure P7.11). The PLC analog output is a signal in the range of 4 to 20 mA that is converted into a desired speed frequency of 0 to 180 Hz. The input integer value to the DAC of the analog output module corresponds to the lowest and highest frequencies as:

Frequency	Modicon	CLogix	PLC-5	SLC-500	Siemens	GE Fanuc
0	0	-20,030	0	6242	5530	0
180	32,000	30,920	4095	31,208	27,648	32,000

Find the equation that converts the desired frequency, in Hz, into the DAC input integer for

(a) Modicon (d) SLC-500
(b) ControlLogix (e) Siemens S7
(c) PLC-5 (f) GE Fanuc 90-30

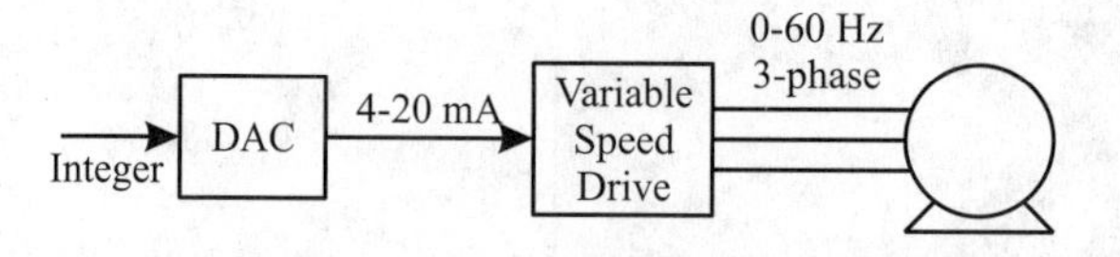

Figure P7.11. Motor controller.

General instructions for problems P7-12 to P7-31:

Write a ladder logic program for the application and implement it for one of the following PLC ladder logic languages:

Modicon Concept, **or**

Allen-Bradley ControlLogix, **or**

Allen-Bradley PLC-5/SLC-500, **or**

Siemens S7, **or**

GE Fanuc 90-30 (with floating point)

If any part of the operation is ambiguous, write down your additional assumptions. The physical inputs, physical outputs, and internal variables for each situation are given in the problem. **DO NOT** assign any more physical inputs!

Unless otherwise specified, assume the ADC in the analog input module has an output integer value that corresponds to the lowest and highest sensor value as:

Value	Modicon	Logix	PLC-5	SLC-500	Siemens	GE Fanuc
Lowest	0	-20,030	0	3277	5530	0
Highest	32,000	30,920	4095	16,384	27,648	32,000

In the case of the ControlLogix PLC, the instructor may choose to specify that the output of the ADC is a real number configured to be in the sensor units, for example, level in feet or temperature in °C.

Also, unless otherwise specified, assume the input integer to the DAC of an analog output module corresponds to the lowest and highest values of the output device control as:

Value	Modicon	Logix	PLC-5	SLC-500	Siemens	GE Fanuc
Lowest	0	-20,030	0	6242	5530	0
Highest	32,000	30,920	4095	31,208	27,648	32,000

In the case of the ControlLogix PLC, the instructor may choose to specify that the input to the DAC is a real number configured to be in the actual units of the output device, for example, speed in rpm or valve position in percent of span.

Your solution should include the following:

1. Function chart (if appropriate)
2. Specify the PLC processor used.
3. Ladder logic diagram (with comments). For consistency among the different PLCs, use only variables/symbols/tags in the ladder logic. Use instructions and function blocks consistent with the PLC processor.
4. Table listing additional internal memory (variables/symbols/tags) used and a brief description of their use. For the Allen-Bradley ControlLogix and the Modicon Quantum/Momentum processors, list the internal variables/tags and the data type. For the other processors, list the internal variables/symbols and the associated memory address.

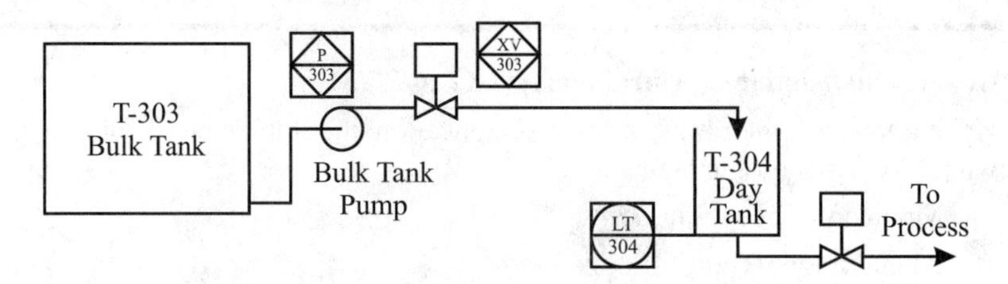

Figure P7.12. Day tank system.

P7-12. Day Tank Level Control. Implement the following calculation and comparison operations for a day tank level control.

A day tank has about one 8-hour shift worth of material to feed into a process. A day tank is located close to the process and is fed from a much larger bulk tank, located some distance from the process to be conveniently loaded from a tanker truck or railcar. The day tank allows much finer control of the material feed into the process and saves energy since the bulk tank pump runs only occasionally. The day tank is only fed from the bulk tank when the day tank level is low (for example, 10%). When the day tank has been filled from the bulk tank to a high level (for example, 90%), the bulk tank pump is shut off.

The PLC implements a simple level control for the T-304 day tank in Figure P7.12. The PLC controls the P-303 pump and XV303 block valve to keep the liquid level in T-304 between two limits, T304_HI_LVL and T304_LO_LVL:

The valve is opened and the pump is turned **on** when

Measured Level < T304_LO_LVL

The valve is closed and the pump is turned **off** when

Measured Level > T304_HI_LVL

The T304_HI_LVL and T304_LO_LVL values, in inches, are already stored in internal memory locations. The level measurement transmitter, LT304, is calibrated to measure from 0 to 45 inches. LT304 is connected to an analog input module having an ADC whose output value (LT304_MEAS) corresponds to the lowest and highest levels as specified in the general instructions prior to P7-12. The LT304_MEAS value should be converted into a level in inches (a real number) and placed in T304_INCH.

Also, in order to protect against illegal values entered by the operator, make sure the T304_HI_LVL is no higher than 40 inches and that the T304_LO_LVL is no lower than 10 inches.

The T304_ENABLE internal coil enables the day tank control. When T304_ENABLE is **on**, the T-304 level is controlled as described above. The valve is closed and the pump does not run when T304_ENABLE is **off**.

The solution should include the equation used to convert the LT304_MEAS value into the level in inches.

For the Modicon PLC, LT304_MEAS is an INT data type. For the PLC-5, do not use file numbers 10-12 for the internal memory and assume that the analog input reading has already been moved into the PLC memory using the BTR instruction.

Assume the following physical inputs, physical outputs and internal variables:

Variable	Description
P303_RUN	P-303 pump control, **on** runs pump.
XV303_SOL	XV303 valve control, **on** opens valve, **off** closes valve.
LT304_MEAS	Raw T-304 level measurement, represents 0 to 45 inches; ADC integer range listed before P7-12.
T304_ENABLE	Enable day tank control; **on** allows day tank control to operate. When **off**, the valve is closed and the pump is off.
T304_LO_LVL	Minimum tank level, in inches (a REAL).
T304_HI_LVL	Maximum tank level, in inches (a REAL).
T304_INCH	Current tank level, in inches (a REAL).

The addresses associated with the physical inputs and outputs are:

Variable	Modicon	PLC-5	ControlLogix	Siemens	GE Fanuc
P303_RUN	000001	O:02/00	Local:2:O.Data.0	Q8.0	%Q1
XV303_SOL	000002	O:02/01	Local:2:O.Data.1	Q8.1	%Q2
LT304_MEAS	300001	N10:4 I:3.0 (SLC)	Local:3:I.Ch0Data	IW288	%AI1

The addresses or data types associated with the internal variables:

	Modicon	PLC-5	Logix	Siemens	GE Fanuc
Variable	Data Type	Addr.	Data Type	Addr.	Addr.
T304_ENABLE	BOOL	B3/20	BOOL	M1.4	%M20
T304_LO_LVL	REAL	F12:0	REAL	MD100	%R100
T304_HI_LVL	REAL	F12:1	REAL	MD104	%R102
T304_INCH	REAL	F12:2	REAL	MD108	%R104

P7-13. Day Tank Alarms. Add low and high alarms to the day tank of problem P7-12 described as follows:

> The alarm indicators consist of high and low level alarm lights (T304_HIALM and T304_LOALM) and an alarm horn, ALM_HORN. There are two low alarm levels and two high alarm levels:
>
> | | |
> |---|---|
> | Low-low alarm | 5 inches |
> | Low alarm | T304_LO_LVL – 3 |
> | High alarm | T304_HI_LVL + 3 |
> | High-high alarm | 44 inches |
>
> The alarm light actions depend on the relationship of the current level with the alarm values:
>
> | | |
> |---|---|
> | Level ≤ Low-low alarm | Low alarm flashes at 2 Hz |
> | Low-low < Level ≤ Low | Low alarm steady on |
> | Low < Level < High | No alarms |
> | High ≤ Level < High-high | High alarm steady on |
> | High-high ≤ Level | High alarm flashes at 2 Hz |
>
> The horn is handled in the following manner. The horn is turned on (steady) whenever the level ≤ low-low alarm or whenever the level ≥ high-high alarm. The

horn remains on until the operator has acknowledged the alarm by pressing the HORN_ACK button. When the HORN_ACK button is pressed, the horn should be silenced and remain silenced when the button is released. If a level ≤ low-low alarm turns on the horn, the horn should remain **on** until acknowledged by the operator, even if the level rises above the low-low alarm value. If a level ≥ high-high alarm turns on the horn, the horn should remain **on** until acknowledged by the operator, even if the level falls below the high-high alarm value.

Assume the following additional physical inputs and outputs.

Variable	Description
HORN_ACK	Horn acknowledge push button switch; **on** when pushed, **off** when released. Operation described above.
T304_HIALM	High level alarm indication, high-high when flashing.
T304_LOALM	Low level alarm indication, low-low when flashing.
ALM_HORN	Alarm horn, **on** to sound horn.

The addresses associated with the physical inputs and outputs are:

Variable	Modicon	PLC-5	ControlLogix	Siemens	GE Fanuc
HORN_ACK	100001	I:01/00	Local:1:I.Data.0	I4.0	%I1
T304_HIALM	000003	O:02/02	Local:2:O.Data.2	Q8.2	%Q3
T304_LOALM	000004	O:02/03	Local:2:O.Data.3	Q8.3	%Q4
ALM_HORN	000005	O:02/04	Local:2:O.Data.4	Q8.4	%Q5

P7-14. Proportional Level Control. Implement the following calculation and comparison operations for a level control.

The PLC implements a simple proportional controller for level control. The controller equations are:

$$\text{Error} = \text{DesiredLevel} - \text{MeasuredLevel}$$

$$\text{ValveOutput} = K_p \times \text{Error} + \text{Bias}$$

The calculation of ValveOutput should be performed every 0.1 seconds.

The K_p and Bias are internal variables, whose locations are given below. The ValveOutput is in the range of 0-100 and represents the 0 to 100% open valve position. Additionally, whenever the measured level is less than 30% of the desired level, an alarm must be turned **on**.

The desired level (in inches) is entered by a thumbwheel switch and appears as a 2-digit BCD number within an internal variable. The desired level must be converted to an integer number (range 0-40) before using in the controller equation. If the desired level is less than 6 inches, assume the operator made an error specifying the desired level and use a desired level of 6 inches. Also, if the desired level is greater than 38 inches, assume the operator made an error specifying the desired level and use a desired level of 38 inches.

Assume the K_p and Bias constants are set so that the result of the controller calculation is a valid number. However, your calculations must ensure that the ValveOutput is between 0 and 100. Assume that the K_p and Bias constants have already been loaded into internal memory locations, and should not be changed.

The level transmitter measures levels between 2 and 40 inches and converts the level into a 4 to 20 mA signal that is connected to an analog input module. The ADC output integer value (LT101_MEAS) corresponds to the lowest and highest levels as specified in the general instructions prior to P7-12. The LT101_MEAS value should be converted into a level in inches (a real number) before using it in the controller equation.

The ValveOutput calculated by the ladder logic must be moved to the DAC of an analog output module connected to a regulatory control valve. The PLC analog output is a signal in the range of 4 to 20 mA that is converted into 0 to 100 percent open (0 is closed; 100 is open). The input integer value (FV101_OUT) to the DAC of the analog output module corresponds to the lowest and highest valve positions as specified in the general instructions prior to P7-12. The ValveOutput should be converted to the DAC integer, FV101_OUT.

The solution should include the equation used to convert LT101_MEAS into the level in inches and the equation used to convert ValveOutput to the proper units for FV101_OUT.

For the Modicon PLC, LEVEL_TW, LT101_MEAS and FV101_OUT are INT data types. For the PLC-5, do not use any other locations in file numbers 10-12 other than those listed below. Assume other locations are defined as other sensor readings, thumbwheel switches, controller internal memory, or analog outputs. Assume that the thumbwheel switch discrete inputs and analog input reading have already been moved into the PLC memory using the BTR instruction.

Assume the following physical inputs, physical outputs and internal variables.

Variable	Description
ALARM	**On** when measured level < 30% of desired level.
LEVEL_TW	Desired level thumbwheel switch (inches), 2 digits BCD.
LT101_MEAS	Raw level measurement, represents 2 to 40 inches; ADC integer range listed before P7-12.
FV101_OUT	Raw analog valve output, represents 0 to 100 percent valve open; DAC integer range listed before P7-12.
KP	K_p constant (a REAL).
BIAS	Bias constant (a REAL).

The addresses associated with the physical inputs and outputs are:

Variable	Modicon	PLC-5	ControlLogix	Siemens	GE Fanuc
ALARM	000001	O:02/00	Local:2:O.Data.0	Q8.0	%Q1
LT101_MEAS	300001	N10:4 I:3.0 (SLC)	Local:3:I.Ch0Data	IW288	%AI1
FV101_OUT	400001	N11:0 O:4.0 (SLC)	Local:4:O.Ch0Data	QW304	%AQ1
LEVEL_TW	300005	D9:0	Local:5:I.Data	IW320	%AI5

The addresses or data types associated with the internal variables:

	Modicon	PLC-5	Logix	Siemens	GE Fanuc
Variable	Data Type	Addr.	Data Type	Addr.	Addr.
KP	REAL	F12:0	REAL	MD100	%R100
BIAS	REAL	F12:1	REAL	MD104	%R102

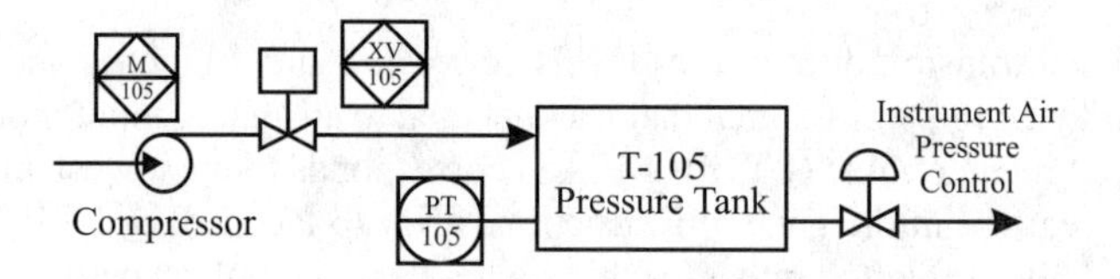

Figure P7.15. Pressure tank system.

P7-15. Simple Pressure Control. Implement the following calculation and comparison operation for a pressure tank.

The PLC implements a simple pressure control for an air tank that supplies instrument air for the plant section (Figure P7.15). The PT105 pressure sensor measures the pressure. The PLC turns on an air compressor (M-105) and an air inlet valve (XV105) to increase the tank pressure when the pressure is **below** a set minimum and turns off the valve when the pressure is **above** a set maximum. The minimum and maximum pressures are entered by the operator with thumbwheel switches. In addition, the current pressure, in psi, is displayed to the operator with a 3 digit LED display. Additionally, whenever the measured pressure is **greater than** 150% of the set maximum pressure (indicating that the compressor and XV105 valve is stuck on), a high alarm lamp must be turned **on**. Also, whenever the measured pressure is **less than** 75% of the set minimum pressure (indicating that XV105 is stuck on with the compressor off or there is a catastrophic leak), a low alarm lamp must be turned **on**. Whenever either alarm lamp is on, an alarm horn must be sounded.

Both the set minimum and maximum pressures are entered by thumbwheel switches and appear as a 3-digit BCD number within a word (do not concern yourself with how the thumbwheel switch inputs are transferred to the word). The current pressure, in psi must be converted to a BCD number and placed in a specified memory location (again, do not concern yourself about how the BCD number is transferred to the LED display inputs). The pressure measurement transmitter, PT105, is calibrated to measure from 0 to 300 psi. PT105 is connected to an analog input module having an ADC whose output value (PT105_MEAS) corresponds to the lowest and highest levels as specified in the general instructions prior to P7-12. The PT105_MEAS value should be converted into a pressure in psi (a real number).

The solution should include the equation used to convert PT105_MEAS into the pressure in psi.

For the Modicon PLC, PT105_MEAS is an INT data type. Also, use the BCD_INT derived function block (Figure 12.1) for the BCD-to-integer conversion and the INT_BCD block (Figure P12.1) for the integer-to-BCD conversion. For the PLC-5, do not use any locations in files 10 - 12 for any calculation temporary results (any other locations in files 10-12 are for other measurements or analog outputs). Assume that the analog input readings have already been moved into the PLC memory using the BTR instruction.

Assume the following physical input, physical output, and internal memory assignments:

Variable	Description
M105_RUN	M-105 compressor control, **on** runs compressor.

XV105_SOL	XV105 valve control, **on** opens valve, **off** closes valve.
PT105_LO_LA	Low pressure indicator lamp; **on** when measured pressure < 75% of set minimum desired pressure.
PT105_HI_LA	High pressure indicator lamp; **on** when measured pressure > 150% of set minimum desired pressure.
PT105_HORN	Alarm horn; **on** when either alarm lamp is **on**.
PT105_MEAS	Raw PT105 pressure measurement, represents 0 to 300 psi; ADC integer range listed before P7-12
PT105_LO_BCD	Minimum pressure thumbwheel switch reading in psi (3 digits BCD).
PT105_HI_BCD	Maximum pressure thumbwheel switch reading in psi (3 digits BCD).
PT105_BCD	Current tank pressure in psi (BCD), to be transferred to 3-digit LED display.
PT105_VAL	Current tank pressure in psi (a REAL).

The addresses associated with the physical inputs and outputs are:

Variable	Modicon	PLC-5	ControlLogix	Siemens	GE Fanuc
M105_RUN	000001	O:02/00	Local:2:O.Data.0	Q8.0	%Q1
XV105_SOL	000002	O:02/01	Local:2:O.Data.1	Q8.1	%Q2
PT105_LO_LA	000003	O:02/02	Local:2:O.Data.2	Q8.2	%Q3
PT105_HI_LA	000004	O:02/03	Local:2:O.Data.3	Q8.3	%Q4
PT105_HORN	000005	O:02/04	Local:2:O.Data.4	Q8.4	%Q5
PT105_MEAS	300001	N10:4 I:3.0 (SLC)	Local:3:I.Ch0Data	IW288	%AI1

The addresses or data types associated with the internal variables:

	Modicon	PLC-5	Logix	Siemens	GE Fanuc
Variable	Data Type	Addr.	Data Type	Addr.	Addr.
PT105_LO_BCD	INT	D9:1	INT	MW100	%R100
PT105_HI_BCD	INT	D9:2	INT	MW102	%R101
PT105_BCD	INT	D9:3	INT	MW104	%R102
PT105_VAL	REAL	F12:0	REAL	MD106	%R103

P7-16. Plant Waterer Improvements. Modify the plant waterer of problem P5-21 so that the 8-hour interval can be changed as desired by the user and the number of hours to the next watering check is calculated and displayed.

The desired watering interval (WAT_INTERVAL) is an integer, specified by an HMI package. Make sure WAT_INTERVAL is in the range of 0 – 15, inclusive. Do not write to this location, except to make sure it is within range.

Calculate REMAIN_TIME, the number of hours remaining to the next watering interval. Note that REMAIN_TIME is an integer. This number is to be displayed by an HMI package. The number of remaining hours is also displayed as a binary pattern on four discrete outputs. However you do the calculation, the other bits in the discrete output word must not be changed by the result of your calculation.

Start with a copy of either your solution (if correct) or the instructor's solution to P5-21. Mark the rungs that will be changed on it and attach page(s) with the new rungs to replace the old rungs and any additional rungs.

Assume the following additional physical output and internal memory assignments:

Variable	Description
WAT_INTERVAL	Desired watering interval, in hours. Maximum of 15. DO NOT write to this location.
REMAIN_TIME	Remaining hours to the next watering interval.
REMAIN0	Least significant bit (bit 0) of 4-bit display of hours remaining.
REMAIN1	Bit 1
REMAIN2	Bit 2
REMAIN3	Most significant bit (bit 3) of 4-bit display of hours remaining.

The addresses associated with the physical inputs and outputs are:

Variable	Modicon	PLC-5	ControlLogix	Siemens	GE Fanuc
REMAIN0	000003	O:02/02	Local:2:O.Data.2	Q8.2	%Q3
REMAIN1	000004	O:02/03	Local:2:O.Data.3	Q8.3	%Q4
REMAIN2	000005	O:02/04	Local:2:O.Data.4	Q8.4	%Q5
REMAIN3	000006	O:02/05	Local:2:O.Data.5	Q8.5	%Q6

The addresses or data types associated with the internal variables:

Variable	Modicon Data Type	PLC-5 Addr.	Logix Data Type	Siemens Addr.	GE Fanuc Addr.
WAT_INTERVAL	INT	N7:0	INT	MW100	%R100
REMAIN_TIME	INT	N7:1	INT	MW102	%R101

P7-17. Tank Level Indicator and Alarm. The PLC implements a simple level indicator and alarm system for a tank.

The tank level is measured from the top of the tank with an ultrasonic transducer (Figure P7.9). Hence, a longer distance measured by the transducer indicates a lower tank level. The ultrasonic level transmitter measures the level in the tank and converts the level into a 4 to 20 mA signal that is connected to an analog input module. The ADC output integer value corresponds to the lowest and highest levels as:

Level (feet)	Modicon	PLC-5	SLC-500	Siemens	GE Fanuc
0.0 (empty)	32,000	4095	16384	27,648	32,000
50.0 (full)	0	0	3277	5530	0

In the case of the ControlLogix PLC, the analog input is configured to scale the LT1274_MEAS value to be the level in feet. For the other PLCs, the LT1274_MEAS value should be converted into a level in feet (a real number) and placed in the LT1274_VAL location.

There are three indicator lights and an alarm on the operator panel that are operated in the following manner, depending on the tank level:

Level (ft.)	**LT1274_LO**	**LT1274_NM**	**LT1274_HI**	**LT1274_ALM**
< 2.0	Flashing	Off	Off	Off
≥ 2.0 and < 5.0	On	Off	Off	Off
≥ 5.0 and ≤ 40.0	Off	On	Off	Off
> 40.0 and ≤ 45.0	Off	Off	On	Off
> 45.0 and ≤ 50.0	Off	Off	Flashing	See below

When a light is flashing, it should flash with an **on** period and **off** period of 0.5 second each.

The LT1274_ALM is handled in the following manner. LT1274_ALM is turned **on** for any of the following conditions:

1. The level becomes greater than 45.0 feet
2. The alarm has been acknowledged by the operator, but the level has remained above 45.0 feet for five minutes.

LT1274_ALM is turned **off** for the following condition:

The operator acknowledges the alarm by pushing ALM_ACK.

Even if the level drops below 45.0 feet while LT1274_ALM is **on**, the alarm should remain **on** until acknowledged by the operator. If the level falls to 45.0 feet or below during the five minutes after alarm acknowledgment, the timing interval is completely canceled and the next time the level goes above 45.0 is treated as if it is the first time the level has gone above 45.0.

The ALM_ACK input is a push button switch. Do not assume it remains **on** for the 5-minute interval that starts when the ALM_ACK switch is pushed. Also, do not assume ALM_ACK is **off** after 5 minutes (it could be taped down). It has to turn **off** in order for it to turn **on** to acknowledge the next alarm.

The solution should include the equation used to convert LT1274_MEAS into the level in inches.

For the Modicon PLC, LT1274_MEAS is an INT data type. For the PLC-5, do not use any locations in files 10 - 12 for any calculation temporary results (any other locations in files 10-12 are for other measurements or analog outputs). Assume that the analog input readings have already been moved into the PLC memory using the BTR instruction.

Assume the following input, output, and internal memory assignments:

Variable	Description
ALM_ACK	Alarm acknowledge push button switch; **on** when pushed, **off** when released. Operation described above.
LT1274_HI	High level indication, high-high when flashing.
LT1274_NM	Normal level indication.
LT1274_LO	Low level indication, low-low when flashing.
LT1274_ALM	Level alarm horn, **on** sounds horn.
LT1274_MEAS	Raw T-1274 level measurement, represents 0 to 50 feet; ADC integer range listed above.
LT1274_VAL	Level of tank, in feet (a REAL).

The addresses associated with the physical inputs and outputs are:

Variable	Modicon	PLC-5	ControlLogix	Siemens	GE Fanuc

ALM_ACK	100001	I:01/00	Local:1:I.Data.0	I4.0	%I1
LT1274_HI	000001	O:02/00	Local:2:O.Data.0	Q8.0	%Q1
LT1274_NM	000002	O:02/01	Local:2:O.Data.1	Q8.1	%Q2
LT1274_LO	000003	O:02/02	Local:2:O.Data.2	Q8.2	%Q3
LT1274_ALM	000004	O:02/03	Local:2:O.Data.3	Q8.3	%Q4
LT1274_MEAS	300001	N10:4 I:3.0 (SLC)	Local:3:I.Ch0Data	IW288	%AI1

The addresses or data types associated with the internal variables:

Variable	Modicon Data Type	PLC-5 Addr.	Logix Data Type	Siemens Addr.	GE Fanuc Addr.
LT1274_VAL	REAL	F12:0	REAL	MD100	%R100

P7-18. Flow Meter Accumulator. Use ladder logic to implement an accumulator that converts the reading from a flow meter (gal/min) to the volume of material (gallons) that passes through the flow meter. *Do not implement a function chart.*

The accumulator converts flow into volume by implementing a simple integrator that integrates the flow rate converting it into a volume. In order to do the integrator operation in the PLC, the flow rate is sampled at 1-second intervals and the volume is updated accordingly. Given samples of the flow, the general equation for the volume at the *i*-th time interval is

$$\text{Volume}_i = T\sum_{k=0}^{i}\text{Flow}_k \tag{P7-18.1}$$

where T is the sample period (1 second in this case). In words, the volume can be calculated by summing all previous flow samples and multiplying this sum by T. However, it is not necessary to keep all previous values of the flow, because the volume can be updated with each new sample of the flow rate by the formula

$$\text{Volume}_i = \text{Volume}_{i-1} + T \times \text{Flow}_i \tag{P7-18.2}$$

In words, the volume is updated by adding to it the product of the current flow rate and the sample period.

What your code needs to do:

(1) Implement equation (P7-18.2) every 1 second. In order to make the units consistent, $T = 1/60 = 0.01667$ (since volume is gallons and the flow rate units are gallons/minute). Just update the current value of VOLUME. Do not save the previous value of VOLUME.

(2) When the RESET_ACCUM internal coil is ON, reset the accumulator, that is, set the volume to zero.

The FTXXX_VAL value has already been converted from the raw analog input channel value into an integer with units of gallons/minute.

All time intervals must be accurate to within 0.01 second.

If using the PLC-5, do not use any locations in files 10 - 11 for any calculation temporary results (any other locations in files 10-11 are for other measurements or calculations).

Assume the following internal memory assignments.

Variable	Description
FTXXX_VAL	Current flow rate, in gallons/minute (a REAL).
VOLUME	Volume of material that has passed through flow meter since the accumulator has been reset, in gallons (a REAL).
RESET_ACCUM	**On** to reset accumulator (set VOLUME to zero).

The addresses or data types associated with the internal variables:

Variable	Modicon Data Type	PLC-5 Addr.	Logix Data Type	Siemens Addr.	GE Fanuc Addr.
FTXXX_VAL	REAL	F8:6	REAL	MD112	%R112
VOLUME	REAL	F8:7	REAL	MD116	%R114
RESET_ACCUM	BOOL	B3/201	BOOL	M12.7	%M202

P7-19. Test Panel Lamps. An operator panel needs a function to test the lamps on the panel (Figure P7.19*a*). Normally, a push button switch is added to the panel and when this switch is pressed, all lamps on the panel are lit and those that are burned out can be readily identified. To implement this function in ladder logic, a contact referring to the test push button is added in parallel with the other logic driving each lamp, to turn **on** each lamp when the lamp test push button is pressed. However, when implemented in this manner, you

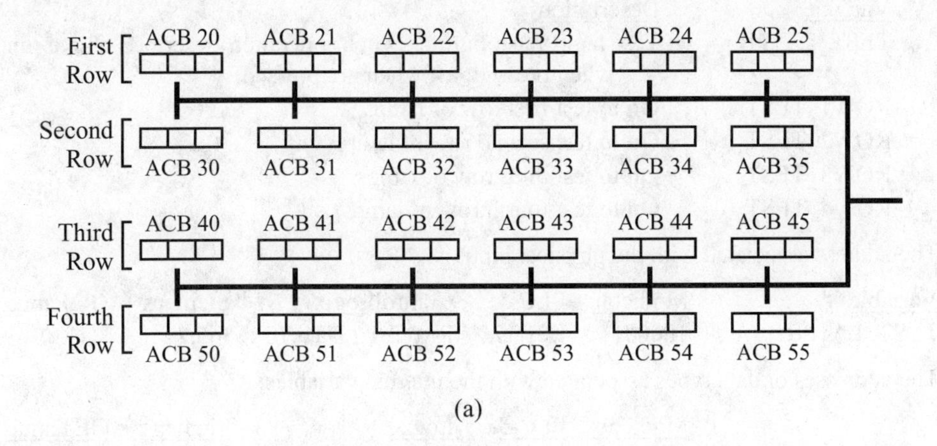

(a)

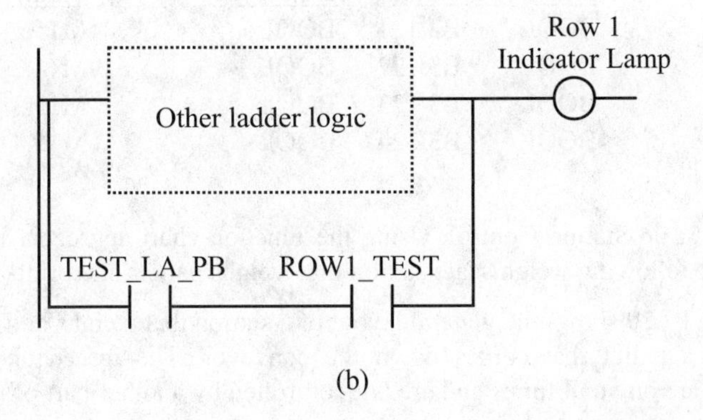

(b)

Figure P7.19. Operator panel: *(a)* partial view of lamps; *(b)* typical test lamp logic.

discover that the 24-volt power supply does not have the capacity to light all 200 lamps simultaneously. In fact, when lighting less than half of the lamps, the power supply voltage dips enough to cause some alarms to annunciate (to your embarrassment).

Implement the panel lamp test in the following manner. The panel is divided into four rows of lamps and only one row of lamps is tested at a time. The first time the TEST_LA_PB push button is pressed, the first row of lamps is turned **on** and remains **on** as long as TEST_LA_PB is held down. The second time the TEST_LA_PB push button is pressed, the second row of lamps is turned **on** and remains **on** as long as TEST_LA_PB is held down. The third and fourth rows of lamps are tested in a similar manner on successive presses of TEST_LA_PB. On the fifth press of TEST_LA_PB, the pattern is repeated and the first row of lamps is tested again. If the TEST_LA_PB button has not been pushed for 2 minutes, then set any internal logic so that the next press of TEST_LA_PB tests the first row of lamps. The latter feature ensures that the first row is always the first one tested after a period of inactivity. That is, no matter which row was tested last, after a reasonable amount of inactivity, the test reverts to start with the first row.

Implement the ladder logic code to generate the internal coils, ROW1_TEST, ROW2_TEST, ROW3_TEST, and ROW4_TEST that will be added to the lamp logic. An example use of ROW1_TEST is shown in Figure P7.19*b*. **Use only one counter.**

Assume the following input, output, and internal memory assignments.

Variable	Description
TEST_LA_PB	Test lamp push button switch, operation described above, **on** when pressed, **off** when not pressed.
ROW1_TEST	**On** to test first row of lamps.
ROW2_TEST	**On** to test second row of lamps.
ROW3_TEST	**On** to test third row of lamps.
ROW4_TEST	**On** to test fourth row of lamps.

The address associated with the physical input is:

Variable	Modicon	PLC-5	ControlLogix	Siemens	GE Fanuc
TEST_LA_PB	100001	I:21/12	RM_2:1:I.Data.10	I65.2	%I130

The addresses or data types associated with the internal variables:

Variable	Modicon Data Type	PLC-5 Addr.	Logix Data Type	Siemens Addr.	GE Fanuc Addr.
ROW1_TEST	BOOL	B3/121	BOOL	M15.1	%M121
ROW2_TEST	BOOL	B3/122	BOOL	M15.2	%M122
ROW3_TEST	BOOL	B3/123	BOOL	M15.3	%M123
ROW4_TEST	BOOL	B3/124	BOOL	M15.4	%M124

P7-20. Weigh Scale Station Control. Using the function chart approach, implement the program for the following weigh scale station that weighs pallets and prints the weight.

Figure P7.20 shows the general layout of a station that weighs and prints the weight of a pallet that comes down the conveyor. The infeed and outfeed conveyors are on at all times and are not controlled by another part of the ladder

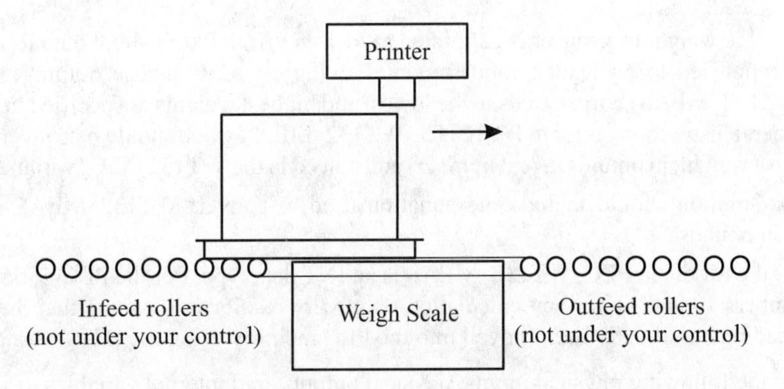

Figure P7.20. Weigh scale station.

logic. The weigh scale has its own small conveyor belt that can be stopped to weigh the pallet. The operation is described in the following manner:

> The weigh scale belt runs continuously until the weigh scale senses at least 5 pounds. The presence of the pallet is sensed by the weigh scale and not by any limit switches or photoelectric "eyes."
>
> When the weigh scale detects a weight of greater than 5 pounds, then the conveyor belt is stopped.
>
> After a pause of 4 seconds, to allow the weight to stabilize, the spray printer is activated to spray the weight on the pallet. In order to keep the problem simple, you will not need to know how to send the weight to the printer. All your ladder needs to do is to make sure the weight, in pounds, is in the proper memory location and turn **on** the DO_PRINT internal coil. Another internal coil, called PRINT_DONE, is set by another part of the ladder to signal that the weight has been printed.
>
> After the printer has sprayed the pallet, then the weigh scale conveyor is activated until the weight has been less than 5 pounds for 2 seconds to move the pallet out of the weigh station and onto the outfeed conveyor.

After the pallet has been moved off, the weigh scale station repeats its operation, running the conveyor until the next pallet is processed. Assume the pallets are spaced far enough apart so that the next pallet arrives after the pallet has left the station.

Upon initial startup, assume there are no pallets in the station, and the conveyor runs until a pallet is detected as detailed above. When the stop push button is pressed (turned **off**) the operation should pause and the conveyor must be turned **off**. Pressing the start switch while the operation of the station is paused causes the station to resume its suspended operation.

There is a reset push button that when pressed, resets any internal steps so that when the start switch is pressed, no pallets are assumed to be in the station. The reset switch should be ignored if the station is running. Assume the pallets are removed before RESET_PB is pressed.

The weight transducer is calibrated to measure from 0.0 to 900.0 pounds and is connected to an analog input module having an ADC whose output value (WT132_MEAS) corresponds to the lowest and highest weights as specified in the general instructions prior to P7-12. The WT132_MEAS value should be converted into a weight, in pounds (a real number) and placed in the WT132_VAL variable.

The solution should include the equation used to convert WT132_MEAS into the weight in pounds.

For the Modicon PLC, WT132_MEAS is an INT data type. For the PLC-5, do not use file numbers 10 and 11 for any calculation temporary results and assume that the analog input reading has already been moved into the PLC memory using the BTR instruction.

Assume the following physical inputs, physical outputs, and internal variables.

Variable	Description
START_PB	Start push button, N. O., **on** when starting.
STOP_PB	Stop push button, N. C., **off** when stopping.
RESET_PB	Reset push button, N. O., **on** to restore station to initial state.
CONV_MOTOR	Conveyor motor control, **on** to move conveyor.
WT132_MEAS	Raw pallet weight measurement, represents 0 to 900 lbs.; ADC integer range listed before P7-12.
WT132_VAL	Current weigh scale measurement, in pounds (a REAL).
PRINT_DONE	Indicates that printer has finished spraying weight on box. **On** when printing done. Controlled by another part of the ladder.
DO_PRINT	**On** to activate the spray printer to spray weight on box. Controlled by this part of the ladder.

The addresses associated with the physical inputs and outputs are:

Variable	Modicon	PLC-5	ControlLogix	Siemens	GE Fanuc
START_PB	100001	I:01/00	Local:1:I.Data.0	I4.0	%I1
STOP_PB	100002	I:01/01	Local:1:I.Data.1	I4.1	%I2
RESET_PB	100003	I:01/02	Local:1:I.Data.2	I4.2	%I3
CONV_MOTOR	000001	O:02/00	Local:2:O.Data.0	Q8.0	%Q1
WT132_MEAS	300001	N10:4 I:3.0 (SLC)	Local:3:I.Ch0Data	IW288	%AI1

The addresses or data types associated with the internal variables:

Variable	Modicon Data Type	PLC-5 Addr.	Logix Data Type	Siemens Addr.	GE Fanuc Addr.
WT132_VAL	REAL	F12:0	REAL	MD100	%R100
PRINT_DONE	BOOL	B3/101	BOOL	M104.0	%M102
DO_PRINT	BOOL	B3/102	BOOL	M104.1	%M103

P7-21. Width Check Station Control. Using the function chart approach, implement the program for the following station that checks the width of parts.

Figure P7.21 shows the general layout of a station that checks the width of parts as they come down the conveyor. The section of conveyor at the station is on

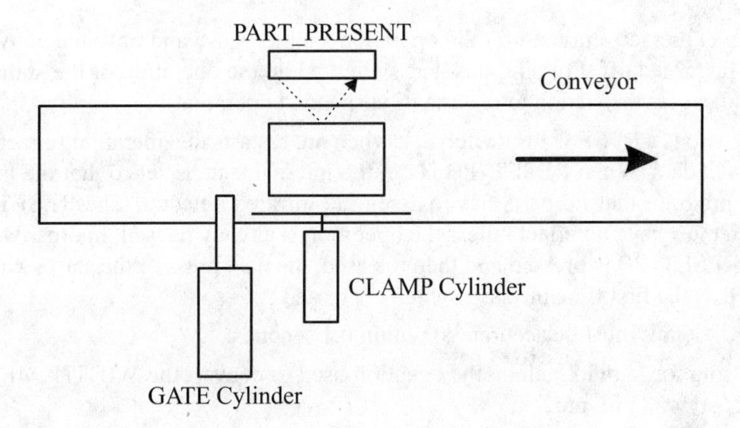

Figure P7.21. Width measurement station.

at all times the station is running. Not every part is checked. Only every tenth part is checked. In summary, when a part is to be checked, a clamp is activated to hold the part and check the width with an LVDT. Delays must be incorporated into the operation to allow the measurement to settle and the part to clear when the part is unclamped. The operation is described in the following manner:

The presence of a part is sensed by the PART_PRESENT reflective infrared sensor.

After 9 parts have passed, the tenth part is checked (when it is present), by activating the clamp cylinder. When the part is clamped, the conveyor is stopped and a gate is also activated to prevent more parts from interfering with the measurement.

After a pause of 2 seconds, to allow the measurement to stabilize, the width is measured. The width measurement is described below.

After the measurement is completed, the clamp is released, the gate is deactivated, the conveyor is restarted, and then there is a 2 second delay to allow the conveyor to restart and move the part out of the station. The NEW_WIDTH internal coil must be **on** in this step, signaling to another part of the ladder that there is a new width measurement.

After the 2 second wait, the station restarts the operation, waiting for the tenth part.

The width of the part is measured using a linear variable differential transformer (LVDT), calibrated to measure from 0.0 to 70.0 mm. The LVDT is connected to an analog input module having an ADC whose output value (WIDTH_MEAS) corresponds to the lowest and highest widths as specified in the general instructions prior to P7-12. The WIDTH_MEAS value should be converted into units of mm and stored in WIDTH_VAL (a real number). The width is only valid at the end of the 2-second period that allows it to be stabilized. DO NOT continuously calculate WIDTH_VAL.

When the start push button is pressed (turned **on**) for the first time only, the station assumes that no parts have passed the infrared detector. When the stop switch is pressed (turned **off**) the operation should pause and only the conveyor must be turned **off**. Pressing the start switch while the operation of the station is paused causes the station to resume its suspended operation.

There is a RESET_PB switch that when **on**, restarts the operation retracts the two cylinders. When RESET_PB is **on**, the internal state is set so that the ladder logic program that no parts have passed the infrared detector. The RESET_PB switch must have no effect unless the operation is already paused. In other words, after RESET_PB is pressed and then released, the next press of the start switch is treated as the first time the start switch is pressed.

All delays must be accurate to within 0.1 seconds.

Your solution should include the equation used to convert the WIDTH_MEAS value into the actual width in mm.

For the Modicon PLC, WIDTH_MEAS is an INT data type. For the Allen-Bradley PLC-5, do not use any locations in files 10 - 12 for any calculation temporary results (any other locations in files 10-12 are for other measurements or values from a supervisory controller). The analog input reading has already been moved into the PLC memory using the BTR instruction.

Assume the following physical input, physical output, and internal memory assignments:

Variable	Description
START_PB	Start push-button switch, **on** (closed) to start.
STOP_PB	Stop push-button switch, **off** (open) to stop.
RESET_PB	Reset push button switch, **on** (closed) to reset.
PART_PRESENT	Proximity sensor, **on** when part present.
CONV_MTR	Conveyor motor, **on** to run conveyor at station.
CLAMP	Clamp cylinder control, **on** to clamp part.
GATE	Gate cylinder control, **on** to activate gate that prevents more parts from interfering with the measurement.
NEW_MEAS	Internal coil, set **on** for 2 seconds by your ladder, to indicate that a new width has been measured.
WIDTH_MEAS	Raw width measurement, represents 0 to 70 mm; ADC integer range listed before P7-12.
WIDTH_VAL	Width of current (or last) part, in mm (a REAL).

The addresses associated with the physical inputs and outputs are:

Variable	Modicon	PLC-5	ControlLogix	Siemens	GE Fanuc
START_PB	100001	I:01/00	Local:1:I.Data.0	I4.0	%I1
STOP_PB	100002	I:01/01	Local:1:I.Data.1	I4.1	%I2
RESET_PB	100003	I:01/02	Local:1:I.Data.2	I4.2	%I3
PART_PRESENT	100004	I:01/03	Local:1:I.Data.3	I4.3	%I4
CONV_MTR	000001	O:02/00	Local:2:O.Data.0	Q8.0	%Q1
CLAMP	000002	O:02/01	Local:2:O.Data.1	Q8.1	%Q2
GATE	000003	O:02/02	Local:2:O.Data.2	Q8.2	%Q3
WIDTH_MEAS	300001	N10:4 I:3.0 (SLC)	Local:3:I.Ch0Data	IW288	%AI1

The addresses or data types associated with the internal variables:

Variable	Modicon Data Type	PLC-5 Addr.	Logix Data Type	Siemens Addr.	GE Fanuc Addr.
NEW_MEAS	BOOL	B3/140	BOOL	M8.11	%M141
WIDTH_VAL	REAL	F12:0	REAL	MD103	%R103

P7-22. Stamping Station Control. Using the function chart approach, implement the program for the following station that stamps a piece of metal.

Figure P7.22 shows the general layout of a station that stamps an impression into a metal piece. Not every piece is stamped. Only those having a particular bar code are stamped. The piece is pushed off the conveyor into the stamping station, where it is stamped before being returned to the conveyor. The required stamping pressure is not constant and is stored in an internal memory location. The actual stamp pressure is measured by a pressure transducer connected to an analog input channel.

The overall operation of the station is first described, followed by the details. The sequence of operation for the station follows these steps:

Metal piece coming down conveyor has its bar code read by the bar code reader. If the bar code indicates the piece is to be stamped, then the following steps are done. Otherwise, the station just waits for the next piece.

When PROX turns **on**, the piece is in position to be pushed into the stamper.

Extend PCYL1 to push piece to stamping position. LS2 turns **on** when in position. When in position, the piece is also against the end of PCYL2

The hydraulic ram, HCYL3 is moved down until the stamping pressure reaches the desired value.

Move HCYL3 up to fully up position (allow 3 seconds)

Simultaneously, PCYL2 is extended and PCYL1 is retracted to push piece onto conveyor (LS1 senses)

Retract PCYL2 (allow 2 seconds). It requires 4 seconds to fully retract PCYL2, but 2 seconds is sufficient time to allow it to clear the conveyor and allow a conveyor restart.

Move piece out of station

The operation then repeats.

The conveyor must be stopped while the part is being pushed off or on the conveyor and while the metal piece is being stamped. Assume pieces are far enough apart on the conveyor so that each piece can be handled individually.

A bar code reader is used to scan the bar code on the metal piece. All you know is that the bar code (a part number) is placed in an internal memory location, called BARCODE, and that an internal coil, NEW_CODE, is **on** when a new bar code has been read and placed into BARCODE. Assume that NEW_CODE is **on** only for the scan when a new barcode is read (it is the output of a rung driven by a one-shot instruction). DES_BARCODE contains the bar code of the parts that must be stamped, and is set by a host PLC or computer.

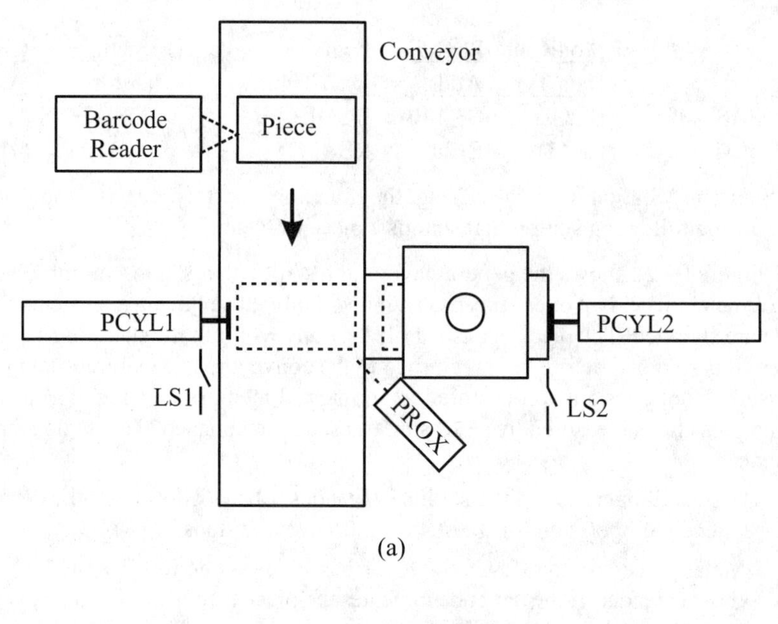

(a)

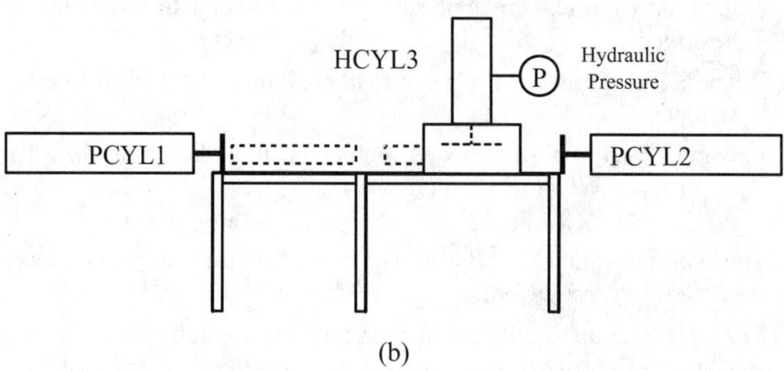

(b)

Figure P7.22. Stamping station: *(a)* top view; *(b)* side view.

PCYL1 is pneumatic ram powered by a double action cylinder. When the PCYL1_EXTEND output is **on**, the PCYL1 ram extends. When the PCYL1_RETRACT output is **on**, the PCYL1 ram retracts. When neither PCYL1 output or both outputs are **on**, the PCYL1 ram stops moving and remains at its present position. However, PCYL1_EXTEND output must remain **on** to hold the piece in position while it is being stamped (even when paused).

PCYL2 is a pneumatic ram powered by a single action cylinder with a spring return. When the PCYL2 output is **on**, the ram extends until it reaches the fully extended position. When the power is removed (PCYL2 is **off**), the ram retracts until it is in its fully retracted position. There is no limit switch that indicates that the ram powered by PCYL2 is fully retracted or extended. When turning off the PCYL2 output, assume that at least 4 seconds are required to go from the fully extended position to the fully retracted position.

The ram that moves the stamp down and up, HCYL3, is a hydraulic ram powered by a double action cylinder (like PCYL1). When the STAMP_DOWN output is **on**, the stamping press moves down. When the STAMP_UP output is **on**, the press moves up. When neither stamp ram output or both outputs are **on**, the cylinder stops moving vertically and remains at its present position. There is no limit switch indicating when HCYL3 is fully up. When moving the press up, assume that at least 3 seconds are required to go from the fully down (extended) position to the fully up (retracted) position.

PROX is used to sense when the metal piece is in position to be pushed into the stamping press. When it is **on** the piece is in position.

The DES_PRESS internal memory location indicates the desired hydraulic stamping pressure in pounds per square inch (psi). Assume this value has been placed in the PLC memory from a supervisory PLC or computer. The hydraulic pressure is measured by a pressure transducer is calibrated to measure from 2000 to 5000 psi and is connected to an analog input module having an ADC whose output value (PT214_MEAS) corresponds to the lowest and highest pressures as specified in the general instructions prior to P7-12. The PT214_MEAS value should be converted into a pressure, in psi (a real number) and placed in the PT214_VAL variable.

Use the pressure measurement, converted to the proper units to determine when to stop the hydraulic stamping ram. The ram pressure increases as the stamping ram extends (stamp lowers) and contacts the metal plate. (Hint: remember, there may be some inaccuracy in the measurement, so using equality to stop the ram is not wise.)

When the start switch is pressed (turned **on**) for the first time only, the station assumes there is no piece in the station and waits for the first piece to arrive. When the stop switch is pressed (turned **off**) the operation should pause and all outputs (except PCYL1 when stamping taking place) must be turned **off**. The operation cannot be paused when the hydraulic stamping press is being moved down (to make sure impression is correct). If the stop switch is pressed while the press is being lowered, the operation should continue to the next step and pause in that step. Pressing the start switch while the operation of the station is paused causes the station to resume its suspended operation.

There is a RESET_PB switch that when **on**, restarts the operation. When RESET is **on**, the internal step is set so that the ladder logic program waits for the next metal piece (but does not actually turn any outputs **on**). Also, retract all rams, including those that are double-acting when RESET_PB is momentarily pressed. All rams must be retracted before START_PB has any effect. START_PB must be pressed to actually restart the station. The RESET_PB switch must have no effect unless the operation is already paused. In other words, after RESET_PB is pressed and then released, the next press of the start switch is treated as the first time the start switch is pressed.

All delays must be accurate to within 0.1 seconds.

The solution should include the equation used to convert PT214_MEAS pressure measurement into the actual pressure in psi.

For the Modicon PLC, PT214_MEAS is an INT data type. For the PLC-5, do not use any locations in files 10 - 12 for any calculation temporary results (any other locations in files 10-12 are for other measurements or values from a supervisory controller). Assume that the analog input readings have already been moved into the PLC memory using the BTR instruction.

Assume the following input, output, and internal memory assignments.

Variable	Description
START_PB	Start push button switch, **on** (closed) to start.
STOP_PB	Stop pushbutton switch, **off** (open) to stop.
RESET_PB	Reset push button switch, **on** (closed) when resetting.
LS1	Limit switch, **on** (closed) when PCYL1 is fully retracted and piece is back on conveyor.
LS2	Limit switch, **on** (closed) when metal piece is in position to be stamped (under stamping press).
PROX	Proximity switch, **on** when piece in position to be moved into stamper.
CONV_MTR	Conveyor motor, **on** to run conveyor.
PCYL1_EXTEND	PCYL1 extend ram control; **on** to extend ram, **off** stops ram movement (but does not retract ram).
PCYL1_RETRACT	PCYL1 retract ram control; **on** to retract ram, **off** stops ram.
PCYL2	PCYL2 ram control; **on** to extend ram, **off** retracts.
STAMP_DOWN	**On** to move stamp ram down, **off** stops movement (but does not retract ram).
STAMP_UP	**On** to move stamp ram up, **off** stops movement.
PT214_MEAS	Raw stamping ram pressure measurement, represents 2000 to 5000 psi.; ADC integer range listed before P7-12.
NEW_CODE	**On** when a new barcode has been read and placed into BARCODE. This part of ladder DOES NOT control it.
PT214_VAL	Current stamping ram pressure, in psi (a REAL).
DES_PRESS	Desired stamping ram pressure, in psi (a REAL).
BARCODE	Bar code read from piece. Only valid when NEW_CODE is ON.
DES_BARCODE	Barcode of those parts that are to be stamped (integer). This part of ladder DOES NOT control it.

The addresses associated with the physical inputs and outputs are:

Variable	Modicon	PLC-5	ControlLogix	Siemens	GE Fanuc
START_PB	100001	I:01/00	Local:1:I.Data.0	I4.0	%I1
STOP_PB	100002	I:01/01	Local:1:I.Data.1	I4.1	%I2
RESET_PB	100003	I:01/02	Local:1:I.Data.2	I4.2	%I3
LS1	100004	I:01/03	Local:1:I.Data.3	I4.3	%I4
LS2	100005	I:01/04	Local:1:I.Data.4	I4.4	%I5
PROX	100006	I:01/05	Local:1:I.Data.5	I4.5	%I6
CONV_MTR	000001	O:02/00	Local:2:O.Data.0	Q8.0	%Q1
PCYL1_EXTEND	000002	O:02/01	Local:2:O.Data.1	Q8.1	%Q2
PCYL1_RETRACT	000003	O:02/02	Local:2:O.Data.2	Q8.2	%Q3

PCYL2	000004	O:02/03	Local:2:O.Data.3	Q8.3	%Q4
STAMP_DOWN	000005	O:02/04	Local:2:O.Data.4	Q8.4	%Q5
STAMP_UP	000006	O:02/05	Local:2:O.Data.5	Q8.5	%Q6
PT214_MEAS	300001	N10:4 I:3.0 (SLC)	Local:3:I.Ch0Data	IW288	%AI1

The addresses or data types associated with the internal variables:

Variable	Modicon Data Type	PLC-5 Addr.	Logix Data Type	Siemens Addr.	GE Fanuc Addr.
NEW_CODE	BOOL	B3/140	BOOL	M8.11	%M141
PT214_VAL	REAL	F8:40	REAL	MD180	%R180
DES_PRESS	REAL	F12:0	REAL	MD300	%R300
BARCODE	INT	N7:45	SINT	MW46	%R46
DES_BARCODE	INT	N13:0	SINT	MW350	%R350

P7-23. Valve Leak Check Station Control. Using the function chart approach, implement the program for the following valve leak check station.

Figure P7.23 shows the layout of a station that checks each assembled valve for leaks. The station pressurizes the valve and then checks that the pressure has not dropped too far within a certain time period.

Another part of the ladder controls the roller conveyor, so assume it is always moving.

Each valve is on a carrier, which ensures that the PROX sensor will turn off between valves, even if there is no spacing between the carriers.

There is no START_PB and STOP_PB because there is an overall start and stop for the line. Instead, there is a RUN internal coil that is **on** when this station is to be running. The station is running as long as valves are being produced.

Upon initial turning on of the RUN internal coil, assume there are no valves in the station. To pressure-check a valve the following happens:

A new valve is sensed (PROX turns **on**).

The HD_DOWN cylinder control is activated in order to move the measuring head down into position. Since this station must work with different valve sizes, the head is moved down until HD_HGT is less than or equal to VLV_HGT. Simultaneously, the LIFT_SOL is activated to raise the valve off the rollers. Assume LIFT_SOL is fast-acting and has finished moving the valve up long before the head is down in position. Do not construct a branch to do this operation.

The valve is pressurized to the desired pressure, DES_PRES. Turn on AIR_VLV to pressurize the valve under test.

Wait 30 seconds. If the valve has a leak, then the measured pressure at the end of this interval will be smaller than DES_PRES. The details about the pressure check appear below.

Activate the HD_UP cylinder control to move measuring head up. UP_LS is **on** when the head is fully up. Simultaneously, deactivate,

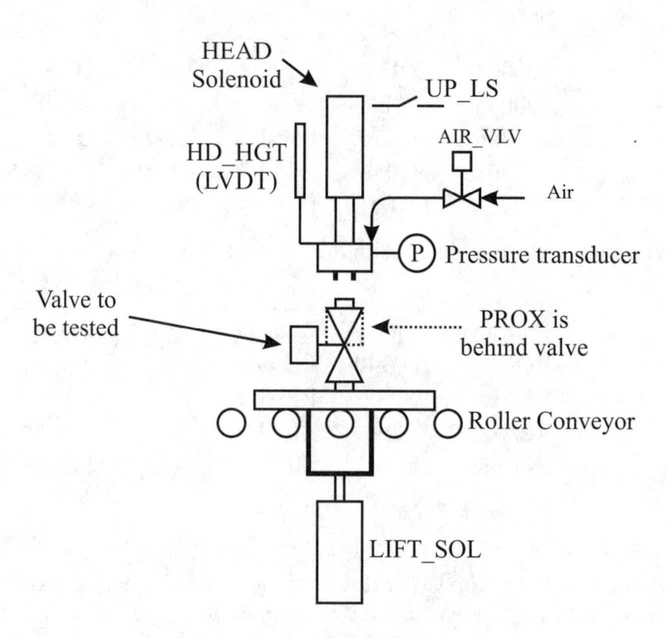

Figure P7.23. Leak check station.

the LIFT_SOL to let the valve fall back onto the conveyor. Assume LIFT_SOL is fast-acting and has finished moving the valve down on to the conveyor long before the head is fully up. Do not construct a branch to do this operation.

The operation then repeats.

The conveyor rollers are not controlled by this section of the ladder, so assume they are always **on**.

The proximity sensor is a reflective infrared sensor (like many of the proximity sensors in the conveyor lab exercise). PROX senses the leading edge of the valve when it is in the proper position. Assume that PROX remains **on** as the valve is being checked for leaks and as it is being lifted off the conveyor.

The LIFT_SOL is a fast-acting single action pneumatic cylinder. When the LIFT_SOL output is energized, the valve on its carrier is raised off the conveyor. The carrier remains up as long as LIFT_SOL is **on**. As soon as LIFT_SOL is turned **off**, the carrier (and valve) fall to the rollers and are conveyed out of the check station. There are limit switches, LU_LS and LD_LS that indicate when the LIFT_SOL is up or down, respectively. However, LIFT_SOL is fast-acting and you are to assume that the pressurizing head (which moves at the same time) is slower. Therefore, do not use LU_LS or LD_LS in you ladder. They would be used for error checking to indicate that the cylinder did not move and is outside the scope of this problem.

The mechanism used to lower and raise the pressurizing head consists of a double-action linear pneumatic cylinder. When the HD_DOWN output is energized, the mechanism moves down and continues to move down as long as power is applied (turned on). When the HD_UP output is energized, the mechanism moves up and continues to move up as long as power is applied (turned on). The mechanism stops if neither output is on, or if they are energized simultaneously. UP_LS is **on** when the pressurizing mechanism is in the fully "up" position.

When AIR_VLV is **on**, air is admitted to pressurize the valve. The valve should be turned **off** when the target pressure, DES_PRES is reached. There are no limit switches indicating that the valve is open or closed.

If the valve pressure (VLV_PRES) drops more than 0.1 psi below DES_PRES during the step while the pressure is being checked, the STAT20_REJ bit is set (latched). This bit is part of a shift register that tracks the good/bad status of the valve as it moves down the line. Do not turn this bit **off**. The instructions used to generate the shift register will move this bit to the STAT21_REJ bit as the STAT19_REJ bit is shifted into the STAT20_REJ bit.

The height of the pressurizing head is measured using a linear variable differential transformer (LVDT) connected to an analog input module having an ADC whose output value (HGT_MEAS) corresponds to the lowest (75.0 mm) and highest (150.0 mm) heights as specified in the general instructions prior to P7-12. The HGT_MEAS value should be converted into units of mm and stored in HD_HGT (a real number).

The pressure on the valve is measured with a pressure transducer connected to an analog input module having an ADC whose output value (PRES_MEAS) corresponds to the lowest (0.0 psi) and highest (100.0 psi) pressures as specified in the general instructions prior to P7-12. The PRES_MEAS value should be converted into units of psi and stored in VLV_PRES (a real number).

When the RUN internal coil is turned **on** for the first time only, the station assumes there are no valves in the station and waits for the first one. When the RUN internal coil is turned **off** the operation should pause at its current step, except when the pressure is being checked. If the RUN is turned off while the pressure is being checked, the timer must run to completion, and the program must advance to the next step. When the operation is paused, LIFT_SOL must remain **on**. All other outputs must be **off** when paused. If RUN is turned **on** while the operation of the station is paused, the station should resume its suspended step. Assume the conveyor is not running when RUN is **off**.

Do not add any more timed steps to those explicitly stated in the problem. In other words, do not put a timer in a step unless it is stated that the step duration is a specific time.

There is a RESET internal coil that when **on**, restarts the operation. When RESET is **on**, the pressurizing head must be raised and the internal steps are set so that the ladder logic program assumes there are no valves in the check station. After a reset, RUN must be turned **on** to actually restart the station. In other words, after RESET is turned **on** and then back **off**, the next time RUN turns **on**, it is treated as the first time RUN turns **on**. The RESET coil must have no effect unless the operation is already paused. RUN must be ignored while the pressurizing head is being raised during the reset operation.

Your solution should include the equation used to convert HGT_MEAS height measurement into the height in mm and the equation used to convert PRES_MEAS pressure measurement into the pressure in psi.

For the Modicon PLC, HGT_MEAS and PRES_MEAS are INT data types. For the PLC-5, do not use any locations in files 10, 21, 24, 33 and 34 for any calculation temporary results (any other locations in files 10, 21, 24, 33 and 34 are for other measurements, or values from a supervisory controller). Assume that the analog input readings have already been moved into the PLC memory using the BTR instruction.

Assume the following internal variable assignments.

Variable	Description
RUN	When **on**, allow pressure check station to run. When **off**, pause (explained above).
RESET	When on resets operation of station (explained above).
HD_HGT	Pressurizing head height, in mm (a REAL). Your part of the ladder needs to calculate this value.
VLV_PRES	Pressure, in psi (a REAL). Your part of the ladder needs to calculate this value.
VLV_HGT	Height of valve, desired height of pressurizing head to do pressure check (a REAL). Set by another part of the ladder.
DES_PRES	Desired test pressure, in psi (a REAL). Set by another part of the ladder.
STAT20_REJ	Set if valve is to be rejected because it will not hold pressure. Cleared by another part of the ladder.

Assume the following physical input and physical output assignments.

Variable	Description
PROX	Reflective proximity switch that is **on** when valve is in position to be pressure-checked.
UP_LS	Limit switch that closes (**on**) when pressurizing head is fully up.
HGT_MEAS	Measurement of pressurizing head height, represents 75 to 150 mm; ADC integer range listed before P7-12.
PRES_MEAS	Measurement of pressure, represents 0 to 100 psi; ADC integer range listed before P7-12.
HD_DOWN	When **on**, moves the pressurizing head down. When **off**, the head does not change position.
HD_UP	When **on**, moves the pressurizing head up. When **off**, the head does not change position
LIFT_SOL	**On** to move carrier (and valve) up and off the conveyor and retain it there. When **off**, the valve and carrier falls into conveyor.
AIR_VLV	Opens air valve pressurize tested valve. **On** to open valve (pressurize), **off** to close.

The addresses or data types associated with the internal variables:

Variable	Modicon Data Type	PLC-5 Addr.	Logix Data Type	Siemens Addr.	GE Fanuc Addr.
RUN	BOOL	B33/20	BOOL	M201.4	%M720
RESET	BOOL	B34/20	BOOL	M251.4	%M770
HD_HGT	REAL	F8:50	REAL	MD190	%R190

VLV_PRES	REAL	F8:51	REAL	MD194	%R192
VLV_HGT	REAL	F24:15	REAL	MD430	%R430
DES_PRES	REAL	F24:16	REAL	MD434	%R432
STAT20_REJ	BOOL	B21/20	BOOL	M161.4	%M564

The addresses associated with the physical inputs and outputs are:

Variable	Modicon	PLC-5	ControlLogix	Siemens	GE Fanuc
PROX	100001	I:01/00	Local:1:I.Data.0	I4.0	%I1
UP_LS	100002	I:01/01	Local:1:I.Data.1	I4.1	%I2
HD_DOWN	000001	O:02/00	Local:2:O.Data.0	Q8.0	%Q1
HD_UP	000002	O:02/01	Local:2:O.Data.1	Q8.1	%Q2
LIFT_SOL	000003	O:02/02	Local:2:O.Data.2	Q8.2	%Q3
AIR_VLV	000004	O:02/03	Local:2:O.Data.3	Q8.3	%Q4
HGT_MEAS	300001	N10:4 I:3.0 (SLC)	Local:3:I.Ch0Data	IW288	%AI1
PRES_MEAS	300002	N10:5 I:3.1 (SLC)	Local:3:I.Ch1Data	IW290	%AI2

P7-24. Hole-drilling Station 2 Control. Using a function chart approach, implement the program for the following station that drills a hole in a piece of metal.

Figure P7.24 shows the general layout of a station that drills a hole in a piece of metal. The horizontal location and depth of the hole is not the same for every piece and so there are two internal memory locations that indicate the desired hole location and depth. The actual horizontal displacement and drill depth are measured by LVDTs (linear variable differential transformers) that are connected to analog input channels and are used to control the horizontal ram and drill ram movement.

The overall operation of the station is first described, followed by the details. The sequence of operation for the station follows these steps:

Metal piece coming down inbound conveyor hits end of conveyor, turning **on** LS1

Extend CYL1 to block next piece coming down inbound conveyor

Extend CYL2 to push piece to desired horizontal drilling position

Move drill down to desired depth, drilling hole

Move drill up to fully up position (LS3 turns **off**)

Extend CYL2 to push piece onto outbound conveyor (PE1 senses)

Retract CYL2 until fully retracted (indicated by LS2 **off**). CYL2 must be fully retracted before CYL1 is retracted.

Retract CYL1

The operation then repeats. The inbound and outbound conveyors are both **on** while the station is running.

CYL1 is a pneumatic ram powered by a single action cylinder with a spring return. When the CYL1 output is **on**, the ram extends until it reaches the fully extended position. When the power is removed (CYL1 is **off**), the ram retracts

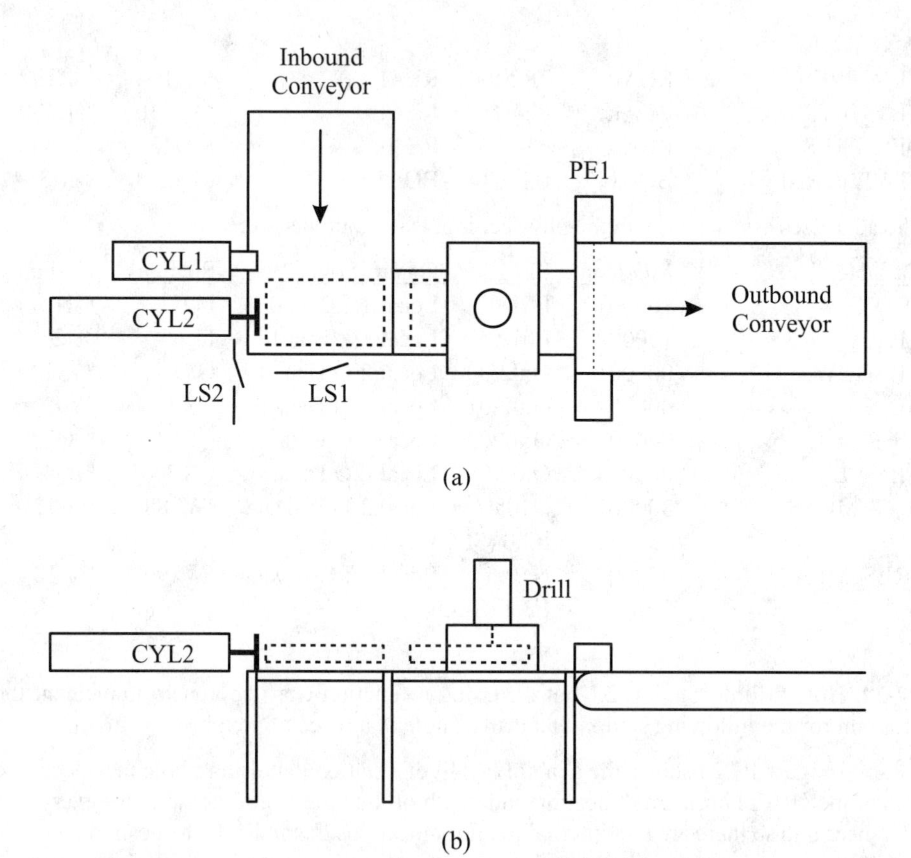

Figure P7.24. Drilling station: *(a)* top view; *(b)* side view.

until it is in its fully retracted position. There is no limit switch that indicates that the ram powered by CYL1 is fully retracted or extended. Activating the CYL1 output for at least 3 seconds is enough to ensure that it goes from the fully retracted to the fully extended position. When turning off the CYL1 output, assume that at least 3 seconds are required to go from the fully extended position to the fully retracted position.

CYL2 is pneumatic ram powered by a double action cylinder. When the CYL2_EXTEND output is **on**, the CYL2 ram extends. When the CYL2_RETRACT output is **on**, the CYL2 ram retracts. When neither CYL2 output or both outputs are **on**, the CYL2 ram stops moving and remains at its present position.

The ram that moves the drill down and up is a pneumatic ram powered by a double action cylinder (like CYL2). When the DRILL_DOWN output is **on**, the drill moves down. When the DRILL_UP output is **on**, the drill moves up. When neither drill ram output or both outputs are **on**, the drill stops moving vertically and remains at its present position.

The DRILL_MOTOR output must be turned **on** when the metal piece is being moved into position so that it is turning at its maximum speed when it is starting to move down. The DRILL_MOTOR output is not turned **off** until the drill is fully up.

The PE1 is used to sense when the metal piece is fully on the outbound conveyor. As the piece is pushed out of the drilling station, the beam is interrupted (input turns **off**) and then turns back **on**. Only when PE1 changes from **off** to **on**, can one be assured that the piece is fully on the outbound conveyor. When the metal piece is in any of the possible horizontal positions for the hole, the PE1 is **on**.

The DES_HORIZ internal memory location indicates the desired hole location in millimeters. The DES_DEPTH internal memory location indicates the desired hole depth in mm. Assume these values have been placed in the PLC memory from a supervisory PLC or computer.

The actual horizontal displacement and drill depth are measured by linear variable differential transformers (LVDTs) that are connected to analog input channels. The range of the horizontal measurement is 100.0 to 250.0 mm and the range of the depth measurement is 10.0 to 35.0 mm. Both measurement values increase as their respective cylinder extends. The ranges of the HORIZ_MEAS and DEPTH_MEAS ADC output integers are specified in the general instructions prior to P7-12. The HORIZ_MEAS and DEPTH_MEAS values should be converted into units of mm and stored in HORIZ_VAL and DEPTH_VAL, respectively (both real numbers). Use the appropriate LVDT measurement, converted to the proper units to determine when to stop the ram (horizontal or drill) at the desired position.

When the start switch is pressed (turned **on**) for the first time only, the station assumes there is no piece being drilled and waits for the first piece to drill. When the stop switch is pressed (turned **off**) the operation should pause, except during drilling, and all outputs (except CYL1 and DRILL_MOTOR) must be turned **off**. If paused during drilling, the operation must not pause until the drill is retracted. Pressing the start switch while the operation of the station is paused causes the station to resume its suspended operation.

There is a RESET_PB switch that when **on**, restarts the operation. When the RESET_PB is **on**, all rams need to be retracted and the internal step is set so that the ladder logic program waits for the next metal piece (but does not actually turn any outputs **on**). All rams must be retracted before the start switch has any effect. The START_PB must be pressed to actually restart the station. The RESET_PB switch must have no effect unless the operation is already paused. Also, the reset switch must be ignored during drilling. After RESET_PB is pressed and then released, the next press of the start switch is treated as the first time the start switch is pressed.

All delays must be accurate to within 0.1 seconds.

The solution should include the equations used to convert the HORIZ_MEAS and DEPTH_MEAS position measurements into the actual horizontal and depth position measurements in mm.

For the Modicon PLC, HORIZ_MEAS and DEPTH_MEAS are INT data types. For the PLC-5, do not use any locations in files 10 - 11 for any calculation temporary results (any other locations in files 10-11 are for other measurements or values from a supervisory controller). Assume that the analog input readings have already been moved into the PLC memory using the BTR instruction.

Assume the following input, output, and internal memory assignments.

Variable	Description
START_PB	Start push button switch, **on** (closed) to start.
STOP_PB	Stop push button switch, **off** (open) to stop.
RESET_PB	Reset pushbutton switch, **on** (closed) when resetting.
LS1	Limit switch, **on** (closed) when metal piece is at end of conveyor.
LS2	Limit switch, **off** (open) when CYL2 ram is retracted.
LS3	Limit switch, **off** (open) when drill ram is up.
PE1	Photoelectric switch, **off** (open) as piece moves on outbound conveyor, **on** when it is fully on conveyor.
IN_CONV	Inbound conveyor motor, **on** to run conveyor.
OUT_CONV	Outbound conveyor motor, **on** to run conveyor.
CYL1	Gate ram control, **on** to extend ram, **off** retracts.
CYL2_EXTEND	Main cylinder extension control; **on** to extend ram, **off** stops ram movement (but does not retract ram).
CYL2_RETRACT	Main cylinder retraction control; **on** to retract ram, **off** stops ram.
DRILL_MOTOR	Drill motor control; **on** to cause drill to turn, **off** stops drill.
DRILL_DOWN	Drill cylinder extension control; **on** to move drill down, **off** stops movement (but does not retract drill ram).
DRILL_UP	Drill cylinder retraction control; **on** to move drill up, **off** stops movement.
HORIZ_MEAS	Measurement of horizontal position, represents 100 to 250 mm; ADC integer range listed before P7-12.
DEPTH_MEAS	Measurement of drill depth, represents 10 to 35 mm; ADC integer range listed before P7-12.
HORIZ_VAL	Actual horizontal position, in mm (a REAL).
DES_HORIZ	Desired horizontal position, in mm (a REAL).
DEPTH_VAL	Actual drill depth, in mm (a REAL).
DES_DEPTH	Desired drill depth, in mm (a REAL).

The addresses associated with the physical inputs and outputs are:

Variable	Modicon	PLC-5	ControlLogix	Siemens	GE Fanuc
START_PB	100001	I:01/00	Local:1:I.Data.0	I4.0	%I1
STOP_PB	100002	I:01/01	Local:1:I.Data.1	I4.1	%I2
RESET_PB	100003	I:01/02	Local:1:I.Data.2	I4.2	%I3
LS1	100004	I:01/03	Local:1:I.Data.3	I4.3	%I4
LS2	100005	I:01/04	Local:1:I.Data.4	I4.4	%I5
LS3	100006	I:01/05	Local:1:I.Data.5	I4.5	%I6
PE1	100007	I:01/06	Local:1:I.Data.6	I4.6	%I7
IN_CONV	000001	O:02/00	Local:2:O.Data.0	Q8.0	%Q1
OUT_CONV	000002	O:02/01	Local:2:O.Data.1	Q8.1	%Q2
CYL1	000003	O:02/02	Local:2:O.Data.2	Q8.2	%Q3
CYL2_EXTEND	000004	O:02/03	Local:2:O.Data.3	Q8.3	%Q4

CYL2_RETRACT	000005	O:02/04	Local:2:O.Data.4	Q8.4	%Q5
DRILL_MOTOR	000006	O:02/05	Local:2:O.Data.5	Q8.5	%Q6
DRILL_DOWN	000007	O:02/06	Local:2:O.Data.6	Q8.6	%Q7
DRILL_UP	000008	O:02/07	Local:2:O.Data.7	Q8.7	%Q8
HORIZ_MEAS	300001	N10:4 I:3.0 (SLC)	Local:3:I.Ch0Data	IW288	%AI1
DEPTH_MEAS	300002	N10:5 I:3.1 (SLC)	Local:3:I.Ch1Data	IW290	%AI2

The addresses or data types associated with the internal variables:

Variable	Modicon Data Type	PLC-5 Addr.	Logix Data Type	Siemens Addr.	GE Fanuc Addr.
HORIZ_VAL	REAL	F8:67	REAL	MD224	%R224
DEPTH_VAL	REAL	F8:68	REAL	MD228	%R226
DES_HORIZ	REAL	F12:0	REAL	MD300	%R300
DES_DEPTH	REAL	F12:1	REAL	MD304	%R302

P7-25. Hole-drilling Station 3 Control. Using the function chart approach, write a ladder logic program for the following station that drills a hole into a piece of metal.

Figure P7.25 shows the general layout of a station that drills a hole into a metal piece. The horizontal X and Y location of the hole is not the same for every piece and so there are two internal memory locations that indicate the desired hole location. The actual x-horizontal displacement and y-horizontal displacement are measured by LVDTs (linear variable differential transformers) that are connected to analog input channels and are used to control the two horizontal ram positions.

The overall operation of the station is first described, followed by the details. The sequence of operation for the station follows these steps:

Metal piece coming down inbound conveyor contacts the stop at the end of the conveyor, turning **on** LS1.

Extend XCYL to push piece to desired x-horizontal drilling position.

Extend YCYL to push piece to desired y-horizontal position.

Extend CLAMP_CYL to clamp piece into drilling position. Simultaneously, retract YCYL. Assume 1 second is required to complete this operation.

Move drill down to fully extended position, pause 1.5 second, and then move drill up to fully retracted position.

Extend XCYL to push piece onto outbound conveyor (PROX senses).

Fully retract XCYL. LS2 turns **on** when it is fully retracted.

The operation then repeats. The inbound and outbound conveyors are both **on** while the station is running. These conveyors are controlled by this station.

XCYL is a pneumatic rams powered by a double action cylinder. When the XCYL_EXTEND output is **on**, the XCYL ram extends. When the XCYL_RETRACT output is **on**, the XCYL ram retracts. When neither XCYL

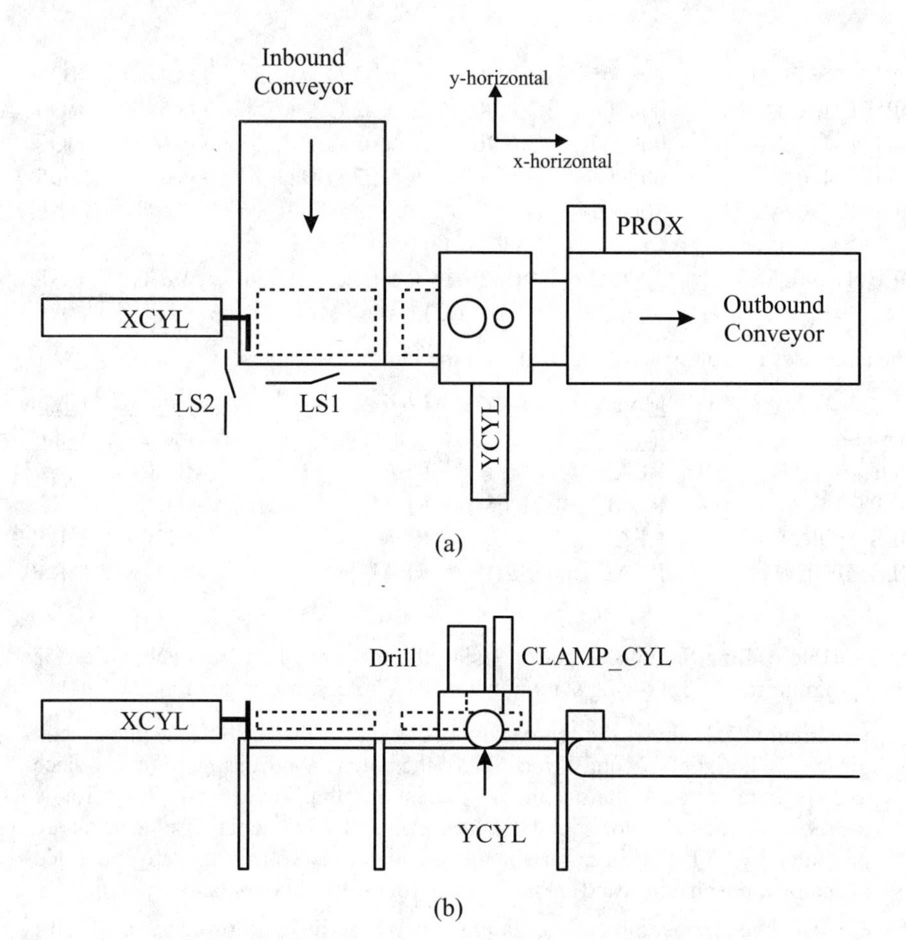

Figure P7.25. Drilling station: *(a)* top view; *(b)* side view.

output or both outputs are **on**, the XCYL ram stops moving and remains at its present position.

YCYL and CLAMP_CYL are pneumatic rams powered by single action cylinders with a spring return. For example, when the YCYL output is **on**, the YCYL ram extends until it reaches the fully extended position. When the power is removed (YCYL is **off**), the ram retracts until it is in its fully retracted position. There is no limit switch that indicates that theses rams are fully retracted or extended. Assume 1 second is required to go from the fully extended position to the fully retracted position, or vice versa. CLAMP_CYL may be retracted at the same time the part is being pushed out of the station.

The ram that moves the drill down and up is a pneumatic ram powered by a double action cylinder (like XCYL). When the DRILL_DOWN output is **on**, the drill moves down. When the DRILL_UP output is **on**, the drill moves up. When neither drill ram output or both outputs are **on**, the drill stops moving vertically and remains at its present position. Limit switch LS3 indicates when the drill is fully up. Limit switch LS4 indicates when the drill is fully down.

The DRILL_MOTOR output must be turned **on** when the metal piece is being moved into its y-horizontal position so that it is turning at its maximum speed when it is starting to move down. The DRILL_MOTOR output is not turned **off** until the drill is fully up.

The PROX sensor is used to sense when the metal piece is fully on the outbound conveyor. As the piece is pushed out of the drilling station, PROX is turned **on** when the piece is at PROX, and then PROX is turned **off**. Only when PROX changes from **on** to **off**, can one be assured that the piece is fully on the outbound conveyor. When the metal piece is in any of the possible horizontal positions for the hole, the PROX is **off**.

The DES_X and DES_Y internal memory locations indicates the desired x-horizontal position and the desired y-horizontal position, respectively, in millimeters. Assume these values have been placed in the PLC memory from a supervisory PLC or computer.

The actual horizontal displacements are measured by linear variable differential transformers (LVDTs) that are connected to analog input channels. The range of the X-horizontal measurement is 150.0 to 300.0 mm and the range of the Y-horizontal measurement is 0.0 to 110.0 mm. For the measurements, the ADC output values (X_MEAS and Y_MEAS) correspond to the lowest and highest values as specified in the general instructions prior to P7-12. The X_MEAS and Y_MEAS values should be converted into units of mm and stored in X_VAL and Y_VAL, respectively (both real numbers).

Use the appropriate LVDT measurement, converted to the proper units to determine when to stop the ram (x-horizontal or y-horizontal) at the desired position. Assume the LVDT measurement increases as the ram extends. (Hint: remember, there may be some inaccuracy in the measurement.)

When the start switch is pressed (turned **on**) for the first time only, the station assumes there is no piece in the station and waits for the first piece to arrive. When the stop switch is pressed (turned **off**) the operation should pause and all outputs (except CLAMP_CYL and DRILL_MOTOR) must be turned **off**. The operation cannot be paused when the drill motor is being moved down (to make sure the hole is correct). If the stop switch is pressed while the drill is being lowered, the drill should continue to be lowered and the operation should be paused at the end of the step. Pressing the start switch while the operation of the station is paused causes the station to resume its suspended operation.

There is a RESET_PB switch that when **on**, restarts the operation. When RESET is **on**, the internal step is set so that the ladder logic program waits for the next metal piece (but does not actually turn any outputs **on**). Also, retract all rams, including those that are double-acting when RESET_PB is momentarily pressed. If the drill must be retracted during reset, the drill motor must be **on**. All rams must be retracted before START_PB has any effect. START_PB must be pressed to actually restart the station. The RESET_PB switch must have no effect unless the operation is already paused. In other words, after RESET_PB is pressed and then released, the next press of the start switch is treated as the first time the start switch is pressed.

All delays must be accurate to within 0.1 seconds.

Your solution should include the equations used to convert the X_MEAS and Y_MEAS position measurements into the actual x-horizontal and y-horizontal position measurements in mm.

For the Modicon PLC, X_MEAS and Y_MEAS are INT data types. For the PLC-5, do not use any locations in files 10 - 12 for any calculation temporary results (any other locations in files 10-12 are for other measurements or values from a supervisory controller). Assume that the analog input readings have already been moved into the PLC memory using the BTR instruction.

Assume the following input, output, and internal memory assignments.

Variable	Description
START_PB	Start push button switch, **on** (closed) to start.
STOP_PB	Stop push button switch, **off** (open) to stop.
RESET_PB	Reset push button switch, **on** (closed) when resetting.
LS1	Limit switch, **on** (closed) when metal piece is at the stop at the end of the conveyor.
LS2	Limit switch, **on** (closed) when XCYL ram is fully retracted.
LS3	Limit switch, **off** (closed) when drill is fully up.
LS4	Limit switch, **on** (closed) when drill is fully down.
PROX	Proximity switch, **on** as piece moves on outbound conveyor, **off** when it is fully on conveyor.
IN_CONV	Inbound conveyor motor control, **on** to run conveyor.
OUT_CONV	Outbound conveyor motor control, **on** to run conveyor.
XCYL_EXTEND	X ram extension control; **on** to extend XCYL ram, **off** stops ram movement (but does not retract ram).
XCYL_RETRACT	X ram retraction control; **on** to retract ram, **off** stops ram.
YCYL	Y ram control; **on** to extend ram, **off** retracts.
CLAMP_CYL	Clamp ram control, **on** to extend ram that clamps piece for drilling, **off** retracts.
DRILL_DOWN	Drill cylinder extension control; **on** to move drill down, **off** stops movement (but does not retract drill ram).
DRILL_UP	Drill cylinder retraction control; **on** to move drill up, **off** stops movement.
DRILL_MOTOR	Drill motor control; **on** to cause drill to turn, **off** stops drill.
X_MEAS	X-horizontal position measurement, represents 150 to 300 mm; ADC integer range listed before P7-12.
Y_MEAS	Y-horizontal position measurement, represents 0 to 110 mm; ADC integer range listed before P7-12.
X_VAL	actual x-horizontal position, in millimeters (a REAL).
Y_VAL	actual y-horizontal position, in millimeters (a REAL).
DES_X	desired x-horizontal position, in millimeters (a REAL).
DES_Y	desired y-horizontal position, in millimeters (a REAL).

The addresses associated with the physical inputs and outputs are:

Variable	Modicon	PLC-5	ControlLogix	Siemens	GE Fanuc
START_PB	100001	I:01/00	Local:1:I.Data.0	I4.0	%I1

STOP_PB	100002	I:01/01	Local:1:I.Data.1	I4.1	%I2
RESET_PB	100003	I:01/02	Local:1:I.Data.2	I4.2	%I3
LS1	100004	I:01/03	Local:1:I.Data.3	I4.3	%I4
LS2	100005	I:01/04	Local:1:I.Data.4	I4.4	%I5
LS3	100006	I:01/05	Local:1:I.Data.5	I4.5	%I6
LS4	100007	I:01/06	Local:1:I.Data.6	I4.6	%I7
PROX	100008	I:01/07	Local:1:I.Data.7	I4.7	%I8
IN_CONV	000001	O:02/00	Local:2:O.Data.0	Q8.0	%Q1
OUT_CONV	000002	O:02/01	Local:2:O.Data.1	Q8.1	%Q2
XCYL_EXTEND	000003	O:02/02	Local:2:O.Data.2	Q8.2	%Q3
XCYL_RETRACT	000004	O:02/03	Local:2:O.Data.3	Q8.3	%Q4
YCYL	000005	O:02/04	Local:2:O.Data.4	Q8.4	%Q5
CLAMP_CYL	000006	O:02/05	Local:2:O.Data.5	Q8.5	%Q6
DRILL_DOWN	000007	O:02/06	Local:2:O.Data.6	Q8.6	%Q7
DRILL_UP	000008	O:02/07	Local:2:O.Data.7	Q8.7	%Q8
DRILL_MOTOR	000009	O:02/10	Local:2:O.Data.8	Q9.0	%Q9
X_MEAS	300001	N10:4 I:3.0 (SLC)	Local:3:I.Ch0Data	IW288	%AI1
Y_MEAS	300002	N10:5 I:3.1 (SLC)	Local:3:I.Ch1Data	IW290	%AI2

The addresses or data types associated with the internal variables:

	Modicon	PLC-5	Logix	Siemens	GE Fanuc
Variable	Data Type	Addr.	Data Type	Addr.	Addr.
X_VAL	REAL	F8:50	REAL	MD190	%R190
Y_VAL	REAL	F8:51	REAL	MD194	%R192
DES_X	REAL	F12:0	REAL	MD300	%R300
DES_Y	REAL	F12:1	REAL	MD304	%R302

P7-26. Part Width Sorter Control Using the function chart approach, write a ladder logic program to control the following station that sorts parts into one of three bins, depending on the size of the part.

A top view of the system is shown in Figure P7.26. As parts proceed down the conveyor, the width is measured and then the part is ejected into one of three bins. To eject the part into a bin, the corresponding eject cylinder control must be **on** for 1 sec (when the part is at the appropriate position). The parts are sorted into bins as follows:

Width	**Bin**
1 ± 0.1"	Bin 1
2 ± 0.1"	Bin 2
All others	Bin 3

The conveyor does not need to be stopped while ejecting the part. The eject mechanisms are each controlled by a single-acting air cylinder. Once an eject control is energized, the eject bar is extended, causing the part to be pushed into the

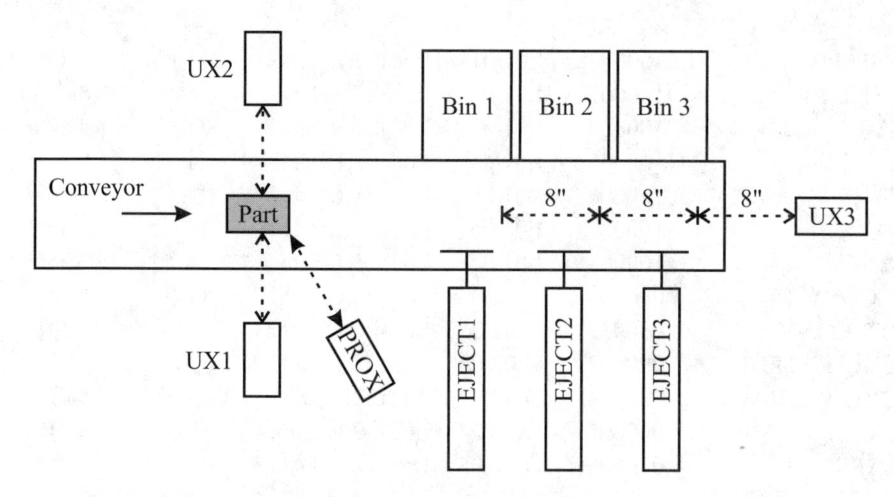

Figure P7.26. Width sorting station.

bin. The eject bar remains extended as long as power is applied (turned **on**). The eject bar retracts when power is removed (turned **off**).

The width is measured by using the two ultrasonic distance transducers UX1 and UX2. When PROX is ON (indicating part is in position to be measured), the width is determined by subtracting the sum of the two transducer, UX1 and UX2, readings from 16 (UX1 and UX2 are 16 inches apart):

Part width (inches) = 16 – (UX1 + UX2)

The reading and conversion to part width must be done instantaneously and does not require that the conveyor belt be stopped.

The position at which a part is to be ejected into a bin is a certain distance from the UX3 ultrasonic distance transducer:

Bin	Distance from UX3
Bin 1	24"
Bin 2	16"
Bin 3	8"

Note that as soon as an eject cylinder control is turned **on**, the UX3 reading is invalid because the part is being moved off the conveyor. The actual distances are measured by ultrasonic transducers that are connected to analog input channels. The highest and lowest values of all three distance measurements are 4.0 and 30.0 inches, respectively. The ADC output values (UX1_MEAS, UX2_MEAS, and UX3_MEAS) correspond to the lowest and highest values as specified in the general instructions prior to P7-12. The distance values should be converted into units of inches and stored in internal memory locations (real numbers).

The conveyor is **on** whenever the station is running.

A RUN internal coil that operates as a start/pause. When RUN is **on**, the station operates. When it is **off**, the station operation is paused. When it is turned **on** for the first time, no parts are assumed on the conveyor from PROX1 to UX3.

If the station is paused during the time that the part is being ejected into a bin, the step should **complete**. The operation **must not** pause when any of the eject cylinder controls are **on**. If the RUN coil is turned **off** during the time the piece is being ejected, the step should be completed (and advanced to the next step) before pausing. When the RUN internal coil turns **on** when the operation is paused, the station should resume the suspended step. When paused, **it is permissible to advance** to the next step as long as equipment will not be damaged. When the station is paused, the conveyor should be turned off.

A separate INT_RESET internal coil is provided which resets any internal states so that when the RUN internal coil is turned **on**, the conveyor has already been cleared of any items from PROX1 to UX3. You may assume that the INT_RESET coil can be ON only when RUN is OFF.

The RUN and INT_RESET internal coils are **inputs**. Your ladder logic cannot control them and thus **must** not appear as an output on any rung!

Assume the tolerance on all timer values is 0.1 seconds.

The solution should include the equations used to convert the UX1, UX2, and UX3 distance measurements into the actual distances in inches.

For the Modicon PLC, UX1_MEAS, UX2_MEAS, and UX3_MEAS are INT data types. For the Allen-Bradley PLC-5, do not use any locations in files 10 and 11 for temporary results (any other locations in files 10 and 11 are for other measurements) and assume that the analog input reading have already been moved into the PLC memory using the BTR instruction.

Assume the following input, output, and internal memory assignments.

Variable	Description
PROX	Proximity sensor, **on** when part is in position for width measurement.
UX1_MEAS	Distance sensor raw measurement, represents 4 – 30 inches; ADC integer range listed before P7-12.
UX2_MEAS	Distance sensor, same format and range as UX1_MEAS.
UX3_MEAS	Distance sensor, same format and range as UX1_MEAS.
RUN	When **on**, allow system to operate. When **off**, pause (explained above).
INT_RESET	When on resets operation of station (explained above)
CONV_MTR	Conveyor motor control; **on** to run conveyor belt.
EJECT1	**On** to operate cylinder to eject part into bin 1, must remain **on** for 1 sec to eject part.
EJECT2	**On** to operate cylinder to eject part into bin 2. Operates in similar manner as EJECT1.
EJECT3	**On** to operate cylinder to eject part into bin 3. Operates in similar manner as EJECT1.

The addresses associated with the physical inputs and outputs are:

Variable	Modicon	PLC-5	ControlLogix	Siemens	GE Fanuc
PROX	100001	I:01/00	Local:1:I.Data.0	I4.0	%I1
CONV_MTR	000001	O:02/00	Local:2:O.Data.0	Q8.0	%Q1

EJECT1	000002	O:02/01	Local:2:O.Data.1	Q8.1	%Q2
EJECT2	000003	O:02/02	Local:2:O.Data.2	Q8.2	%Q3
EJECT3	000004	O:02/03	Local:2:O.Data.3	Q8.3	%Q4
UX1_MEAS	300001	N10:4 I:3.0 (SLC)	Local:3:I.Ch0Data	IW288	%AI1
UX2_MEAS	300002	N10:5 I:3.1 (SLC)	Local:3:I.Ch1Data	IW290	%AI2
UX3_MEAS	300003	N10:6 I:3.2 (SLC)	Local:3:I.Ch2Data	IW292	%AI3

The addresses or data types associated with the internal variables:

Variable	Modicon Data Type	PLC-5 Addr.	Logix Data Type	Siemens Addr.	GE Fanuc Addr.
RUN	BOOL	B33/20	BOOL	M201.4	%M720
INT_RESET	BOOL	B34/20	BOOL	M251.4	%M770

P7-27. Part Height Sorter Control. Using the function chart approach, write a ladder logic program to control the following station that sorts parts onto one of four outbound conveyors, depending on the height of the part.

Top and side views of the station are shown in Figure P7.27. There are multiple conveyor sections. Parts come into the station on the inbound conveyor, CONV_1. Assume that the inbound and outbound conveyors are controlled by another PLC. A short conveyor, CONV_2, is not much longer than the part and holds the part as it is being measured. This conveyor must be stopped while the part height is being measured. Following the measurement conveyor, the eject conveyor, CONV_3 conveys the part to the appropriate place where the part is ejected onto one of four outbound conveyors. To eject the part onto a conveyor, the corresponding eject cylinder control must be **on** for 1 second (when the part is at the appropriate eject position). The parts are sorted onto the conveyors as follows:

Height	**Outbound Conveyor**
60 ± 4 mm	OUTCONV_1
75 ± 4 mm	OUTCONV_2
90 ± 4 mm	OUTCONV_3
All others	OUTCONV_4

The sequence of measuring each part and ejecting it onto the proper conveyor is as follows:

Wait for next part coming down conveyor, sensed by PROX

CONV_2 is stopped, the gate cylinder is extended, and the MEAS_RAM is extended to measure the part. Since the part height is variable, the extension of MEAS_RAM must be timed. Allow 2 seconds for the maximum extension. The pressure exerted by the ram will not damage the part.

Measure the height and display it on the 2-digit LED display.

Retract the MEAS_RAM. LS1 is **on** when the ram is fully retracted.

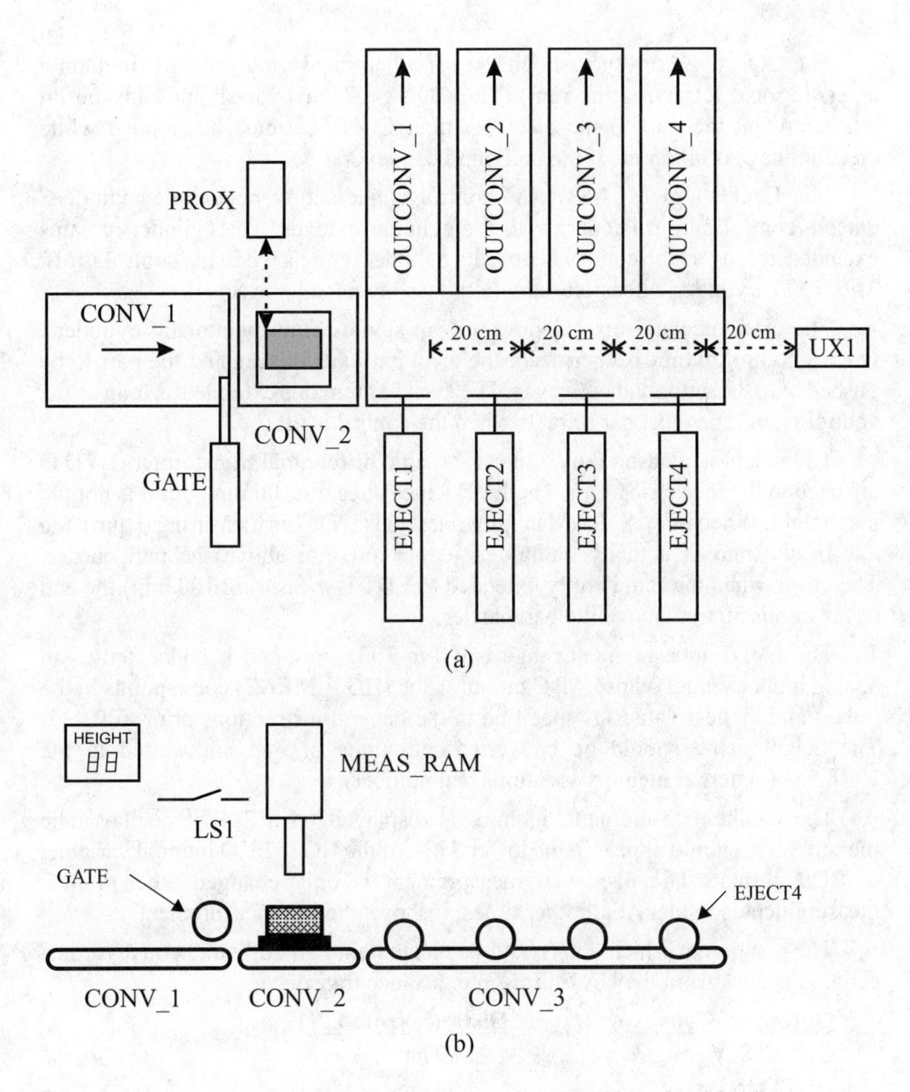

Figure P7.27. Height sorting station: *(a)* top view; *(b)* side view.

Move the part onto the eject conveyor and to the proper eject position.

When the part is at the proper eject position, CONV_3 is stopped and the part is ejected onto the proper outbound conveyor.

The GATE cylinder is retracted and the operation is repeated.

The parts are on carriers, so that even when the carriers are next to each other on the inbound conveyor, there is sufficient space between parts for the GATE ram to extend and allow the first part into the station and keep all others out. The PROX sensor is in such a position that activating the gate will prevent the next part from entering the measuring station. When PROX is **on**, the part is also in position to be measured.

The CONV_2 conveyor should be **off** when measuring the part (including extending and retracting the ram). The CONV_3 conveyor should only be **on** when moving the part to the eject position. CONV_3 must be stopped while ejecting the part onto one of the outbound conveyors.

The GATE and MEAS_RAM control single-acting pneumatic cylinders. Once a control output is energized, the cylinder extends. The cylinder remains extended as long as the control is **on**. The cylinder retracts when the control is **off**. The GATE cylinder extension/retraction does not need to be timed.

The eject mechanisms are powered by single-acting pneumatic cylinders. Once a control output is energized, the eject bar extends, causing the part to be pushed onto the outbound conveyor. The eject bar remains extended as long as the control is **on**. The eject bar retracts when the control is **off**.

The height is measured by a linear variable differential transformer (LVDT) attached to the measuring ram. The LVDT measures 0 – 100 mm, but it is not the part height. When MEAS_RAM is fully retracted (LVDT is measuring 0 mm), the end of the ram is actually calibrated to be 150 mm above the part carrier. Therefore, when the ram is fully extended (LVDT is measuring 100 mm) the end of the ram is 50 mm above the part carrier.

The LVDT measurement range is 0.0 to 100.0 mm and is connected to an analog input channel whose ADC output value (HGT_MEAS) corresponds to the lowest and highest values as specified in the general instructions prior to P7-12. The height value should be converted into units of mm and stored in the HGT_VAL internal memory location (real number).

The height measurement, in mm, is displayed on a 2-digit display. The measurement should appear in the lower 8 bits of the HGT_BCD internal variable, in BCD format. The displayed measurement is only changed when a new measurement is made. At all other times, it shows the last measurement.

The position at which a part is to be ejected onto an outbound conveyor is a certain distance from the UX1 ultrasonic distance transducer:

Outbound Conveyor	Distance from UX1
OUTCONV_1	80 cm
OUTCONV_2	60 cm
OUTCONV_3	40 cm
OUTCONV_4	20 cm

Note that as soon as an eject cylinder control is turned **on**, the UX1 reading is invalid because the part is being moved off the conveyor. The actual distance is measured by an ultrasonic transducer connected to an analog input channel. The highest and lowest value of the distance measurement is 15.0 and 100.0 cm, respectively. The ADC output value (UX1_MEAS) corresponds to the lowest and highest values as specified in the general instructions prior to P7-12. The distance value should be converted into units of cm and stored in an internal memory location (real number).

The RUN internal coil operates as a start/pause. Assume it is controlled by another part of the ladder. When RUN is **on,** the station operates. When RUN is **off**, the station operation is paused. When it is turned **on** for the first time, no parts are assumed on the conveyor from PROX1 to UX1.

If the station is paused during the time that the part is being ejected onto an outbound conveyor, the step should **complete**. The operation **must not** pause when any of the eject cylinder controls are **on**. If the RUN coil is turned **off** during the time the part is being ejected, the step should be completed (and advanced to the next step) before pausing. When the RUN internal coil turns **on** when the operation is paused, the station should resume the suspended step. When paused, **it is permissible to advance** to the next step as long as equipment will not be damaged. When the station is paused, the conveyors should be turned **off**.

A separate INT_RESET internal coil is provided which retracts the rams and resets any internal states so that when the RUN internal coil is turned **on**, the conveyor has already been cleared of any items from PROX1 to UX1. You may assume that the INT_RESET coil can be **on** only when RUN is **off**.

The RUN and INT_RESET internal coils are **inputs**. Your ladder logic cannot control them and thus **must** not appear as an output on any rung!

Assume the tolerance on all timer values is 0.1 seconds.

The solution should include the equation used to convert the LVDT measurement into a part height and the equation used to convert the UX1 distance measurement into the actual distances in cm.

For the Modicon PLC, HGT_MEAS and UX1_MEAS are INT data types, and the INT_BCD block (P12-1) is availale to perform the conversion to BCD. For the Allen-Bradley PLC-5, do not use any locations in files 10 - 12 for temporary results (any other locations in files 10 and 11 are for other measurements) and assume that the analog input reading have already been moved into the PLC memory using the BTR instruction.

Assume the following input, output, and internal memory assignments.

Variable	Description
PROX	Proximity sensor, **on** when part is in position for height measurement.
LS1	Limit switch, **on** when MEAS_RAM retracted.
HGT_MEAS	LVDT length measurement, represents 0 – 100 mm; ADC integer range listed before P7-12.
UX1_MEAS	Distance sensor raw measurement, represents 15 – 100 cm; ADC integer range listed before P7-12.
RUN	When **on**, allow system to operate. When **off**, pause (explained above).
INT_RESET	When on resets operation of station (explained above)
GATE	Gate ram control; **on** to extend ram, **off** retracts ram.
MEAS_RAM	Measuring ram control; **on** to extend ram, **off** retracts ram.
CONV_2	Short conveyor motor control; **on** to run conveyor belt.
CONV_3	Eject conveyor motor control; **on** to run conveyor belt.
EJECT1	**On** to operate cylinder to eject part onto OUTCONV_1, must remain **on** for 1 sec to eject part.
EJECT2	**On** to operate cylinder to eject part onto OUTCONV_2.
EJECT3	**On** to operate cylinder to eject part onto OUTCONV_3.
EJECT4	**On** to operate cylinder to eject part onto OUTCONV_4.

HGT_VAL	Part height, in mm (a REAL).
HGT_BCD	Part height, in mm, 2 digits BCD.
UX1_VAL	Distance, in cm (a REAL).

The addresses associated with the physical inputs and outputs are:

Variable	Modicon	PLC-5	ControlLogix	Siemens	GE Fanuc
PROX	100001	I:01/00	Local:1:I.Data.0	I4.0	%I1
LS1	100002	I:01/01	Local:1:I.Data.1	I4.1	%I2
GATE	000001	O:02/00	Local:2:O.Data.0	Q8.0	%Q1
MEAS_RAM	000002	O:02/01	Local:2:O.Data.1	Q8.1	%Q2
CONV_2	000003	O:02/02	Local:2:O.Data.2	Q8.2	%Q3
CONV_3	000004	O:02/03	Local:2:O.Data.3	Q8.3	%Q4
EJECT1	000005	O:02/04	Local:2:O.Data.4	Q8.4	%Q5
EJECT2	000006	O:02/05	Local:2:O.Data.5	Q8.5	%Q6
EJECT3	000007	O:02/06	Local:2:O.Data.6	Q8.6	%Q7
EJECT4	000008	O:02/07	Local:2:O.Data.7	Q8.7	%Q8
HGT_MEAS	300001	N10:4 I:3.0 (SLC)	Local:3:I.Ch0Data	IW288	%AI1
UX1_MEAS	300002	N10:5 I:3.1 (SLC)	Local:3:I.Ch1Data	IW290	%AI2

The addresses or data types associated with the internal variables:

Variable	Modicon Data Type	PLC-5 Addr.	Logix Data Type	Siemens Addr.	GE Fanuc Addr.
RUN	BOOL	B33/20	BOOL	M201.4	%M720
INT_RESET	BOOL	B34/20	BOOL	M251.4	%M770
HGT_VAL	REAL	F8:50	REAL	MD190	%R190
HGT_BCD	INT	D11:2	INT	MW102	%R102
UX1_VAL	REAL	F8:51	REAL	MD194	%R192

P7-28. Batch Reactor Control. Using the function chart approach, implement the program for the following batch process.

This application deals with the automation of a batch process. Figure P7.28 shows the process and its associated equipment. There are two ingredients, A and B that will be mixed in the reactor tank. The two ingredients react as they are agitated to form a thicker product. Therefore, the agitator speed is controlled throughout the reaction time and then the product is dumped into a product tank, called a QA tank. The overall operation of the batch cycle is first described, followed by the details. The batch cycle sequence follows these major steps:

Wait for READY signal to be **on** (When on, it signifies that the QA tank has enough room for this batch, and other permissives)

Fill desired amount of ingredient A

Fill desired amount of ingredient B

Agitate at constant speed (500 rpm) for 10 minutes

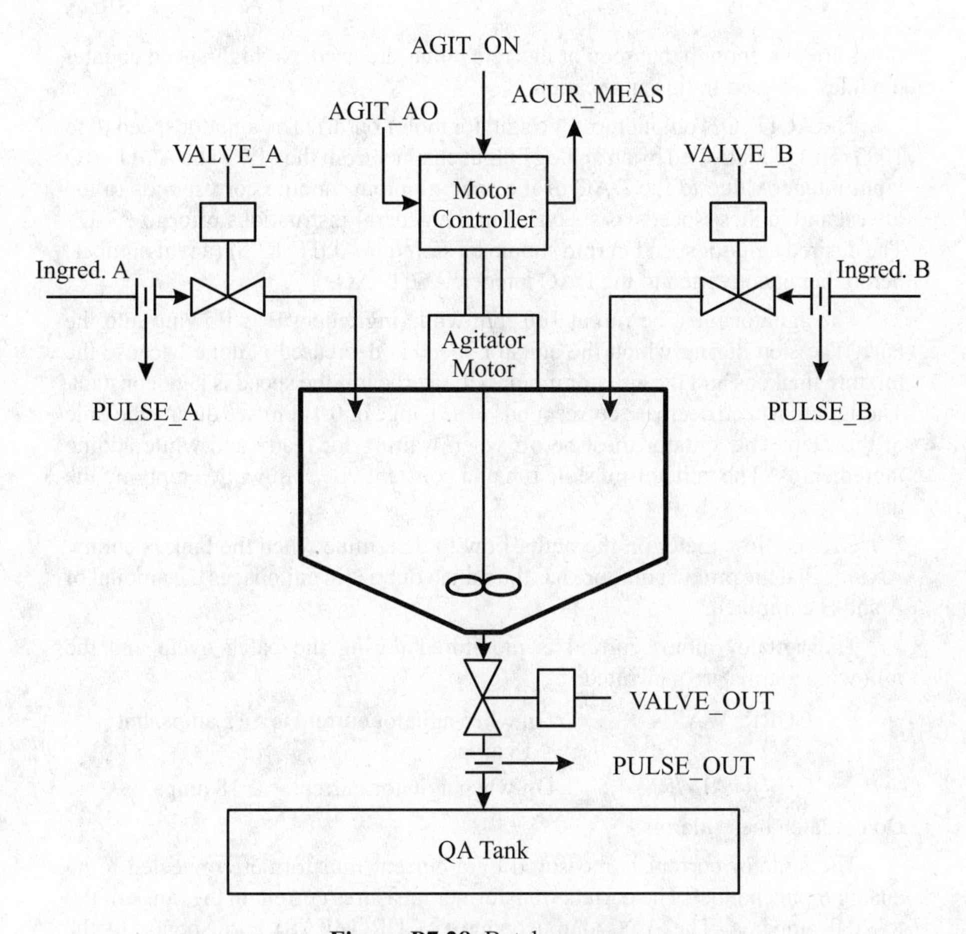

Figure P7.28. Batch process.

Agitate at decreasing speed (500 - 260 rpm) over a period of 40 minutes (2400 seconds)

Dump into QA tank (agitate at 260 rpm)

The operation then repeats. The READY signal is controlled by another part of the ladder and thus must not appear as an output on any rung of your solution.

Ingredient A is added to the tank by opening the VALVE_A solenoid valve. Ingredient B is added to the tank by opening the VALVE_B solenoid valve. The desired amount (gallons) of A and B to be loaded into the reactor are in the DES_A and DES_B integer locations, respectively. The values in these locations are from a recipe and are therefore read-only (do not write into these locations).

Ingredient B may only be added after the desired amount of A has been added to the tank.

The A and B inlet flows and the outlet flow are monitored by pulse-type flow meters. These meters output a pulse for every gallon that passes through the flow meter. Therefore, to measure the amount of material that flows in the stream, one must count the flow meter pulses (PULSE_A, PULSE_B, or PULSE_OUT). The flows are low enough that regular discrete inputs are used. No high-speed counter modules are used in this application.

The AGIT_ON output turns the agitator motor on/off. The agitator speed (0 to 1000 rpm) is controlled by an analog output channel from the PLC. The AGIT_AO input integer value to the DAC of the analog output module corresponds to the lowest and highest speeds as specified in the general instructions prior to P7-12. The desired agitator speed in rpm should be stored in AGIT_RPM (a real number) before being converted to the DAC integer, AGIT_AO.

The agitator must be run at 100 rpm while ingredient B is flowing into the tank. The step during which the agitator speed is decreased is done because the mixture thickens and the agitator motor will overheat if the speed is kept constant. The agitator speed decrease corresponds to a change of 0.1 rpm/sec during the time of this step. The agitator must be **off** when waiting for ready and while adding ingredient A. The agitator must be run at a constant 260 rpm while emptying the tank.

Use the flow meter on the outlet flow to determine when the tank is empty. Assume that the product mixture has the same volume (in gallons) as the amount of A and B combined.

The agitator motor current is monitored during the batch cycle and the following alarms are generated:

CURR_WARN	**On** when agitator current is ≥ 15 amps, but < 18 amps
CURR_ALARM	**On** when agitator current is ≥ 18 amps

Do not latch these alarms.

The agitator current is measured by a current transformer connected to an analog input channel. The current transformer measures current in the range of 0.0 to 20.0 amperes. The ADC output value (ACUR_MEAS) corresponds to the lowest and highest values as specified in the general instructions prior to P7-12. The measurement values should be converted into units of amperes and stored in AGIT_CURR (a real number).

When the start switch is pressed (turned **on**) for the first time, the batch process goes to the step that waits for the READY signal. When the stop switch is pressed (turned **off**) the operation should pause and all outputs must be turned **off**. When paused, all timer values must be retained. The agitator speed is ignored when the AGIT_ON output is **off**, and so the agitator speed command does not change when paused. The operation can be paused in any step. Pressing the start switch while the batch operation is paused causes the batch operation to resume its suspended operation.

There is no provision for resetting the batch operation. All time delays must be accurate to within 1 second.

The solution should include the equation used to convert desired speed of agitator motor, in rpm, into the value written into AGIT_AO and the equation used to convert ACUR_MEAS agitator motor current measurement into the actual current in amps.

For the Modicon PLC, ACUR_MEAS and AGIT_AO are INT data types. For the PLC-5, do not use any locations in files 10 - 12 for any calculation temporary results (any other locations in files 10-12 are for other measurements, analog outputs, or values from a supervisory controller). Assume that the analog input readings have already been moved into the PLC memory using the BTR instruction.

Assume the following input, output, and internal memory assignments.

Variable	Description
START_PB	Start push button switch, **on** (closed) to start.
STOP_PB	Stop push button switch, **off** (open) to stop.
PULSE_A	used to indicate amount of ingredient A that is flowing past flow meter. Each pulse indicates that 1 (one) gallon has flowed past.
PULSE_B	used to indicate amount of ingredient B that is flowing past flow meter. Each pulse indicates that 1 (one) gallon has flowed past.
PULSE_OUT	used to indicate amount of outlet material that is flowing past flow meter. Each pulse indicates that 1 (one) gallon has flowed past.
VALVE_A	**On** to open solenoid valve to allow ingredient A to flow into mixing vessel. **Off** closes valve.
VALVE_B	**On** to open solenoid valve to allow ingredient B to flow into mixing vessel. **Off** closes valve.
VALVE_OUT	**On** to open solenoid valve to allow mixture to flow out of mixing vessel. **Off** closes valve.
AGIT_ON	**On** to run agitator motor, when OFF, agitator speed command is ignored.
CURR_WARN	**On** when agitator current is ≥ 15 amps, but < 18 amps.
CURR_ALARM	**On** when agitator current is ≥ 18 amps.
ACUR_MEAS	Raw agitator motor current measurement, represents 0 – 20 amps; ADC integer range listed before P7-12.
AGIT_AO	Agitator motor controller speed command, represents 0 – 1000 rpm; DAC integer range listed before P7-12.
READY	Ready signal, ON when permissives are satisfied and batch cycle may begin by adding ingredient A.
DES_A	Desired amount of ingredient A to add, in gallons (a REAL).
DES_B	Desired amount of ingredient B to add, in gallons (a REAL).
AGIT_RPM	Commanded agitator speed, 0 to 1000 rpm (a REAL).
AGIT_CURR	Agitator motor current, 0 to 20 amps (a REAL).

The addresses associated with the physical inputs and outputs are:

Variable	Modicon	PLC-5	ControlLogix	Siemens	GE Fanuc
START_PB	100001	I:01/00	Local:1:I.Data.0	I4.0	%I1
STOP_PB	100002	I:01/01	Local:1:I.Data.1	I4.1	%I2
PULSE_A	100003	I:01/02	Local:1:I.Data.2	I4.2	%I3
PULSE_B	100004	I:01/03	Local:1:I.Data.3	I4.3	%I4
PULSE_OUT	100005	I:01/04	Local:1:I.Data.4	I4.4	%I5
VALVE_A	000001	O:02/00	Local:2:O.Data.0	Q8.0	%Q1

VALVE_B	000002	O:02/01	Local:2:O.Data.1	Q8.1	%Q2
VALVE_OUT	000003	O:02/02	Local:2:O.Data.2	Q8.2	%Q3
AGIT_ON	000004	O:02/03	Local:2:O.Data.3	Q8.3	%Q4
CURR_WARN	000005	O:02/04	Local:2:O.Data.4	Q8.4	%Q5
CURR_ALARM	000006	O:02/05	Local:2:O.Data.5	Q8.5	%Q6
ACUR_MEAS	300001	N10:4 I:3.0 (SLC)	Local:3:I.Ch0Data	IW288	%AI1
AGIT_AO	400001	N11:0 I:4.0 (SLC)	Local:4:O.Ch0Data	IW304	%AQ1

The addresses or data types associated with the internal variables:

Variable	Modicon Data Type	PLC-5 Addr.	Logix Data Type	Siemens Addr.	GE Fanuc Addr.
READY	BOOL	B33/20	BOOL	M201.4	%M720
AGIT_RPM	REAL	F8:50	REAL	MD190	%R190
AGIT_CURR	REAL	F8:51	REAL	MD194	%R192
DES_A	REAL	F12:0	REAL	MD300	%R300
DES_B	REAL	F12:1	REAL	MD304	%R302

P7-29. Multi-tank Batch Control. Using the function chart approach, implement the program for the following batch process.

A plant consists of four tanks with valves to transfer the materials through the system (Figure P7.29). Each tank is fitted with a load cell that measures weight, and thus determines the level. Tank 3 has an electric heating element wrapped around it and an associated temperature sensor. Tank 4, the reaction vessel, is equipped with a stirrer to mix the materials while they are being transferred into the reaction vessel and the reaction is taking place. The reaction tank has the capacity of tanks 1, 2, and 3 combined.

The process is operated as follows:

Tanks 1, 2 and 3 are to be filled simultaneously from supply reservoirs of chemicals, by opening valves XV101, XV102, and XV103. The inlet valve for each tank should be closed as soon as each tank is filled.

As soon as tank 3 is full, the heating element in tank 3 is activated, raising the liquid temperature to 70°C.

When all tanks are filled and the temperature of tank 3 is 70°C, valves XV104, XV105 and XV106 are opened and pumps P-105 and P-106 are run to transfer all the material in tank 1 and half of the contents of tanks 2 and 3 to the reaction vessel, tank 4. The vibrator must be turned **on** when tank 1 is being emptied. The stirrer must run when tank 4 has anything in it. When any tank becomes empty, its outlet valve must be closed and pump stopped (e.g., when tank 1 is empty, valve XV104 must be closed).

After tank 1 and half of tanks 2 and 3 have been emptied into tank 4, the stirrer is kept **on** for an additional 20 seconds.

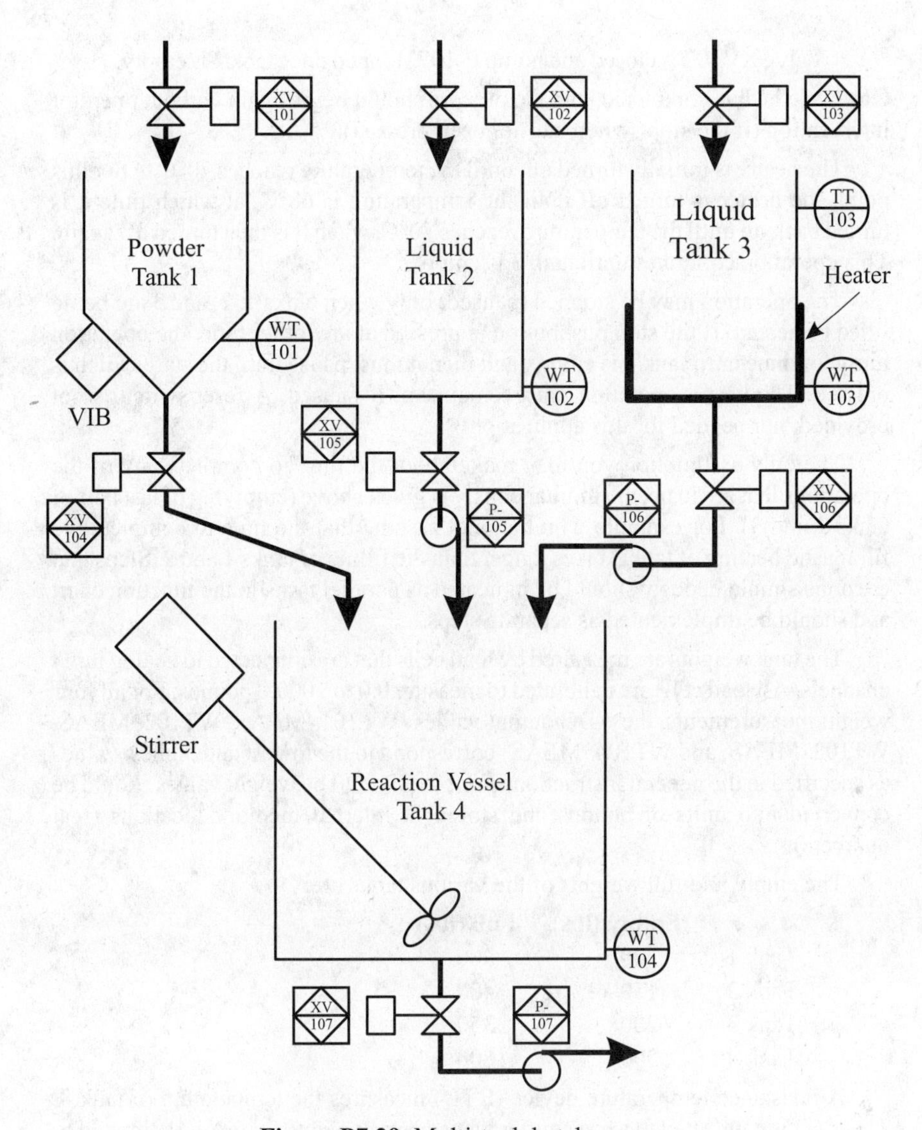

Figure P7.29. Multi-tank batch process.

After the end of this 20 second interval, a 250 second interval is started. During this interval, the remainder of tanks 2 and 3 are emptied into tank 4. Assume that it takes less than 250 seconds to empty the last half of tanks 2 and 3. The corresponding valve to empty a tank must be turned **off** as soon as the tank is empty and the heater for tank 3 must be turned off when tank 3 is empty (do not wait for the end of the 250 second interval).

When the stirrer has been **on** for the 250 second interval, valve XV107 is opened and pump P-107 is run to transfer the product to another tank.

Valve XV107 is closed and pump P-107 stopped once tank 4 is empty.

One cycle is thus completed, and the process should begin again without operator intervention (if the stop switch has not been pressed).

The heater is initially turned **on**, until the temperature reaches 70°C. After this point, the heater is turned **off** until the temperature is 68°C, at which time it is turned back **on** until the temperature reaches 70°C, when it is then turned **off** again. This operation continues until tank 3 is empty.

The operation may be stopped (paused) only when tanks 1, 2, and 3 are being filled or heated. If the stop pushbutton is pressed at any other time, the operation must continue until tank 4 is empty, and then it must pause until the start switch is pressed. The heater operation must remain **on**, if paused. A reset switch is not provided, nor needed for this application.

The only assumption you may make about the time to complete any of the operations that are to occur simultaneously is given above (emptying of last half of tanks 2 and 3). For example, you may not assume that the time to complete the filling and heating of tank 3 takes longer than the filling of tanks 1 and 2. Steps that are done simultaneously should be indicated as parallel tasks in the function chart and should be implemented as separate steps.

The tank weights are measured by load cells that are connected to analog input channels. All load cells are calibrated to measure 0.0 to 1000.0 pounds. For all four weight measurements, the ADC output values (WT101_MEAS, WT102_MEAS, WT103_MEAS, and WT104_MEAS) correspond to the lowest and highest values as specified in the general instructions prior to P7-12. The weight values should be converted into units of pounds and stored in internal memory locations (real numbers).

The empty and full weights of the various tanks are:

	Empty (lbs)	**Full (lbs)**
Tank 1	200	300
Tank 2	150	400
Tank 3	200	350
Tank 4	300	800

A resistance temperature device (RTD) measures the temperature of tank 3. The RTD is connected to a transmitter whose output of 4 to 20 mA is calibrated to represent 0 to 100 °C. The transmitter output is connected to an analog input module having an ADC whose output integer value (TT103_MEAS) corresponds to the lowest and highest temperatures as specified in the general instructions prior to P7-12. The temperature measurement value should be converted into units of °C and stored in an internal memory location (real numbers).

The solution should include the equation used to convert the weight measurements into the weight in pounds.

For the Modicon PLC, all weight and temperature measurements are INT data types. For an implementation with the PLC-5, do not use file number 10 for any calculation results and assume that the analog readings have already been moved into the PLC memory using the BTR instruction.

Assume the following physical input and output assignments:

Variable	Description
START_PB	Start push button switch, **on** (closed) to start.
STOP_PB	Stop push button switch, **off** (open) to stop.
WT101_MEAS	Tank 1 weight measurement, represents 0 – 1000 pounds; ADC integer range listed before P7-12.
WT102_MEAS	Tank 2 weight, same format and range as WT101_MEAS.
WT103_MEAS	Tank 3 weight, same format and range as WT101_MEAS.
WT104_MEAS	Tank 4 weight, same format and range as WT101_MEAS.
TT103_MEAS	Tank 3 temperature measurement, represents 0 – 100 °C; ADC integer range listed before P7-12.
XV101_SOL	**On** to open XV101. **Off** closes valve.
XV102_SOL	**On** to open XV102. **Off** closes valve.
XV103_SOL	**On** to open XV103. **Off** closes valve.
XV104_SOL	**On** to open XV104. **Off** closes valve.
XV105_SOL	**On** to open XV105. **Off** closes valve.
XV106_SOL	**On** to open XV106. **Off** closes valve.
XV107_SOL	**On** to open XV107. **Off** closes valve.
P105_RUN	**On** to run pump P-105. **Off** stops pump.
P106_RUN	**On** to run pump P-106. **Off** stops pump.
P107_RUN	**On** to run pump P-107. **Off** stops pump.
STIR_ON	Tank 4 stirrer control, **on** to stir tank 4.
HEAT_RLY	Tank 3 heat relay control, **on** to heat tank 3.
VIB_ON	Tank 1 vibrator control, **on** to vibrate tank during emptying.
WT101_VAL	Tank 1 weight, in lbs. (a REAL).
WT102_VAL	Tank 2 weight, in lbs. (a REAL).
WT103_VAL	Tank 3 weight, in lbs. (a REAL).
WT104_VAL	Tank 4 weight, in lbs. (a REAL).
TT103_VAL	Tank 3 weight, in C (a REAL).

The addresses associated with the physical inputs and outputs are:

Variable	Modicon	PLC-5	ControlLogix	Siemens	GE Fanuc
START_PB	100001	I:01/00	Local:1:I.Data.0	I4.0	%I1
STOP_PB	100002	I:01/01	Local:1:I.Data.1	I4.1	%I2
XV101_SOL	000001	O:02/00	Local:2:O.Data.0	Q8.0	%Q1
XV102_SOL	000002	O:02/01	Local:2:O.Data.1	Q8.1	%Q2
XV103_SOL	000003	O:02/02	Local:2:O.Data.2	Q8.2	%Q3
XV104_SOL	000004	O:02/03	Local:2:O.Data.3	Q8.3	%Q4
XV105_SOL	000005	O:02/04	Local:2:O.Data.4	Q8.4	%Q5
XV106_SOL	000006	O:02/05	Local:2:O.Data.5	Q8.5	%Q6
XV107_SOL	000007	O:02/06	Local:2:O.Data.6	Q8.6	%Q7
P105_RUN	000008	O:02/07	Local:2:O.Data.7	Q8.7	%Q8
P106_RUN	000009	O:02/10	Local:2:O.Data.8	Q9.0	%Q9
P107_RUN	000010	O:02/11	Local:2:O.Data.9	Q9.1	%Q10

STIR_ON	000011	O:02/12	Local:2:O.Data.10	Q9.2	%Q11
HEAT_RLY	000012	O:02/13	Local:2:O.Data.11	Q9.3	%Q12
VIB_ON	000013	O:02/14	Local:2:O.Data.12	Q9.4	%Q13
WT101_MEAS	300001	N10:4 I:3.0 (SLC)	Local:3:I.Ch0Data	IW288	%AI1
WT102_MEAS	300002	N10:5 I:3.1 (SLC)	Local:3:I.Ch1Data	IW290	%AI2
WT103_MEAS	300003	N10:6 I:3.2 (SLC)	Local:3:I.Ch2Data	IW292	%AI3
WT104_MEAS	300004	N10:7 I:3.3 (SLC)	Local:3:I.Ch3Data	IW294	%AI4
TT103_MEAS	300005	N10:8 I:3.4 (SLC)	Local:3:I.Ch4Data	IW296	%AI5

The addresses or data types associated with the internal variables:

Variable	Modicon Data Type	PLC-5 Addr.	Logix Data Type	Siemens Addr.	GE Fanuc Addr.
WT101_VAL	REAL	F8:4	REAL	MD200	%R200
WT102_VAL	REAL	F8:5	REAL	MD204	%R202
WT103_VAL	REAL	F8:6	REAL	MD208	%R204
WT104_VAL	REAL	F8:7	REAL	MD212	%R206
TT103_VAL	REAL	F8:8	REAL	MD216	%R208

P7-30. Repeat problem P7-26, but show the parallel paths (depending on part width) on your function chart. SHOW THE PARALLEL OPERATIONS ON YOUR FUNCTION CHART AS SEPARATE STEPS. Implement the revised function chart in ladder logic. Do not try to combine steps.

P7-31. Repeat problem P7-27, but show the parallel paths (depending on part height) on your function chart. SHOW THE PARALLEL OPERATIONS ON YOUR FUNCTION CHART AS SEPARATE STEPS. Implement the revised function chart in ladder logic. Do not try to combine steps.

8 Other Ladder Logic Instructions

Chapter Topics:

- Bit shift registers
- First-in/first-out (FIFO) and last-in/first out (LIFO) queues
- Array functions
- Program control
- Shift register and FIFO/LIFO queue applications

OBJECTIVES

- Upon completion of this chapter, you will be able to:
- Describe the function of shift registers and FIFO/LIFO queues
- Describe the function and application of special array function blocks
- Apply shift registers and FIFO/LIFO queues to industrial situations
- Understand the use of program control and its use in applications

Scenario: Displaying the step number of a sequence.

A step number needs to be determined for a sequential system implemented with the technique of Chapter 6. A PLC-5 processor implements the sequential operation, where the step-in-progress bits are B20/1 through B20/21 (steps 1 - 21). The initial step is indicated by B20/0. The step number that corresponds to a particular step-in-progress bit needs to be calculated so that it can be displayed on an operator interface.

***Solution*:** The PLC-5 has a function block called FBC (file bit comparison) that can be used for this purpose. Figure 8.1 shows the ladder logic to accomplish this task and an example calculation of the step number. The FBC block basically compares two bit arrays and reports the bit number(s) that are dissimilar. The reference bit array of 32 zero bits is set up in N7:50 and N7:51. The step-in-progress bits are all in words B20:0 and B20:1, which makes up an array of up to 32 bits. Only one bit is set and so the one mismatch is recorded in N7:52, a one-element result array. The number in N7:52 is thus the current step number of the sequential operation. The N.C. contact toggles the function block execution so that it executes on alternate program scans.

8.1 INTRODUCTION

The shift register, FIFO/LIFO, and special array ladder logic function blocks described in this chapter are used less frequently but are necessary for certain applications. In addition, the instructions that modify ladder logic execution are described. This chapter describes

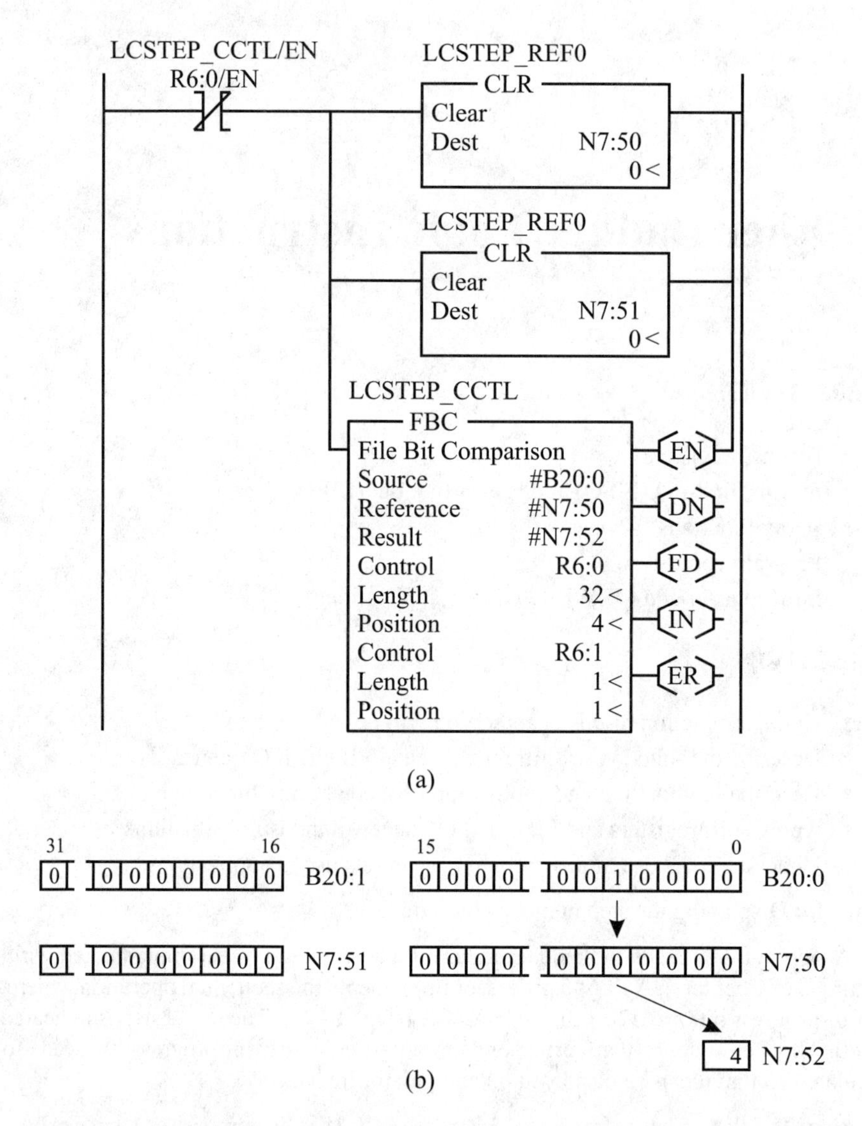

Figure 8.1. Determining current step number: *(a)* ladder logic; *(b)* example.

these types of function blocks for the PLCs covered by this text. As in previous chapters, the function blocks for a particular PLC are described in separate sections. That is, only the section(s) pertaining to the PLC(s) of interest need to be studied. Following these descriptions, simple examples illustrate their application.

The shift register function blocks provide the ability to track the flow of material in a manufacturing system. The shift register can be implemented as an array of Booleans (bits) or as an array of integers. A bit array shift register is often used to track the progress of a generic item (e.g., can, bottle, defective part) as it moves down the line. Depending on how items are removed from the integer array shift register, it is called a first-in/first-out (FIFO) queue or a last-in/first-out (LIFO) queue. A FIFO queue can track parts represented by part numbers or an assembly code as parts move down the line. In a LIFO queue, items are removed in reverse order, and so it is useful when tracking items having a serial number that are being stacked and unstacked.

Many of the PLCs covered by this text provide special functions to handle array calculations or other special array operations. Program control function blocks provide a way to modify the ladder logic scanning.

8.2 OTHER IEC FUNCTION BLOCKS

The IEC 61131-3 standard defines four bit shift function blocks, similar to the Modicon function blocks. As described in the standard, the operation of each of these function blocks is identical to a Modicon function block of the same name. The only difference is that the name of the Modicon function blocks have a data type suffix appended to the IEC name, which is allowed in IEC 61131-3. The names and description of these function blocks are:

IEC Function Block	Description
SHL	Bit shift left
SHR	Bit shift right
ROL	Bit rotate left
ROR	Bit rotate right

The next section details the operation and use of these function blocks.

The IEC 61131-3 standard does not define any FIFO and LIFO queues or other array function blocks. Most of the program control functions defined by 61131-3 are for the structured text and instruction list. However, the EN input for the timer, counter, computation, and comparison function blocks is a form of execution control.

The IEC 61131-3 standard defines some ladder program control elements, illustrated in Figure 8.2. A *jump* can be used to skip execution of certain ladder logic rungs and is shown as a horizontal line terminated in a double arrowhead. Program execution is directed to the designated label. A jump can be conditional or unconditional. For example, in Figure 8.2 when LS_101 and LS_102 are both **on**, the second and third rungs are skipped and Check_LS_202 is always turned **on**. If LS_101 and LS_102 are not both **on**, then the state of Check_LS_202 is determined by the logic of the second rung and the unconditional jump in rung 3 causes program execution to skip to the fifth rung. A jump and its target (label) must occur in the same program organization unit. A *return* program control element transfers control back to the invoking program entity. In IEC 61131-3, a return in a ladder diagram makes sense only if the ladder logic program is implementing a function block (Figure 3.1). Figure 8.2 shows a ladder diagram with a conditional return and an unconditional return.

8.3 OTHER MODICON FUNCTION BLOCKS

The Modicon Quantum and Momentum PLCs provide ladder logic function blocks for bit shifting, FIFO/LIFO, array search/copy, and some program control. Compared to the Allen-Bradley processors, the set of function blocks is limited. A user needing more sophisticated array function blocks will need to program a derived function block (Chapter 11) with the desired function.

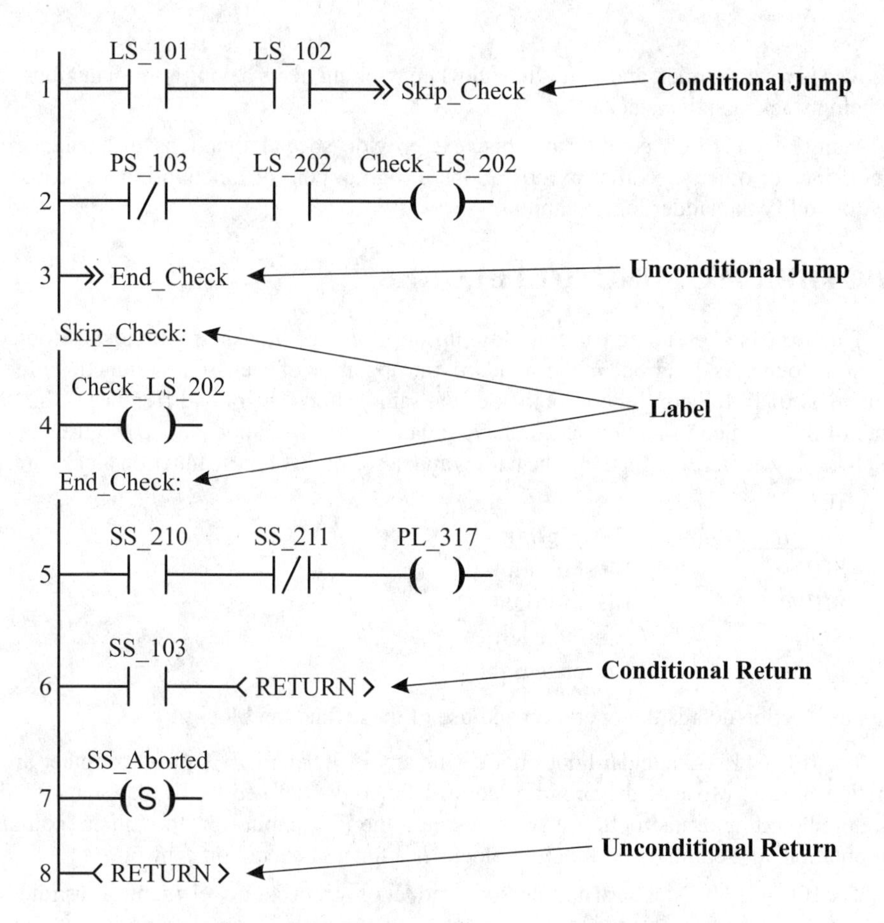

Figure 8.2. IEC 61131-3 ladder execution control examples.

8.3.1 Shift Bit in Register

The bit shifting function blocks and the operation that occurs for each one are:

Block Name	Operation Result
ROL_***	Bit rotate left
ROR_***	Bit rotate right
SHL_***	Bit shift left (zeros filled from right)
SHR_***	Bit shift right (zeros filled from left)

where *** is either BYTE or WORD and represents the data type of the input and output. An example ROL_WORD block is shown in Figure 8.3*a* and an example SHL_WORD block is shown in Figure 8.3*c*. For these blocks, the IN input is the word to be rotated or shifted and the N input is a UINT data type and indicates the number of bits to rotate or shift. The unlabeled output is the result of the rotate or shift operation. Note that for the SHL and SHR function blocks, zeros are shifted into the destination. As an example, Figure 8.3 shows the result of rotating the word AW two bits left (Figure 8.3*b*) and shifting AW two bits left (Figure 8.3*d*).

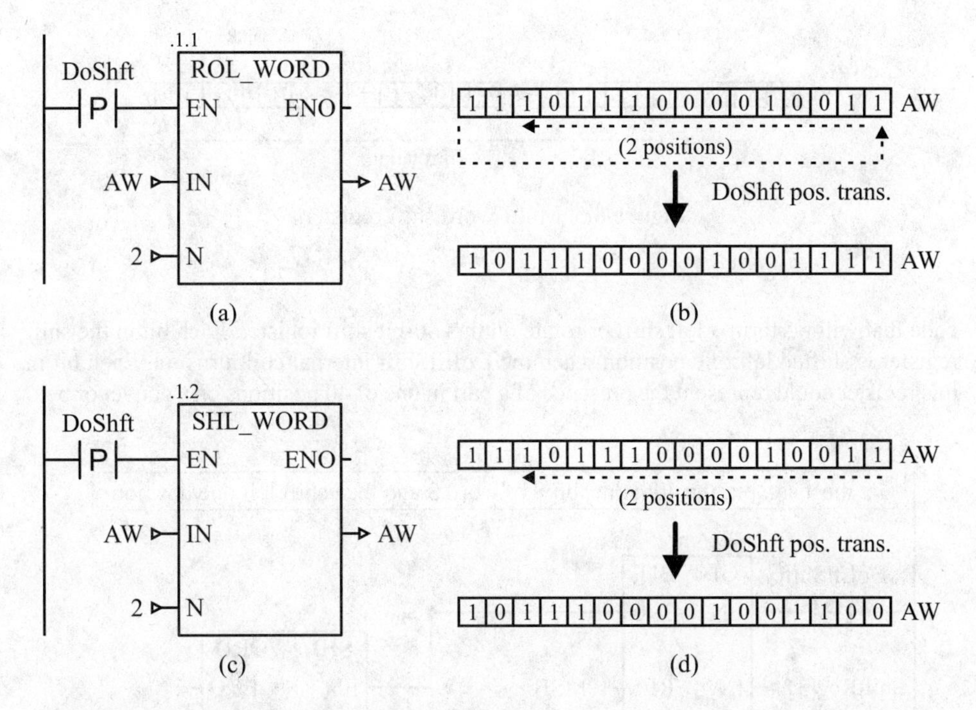

Figure 8.3. Modicon bit shift examples: *(a)* ROL block; *(b)* ROL input and shift result; *(c)* SHL block; *(d)* SHL input and shift result.

The GET_BIT and SET_BIT function blocks, shown in Figure 8.4, provide a convenient way to read and write individual bits in a word. For both blocks, the NO input is a UINT that specifies the bit to be read or written. The GET_BIT function block reads the NO bit of the IN input and writes the current state of the bit to the RES output. The SET_BIT function block sets the NO bit of the RES output to the value of IN. For these two blocks, the bits within the word are numbered from 1 to 16 (Figure 8.4*c*), rather than 0 to 15.

Shift registers longer than 16 bits can be constructed from individual WORDs, but external logic must transfer bits between words. As an example, Figure 8.5 shows the construction of a 40-bit shift register from three words. Figure 8.6 shows the ladder logic

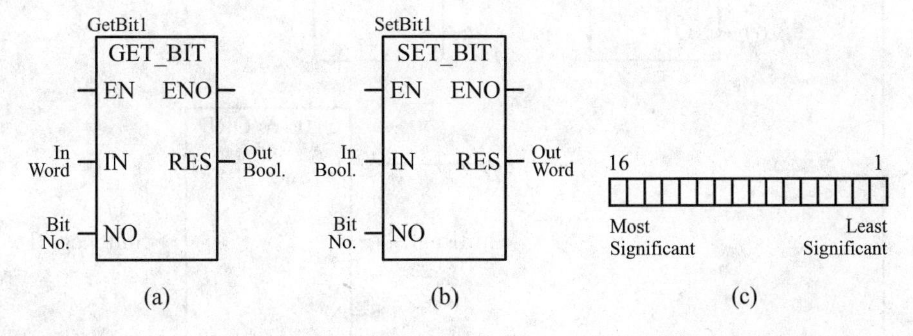

Figure 8.4. Modicon get and set bit function blocks: *(a)* GET_BIT; *(b)* SET_BIT; *(c)* bit numbering within word.

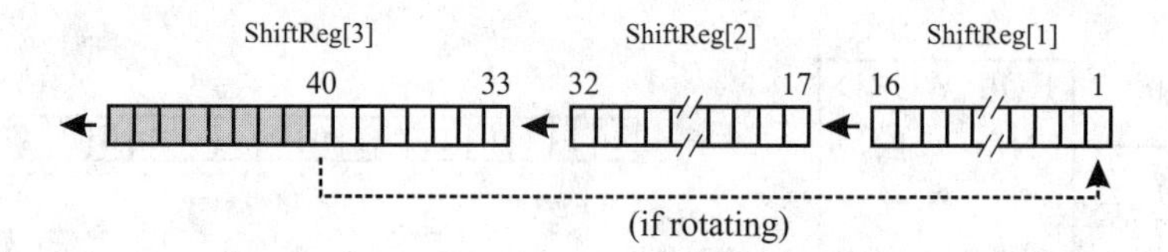

Figure 8.5. Multi-word shift register.

code that will perform a left shift or rotate on this 40-bit shift register. Each bit in the shift register is shifted left one position when the DoLftShift internal coil turns **on**. Each bit in this register could represent the presence of a part in one of 40 positions on a conveyor belt.

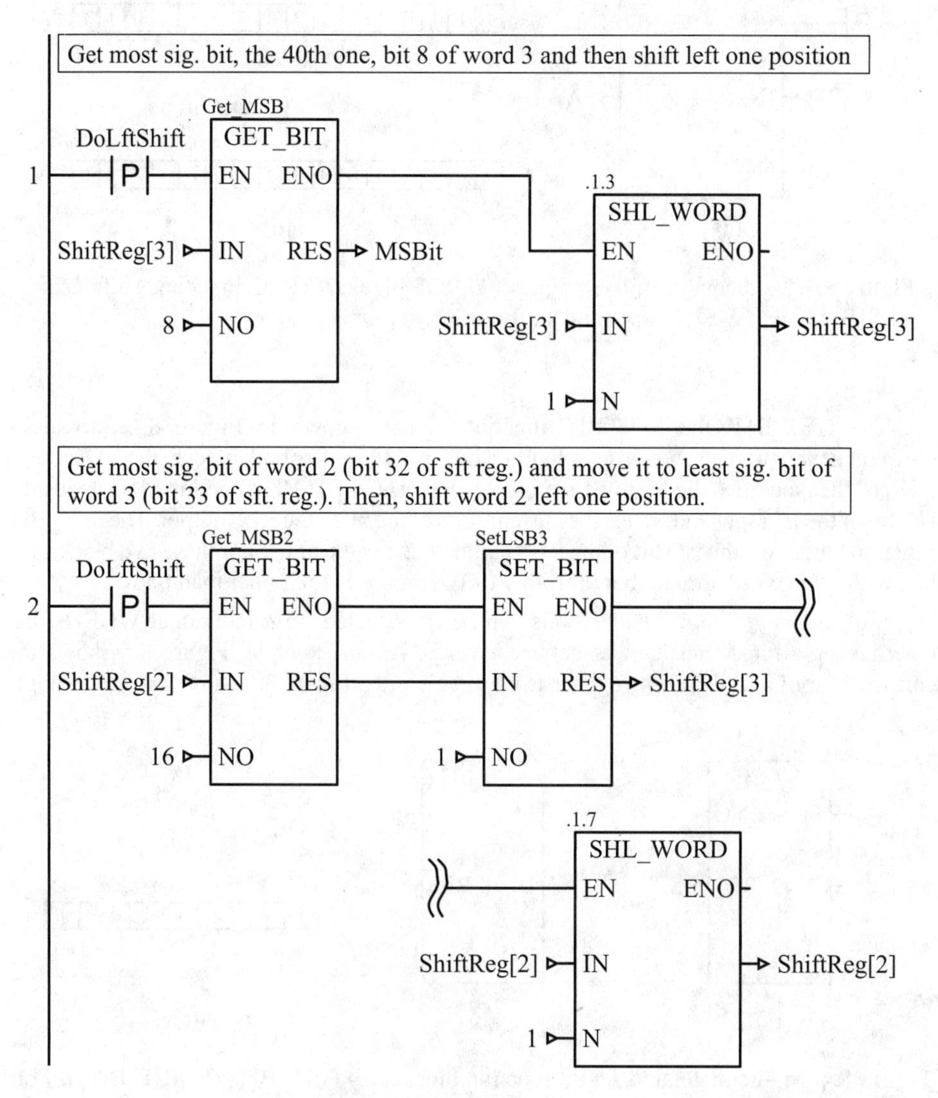

Figure 8.6. Modicon bit shift for multiple words. *(continued)*

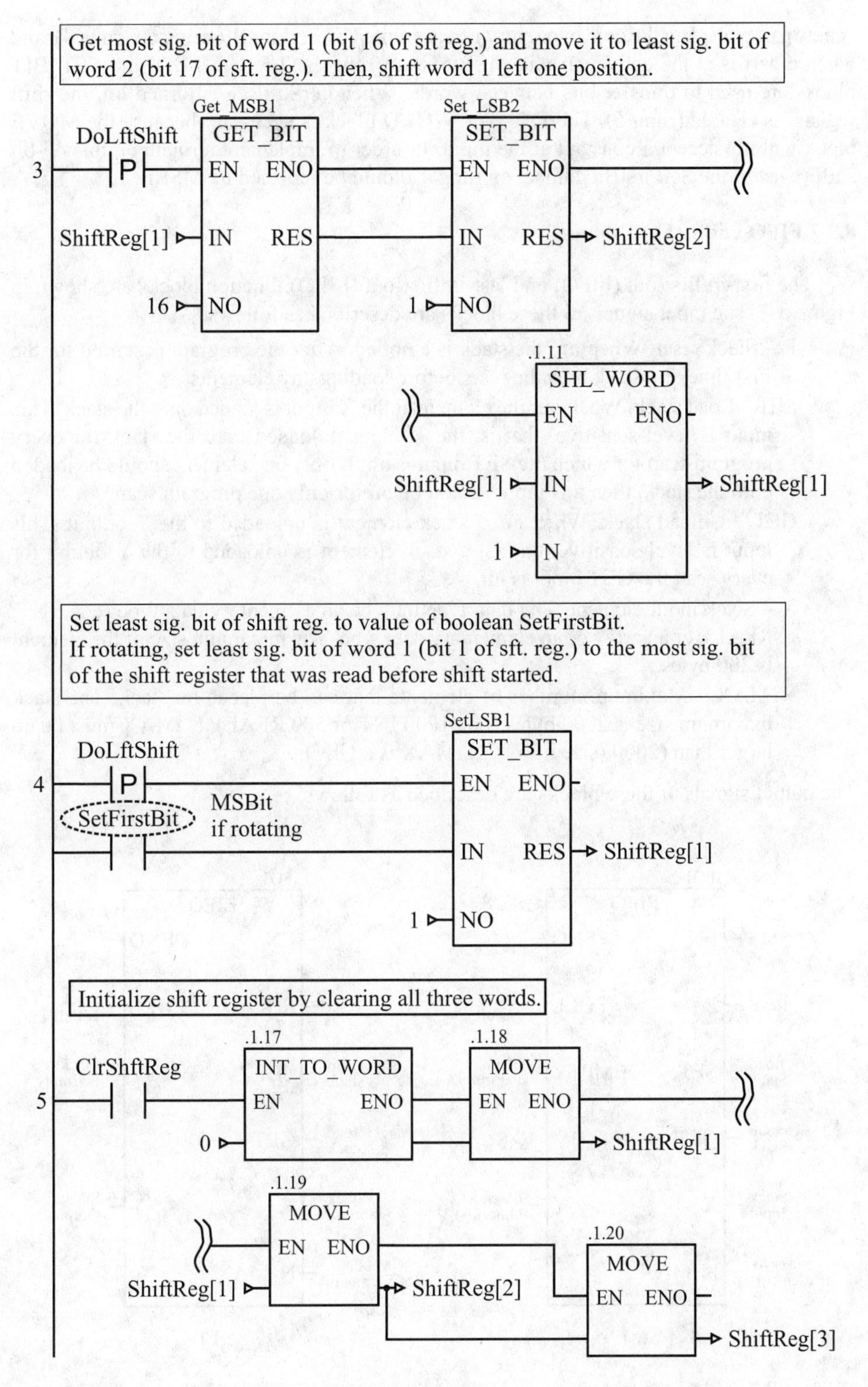

Figure 8.6. *(continued)*

A new part placed on the conveyor entry is represented by SetFirstBit being **on** (rung 4). and when a part is at the conveyor exit, MSBit is **on** (rung 1). The GET_BIT and SET_BIT blocks are used to transfer bits between words. When ClrShftReg is turned **on**, the shift register is cleared (rung 5). The INT_TO_WORD block is necessary because the MOVE block will not accept a constant at the input. In order to implement a rotate on this 40-bit shift register, the SetFirstBit contact on rung 4 should be replaced by MSBit.

8.3.2 FIFO and LIFO Queues

The first-in/first-out (FIFO) and last-in/first-out (LIFO) function blocks are shown in Figure 8.7. The input signals to these blocks are described as follows:

R – Stack reset. When **on**, the stack is emptied. After the program is started for the first time, the stack must be reset before loading any elements.

SET – Load stack. When **on**, the element at the X input is loaded onto the stack. This input is level-sensitive, that is, the X input is loaded onto the stack for every program scan for which the SET input is **on**. If only one element should be loaded onto the stack, then this input should be **on** for only one program scan.

GET – Unload stack. When **on**, a stack element is unloaded to the Y output. This input is level-sensitive, that is, a stack element is unloaded to the Y output for every scan the GET input is **on**.

X – Stack input element. The data type may be an elementary data type (e.g., INT, REAL), or an array of an elementary data type. The maximum size of the element is 200 bytes.

N_MAX – Maximum number of elements that can be placed on stack. The stack maximum size is 2000 bytes (i.e., 1000 INT or 500 REAL). N_MAX must be no larger than (2000/(size of X)). N_MAX is a UINT.

The output signals of these blocks are described as follows:

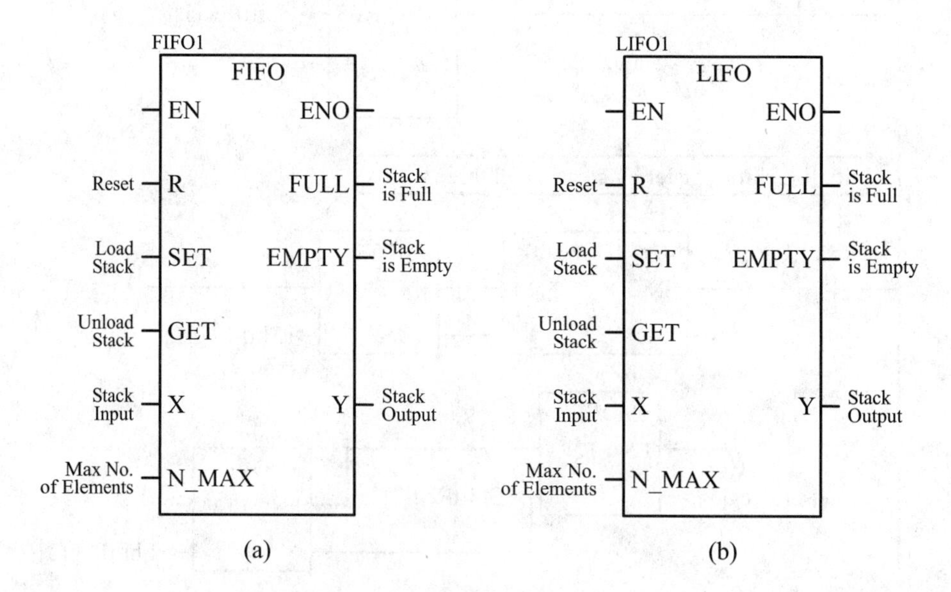

Figure 8.7. Modicon stack function blocks: *(a)* First in – first out; *(b)* Last in – first out.

FULL – **On** if the stack is full.

EMPTY - **On** if the stack is empty.

Y – Stack output element. Must be the same data type as X.

The basic difference between the operation of the FIFO and LIFO instructions is the order in which the stack is unloaded. For the FIFO, elements are unloaded in the same order as they are loaded. For the LIFO, elements are unloaded in the opposite order as they are loaded. The stack is part of the internal state of the block, and individual elements are not accessible to the user.

An example operation of the FIFO is shown in Figure 8.8. In this example, N_MAX is five. After the FIFO is reset, five INTs are loaded onto the stack and then unloaded. The contents of the stack before and after the numbered scans are also shown. Since the actual stack format is unknown, the stack format in the figure is for illustrative purposes only. The "x" indicates unknown stack element contents. The arrow on the left of the stack indicates the X input that will be loaded and the arrow on the right indicates the Y output that was unloaded. The stack is loaded with 67, 14, 37, 25, and 40. When the stack is unloaded, the

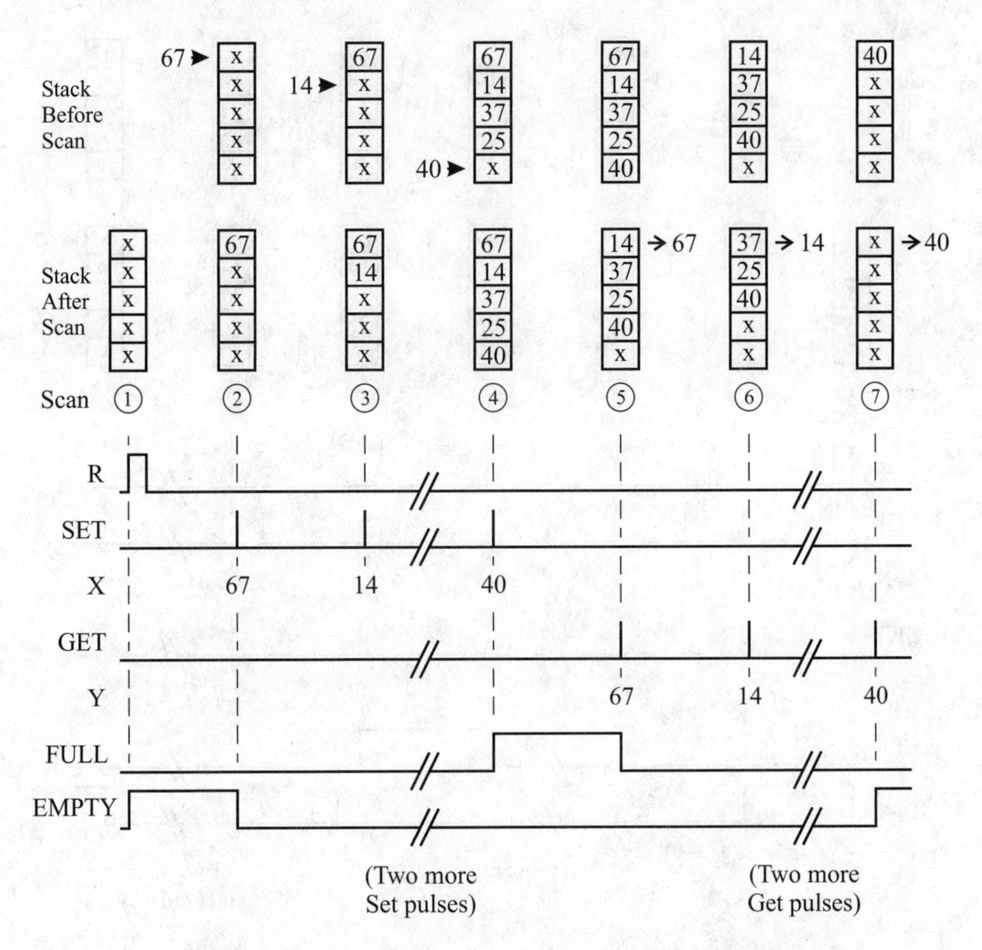

Figure 8.8. Operation of Modicon FIFO function block.

elements unload in the order 67, 14, 37, 25, and 40. The action at each of the numbered scans is as follows:

1. Reset stack, EMPTY turned **on**.
2. Load stack with X = 67, EMPTY turned **off**.
3. Load stack with X = 14
   (37 and 25 loaded between scans 3 and 4)
4. Load stack with X = 40, FULL turned **on**.
5. Unload stack, Y set to 67, FULL turned **off**.
6. Unload stack, Y set to 14
   (37 and 25 unloaded between scans 6 and 7)
7. Unload stack, Y set to 40, EMPTY turned **on**.

An example operation of the LIFO is shown in Figure 8.9. Like the previous example, N_MAX is five. After the LIFO is reset, five INTs are loaded onto the stack and then unloaded. The stack is loaded with 67, 14, 37, 25, and 40. When the stack is unloaded, the elements unload in the order 40, 25, 37, 14, and 67. The operation at each of the numbered scans is as follows:

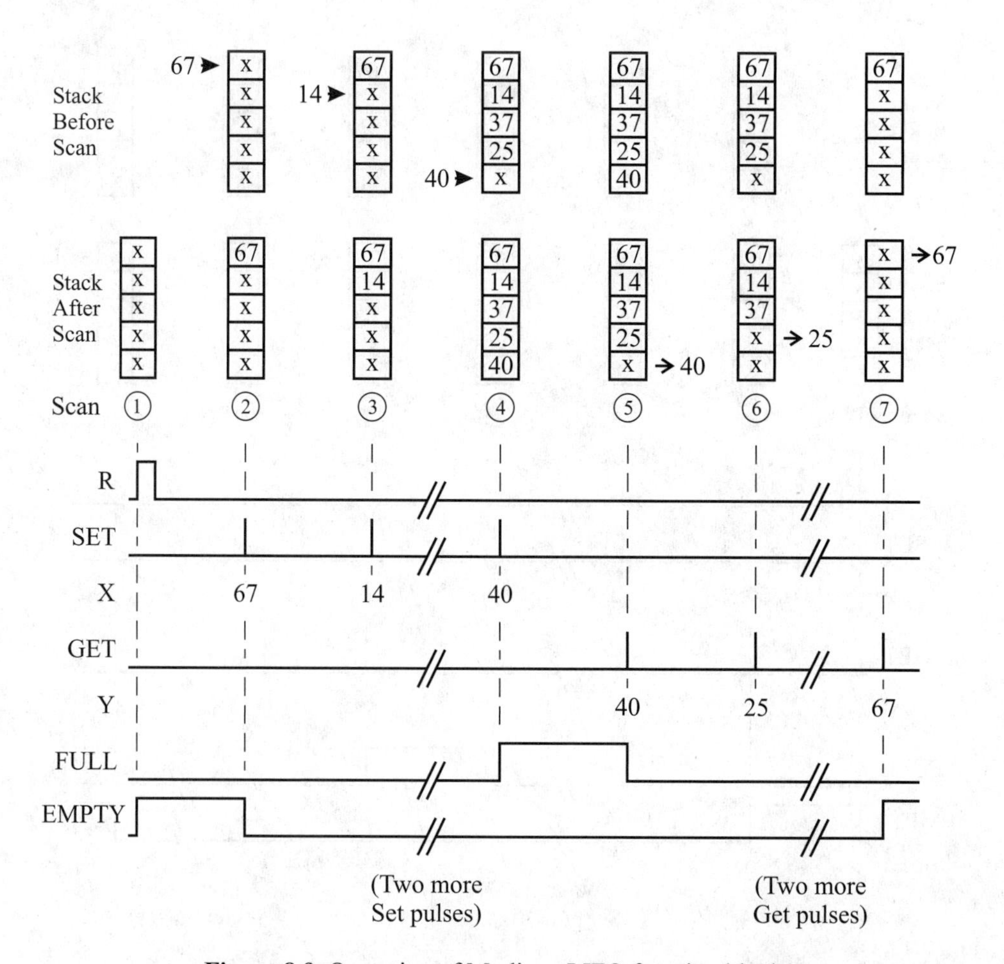

Figure 8.9. Operation of Modicon LIFO function block.

1. Reset stack, EMPTY turned **on**.
2. Load stack with X = 67, EMPTY turned **off**.
3. Load stack with X = 14
   (37 and 25 loaded between scans 3 and 4)
4. Load stack with X = 40, FULL turned **on**.
5. Unload stack, Y set to 40, FULL turned **off**.
6. Unload stack, Y set to 25
   (37 and 14 unloaded between scans 6 and 7)
7. Unload stack, Y set to 67, EMPTY turned **on**.

8.3.3 Other Array Function Blocks

The Modicon PLCs provide the following three ladder logic function blocks that operate on arrays:

Block Name	Operation Result
SRCH_***	Search array
T2T	Copy array
R2T_***	Copy element into array

where *** is DINT, INT, REAL, UDINT, or UINT and represents the data type of each element in the array.

The SRCH function block (Figure 8.10) searches an array for the next element that matches a particular pattern. The input signals to this block are described as follows:

TRIG – Trigger. When transitions **on**, the next element in the array is checked.
CONT – Continue search. When **on**, the search checks the element at the next index. When **off**, the search starts at the first element (index = 1).
SRC – Search table. Array of DINT, INT, REAL, UDINT, or UINT (consistent with the suffix of the block name).
PATTERN – Search pattern. Check array element for this value.

The output signals of this block are described as follows:

FOUND – **On** if the SRC element at the INDEX is equal to the PATTERN input.
INDEX – Current array index being checked.

An example use of the SRCH function block in Figure 8.10 searches for the first occurrence of the "SPatt" value in the "Table" DINT array. The "Do_Srch" is on to perform the search. On the positive transition of "Do_Srch", the trigger is turned **on** and the CONT input to the SRCH block is turned **off** to initialize the search at the first table index. After this, CONT is held **on** during the search so that it proceeds through the table. The TRIG input must be toggled in order to perform the search, and so it changes value on each scan. This oscillation makes the search proceed through the array until a match is found or the end of the array is reached. If the entire table is searched without finding a match, the "At_End" coil is turned **on**.

The T2T function block incrementally copies the contents of one array to another. Each time this block is executed, a selected number of words is copied from one array to another. An example T2T (table-to-table) function block is shown in Figure 8.11*a*. The input signals to this block are described as follows:

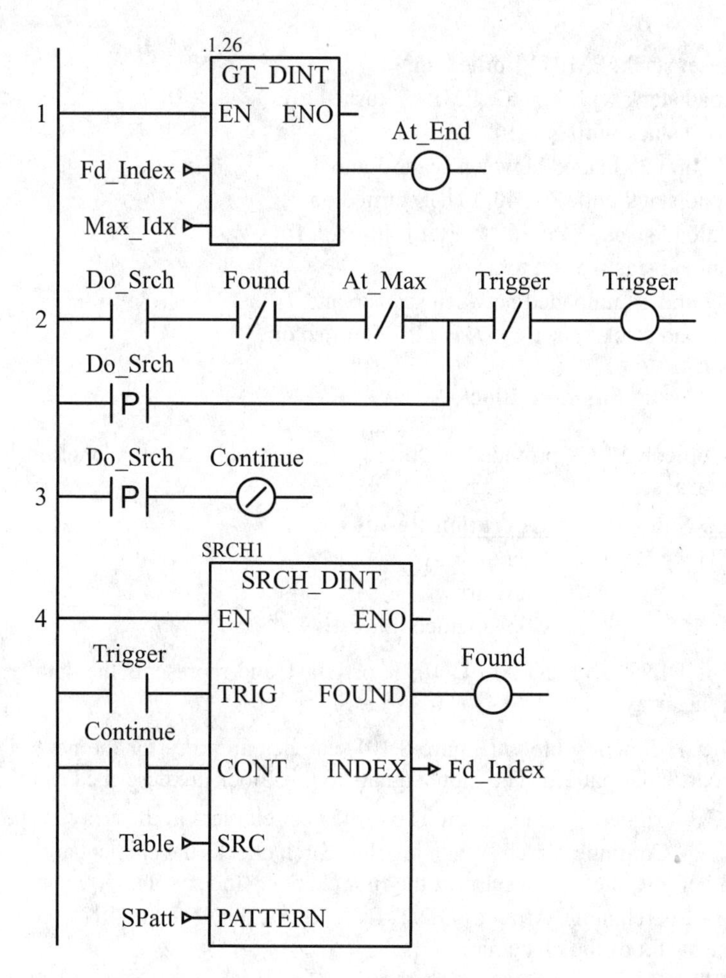

Figure 8.10. Example use of Modicon SRCH function block.

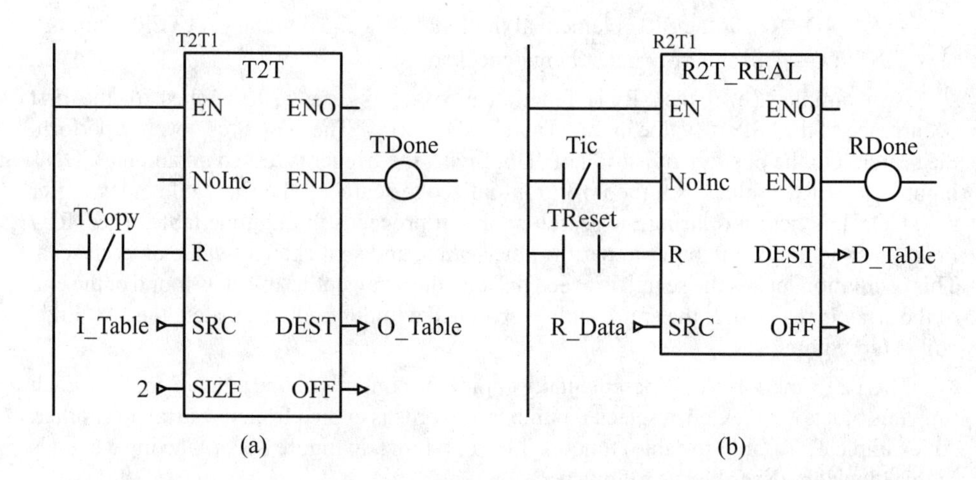

Figure 8.11. Modicon array copy blocks: *(a)* table-to-table; *(b)* register-to-table.

NoInc – When **on**, the offset (OFF) is not incremented.

R – Reset. When **on**, resets the offset (OFF) to one. One side effect of reset is that the first SIZE words of the SRC array are copied to the DEST array. If NoInc is **off**, the offset is also incremented.

SRC – Source array. Can be an array of any type, including an array of structures.

SIZE – Number of 16-bit words that are copied on each scan of the function block (when EN is **on**).

The output signals of this block are described as follows:

END – **On** when the end of the array is reached. If the SRC and DEST arrays are not the same length, this output is turned **on** when the end of the shorter of the two arrays is reached.

DEST – Destination array. Source array copied to this array.

OFF – Current WORD offset of array. Index for the SRC array and the DEST array.

The T2T example in Figure 8.11*a* copies the contents of the I_Table array to the O_Table array. While TCopy is **on**, the function block copies 2 words of the I_Table array to the O_Table array on every scan until the end of one of the arrays is reached. After each scan, the OFF output is incremented by 2 (the value of SIZE). This process continues until OFF becomes larger than either I_Table or O_Table. When that happens, TDone is turned **on** and no more data is copied. When TCopy is **off**, the OFF output is set to one and the first 2 words of I_Table are copied to O_Table every time the block is scanned.

The R2T function block incrementally copies one element into an array and is very useful for generating trend data. An example R2T (register-to-table) function block is shown in Figure 8.11*b*. This function block operates similarly to the T2T function block except that the source (SRC connection) is one of the elementary data types DINT, INT, REAL, UDINT, or UINT. The suffix of the block name is the data type of the SRC input.

The R2T example in Figure 8.11*b* samples the R_Data value, placing it into the D_Table array. The Tic internal coil is a timer tick, generated by a TON, similar to Figure 5.67. When Tic is **off**, the current value of R_Data is copied to the current index of D_Table and OFF is held constant. When Tic is **on**, R_Data is copied to the current index of D_Table and the array index increments (by one), essentially sampling the value of R_Data. This process continues until OFF becomes larger than D_Table. When that happens, RDone is turned **on** and no more data is copied. When TReset is **on**, the array index is set to one.

8.3.4 Program Execution Control

Like IEC 61131-3, most of the program control functions defined for the Modicon Quantum and Momentum PLCs are for the structured text and instruction list languages. The EN input for the timer, counter, computation, and comparison function blocks is a form of execution control. However, two ladder function blocks, shown in Figure 8.12, have a direct effect on ladder logic execution.

The SKP_RST_SCT_FALSE (Skip Rest of Section if False) skips the scan of the remainder of the ladder logic section if its DoNotSkp input is **off**. In some sense, the SKP_RST_SCT_FALSE block functions like a master control relay, except that the output coils in the remainder of the section are not changed (a master control relay turns them **off**) when the rungs are skipped. The OUT output mimics the DoNotSkp input. However, if an ordinary coil is connected to OUT, it will not turn **off** when DoNotSkp is turned **off**, since

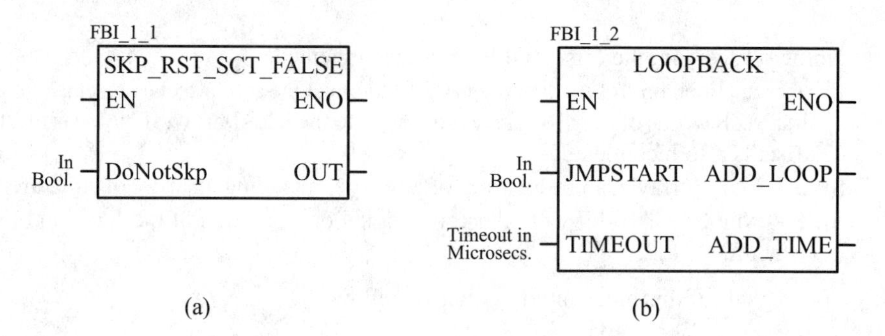

Figure 8.12. Modicon program execution control: *(a)* Skip rest of section; *(b)* Loopback.

the coil is part of the ladder logic that will be skipped. Hence, one should determine whether the ladder logic after this block is executed by monitoring the input condition to this block and not the OUT output.

The LOOPBACK function forces the program to jump back to the start of the program. When the JMPSTART input is **on**, the program execution jumps to the start of the program as long as the time specified by the TIMEOUT input has not expired. The program execution will continue to loop in this fashion until the elapsed time from the start of the looping is larger than the TIMEOUT time. The TIMEOUT input is an UDINT, expressing time in microseconds (1,000,000 = 1 sec.). The jump is executed only if the TIMEOUT value is greater than the actual program execution time. The ADD_LOOP output (UINT) is the number of program loop cycles that were executed before the end of the timeout time. The ADD_TIME output (UDINT) is the number of microseconds required to execute the additional cycles, which is higher than the timeout time. If the LOOPBACK jump is executed, one side effect is that the program scan time is increased by the ADD_TIME time.

8.4 OTHER CONTROLLOGIX FUNCTION BLOCKS

The ControlLogix PLC provides a rich set of ladder function blocks for bit shifting, FIFO/LIFO queues, special array functions, and program control. The basic operation and simple applications of these function blocks are described in this section. Longer bit shifting and FIFO/LIFO applications are presented in section 8.8.

Many of these instructions use the CONTROL data type structure, shown in Figure 8.13. The parts of this structure that are pertinent to each function block are described in conjunction with the function block.

8.4.1 Shift Bit in Register

The bit shifting function blocks and the operation that occurs for each one are:

Block Name	Operation Result
BSL	Bit shift left
BSR	Bit shift right

An example BSL (bit shift left) function block is shown in Figure 8.14*a*, and an example BSR (bit shift right) function block is shown in Figure 8.15*a*. The operands of both of these blocks are described as follows:

31	30	29	28	27	26	25	24	0
EN	EU	DN	EM	ER	UL	IN	FD	
Length value (DINT)								
Position value (DINT)								

Individual CONTROL fields:

Name.LEN	Length value
Name.POS	Position value
Name.EN	Enable bit
Name.EU	Enable-unload bit
Name.DN	Done bit
Name.EM	Empty bit
Name.ER	Error bit
Name.UL	Unload bit
Name.IN	Inhibit bit
Name.FD	Found bit

Figure 8.13. ControlLogix CONTROL data type structure.

Array – Start of bit array. Must be an element of a DINT array data type.
Control – CONTROL structure data type (Figure 8.13).
Source Bit – Bit (Boolean) that will be shifted into the bit array
Length – Number of bits in the bit array.

For the "Control" tag defined in Figure 8.14*a*, the individual parts (fields) of the CONTROL structure are addressed as follows:

Reference	Description
Cnv1_PCtl.UL	Unload (bit that was shifted out)
Cnv1_PCtl.EN	Enable
Cnv1_PCtl.ER	Error (length < 0)
Cnv1_PCtl.LEN	Length of bit array

For each **off**-to-**on** transition of the BSL input, the bit array is shifted left one position. The "Source Bit" value replaces the rightmost bit, and the .UL bit is set to the value of the (shifted out) leftmost bit in the bit array. The .EN bit is identical to the block input condition. The .ER bit is set if the .LEN field is less than zero. The value of the array length (.LEN) can be accessed as a DINT. An example application of the BSL function block is shown in Figure 8.14*a*, and example bits in the bit array before and after a shift are shown in Figure 8.14*b*.

For each **off**-to-**on** transition of the BSR input, the bit array is shifted right one position. The "Source Bit" value replaces the leftmost bit, and the .UL bit is set to the value of the (shifted out) rightmost bit in the bit array. The .EN and .ER bits as well as the .LEN field have the same function as for the BSL block. An example application of the BSR function block is shown in Figure 8.15*a*, and the bits in the bit array before and after a shift are shown in Figure 8.15*b*.

To rotate the bits in a shift register, the "Source Bit" is set to the appropriate bit at the end of the bit array that is copied to the .UL bit when the bits are shifted. For example, for the BSL in Figure 8.14*a*, using Cnv1_PPos[0].19 for the "Source Bit" will convert the left shift into a left rotate. In Figure 8.15*a*, using Belt_Pos[0].0 for the "Source Bit" will change the right shift into a right rotate.

Shift registers longer than 32 bits are handled automatically since the "Array" operand is already treated as an array of DINTs. For example, the right shift of Figure 8.15*a* can easily be a 70-bit shift register by defining Belt_Pos as a 3 DINT array and changing the

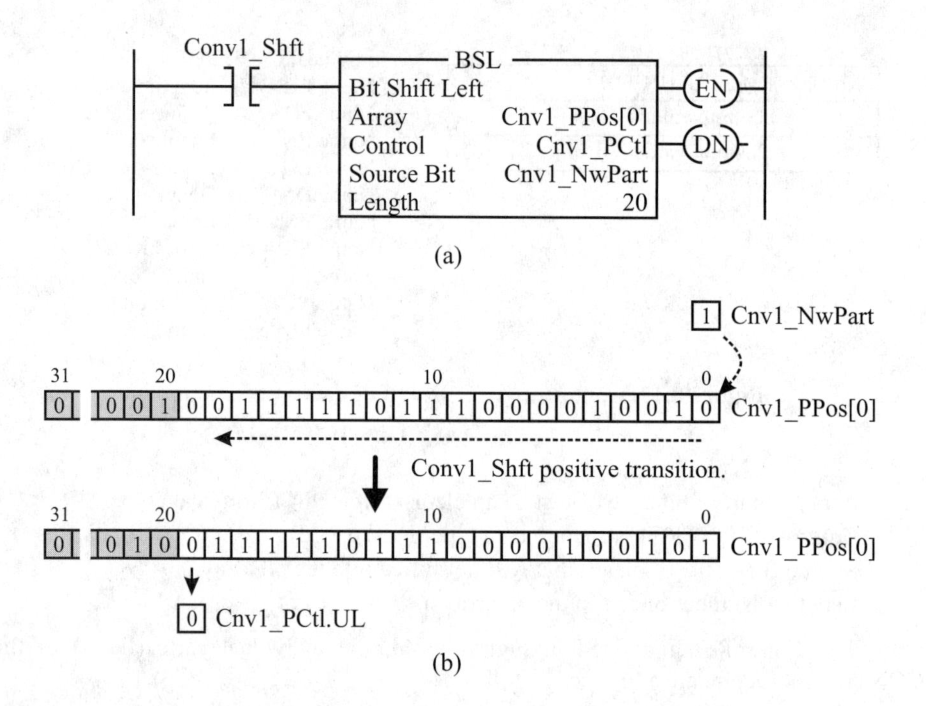

Figure 8.14. ControlLogix bit-shift left: *(a)* example BSL block; *(b)* bit array before and after shift.

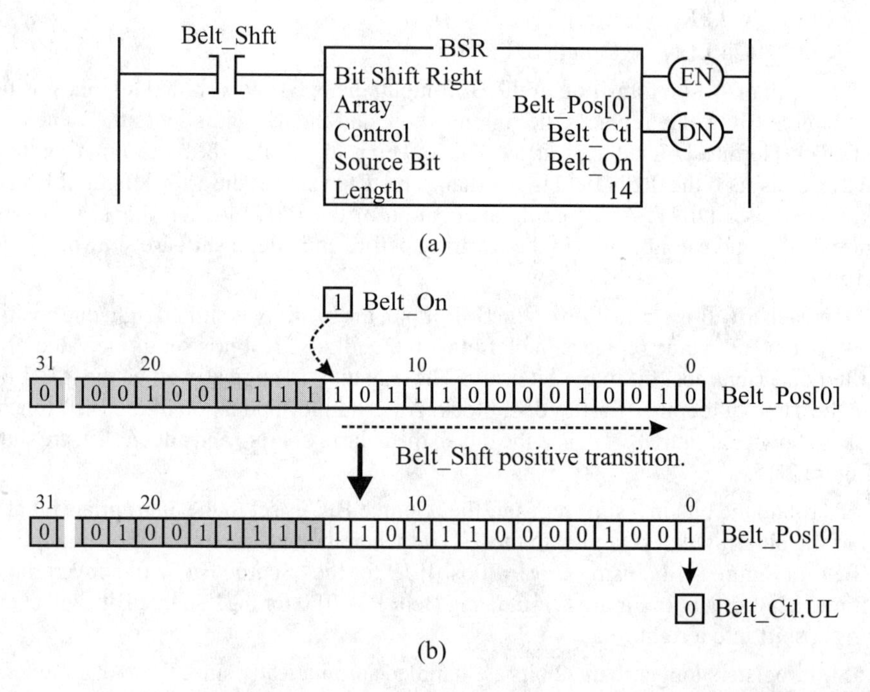

Figure 8.15. ControlLogix bit-shift right: *(a)* example BSR block; *(b)* bit array before and after shift.

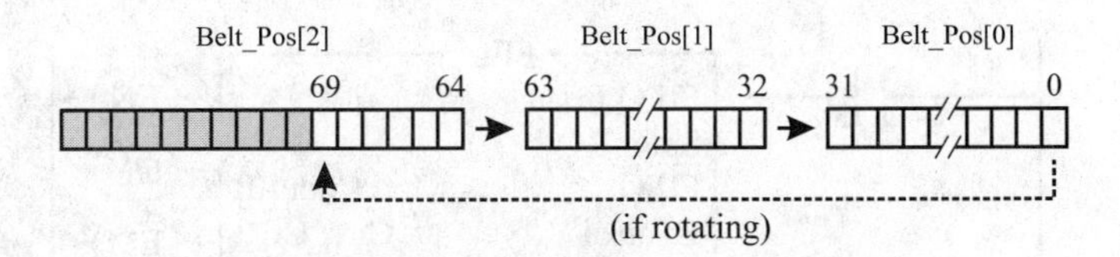

Figure 8.16. Multi-DINT shift register.

length to 70. In this case, the shift register is constructed as in Figure 8.16. The BSR function block handles the transfer of bits between DINTs automatically. To clear a shift register consisting of multiple DINTs, use the FLL block described in section 8.4.3.

8.4.2 FIFO and LIFO Queues

The array (queue) shifting function blocks and the operation that occurs for each one are:

Block Name	Operation Result
FFL	Load value to the next FIFO position
FFU	Unload value from first FIFO position
LFL	Load value to the next LIFO position
LFU	Unload value from last LIFO position

The basic difference between the operation of a first-in/first-out (FIFO) and a last-in/first-out (LIFO) array is the order in which the array unloads elements. For the FIFO array, elements unload in the same order as they are loaded. For the LIFO array, elements unload in the opposite order as they are loaded.

Normally, the FFL and FFU are used together to construct a FIFO data array. An example application of the FFL and FFU blocks is shown in Figure 8.17. For the FFL and FFU function blocks, the operands are described as follows:

FIFO – First element in a DINT or REAL array data type.
Control – CONTROL structure data type (Figure 8.13).
Length – Maximum length of the FIFO array.
Position – Position where the next data will be loaded.
Source – (FFL only) Tag of the data that will be stored in the array.
Dest – (FFU only) Tag where the data will be placed after it is unloaded from the FIFO.

Typically, the FFL and FFU refer to the same "Control" tag. For the control tag defined in Figure 8.17, the individual fields of the CONTROL structure are addressed as follows:

Reference	Description
Cnv_CCtl.EN	Load enabled
Cnv_CCtl.EU	Unload enabled
Cnv_CCtl.DN	FIFO full
Cnv_CCtl.EM	FIFO empty
Cnv_CCtl.LEN	FIFO array length
Cnv_CCtl.POS	Next entry will load here

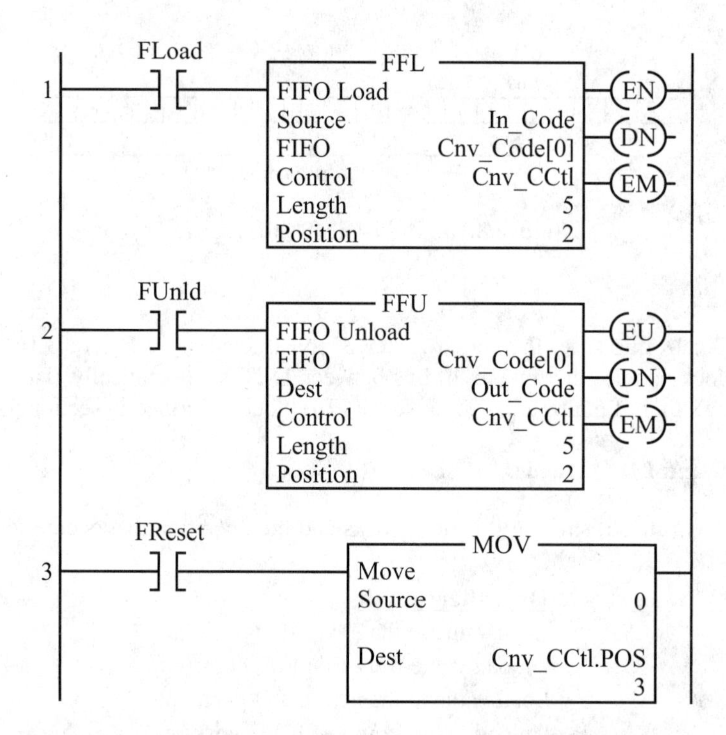

Figure 8.17. ControlLogix FIFO array function blocks.

For each **off**-to-**on** transition of the FFL input, the "Source" value is placed in the FIFO array at the current position, and the position (.POS) is incremented by one. The .EN bit is identical to the FFL block input condition. The .DN bit is set if the .POS is equal to the array length. If data is added to an already full FIFO, the new data replaces the previously added data entry. The position value of the FIFO (.POS) can be accessed as DINT. In order to reset a FIFO array, set the .POS to zero.

For each **off**-to-**on** transition of the FFU input, the first element in the FIFO array is copied to "Dest", and the remaining data in the array is shifted one position toward the beginning of the array. The position is also decremented by one. The .EU bit is identical to the FFU block input condition. The .EM bit is set if the FIFO is empty (.POS=0). A zero is placed into "Dest" if one attempts to unload an already empty FIFO.

An example operation of the FFL and FFU of Figure 8.17 is shown in Figure 8.18. This example assumes the FIFO starts empty. Five DINTs are loaded onto the FIFO and then unloaded. The contents of the FIFO before and after the numbered scans are also shown. The arrow on the left of the array indicates the .POS value, and the arrow on the right indicates the value unloaded into Out_Code. The FIFO is loaded with 67, 14, 37, 25, and 40. When the FIFO is unloaded, the elements unload in the order 67, 14, 37, 25, and 40. The action at each of the numbered scans is as follows:

1. Load stack with In_Code = 67, .EM turned **off**.
2. Load stack with In_Code = 14
   (37 and 25 loaded between scans 2 and 3)
3. Load stack with In_Code = 40, .DN turned **on**.
4. Unload stack, Out_Code set to 67, .DN turned **off**.
5. Unload stack, Out_Code set to 14

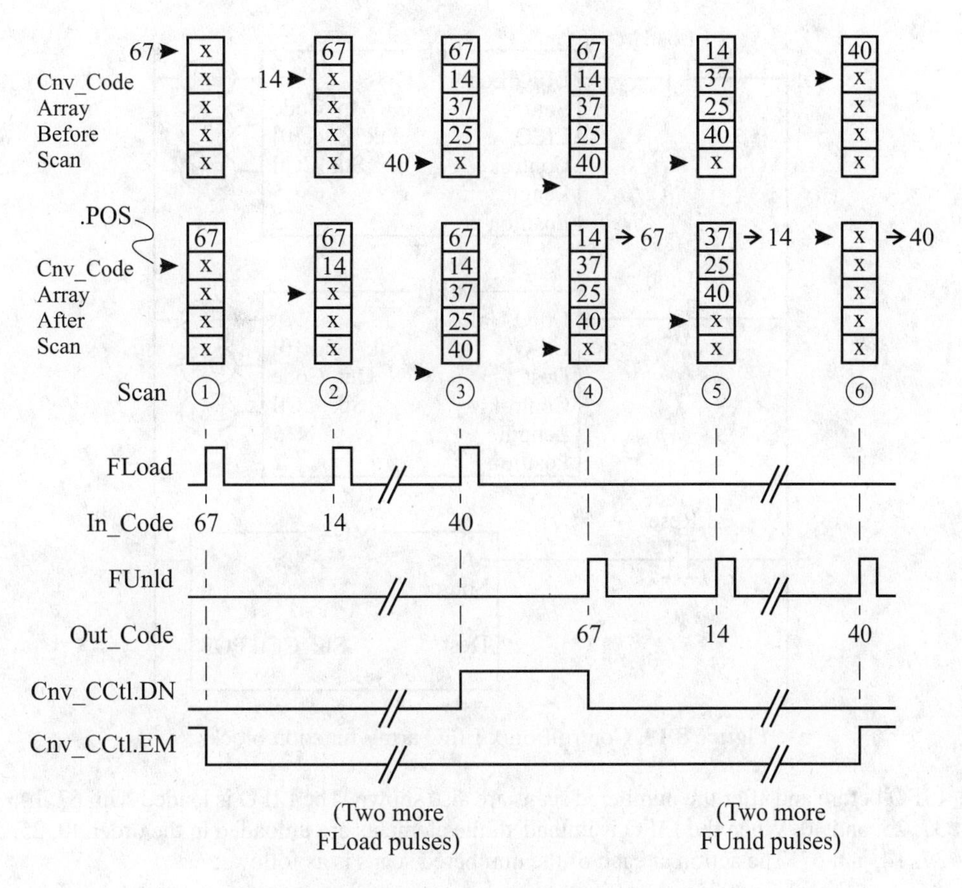

Figure 8.18. ControlLogix FIFO array operation.

(37 and 25 unloaded between scans 5 and 6)

6. Unload stack, Out_Code set to 40, .EM turned **on**.

Normally, the LFL and LFU are used together to construct a LIFO data array. An example application of the LFL and LFU blocks is shown in Figure 8.19. The operands for these instructions are identical to the FFL/FFU except for the "LIFO" operand, which is the first element of the LIFO array.

For each **off**-to-**on** transition of the LFL input, the "Source" value is placed in the LIFO array at the current position, and the position (.POS) is incremented by one. The .EN bit is identical to the block input condition. The .DN bit is set if the .POS is equal to the array length. If data is added to an already full LIFO, the new data replaces the previously added data entry. The position value of the LIFO (.POS) can be accessed as DINT. In order to reset a LIFO array, set the .POS to zero.

For each **off**-to-**on** transition of the LFU input, the last element in the LIFO array is copied to "Dest", and the position is decremented by one. The .EU bit is identical to the block input condition. The .EM bit is set if the LIFO is empty (.POS=0). A zero is placed into "Dest" if one attempts to unload an already empty LIFO.

Figure 8.20 shows an example operation of the LFL and LFU of Figure 8.19. The LIFO starts empty. Five DINTs are loaded onto the LIFO and then unloaded. The contents of the

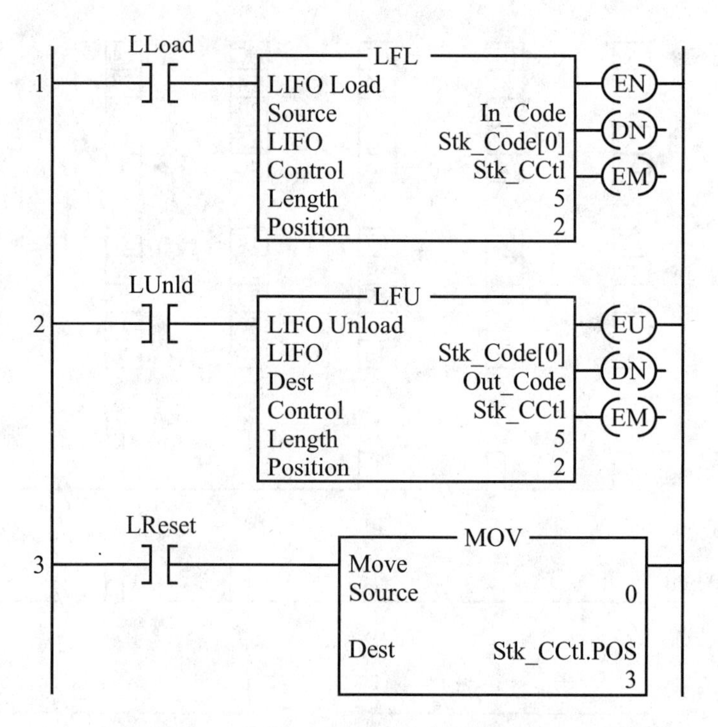

Figure 8.19. ControlLogix LIFO array function blocks.

LIFO before and after the numbered scans are also shown. The LIFO is loaded with 67, 14, 37, 25, and 40. When the LIFO is unloaded, the elements are unloaded in the order 40, 25, 37, 14, and 67. The action at each of the numbered scans is as follows:

1. Load stack with In_Code = 67, .EM turned **off**.
2. Load stack with In_Code = 14
   (37 and 25 loaded between scans 2 and 3)
3. Load stack with In_Code = 40, .DN turned **on**.
4. Unload stack, Out_Code set to 40, .DN turned **off**.
5. Unload stack, Out_Code set to 25
   (37 and 14 unloaded between scans 5 and 6)
6. Unload stack, Out_Code set to 67, .EM turned **on**.

8.4.3 Other Array Function Blocks

Other specialized numerical and bit array function blocks and the operation that occurs for each one are:

Block Name	Operation Result
FAL	Array (file) arithmetic and logic
FSC	Array (file) search and compare
FLL	Fill array with a value
COP	Copy values or structures
FBC	Find mismatches between two bit arrays
DDT	Find and correct mismatched bit arrays

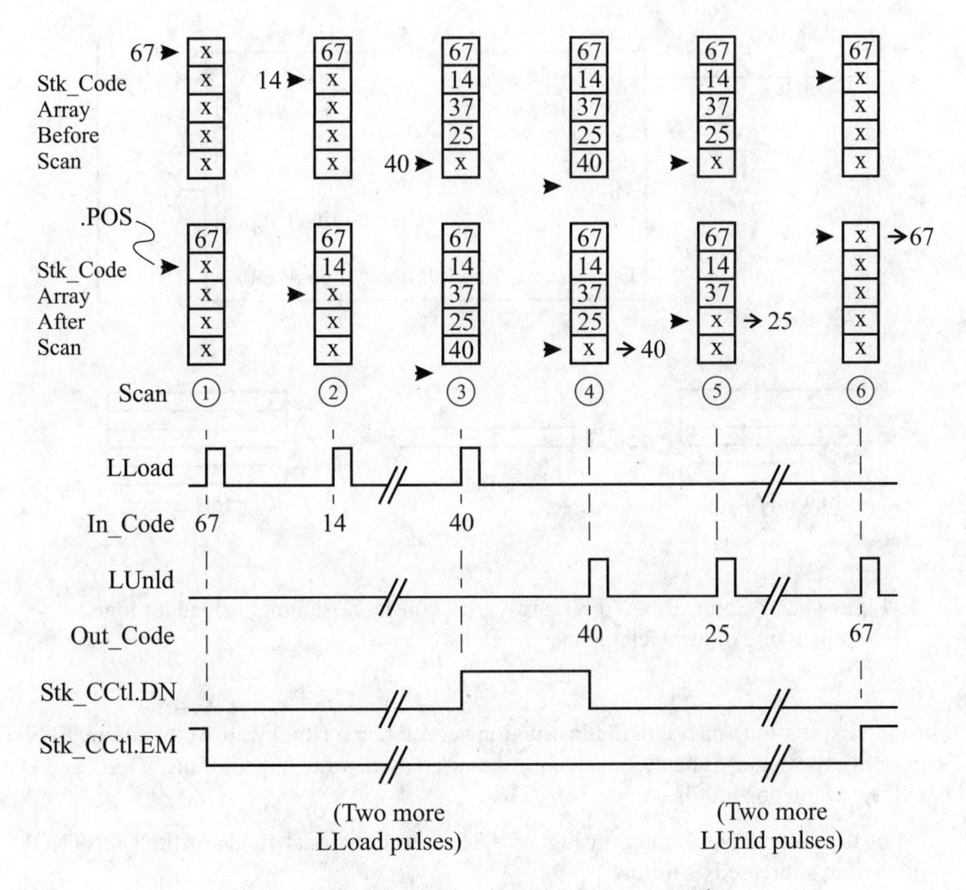

Figure 8.20. ControlLogix LIFO array operation.

The operation of each of these instructions is explained and illustrated with short examples. Other array functions are available (e.g., array sorting and averaging) but are not covered in this text.

The FAL (file arithmetic/logic) function block performs the same operations on arrays as the CPT (compute) function block performs on individual elements. In addition, this block can be programmed to perform the operation on the entire array when it executes or incrementally, that is, perform only a few operations each time the block is scanned. The latter mode is useful when processing large arrays or data that are not time-critical. Only simple applications are described in this section. The interested reader should consult the instruction set reference (Rockwell Automation, 1999) for more details.

An example FAL function block is shown in Figure 8.21. The operands are as follows:

Control – CONTROL structure data type (Figure 8.13).

Length – Number of elements in the array to be manipulated.

Position – Current position in the array, initially it is typically zero.

Mode – How array elements are processed (all, inc, or a number).

Dest – Tag of the expression result.

Expression – A valid arithmetic, logical, conversion, and copy operation.

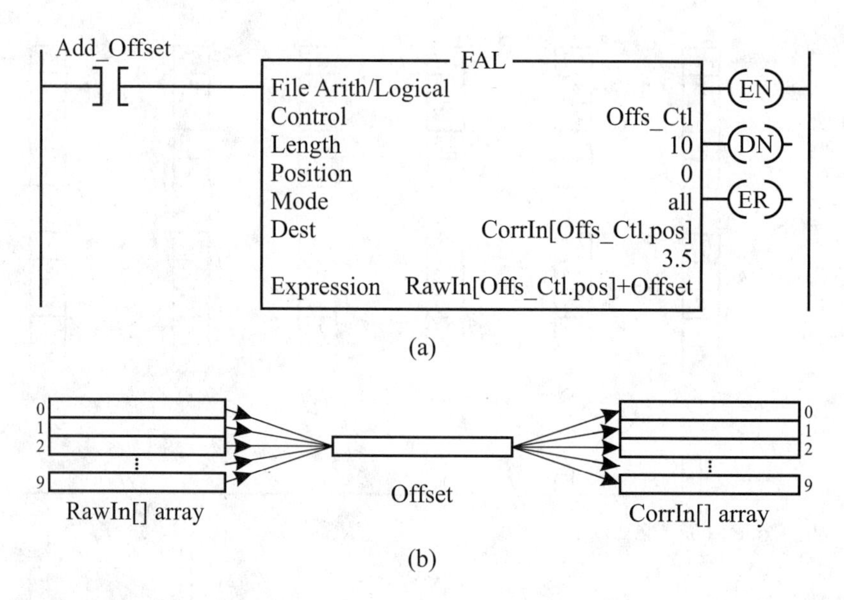

Figure 8.21. ControlLogix FAL array plus constant example: *(a)* ladder logic; *(b)* processing of array elements.

For the "Expression" operand, the instruction set reference (Rockwell Automation, 1999) lists valid expressions. The .POS value is often used as an array index for the "Dest" and/or the "Expression" operands.

For the control tag defined in Figure 8.21*a*, the individual fields of the CONTROL structure are addressed as follows:

Reference	Description
Offs_Ctl.EN	FAL enabled
Offs_Ctl.DN	Operation done
Offs_Ctl.ER	Overflow for one array element
Offs_Ctl.LEN	Number of elements in array
Offs_Ctl.POS	Index of current element being processed

The possible values of "Mode" are:

all — When block input condition changes from **off** to **on**, all specified array elements are processed.

inc — One specified array element processed for each **off**-to-**on** transition of the block input condition. The .DN bit is set when all array elements have been processed.

[number] — When block input condition changes from **off** to **on**, [number] of array elements are processed on each scan of this instruction until all specified array elements are processed. The .DN bit is set when all array elements have been processed. The [number] is any valid non-zero positive DINT.

Figure 8.21 shows an example FAL used to add a constant value (Offset) to every element in the RawIn array and store the results in the CorrIn array. The operation is in the

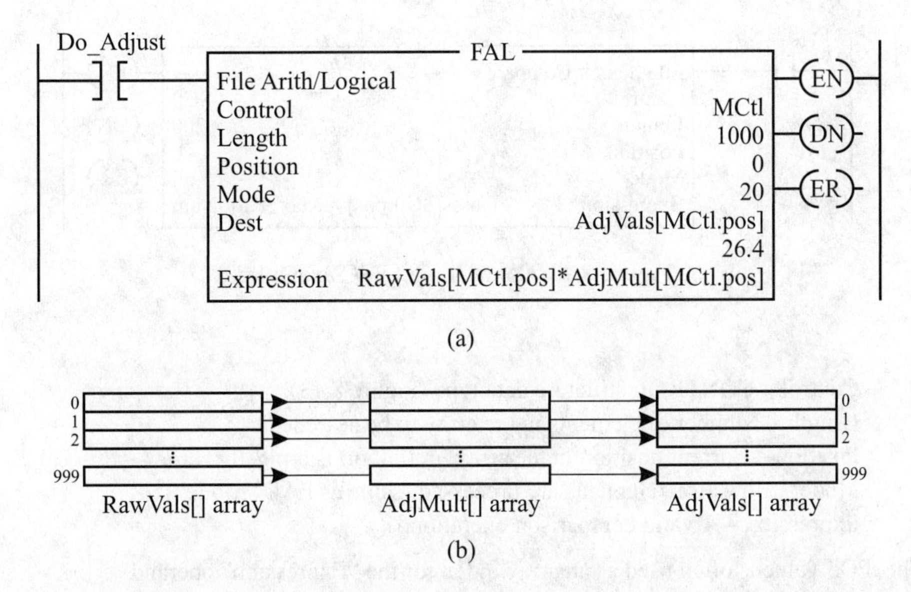

Figure 8.22. ControlLogix FAL array multiplication example: *(a)* ladder logic; *(b)* processing of array elements.

"all" mode, meaning all 10 specified additions are processed for each **off**-to-**on** transition of the FAL input. If the "Mode" operand is set to "3", then it will require 4 program scans to process all 10 array elements. If the "Mode" operand is set to "inc", then 10 **off**-to-**on** transitions of Add_Offset are required to process all 10 elements of the arrays.

Figure 8.22 shows an example FAL used to do an element-by-element multiplication of one array by another array to produce a third array. Each element of RawVals is multiplied by the corresponding element in AdjMult to produce an element of the AdjVals array. Since this is a large array, the "Mode" operand is set to "20", and it will require 50 program scans to process all 1000 array elements.

Design Tip

The FAL function block is useful for performing a wide variety of arithmetic operations on data arrays.

The FSC (file search/compare) function block performs a similar operation on arrays as the CMP (compare) function block performs on individual elements, except that it finds the first array element that satisfies the comparison. Like the FAL block, the FSC block can be programmed to perform the comparison on the entire array when it executes or incrementally, that is, perform only a few comparisons each time the block is scanned. The latter mode is useful when processing large arrays or data that are not time-critical.

An example FSC function block is shown in Figure 8.23. The operands are as follows:

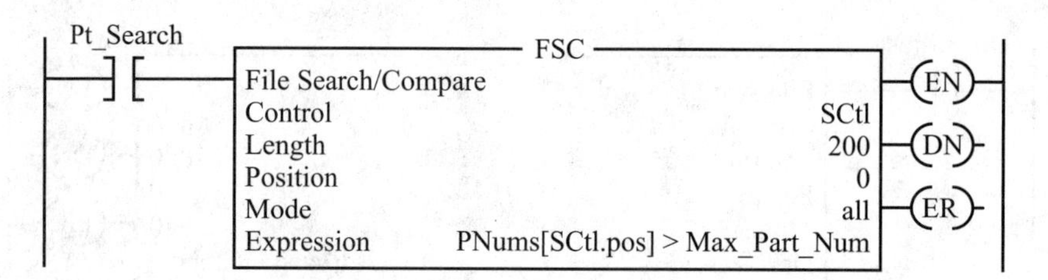

Figure 8.23. ControlLogix FSC example.

Control – CONTROL structure data type (Figure 8.13).
Length – Number of elements in the array to be searched.
Position – Current position in the array, initially it is typically zero.
Mode – How array elements are processed (same as FAL "Mode").
Expression – A valid comparison operation.

The .POS value is often used as an array index for the "Expression" operand.

For the control tag defined in Figure 8.23, the individual fields of the CONTROL structure are addressed as follows:

Reference	Description
SCtl.EN	FSC enabled
SCtl.DN	Searched to end of array
SCtl.IN	Inhibit bit, **on** when true comparison detected; must clear to continue search
SCtl.FD	Found bit, **on** when true comparison detected
SCtl.LEN	Number of elements in array
SCtl.POS	Index of current element being processed

Figure 8.23 shows an example FSC used to search an array of part numbers for the first one that is greater than the value in Max_Part_Num. The operation is in the "all" mode, meaning that all 200 array elements may be searched for each **off**-to-**on** transition of the FSC input. The SCtl.FD and SCtl.IN bits will be set if a part number that matches the expression is found. The value of SCtl.POS is the index of the PNums array that has the part number matching the search criterion. If one wanted to search for another match, leave SCtl.POS unmodified, unlatch the SCtl.IN bit, and re-initiate the FSC function block.

The FLL (fill) function block fills the elements of an array with the same value and is useful for initialization. An example FLL block is shown in Figure 8.24. The "Source" operand is either the tag containing the value to copy or a constant value. The "Dest" is the tag of the first element in an integer or real array data type. The "Length" is the number of

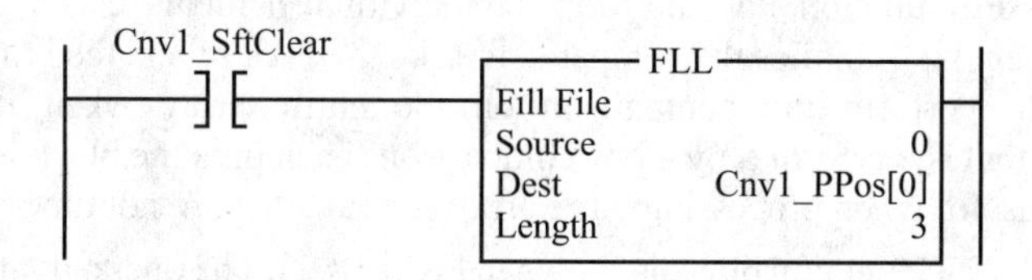

Figure 8.24. ControlLogix FLL example.

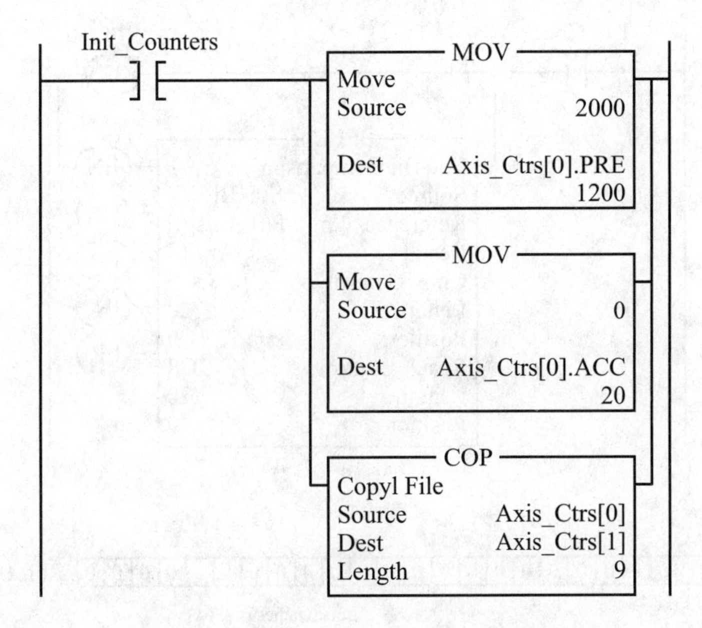

Figure 8.25. ControlLogix COP example.

elements to fill. For best results, the data type of the "Source" should match the data type of each element of the "Dest" array.

The COP (copy) function block is similar to the FLL function block, except it will also initialize arrays of structures (e.g., an array of counters or timers). An example application of the COP block is shown in Figure 8.25 that initializes an array of counters. The first counter in the array is initialized and then it is copied to the other 9 counters in the array. The "Source" and "Dest" operands are basically the same as for the FLL block, except that the "Source" can be a structure data type and the "Dest" can be the element of an array of structures.

The FBC (file bit compare) function block compares two bit arrays and records the bit number of each difference in a result array. An example FBC block is shown in Figure 8.26. The operands of this block are described as follows:

Source – Bit array compared to reference. First location of DINT array.
Reference – Reference bit array. First location of DINT array.
Result – Array to store search results. First location of DINT array.
Cmp. Control – CONTROL structure for compare.
Length – Number of bit locations to compare
Position – Current position in source array. Typically initialized to zero.
Result Control – CONTROL structure for the results.
Length – Number of storage locations in result array.
Position – Current position in result array. Typically initialized to zero.

The "Cmp. Control" and "Result Control" operand must be different tags and a CONTROL data type (Figure 8.13). For the "Cmp. Control" tag defined in Figure 8.26, the individual fields of the CONTROL structure are addressed as follows:

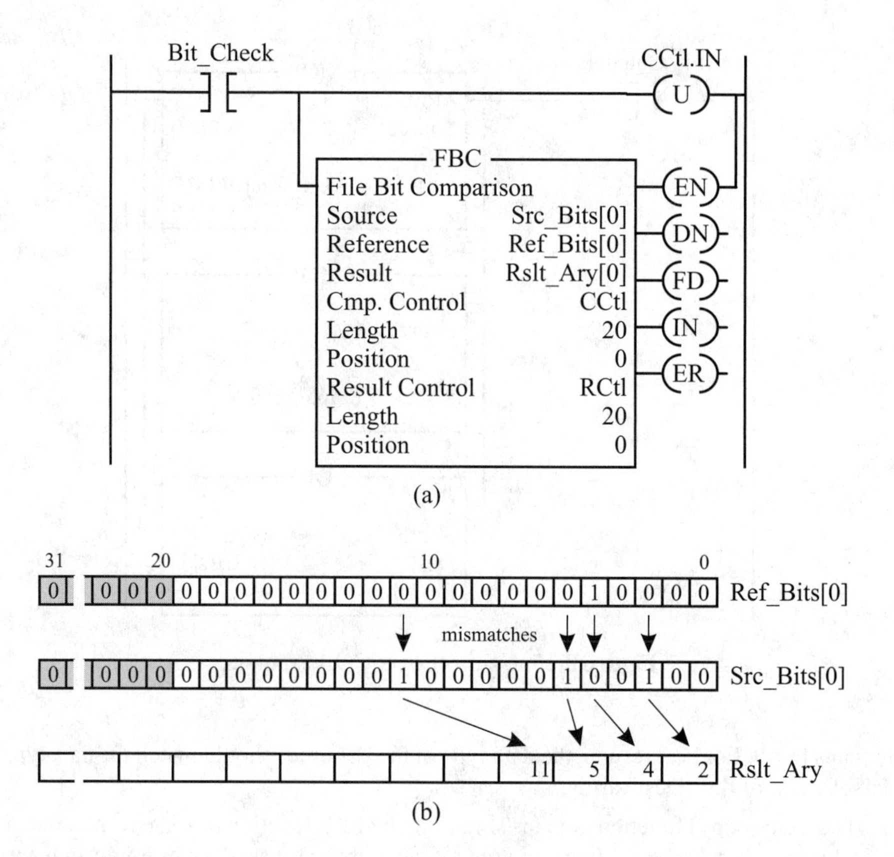

Figure 8.26. ControlLogix FBC example: *(a)* ladder logic; *(b)* FBC execution results.

Reference	Description
CCtl.EN	FBC enabled
CCtl.DN	Set when last bit in array compared.
CCtl.FD	Set when mismatch recorded (one-at-a-time operation) or all mismatches recorded (all-per-scan) operation.
CCtl.IN	Search mode bit, **off** to search for all mismatches, **on** to search for next mismatch only.
CCtl.ER	Error bit, **on** when parameters illegal.
CCtl.LEN	Number of bits to compare.
CCtl.POS	Index of current bit.

For the "Result Control" tag defined in Figure 8.26, the individual fields of the CONTROL structure are addressed as follows:

Reference	Description
RCtl.DN	Set when result array full.
RCtl.LEN	Length of result array.
RCtl.POS	Current position in result array.

For the "Source," "Reference," and "Result" tags, one should not use .POS as the array subscript.

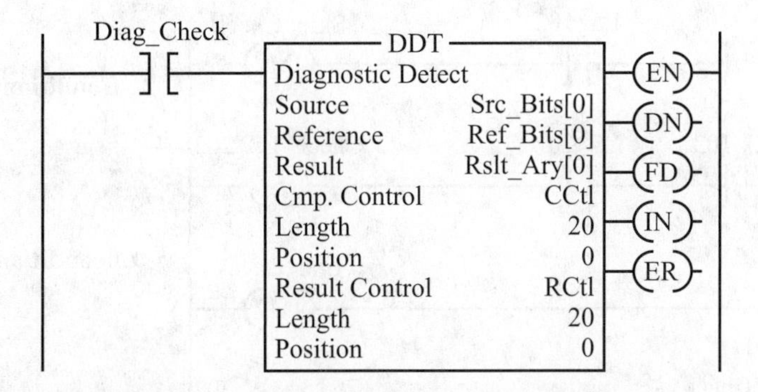

Figure 8.27. ControlLogix DDT function block.

Figure 8.26*a* shows an example FBC used to compare 20 bits of Src_Bits[0] with 20 bits of Ref_Bits[0]. The CCtl.IN bit is **off** to search for all mismatches, and the results are placed in Rslt_Ary. For particular values of the bit arrays, the result of the function block execution is shown in Figure 8.26*b*.

The DDT (diagnostic detect) function block compares two bit arrays, records the bit number of each difference in a result array, and then changes the bit in the reference array to match the bit in the source array. The DDT function block functions in the same manner as the FBC function block except that the DDT function block changes the reference bits to match the source bits. An example DDT block is shown in Figure 8.27.

8.4.4 Program Execution Control

The ControlLogix PLC offers a number of instructions that can control ladder logic execution. The names and the operation that occurs for each one are:

Block Name	Operation Result
JMP	Jump to a defined label
LBL	Jump destination
JSR	Jump to subroutine, passing data
SBR	Pass data to subroutine
RET	Return results from subroutine
MCR	Master control relay; disable logic section
FOR	Repeatedly execute a routine
BRK	Terminate the repeated execution of a routine.
AFI	Disable rung logic
NOP	No operation
TND	Mark temporary end of ladder

Depending on the particular instruction, it may be a contact, or a coil, or a function block. The operation of each of these instructions is explained and illustrated with short examples.

The JMP (jump) coil and LBL (label) contact are used together to skip portions of ladder logic. When the JMP coil is turned **on**, the ladder scan skips to the referenced LBL contact. One can jump either forward or backward. Jumping backward lets the controller iterate certain sections of logic. However, jumping backward an excessive number of times

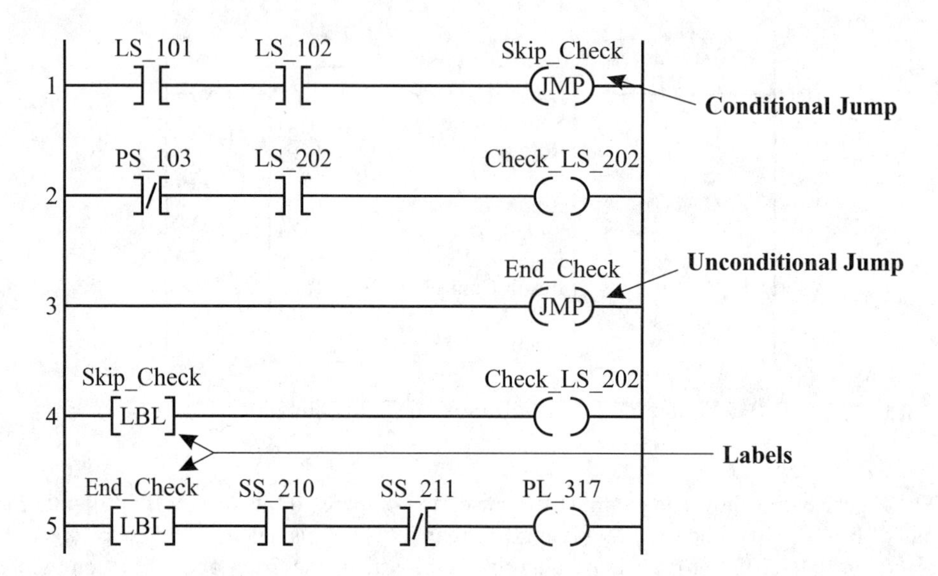

Figure 8.28. ControlLogix JMP and LBL example.

will cause the controller to fault if the scan time is too long. Jumping forward decreases the scan time by skipping logic segments until needed. One drawback to jumping forward is that the logic between the jump coil and the label contact is not scanned, so any output coils are not changed. An example ladder segment with two jump and two label instructions is shown in Figure 8.28.

The JSR (jump to subroutine), SBR (subroutine), and RET (return) function blocks are used to execute routines other than the main program routine. Large programs are often broken into subroutines which are called from the main routine. When enabled, the JSR function block directs logic execution to the first rung of the specified routine, and if needed, passes parameters to the routine. If parameters are passed to the subroutine, the first rung of the subroutine must have a SBR function block. Otherwise, if no parameters are passed to the subroutine, the SBR block is not needed. Likewise, the RET function block appears on the last rung of a subroutine if parameters are passed back to the calling routine. Actually, the RET block can have conditions to enable it and occur before the last subroutine rung. In this case, if the RET block is not executed, ladder logic execution continues after the rung that contains the RET block. If the RET block is omitted, the subroutine automatically returns back to the calling routine after the last subroutine rung is scanned, but no parameters are passed back.

Subroutines can call other subroutines, often called *nested subroutines*, as shown in Figure 8.29. Other than controller memory, there is no limit on the number of nested subroutines.

The parameters are passed into and out of a subroutine by value. The values are copied back and forth between the memory of the calling routine and the subroutine, which increases execution time. Directly accessing program-scoped and controller-scoped tags from within the subroutine will reduce execution time. However, the subroutines may not be easily reused in another PLC program because it will require certain globally-defined tags. Array elements, structures, and entire arrays can all be passed as parameters. In all

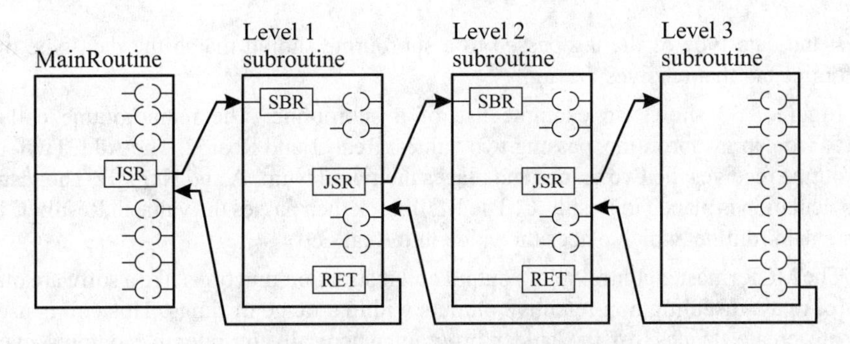

Figure 8.29. Nested subroutines.

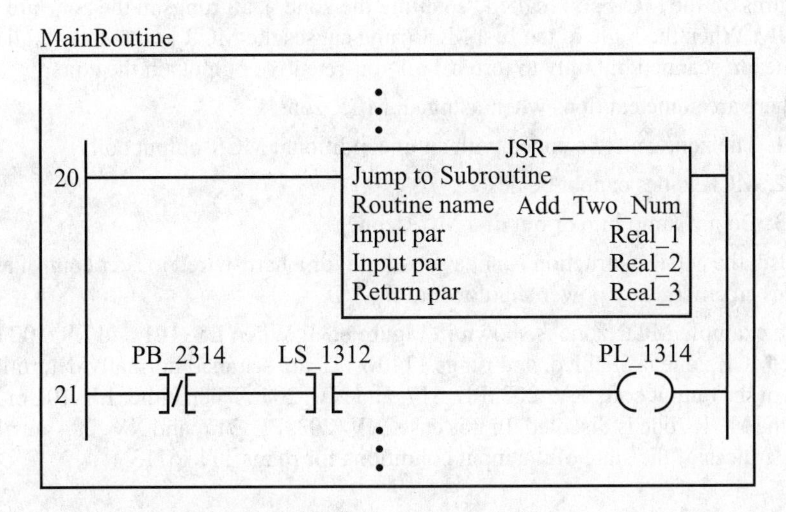

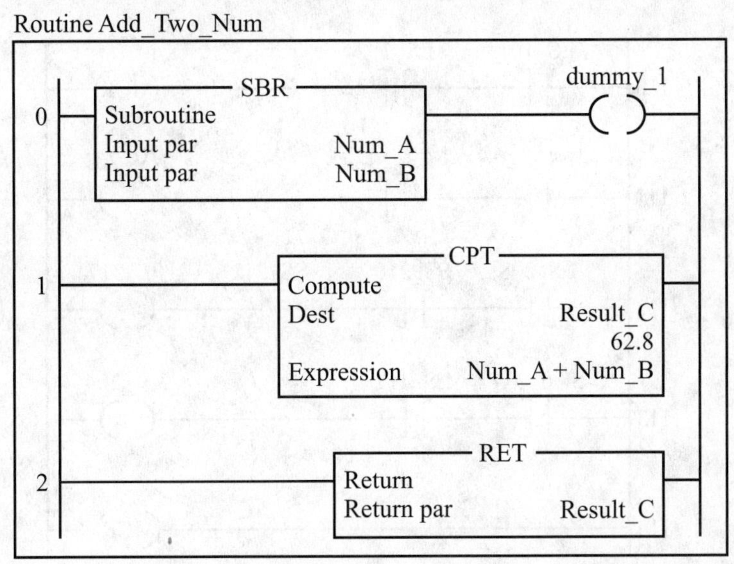

Figure 8.30. ControlLogix JSR/SBR/RET example.

cases, the data type of the tag passed to a subroutine should match the data type of the subroutine tag that receives the tag.

Figure 8.30 shows an example use of a subroutine. The main routine calls the Add_Two_Num subroutine, passing two values, Real_1 and Real_2. The Add_Two_Num subroutine receives the two values and places them into Num_A and Num_B. The result of the calculation is placed in Result_C. The RET block then passes the value in Result_C back to the main routine, which places the value into Real_3.

The MCR (master control relay) output coil instruction functions like a software master control relay, disabling non-retentive outputs within a range of rungs. This coil is used in pairs to create "zones" of the ladder program where all non-retentive outputs may be disabled. One MCR defines the start of the zone, and one MCR defines the end of the zone. Rung logic on the rung of the first MCR controls execution of the zone. When this rung logic turns **on** the MCR coil (called "enabling the zone"), all rungs in the zone are scanned normally. When the logic of the first MCR rung causes the MCR coil to be **off**, all rungs in the zone are scanned but only to turn **off** all non-retentive outputs in the zone.

There are some cautions when using an MCR zone:

1. The zone must be ended with an unconditional MCR output coil.
2. MCR zones cannot be nested.
3. Do not jump into or out of a MCR zone.

Also, the MCR instruction is not a substitute for a hard-wired master control relay that provides an emergency power shutdown to the I/O.

An example MCR zone is shown in Figure 8.31. When LS_101 and LS_102 are both **on**, the MCR zone is enabled, and rungs 111 to 113 are scanned normally determining the values of the output coils XV_203, PL_317, and XV_204. When either LS_101 or LS_102 is **off**, the MCR zone is disabled. In this case, XV_203, PL_317, and XV_204 are all turned **off**, regardless of the state of the input conditions for rungs 111 to113.

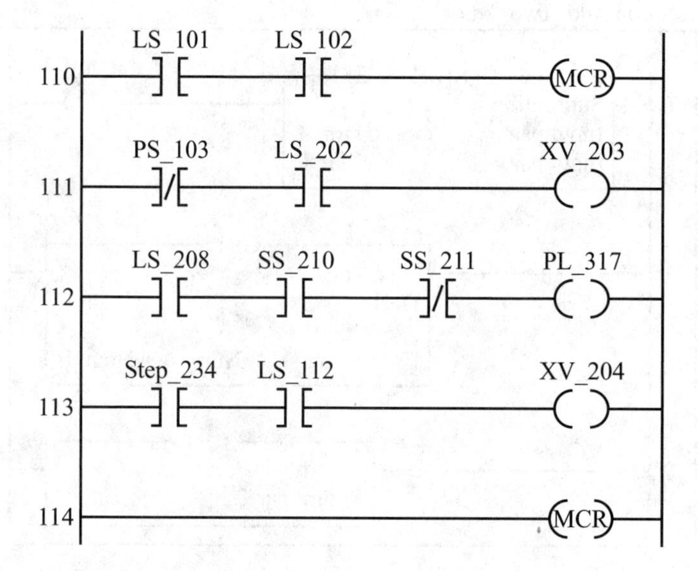

Figure 8.31. ControlLogix MCR example.

The FOR function block is used to repeatedly call a subroutine. The BRK output coil is used within the subroutine to exit the subroutine and exit the FOR loop. A RET output coil in the subroutine exits the subroutine but does not exit the FOR loop (unless the index is greater than or equal to the terminal value). An example FOR function block is shown in Figure 8.32. When enabled, the FOR function block repeatedly executes the "Routine name" until the "Index" value is greater than or equal to the "Terminal value". After each execution of the subroutine, the "Step size" is added to the "Index" and then compared to the "Terminal value".

The FOR block in Figure 8.32 executes the Do_Check subroutine ten times. This example also shows the use of the BRK output coil and the RET block in the subroutine called by the FOR function block. If rung 31 is scanned and LS_823 is **off** and XV_813 is **on**, then the BRK output coil causes the Do_Check subroutine to be exited and the FOR

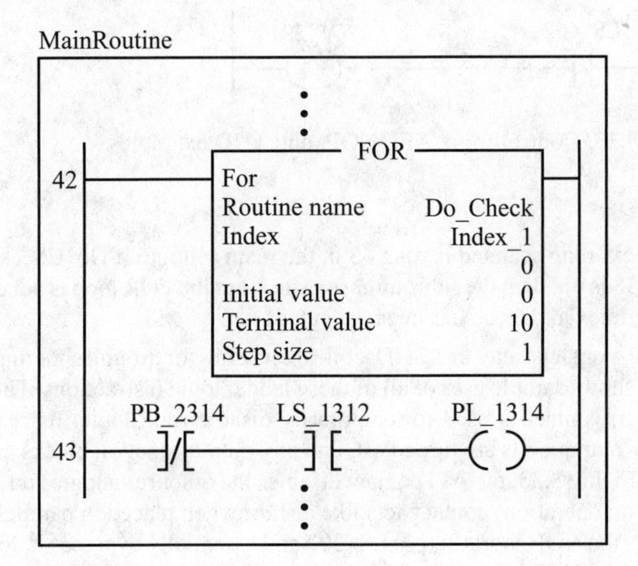

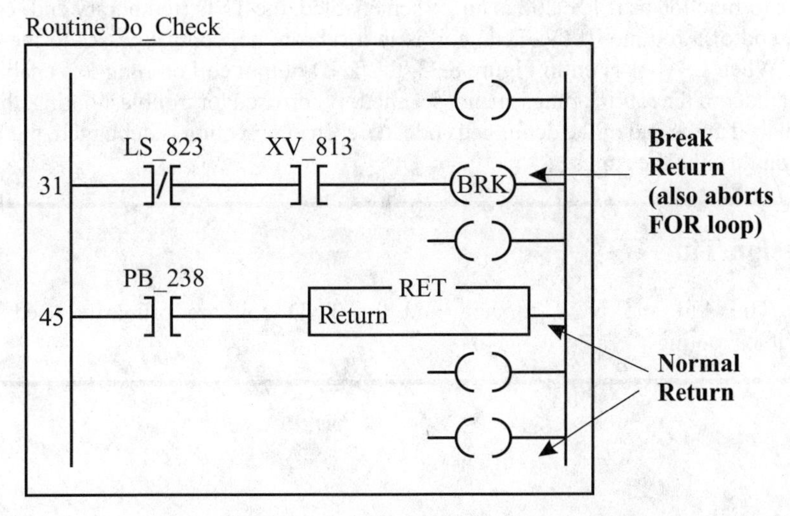

Figure 8.32. ControlLogix FOR and BRK example.

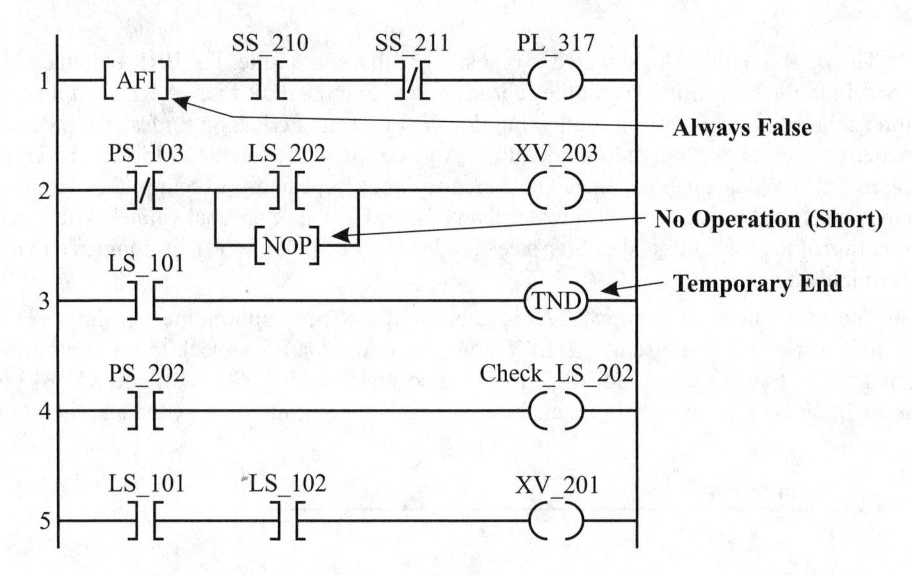

Figure 8.33. ControlLogix AFI, NOP, and TND examples.

loop to be exited. The next rung scanned is rung 43 in the main routine. If Do_Check rung 45 is scanned and PB_238 is **on**, then the subroutine is exited, but the FOR loop is not exited (unless this is the tenth time Do_Check has been executed).

The AFI and NOP contacts and the TND coil are useful for troubleshooting and debugging. Figure 8.33 shows sample uses of all of these ladder logic instructions. The AFI (always false instruction) contact is used to temporarily disable rung logic. Its result is always false, and so any output coils are turned **off**, and any output function blocks are not executed. For rung 1 of Figure 8.33, the AFI contact disables the other rung logic and keeps PL_317 **off**. The NOP (no operation) contact acts like a short when placed in parallel with other contacts. In rung 2, the NOP shorts across LS_202 and essentially bypasses it, forcing the logic to function as if LS_202 is **on**. When enabled, the TND (temporary end) coil acts like the end of a routine. If the TND coil is in a subroutine, control passes to the calling routine. When LS_101 is **on** in Figure 8.33, the TND output coil on rung 3 is enabled and the remainder of the routine rungs are not scanned. When used for troubleshooting, the TND coil is placed at the end of the debugged code. As each new section is debugged, the TND is moved on through the rungs.

Design Tip

The AFI and NOP contacts and the TND coil are primarily used for troubleshooting.

8.5 OTHER PLC-5/SLC-500 FUNCTION BLOCKS

The PLC-5/SLC-500 PLCs provide ladder function blocks for bit shifting, FIFO/LIFO queues, special array functions, and program control. The basic operation and simple application of these function blocks are described in this section. Longer bit shifting and FIFO/LIFO applications are presented in section 8.8.

The PLC-5 and SLC-500 function blocks described in this section are very similar to the ControlLogix function blocks of the same name. However, there are enough differences between the operation of the corresponding ControlLogix and PLC-5/SLC-500 function blocks that the operation of each block is described instead of just referring to the description in section 8.4. One major difference is that the block parameters are shown as addresses and not as symbols. The symbols can be used when entering the blocks into the ladder logic program, but the programming software displays the addresses in the function block.

The specific function blocks that are supported vary among the different PLC-5 and SLC-500 processors. Table 8.1 shows which function blocks are supported by the PLC-5 and SLC-500 PLCs. None of them support the ControlLogix NOP (no operation) contact. Many of these instructions use the file control data file element (R6:*n*) structure, shown in Figure 8.34. The parts of this structure that are pertinent to each function block are described in conjunction with the function block.

Table 8.1 Function Blocks Supported by PLC-5 and SLC-500

Block Name	Processor Model		
	Original PLC-5	Enhanced PLC-5	SLC-500
BSL, BSR	X	X	X
FFL, FFU	X	X	X[1]
LFL, LFU		X	X[1]
FAL, FSC	X	X	
FLL, COP	X	X	X
FBC, DDT	X	X	X[2]
JMP, LBL	X	X	X
JSR, SBR, RET	X	X	X[3]
MCR	X	X	X
FOR, NXT, BRK	X	X	
AFI	X	X	
TND	X	X	X

Notes:

1. SLC-5/02 and higher
2. Series C SLC-5/03 and higher
3. Limits on subroutine nesting

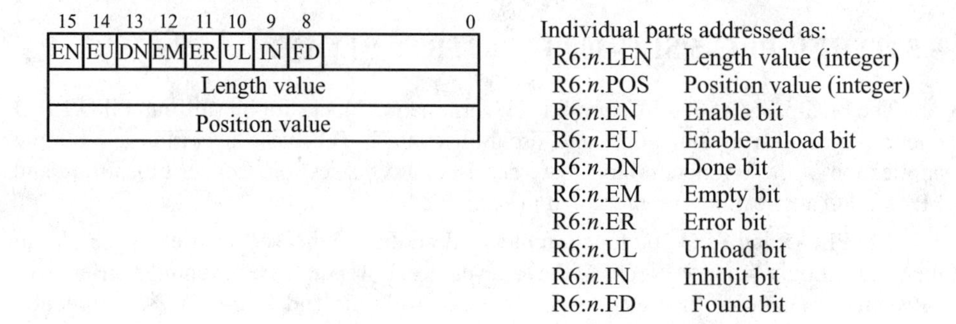

Figure 8.34. PLC-5 control element structure.

8.5.1 Shift Bit in Register

The bit shifting function blocks and the operation that occurs for each one are:

Block Name	Operation Result
BSL	Bit shift left
BSR	Bit shift right

An example BSL function block is shown in Figure 8.35*a*, and an example BSR function block is shown in Figure 8.36*a*. The operands of both of these blocks are described as follows:

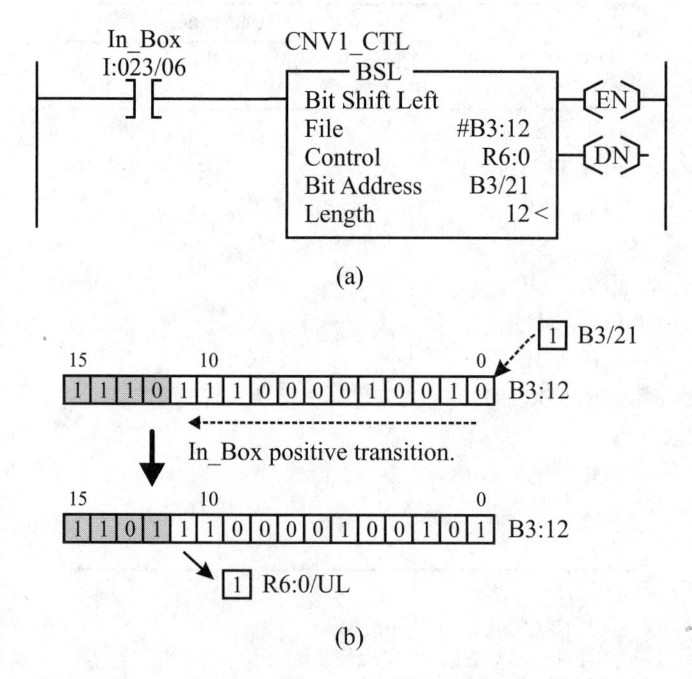

Figure 8.35. PLC-5 bit-shift left: *(a)* example BSL block; *(b)* bit array before and after shift.

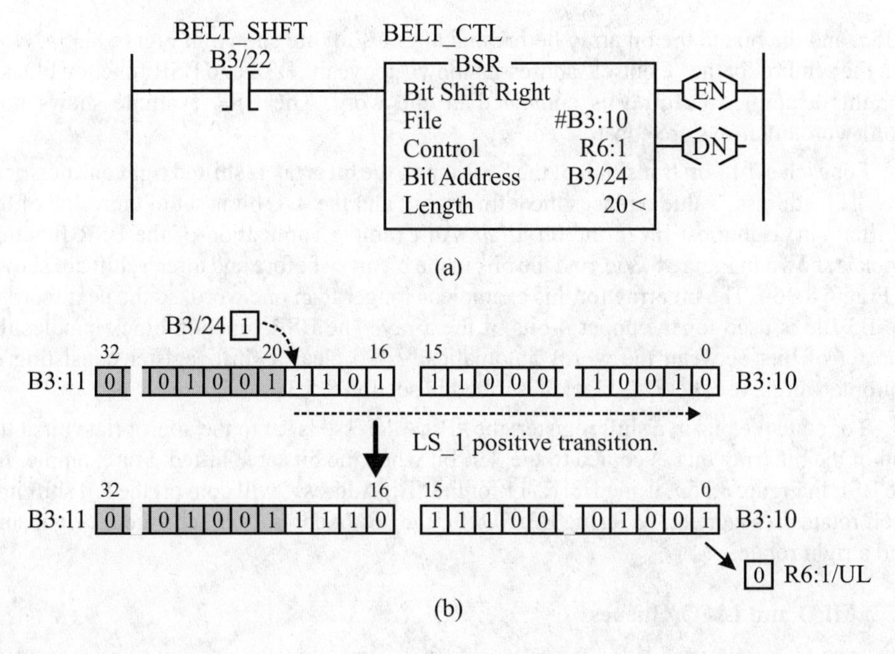

Figure 8.36. PLC-5 bit-shift right: *(a)* example BSR block; *(b)* bit array before and after shift.

File – Start of bit array. Must be the address of a 16-bit word.
Control – Address of control structure (Figure 8.34).
Bit Address – Bit (Boolean) that will be shifted into the bit array
Length – Number of bits in the bit array.

The least-significant bit of the bit array is always bit 0 of the "File" word address. For the "Control" address defined in Figure 8.35*a*, the individual parts (fields) of the structure are addressed as follows:

Symbol Reference	**Address Reference**	**Description**
CNV1_CTL/UL	R6:0/UL	Unload (bit shifted out)
CNV1_CTL/EN	R6:0/EN	Enable
CNV1_CTL/ER	R6:0/ER	Error (length < 0)
CNV1_CTL.LEN	R6:0.LEN	Bit array length

When entering the symbol reference into a block parameter, a "/" or "." can be used to separate the symbol or address from the field name, but the above table shows how they are displayed.

For each **off**-to-**on** transition of the BSL input, the bit array is shifted left one position. The "Bit Address" value replaces the rightmost bit, and the .UL bit is set to the value of the (shifted out) leftmost bit in the bit array. The .EN bit is identical to the block input condition. The .ER bit is set if the .LEN field is less than zero. The value of the array length (.LEN) can be accessed as an integer. An application of the BSL function block is shown in Figure

8.35*a*, and the bits in the bit array before and after a shift are shown in Figure 8.35*b*. Note that the symbol for the "Control" address is shown above the BSL and BSR function blocks. For this example, the array is contained in one word. The BSR example shows how multi-word bit arrays are constructed.

For each **off**-to-**on** transition of the BSR input, the bit array is shifted right one position. The "Bit Address" value replaces the leftmost bit, and the .UL bit is set to the value of the (shifted out) rightmost bit in the bit array. An example application of the BSR function block is shown in Figure 8.36*a*, and the bits in the bit array before and after a shift are shown in Figure 8.36*b*. The bit array for this example is longer than one word, so the next word in the B3 file is used for the upper 4 bits of the array. The BSR function block handles the transfer of bits between the words automatically. To clear a shift register consisting of multiple words, use the FLL block described in section 8.5.3.

To rotate the bits in a shift register, the "Bit Address" is set to the appropriate bit at the end of the bit array that is copied to the .UL bit when the bits are shifted. For example, for the BSL in Figure 8.35*a*, using B3:12/11 for the "Bit Address" will convert the left shift into a left rotate. In Figure 8.36*a*, using B3:10/0 for the "Bit Address" will change the right shift into a right rotate.

8.5.2 FIFO and LIFO Queues

The array (queue) shifting function blocks and the operation that occurs for each one are:

Block Name	Operation Result
FFL	Load value to the next FIFO position
FFU	Unload value from first FIFO position
LFL	Load value to the next LIFO position
LFU	Unload value from last LIFO position

The LFL and LFU blocks are not valid for the original PLC-5 and some SLC-500 processors.

Typically, the FFL and FFU are used together to construct a FIFO data array. An example application of the FFL and FFU blocks is shown in Figure 8.37. For the FFL and FFU function blocks, the parameters are described as follows:

FIFO – Address of first integer in FIFO array.
Control – Address of control structure (Figure 8.34).
Length – Maximum length of the FIFO array.
Position – Position where the next data will be loaded.
Source – (FFL only) Tag of the integer that will be stored in the array.
Dest – (FFU only) Tag where the integer will be placed after it is unloaded from the FIFO.

Normally, the FFL and FFU refer to the same "Control" address. For the control address defined in Figure 8.37, the individual fields of the CONTROL structure are addressed as follows:

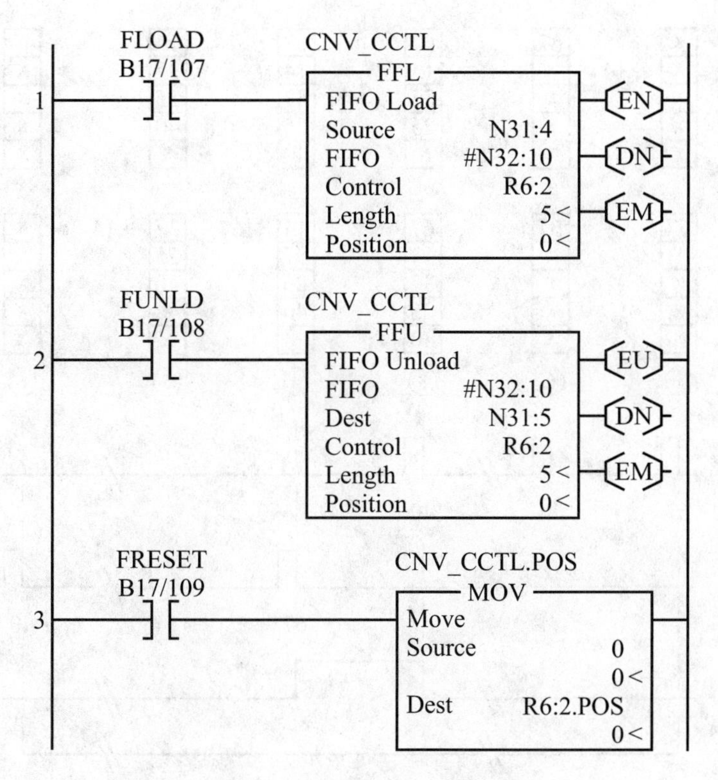

Figure 8.37. PLC-5 FIFO array function blocks.

Symbol **Reference**	**Address** **Reference**	**Description**
CNV_CCTL/EN	R6:2/EN	Load enabled
CNV_CCTL/EU	R6:2/EU	Unload enabled
CNV_CCTL/DN	R6:2/DN	FIFO full
CNV_CCTL/EM	R6:2/EM	FIFO empty
CNV_CCTL.LEN	R6:2.LEN	FIFO array length
CNV_CCTL.POS	R6:2.POS	Next entry will load here

For each **off**-to-**on** transition of the FFL input, the "Source" value is placed in the FIFO array at the current position, and the position (.POS) is incremented by one. The .EN bit is identical to the FFL block input condition. The .DN bit is set if the .POS is equal to the array length. If data is added to an already full FIFO, the new data replaces the previously added data entry. The position value of the FIFO (.POS) can be accessed as an integer. In order to reset a FIFO array, set the .POS to zero.

For each **off**-to-**on** transition of the FFU input, the first element in the FIFO array is copied to "Dest", and the remaining data in the array is shifted one position toward the beginning of the array. The position is also decremented by one. The .EU bit is identical to the FFU block input condition. The .EM bit is set if the FIFO is empty (.POS=0). A zero is placed into "Dest" if one attempts to unload an already empty FIFO.

An example operation of the FFL and FFU of Figure 8.37 is shown in Figure 8.38. This example assumes the FIFO starts empty. Five integers are loaded onto the FIFO and then

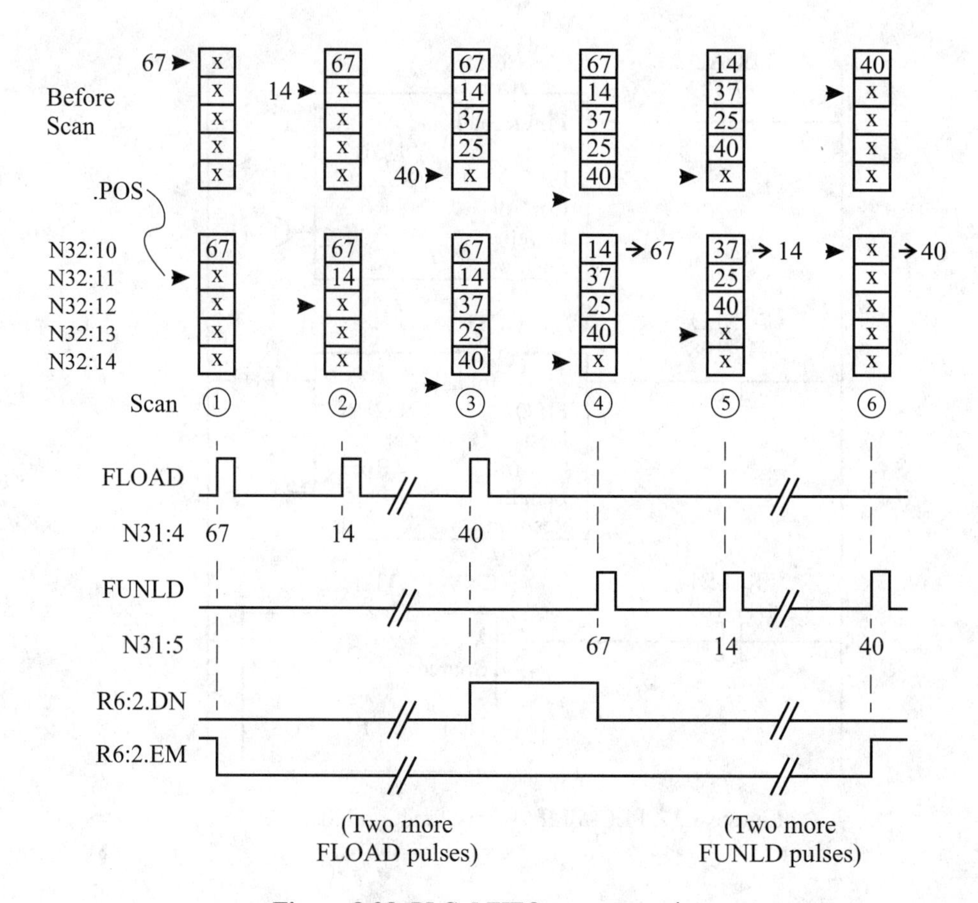

Figure 8.38. PLC-5 FIFO array operation.

unloaded. The FIFO array starts at N32:10 and ends at N32:14. The contents of the FIFO before and after the numbered scans are also shown. The arrow on the left of the array indicates the .POS value, and the arrow on the right indicates the value unloaded into Out_Code. The FIFO is loaded with 67, 14, 37, 25, and 40. When the FIFO is unloaded, the elements unload in the order 67, 14, 37, 25, and 40. The action at each of the numbered scans is as follows:

1. Load stack with In_Code = 67, .EM turned **off**.
2. Load stack with In_Code = 14
   (37 and 25 loaded between scans 2 and 3)
3. Load stack with In_Code = 40, .DN turned **on**.
4. Unload stack, Out_Code set to 67, .DN turned **off**.
5. Unload stack, Out_Code set to 14
   (37 and 25 unloaded between scans 5 and 6)
6. Unload stack, Out_Code set to 40, .EM turned **on**.

Normally, the LFL and LFU are used together to construct a LIFO data array. An example application of the LFL and LFU blocks is shown in Figure 8.39. The operands for these instructions are identical to the FFL/FFU except for the "LIFO" operand, which is the first element of the LIFO array.

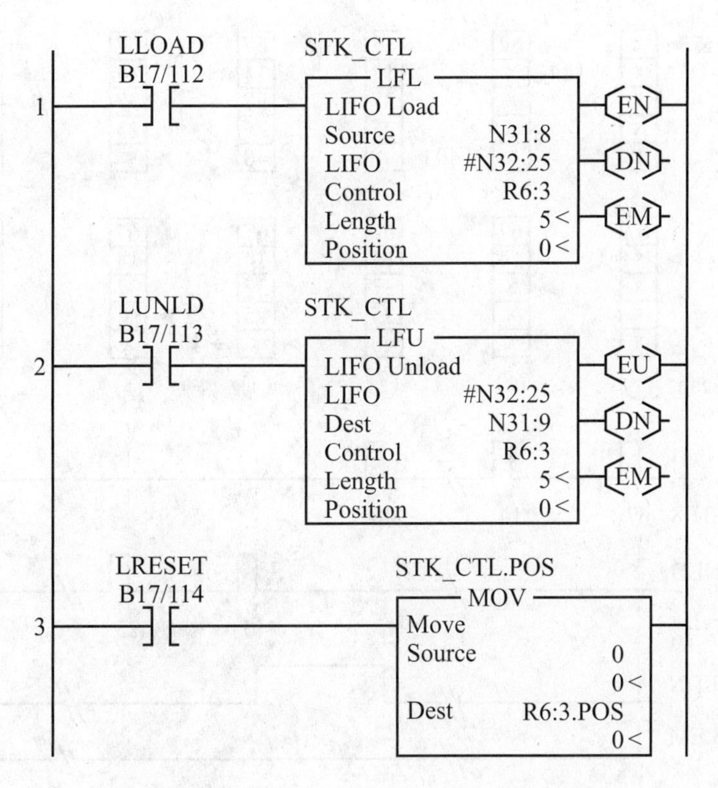

Figure 8.39. PLC-5 LIFO array function blocks.

For each **off**-to-**on** transition of the LFL input, the "Source" value is placed in the LIFO array at the current position, and the position (.POS) is incremented by one. The .EN bit is identical to the LFL block input condition. The .DN bit is set if the .POS is equal to the array length. If data is added to an already full LIFO, the new data replaces the previously added data entry. The position value of the LIFO (.POS) can be accessed as DINT. In order to reset a LIFO array, set the .POS to zero.

For each **off**-to-**on** transition of the LFU input, the last element in the LIFO array is copied to "Dest", and the position is decremented by one. The .EU bit is identical to the LFU block input condition. The .EM bit is set if the LIFO is empty (.POS=0). A zero is placed into "Dest" if one attempts to unload an already empty LIFO.

Figure 8.40 shows an example operation of the LFL and LFU of Figure 8.39. The LIFO starts empty. Five DINTs are loaded onto the LIFO and then unloaded. The contents of the LIFO before and after the numbered scans are also shown. The LIFO is loaded with 67, 14, 37, 25, and 40. When the LIFO is unloaded, the elements are unloaded in the order 40, 25, 37, 14, and 67. The action at each of the numbered scans is as follows:

1. Load stack with In_Code = 67, .EM turned **off**.
2. Load stack with In_Code = 14
   (37 and 25 loaded between scans 2 and 3)
3. Load stack with In_Code = 40, .DN turned **on**.
4. Unload stack, Out_Code set to 40, .DN turned **off**.
5. Unload stack, Out_Code set to 25

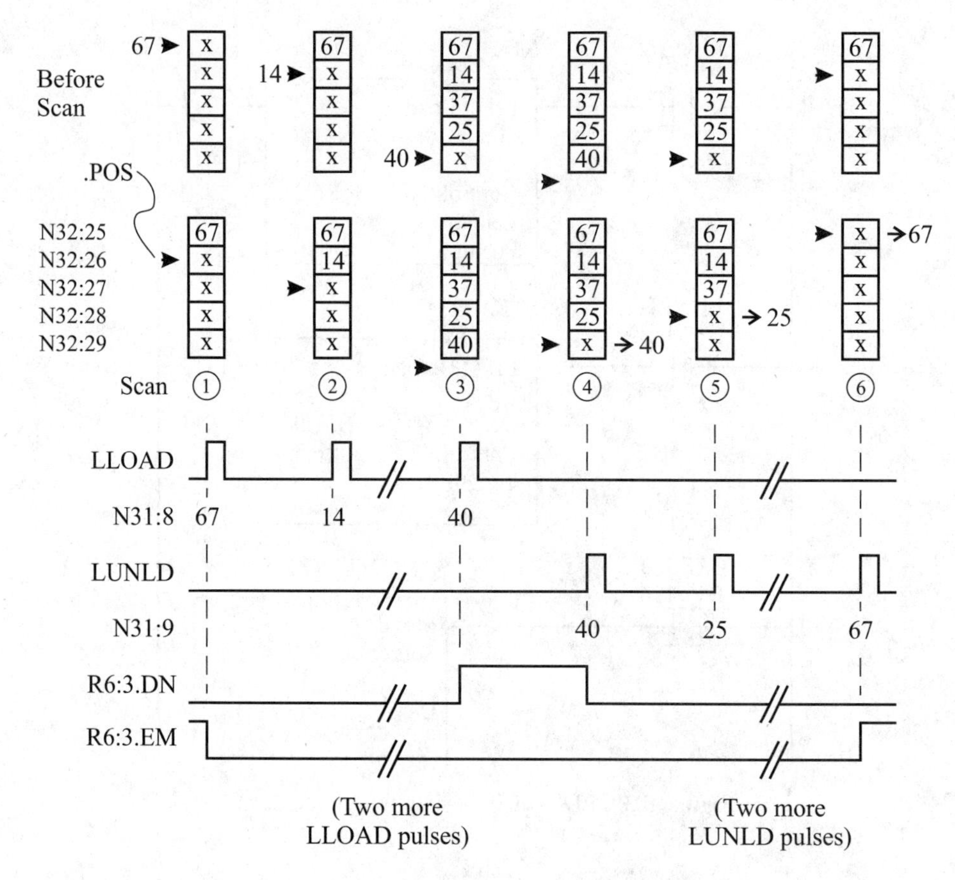

Figure 8.40. PLC-5 LIFO array operation.

(37 and 14 unloaded between scans 5 and 6)

6. Unload stack, Out_Code set to 67, .EM turned **on**.

8.5.3 Other Array Function Blocks

Other specialized numerical and bit array function blocks and the operation that occurs for each one are:

Block Name	Operation Result
FAL	Array (file) arithmetic and logic
FSC	Array (file) search and compare
FLL	Fill array with a value
COP	Copy values, arrays, or structures
FBC	Find mismatches between two bit arrays
DDT	Find and correct mismatched bit arrays

The operation of each of these instructions is explained and illustrated with short examples. Other array functions are available (e.g., array sorting and averaging), but are not covered in this text.

The FAL (file arithmetic/logic) function block performs the same operations on arrays as the CPT (compute) function block performs on individual elements. In addition, this block can be programmed to perform the operation on the entire array when it executes or incrementally, that is, perform only a few operations each time the block is scanned. The latter mode is useful when processing large arrays or data that is not time-critical. Only simple applications are described in this section. The interested reader should consult the instruction set reference (Rockwell Automation, 1998) for more details.

An example FAL function block is shown in Figure 8.41. The parameters are as follows:

Control – Address of control structure (Figure 8.34).

Length – Number of elements in the array to be manipulated.

Position – Current position in the array, initially it is typically zero.

Mode – How array elements are processed (ALL, INC, or a number).

Dest – Tag of the expression result.

Expression – A valid arithmetic, logical, conversion, and copy operation.

For the "Expression" operand, the instruction set reference (Rockwell Automation, 1998) lists valid expressions. In the "Dest" and "Expression" operands, a "#" sign before the address signifies the address as the start of an array and therefore .POS is the index into the array. The "#" sign also means that this function block will modify the contents of the index register (S:24).

For the control tag defined in Figure 8.41*a*, the individual fields of the R6:5 control structure are addressed as follows:

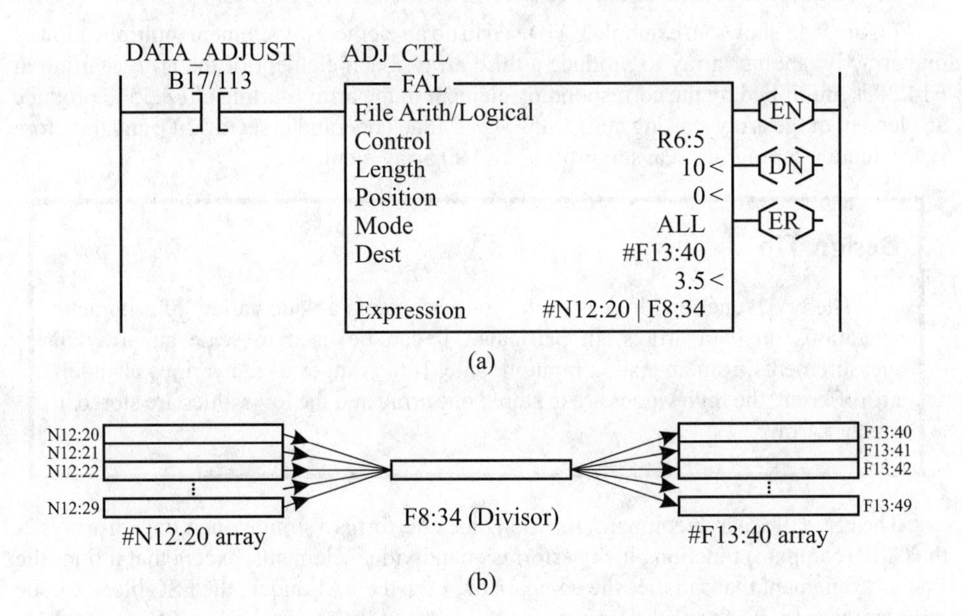

Figure 8.41. PLC-5 FAL array divided by constant example: *(a)* ladder logic; *(b)* processing of array elements.

Symbol Reference	Address Reference	Description
ADJ_CTL/EN	R6:5/EN	FAL enabled
ADJ_CTL/DN	R6:5/DN	Operation done
ADJ_CTL/ER	R6:5/ER	Overflow for one element
ADJ_CTL.LEN	R6:5.LEN	Number of elements to process
ADJ_CTL.POS	R6:5.POS	Index of current element being processed

The possible values of "Mode" are:

ALL When block input condition changes from **off** to **on**, all specified array elements are processed.

INC One specified array element processed for each **off**-to-**on** transition of the block input condition. The .DN bit is set when all array elements have been processed.

[number] When block input condition changes from **off** to **on**, [number] of array elements are processed on each scan of this instruction until all specified array elements are processed. The .DN bit is set when all array elements have been processed. The [number] is any valid non-negative integer.

Figure 8.41 shows an example FAL used to divide every element of the integer array starting at N12:20 by the floating-point value in F8:34 and place the results in the floating-point array starting at F13:40. The operation is in the "ALL" mode, meaning all 10 specified divisions are processed for each **off**-to-**on** transition of the FAL input. If the "Mode" operand is set to "3", then it will require 4 program scans to process all 10 array elements. If the "Mode" operand is set to "INC", then 10 **off**-to-**on** transitions of DATA_ADJUST are required to process all 10 elements of the arrays.

Figure 8.42 shows an example FAL used to do an element-by-element multiplication of one array by another array to produce a third array. Each element of the array starting at F14:20 is multiplied by the corresponding element in the array starting at F8:35 to produce an element of the array starting at F15:35. The "Mode" operand is set to "20", and therefore it will require 5 program scans to process all 100 array elements.

Design Tip

The FAL function block is useful for performing a wide variety of arithmetic operations on data arrays. In particular, it can be used to scale an array of measurements from an analog input module. If the ranges of the various channels are different, the high values are in stored one array and the low values are stored in another array.

The FSC (file search/compare) function block performs a similar operation on arrays as the CMP (compare) function block performs on individual elements, except that it finds the first array element that satisfies the comparison. Like the FAL block, the FSC block can be programmed to perform the comparison on the entire array when it executes or incrementally, that is, perform only a few comparisons each time the block is scanned. The latter mode is useful when processing large arrays or data that is not time-critical.

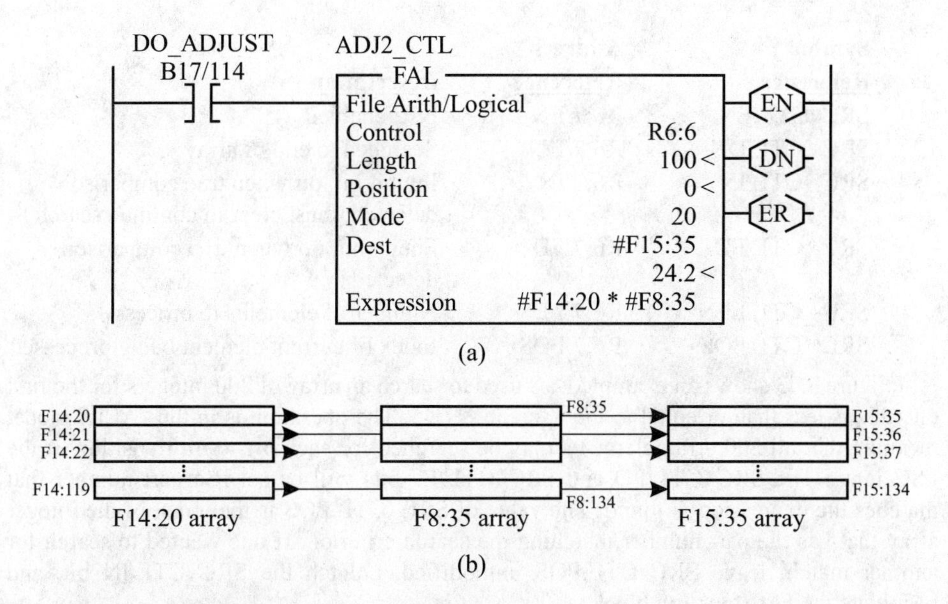

Figure 8.42. PLC-5 FAL array multiplied by array example: *(a)* ladder logic; *(b)* processing of array elements.

An example FSC function block is shown in Figure 8.43. The parameters are as follows:

Control – Address of control structure (Figure 8.34).
Length – Number of elements in the array to be searched.
Position – Current position in the array, initially it is typically zero.
Mode – How array elements are processed (same as FAL "Mode").
Expression – A valid comparison operation.

A "#" sign before the address in the "Expression" operand signifies the address as the start of an array, and therefore .POS is the index into the array. The "#" sign also means that this function block will modify the contents of the index register (S:24).

For the control tag defined in Figure 8.43, the individual fields of the R6:7 control structure are addressed as follows:

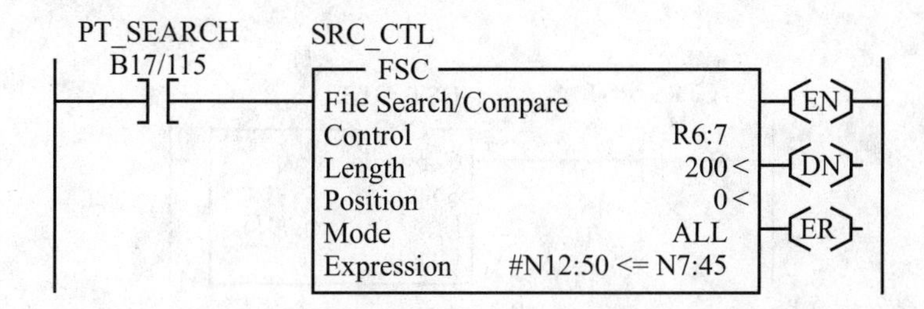

Figure 8.43. PLC-5 FSC example.

Symbol Reference	**Address Reference**	**Description**
SRC_CTL/EN	R6:7/EN	FSC enabled
SRC _CTL/DN	R6:7/DN	Searched to end of array
SRC _CTL/IN	R6:7/IN	Inhibit bit, **on** when true comparison detected; must clear to continue search
SRC _CTL/FD	R6:7/FD	Found bit, **on** when true comparison detected
SRC _CTL.LEN	R6:7.LEN	Number of elements to process
SRC _CTL.POS	R6:7.POS	Index of current element being processed

Figure 8.43 shows an example FSC used to search an array of 200 integers for the first one that is less than or equal to the value in N7:45. The operation is in the "ALL" mode, meaning that all 200 array elements may be searched for each **off**-to-**on** transition of the FSC input. The SRC_CTL/FD and SRC_CTL/IN bits will be set if a part number that matches the expression is found. The value of SRC_CTL.POS is the index of the integer array that has the part number matching the search criterion. If one wanted to search for another match, leave SRC_CTL.POS unmodified, unlatch the SRC_CTL/IN bit, and re-initiate the FSC function block.

The FLL (fill) function block fills the elements of an array with the same value and is useful for initialization. An example FLL block is shown in Figure 8.44. The "Source" operand is either the address containing the value to copy or a constant value. The "Dest" is the address of the first element in an integer or floating-point array. The address must be prefixed with the "#" character. The "Length" is the number of elements to fill. The symbol shown above the block is the symbol for the "Dest" address. The "Source" and "Dest" should be the same data type since there is no conversion between data types.

The COP (copy) function block copies arrays. The array can be a simple type (e.g., integer, word, floating point) or an array of structures (e.g., an array of counters or timers). An example application of the COP block is shown in Figure 8.45 that copies an array of 5 counters to another array of 5 counters. The "Source" and "Dest" operands are addresses of

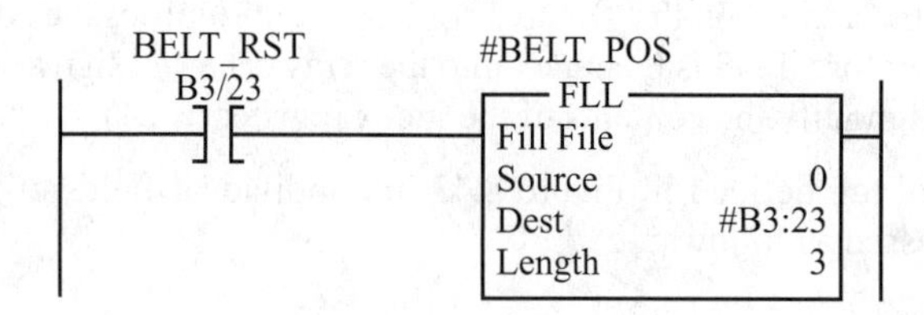

Figure 8.44. PLC-5 FLL example.

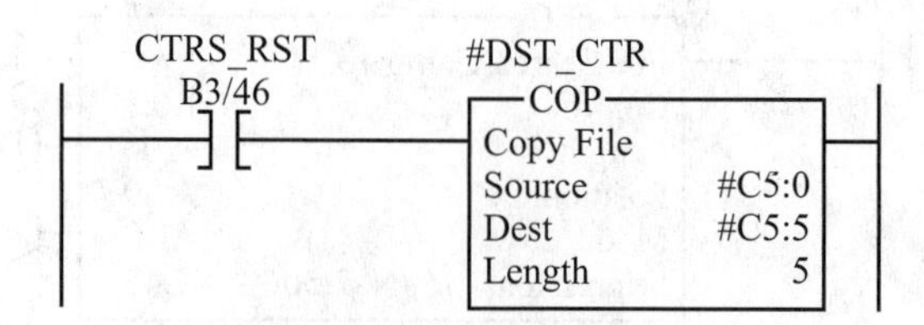

Figure 8.45. PLC-5 COP example.

the source and destination arrays, respectively. The “Length” is the number of elements to write in the destination file. The symbol shown above the block is the symbol for the “Dest” address. As for the FLL, the “Source” and “Dest” should be the same data type since there is no conversion between data types. If the “Source” is an array of integers, “Dest” is an array of timers, and the “Length” is 5, 15 integers are copied into 5 timer structures.

The FBC (file bit compare) function block compares two bit arrays and records the bit number of each difference in a result array. An example FBC block is shown in Figure 8.46. The parameters of this block are described as follows:

Source – Start address of bit array compared to reference.
Reference – Start address of reference bit array.
Result – Start address of integer array to store search results.
(Cmp.) Control – Control structure for compare.
Length – Number of bit locations to compare
Position – Current position in source array. Typically initialized to zero.
(Result) Control – Control structure for the results.
Length – Number of storage locations in result array.
Position – Current position in result array. Typically initialized to zero.

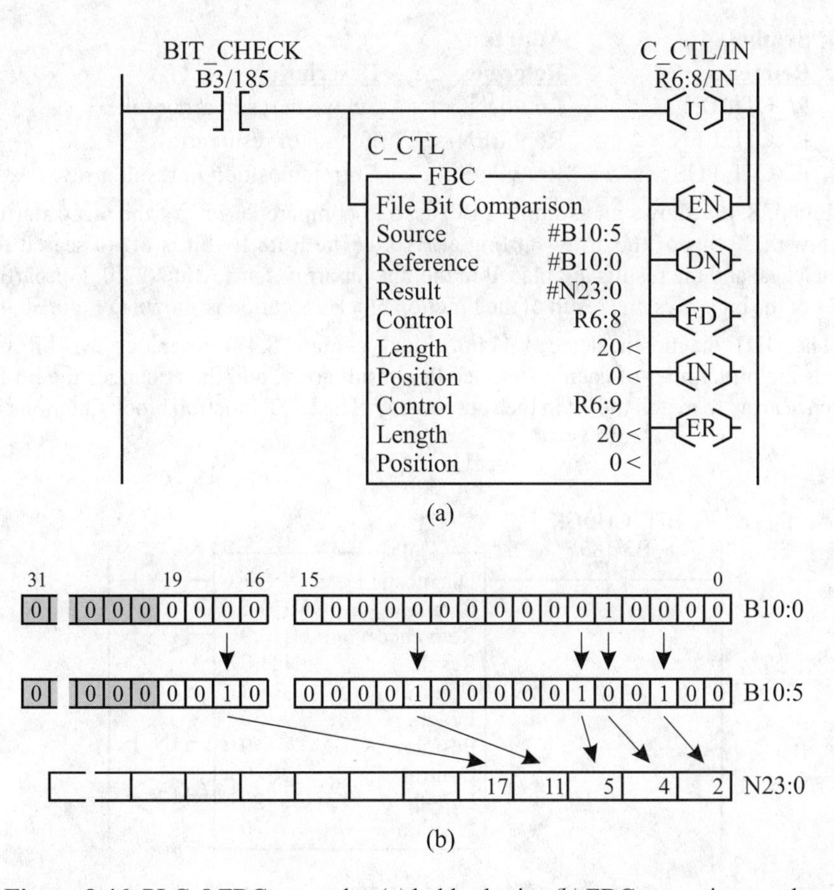

Figure 8.46. PLC-5 FBC example: *(a)* ladder logic; *(b)* FBC execution results.

The two "Control" operands must be different addresses of a control structure (Figure 8.34). The first "Control" address is for the comparison and for the address defined in Figure 8.46, the individual fields of the control structure are addressed as:

Symbol Reference	**Address Reference**	**Description**
C_CTL/EN	R6:8/EN	FBC enabled
C_CTL/DN	R6:8/DN	Set when last bit in array compared.
C_CTL/FD	R6:8/FD	Set when mismatch recorded (one-at-a-time operation) or all mismatches recorded (all-per-scan) operation.
C_CTL/IN	R6:8/IN	Search mode bit, **off** to search for all mismatches, **on** to search for next mismatch only.
C_CTL.LEN	R6:8.LEN	Number of bits to compare.
C_CTL.POS	R6:8.POS	Index of current bit.

The second "Control" address is for the result array. If the address of this operand in Figure 8.46 is defined as R_CTL, the individual fields of the control structure are addressed as:

Symbol Reference	**Address Reference**	**Description**
R_CTL/DN	R6:9/DN	Set when result array full.
R_CTL.LEN	R6:9.LEN	Length of result array.
R_CTL.POS	R6:9.POS	Current position in result array.

Figure 8.46*a* shows an example FBC used to compare 20 bits of the array starting at B10:5 with 20 bits of the array starting at B10:0. The R6:8/IN bit is **off** to search for all mismatches, and the results are placed in the integer array starting at N23:0. For particular values of the bit arrays, the result of the function block execution is shown in Figure 8.46*b*.

The DDT diagnostic detect function block (Figure 8.47) compares two bit arrays, records the bit number of each difference in a result array, and then changes the bit in the reference array to match the bit in the source array. The DDT function block functions in the

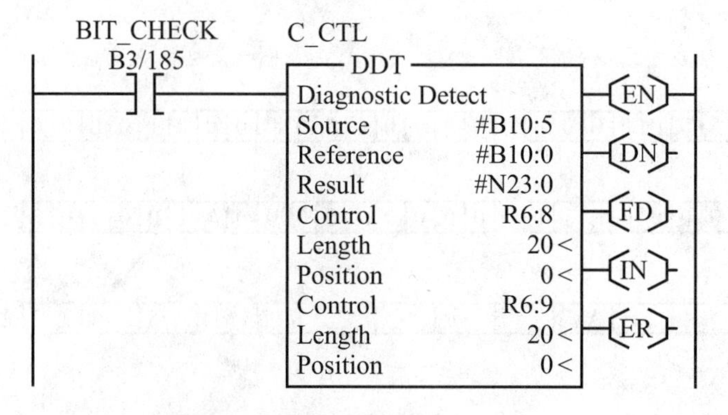

Figure 8.47. PLC-5 DDT function block.

same manner as the FBC function block except that the DDT function block changes the reference bits to match the source bits.

8.5.4 Program Execution Control

The PLC-5 offers a number of instructions that can control ladder logic execution. The SLC-500 processors also support many of these instructions. The names and the operation that occurs for each one are:

Block Name	Operation Result
JMP	Jump to a defined label
LBL	Jump destination
JSR	Jump to subroutine, passing data
SBR	Pass data to subroutine
RET	Return results from subroutine
MCR	Master control relay; disable logic section
FOR	Repeatedly execute rungs
NXT	Defines last rung repeated by For-Next loop
BRK	Abnormal exit of For-Next loop.
AFI	Disable rung logic
TND	Mark temporary end of ladder

Depending on the particular instruction, it may be a contact, or a coil, or a function block. The operation of each of these instructions is explained and illustrated with short examples.

The JMP (jump) coil and LBL (label) contact are used together to skip portions of ladder logic. When the JMP coil is turned **on**, the ladder scan skips to the referenced LBL contact. The labels are numbers, 0-255 for the enhanced PLC-5 and SLC-500 processors, and 0-31 for the original PLC-5 processors. The label is displayed as Q*n*:*x*, where *n* is the ladder logic file number and *x* is the label number. One can jump either forward or backward. Jumping backward lets the controller iterate certain sections of logic. However, jumping backward an excessive number of times will cause the controller to fault if the scan time is too long. Jumping forward decreases the scan time by skipping logic segments until needed. One drawback to jumping forward is that the logic between the jump coil and the label contact is not scanned, so any output coils are not changed. An example ladder segment with two jump and two label instructions is shown in Figure 8.48. For simplicity, the ordinary contact and coil addresses are not shown.

The JSR (jump to subroutine), SBR (subroutine), and RET (return) function blocks are used to execute program files other than the main ladder program file. Large programs are often broken into subroutine program files, which are called from the main program. When enabled, the JSR function block directs logic execution to the first rung of the specified program file, and if needed, passes parameters to the file. If parameters are passed to the subroutine, the first rung of the subroutine file must have a SBR function block. Otherwise, if no parameters are passed to the subroutine, the SBR block is not needed. Likewise, the RET function block appears on the last rung of a subroutine file if parameters are passed back to the calling routine. Actually, the RET block can have conditions to enable it and occur before the last subroutine rung. In this case, if the RET block is not executed, ladder logic execution continues after the rung that contains the RET block. If the RET block is

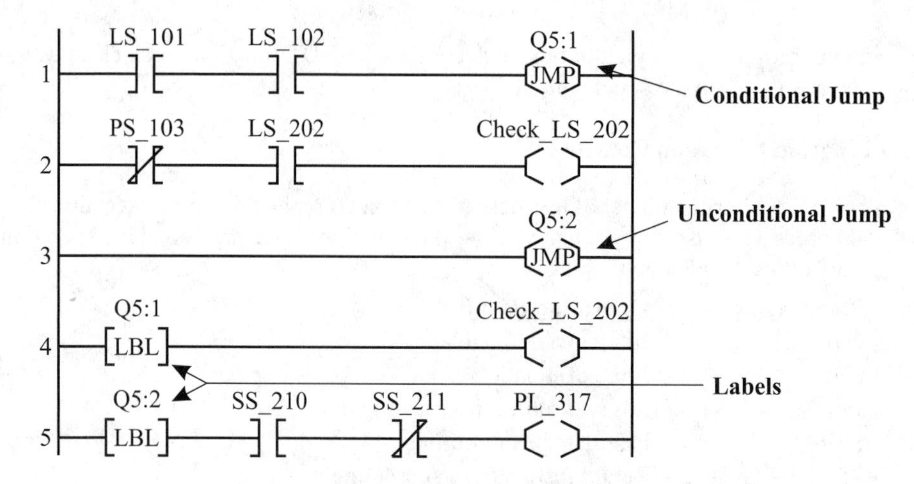

Figure 8.48. PLC-5 JMP and LBL example.

omitted, the subroutine automatically returns back to the calling routine after the last subroutine rung is scanned, but no parameters are passed back.

Subroutines can call other subroutines, often called *nested subroutines*, as shown in Figure 8.29. A program can have up to eight levels of nested subroutines (four for SLC 5/01).

The parameters are passed into and out of a subroutine by value. A JSR input parameter is copied to the memory location specified in the SBR input parameter. The first JSR input parameter is copied to the first address in the SBR block of the subroutine program file. A RET return parameter is copied to the memory location specified as a return parameter of the calling JSR. Constants, addresses (word, integer, or floating point), and structure elements (e.g., counter accumulator) are valid parameters. The data type of the element passed to a subroutine should match the data type of the address specified in the SBR block.

Figure 8.49 shows an example use of a subroutine. The main program file (file 2) calls subroutine (program) file 10, passing two values, N7:29 and F8:41. The subroutine receives the two values and places them into N23:0 and F24:0. The result of the calculation is placed in F24:1. The RET block then passes the value in F24:1 back to the main routine, which places the value into F8:42.

The MCR (master control relay) output coil instruction functions like a software master control relay, disabling non-retentive outputs within a range of rungs. This coil is used in pairs to create "zones" of the ladder program where all non-retentive outputs may be disabled. One MCR defines the start of the zone, and one MCR defines the end of the zone. Rung logic on the rung of the first MCR controls execution of the zone. When this rung logic turns **on** the MCR coil (called "enabling the zone"), all rungs in the zone are scanned normally. When the logic of the first MCR rung causes the MCR coil to be **off**, all rungs in the zone are scanned, but only to turn **off** all non-retentive outputs in the zone.

There are some cautions when using an MCR zone:

1. The zone must be ended with an unconditional MCR output coil.
2. MCR zones cannot be nested.
3. Do not jump into or out of a MCR zone.

Main Ladder program file 2

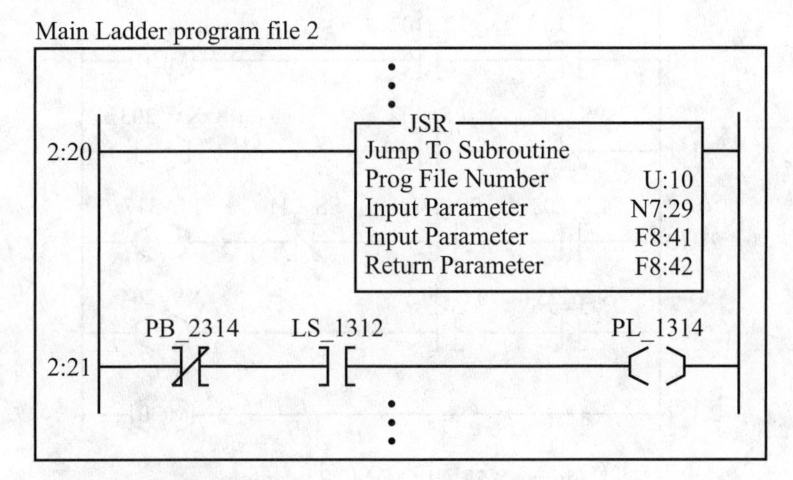

Subroutine program file 10

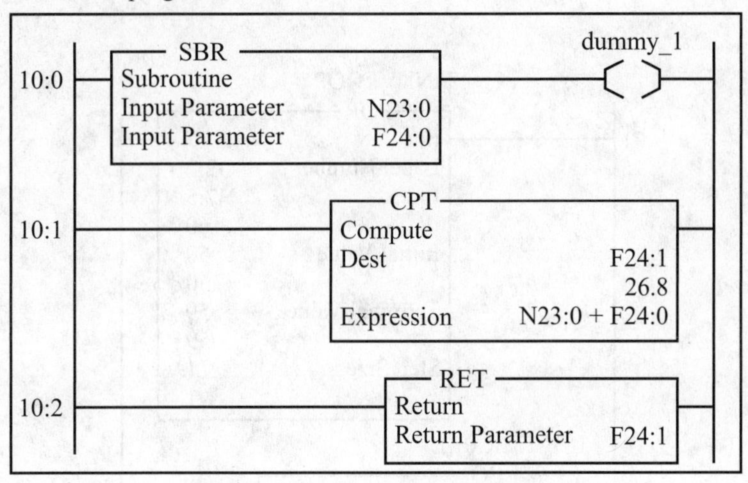

Figure 8.49. PLC-5 JSR/SBR/RET example.

Also, the MCR instruction is not a substitute for a hard-wired master control relay that provides an emergency power shutdown to the I/O.

An example MCR zone is shown in Figure 8.50. When LS_101 and LS_102 are both **on**, the MCR zone is enabled and rungs 2:111 to 2:113 are scanned normally determining the values of the output coils XV_203, PL_317, and XV_204. When either LS_101 or LS_102 is **off**, the MCR zone is disabled. In this case XV_203, PL_317, and XV_204 are all turned **off**, regardless of the state of the input conditions for rungs 2:111 to 2:113.

The FOR and NXT function blocks are used to create a For-Next loop in the ladder logic, that is, define rungs that are repeatedly scanned a certain number of times. The rungs to be repeatedly scanned are between the FOR and NXT function blocks. When executed, the BRK output coil aborts a For-Next loop. An example FOR function block is shown in Figure 8.51. When enabled, the FOR function block repeatedly scans the rungs between the FOR block and the NXT block that refers to the same label until the "Index" value is greater than or equal to the "Terminal Value." When the NXT block is scanned, the "Step Size" is

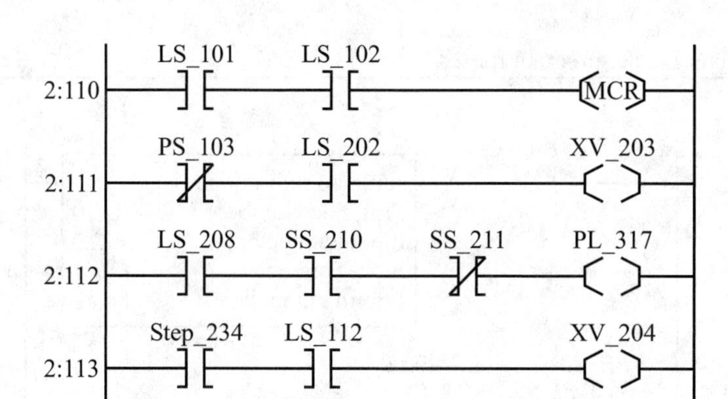

Figure 8.50. PLC-5 MCR example.

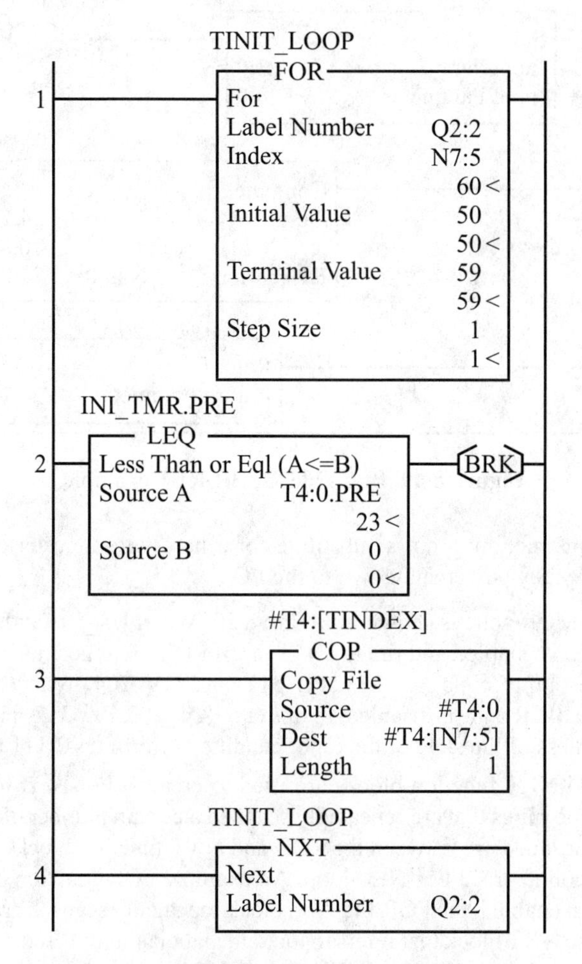

Figure 8.51. PLC-5 FOR/NXT/BRK example.

added to the “Index” and then compared to the “Terminal Value.” If the “Index” value is greater than or equal to the “Terminal Value,” the loop is exited and scanning resumes at the rung following the NXT block.

The FOR loop in Figure 8.51 initializes an array of timers, T4:50 to T4:59 to the preset and accumulator of timer T4:0. This example also illustrates the use of the BRK output coil. If the preset of the T4:0 is not positive, the loop is exited, and T4:50 to T4:59 are not initialized. Note the use of the loop index value (N7:5) to form the indirect address to specify the destination of the COP function block.

The AFI contact and the TND coil are useful for troubleshooting and debugging. Figure 8.52 shows sample uses of these ladder logic instructions. The AFI (always false instruction) contact is used to temporarily disable rung logic. Its result is always false, and so any output coils are turned **off**, and any output function blocks are not executed. For rung 1 of Figure 8.52, the AFI contact disables the other rung logic and keeps PL_317 **off**. When enabled, the TND (temporary end) coil acts like the end of the ladder file. If the TND coil is in a subroutine file, control passes to the calling routine. When LS_101 is **on** in Figure 8.52, the TND output coil on rung 3 is enabled and the remainder of the routine rungs are not scanned. When used for troubleshooting, the TND coil is placed at the end of the debugged code. As each new section is debugged, the TND is moved on through the rungs.

Design Tip

The AFI contact and the TND coil are primarily used for troubleshooting.

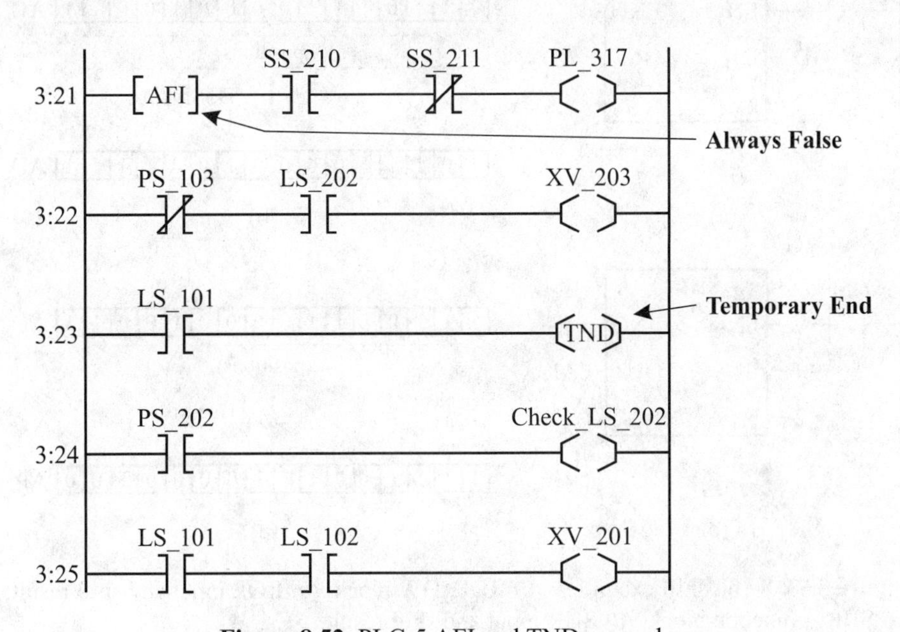

Figure 8.52. PLC-5 AFI and TND examples.

8.6 OTHER SIEMENS S7 FUNCTION BLOCKS

The Siemens S7-300/400 processors support ladder logic function blocks for bit shifting, FIFO/LIFO tables, other table functions, and program control. String processing functions are available, but are not covered in this text. For the S7-200 processors, only the IEC-compatible function blocks are covered. Of the function blocks discussed in this chapter, the S7-200 processors only support the bit shifting functions and some of the program control functions.

8.6.1 Shift Bit in Register

The bit shifting function blocks and the operation that occurs for each one are:

Block Name	Operation Result
ROL_DW	Bit rotate left, double word
ROR_DW	Bit rotate right, double word
SHL_W	Bit shift left, word (zeros filled from right)
SHL_DW	Bit shift left, double word (zeros filled from right)
SHR_I	Bit shift right, integer (sign filled from left)
SHR_DI	Bit shift right, double integer (sign filled from left)
SHR_W	Bit shift right, word (zeros filled from left)
SHR_DW	Bit shift right, double word (zeros filled from left)

Note that all bit shifting functions are not available for all data types. An example ROL_DW block is shown in Figure 8.53*a* and an example SHR_I block is shown in Figure 8.53*c*. For these blocks, the IN input is the word, double word, integer, or double integer to be rotated

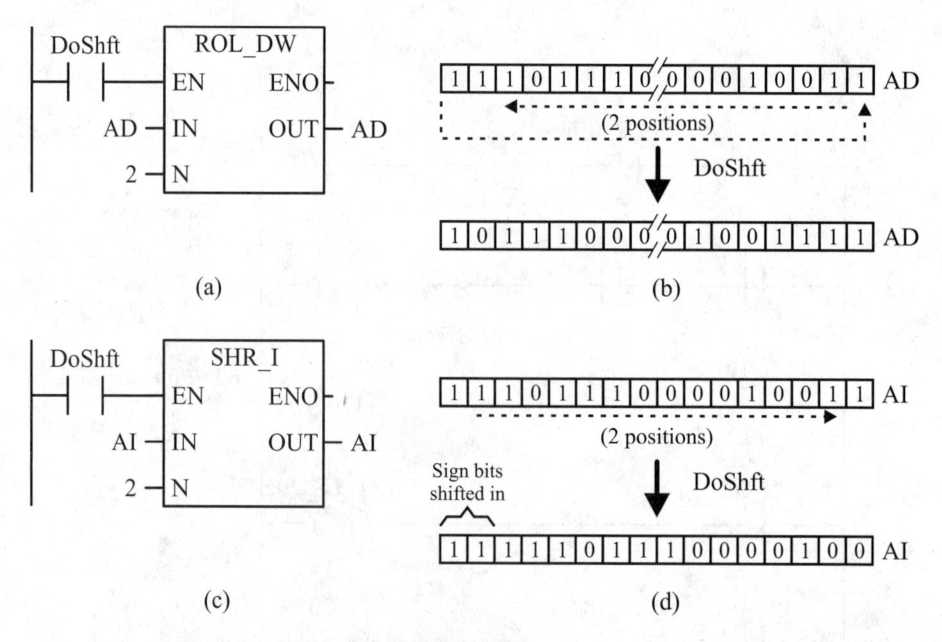

Figure 8.53. S7 bit shift examples: *(a)* ROL_DW block; *(b)* ROL input and shift result; *(c)* SHR_I function block; *(d)* SHR input and shift result.

or shifted and the N input is a WORD data type and indicates the number of bits to rotate or shift. The OUT output is the result of the rotate or shift operation. The ENO output echoes the EN input. Note that the right-shift function blocks operate differently for words and integers. For words, zeros are shifted into the destination. For integers, the bits shifted in from the left are the same as the sign bit of IN. Thus, shifting right does not change the sign of the number. As an example, Figure 8.53 shows the result of rotating the double word AD two bits left (Figure 8.53*b*) and shifting the integer AI two bits right (Figure 8.53*d*). Note that AI is a negative number so "1" bits are shifted in from the left.

Shift registers longer than 32 bits can be constructed from individual BYTEs, but the only provided function, SHRB executes a left shift. SHRB is a FC function. In order to right shift a shift register longer than 32 bits, external logic must transfer bits between words, as done with the Modicon PLC in Figures 8.5 and 8.6. However, individual bits can be addressed in the words and so contacts and coils transfer bits between words.

An example SHRB block is shown in Figure 8.54. The input signals to this block are described as follows:

DATA – Boolean data to be shifted into register.

RESET – Reset shift register. When **on**, clears all bits.

S_BIT – Pointer to the first (rightmost) bit of the shift register.

N – Length of shift register, in bits (WORD).

When EN is **on**, the entire register is shifted left one position and the DATA bit is placed in the first (rightmost) position. The only output, ENO, is turned **on** if the block executes without error. When RESET is **on**, all shift register bits are turned **off**.

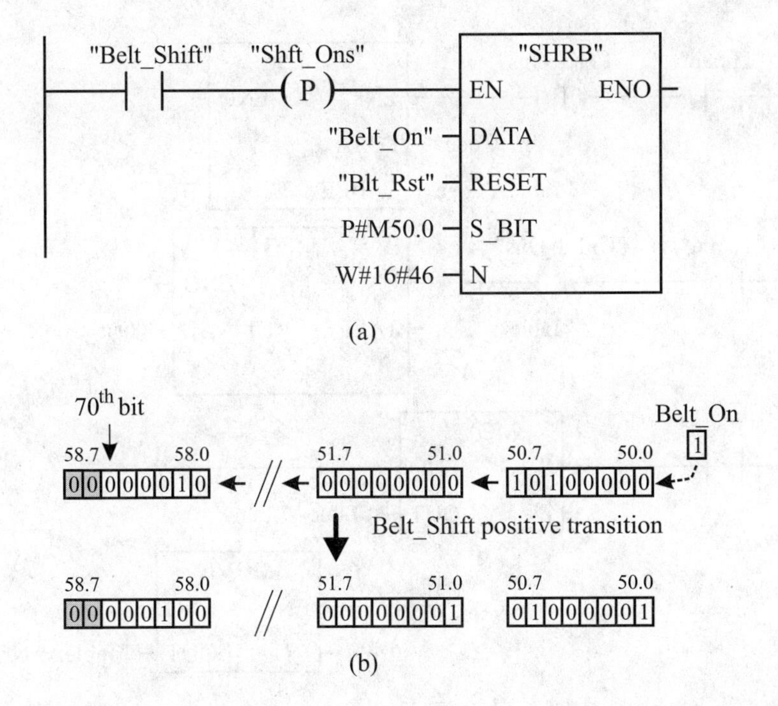

Figure 8.54. S7 SHRB example: *(a)* ladder logic; *(b)* bit array before and after shift.

Figure 8.54 shows an example use of SHRB with a 70-bit shift register constructed from eight bytes. Figure 8.54*a* shows the ladder logic code, and the bits in the array before and after a shift are shown in Figure 8.54*b*.

The S7-200 processors support the four bit shift functions (rotate-left, rotate-right, shift-left, and shift-left) for BYTE, WORD, and DWORD data types. The blocks have the same name as the S7-300/400 block without the data type suffix. The inputs and outputs for these blocks are identical to the S7-300/400 blocks.

8.6.2 FIFO and LIFO Tables

The FIFO and LIFO function blocks and the operation that occurs for each one are:

Block Name	Operation Result
ATT	Add value to table
FIFO	Unload oldest value from table
LIFO	Unload newest value from table

All of these blocks are FC function blocks. The ATT block adds data to both FIFO and LIFO tables. The operation of a table is determined by which function block is used to remove elements. When the FIFO block is used, elements unload in the same order as they are loaded. When the LIFO block is used, elements unload in the opposite order as they are loaded.

Normally, the ATT and FIFO are used together to construct a FIFO data array. An example application of the ATT and FIFO blocks is shown in Figure 8.55. For the ATT and FIFO function blocks, the input signals are described as follows:

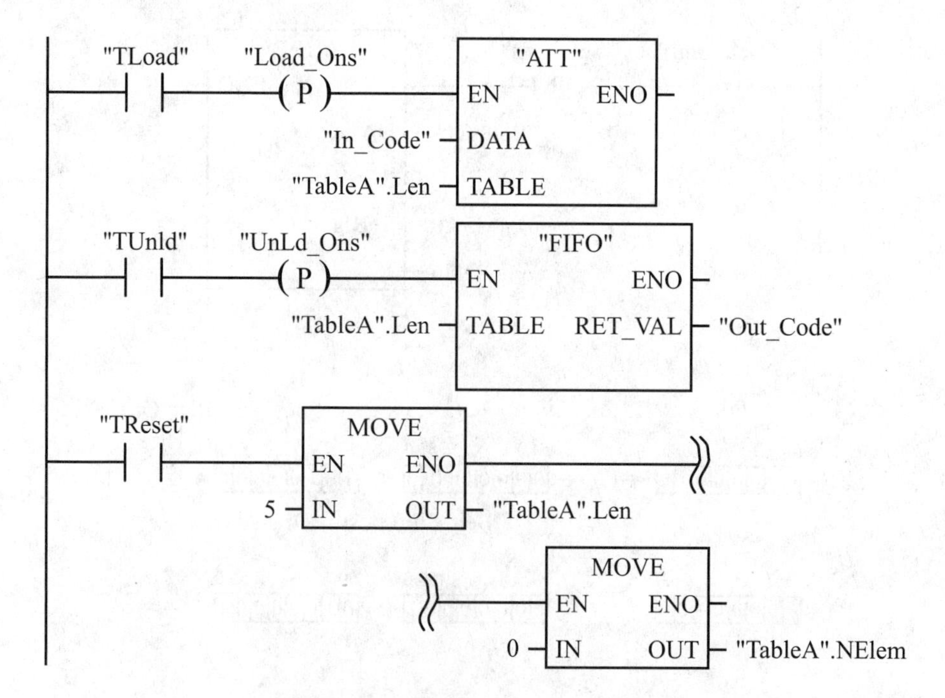

Figure 8.55. S7 FIFO table function blocks.

DATA – WORD data to be loaded to table.

TABLE – Pointer to table.

For the FIFO function block, the RET_VAL output is the WORD data unloaded from the table. The table is structured as follows:

Word 1:	Length of table
Word 2:	Number of table elements
Word 3:	First data word
Word 4:	Second data word
(and so on)	

Before elements can be added to a table, the first two words must be initialized. There are no special instructions to initialize the table.

Each time the ATT block is executed (EN is **on**), the data is transferred to the next position in the table, and the number of table elements (the second word of the table) is incremented. If the table is full when the ATT block is executed, the table is not changed and ENO is turned **off**. Otherwise, ENO is **on**. Each time the FIFO block is executed, the first table element (word) is transferred to the RET_VAL output, the number of table elements is decremented, and the remaining elements in the array are shifted one position toward the beginning of the array. For example, word 4 is moved to word 3, word 5 is moved to word 4, and so on. If the table is empty when the FIFO block is executed, RET_VAL is not changed and ENO is turned **off**. The ENO outputs of the ATT and FIFO functions are not reliable indicators of the full/empty status. One should check the second word in the table to determine whether the table is full or empty.

An example operation of the ATT and FIFO of Figure 8.55 is shown in Figure 8.56. The table is contained in DB2 and consists of seven words (maximum number of elements is therefore five). The "TableA".Len symbol refers to the first word address of the table and "TableA".NElem is the second word address. Two MOVE blocks initialize the first two words of the table. Five WORDs are loaded onto the table and then unloaded. The contents of the table before and after the numbered scans are also shown. The arrow on the left of the array indicates the In_Code value that will be loaded, and the arrow on the right indicates the value unloaded into Out_Code. The table is loaded with 67, 14, 37, 25, and 40. When the table is unloaded, the elements unload in the order 67, 14, 37, 25, and 40. The action at each of the numbered scans is as follows:

1. Load stack with In_Code = 67
2. Load stack with In_Code = 14
   (37 and 25 loaded between scans 2 and 3)
3. Load stack with In_Code = 40
4. Unload stack, Out_Code set to 67
5. Unload stack, Out_Code set to 14
   (37 and 25 unloaded between scans 5 and 6)
6. Unload stack, Out_Code set to 40

The LIFO block has the same inputs and output as the FIFO block. Each time the LIFO block is executed, the last table element (word) is transferred to the RET_VAL output and the number of table elements is decremented. If the table is empty when the FIFO block is executed, RET_VAL is not changed and ENO is turned **off**.

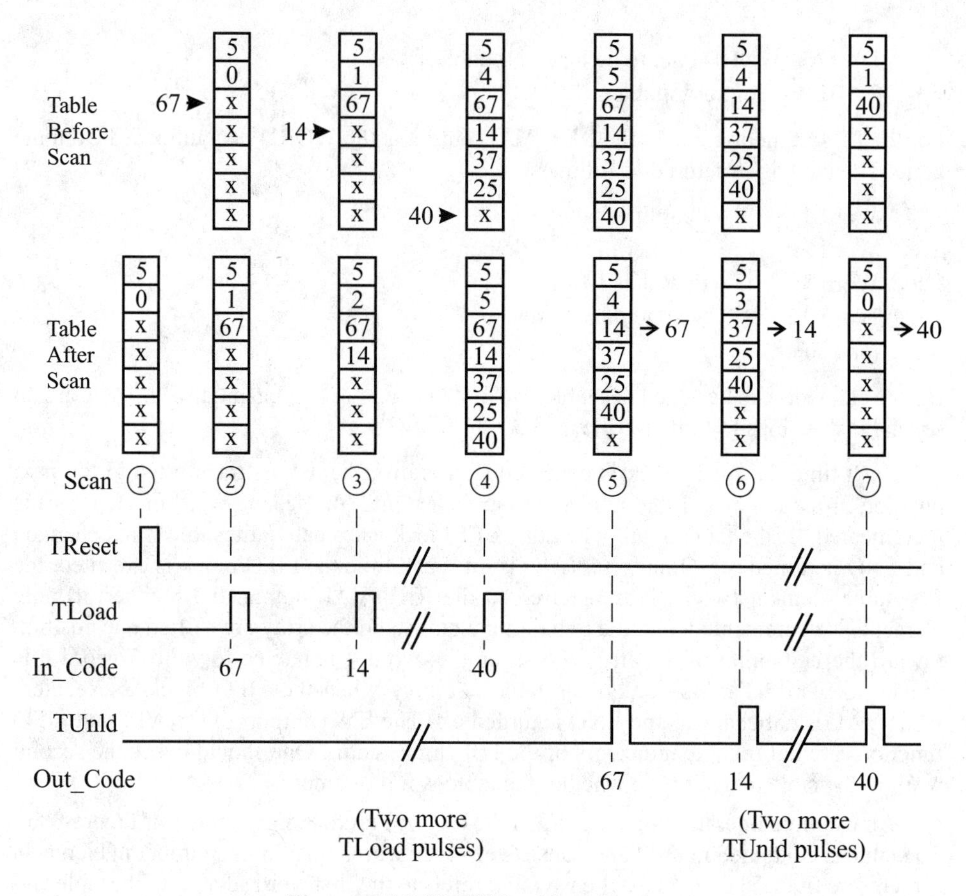

Figure 8.56. S7 FIFO table operation.

If the FIFO block of Figure 8.55 is replaced by a LIFO block, the ladder logic operates as shown in Figure 8.57. The data is loaded in the same manner as for the FIFO operation shown in Figure 8.56. When unloaded, the data appears in the opposite order as it was loaded. The table is loaded with 67, 14, 37, 25, and 40. When the table is unloaded, the elements unload in the order 40, 25, 37, 14, and 67. The action at each of the numbered scans is as follows:

1. Load stack with In_Code = 67
2. Load stack with In_Code = 14
   (37 and 25 loaded between scans 2 and 3)
3. Load stack with In_Code = 40
4. Unload stack, Out_Code set to 40
5. Unload stack, Out_Code set to 25
   (37 and 14 unloaded between scans 5 and 6)
6. Unload stack, Out_Code set to 67

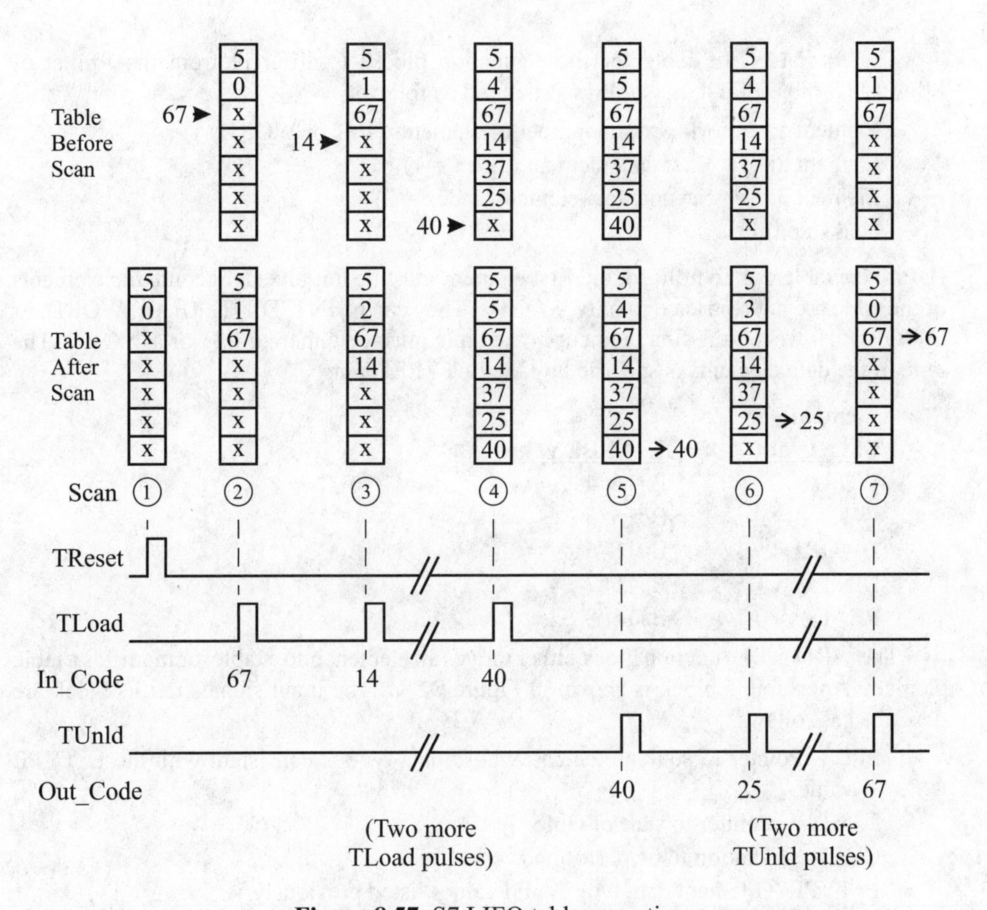

Figure 8.57. S7 LIFO table operation.

8.6.3 Other Table (Array) Function Blocks

Other specialized numerical and bit array function blocks and the operation that occurs for each one are:

Block Name	Operation Result
WRD_TBL	Modify one table element with source data
TBL_WRD	Copy one table element
TBL	Table element modification
TBL_TBL	Table-to-table simple arithmetic
TBL_FIND	Search table for a pattern
CDT	Locate table element in a correlated table
BLKMOV	Copy blocks of data
FILL	Initialize memory area
WSR	Word shift register

All of these blocks are FC functions. The table functions are described first and illustrated with short examples.

The format of the table for these function blocks is different from the format of FIFO/LIFO tables. First, the table is structured as follows:

Element 1: Maximum number of elements (INT or WORD)
Element 2: First data element (index = 1)
Element 3: Second data element (index = 2)
(and so on)

Before the table can be utilized, the first element must be initialized. Second, the elements of the table are not restricted to only WORDs. They can be INT, DINT, REAL, WORD, or DWORD. However, the first element in the table must be either an INT or a WORD. The type of the data elements is specified by the E_TYPE input:

Element Data Type	E_TYPE value
WORD	B#16#4
INT	B#16#5
DWORD	B#16#6
DINT	B#16#7
REAL	B#16#8

The WRD_TBL function block either moves an element into a table, or modifies a table element. An example block is shown in Figure 8.58*a*. The input signals to this block are described as follows:

SRC – Pointer to source element, whose data type is consistent with the E_TYPE value.

TABLE – Pointer to start of table.

CMD – Operation to be performed.

E_TYPE – Element data type. Valid values listed previously.

INDX – Table index of element to be replaced or modified.

The valid values of CMD and the operation that is performed are:

CMD Value	Operation
B#16#7	Logical AND of SRC and table element
B#16#8	Logical OR of SRC and table element
B#16#9	Logical exclusive-OR of SRC and table element
B#16#E	Move SRC to table element

If the table elements are REAL, the only valid command is "move." The output signals of this block are described as follows:

RET_VAL – Error information (WORD). A nonzero value indicates an error. Error codes are listed in Siemens (2000).

Q - **On** if INDX is the index of the last table element.

The RET_VAL and Q outputs must be connected to variables. The ENO output is **on** if the function block executes without an error.

When the EN input is **on**, the indicated CMD operation is performed between the SRC data and the INDX element in the TABLE, placing the result in the INDX element in the TABLE. The value of the INDX element is incremented after the operation is complete, if not at the end of the table.

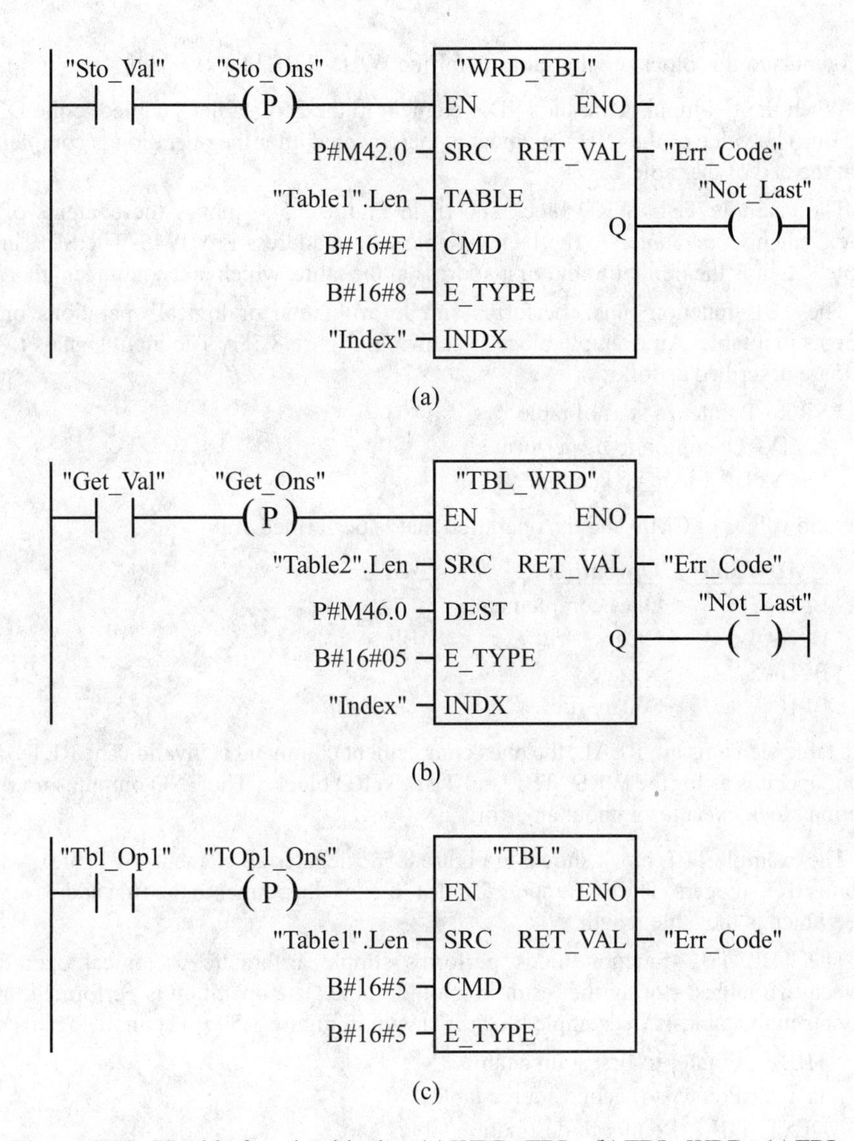

Figure 8.58. S7 table function blocks: *(a)* WRD_TBL; *(b)* TBL_WRD; *(c)* TBL.

The example WRD_TBL block shown in Figure 8.58*a* moves the contents of the REAL variable whose address is MD42 (SRC input P#M42.0) to the "Index" element of Table1. The TABLE input, "Table1".Len is the pointer to the first address in the table, which is the table length.

The TBL_WRD function block copies one table element to another location. An example block is shown in Figure 8.58*b*. The E_TYPE and INDX input signals to this block function in the same manner as for the WRD_TBL function block. The other input signals are:

SRC – Pointer to start of table.

DEST – Pointer to destination, whose data type is consistent with the E_TYPE value.

The outputs to this block are the same as for the WRD_TBL block.

When the EN input is **on**, the INDX element in the SRC table is copied to the DEST location. The value of the INDX element is incremented after the operation is complete, if not at the end of the table.

The example TBL_WRD block shown in Figure 8.58*b* moves the contents of the "Index" element of Table2 to the INT variable whose address is MW46. The SRC input, "Table2".Len is the pointer to the first address in the table, which is the table length.

The TBL function block performs simple arithmetic or logical operations on all elements in a table. An example block is shown in Figure 8.58*c*. The input signals to this block are described as follows:

SRC – Pointer to start of table.
CMD – Operation to be performed.
E_TYPE – Element data type.

The valid values of CMD and the operation that is performed are:

CMD Value	Operation
B#16#3	Ones complement
B#16#4	Clear
B#16#5	Negate
B#16#6	Square root

If the table elements are REAL, the ones complement command is invalid. The RET_VAL output operates as for the WRD_TBL and TBL_WRD blocks. The ENO output is **on** if the function block executes without an error.

The example TBL block shown in Figure 8.58*c* negates all elements of Table1, which contains INT integers. The SRC input, "Table1".Len is the pointer to the first address in the table, which is the table length.

The TBL_TBL function block performs simple arithmetic or logical operations between two tables, storing the result in another table. The operation is performed on all elements in the tables. An example block is shown in Figure 8.59*a*. The input signals are:

TBL1 – Pointer to first source table.
TBL2 – Pointer to second source table.
DEST_TBL – Pointer to destination table.
CMD – Operation to be performed.
E_TYPE – Element data type.

All of the tables must be the same length. The valid values of CMD and the operation that is performed are:

CMD Value	Operation
B#16#7	Logical AND
B#16#8	Logical OR
B#16#9	Logical exclusive-OR
B#16#A	Addition
B#16#B	Subtraction (TBL1 – TBL2)
B#16#C	Multiplication
B#16#D	Division (TBL1 ÷ TBL2)

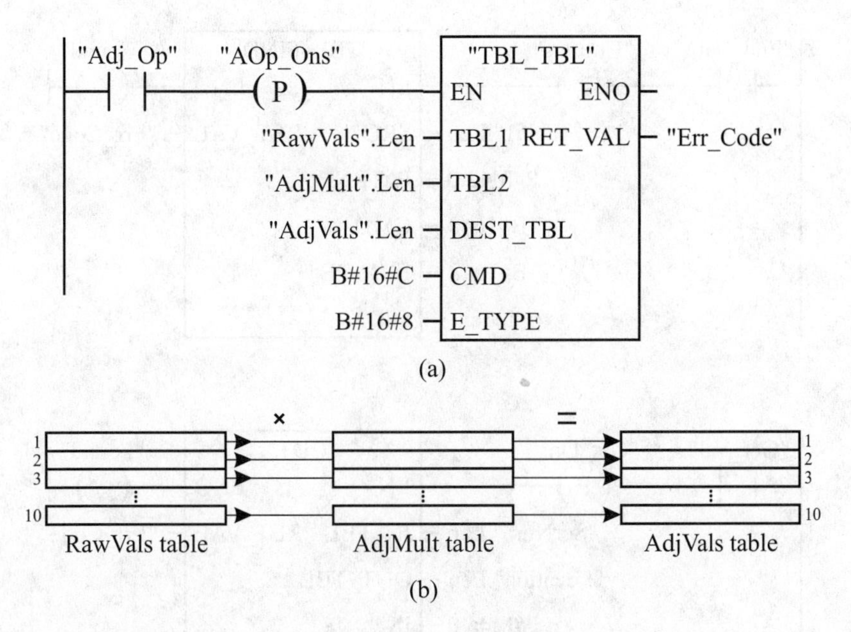

Figure 8.59. S7 TBL_TBL table multiplication example: *(a)* ladder logic; *(b)* processing of table elements.

If the table elements are REAL, the logical operations are invalid. The RET_VAL output operates as for the other table function blocks. The ENO output is **on** if the function block executes without an error.

The example TBL_TBL block shown in Figure 8.59*a* does an element-by-element multiplication of one table by another table to produce a third table. Each element of RawVals is multiplied by the corresponding element in AdjMult to produce an element of the AdjVals table. All elements in the three arrays are REAL.

The TBL_FIND and CDT (correlation data table) function blocks both search for table elements. However, they are useful for different applications.

The TBL_FIND finds the first table element that either matches or does not match a desired pattern. An example TBL_FIND function block is shown in Figure 8.60*a*. The input signals to this block are described as follows:

SRC – Pointer to table.

PATRN – Pointer to pattern. Same as table element data type.

CMD – Search to be performed: B#16#0 – search for equal; B#16#1 – search for not equal.

E_TYPE – Element data type.

INDX – Starting index and index of found element.

The RET_VAL output operates as for the other table function blocks.

The TBL_FIND function starts its search with the element **after** the value in INDX. Each element in the SRC table is compared with the source pattern (PATRN). If CMD=0, the function locates the next element that matches the pattern and updates INDX with the element index. If CMD=1, the function locates the next element that **does not** match the

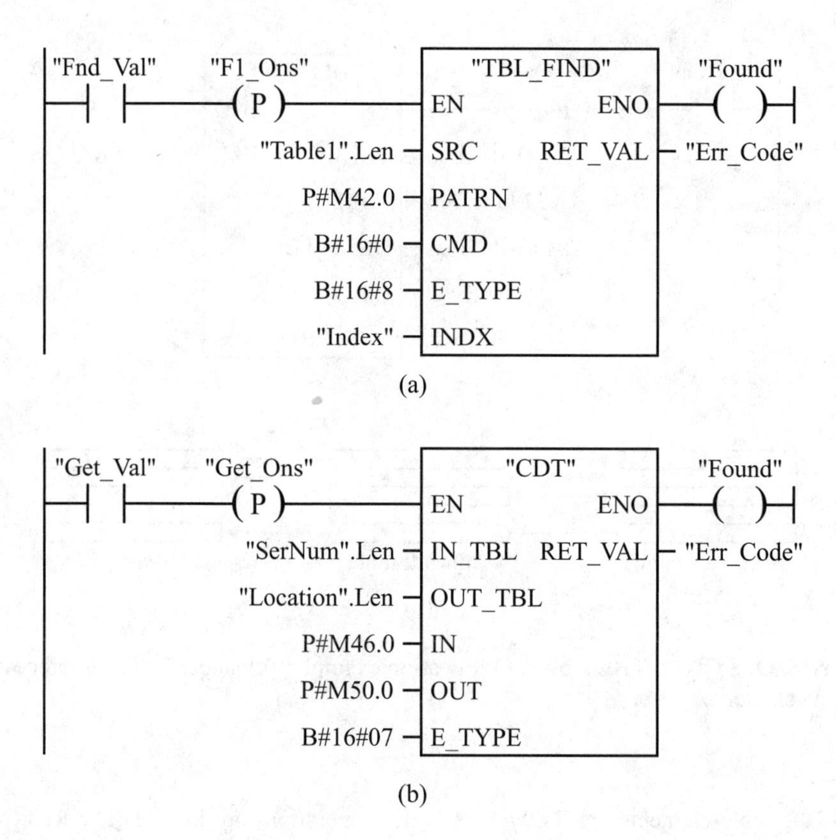

Figure 8.60. S7 table search function blocks: *(a)* TBL_FIND; *(b)* CDT (correlated data table).

pattern and updates INDX with the element index. If a match (or mismatch) is found, the ENO output is turned **on**. If no match (or mismatch is found), the value of INDX points to an element past the end of the table and the ENO output is turned **off**.

The example TBL_FIND block shown in Figure 8.60*a* searches for a pattern in Table1, a table of real elements. Starting from the table index in "Index," the table elements are searched for the first element that matches the real value stored at MD42. The Found coil is turned **on** if a match is found.

The CDT (correlated data table) function block finds the first element in one table that is greater than or equal to a desired value and then uses this index to access the corresponding element in a second table. One possible application for this function is to determine the location for a given component serial number. One table contains the serial numbers in ascending order and the second table contains the location (coded in a DINT) for each serial number. The same index used to access the serial number is also the index of the location of that part. An example CDT function block is shown in Figure 8.60*b*. The input signals to this block are described as follows:

IN_TBL – Pointer to the input table.
OUT_TBL – Pointer to the output table.
IN – Pointer to value used for input table comparison.
OUT – Pointer to location where result will be stored.
E_TYPE – Element data type. Only INT, DINT, and REAL types are valid.

The RET_VAL output operates as for the other table function blocks.

The CDT function starts its search with the first element in IN_TBL. Each element in the IN_TBL table is compared with the input value (pointed to by IN). When a table element is greater than or equal to the input value, the search ends (*bw*) and the index is noted. This index is used to access the corresponding element in OUT_TBL and this element is copied to the location pointed to by OUT. In this situation, the ENO output is turned **on**. If no IN_TBL element is found, the ENO output is turned **off** and RET_VAL is set to an error code.

In order for this function to work properly, the elements in IN_TBL should be in ascending order. The first table element should have the smallest value and the last table element should have the largest value. Also, the IN_TBL and OUT_TBL must have the same length.

The example CDT block shown in Figure 8.60*b* searches for a serial number in SerNum, a table of double integers. When a serial number equal to or greater than the value in MD46 is located, its index is used to copy the location from the Location table to the double integer in MD50. The Found coil is turned **on** if a match is found.

The BLKMOV function block (Figure 8.61*a*) copies the contents of one block of data to another block. The SRCBLK connection is the source data block and the DSTBLK connection is the destination data block. Both blocks are specified as a symbol or starting address of any simple or complex data type (e.g., ARRAY or STRUCT) excluding arrays of the STRING data type. The source and destination blocks should not overlap. If the size of the destination block is larger than the source data block, the BLKMOV function copies the entire source block, and no more, to the destination block. If the destination block is smaller than the source block, the function only copies as much data to fill the destination block. If an error occurs while the block is executed, the error code is saved to the variable connected to the RET_VAL output.

The FILL function block (Figure 8.61*b*) operates similarly to the BLKMOV function block. The two differences are: (1) if the destination block is larger than the source block, the source block copy is repeated until the destination block is full, and (2) the connections are labeled differently. The BVAL input is the source contents and is the same as the

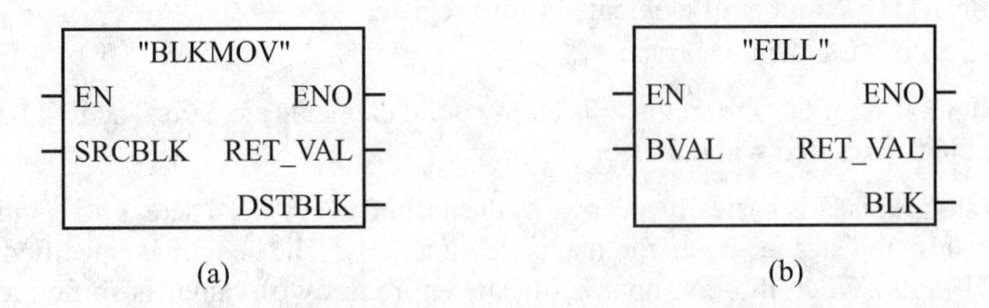

Figure 8.61. S7 block move function blocks: *(a)* BLKMOV; *(b)* FILL.

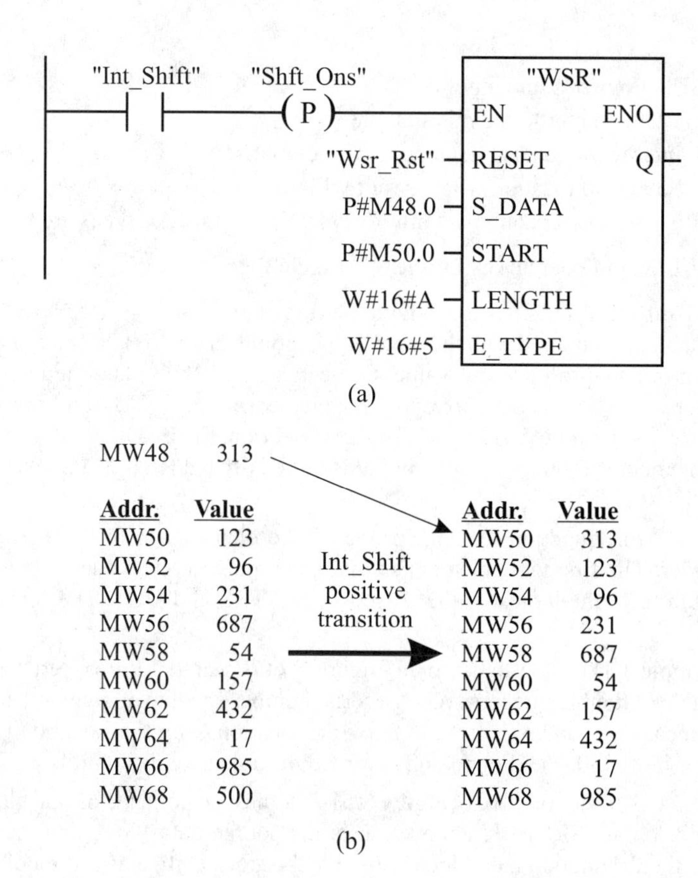

Figure 8.62. S7 word shift register example: *(a)* ladder logic; *(b)* integer array before and after shift.

SRCBLK connection for the BLKMOV function. The BLK output is the destination and is the same as the DSTBLK connection for the BLKMOV function.

The WSR (word shift register) function block (Figure 8.62) implements a shift register that consists of INT, DINT, WORD, DWORD, or REAL values. The input signals to this block are described as follows:

RESET – Sets all elements to zero when **on**.
S_DATA – Pointer to source data to be shifted in.
START – Pointer to the start of the shift register.
LENGTH – Number of elements in shift register.
E_TYPE – Element data type.

The Q output is **on** if the shift register is empty or all elements are zero. The ENO output is **on** if the block executed without error.

The shift register is basically an array of the desired data type. There is no length stored with the shift register as done for the table functions. The length is specified by the LENGTH input. When the EN input is **on**, the entire array of values is shifted to higher memory addresses and the last value is lost. The source data is then placed in the first register location. When the EN and RESET inputs are **on**, all register locations are cleared.

Figure 8.62 shows an example use of WSR with a 10-integer shift register. Figure 8.62*a* shows the ladder logic code, and the integers in the array before and after a shift are shown in Figure 8.62*b*.

8.6.4 Program Execution Control

The S7-300/400 processors offer a number of coil instructions that can control ladder logic execution. The names and the operation that occurs for each one are:

Instruction	Operation Result
JMP	Jump to a defined label if rung condition true
JMPN	Jump to a defined label if rung condition false
label	Jump destination
CALL	Call a function block (FC/SFC) with no parameters
RET	Exit organization block or function block
MCRA	Master control relay activate
MCRD	Master control relay disable
MCR<	Master control relay zone start
MCR>	Master control relay zone end

The S7-200 processors also support many of these instructions. All S7-200 processors support a JMP-to-label coil. All but the S7-210 processor support subroutines, which act similarly to S7-300/400 functions (FCs). However, there is some inconsistency among processors. The S7-21x processors support the CALL coil. The S7-22x processors support a SBR function block (with input and output parameters) that appears similar to a FC/SFC call. None of the S7-200 processors support master control relay instructions.

The JMP (jump) and JMPN (jump-if-not) coils are used with a label to skip portions of ladder logic. When the JMP coil input is **on**, the ladder scan skips to the referenced label. When the JMPN coil input is **off**, the ladder scan skips to the referenced label. A label is defined at the beginning of a rung, but appears within a box above the left side of a rung. A label consists of up to four alphanumeric characters and the first character must be a letter. One can jump either forward or backward. Jumping backward lets the controller iterate certain sections of logic. However, jumping backward an excessive number of times will cause the controller to fault if the scan time is too long. Jumping forward decreases the scan time by skipping logic segments until needed. One drawback to jumping forward is that the logic between the jump coil and the label contact is not scanned, so any output coils are not changed. An example ladder segment with two jump coils and two labels is shown in Figure 8.63.

The program in an organization block can call function blocks or functions (Figure 3.34). Therefore, there is no jump-to-subroutine construct for the S7 processors. Basically, function blocks or functions are subroutines. Many of the function blocks (for example, IEC timers and counters) already discussed in the text are function calls. A call to a user-defined function or function block is no different. A function block must also have an instance data block associated with it. If a function does not have any parameters, a CALL coil (Figure 8.64*a*) can be used to execute it. Function block programming is covered in Chapter 11.

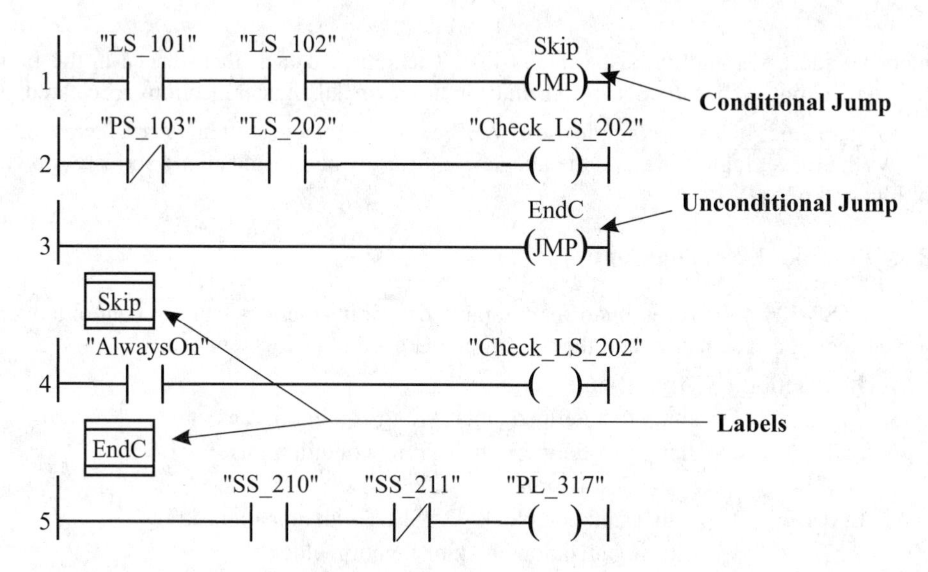

Figure 8.63. S7 JMP and label example.

"FC/SFC name"
—(CALL)—| (a)

—(RET)—| (b)

Figure 8.64. S7 program control: *(a)* CALL coil; *(b)* RET (return) coil.

An organization block can be conditionally exited with the RET coil (Figure 8.64*b*). The RET coil must be preceded with logic. The RET coil is equivalent to jumping to the end of the organization block.

The MCR (master control relay) coils function like a software master control relay, disabling non-retentive outputs within a range of rungs. The MCR< and MCR> coils are used in pairs to create "zones" of the ladder program where all outputs may be disabled. An MCR< coil defines the start of the zone, and an MCR> coil defines the end of the zone. Zones may be nested (up to eight nested zones). Logic preceding the MCR< coil controls execution of the zone. When this rung logic turns **on** the MCR< coil (called "enabling the zone"), all rungs in the zone are scanned normally. When the rung logic causes the MCR< coil to be **off** (called "disabling the zone"), all rungs in the zone are scanned but only to turn **off** all non-retentive outputs in the zone. The following elements are affected when a zone is disabled:

Element	**When zone disabled**
Coil	output always off
Set coil	output not affected
Reset coil	output not affected
Midline coil	always off
RS block	not executed
SR block	not executed
MOVE block	not executed

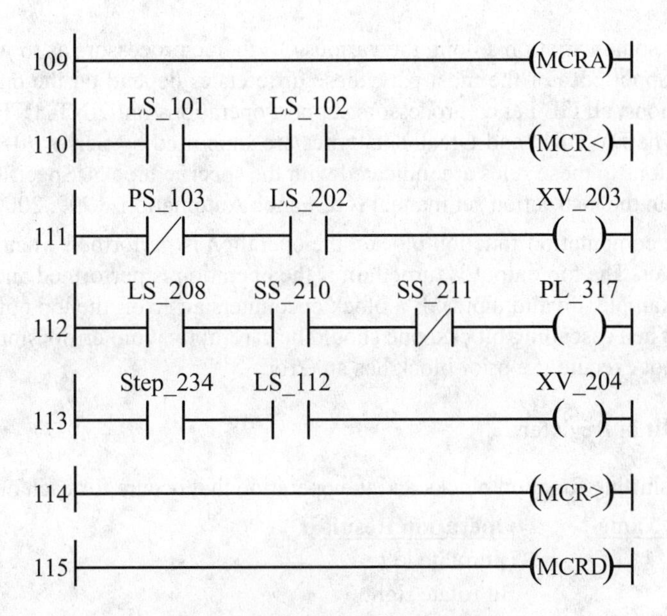

Figure 8.65. S7 MCR example.

The MCRA coil activates the master control relay functions. A rung with the MCRA coil must preceded any MCR< and MCR> coils. The MCRD coil deactivates the master control relay functions. Any MCR< and MCR> coils before the MCRA coil and after the MCRD coil are ignored.

There are some cautions when using an MCR zone:

1. Do not jump into or out of a MCR zone.
2. When accessing components of complex FC or FB parameters of the type STRUCT, UDT, ARRAY, or STRING, the result will be undefined or the processor will stop (Siemens, 2002a)

Also, the MCR instruction is not a substitute for a hard-wired master control relay that provides an emergency power shutdown to the I/O.

An example MCR zone is shown in Figure 8.65. When LS_101 and LS_102 are both **on**, the MCR zone is enabled, and rungs 111 to 113 are scanned normally determining the values of the output coils XV_203, PL_317, and XV_204. When either LS_101 or LS_102 is **off**, the MCR zone is disabled. In this case, XV_203, PL_317, and XV_204 are all turned **off**, regardless of the state of the input conditions for rungs 111 to113.

8.7 OTHER GE FANUC FUNCTION BLOCKS

The GE Fanuc processors support ladder logic function blocks for bit shifting, FIFO/LIFO tables, other table functions, and program control.The basic operation and simple applications of these function blocks are described in this section. Longer bit shifting and FIFO/LIFO applications are presented in section 8.8.

There is some variation among the various GE Fanuc processors as to which specific blocks are supported. For the most part, these differences depend on the data type. With some exceptions, all GE Fanuc processors support operations on DINT, INT, and WORD data types. The DWORD and UINT data types are supported by Series 90-70 processors only. Exceptions to these rules are indicated with the specific blocks. Specific information is contained in the instruction set manual (GE Fanuc Automation, 1999, 2000, 2001).

Like the computation function blocks, the operation is performed when the top input receives power. The top output is turned **on** if the operation is performed and there are no errors (for example, invalid input). If a block encounters an error, the top output is always turned **off**. When cascading blocks, one should be careful to avoid errors since subsequent blocks will not execute if a prior block has an error.

8.7.1 Shift Bit in Register

The bit shifting function blocks and the operation that occurs for each one are:

Block Name	Operation Result
ROL_***	Bit rotate left
ROR_***	Bit rotate right
SHIFTL_***	Bit shift left
SHIFTR_***	Bit shift right

where *** is either DWORD or WORD and represents the data type of the input and output. An example ROL_WORD block is shown in Figure 8.66*a* and an example SHIFTR_WORD block is shown in Figure 8.66*c*. For these blocks, the IN input is the word to be rotated or shifted and the N input is a INT data type and indicates the number of bits to

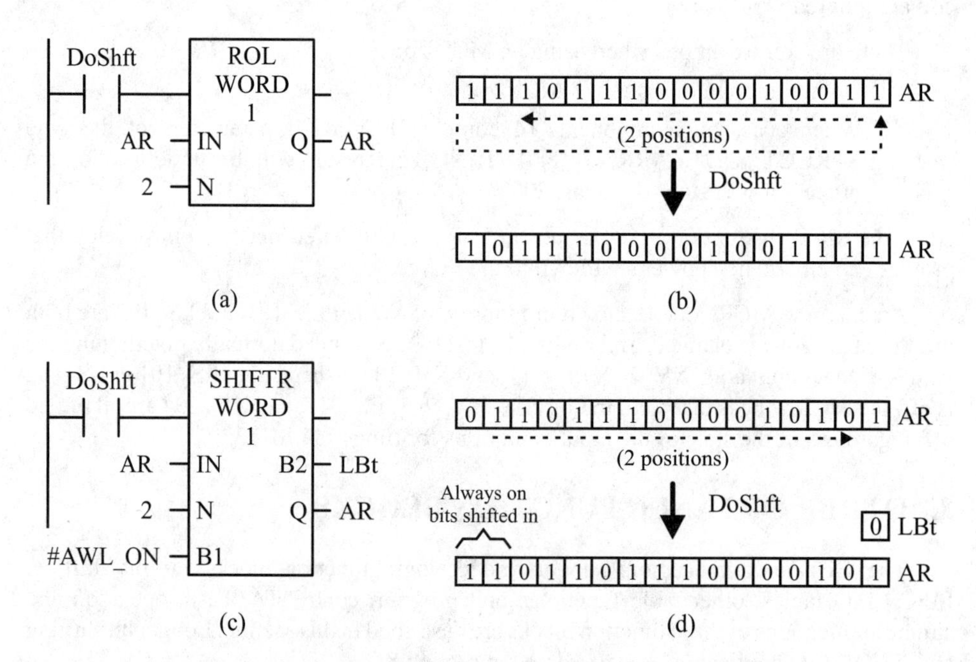

Figure 8.66. GE Fanuc bit shift examples: *(a)* ROL_WORD block; *(b)* word before and after rotate; *(c)* SHIFTR_WORD block; *(d)* word before and after shift.

rotate or shift. The Q output is the result of the rotate or shift operation. The number below the name of the function block is the number of WORDs or DWORDs that compose the shift register, from 1 to 256. For the SHIFTL and SHIFTR function blocks, the B1 input specifies the bit value (0 or 1) to be shifted into the destination. The B2 output is the last bit shifted out of the source. As an example, Figure 8.3 shows the result of rotating the word AR two bits left (Figure 8.66*b*) and shifting AR two bits right (Figure 8.66*d*). Note that in Figure 8.66*d*, the #AWL_ON (always on) system bit is used to shift 1's into AR from the left.

The N input must be at least 1 and no greater than the number of bits in the bit string. If N is out of range for the ROL and ROR functions, there is no rotation and the unlabeled output is **off**. If N is out of range for the SHIFTL and SHIFTR functions, the behavior depends on the processor. For the 90-70 processor, no shift occurs and unlabeled output is **off**. For the other processors, if N is less than 1, no shift occurs and the B1 input is copied to unlabeled output. If N is greater than the number of bits in the bit array, the Q output is filled with the B1 input and the B2 input Boolean is copied to the unlabeled output.

8.7.2 FIFO and LIFO Queues

The FIFO and LIFO function blocks and the operation that occurs for each one are:

Block Name	**Operation Result**
FIFO_RD_***	Unload value from first FIFO position
FIFO_WRT_***	Load value to next FIFO position
LIFO_RD_***	Unload value from last LIFO position
LIFO_WRT_***	Load value to next LIFO position
TBL_RD_***	Unload value from circular FIFO position
TBL_WRT_***	Load value to next circular FIFO position

where *** is DINT, DWORD, INT, UINT, or WORD (the data type of the elements). These blocks are valid only for the 90-70 processors.

Typically, the FIFO_WRT and FIFO_RD blocks are used together to construct a FIFO data array. An example application of these blocks is shown in Figure 8.67*a*. For the FIFO_WRT and FIFO_RD function blocks, the input signals are described as follows:

TB – Address/symbol of first element in FIFO array.
PTR – Index of current last element in array (INT).
IN – (FIFO_WRT only) Element that will be stored in the array. Data type must be consistent with block suffix.

The output signals are:

FL – (FIFO_WRT only) Full indication. **On** when FIFO full.
Q – (FIFO_RD only) Where element will be placed after it is unloaded from the FIFO. Data type must be consistent with block suffix.
EM – (FIFO_RD only) Empty indication. **On** when FIFO empty.

The length of the array is indicated by the number below the function name. There can be from 1 to 32,767 elements. In order to reset a FIFO array, set the PTR to zero.

Each time the upper input of FIFO_WRT is **on**, PTR is incremented by one and the IN value is placed in the FIFO array at the new position. The FL output is set **on** if the PTR is

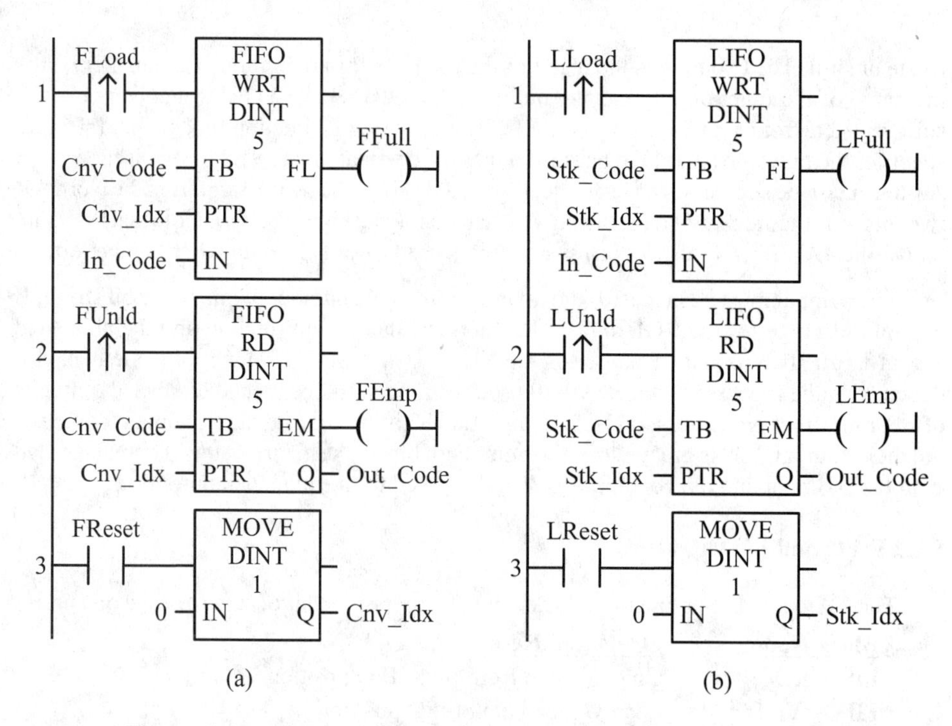

Figure 8.67. GE Fanuc FIFO/LIFO: *(a)* FIFO array; *(b)* LIFO array.

equal to the array length. If data is added to an already full FIFO, the new data is not added to the FIFO array. The upper output passes power if the element was successfully added.

Each time the upper input of FIFO_RD is **on**, the first element in the FIFO array is copied to Q, and the remaining elements in the array are shifted one position toward the beginning of the array. Also, PTR is decremented by one. The EM output is set if the FIFO array is empty (PTR=0). If data is removed from an already empty FIFO, the Q output is not changed. The upper output passes power if PTR is greater than zero and less than the array length.

The operation of the FIFO_WRT and FIFO_RD of Figure 8.67*a* is very similar to the ControlLogix FFL/FFU diagram shown in Figure 8.18. The FFull and FEmp outputs of Figure 8.67*a* are equivalent to Cnv_CCtl.DN and Cnv_CCtl.EM of Figure 8.18, respectively. Also, the Cnv_Idx of Figure 8.67*a* is one less than the .POS value of Figure 8.18. This example assumes the FIFO starts empty. Five DINTs are loaded onto the FIFO and then unloaded. The contents of the FIFO before and after the numbered scans are also shown. The arrow on the left of the array is one more than the Cnv_Idx value, and the arrow on the right indicates the value unloaded into Out_Code. The FIFO is loaded with 67, 14, 37, 25, and 40. When the FIFO is unloaded, the elements unload in the order 67, 14, 37, 25, and 40.

Typically, LIFO_WRT and LIFO_RD are used together to construct a LIFO data array. An example application of these blocks is shown in Figure 8.67*b*. The inputs and outputs of these blocks have the same function as the inputs and outputs of the FIFO_WRT/FIFO_RD blocks. In order to reset a LIFO array, set the PTR to zero.

Each time the upper input of LIFO_WRT is **on**, PTR is incremented by one and the IN value is placed in the LIFO array at the new position. The FL output is set **on** if the PTR is equal to the array length. If data is added to an already full LIFO, the new data is not added to the LIFO array. The upper output passes power if the element was successfully added.

Each time the upper input of LIFO_RD is **on**, the element in the LIFO array at the PTR index is copied to Q, and PTR is decremented by one. The EM output is set if the LIFO array is empty (PTR=0). If data is removed from an already empty LIFO, the Q output is not changed. The upper output passes power if PTR is greater than zero and less than the array length.

The operation of the LIFO_WRT and LIFO_RD of Figure 8.67*b* is very similar to the ControlLogix LFL/LFU diagram shown in Figure 8.20. The LFull and LEmp outputs of Figure 8.67*b* are equivalent to Stk_CCtl.DN and Stk_CCtl.EM of Figure 8.20, respectively. Also, the Stk_Idx of Figure 8.67*b* is one less than to the .POS value of Figure 8.20. This example assumes the LIFO starts empty. Five DINTs are loaded onto the LIFO and then unloaded. The contents of the LIFO before and after the numbered scans are also shown. The arrow on the left of the array indicates one more than the Stk_Idx value, and the arrow on the right indicates the value unloaded into Out_Code. The LIFO is loaded with 67, 14, 37, 25, and 40. When the LIFO is unloaded, the elements unload in the order 40, 25, 37, 14, and 67.

Typically, the TBL_WRT and TBL_RD blocks are used together to construct a circular FIFO to transfer data between applications where the data generation is not synchronized with the data processing. An example application of these blocks is shown in Figure 8.68. The inputs and outputs of these blocks have a similar function as the inputs and outputs of the FIFO_WRT/FIFO_RD blocks. In order to reset a circular FIFO, set the PTR for both TBL_WRT and TBL_RD to zero.

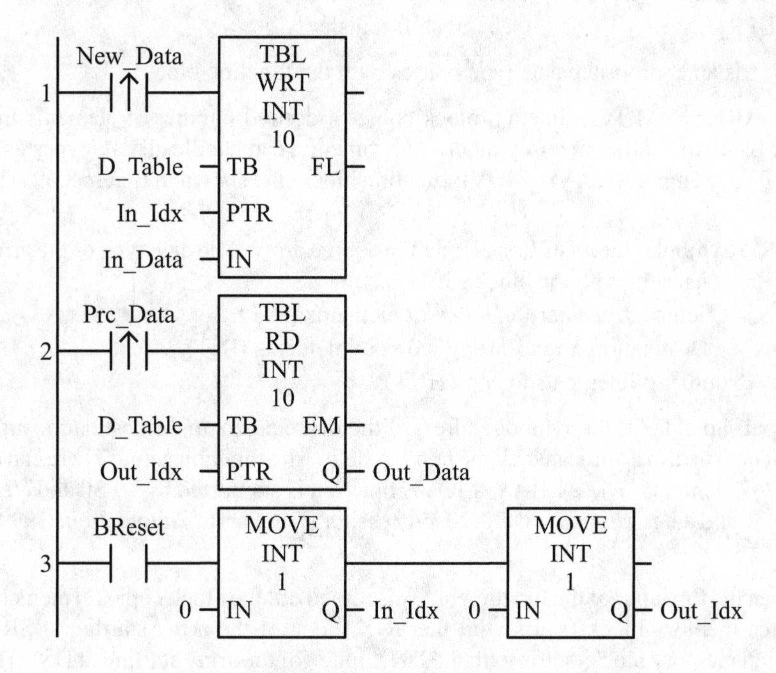

Figure 8.68. GE Fanuc circular FIFO array.

Each time the upper input of TBL_WRT is **on**, the position (PTR) is incremented by one and the IN value is placed in the array at the new position. The FL output is set **on** if the PTR is equal to the array length. If data is added to an already full array, PTR is set to one and the new data is added at this position. The upper output always passes power if the block is executed.

Each time the upper input of TBL_RD is **on**, PTR is incremented by one and the element at the PTR index in the FIFO array is copied to Q. The EM output is set if the index is at the end of the array. If PTR is at the end of the array, PTR is set to one and data is removed from this position. The upper output always passes power if the block is executed.

The combination of TBL_WRT and TBL_RD in Figure 8.68 implements a circular FIFO queue. Every time a new value of In_Data is generated, it is added to the D_Table buffer by a positive transition of New_Data. When a value can be processed, it is removed from D_Table by a positive transition of Prc_Data. Note that each block maintains its own PTR value. This figure illustrates the basic functionality of these two blocks. Extra logic should be added if it is important that the circular FIFO does not overrun or that data is not removed from an empty queue. In either case, the FL and EM outputs will not reliably check these conditions and In_Idx and Out_Idx must be compared.

8.7.3 Other Array Functions

Other numerical array function blocks and the operation that occurs for each one are:

Block Name	Operation Result
ARRAY_MOVE_***	Copy elements between arrays
SEARCH_??_***	Search array for first value meeting criteria
BLKMOV_***	Copy 7 constants to consecutive locations
BLK_CLR_WORD	Clear block of memory
SHFR_***	General shift register

where *** is an appropriate data type (varies with the function block).

The ARRAY_MOVE function block copies a desired number of elements from one memory block to another memory block. This function can handle all data types except for REAL. Two example ARRAY_MOVE function blocks are shown in Figure 8.69. The input signals are:

SR – Symbol/address of first element in source array. The data type of the array must be consistent with the block suffix.

SNX – Source array starting index of elements (INT).

DNX – Destination array starting index of elements (INT).

N – Number of elements to copy (INT).

The output signal DS is the symbol/address of the first element in the destination array. The length of both arrays is indicated by the number below the function name. There can be from 1 to 32,767 elements. The ARRAY_MOVE function is supported by 90-30 and VersaMax processors and later versions of 90-70 processors (GE Fanuc Automation, 1999, 2000, 2001).

When the top input of the function block is turned **on**, the block copies N elements from the source memory block (starts with the SNX index of the array starting at SR) to the destination memory block (starts with the DNX index of the array starting at DS). The SNX

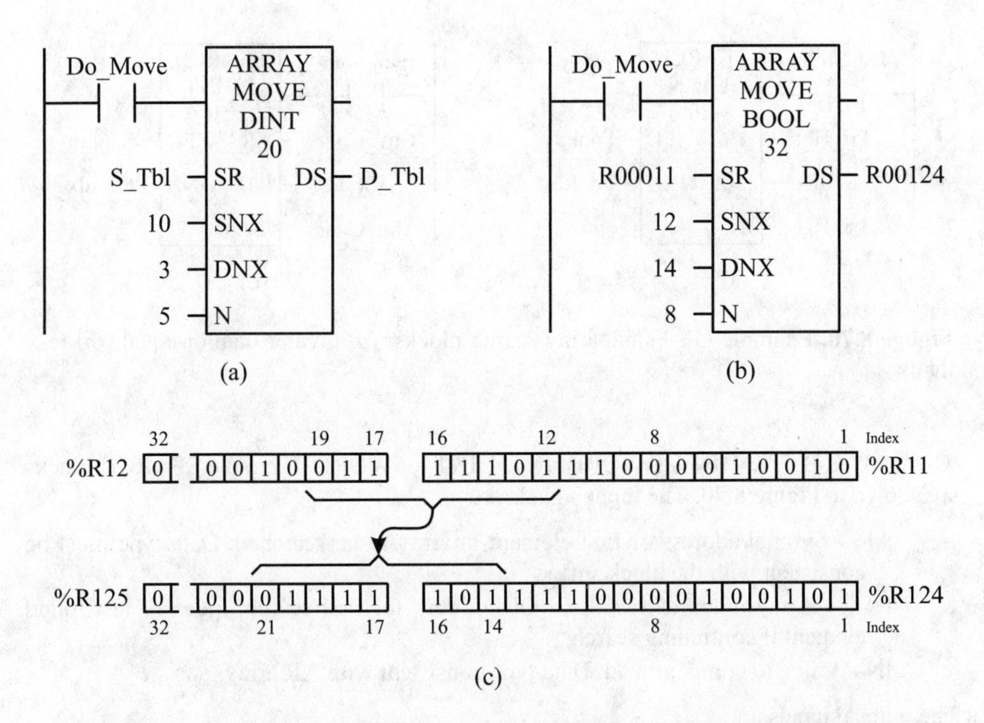

Figure 8.69. Example GE Fanuc array move blocks: *(a)* ARRAY_MOVE_INT; *(b)* ARRAY_MOVE_BOOL; *(c)* operation of ARRAY_MOVE_BOOL.

and DNX array indices are 1-based, that is, the first element in each array has an index of one. If the N+SNX or N+DNX index falls outside either the source or destination memory blocks, the copy is not performed. The top output is turned **on** if the function is executed and the copied block lies within both memory blocks.

Example uses of the ARRAY_MOVE function are shown in Figure 8.69. In Figure 8.69*a*, five DINTs are copied, starting from the tenth element of S_Tbl, to the array starting from the third element of D_Tbl. Suppose S_Tbl starts at register address %R*m* and D_Tbl starts at register address %R*n*. The addresses of the source block are %R*m*+(10-1)*2 to %R*m*+(14-1)*2+1 and the addresses of the destination block are %R*n*+(3-1)*2 to %R*n*+(7-1)*2+1. In Figure 8.69*b*, 8 bits are copied from one 32-bit array to another. In this case, the source and destination addresses are registers. Figure 8.69*c* shows how this move operation is accomplished, crossing register boundaries.

The SEARCH function block searches an array for the first value meeting the specified search criteria. The types of comparison allowed are:

Block Name	Search Description
SEARCH_EQ_***	Search for first element = IN
SEARCH_GE_***	Search for first element ≥ IN
SEARCH_GT_***	Search for first element > IN
SEARCH_LE_***	Search for first element ≤ IN
SEARCH_LT_***	Search for first element < IN
SEARCH_NE_***	Search for first element ≠ IN

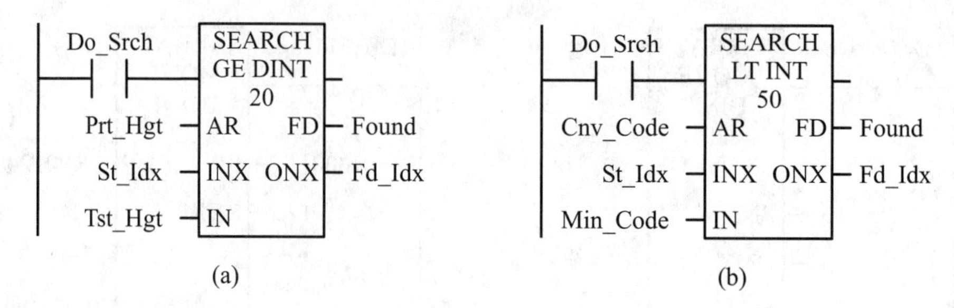

Figure 8.70. Example GE Fanuc array search blocks: *(a)* greater than or equal; *(b)* less than.

where *** is BYTE, DINT, DWORD, INT, UINT, or WORD. Example SEARCH blocks are shown in Figure 8.70. The input signals are:

AR – Symbol/address of first element in array to be searched. Data type must be consistent with the block suffix.

INX – Array index of search (WORD): zero for first search; index of last found element if continuing search.

IN – Value to compare with. Data type consistent with AR array.

The output signals are:

FD – Found indication. **On** if element found that satisfies criterion.

ONX – Array index of found element (WORD). The first index is one.

The **register** length of the array is indicated by the number below the function name. There can be from 1 to 32,767 words (in contrast to previously-described array function blocks which specified the length in elements which could be DINTs).

When the top input to this block is energized, the search begins at the INX+1 index of the array starting at AR. The search continues until an array element is found that satisfies the search criterion or until the end of the array is reached. If an array element is found, the FD output is turned **on** and the ONX is set to the index of the found array element. If no array element is found, the FD output is turned **off** and ONX is set to zero. The top output echoes the top input when the block executes without error. If INX is outside its valid range, the top output is turned **off**. To repeat the search, the ONX value is simply copied to the INX variable before the next block execution.

The BLKMOV function block copies 7 constants to consecutive array locations. An example BLKMOV function is shown in Figure 8.71*a*. All GE Fanuc processors can handle the INT and WORD data types. The DINT, DWORD, and UINT data types are valid for 90-70 processors. Operations with REAL data types can be done only by processors that support floating-point operations. When the top input receives power, the 7 constants specified by IN1 to IN7 are copied to 7 consecutive array locations, starting with the element specified by the Q output. The data type of the variable at the Q output must be consistent with the BLKMOV function block name suffix.

The BLK_CLR_WORD function block clears a block of memory. An example BLK_CLR_WORD is shown in Figure 8.71*b*. The number of words in the block is indicated by the number beneath the block name. When the top input receives power, the specified number of word (register) locations, starting with the location specified by the IN

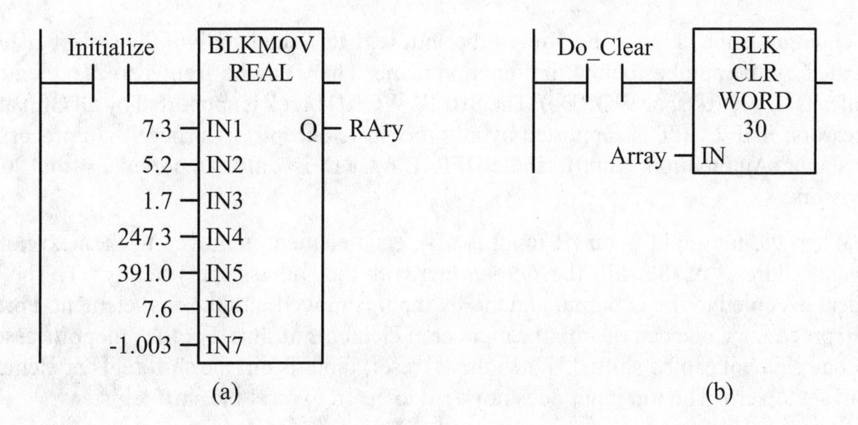

Figure 8.71. Example GE Fanuc block initialization functions: *(a)* set 7 consecutive constants; *(b)* block clear.

input, is filled with zeros. Note that the number of words in the block is specified. Therefore, if the block is an array of DINTs, the number of words is twice the number of DINTs. The data type of IN does not need to be WORD. It can be any of the data types supported by the processor except BOOL and BYTE.

The SHFR function block is a generalized shift register. The suffix can be BIT, DWORD, or WORD and is the data type of the shift register. The SHFR_BIT function block is similar to SHIFTL_WORD, except that the bit array consists of Booleans, rather than bits within words. Example SHFR_WORD function blocks are shown in Figure 8.72. The block for the 90-70 processors has an additional input. The input signals are:

R – Reset input. When **on**, the shift register is filled with zeros.

N – Number of elements to shift (90-70 only). A constant.

IN – Value to be shifted in. Data type consistent with ST.

ST – Symbol/address of first element in shift register. Data type must be consistent with block suffix.

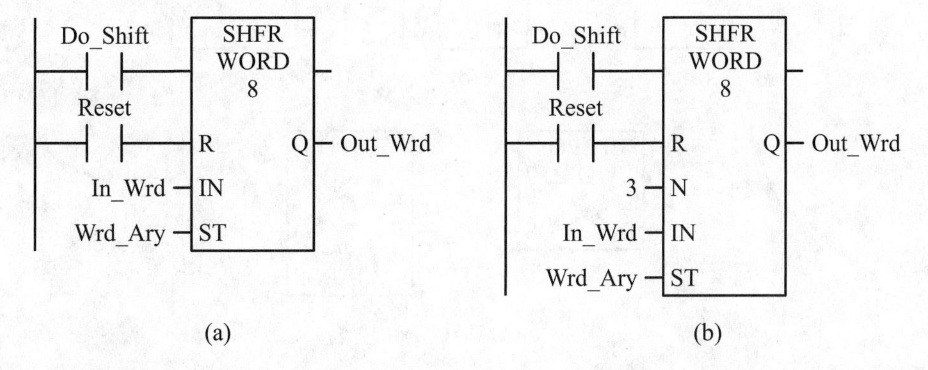

Figure 8.72. Example GE Fanuc general shift register functions: *(a)* 90-30 and VersaMax processors; *(b)* 90-70 processors.

The Q output is the value shifted out of the shift register. The length of the shift register is indicated by the number below the function name. There can be from 1 to 256 elements (Booleans, DWORDs, or WORDs). The SHFR_WORD block is supported by all GE Fanuc processors; SHFR_BIT is supported by all processors except for earlier 90-70 processors (GE Fanuc Automation, 2000); and SHFR_DWORD is only supported by the 90-70 processors.

When the top input is **on** (R input is **off**), each element is moved to the next higher element (address) of the shift register starting with the address specified by ST. The last element is copied to the Q output and the IN input is moved into the first element. For the 90-70 processors, one can specify the number of elements to shift. For the other processors, only one element can be shifted. When the R (reset) input is **on**, the shift register elements are all set to zero. The top input does not need to be on to reset the shift register.

The example SHFR_WORD in Figure 8.72*a* is an 8-element WORD shift register. The example SHFR_WORD in Figure 8.72*b* (for the 90-70 processors) is also an 8-element WORD shift register, but every time this block is executed, three words are shifted into the register. In this case, the Out_Wrd output contains the last (third) word shifted out.

Bit array function blocks and the operation that occurs for each one are:

Block Name	**Operation Result**
BIT_CLR_***	Clear bit in array
BIT_POS_***	Find position of bit in array
BIT_SET_***	Set bit in array
BIT_TEST_***	Test value of bit in array
MASK_COMP_***	Masked comparison of two bit arrays

where *** is WORD or DWORD. For all of these functions, a bit array is constructed from WORDs or DWORDs. All of these blocks except for the MASK_COMP function block are shown in Figure 8.73. The MASK_COMP function block is shown in Figure 8.74.

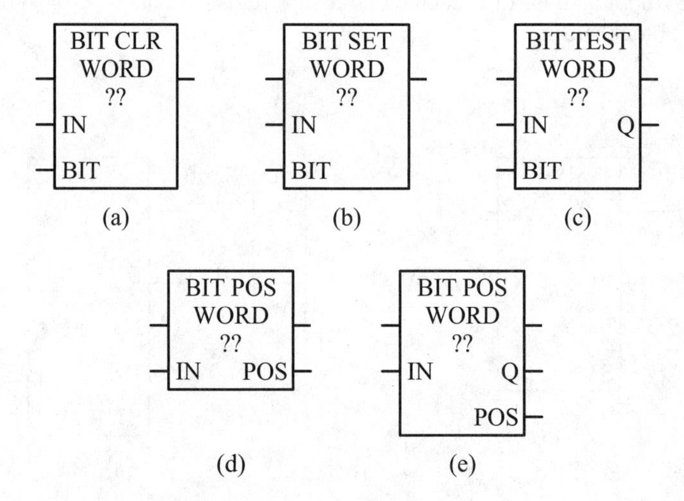

Figure 8.73. GE Fanuc bit array functions: *(a)* clear bit; *(b)* set bit; *(c)* test bit; *(d)* bit position (90-30 and VersaMax); *(e)* bit position (90-70).

For all blocks in Figure 8.73, the IN input is the starting WORD (or DWORD) of the bit array and the BIT input is the bit number being changed or tested. The least significant bit is bit one. The "??" field is the number of WORDs or DWORDs that constitute the array, from 1 to 256.

The BIT_CLR and BIT_SET function blocks, shown in Figure 8.73*a,b*, provide a convenient way to write individual bits in the array. BIT_CLR clears the specified bit (sets its value to "0") and BIT_SET sets the specified bit to "1." The BIT_TEST function (Figure 8.73*c*) copies the value of the specified bit to the Q output. For all three of these blocks, the top output is **on** whenever the top input is **on** and the BIT value is a valid number. An application of the BIT_TEST block is shown in section 9.2.5.

The BIT_POS function finds the position of the first bit in the array that is "1." The POS output is set to that position. If none of the bits are "1," the POS output is set to zero. The 90-70 implementation of this block has another output, Q, that is **on** if the array contained a bit set to "1," and **off** otherwise. The top output is **on** whenever the top input is **on**.

The MASK_COMP function block (Figure 8.74) compares two bit arrays and returns the next position where they differ. One can also specify a mask. The input signals are:

IN1 – Symbol/address of first element of first bit array.
IN2 – Symbol/address of first element of second bit array.
M – Bit array compare mask.
BIT – Array index of search: zero for first search; index of last found element if continuing search (UINT).

The output signals are:

MC – Miscompare indication. **On** if miscompare found.
Q – Output copy of compare mask.
BN – Bit array index of last miscompare (WORD).

The number below the block name is the number of WORDs or DWORDs that constitute the array, from 1 to 256.

When the top input of the function block is turned **on**, the bits in the first bit array (IN1) are compared with the corresponding bits in the second bit array (IN2). The comparison starts at the BIT+1 index and increments through the arrays. The mask (M) indicates which

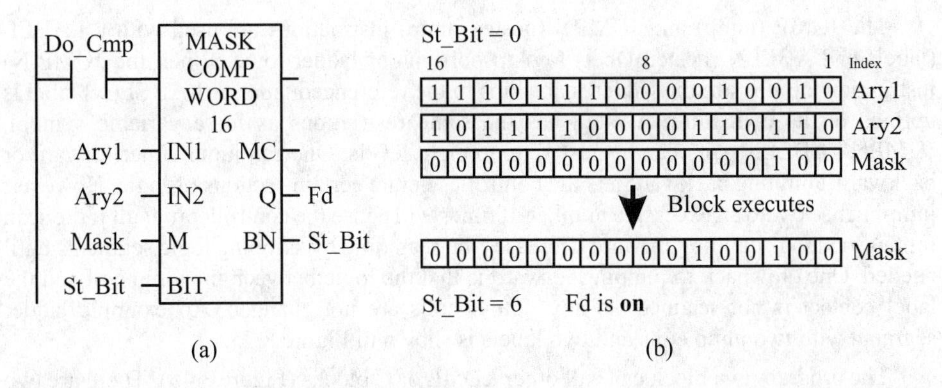

Figure 8.74. GE Fanuc bit array compare function: *(a)* ladder logic; *(b)* operation.

miscompares should be ignored. A “1” in the mask indicates that a miscompare in this position should be ignored. Initially, the input mask (M) is copied to the Q output. When a miscompare is detected, that is, a bit in the first array is not equal to the corresponding bit in the second array, the corresponding bit in the mask array (M) is checked. If the mask bit is ”1,” the miscompare is ignored and the next index is checked. If the mask bit is “0,” the following happens: (1) set the corresponding mask bit in M to “1,” (2) update Q to match M, (3) set the miscompare (MC) output to **on**, (4) set the bit number (BN) output to the current index, and (5) stop the comparison. If the end of the bit array is reached and a miscompare is not found, the MC output is turned **off** and the BN output is set to the highest bit number in the bit array.

To repeat the function and find the next mismatch, the value of the BN output is copied to the BIT input (or BN and BIT are connected to the same variable).

An example application of the MASK_COMP block is shown in Figure 8.74. The ladder logic is shown in Figure 8.74*a* and the operation is illustrated in Figure 8.74*b*. Before the block is executed, St_Bit is set to zero. When the block executes, Ary1 and Ary2 are compared. The first mismatch is at index 3, but the mask bit is set, so this mismatch is ignored. The next mismatch is at index 6 and the mask bit is “0,” so the comparison is stopped. The BN output (St_Bit) and the mask are updated accordingly. This example is set up to continue the comparison.

8.7.4 Program Execution Control

The GE Fanuc processors offer a number of instructions that can control ladder logic execution. The names and the operation that occurs for each one are:

Instruction	Operation Result
JUMP(N)	Jump to a defined label if rung condition true
LABEL(N)	Jump destination
CALL	Call a function block (FC/SFC) with no parameters
MCR(N)	Master control relay activate
MCREND(N)	Master control relay disable
END	Mark end of ladder

Except for CALL and END, there are two versions of the instructions. The version ending in “N” means “nested” and is supported by all GE Fanuc processors. The instructions without the “N” are only supported by certain 90-30 processors (GE Fanuc Automation, 1999).

The JUMP (jump) and JUMPN (nested jump) instructions are used with a LABEL (label) or LABELN (nested label) to skip portions of ladder logic. When the JUMP(N) instruction input is **on**, the ladder scan skips to the referenced label. A LABEL(N) label is defined on its own rung. A label has the same restrictions as for a variable symbol. JUMPN/LABELN pairs can be nested up to eight levels. One can jump either forward or backward. Jumping backward lets the controller iterate certain sections of logic. However, jumping backward an excessive number of times will cause the controller to fault if the scan time is too long. Jumping forward decreases the scan time by skipping logic segments until needed. One drawback to jumping forward is that the logic between the jump coil and the label contact is not scanned, so any output coils are not changed. An example ladder segment with two jump coils and two labels is shown in Figure 8.75.

The program in a block can call other LD, IL or C blocks (Figure 3.45). There are two types of calls, non-parameterized (Figure 8.76*a*) and parameterized (Figure 8.76*b*). A

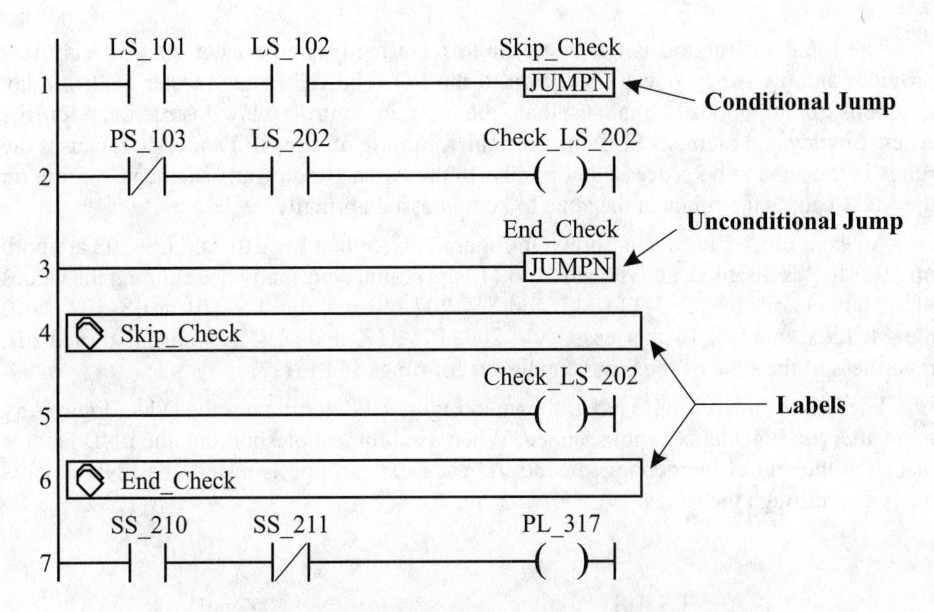

Figure 8.75. GE Fanuc JUMPN and LABELN example.

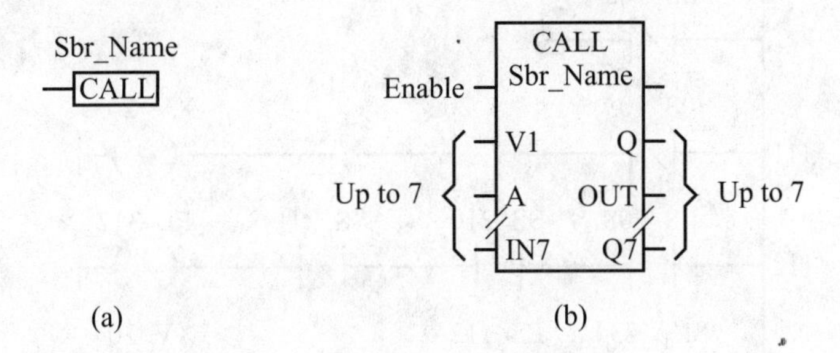

Figure 8.76. GE Fanuc subroutine call: *(a)* non-parameterized; *(b)* parameterized (90-70 only).

non-parameterized call does not pass values into or out of the block. The name of the block appears above the call rectangle. Parameterized calls are supported by 90-70 processors only. In this case, one can define up to seven input and output parameters for the block.

The MCR(N) (master control relay) instructions function like a software master control relay, disabling non-retentive outputs within a range of rungs. The MCR(N) instruction ENDMCR(N) label are used in pairs to create "zones" of the ladder program where all outputs may be disabled. An MCR(N) defines the start of the zone, and an ENDMCR(N) having the same name as the MCR(N) defines the end of the zone. Zones may be nested up to eight levels deep. Logic preceding the MCR(N) instruction controls execution of the zone. When this rung logic turns **off** the MCR(N) all rungs in the zone are scanned normally. When the rung logic causes the MCR(N) to be **on**, all rungs in the zone are scanned but only to turn **off** all non-retentive outputs in the zone. All normal coils are turned **off** and all negated coils are turned **on**. All non-retentive timers are reset and all blocks are not executed.

The MCR instruction is not a substitute for a hard-wired master control relay that provides an emergency power shutdown to the I/O. The GE Fanuc master control relay functions in an opposite manner than the master control relay instructions for the Allen-Bradley and Siemens PLCs. In particular, turning off the GE Fanuc MCR causes the rungs in the zone to be processed normally. In the Allen-Bradley and Siemens, turning on the MCR causes the rungs in the zone to be processed normally.

An example MCR zone is shown in Figure 8.77. When LS_101 and LS_102 are both **on**, the MCR is disabled, and rungs 111 to 113 are scanned normally determining the values of the output coils XV_203, PL_317, and XV_204. When either LS_101 or LS_102 is **off**, the MCR is enabled. In this case, XV_203, PL_317, and XV_204 are all turned **off**, regardless of the state of the input conditions for rungs 111 to113.

The END (End of Logic) label, shown in Figure 8.78, terminates the ladder logic. Any logic after the END label is not scanned. When used for troubleshooting, the END label is placed at the end of the debugged code. As each new section is tested, the END label is moved on through the rungs.

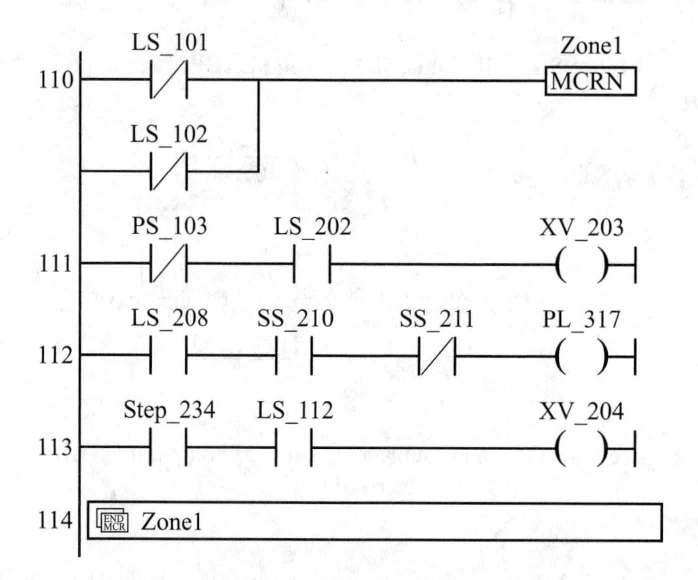

Figure 8.77. GE Fanuc MCR example.

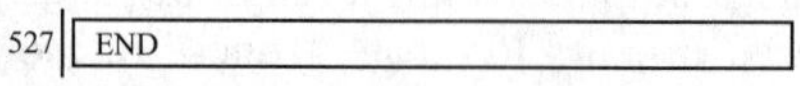

527 END

Figure 8.78. GE Fanuc END label.

8.8 EXAMPLES

The following three examples illustrate the application of shift registers and FIFO/LIFO queues to track material as it moves down a production line. The first example uses a shift register to track part defects. The second example tracks part numbers as they move on a conveyor and as they are stacked and unstacked. Modifying the system to allow parts to be placed on intermediate stations on the transport conveyor produces the third example.

> **Design Tip**
>
> Shift registers and FIFO/LIFO queues are useful for tracking the status or identification of a part as it moves down an assembly line.

Example 8.1. Defect tracking. Implement a defect tracking system for a production system. The system is modeled as 25 stations (Figure 8.79*a*) and a part moves along the system, spending 2 seconds in each station and then 0.5 seconds to move between stations. If a part is determined to be defective at any station, a defect indication is set that follows the part as it moves through the remaining stations. The last station (#25) is the reject station. If the part is marked as defective at the reject station, a reject solenoid is activated for 1.0 seconds to kick the part off the conveying system.

Assume the following physical input, physical output, and internal memory assignments:

Variable	Description
Run	Internal coil, **on** when system running (set by another part of the ladder).
Int_Reset	Internal coil, **on** to clear all defect indications. Assume that Run is already **off** when this turns **on** (set by another part of the ladder).
REJECT_SOL	Reject solenoid; **on** for 1.0 second to push defective part off conveying system.

The addresses associated with the physical output is:

Variable	Modicon	PLC-5	ControlLogix	Siemens	GE Fanuc
REJECT_SOL	000016	O:2/17	Local:2:O.Data.15	Q5.7	%Q16

The addresses or data types associated with the internal variables:

Variable	Modicon Data Type	PLC-5 Addr.	Logix Data Type	Siemens Addr.	GE Fanuc Addr.
Run	BOOL	B3/100	BOOL	M62.0	%M100
Int_Reset	BOOL	B3/101	BOOL	M62.1	%M101

Solution. A 25-bit shift register will be used to store the defect indication. The appropriate bit is set by the defect-checking logic at individual stations, and the defect indication must shift with the part as it moves down the line. The logic to generate the signals that indicate when the part is moving (Mv_Part) and when it is being processed (Dwell) will also be

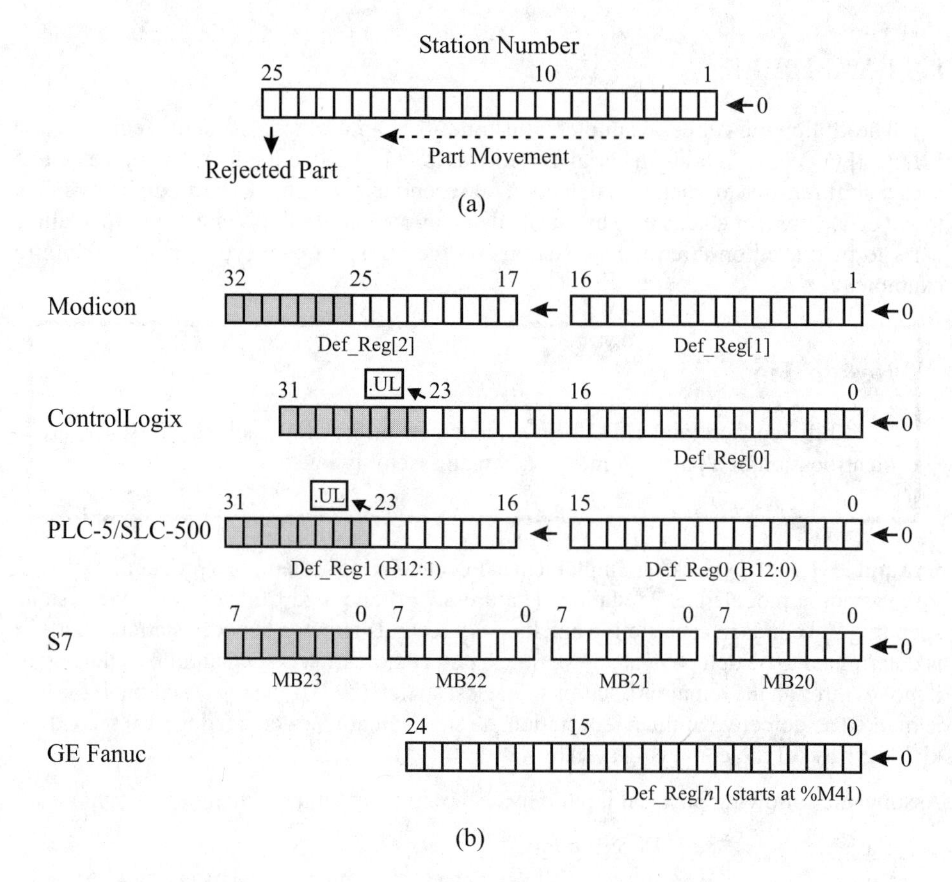

Figure 8.79. Production system defect tracking: *(a)* model of stations; *(b)* shift registers for implementation.

shown, though that is not part of the problem. As an example, the logic to set the defect indication for station 10 is shown. The logic for any other station that sets a defect bit is similar.

The structure of the shift register for each of the PLCs is shown in Figure 8.79*b*. The solutions are shown in Figures 8.80 to 8.84. For all of the implementations, the shift register is shifted at the start of the dwell time, and if a defective part is present at station 25, the reject solenoid is activated. A station defect indication is set at the start of part movement (end of dwell), allowing the dwell time to test for a defect.

The Modicon solution for this problem is shown in Figure 8.80. The function of each rung is as follows:

1. Generate Dwell (part processing) and Mv_Part (part moving).

2.-3. Shift defect indications left one position. A shorter version of the 40-bit shift register in Figure 8.6.

4. Clear shift register on reset.

5. Eject part if station 25 defect bit turned on (Def_Bit, from rung 2).

6. Set station 10 defect if defect detected.

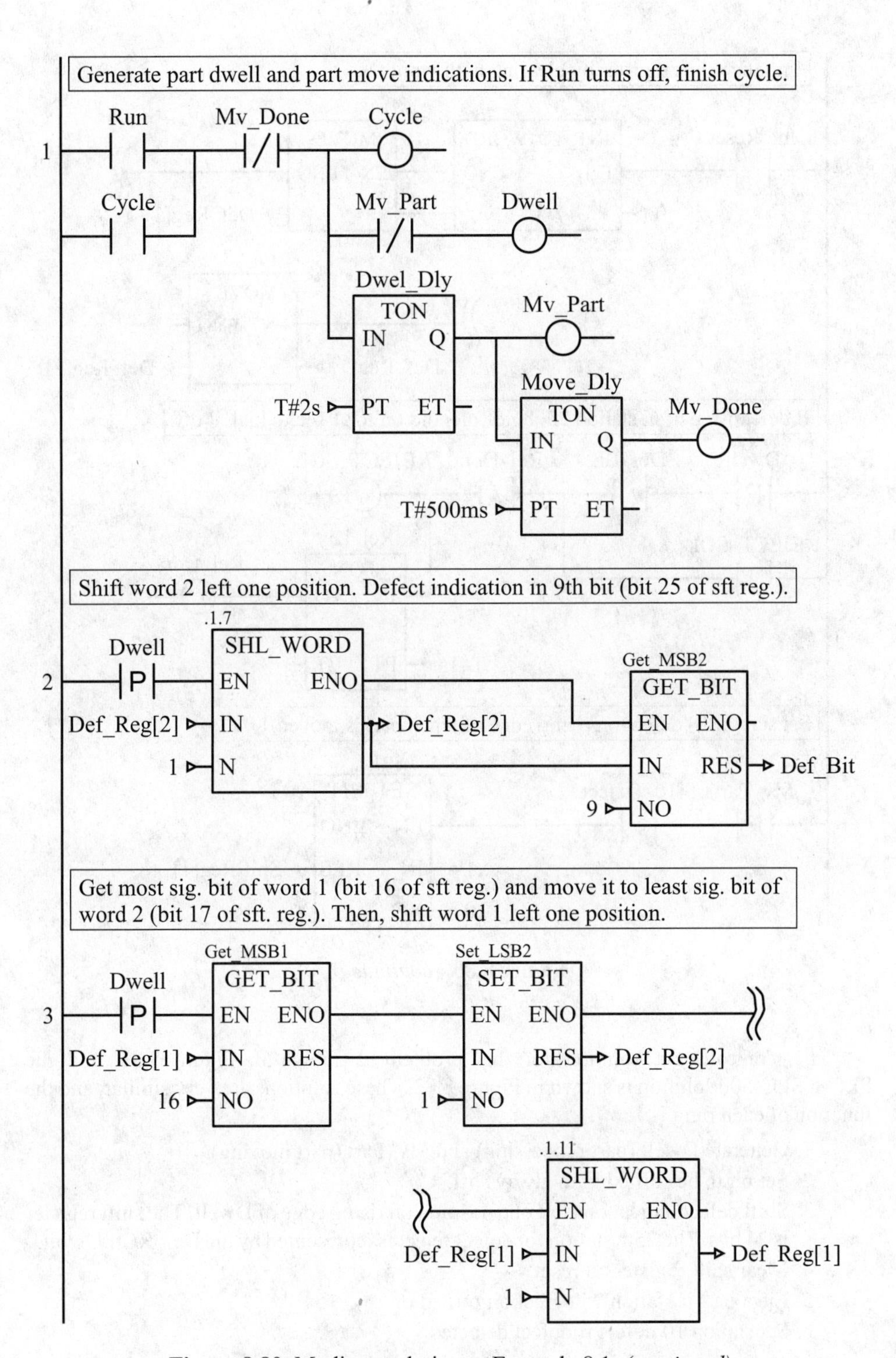

Figure 8.80. Modicon solution to Example 8.1. *(continued)*

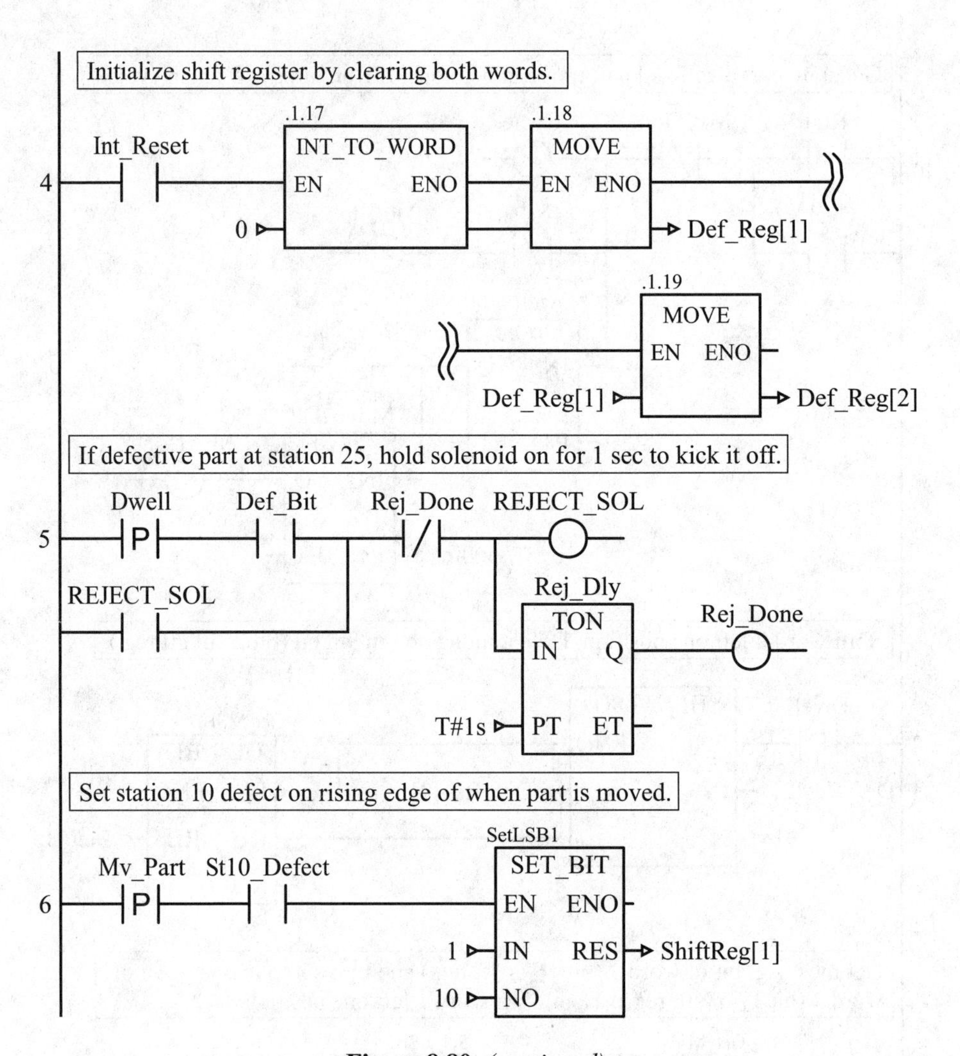

Figure 8.80. *(continued)*

The ControlLogix solution for this problem is shown in Figure 8.81, and the PLC-5/SLC-500 solution is shown in Figure 8.82. These solutions are very similar, and the function of each rung is:

1. Generate Dwell (part processing) and Mv_Part (part moving).
2. Set bit to be shifted in to always **off**.
3. Shift defect indications left one position on rising edge of Dwell. The shift register is 24 bits. The 25th station for defect reject is represented by the Def_RCtl.UL bit.
4. Clear shift register on reset.
5. Eject part if station 25 defect bit turned on.
6. Set station 10 defect if defect detected.

The Siemens S7-300/400 solution for this problem is shown in Figure 8.83, and the GE Fanuc 90-30 solution is shown in Figure 8.84.The function of each rung of the S7 solution is:

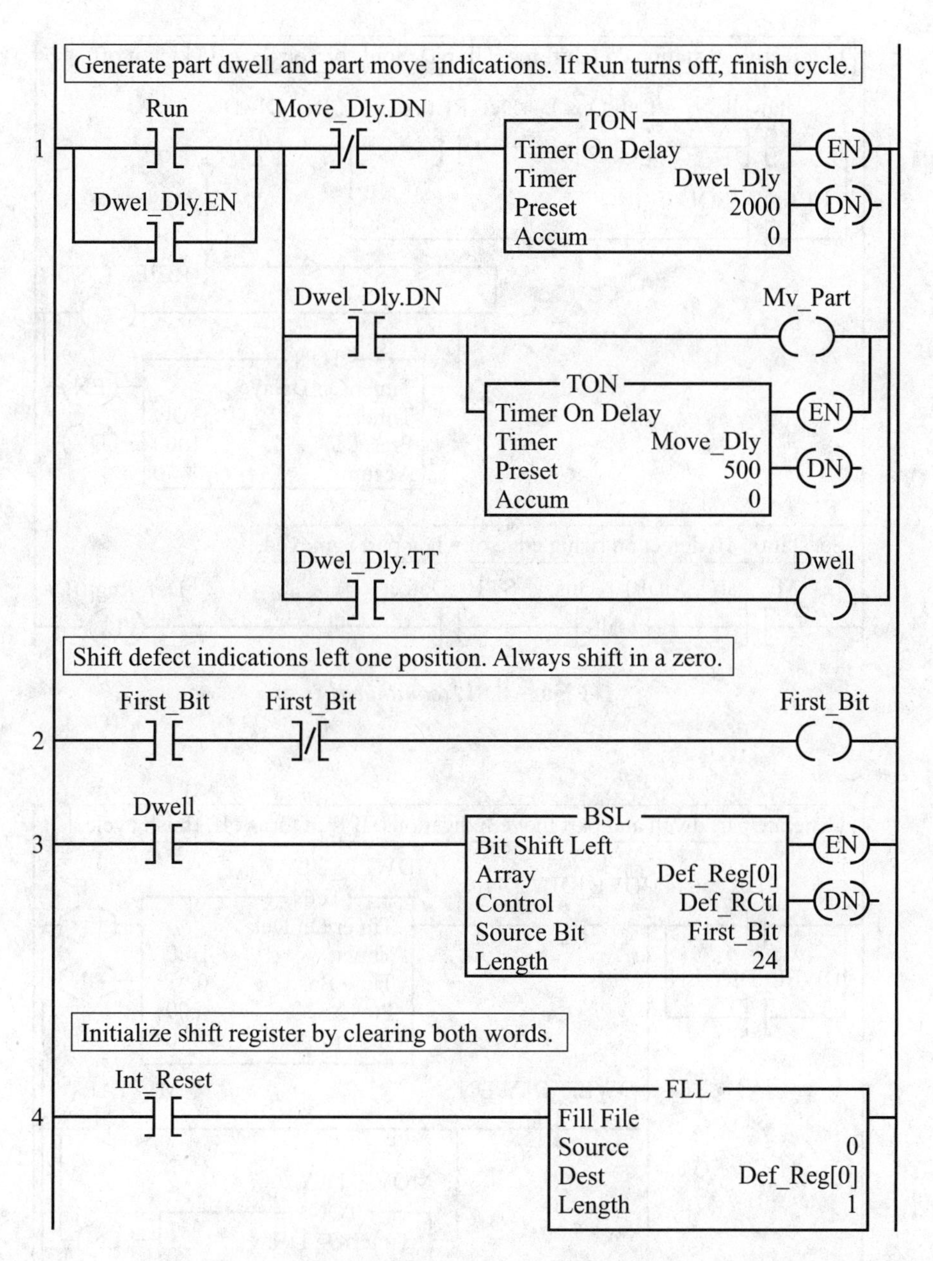

Figure 8.81. ControlLogix solution to Example 8.1. *(continued)*

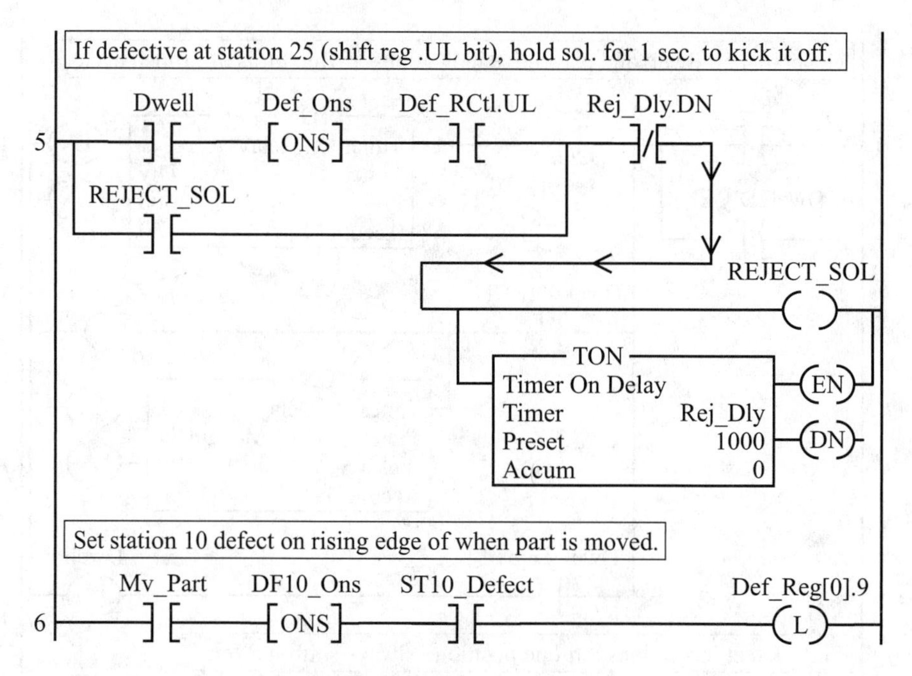

Figure 8.81. *(continued)*

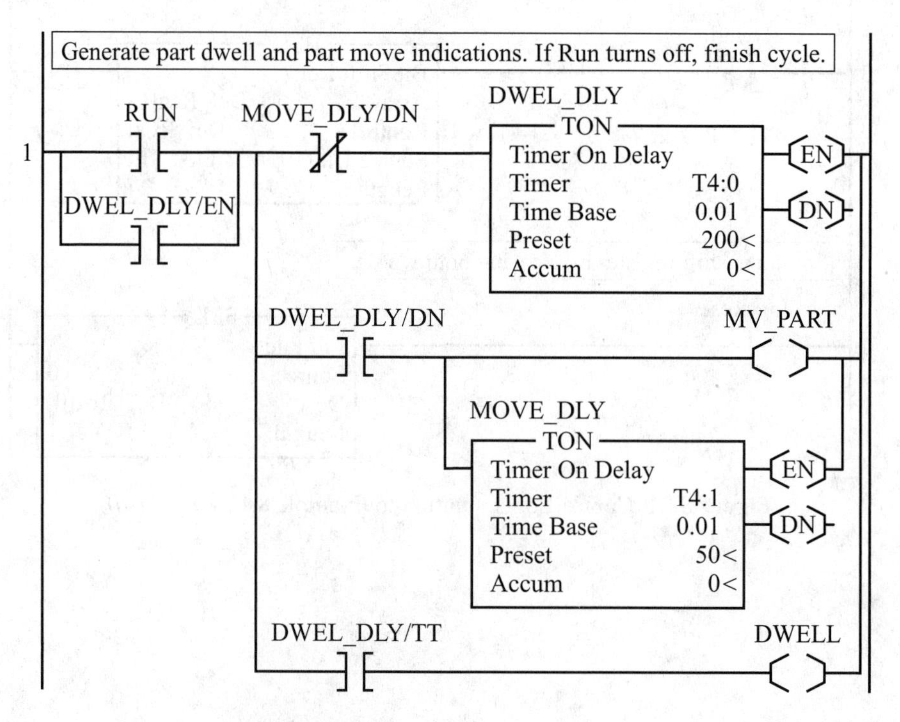

Figure 8.82. PLC-5/SLC-500 solution to Example 8.1. *(continued)*

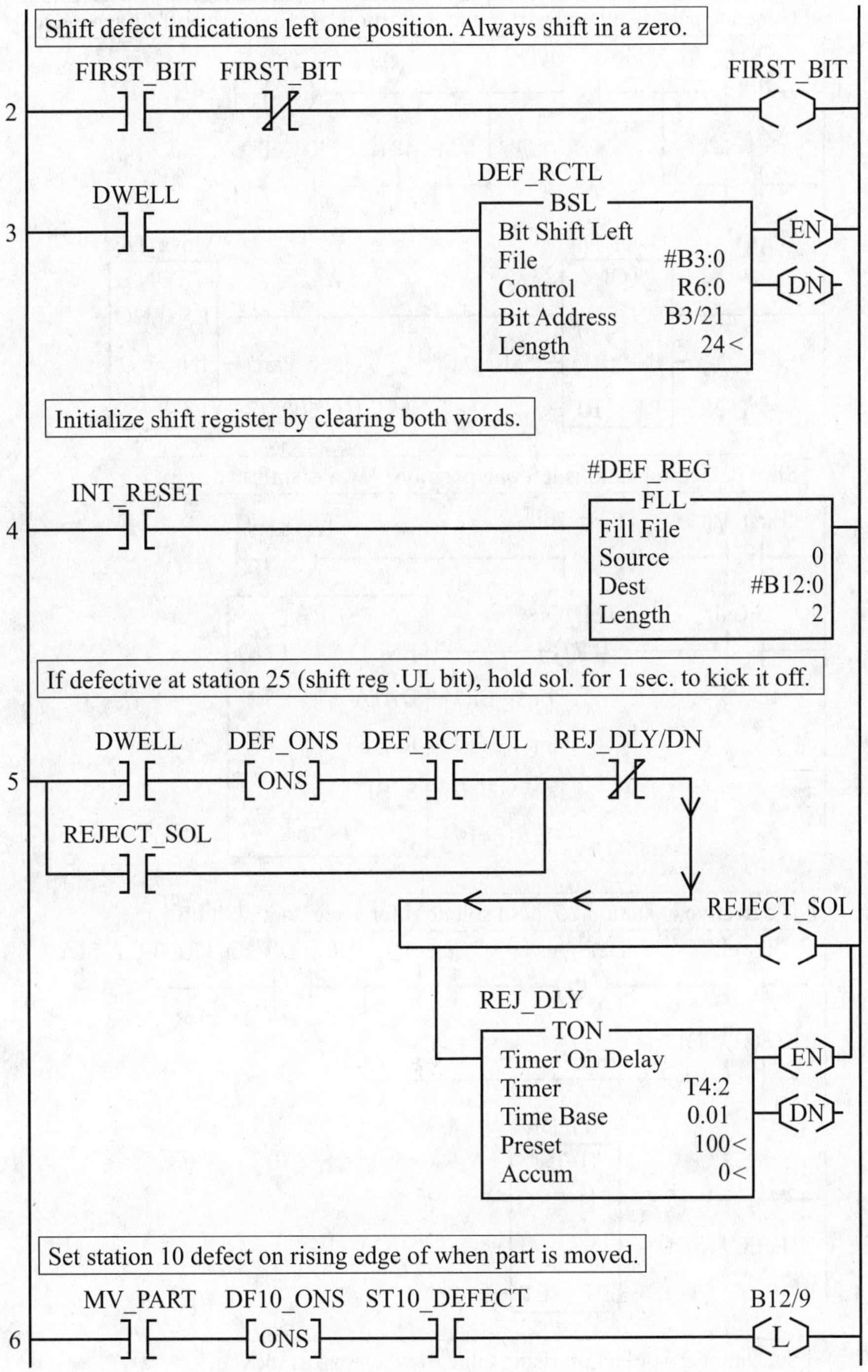

Shift defect indications left one position. Always shift in a zero.

2 FIRST_BIT] [FIRST_BIT]/[—— ( ) FIRST_BIT

3 DWELL] [—— DEF_RCTL BSL
Bit Shift Left
File #B3:0
Control R6:0
Bit Address B3/21
Length 24<
(EN)
(DN)

Initialize shift register by clearing both words.

4 INT_RESET] [—— #DEF_REG FLL
Fill File
Source 0
Dest #B12:0
Length 2

If defective at station 25 (shift reg .UL bit), hold sol. for 1 sec. to kick it off.

5 DWELL] [DEF_ONS [ONS] DEF_RCTL/UL] [REJ_DLY/DN]/[
REJECT_SOL] [
REJECT_SOL ( )
REJ_DLY TON
Timer On Delay
Timer T4:2
Time Base 0.01
Preset 100<
Accum 0<
(EN)
(DN)

Set station 10 defect on rising edge of when part is moved.

6 MV_PART] [DF10_ONS [ONS] ST10_DEFECT] [—— B12/9 (L)

Figure 8.82. *(continued)*

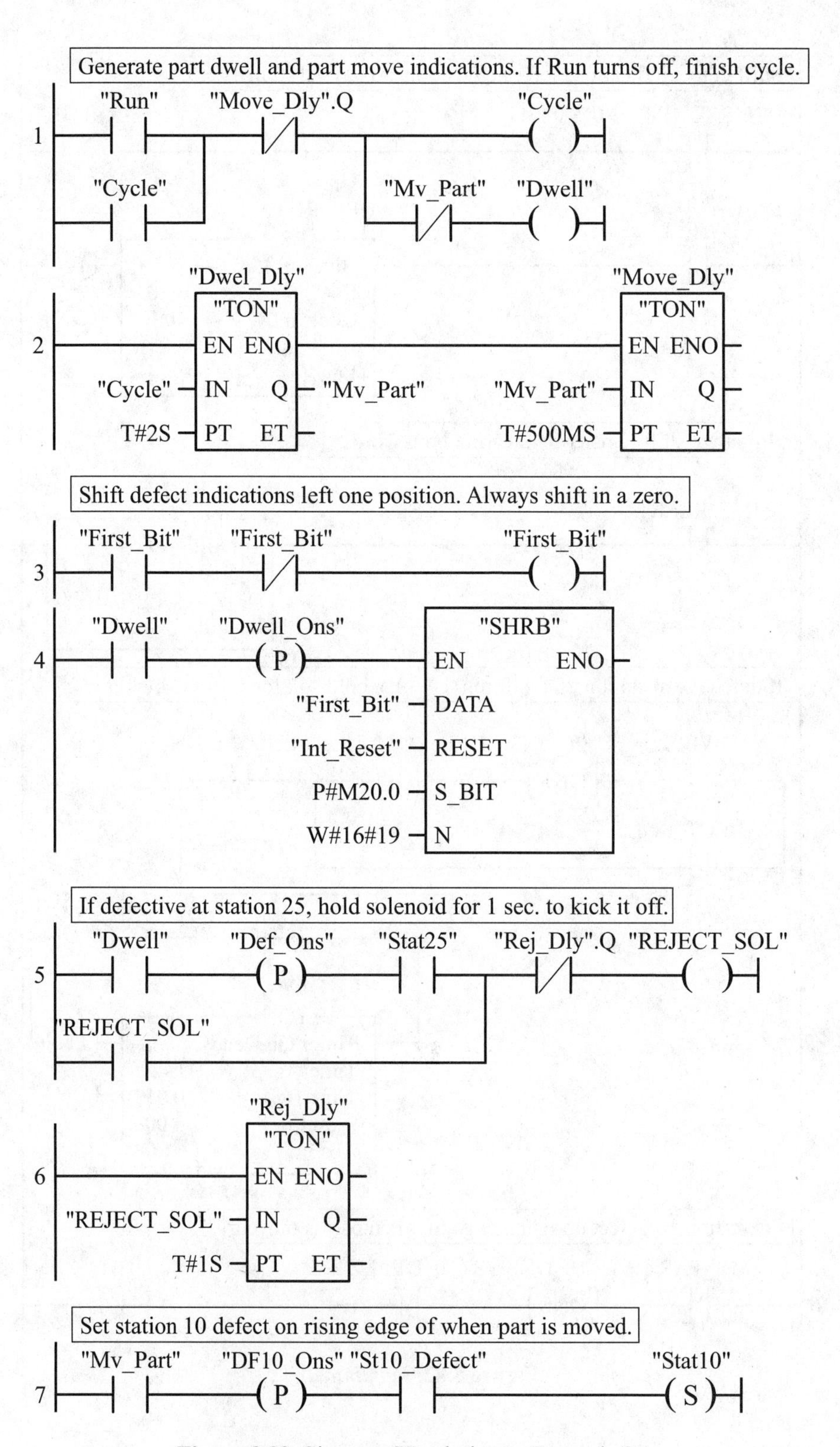

Figure 8.83. Siemens S7 solution to Example 8.1.

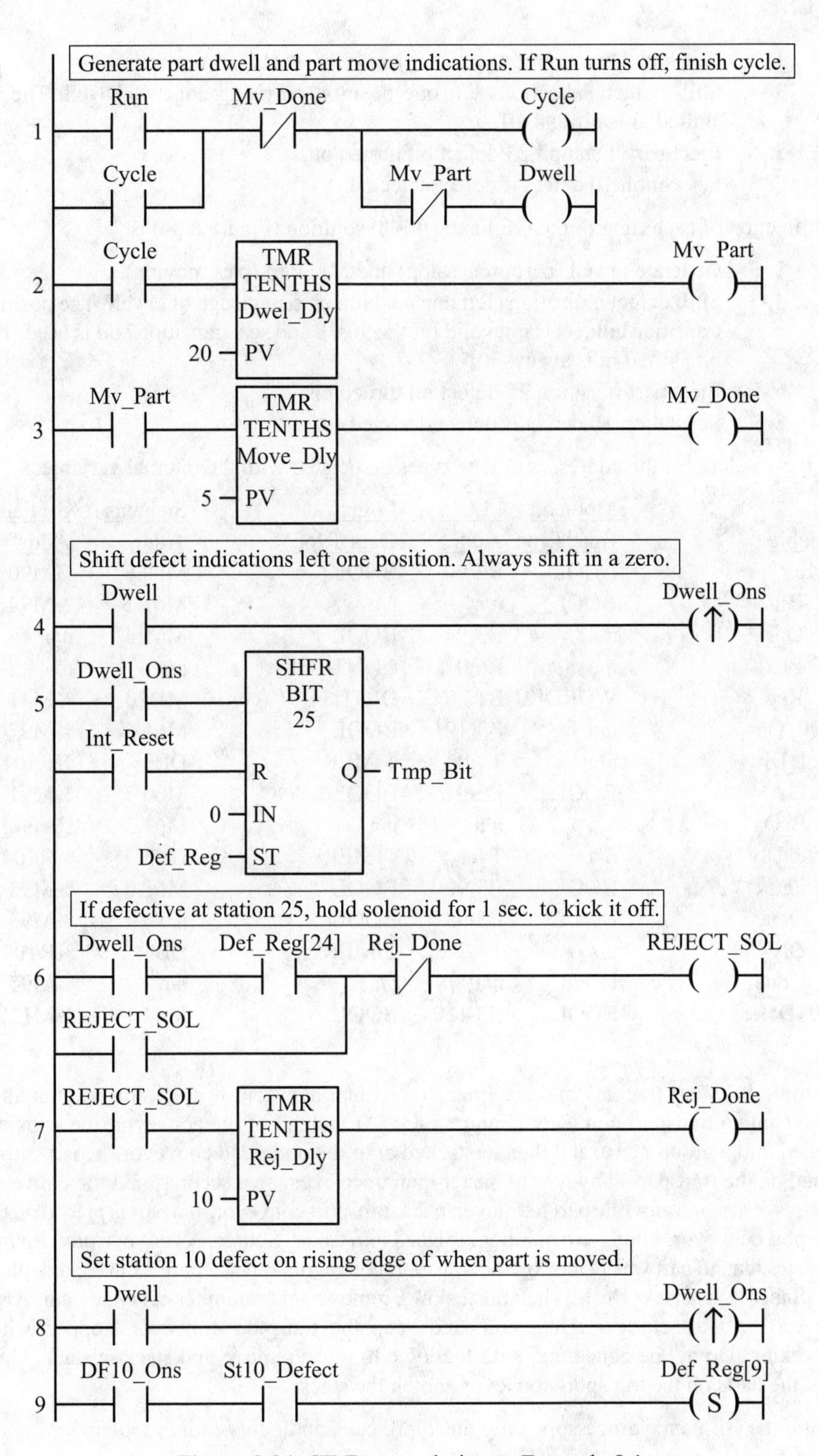

Figure 8.84. GE Fanuc solution to Example 8.1.

1.-2. Generate Dwell (part processing) and Mv_Part (part moving).
3.-4. Shift defect indications left one position on rising edge of Dwell. The bit shifted in is always **off**.
5.-6. Eject part if station 25 defect bit turned on.
7. Set station 10 defect if defect detected.

The function of each rung of the GE Fanuc 90-30 solution (Figure 8.84) is:

1.-3. Generate Dwell (part processing) and Mv_Part (part moving).
4.-5. Shift defect indications left one position on rising edge of Dwell. The positive transition contact is not valid for the 90-30 and so a transition coil is used. The bit shifted in is always **off**.
6.-7. Eject part if station 25 defect bit turned on.
8.-9. Set station 10 defect if defect detected.

For these solutions, the addresses or data types associated with the internal variables:

Variable	Modicon Data Type	PLC-5 Addr.	Logix Data Type	Siemens Addr.	GE Fanuc Addr.
Cycle	BOOL	B3/90	BOOL	M60.6	%M90
Def_Bit	BOOL	n/a	n/a	M61.2	%M94
Def_Ons	n/a	B3/94	BOOL	M61.4	n/a
Def_RCtl	n/a	R6:0	CONTROL	n/a	n/a
Def_Reg	WORD[2]	B12:0	DINT[1]	MD20	%M41
DF10_Ons	n/a	B3/121	BOOL	M61.5	%M97
Dwel_Dly	n/a	T4:0	TIMER	DB2	%R101
Dwell	BOOL	B3/91	BOOL	M60.7	%M91
Dwell_Ons	n/a	n/a	n/a	M61.3	%M96
Move_Dly	n/a	T4:1	TIMER	DB3	%R104
Mv_Part	BOOL	B3/92	BOOL	M61.0	%M92
Mv_Done	BOOL	B3/93	BOOL	n/a	%M93
Rej_Dly	n/a	T4:2	TIMER	DB4	%R107
Rej_Done	BOOL	n/a	n/a	n/a	%M95
St10_Defect	BOOL	B3/120	BOOL	M64.1	%M120

Example 8.2. Part tracking and stacking. Implement a system to track the parts as they move along a transport conveyor (Figure 8.85). At the end of the conveyor, the parts are stacked into a group of 10, and then unstacked onto the outbound conveyor. A part can be placed on the transport conveyor no faster than once every two seconds and the conveyor requires 40 seconds for one part to tranverse the transport conveyor. If a part is placed on the transport conveyor, a non-zero number is placed into Conv_Source. A zero in Conv_Source indicates that no part was placed on the transport conveyor. When a part is unstacked, place its number in Unstack_Dest. When unstacking, remove a part number every second. Also, turn **on** the Unstacking internal coil, and keep the transport conveyor stopped when unstacking. Do not be concerned with the logic to place/remove and stack/unstack. Only track the parts on the transport conveyor and on the stack.

Of the GE Fanuc processors, only the 90-70 can handle this entire problem.

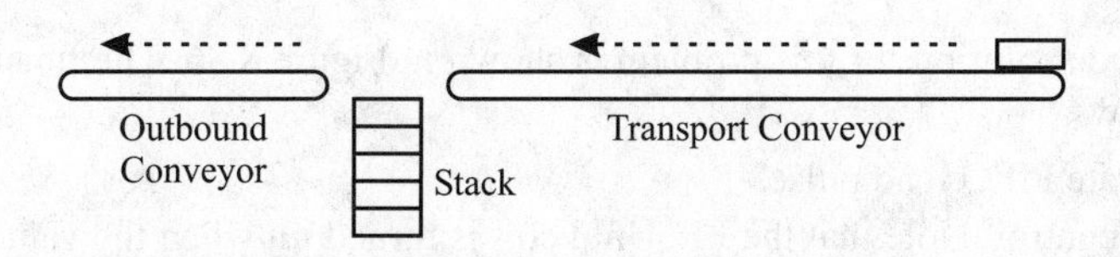

Figure 8.85. System of Example 8.2.

Assume the following physical input, physical output, and internal memory assignments:

Variable	Description
Conv_Run	Internal coil, **on** when transport conveyor may run (set by another part of the ladder).
Int_Reset	Internal coil, **on** to reset all queues. Assume that Conv_Run is already **off** when this turns **on** (set by another part of the ladder).
Conv_Source	Number of part being placed on transport conveyor.
Unstack_Dest	Number of part being unstacked from stack.
Unstacking	Indicates stack is being unstacked; **on** when unstacking (set by this part of ladder)
M1	Transport conveyor motor; **on** to run conveyor.

The addresses associated with the physical output is:

Variable	Modicon	PLC-5	ControlLogix	Siemens	GE Fanuc
M1	000016	O:2/17	Local:2:O.Data.15	Q4.0	%Q16

The addresses or data types associated with the internal variables:

	Modicon	PLC-5	Logix	Siemens	GE Fanuc
Variable	Data Type	Addr.	Data Type	Addr.	Addr.
Conv_Run	BOOL	B3/0	BOOL	M2.0	%M10
Int_Reset	BOOL	B3/1	BOOL	M2.1	%M11
Unstacking	BOOL	B3/3	BOOL	M2.3	%M13
Conv_Source	INT	N14:0	DINT	MW10	%R5
Unstack_Dest	INT	N14:50	DINT	MW20	%R10

Solution. The transport conveyor is modeled by a 20-element FIFO queue, and the stack is modeled by a 10-element LIFO queue. The FIFO queue is initialized to empty, and then when M1 (the conveyor motor) is running, the value of Conv_Source (part number) is loaded into the FIFO every 2 seconds. When the FIFO is full, then a part number is unloaded into Conv_Dest. If this number is non-zero, then a part is at the end of the conveyor, and it is loaded into the LIFO queue. This process continues until the LIFO is full. When the LIFO is full, the transport conveyor is stopped and the LIFO is unloaded, once per second until it is empty. Then the transport conveyor is allowed to run, and the process continues.

A timer (Conv_Tmr) generates a two-second tick to coordinate the FIFO load and unload. In order to simplify the logic, the handling of the situation when Conv_Run is turned off during this two-second interval is not considered. The Unld_Tmr generates the one-second tick to unload the LIFO.

The Modicon solution for this problem is shown in Figure 8.86. The function of each rung is as follows:

1. Generate FIFO load pulse.
2. FIFO control. Note that the FF_Unld coil is turned **on** when the value is actually unloaded from the FIFO. FF_Full cannot be used to load a value in to the LIFO since it is **on** for only one scan and is **off** when the unloaded value is possibly loaded into the LIFO.
3. Check for nonzero FIFO unloaded value before loading it onto LIFO.

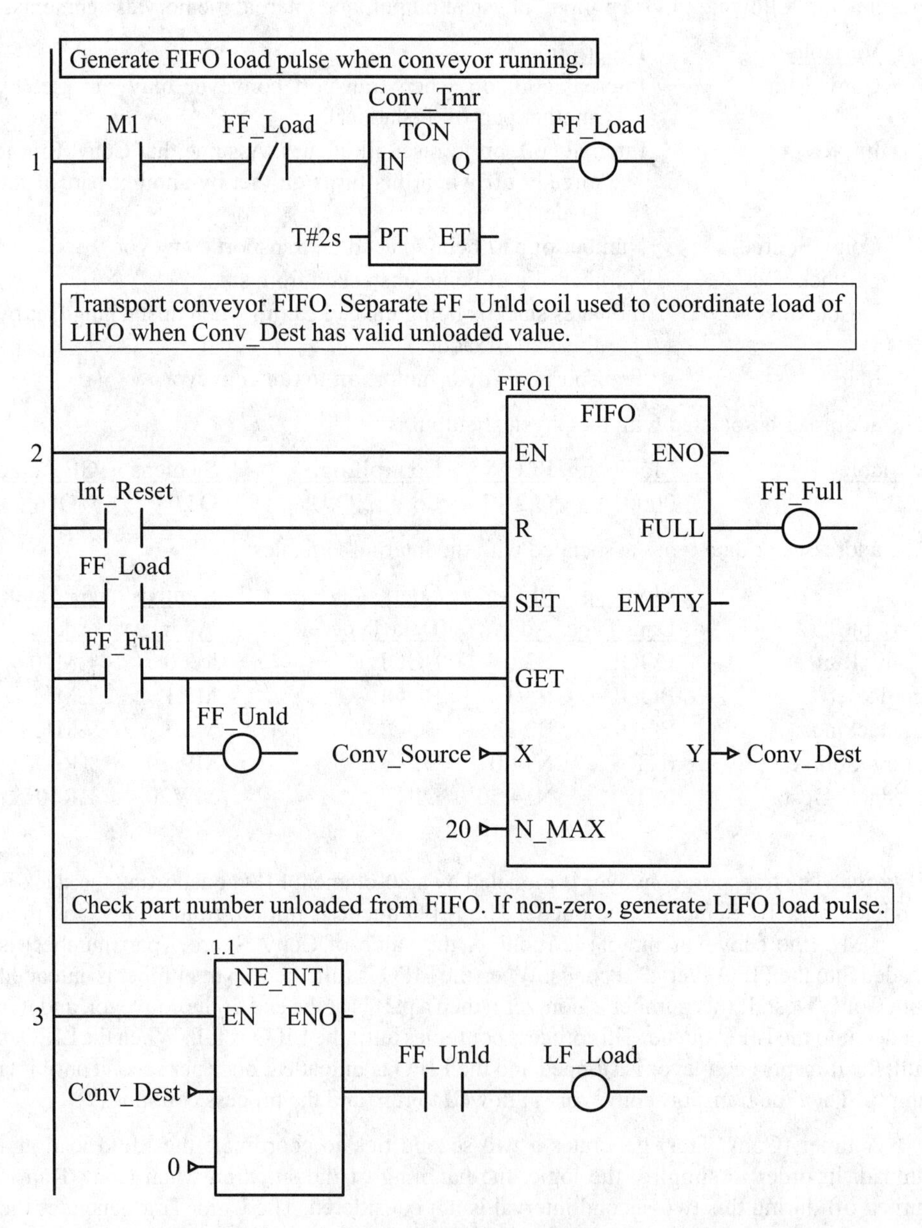

Figure 8.86. Modicon solution to Example 8.2. *(continued)*

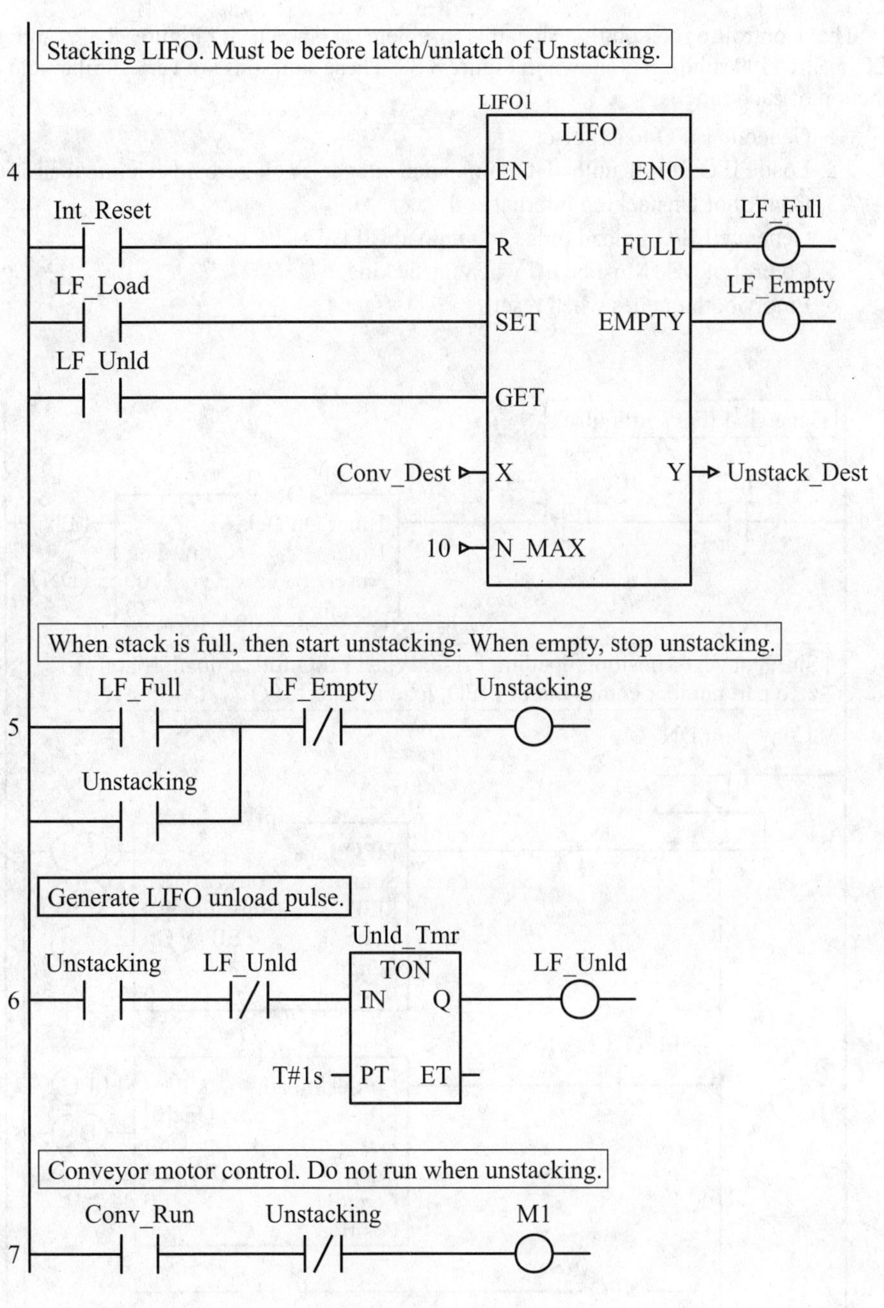

Figure 8.86. *(continued)*

4. LIFO control.
5. Control of Unstacking internal coil.
6. Generate LIFO unload pulse.
7. Control of M1. Must be **off** when unstacking.

The ControlLogix solution for this problem is shown in Figure 8.87, and the PLC-5/SLC-500 solution is shown in Figure 8.88. These solutions are very similar, and the function of each rung is:

1. Generate FIFO load pulse.
2. Load FIFO. If full, unload it. If unloaded integer is non-zero, load it into the LIFO.
3. Control of Unstacking internal coil.
4. Generate LIFO unload pulse and unload LIFO.
5. Control of M1. Must be **off** when unstacking.
6. Empty both queues when reset.

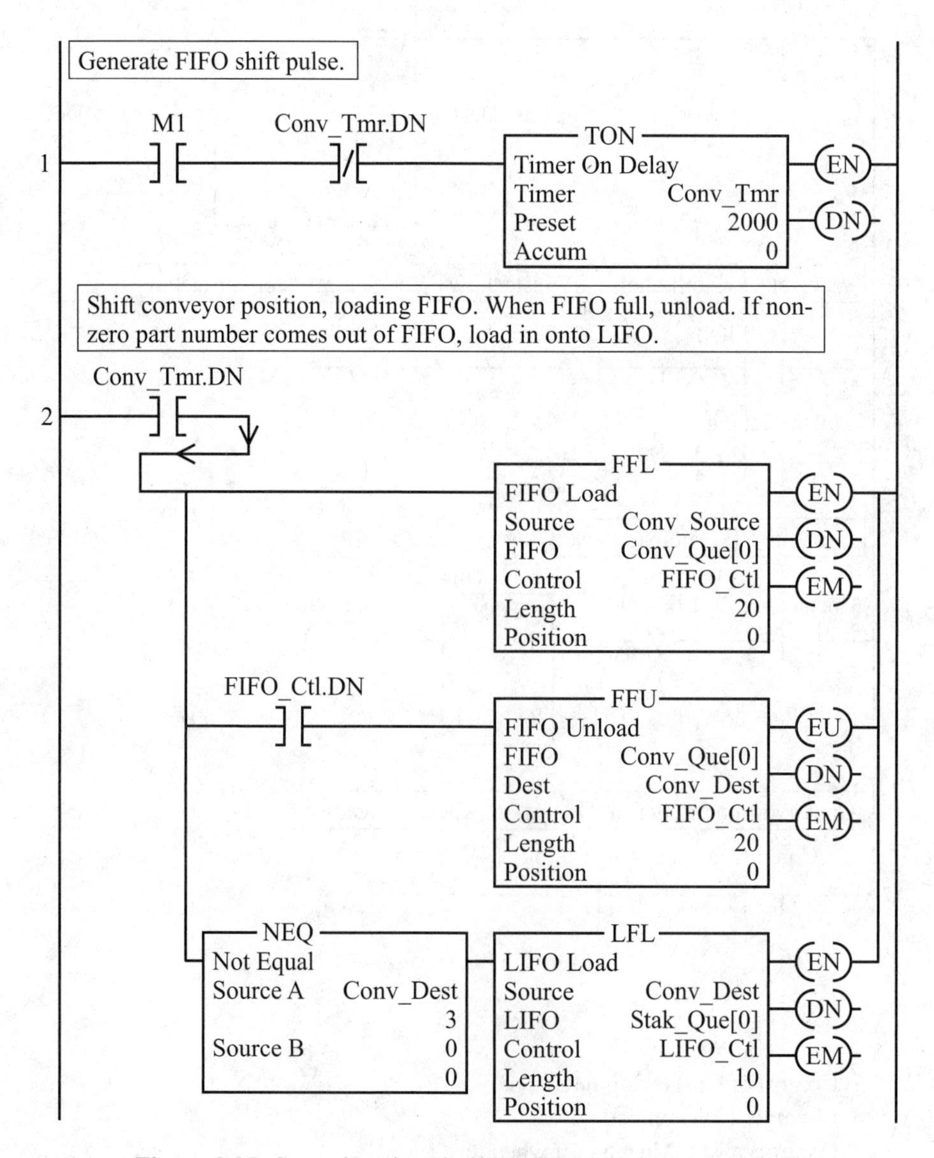

Figure 8.87. ControlLogix solution to Example 8.2. *(continued)*

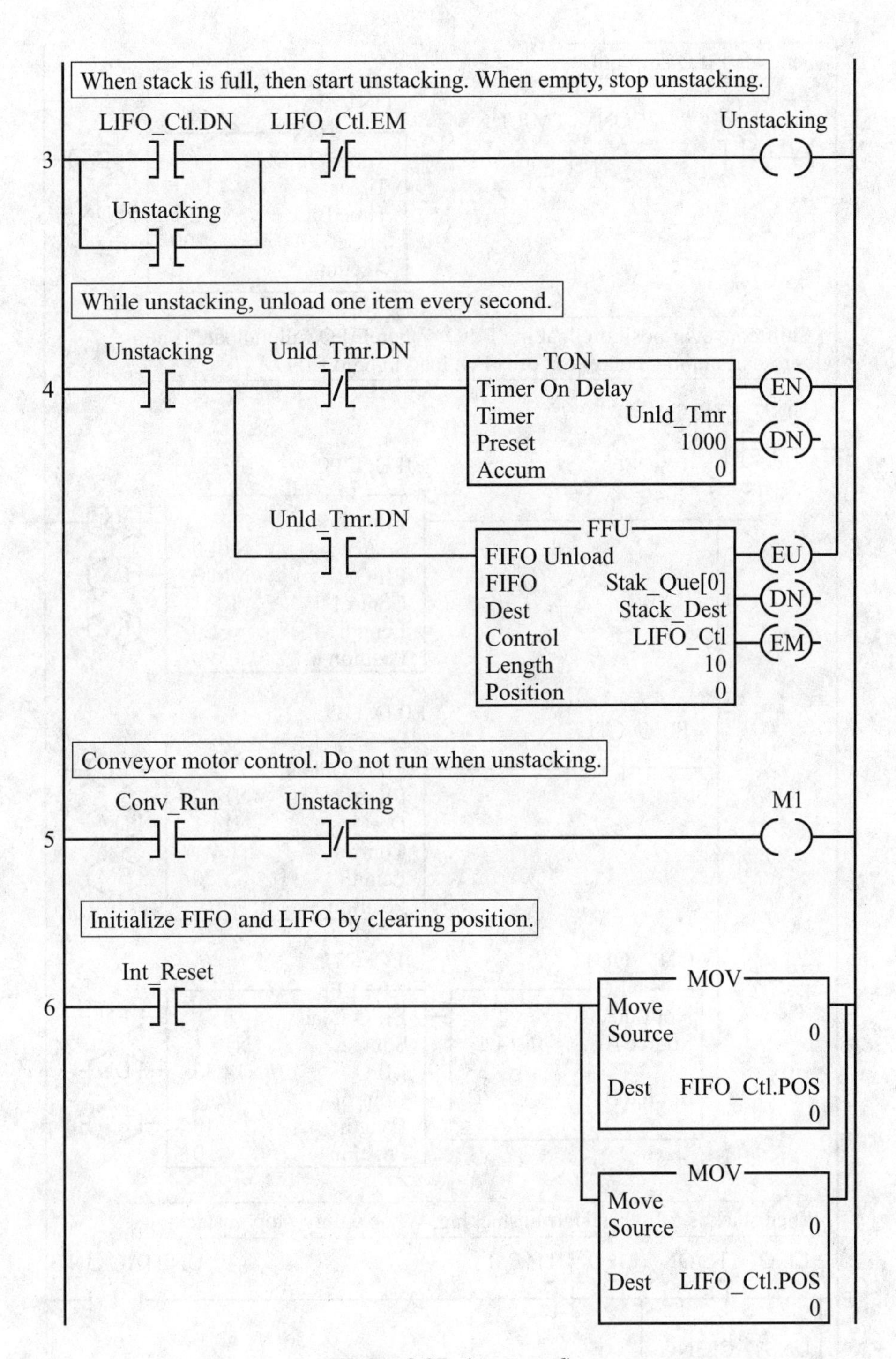

Figure 8.87. *(continued)*

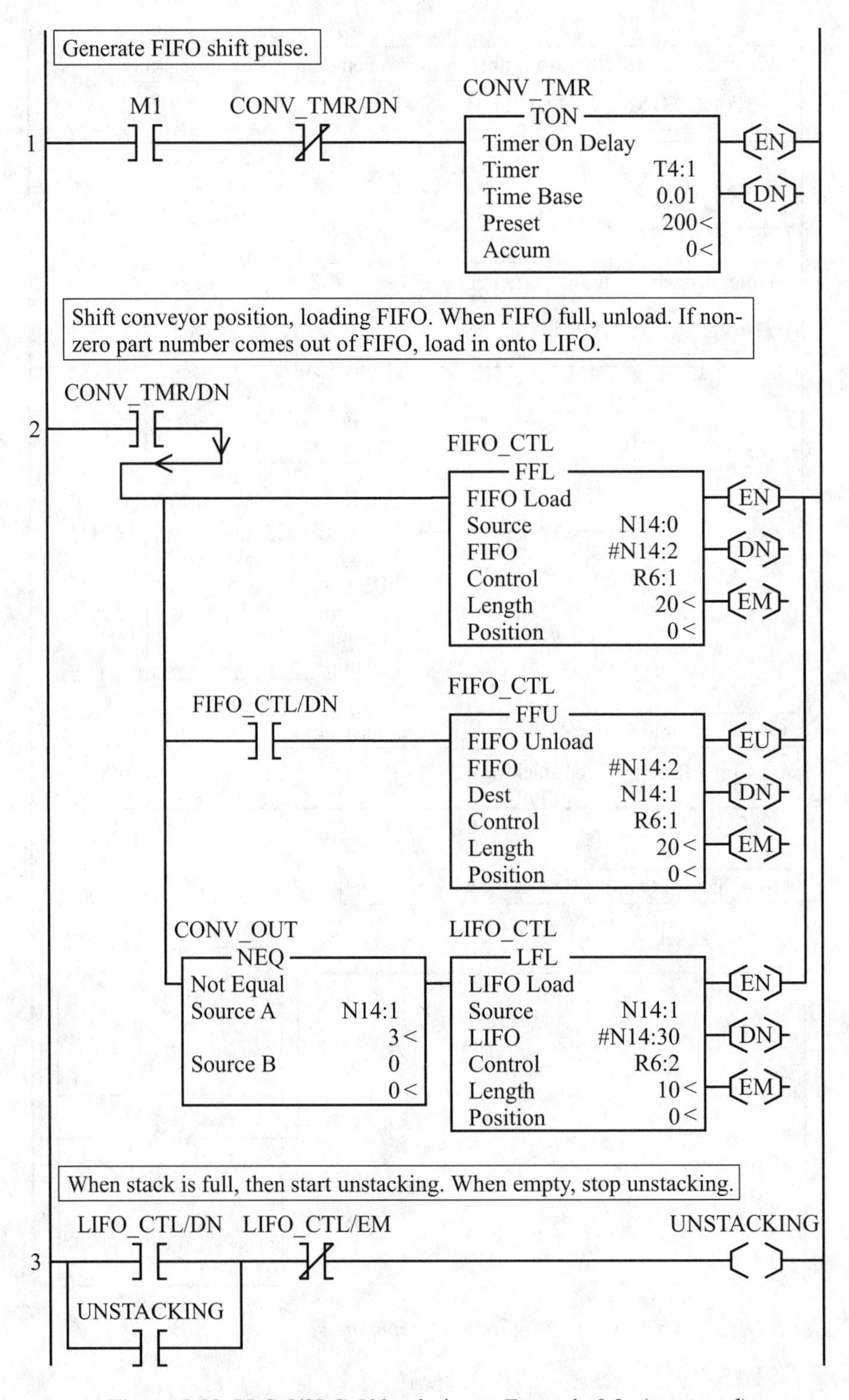

Figure 8.88. PLC-5/SLC-500 solution to Example 8.2. *(continued)*

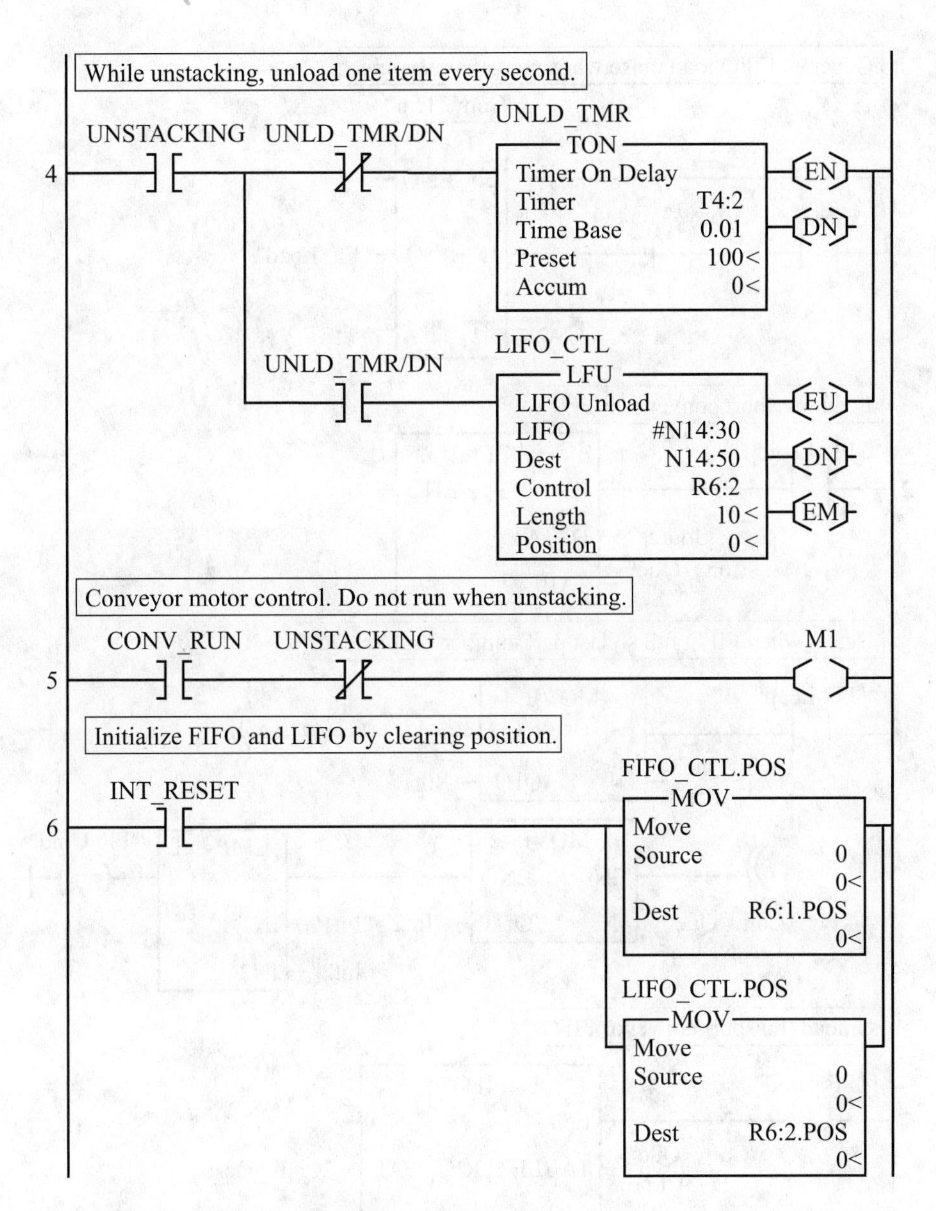

Figure 8.88. *(continued)*

The S7 solution for this problem is shown in Figure 8.89. The data type for the FIFO and LIFO queues is a user-defined type (UDT1), named FIFO20, defined as shown in Figure 8.90. The table for the conveyor FIFO queue is named "A" and is stored in DB2 and the LIFO queue is stored in DB3. The function of each rung is:

1. Generate FIFO load pulse.
2. Load FIFO.
3. Check for full FIFO. If full, generate pulse to unload it. Note that words must be converted to integers before they can be compared.

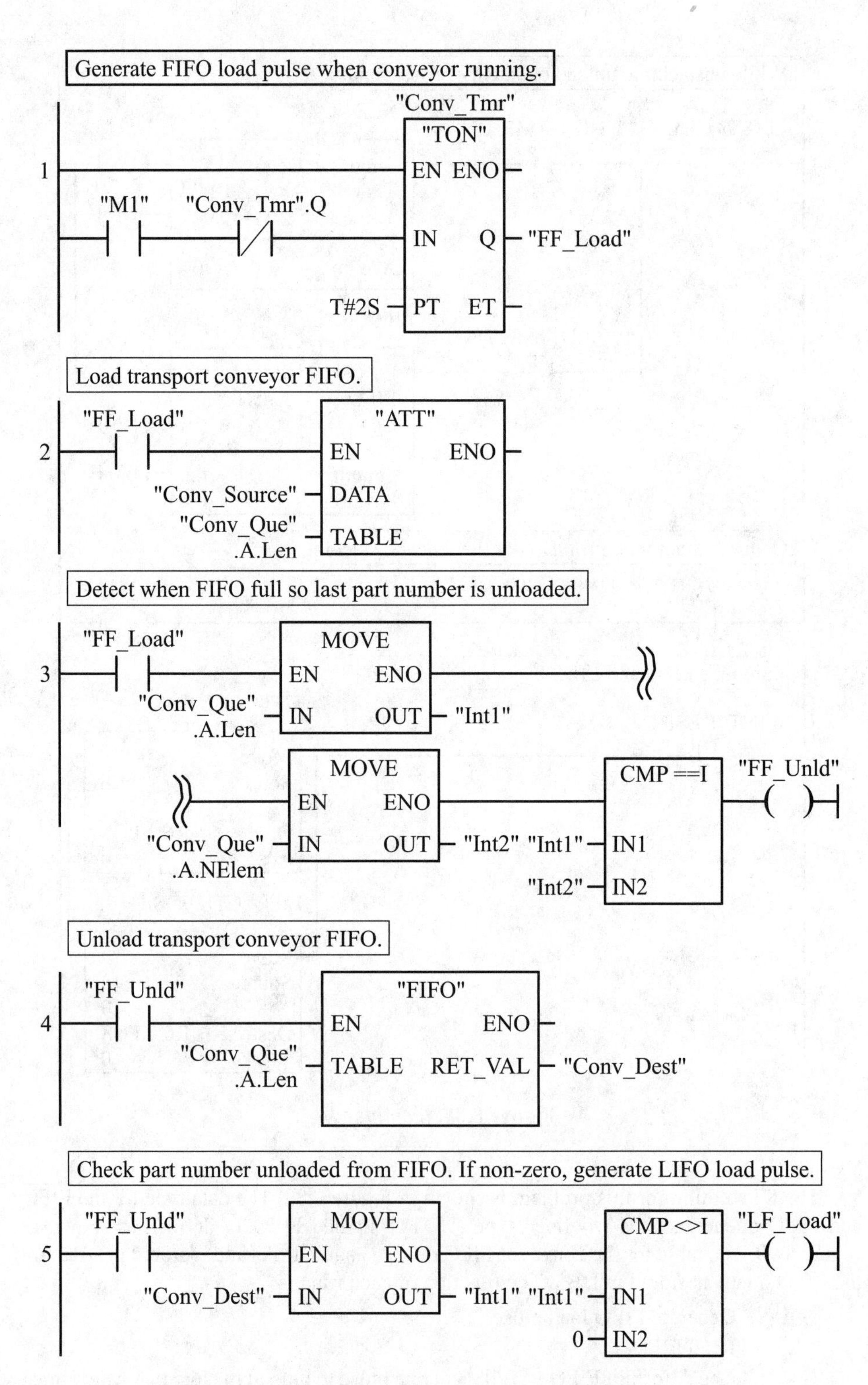

Figure 8.89. S7-300/400 solution to Example 8.2. *(continued)*

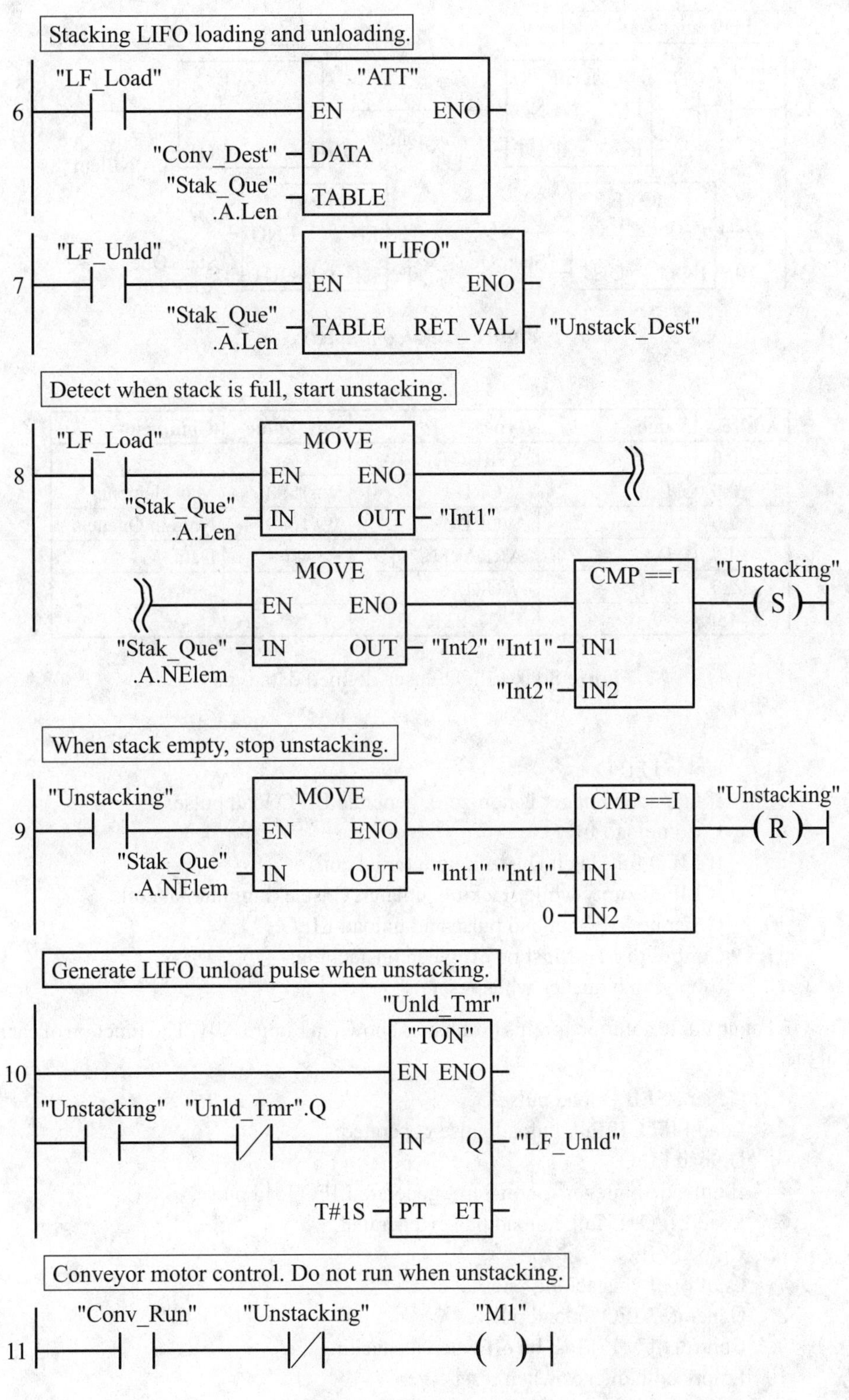

Figure 8.89. *(continued)*

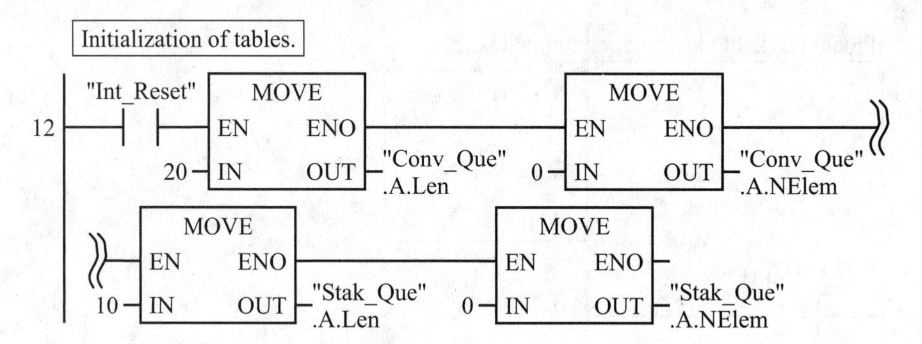

Figure 8.89. *(continued)*

Address	Name	Type	Init. Value	Comment
0.0		STRUCT		
+0.0	Len	WORD	W#16#0	Max elements
+2.0	NElem	WORD	W#16#0	Num in Queue
+4.0	D	ARRAY[1..20]		Data
*2.0		WORD		
=44.0		END_STRUCT		

Figure 8.90. FIFO20 user-defined data type.

4. Unload FIFO.
5. If unloaded integer is non-zero, generate LIFO load pulse.
6.-7. Load/unload LIFO.
8. If LIFO full, latch Unstacking internal coil.
9. If LIFO empty while stacking, unlatch Unstacking internal coil.
10. Generate LIFO unload pulse and unload LIFO.
11. Control of M1. Must be **off** when unstacking.
12. Empty both queues when reset.

The GE Fanuc 90-70 solution for this problem is shown in Figure 8.91. The function of each rung is:

1. Generate FIFO load pulse.
2. Load FIFO. If full, unload pulse generated.
3. Unload FIFO.
4. If unloaded integer is non-zero, generate LIFO load pulse.
5. Load LIFO. If full, unload pulse generated.
6. Unload LIFO.
7. Control of Unstacking internal coil.
8. Generate LIFO unload pulse.
9. Control of M1. Must be **off** when unstacking.
10. Empty both queues when reset.

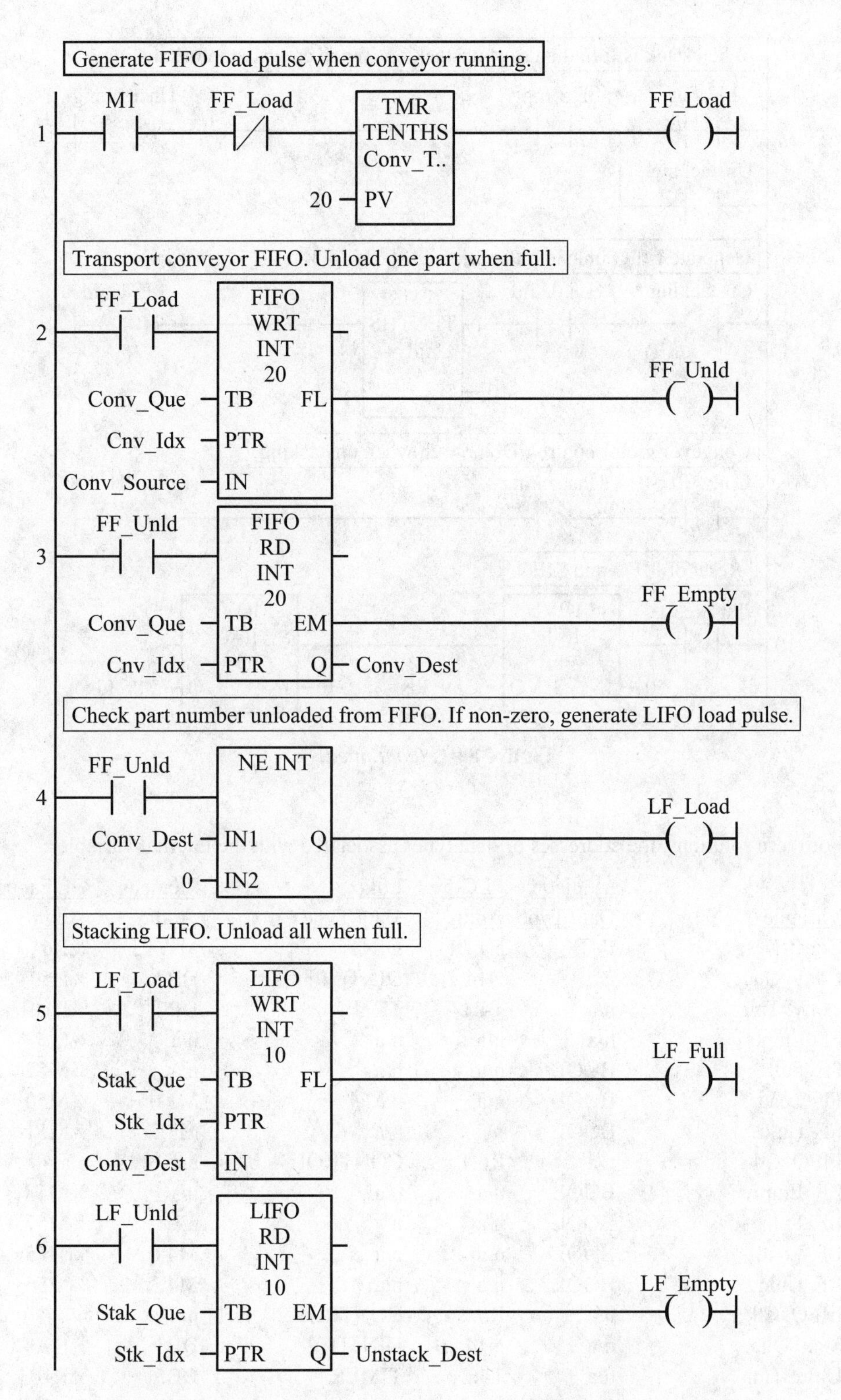

Figure 8.91. GE Fanuc 90-70 solution to Example 8.2. *(continued)*

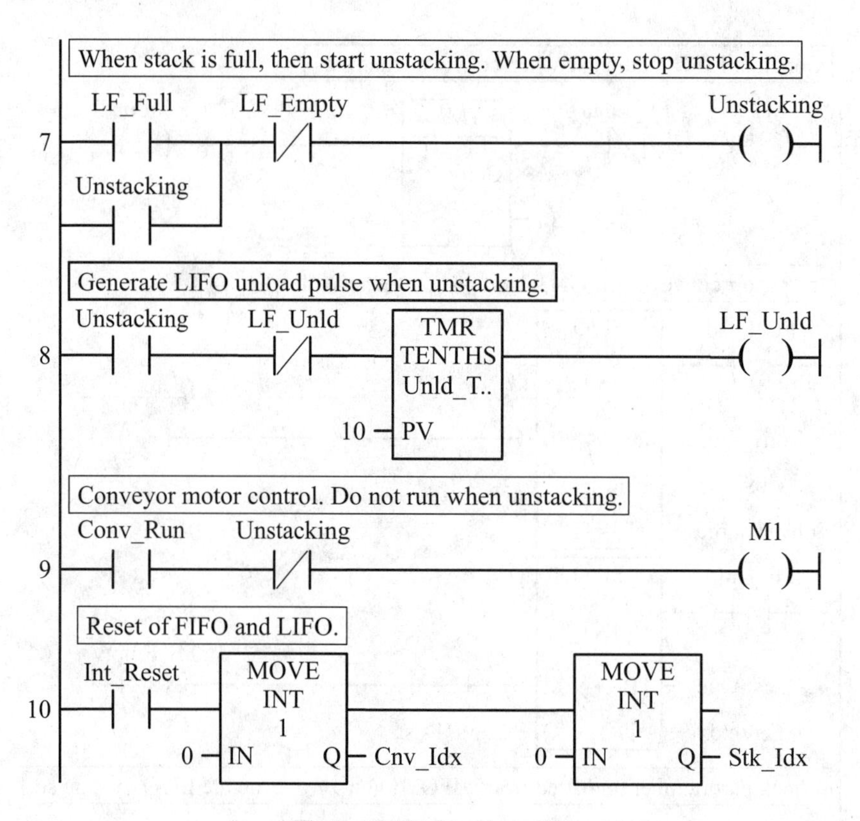

Figure 8.91. *(continued)*

For these solutions, the addresses or data types associated with the internal variables:

Variable	Modicon Data Type	PLC-5 Addr.	Logix Data Type	Siemens Addr.	GE Fanuc Addr.
Conv_Dest	INT	N14:1	DINT	MW12	%R6
Conv_Que	n/a	N14:2	DINT[20]	DB2	%R50
Conv_Tmr	n/a	T4:1	TIMER	DB4	%R101
FF_Empty	n/a	n/a	n/a	n/a	%M53
FF_Full	BOOL	n/a	n/a	n/a	%M52
FF_Load	BOOL	n/a	n/a	M3.0	%M50
FF_Unld	BOOL	n/a	n/a	M3.3	%M51
FIFO_Ctl	n/a	R6:1	CONTROL	n/a	n/a
LF_Empty	BOOL	n/a	n/a	n/a	%M58
LF_Full	BOOL	n/a	n/a	n/a	%M57
LF_Load	BOOL	n/a	n/a	M4.0	%M55
LF_Unld	BOOL	n/a	n/a	M4.3	%M56
LIFO_Ctl	n/a	R6:2	CONTROL	n/a	n/a
Stak_Que	n/a	N14:30	DINT[10]	DB3	%R70
Unld_Tmr	n/a	T4:2	TIMER	DB5	%R104

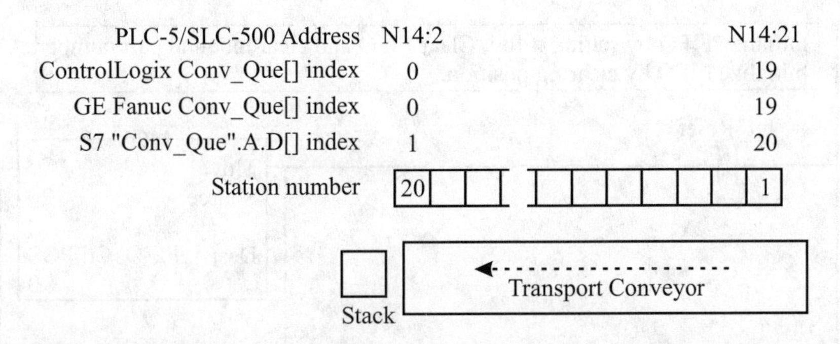

Figure 8.92. Mapping of stations to FIFO queue elements for Example 8.3.

Example 8.3. Modified part tracking and stacking. The transport conveyor of Example 8.2 is modified to be the conveyor that transports manufactured parts from a series of stations to the stacker. When a station places a part on the transport conveyor, the part number is copied to the element in the FIFO corresponding to that station.

Solution. The Modion FIFO function blocks cannot be used for this problem since access to the individual FIFO queue elements is not possible. As in Example 8.2, the transport conveyor is modeled by a 20-element FIFO queue, and the stack is modeled by a 10-element LIFO queue. Using the same definitions as for the solution to Example 8.2, the addresses of the FIFO queue elements that correspond to conveyor stations are shown in Figure 8.92. Looking at the FIFO and LIFO queues, the only difference between the solution for Example 8.3 and the solution for Example 8.2 is the FIFO queue initialization. In this example, the FIFO queue is initialized to a full condition, and all entries are zeroed. In addition, Conv_Source is always zero.

For the ControlLogix solution (Figure 8.87) rung 6 changes to the rung shown in Figure 8.93. The rung for the PLC-5/SLC-500 solution is very similar. For the S7 solution (Figure 8.89) rung 12 changes to the rung shown in Figure 8.94.The FILL block is used to fill the table with zeros. The last rung of the GE Fanuc solution (Figure 8.91) changes to the rung shown in Figure 8.95.

8.9 CHAPTER SUMMARY

For the PLCs covered by this text, this chapter describes shift register, FIFO/LIFO, and special array ladder logic function blocks. Though used less frequently, these function blocks are necessary for certain applications. In addition, the instructions that modify ladder logic execution are described. Following these descriptions, applications of shift registers and FIFO/LIFO queues are illustrated.

REFERENCES

GE Fanuc Automation, 1999. *Series 90^{TM}-30/20/Micro PLC CPU Instruction Set: Reference Manual,* pub. GFK-0467L, GE Fanuc Automation North America, Inc., Charlottesville, VA.

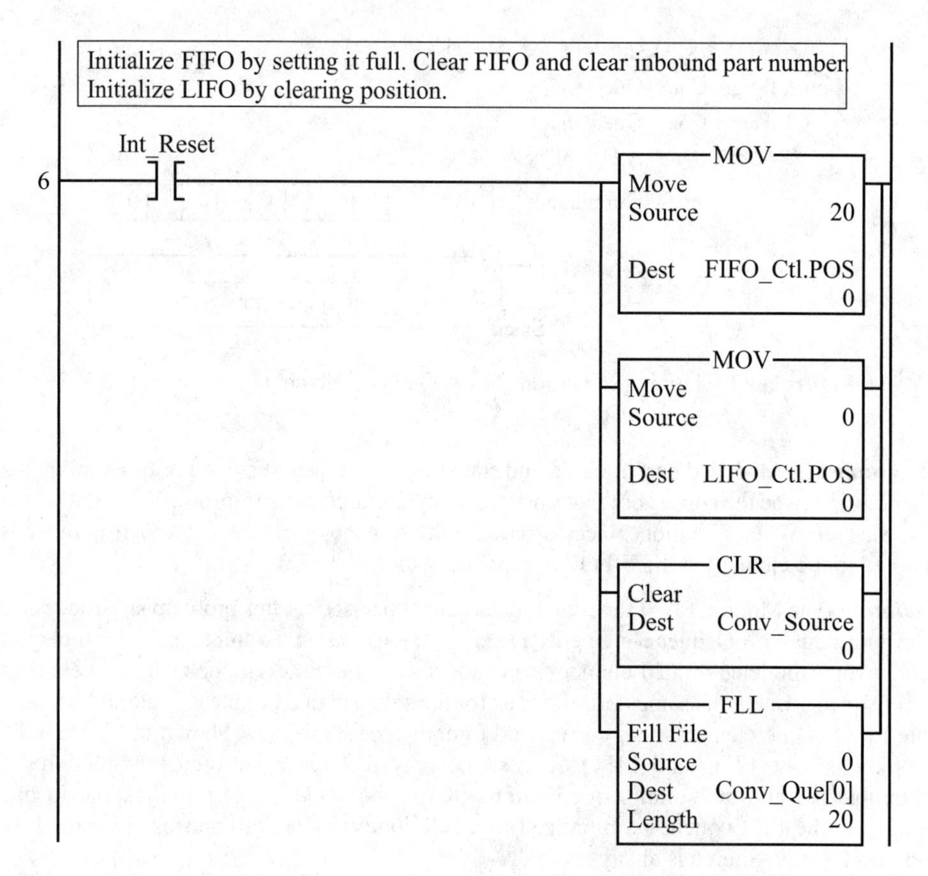

Figure 8.93. Modified ControlLogix rung 6 for Example 8.3 solution.

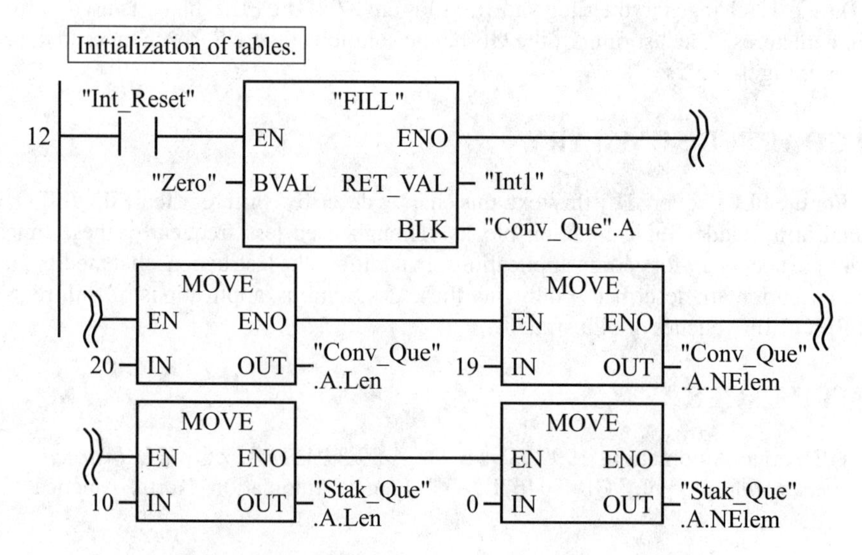

Figure 8.94. Modified S7 rung 12 for Example 8.3 solution.

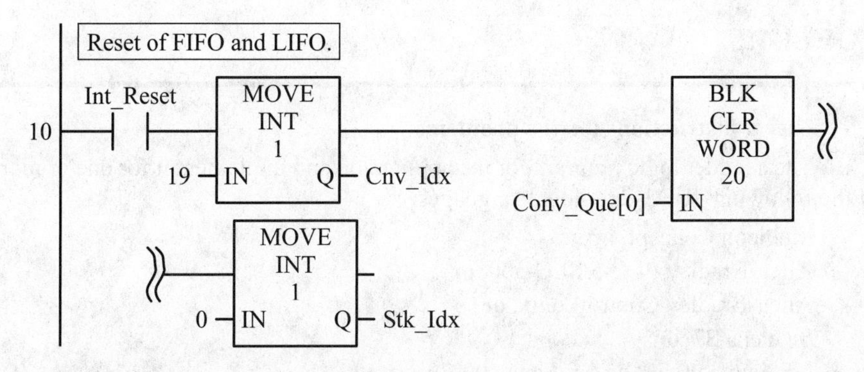

Figure 8.95. Modified GE Fanuc rung 10 for Example 8.3 solution.

GE Fanuc Automation, 2000. *Series 90™-70 PLC CPU Instruction Set: Reference Manual,* pub. GFK-0265J, GE Fanuc Automation North America, Inc., Charlottesville, VA.

GE Fanuc Automation, 2001. *VersaMax® PLC: User's Manual,* pub. GFK-1503C, GE Fanuc Automation North America, Inc., Charlottesville, VA.

IEC, 1993. *IEC 1131-3: Programmable Logic Controllers - Part 3: Programming Languages*, International Electrotechnical Commission, Geneva, Switzerland.

Rockwell Automation, 1998a. *PLC-5 Family Instruction Set Reference Manual*, pub. 1785-6.1, Rockwell Automation, Milwaukee, WI.

Rockwell Automation, 1998b. *SLC Modular Processors Instruction Set Reference Manual*, pub. 1747-6.15, Rockwell Automation, Milwaukee, WI.

Rockwell Automation, 2002. *Logix5000™ Controllers General Instructions*, pub. 1756-RM003F-EN-P, Rockwell Automation, Milwaukee, WI, May.

Schneider Automation, 1998. *Concept Block Library IEC,* vol. 1, ver. 2.1, pub. 840 USE 462 00, Schneider Automation, Inc., North Andover, MA.

Siemens, 2000. *System Software for S7-300 and S7-400 System and Standard Functions Part 2: Reference Manual,* Edition 03, pub. A5E00066867-03, Siemens AG, Nuernberg, Germany.

Siemens, 2002a. *Ladder Logic (LAD) for S7-300 and S7-400 Programming: Reference Manual,* Edition 11/2002, pub. A5E00171231-01, Siemens AG, Nuernberg, Germany.

Siemens, 2002b. *System Software for S7-300/400 System and Standard Functions: Reference Manual,* Edition 12/2002, pub. A5E00171234-01, Siemens AG, Nuernberg, Germany.

PROBLEMS

General instructions for the problems:

Write a ladder logic program for the application and implement it for one or more of the following PLC ladder logic languages:

Modicon Concept, **or**
Allen-Bradley PLC-5/SLC-500, **or**
Allen-Bradley ControlLogix, **or**
Siemens S7, **or**
GE Fanuc 90-30, **or** GE Fanuc 90-70

If any part of the operation is ambiguous, write down your additional assumptions.

The physical inputs, physical outputs, and internal variables for each problem are given in the problem. **DO NOT** assign any more physical inputs!

Your solution should include the following:

1. Specify the PLC processor used.
2. Ladder logic diagram (with comments). For consistency among the different PLCs, use only variables/symbols/tags in the ladder logic. Use instructions consistent with the PLC processor.
3. Table listing additional internal memory (variables/symbols/tags) used and a brief description of their use. For the Allen-Bradley ControlLogix and the Modicon Quantum/Momentum processors, list the internal variables/tags and the data type. For the other processors, list the internal variables/symbols and the associated memory address.

P8-1. Defect tracking for a diaper-making machine. The production system produces approximately two disposable diapers per second. A diaper is made by combining the various materials onto the base material, called the web. A simplified diagram of the system is shown in Figure P8.1*a*. The web and partially made diapers are checked at various points during processing, but defective diapers are rejected just before they enter the packaging machine. Any detected defect should then be noted and essentially travel with the web to the point at which the diaper containing the defect is removed from line. Model the system as a 200-bit shift register (Figure P8.1*b*) that is shifted upon command (Sync_Pulse transitions from **off** to **on**). The Sync_Pulse internal coil is a pulse train that is assumed on for no longer than one scan and has a nominal 0.2 second period. Sync_Pulse is synchronized to the line speed, and therefore its period may vary.

A finished diaper is represented by 2.5 bits of the reject shift register. There is also some inaccuracy in the defect tracking and so not only is the diaper with the expected defect rejected, but also the one preceding it and the one following it. Therefore, if any of the last 7 bits of the shift register are **on**, the REJECT_ROT is activated for 0.75 seconds to move a rotary arm that removes these diapers. Also, the last 7 bits of the shift register must be cleared when the defective diapers are removed.

Also, show the logic to set the defect bit at the following positions (position 1 is the start of the line and 200 is the end of the line): 20, 42, 49, 67, 82, 114, and 132. With your

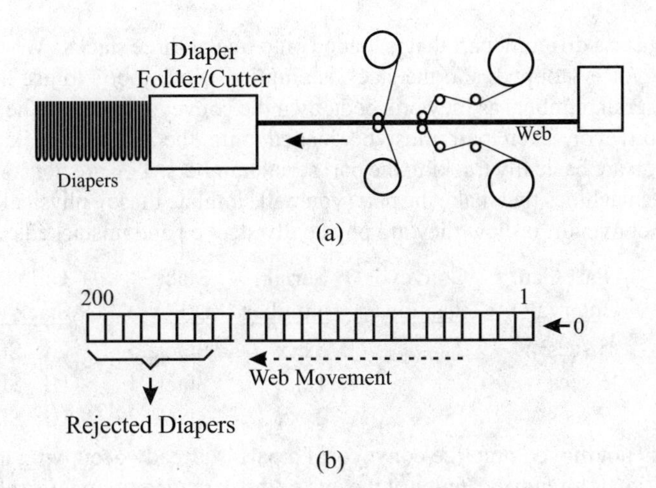

Figure P8.1. Diaper-making machine: *(a)* simplified schematic; *(b)* defect-tracking shift register.

solution, specify the tags (ControlLogix) or addresses (PLC-5/SLC-500, Siemens, or GE Fanuc) for the defect bits for these positions.

Assume the following physical input, physical output, and internal memory assignments:

Variable	Description
Run	Internal coil, **on** when system running (set by another part of the ladder).
Int_Reset	Internal coil, **on** to clear all defect indications. Assume that Run is already **off** when this turns **on** (set by another part of the ladder).
Sync_Pulse	Line synchronizing pulse. Shift defect-tracking bits when it transitions **on**. Assume it is **on** for only one scan and has a nominal period of 0.2 seconds.
REJECT_ROT	Reject mechanism; **on** for 0.75 second to remove 3 defective diapers from line.

The addresses associated with the physical output is:

Variable	Modicon	PLC-5	ControlLogix	Siemens	GE Fanuc
REJECT_ROT	000015	O:2/16	Local:2:O.Data.14	Q5.6	%Q15

The addresses or data types associated with the internal variables:

Variable	Modicon Data Type	PLC-5 Addr.	Logix Data Type	Siemens Addr.	GE Fanuc Addr.
Run	BOOL	B3/100	BOOL	M62.0	%M100
Int_Reset	BOOL	B3/101	BOOL	M62.1	%M101

P8-2. Part tracking for production line. The solution is not possible for the Modicon and GE Fanuc 90-30 PLCs. Figure P8.2 shows a production line that consists of 3 machines. Each machine produces a different part that is loaded onto one of three stacks. When any stack is full, the conveyor is stopped, and the stack is emptied. Your job is to use ladder logic to track the part serial numbers as they proceed down the conveyor and onto the stacks. At the end of the conveyor, each part must be loaded onto the appropriate stack. For this assignment, you are basically tracking the part serial numbers. You are not concerned about controlling the machines that make the part (you will simulate these), physically moving the parts onto the conveyor, or how they are physically stacked and unstacked.

Machine	Part Gen. Interval	Conveyor Position	Serial Number	Stack LIFO	Unload Stack to
A	5 secs	2	5xxx	Stack_5	UL_Stack_5
B	6 secs	7	1xxx	Stack_1	UL_Stack_1
C	7 secs	13	2xxx	Stack_2	UL_Stack_2

The part is not moved onto the conveyor if a part is already occupying the spot. If the conveyor position is already occupied at the end of the part generation interval, the machine waits until the position is unoccupied and then moves a part onto the conveyor. While waiting, the part generation operation pauses. To "move" the part onto the conveyor, move the serial number into the appropriate FIFO position. When the part is moved onto the conveyor, the part generation timer is restarted, and the "xxx" part of the serial number is incremented.

Shift parts on the conveyor FIFO every 1.6 seconds when the conveyor is running. The conveyor is represented by the FIFO from N15:17 (conveyor position 1) to N15:2 (conveyor position 16). The conveyor FIFO is loaded from Conv_Fifo_Ld (a constant zero) and unloaded to Conv_Fifo_Ul.

When the conveyor FIFO is unloaded, the part is placed into one of 3 stacks, depending on the serial #. The stacks are modeled as 10 position LIFO's. When one of the stacks is full,

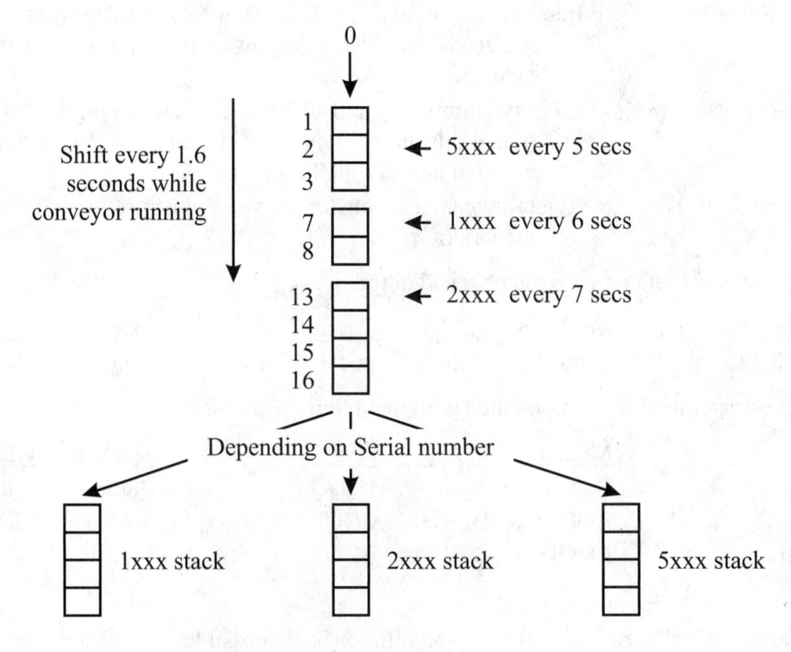

Figure P8.2. Part-tracking system.

the conveyor should be stopped (and stop shifting the FIFO), and the stack unloaded into the appropriate location. Use a one-second timer to simulate the removal of all of the parts from the stack. When the stack is empty, the conveyor should start, and the tracking of parts on the conveyor resumes.

The start and stop pushbuttons are for the line. When START_PB is pressed, the conveyor moves, and the machines generate parts. When the STOP_PB is pressed, the system operation pauses. When paused, the conveyor should be stopped and any unstacking is also paused. When the operation is paused, the timers used to simulate part generation should be paused and the accumulator retained. When RESET_PB is pressed (and the system is not running), the conveyor and pallet queues are cleared, all machine part interval generation timers are reset, and the "xxx" part of all part serial numbers are set to zero.

The conveyor motor (PLC output) should be driven by your ladder logic.

Assume the following physical input, physical output, and internal memory assignments:

Variable	Description
START_PB	Start push button switch, **on** (closed) to start or resume.
STOP_PB	Stop push button switch, **off** (open) to stop or pause.
RESET_PB	Reset push button switch, **on** (closed) resets operation of station (explained above).
CONV_MTR	Conveyor motor starter, **on** to move conveyor.
Conv_Fifo_Ld	Conveyor FIFO is loaded from this location.
Conv_Fifo_Ul	Conveyor FIFO is unloaded to this location.
Conv_Fifo	Conveyor FIFO
Stack_1	Start of LIFO stack for 1xxx parts.
Stack_2	Start of LIFO stack for 2xxx parts.
Stack_5	Start of LIFO stack for 5xxx parts.
UL_Stack_1	LIFO stack for 1xxx parts is unloaded to this location.
UL_Stack_2	LIFO stack for 2xxx parts is unloaded to this location.
UL_Stack_5	LIFO stack for 5xxx parts is unloaded to this location.

The addresses associated with the physical inputs and output are:

Variable	PLC-5	ControlLogix	Siemens	GE Fanuc
START_PB	I:04/00	Local:4:I.Data.0	I0.0	%I1
STOP_PB	I:04/01	Local:4:I.Data.1	I0.1	%I2
RESET_PB	I:04/02	Local:4:I.Data.2	I0.2	%I3
CONV_MTR	O:05/11	Local:5:O.Data.9	Q4.0	%Q1

The addresses or data types associated with the internal variables:

Variable	PLC-5 Addr.	Logix Data Type	Siemens Addr.	GE Fanuc Addr.
Conv_Fifo_Ld	N15:0	DINT	MW10	%R5
Conv_Fifo_Ul	N15:1	DINT	MW12	%R6
Conv_Fifo	N15:2	DINT[16]	DB1	%R50
Stack_1	N15:30	DINT[10]	DB2	%R70
Stack_2	N15:40	DINT[10]	DB3	%R80

Stack_5	N15:50	DINT[10]	DB4	%R90
UL_Stack_1	N15:71	DINT	MW20	%R10
UL_Stack_2	N15:72	DINT	MW22	%R11
UL_Stack_5	N15:73	DINT	MW24	%R12

The Siemens S7 data blocks DB1 – DB4 are defined to be the FIFO20 data type of Example 8.2.

P8-3. Alarm history display. The last ten alarms and the time they occurred need to be displayed on an operator interface screen (Figure P8.3). Program an array of these alarm numbers and their associated time stamp. The time stamp should contain the seconds, minutes, hour, day, and month the alarm occurred. The operator interface will display the number of the alarm, the time and date it occurred, and a text description. Do not generate the text description.

When the Alarm_Trigger transitions from **off**-to-**on**, save the Alarm_Number and the current time in the alarm history. If the history already contains 10 alarms, then the oldest alarm is removed from the list before the new one is added. When Alm_Hist_Rst is **on**, clear the alarm history list, and insert zeros for all alarm numbers and the time stamp.

With your solution, specify the tags (ControlLogix) or addresses (PLC-5, Siemens, GE Fanuc) for the most recent to the oldest alarm information to be used by the HMI programmer.

Variable	Description
Alarm_Trigger	Internal coil, **off**-to-**on** transition means the Alarm_Number and the current timestamp should be saved in the history (set by another part of the ladder).
Alarm_Number	Number of alarm to place in alarm history (set by another part of the ladder).
Alm_Hist_Rst	Alarm history reset. When **on**, clear the alarm history list and insert zeros for all alarm numbers and the time stamp (set by another part of the ladder).

The addresses or data types associated with the internal variables:

Variable	Modicon Data Type	PLC-5 Addr.	Logix Data Type	Siemens Addr.	GE Fanuc Addr.
Alarm_Trigger	BOOL	B3/100	BOOL	M62.0	%M100
Alm_Hist_Rst	BOOL	B3/101	BOOL	M62.1	%M101
Alarm Number	INT	N7:24	DINT	MW102	%R102

Date	Time	No.	Alarm Description
04/07/03	10:19:02	323	T304 at 90% level
04/07/03	10:10:15	125	P124 needs servicing
04/07/03	08:03:23	21	B24 at low level
04/07/03	06:43:32	227	TT235 high temperature

Figure P8.3. Alarm display (partial).

9 Other Function Chart Implementations

Chapter Topics:

- Counter-based function chart implementation
- Shift register function chart implementation
- Sequencer function blocks
- Unstructured function chart implementation

OBJECTIVES

Upon completion of this chapter, you will be able to:

- Implement a sequential operation using a counter
- Implement a sequential operation using a shift register
- Implement a sequential operation using sequencer function blocks
- Understand a commonly used, but flawed technique for implementing sequential operations.

Scenario: Memory savings using indirect addressing on counter-based sequencer.

You are using a PLC-5/80E to implement a counter-based sequencer where the counter accumulator is the step number. The appropriate step-in-progress bit is set based on the value of the accumulator. When in a particular step and its transition conditions are satisfied, a step-done bit is set. The step-done bit is then used to increment the counter to the next step. The parts of this implementation of a sequential operation are shown in Figure 9.1.

You are writing the PLC code for a process that consists of four identical units and has a large number of sequential operations. It appears that the project will require another PLC processor. However, that will cost an extra $8,000 for the processor alone, disregarding the costs of reassigning I/O points, programming the inter-processor communication, and revising drawings. You need to find an alternate approach that requires less program memory.

Solution: In order to verify your suspicions that there is not enough PLC memory for the program, you estimate the program memory for an individual sequence. Going to an existing program, you take a typical sequence and delete one step to obtain an estimate of the memory for one step. Then you delete all steps, note the size of the program, and then delete the overhead to estimate the overhead needed for each sequential operation. Armed with this information, an estimate of the number of sequences required, and an estimate to the number of steps in each sequence, you estimate that the completed program will require at least a PLC-5/40E processor.

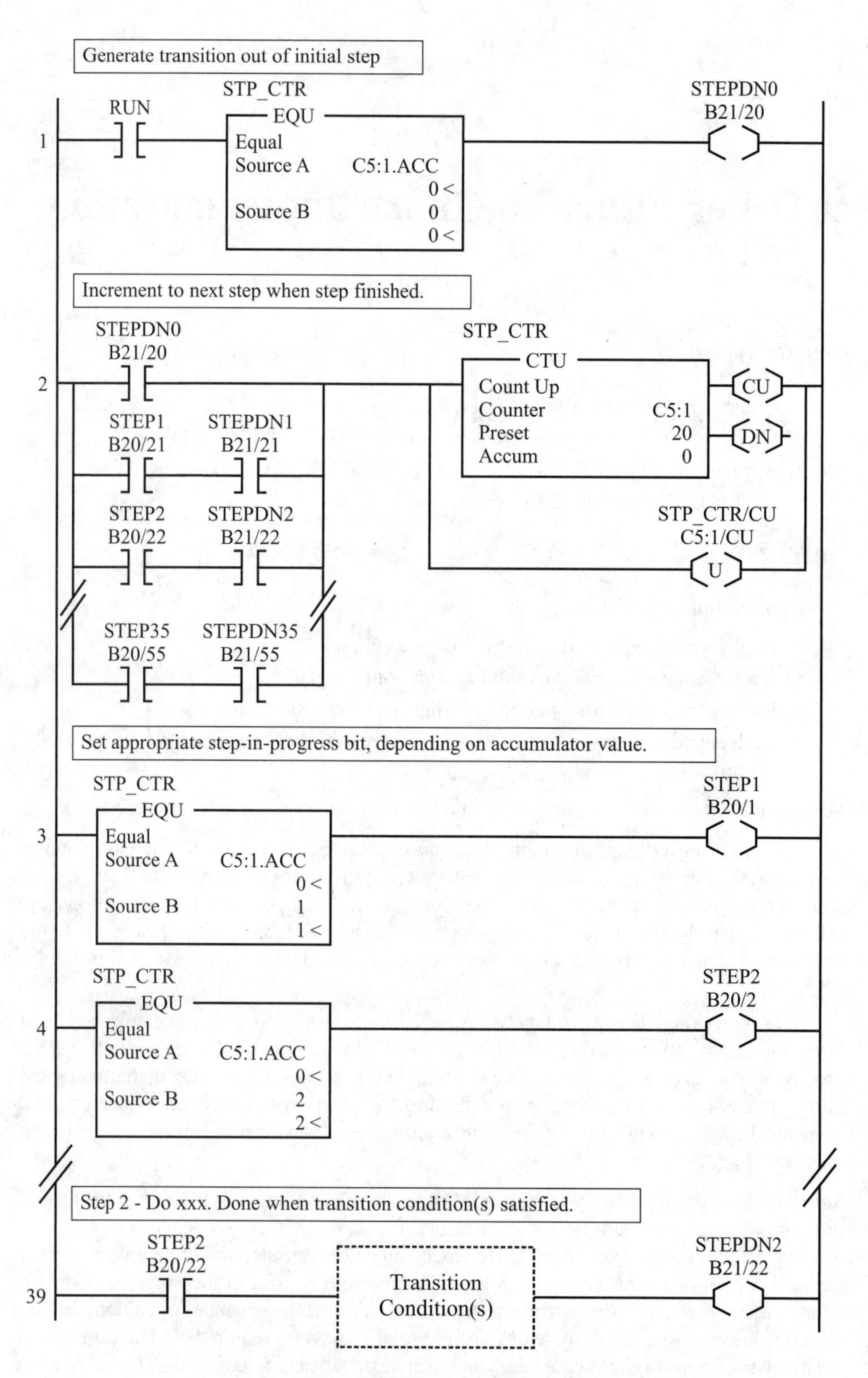

Figure 9.1. Original PLC-5 counter-based sequence.

A colleague suggests an approach using PLC-5 indexed addressing to reduce the program size. You and some others try some ideas and eventually settle on the implementation outlined in section 9.2.3. When you estimate the memory required for each step, it is 10 words less than the current approach, but the overhead for every sequence grows by 59 words. Therefore, the indexed addressing approach uses less memory if the sequence has at least 6 steps. When you recalculate the expected program requirements, it still exceeds the amount of memory in the PLC-5/80E, but only by about 1000 words. You present this information to your project manager, and he decides to try the new approach anyway. If nothing else, the time to enter the program will be reduced.

The project is implemented in stages, and after the first unit is installed and operational, the memory requirements are reassessed. It now appears that the complete program will fit in the processor, but it will be very close. When all four units are operational, there are less than 200 words of free memory in the processor! You hope there will be few future changes!

9.1 INTRODUCTION

The approach to implementing function charts that is described in Chapter 6 is simple and easy to understand. This chapter describes other ways to implement a function chart, also called a sequence, with ladder logic.

In a counter-based implementation of a function chart, the counter accumulator holds the current step number, and a transition to the next step involves a counter increment. For a shift register-based implementation, the transition is handled as a shift of the register. The Allen-Bradley PLC processors have sequencer function blocks that can be adapted to implement function charts.

Why would one consider these alternative implementations? The main reason is that there are typically fewer errors when revising the ladder logic. In any project, modifications to the function chart are inevitable. With these alternative approaches, the required ladder logic changes are often easier and involve fewer changes to the code, thus decreasing potential programming errors.

There are some other reasons for considering these alternative implementations. In a counter-based implementation, the counter accumulator holds the current step number and can easily be displayed on an operator interface. Alternatively, the step number can be the index into an array of messages, displaying the appropriate one for the current step. A function chart implemented with a shift register is a little shorter since all of the transition conditions appear on the same rung.

The chapter concludes by presenting an unstructured approach to a sequential control solution. Unfortunately, one will often encounter this approach, especially when modifying existing programs. The most important disadvantage of this approach is that it requires more time to design, program, and troubleshoot the initial solution and any future modifications.

9.2 COUNTER-BASED SEQUENCE

A counter is the heart of this implementation of a function chart. The counter accumulator is the step number. Normally, when in a particular step and its transition conditions are satisfied, the counter accumulator is incremented to the next step. However, when an operation repeats, the succeeding step after the final step is the first step and so some form of branching needs to be provided. To implement a branch, the counter accumulator is set to the next step rather than doing the normal counter increment.

The step-in-progress bits are an array of bits and the counter accumulator serves as the index into the array. The step-in-progress bit of a particular step is set when entering that step and reset when exiting the step. There is also an array of step-done bits. The step-done bit of a particular step is turned **on** when the transition conditions out of a step are satisfied and causes the counter accumulator to increment. A zero counter accumulator indicates the operation has been reset and is thus in the initial step.

Design Tip

Use a counter-based implementation of a function chart when needing to display the step number on an operator interface.

The counter-based implementation of the function chart basically replaces the portion of the ladder logic that handles the initial start and the transition between steps. The start/stop/pause rung remains the same. The step actions basically remain the same, but the references to the steps will change. The main parts of the ladder logic that are different are:

First start

Set/clear step-in-progress bit

Counter increment

Transition between steps

The implementation details specific to each type of PLC are described and then illustrated with an example.

9.2.1 Modicon

The parts of a Modicon implementation of a counter-based sequence are shown in Figure 9.2. The variables are:

Variable	Type	Description
Stp_Ary	StepArray50	Array of step-in-progress bits.
StpDn_Ary	StepArray50	Array of step-done bits.
Stp_Idx	INT	Current step; index into arrays.
Ctr_Acc	INT	Counter accumulator value.
Int_Reset	BOOL	**On** when resetting sequence.
Do_Jump	BOOL	**On** when jumping to step.
Step_Jump	INT	Step number that is destination of jump

where the StepArray50 type is defined as an ARRAY [0..50] of BOOL.

The first start is handled as shown in rung 1 of Figure 9.2. When the current step (Stp_Idx) is zero and Run is **on**, then the step-done bit for step zero is turned **on**, which will increment the counter accumulator in rung 3.

Rung 2 contains the ladder logic that moves the step-in-progress bit from one step to the next. The SET_STEP function block is a derived function block (DFB) that either clears or sets an element of a StepArray50 Boolean array. The input signals to this block are described as follows:

SArray – Array of step-in-progress bits (of type StepArray50).

In – New value of element; 0 resets and 1 sets.

StpNum – Index of array element to reset or set.

The output signal of this block is described as follows:

Res – Updated array of step-in-progress bits.

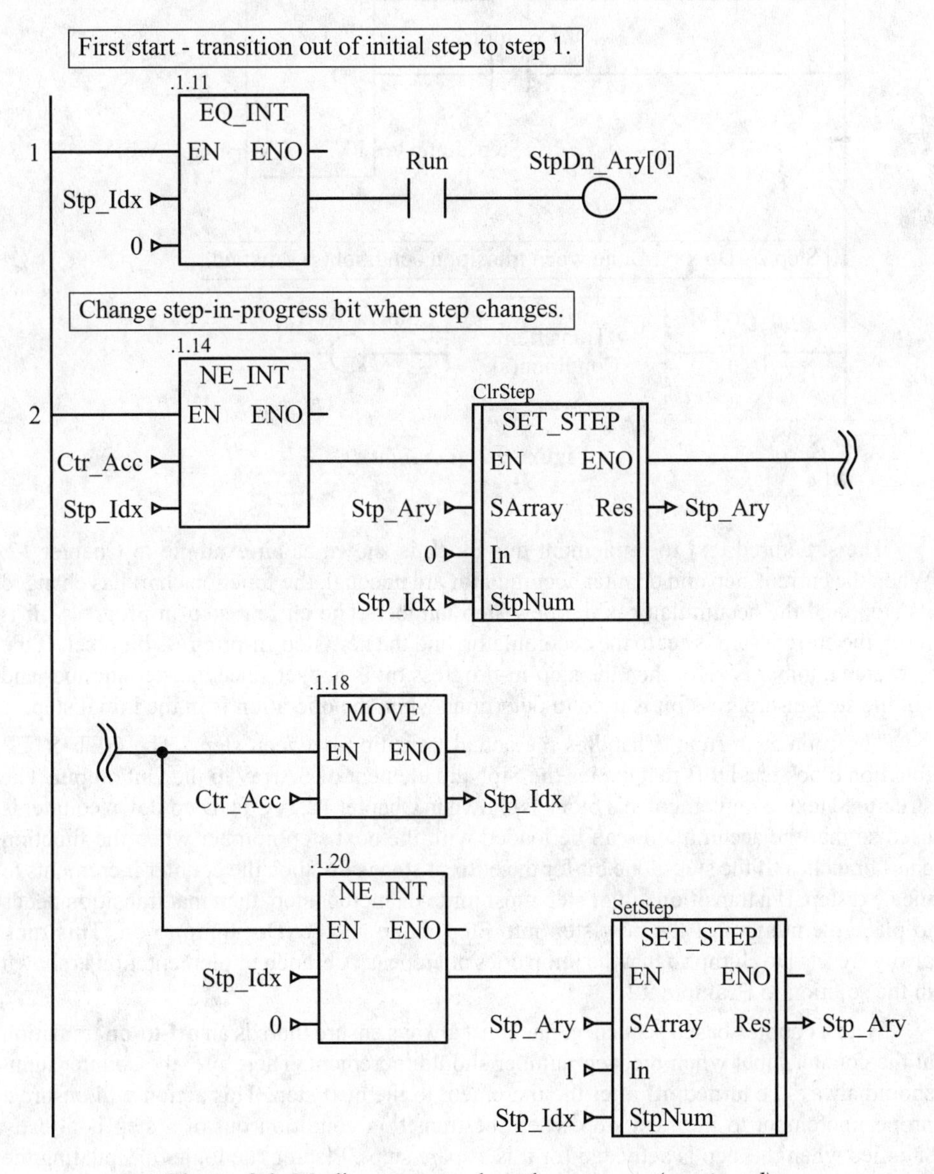

Figure 9.2. Modicon counter-based sequence. *(continued)*

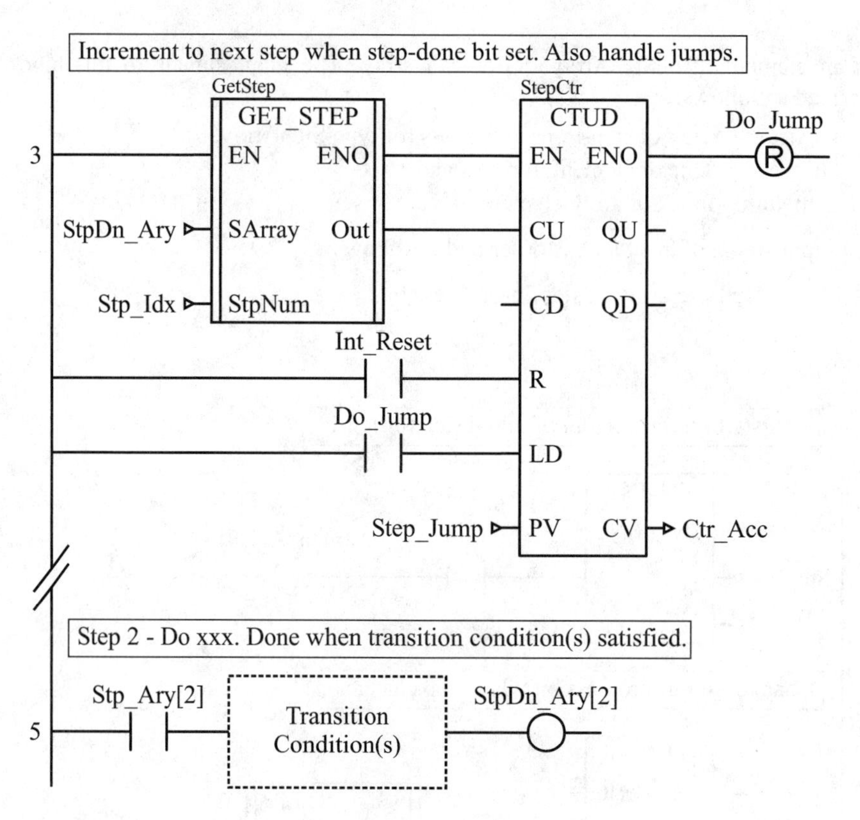

Figure 9.2. *(continued)*

The structured text to implement this block is shown as an example in Chapter 12. When the current step and counter accumulator are unequal, the function chart has changed its step, and the accumulator is the new step number. The current step-in-progress bit is reset, the current step is set to the accumulator, and the new step-in-progress bit is set. If the new step number is zero, then the step-in-progress bit is not set since the step number and not the step-in-progress bit is used to determine when the operation is in the initial step.

The counter in rung 3 handles the actual transition between steps. The GET_STEP function block is a DFB that copies the StpNum element of SArray to the Out output. The structured text to implement this block is shown in Chapter 12. A CTUD up/down counter is used so that the accumulator can be loaded with the next step number when the function chart branches. If the step-done bit for the current step is **on**, then the counter increments to the next step. If a transition out of step must jump to another step, then that transition needs to place the number of the next step into Step_Jump and set Do_Jump to **on**. This rung always resets Do_Jump so that the jump does not repeat. A branch implementation is shown in the solution to Example 9.1.

With a counter-based sequence, one must always ensure there is an **off**-to-**on** transition at the counter input when the step number should increment. Therefore, the counter input should always be turned **off** after the increment to the next step. This action will ensure a proper increment to the next step when the transition condition out of a step is already satisfied when the step is activated (or it is a spare step). Placing the logic for updating the step-in-progress bit (rung 2) ***before*** the counter increment (rung 3) satisfies this requirement concerning the counter input. When the counter increments, the index into the step-in-progress bit array changes on the next scan. When this index is changed, the step-done bit of the new step is always **off** because the rung that handles the transition out of the new step has not been scanned to turn it **on**. Hence, the counter input is **off** during the program scan after the counter accumulator changes. If the transition condition of the new step is already satisfied, then the step-done bit of the new step is turned **on** during this scan, and the counter is incremented on the next scan. If rungs 2 and 3 are swapped so that the counter increment is before the logic that updates the step-in-progress bit, the counter input will not change under certain conditions. Specifically, the counter will not increment to the next step after a step whose transition condition out of the step is already satisfied when entering the step. In this case, the following actions happen on the same scan: (1) the counter increments because the step-done bit of the current step is on, (2) the step-in-progress bit of the new step is turned **on**, and (3) the step-done bit of the new step turns **on**. Therefore, on the next program scan, the counter input is still **on**, and the counter will not increment to the next step.

The ladder logic for a typical step transition is shown in rung 5. When the particular step-in-progress bit is **on** and the transition logic is satisfied, then the step-done bit is turned **on**. It is similar to the logic of Figure 6.17 except that an array index defines the step-in-progress bit. The output is the step-done bit rather than setting the next step-in-progress bit and resetting the current step-in-progress bit.

9.2.2 ControlLogix

The parts of a ControlLogix implementation of a counter-based sequence are shown in Figure 9.3. The tags are:

Tags	Type	Description
Stp_Ary	BOOL[64]	Array of step-in-progress bits.
StpDn_Ary	BOOL[64]	Array of step-done bits.
Stp_Idx	DINT	Current step; index into arrays.
Stp_Ctr	COUNTER	Step counter.
Int_Reset	BOOL	**On** when resetting sequence.

The first start is handled as shown in rung 1 of Figure 9.3. When the current step (Stp_Idx) is zero and Run is on, then the step-done bit for step zero is turned **on**, which will increment the counter accumulator in rung 3.

The rung 2 ladder logic moves the step-in-progress bit from one step to the next. When the current step index and counter accumulator are unequal, the step number has changed, and the accumulator is the new step number. The current step-in-progress bit is unlatched, the current step is set to the accumulator, and the new step-in-progress bit is latched. If the new step number is zero, then the step-in-progress bit is not latched since the step number and not the step-in-progress bit is used to determine when the operation is in the initial step.

The counter in rung 3 handles the actual transition between steps. If the step-done bit for the current step is **on**, then the counter increments to the next step. If the transition out of a step must jump to another step, then that transition needs to use the MOV block to place the number of the next step into the Stp_Ctr accumulator. The RES coil must be used to reset the step counter (rung 4). Note that the logic for updating the step-in-progress bit (rung

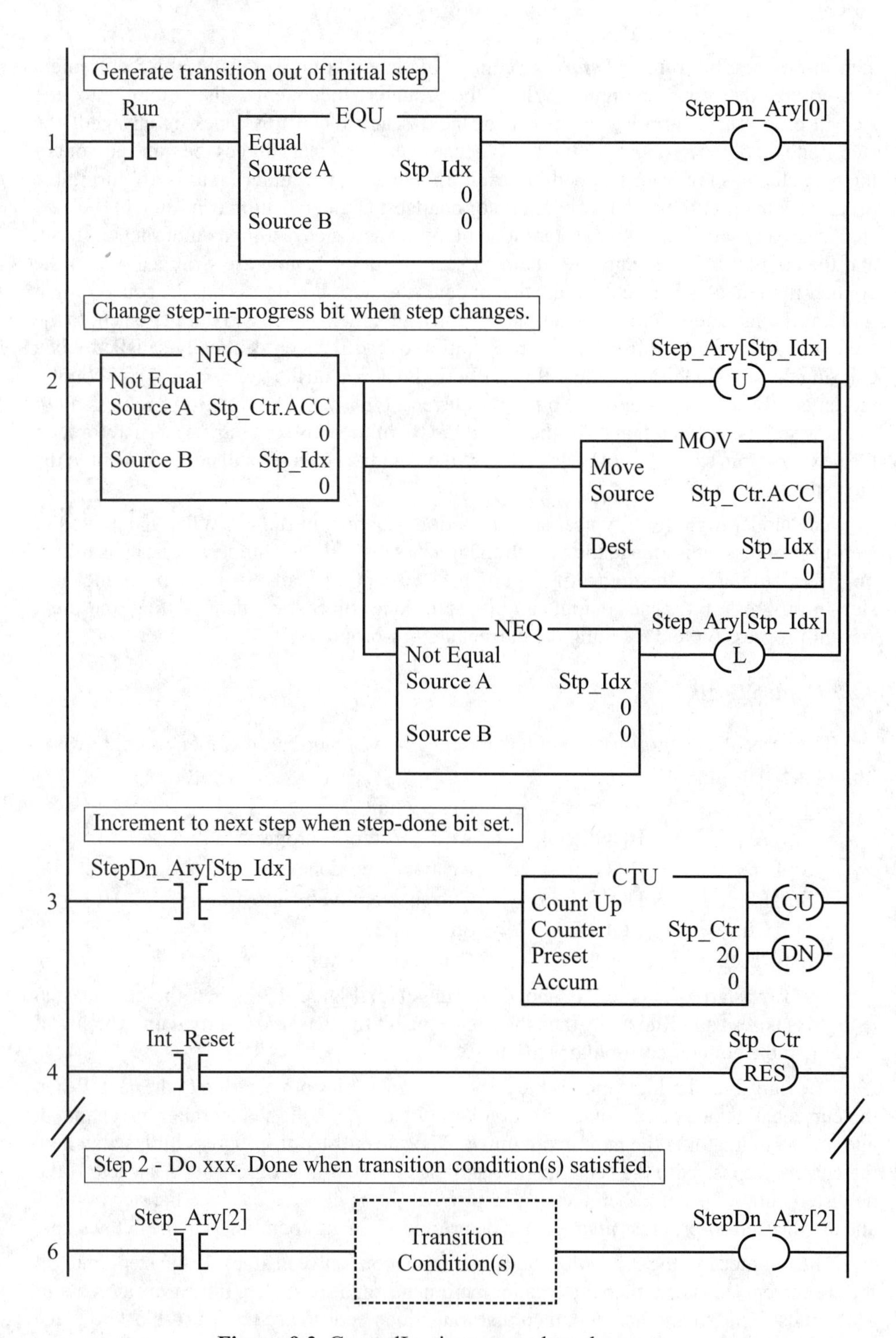

Figure 9.3. ControlLogix counter-based sequence.

2) is placed ***before*** the counter increment (rung 3). The reason for this order is explained in the previous subsection, in conjunction with the Modicon counter-based sequencer.

The ladder logic for a typical step transition is shown in rung 6. When the particular step-in-progress bit is **on** and the transition logic is satisfied, then the step-done bit is turned **on**. It is similar to the logic of Figure 6.17 except that an array index defines the step-in-progress bit. The output is the step-done bit rather than setting the next step-in-progress bit and resetting the current step-in-progress bit.

9.2.3 PLC-5/SLC-500

The parts of a PLC-5/SLC-500 implementation of a counter-based sequence are shown in Figure 9.4. The symbols and addresses are:

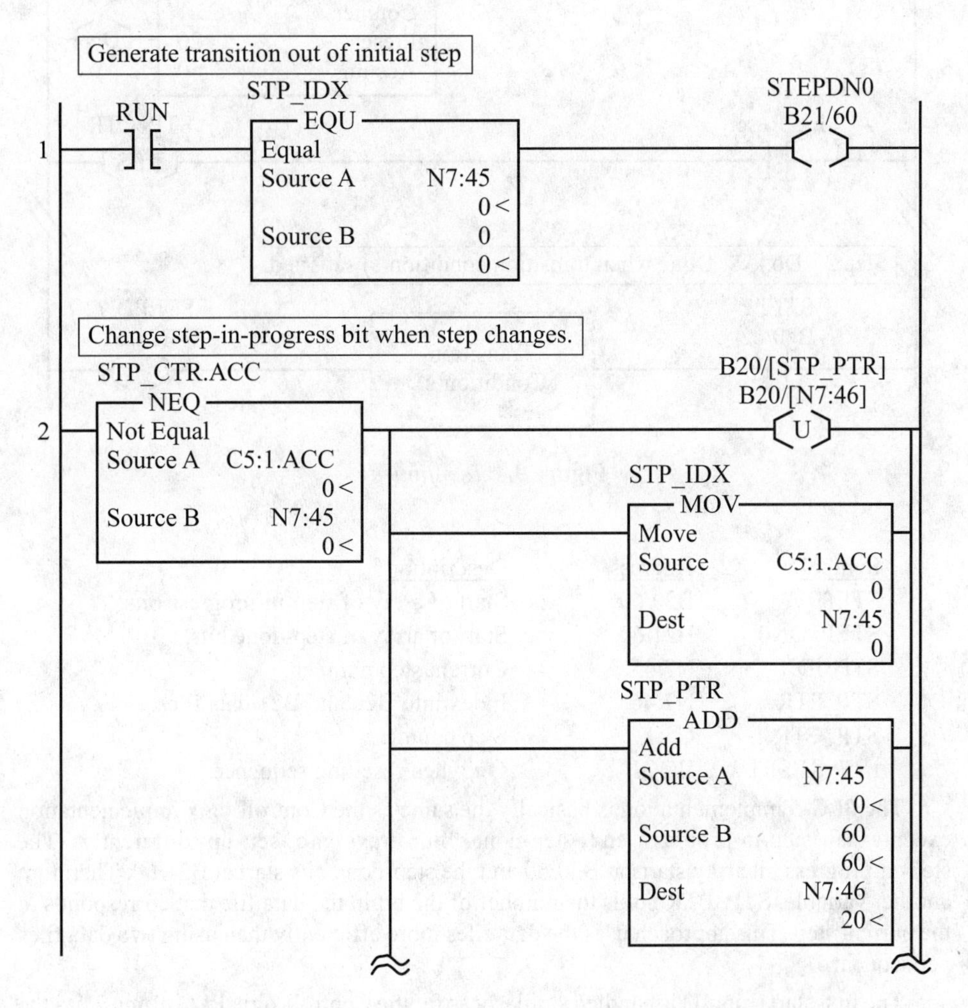

Figure 9.4. PLC-5 counter-based sequence. *(continued)*

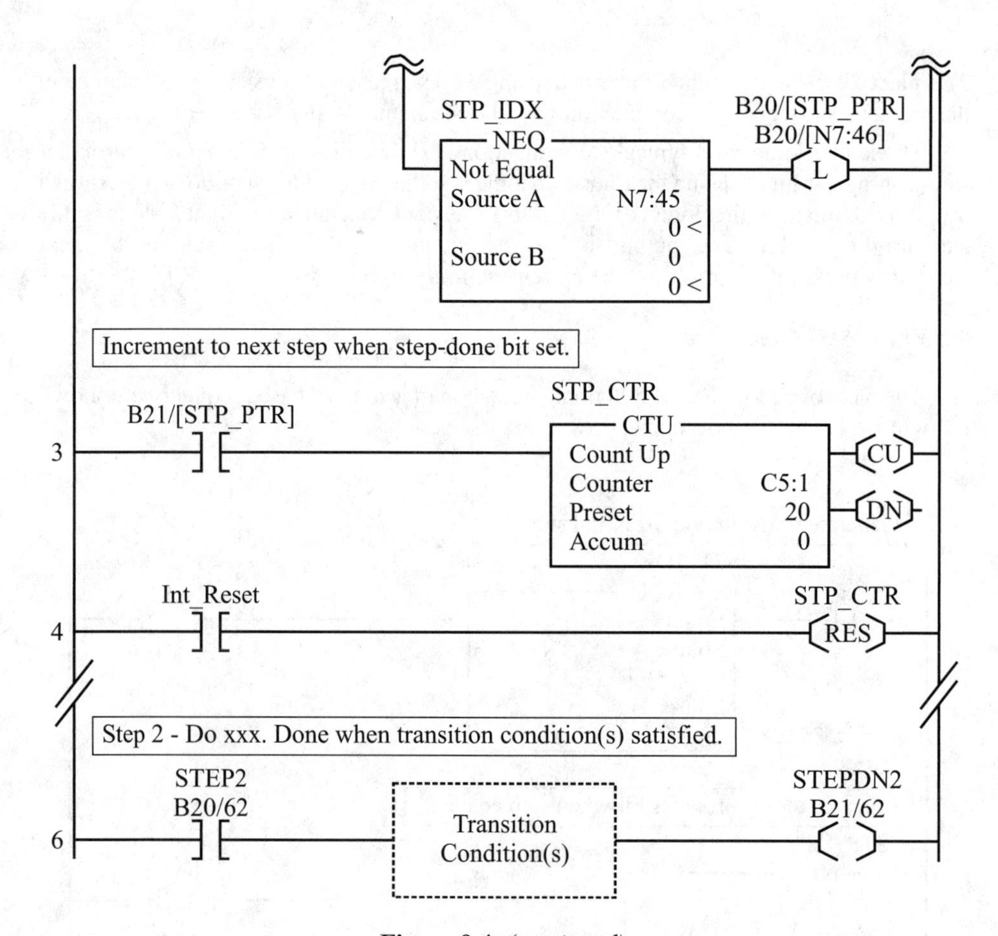

Figure 9.4. *(continued)*

Symbol	Address	Description
STEP0	B20/60	Start of array of step-in-progress bits.
STEP_DN0	B21/60	Start of array of step-done bits.
STP_IDX	N7:45	Current step number.
STP_PTR	N7:46	Index into B20 and B21 data files.
STP_CTR	C5:1	Step counter.
INT_RESET	BOOL	**On** when resetting sequence.

The PLC-5 implementation is basically the same as the ControlLogix implementation except that step-in-progress and step-done bit arrays are set up differently. The step-in-progress bit array starts at B20/60 and the step-done bits start at B21/60. Therefore another variable, STP_PTR holds the number of the bit in the data file that corresponds to the current step. This approach uses the data files more efficiently than using two data files per sequence.

The first start (rung 1) is handled similarly as for the ControlLogix PLC. Rung 2 has the ladder logic that changes the step-in-progress bit when the step changes. The STP_PTR location is the bit number of the B20 and B21 data files corresponding to the current step and is calculated as the STP_IDX plus 60.

9.2.4 S7-300/400

The parts of a Siemens S7-300/400 implementation of a counter-based sequence are shown in Figure 9.5. The variables are:

Variable	Type	Description
Step.Ary	ARRAY[0..50]	Array of step-in-progress bits.
Step.Dn_Ary	ARRAY[0..50]	Array of step-done bits.
Step.Idx	INT	Current step; index into arrays.
Int_Reset	BOOL	**On** when resetting sequence.
Do_Jump	BOOL	**On** when jumping to step.
Step_Jump	INT	Step number that is destination of jump

where Step is the name of a data block, structured as follows:

```
        STRUCT
Idx     DINT
Ary     ARRAY[0..50]
        BOOL
Dn_Ary  ARRAY[0..50]
        BOOL
        END_STRUCT
```

The first start is handled as shown in rung 1 of Figure 9.5 and is similar to the Modicon implementation. When the current step ("Step".Idx) is zero and Run is **on**, then the step-done bit for step zero is turned **on**, which will increment the counter accumulator in rung 3.

Rung 2 contains the ladder logic that moves the step-in-progress bit from one step to the next. The SET_STEP function block is a user-programmed function block (FC) that either clears or sets an element of an ARRAY[0..50] of BOOL array. The input signals to this block are described as follows:

In – New value of element; 0 resets and 1 sets.

StpNum – Index of array element to reset or set.

SArray – Array of step-in-progress bits (of type ARRAY[0..50] of BOOL).

The SArray connection is an input/output signal. The structured text to implement this block is shown as an example in Chapter 12. When the current step and counter accumulator are unequal, the step has changed, and the accumulator is the new step number. The current step-in-progress bit is reset, the current step is set to the accumulator, and the new step-in-progress bit is set. If the new step number is zero, then the step-in-progress bit is not set since the step number is used to determine when the operation is in the initial step.

The counter in rung 3 handles the actual transition between steps. The GET_STEP function block is a user-programmed FC that copies the StpNum element of SArray to the Out output. The structured text to implement this block is shown in Chapter 12. A CTUD up/down counter is used so that the accumulator can be loaded with the next step number when the function chart branches. If the step-done bit for the current step is **on**, then the counter increments to the next step. If a transition out of step must jump to another step, then that transition needs to place the number of the next step into Step_Jump and set Do_Jump to **on**. This rung always resets Do_Jump so that the jump does not repeat.

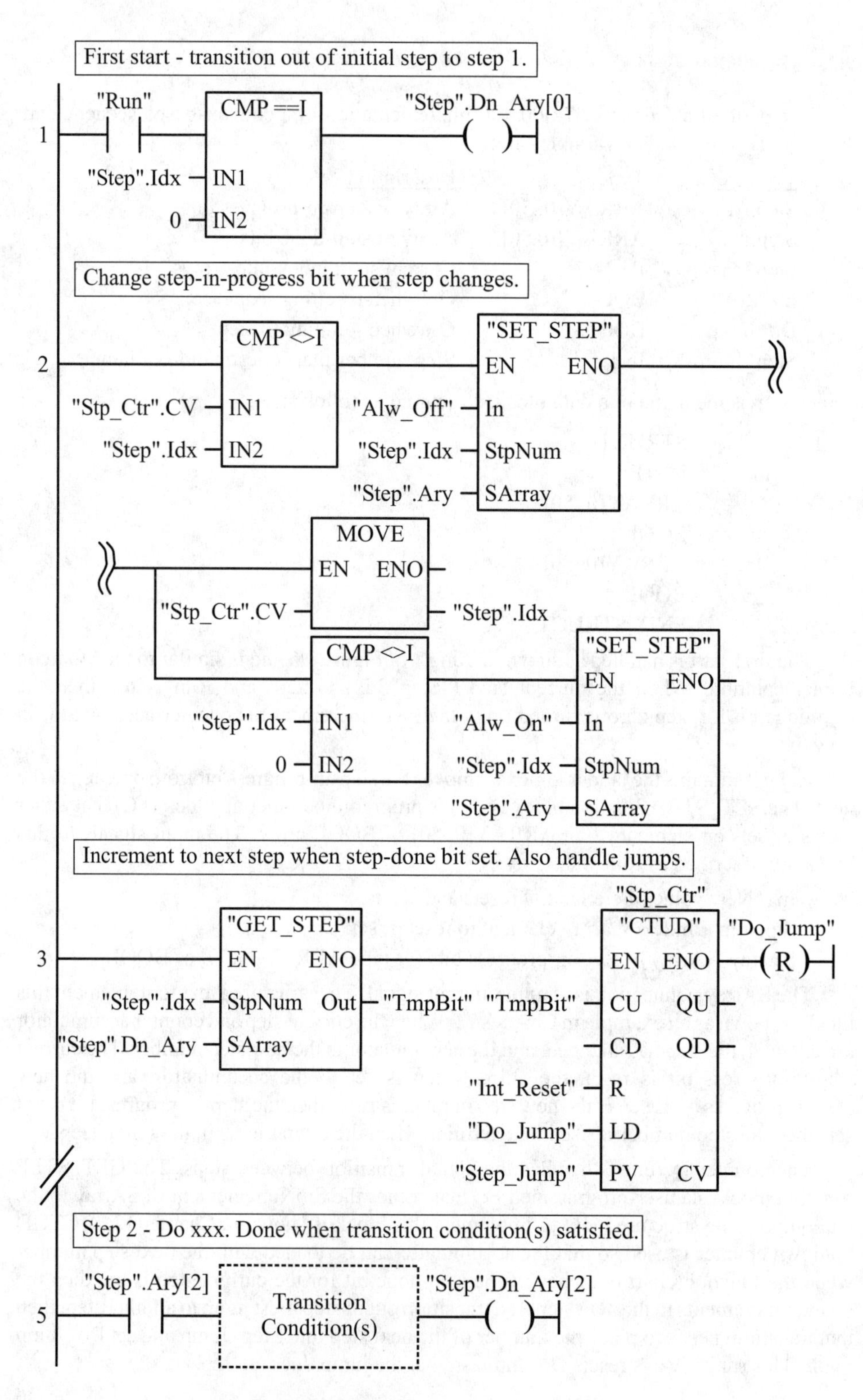

Figure 9.5. S7 counter-based sequence.

Like the Modicon implementation, an **off**-to-**on** transition at the counter input is always ensured when the step number changes, even if the transition condition out of the next step is already met.

The approach discussed in this section cannot be done with a S7-200 processor. To implement a counter-based function chart with a S7-200 processor, one must use the approach outlined in Figure 9.1.

9.2.5 GE Fanuc

A counter-based sequence could be constructed in a manner similar to the Modicon and S7 implementations and use the BIT_CLR, BIT_SET, and BIT_TEST blocks with a bit array defined in %M memory. However, GE Fanuc has a BIT_SEQ function block that includes a counter and handles the set/clear of the step-in-progress bits. A GE Fanuc counter-based sequence that uses the BIT_SEQ block is shown in Figure 9.6. The variables and addresses are:

Symbol	Type	Addr.	Description
Stp_Ary	BYTE	%M33	Array of step-in-progress bits.
Step_1	BOOL	%M33	Step 1 step-in-progress bit.
Step_2	BOOL	%M34	Step 2 step-in-progress bit.
…			
Step_16	BOOL	%M48	Step 16 step-in-progress bit.
StpDn_Ary	BYTE	%M49	Array of step-done bits.
StpDn_1	BOOL	%M49	Step 1 done bit.
StpDn_2	BOOL	%M50	Step 2 done bit.
…			
StpDn_16	BOOL	%M64	Step 16 done bit.
Stp_Ctr	INT (3)	%R21	Step counter for sequencer.
Step_Inc	BOOL	%M21	**On** when needing to increment to next step.
Do_Jump	BOOL	%M20	**On** when jumping to step.
Step_Jump	INT	%R24	Step number destination of step.
Int_Reset	BOOL	%M22	**On** when resetting sequence.

Note that the step-in-progress bits and the step-done bits are addressed as Booleans and as BYTEs. The BYTE addresses are needed by the BIT_SEQ and BIT_TEST blocks. The Boolean addresses are needed by the transition logic. This addressing is legal, as long as the starting %M number for the BYTE is a multiple of 16 plus one.

The inputs of the BIT_SEQ block are described as follows:

R – Reset. **On** to reset sequencer to step number indicated by N input.

DIR – Step number increment/decrement. When **on**, step number increments on **off**-to-**on** transition of the top input. When DIR is **off**, step number decrements.

N – Step number sequencer is set to when reset. If < 1, then 1 is assumed. If > max. step number, then the max. step number is assumed.

ST – Address/variable of first element in byte array that contains step-in-progress bits. Can be mapped to %M address so one can easily access step-in-progress bits.

The field below the block name is the symbol or address of the BIT_SEQ sequencer control, three consecutive register addresses to store internal information. As for the timers and counters, only the symbol or register address of the first word is specified as part of the

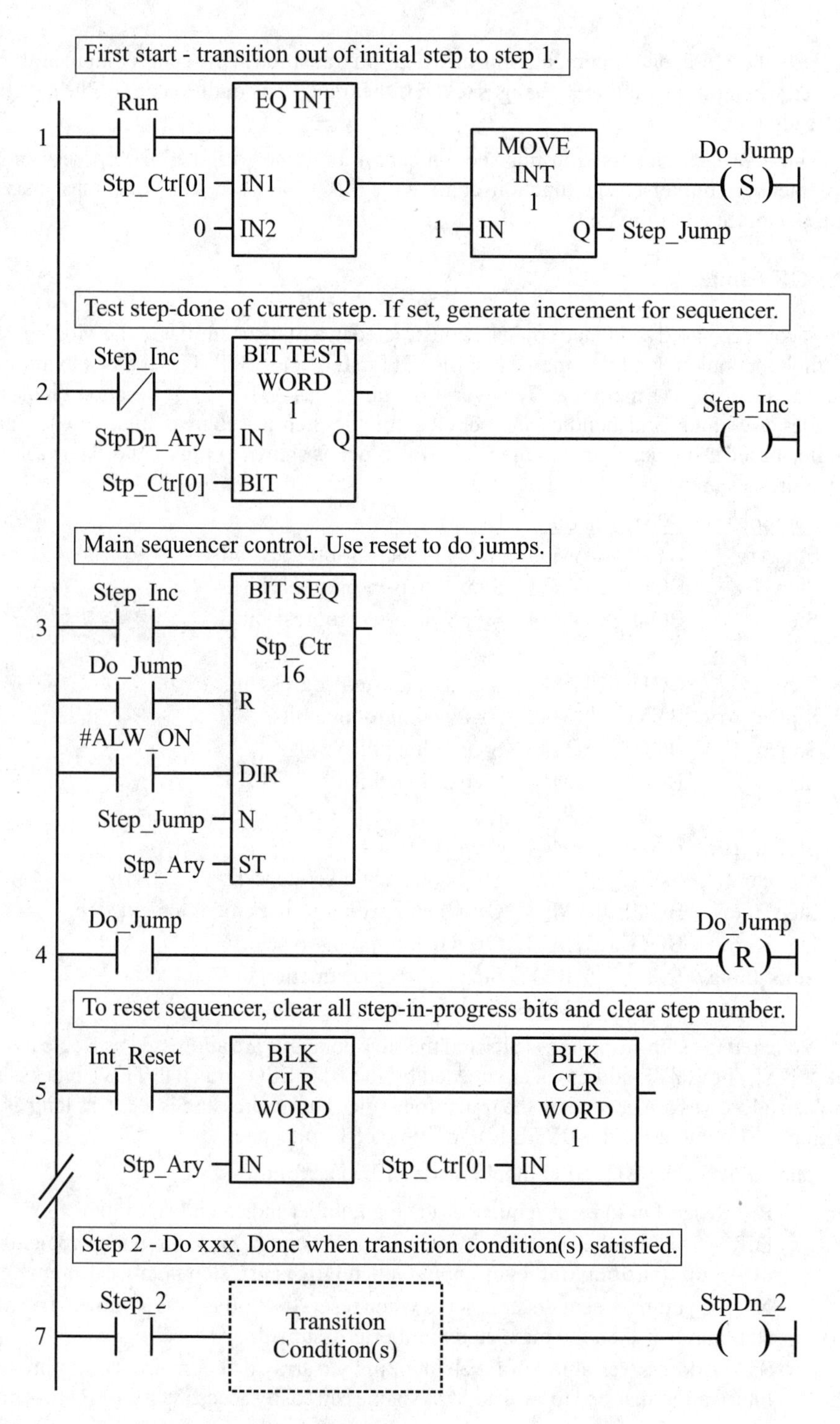

Figure 9.6. GE Fanuc counter-based sequence.

function block. The other register addresses are assumed. The first word contains the current step number, which can be addressed as "Sym[0]" if "Sym" is in this field. The maximum step number is placed in the field below the sequencer control. There can be up to 256 steps.

The BIT_SEQ block operates in the following manner. When R is **on**, all step-in-progress bits are reset, the step number is set to the N input, and the corresponding step-in-progress bit is set **on**. When R is **off**, and there is an **off**-to-**on** transition on the top input, the step number is changed in accordance with the INC input. When the step number changes, the current step-in-progress bit is cleared and the new step-in-progress bit is set **on**.

The first start is handled as shown in rung 1 of Figure 9.6. When the current step (Stp_Ctr[0]) is zero and Run is **on**, then the parameters are set up for a jump to the first step.

Rung 2 contains the ladder logic that determines if the step number needs to be incremented to the next step. The BIT_TEST_WORD function block sets Step_Inc when the step-done bit for the current step is **on**. One must always ensure there is an **off**-to-**on** transition at the BIT_SEQ input when the step number should increment. Therefore, Step_Inc must be **off** before any step-done bit is tested.

The BIT_SEQ block in rung 3 handles the actual transition between steps. Note that the reset input of the BIT_SEQ block is used to jump to a step that is not one more than the current step. If a transition out of step must jump to another step, then that transition needs to place the number of the next step into Step_Jump and set Do_Jump to **on**. Rung 4 always resets Do_Jump so that the jump does not repeat. A branch implementation is shown in the solution to Example 9.1. Rung 5 resets the sequence by clearing the step-in-progress bits and clearing the current step number, Stp_Ctr[0].

The ladder logic for a typical step transition is shown in rung 7. When the particular step-in-progress bit is **on** and the transition logic is satisfied, then the step-done bit is turned **on**. It is similar to the logic of Figure 6.19. The output is the step-done bit rather than setting the next step-in-progress bit and resetting the current step-in-progress bit.

If the sequence contains more than 16 steps, then the number in the BIT_TEST block on rung 2 and in the first BLK_CLR_WORD on rung 5 need to be increased accordingly. The number should be [(number of steps) MOD 16]+1.

9.2.6 Example

The counter-based function chart implementation is illustrated by reworking a previous example from Chapter 6. This example includes a function chart for the reset operation and so the interplay between these two function charts can be illustrated.

Example 9.1. Engine Inverter Station Control. Implement the engine inverter control of Example 6.4 using the counter-based approach of this section.

Solution. The general approach to the counter-based implementation has already been explained. The Modicon solution for this problem is shown in Figure 9.7. The function of each rung is explained in the comments. There are a few parts that need further explanation. The transition from step 13 to step 1 is handled by the logic on rung 17. When step 13 is done, Step_Jump is set to 1 and Do_Jump is set. The actual jump will happen when rung 4 is scanned. The LIM_INT block is used on rungs 24 and 25 to turn **on** a physical output for multiple steps. For this function block, when the value of IN is between the MN and MX values, inclusive, the Res output is **on**. This function block is implemented in the structured

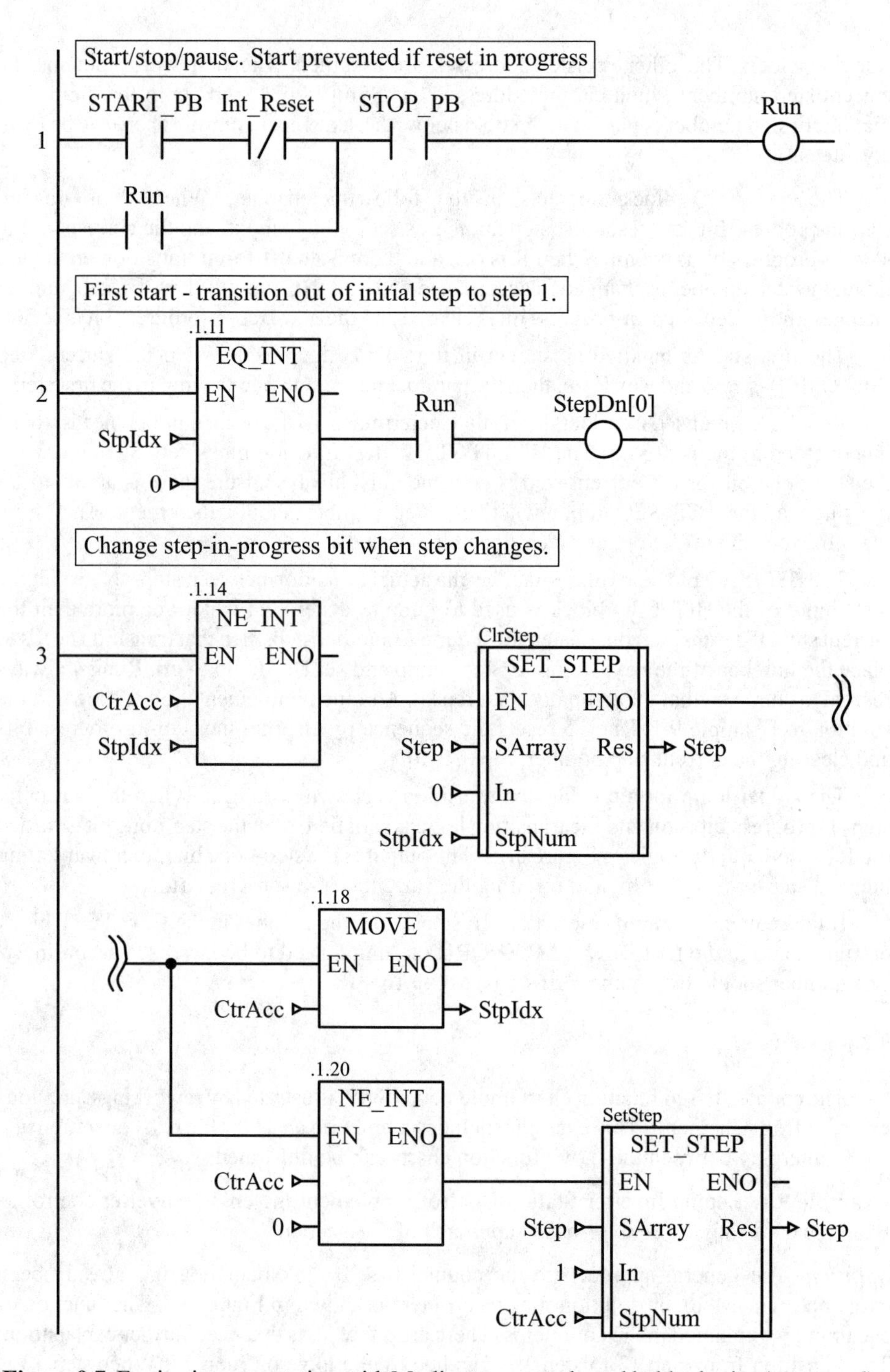

Figure 9.7. Engine inverter station with Modicon counter-based ladder logic. *(continued)*

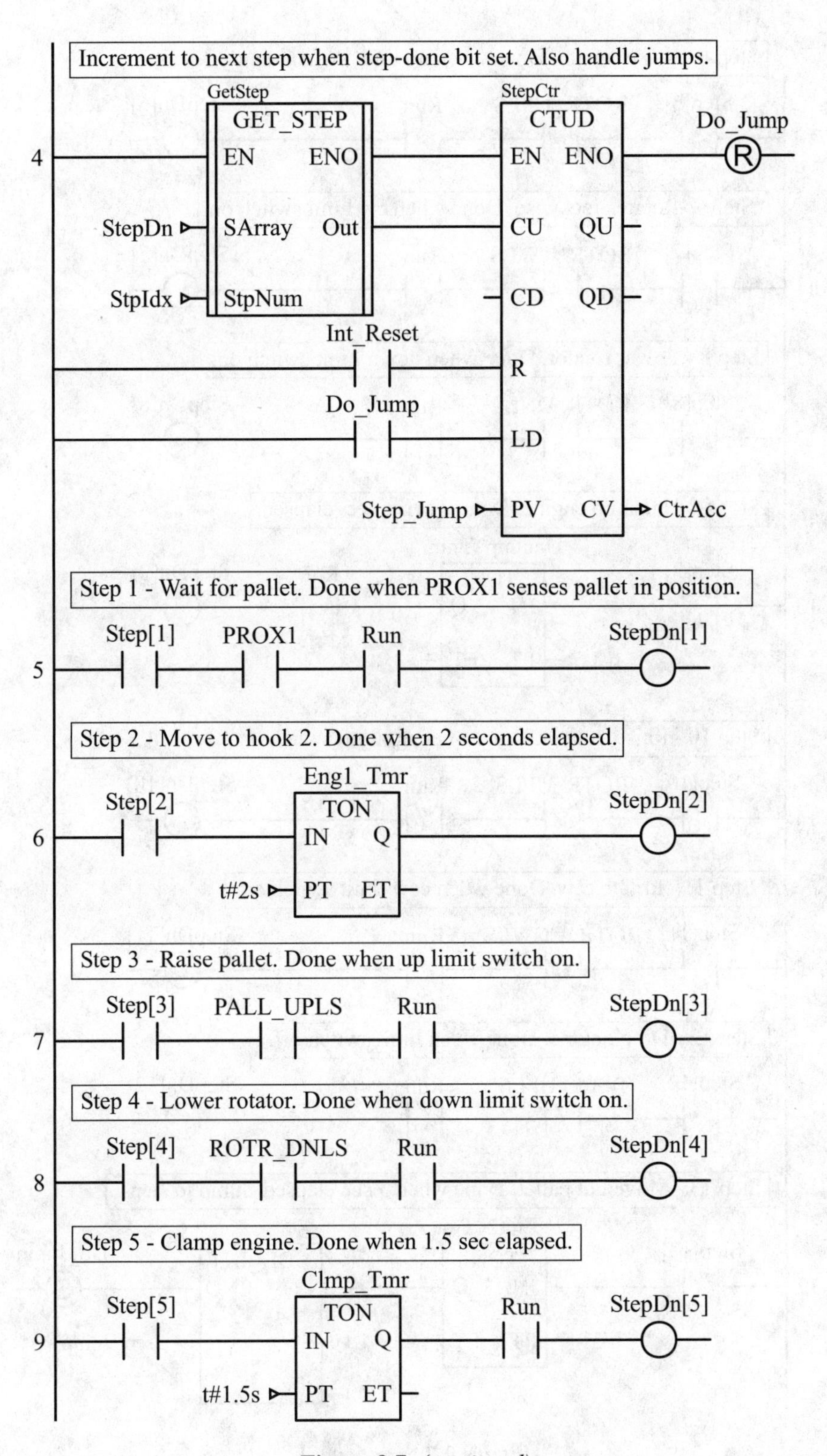

Figure 9.7. *(continued)*

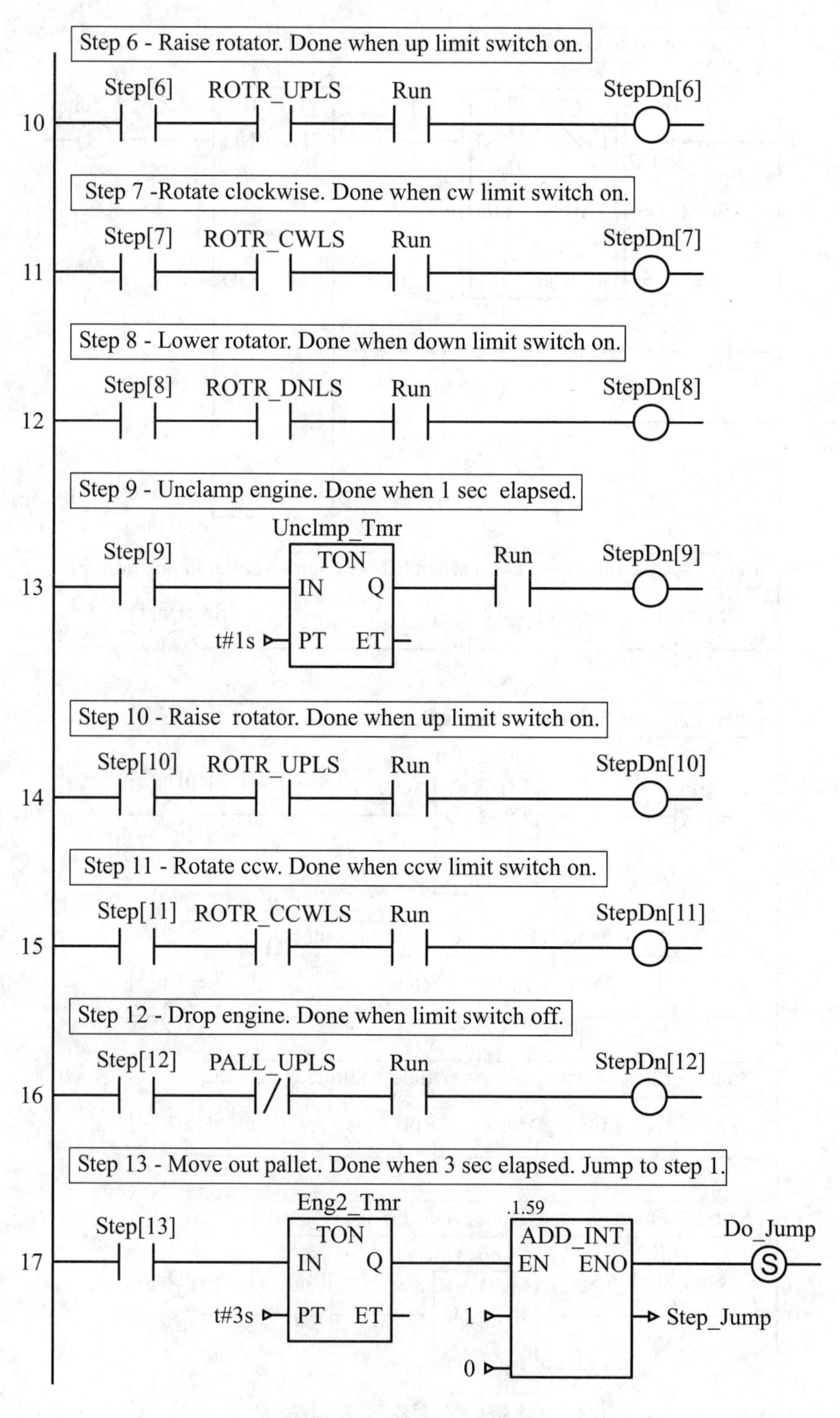

Figure 9.7. *(continued)*

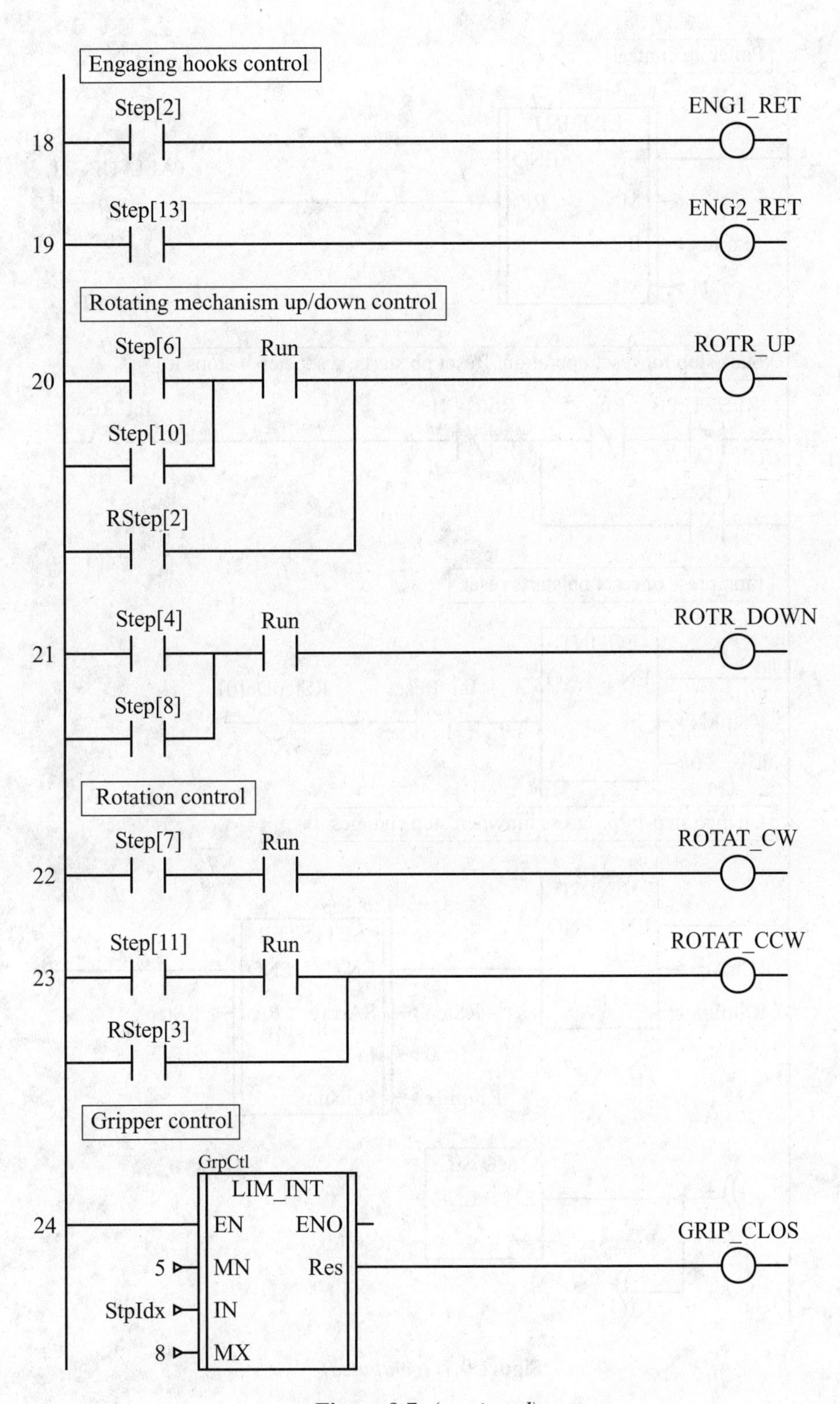

Figure 9.7. *(continued)*

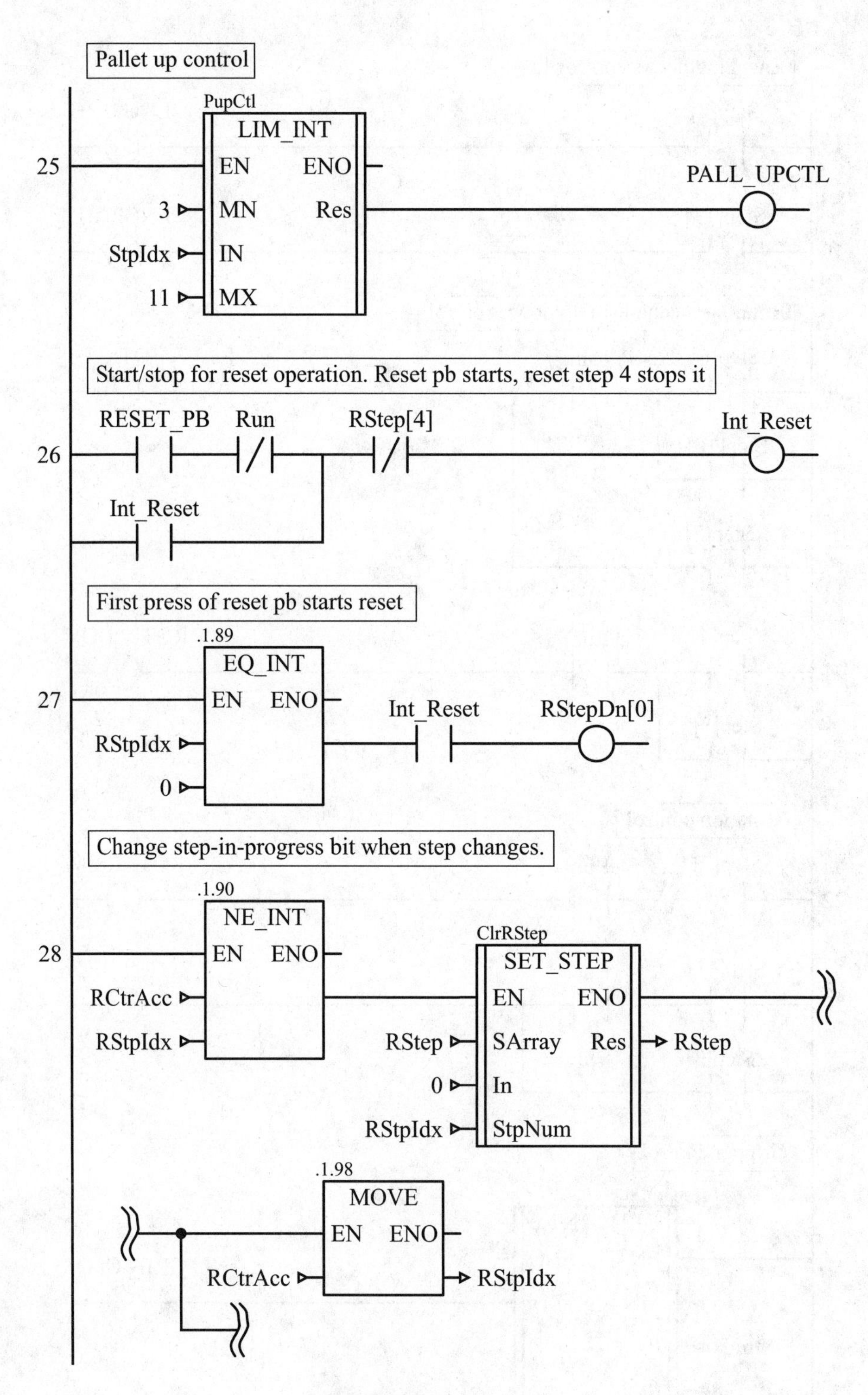

Figure 9.7. *(continued)*

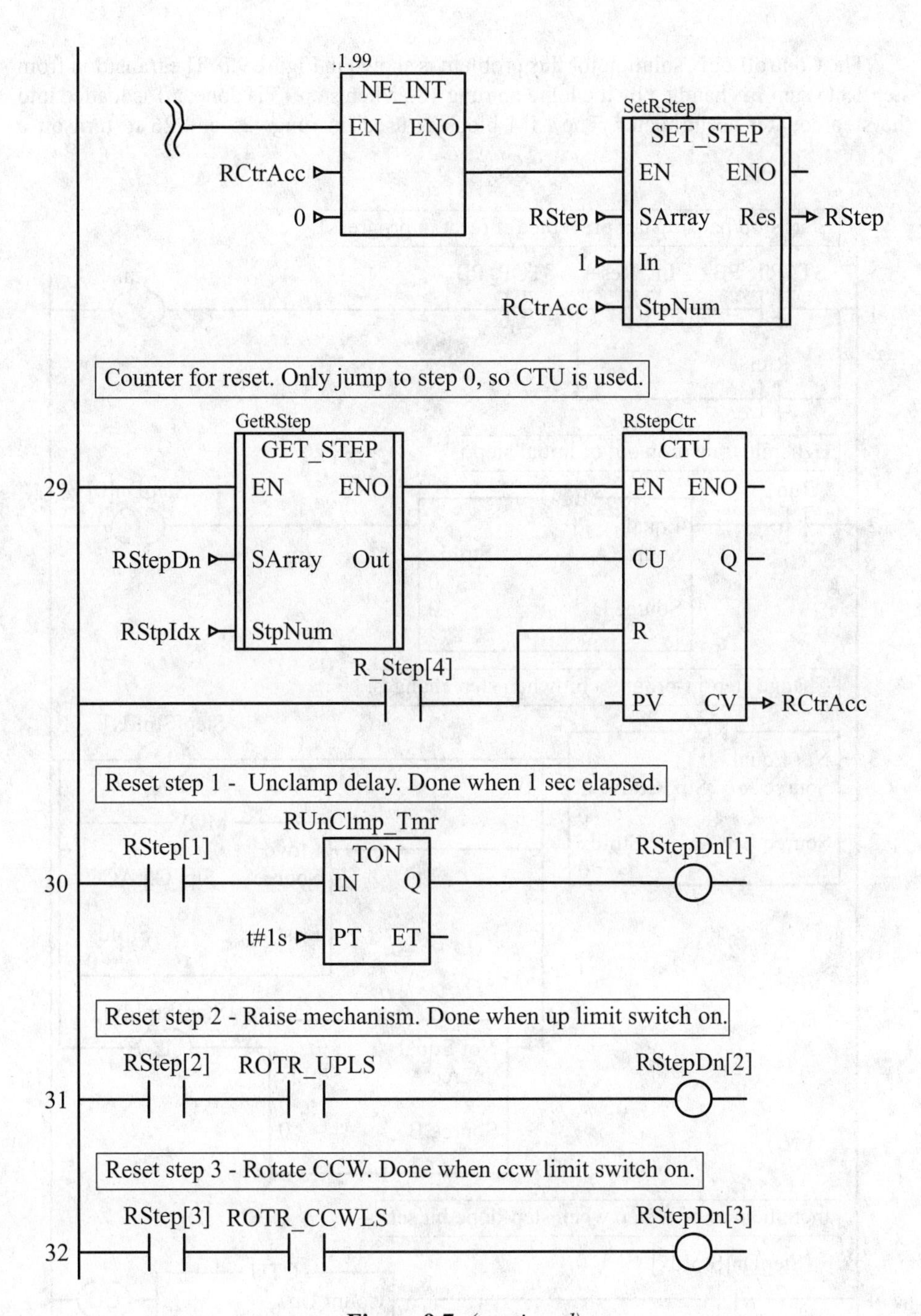

Figure 9.7. *(continued)*

text language and is an example from Chapter 12. The counter for the reset function chart (rung 29) is a CTU instead of a CTUD. Since the only jump in this function chart is back to the initial (zero) step, there is no need to load the counter accumulator with a nonzero value. The R_Step[4] bit is used to reset the counter.

The ControlLogix solution for this problem is shown in Figure 9.8. The transition from step 13 to step 1 is handled by the logic on rung 18. When step 13 is done, a 1 is loaded into the step counter accumulator. The LIM block is used on rungs 25 and 26 to turn **on** a

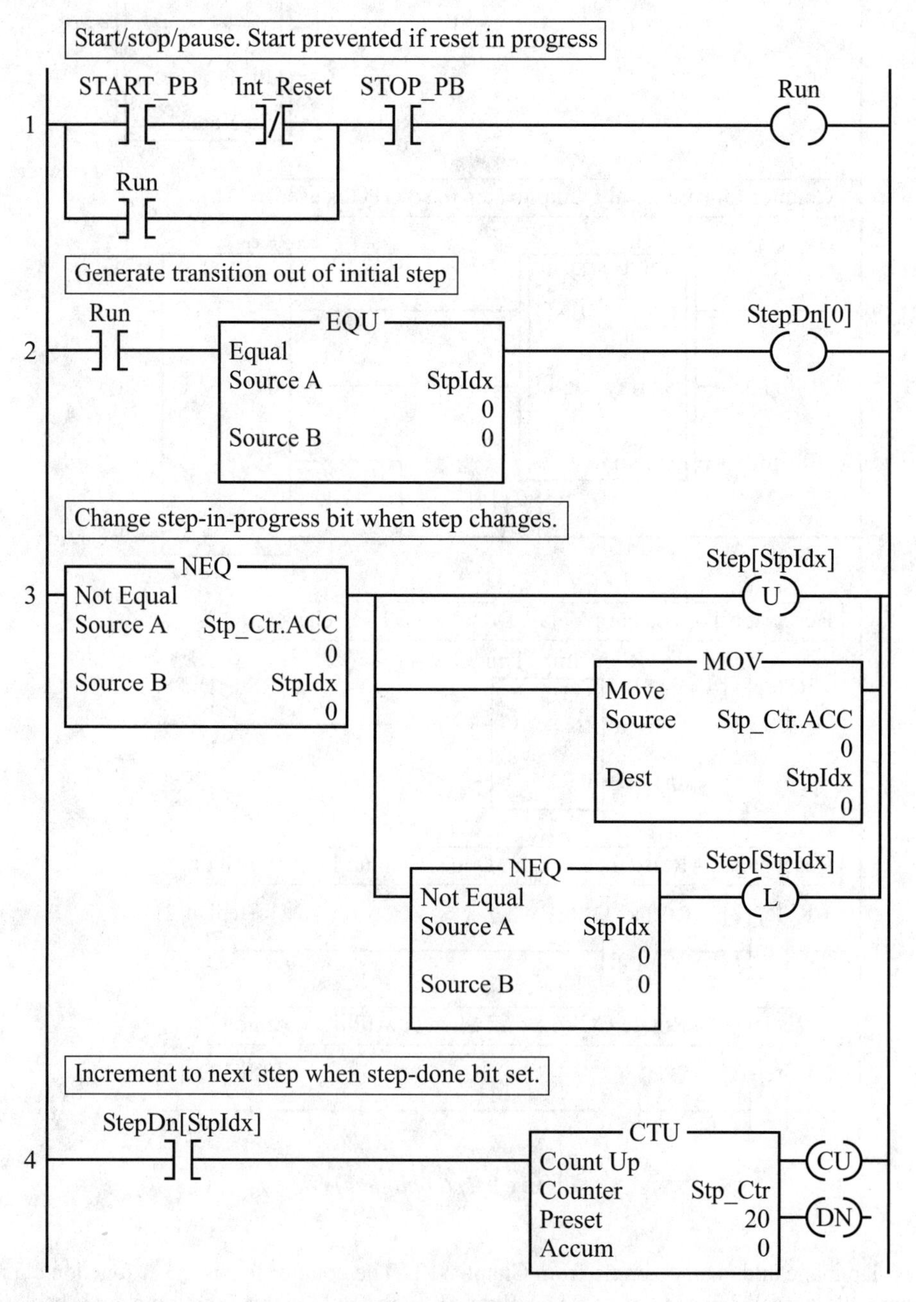

Figure 9.8. Engine inverter station with ControlLogix counter-based ladder logic. *(continued)*

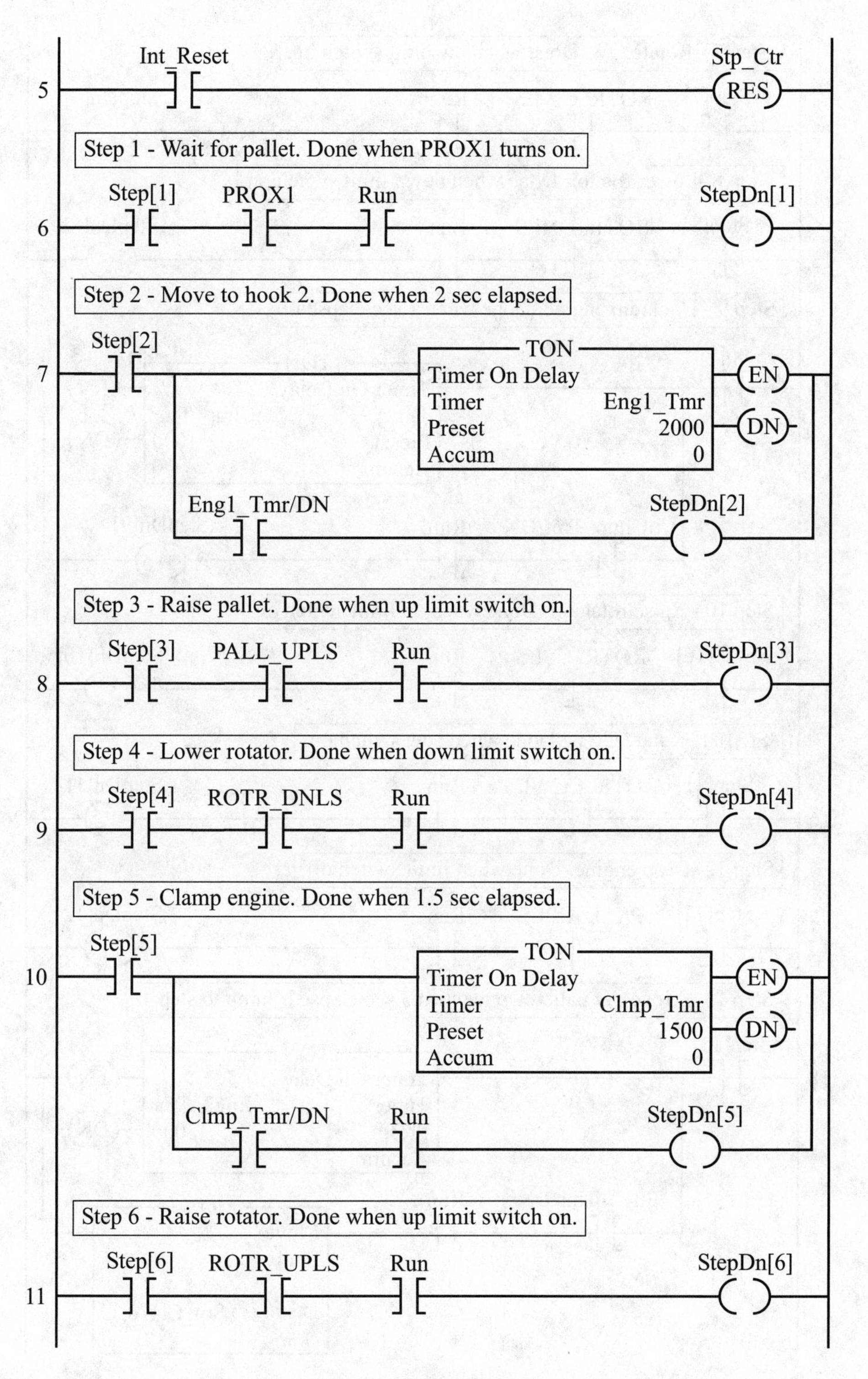

Figure 9.8. *(continued)*

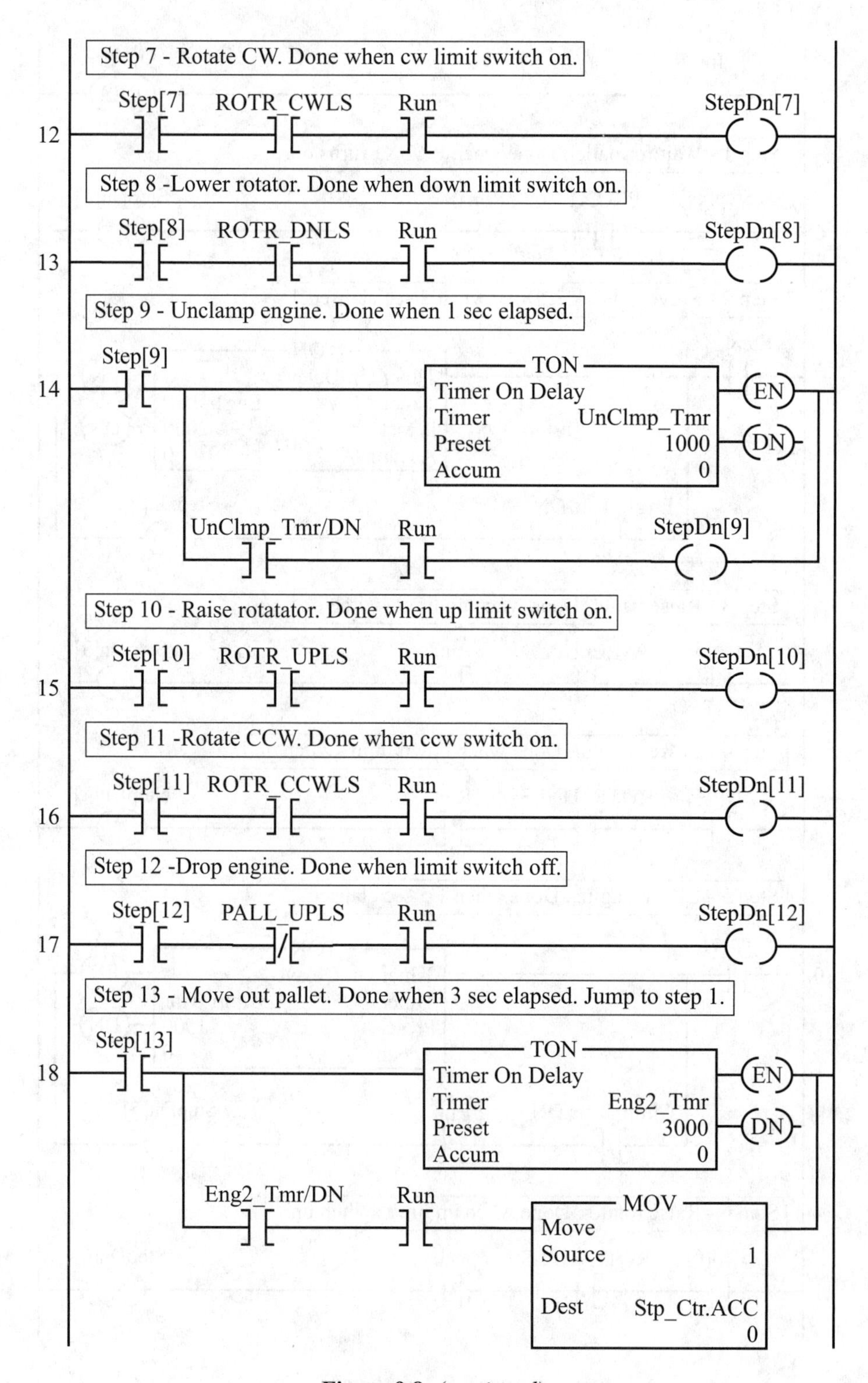

Figure 9.8. *(continued)*

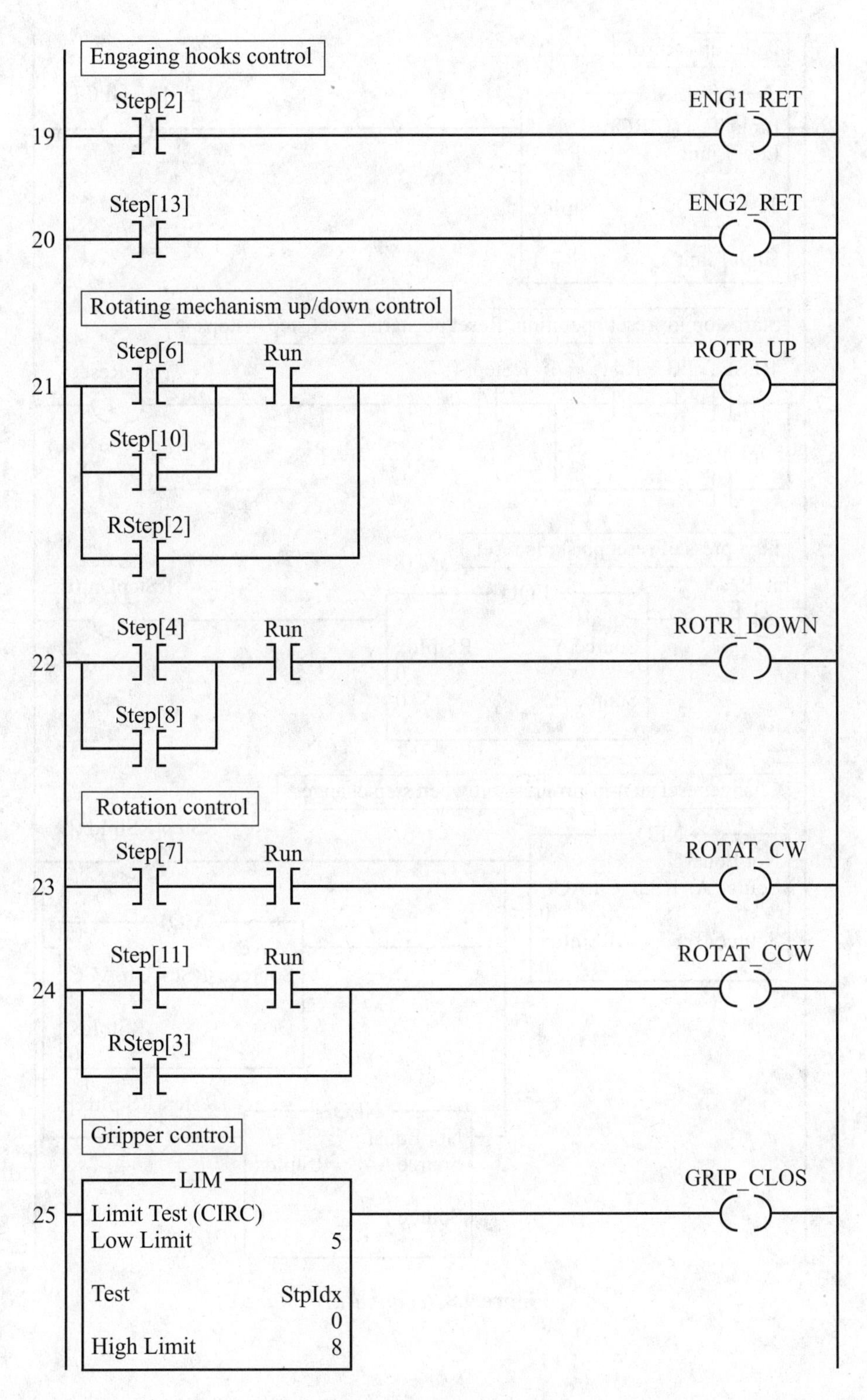

Figure 9.8. *(continued)*

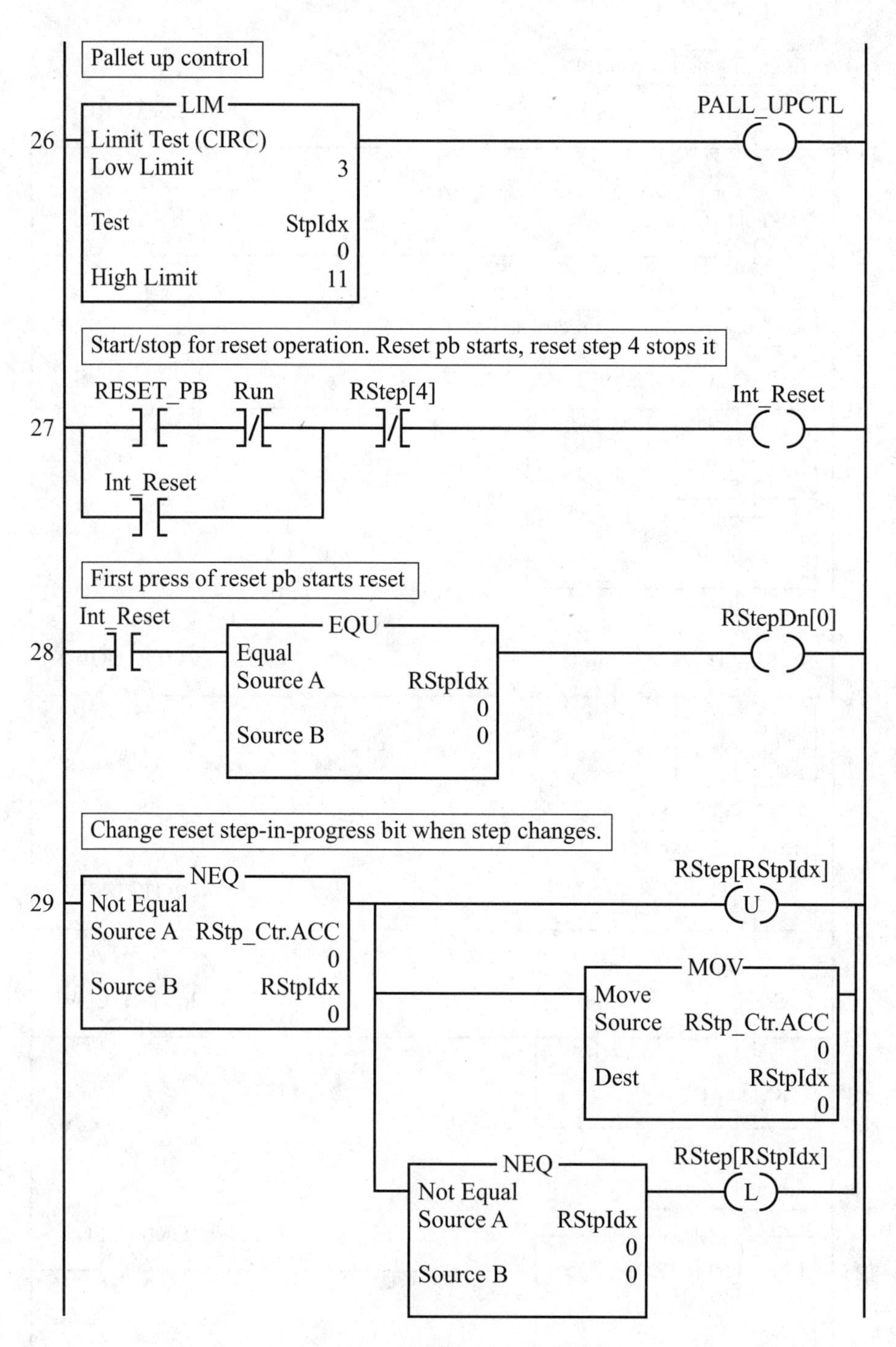

Figure 9.8. *(continued)*

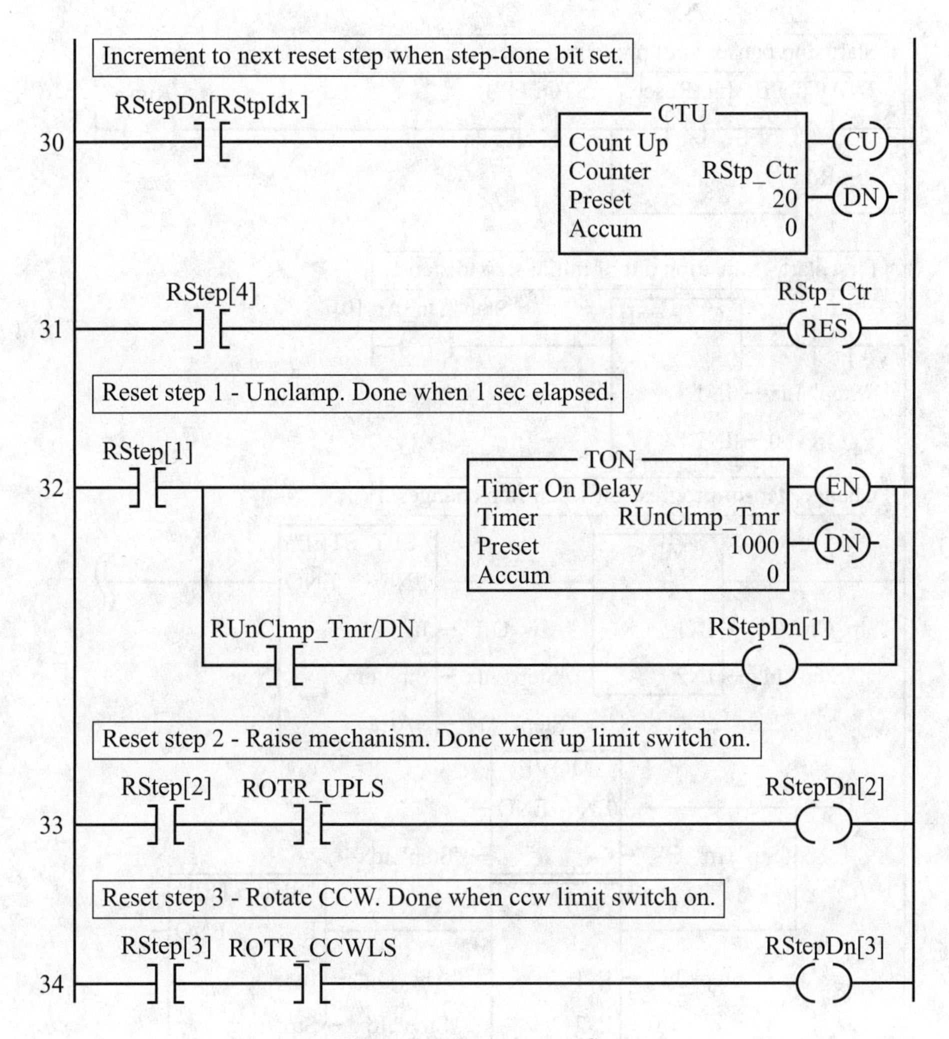

Figure 9.8. *(continued)*

physical output for multiple steps. The R_Step[4] bit is used to reset the counter for the reset sequence (rung 31).

A partial S7 solution for this problem is shown in Figure 9.9. Since it is very similar to the Modicon solution of Figure 9.7, only the first six rungs are shown. Also, the transition out of step 13 that jumps back to step 1 is shown. The IStep and RStep data blocks are defined to be the same as the Step structure in section 9.2.4.

The GE Fanuc solution for this problem is shown in Figure 9.10. Rather than show a complete solution, only the rungs dealing with the sequencer and the jumps are shown. The rungs that handle the transitions and the physical outputs are similar to the Modicon solution in Figure 9.7.

The solutions use the following internal variables:

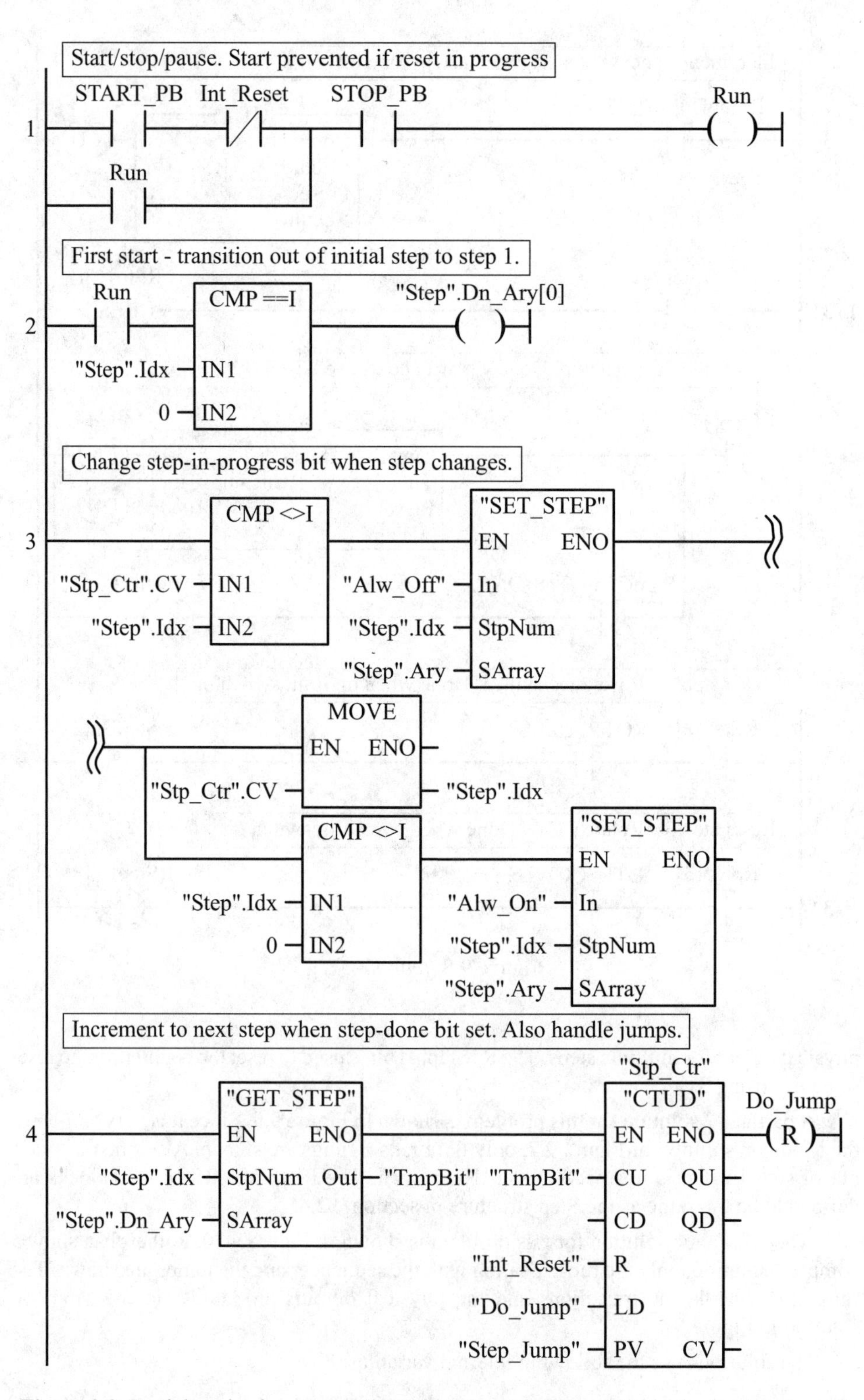

Figure 9.9. Partial engine inverter station with S7 counter-based ladder logic. *(continued)*

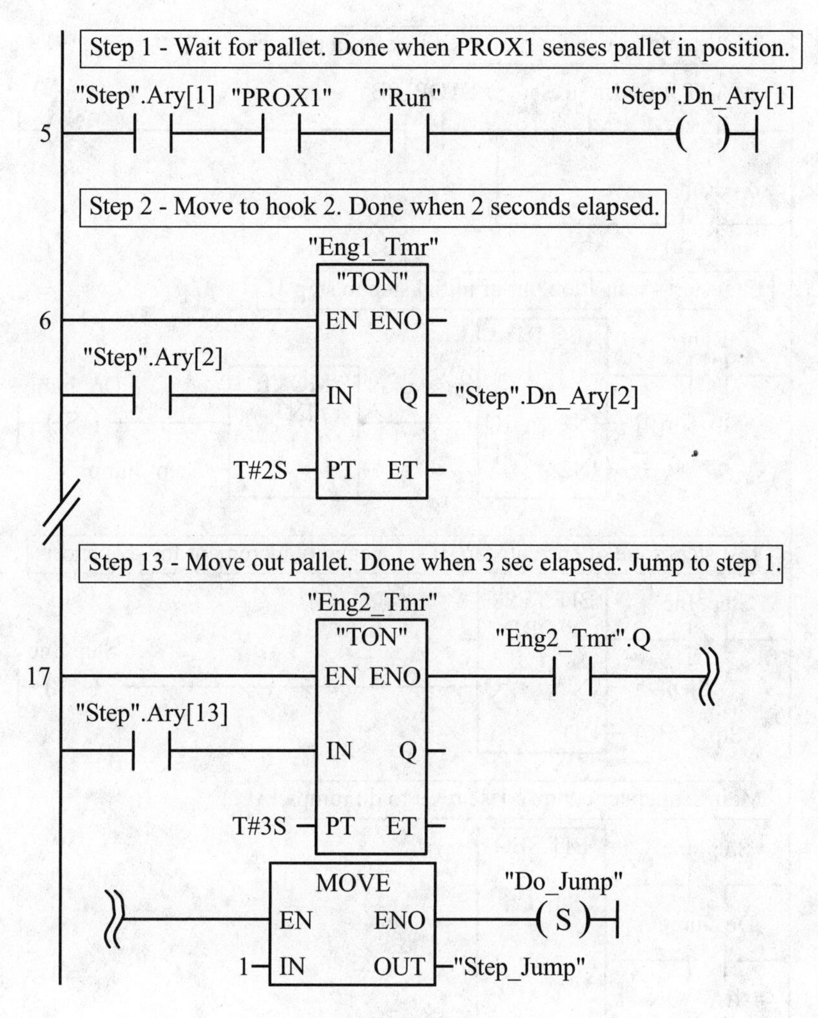

Figure 9.9. *(continued)*

Variable	Description
Run	Internal coil, **on** when system running.
Int_Reset	Internal coil, **on** to reset operation.
StpIdx	Current step number for inverter normal sequence.
Step	Array of step-in-progress bits for normal sequence.
StepDn	Array of step-done bits for normal sequence.
Stp_Ctr	Counter for normal sequence (A-B and GE Fanuc).
CtrAcc	Counter accumulator for normal sequence (Modicon and S7).
RStpIdx	Current step number for reset sequence.
RStep	Array of step-in-progress bits for reset sequence.
RStepDn	Array of step-done bits for reset sequence.
RStp_Ctr	Counter for reset sequence (A-B and GE Fanuc).
RCtrAcc	Counter accumulator for reset sequence (Modicon and S7).

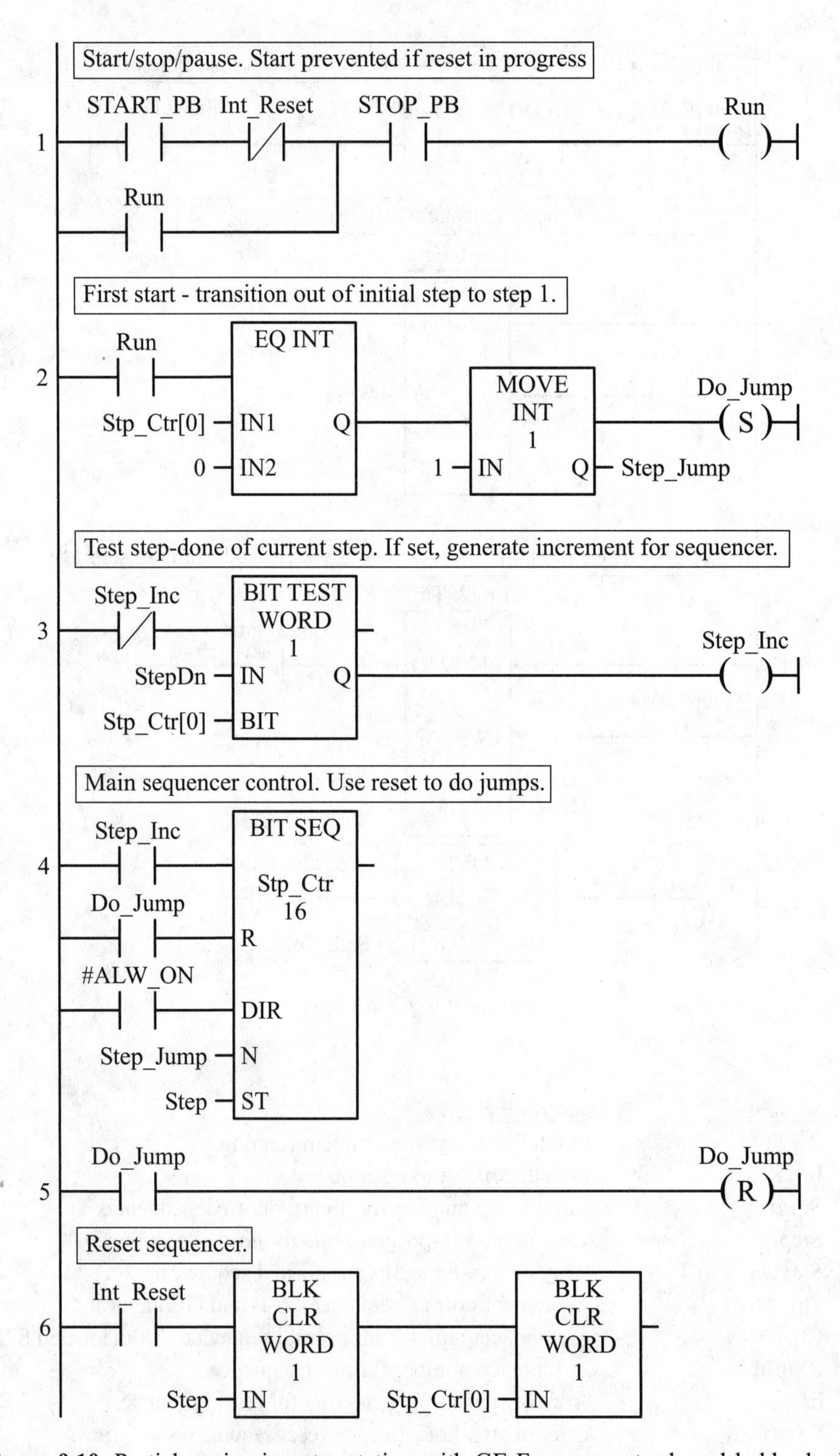

Figure 9.10. Partial engine inverter station with GE Fanuc counter-based ladder logic. *(continued)*

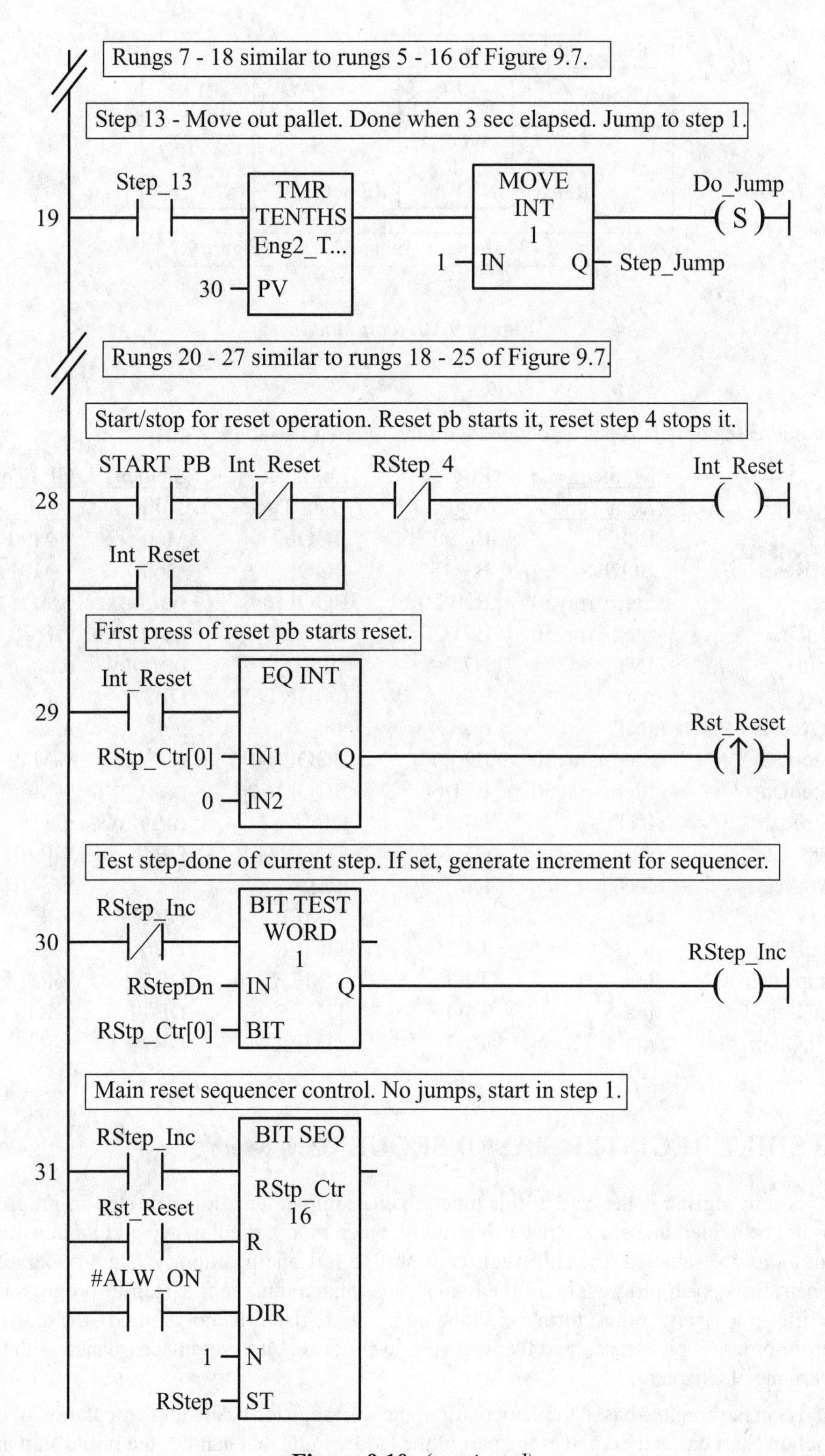

Figure 9.10. *(continued)*

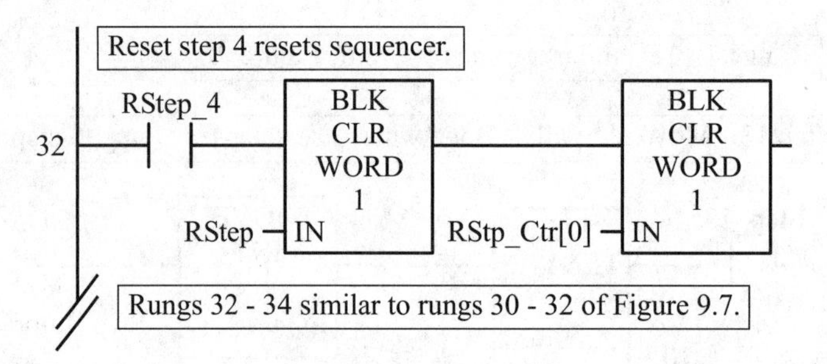

Figure 9.10. *(continued)*

The addresses or data types associated with the internal variables:

Variable	Modicon Data Type	PLC-5 Addr.	Logix Data Type	Siemens Addr.	GE Fanuc Addr.
Run	BOOL	B3/90	BOOL	M60.6	%M90
Int_Reset	BOOL	B3/91	BOOL	M60.7	%M91
Step	StepArray50	B20/20	BOOL[64]	DB1.DBX2	%M17
StepDn	StepArray50	B21/20	BOOL[64]	DB1.DBX10	%M33
StpIdx	INT	N7:30	DINT	DB1.DBW0	n/a
Stp_Ctr	n/a	C5:1	COUNTER	DB3	%R95
CtrAcc	INT	n/a	n/a	n/a	n/a
RStep	StepArray50	B20/60	BOOL[64]	DB2.DBX2	%M49
RStepDn	StepArray50	B21/60	BOOL[64]	DB2.DBX10	%M65
RStpIdx	INT	N7:32	DINT	DB2.DBW0	n/a
RStp_Ctr	n/a	C5:2	COUNTER	DB4	%R105
RCtrAcc	INT	n/a	n/a	n/a	n/a
Eng1_Tmr	n/a	T4:1	TIMER	DB51	%R1
Eng2_Tmr	n/a	T4:2	TIMER	DB6	%R4
Clmp_Tmr	n/a	T4:3	TIMER	DB7	%R7
UnClmp_Tmr	n/a	T4:4	TIMER	DB8	%R10
RUnClmp_Tmr	n/a	T4:5	TIMER	DB9	%R13

9.3 SHIFT REGISTER-BASED SEQUENCE

A shift register is the core of this function chart implementation. The step-in-progress bits are contained in a shift register. Normally, when in a particular step and its transition conditions are satisfied, the shift register is shifted left one position. When an operation repeats, the step-in-progress bit of the final step is rotated into the first step-in-progress bit. To implement any other form of branching, the register is not shifted, the current step-in-progress bit is reset, and the next step-in-progress bit is set in accordance with the technique of Chapter 6.

As in the counter-based implementation, the shift register-based implementation of the function chart basically replaces the part of the ladder logic that handles the initial start and transitions between steps. The start/stop/pause rung remains the same. The step actions basically remain the same, but the references to the steps will change. The main parts of the ladder logic that are different are:

First start

Transition between steps

Step-in-progress array (register) shift

The implementation details specific to each type of PLC are described and then illustrated with an example.

9.3.1 Modicon

The parts of a Modicon implementation of a shift register-based sequence are shown in Figure 9.11. The ladder logic to handle the 40-bit shift register is shown in Figure 8.6. The variables are:

Variable	Type	Description
ShiftReg	WordArr5	Shift register, contains step-in-progress bits.
SetFirstBit	BOOL	**On** when starting for first time.
Step_x	BOOL	Step-in-progress bits for transitions.

where the WordArr5 type is a default type, defined as an ARRAY [1..5] of WORD.

The first start is handled as shown in rung 1 of Figure 9.11. When all bits of the shift register are zero, then SetFirstBit is turned **on**, which will also initiate a shift in rung 5.

Rungs 2 – 4 extract the step-in-progress bit from the shift register words. The transitions are all handled as parallel conditions to cause a left shift in the shift register (rung 5). Note that the N.C. DoLeftShift contact ensures that DoLeftShift is turned **off** for at least one scan after a transition. This N.C. contact ensures a proper shift to the next step when the transition condition out of a step is already satisfied when the step is entered (e.g., it is a spare step).

9.3.2 ControlLogix

The parts of a ControlLogix implementation of a shift register-based sequence are shown in Figure 9.12. The variables are:

Variable	Type	Description
Step	DINT[2]	Shift register, contains step-in-progress bits.
First_Start	BOOL	**On** when starting for first time.
Do_Shift	BOOL	**On** when any transition is true.
Src_Bit	BOOL	Bit shifted into register.
Shift_Ctl	CONTROL	Control for shift register.

The first start is handled as shown in rung 1 of Figure 9.12. When all bits of the shift register are zero, then First_Start is turned **on**, which will also cause a transition (in rung 2).

The transitions are all handled as parallel conditions to cause a left shift in the shift register (rung 2). Note that the step numbers are not the same as the shift register bit number. Step 1 is bit 0 (zero), step 2 is bit 1, and so on. The shift register is handled on rungs 3 – 5. The Src_Bit output on rung 3 is the bit that is shifted into the first position of the shift register (step 1). Note that the N.C. Shift_Ctl.EN contact ensures that the BSL input is

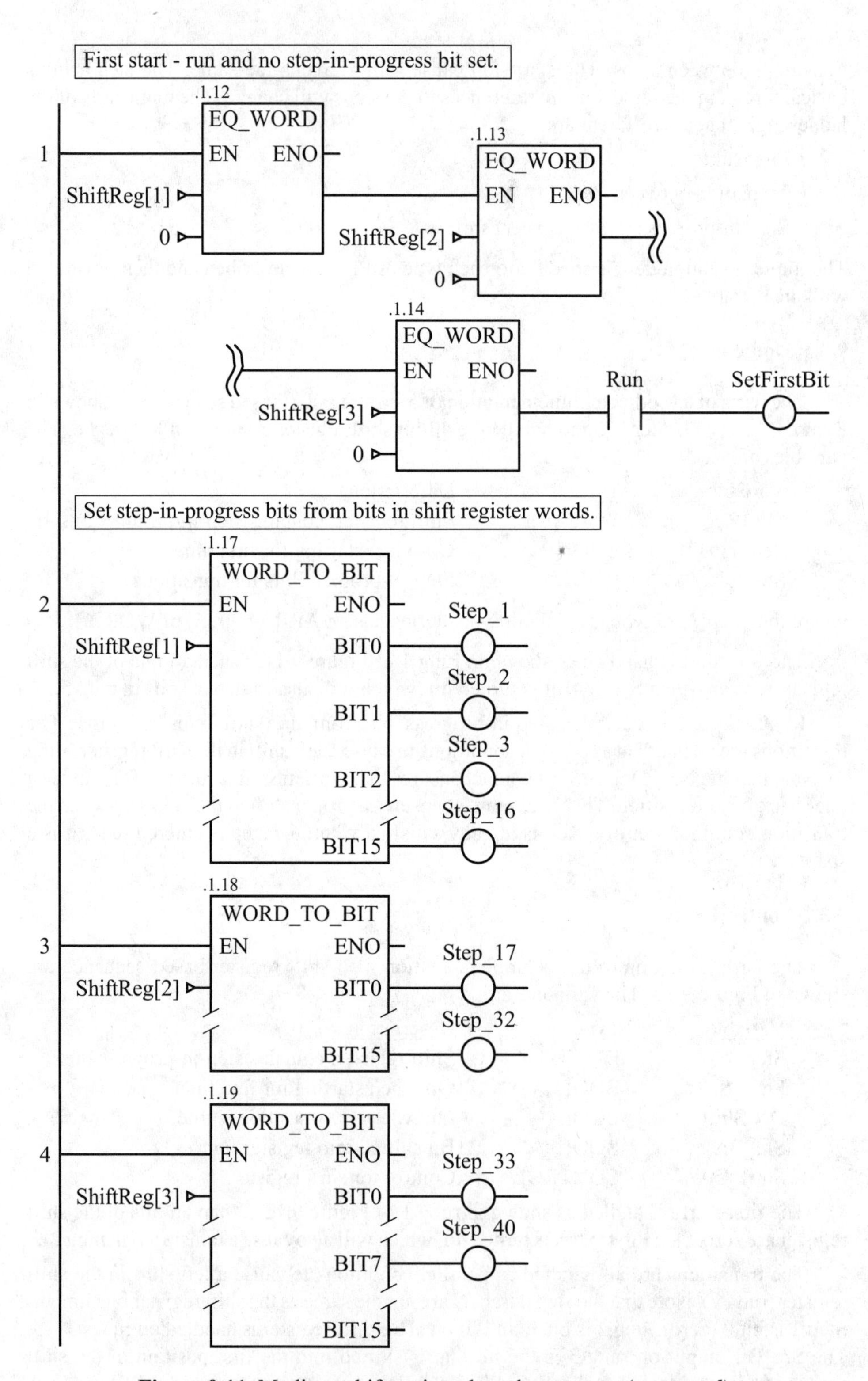

Figure 9.11. Modicon shift register-based sequence. *(continued)*

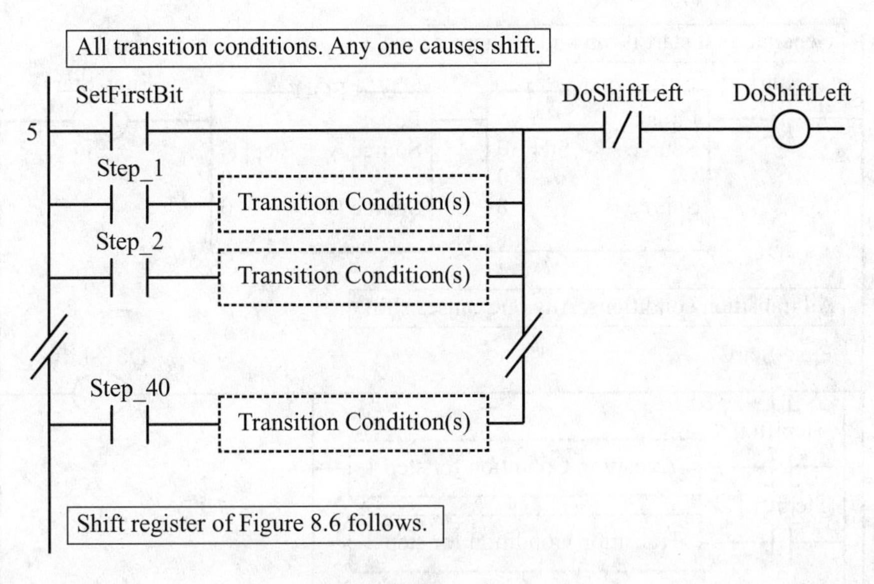

Figure 9.11. *(continued)*

turned **off** for at least one scan after a transition. This N.C. contact ensures a proper shift to the next step when the transition condition out of a step is already satisfied when the step is entered (e.g., it is a spare step). The FLL block clears all step-in-progress bits when the operation is reset.

9.3.3 PLC-5/SLC-500

A PLC-5 and SLC-500 implementation of a shift register-based sequence is very similar to a ControlLogix implementation. The only basic difference is that the shift register is constructed with 16-bit words or integers. Therefore, this implementation is not shown.

9.3.4 S7-300/400

The parts of a S7-300/400 implementation of a shift register-based sequence are shown in Figure 9.13. The variables and addresses are:

Symbols	Type	Addr.	Description
SReg0	INT	%MW50	First word of step-in-progress bits.
SReg1	INT	%MW52	Second word of step-in-progress bits.
Step_1	BOOL	%M50.0	Step 1 step-in-progress bit.
Step_2	BOOL	%M50.1	Step 2 step-in-progress bit.
…			
Step_16	BOOL	%M51.7	Step 16 step-in-progress bit.
First_Start	BOOL	%M10.0	First start when no steps active.
Src_Bit	BOOL	%M10.1	Bit shifted into shift register.
Do_Shift	BOOL	%M10.2	**On** when transition causes shift.
Int_Reset	BOOL	%M10.3	**On** when resetting sequence.

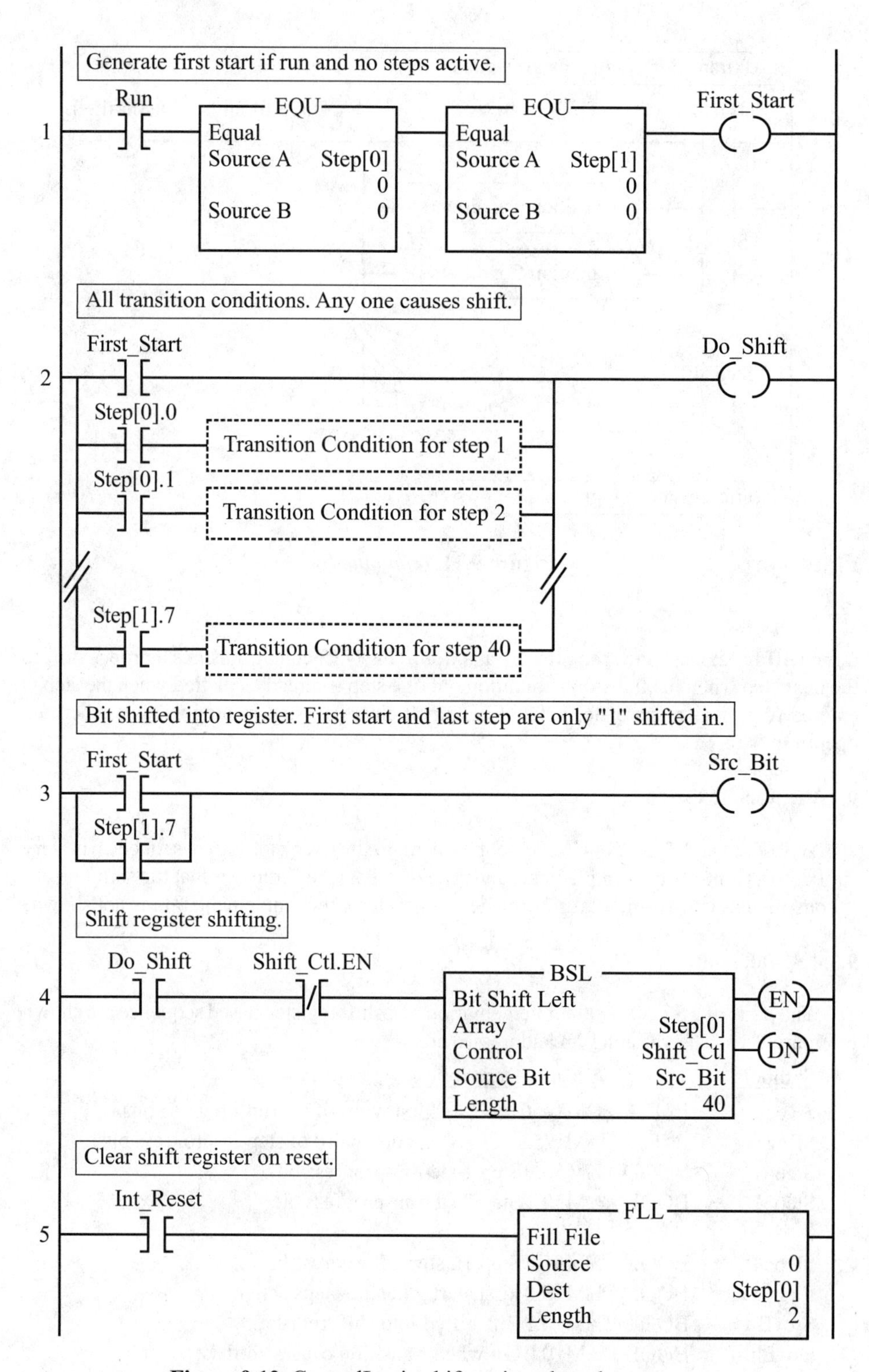

Figure 9.12. ControlLogix shift register-based sequence.

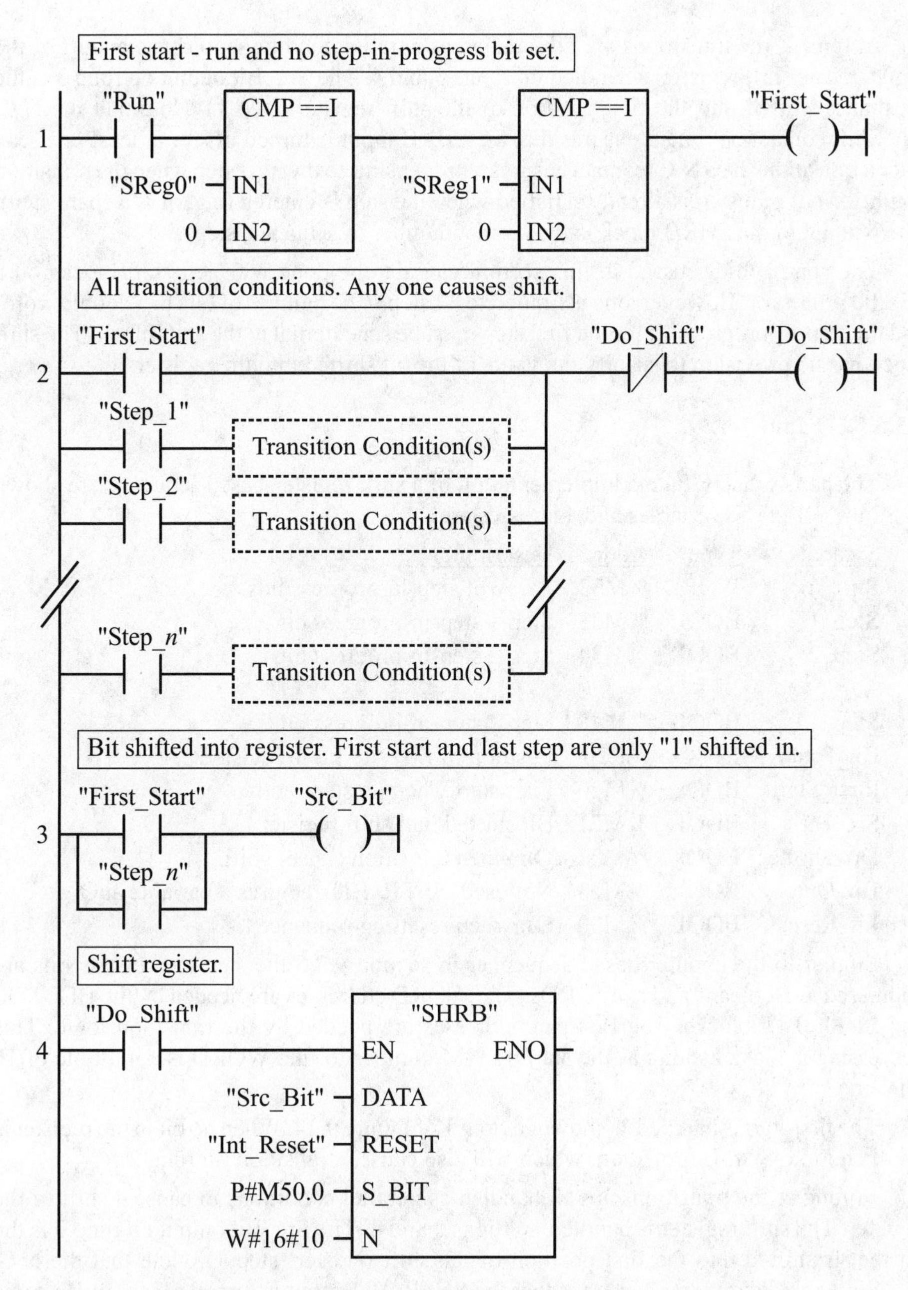

Figure 9.13. S7-300/400 shift register-based sequence.

The step-in-progress bits are addressed as Booleans and as INTs. The INT address is needed by the comparison blocks that check for any step in progress. The Boolean addresses are needed by the transition logic.

The first start is handled as shown in rung 1 of Figure 9.13. When no bit in the register is **on**, then First_Start is turned **on**, which will also cause a transition (in rung 2).

In rung 2, the transitions are all handled as parallel conditions to cause a shift of the register. The shift register is handled on rungs 3 and 4. The Src_Bit output on rung 3 is the bit that is shifted into the first position of the shift register (step 1). Note that the N.C. Do_Shift contact on rung 2 ensures that the SHRB input is turned **off** for at least one scan after a transition. This N.C. contact ensures a proper shift to the next step when the transition condition out of a step is already satisfied when the step is entered (e.g., it is a spare step). The N input to the SHRB block is the correct number of sequence steps.

The approach discussed in this section can also be done with left-shift blocks on a S7-200 processor. However, one is limited to 32 steps (the number of bits in a double word) and the step-in-progress bit for the first step must be set external to the shift block. The shift block has no provision to specify the value of the bit shifted into the register.

9.3.5 GE Fanuc

The parts of a GE Fanuc implementation of a shift register-based sequence are shown in Figure 9.14. The variables and addresses are:

Symbols	Type	Addr.	Description
Stp_Ary	WORD	%M33	Array of step-in-progress bits.
Step_1	BOOL	%M33	Step 1 step-in-progress bit.
Step_2	BOOL	%M34	Step 2 step-in-progress bit.
…			
Step_16	BOOL	%M48	Step 7 step-in-progress bit.
Bit_Pos	INT	%R20	Position of first “1” bit in register.
First_Start	BOOL	%M20	First start when no steps active.
Src_Bit	BOOL	%M21	Bit shifted into shift register.
Do_Shift	BOOL	%M22	**On** when transition causes shift.
Bit_Out	BOOL	%M23	Not used. SHFR_BIT requires a variable at Q.
Int_Reset	BOOL	%M30	**On** when resetting sequence.

Similar to the counter-based sequencer in section 9.2.5 the step-in-progress bits are addressed as Booleans and as WORDs. The WORD addresses are needed by the BIT_POS and SHFR_BIT blocks. The Boolean addresses are needed by the transition logic. This addressing is legal, as long as the starting %M number for the WORD is a multiple of 16 plus one.

The first start is handled as shown in rung 1 of Figure 9.14. When no bit in the register is **on**, then First_Start is turned **on**, which will also cause a transition (in rung 2).

In rung 2, the transitions are all handled as parallel conditions to cause a shift of the register. The shift register is handled on rungs 3 and 4. The Src_Bit output on rung 3 is the bit that is shifted into the first position of the shift register (step 1). Note that the N.C. Do_Shift contact on rung 2 ensures that the SHFR_BIT input is turned **off** for at least one scan after a transition. This N.C. contact ensures a proper shift to the next step when the transition condition out of a step is already satisfied when the step is entered (e.g., it is a spare step). If the sequence contains more than 16 steps, then the number in the BIT_POS block on rung 1 needs to be increased accordingly. The number should be [(number of steps) MOD 16]+1.

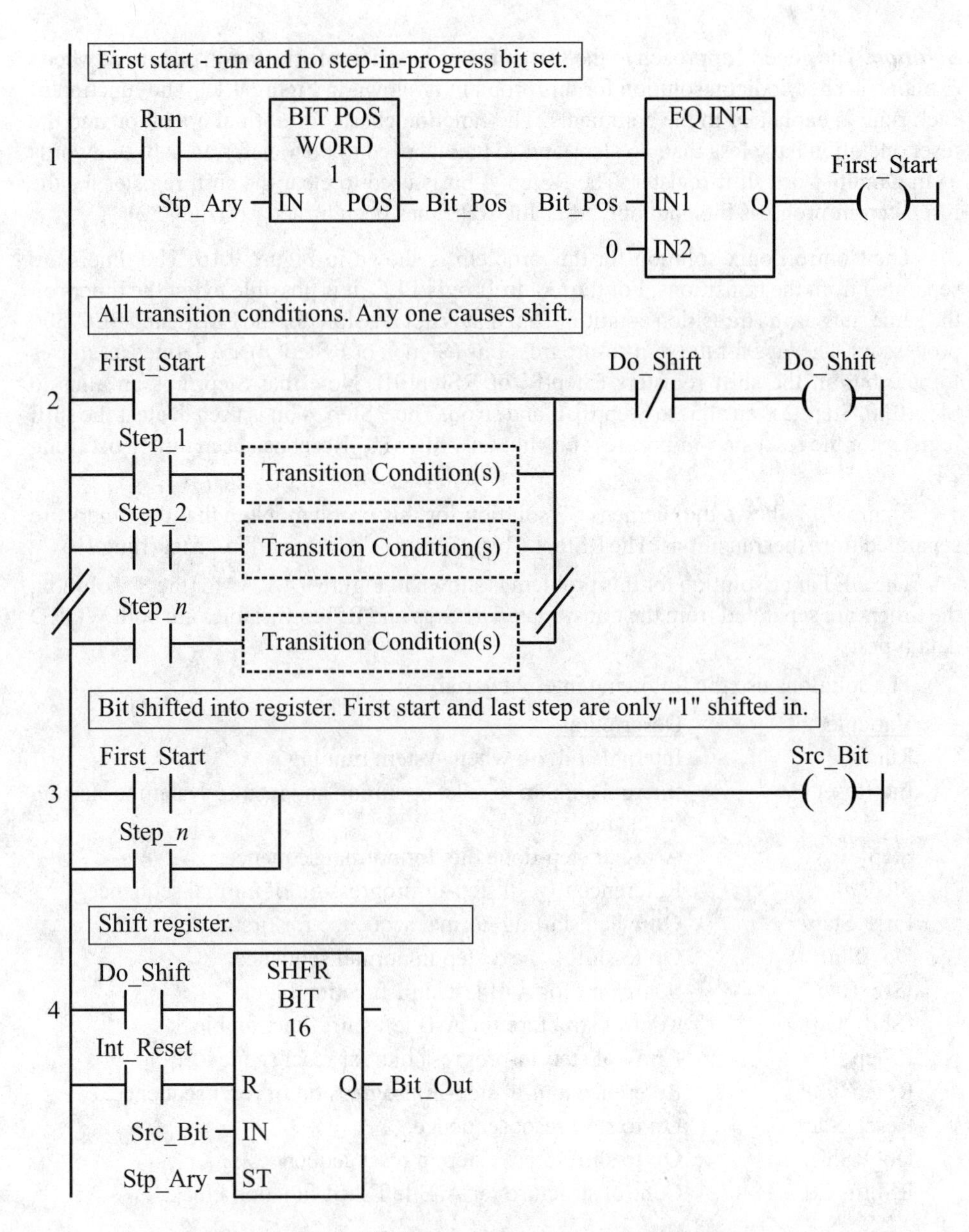

Figure 9.14. GE Fanuc shift register-based sequence.

9.3.6 Example

The shift register-based function chart implementation is illustrated by reworking the previous example. This example includes a function chart for the reset operation and so the interplay between these two function charts can be illustrated.

Example 9.2. Engine Inverter Station Control. Implement the engine inverter control of example 6.4 using the shift register-based approach of this section.

Solution. The general approach to the shift register-based implementation has already been explained. The Modicon solution for this problem is shown in Figure 9.15. The function of each rung is explained in the comments. The function charts for normal operation and the reset operation have less than 16 steps and so no bits need to be transferred between words as in a multi-word shift register. The RStep_4 bit is used to clear the shift register for the reset step-in-progress bits, but only after Int_Reset has been turned off (rung 22).

The ControlLogix solution for this problem is shown in Figure 9.16. The timers are separated from the transitions. For the ControlLogix PLC, it is possible to put the timers on the same rung as the transition condition, but that is not possible for the PLC-5 and SLC-500 processors. The tags for the step-in-progress bits (Step_*n* or RStep_*n*) are defined as aliases for the bits in the shift registers (Step[0] or RStep[0]). Note that Step_1 is an alias to Step[0].0, Step_2 is an alias to Step[0].1, and so on. The RStep_4 bit is used to clear the shift register for the reset step-in-progress bits but only after Int_Reset has been turned off (rung 24).

Figure 9.17 shows the Siemens S7 solution for this problem. Note that the timers are separated from the transitions. The RStep_4 bit is used to clear the shift register (rung 19).

The GE Fanuc solution for this problem is shown in Figure 9.18. As for the S7 solution, the timers are separated from the transitions. The Step and RStep variables are both WORD data types.

The solutions use the following internal variables:

Variable	Description
Run	Internal coil, **on** when system running.
Int_Reset	Internal coil, **on** to reset operation and restore system to starting state.
Step	Array of step-done bits for normal sequence.
Step_*n*	Reference to *n*-th step-in-progress bit of normal sequence.
First_Start	**On** when starting normal sequence for first time.
Do_IShift	**On** to shift to next step in normal sequence.
ISrc_Bit	Source bit for A-B left shift function block.
IShift_Ctl	Control structure for A-B left shift function block.
RStep	Array of step-in-progress bits for reset sequence.
RStep_*n*	Reference to *n*-th step-in-progress bit of reset sequence.
Reset_Start	**On** to start reset sequence.
Do_RShift	**On** to shift to next step in reset sequence.
RShift_Ctl	Control structure for A-B left shift function block.

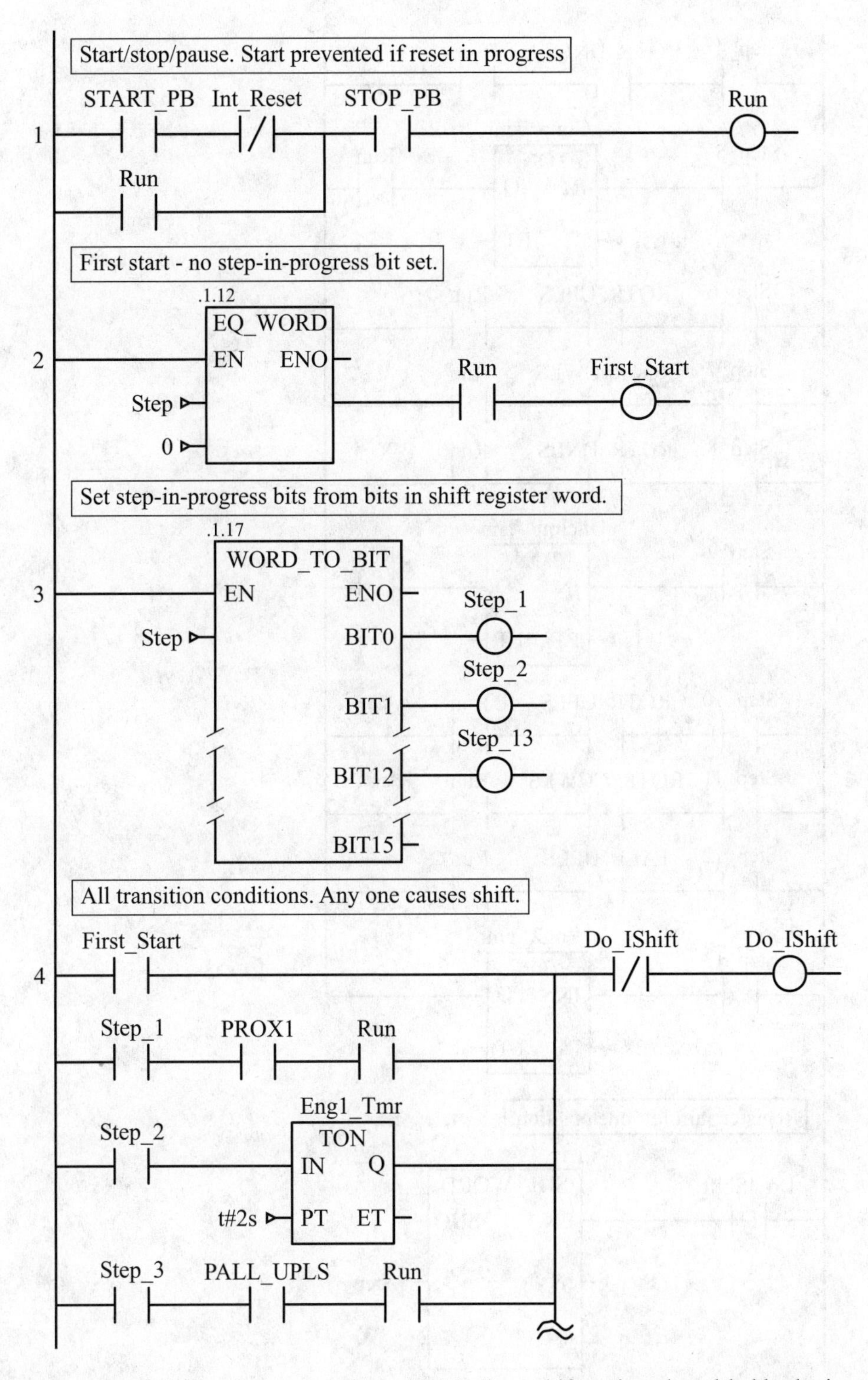

Figure 9.15. Engine inverter station with Modicon shift register-based ladder logic. *(continued)*

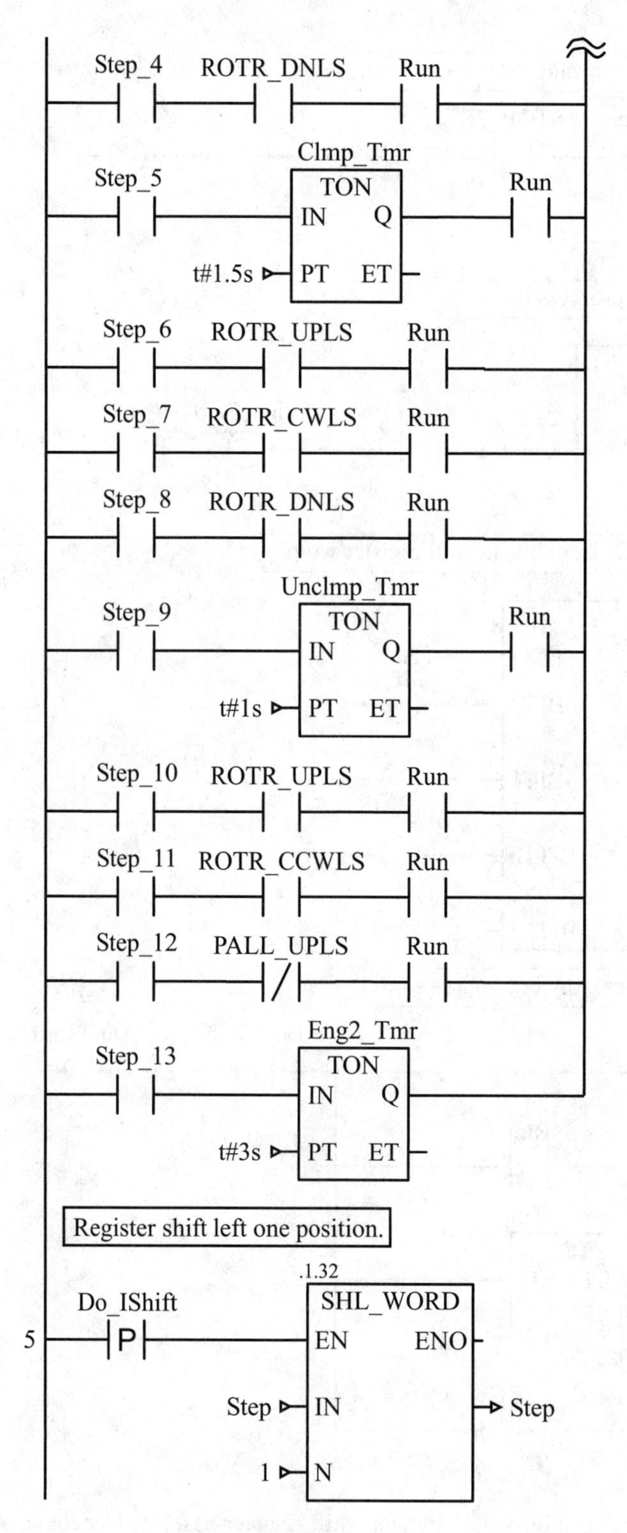

Figure 9.15. *(continued)*

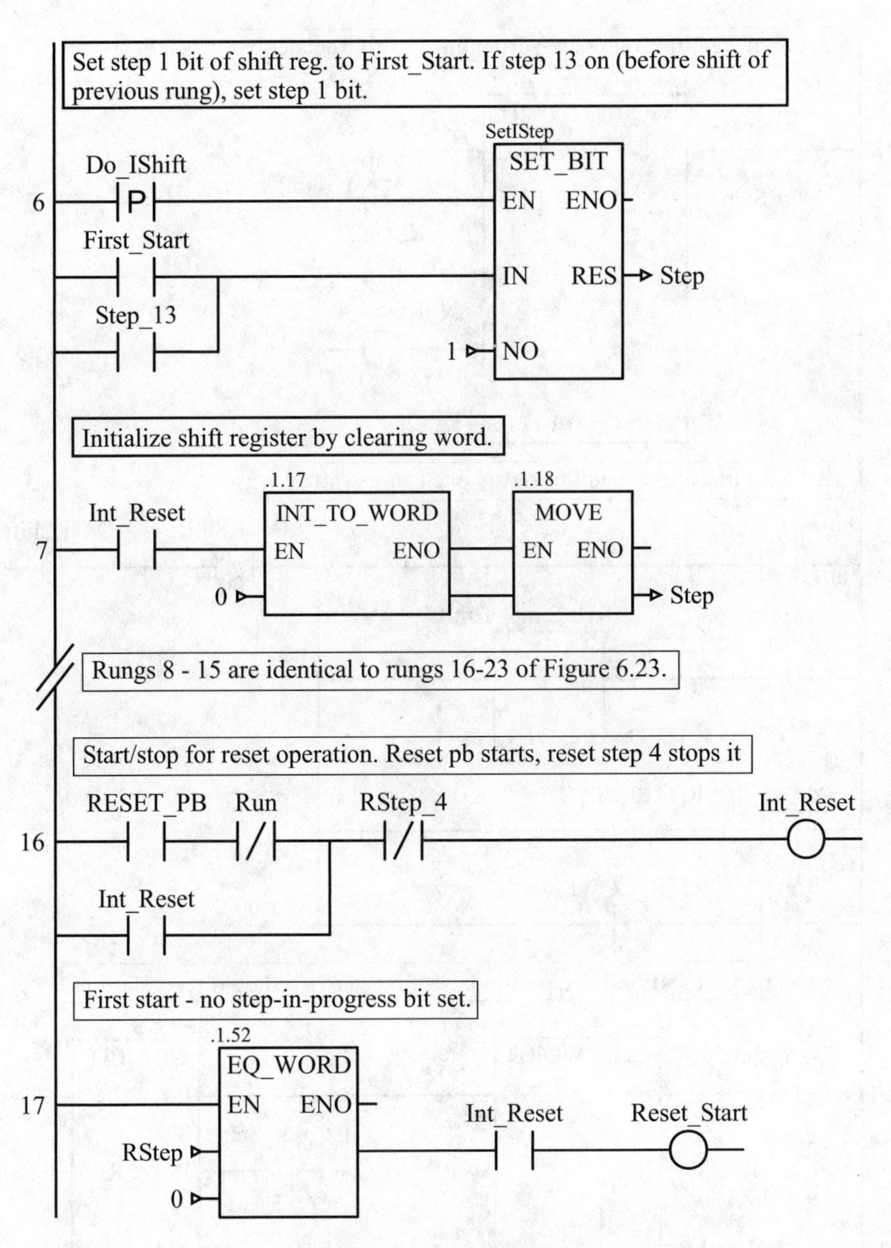

Figure 9.15. *(continued)*

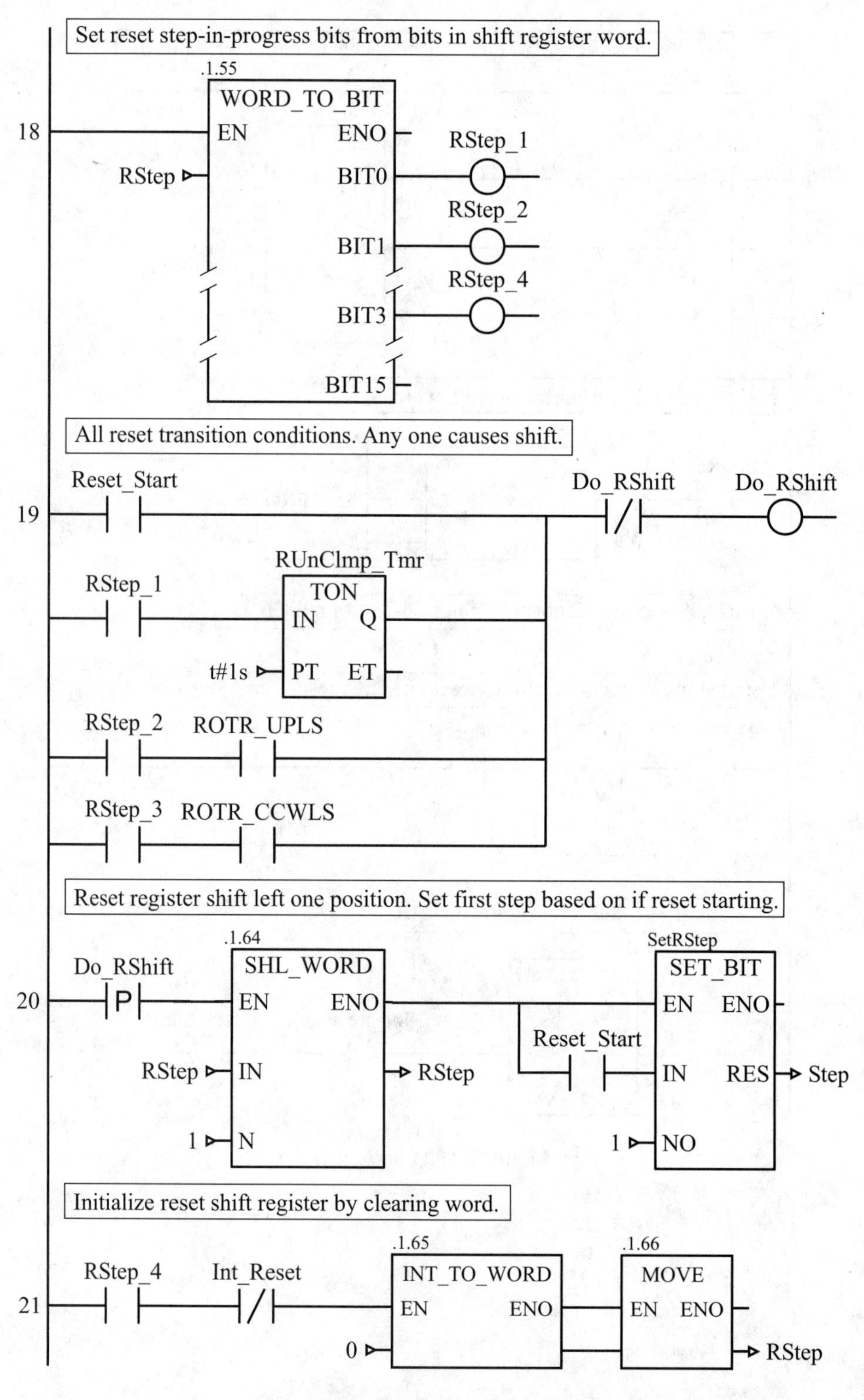

Figure 9.15. *(continued)*

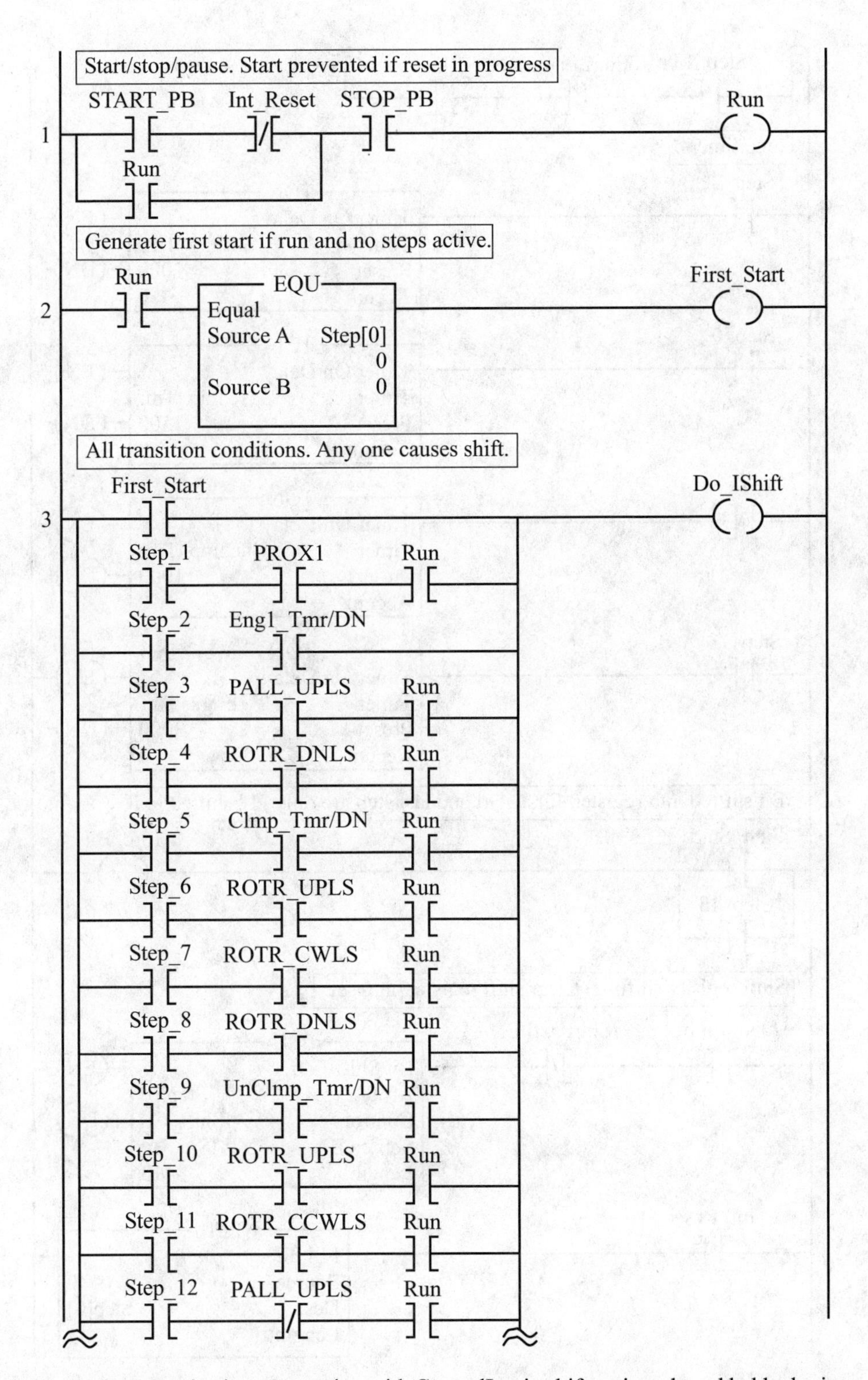

Figure 9.16. Engine inverter station with ControlLogix shift register-based ladder logic. *(continued)*

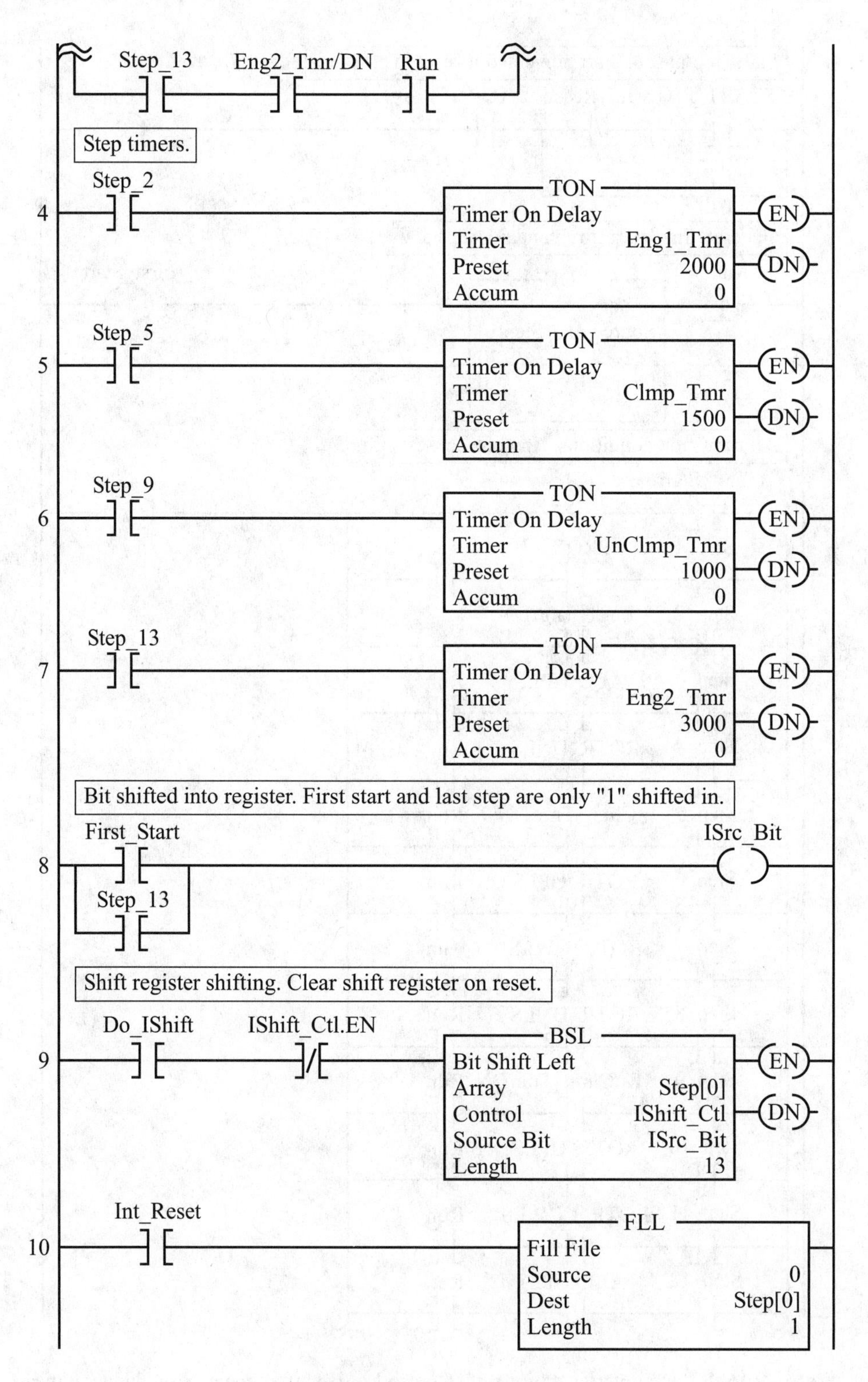

Figure 9.16. *(continued)*

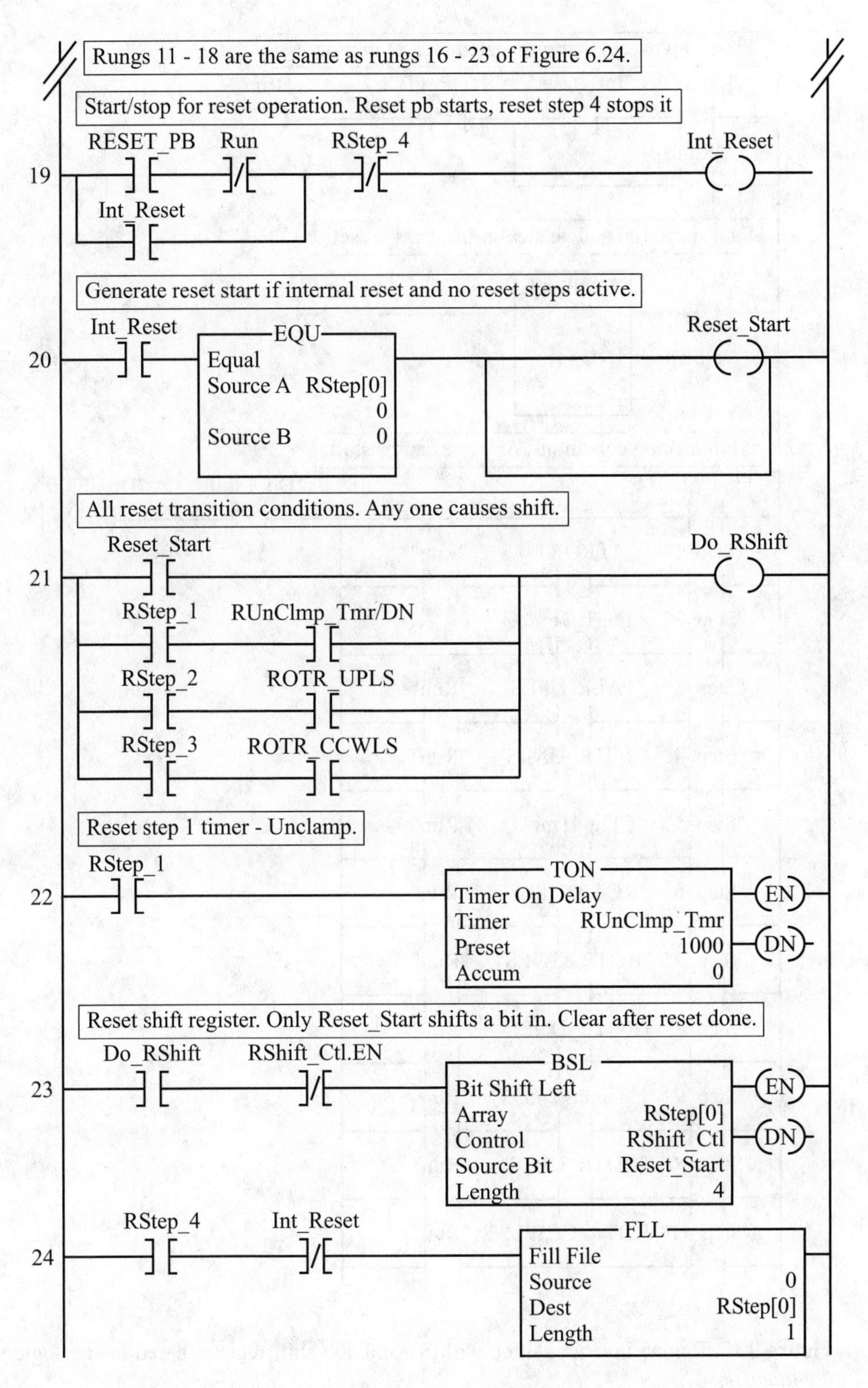

Figure 9.16. *(continued)*

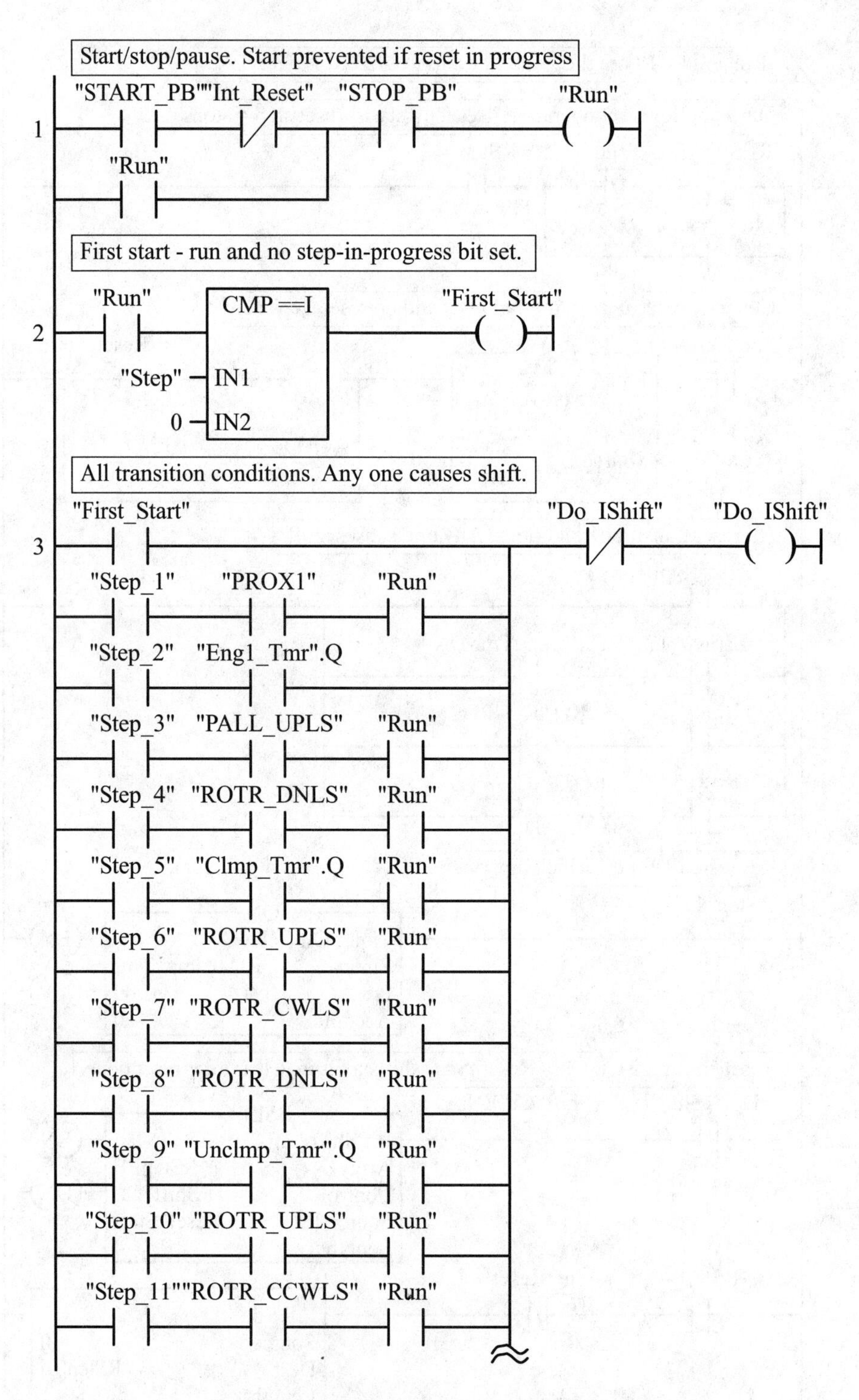

Figure 9.17. Engine inverter station with S7-300/400 shift register-based ladder logic. *(continued)*

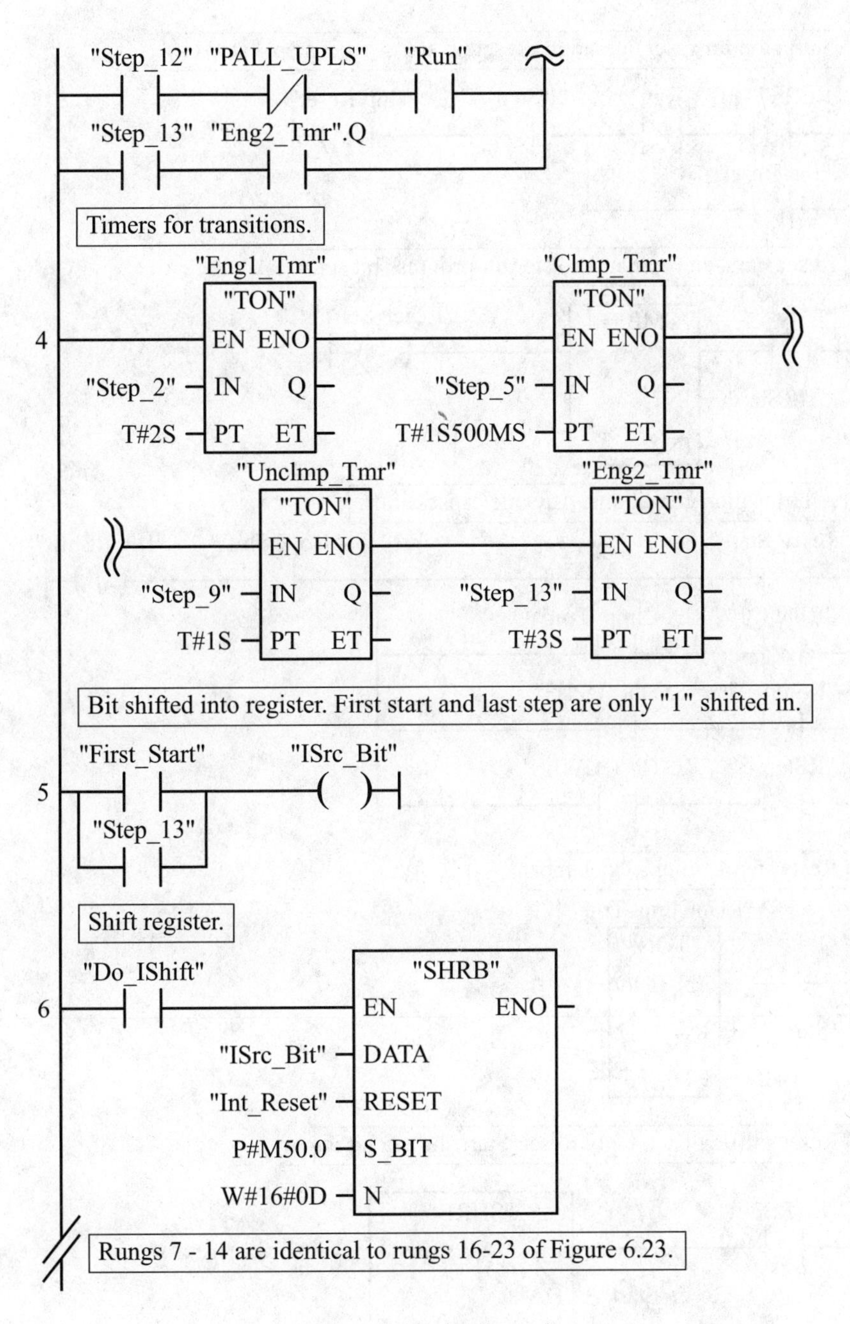

Figure 9.17. *(continued)*

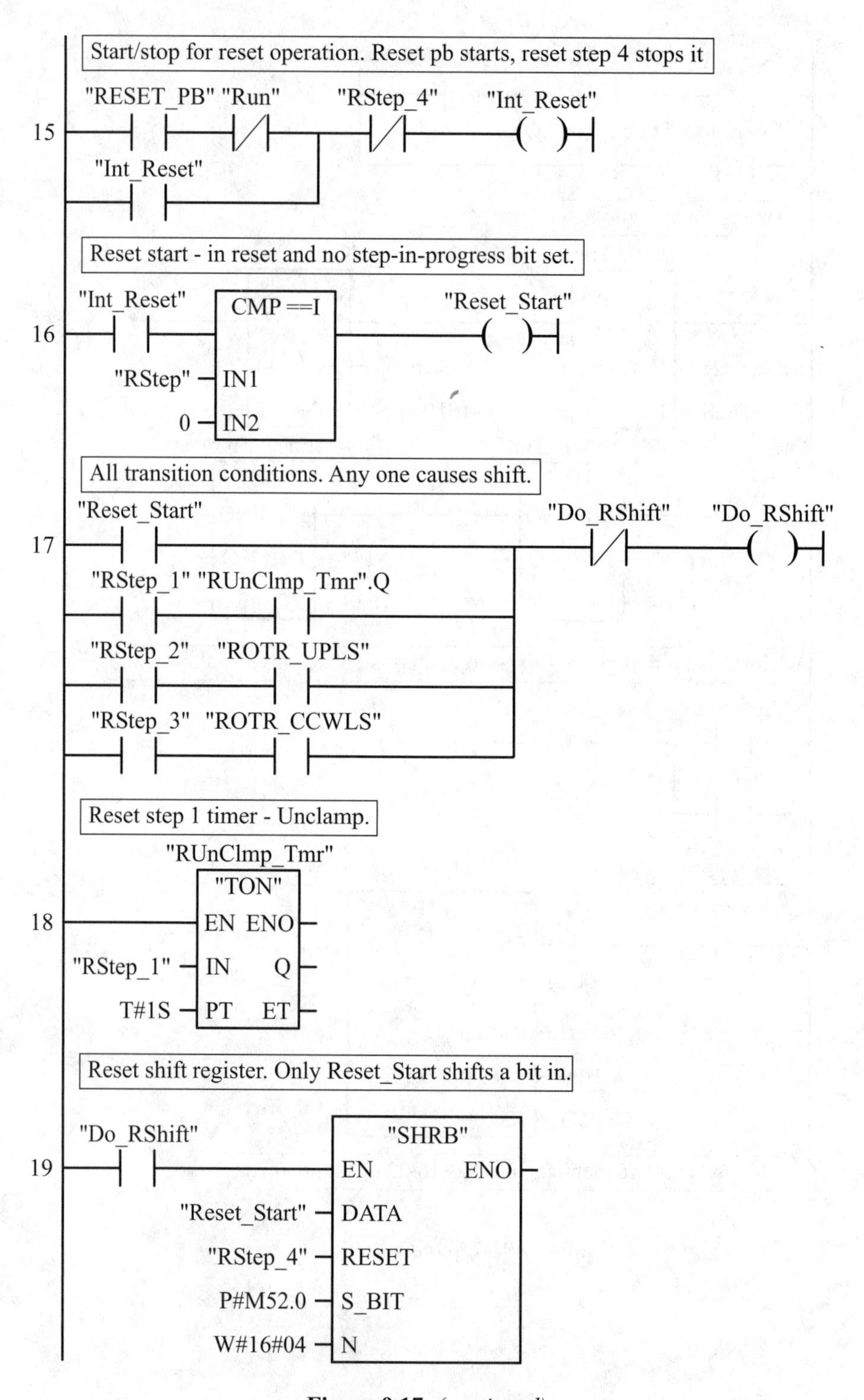

Figure 9.17. *(continued)*

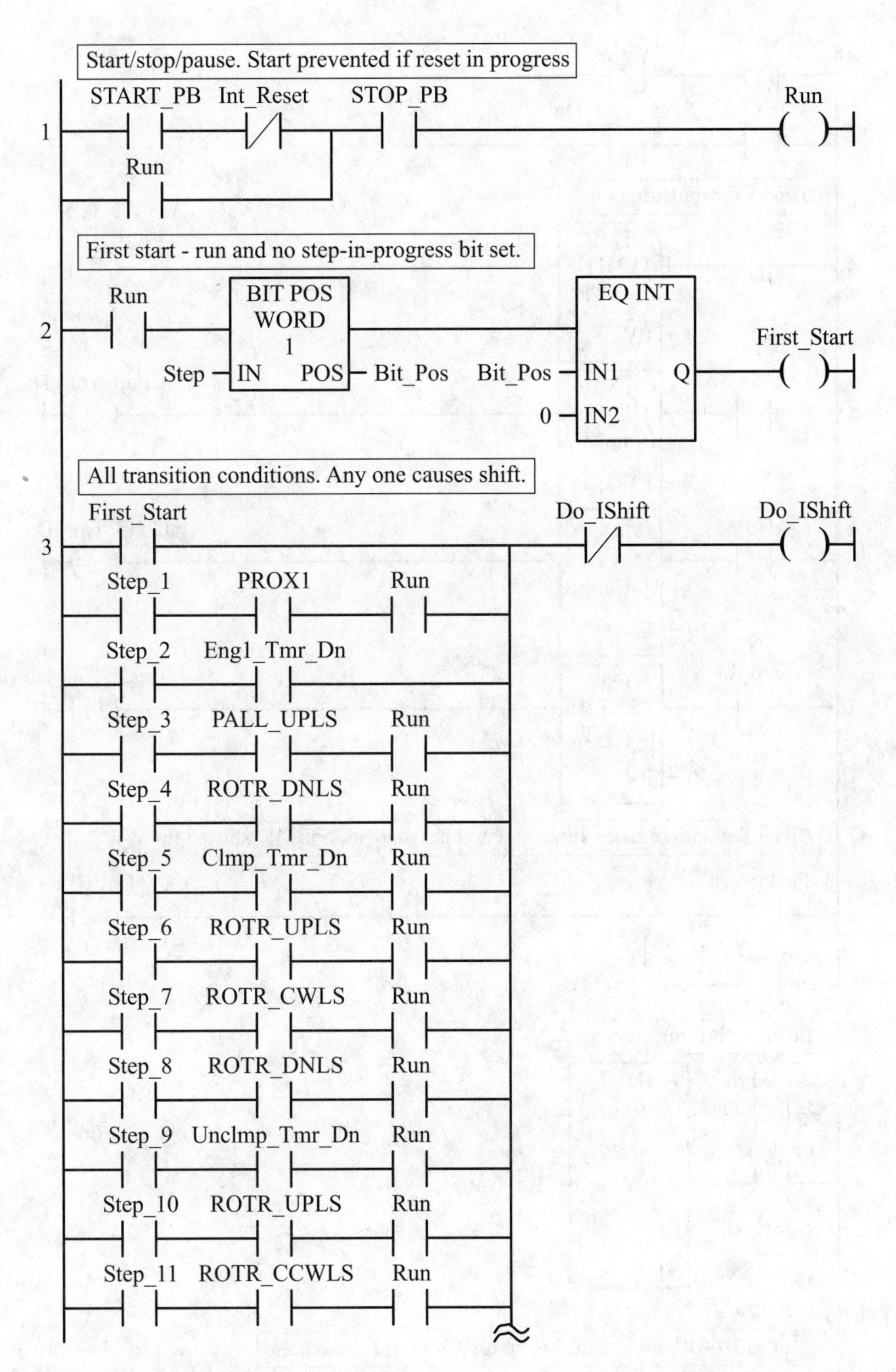

Figure 9.18. Engine inverter station with GE Fanuc shift register-based ladder logic. *(continued)*

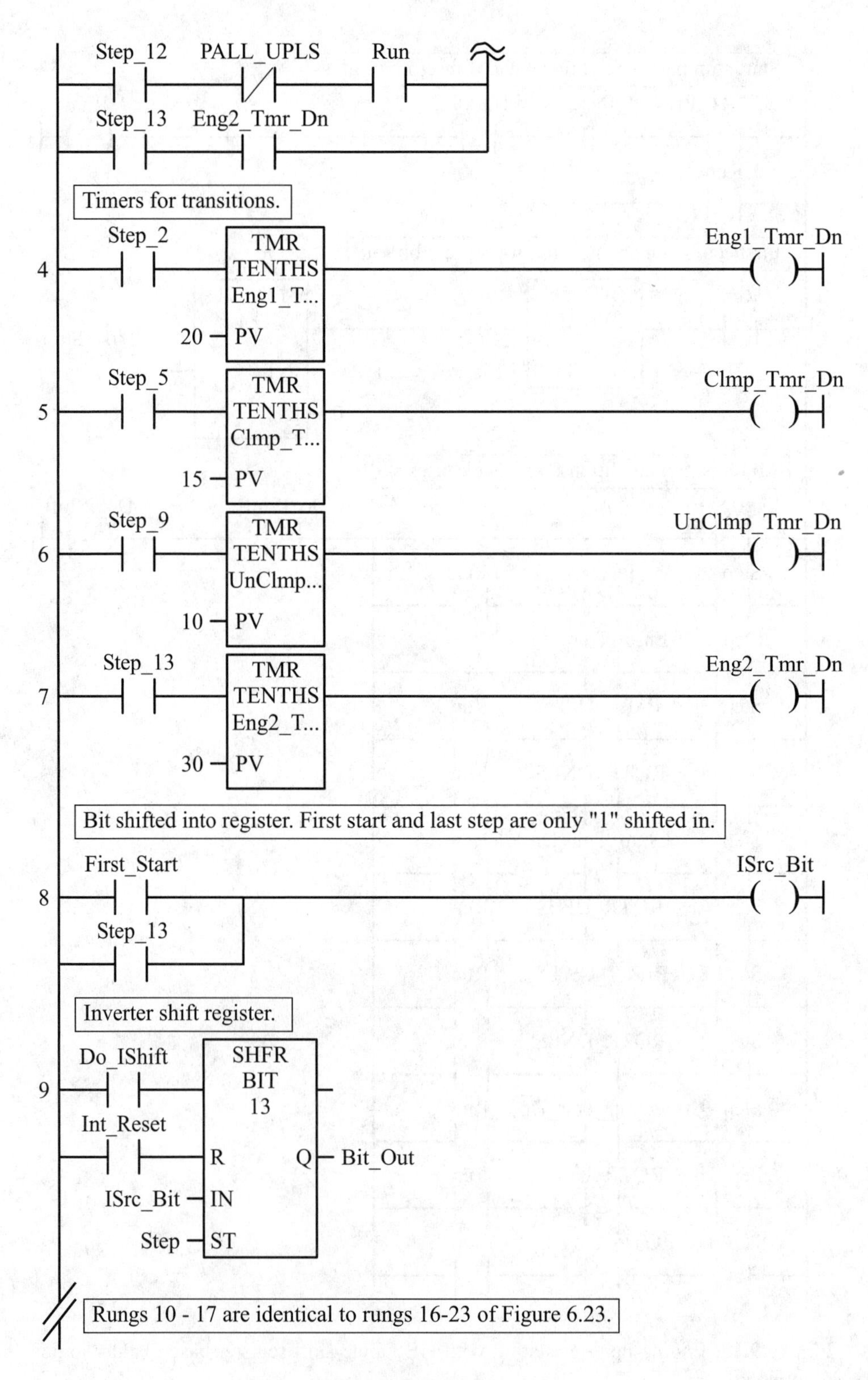

Figure 9.18. *(continued)*

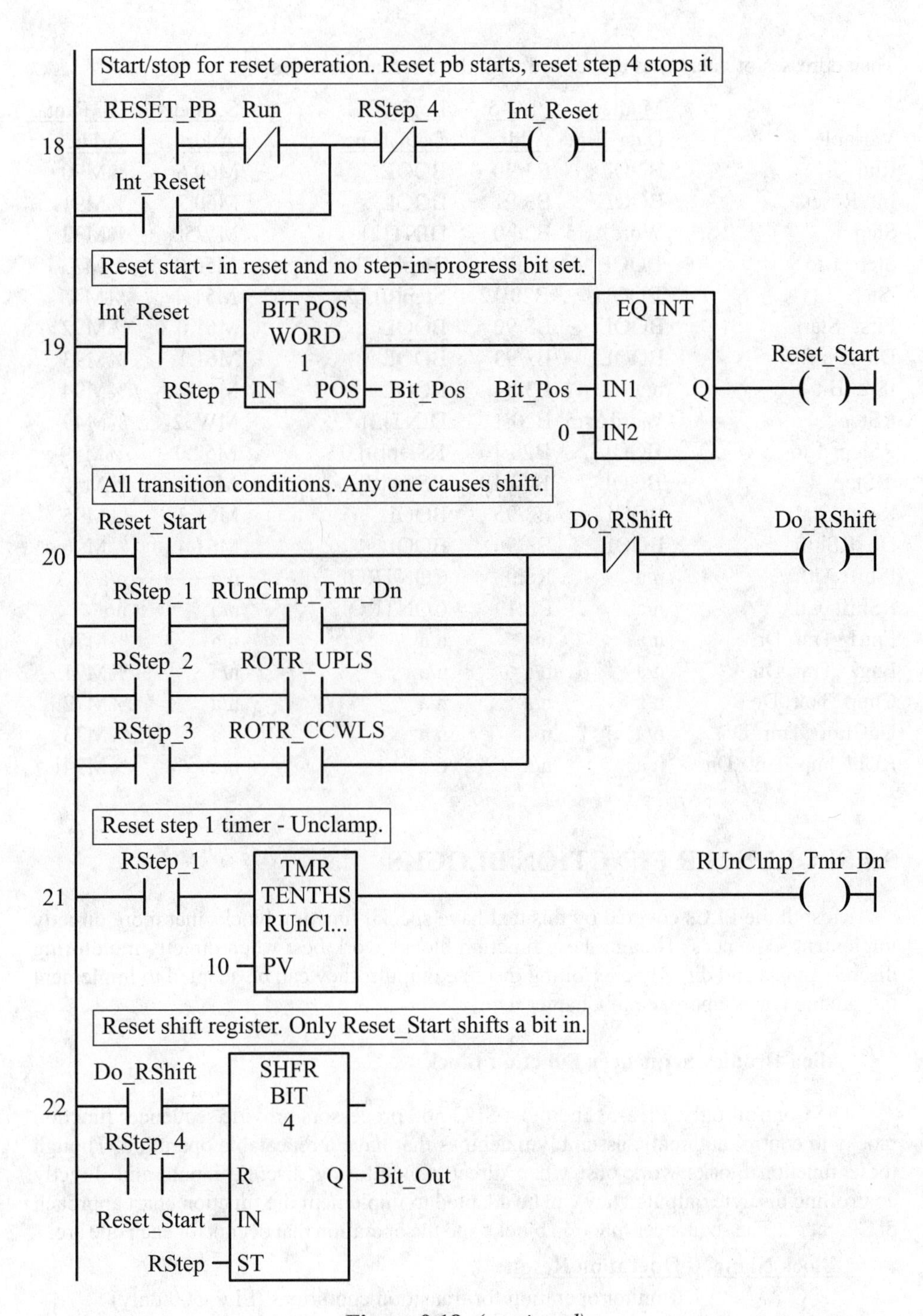

Figure 9.18. *(continued)*

The addresses or data types associated with the internal variables:

Variable	Modicon Data Type	PLC-5 Addr.	Logix Data Type	Siemens Addr.	GE Fanuc Addr.
Run	BOOL	B3/90	BOOL	M60.6	%M90
Int_Reset	BOOL	B3/91	BOOL	M60.7	%M91
Step	WordArr5	B20:0	DINT[2]	MW50	%M33
Step_1 to	BOOL	B20/0	Step[0].0	M50.0	%M33
Step_13	BOOL	B20/12	Step[0].12	M51.4	%M45
First_Start	BOOL	B3/92	BOOL	M61.0	%M92
Do_IShift	BOOL	B3/93	BOOL	M61.1	%M93
ISrc_Bit	n/a	B3/94	BOOL	M61.2	%M94
RStep	WordArr5	B20:1	DINT[2]	MW52	%M49
RStep_1 to	BOOL	B20/16	RStep[0].0	M52.0	%M49
RStep_4	BOOL	B20/19	RStep[0].3	M52.3	%M52
Reset_Start	BOOL	B3/95	BOOL	M61.3	%M95
Do_RShift	BOOL	B3/96	BOOL	M61.4	%M96
IShift_Ctl	n/a	R6:0	CONTROL	n/a	n/a
RShift_Ctl	n/a	R6:1	CONTROL	n/a	n/a
Eng1_Tmr_Dn	n/a	n/a	n/a	n/a	%M70
Eng2_Tmr_Dn	n/a	n/a	n/a	n/a	%M71
Clmp_Tmr_Dn	n/a	n/a	n/a	n/a	%M72
UnClmp_Tmr_Dn	n/a	n/a	n/a	n/a	%M73
RUnClmp_Tmr_Dn	n/a	n/a	n/a	n/a	%M74

9.4 SEQUENCER FUNCTION BLOCKS

Most of the PLCs covered by this text have special function blocks that more directly implement sequences. Though these function blocks work best when directly monitoring discrete inputs and directly controlling discrete outputs, they can be adapted to implement the function chart approach of Chapter 6.

9.4.1 Allen-Bradley Sequencer Function Block

The ControlLogix, PLC-5, and most SLC-500 processors provide sequencer function blocks to control automatic assembly machines that have a repeatable operation. Though these function blocks work best when directly monitoring discrete inputs and directly controlling discrete outputs, they can be adapted to implement the function chart approach of Chapter 6. The sequencer function blocks and the operation that occurs for each one are:

Block Name	Operation Result
SQC	Monitor operation for transition conditions (SLC-500 only)
SQI	Monitor operation for transition conditions (except SLC-500)
SQL	Load reference conditions
SQO	Control outputs

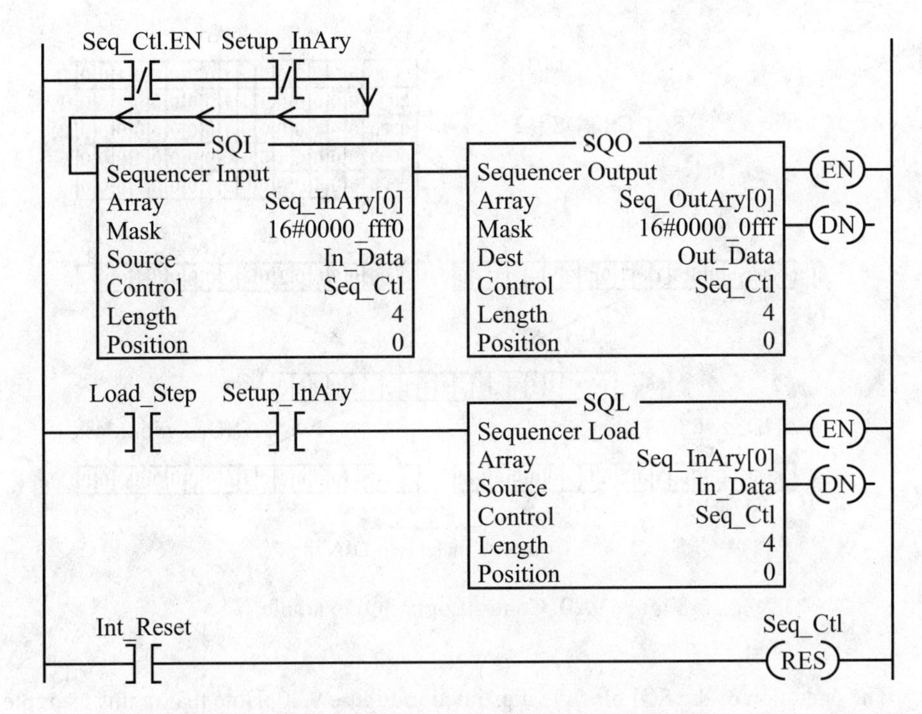

Figure 9.19. ControlLogix sequencer function blocks.

Normally, the SQI (or SQC) and SQO are used together to construct a sequencer. An example application of the SQI, SQO, and SQL blocks for the ControlLogix processor appears in Figure 9.19. The function block operands are described as follows:

Array – First element in the sequencer array, a DINT array data type.

Mask – Bits to block or pass (constant, tag, or tag indexed by .POS)

Source – Input data to be compared with the current sequencer array element (SQI) or loaded into array (SQL).

Dest –Tag where the current sequencer array data will be placed (SQO).

Control – CONTROL structure data type (Figure 8.13).

Length – Number of elements in sequencer array.

Position – Current position in the array.

Normally, the SQI, SQO, and SQL refer to the same "Control" tag. For the control tag defined in Figure 9.19, the individual fields of the CONTROL structure are addressed as follows:

Reference	**Description**
Seq_Ctl.EN	SQO or SQL is enabled
Seq_Ctl.DN	Current position is at last element
Seq_Ctl.ER	Illegal length or position
Seq_Ctl.LEN	Number of steps in sequencer array
Seq_Ctl.POS	Sequencer array element currently being compared (SQI) or being copied (SQO and SQL)

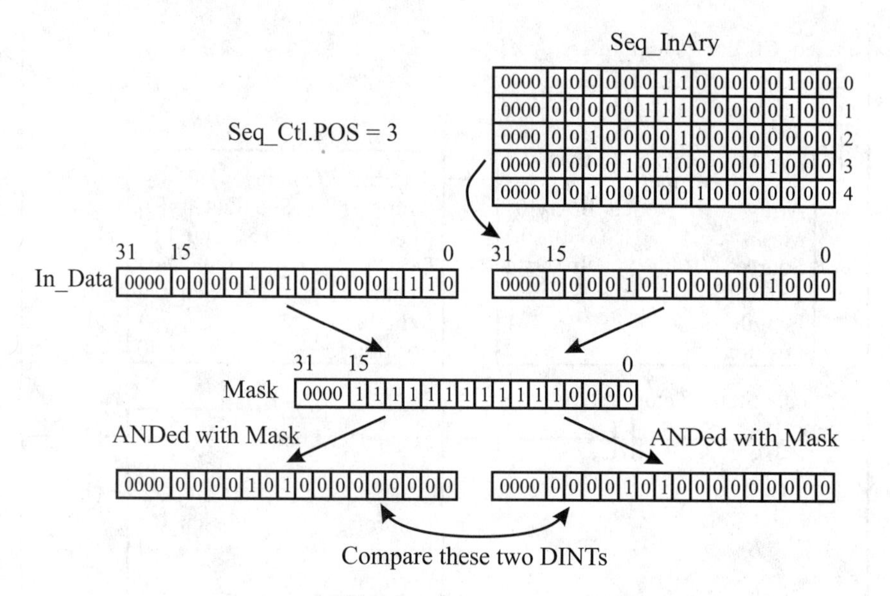

Figure 9.20. ControlLogix SQI example.

The operation of the SQI block is illustrated in Figure 9.20. Note that in this example the upper 16 bits of all DINTs are zero. When the input to the SQI block is enabled, the current value of the "Source" is compared to the value of the current array element (.POS). Like the MEQ (masked equal) block, the "Source" value and the array element are logically ANDed with the "Mask" before being compared. If these values are equal, the output of the function block is true (**on**). For the example shown in Figure 9.20, the comparison is true. If the .POS value is used as an array index for the "Mask" operand, a different mask can be defined for each step in the sequence. The RES output coil is used to reset the .POS value to zero.

Normally, the output of the SQI block is connected to the input of an SQO block. Figure 9.21 shows the operation of the SQO block. When the SQO block is scanned, the array element at the .POS index is copied to the "Dest" tag. When the input of the SQO block transitions from **off**-to-**on**, the .POS value is incremented, and then the new array element is copied to the "Dest" tag. As long as the input to the SQO block is **on**, the array element at the .POS index is copied to the "Dest" tag. If the .POS value is larger than the length of the array, .POS is set to one. The Seq_Ctl.EN normally-closed contact at the beginning of the first rung in Figure 9.19 ensures that the sequence properly increments when the transition conditions are already satisfied when the step is entered.

Normally, the data in the files used by the SQI and SQO blocks are loaded as part of the ladder logic programming. However, the SQL function block provides a alternate way to load the reference array. When the SQL input transitions from **off**-to-**on**, the .POS value is incremented and the "Source" value is loaded into that index in the array. As long as the input remains **on**, the "Source" is loaded into the current array position. One steps the machine through its normal operation, pulsing the SQL input when each transition condition is established. The SQL block in Figure 9.19 loads data into the Seq_InAry array. When Setup_InAry is **on**, each **off**-to-**on** transition of Load_Step copies the contents of

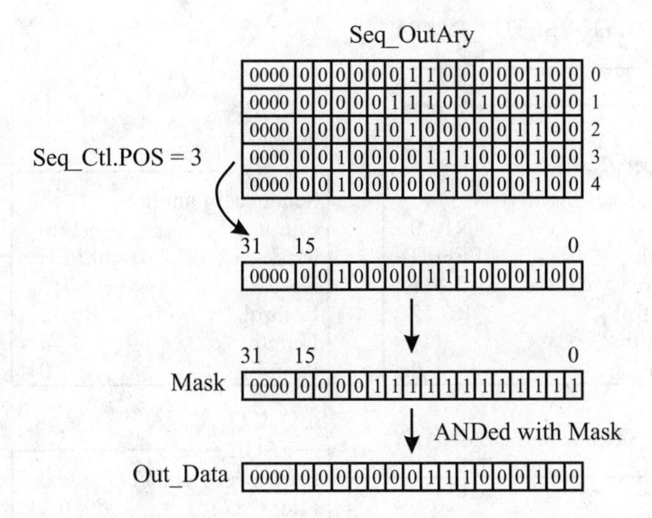

Figure 9.21. ControlLogix SQO example.

In_Data to the current position in Seq_InAry. In order to load Seq_InAry, one does the following:

1. Turn **on** Setup_InAry.
2. Turn **on** Load_Step.
3. Pulse Int_Reset **on** to reset the sequencer position.
4. Set the PLC physical inputs to the condition that should cause a transition out the initial (.POS=0) step.
5. Pulse Load_Step **off**.
   Repeat steps 4 and 5 as necessary to load Seq_InAry.
6. Turn **off** Setup_InAry.
7. Turn **off** Load_Step.

The arrays for these sequencer function blocks are all DINTs (32 bits). The SQI blocks may be connected in series to handle multiples of 32 discrete inputs. Similarly, place SQO blocks in parallel to handle more than 32 discrete outputs. When using multiple SQI blocks in this fashion, all SQI blocks must refer to the same "Control" tag. When using multiple SQO blocks in this fashion, only the first SQO block should have the same "Control" tag as the "Control" tag for the SQI(s).

The PLC-5 sequencer function blocks are shown in Figure 9.22. These blocks are very similar to the ControlLogix function blocks except that the "File" operand is the starting address of a word or integer array and is prefixed by a "#" character. In addition, the PLC-5 blocks operate on 16 bits at a time.

The SLC-500 sequencer function blocks are shown in Figure 9.23. The SQL block is not available for the SLC-5/01. The SQC block operates quite differently from the PLC-5 SQL function block, though both of them compare the "Source" to the current index of the array starting at the "File" address. When the comparison for the SQC block is true, the .POS value is incremented, and the .FD bit is turned **on**. This .FD bit is then used to drive the SQO function block. Note that the "Control" address must not be shared by the SQC and

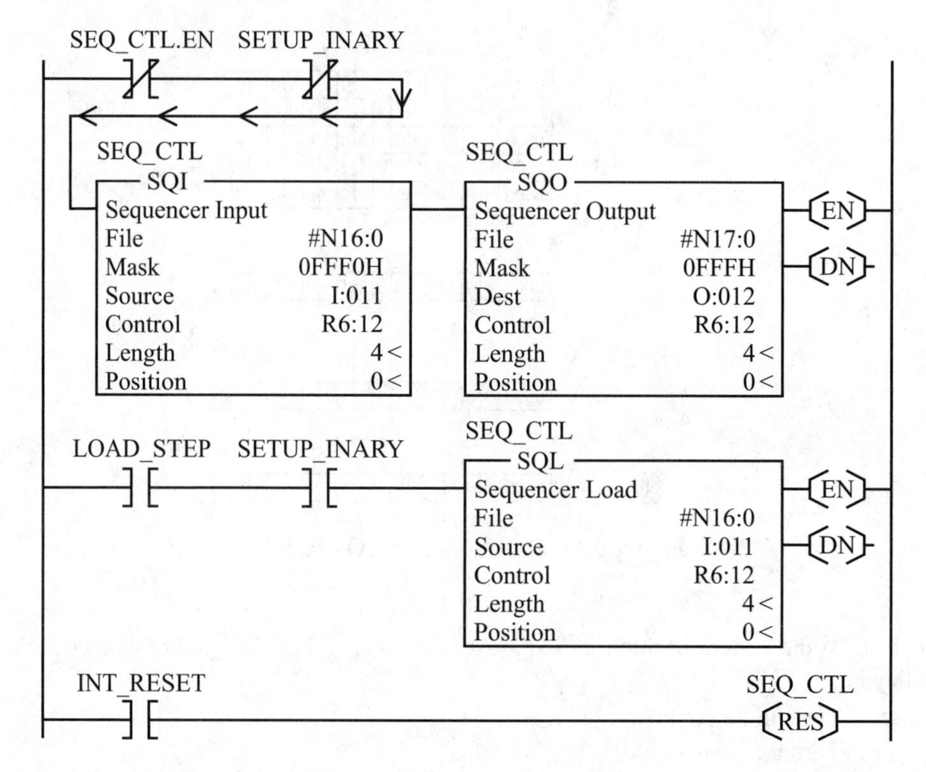

Figure 9.22. PLC-5 sequencer function blocks.

SQO blocks. The SLC-500 SQO and SQL function blocks operate in the same manner as the PLC-5 SQO and SQL blocks.

The sequencer function blocks are basically intended to directly read discrete inputs and directly control discrete outputs. Internal coils, timers, counters, and arithmetic comparisons are not handled directly by the sequencer. Also, the sequencer cannot selectively turn off certain outputs when paused. Thus, implementing a function chart is not always an easy task. Instead, all of these internal details must be "mapped" to the "Source" and "Dest" tags. Each physical input, timer/counter done-bit, and comparison result that is a transition condition must be copied to a bit in In_Data. Also, the Out_Data bits must be copied to the physical outputs and timer/counter inputs, if used. Finally, the value of each element of the input array, mask array, and output array must be specified. Normally, the mask is different for each step.

9.4.2 S7-300/400 DRUM Function Block

The S7-300/400 DRUM function block implements an electromechanical drum sequencer (Figure 1.8) with up to 16 steps and 16 outputs. The drum advances its step based on an event and/or a programmed time. Figure 9.24 shows a typical sequencer implemented with a DRUM block. The inputs of the DRUM block are described as follows:

RESET – Reset. **On** to reset step to Preset Step (DSP) stored in drum instance data block and copy the appropriate bit pattern to the outputs.

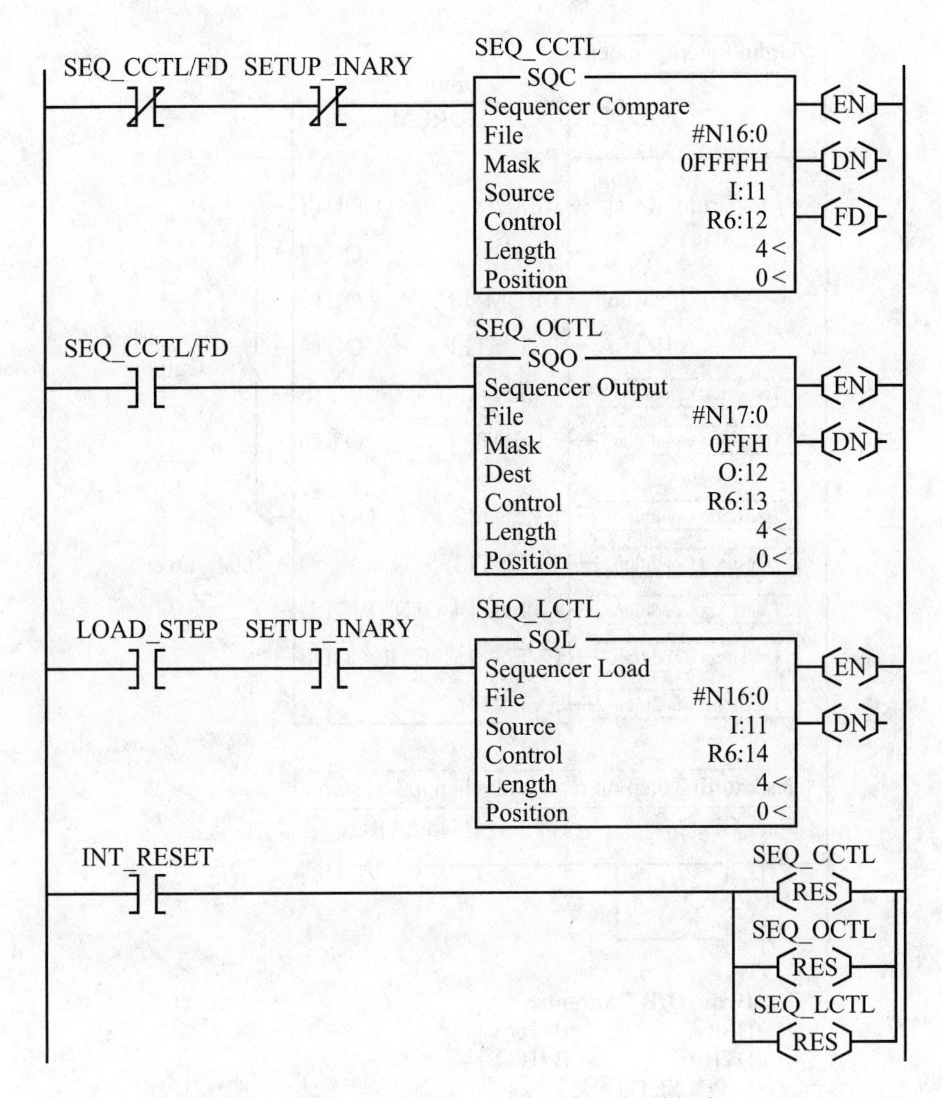

Figure 9.23. SLC-500 sequencer function blocks.

JOG – Jog. **Off**-to-**on** transition increments to next step.

DRUM_EN – Drum enable. When **on**, the drum advances to the next step based on the timing and event criteria.

LST_STEP – Last step. Number of last step (a BYTE).

EVENTi – Event for i-th step. When **on** and at end of defined timing interval, the drum advances to the next step.

The outputs of the DRUM block are described as follows:

OUTi – Step output bits. The 16 bits for the current step are conditioned by the mask (S_MASK) and transferred to these outputs.

Q – Last step. Output is **on** when the drum is in the last step (LST_STEP).

OUT_WORD – Sixteen outputs combined into a WORD.

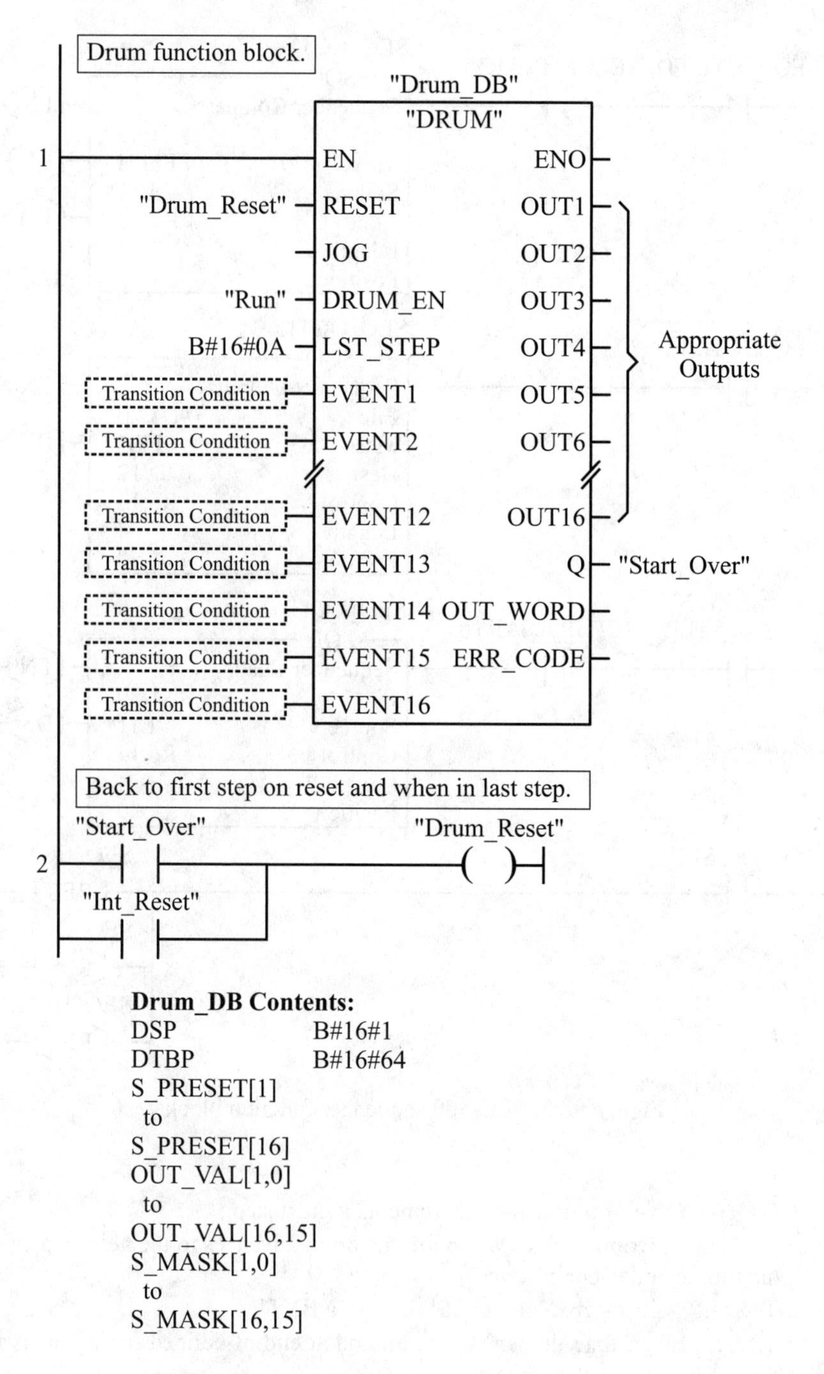

Drum_DB Contents:
DSP B#16#1
DTBP B#16#64
S_PRESET[1]
to
S_PRESET[16]
OUT_VAL[1,0]
to
OUT_VAL[16,15]
S_MASK[1,0]
to
S_MASK[16,15]

Figure 9.24. Sequencer using S7 DRUM function block

ERR_CODE – Error code. A non-zero value indicates an error when executing the block.

The drum instance data block contains further configuration information including:

DSP – Preset step. When the drum is reset, it goes to this step number.

DSC – Current step

DTBP – Time base preset. The time base for all step timers, in milliseconds.

S_PRESET[*i*] – Step preset time for the *i*-th step. The actual time, in milliseconds, is this value multiplied by DTBP.

OUT_VAL[*i,j*] – Bit for *j+1*-st output of the *i*-th step. A TRUE value means this output will be set and a FALSE value means this output will be cleared (assuming S_MASK[*i,j*] is TRUE).

S_MASK[*i,j*] – Mask bit for *j+1*-st output of the *i*-th step. A TRUE value means OUT_VAL[*i,j*] is copied to the appropriate output. A FALSE value means the *j+1*-st output is not changed.

In operation, the DRUM block drives output bits (OUT1 to OUT16) with the OUT_VAL of the current step conditioned by the step S_MASK while the DRUM is at that step. The DRUM advances to the next step when either the event for the step is true and the programmed time for the current step has expired, or the JOG input transitions from **off**-to-**on**. The step preset time, in milliseconds, is the S_PRESET for that step multiplied by the time base preset (DTBP). A particular step may be programmed with an event, a time interval, or both an event and a time interval. If a step has a zero preset time, then the drum advances to the next step when the event input turns **on**. If the event input is unconnected, then the drum advances when the preset time expires. If a step has both an event connected and a nonzero preset time, the time interval starts only when the event input turns **on**.

If "Run" is a transition for all steps, that is handled by the "Run" condition on the DRUM_EN input. If some steps must transition even when paused, then the DRUM_EN input must be always connected to a Boolean that is always **on** and "Run" will appear as part of the appropriate transition conditions. Also note that the initial step is step 1 and the first start of the sequence is handled as a transition condition of "Run" out of step 1.

When the drum step number is the same as the last step (LST_STEP) and that step time has expired, the Q output is turned **on**. Once Q is turned **on**, it remains **on** until the drum is reset. In Figure 9.24, the Q output is used to reset the drum back to the first step.

The OUT_WORD output has all 16 output bits packed into one word. The OUT1 output bit corresponds to the least-significant bit of the OUT_WORD word output and OUT16 corresponds with the most-significant bit of OUT_WORD.

The configurable mask (S_MASK) allows the selection of the individual output bits (OUT1 to OUT16) to be set/reset by the output values (OUT_VAL). When S_MASK[*i,j*] is true, OUT_VAL[*i,j*] is copied to the *j+1*-st output during the *i*-th step. When S_MASK[*i,j*] is false, the *j+1*-st output is not changed when entering the *i*-th step. Figure 9.25 shows the operation of the DRUM block OUT_VAL and S_MASK arrays in determining the OUT*i* outputs. Note that bits 12 – 15 of the mask for step 4 are cleared, meaning that OUT13 – OUT16 are not modified during step 4. They keep the values determined at step 3.

It is possible to extend the DRUM blocks to handle more than 16 outputs and/or 16 steps. To handle more than 16 outputs, use multiple DRUM blocks with identical inputs and identical S_PRESET arrays. To handle more than 16 steps, the Q output of the DRUM

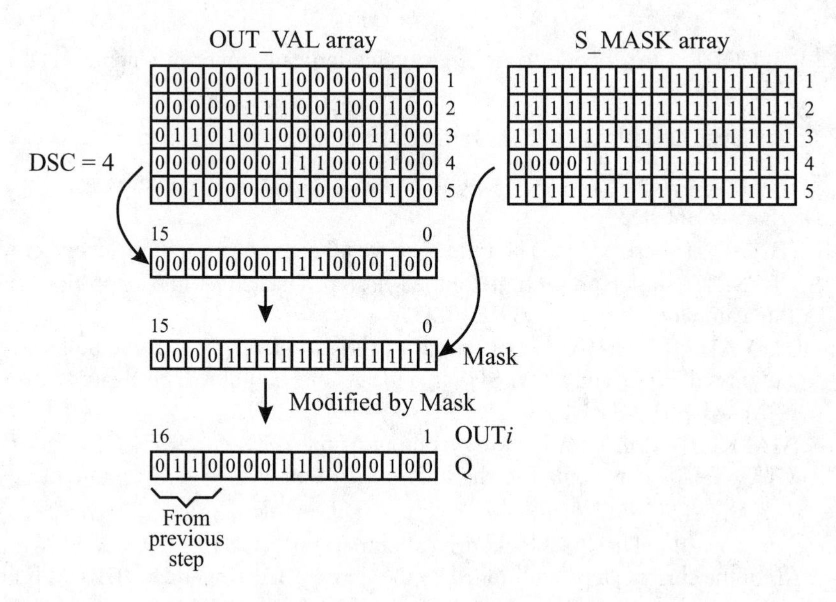

Figure 9.25. Operation of S7 DRUM outputs.

handling the first 16 steps controls the EN input of the DRUM handling the next 16 steps. The individual DRUM OUT*i*'s must be logically or'd to control the actual outputs.

The S7-200 processors have a set of sequential relay instructions that can be used to implement sequential operations. These instructions are discussed in Siemens (2000a).

9.4.3 GE Fanuc DRUM Function Block

Like the S7 DRUM function block, the GE Fanuc DRUM block implements an electromechanical drum sequencer (Figure 1.8) with up to 256 steps and 16 outputs. The inputs of the DRUM block (Figure 9.26) are described as follows:

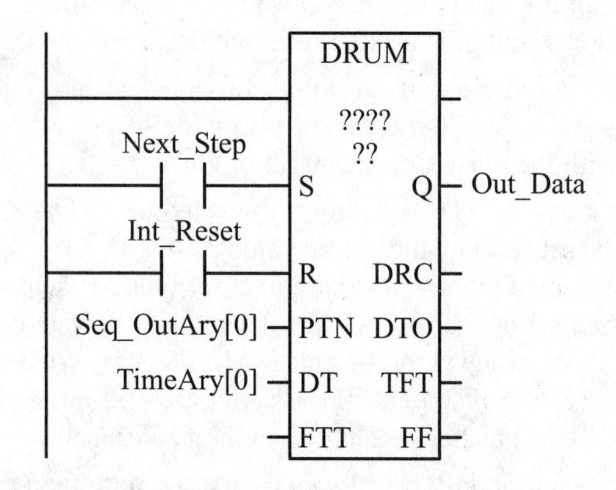

Figure 9.26. GE Fanuc DRUM function block.

S – Step. **Off**-to-**on** transition increments to next step.

R – Reset. **On** to reset step to the Preset Step stored in the drum control array and copy its bit pattern to Q.

PTN – Pattern array. Symbol/address of the first element of the pattern array (WORD array). The array must be as long as the number of steps in the sequence. Each pattern word is the desired combination of outputs for a particular step. The first pattern is for the first step.

DT – Dwell time array. Symbol/address of the first element of a dwell time array (WORD array). The array must be as long as the number of steps in the sequence. Each element is the dwell time for the corresponding step, in 0.1 second units. If a dwell time is specified for a step, the drum cannot advance to the next step until the dwell time has expired. When the dwell time expires for a given step, the DTO output bit is turned **on**. The input is optional. If the DT input is used, the DTO output must be connected.

FTT – Fault timeout array. Symbol/address of the first element of a fault time array (WORD array). The array must be as long as the number of steps in the sequence. Each element is the fault time for the corresponding step, in 0.1 second units. If the drum is in a given step when the fault time expires for that step, the TFT output bit is turned **on**. The input is optional. If the FTT input is used, the TFT output must be connected.

The outputs of the DRUM block are described as follows:

Q – Step outputs. The 16-bit pattern for the current step is transferred to the 16 bits starting with this symbol/address (a WORD). The address is normally in the %M or %Q memory areas.

DRC – Drum coil. **On** whenever the top input is **on** and the current step is not equal to the preset step.

DTO – Dwell timeout output. **On** when the dwell time has expired for the current step. If the DTO output is used, the DT input must be connected.

TFT – Timeout fault output. **On** when the drum has been in the current step longer than its fault timeout time. If the TFT output is used, the FTT input must be connected.

FF – First Follower. The starting symbol/address of a BYTE array that is long enough to hold the number of bits equal to the number of steps in the sequence. Each bit in the bytes is a step-in-progress bit. The first bit is the step-in-progress bit of the first step. If this address is in the %M memory area, the step-in-progress bits can be accessed as Booleans. This output is optional.

The "????" field is the symbol or address of the start of five consecutive register addresses to store the drum control information. As for the timers and counters, only the symbol or register address of the first word is specified as part of the function block. The other register addresses are assumed. The five words of the drum control information are:

Reference	**Description of Register**
Sym[0]	Current step number
Sym[1]	Preset step number
Sym[2]	Step control (do not modify this register)
Sym[3]	Step timer (do not modify this register)
Sym[4]	Step timer (do not modify this register)

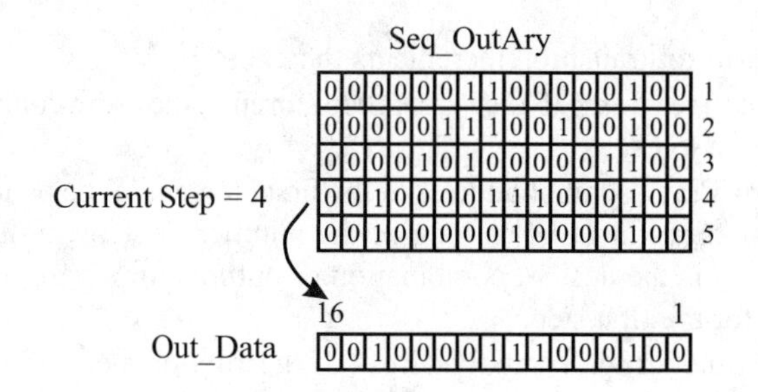

Figure 9.27. Operation of GE Fanuc DRUM outputs.

assuming “Sym” is in the “????” field. The maximum step number is placed in the “??” field. There can be up to 256 steps.

The preset step number and current step number in the drum control must be properly initialized before the DRUM can be executed (must be between 1 and the maximum step number). The preset step must be initialized, even if not utilized.

The DRUM block operates in the following manner. When R is **on**, the active step is set to the preset step number. The R input overrides the S input. When top input is **on**, the 16-bit pattern of the current step is copied to the Q output. When R is **off**, and there is an **off**-to-**on** transition at the S input, the step number is incremented and the 16-bit pattern of the new step is copied to the Q output. When the step number changes, both the DTO and TFT outputs are initially **off**.

Figure 9.27 shows the operation of the DRUM block Q output. When the top input is **on**, the current step is used as an index into the PTN array. The array element at the current index is copied to the Q output. When the S input of the DRUM block transitions from **off**-to-**on**, the current step is incremented, and then the new array element is copied to the Q output.

A sequencer constructed with DRUM block is shown in Figure 9.28. The Stp_Ary connected to the FF output is also mapped to the step-in-progress bits. Like the shift register implementation, all of the transition conditions are connected in parallel to cause the drum to advance to the next step. For those steps that are strictly timed, the dwell-time array is used for timing. Therefore, only the step-in-progress bit appears in these transition conditions and the actual transition is handled by the Dwell_Done (DTO output). If “Run” is a transition for all steps, that is handled by the “Run” condition on the top input of the DRUM block. If some steps must transition even when paused, then the top input to the DRUM must be always connected to the power rail and “Run” will appear as part of the appropriate transition conditions. Also note that the initial step is step 1 and the first start of the sequence is handled as a transition condition of “Run” out of step 1.

To handle more than 16 outputs, use multiple DRUM blocks with identical S and R inputs. Only one of the DRUM blocks needs to use the DT and FTT inputs and the DRC, DTO, TFT, and FF outputs.

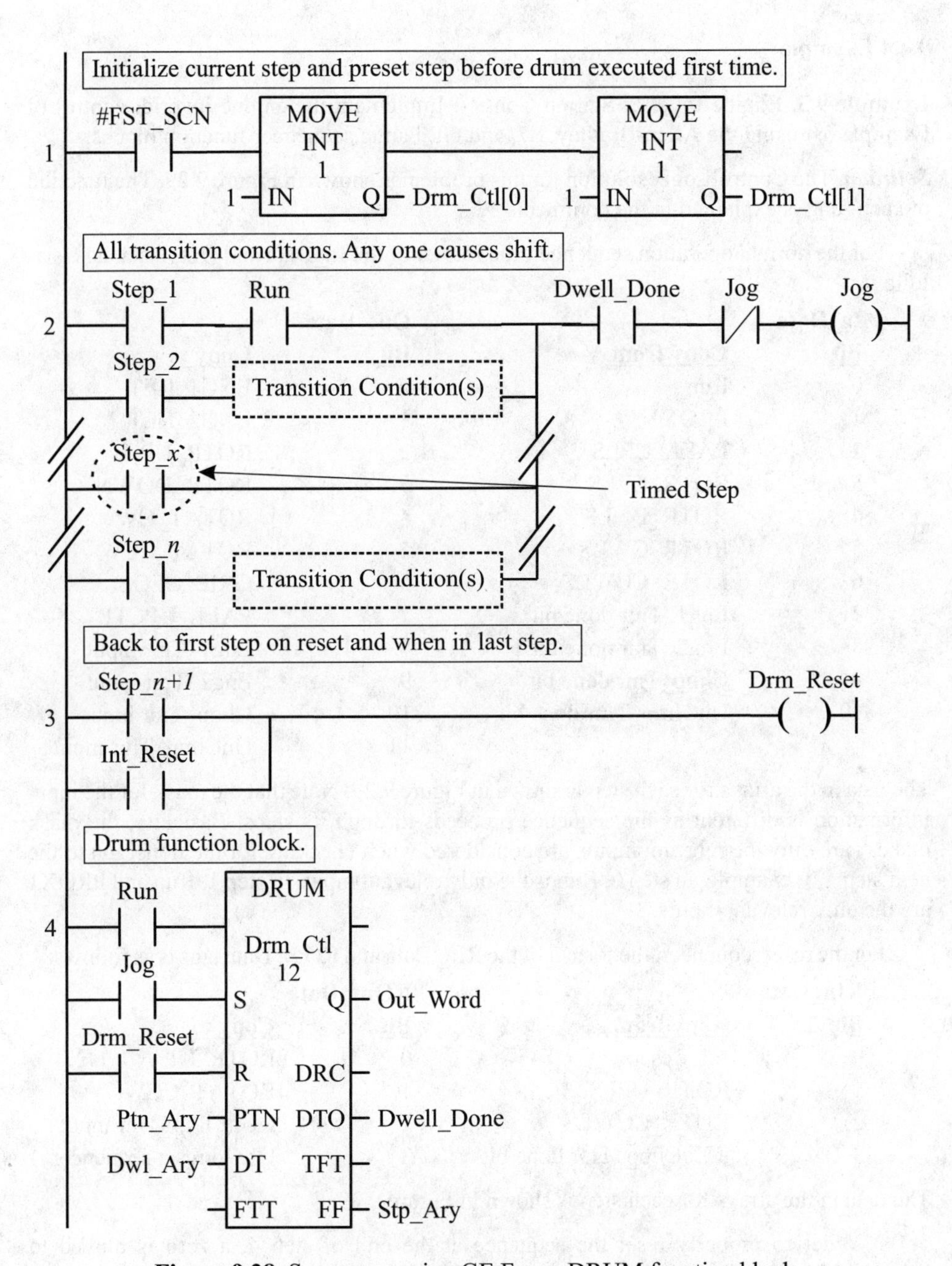

Figure 9.28. Sequencer using GE Fanuc DRUM function block.

9.4.4 Example

Example 9.3. Engine Inverter Station Control. Implement the engine inverter control of Example 6.4 using the Allen-Bradley, S7, and GE Fanuc sequencer function blocks.

Solution. The ControlLogix solution for this problem is shown in Figure 9.29. The function of each rung is explained in the comments.

For the normal operation sequencer, the format of the In_Data and Out_Data tags is as follows:

In_Data		**Out_Data**	
Bit	**Copy from**	**Bit**	**Copy to**
0	Run	0	ENG1_RET
1	PROX1	1	ENG2_RET
2	PALL_UPLS	2	ROTR_UP
3	ROTR_UPLS	3	ROTR_DOWN
4	ROTR_DNLS	4	ROTAT_CW
5	ROTR_CWLS	5	ROTAT_CCW
6	ROTR_CCWLS	6	GRIP_CLOS
7	Eng1_Tmr done bit	7	PALL_UPCTL
8	Eng2_Tmr done bit	8	Eng1_Tmr input
9	Clmp_Tmr done bit	9	Eng2_Tmr input
10	UnClmp_Tmr done bit	10	Clmp_Tmr input
		11	UnClmp_Tmr input

The data in the arrays for each step is shown in Figure 9.29. Note that the mask for the input information is different as the sequence proceeds through its steps. Basically, the mask makes sure only the relevant inputs are considered when checking for the transition to the next step. For example, in step 0, Run is the only relevant input. In step 1, Run and PROX1 are the only relevant inputs.

For the reset sequencer, the format of the RIn_Data and ROut_Data tags is as follows:

RIn_Data		**ROut_Data**	
Bit	**Copy from**	**Bit**	**Copy to**
0	Int_Reset	0	ROTR_UP
1	ROTR_UPLS	1	ROTAT_CCW
2	ROTR_CCWLS	2	RUnClmp_Tmr input
3	RUnClmp_Tmr done bit	3	Use to reset sequencer

The data in the arrays for each step is shown in Figure 9.29.

In order to properly reset the sequence at the end of step 4, a zero is moved to RSeq_Ctl.POS on rung 28. This move must occur after rung 27 so that Int_Reset can be turned **off**. Also, this move must occur before the SQI/SQO rung so that when they are scanned, the outputs are set properly.

The S7-300/400 solution for this problem is shown in Figure 9.30. The function of each rung is explained in the comments. The data in the OUT_VAL, S_PRESET, and S_MASK arrays for each drum is shown with the ladder logic code. The mask is not used, so all mask bits are set to "1." Note that since some transitions do not use the Run contact, the DRUM_EN for the normal inverter operation is always **on**.

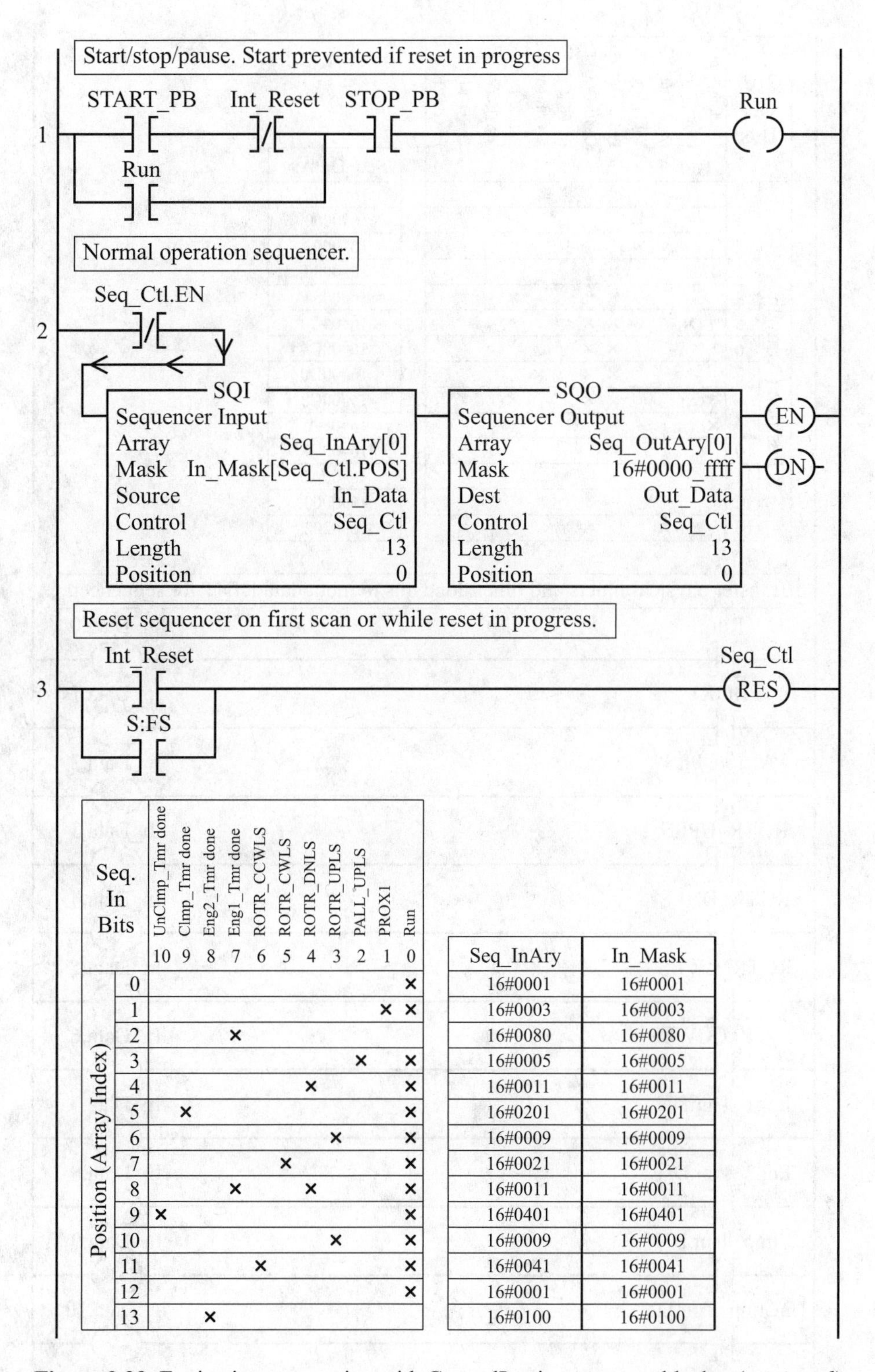

Position (Array Index) \ Seq. In Bits	10 UnClmp_Tmr done	9 Clmp_Tmr done	8 Eng2_Tmr done	7 Eng1_Tmr done	6 ROTR_CCWLS	5 ROTR_CWLS	4 ROTR_DNLS	3 ROTR_UPLS	2 PALL_UPLS	1 PROX1	0 Run
0											×
1										×	×
2				×							
3									×		×
4							×				×
5		×									×
6								×			×
7						×					×
8				×			×				×
9	×										×
10								×			×
11					×						×
12											×
13			×								

Seq_InAry	In_Mask
16#0001	16#0001
16#0003	16#0003
16#0080	16#0080
16#0005	16#0005
16#0011	16#0011
16#0201	16#0201
16#0009	16#0009
16#0021	16#0021
16#0011	16#0011
16#0401	16#0401
16#0009	16#0009
16#0041	16#0041
16#0001	16#0001
16#0100	16#0100

Figure 9.29. Engine inverter station with ControlLogix sequencer blocks. *(continued)*

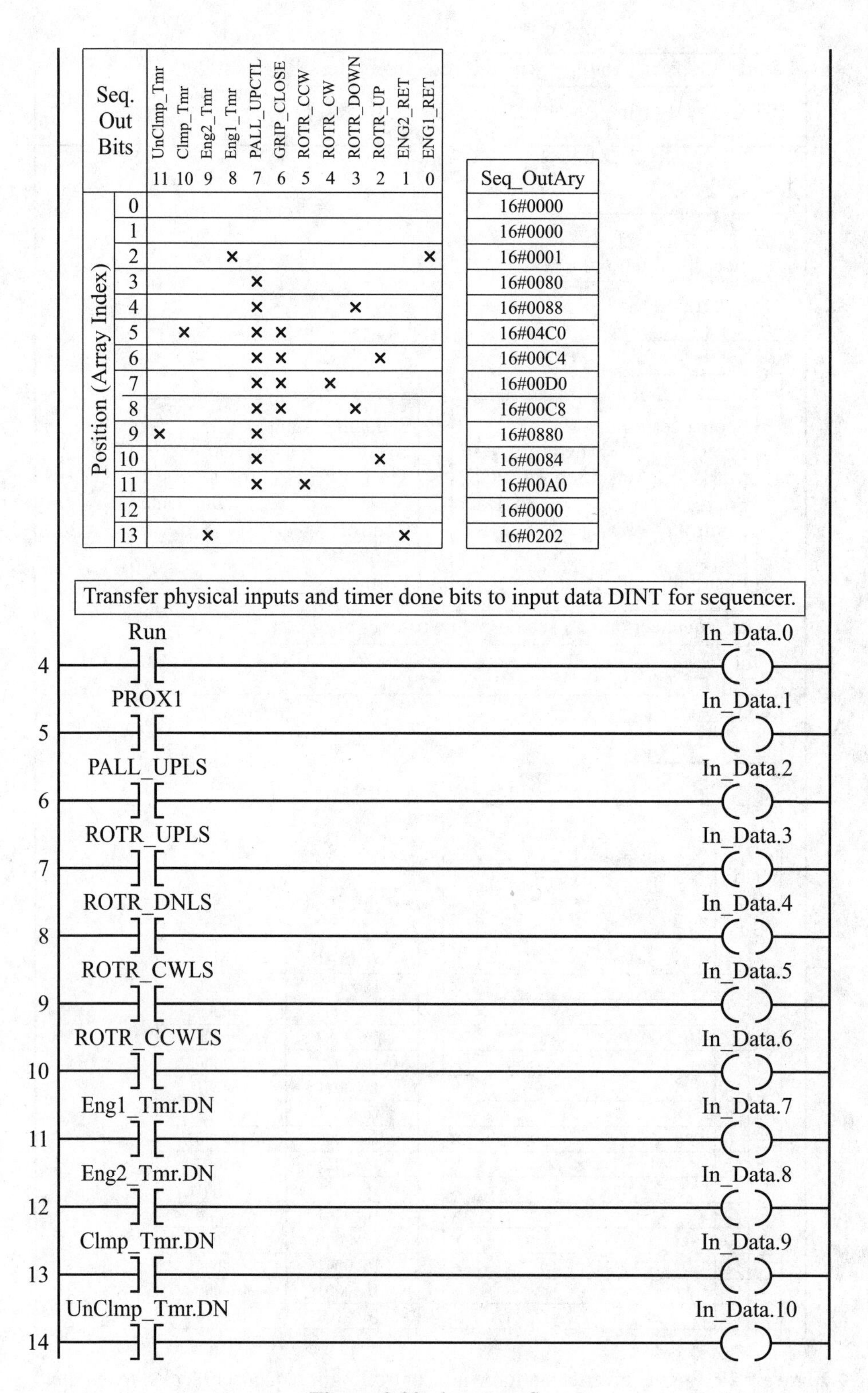

Position (Array Index)	11 UnClmp_Tmr	10 Clmp_Tmr	9 Eng2_Tmr	8 Eng1_Tmr	7 PALL_UPCTL	6 GRIP_CLOSE	5 ROTR_CCW	4 ROTR_CW	3 ROTR_DOWN	2 ROTR_UP	1 ENG2_RET	0 ENG1_RET	Seq_OutAry
0													16#0000
1													16#0000
2				×								×	16#0001
3					×								16#0080
4					×				×				16#0088
5		×			×	×							16#04C0
6					×	×				×			16#00C4
7					×	×		×					16#00D0
8					×	×			×				16#00C8
9	×				×								16#0880
10					×					×			16#0084
11					×		×						16#00A0
12													16#0000
13			×								×		16#0202

Figure 9.29. *(continued)*

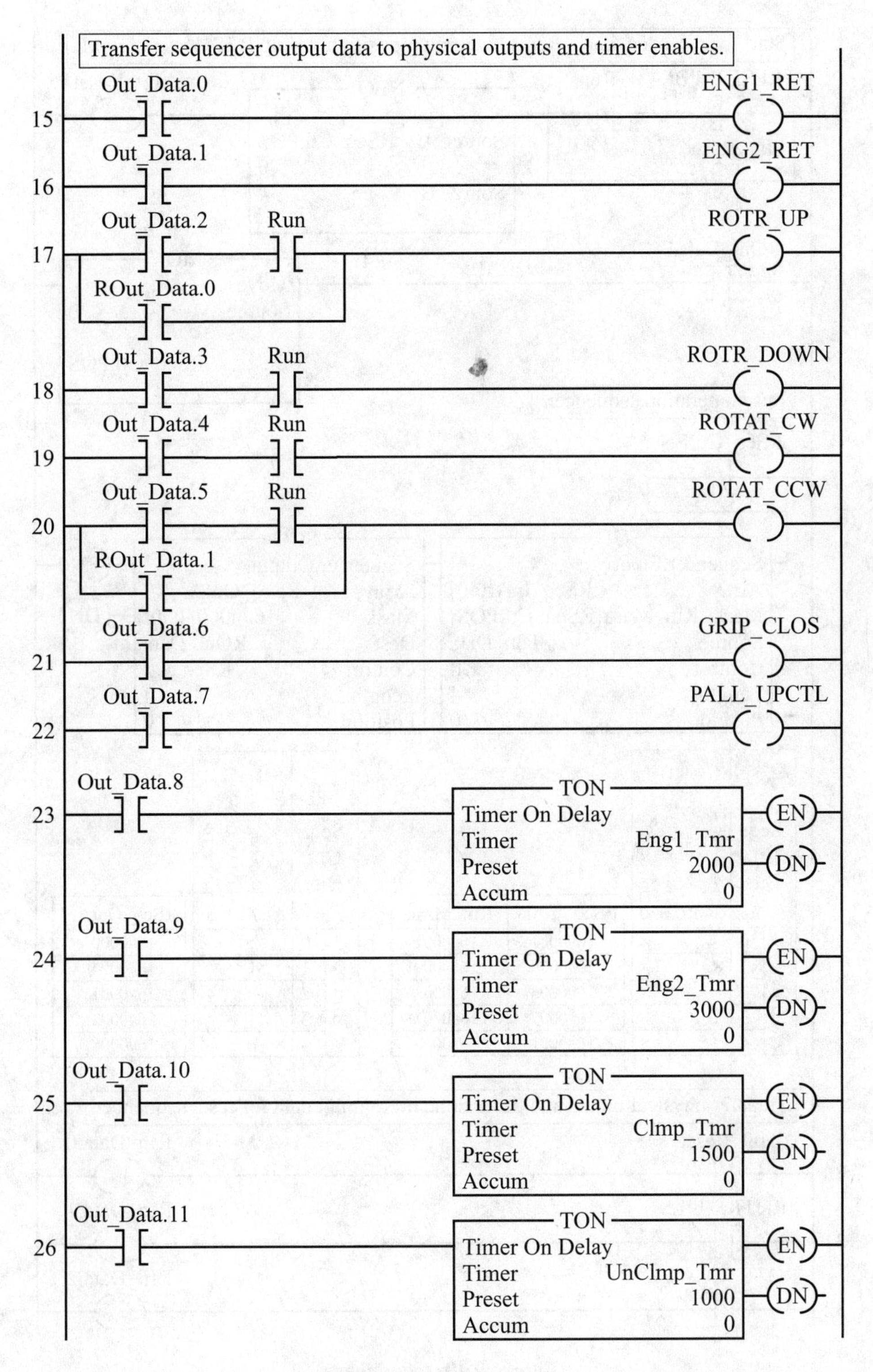

Figure 9.29. *(continued)*

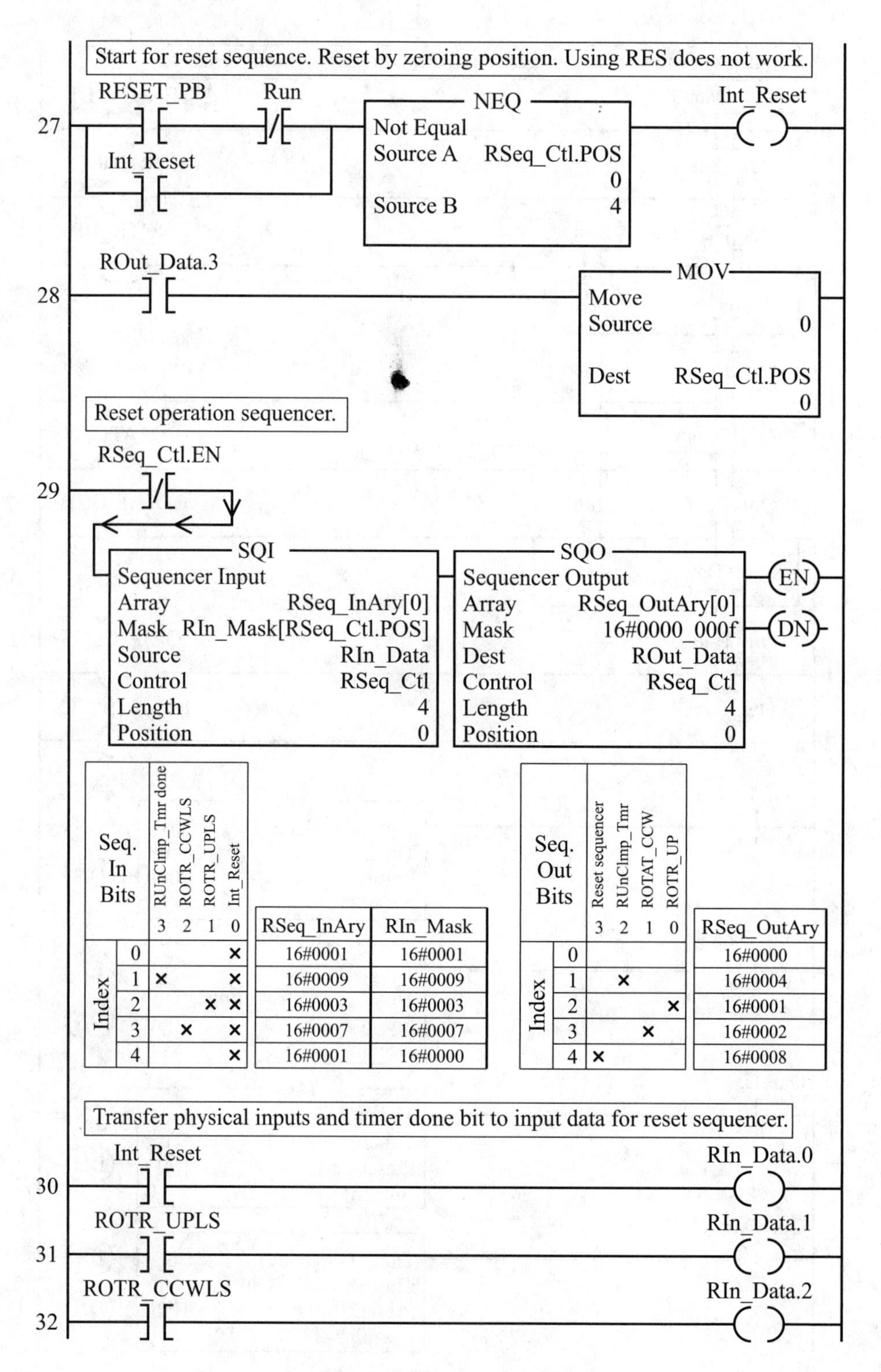

Seq. In Bits	RUnClmp_Tmr done (3)	ROTR_CCWLS (2)	ROTR_UPLS (1)	Int_Reset (0)	RSeq_InAry	RIn_Mask
Index 0				×	16#0001	16#0001
1	×			×	16#0009	16#0009
2			×	×	16#0003	16#0003
3		×		×	16#0007	16#0007
4				×	16#0001	16#0000

Seq. Out Bits	Reset sequencer (3)	RUnClmp_Tmr (2)	ROTAT_CCW (1)	ROTR_UP (0)	RSeq_OutAry
Index 0					16#0000
1		×			16#0004
2				×	16#0001
3			×		16#0002
4	×				16#0008

Figure 9.29. *(continued)*

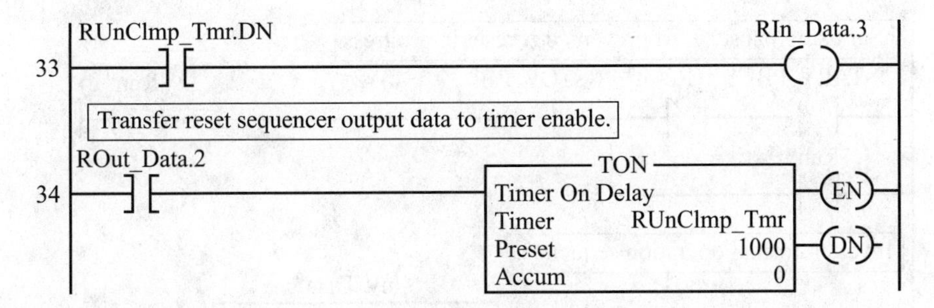

Figure 9.29. *(continued)*

For the normal operation sequencer, the OUT_VAL word bits are mapped to the individual physical outputs as follows:

OUT*i*	Copy to
1	ENG1_RET
2	ENG2_RET
3	ROTR_UP
4	ROTR_DOWN
5	ROTAT_CW
6	ROTAT_CCW
7	GRIP_CLOS
8	PALL_UPCTL

For the reset sequencer, the OUT_VAL word bits are mapped to the individual physical outputs as follows:

OUT*i*	Copy to
3	ROTR_UP
6	ROTAT_CCW
9	Int_Reset

The GE Fanuc solution for this problem is shown in Figure 9.31. The function of each rung is explained in the comments. The data in the pattern and dwell time arrays is shown with the ladder logic code.

For the normal operation sequencer, the Out_Word word bits are mapped to %M33 and the individual bits are as follows:

Out_Data bit	Symbol	Copy to
%M33	D_Eng1_Ret	ENG1_RET
%M34	D_Eng2_Ret	ENG2_RET
%M35	D_Rotr_Up	ROTR_UP
%M36	D_Rotr_Down	ROTR_DOWN
%M37	D_Rotat_Cw	ROTAT_CW
%M38	D_Rotat_Ccw	ROTAT_CCW
%M39	D_Grip_Clos	GRIP_CLOS
%M40	D_Pall_UpCtl	PALL_UPCTL

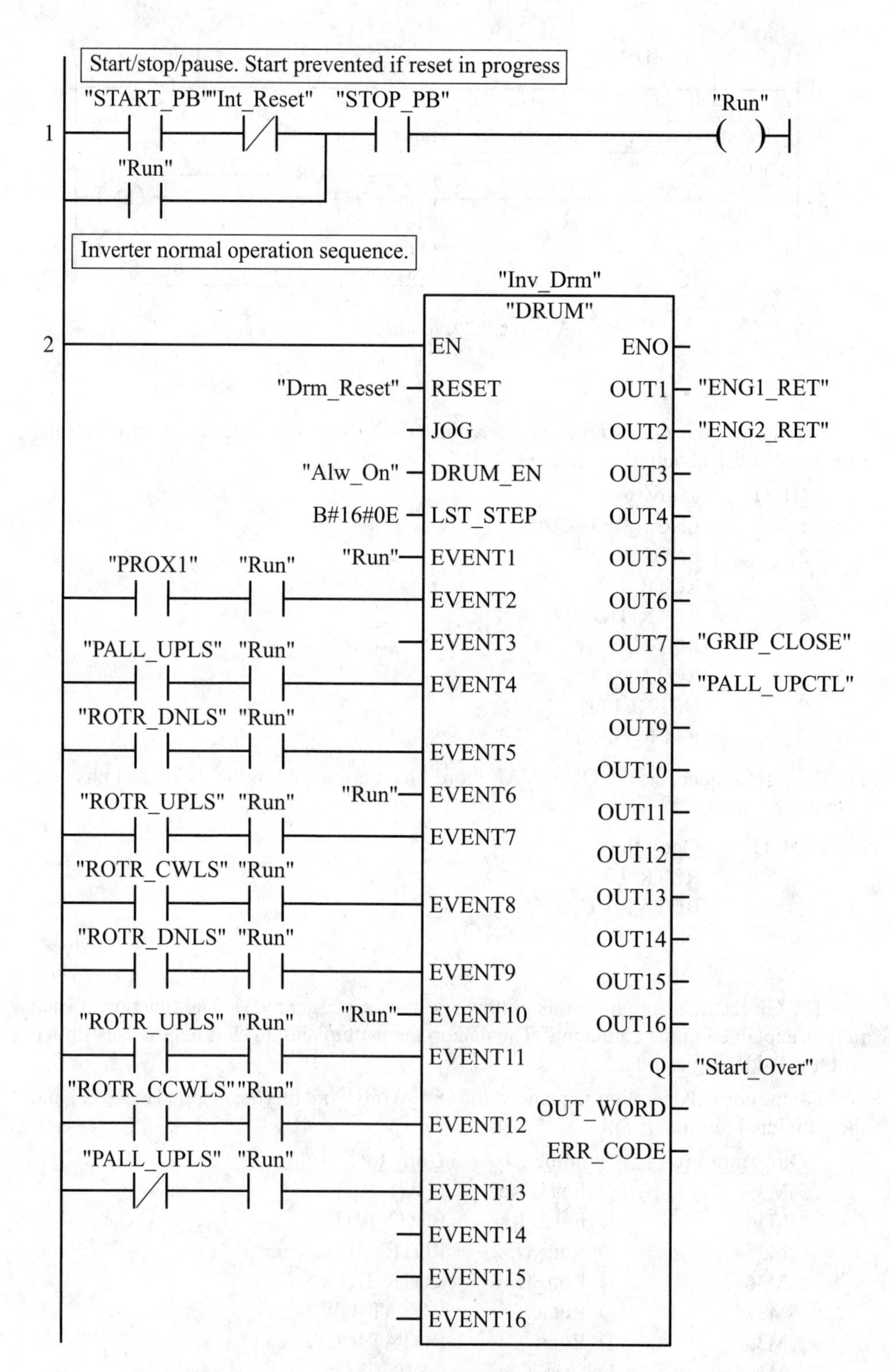

Figure 9.30. Engine inverter station with S7 DRUM blocks. *(continued)*

STEP	8 PALL_UPCTL	7 GRIP_CLOSE	6 ROTR_CCW	5 ROTR_CW	4 ROTR_DOWN	3 ROTR_UP	2 ENG2_RET	1 ENG1_RET	OUT_VAL	S_PRESET	S_MASK
1									W#16#0	W#16#0	W#16#FFFF
2									W#16#0	W#16#0	W#16#FFFF
3								×	W#16#1	W#16#14	W#16#FFFF
4	×								W#16#80	W#16#0	W#16#FFFF
5	×				×				W#16#88	W#16#0	W#16#FFFF
6	×	×							W#16#C0	W#16#F	W#16#FFFF
7	×	×				×			W#16#C4	W#16#0	W#16#FFFF
8	×	×		×					W#16#D0	W#16#0	W#16#FFFF
9	×	×			×				W#16#C8	W#16#0	W#16#FFFF
10	×								W#16#80	W#16#A	W#16#FFFF
11	×					×			W#16#84	W#16#0	W#16#FFFF
12	×		×						W#16#A0	W#16#0	W#16#FFFF
13									W#16#0	W#16#0	W#16#FFFF
14							×		W#16#2	W#16#1E	W#16#FFFF

Other Inv_Drm DB Contents:

DSP B#16#1

DTBP B#16#64

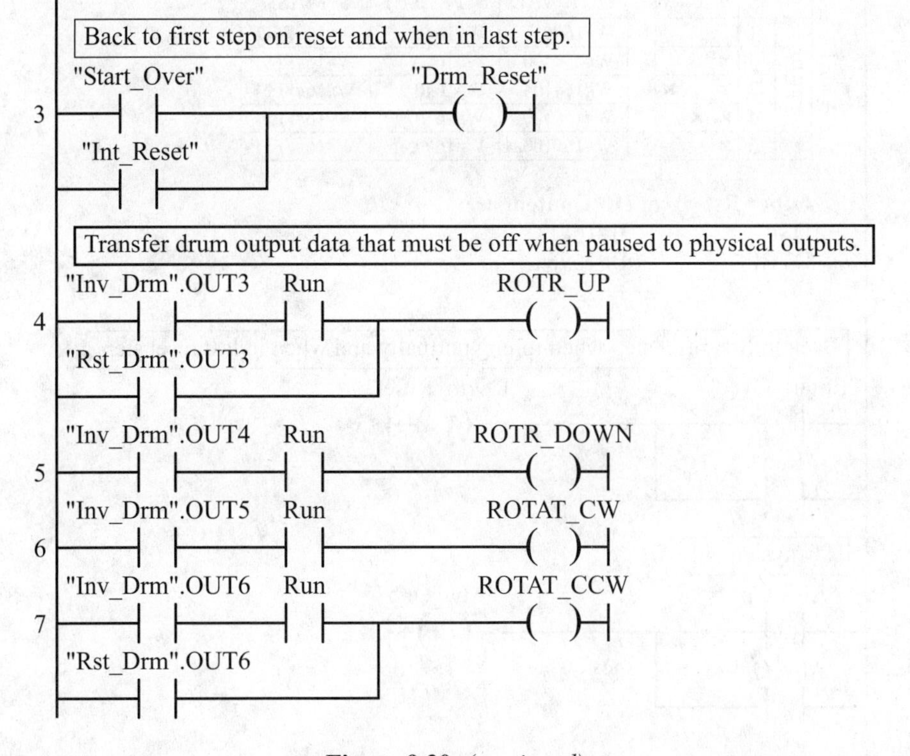

Figure 9.30. *(continued)*

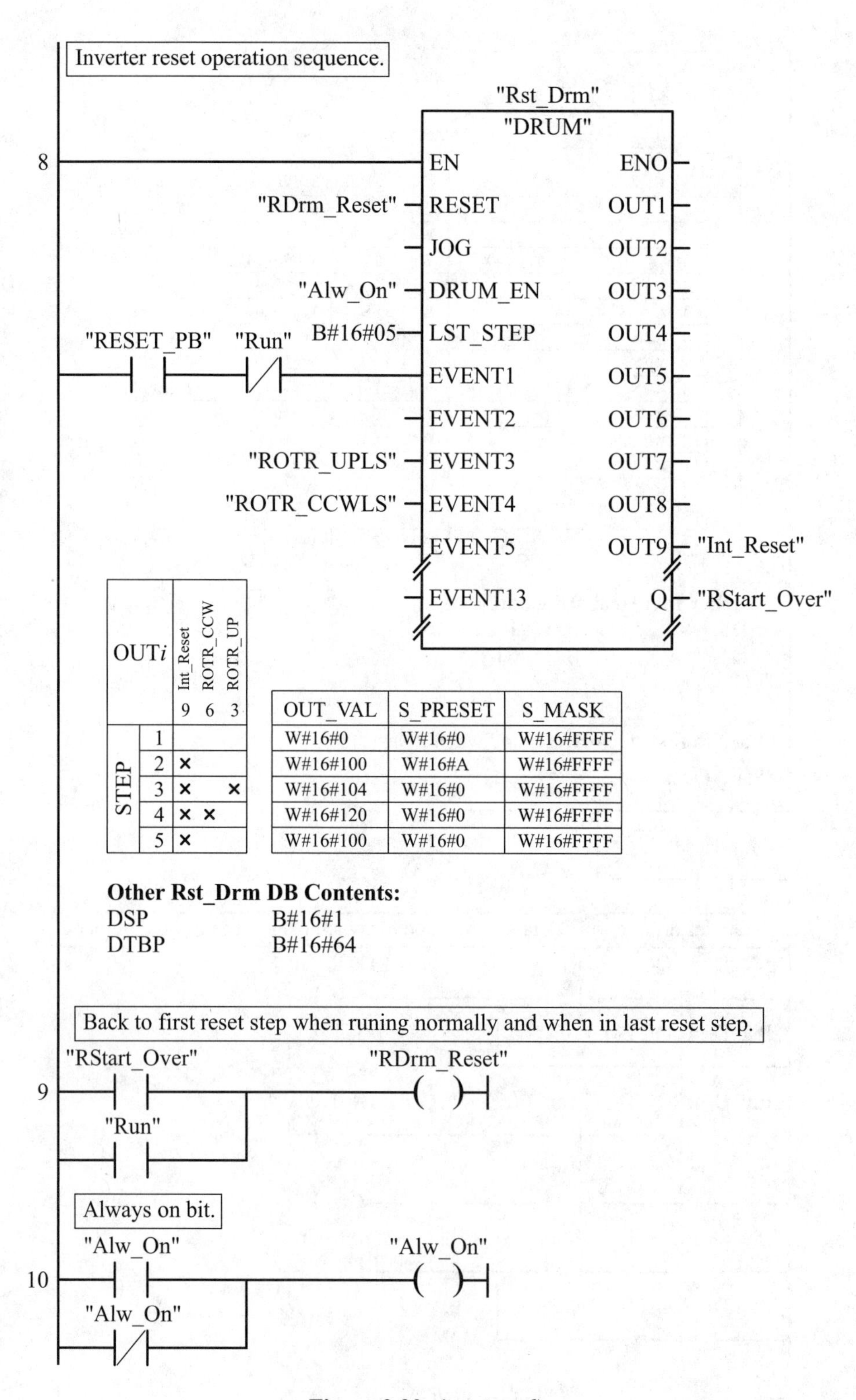

STEP \ OUT*i*	9 Int_Reset	6 ROTR_CCW	3 ROTR_UP
1			
2	×		
3	×		×
4	×	×	
5	×		

OUT_VAL	S_PRESET	S_MASK
W#16#0	W#16#0	W#16#FFFF
W#16#100	W#16#A	W#16#FFFF
W#16#104	W#16#0	W#16#FFFF
W#16#120	W#16#0	W#16#FFFF
W#16#100	W#16#0	W#16#FFFF

Figure 9.30. *(continued)*

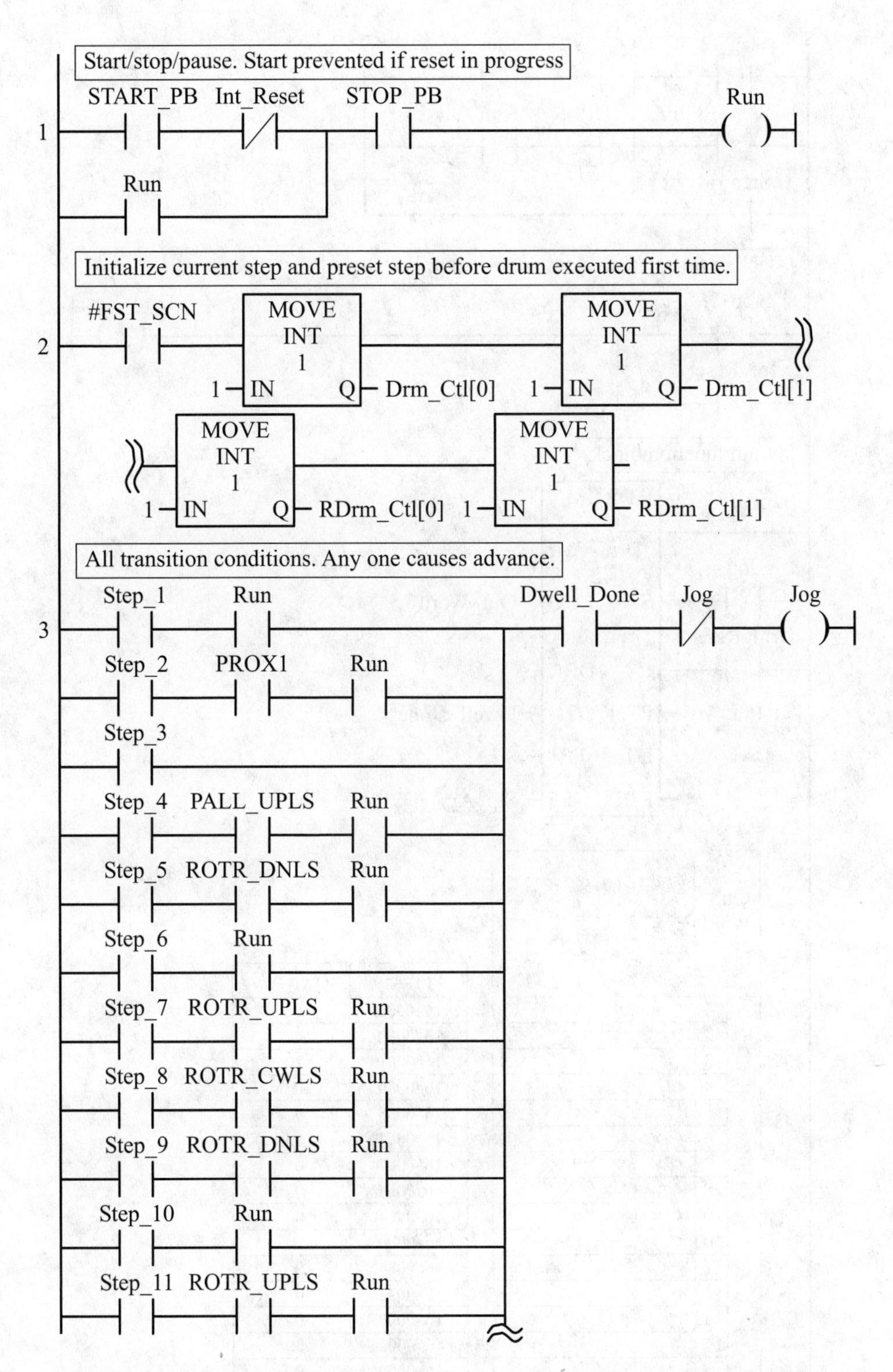

Figure 9.31. Engine inverter station with GE Fanuc DRUM blocks. *(continued)*

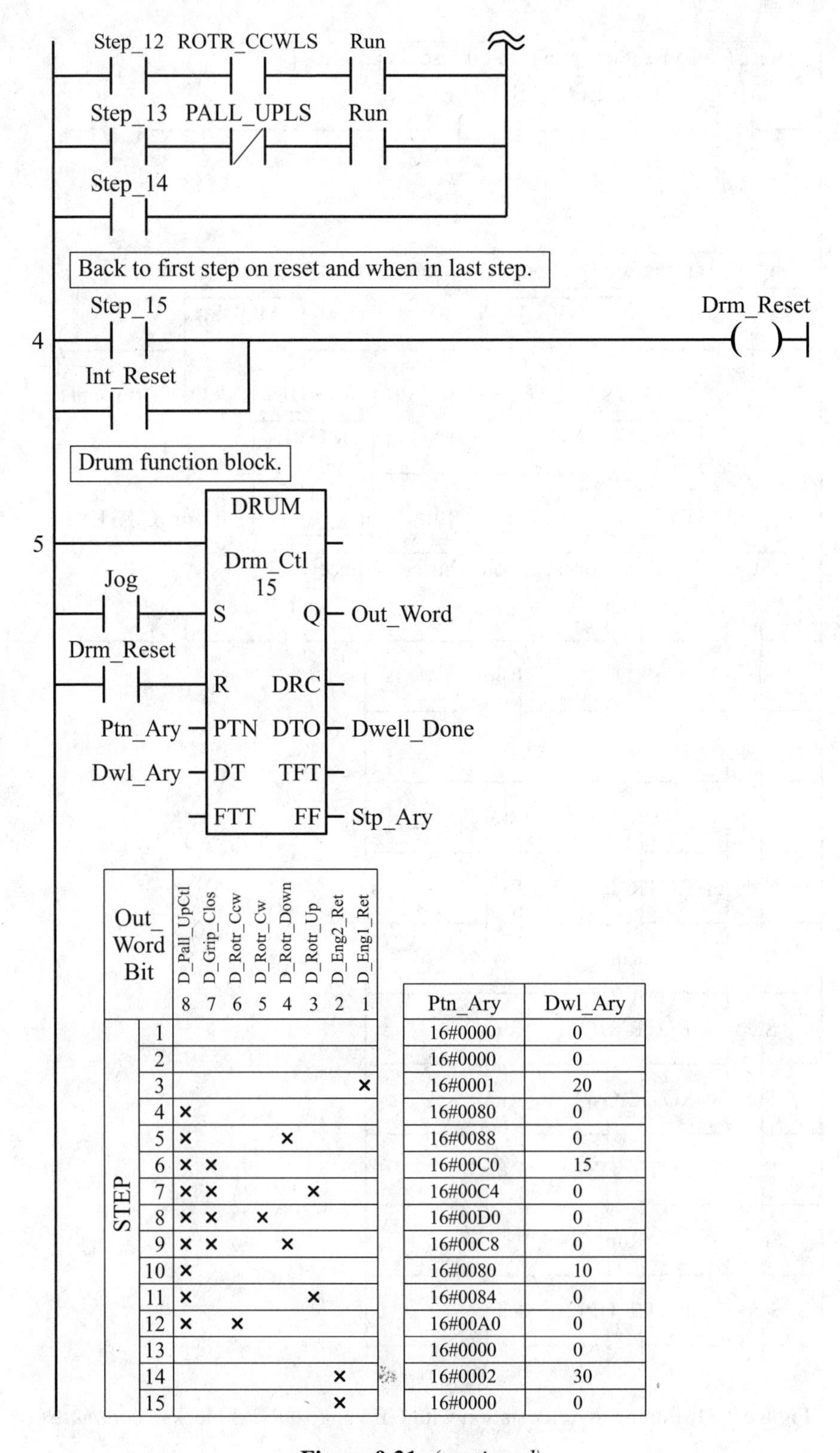

STEP	Out_Word Bit	8 D_Pall_UpCtl	7 D_Grip_Clos	6 D_Rotr_Ccw	5 D_Rotr_Cw	4 D_Rotr_Down	3 D_Rotr_Up	2 D_Eng2_Ret	1 D_Eng1_Ret	Ptn_Ary	Dwl_Ary
	1									16#0000	0
	2									16#0000	0
	3								×	16#0001	20
	4	×								16#0080	0
	5	×				×				16#0088	0
	6	×	×							16#00C0	15
	7	×	×				×			16#00C4	0
	8	×	×		×					16#00D0	0
	9	×	×			×				16#00C8	0
	10	×								16#0080	10
	11	×					×			16#0084	0
	12	×		×						16#00A0	0
	13									16#0000	0
	14							×		16#0002	30
	15							×		16#0000	0

Figure 9.31. *(continued)*

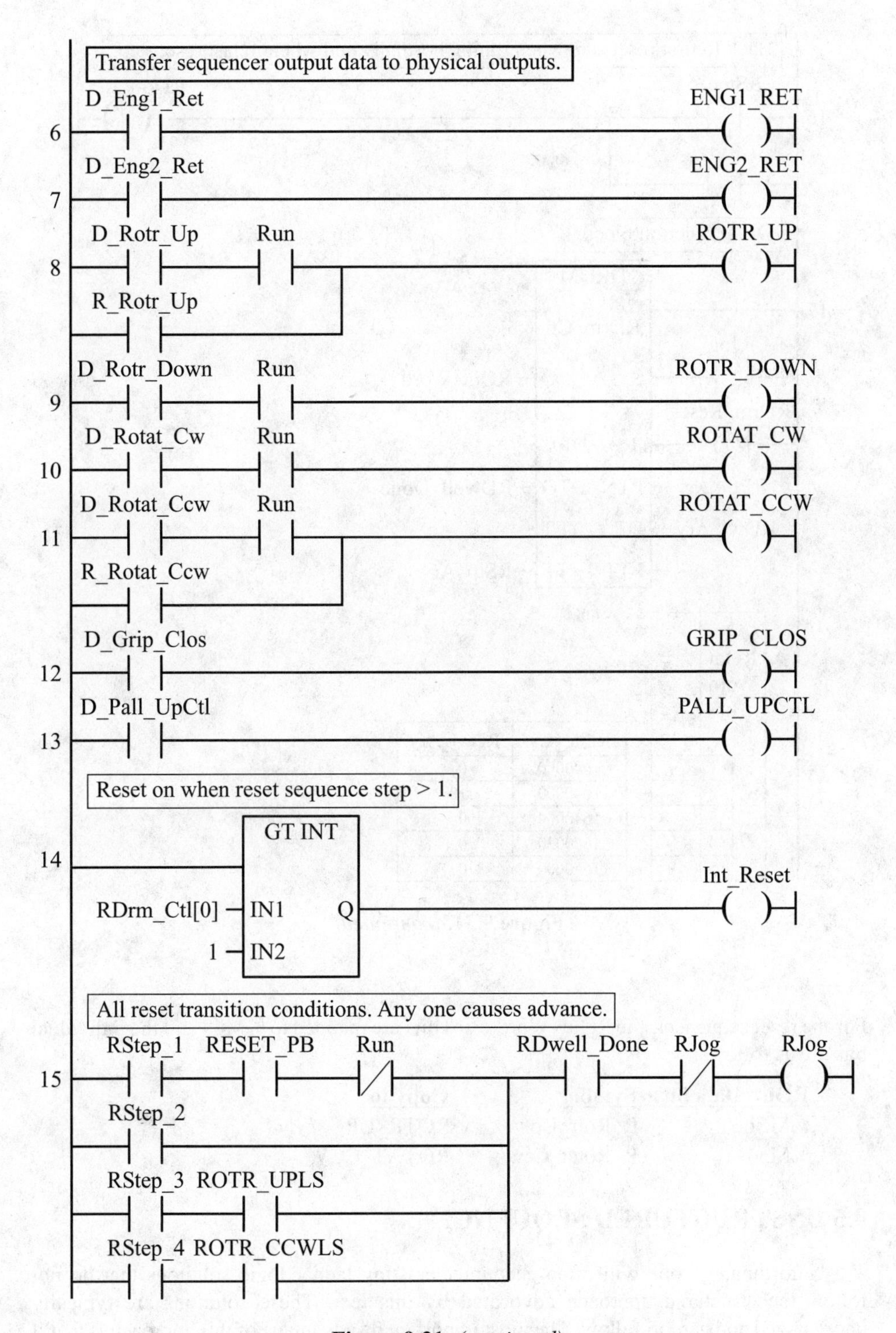

Figure 9.31. *(continued)*

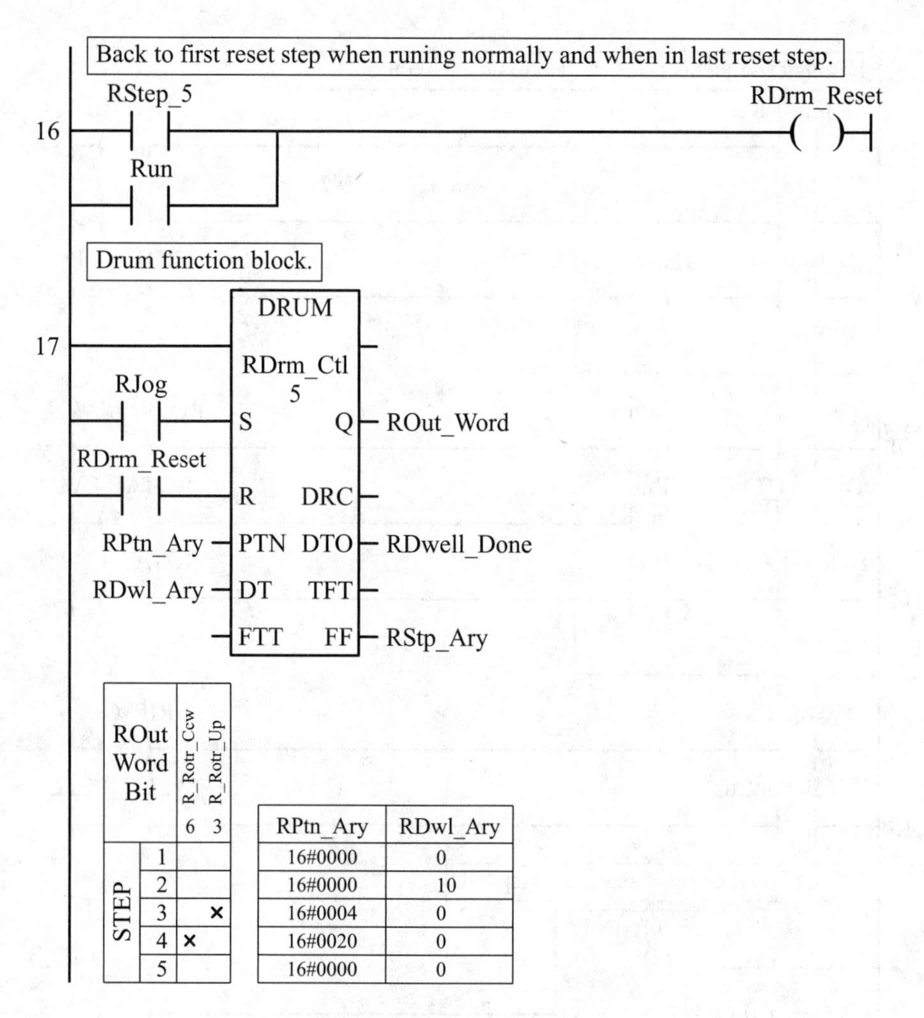

RPtn_Ary	RDwl_Ary
16#0000	0
16#0000	10
16#0004	0
16#0020	0
16#0000	0

Figure 9.31. *(continued)*

For the reset sequencer, the ROut_Word word bits are mapped to %M49 and the individual bits are as follows:

ROut_Data bit	Symbol	Copy to
%M51	R_Rotr_Up	ROTR_UP
%M54	R_Rotat_Ccw	ROTAT_CCW

9.5 UNSTRUCTURED SEQUENCE

Unfortunately, one will often encounter existing ladder logic solutions that do not follow the structured approach advocated by this text. These solutions are typically unorganized and hard to follow. The most important disadvantage of this approach is that it requires more time to design, program, and troubleshoot the initial solution and any future modifications. These disadvantages are illustrated by the following example.

Example 9.4. Engine Inverter Station Control. Implement the engine inverter control of Example 6.4 without using any of the structured techniques of this text.

Solution. Once one is exposed to the function chart design approach to design controls for sequential operations, it is hard to implement an unstructured approach. One approach to a solution that does not use the function chart as a design tool is described here. It is best described as "determine the start and stop conditions for each physical output and program the ladder logic accordingly." A Modicon solution for this problem is shown in Figure 9.32. The function of each rung is explained in the comments. Note that the normal operation start/stop/pause and the reset start/stop are handled as in previous examples. Internal coils are added as needed to define transitional conditions. Note the large number of transitional contacts. These are necessary since little "step" or "state" information is retained by the program. The logic of starting and stopping a particular physical output is largely determined by examining the state of the physical inputs. This solution does not exactly implement the operation as described in Example 6.4. On an initial start, there is a 2-second delay (engage 2 timer) before the next pallet is brought in, even if PROX1 is on when the operation is initially started. Also, it required about three times longer to design, program and troubleshoot this solution compared to the solution of Example 6.4.

Other examples of sequential control applications using unstructured approaches to the ladder logic appear in Bolton, 2000 (chapter 10 examples); Bryan and Bryan, 1997 (batching example in section 11-6); Geller, 2005 (chapter 12); Petruzella, 2005 (section 6-11); and Webb and Reis, 2003 (section 7-3). Many of these examples construct a flow chart to document the operation, but they use an approach similar to this section to design the ladder logic.

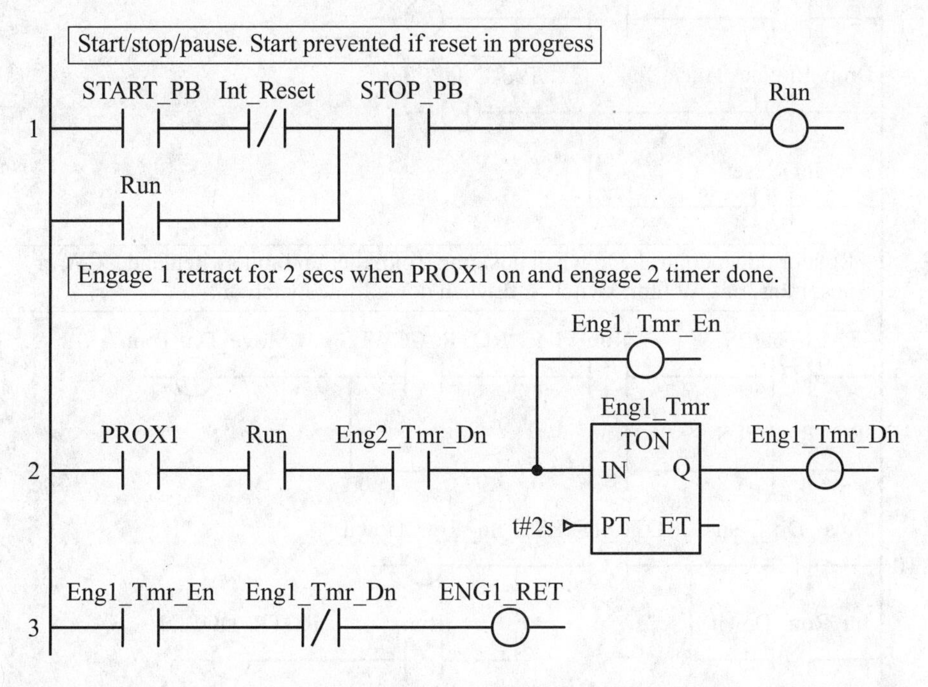

Figure 9.32. Unstructured Modicon solution to engine inverter station control. *(continued)*

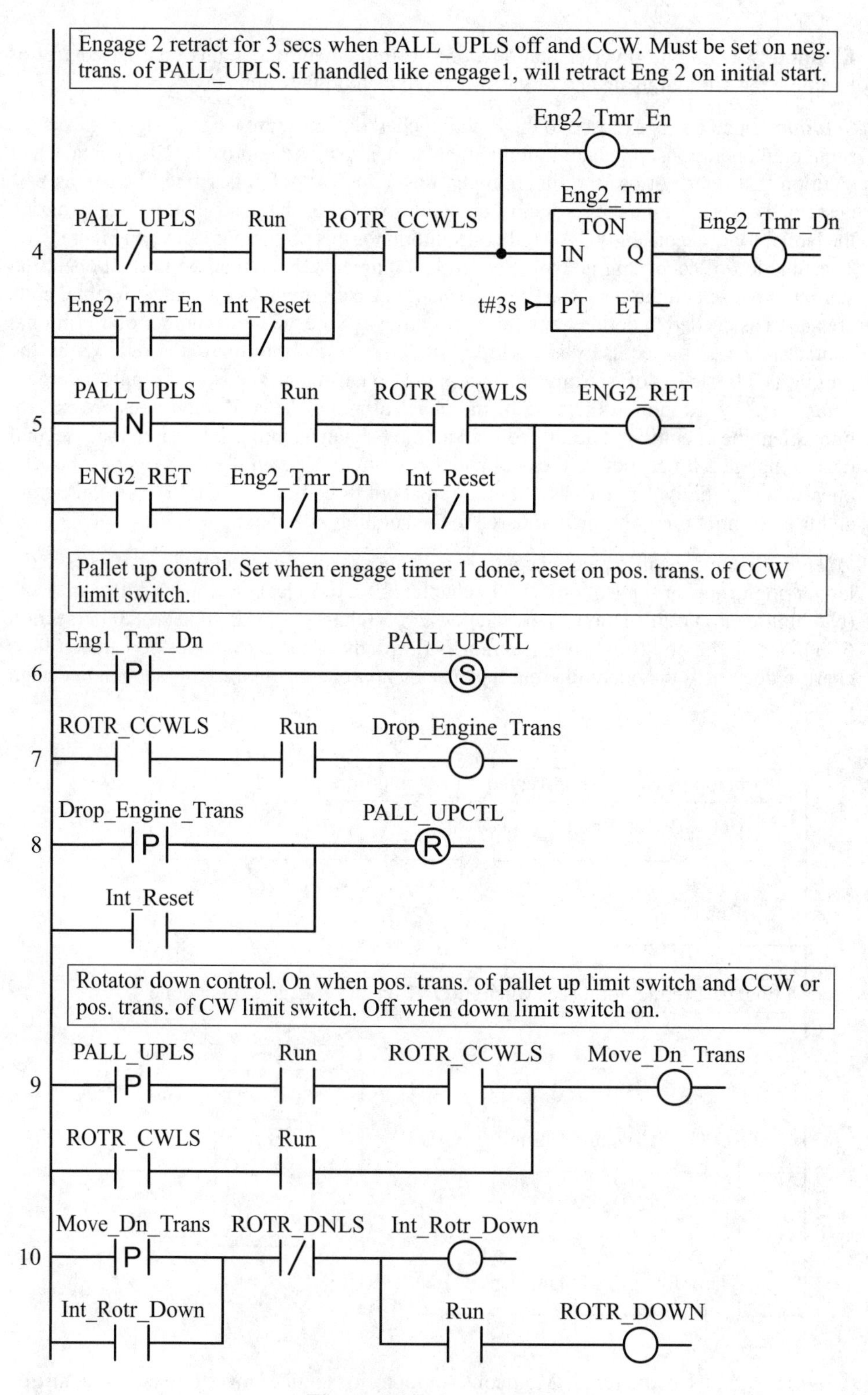

Figure 9.32. *(continued)*

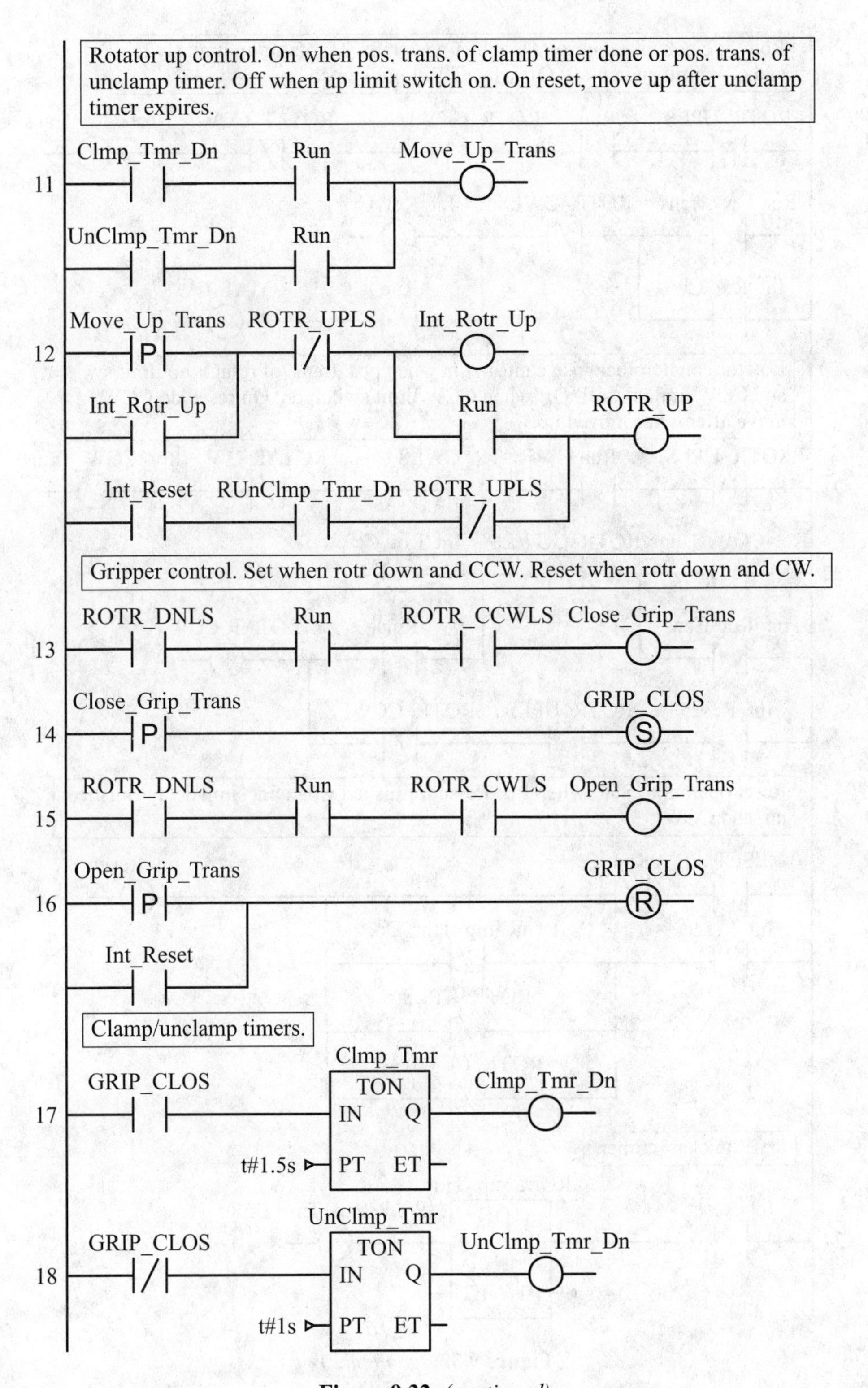

Figure 9.32. *(continued)*

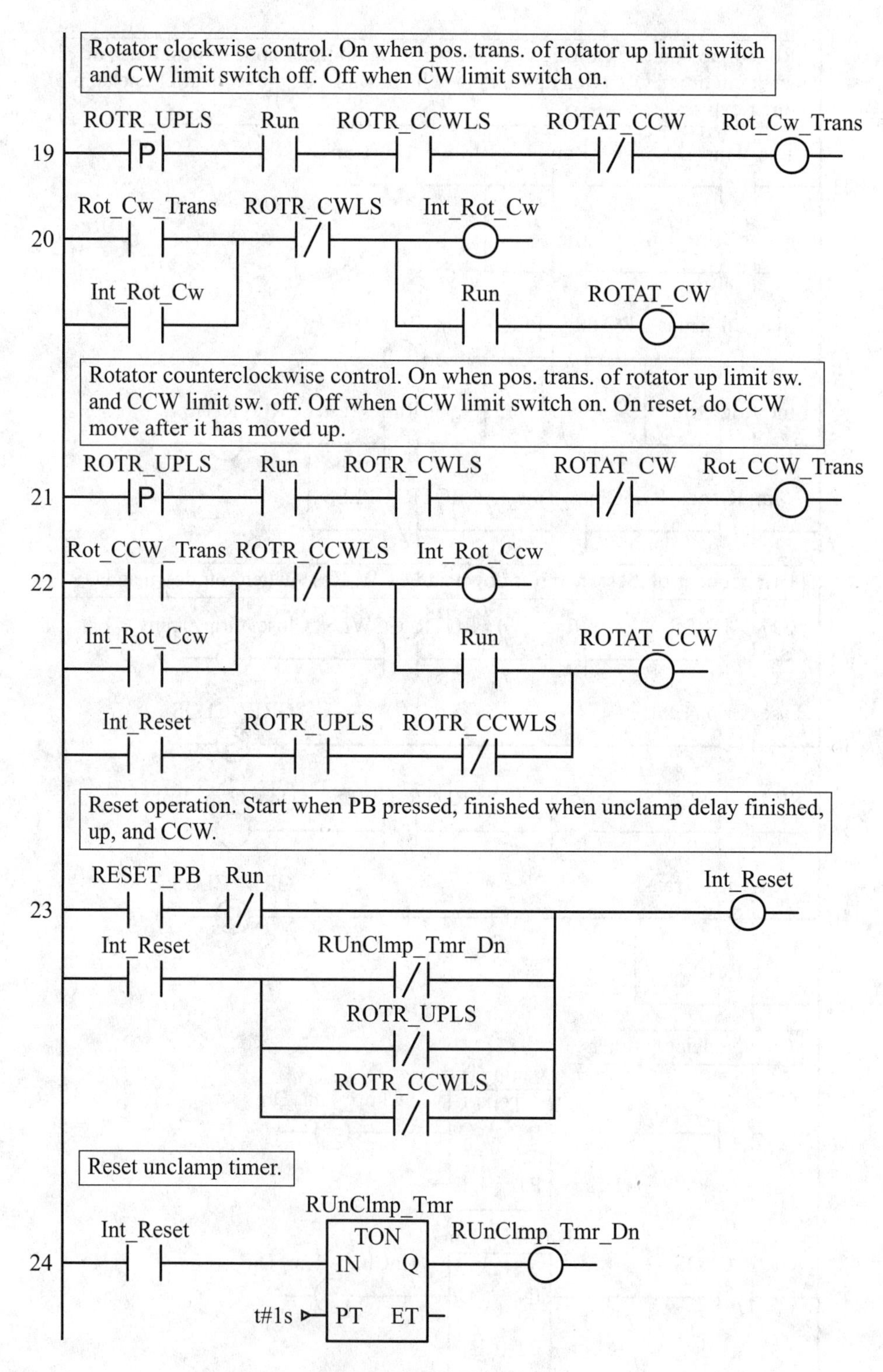

Figure 9.32. *(continued)*

9.6 CHAPTER SUMMARY

This chapter describes implementations of a function chart based on a counter, a shift register, and the Allen-Bradley sequencer function block. Each of these implementations is illustrated by repeating the engine inverter station example from Chapter 6. The chapter concludes by presenting an unstructured sequential control solution and emphasizing its drawbacks.

REFERENCES

Bolton, W., 2000. *Programmable Logic Controllers*, 2nd Ed., Newnes.

Bryan, L. A. and Bryan, E. A., 1997. *Programmable Logic Controllers: Theory and Implementation*, 2nd Ed., Industrial Text.

GE Fanuc Automation, 1999. *Series 90TM-30/20/Micro PLC CPU Instruction Set: Reference Manual,* pub. GFK-0467L, GE Fanuc Automation North America, Inc., Charlottesville, VA.

GE Fanuc Automation, 2000. *Series 90TM-70 PLC CPU Instruction Set: Reference Manual,* pub. GFK-0265J, GE Fanuc Automation North America, Inc., Charlottesville, VA.

GE Fanuc Automation, 2001. *VersaMax® PLC: User's Manual,* pub. GFK-1503C, GE Fanuc Automation North America, Inc., Charlottesville, VA.

Geller, David A., 2005. *Programmable Controllers Using the Allen-Bradley SLC-500 Family*, 2nd Ed., Pearson Education, Inc.

IEC, 1993. *IEC 1131-3: Programmable Logic Controllers - Part 3: Programming Languages*, International Electrotechnical Commission, Geneva, Switzerland.

Petruzella, Frank D., 2005. *Programmable Logic Controllers*, 3rd Ed., McGraw-Hill.

Rockwell Automation, 1998a. *PLC-5 Family Instruction Set Reference Manual*, pub. 1785-6.1, Rockwell Automation, Milwaukee, WI.

Rockwell Automation, 1998b *SLC Modular Processors Instruction Set Reference Manual*, pub. 1747-6.15, Rockwell Automation, Milwaukee, WI.

Rockwell Automation, 2002. *Logix5000TM Controllers General Instructions*, pub. 1756-RM003F-EN-P, Rockwell Automation, Milwaukee, WI, May.

Schneider Automation, 1998. *Concept Block Library IEC,* vol. 1, ver. 2.1, pub. 840 USE 462 00, Schneider Automation, Inc., North Andover, MA.

Siemens, 2000a. *S7-200 Programmable Controller: System Manual,* pub. A5E00066097-02, Siemens AG, Nuernberg, Germany.

Siemens, 2000b. *System Software for S7-300 and S7-400 System and Standard Functions Part 2: Reference Manual,* Edition 03, pub. A5E00066867-03, Siemens AG, Nuernberg, Germany.

Siemens, 2002a. *Ladder Logic (LAD) for S7-300 and S7-400 Programming: Reference Manual,* Edition 11/2002, pub. A5E00171231-01, Siemens AG, Nuernberg, Germany.

Siemens, 2002b. *System Software for S7-300/400 System and Standard Functions: Reference Manual,* Edition 12/2002, pub. A5E00171234-01, Siemens AG, Nuernberg, Germany.

Webb, John W. and Reis, Ronald A., 2003. *Programmable Logic Controllers: Principles and Applications*, 5th Ed., Pearson Education, Incl.

PROBLEMS

General instructions for the problems:

Write a ladder logic program for the application and implement it for one of the following PLC ladder logic languages:

Modicon Concept, **or**

Allen-Bradley ControlLogix, **or**

Allen-Bradley PLC-5/SLC-500, **or**

Siemens S7, **or**

GE Fanuc 90-30 (with floating point)

If any part of the operation is ambiguous, write down your additional assumptions. The physical inputs, physical outputs, and internal variables for each situation are given in the problem. **DO NOT** assign any more physical inputs!

Unless otherwise specified, assume the ADC in the analog input module has an output integer value that corresponds to the lowest and highest sensor value as:

Value	Modicon	Logix	PLC-5	SLC-500	Siemens	GE Fanuc
Lowest	0	-20,030	0	3277	5530	0
Highest	32,000	30,920	4095	16,384	27,648	32,000

In the case of the ControlLogix PLC, the instructor may choose to specify that the output of the ADC is a real number configured to be in the sensor units, for example, level in feet or temperature in °C.

Also, unless otherwise specified, assume the input integer to the DAC of an analog output module corresponds to the lowest and highest values of the output device control as:

Value	Modicon	Logix	PLC-5	SLC-500	Siemens	GE Fanuc
Lowest	0	-20,030	0	6242	5530	0
Highest	32,000	30,920	4095	31,208	27,648	32,000

In the case of the ControlLogix PLC, the instructor may choose to specify that the input to the DAC is a real number configured to be in the actual units of the output device, for example, speed in rpm or valve position in percent of span.

Your solution should include the following:

1. Function chart (if appropriate)
2. Specify the PLC processor used.
3. Ladder logic diagram (with comments). For consistency among the different PLCs, use only variables/symbols/tags in the ladder logic. Use instructions and function blocks consistent with the PLC processor.
4. Table listing additional internal memory (variables/symbols/tags) used and a brief description of their use. For the Allen-Bradley ControlLogix and the Modicon Quantum/Momentum processors, list the internal variables/tags and the data type. For the other processors, list the internal variables/symbols and the associated memory address.

P9-1. Carton Sealer Control. Implement the carton sealing control of problem P6-1 using the counter-based approach of section 9.2.

P9-2. Batch Process Control. Implement the batch control of problem P6-2 using the counter-based approach of section 9.2.

P9-3. Bag Sealing Control. Implement the ladder logic for the bag sealer of problem P6-4 using the counter-based approach of section 9.2.

P9-4. Erbia Elevator Control. Implement the erbia elevator control of problem P6-5 using the counter-based approach of section 9.2.

P9-5. Transfer Station Control. Implement the transfer station control of problem P6-6 using the counter-based approach of section 9.2.

P9-6. Hole Drilling Station 1 Control. Implement the drilling station control of problem P6-8 using the counter-based approach of section 9.2.

P9-7. Oiler Station Control. Implement the oiler station control of problem P6-9 using the counter-based approach of section 9.2.

P9-8. Pressing Station Control. Implement the pressing station control of problem P6-10 using the counter-based approach of section 9.2.

P9-9. Case Erector Control. Implement the case erector control of problem P6-11 using the counter-based approach of section 9.2.

P9-10. Batch Process Control. Implement the batch control system of problem P6-12 using the counter-based approach of section 9.2.

P9-11. Erbia Can Tipper/Rotator Control. Implement the station of problem P6-15 using the counter-based approach of section 9.2.

P9-12. Bagging Machine Control. Implement the bagging machine control of problem P6-17 using the counter-based approach of section 9.2.

P9-13. Drilling Station Control. Implement the drilling station control of problem P6-18 using the counter-based approach of section 9.2.

P9-14. Bolt Driving Station Control. Implement the bolt-driving station control of problem P6-19 using the counter-based approach of section 9.2.

P9-15. Palletizing Station Control. Implement the palletizer control of problem P6-20 using the counter-based approach of section 9.2.

P9-16. Weigh Scale Station Control. Implement the weigh scale station control of problem P7-20 using the counter-based approach of section 9.2.

P9-17. Width Check Station Control. Implement the width check station control of problem P7-21 using the counter-based approach of section 9.2.

P9-18. Stamping Station Control. Implement the stamping station control of problem P7-22 using the counter-based approach of section 9.2.

P9-19. Leak Check Station Control. Implement the valve leak check station control of problem P7-23 using the counter-based approach of section 9.2.

P9-20. Hole-drilling Station 2 Control. Implement the drilling station control of problem P7-24 using the counter-based approach of section 9.2.

P9-21. Hole-drilling Station 3 Control. Implement the drilling station control of problem P7-25 using the counter-based approach of section 9.2.

P9-22. Batch Reactor Control. Implement the batch reactor control of problem P7-28 using the counter-based approach of section 9.2.

P9-23. Carton Sealer Control. Implement the carton sealing control of problem P6-1 using the shift register-based approach of section 9.3.

P9-24. Batch Process Control. Implement the batch control of problem P6-2 using the shift register-based approach of section 9.3.

P9-25. Bag Sealing Control. Implement the ladder logic for the bag sealer of problem P6-4 using the shift register-based approach of section 9.3.

P9-26. Erbia Elevator Control. Implement the erbia elevator control of problem P6-5 using the shift register-based approach of section 9.3.

P9-27. Transfer Station Control. Implement the transfer station control of problem P6-6 using the shift register-based approach of section 9.3.

P9-28. Hole Drilling Station 1 Control. Implement the drilling station control of problem P6-8 using the shift register-based approach of section 9.3.

P9-29. Oiler Station Control. Implement the oiler station control of problem P6-9 using the shift register-based approach of section 9.3.

P9-30. Pressing Station Control. Implement the pressing station control of problem P6-10 using the shift register-based approach of section 9.3.

P9-31. Case Erector Control. Implement the case erector control of problem P6-11 using the shift register-based approach of section 9.3.

P9-32. Batch Process Control. Implement the batch control system of problem P6-12 using the shift register-based approach of section 9.3.

P9-33. Erbia Can Tipper/Rotator Control. Implement the station of problem P6-15 using the shift register-based approach of section 9.3.

P9-34. Bagging Machine Control. Implement the bagging machine control of problem P6-17 using the shift register-based approach of section 9.3.

P9-35. Drilling Station Control. Implement the drilling station control of problem P6-18 using the shift register-based approach of section 9.3.

P9-36. Bolt Driving Station Control. Implement the bolt-driving station control of problem P6-19 using the shift register-based approach of section 9.3.

P9-37. Palletizing Station Control. Implement the palletizer control of problem P6-20 using the shift register-based approach of section 9.3.

P9-38. Weigh Scale Station Control. Implement the weigh scale station control of problem P7-20 using the shift register-based approach of section 9.3.

P9-39. Width Check Station Control. Implement the width check station control of problem P7-21 using the shift register-based approach of section 9.3.

P9-40. Stamping Station Control. Implement the stamping station control of problem P7-22 using the shift register-based approach of section 9.3.

P9-41. Leak Check Station Control. Implement the valve leak check station control of problem P7-23 using the shift register-based approach of section 9.3.

P9-42. Hole-drilling Station 2 Control. Implement the drilling station control of problem P7-24 using the shift register-based approach of section 9.3.

P9-43. Hole-drilling Station 3 Control. Implement the drilling station control of problem P7-25 using the shift register-based approach of section 9.3.

P9-44. Batch Reactor Control. Implement the batch reactor control of problem P7-28 using the shift register-based approach of section 9.3.

P9-45. Transfer Station Control. Implement the transfer station control of problem P6-6 using the Allen-Bradley sequencer function blocks.

P9-46. Pressing Station Control. Implement the pressing station control of problem P6-10 using the Allen-Bradley sequencer function blocks.

P9-47. Case Erector Control. Implement the case erector control of problem P6-11 using the Allen-Bradley sequencer function blocks.

P9-48. Batch Process Control. Implement the batch control system of problem P6-12 using the Allen-Bradley sequencer function blocks.

P9-49. Erbia Can Tipper/Rotator Control. Implement the station of problem P6-15 using the Allen-Bradley sequencer function blocks.

P9-50. Bagging Machine Control. Implement the bagging machine control of problem P6-17 using the Allen-Bradley sequencer function blocks.

P9-51. Drilling Station Control. Implement the drilling station control of problem P6-18 using the Allen-Bradley sequencer function blocks.

P9-52. Bolt Driving Station Control. Implement the bolt-driving station control of problem P6-19 using the Allen-Bradley sequencer function blocks.

P9-53. Spray Painting Station Control. Implement the sprayer station control of problem P6-20 using the Allen-Bradley sequencer function blocks.

P9-54. Weigh Scale Station Control. Implement the weigh scale station control of problem P7-20 using the Allen-Bradley sequencer function blocks.

P9-55. Stamping Station Control. Implement the stamping station control of problem P7-22 using the Allen-Bradley sequencer function blocks.

P9-56. Leak Check Station Control. Implement the valve leak check station control of problem P7-23 using the Allen-Bradley sequencer function blocks.

P9-57. Hole-drilling Station 2 Control. Implement the drilling station control of problem P7-24 using the Allen-Bradley sequencer function blocks.

P9-58. Hole-drilling Station 3 Control. Implement the drilling station control of problem P7-25 using the Allen-Bradley sequencer function blocks.

P9-59. Batch Reactor Control. Implement the batch reactor control of problem P7-28 using the Allen-Bradley sequencer function blocks.

10 PID Control

Chapter Topics:

- General features of feedback control
- PID controller theory and tuning
- PID control enhancements
- Operational aspects of PID control
- PLC PID control implementation

OBJECTIVES

Upon completion of this chapter, you will be able to:

- Understand the basic operation of a PID controller
- Understand how to tune a PID controller
- Understand when to use cascade and feedforward control
- Implement PID control in a PLC

Scenario: Peak shaving load control. A university has contracted with you to install an automatic load control for Generator #3, their diesel-powered generator. The power plant mainly supplies steam to heat and cool campus buildings. However, it has two electric generators. Generator #1 is driven by a non-condensing steam turbine and supplies a maximum of 250 kW. Generator #3 is a 1000 kW diesel generator normally used to supply power to the power plant equipment when the utility power source fails. Generator #2 was removed a few years ago.

In order to save money, Generator #3 is being used to "shave" the peak electricity demand in the summer. The cost of the electicity is a certain rate as long as the campus demand stays below a certain peak level (determined weekly). If the campus demand remains above this peak for at least 15 minutes, the utility adds a hefty "demand charge" to the monthly bill. Even though the cost of electricity from the diesel generator is more than the normal charge from the utility, there is substantial cost savings to running generator #3 to keep the campus demand below the peak.

The generator load is controlled by a potentiometer on the power plant panel. When the campus demand approaches the peak demand, the operator starts the diesel, synchronizes it to the bus, connects it to the bus, and then adjusts the generator load to keep the campus demand just below the peak. An operator has other duties, so s/he does not always watch the campus demand meter. As a consequence, the campus has incurred demand charges because the operator was busy with other duties when the demand initially exceeded the

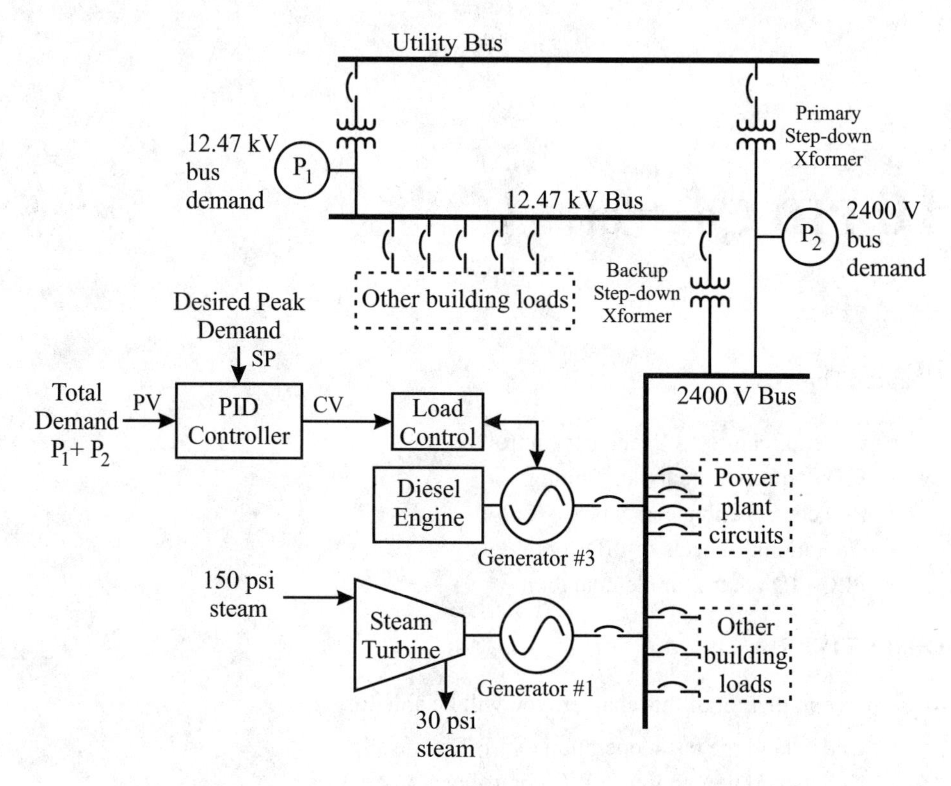

Figure 10.1. Simplified diagram of peak shaving system.

peak, or when the load control needed to be increased enough to keep the demand below the peak during the day.

Therefore, you added functionality to the existing PLC-5 to automatically control the Generator #3 load to keep the campus demand below the peak. This scenario focuses on the tuning of the PID controller that controls the generator load to keep the campus demand below the peak. Modification of the control scheme to prevent negative power flow through the primary step-down transformer is covered in Example 10.7.

Figure 10.1 shows how the PID control fits into the system. The setpoint (SP) is the desired peak demand, the process variable (PV) measurement is the total demand, and the control variable (CV) is the desired generator load, 0 – 1000 kW. You did some initial tests to determine how fast the generated power changed when the load control was changed by a small amount (50 kW) and calculated the initial PID controller parameters as $K_P = 1.0$, $K_I = 6$, and $K_D = 0.0$. The ladder logic and PID parameters are shown in Figure 10.2.

When you install the system and observe its operation during commissioning, the control seems to hold the demand reasonably close to the desired peak. The campus demand has some fluctuation, and so the generated power fluctuates as well. However, the next day you are called because the generated power seems to be fluctuating more than it should be. You cannot come immediately, and so they revert to manual control of the generator load to finish the day.

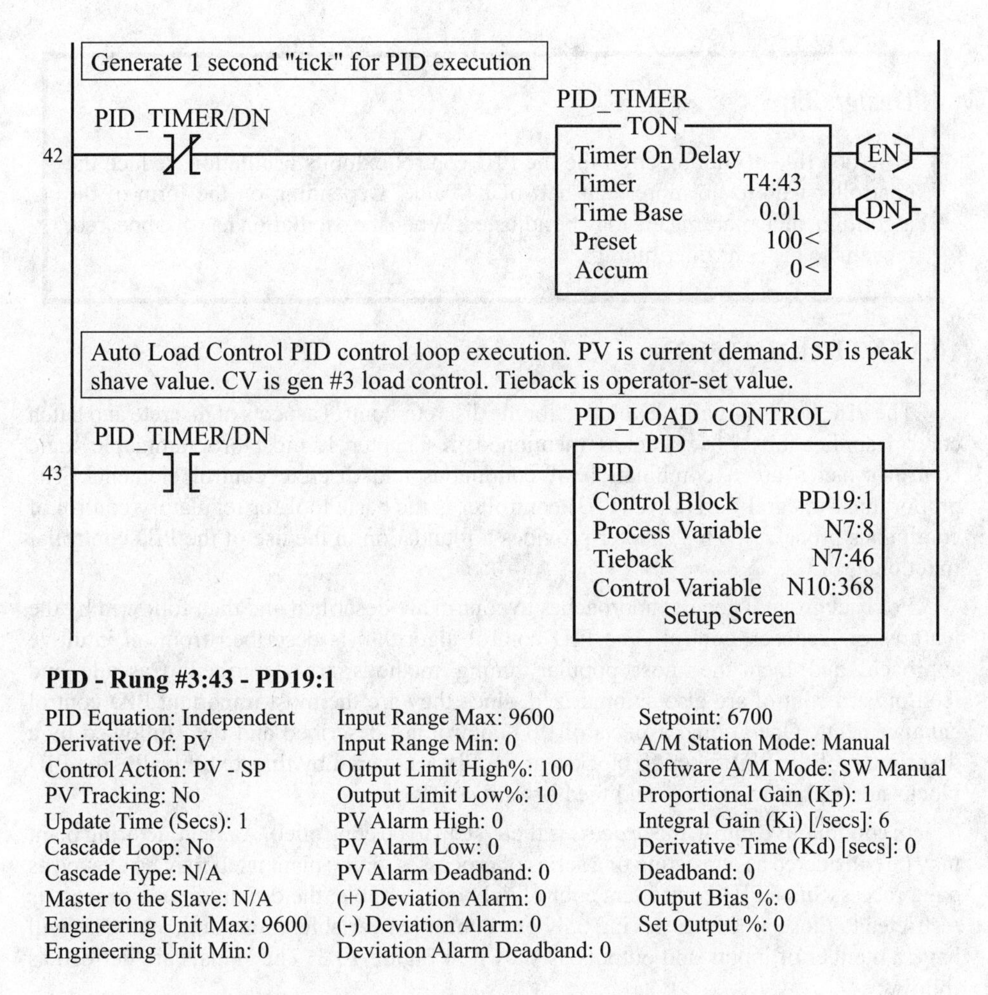

Figure 10.2. PLC-5 ladder logic for PID controller.

The next day, you investigate the PID controller a little more carefully when it is controlling the generator load. The meter displaying the generated power has some reasonable fluctuation. However, when you examine the PID controller CV, it is definitely oscillating, from 10% to 60%, with a period of about 25 seconds. What should you do?

***Solution*:** As a rule of thumb, any time one observes oscillation, the gain of the controller, K_P, should be reduced by at least half. You reduce both the proportional and integral gain to $K_P = 0.5, K_I = 3$. The oscillation disappears, and the generator load levels out. The control of the campus demand is not as "tight," that is, it seems to fluctuate a little more around the desired peak, but that is acceptable since the desired peak value is below the demand charge value.

Design Tip

As a rule of thumb, any time the PID control exhibits oscillation, reduce the controller gain to no more than half of its value. Depending on the form of the algorithm, other parameters may be adjusted. When the oscillation has disappeared, reevaluate the controller tuning.

10.1 INTRODUCTION

The PLC was originally developed for the discrete-control aspects of discrete and batch control applications. However, as mentioned in Chapter 1, most programmable logic control systems are a combination of continuous and discrete control elements. The proportional-integral-derivative (PID) controller is the basic tool for regulatory control of continuous processes. This chapter provides a foundation in the use of the PID controller function in PLCs.

For background, general approaches to control are described and then followed by the features of feedback control. The PID control algorithm is described from an intuitive approach, and then the most popular tuning methods are described. Cascade and feedforward control are also summarized, since they are the most important PID control enhancements. Operational aspects of PID control are described and then followed by a description of the PID function blocks for the PLCs covered by this text. Finally, the PID blocks are applied to cascade and feedforward control.

In continuous control, the *process* is the system to be controlled. A manufacturing plant may be considered as consisting of a series of processes, or the plant itself may be viewed as one process. Since PID controllers control only one variable, the definition of a process is restricted to those processes having only one controlled variable. In general, a process will have a number of inputs and outputs as shown in Figure 10.3. The signals are defined as follows:

Process Variable (PV) - Process output which is to be maintained at a desired value by adjustment of a process input.

Control Variable (CV) - The process input that is adjusted to maintain the process variable at the setpoint. This input is also commonly called the manipulated variable (MV) or valve out (VO).

Disturbance – A process input other than the control variable that affects the process variable.

A simple flow process is shown in Figure 10.4*a*, and its corresponding block diagram representation is shown in Figure 10.4*b*. The process variable is the flow, and the control

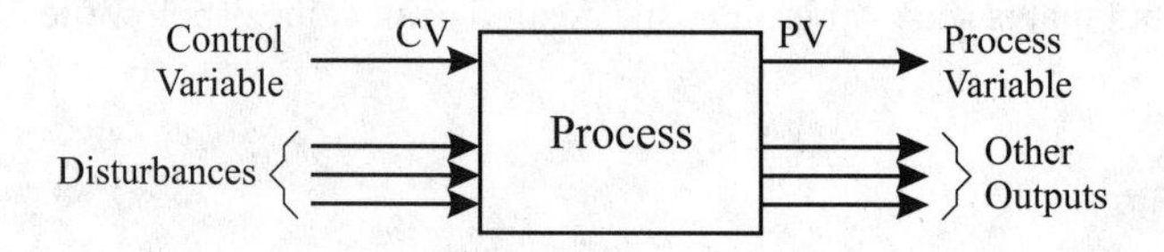

Figure 10.3. Block diagram of a general process.

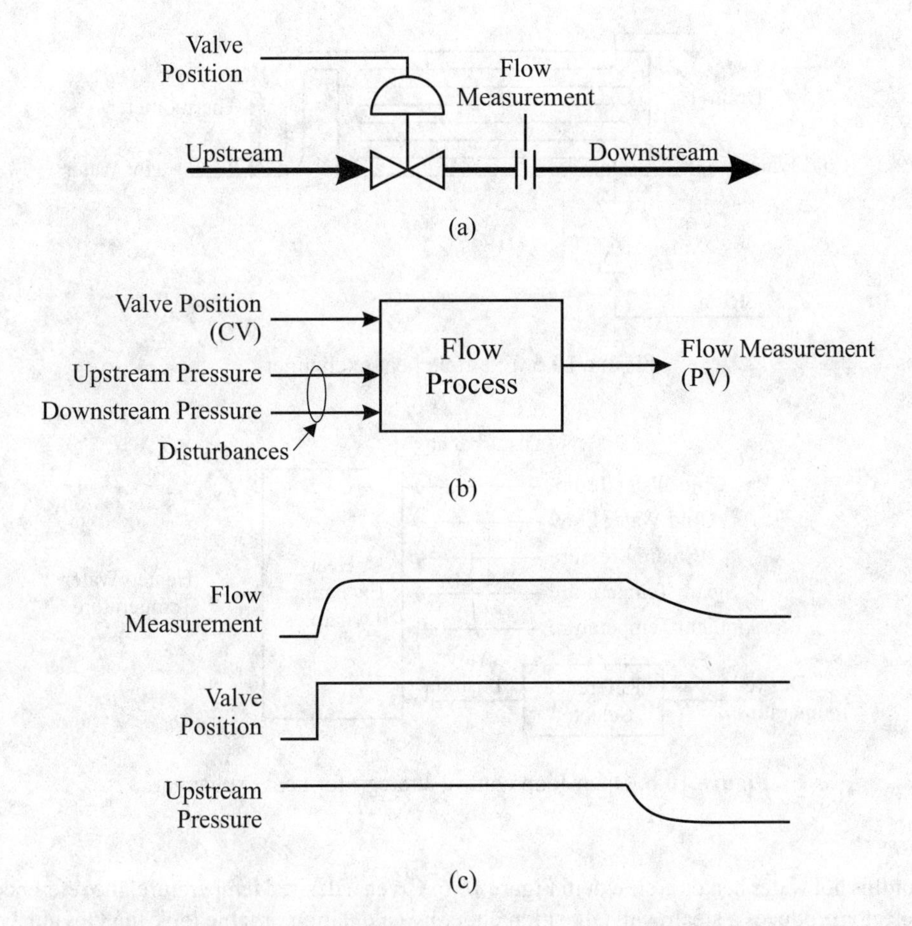

Figure 10.4. Example flow process: *(a)* process; *(b)* as block diagram; *(c)* effect of valve position and upstream pressure on flow.

variable is valve position. The upstream and downstream pressures are both disturbances, since either one can affect the flow. As illustrated in Figure 10.4*c*, both the valve position (control variable) and the upstream pressure (disturbance) determine the actual flow (process variable).

In order to place the material in this chapter in its proper context, the most common strategies for regulatory control are described and related to each other.

Open-Loop Control. If a process has no disturbances, or their effect on the process variable is negligible, then open-loop control is sufficient. Based on an indicated value of the process variable, the control variable is adjusted by a plant operator. In this control strategy, the control variables are simply set to their design values and held there. Many people consider this strategy as no control, but by setting the control variables, the control system is influencing the process. For example, consider the control of a heat exchanger, depicted in Figure 10.5, which uses steam to heat cold water and produce hot water. The goal is to control the hot water temperature to a desired value, ±2°C. An open-loop control strategy

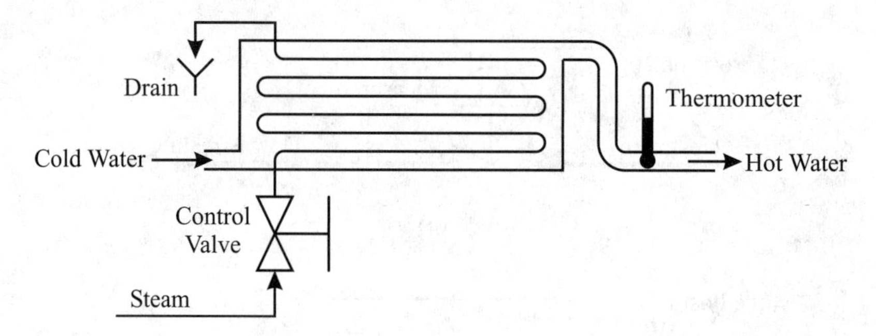

Figure 10.5. Example heat exchanger.

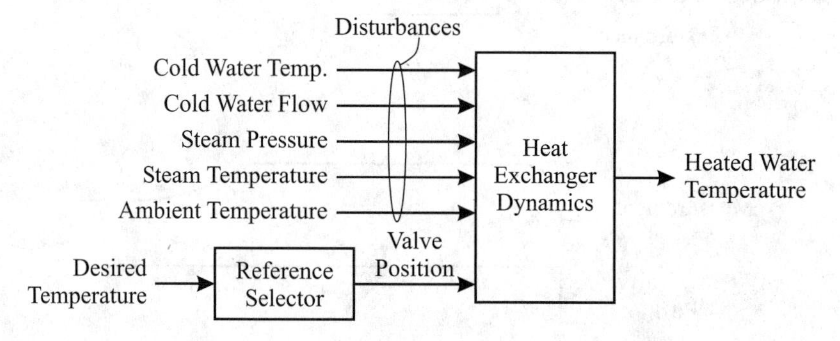

Figure 10.6. Open-loop control strategy for heat exchanger.

for this hot water heater is shown in Figure 10.6. Given a desired temperature, the reference selector produces a steam valve position either by calculation or table look-up. Obviously, any variations in the cold-water temperature or steam pressure, among other external influences, will affect the hot water temperature and the reference selector will not account for them.

This strategy is useful for those systems that have no or small disturbance effects. Obviously, if the system is subject to significant disturbances, then some more sophisticated control is needed.

Feedforward Control. If one knows the types of disturbances that can influence a process, then the reference selector can be modified to measure these disturbances and modify the calculation of the control variable. For example, the heat exchanger of Figure 10.5 is subject to the following disturbances:

Cold water temperature	Steam temperature
Cold water flow	Ambient temperature
Steam pressure	

All of these influences are called *disturbances* because they affect the output but are not manipulated. To construct a feedforward controller, the important disturbances are measured and used by the reference selector, along with the desired value of the output to calculate the control variable value. For example, Figure 10.7 shows a possible feedforward controller for the heat exchanger. The important disturbances, cold water temperature, cold

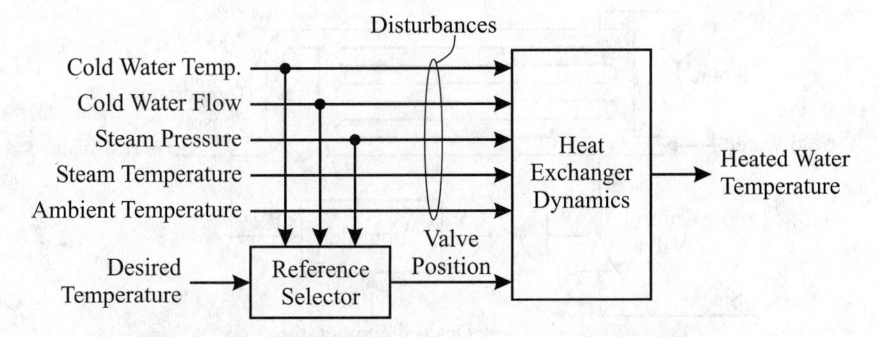

Figure 10.7. Feedforward control strategy for heat exchanger.

water flow, and steam pressure are considered to be either the disturbances that have the biggest effect or the ones most likely to change. The other disturbances are unmeasured and still influence the process to some extent.

This strategy is useful for those cases where the process operating point does not change and the process is subject to significant disturbances whose effect on the process variable is known. The disturbances not used in this strategy must have small effects on the process variable.

Manual Feedback Control. The strategy of using knowledge of the output to take corrective action is called *feedback*. In manual feedback control, operating personnel monitor the process variable of interest and take corrective action in order to maintain the desired value. A manual feedback control scheme for the heat exchanger is shown in Figure 10.8. An operator periodically monitors the hot-water temperature and adjusts the steam valve position in order to maintain the hot-water temperature.

Manual control is useful in a large number of applications whose process variable is not critical, whose disturbances are few, or where the cost of automation is too high to justify automatic (open-loop or feedback) control.

Automatic Feedback Control. When the operator in a manual feedback strategy is replaced by a controller device that continuously measures the process variable, then one has automatic feedback control. Automatic control helps to eliminate disturbance effects. To

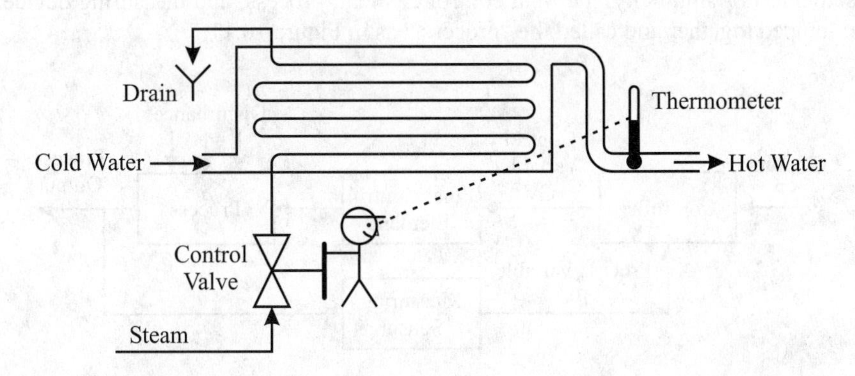

Figure 10.8. Manual feedback control for heat exchanger.

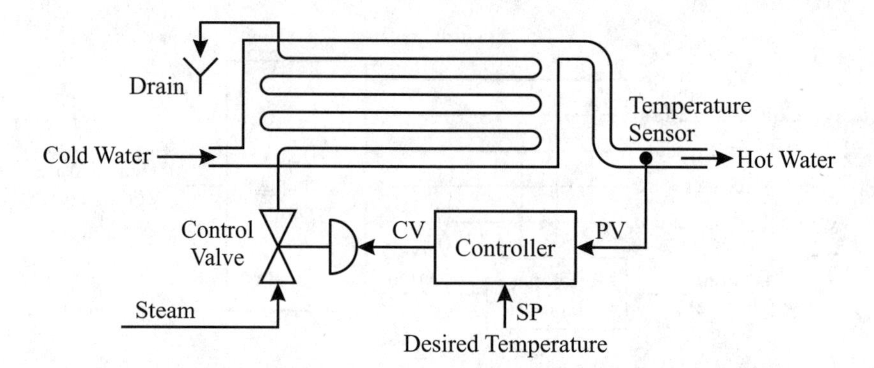

Figure 10.9. Automatic feedback control for heat exchanger.

maintain the process variable at the setpoint, the control variable is adjusted each time there is a change in the process variable. For the heat exchanger example, the operator is replaced by an automatic feedback controller (Figure 10.9). The *setpoint* (SP) is the desired value of the process variable, the hot-water temperature. The combination of feedback and feedforward control is considered later in this chapter. The only drawback to automatic feedback control is its cost. Beyond the hardware cost, an installation, tuning, and maintenance cost is incurred.

Feedback control also applies to discrete processes. For example, a solenoid valve has only two valid states, open or closed. Often limit switches are attached to the valve to determine if the valve reaches the commanded state. If the controller commands the valve to open and the open limit switch is still **off** after 10 seconds, then the valve (or the limit switch) has failed, and the system must take corrective action, such as shutting down the system. At the very least, an alarm is generated to inform the operator of the problem. In this example, the limit switches provide the feedback to the discrete controller.

10.2 FEEDBACK CONTROL PERFORMANCE

The block diagram of a typical feedback control system for a single-input, single-output (SISO) control system is shown in Figure 10.10. A controller compares the process variable measurement with the setpoint and calculates a control variable to maintain the setpoint. For simplicity, the final control element, process, and measuring device are often lumped together and called the "process," as in Figure 10.11.

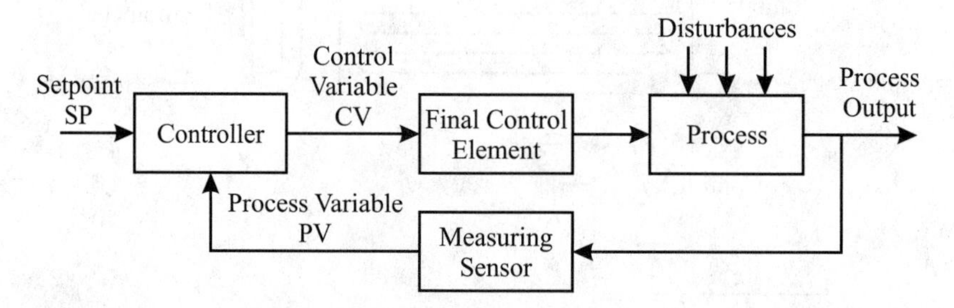

Figure 10.10. General single-input, single-output (SISO) control system.

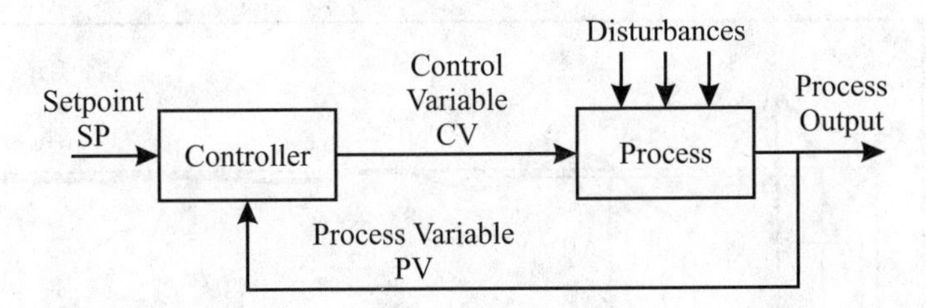

Figure 10.11. Simplified SISO control system.

Regardless of the particular controller algorithm, there are four general advantages of a feedback control system compared with an open-loop system (Dorf, 2000; Erickson and Hedrick, 1999; Phillips and Harbor, 1999):

1. Increased speed of response
2. Reduced error
3. Disturbance rejection
4. Reduced sensitivity to modeling errors

Ultimately, the controller forces the process variable to follow a setpoint value by adjusting the control variable. Sometimes, the setpoint is not a constant but a trajectory. For most systems, it is impossible to make the process variable perfectly follow the setpoint. Hence, quantitative control performance measures are needed to judge the quality of the controller. These performance measures are based on the response to the two external inputs to the system: setpoint changes and disturbance changes.

10.2.1 Setpoint Input Changes

The most common control loop performance measures are based on changes to the setpoint. In many processes, the setpoint is held constant for long periods of time, as in the pressure of a steam header. In others, the setpoint is changed at frequent intervals, as in the temperature of a batch reactor. In still other cases, the setpoint assumes a profile. For example, in metal annealing, the furnace temperature is ramped from an initial temperature to a final temperature, held constant for a period of time, and then ramped back to the initial temperature. However, the common control performance measures are based on a step change in the setpoint, which corresponds to the situation where an operator or supervisory controller makes an abrupt change in the setpoint and waits for the process variable to reach a steady-state value. Typical control variable and process variable responses are shown in Figure 10.12. The responses in Figure 10.12 are indicative of an *underdamped* process. The following aspects of these curves are used to evaluate the control system performance.

Offset. The difference between the setpoint and the process variable when the system has reached steady state is called the offset. For most systems, the desired offset is zero.

Rise Time. The time required for the process variable to go from 10% to 90% of the steady-state change is the rise time T_r. Generally, a short rise time is desired, although a short rise time often requires a rapid control variable change, leading to increased wear of the final control element. The short rise time is only relative and usually refers to a rise time shorter than the rise time of the system with no control. The rise time cannot be arbitrarily

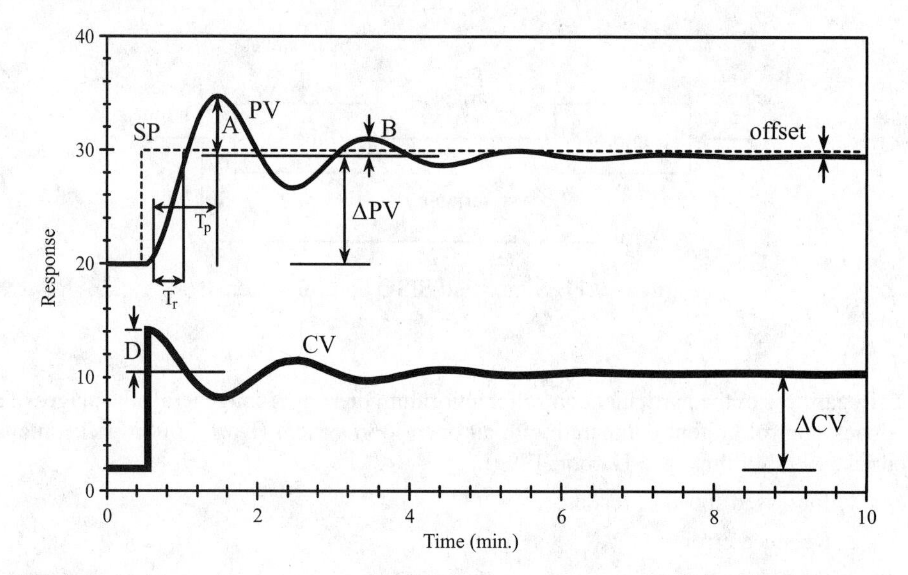

Figure 10.12. Typical process and control variable response to step setpoint change.

short, since given the constraints on the magnitudes of the control variable, there is a shortest achievable rise time.

Percent Overshoot. The amount that the process variable proceeds beyond its final value is called the overshoot (*A* in Figure 10.12). Obviously, if the process variable response does not contain a peak whose value exceeds the final value (commonly called an overdamped response), the overshoot is zero. The *percent overshoot* (PO), defined as

$$\mathrm{PO} = \frac{\mathrm{A}}{\Delta \mathrm{PV}} \times 100\%$$

is often used as the performance measure in place of the overshoot, since it is a relative measure that does not depend on the setpoint change magnitude. Generally, little or no overshoot is desirable in a process control system since overshoot has a detrimental effect on downstream processes.

Peak Time. The peak time T_p is the time from the setpoint step change to the time of the first peak of an underdamped process variable response. The peak time and the rise time are closely related, and so usually only one of them is used.

Damping Ratio. If the process variable response is underdamped, the damping ratio is the ratio of the second peak to the first peak in the response (*B*/*A* in Figure 10.12). Usually, a small ratio is desired.

Settling Time. The settling time T_s is the time from the setpoint change to the time that the process variable response has settled within a certain percentage band of the final value, usually 2 or 5%. Generally, a short rise time also means a short settling time. As for the rise time, a short settling time is desired.

Integral Error. The cumulative deviation of the process variable from the setpoint can be measured a number of ways. The two most frequently used measurements are:

Integral of the absolute error (IAE):

$$\text{IAE} = \int_0^\infty |\text{SP}(t) - \text{PV}(t)|\,dt \tag{10.1}$$

Integral of the product of time and the absolute error (ITAE):

$$\text{ITAE} = \int_0^\infty t|\text{SP}(t) - \text{PV}(t)|\,dt \tag{10.2}$$

The IAE is the most common performance measurement in this group. When the process variable is a quality measurement, like concentration, the IAE basically measures the total amount of off-specification material produced by the system. The ITAE penalizes deviations that endure for a long time.

Control Variable Percent Overshoot. The control (manipulated) variable overshoot is calculated in the same manner as the percent overshoot of the process variable. It is an indication of the amount of control effort needed to produce the closed-loop process variable response. A higher control variable percent overshoot (CVPO) usually means more wear on the final control element, a valve in many process control systems:

$$\text{CVPO} = \frac{\text{D}}{\Delta\text{CV}} \times 100\%$$

10.2.2 Disturbance Input Changes

Disturbances are uncontrolled inputs to the process that affect the process variable. These inputs generally cause significant deviations from the setpoint if corrective action is not taken. The major types of disturbances encountered in process control are step disturbances, stochastic disturbances, and ramp disturbances.

Step Disturbance. A disturbance characterized by a large, abrupt change in its value is modeled as a step signal. Typical manipulated variable and process variable responses to a step disturbance are shown in Figure 10.13. The performance measures for the process variable response are largely the same, except that the rise time and percent overshoot are replaced by the *maximum deviation*, which has meaning only in the context of a disturbance response. The maximum deviation measures the maximum effect of the disturbance on the

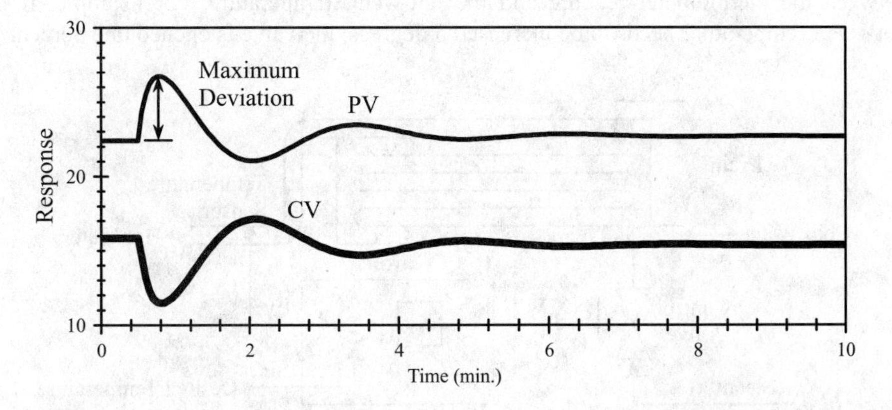

Figure 10.13. Typical process and control variable response to step disturbance change.

process variable response, and obviously, a small value is desired. In the heat exchanger (Figure 10.5), an abrupt change in the heated water flow is a step disturbance.

Stochastic Disturbance. Stochastic disturbances are those seemingly random upsets that disturb the system from the steady state. Their average value is zero, so they do not have the major effects on the process variable that step disturbances have. Nevertheless, their effect can be dramatic on the expected performance as will be demonstrated by the controller tuning examples. The only stochastic disturbance considered in this text is measurement noise, since a small amount of it is present in any real system and the quantization process used to convert the measurement into a value to be used by the digital control algorithm introduces its own noise.

Ramp Disturbance. Ramp-like disturbances generally correspond to environmental factors such as ambient outside temperature. They will not be directly used in the design procedure.

10.3 PID CONTROLLER

The most common industrial controller is based on the PID algorithm. After explaining each part of the basic algorithm, other parameters that must be set in a commercial PID controller are explained. The operational modes of a PID controller are described and then guidance concerning which terms should be selected is presented before the tuning procedures are presented.

Even though all of the PLC vendors implement some form of the digital PID controller, both the analog and digital PID terms are described. Historically, the analog PID controller has existed much longer. Also, its equations are simpler and therefore easier to understand.

10.3.1 PID Controller Terms

The three parts (often called *terms*) of the PID controller are (1) proportional, (2) integral, and (3) derivative. These terms are first explained from an intuitive viewpoint and then the specific equations are described. Each part of the algorithm is explained as follows:

1. *Proportional*. The control variable is calculated as a constant (gain) multiplied by the error (setpoint minus process variable). The proportional gain is analogous to the operator in Figure 10.8 adjusting the valve position in an amount proportional to the difference between the thermometer reading and the hot-water temperature. For example, if the hot-water temperature needs to be increased 5 degrees, the valve is opened one percent. A

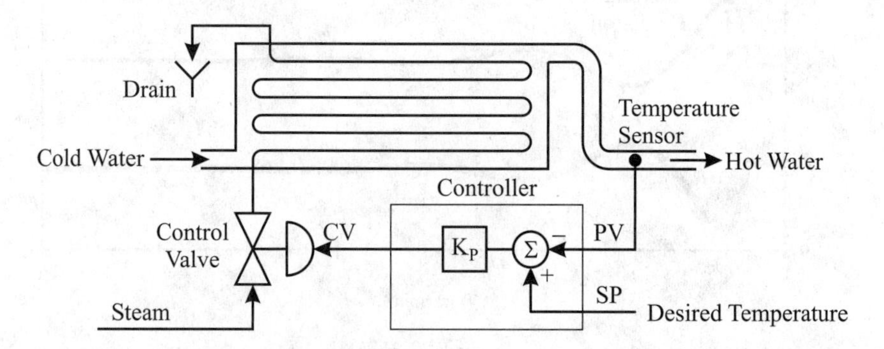

Figure 10.14. Proportional control for heat exchanger.

proportional-only controller for the heat exchanger is shown in Figure 10.14. The equation for the proportional term is commonly expressed as

$$\mathrm{CV}(t) = K_P(\mathrm{SP}(t) - \mathrm{PV}(t)) = K_P e(t)$$

where K_P is the proportional gain and e is the error. The proportional action reduces the error between the setpoint and the process variable but does not eliminate it. Increasing the proportional gain also speeds up the response of the closed-loop system. However, there is usually a practical upper limit because increasing the proportional gain often causes increased oscillation. If the proportional gain is too high, the system is usually unstable.

2. *Integral.* The control variable calculation is based on the integrated error. The integral term is analogous to the operator in Figure 10.8 returning periodically to check the hot-water temperature. Each time the hot-water temperature is checked, the valve position is adjusted by an amount proportional to the difference between the thermometer reading and the desired hot-water temperature. For example, every hour the hot-water temperature is checked and the valve is opened one percent for every 3 degrees low and closed one percent for every 3 degrees high. As long as the hot-water temperature is not equal to the desired temperature, the steam valve position is changed. Integral action is added to the heat exchanger controller in Figure 10.15. Integral action drives the error to zero. Integral action is also called reset. The equation for integral action is commonly

$$\mathrm{CV}(t) = \frac{1}{T_I}\int_0^t e(t)dt \qquad \text{or} \qquad \mathrm{CV}(t) = K_I\int_0^t e(t)dt$$

where T_I is called the integral time constant in units of minutes or seconds. On some controllers, the integral gain is specified, which is related to the integral time constant as

$$K_I = 1/T_I$$

and whose units are repeats per minute or repeats per second. In digital controllers, the integration is approximated by a summation,

$$\mathrm{CV}(n) = \frac{T}{T_I}\sum_{i=0}^{n} e(i) = \mathrm{CV}(n-1) + \frac{T}{T_I}[e(n)]$$

where T is the sample period, n is the current sample number, and $e(n)$ is the error at the nth sampling instant.

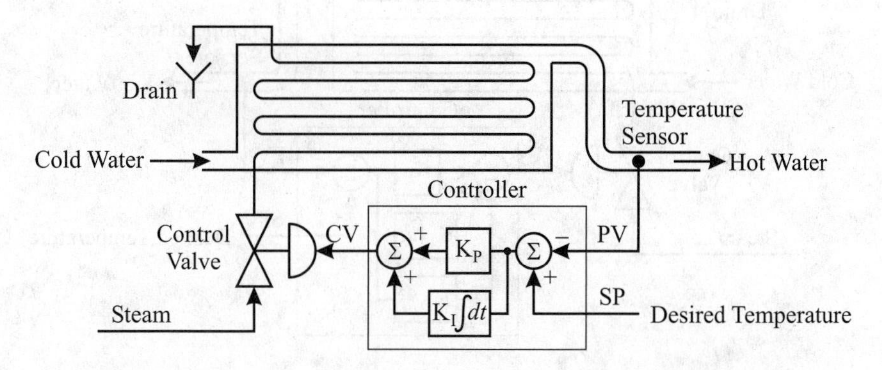

Figure 10.15. Proportional and integral (PI) control for heat exchanger.

The integral term is mainly used to force the offset to zero. However, it generally tends to slow the system down, in contrast to the proportional term. As the integral time constant is reduced (integral gain increased), the system response becomes more oscillatory. A small enough value of the integral time constant will cause the system to become unstable.

When a controller has integral action, a persistent error will cause the integral term to increase (or decrease) to a value of large magnitude. The integral term does not become smaller until the sign of the error changes. This situation is called integral windup. Many commercial controllers limit the value of the integral term and/or modify the integral action when this situation is encountered to temporarily decrease the integral gain as the magnitude of the error decreases but before the error changes sign.

3. *Derivative*. Also called *rate action*, the control variable calculation is based on the rate of change of the process variable. The derivative term is analogous to the operator in Figure 10.8 "spiking" the steam valve position in an amount proportional to the difference between the thermometer reading and the new hot-water temperature. For example, if the hot-water temperature needs to be increased quickly 5 degrees, the valve is opened 5 percent for one minute and then closed 4 percent. Derivative action is added to the heat exchanger controller in Figure 10.16. The equation for derivative action is

$$\mathrm{CV}(t)=T_D\frac{d}{dt}[e(t)] \qquad \text{or} \qquad \mathrm{CV}(t)=K_D\frac{d}{dt}[e(t)]$$

where T_D is called the derivative time constant in minutes or seconds. On some controllers, the derivative gain, K_D, is specified, which is equal to the derivative time constant. In reality, a pure derivative amplifies any measurement noise so controllers implement a filtered derivative,

$$T_D s \approx \frac{T_D s}{\alpha s+1} \qquad \text{or} \qquad T_D s \approx \frac{T_D s+1}{\alpha T_D s+1}, \tag{10.3}$$

where α has a value of about 10. In digital controllers, the derivative may be approximated by a difference,

$$\mathrm{CV}(n)=\frac{T_D}{T}[e(n)-e(n-1)]=\frac{T_D}{T}\Delta e(n)$$

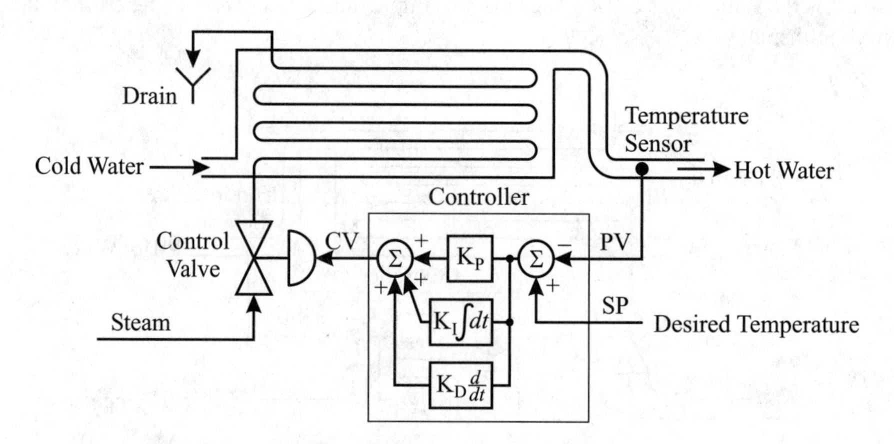

Figure 10.16. Proportional-integral-derivative (PID) control for heat exchanger.

where T is the sample period and n is the current sample number. Most PLC vendors use a discrete equivalent of (10.3) as the derivative term for the digital PID controller.

Major changes in disturbances are anticipated by derivative (rate) action. The derivative term also tends to cancel the effect of the integral action in slowing down the system response. However, the use of derivative action should be restricted to those processes where the process variable, the controlled variable measurement, is noise free. Derivative action tends to amplify any noise in the measurement.

Of course, there are many possible combinations of these three actions. For example, a P controller has only proportional action, a PI controller has proportional and integral action, and so on. The K_P, T_I, and T_D (or K_P, K_I, and K_D) are called the PID tuning parameters.

10.3.2 Forms of the Equation

There are essentially eight forms of the basic PID equation. Depending on the vendor, one may or may not have a chance to select the particular PID algorithm form. The various choices for algorithm type are:

Interacting (ISA standard) versus noninteracting (independent gains)
Derivative-on-error versus derivative-on-measurement
Positional versus velocity

In the noninteracting form of the PID equation, all three terms are calculated independently and summed to obtain the manipulated variable. In the interacting form, the K_P modifies the integral and derivative terms. In most industrial situations, derivative action on the measurement is generally preferred to derivative action on the error, because then setpoint changes do not cause a large change in the control variable. In the positional form of the PID algorithm, the value of the control variable is calculated. In order to initialize the algorithm correctly, an initial bias term must be specified. In the velocity form of the PID, the change in the control variable is calculated. The velocity form may also be called the incremental form. Block diagrams of all combinations of interaction and derivative action are shown in Figures 10.17 and 10.18 for the positional form of the algorithm. For the continuous (analog) PID, the four possible equations for the positional forms of the algorithm are:

Interacting, derivative on error (Figure 10.17*a*):

$$\text{CV}(t) = K_P\left(e(t) + \frac{1}{T_I}\int e(t) + T_D\frac{d}{dt}e(t)\right) + \text{Bias}$$

Interacting, derivative on measurement (Figure 10.17*b*):

$$\text{CV}(t) = K_P\left(e(t) + \frac{1}{T_I}\int e(t) - T_D\frac{d}{dt}\text{PV}(t)\right) + \text{Bias}$$

Noninteracting, derivative on error (Figure 10.18*a*):

$$\text{CV}(t) = K_P e(t) + \frac{1}{T_I}\int e(t) + T_D\frac{d}{dt}e(t) + \text{Bias}$$

Noninteracting, derivative on measurement (Figure 10.18*b*):

$$\text{CV}(t) = K_P e(t) + \frac{1}{T_I}\int e(t) - T_D\frac{d}{dt}\text{PV}(t) + \text{Bias}$$

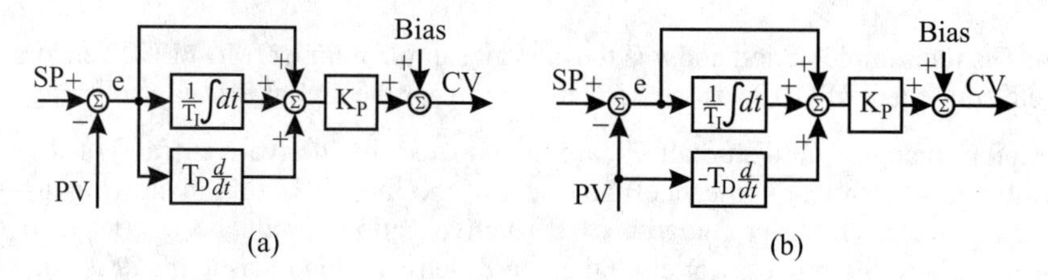

Figure 10.17. Forms of the interacting positional PID algorithm: *(a)* derivative on error; *(b)* derivative on measurement.

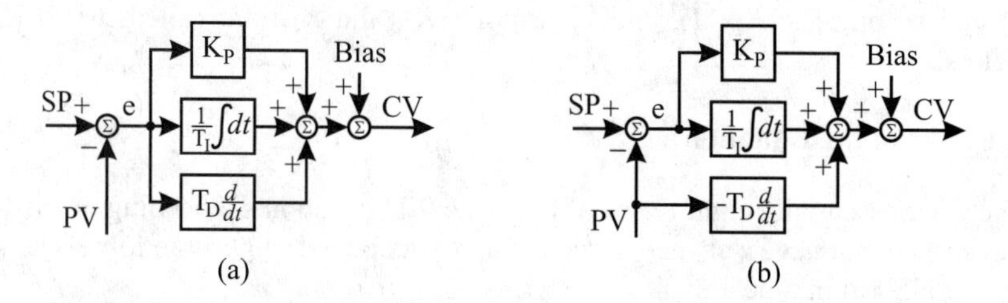

Figure 10.18. Forms of the noninteracting positional PID algorithm: *(a)* derivative on error; *(b)* derivative on measurement.

When implemented in a PLC, the four possibilities for the positional form of the digital PID equation are:

Interacting, derivative on error (Figure 10.17*a*):

$$\mathrm{CV}(n) = K_P\left(e(n) + \frac{T}{T_I}\sum_i e(i) + \frac{T_D}{T}\Delta e(n)\right) + \mathrm{Bias}$$

Interacting, derivative on measurement (Figure 10.17*b*):

$$\mathrm{CV}(n) = K_P\left(e(n) + \frac{T}{T_I}\sum_i e(i) - \frac{T_D}{T}\Delta \mathrm{PV}(n)\right) + \mathrm{Bias}$$

Noninteracting, derivative on error (Figure 10.18*a*):

$$\mathrm{CV}(n) = K_P e(n) + \frac{T}{T_I}\sum_i e(i) + \frac{T_D}{T}\Delta e(n) + \mathrm{Bias}$$

Noninteracting, derivative on measurement (Figure 10.18*b*):

$$\mathrm{CV}(n) = K_P e(n) + \frac{T}{T_I}\sum_i e(i) - \frac{T_D}{T}\Delta \mathrm{PV}(n) + \mathrm{Bias}$$

For the continuous PID controller, the velocity forms of the equations are not possible. So, the velocity form only applies to the digital PID algorithm. The four types of PID equations are obtained by subtracting CV*(n-1)* from CV*(n)*. The block diagrams of these equations look similar to the diagrams for the positional PID (Figures 10.17 and 10.18) except that the *Bias* signal is replaced by CV*(n-1)*. For brevity, only the equation for the interacting, derivative on error (Figure 10.17*a*) is shown:

$$\mathrm{CV}(n) = \mathrm{CV}(n-1) + K_P\left(\Delta e(n) + \frac{T}{T_I}e(n) + \frac{T_D}{T}[e(n) - 2e(n-1) + e(n-2)]\right)$$

Note that actual implementations of the digital PID controller are more complex than the equations presented here. As indicated earlier, the derivative term is generally filtered. Also, the integral gain is often modified to handle integral windup.

Concerning these PID algorithm choices, only the derivative-on-error versus derivative-on-measurement may be critical to the control engineer. If the user needs the derivative action, then derivative-on-measurement is preferred because a setpoint change does not induce a large change in the controller output, which happens if the derivative is on the error. The vendor has often already made the choice of positional versus velocity forms of the equations. The particular choice will have an impact on such issues as initialization and bumpless transfer. The choice between interacting versus noninteracting affects the tuning rule equations. For example, if the tuning rules calculate the parameters for an interacting PID, divide the T_I by K_P and multiply the T_D by K_P to obtain the noninteracting parameters.

10.3.3 Other Controller Parameter Selections

Besides the main PID parameters K_P, T_I, and T_D and the choices for the PID equation form, there are other parameter selections that must be made before the controller can be operational.

Direct and Reverse Action. The sign relationship of the process variable to the control variable is specified through the direct/reverse selection. Direct and reverse action refers to the sign of the gain of the controller. The control action should be set as follows:

Specify the control action as *direct acting* if the CV must increase to correct for an increasing PV.

Specify the control action as *reverse acting* if the CV must decrease to correct for an increasing PV.

For a reverse-acting controller (Figures 10.17 and 10.18), the error is

Error = SP - PV

For a direct-acting controller, the error is

Error = PV - SP

Note that a reverse-acting controller is connected to a direct-acting process, that is, an increase in CV causes an increase in the PV measurement. A direct-acting controller is connected to a reverse-acting process, that is, an increase in CV causes a decrease in the PV measurement.

The difference between reverse- and direct-acting controllers is illustrated in the two possible level control schemes of Figure 10.19. Assume the valves are increase-open, that is, an increase in the CV output from the controller causes the valve to open further. In this case, the PID controller in Figure 10.19*a* is direct acting. When the level measurement is above the setpoint, the outlet valve needs to be opened to decrease the level to the setpoint. If the control valve is moved to control the inlet flow (Figure 10.19*b*), the controller is reverse acting. In this case, when the level measurement is above the setpoint, the inlet valve needs to be closed to decrease the level to the setpoint.

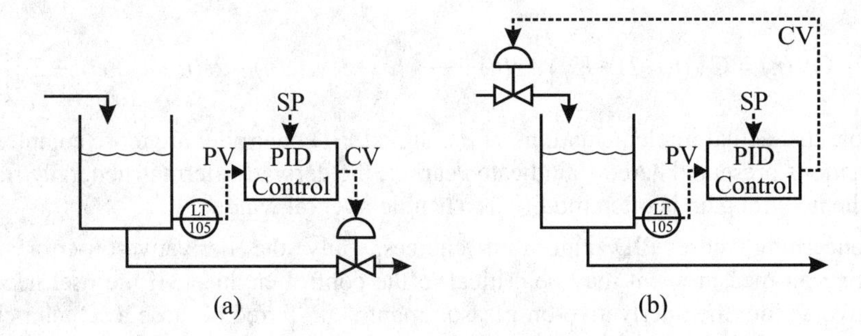

Figure 10.19. Direct- versus reverse-acting control (increase-open valves): *(a)* direct-acting control; *(b)* reverse-acting control.

The type of valve is selected based on whether the valve should fail open or fail closed if the control system fails and/or system power is removed. Note that if the valves in Figure 10.19 are increase-close, then the type of controller also changes. For an increase-close valve, the controller in Figure 10.19*a* is reverse acting, and the controller in Figure 10.19*b* is direct acting.

If one happens to set this parameter to the wrong value, the manipulated variable will often move to its maximum or minimum value and remain there, often causing the process variable to go to one extreme, generally an undesirable response.

Design Tip

Make sure you properly set the reverse/direct parameter.

Bumpless Transfer. This important parameter is often overlooked when configuring a controller. Without bumpless transfer, when the controller mode is switched from manual to automatic, the error between the process variable and setpoint generally causes an abrupt change in the control variable. This abrupt change can damage equipment (e.g., "bang valves") and/or upset downstream processes with the process variable oscillations that often result. With bumpless transfer, when the controller mode is switched from manual to automatic, the initial CV output is not changed, and the CV is ramped to the calculated value. The equipment and the process better tolerate this gradual change in the control variable. Depending on the controller vendor, bumpless transfer may be part of the algorithm and cannot be disabled. For others, specifying a parameter enables/disables bumpless transfer.

Loop Sample Period. The PID algorithm should be executed at a fixed, periodic interval called the loop sample period or loop sample time. The loop sample period is related to the dynamics of the controlled process. For example, a slow process, such as a temperature process will need a loop sample period of one second or longer. A flow loop generally requires a loop sample period of about 0.25 seconds. Motion control may require a loop sample period of milliseconds, which is why motion control is often not done in the PLC but in dedicated motion control modules.

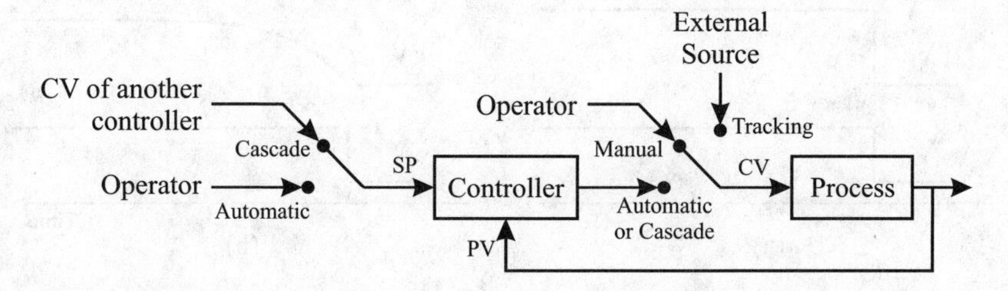

Figure 10.20. Controller setpoint and control variable source determined by mode switch.

10.3.4 Basic Controller Modes

The term *mode* indicates the state of the controller. The PID algorithm really only has two states: manual and automatic. Nevertheless, control vendors usually assign modes to the algorithm that indicate the source of the setpoint and/or the source of the controller output, the control variable. The most common modes are manual, automatic, tracking, and cascade. These modes indicate who or what has control of the setpoint and/or control variable and generally provide some protection against inadvertent manipulation of the setpoint or control variable by another device or operator. When the controller is in the automatic mode, the controller calculates the manipulated variable according to the PID equation, and the operator changes the setpoint. When the controller is in the manual mode, the operator sets the control variable, and the PID equation is not executed. When the controller is in the tracking mode, the control variable tracks another variable, usually the output of another controller. When in the manual or tracking modes, the internal variables of the PID algorithm are modified so that the calculated CV matches the tracked variable so there is a bumpless transfer when the mode is changed to automatic. When the controller is in the cascade mode, the setpoint is supplied from another controller or device (not the operator) and the PID algorithm calculates the control variable. The cascade mode is prevalent among the DCS vendors and not common in PLCs. The mode can be considered as a switch at the controller output and/or setpoint, as in Figure 10.20.

Ordinarily, when the controller starts up, it is in the manual mode. When the controller mode is switched from manual to automatic, most controllers implement some form of bumpless transfer, so that the control variable does not make an abrupt change due to any error between the process variable and the setpoint. When the controller mode is switched from automatic to manual, the control variable is retained at its last calculated value or some default value (if the controller can be configured in this manner).

10.3.5 PID Term Selection

Depending on the controller manufacturer, different combinations of proportional, integral, and derivative terms may be selected. Also, by setting the derivative gain to zero, the controller reduces to a PI controller. By setting the proportional gain and the derivative gain of a noninteracting PID controller to zero, the PID controller reduces to an I-only controller. The selection of controller terms should be based on the type of process, that is, how the process variable reacts to a change in the control variable.

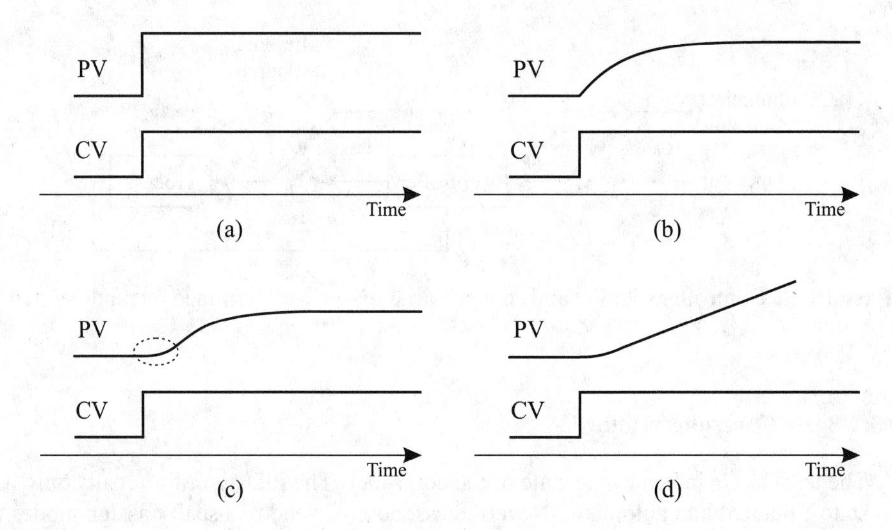

Figure 10.21. Process responses: *(a)* gain-only; *(b)* first-order lag; *(c)* second-order lag; *(d)* integrating.

Gain-Only Process: I Controller. When the response of the process variable to a change in the manipulated parameter is instantaneous (Figure 10.21*a*), the process is a gain only, and only the integral term is required. Example processes that are essentially only a gain are:

Speed control of centrifugal compressors
Liquid flow control when a fast actuator is used

First-Order Lag Process: PI Controller. When the process can be adequately represented as a first-order lag (Figure 10.21*b*), both proportional and integral terms should be used. The majority of industrial processes fall into this category. Example first-order processes are:

Gas pressure control
Liquid flow control with slow actuators
Concentration control

Second-Order Low-Noise Process: PID Controller. When the process is best represented as a second-order lag (Figure 10.21*c*) ***and*** the process variable contains little noise, then the derivative term should be used with the proportional and integral terms. It is important to remember that the derivative term will amplify any noise present on the process variable. Therefore, the derivative term is generally used sparingly. An example low-noise second-order process is:

Temperature control loops, where the lag of the temperature bulb and thermowell is significant when compared to the process lag

Note that the second-order response is distinguished from the first-order response by the more gradual initial change in the process variable.

Integrating Process: P Controller. If the process is best represented as an integrator (Figure 10.21*d*), the process is not self-regulating, and only the proportional term is required.

However, some integral action may be needed if the integration time is long (slope of process variable response curve is small). An example integrating process is:

Tank level control by regulation of the outflow or inflow.

10.4 PID CONTROLLER TUNING

There are many techniques of controller tuning. The ones presented here are the most popular techniques and will allow one to determine the parameters for reasonably good control. In many cases, the performance of the system may be adequate when tuned with these methods. In practice, one will use one or more of the following techniques to get the parameters "in the ballpark" and then adjust the parameters until the desired performance is obtained, or until one runs out of time.

Most processes may be approximated as being linear over a small operating range. However, over a wide range of operation, most processes will exhibit some nonlinearity in the form of a process gain change. As a general rule, tuning should be done at the operating point where the maximum gain occurs. Then when the process moves to an operating point where the gain is lower, the control becomes more sluggish but does not become unstable.

The specification of the desired system response should include both the desired process variable and control (manipulated) variable responses. Some general rules follow:

- There is a trade-off between speed of response and the amount of overshoot in the process response. Usually, a fast process variable response also causes the process variable to overshoot its desired value before settling to the desired value.
- The required control variable changes to achieve the desired process variable response should be considered. A process variable response that closely follows a setpoint generally requires vigorous control variable action and excessive wear on the final control element. If the apparent process gain increases because the process is at a new operating point, the system may become unstable.
- For a given set of tuning parameters, the response to a setpoint change will not be the same as the response to a disturbance change.

There are two major categories of tuning methods: (1) closed-loop and (2) open-loop tuning. Closed-loop tuning refers to tuning the controller while it is operating in the automatic mode, and thus is operating in the closed loop. Open-loop tuning methods base the initial tuning of the PID parameters on the empirical first-order-plus-deadtime process model, obtained while the controller is in the manual mode. Both of these methods have their advantages and disadvantages.

Closed-loop tuning, whether done by the operator or autotuned by the controller, is probably the most popular technique of controller tuning. Autotuning available for the Modicon PLC is discussed since it is a standard function block. For the other PLCs discussed in this text, autotuning is provided by third-party vendors and are not discussed in this text. All tuning techniques, including autotuning, require that the process be "bumped" in order to evaluate the effect of the tuning parameters and/or calculate a new set of tuning parameters. Closed-loop tuning techniques are applicable to reasonably fast processes that can tolerate process variable oscillations. On the other hand, open-loop tuning techniques work well for slow processes but require a process model. In the author's opinion, the Fertik open-loop tuning method yields the best response for process control since the overshoot is minimal.

Design Tip

Be mindful of the unit used to measure time. Whatever unit (seconds or minutes) the vendor uses should be used throughout the calculations for any of the tuning methods. For example, if T_I is expressed in seconds, then any time that is measured as part of the tuning procedure should be measured in seconds.

10.4.1 Settings for Plant Startup

Initial controller parameter values that may be used during a plant startup are given in Table 10.1. The values are conservative and will normally result in a sluggish process variable response. These parameter values are general guidelines and serve to get a plant operating, after which the tuning techniques outlined in the succeeding sections should be used to change the parameters to provide the desired response at normal operating conditions.

Table 10.1 Initial PID Controller Parameter Values

	K_P	T_I (min.)	T_D (min.)
Flow	0.3	1.0	0
Temperature	1.3	0.5	0.05
Liquid level	2.0	50.0	0
Gas pressure	5.0	50.0	0

10.4.2 Effects of Controller Terms

The following tuning techniques are based on the following observations about the process (closed-loop) response:

- As the controller proportional gain is increased, the response to setpoint changes becomes more oscillatory, commonly called underdamped (Figure 10.22*a*).
- At some greater gain, the response of the control loop will become a steady-state oscillation (Figure 10.22*b*). The manipulated variable and process variable will be one-half of a cycle (180°) out of phase at this gain. The system is called "marginally stable."
- If the gain is increased past the point where steady-state oscillation is observed, the control loop will become unstable, and the oscillations will increase in amplitude (Figure 10.22*c*). The frequency of the oscillation is determined by the process dynamics.

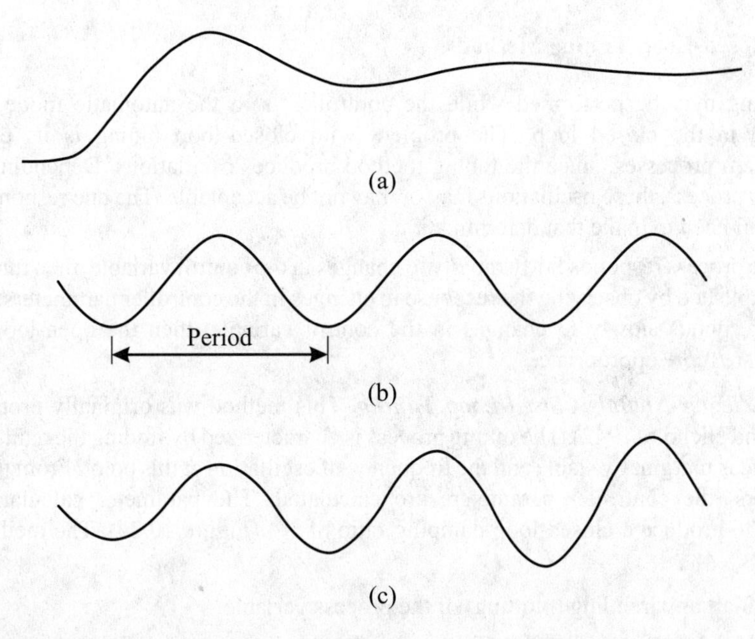

Figure 10.22. Types of oscillatory response: *(a)* underdamped; *(b)* sustained oscillation; *(c)* unstable.

The effect of the proportional, integral, and derivative gains on controller gains at different frequencies may be illustrated by examining the contribution of each controller term to a slow change in the error signal (low frequency) and a fast change in the error signal (high frequency), as shown in Figure 10.23:

The effect of the proportional gain is the same for all frequencies.

Integral gain is more responsive to low frequencies.

Derivative gain is more responsive to high frequencies.

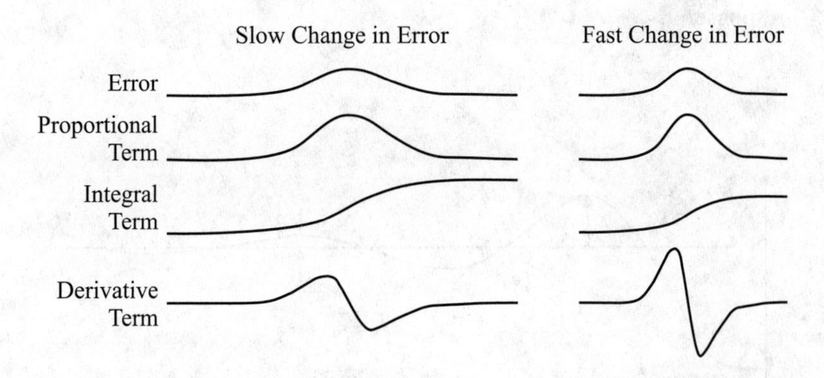

Figure 10.23. Contribution of each controller term to a change in error.

10.4.3 Closed-Loop Tuning Methods

Tuning may be performed while the controller is in the automatic mode, that is, operating in the closed loop. The problem with closed-loop tuning is its effect on downstream processes, since the tuning method produces oscillations. Depending on the particular process, these oscillations may or may not be acceptable. The one responsible for tuning will need to make that determination.

If the process responds fairly rapidly to changes in the control variable, then tuning may be accomplished by observing the response to changes in the controller parameters. When a process responds slowly to changes in the control variable, then the open-loop tuning methods are more appropriate.

10.4.3.1 Ziegler-Nichols Closed-Loop Tuning. This method was originally proposed by Ziegler and Nichols (1942). The tuning process is characterized by finding the gain at which the system is marginally stable and the frequency of oscillation at this point. From these two parameters, the controller parameters are calculated. The parameter calculations are intended to produce a closed-loop damping ratio of 1/4 (Figure 10.24). The method is as follows:

1. Start any trending (plotting) of the process variable.
2. If the process is listed in Table 10.1, set the K_P to the initial gain in Table 10.1. Otherwise, set K_P to a small value. Set T_D to zero and the T_I time constant to its maximum value (or K_I to zero). Now place the controller in the automatic mode.
3. If one is not sure how the process will react, increase the proportional gain in small steps. If small changes in K_P are not causing oscillation, make larger changes, but no larger than doubling the K_P. After each adjustment, observe the process variable or control variable response to a setpoint change. When sustained oscillations (**Figure 10.22*b***) are observed, note the value of the proportional gain and the period of the oscillations:

   G_u = proportional gain for sustained oscillations

   P_u = period of oscillations (in appropriate time units)
4. Calculate the controller settings as shown in Table 10.2.
5. Make any final adjustments in K_P, T_I, or T_D to obtain the desired process variable response.

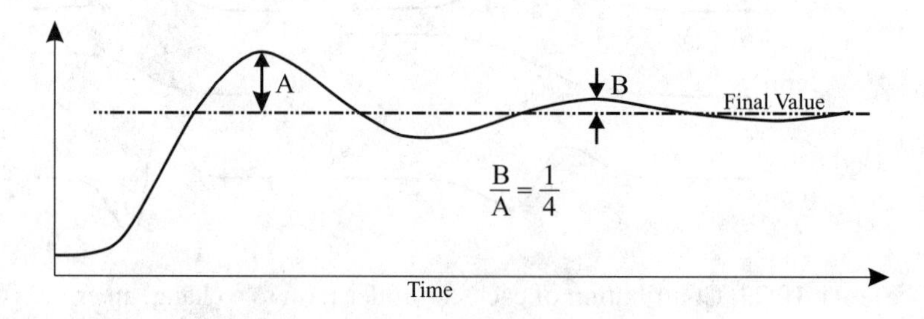

Figure 10.24. One-fourth damping ratio.

Table 10.2 Ziegler-Nichols Closed-Loop Tuning PID Parameters

	Interacting Equation	Noninteracting Equation
P controller		
K_P	$0.5G_u$	$0.5G_u$
PI controller		
K_P	$0.45G_u$	$0.45G_u$
T_I	$P_u/1.2$	$P_u/(1.2K_P)$
PID controller		
K_P	$0.6G_u$	$0.6G_u$
T_I	$P_u/2.0$	$P_u/(2.0K_P)$
T_D	$P_u/8.0$	$(P_uK_P)/8.0$

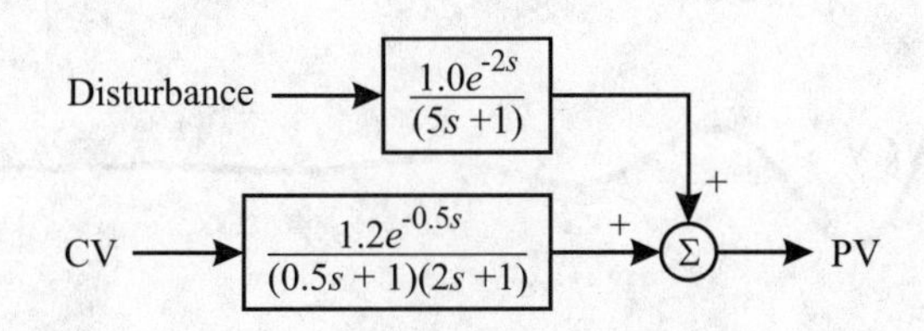

Figure 10.25. Process used for self-regulating tuning examples.

Example 10.1. For the process shown in block diagram in Figure 10.25, where the time constants are measured in minutes, tune a PI controller to control this process using the Ziegler-Nichols closed-loop tuning method.

Solution. The starting values of the controller parameters are

$$K_P = 0.1,\ T_I = 1000 \text{ min.},\ T_D = 0 \text{ min.}$$

Using proportional-only control, the gain K_P is increased until the response exhibits a sustained oscillation when the setpoint is changed by a small amount. The value of K_P for sustained oscillation is 5.0, and the sustained oscillation appears as in Figure 10.26. Actually, the oscillation is growing slightly for this gain. However, this situation corresponds to tuning under actual process conditions, since one does not usually have the time to observe very many oscillations. Thus the values of the ultimate gain and ultimate period are

$$G_u = 5.0$$

$$P_u = 3.1 \text{ min.}$$

If a PI controller is desired, the tuning parameters are:

$$K_P = 0.45\ G_u = 0.45 \times 5.0 = 2.25$$

$$T_I = P_u\ /1.2 = 3.1/1.2 = 2.58 \text{ min.}$$

The setpoint change response of the system with this PI controller is shown in Figure 10.27. The damping ratio is actually smaller than 1/4.

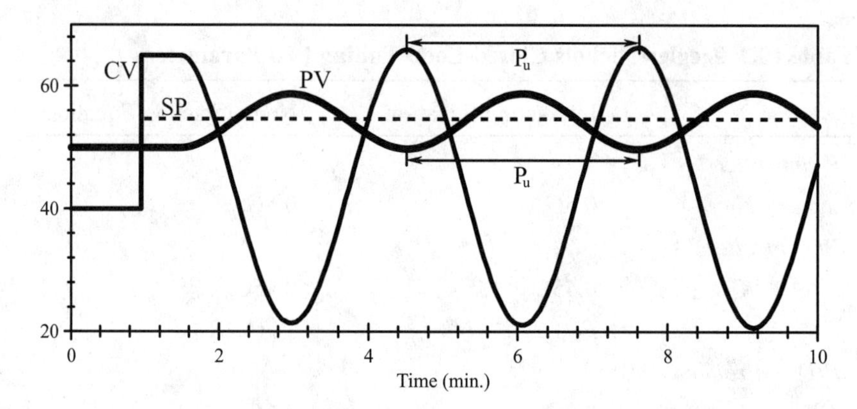

Figure 10.26. Sustained oscillations used in Zeigler-Nichols closed-loop tuning.

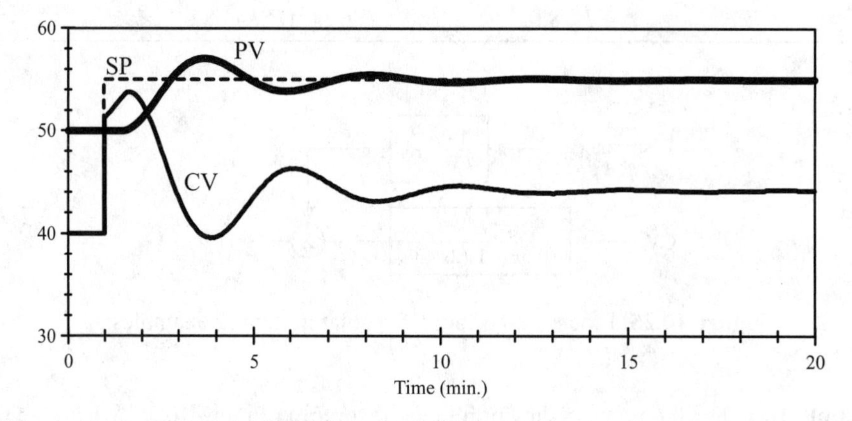

Figure 10.27. Response of system to a setpoint change when PI controller is tuned with Ziegler-Nichols closed-loop method.

10.4.3.2 Damped Oscillation Tuning Method. When it is undesirable to allow sustained oscillations, the following method is used. The process is characterized by finding the proportional gain at which the system has a one-fourth damping ratio (Figure 10.24) and the frequency of oscillation at this point. Similar to the Ziegler-Nichols method, the controller parameters are calculated from the gain and oscillation frequency. The method is as follows:

1. Start any trending (plotting) of the process variable.
2. If the process is listed in Table 10.1, set the K_P to the initial gain in Table 10.1. Otherwise, set K_P to a small value. Set T_D to zero and the T_I time constant to its maximum value (or K_I to zero). Now place the controller in the automatic mode.
3. Increase the proportional gain in small steps. After each adjustment, observe the process variable response to a setpoint change. When a one-fourth damping ratio is observed, note the value of the proportional gain and the period of the oscillations.

Table 10.3 Damped Oscillation Closed-Loop Tuning PID Parameters

	Interacting Equation	Noninteracting Equation
P controller		
K_P	$1.1G_d$	$1.1G_d$
PI controller		
K_P	$1.1G_d$	$1.1G_d$
T_I	$P_d/2.6$	$P_d/(2.6K_P)$
PID controller		
K_P	$1.1G_d$	$1.1G_d$
T_I	$P_d/3.6$	$P_d/(3.6K_P)$
T_D	$P_d/9.0$	$(P_dK_P)/9.0$

G_d = proportional gain for damping ratio of 1/4
P_d = period of oscillations (in appropriate time units)

4. Calculate the controller settings as shown in Table 10.3.
5. Make any final adjustments in K_P, T_I, or T_D to obtain the desired process variable response.

Example 10.2. For the same process as in Example 10.1, tune a PI controller to control this process using the damped oscillation tuning method.

Solution. The starting values of the controller parameters are:

$$K_P = 0.1,\ T_I = 1000 \text{ min.},\ T_D = 0 \text{ min.}$$

Using proportional-only control, the gain K_P is increased until the response exhibits a response with quarter-wave damping when the setpoint is changed by a small amount. The value of K_P for one-fourth damped oscillation is 2.75 and the period of the oscillation is 3.7 min. Thus,

$$G_d = 2.75$$
$$P_d = 3.7 \text{ min.}$$

If a PI controller is desired, the tuning parameters are:

$$K_P = 1.1G_d = 1.1 \times 2.75 = 3.0$$
$$T_I = P_d/2.6 = 3.7/2.6 = 1.42 \text{ min.}$$

The setpoint change response of the system with this PI controller is shown in Figure 10.28. Obviously, in this case the method does not produce acceptable results. Comparing the PI parameters to the previous example, the gain is too high and the integral time constant is too low. However, as indicated in the introductory remarks of this chapter, all of the tuning methods in this chapter are only designed to provide the engineer with a good starting point from which the parameters are further refined.

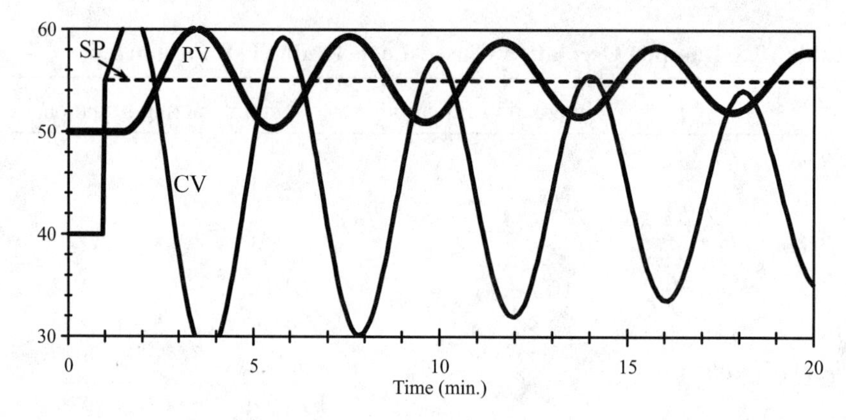

Figure 10.28. Response of system to a setpoint change when PI controller is tuned with damped oscillation method.

10.4.4 Open-Loop Tuning Methods

Tuning may be determined based on the process response to a step change in the control variable while the controller is in manual mode. However, the process is not being controlled during such tests. This technique can be used to determine the tuning of slow processes. All of the open-loop tuning methods for self-regulating processes (reaches a steady-state value after a step change in the manipulated variable) use a first-order-plus-deadtime model of the process. An integrator-plus-deadtime model is used to tune non-self-regulating processes. Open-loop tuning methods are most amenable to slow processes or for those processes for which a model has been determined.

10.4.4.1 First-Order Model of Self-Regulating Process. The transfer function of a general first-order-plus-deadtime (FODT) model is

$$G_{FODT}(s) = \frac{Ke^{-s\theta_D}}{\tau s+1} \tag{10.4}$$

where

K = process gain,

θ_D = apparent process deadtime,

τ = apparent process time constant.

Many processes are higher than first order (contain more than one lag term) and so any first-order model will only be an approximation. However, the approximation is sufficient for tuning PID controllers.

The graphical procedure for determining the model is based on Ziegler and Nichols (1942). This method is based on features of the response of (10.4) to a step input of magnitude A,

$$y(t) = KA\left(1 - e^{-(t-\theta_D)/\tau}\right)$$

This response is evaluated when the exponent is one ($t = \theta_D + \tau$). When the exponent is one, the value of the response is

$$y(t) = KA\left(1 - e^{-1}\right) = 0.632KA$$

In other words, the response reaches 63.2% of its change when $t = \theta_D + \tau$. Given a response plot as shown in Figure 10.29, the procedure to find the gain, apparent deadtime, and apparent time constant is as follows:

1. Start any trending (plotting) of the PV and CV. The units of the PV and CV must be in percent of span since that is the unit used in the controller calculation.
2. Place the controller in manual mode and allow the process to reach steady state (PV is a "flat line").
3. Impose a step change in the controller output (CV).
4. Allow the process to reach steady state.
5. Stop any trending of the PV and CV and get a hard copy of the response curves.
6. Draw a tangent to the process variable response curve at its point of maximum slope, the point of inflection (Figure 10.29). In practice, this step may be tricky, especially if the response contains noise.
7. The term T_1 is the time at which the step change in the manipulated variable was imposed. T_2 is the time at which the tangent drawn in the previous step intersects the time axis, *drawn horizontally from the beginning of the process variable response curve*. The apparent process deadtime $\theta_D = T_2 - T_1$.
8. The term T_3 is the time at which the process variable response has made 63% of its total change. The apparent process time constant $\tau = T_3 - T_2$.
9. The process gain is the change in the process variable divided by the change in the control variable,

$$K = \frac{\Delta \text{PV}}{\Delta \text{CV}} = \frac{\text{PV}_2 - \text{PV}_1}{\text{CV}_2 - \text{CV}_1}$$

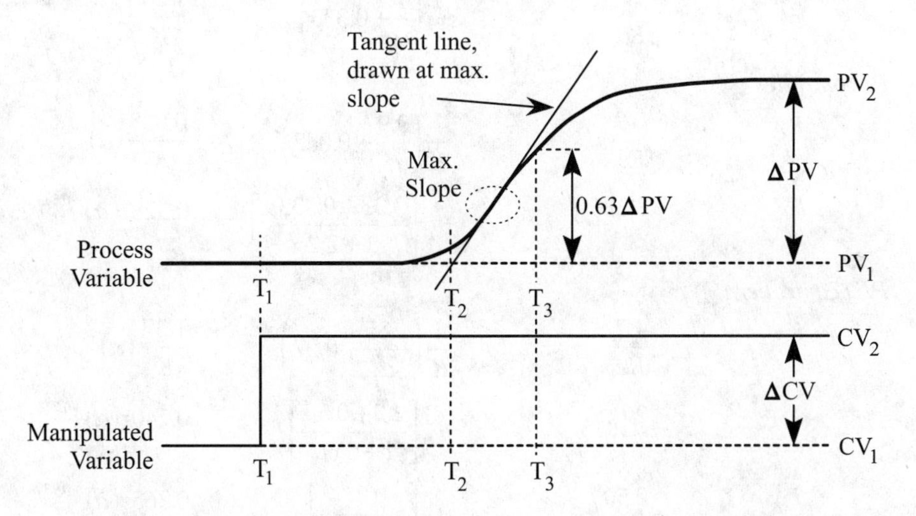

Figure 10.29. Determination of first-order approximate model.

10.4.4.2 Open-Loop Tuning of Self-Regulating Process. Given a first-order-plus-deadtime model that approximates the self–regulating process, there are a few methods one can use to calculate the tuning parameters. The Ziegler-Nichols open-loop tuning method (Ziegler and Nichols, 1942) and the two Cohen-Coon tuning methods (Cohen and Coon, 1953) result in similar tuning parameters. These three methods usually yield a set of parameters that generates an oscillatory response. A fourth method, proposed by Fertik (1975), yields a different set of tuning parameters. The Fertik method generally yields a nonoscillatory response, which is desirable for most process control applications. The rationales behind each of these methods are:

Ziegler-Nichols open-loop	Quarter-wave damping
Cohen-Coon	Quarter-wave damping
Cohen-Coon with constraints	Minimum IAE (Eqn. 10.1)
Fertik	Minimum ITAE (Eqn 10.2), <8% overshoot

Each method assumes a first order plus deadtime process model of the form of (10.4). The Ziegler-Nichols and Cohen-Coon open-loop tuning methods assume a process controllability, α,

$$\alpha = \frac{\theta_D}{\tau}$$

Table 10.4 Open-loop Tuning PID Parameters for Self-regulating Process

	Ziegler-Nichols open-loop	Cohen-Coon	Cohen-Coon with constraints
P controller			
K_P	$\frac{1}{K\alpha}$	$\frac{1}{K}\left(\frac{1}{\alpha}+0.333\right)$	$\frac{1.208}{K}(\alpha)^{-0.956}$
PI controller			
K_P	$\frac{0.9}{K\alpha}$	$\frac{1}{K}\left(\frac{0.9}{\alpha}+0.082\right)$	$\frac{0.928}{K}(\alpha)^{-0.946}$
T_I	$3.33\theta_D$	$\theta_D\left[\frac{3.33+0.333\alpha}{1+2.2\alpha}\right]$	$0.928\tau(\alpha)^{+0.583}$
PID controller			
K_P	$\frac{1.2}{K\alpha}$	$\frac{1}{K}\left(\frac{1.35}{\alpha}+0.27\right)$	$\frac{1.37}{K}(\alpha)^{-0.95}$
T_I	$2\theta_D$	$\theta_D\left[\frac{2.5+0.5\alpha}{1+0.6\alpha}\right]$	$0.740\tau(\alpha)^{+0.738}$
T_D	$0.5\theta_D$	$\theta_D\left[\frac{0.37}{1+0.2\alpha}\right]$	$0.365\tau(\alpha)^{+0.95}$

The K_P, T_I, or T_D are calculated from the first-order-plus-deadtime model parameters. The calculations also depend on the type of controller (P only, PI, or PID). Table 10.4 summarizes these calculations for the interacting PID equation.

Example 10.3. For the same process as in Example 10.1, tune a PI and a PID controller to control this process using the Ziegler-Nichols open-loop tuning method. Show the response of the system to setpoint and disturbance changes.

Solution. First, a first-order-plus-deadtime approximation to this process must be determined. The controller is placed in manual mode, and the PV response to a step change in CV is recorded in Figure 10.30. The approximate first-order-plus-deadtime model is obtained using the method outlined in section 10.4.4.1 and the pertinent information is marked on the response in Figure 10.30.

$\Delta CV = 8$

$\Delta PV = 44.6 - 35 = 9.6$

$T_1 = 12$ min.

$T_2 \approx 12.7$ min.

$T_3 \approx 15.1$ min. $\quad (0.63\Delta PV + PV_1 = 0.63(9.6) + 35 = 41.05)$

The model parameters are calculated as:

$$\theta_D = T_2 - T_1 = 12.7 - 12 = 0.7 \text{ min.}$$

$$\tau = T_3 - T_2 = 15.1 - 12.7 = 2.4 \text{ min.}$$

$$\text{Gain} = K = \frac{\Delta PV}{\Delta CV} = \frac{9.6}{8} = 1.2$$

The approximate model is thus

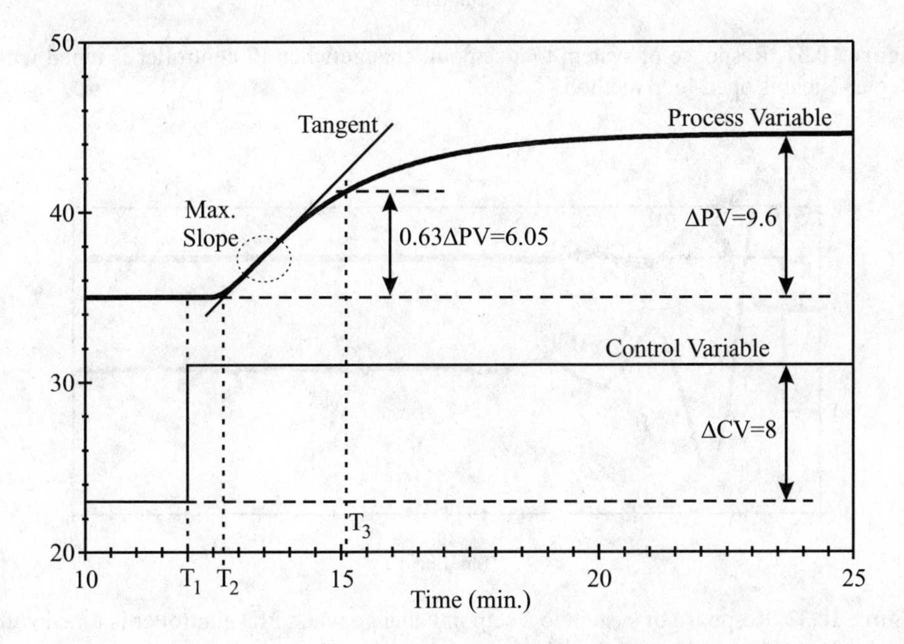

Figure 10.30. First-order process model from graphical data for Example 10.3.

$$G_{FODT}(s) = \frac{1.2e^{-0.7s}}{2.4s+1}$$

Using the equations in Table 10.4, the interacting PI controller parameters are determined to be

$K_P = 2.57$, $T_I = 2.33$ min., $T_D = 0$ min.

and the interacting PID controller parameters are

$K_P = 3.43$, $T_I = 1.4$ min., $T_D = 0.35$ min.

The setpoint change response of the system with this PI controller is shown in Figure 10.31 and has more overshoot than the PI controller in Example 10.1. The PID controller response is shown in Figure 10.32 and illustrates the magnification of the measurement noise by the derivative term. The CV makes small changes even when there are no apparent PV changes. The addition of the derivative term gives a better process variable response at

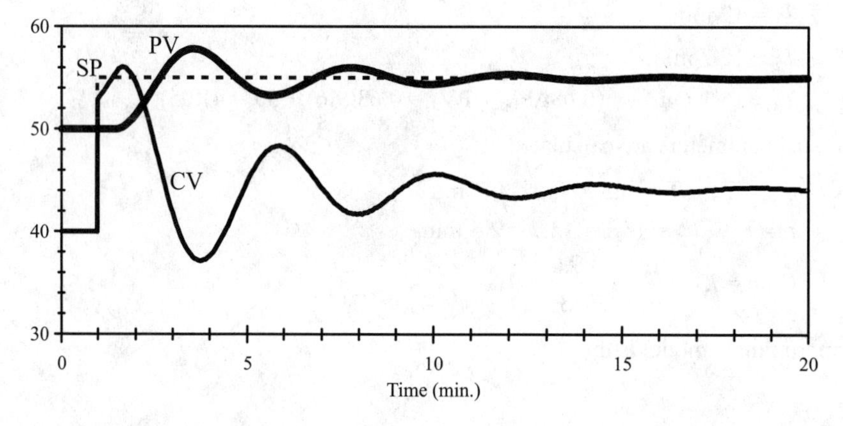

Figure 10.31. Response of system to a setpoint change when PI controller is tuned with Ziegler-Nichols open-loop method.

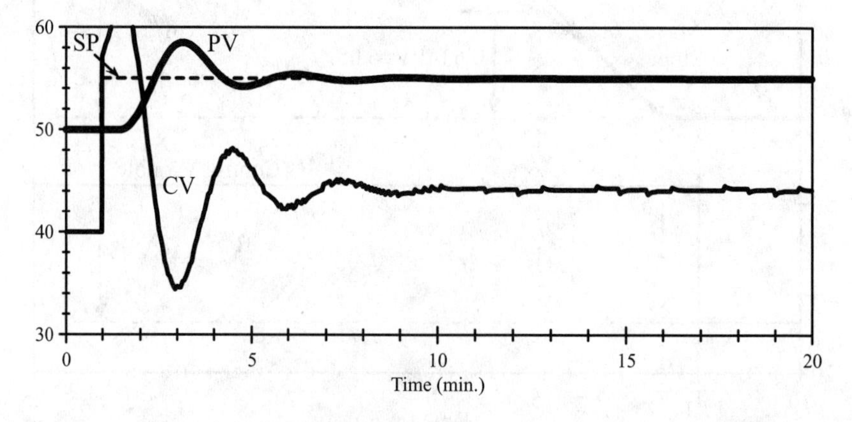

Figure 10.32. Response of system to a setpoint change when PID controller is tuned with Ziegler-Nichols open-loop method.

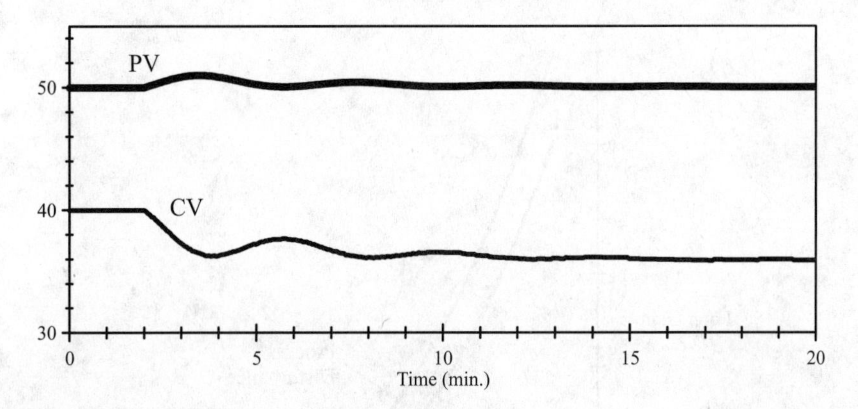

Figure 10.33. Response of system to a step disturbance change of +5 when PI controller is tuned with Ziegler-Nichols open-loop method.

the expense of more vigorous control variable action. The response to a disturbance of +5 is shown in Figure 10.33 for the PI controller.

Tuning using the Fertik method entails determining the type of controller (PI or PID), calculating the Fertik controllability, α_F, as

$$\alpha_F = \frac{\theta_D}{\theta_D + \tau} = \frac{T_d}{T_{ps}},$$

$$T_d = \theta_D$$

$$T_{ps} = \theta_D + \tau$$

and then reading the normalized parameters from the set of graphs in Figures 10.34 – 10.38. The parameters may be optimized for setpoint response or for disturbance response. Note that the PID controller is not recommended for those processes whose Fertik controllability is greater than 0.5. These processes are dominated by deadtime.

Example 10.4. For the same process as in Example 10.1, tune a PI and a PID controller to control this process using the Fertik open-loop tuning method. Tune the controller for an "optimal" setpoint response and show its response to a setpoint change. Also tune the controller for an "optimal" disturbance response and demonstrate its response to a step disturbance.

Solution. The first-order-plus-deadtime approximation to this process is determined in the same manner as for Example 10.3

$$G_{FODT}(s) = \frac{Ke^{-s\theta_D}}{\tau s + 1} = \frac{1.2e^{-0.7s}}{2.4s + 1}$$

The Fertik controllability is determined as $\alpha_F = 0.23$. The value of $T_{ps} = 3.1$. Using the graphs in Figures 10.34 and 10.35, the PI controller parameters for a setpoint change are

$$KK_P \approx 1.4 \Rightarrow K_P = 1.4/1.2 = 1.17$$

$$T_I / T_{ps} \approx 0.86 \Rightarrow T_I = 0.86 \times 3.1 = 2.67 \text{ min.}$$

and the PID controller parameters for a setpoint change are determined using the graphs in Figures 10.36 - 10.38:

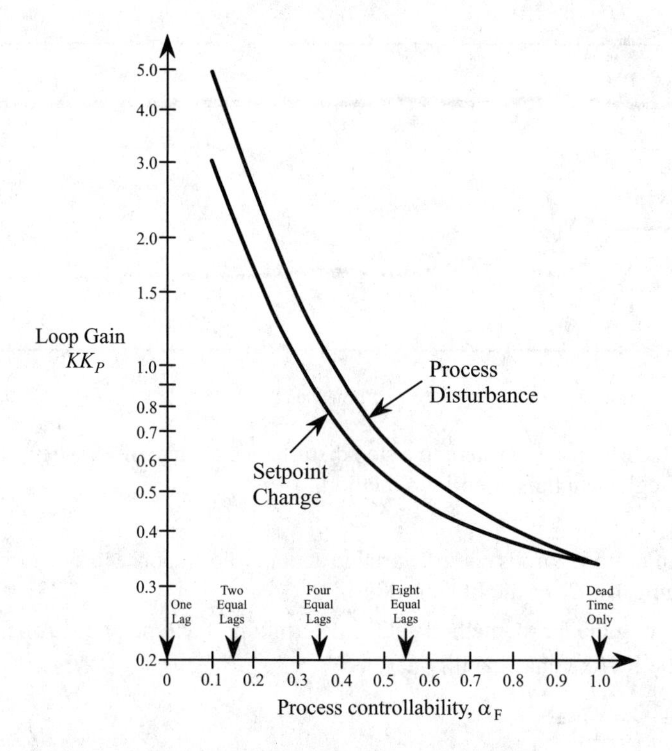

Figure 10.34. Fertik controller gain for PI control. (Copyright 1975, ISA - The Instrumentation, Systems, and Automation Society. All rights reserved. Used with permission of ISA.)

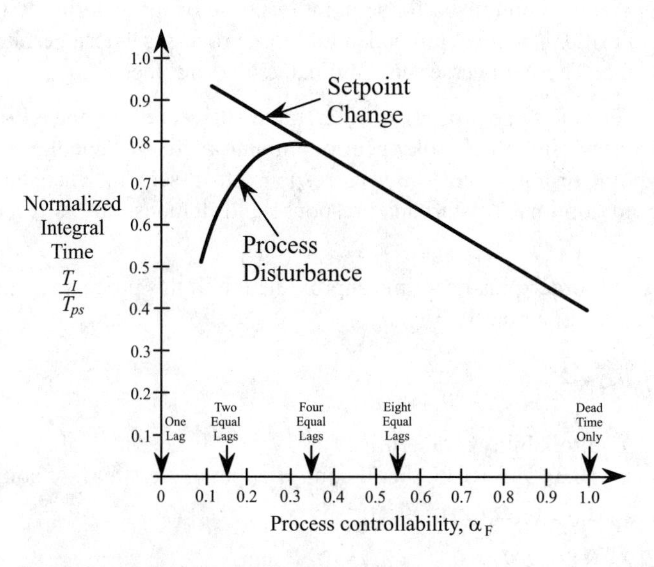

Figure 10.35. Fertik controller integral time for PI control. (Copyright 1975, ISA - The Instrumentation, Systems, and Automation Society. All rights reserved. Used with permission of ISA.)

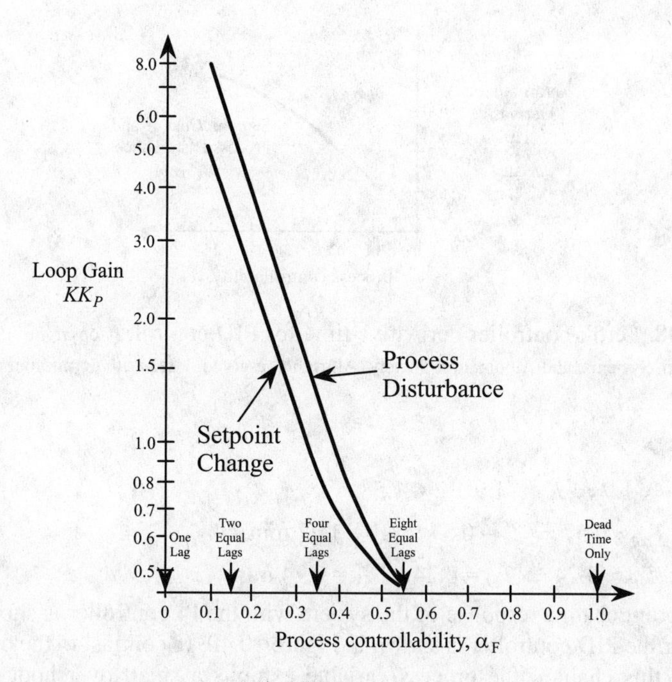

Figure 10.36. Fertik controller gain for PID control.

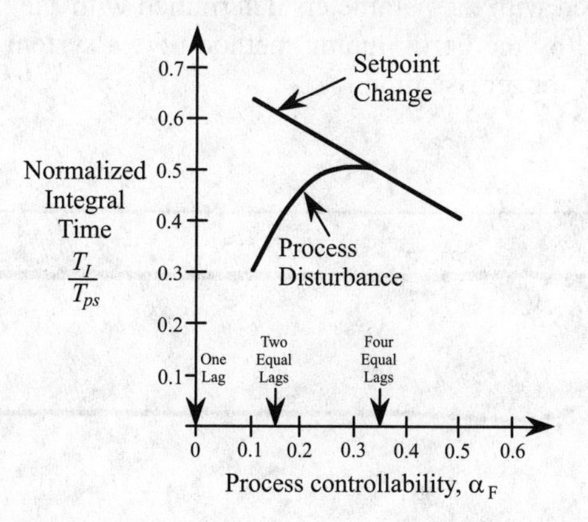

Figure 10.37. Fertik controller integral time for PID control.

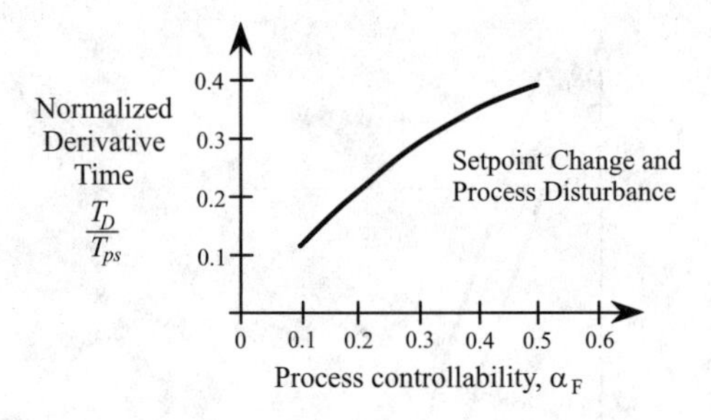

Figure 10.38. Fertik controller derivative time for PID control. (Copyright 1975, ISA - The Instrumentation, Systems, and Automation Society. All rights reserved. Used with permission of ISA.)

$KK_P \approx 1.9 \Rightarrow K_P = 1.9/1.2 = 1.58$

$T_I / T_{ps} \approx 0.57 \Rightarrow T_I = 0.57 \times 3.1 = 1.77$ min.

$T_D / T_{ps} \approx 0.24 \Rightarrow T_D = 0.24 \times 3.1 = 0.74$ min.

The setpoint change response of the system with the PI controller is shown in Figure 10.39 and for the PID controller is shown in Figure 10.40. In contrast to the other methods presented in this chapter, the process variable exhibits a small overshoot to a setpoint change, but a slower rise time. In a similar manner, the PI parameters for good disturbance response are:

$K_P = 1.67$, $T_I = 2.39$ min., $T_D = 0.0$ min.

and the PID parameters for good disturbance response are:

$K_P = 2.5$, $T_I = 1.52$ min., $T_D = 0.74$ min.

The response of the system to a step disturbance of +5 with the PI controller is shown in Figure 10.41. Compared with the parameters determined with Ziegler-Nichols tuning, the parameters determined by the Fertik tuning method give a system response with smaller deviation but a slightly longer rise time.

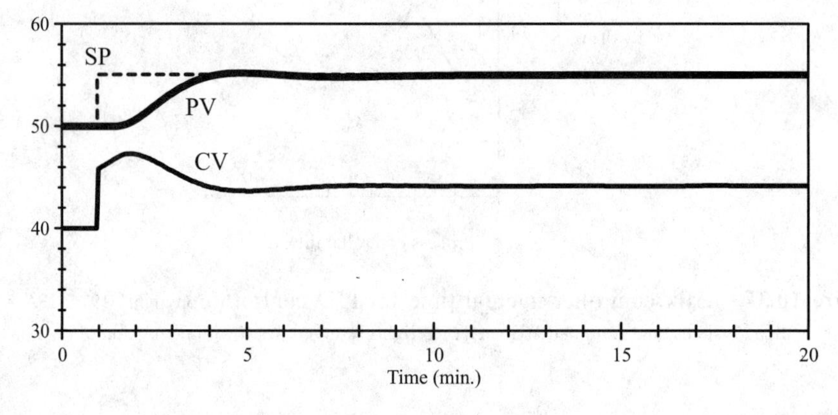

Figure 10.39. Response of system to a setpoint change when PI controller is tuned according to the Fertik open-loop method.

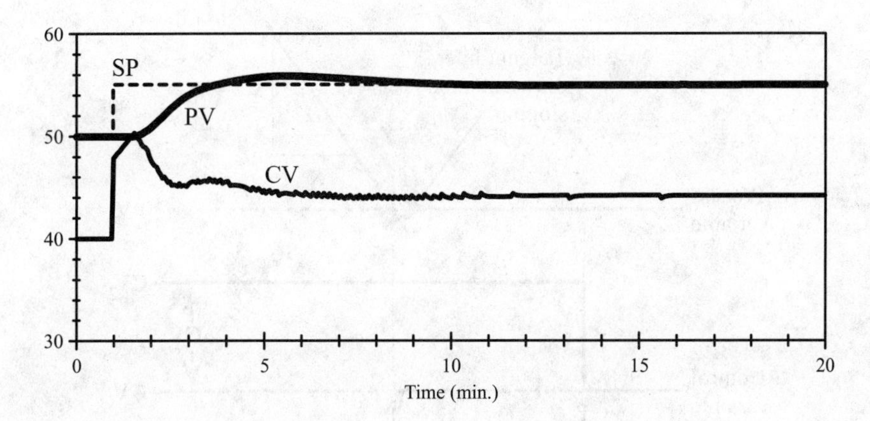

Figure 10.40. Response of system to a setpoint change when PID controller is tuned according to the Fertik open-loop method.

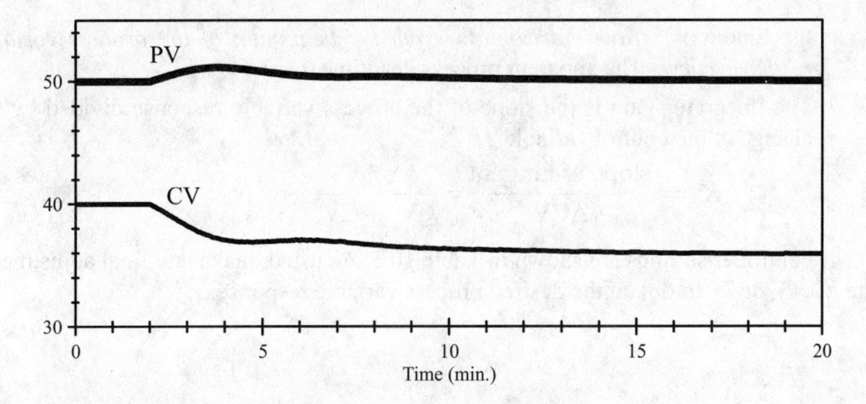

Figure 10.41. Response of system to a step disturbance change of +5 when PI controller is tuned with the Fertik open-loop method.

10.4.4.3 Integrating Processes. This method was originally proposed by Ziegler and Nichols (1942) and may be used to determine the tuning parameters for a non-self-regulating process.

1. Start any trending (plotting) of the PV and CV.
2. Place the controller in manual mode and allow the process to reach steady state.
3. Impose a step change in the controller output (CV).
4. When there is enough trend information, put the controller back in automatic mode (so the process does not "run away").
5. Using the recorded process response curve, draw a straight line tangent to the process response curve at its point of maximum rate of ascent as shown in Figure 10.42.
6. The term T_1 is the time at which the step change in the manipulated variable was imposed. T_2 is the time at which the tangent drawn in the previous step intersects

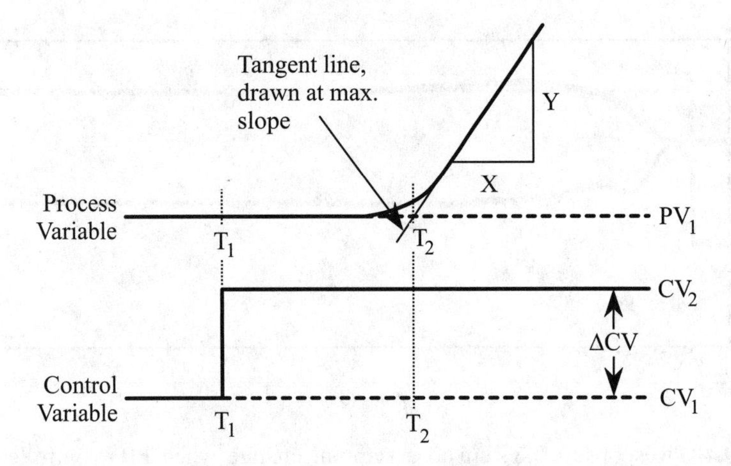

Figure 10.42. Determination of parameters for non-self-regulating process PID tuning.

the time axis, *drawn horizontally from the beginning of the process variable response curve.* The apparent process deadtime $\theta_D = T_2 - T_1$.

7. The integrator gain is the slope of the process variable response divided by the change in the control variable,

$$K_S = \frac{\text{slope of tangent}}{\Delta \text{CV}} = \frac{\text{Y/X}}{\text{CV}_2 - \text{CV}_1}$$

The controller settings are shown in Table 10.5. As usual, make any final adjustments in the K_P, T_I, or T_D to obtain the desired process variable response.

Table 10.5 Open-loop Tuning PID Parameters for Integrating Process

	Interacting Equation	Noninteracting Equation
P controller		
K_P	$1/(K_S\theta_D)$	$1/(K_S\theta_D)$
PI controller		
K_P	$0.9/(K_S\theta_D)$	$0.9/(K_S\theta_D)$
T_I	$3.3\theta_D$	$3.3\theta_D/K_P$
PID controller		
K_P	$1.2/(K_S\theta_D)$	$1.2/(K_S\theta_D)$
T_I	$3.3\theta_D$	$3.3\theta_D/K_P$
T_D	$0.5\theta_D$	$0.5\theta_D K_P$

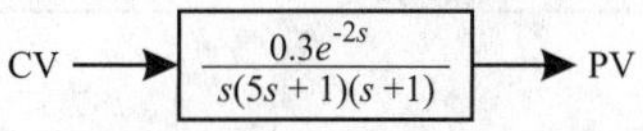

$$\text{CV} \longrightarrow \boxed{\frac{0.3e^{-2s}}{s(5s+1)(s+1)}} \longrightarrow \text{PV}$$

Figure 10.43. Process used for non-self-regulating tuning example.

Example 10.5. Assume the process is represented by the block diagram in Figure 10.43, where the time constants are measured in minutes. Tune a PI and a PID controller to control this process using the Ziegler-Nichols open-loop tuning method for integrating processes.

Solution. First, an approximate model must be determined. In order to keep the process variable from moving too far away from the operating point, as soon as the response seems to assume a constant slope, the control variable is changed to a step in the negative direction and for the same duration as the original change. This change brings the process back to its original operating point.

The appropriate information needed to determine the approximate process is marked in Figure 10.44. The model parameters are thus

$$\theta_D = T_2 - T_1 \approx 8 - 2 = 6 \text{ min.}$$

$$K_S = \frac{\text{slope of tangent}}{\Delta\text{CV}} \approx \frac{4/(12-8.8)}{5} = 0.25$$

The PI parameters are calculated to be

$$K_P = \frac{0.9}{K_S\theta_D} = \frac{0.9}{0.25 \times 6} = 0.6$$

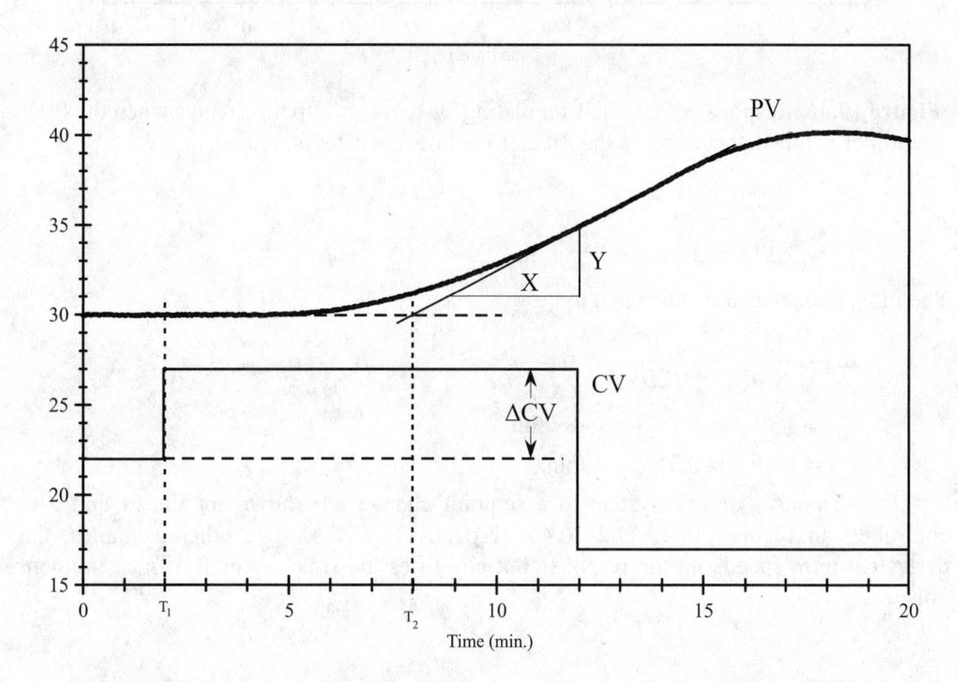

Figure 10.44. Non-self-regulating process model parameters for Example 10.5.

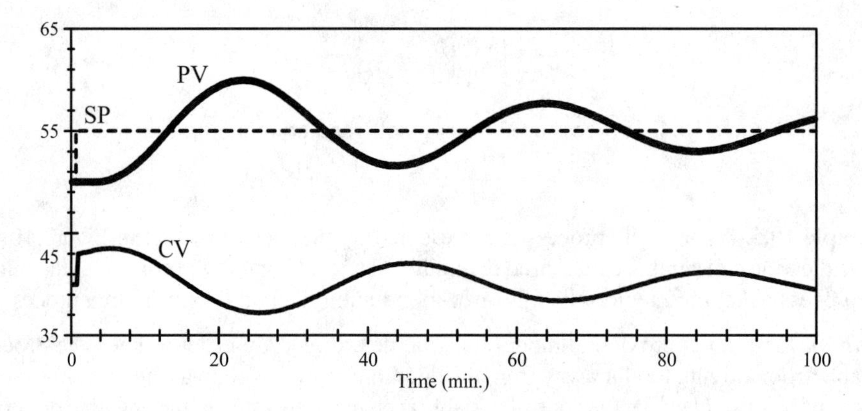

Figure 10.45. Response of non-self-regulating system to a setpoint change when the PI controller is tuned according to the Ziegler-Nichols open-loop method.

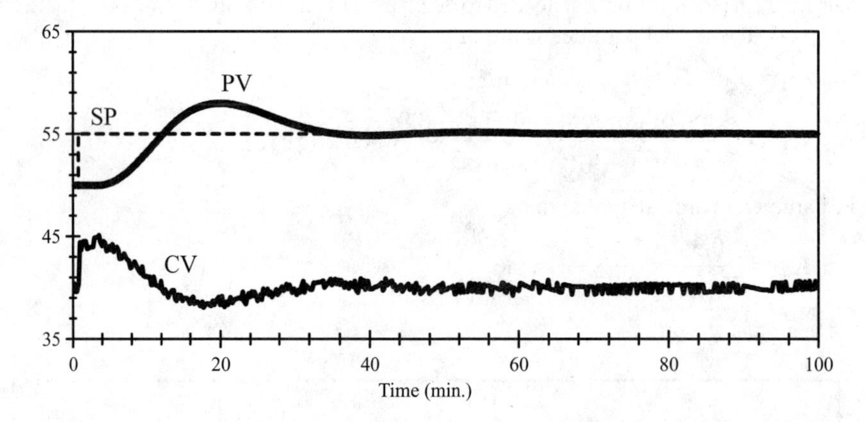

Figure 10.46. Response of non-self-regulating system to a setpoint change when the PID controller is tuned according to the Ziegler-Nichols open-loop method.

$$T_I = 3.3\theta_D = 3.3 \times 6 = 19.8 \text{ min.}$$

The PID parameters are calculated to be

$$K_P = \frac{1.2}{K_S \theta_D} = \frac{1.2}{0.25 \times 6} = 0.8$$

$$T_I = 3.3\theta_D = 3.3 \times 6 = 19.8 \text{ min.}$$

$$T_D = 0.5\theta_D = 0.5 \times 6 = 3 \text{ min.}$$

The responses of this system to a setpoint change are shown for the PI and PID controllers in Figures 10.45 and 10.46, respectively. As seen in other examples, the derivative term speeds up the response but amplifies the small amount of measurement noise.

Table 10.6 Situations for PID Control Enhancements

Enhancement	Situation
Cascade	Control of any non-flow variable that uses a valve as its final control element.
Feedforward	Eliminate or reduce disturbance effect on the process variable.
Ratio	Blending or other applications where the flow of two streams need to be held in constant ratio to each other.
Split Range	Process has one process variable and more than one control variable.
Override	Protection of process equipment or personnel.

10.5 PID CONTROL ENHANCEMENTS

While the PID controller works adequately in many process control situations, there are many applications where enhancements to the basic controller can dramatically improve its performance. Each enhancement is appropriate for certain situations, as shown in Table 10.6. Other enhancements are possible, but these are the more important ones. This section only surveys these enhancements. More information may be found in a process control text like Erickson and Hedrick (1999), Marlin (2000) and Riggs (1999).

10.5.1 Cascade Control

In many cases a controlled process may be considered as two processes in series. When a PID controller is used in such a situation, as shown in Figure 10.47, disturbances in the secondary process are not measured until they have already affected the output of the primary process. Control performance can be improved by the addition of another feedback loop, as shown in Figure 10.48. This control scheme is called cascade control. The output of the primary (master) loop becomes the setpoint of the secondary (slave) loop. With cascade control, disturbances to the secondary control loop are corrected by the secondary controller and thus have little effect on the controlled output. For a cascade control loop to function properly, the dynamics of the secondary loop must be at least as fast as the primary loop, and

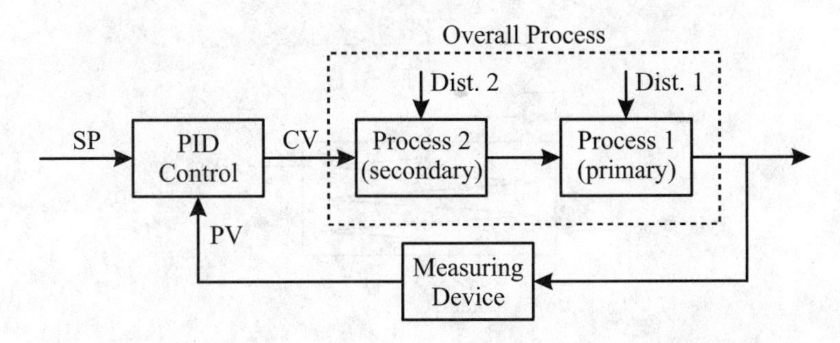

Figure 10.47. Single-loop control of two cascaded processes.

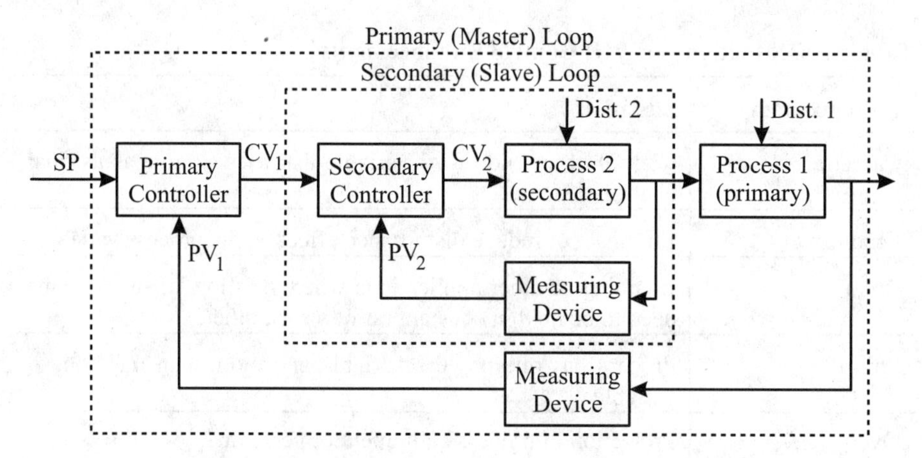

Figure 10.48. Cascade control.

preferably much faster. Usually, two loops are cascaded, although the strategy can be extended to more than two loops. In any case, only one loop directly manipulates the physical variable (usually a flow). The second loop output is the setpoint of the first loop, the third loop output is the setpoint of the second, and so on.

As an example, consider the PID control of a heat exchanger in Figure 10.49. The objective is to control the outlet temperature, sensed by TT2501. With a single-loop PID controller, the steam control valve is manipulated by the temperature controller to maintain a desired outlet temperature. However, disturbances in the steam header pressure, which cause the steam flow to change, are not detected by the temperature controller until their effect is seen as a change in the outlet temperature. In order to control the outlet temperature better, a slave loop maintains the steam flow. The temperature controller then manipulates the flow controller setpoint, as shown in Figure 10.50. The performance improvement of cascade control when there is a steam pressure disturbance is demonstrated in Figure 10.51. With cascade control, the outlet temperature response to a change in the steam header pressure is negligible.

Another example of cascade control is shown in Figure 10.52. Cascade control is used to regulate the temperature of a process stream that exits from a furnace. Because the dynamics between the fuel pump speed and the exit temperature are slow, direct adjustment of the pump speed by TIC1102 will lead to poor regulation to fuel pressure changes. The

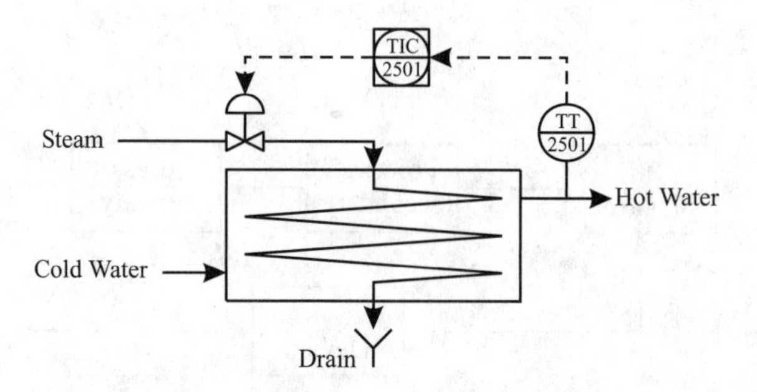

Figure 10.49. Single-loop control of heat exchanger.

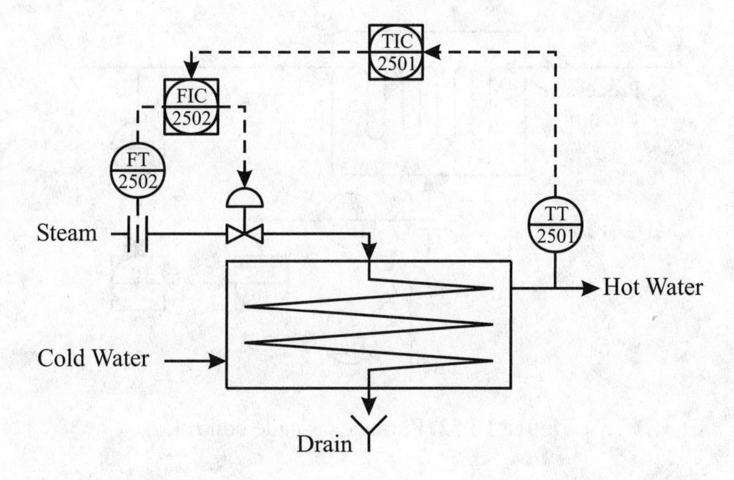

Figure 10.50. Cascade control of heat exchanger.

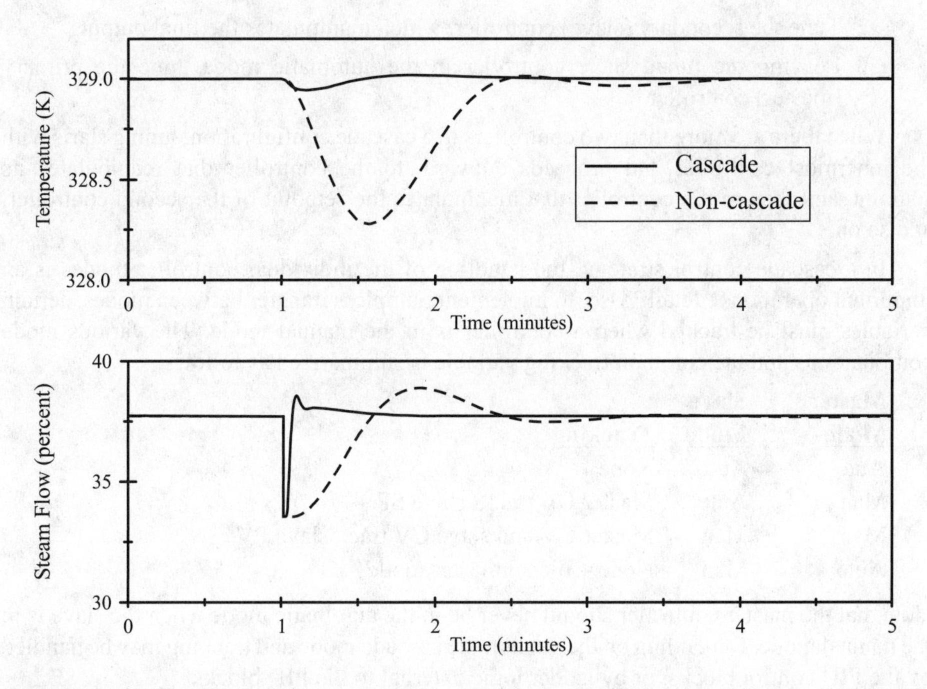

Figure 10.51. Cascade versus non-cascade control of heat exchanger subject to a –10% step disturbance in steam pressure.

primary control loop adjusts the flow of the fuel in order to maintain the process stream exit temperature. The secondary controller (FIC1103) adjusts the fuel pump speed and compensates for changes in the fuel pressure. The pump speed control (SC1103) contains its own controller, so this example demonstrates two levels of cascade control.

The controllers that make up a cascade control strategy must be tuned individually. The tuning process should start with the controller that manipulates the final output:

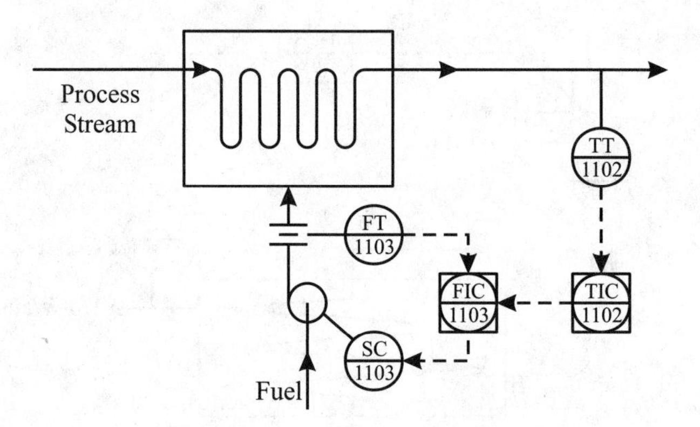

Figure 10.52. Furnace cascade control.

1. Place all controllers involved in the cascade control strategy in manual mode.
2. Tune the secondary (slave) controller, which manipulates the final output.
3. Leaving the tuned slave controller in the automatic mode, tune the primary (master) controller.

When there are more than two controllers in a cascade configuration, tuning starts with the innermost controller and proceeds outward, to the controller that manipulates its setpoint, and then to the controller that manipulates the setpoint of the second controller, and so on.

In a cascade control strategy, the handling of the individual controller modes is an important operational detail. Also, to implement bumpless transfer between modes, certain variables must be tracked when a controller is in the manual mode. The various mode combinations and the common tracking variable is summarized as follows:

Master Mode	Slave Mode	Tracking
Auto	Auto	None
Man	Auto	Master CV tracks slave SP
Man	Man	Master CV and slave CV track slave PV
Auto	Man	None – illegal master mode

Note that the master controller should never be in the automatic mode when the slave is in the manual mode. Depending on the vendor, the cascade mode and tracking may be handled by the PID control blocks, or by ladder logic external to the PID blocks.

Design Tip

Handling the modes and tracking of the individual controllers in a cascade configuration is an important, and often overlooked, detail.

10.5.2 Feedforward Control

Feedback control mitigates the effect of a disturbance by measuring its effect on the process variable and then adjusting the control (manipulated) variable accordingly. In contrast, feedforward control measures the disturbance and changes the manipulated variable in order to counteract the disturbance before it affects the process variable.

Consider the heat exchanger control of Figure 10.50. The cascade control scheme mitigates the effect of disturbances in the steam pressure. However, the system is still subject to the following disturbances:

Cold water temperature	Steam temperature
Cold water flow	Ambient temperature

A feedforward controller could be constructed for each of these disturbances. However, it may not be appropriate to construct a feedforward controller for each disturbance. The ambient temperature does not vary rapidly and so can be easily handled by the feedback controller. Of the remaining disturbances, the major one is the cold-water flow, since it can change rapidly depending on the demand. A block diagram of the combination feedforward and cascade control system is shown in Figure 10.53. Response to a +2-gpm change in cold-water flow with and without dynamic feedforward control is shown in Figure 10.54. Note that the feedforward control does not completely cancel the disturbance effect due to imperfect process knowledge.

How does one design a feedforward controller? When a feedforward controller is added to a feedback control system, the resulting system block diagram appears as in Figure 10.55. Note that the process model is depicted as two parts, the dynamic effect of the CV on the PV (G_p) and the dynamic effect of the disturbance on the PV (G_d).

Only one disturbance is shown, but designing a separate feedforward controller for each disturbance can accommodate more disturbances.

In order for the disturbance to be completely rejected, it can be shown (Erickson and Hedrick, 1999) that the feedforward controller $G_{ff}(s)$ is

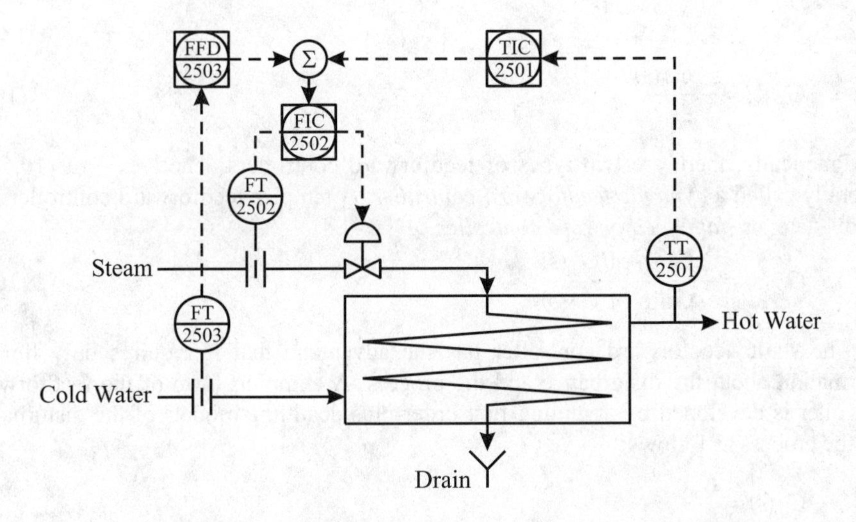

Figure 10.53. Feedforward and cascade control of heat exchanger.

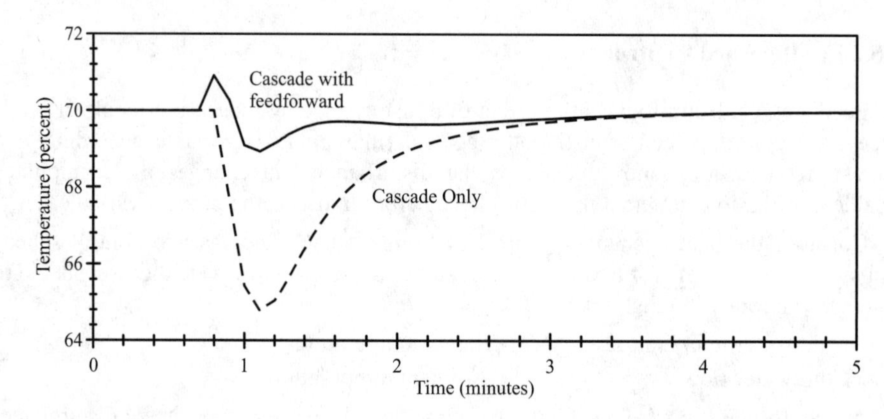

Figure 10.54. Hot water response to a +2-gpm change in cold-water flow without and with dynamic feedforward control.

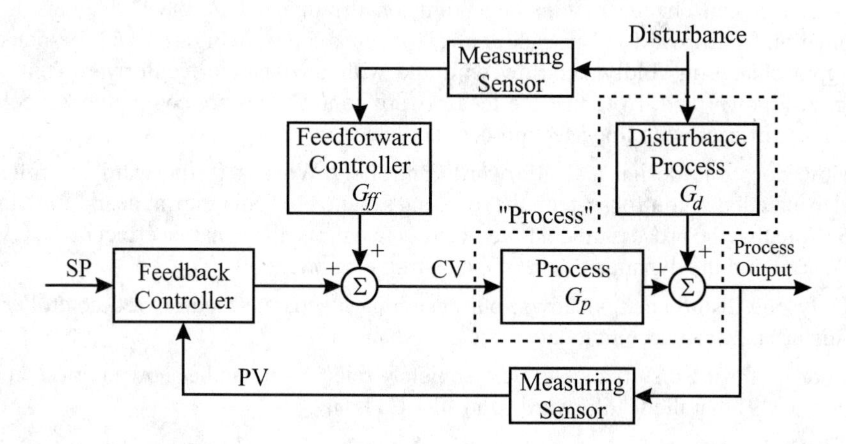

Figure 10.55. Block diagram of combined feedback and feedforward control.

$$G_{ff}(s) = -\frac{G_d(s)}{G_p(s)} \tag{10.5}$$

Practically, there are two types of feedforward controllers. The of (10.5) is generally called a *dynamic feedforward controller*. A simpler feedforward controller is a steady-state, or *static feedforward controller*,

$$G_{ff}(s) = -\frac{\text{Gain of } G_d(s)}{\text{Gain of } G_p(s)} \tag{10.6}$$

The static feedforward controller has the advantage that it requires only limited information about the disturbance and the process. A common form of the feedforward controller is developed by assuming first-order-plus-deadtime models of the disturbance and the process as follows:

$$G_d(s) = \frac{K_d e^{-\theta_d s}}{\tau_d s + 1}$$

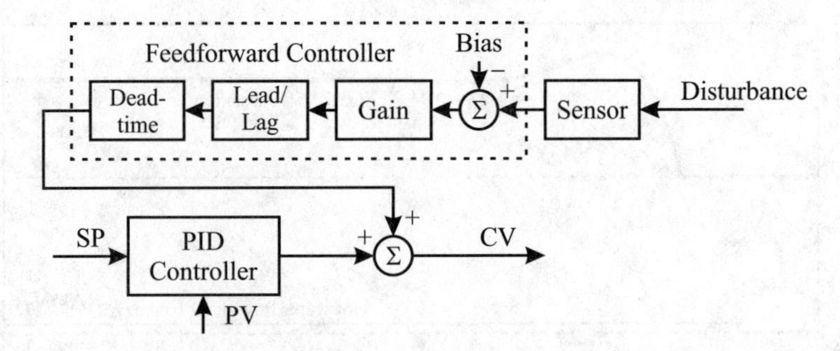

Figure 10.56. Feedforward controller implementation.

$$G_p(s) = \frac{K_p e^{-\theta_p s}}{\tau_p s + 1}$$

Using (10.5), the dynamic feedforward controller transfer function is

$$G_{ff}(s) = -\frac{K_d(\tau_p s + 1)}{K_p(\tau_d s + 1)} e^{-(\theta_d - \theta_p)s} \tag{10.7}$$

The controller consists of three parts: (1) gain, (2) lead/lag, and (3) deadtime. Thus in a control system these three blocks are combined to implement a dynamic feedforward controller. A static feedforward controller has only the gain block. Depending on the disturbance measurement, a bias may be subtracted from the feedforward measurement so the net effect of the feedforward controller is zero at the operating point. Also, the feedforward controller output is added to the feedback controller output. Thus, the general block diagram of a feedforward controller implementation is shown in Figure 10.56.

When designing a dynamic feedforward controller, the *realizability* of the resulting controller becomes an issue. In order for the feedforward transfer function (10.7) to be realizable, the deadtime must be nonnegative,

$$\theta_d - \theta_p \geq 0 \qquad \text{or} \qquad \theta_d \geq \theta_p$$

Physically, this inequality makes sense. In order to completely cancel the effect of the disturbance, the combination of the feedforward controller and the process must have a smaller deadtime than the deadtime from the disturbance measurement and the process variable. What does one do if the designed dynamic feedforward controller has a negative deadtime (positive exponent of e)? The best one can do is to use a feedforward controller with a zero deadtime. It will not completely cancel the disturbance effect but may be the best one can do. The only other alternative is to physically move the final control element in order to decrease the apparent process deadtime. However, depending on the system, this may not be possible.

In order to design a feedforward controller using (10.5) or (10.6), a model of the disturbance effect and a process model must be known. When the system contains a feedback controller, there is a simple way to design a static feedforward controller by monitoring the disturbance and the control variable which in automatic mode. The static feedforward gain is the negative of the ratio of the control variable change to the disturbance change. For example, a typical disturbance and corresponding control variable response is shown in Figure 10.57. The static feedforward gain is

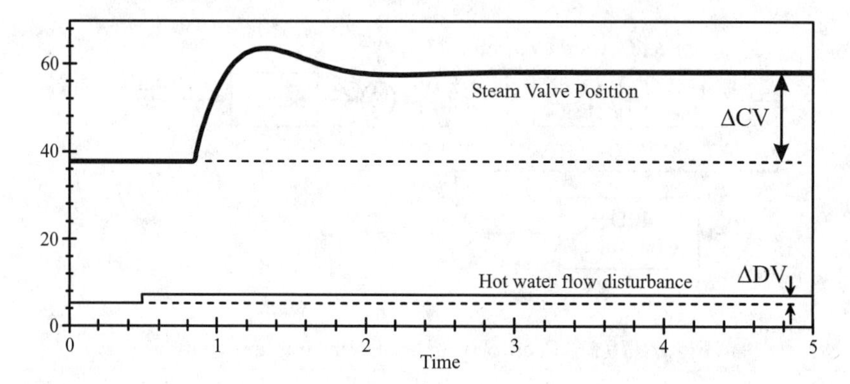

Figure 10.57. Information needed to obtain simple static feedforward controller.

$$G_{ff_{ss}}(s) = +\frac{\Delta \text{CV}}{\Delta \text{DV}} \tag{10.8}$$

This design technique is illustrated by the following example.

Example 10.6. For the heat exchanger of Figure 10.53, design a static feedforward controller that compensates for changes in the cold water flow. Obtain the static feedforward gain with a feedback controller and (10.8).

Solution. A +2-gpm cold water flow change and the response of the temperature controller output (setpoint to flow controller) is shown in Figure 10.57. The static feedforward controller is thus

$$G_{ff_{ss}}(s) = \frac{\Delta \text{CV}}{\Delta \text{DV}} = \frac{58.27 - 37.70}{7 - 5} = 10.29$$

When implementing this controller using the block diagram of Figure 10.56, the bias is 5, the presumed cold water flow operating point since it is the starting point for the disturbance change in Figure 10.57.

Another example of feedforward control is the boiler level control of Figure 10.58. The objective is to keep the boiler level constant. The principal disturbances are the feedwater pressure and the steam flow from the boiler, dictated by varying demand in the plant. The former is handled by cascade control, and the latter is handled with a feedforward controller.

10.5.3 Ratio Control

Ratio control is used to maintain a constant ratio between the flow rates of two or more streams. It is commonly used in such situations as adding ingredients to a batch reactor where a constant ratio between ingredients must be maintained as they are added.

In a ratio control scheme, all stream flow rates are measured and all but one stream is controlled. The uncontrolled stream is usually called the *wild* stream. The flows of the other streams are set based on a ratio of the wild stream. The usual configuration multiplies the wild stream flow by the desired ratio to generate the setpoint to a PID controller for the manipulated stream (Figure 10.59). This scheme is basically feedforward, because the downstream ratio is not measured and used in a feedback controller. Thus, in a situation where two or more streams are blended, this scheme does not guarantee zero offset between

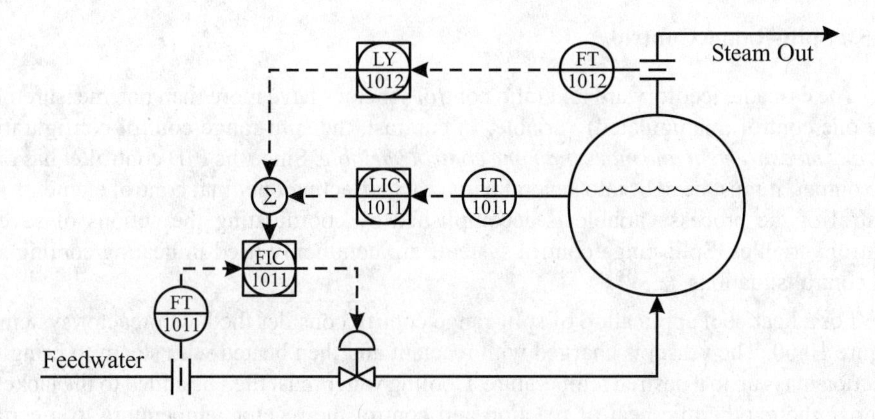

Figure 10.58. Boiler level feedforward control.

the actual and desired composition of the blended stream. Erickson and Hedrick (1999) show the configuration of a ratio control that accurately controls the blended stream composition, but it requires an often expensive composition sensor.

Ratio control is used in the following process control situations:

1. Control the ratio of two reactants into a continuous or batch reactor.
2. Hold the ratio of two or more blended streams constant in order to maintain the blend composition at the desired value.
3. Hold the ratio of a recycle stream to the forward stream constant.
4. Maintain the fuel/air ratio of a burner for most efficient combustion.
5. Keep a constant ratio between the feed flow rate and steam flow rate for a distillation column reboiler.
6. Maintain a constant reflux ratio in a distillation column.

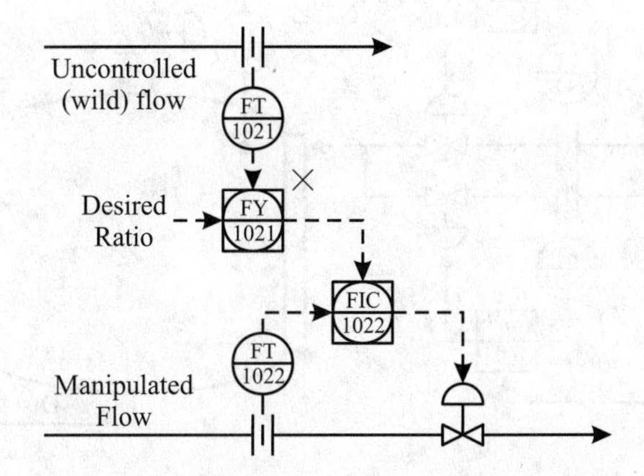

Figure 10.59. Ratio control scheme.

10.5.4 Split-Range Control

The cascade, feedforward and ratio control schemes have more than one measurement and one control (manipulated) variable. In contrast, the split-range control configuration has *one measurement and more than one control variable.* Since the PID controller has only one output, it must be split into several parts, each affecting one final control element. The control of the process variable is accomplished by coordinating the actions of several control variables. Split-range control systems are commonly used in heating/cooling and pH control situations.

For a heat/cool application of split-range control consider the batch reactor system of Figure 10.60. The vessel is charged with reactant and then heated with steam to bring the reaction mass up to a desired temperature. Cooling water must then be added to the jacket to remove the exothermic heat of reaction and control the reactor temperature to a certain profile. There is one measurement, the reactor temperature, TT1401, and two control variables, the steam and chilled water flows. Both of the flows are controlled by individual flow loops, FIC1402 and FIC1403. The one output from TT1401 must be split between the two flow setpoints. The two flow setpoints corresponding to the controller output are shown in Figure 10.61. In operation, when the TT1401 controller is switched to automatic in order to heat up the reactor, the controller output is 100%, meaning the steam flow is at is maximum. As the temperature approaches the desired initial value, the steam flow is incrementally decreased and is zero when the temperature is at the desired initial value. At this point, the reaction becomes exothermic, and the chilled water flow must be increased from zero in order to maintain the reactor temperature. The chilled water flow is manipulated in order to follow a desired temperature profile during the remainder of the batch process. The controller bias parameters must be set up so that the controller output is 50% when the error between the actual and desired temperature is zero. The chilled water valve, is set up to be reverse-acting (air-to-close) and the steam valve is set up to be direct acting (air-to-open). For safety, the chilled water valve is fully open and the steam valve is fully closed upon loss of air pressure or controller failure so that the system always cools the reactor. If the chilled water and steam valve are controlled directly (no cascade control) then the valves can be configured as *split-ranged valves*. Normally, the 4-20 mA analog output

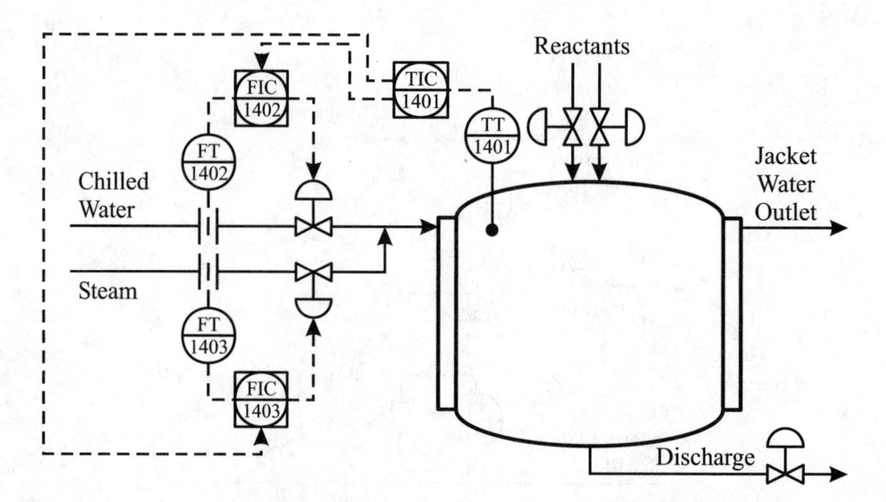

Figure 10.60. Split-range control for batch reactor temperature.

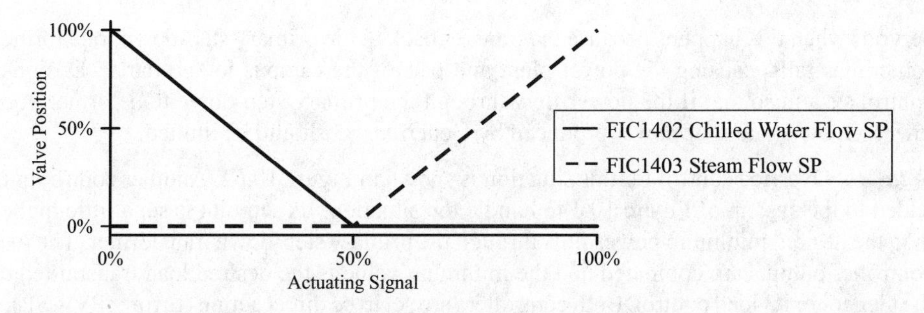

Figure 10.61. Split-ranging flow setpoints as function of temperature controller output.

of the PLC is converted to a 3-15 psig signal that drives the valve. When the valves are set up as split-ranged valves, they are set up to respond to either the upper half of this pressure signal range or the lower half of the range. The valve position for the two valves corresponds to the setpoints shown in Figure 10.61. As an alternative to split ranging the valves, the PLC can calculate the two actuating signals, one for each valve. The cost is higher since two current-to-pressure converters are required. But, the split-point, the point at which both valves are closed can easily be adjusted by changing one parameter instead of adjusting two valve actuators.

In most systems of this nature, the heating and cooling dynamics are different. There are three solutions to this dilemma. The controller could be tuned strictly for the cooling phase, if control during the heating phase is not critical. The controller tuning parameters could represent some compromise between the cooling and heating tuning. In order for the control to be most effective, the controller tuning parameters are changed when it switches from heating to cooling.

10.5.5 Override Control

During startup, normal operation or shutdown of a process it is possible that conditions can arise that lead to damage to equipment and plant personnel. In such situations, the normal control action must be changed, and a different control action must prevent the process variable from exceeding an allowable upper or lower limit. Special types of control switches are used to accomplish this function. The *high selector switch* (HSS) is used to select the highest of two or more signals and the *low selector switch* (LSS) is used to select the lowest of two or more signals. Generally, a HSS is used to prevent a variable from exceeding an upper limit and a LSS is used to prevent a variable from exceeding a lower limit. However, in order to apply them correctly, each situation must be analyzed since the type of actuator, dictated by safety concerns determines the type of selector switch. One situation is described in this section. Other override control situations are presented in Erickson and Hedrick (1999) and Marlin (2000).

Example 10.7. Consider the peak shaving system introduced in the scenario at the beginning of this chapter. One constraint on the amount of power that Generator #3 can produce is that the power flow through the primary step-down transformer should not be negative. The circuit breaker that connects the 2400-volt bus to the utility will trip in this situation. The backup step-down transformer is normally open and so it will close when the primary step-down transformer trips. There is no loss in power, but the operators are nervous when this happens because the transfer back to the primary step-down transformer sometimes fails, causing the power plant and part of the campus to "go dark." Design a control system so that if the power flow through the primary step-down transformer goes low, then the amount of power produced by Generator #3 should be limited.

Solution. Override control for this situation is shown in Figure 10.62. Another controller is added to the system of Figure 10.1 to handle the situation. Its setpoint is set a little higher than the desired minimum power flow through the primary step-down transformer. The two controller outputs are compared and the minimum value is the desired load transmitted to the Generator #3 load control. Both controllers are set to be direct acting (Error = PV – SP).

Assume Generator #3 is running and both controllers are in the automatic mode. As the total demand increases, the load controller increases its CV to increase the generated power and thus decrease the total demand. As long as P_2 stays well above the setpoint to the step-down controller, the step-down controller integral action will "wind up" causing the CV to be at its maximum value. The LSS will select the load controller output to control the generator load. As the generator demand increases during the day, P_2 will decrease. When P_2 gets close to the step-down controller setpoint, the step-down controller CV will decrease from its high limit, eventually becoming lower than the load controller CV. At this point, the LSS will select the step-down controller CV to control the generator load. Obviously, in this situation the campus could be subject to a demand charge, but that is deemed acceptable versus the possibility of causing the power plant to totally lose power.

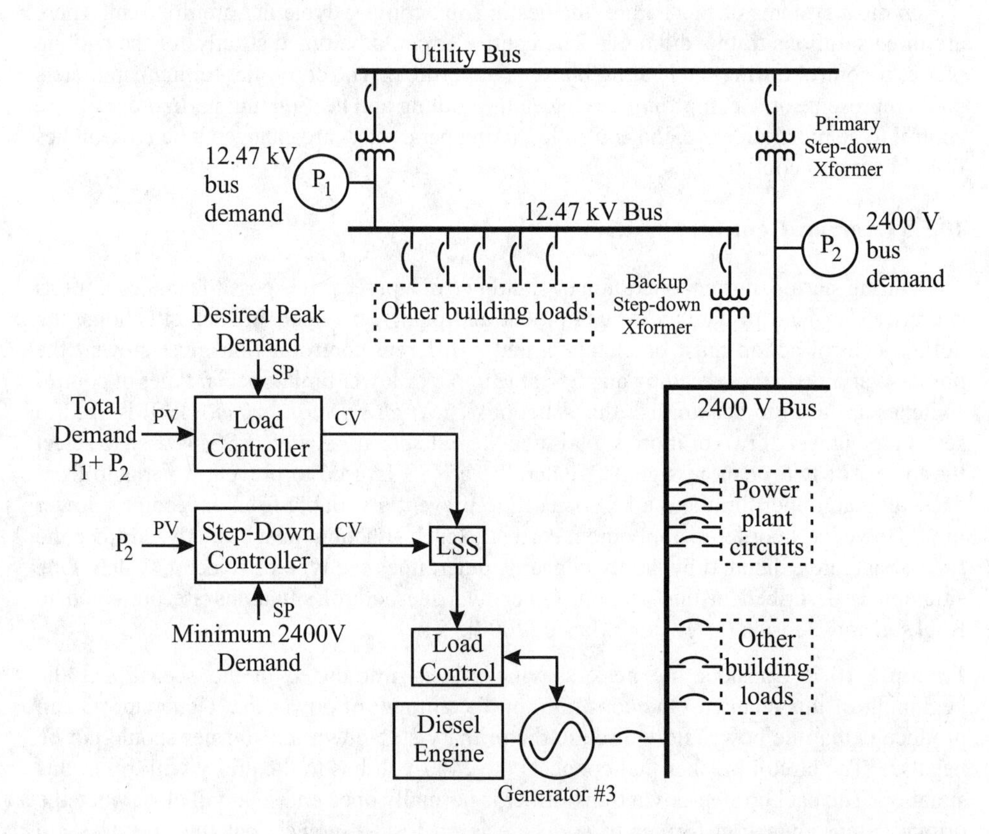

Figure 10.62. Override control for peak shaving system.

The step-down controller will continue to hold P_2 at its minimum until the campus demand decreases enough that the load controller CV is less than the step-down controller CV.

10.6 OPERATIONAL ASPECTS

The previous section introduced some of the functions external to the PID controller algorithm that must be employed in certain applications. In general, there are a number of external functions that must be used in conjunction with a PID controller. These functions are grouped into measurement conditioning, setpoint management, and output processing. In addition, alternative controllers are also described.

Measurement conditioning. Depending on the type of measurement, it may need to be conditioned before it can be used for control. This type of conditioning also includes the blocks needed to implement feedforward control.

Scaling – Changes the scale of a raw analog input value into appropriate units or changes the CV into an analog output value. Depending on the vendor, this function may be handled in the analog input or output module.

Filtering – Filters noise from a measurement, making it "smoother." Sometimes called a lag function block. Heavy filtering of the PV will affect the performance of the PID controller and may cause it to be unstable.

Square root – Converts the differential pressure measurement from orifice-plate flow meters into a volumetric flow rate. This conversion is a weighted square root calculation.

Mass flow calculation – Converts a volumetric gas flow rate into a mass flow rate. It requires a temperature and pressure measurement.

Totalizer – Integrates a flow rate to calculate the volume of material that has passed through the flow meter. Basically, an integrator with more features.

Lead/lag – Implements the lead/lag transfer function. It is essentially a PD controller with filtering. It will also implement the lead/lag block for feedforward compensation.

Time delay – Delays an input signal. It can be used to implement the time-delay function for feedforward control.

Differentiator – Takes the derivative of a variable, for example, to calculate acceleration from a velocity measurement. It may be combined into with some filtering and called a lead function block.

Integrator – Integrates a variable, for example, to calculate the position from a velocity measurement.

Setpoint management. Depending on the application, the setpoint may be more complicated than a constant value.

Bumpless transfer – Smooths transfer between an operator-generated setpoint and a program-generated setpoint.

Ramp/soak generation – Generates the temperature setpoint for applications (e.g., metal processing) that require a ramp/soak profile (Figure 10.63).

Ratio – Calculates a setpoint by multiplying one variable by a ratio, needed for ratio control.

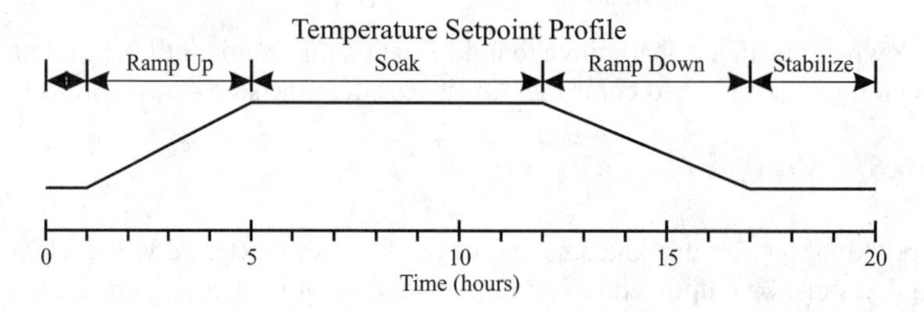

Figure 10.63. Typical temperature ramp/soak profile.

Output processing. Depending on the final control element, the controller output may need to be modified rather than used directly.

Velocity limiter – limits the rate of change of the control variable. This function may be integrated into the PID control algorithm.

High/low selector – Selects the maximum/minimum among multiple signals. It is needed for constraint control.

Split range – Implements split-ranging where two (or more) actuators cover the full range of the control variable.

Servo control – If the valve is controlled by an electric servomotor, the CV must be converted to two logic outputs to the motor, typically open/close or raise/lower.

Pulse-width modulation – Convert the CV analog output into a binary output signal where the pulse width is proportional to the CV value.

Manual station – Allows an operator to switch between automatic and manual modes. Coordinates the source of the CV in automatic and manual modes. This function may be integrated into the PID function block.

Alternative controllers. If the process variable measurement is an analog signal and the final control element is a discrete device, then there are simpler alternatives to the full PID algorithm. For example, a home heating system is a simple on-off control. The temperature is the measurement and the only actuating signal turns the heater (and fan) **on** when the temperature is below a setpoint and turns the heater **off** when the temperature is some value above the setpoint. This approach can be extended to a system that has two discrete actuators, for example, one actuator to control heating and another to control cooling. Among the PLCs covered by this text, the function blocks to implement this type of control are currently only provided by the Modicon PLC and so are described in the section that describes the Modicon PID control function blocks.

10.7 PLC PID FUNCTION BLOCKS

The implementation of the PID function block varies significantly among the vendors. In addition, the IEC 61131-3 standard does not define a standard PID function block, though it presents an example PID function block in one of the appendices (IEC, 1993).

As done in previous chapters, the PID control and related function blocks for a particular PLC are briefly described in separate sections. The reader is referred to the appropriate vendor's documentation for more details. Each section illustrates the ladder logic to implement a single PID loop. Following these descriptions, examples illustrate the application to cascade and feedforward control.

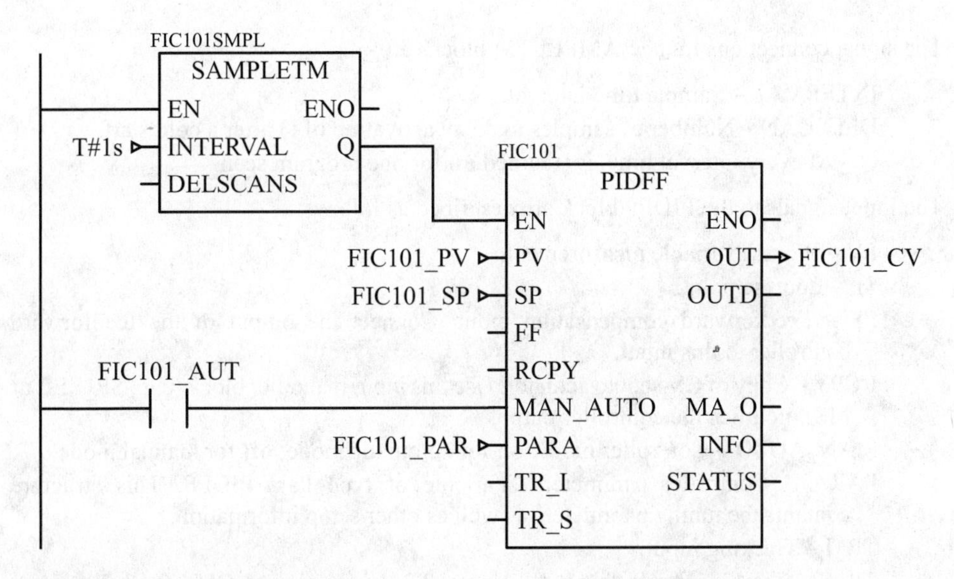

Values in FIC101_PAR

pv_inf	0.0 (PV lo bound)	bump	FALSE (bumpless on)
pv_sup	2.0 (PV up bound)	dband	0.0 (deadband)
out_inf	0.0 (CV lo bound)	gain_kp	0.0 (dband prop. act.)
out_sup	100.0 (CV up bound)	ovs_att	0.0 (overflow atten)
rev_dir	FALSE (rev action)	outbias	0.0 (CV bias)
mix_par	FALSE (interacting)	out_min	0.0 (CV lo limit)
aw_type	FALSE (normal)	out_max	100.0 (CV up limit)
en_rcpy	FALSE	outrate	10.0 (CV vel. limit)
kp	1.17	ff_inf	0.0 (feedforward)
ti	t#2.67m	ff_sup	0.0
td	t#0s	otff_inf	0.0
kd	0.0	otff_sup	0.0
pv_dev	FALSE (PV deriv.)		

Figure 10.64. Example PID loop with Modicon PIDFF function block.

10.7.1 Modicon Concept PID function blocks

The PIDFF function block fully implements the PID control algorithm and includes anti-reset windup and accommodations for feedforward compensation. An example PID loop is constructed from the SAMPLETM and PIDFF function blocks as shown in Figure 10.64. This example assumes that the PV and SP are already in appropriate units and that the CV will be converted to a proper value to drive an analog output.

The SAMPLETM function block executes the PIDFF function block at the set interval (1 second). The SAMPLETM is not necessary because the PIDFF will determine its sample interval based on the setup parameters. Nevertheless, the SAMPLETM is useful for the following reasons:

1. To match the sample period to the process dynamics. A sample period that is too small will often lead to aggressive control and possible increased actuator wear.
2. To distribute the execution of multiple PID blocks to "level out" program scan times.

The signal connections to the SAMPLETM blocks are:

INTERVAL – Sample time interval.

DELSCAN – Number of samples to delay activation of Q after a cold start.

Q – At every interval time, it is turned **on** for one program scan.

The input signals to the PIDFF block are described as follows:

PV – Process variable measurement.

SP – Loop setpoint.

FF – Feedforward compensation input. Connect the output of the feedforward controller to this input.

RCPY – Copy of CV sent to actuator. Use this input if another block (e.g., SP_SEL or MS) modifies the controller output.

MAN_AUTO – Controller mode: **on** for automatic mode; **off** for manual mode.

PARA – Controller parameters. Variable of type Para_PIDFF. This structure contains the tuning parameters as well as other setup information.

TR_I – Tracking input.

TR_S – Tracking mode force. When **on**, TR_I is copied to OUT (with limiting). When **off**, MAN_AUTO determines mode.

The output signals of the PIDFF block are described as follows:

OUT – Control variable.

OUTD – Incremental CV. Difference between the current CV and the CV calculated at the last PIDFF execution.

MA_O – Current controller mode: **on** for automatic mode; **off** for manual or tracking modes.

INFO – Control information. Variable of type Info_PIDFF. Contains the current error and the feedforward correction.

STATUS – Reports internal calculation errors.

When in manual mode (FIC101_AUT **off**) the PIDFF does not set FIC101_CV, allowing the operator to modify its value. However, the PIDFF block does ensure FIC101_CV is within the out_inf and out_sup limits (part of the PARA structure). If another part of the program uses something like a MOVE block to continuously overwrite FIC101_CV when in manual mode, then the STATUS word must be monitored for an OUT out-of-range condition and the source of the MOVE block modified accordingly.

Example values for the PARA structure are shown in Figure 10.64. The tuning parameters are those for the PI controller of Example 10.4. The elements of the PARA control parameter structure include:

Upper and lower bounds of the PV

Upper and lower bounds of the CV

Reverse/direct action

Interacting or noninteracting form of the algorithm

Type of anti-reset windup

Enable of RCPY input

K_P, T_I, and T_D

Derivative on PV/error

Bumpless transfer disable

Deviation deadband – if the error magnitude is within the deadband, the controller considers the error to be zero.
Upper and lower limits of the CV calculation (may be smaller range than bounds)
CV velocity limit
Feedforward scaling

The actual algorithms used to calculate the CV differ somewhat from the PID algorithm equations in section 10.3.2. The velocity form of the algorithm is used if the controller contains integral action, otherwise the positional form is used. The feedforward scaling can easily accommodate static feedforward compensation and is shown in Example 10.9.

The PI_B function block is offered where a simple PI controller is sufficient, but it does not include anti-reset windup and has no accommodation for feedforward corrections. In addition, a change from manual to automatic mode is bumpless only if the integral term is enabled. Other P/PI/PID controller function blocks are also offered.

There is also an AUTOTUNE function block that performs automatic tuning of both the PIDFF and PI_B function blocks. An example connection of AUTOTUNE with the PIDFF block is shown in Figure 10.65. When autotuning is started (FIC101_AT **on** for one scan), the AUTOTUNE block uses the tracking inputs of the PID to disable the PID execution and identifies the process in three stages:

1. Analyze the process noise and stability.
2. Step the CV by a set amount and obtain a model.
3. Restore the CV to its final value and refine the model.

The reader is referred to the Concept documentation (Schneider Automation, 1998) for further details. In practice, automatic tuning of the PID controller is mainly used when commissioning a process. Operators are generally wary of automatic tuning since it introduces a "bump" into the process and there is a period of time in which the loop is not being controlled.

Some of the more important signal conditioning blocks are shown in Figure 10.66. The DTIME block delays the IN signal by the T_DELAY time and then transfers the value to the OUT output. The time delay can be a variable. The delay buffer length is the number of elements in the BUFFER array. An alternative time delay block, QDTIME, allows a constant time delay and fixed buffer length of 128 real numbers. The TR_I and TR_S inputs function like the PIDFF inputs of the same name. The K_SQRT block is a weighted square root calculation to linearize the differential pressure measurement from an orifice-plate flow meters into a volumetric flow rate. The calculation is IN $= K\sqrt{\text{IN}}$ when IN is above the CUTOFF value. When IN is less than CUTOFF, OUT is zero. The LDLG function block implements a lead/lag transfer function block,

$$G_{ll}(s) = K\frac{(\tau_1 s + 1)}{(\tau_2 s + 1)} \tag{10.9}$$

which is equation (10.7) without the time delay. The IN connection is the input, and the OUT connection is the calculation result. The GAIN, LEAD, and LAG inputs correspond to K, τ_1, and τ_2, respectively of (10.9).

Among the other conditioning function blocks that are available are:

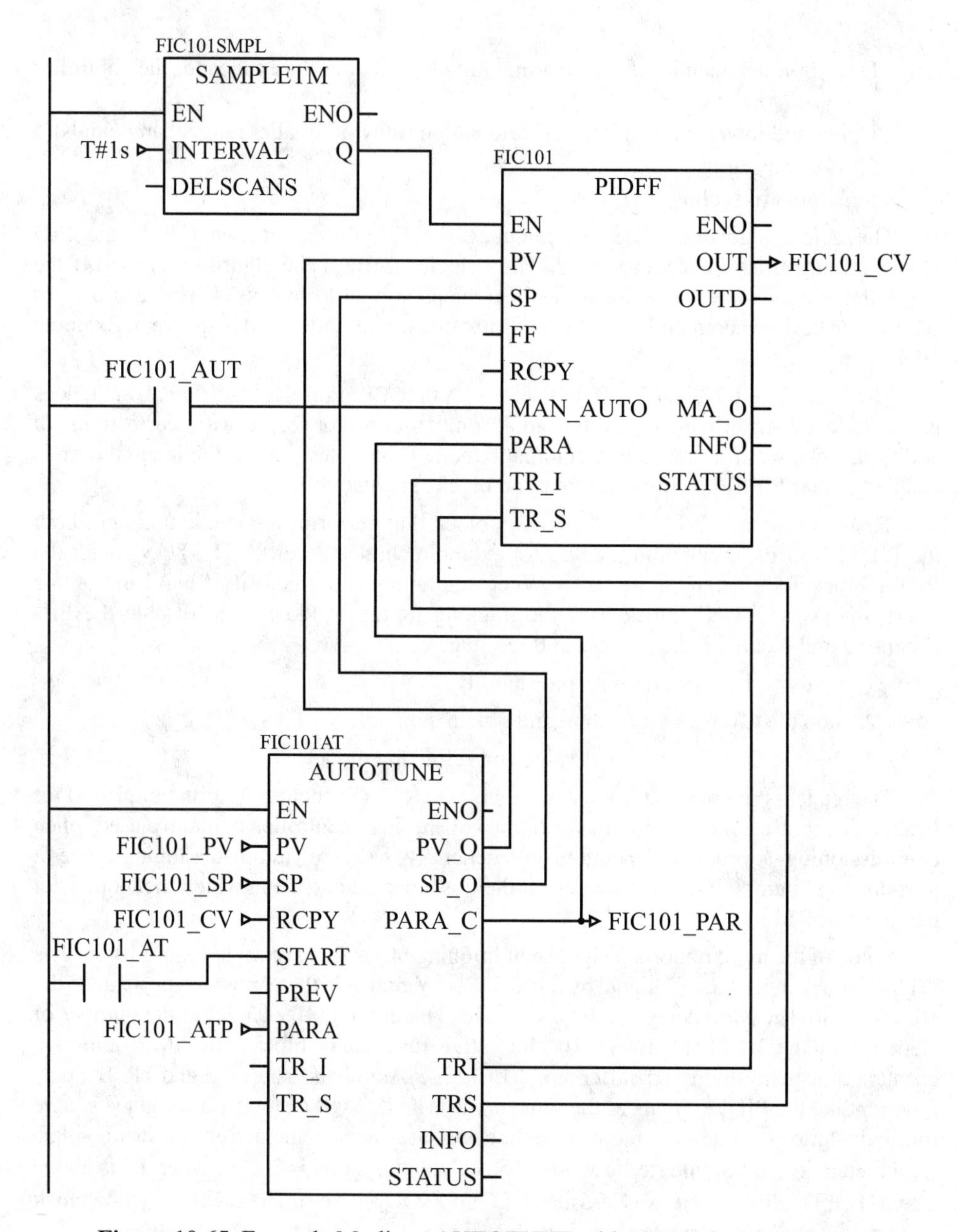

Figure 10.65. Example Modicon AUTOTUNE with PIDFF function block.

LAG_FILTER – Filters noise from a measurement. Implements (10.9) without the numerator.

LEAD – Implements a filtered derivative.

MFLOW – Converts a volumetric gas flow rate into a mass flow rate. Requires a temperature and pressure measurement.

SCALING – Changes the scale of a raw analog input value into appropriate units.

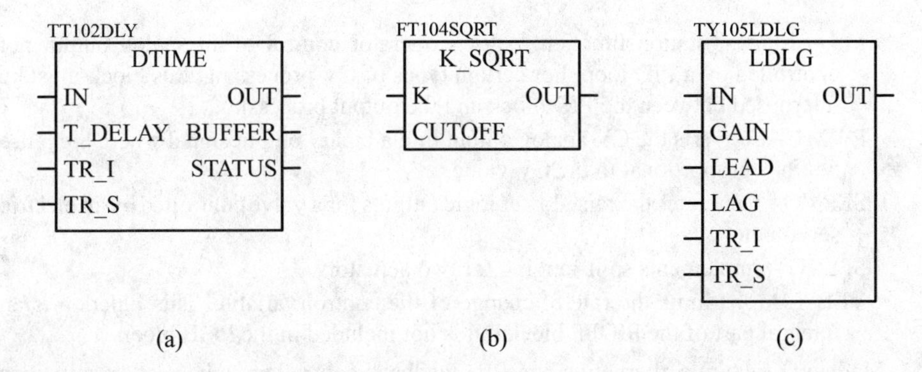

Figure 10.66. Signal conditioning blocks *(a)* time delay; *(b)* weighted square root; *(c)* lead/lag.

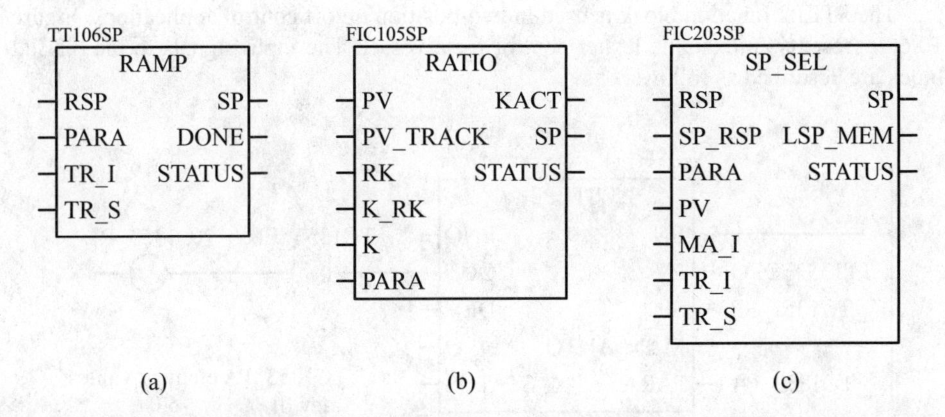

Figure 10.67. Setpoint management blocks: *(a)* ramp between two values; *(b)* setpoint for ratio control; *(c)* setpoint selector.

TOTALIZER – Integrates a flow rate to calculate the volume of material that has passed through the flow meter.

The function blocks that are available for setpoint management are shown in Figure 10.67 and briefly described as:

RAMP – Generates temperature setpoint for applications that require a ramp/soak profile.

RATIO – Calculates a setpoint by multiplying one variable by a ratio, needed for ratio control.

SP_SEL – Smooths transfer between an operator-generated setpoint and a program-generated setpoint. Also used for cascade control.

The SP_SEL function is applied in the cascade control example (Example 10.8).

Function blocks that modify the controller output for certain applications are briefly described.

MS – Manual station function. Allows operator control of an analog output not controlled by a PID loop. For certain types of CV processing, this block must be interposed between the PID block and the output processing.

PWM1 – Converts the CV analog output into a binary output signal where the pulse width is proportional to the CV value.

SERVO – Generates the raise/lower logic outputs for a valve controlled by an electric servomotor

SPLRG – Implements split-ranging for two actuators.

VEL_LIM – Limits the rate of change of the control variable. This function is an integral part of the PIDFF block but is not included in the PI_B block.

Modicon offers two alternative non-PID feedback controllers to be used in situations where the final control element is a discrete device. Both of these controllers will generally not control as well as a PID controller, but in applications where a regulating final control element (e.g., regulating valve) is not available, the options for control are limited.

The STEP2 function block is used in two-position on/off control applications. Figure 10.68*a* presents an example heater control for a vessel. The input signals to the STEP2 block are described as follows:

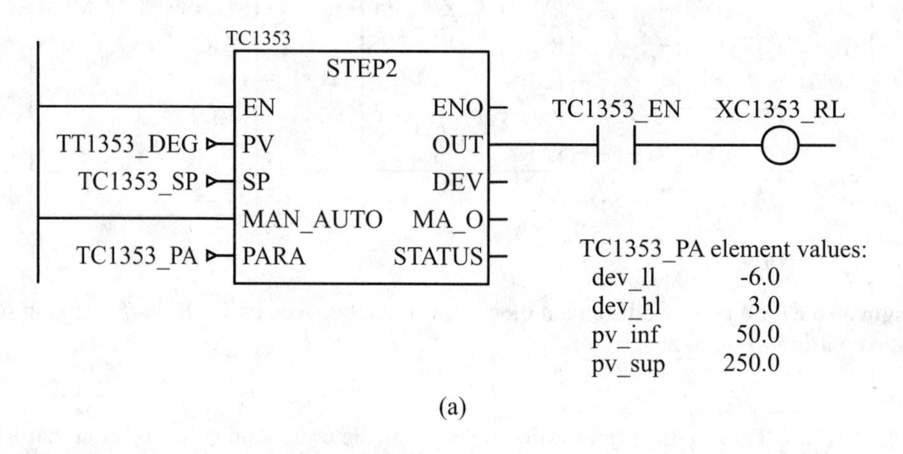

(a)

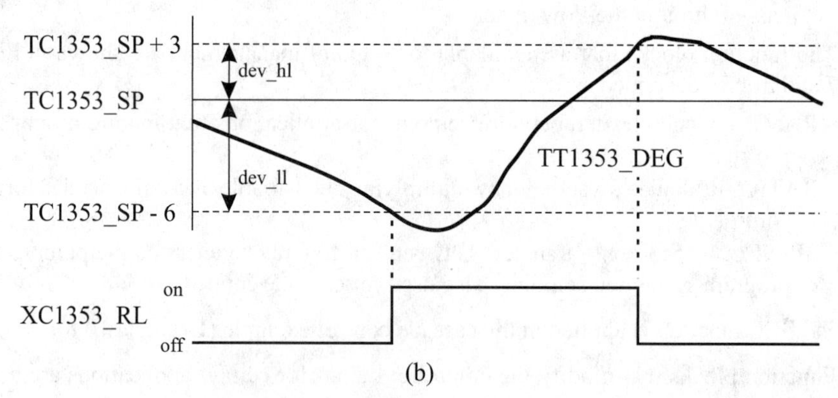

(b)

Figure 10.68. Two-position on/off control: *(a)* ladder logic program; *(b)* example operation.

PV – Process variable measurement.

SP – Loop setpoint.

MAN_AUTO – Controller mode: **on** for automatic mode; **off** for manual mode.

PARA – Controller parameters. Variable of type Para_STEP2. This structure contains the upper and lower deviation threshold and the upper and lower boundaries of PV.

The output signals of the STEP2 block are described as follows:

OUT – Discrete control variable.

DEV – Current deviation (PV – SP).

MA_O – Current controller mode: **on** for automatic mode; **off** for manual mode.

STATUS – Reports internal calculation errors.

The values of the TC1353_PA structure that contains the deviation thresholds are also shown. The STEP2 block turns **on** OUT when the deviation (PV – SP) drops below the lower threshold and then turns it **off** when the deviation rises above the upper threshold, as illustrated in Figure 10.68*b*. The STEP2 mode is always set to automatic for this application because manual mode does not set OUT to a default value. The TC1353_EN Boolean enables the heater operation when it is **on**.

The STEP3 function blocks extends the operation of STEP2 to two discrete actuators: one to control heating and the other to control cooling.

10.7.2 A-B ControlLogix PID function block

The ControlLogix PID function block fully implements the PID control algorithm and includes anti-reset windup and accommodations for feedforward compensation. An example PID loop is shown in Figure 10.69.

This example uses a timer to trigger execution of the PID block. This trigger method is recommended only if the sample period (called the update time) is at least a second and is several times longer than the continuous task scan time. For processes that require shorter sample periods, the PID block should be placed in a periodic task whose execution rate is the desired sample period. In either case, the analog input module should be producing the process variable tag five to ten times faster than the loop sample period. The real time sampling (RTS) feature of the analog input modules is the most accurate way of executing a PID block. When the data timestamp for the analog input module changes, then execute the PID block. In this case, the real time sampling rate becomes the loop update rate.

The operands of the PID block are described as follows:

PID – PID structure tag.

Process variable – Tag of process variable.

Tieback – Tag of value copied to CV when in manual mode.

Control variable – Tag of control variable.

PID Master Loop – Tag of PID structure for master (outer) loop in cascade control if this loop is the slave (inner) loop.

Inhold bit – Inhold bit from analog output module that receives the CV. Supports bumpless restart when controller changes to run mode.

Inhold Value – Data readback from analog output module to support bumpless restart.

Setpoint – Displays current value of setpoint.

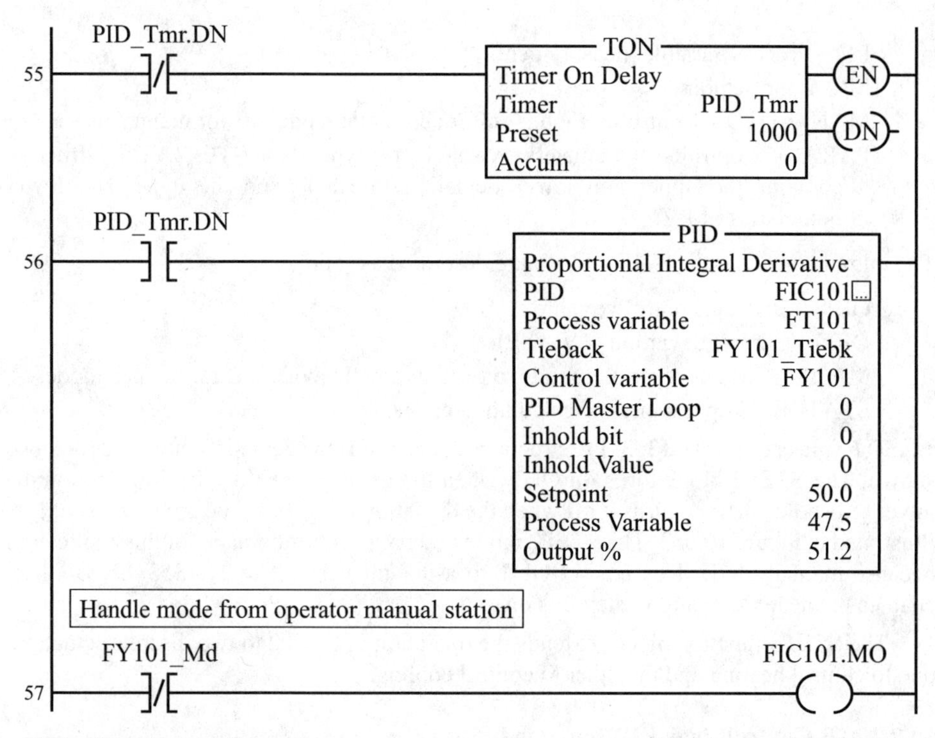

PID - FIC101 Configuration

Setpoint: 1.2
Set Output %: 0.0
Output Bias: 0.0
Proportional Gain: 1.17
Integral Gain (Ti) [mins/rep]: 2.67
Derivative Time (Td) [mins]: 0.0
A/M Station Mode: Auto
Software A/M Mode: Auto
PID Equation: Dependent
Control Action: SP - PV
Derivative Of: PV

Update Time (Secs): 1.0
CV High Limit%: 100
CV Low Limit%: 0
Deadband: 0
PV Tracking: No
Cascade Loop: No
Cascade Type: N/A
PV Alarm High: 0
PV Alarm Low: 0
PV Alarm Deadband: 0
Pos. Deviation Alarm: 0

Neg. Deviation Alarm: 0
Deviation Alm Deadband: 0
PV Unscaled Max: 30920
PV Unscaled Min: -20030
Engineering Unit Max: 2.0
Engineering Unit Min: 0.0
CV Max (at 100%): 30920
CV Min (at 0%): -20030
Tieback Max (at 100%): 30920
Tieback Min (at 0%): -20030

Figure 10.69. Example ControlLogix PID loop.

Process Variable – Displays current value of scaled process variable.

Output % – Displays current value of control variable, in % of range.

The "Process variable" operand should be the tag corresponding to the unscaled analog input channel reading. Also, the "Control variable" operand should be the tag corresponding to the unscaled analog output channel value. When cascading two PID loops, the slave PID block automatically converts the output from the master loop into the correct units for the setpoint of the slave loop.

For the PID tag defined in Figure 10.69, the individual fields of the PID structure that are useful for programmatic control of the PID loop are addressed as follows:

Reference	**Description**
FIC101.SP	Setpoint
FIC101.MO	Manual mode: **on** for manual, **off** for automatic
FIC101.SWM	Software manual mode: **on** for manual, **off** for automatic
FIC101.SO	CV (in %) when SWM bit is **on**.
FIC101.BIAS	Bias term added to output. Feedforward added here.
FIC101.OUT	CV, in percent (0-100)

The PID block offers two manual modes. When the .MO bit is set, the value in the Tieback tag is scaled and copied to the controller output. When the .SWM bit is set, the value in the .SO field is copied to the controller output. The .MO bit overrides the .SWM bit if both are set. The .MO bit is intended to be set from an operator manual station and the tieback value is the analog input readback of the operator-set control variable, as shown in Figure 10.70. FY101_Md is **on** when the controller should be in automatic mode. The transfer of the mode from the operator station to the PID block is on the third rung of Figure 10.69. If the particular loop does not have an operator manual station, then the .MO bit alone can be used to programmatically control the controller mode.

To implement a feedforward correction, copy the feedforward value to the BIAS field. However, keep in mind that if the controller does not use integral action when the mode is changed from manual to automatic, the BIAS term is modified to make the calculated CV output match the tieback (or SO value) when the mode is changed. In this case, any feedforward correction should be disabled when in the manual or software manual mode and not re-enabled until some time after changing to the automatic mode. Setting the .NOBC bit will disable the bias term back-calculation, but then there is no bumpless transfer when the controller does not have integral action.

An example PID configuration is shown in Figure 10.69. The tuning parameters are those for the PI controller of Example 10.4. The configuration in the PID structure includes:

K_P, T_I, and T_D or K_P, K_I, and K_D
Interacting or noninteracting form of the algorithm
Reverse/direct action
Derivative on PV/error
Loop update time
Upper and lower limits of the CV calculation (may be smaller range than bounds)
Deviation deadband – if the error magnitude is within the deadband, the controller considers the error to be zero.
Alarms: PV high, PV low, and deviation
Upper and lower bounds of the PV
Upper and lower bounds of the CV
Upper and lower bounds of tieback value

The actual algorithms used to calculate the CV are very similar to the PID algorithm equations in section 10.3.2. The positional form of the algorithm is used. The user may select either the dependent gains (interacting) or independent gains (noninteracting) form of the algorithm. For the dependent gains, the tuning parameters are K_P, T_I, and T_D, and time is measured in minutes. For the independent gains form of the algorithm, the tuning parameters are K_C, K_I, and K_D, and time is measured in seconds.

Regardless of the method used to trigger the PID block (timer, periodic task, or real-time sampling), the loop update time is specified as a separate configuration parameter.

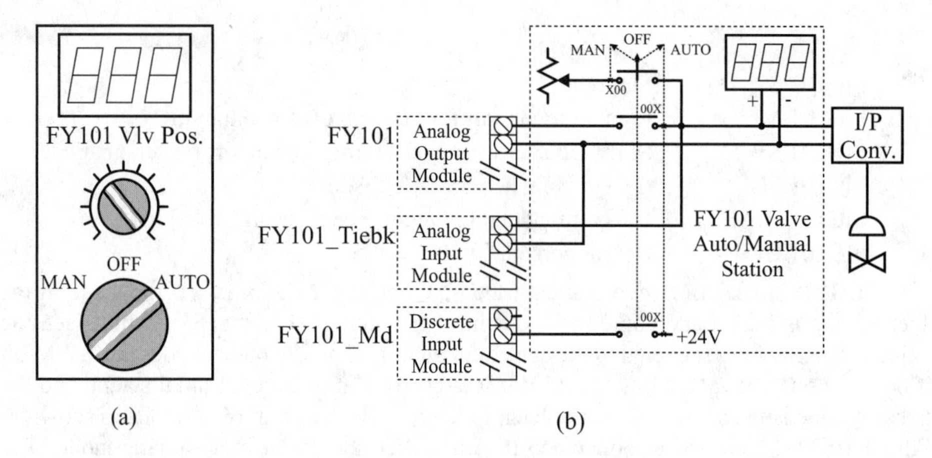

Figure 10.70. Operator manual station: *(a)* panel; *(b)* PLC connections.

The loop update time must match the actual sample period or the algorithm calculation will be incorrect.

The ControlLogix does not have ladder logic function blocks to handle signal conditioning, setpoint management, or output processing. These functions are provided by the FBD function blocks, described in Chapter 11.

10.7.3 A-B PLC-5/SLC-500 PID function block

The PLC-5 PID function block fully implements the PID control algorithm and includes anti-reset windup and accommodations for feedforward compensation. The example PID loop shown in Figure 10.71 is very similar to the ControlLogix PID block.

This example uses a timer to trigger execution of the PID block. This trigger method is recommended only if the loop sample period (update time) is greater than 0.1 second and is several times longer than the program scan time. For processes that require shorter sample periods, the PID block should be placed in a selectable timed interrupt (STI) program file set to execute at the desired loop sample time. In either case, the block transfers for the analog modules should occur as fast as possible, preferably five to ten times faster than the loop sample period. The block transfers may be synchronized with the PID block execution, but this leads to inconsistent loop sample times and is not recommended by the author. For fast PID loops, the analog modules should be in the same chassis as the processor. If the analog input module can be configured for real time sampling (RTS), it can be used to execute a PID block. With RTS, a block transfer read (BTR) will not initiate until new data is available and thus the BTR done bit can execute the PID block. In this case, the real time sampling rate becomes the loop update rate.

The operands of the PID block are described as follows:

Control Block – Address of PID structure.

Process variable – Address of process variable (must be a word).

Tieback – Address of value copied to CV when in manual mode.

Control variable – Address of control variable (must be a word).

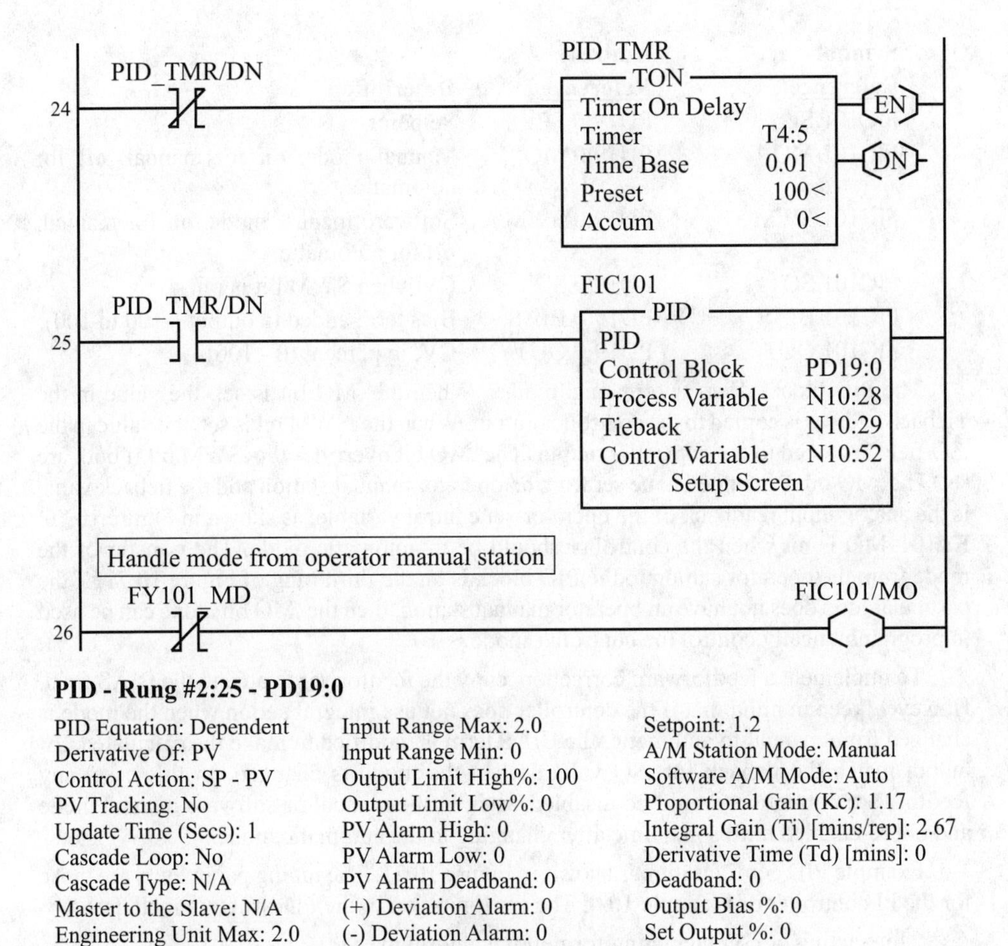

Figure 10.71. Example PLC-5 PID loop.

The "Process Variable" operand should be the address of an unscaled analog input channel reading in the range of 0 - 4095. If the analog input module has been configured to produce scaled readings, they must be descaled before the PID block uses them. Also, the "Control Variable" calculated by the PID block is in the range of 0 – 4095 which corresponds to the range of an unscaled analog output channel value. When cascading two PID loops, the slave (inner) PID block automatically converts the output from the master (outer) loop into the correct units for the setpoint of the slave loop.

The PID structure can be defined as an array of 23 integers or as an element of the PD file type (enhanced PLC-5 only). This section describes the information in a PD control block. The integer structure is very similar, but information is addressed as integers or bits within integers. For the "Control Block" address defined in Figure 10.71, the individual fields of the PD structure that are useful for programmatic control of the PID loop are addressed as follows:

Symbol Reference	**Address Reference**	**Description**
FIC101.SP	PD19:0.SP	Setpoint
FIC101/MO	PD19:0/MO	Manual mode: **on** for manual, **off** for automatic
FIC101/SWM	PD19:0/SWM	Software manual mode: **on** for manual, **off** for automatic
FIC101.SO	PD19:0.SO	CV when SWM bit is **on**.
FIC101.BIAS	PD19:0.BIAS	Bias term added to output (-100 to 100).
FIC101.OUT	PD19:0.OUT	CV, in percent (0 - 100)

The PID block offers two manual modes. When the .MO bit is set, the value in the Tieback address is copied to the controller output. When the .SWM bit is set, the value in the .SO field is copied to the controller output. The .MO bit overrides the .SWM bit if both are set. The .MO bit is intended to be set from an operator manual station and the tieback value is the analog input readback of the operator-set control variable, as shown in Figure 10.70. FY101_MD is **on** when the controller should be in automatic mode. The transfer of the mode from the operator station to the PID block is on the third rung of Figure 10.71. If the particular loop does not have an operator manual station, then the .MO bit alone can be used to programmatically control the controller mode.

To implement a feedforward correction, copy the feedforward value to the BIAS field. However, keep in mind that if the controller does not use integral action when the mode is changed from manual to automatic, the BIAS term is modified to make the calculated CV output match the tieback (or .SO value) when the mode is changed. In this case, any feedforward correction should be disabled when in the manual or software manual mode and not re-enabled until some time after changing to the automatic mode.

Example PID configuration is shown in Figure 10.71. The tuning parameters are those for the PI controller of Example 10.4. The configuration in the PD structure includes:

Interacting or noninteracting form of the algorithm
Derivative on PV/error
Reverse/direct action
Loop update time
Upper and lower bounds of the PV
Upper and lower limits of the CV calculation
Alarms: PV high, PV low, and deviation
K_P, T_I, and T_D or K_P, K_I, and K_D
Deviation deadband – if the error magnitude is within the deadband, the controller considers the error to be zero.

The actual algorithms used to calculate the CV are very similar to the PID algorithm equations in section 10.3.2. The positional form of the algorithm is used. The user may select either the dependent gains (interacting) or independent gains (noninteracting) form of the algorithm. For the dependent gains, the tuning parameters are K_P, T_I, and T_D and time is measured in minutes. For the independent gains form of the algorithm, the tuning parameters are K_C, K_I, and K_D and time is measured in seconds.

Regardless of the method used to trigger the PID block (timer or STI program), the loop update time is specified as a separate configuration parameter. The loop update time must match the actual sample period or the algorithm calculation will be incorrect.

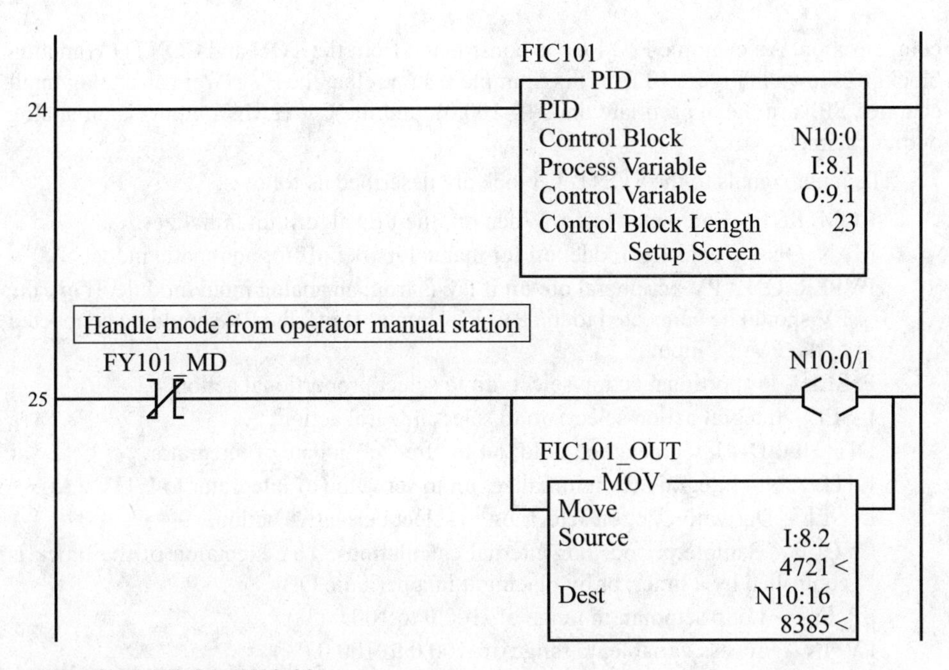

PID - Rung #2:24 - N10:23

Controller Gain, Kc: 1.2
Reset Term, Ti: 2.7
Rate Term, Td: 0.00
Loop Update Time: 1.00
Control Mode: E = SP - PV
PID Control: Manual
Time Mode: Timed
Output Limiting: Yes
Reset and Gain: No

Setpoint: 120
Maximum Setpoint Limit: 200
Minimum Setpoint Limit: 0
Control Variable Percent (CV%): 60
Output Max CV(%): 100
Output Min CV(%): 0
Derivative Action (DA): No
Deadband: 0

Figure 10.72. Example SLC-500 PID loop.

The PLC-5 does not have ladder logic function blocks to handle signal conditioning, setpoint management, or output processing. The available arithmetic function blocks must be used to provide these functions.

The PID function block for the SLC-500 is slightly different from the PLC-5. An example PID block is shown in Figure 10.72. Note the lack of a timer to initiate execution. If placed in a normal program file, the "Time Mode" parameter is set to "Timed," which causes the PID block to execute at rate set in the "Loop Update" value (0.01 to 10.23 seconds). If placed in a STI program file, the "Time Mode" parameter is set to "STI," and the "Loop Update" value is set to the STI time interval. The SLC-500 PID block only executes the interacting form of the PID equation (time units in minutes) and has only one manual mode.

10.7.4 Siemens S7 PID function blocks

For the S7-300/400 processors, the CONT_C function block fully implements the PID control algorithm and includes anti-reset windup and accommodations for feedforward compensation. An example PID loop is constructed from the TON and CONT_C function blocks as shown in Figure 10.73. This example assumes that the PV is from an analog input channel, SP is in the appropriate units (0-100.0), and the CV (LMN output) is an analog output channel.

The input signals to the CONT_C block are described as follows:

COM_RST – Complete restart. When **on**, the PID algorithm initializes.

MAN_ON – Controller mode: **on** for manual mode; **off** for automatic mode.

PVPER_ON – PV peripheral on: **on** if PV is from an analog input module. If **on**, the PV should be connected to the PV_PER input. If **off**, the PV should be connected to the PV_IN input.

P_SEL – Proportional action select: **on** to select proportional action.

I_SEL – Integral action select: **on** to select integral action.

INT_HOLD – Integral action hold: **on** to "freeze" update of integrator.

I_ITL_ON – Integral action initialize: **on** to set value of integrator to I_ITLVAL.

D_SEL – Derivative action select: **on** to select derivative action.

CYCLE – Sample period. For internal calculations. The execution of the block is controlled by a timer, or by placing it in a periodic OB.

SP_INT – Loop setpoint, in range of -100.0 to 100.0 (%).

PV_IN – Process variable, in range of -100.0 to 100.0 (%).

PV_PER – Process variable measurement, in analog input channel units (WORD). Internally, converted to range of -100.0 to 100.0 (%) before it is subtracted from SP_INT.

MAN – Manual value. Copied to LMN output if MAN_ON input is **on**.

GAIN – Proportional gain.

TI – Integral time constant (TIME).

TD – Derivative time (TIME).

TM_LAG – Additional lag time that can be added to derivative action.

DEADB_W – Deadband width. Error deadband, in the same units as the PV and SP, 0 to 100.0 (%).

LMN_HLM – Manipulated variable high limit, in range of LMN_LLM to 100.0 (REAL).

LMN_LLM – Manipulated variable low limit, in range of -100.0 to LMN_HLM (REAL).

PV_FAC – PV factor. Multiplies PV_PER for simple range adaptation. Default value is 1.0 (no scaling).

PV_OFF – PV offset. Added to PV_PER for range adaptation. Default value is 0.0 (no offset).

LMN_FAC – CV factor. Multiplies controller output for simple range adaptation. Default value is 1.0 (no scaling).

LMN_OFF – CV offset. Added to controller output for simple range adaptation. Default value is 1.0 (no scaling).

I_ITLVAL – Integral action initialization value. Output of integrator is set to this value if I_ITL_ON is **on**. Range is -100.0 to 100.0 (%).

DISV – Disturbance variable. Connect the output of the feedforward controller to this input.

The output signals of the CONT_C block are described as follows:

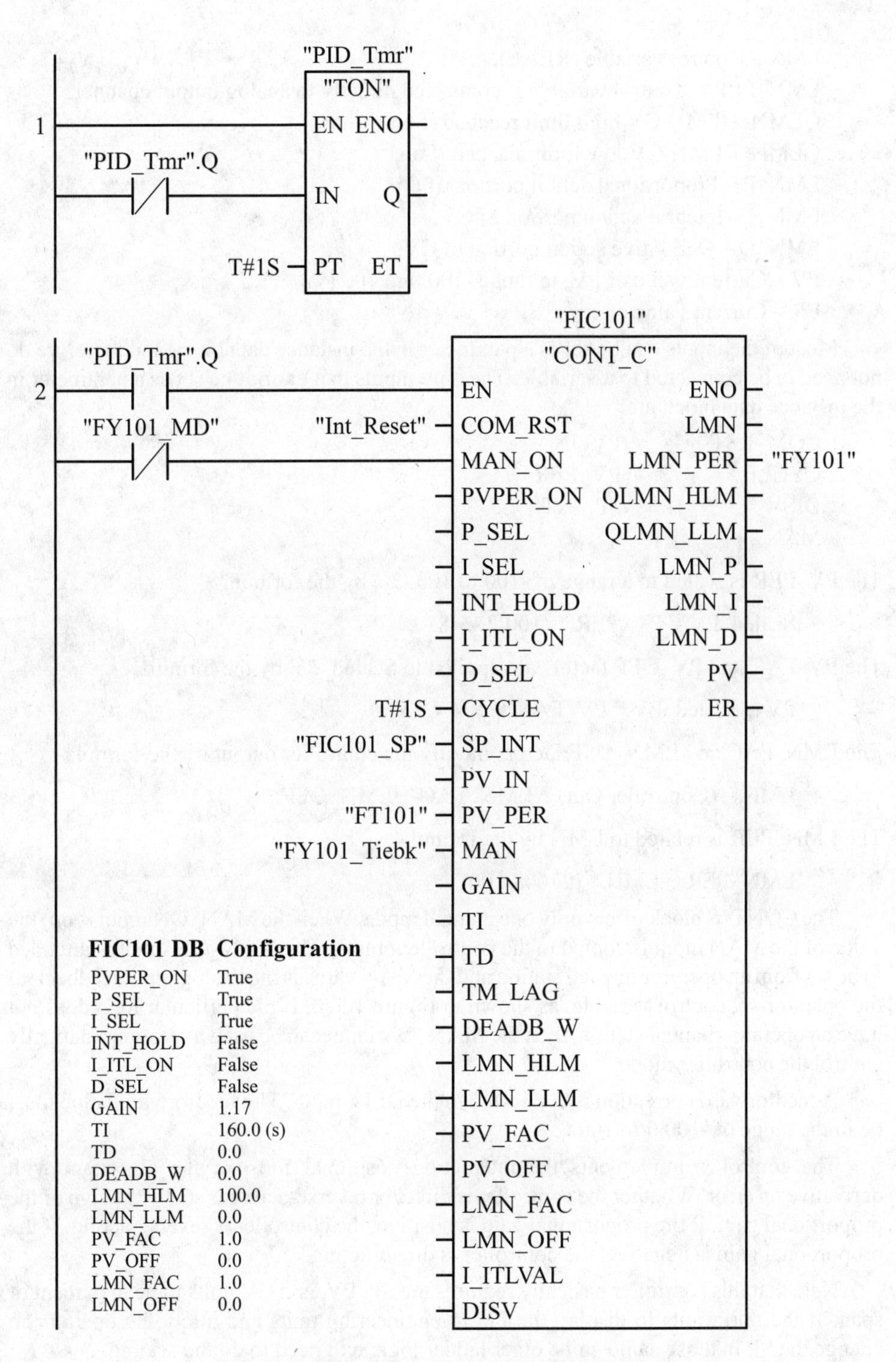

Figure 10.73. Example S7-300/400 PID loop.

LMN – Control variable (REAL).
LMN_PER – Control variable if connected directly to analog output channel.
QLMN_HLM – CV high limit reached if **on**.
QLMN_LLM – CV low limit reached if **on**.
LMN_P – Proportional action portion of CV.
LMN_I – Integral action portion of CV.
LMN_D – Derivative action portion of CV.
PV – Current value of PV, in range -100.0 to 100 (%)
ER – Current value of error, SP – PV.

Most of the inputs can be set as a parameter in the instance data block and therefore do not need to be connected to a variable. The only inputs that **cannot** be set as a parameter in the instance data block are:

COM_RST	PV_IN
CYCLE	PV_PER
DISV	SP_INT
MAN	

The PV_PER is scaled to a range of -100 to 100 (%) by the formula

Scaled_PV = PV_PER * (100/27648)

The PV_FAC and PV_OFF factors are applied to Scaled_PV by the formula

PV = Scaled_PV * PV_FAC + PV_OFF

The LMN_FAC and LMN_OFF factors modify the controller output by the formula

LMN = (Controller Out) * LMN_FAC + LMN_OFF

The LMN_PER is related to LMN by the formula

LMN_PER = LMN * (27648/100)

The CONT_S block offers only one manual mode. When the MAN_ON input is **on**, the value of the MAN input is copied to the controller output. The MAN_ON input is intended to be set from an operator manual station and the MAN value is the analog input readback of the operator-set control variable, as shown in Figure 10.70. If the particular loop does not have an operator manual station, then the MAN_ON input can be used to programmatically control the controller mode.

A feedforward correction is connected to the DISV input. The feedforward value must be in the range of -100.0 to 100.0.

The controller implements the interacting positional form of the algorithm with derivative on error. Whether the controller is direct or reverse-acting is set by the sign of the proportional gain. If the proportional gain is positive, the controller is reverse-acting. If the proportional gain is negative, the controller is direct-acting.

Note that this controller basically requires the SP, PV, and CV units to be in percent of span. If the one wants to display the PV in engineering units and allow the operator to change the SP in those same units, other ladder logic will need to do the scaling.

The CONT_S function block is offered where the controller must generate the raise/lower logic outputs for a valve controlled by an electric servomotor. The PULSEGEN function block converts the output of the CONT_C controller to a binary output signal where the pulse width is proportional to the CV value. The S7-300/400 processors have a special function block, LEAD_LAG which implements a lead/lag function (equation 10.7). Any other signal conditioning or setpoint management must use the available arithmetic function blocks.

For the S7-200 processors, the PID block is used for PID control. It has fewer features than the S7-300/400 CONT_C block and implements the basic PID algorithm. A sample PID loop with this block is shown in Figure 10.74. This example assumes the ladder logic is contained in a timed interrupt routine. The input signals to the PID block (rung 2) are described as follows:

EN – Enable. When **on**, algorithm executes. Normally used for controller mode: **on** for automatic mode; **off** for manual mode.

TBL – Loop table. Starting address of 36-byte table containing parameters and some internal algorithm variables.

LOOP – Loop number (0-7). Only a maximum of 8 PID loops can be configured.

Not all S7-200 processors support the PID block. For the processors that support both SIMATIC and IEC block libraries, the PID block is contained in the SIMATIC library.

The loop table contains the following ("Start" is the starting address):

Address	Type	Description
Start	REAL	Current process variable, in range of 0.0 to 1.0.
Start+4	REAL	Setpoint, in range of 0.0 to 1.0.
Start+8	REAL	Output, CV, in range of 0.0 to 1.0.
Start+12	REAL	Proportional gain.
Start+16	REAL	Sample time, in seconds.
Start+20	REAL	Integral time constant, in minutes.
Start+24	REAL	Derivative time, in minutes.
Start+28	REAL	Bias, or integral sum value, in range 0.0 to 1.0.
Start+32	REAL	Process variable at last block execution.

The PID block calculates the CV and the previous PV. Therefore, the user is responsible for setting up all of the other variables, either by initializing the locations prior to downloading the processor, or by using MOVE blocks to set the values on the first scan of the program.

The controller implements the interacting positional form of the algorithm with derivative on PV. Whether the controller is direct or reverse-acting is set by the sign of the proportional gain. If the proportional gain is positive, the controller is reverse-acting. If the proportional gain is negative, the controller is direct-acting. There is no special controller mode processing. The EN input is basically the automatic/manual mode. The controller does implement bumpless transfer when the EN transitions from **off**-to-**on**.

10.7.5 GE Fanuc PID function blocks

There are two PID control blocks supported by GE Fanuc processors. Both of these function blocks fully implement the PID control algorithm and include anti-reset windup and accommodations for feedforward compensation. The PID_ISA block implements the interacting form of the PID algorithm (Figure 10.17) and the PID_IND block implements the noninteracting form of the PID algorithm (Figure 10.18). An example PID loop is

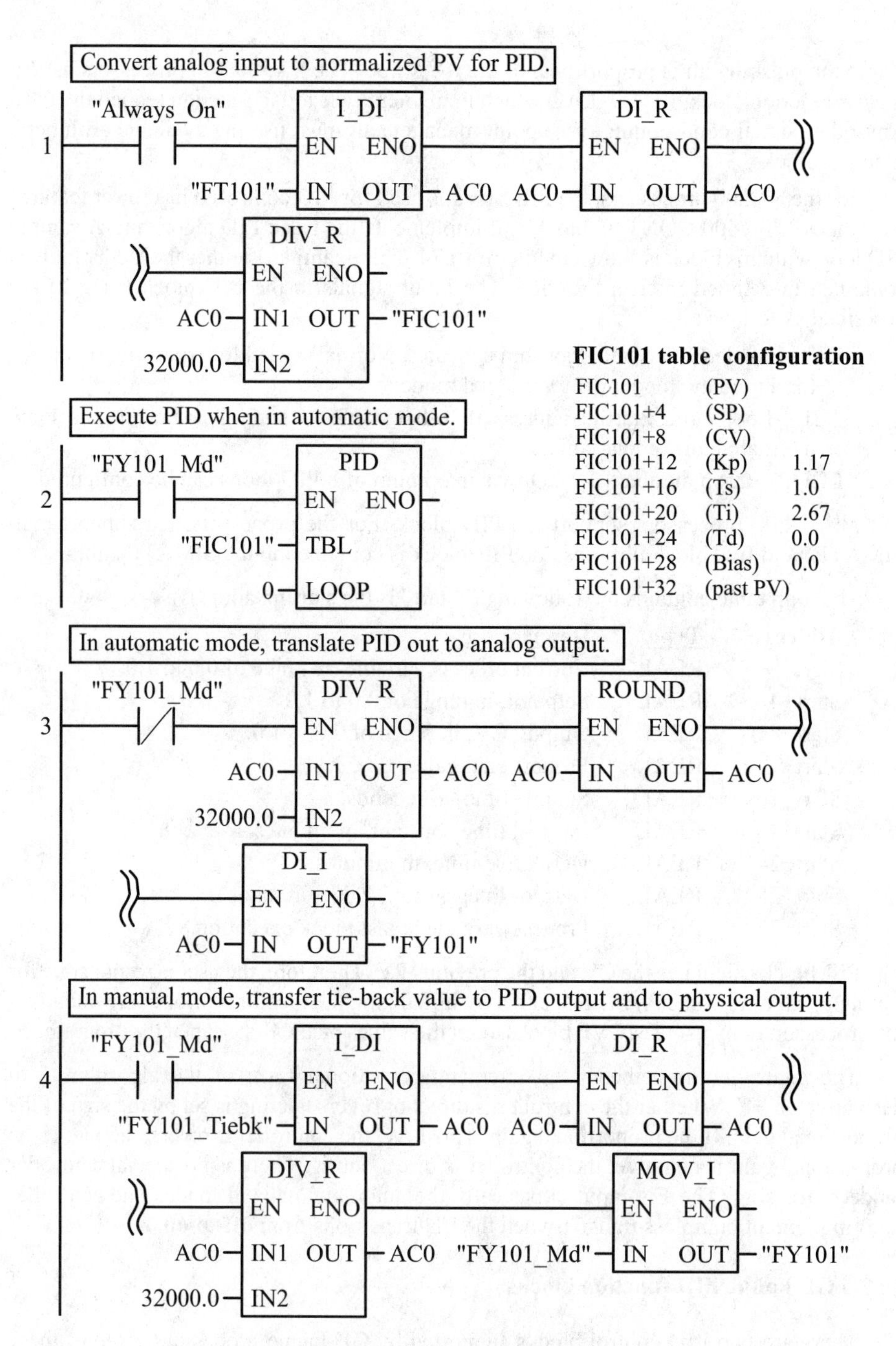

Figure 10.74. Example S7-200 PID loop.

shown in Figure 10.75. This example assumes that the PV is from an analog input channel, SP is in the analog input units (-32000 to 32000), and the CV is an analog output channel.

The input signals to the PID_ISA and PID_IND blocks are described as follows:

SP – Loop setpoint, in analog input channel units, -32000 to 32000.

PV – Process variable measurement, in analog input channel units, -32000 to 32000.

MAN – Controller mode: **on** for manual mode; **off** for automatic mode.

UP – CV increase. When **on** and MAN is **on**, adjusts the CV up by 1 every sample period.

DN – CV decrease. When **on** and MAN is **on**, adjusts the CV down by 1 every sample period.

The UP and DN inputs must be connected to contacts. If either or both of these inputs are not used, the #ALW_OFF symbol may be utilized. The CV output signal, the control

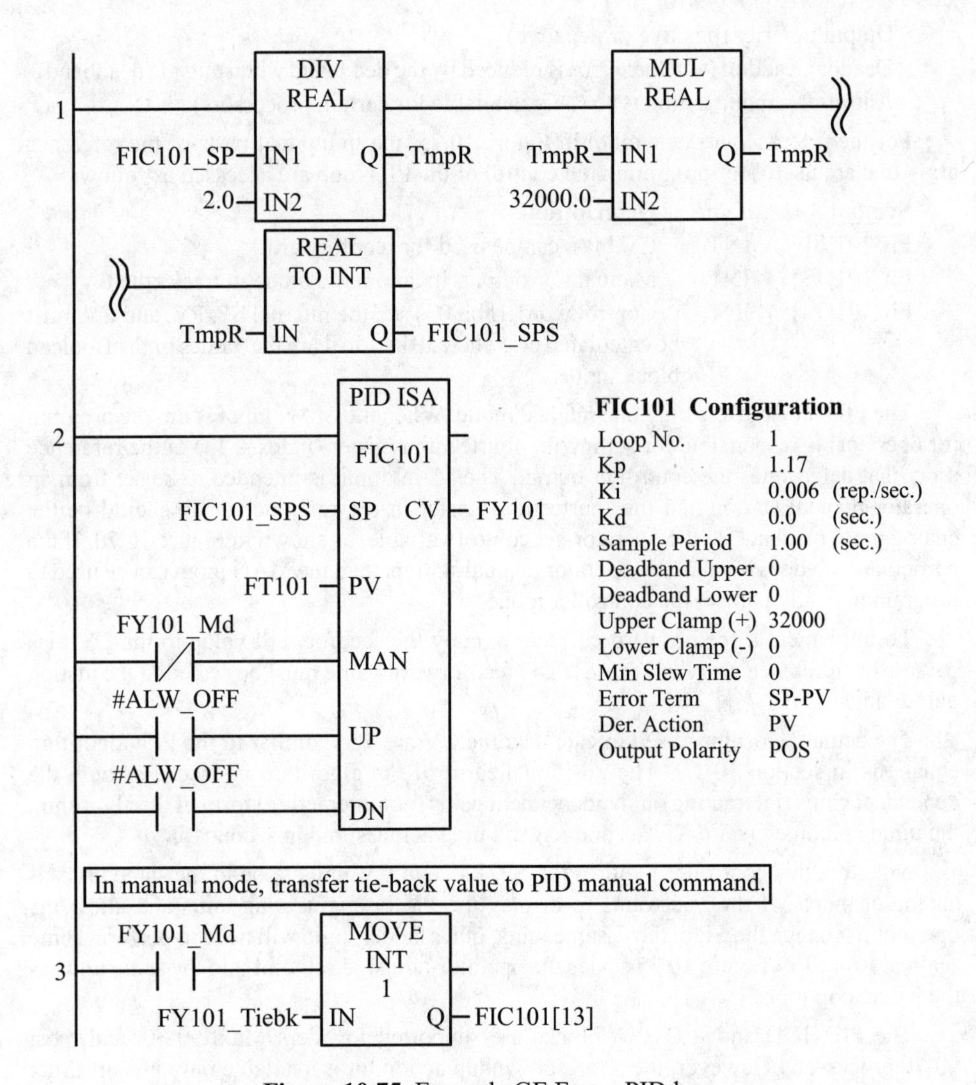

Figure 10.75. Example GE Fanuc PID loop.

variable output, is in analog output channel units, -32000 to 32000. The top output is **on** when the block executes without error. The field below the block name is the symbol or address of a 40-register PID reference array.

The configuration information in the reference array includes:

PID loop number (optional; for operator display)
K_P, K_I, and K_D
Sample period
Deviation deadband – if the error magnitude is within the deadband, the controller considers the error to be zero.
Upper and lower bounds of the CV
Minimum output slew time
Error is SP-PV/PV-SP
Derivative on PV/error
Output polarity (positive or negative)
Deadband action (whether error is reduced by the deadband when outside deadband)
Antireset windup action type (only available for certain processors)

For the reference array symbol in Figure 10.75, the individual parts of the reference array that are useful for programmatic control of the PID loop are accessed as follows:

Symbol	Type	Description
FIC101[8]	INT	CV bias, can be used for feedforward.
FIC101[13]	INT	Manual CV output. In automatic mode, it tracks the CV.
FIC101[14]	INT	Control word. If bit 0 is set, the internal SP, PV, and CV must be calculated elsewhere. Bits 1 to 4 are the values of the Boolean block inputs.

The PID block offers only one manual mode. When the MAN input is **on**, the program (or operator) is responsible for setting the fourteenth register (index = 13) in the reference array that determines the controller output. The MAN input is intended to be set from an operator manual station and the fourteenth register in the reference array should be the analog input readback of the operator-set control variable, as shown in Figure 10.70. If the particular loop does not have an operator manual station, then the MAN input can be used to programmatically control the controller mode.

To implement a feedforward correction, copy the feedforward value to the CV bias parameter (reference array index = 8). The feedforward value must be scaled to the analog output units.

The actual algorithms used to calculate the CV are very similar to the PID algorithm equations in section 10.3.2. The positional form of the algorithm is used. For both the dependent gains (interacting) and independent gains (noninteracting) form of the algorithm, the tuning parameters are K_P, K_I, and K_D and time is measured in seconds.

Note that this controller requires the SP, PV, and CV units to be in the same units as analog channels. If the one wants to display the PV in engineering units and allow the operator to change the SP in those same units, other ladder logic will need to perform some scaling. Rung 1 of Figure 10.75 scales the operator-adjusted setpoint into the same units as the PV analog input.

The PID_IND and PID_ISA blocks are supported for VersaMax, 90-30, and most 90-70 processors. However, the antireset windup action bit is available only in VersaMax processors, and in later 90-30 and 90-70 processors (GE Fanuc Automation, 1999, 2000, 2001).

10.8 EXAMPLES

Examples of single-loop control for the PLCs covered by this text were shown in the previous section. Two more examples will be presented: cascade control and feedforward control.

Example 10.8. Cascade Control. Implement cascade control for the heat exchanger of Figure 10.50. The program must also handle an operator interface. The cascade control has basically three states:

Temperature Control – The operator sets the desired hot water temperature, the SP of FIC2501. The cascade loop functions normally.

Steam Flow Control – The operator sets the desired steam flow. The temperature loop is in manual mode, and the flow loop is in automatic mode. While in this mode of control, the output of TIC2501 should match the SP of FIC2502 so that there will be a bumpless transfer when going to full temperature control.

Manual Control – The operator can manually control the steam valve position. Both controllers are in manual mode. The TIC2501 output should track the actual steam flow.

There are two Booleans that are set to indicate the state of the cascade loop:

HEX_TEMP	STM_FLOW	State
On	Off	Temperature Control
Off	On	Steam Flow Control
Off	Off	Manual Control

The solution should specify the locations of the following operator-adjusted values:

TIC2501 SP	Desired hot water temperature, set by operator
FIC2502 SP	Desired steam flow, set by operator when STM_FLOW is **on**. Otherwise, it should just mimic the current flow setpoint.
FY2502 CV	Desired steam valve position, set by operator when both STM_FLOW and HEX_TEMP are **off**. Otherwise, it should just mimic the current valve position.

The hot water temperature transducer TT2501 is calibrated to measure from 280 °K to 370 °K and is connected to an analog input module having an ADC whose output value (TT2501) corresponds to the lowest and highest temperatures as:

Value	Modicon	Logix	PLC-5	SLC-500	Siemens	GE Fanuc
Lowest	0	-20,030	0	3277	5530	0
Highest	32,000	30,920	4095	16,384	27,648	32,000

The steam flow transducer FT2502 is calibrated to measure from 0 to 8 gpm and is connected to an analog input module having an ADC whose output value (FT2502) corresponds to the lowest and highest flows with the same ranges as given above.

The steam valve position is commanded by an analog output, FY2502, whose DAC input integer corresponds to the lowest and highest values of the output device control as:

Value	Modicon	Logix	PLC-5	SLC-500	Siemens	GE Fanuc
Lowest	0	-20,030	0	6242	5530	0
Highest	32,000	30,920	4095	31,208	27,648	32,000

The master loop, TIC2501 has the following tuning parameters: $K_P = 0.79$, $T_I = 0.83$ min., and $T_D = 0.0$. The slave loop, FIC2502 has the following tuning parameters: $K_P = 4.46$, $T_I = 0.17$ min., and $T_D = 0.0$.

The temperature loop sample period should be 1.0 seconds, and the flow loop sample period should be 0.25 seconds.

Assume the following physical input, physical output, and internal memory assignments:

Variable	Description
TT2501	Hot water temperature measurement, see range above.
FT2502	Steam flow measurement, see range above.
FY2502	Commanded valve position, see range above.
HEX_TEMP	Heat exchanger hot water temperature control enable; **on** to control hot water temperature (and enable cascade control).
STM_FLOW	Steam flow control enable; **on** to control steam flow only.

The addresses associated with the physical inputs and outputs are:

Variable	Modicon	PLC-5	ControlLogix	Siemens	GE Fanuc
TT2501	300002	N11:4	Local:4:I.Ch0Data	IW304	%AI1
FT2502	300003	N11:5	Local:4:I.Ch1Data	IW306	%AI2
FY2502	400002	N11:21	Local:5:O.Ch0Data	QW316	%AQ1

The addresses or data types associated with the internal variables are:

	Modicon	PLC-5	Logix	Siemens	GE Fanuc
Variable	Data Type	Addr.	Data Type	Addr.	Addr.
HEX_TEMP	BOOL	B3/121	BOOL	M15.1	%M121
STM_FLOW	BOOL	B3/122	BOOL	M15.2	%M122

Solution. The STM_FLOW and HEX_TEMP Booleans are translated into the mode commands for the individual loops. Basically, TIC2501 is in automatic only when HEX_TEMP is **on**, and FIC2502 is in automatic when either STM_FLOW or HEX_TEMP are **on**. For the various implementations, the operator-adjusted values are:

Operator	Modicon	PLC-5	CLogix	Siemens	GE Fanuc
Adjustment	Variable	Addr.	Variable	Addr.	Addr.
TIC2501 SP	TIC2501_SP	PD19:1.SP	TIC2501.SP	MD100	%R100
FIC2502 SP	FIC2502_SP	PD19:2.SP	FIC2502.SP	MD104	%R102
FY2502 CV	FY2502_R	PD19:2.SO	FIC2502.SO	MD108	%R104

The Modicon implementation of this cascade control is shown in Figure 10.76. The analog inputs must be scaled into the proper units, and the output of the FIC2502 flow controller must be descaled into the raw analog output value. The SP_SEL function block connects the TIC2501 output to the FIC2502 setpoint when TIC2501 is in automatic mode and lets it be determined by the operator when TIC2501 is in manual mode. Essentially, the

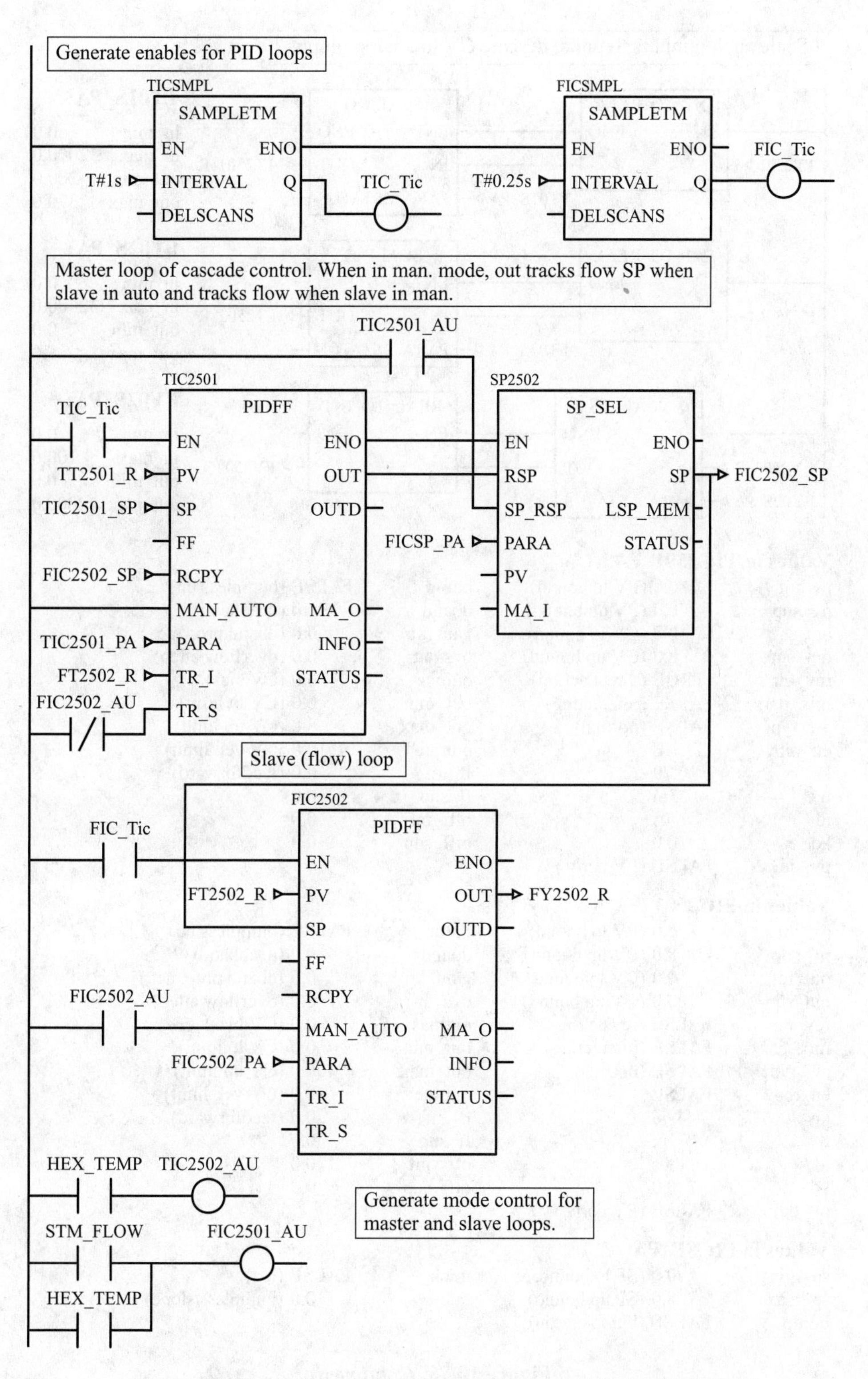

Figure 10.76. Modicon ladder logic cascade control. *(continued)*

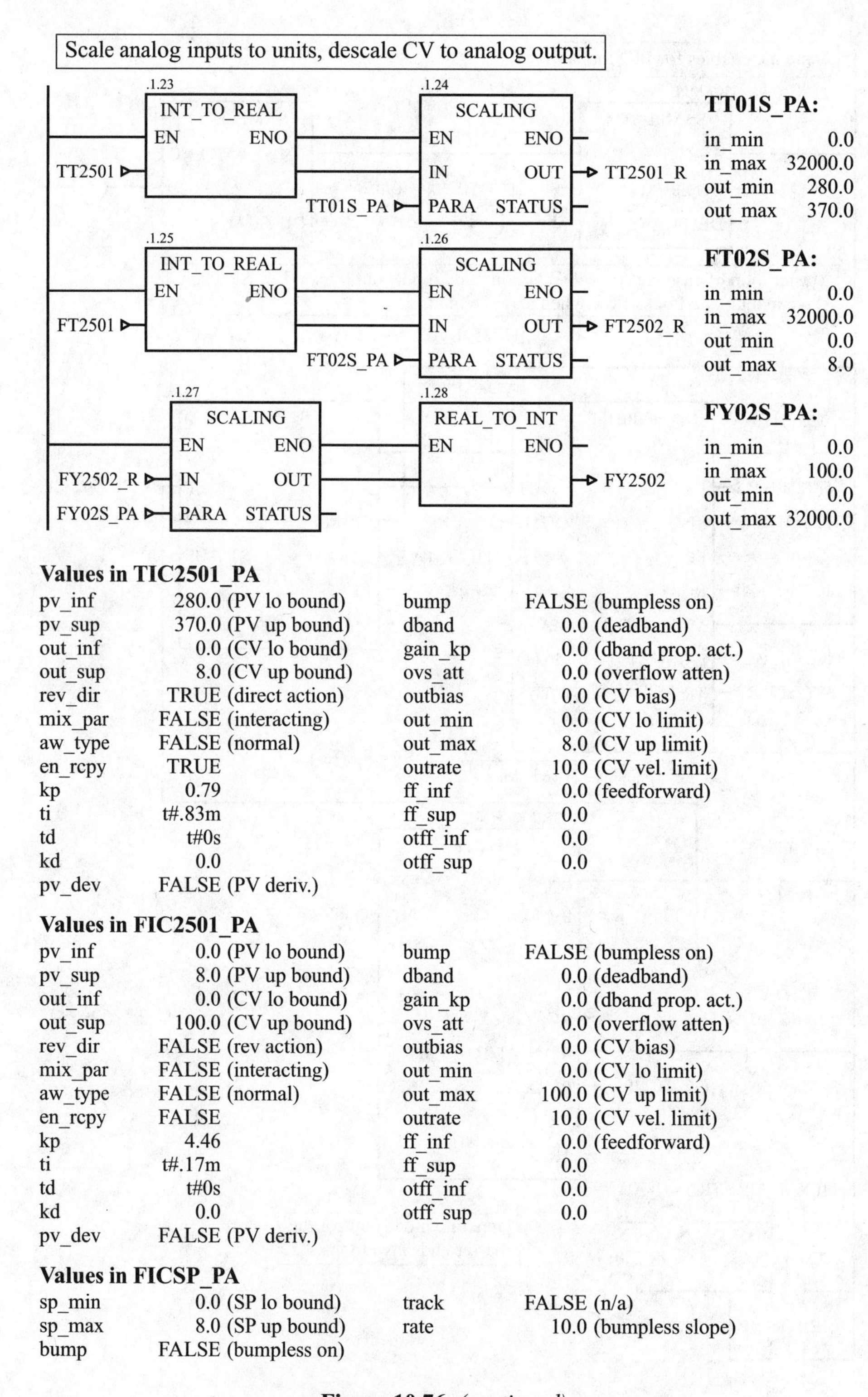

Values in TIC2501_PA

pv_inf	280.0 (PV lo bound)	bump	FALSE (bumpless on)
pv_sup	370.0 (PV up bound)	dband	0.0 (deadband)
out_inf	0.0 (CV lo bound)	gain_kp	0.0 (dband prop. act.)
out_sup	8.0 (CV up bound)	ovs_att	0.0 (overflow atten)
rev_dir	TRUE (direct action)	outbias	0.0 (CV bias)
mix_par	FALSE (interacting)	out_min	0.0 (CV lo limit)
aw_type	FALSE (normal)	out_max	8.0 (CV up limit)
en_rcpy	TRUE	outrate	10.0 (CV vel. limit)
kp	0.79	ff_inf	0.0 (feedforward)
ti	t#.83m	ff_sup	0.0
td	t#0s	otff_inf	0.0
kd	0.0	otff_sup	0.0
pv_dev	FALSE (PV deriv.)		

Values in FIC2501_PA

pv_inf	0.0 (PV lo bound)	bump	FALSE (bumpless on)
pv_sup	8.0 (PV up bound)	dband	0.0 (deadband)
out_inf	0.0 (CV lo bound)	gain_kp	0.0 (dband prop. act.)
out_sup	100.0 (CV up bound)	ovs_att	0.0 (overflow atten)
rev_dir	FALSE (rev action)	outbias	0.0 (CV bias)
mix_par	FALSE (interacting)	out_min	0.0 (CV lo limit)
aw_type	FALSE (normal)	out_max	100.0 (CV up limit)
en_rcpy	FALSE	outrate	10.0 (CV vel. limit)
kp	4.46	ff_inf	0.0 (feedforward)
ti	t#.17m	ff_sup	0.0
td	t#0s	otff_inf	0.0
kd	0.0	otff_sup	0.0
pv_dev	FALSE (PV deriv.)		

Values in FICSP_PA

sp_min	0.0 (SP lo bound)	track	FALSE (n/a)
sp_max	8.0 (SP up bound)	rate	10.0 (bumpless slope)
bump	FALSE (bumpless on)		

Figure 10.76. *(continued)*

SP_SEL block handles the automatic/manual mode for TIC2501. The RCPY input of TIC2501 tracks the operator-adjusted FIC2502 setpoint when TIC2501 is in manual. When the slave loop (FIC2502) is in the manual mode, the output of TIC2502 tracks the flow (FT2502), handled by the tracking inputs, TR_I and TR_S.

Figure 10.77 shows the ControlLogix implementation of the cascade control. The scaling of the analog inputs and analog output are handled automatically by the PID blocks. Since the mode bit is **on** when in manual mode, the logic to handle the mode is essentially opposite of the Modicon logic. Also, the tracking of the flow by the master when both loops are in manual mode is set by the "PV Tracking" parameter of FIC2502. However, when the slave (FIC2502) is in automatic and the master (TIC2501) is in manual, the output of the master must be forced to follow the operator-adjusted FIC2502 setpoint. Note that the SP must be scaled to the proper units before it is copied to the master loop output.

The PLC-5 implementation is shown in Figure 10.78 and closely follows the ControlLogix implementation.

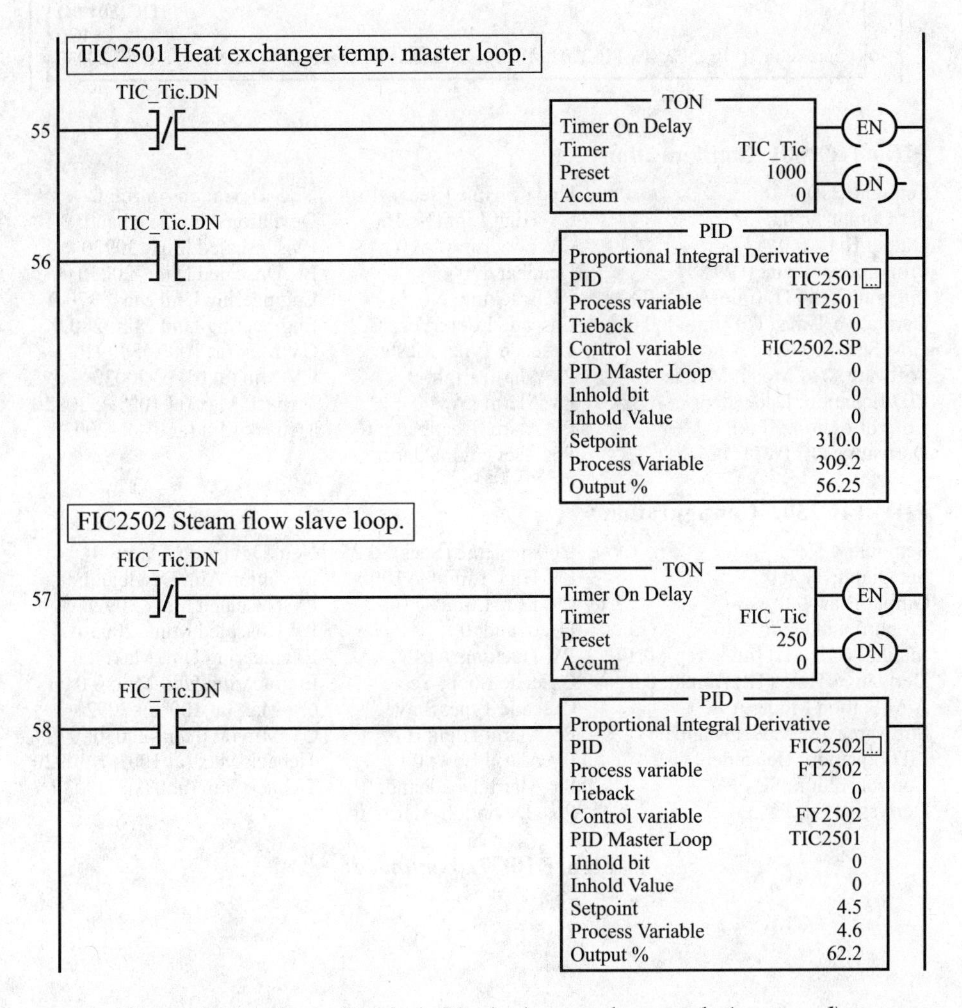

Figure 10.77. ControlLogix ladder logic cascade control. *(continued)*

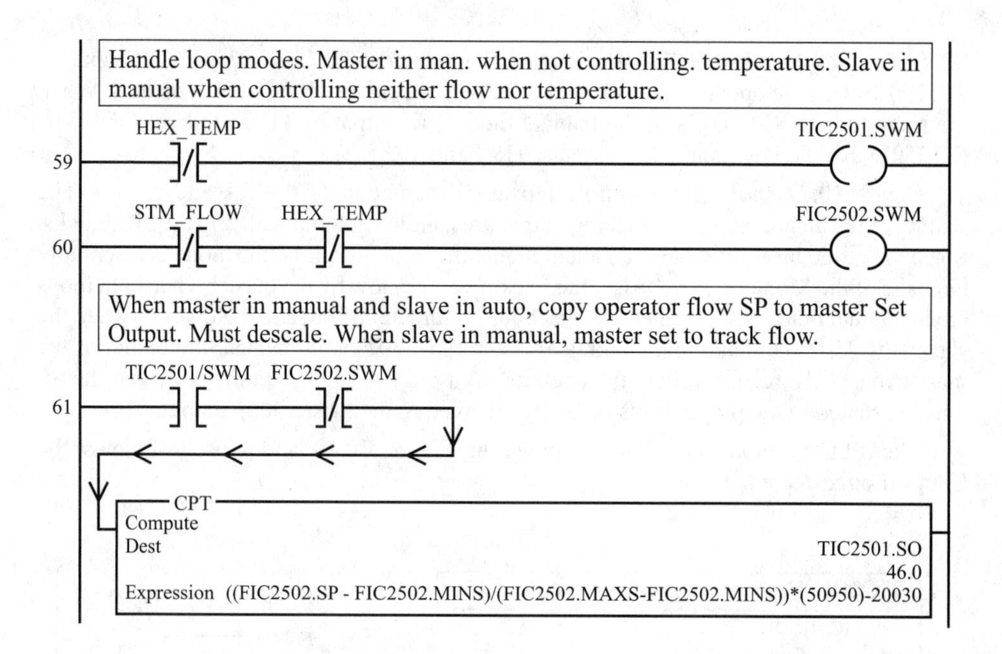
Handle loop modes. Master in man. when not controlling. temperature. Slave in manual when controlling neither flow nor temperature.
59
HEX_TEMP
TIC2501.SWM
60
STM_FLOW
HEX_TEMP
FIC2502.SWM
When master in manual and slave in auto, copy operator flow SP to master Set Output. Must descale. When slave in manual, master set to track flow.
61
TIC2501/SWM
FIC2502.SWM
CPT
Compute
Dest
TIC2501.SO
46.0
Expression ((FIC2502.SP - FIC2502.MINS)/(FIC2502.MAXS-FIC2502.MINS))*(50950)-20030

PID - TIC2501 Configuration

Setpoint: 310.0
Set Output %: 0.0
Output Bias: 0.0
Proportional Gain: 0.79
Integral Gain (Ti) [mins/rep]: 0.83
Derivative Time (Td) [mins]: 0.0
A/M Station Mode: Auto
Software A/M Mode: Manual
PID Equation: Dependent
Control Action: SP - PV
Derivative Of: PV

Update Time (Secs): 1.0
CV High Limit%: 100
CV Low Limit%: 0
Deadband: 0
PV Tracking: No
Cascade Loop: Yes
Cascade Type: Master
PV Alarm High: 0
PV Alarm Low: 0
PV Alarm Deadband: 0
Pos. Deviation Alarm: 0

Neg. Deviation Alarm: 0
Deviation Alm Deadband: 0
PV Unscaled Max: 30920
PV Unscaled Min: -20030
Engineering Unit Max: 370.0
Engineering Unit Min: 280.0
CV Max (at 100%): 30920
CV Min (at 0%): -20030
Tieback Max (at 100%): 30920
Tieback Min (at 0%): -20030

PID - FIC2502 Configuration

Setpoint: 4.5
Set Output %: 0.0
Output Bias: 0.0
Proportional Gain: 4.46
Integral Gain (Ti) [mins/rep]: 0.17
Derivative Time (Td) [mins]: 0.0
A/M Station Mode: Auto
Software A/M Mode: Manual
PID Equation: Dependent
Control Action: SP - PV
Derivative Of: PV

Update Time (Secs): 0.25
CV High Limit%: 100
CV Low Limit%: 0
Deadband: 0
PV Tracking: Yes
Cascade Loop: Yes
Cascade Type: Slave
PV Alarm High: 0
PV Alarm Low: 0
PV Alarm Deadband: 0
Pos. Deviation Alarm: 0

Neg. Deviation Alarm: 0
Deviation Alm Deadband: 0
PV Unscaled Max: 30920
PV Unscaled Min: -20030
Engineering Unit Max: 8.0
Engineering Unit Min: 0.0
CV Max (at 100%): 30920
CV Min (at 0%): -20030
Tieback Max (at 100%): 30920
Tieback Min (at 0%): -20030

Figure 10.77. *(continued)*

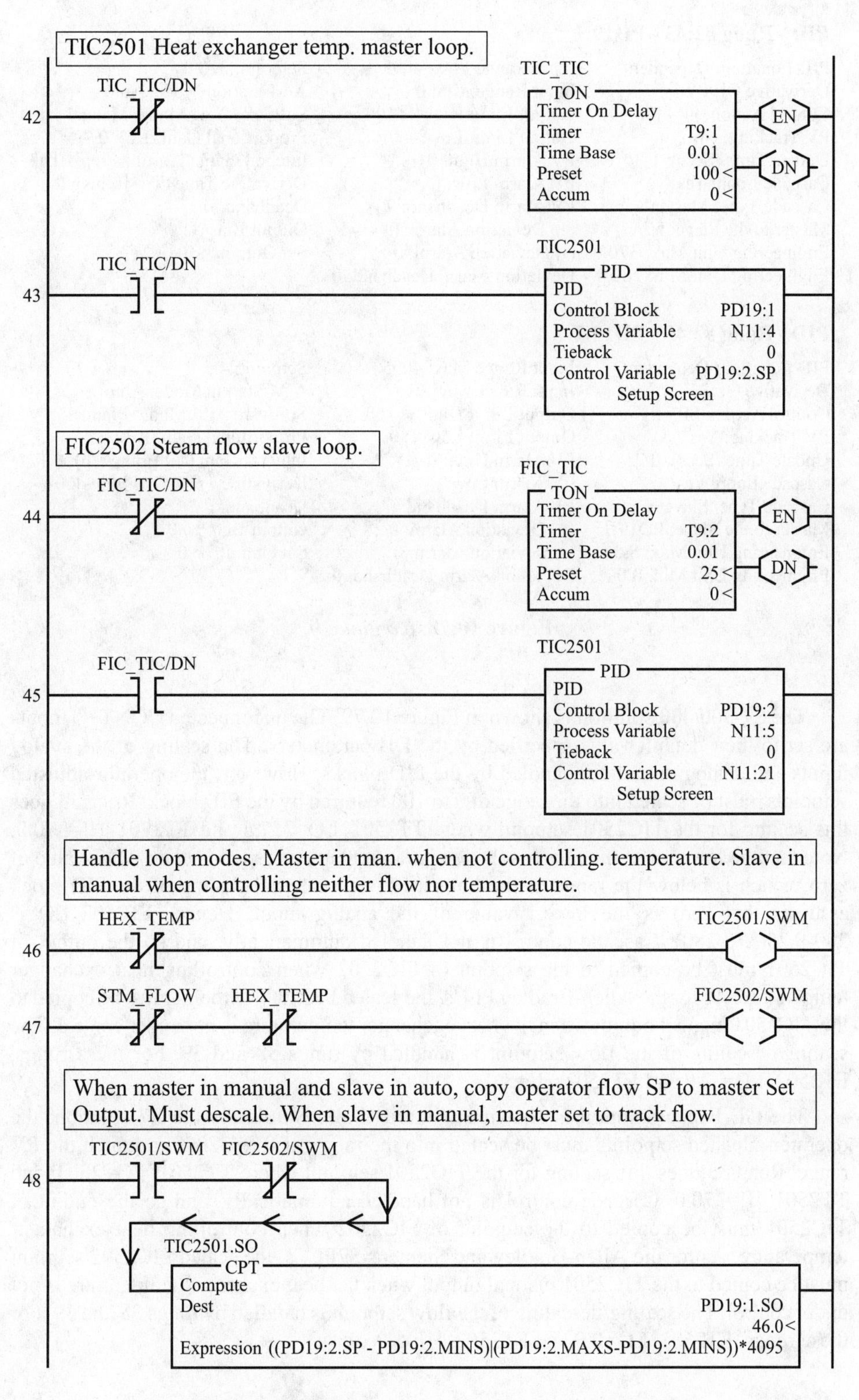

Figure 10.78. PLC-5 cascade control. *(continued)*

PID - Rung #2:43 - PD19:1

PID Equation: Dependent	Input Range Max: 4095	Setpoint: 310.0
Derivative Of: PV	Input Range Min: 0	A/M Station Mode: Auto
Control Action: SP - PV	Output Limit High%: 100	Software A/M Mode: Manual
PV Tracking: No	Output Limit Low%: 0	Proportional Gain (Kc): 0.79
Update Time (Secs): 1	PV Alarm High: 0	Integral Gain (Ti) [mins/rep]: 0.83
Cascade Loop: Yes	PV Alarm Low: 0	Derivative Time (Td) [mins]: 0
Cascade Type: Master	PV Alarm Deadband: 0	Deadband: 0
Master to the Slave: N/A	(+) Deviation Alarm: 0	Output Bias %: 0
Engineering Unit Max: 370.0	(-) Deviation Alarm: 0	Set Output %: 0
Engineering Unit Min: 280.0	Deviation Alarm Deadband: 0	

PID - Rung #2:45 - PD19:2

PID Equation: Dependent	Input Range Max: 4095	Setpoint: 4.5
Derivative Of: PV	Input Range Min: 0	A/M Station Mode: Auto
Control Action: SP - PV	Output Limit High%: 100	Software A/M Mode: Manual
PV Tracking: Yes	Output Limit Low%: 0	Proportional Gain (Kc): 4.46
Update Time (Secs): 0.25	PV Alarm High: 0	Integral Gain (Ti) [mins/rep]: 0.17
Cascade Loop: Yes	PV Alarm Low: 0	Derivative Time (Td) [mins]: 0
Cascade Type: Slave	PV Alarm Deadband: 0	Deadband: 0
Master to the Slave: PD19:1	(+) Deviation Alarm: 0	Output Bias %: 0
Engineering Unit Max: 8.0	(-) Deviation Alarm: 0	Set Output %: 0
Engineering Unit Min: 0.0	Deviation Alarm Deadband: 0	

Figure 10.78. *(continued)*

The S7-300/400 solution is shown in Figure 10.79. The unconnected CONT_C inputs are set to their default value specified by the DB parameters. The scaling of the analog inputs and analog output are handled by the PID blocks. However, the operator-adjusted setpoints must be scaled into the range of 0 to 100 required by the PID block. Rung 33 does this scaling for the TIC2501 setpoint where TT2501_LO=257.5 and TT2501_HI=370.0. Note that the low end of the range is the temperature that corresponds to an ADC value of zero, which is below the range of the transducer. The internal scaling of the PID block assumes that zero is the lowest value of the analog input. Hence, TT2502_LO is 280-0.25(370-280). Cascade control is not handled automatically, and so the output of TIC2501 must be copied to the setpoint of FIC2502 when controlling heat exchanger temperature. As for the Allen-Bradley PLCs, the scaled FIC2502 setpoint must be copied to the TIC2501 manual output when the heat exchanger temperature is not under control. The scaling/descaling of the flow setpoint is handled by rungs 38 and 39. For these rungs, FT2502_LO=-2.0 and FT2502_HI=8.0.

The GE Fanuc solution is shown in Figure 10.80. Similar to the S7 solution, the operator-adjusted setpoints must be scaled into the range of 0 to 32000 to match the PV range. Rung 33 does this scaling for the TIC2501 setpoint where TT2501_LO=280.0 and TT2501_HI=370.0. Cascade control is not handled automatically, and so the output of TIC2501 must be copied to the setpoint of FIC2502 when controlling heat exchanger temperature. As for the Allen-Bradley and Siemens S7PLCs, the scaled FIC2502 setpoint must be copied to the TIC2501 manual output when the heat exchanger temperature is not under control. The scaling/descaling of the flow setpoint is handled by rungs 38 and 39. For these rungs, FT2502_LO=0.0 and FT2502_HI=8.0.

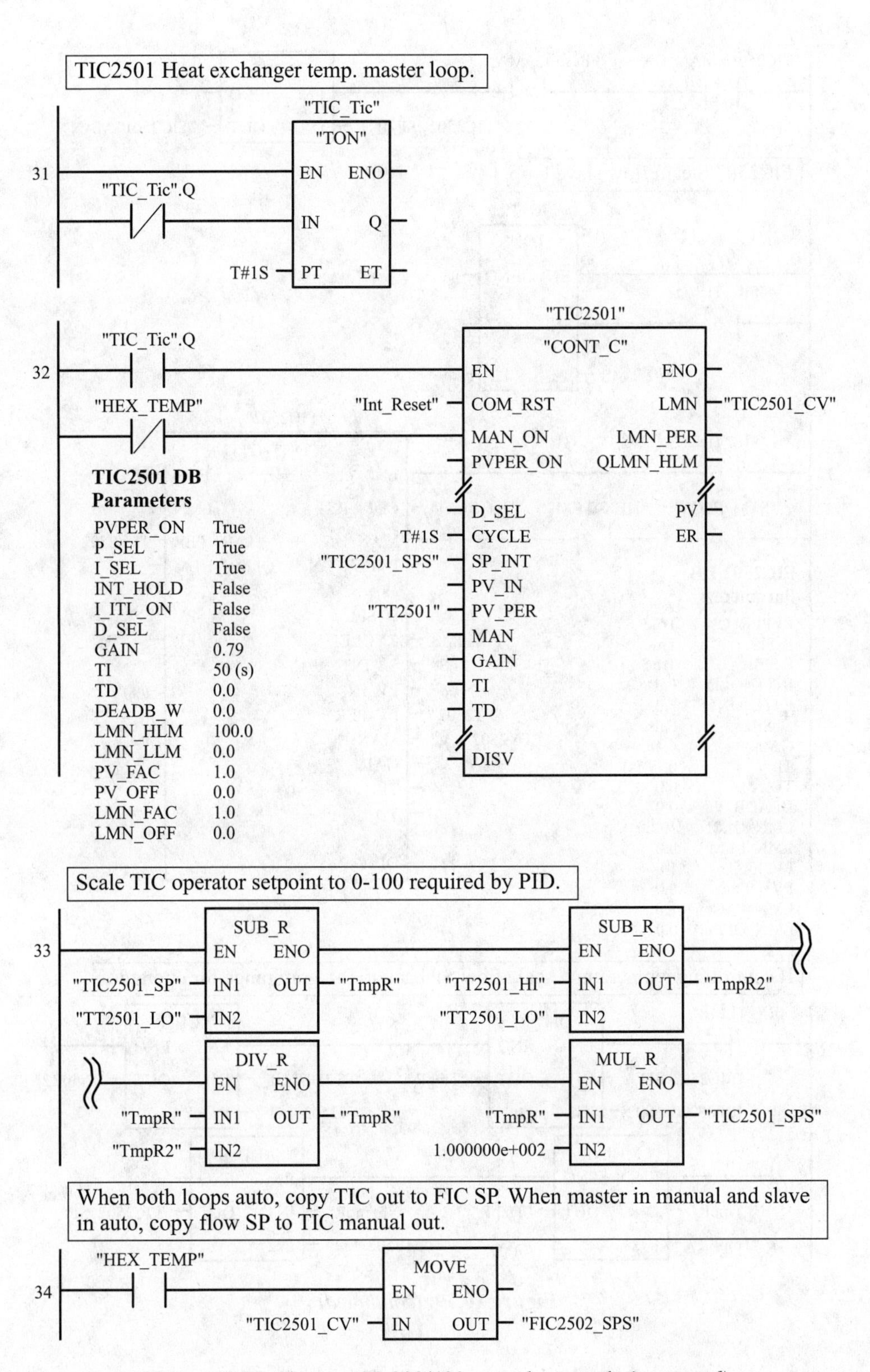

Figure 10.79. Siemens S7-300/400 cascade control. *(continued)*

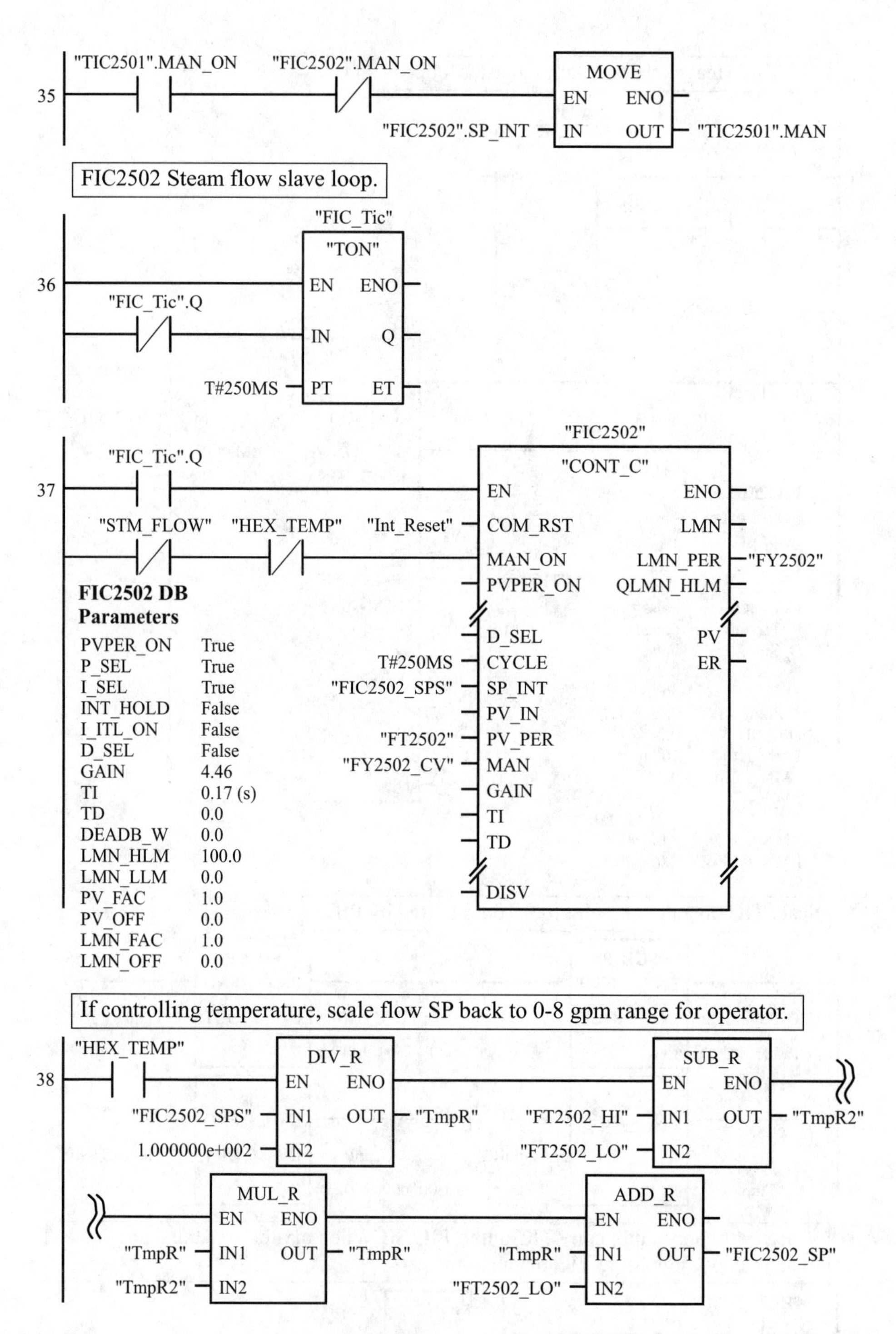

Figure 10.79. *(continued)*

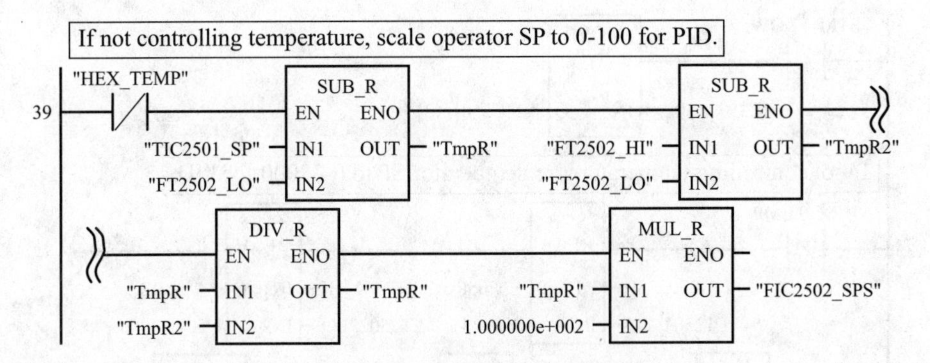

Figure 10.79. *(continued)*

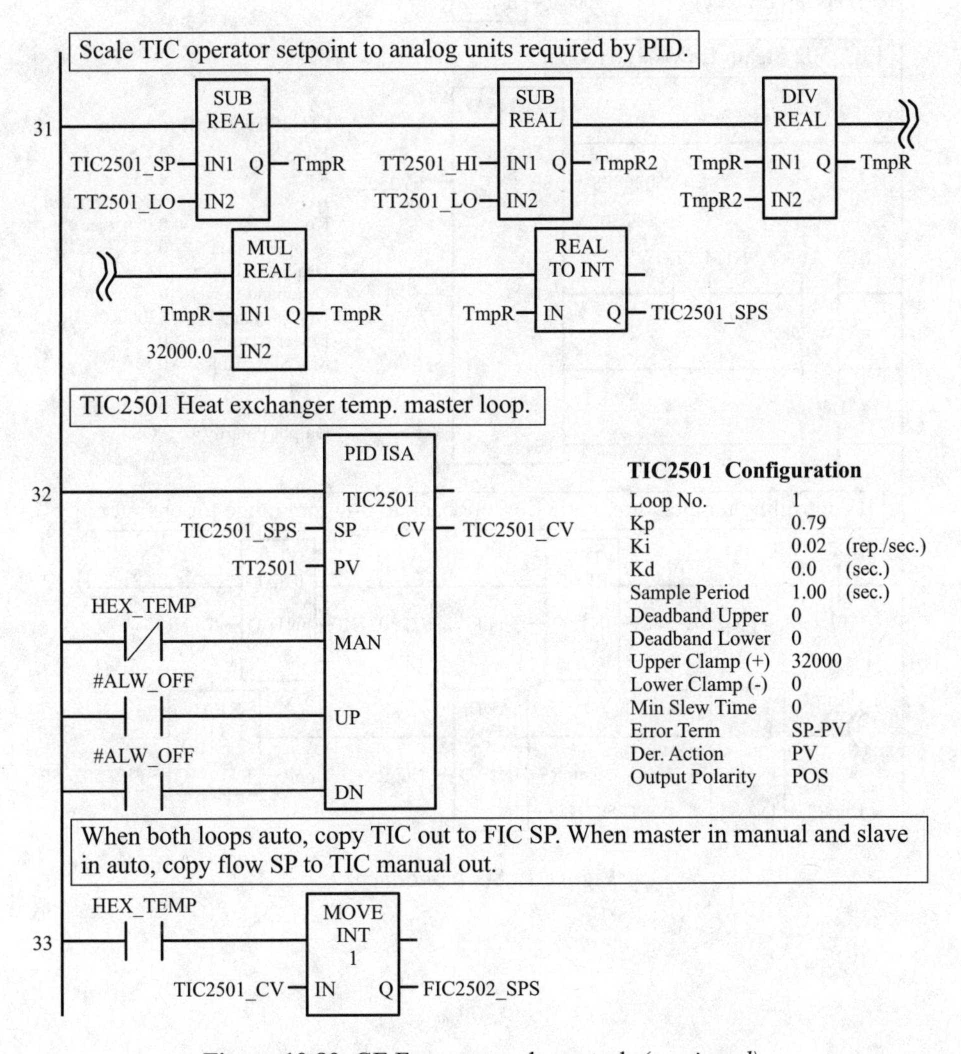

Figure 10.80. GE Fanuc cascade control. *(continued)*

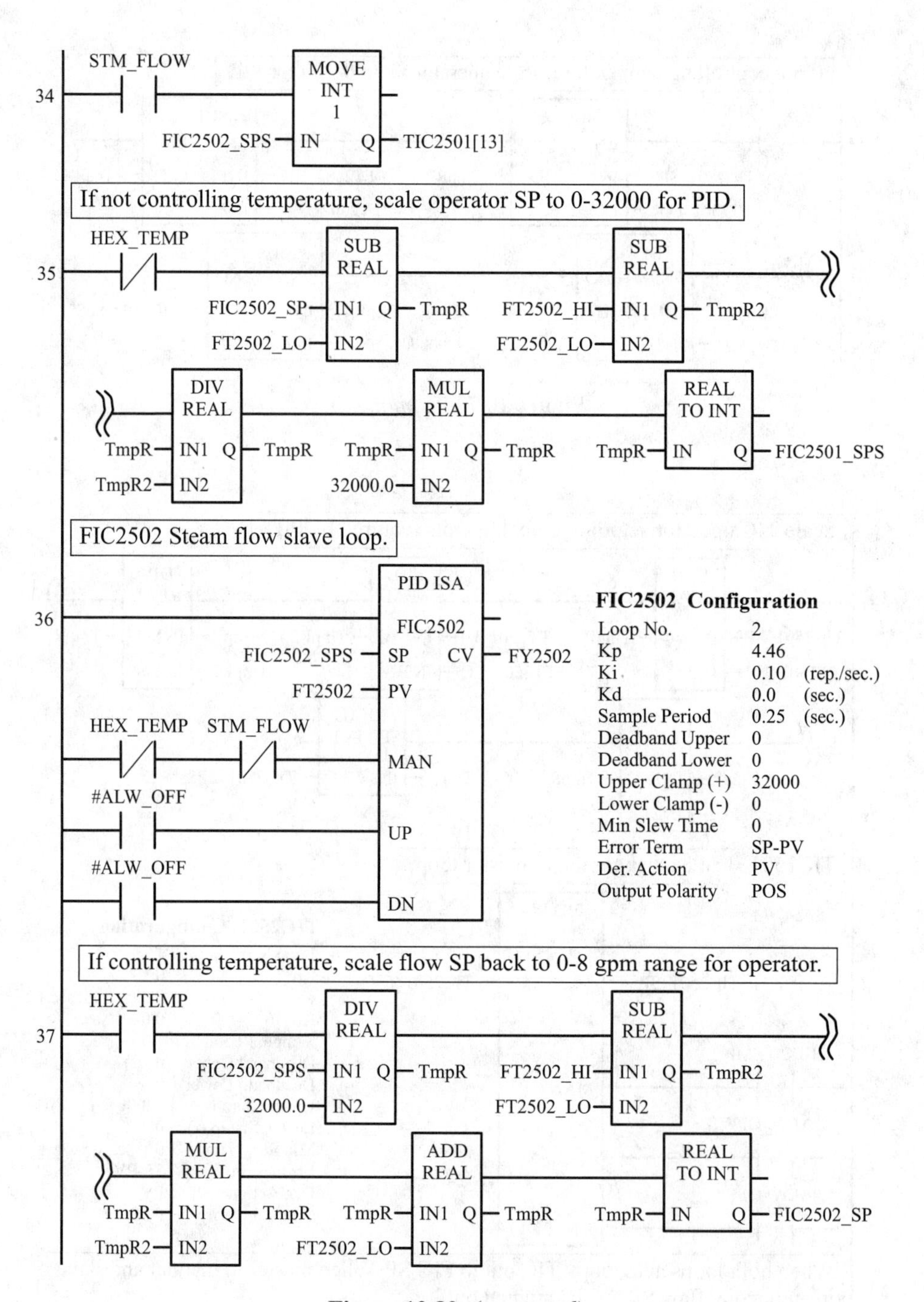

Figure 10.80. *(continued)*

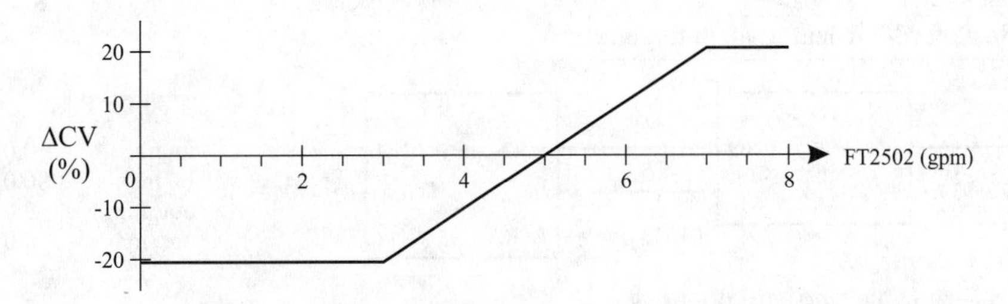

Figure 10.81. Static feedforward correction to CV.

Example 10.9. Feedforward Control. Add the static feedforward control designed in Example 10.6 to the cascade control for the heat exchanger of Example 10.8. The entire system corresponds to Figure 10.53.

The cold-water flow transducer FT2503 is calibrated to measure from 0 to 8 gpm and is connected to an analog input module having an ADC whose output value (FT2503) corresponds to the lowest and highest flows with the same ranges given in Example 10.8.

Solution. There will need to be an assumption about the range of cold-water flow for which the static feedforward correction is valid. The operating point is for a cold-water flow of 5 gpm, and the cold water flow can range from 0 to 8 gpm. Also, the feedforward correction designed in Example 10.6 is a CV change of 10.29 for every 1 gpm change in cold-water flow. A reasonable assumption is to assume that the feedforward correction will only be applied for a maximum deviation of 2 gpm cold-water flow. Therefore, the feedforward correction to the CV as a function of the cold-water flow is shown graphically in Figure 10.81.

Figure 10.82 shows the modifications to the Modicon cascade control of Figure 10.76. All that is needed is to connect the FT2503 reading to the FF input of the PIDFF block labeled TIC2501 and change the four feedforward parameters for the TIC2501 block.

For the Allen-Bradley and S7-300/400 controllers, the feedforward correction to the controller output is calculated as:

$$\text{Out Corr (in \%)} = (\text{FT2503} - 5) \times 10.29$$

with a FT2503 maximum 7 and a minimum of 3.

The additional rungs to implement feedforward for the ControlLogix solution are shown in Figure 10.83. After scaling the FT2503 reading into the proper units, limiting the range, and calculating the correction, it is copied to the bias parameter of the TIC2501 controller. The PLC-5 solution differs only in the scaling from the analog input value to the proper units and is not shown.

The additional rungs to implement feedforward for the S7-300/400 solution (Figure 10.79) are shown in Figure 10.84. After scaling the FT2503 reading into the proper units, limiting the range, and calculating the correction, it is copied to the disturbance variable of the TIC2501 controller.

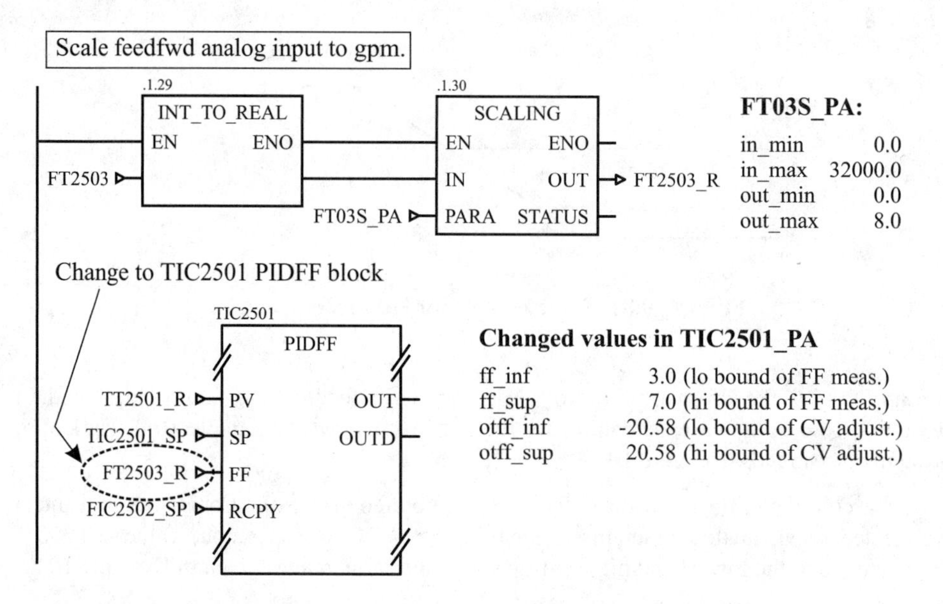

Figure 10.82. Modicon ladder logic feedforward control.

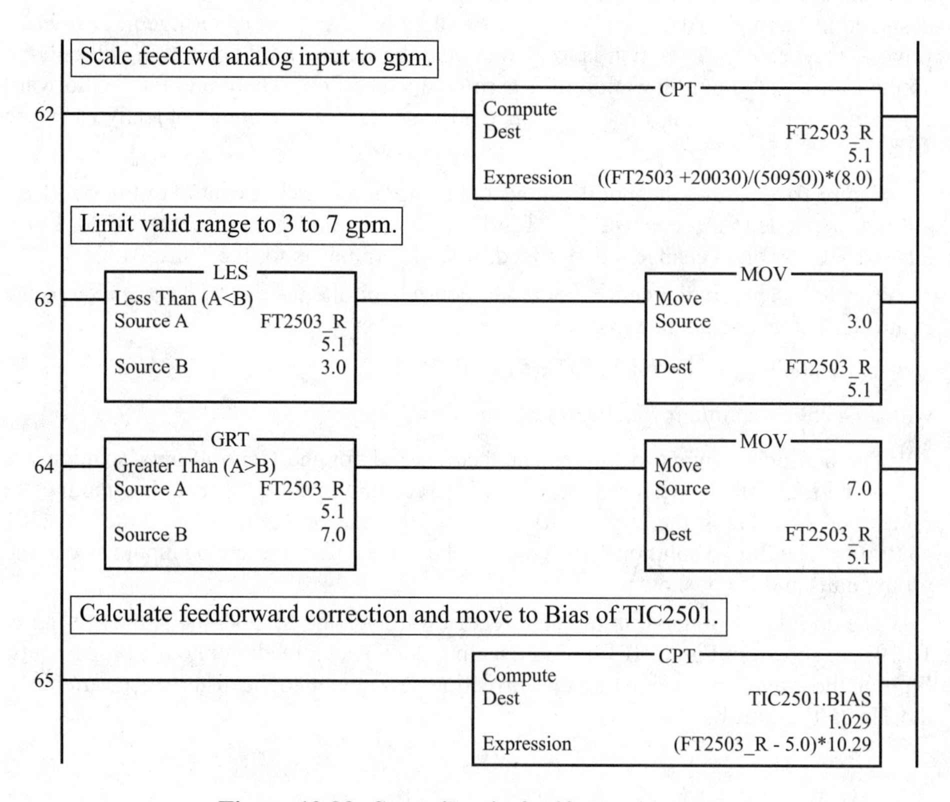

Figure 10.83. ControlLogix feedforward control.

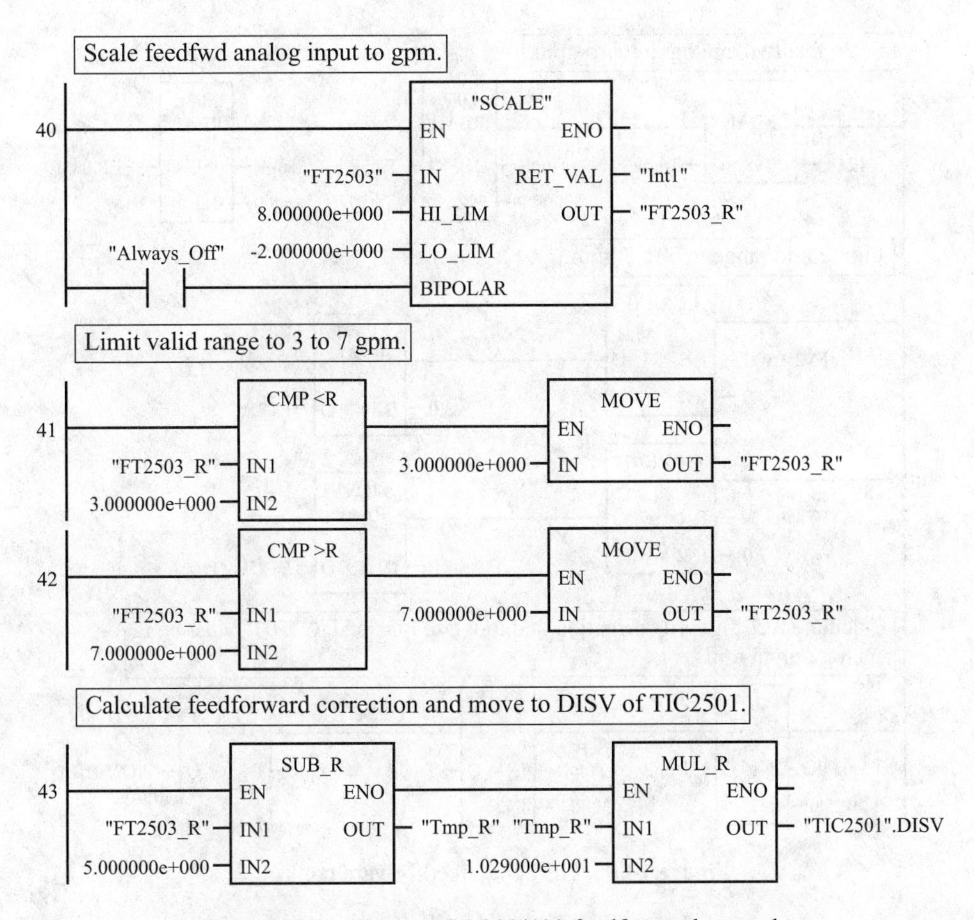

Figure 10.84. Siemens S7-300/400 feedforward control.

For the GE Fanuc controllers, the feedforward correction to the controller output is different since it must be scaled to the analog output units. The correction is thus:

$$\text{Out Corr.} = (\text{FT2503} - 5) \times 10.29 \times (32000/100).$$

Like the other solutions, the additional rungs to be added to the solution of Figure 10.80 are shown in Figure 10.85.

10.9 CHAPTER SUMMARY

This chapter describes PID control in the context of a PLC implementation. After introducing general features of feedback control, the PID control algorithm is described from an intuitive approach. Operational aspects of PID control are also delineated. The most popular methods of calculating the PID tuning parameters are described and illustrated. The important PID enhancements of cascade and feedforward control then are summarized. Operational aspects of PID control are described and then followed by a description of the PID function blocks for the PLCs covered by this text. The chapter concludes with cascade and feedforward control examples.

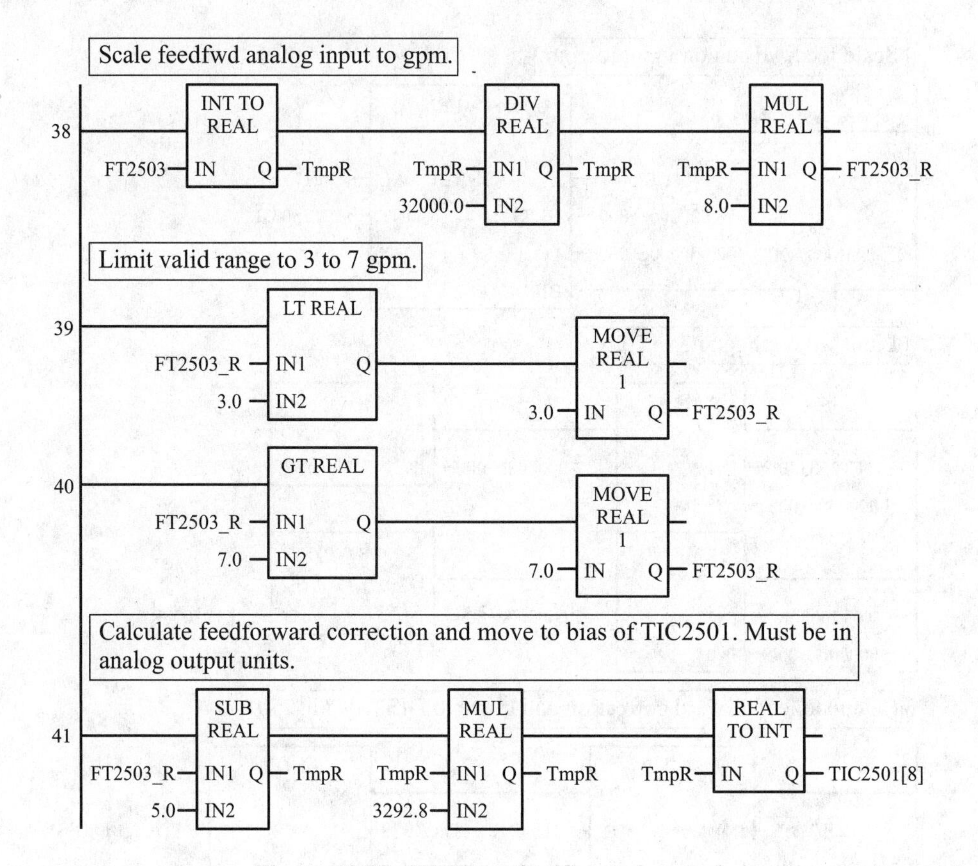

Figure 10.85. GE Fanuc feedforward control.

REFERENCES

Cohen, G. H. and G. A. Coon, 1953. “Theoretical Considerations of Retarded Control,” *Trans. of the ASME*, **75** (7), 827-834.

Dorf, R.C. and R. H. Bishop, 2000. *Modern Control Systems*, 9th cd., Prcnticc Hall, New York.

Erickson, K. T. and J. L. Hedrick, 1999. *Plantwide Process Control*, John Wiley & Sons, New York.

Fertik, H. A., 1975. “Tuning Controllers for Noisy Processes,” *ISA Trans.*, **14** (4), 292-304.

GE Fanuc Automation, 1999. *Series 90*^{TM}*-30/20/Micro PLC CPU Instruction Set: Reference Manual,* pub. GFK-0467L, GE Fanuc Automation North America, Inc., Charlottesville, VA.

GE Fanuc Automation, 2000. *Series 90*^{TM}*-70 PLC CPU Instruction Set: Reference Manual,* pub. GFK-0265J, GE Fanuc Automation North America, Inc., Charlottesville, VA.

GE Fanuc Automation, 2001. *VersaMax® PLC: User's Manual,* pub. GFK-1503C, GE Fanuc Automation North America, Inc., Charlottesville, VA.

IEC, 1993. *IEC 1131-3: Programmable Logic Controllers - Part 3: Programming Languages*, International Electrotechnical Commission, Geneva, Switzerland.

Marlin, T. E, 2000. *Process Control: Designing Processes and Control Systems for Dynamic Performance*, 2nd Ed., McGraw-Hill, New York.

Phillips, C.L. and R. D. Harbor, 1999. *Feedback Control Systems*, 4th ed., Prentice Hall, New York.

Riggs, J. B, 1999. *Chemical Process Control*, Ferret Pub., Lubbock, TX.

Rockwell Automation, 1998a. *PLC-5 Family Instruction Set Reference Manual*, pub. 1785-6.1, Rockwell Automation, Milwaukee, WI.

Rockwell Automation, 1998b. *SLC Modular Processors Instruction Set Reference Manual*, pub. 1747-6.15, Rockwell Automation, Milwaukee, WI.

Rockwell Automation, 2002a. *Logix5000™ Controllers General Instructions*, pub. 1756-RM003F-EN-P, Rockwell Automation, Milwaukee, WI, May.

Rockwell Automation, 2002b. *Logix5000™ Controllers Process Control and Drives Instructions*, pub. 1756-RM006B-EN-P, Rockwell Automation, Milwaukee, WI, May.

Schneider Automation, 1998. *Concept Block Library IEC,* vol. 2, ver. 2.1, pub. 840 USE 462 00, Schneider Automation, Inc., North Andover, MA.

Siemens, 1996. *System Software for S7-300 and S7-400 - PID Control: Reference Manual,* pub. C79000-G7076-C516-01, Siemens AG, Nürnberg, Germany.

Siemens, 2000. *S7-200 Programmable Controller: System Manual,* pub. A5E00066097-02, Siemens AG, Nuernberg, Germany.

Siemens, 2002. *System Software for S7-300/400 System and Standard Functions: Reference Manual,* Edition 12/2002, pub. A5E00171234-01, Siemens AG, Nürnberg, Germany.

Ziegler, J. G. and N. B. Nichols, 1942. "Optimum Settings for Automatic Controllers," *ASME Trans.*, **64**, 759-768.

PROBLEMS

> **General instructions for the tuning problems (P10-1 to P10-14):**
> The controller tuning problems assume that you have access to a PID tuning demonstrator program, like the "PIDTune" program provided by the author. You can also use SIMULINK or VisSim to construct a process simulation and generate graphs of the responses.

P10-1. Tune a PID controller for the following first-order process:

Gain = 1.3
Deadtime = 2.0 minutes
First time constant = 3.0 minutes

(a) Find the PI and PID controller parameters using the Ziegler-Nichols closed-loop method. Attach the plot of the sustained oscillations used to determine the controller parameters. Also, attach the plot of the closed-loop setpoint response of the system with a PI controller whose parameters have been determined with the Ziegler-Nichols closed-loop method. Use a setpoint change of plus or minus 5.

(b) Find the PI and PID controller parameters using the four open-loop methods (Ziegler-Nichols, Cohen-Coon, Cohen-Coon with constraints, and Fertik). For the Fertik method, tune for a **setpoint** response. Attach the plot of the closed-loop setpoint response of the system with a PI controller tuned with Fertik's method.

P10-2. Tune a PID controller for the following first-order process:

Gain = 1.0
Deadtime = 3.0 minutes
First time constant = 2.0 minutes

(a) Find the PI and PID controller parameters using the Ziegler-Nichols closed-loop method. Attach the plot of the sustained oscillations used to determine the controller parameters. Also, attach the plot of the closed-loop setpoint response of the system with a PI controller whose parameters have been determined with the Ziegler-Nichols closed-loop method. Use a setpoint change of plus or minus 5.

(b) Find the PI and PID controller parameters using the four open-loop methods (Ziegler-Nichols, Cohen-Coon, Cohen-Coon with constraints, and Fertik). For the Fertik method, tune for a **setpoint** response. Attach the plot of the closed-loop setpoint response of the system with a PI controller tuned with Fertik's method.

P10-3. Tune a PID controller for the following first-order process:

Gain = 1.4
Deadtime = 1.2 minutes
First time constant = 2.5 minutes

(a) Find the PI and PID controller parameters using the Ziegler-Nichols closed-loop method. Attach the plot of the sustained oscillations used to determine the controller parameters. Also, attach the plot of the closed-loop setpoint response of the system with a PI controller whose parameters have been determined with the Ziegler-Nichols closed-loop method. Use a setpoint change of plus or minus 5.

(b) Find the PI and PID controller parameters using the four open-loop methods (Ziegler-Nichols, Cohen-Coon, Cohen-Coon with constraints, and Fertik). For the Fertik method, tune for a **setpoint** response. Attach the plot of the closed-loop setpoint response of the system with a PI controller tuned with Fertik's method.

P10-4. Tune a PID controller for the following first-order process:

Gain = 1.1
Deadtime = 2.0 minutes
First time constant = 4.0 minutes

(a) Find the PI and PID controller parameters using the Ziegler-Nichols closed-loop method. Attach the plot of the sustained oscillations used to determine the controller parameters. Also, attach the plot of the closed-loop setpoint response of the system with a PI controller whose parameters have been determined with the Ziegler-Nichols closed-loop method. Use a setpoint change of plus or minus 5.

(b) Find the PI and PID controller parameters using the four open-loop methods (Ziegler-Nichols, Cohen-Coon, Cohen-Coon with constraints, and Fertik). For the Fertik method, tune for a **setpoint** response. Attach the plot of the closed-loop setpoint response of the system with a PI controller tuned with Fertik's method.

P10-5. Tune a PID controller for the following first-order process:

Gain = 1.1
Deadtime = 4.0 minutes
First time constant = 5.0 minutes

(a) Find the PI and PID controller parameters using the Ziegler-Nichols closed-loop method. Attach the plot of the sustained oscillations used to determine the controller parameters. Also, attach the plot of the closed-loop setpoint response of the system with a PI controller whose parameters have been determined with the Ziegler-Nichols closed-loop method. Use a setpoint change of plus or minus 5.

(b) Find the PI and PID controller parameters using the four open-loop methods (Ziegler-Nichols, Cohen-Coon, Cohen-Coon with constraints, and Fertik). For the Fertik method, tune for a **setpoint** response. Attach the plot of the closed-loop setpoint response of the system with a PI controller tuned with Fertik's method.

P10-6. Tune a PID controller for the following first-order process:

Gain = 0.9
Deadtime = 5.0 minutes
First time constant = 5.0 minutes

(a) Find the PI and PID controller parameters using the Ziegler-Nichols closed-loop method. Attach the plot of the sustained oscillations used to determine the controller parameters. Also, attach the plot of the closed-loop setpoint response of the system with a PI controller whose parameters have been determined with the Ziegler-Nichols closed-loop method. Use a setpoint change of plus or minus 5.

(b) Find the PI and PID controller parameters using the four open-loop methods (Ziegler-Nichols, Cohen-Coon, Cohen-Coon with constraints, and Fertik). For the Fertik method, tune for a **setpoint** response. Attach the plot of the closed-loop setpoint response of the system with a PI controller tuned with Fertik's method.

P10-7. Tune a PID controller for the following first-order process:

Gain = 1.1
Deadtime = 1.5 minutes
First time constant = 3.5 minutes

(a) Find the PI and PID controller parameters using the Ziegler-Nichols closed-loop method. Attach the plot of the sustained oscillations used to determine the controller parameters. Also, attach the plot of the closed-loop setpoint response of the system with a PI controller whose parameters have been determined with the Ziegler-Nichols closed-loop method. Use a setpoint change of plus or minus 5.

(b) Find the PI and PID controller parameters using the four open-loop methods (Ziegler-Nichols, Cohen-Coon, Cohen-Coon with constraints, and Fertik). For the Fertik method, tune for a **setpoint** response. Attach the plot of the closed-loop setpoint response of the system with a PI controller tuned with Fertik's method.

P10-8. Tune a PID controller for the following second-order process:

Gain = 1.5
Deadtime = 1.0 minutes
First time constant = 2.0 minutes
Second time constant = 2.5 minutes

(a) Find the PI controller parameters using the Ziegler-Nichols closed-loop method. Attach the plot of the sustained oscillations used to determine the controller parameters. Also, attach the plot of the closed-loop response of the system with a PI controller to a disturbance change of plus or minus 10.

(b) Find the approximate first-order model of the process. Attach the open-loop response of the system used to obtain the approximate model.

(c) Using your first-order approximate model, find the PI controller parameters using the four open-loop methods (Ziegler-Nichols, Cohen-Coon, Cohen-Coon with constraints, and Fertik). For the Fertik method, tune for a **disturbance** response. Attach the plot of the closed-loop disturbance response (a disturbance change of plus or minus 10) of the system with a PI controller tuned with Fertik's method. **DO NOT set the process to the approximate first-order model.** The simulated process should still be the second-order process given above.

P10-9. Tune a PID controller for the following second-order process:

Gain = 1.5
Deadtime = 2.0 minutes
First time constant = 2.0 minutes
Second time constant = 2.5 minutes

(a) Find the PI controller parameters using the Ziegler-Nichols closed-loop method. Attach the plot of the sustained oscillations used to determine the controller parameters. Also, attach the plot of the closed-loop response of the system with a PI controller to a disturbance change of plus or minus 10.

(b) Find the approximate first-order model of the process. Attach the open-loop response of the system used to obtain the approximate model.

(c) Using your first-order approximate model, find the PI controller parameters using the four open-loop methods (Ziegler-Nichols, Cohen-Coon, Cohen-Coon with constraints, and Fertik). For the Fertik method, tune for a **disturbance** response. Attach the plot of the closed-loop disturbance response (a disturbance change of plus or minus 10) of the system with a PI controller tuned with Fertik's method. **DO NOT set the process to the approximate first-order model.** The simulated process should still be the second-order process given above.

P10-10. Tune a PID controller for the following second-order process:

Gain = 1.4
Deadtime = 2.0 minutes
First time constant = 3.0 minutes
Second time constant = 4.0 minutes

(a) Find the PI controller parameters using the Ziegler-Nichols closed-loop method. Attach the plot of the sustained oscillations used to determine the controller parameters. Also, attach the plot of the closed-loop response of the system with a PI controller to a disturbance change of plus or minus 10.

(b) Find the approximate first-order model of the process. Attach the open-loop response of the system used to obtain the approximate model.

(c) Using your first-order approximate model, find the PI controller parameters using the four open-loop methods (Ziegler-Nichols, Cohen-Coon, Cohen-Coon with constraints, and Fertik). For the Fertik method, tune for a **disturbance** response. Attach the plot of the closed-loop disturbance response (a disturbance change of plus or minus 10) of the system with a PI controller tuned with Fertik's method. **DO NOT set the process to the approximate first-order model.** The simulated process should still be the second-order process given above.

P10-11. Tune a PID controller for the following second-order process:

Gain = 1.3
Deadtime = 1.5 minutes
First time constant = 3.0 minutes
Second time constant = 5.0 minutes

(a) Find the PI controller parameters using the Ziegler-Nichols closed-loop method. Attach the plot of the sustained oscillations used to determine the controller parameters. Also, attach the plot of the closed-loop response of the system with a PI controller to a disturbance change of plus or minus 10.

(b) Find the approximate first-order model of the process. Attach the open-loop response of the system used to obtain the approximate model.

(c) Using your first-order approximate model, find the PI controller parameters using the four open-loop methods (Ziegler-Nichols, Cohen-Coon, Cohen-Coon with constraints, and Fertik). For the Fertik method, tune for a **disturbance** response. Attach the plot of the closed-loop disturbance response (a disturbance change of plus or minus 10) of the system with a PI controller tuned with Fertik's method. **DO NOT set the process to the approximate first-order model.** The simulated process should still be the second-order process given above.

P10-12. Tune a PID controller for the following second-order process:

Gain = 0.9
Deadtime = 2.0 minutes
First time constant = 3.5 minutes
Second time constant = 4.0 minutes

(a) Find the PI controller parameters using the Ziegler-Nichols closed-loop method. Attach the plot of the sustained oscillations used to determine the controller parameters. Also, attach the plot of the closed-loop response of the system with a PI controller to a disturbance change of plus or minus 10.

(b) Find the approximate first-order model of the process. Attach the open-loop response of the system used to obtain the approximate model.

(c) Using your first-order approximate model, find the PI controller parameters using the four open-loop methods (Ziegler-Nichols, Cohen-Coon, Cohen-Coon with constraints, and Fertik). For the Fertik method, tune for a **disturbance** response. Attach the plot of the closed-loop disturbance response (a disturbance change of plus or minus 10) of the system with a PI controller tuned with Fertik's method. **DO NOT set the process to the approximate first-order model.** The simulated process should still be the second-order process given above.

P10-13. Tune a PID controller for the following second-order process:

Gain = 1.6
Deadtime = 1.5 minutes
First time constant = 3.0 minutes
Second time constant = 2.5 minutes

(a) Find the PI controller parameters using the Ziegler-Nichols closed-loop method. Attach the plot of the sustained oscillations used to determine the controller parameters. Also, attach the plot of the closed-loop response of the system with a PI controller to a disturbance change of plus or minus 10.

(b) Find the approximate first-order model of the process. Attach the open-loop response of the system used to obtain the approximate model.

(c) Using your first-order approximate model, find the PI controller parameters using the four open-loop methods (Ziegler-Nichols, Cohen-Coon, Cohen-Coon with constraints, and Fertik). For the Fertik method, tune for a **disturbance** response. Attach the plot of the closed-loop disturbance response (a disturbance change of plus or minus 10) of the system with a PI controller tuned with Fertik's method. **DO NOT set the process to the approximate first-order model.** The simulated process should still be the second-order process given above.

P10-14. Tune a PID controller for the following second-order process:

Gain = 1.2
Deadtime = 2.0 minutes
First time constant = 4.0 minutes
Second time constant = 4.5 minutes

(a) Find the PI controller parameters using the Ziegler-Nichols closed-loop method. Attach the plot of the sustained oscillations used to determine the controller parameters. Also, attach the plot of the closed-loop response of the system with a PI controller to a disturbance change of plus or minus 10.

(b) Find the approximate first-order model of the process. Attach the open-loop response of the system used to obtain the approximate model.

(c) Using your first-order approximate model, find the PI controller parameters using the four open-loop methods (Ziegler-Nichols, Cohen-Coon, Cohen-Coon with constraints, and Fertik). For the Fertik method, tune for a **disturbance** response. Attach the plot of the closed-loop disturbance response (a disturbance change of plus or minus 10) of the system with a PI controller tuned with Fertik's method.

General instructions for problems P10-15 to P10-19:

Write a ladder logic program for the application and implement it for one of the following PLC ladder logic languages:

Modicon Concept, **or**

Allen-Bradley ControlLogix, **or**

Allen-Bradley PLC-5/SLC-500, **or**

Siemens S7-300/400, **or** S7-200 , **or**

GE Fanuc 90-30

If any part of the operation is ambiguous, write down your additional assumptions. The physical inputs, physical outputs, and internal variables for each situation are given in the problem. **DO NOT** assign any more physical inputs!

Unless otherwise specified, assume the ADC in the analog input module has an output integer value that corresponds to the lowest and highest sensor value as:

Value	Modicon	Logix	PLC-5	SLC-500	Siemens	GE Fanuc
Lowest	0	-20,030	0	3277	5530	0
Highest	32,000	30,920	4095	16,384	27,648	32,000

In the case of the ControlLogix PLC, the instructor may choose to specify that the output of the ADC is a real number configured to be in the sensor units, for example, level in feet or temperature in °C.

Also, unless otherwise specified, assume the input integer to the DAC of an analog output module corresponds to the lowest and highest values of the output device control as:

Value	Modicon	Logix	PLC-5	SLC-500	Siemens	GE Fanuc
Lowest	0	-20,030	0	6242	5530	0
Highest	32,000	30,920	4095	31,208	27,648	32,000

In the case of the ControlLogix PLC, the instructor may choose to specify that the input to the DAC is a real number configured to be in the actual units of the output device, for example, speed in rpm or valve position in percent of span.

Your solution should include the following:

1. Specify the PLC processor used.
2. Ladder logic diagram (with comments). For consistency among the different PLCs, use only variables/symbols/tags in the ladder logic. Use instructions and function blocks consistent with the PLC processor.
3. Table listing additional internal memory (variables/symbols/tags) used and a brief description of their use. For the Allen-Bradley ControlLogix and the Modicon Quantum/Momentum processors, list the internal variables/tags and the data type. For the other processors, list the internal variables/symbols and the associated memory address.

P10-15. Split-range Control of pH. Implement split range control for the pH control system of Figure P10.15*a* that is neutralizing a waste stream of unknown pH. This problem is concerned with the pH control only. The only interface to the pH control is the PH_ENABLE Boolean, which is set by another part of the program. When PH_ENABLE is **off**, both valve positions should be 0% (closed). When PH_ENABLE is **on**, the two valves should be adjusted to maintain the tank pH, measured by AT1501. Your part of the program should always set the AIC1501 setpoint to 7.0. The AIC1501 loop should be implemented by a PID controller whose CV is split among the two valve positions. The relationship between the AIC1501 CV and the commanded valve positions is shown in Figure P10.15*b*.

The pH transducer AT1501 is calibrated to measure from 0 pH to 14 pH and is connected to an analog input module having an ADC whose output value (AT1501) corresponds to the lowest and highest pH as specified before problem P10-15. Both acid and base valve positions are commanded by an analog output (FY1502 and FY1503, respectively), whose DAC input integer corresponds to the lowest and highest values of the output device control as specified before problem P10-15.

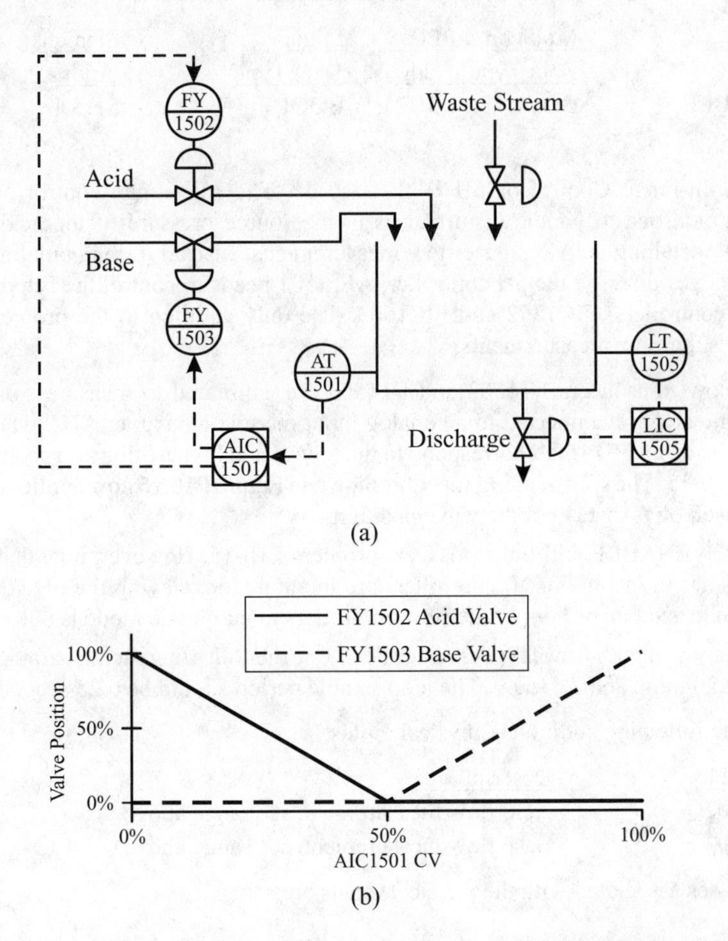

Figure P10.15. Split-range pH control: (a) control scheme; (b) split-ranging valve positions.

The AIC1501 loop has the following tuning parameters: $K_P = 1.0$, $T_I = 0.10$ min., and $T_D = 0.0$. The pH loop sample period should be 1.0 seconds.

Assume the following physical input, physical output, and internal memory assignments:

Variable	Description
AT1501	pH measurement, see range above.
FY1502	Commanded acid valve position, see range above.
FY1503	Commanded base valve position, see range above.
PH_ENABLE	pH control enable; **on** to control pH, **off** to close both valves.

The addresses associated with the physical inputs and outputs are:

Variable	Modicon	PLC-5	ControlLogix	Siemens	GE Fanuc
AT1501	300001	N11:4	Local:4:I.Ch0Data	IW304	%AI1
FY1501	400002	N11:21	Local:5:O.Ch0Data	QW316	%AQ1
FY1502	400003	N11:22	Local:5:O.Ch1Data	QW317	%AQ2

The addresses or data types associated with the internal variables are:

Variable	Modicon Data Type	PLC-5 Addr.	Logix Data Type	Siemens Addr.	GE Fanuc Addr.
PH_ENABLE	BOOL	B3/121	BOOL	M15.1	%M121

P10-16. Split-range Control of pH With Cascade. The split-range control of problem P10-15 is modified to handle disturbances in the source pressure of the acid and base streams by installing acid and base flow measurements. Instead of manipulating the acid and base valves directly, the pH controller, AIC1501 needs to control the setpoints of the two flow controllers, FIC1502 and FIC1503. The only addition to the problem P10-15 statement is the flow measurements.

The flow transducers FT1502 and FT1503 are calibrated to measure from 0 to 40 liters/minute and are connected to an analog input module having an ADC whose output values (FT1502 and FT1503) correspond to the lowest and highest flow as specified before problem P10-15. The split-ranging function shown in Figure P10.16 now applies to the flow controller setpoints instead of the valve positions.

The PH_ENABLE still functions as in problem P10-15. However, note that either all controllers are in manual or all controllers are in automatic. Having the pH controller in manual mode and one or both of the flow controllers in automatic mode is not valid.

The tuning of both flow loops is not critical. Use the following tuning parameters: $K_P =$ 4.0, $T_I = 0.20$ min., and $T_D = 0.0$. The loop sample period should be 0.25 seconds.

Assume the following additional physical inputs:

Variable	Description
FT1502	Acid flow measurement, see range above.
FT1503	Base flow measurement, see range above.

The addresses associated with the physical inputs are:

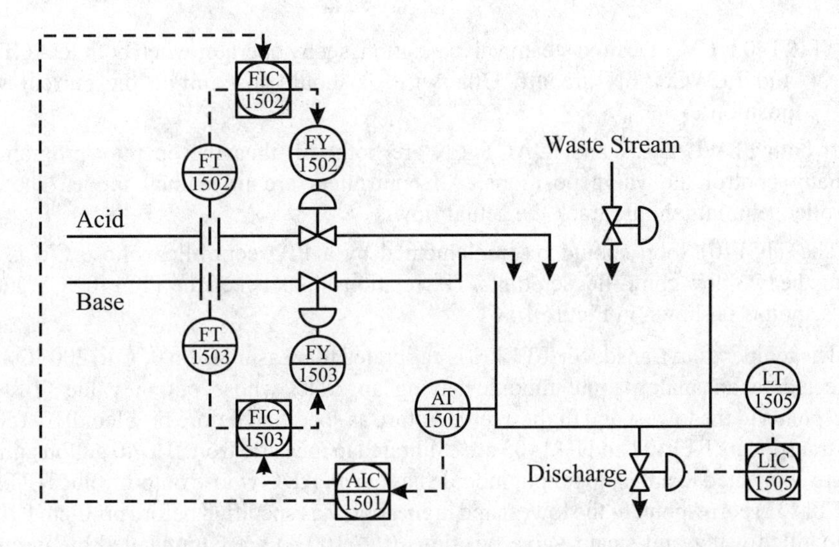

Figure P10.16. Split-range pH control with cascade control of flow.

Variable	Modicon	PLC-5	ControlLogix	Siemens	GE Fanuc
FT1502	300002	N11:5	Local:4:I.Ch1Data	IW305	%AI2
FT1503	300003	N11:6	Local:4:I.Ch2Data	IW306	%AI3

P10-17. Split-range Control of Reactor Jacket. Implement split range control for the batch reactor temperature of Figure 10.60. This problem is only concerned with the temperature control which also includes the flow control of the chilled water and steam. The interface to the temperature control consists of the following internal variables, all set by other parts of the program:

RJACT_EN – Reactor temperature control enable. The operator/program sets the desired jacket temperature, the SP of TIC1401. The cascade loop functions normally.

FLWCN_EN – Control of chilled water and steam flow. The operator sets the desired chilled water and steam flow. The temperature loop is in manual mode and both flow loops are in automatic mode. While in this mode of control, the output of TIC1401 should not be a "back calculation" of the flow setpoints, since both flows may be on simultaneously. There will normally be a "bump" when going to full temperature control.

TIC1401_SP – Desired jacket temperature, set by operator or program.

FIC1402_SP – Desired chilled water flow, set by operator/program when FLWCN_EN is **on**.

FIC1403_SP – Desired steam flow, set by operator/program when FLWCN_EN is **on**.

FIC1402_CV – Desired chilled water valve position, set by operator when both RJACT_EN and FLWCN_EN are **off**. Otherwise, it should just mimic the current valve position.

FIC1403_CV – Desired steam valve position, set by operator when both RJACT_EN and FLWCN_EN are **off**. Otherwise, it should just mimic the current valve position.

If both FLWCN_EN and RJACT_EN are both off, then the operator/program can manually control the valve positions. All controllers are in manual mode. The flow controller setpoints should track the actual flow.

The TIC1401 loop should be implemented by a PID controller whose CV is split among the two flow controller setpoints. The relationship between the TIC1401 CV and the flow setpoints is shown in Figure 10.61.

The temperature transducer TT1401 is calibrated to measure from 0 °C to 200 °C and is connected to an analog input module having an ADC whose output value (TT1401) corresponds to the lowest and highest temperature as specified before problem P10-15. The flow transducers FT1402 and FT1403 are calibrated to measure from 0 to 40 gallons/minute and are connected to an analog input module having an ADC whose output values (FT1402 and FT1403) correspond to the lowest and highest flow as specified before problem P10-15. Both chilled water and steam valve positions (0 – 100%) are commanded by an analog output (FY1402 and FY1403, respectively), whose DAC input integer corresponds to the lowest and highest values of the output device control as specified before problem P10-15.

The TIC1401 loop has the following tuning parameters: $K_P = 0.65$, $T_I = 0.50$ min., and $T_D = 0.0$. The temperature loop sample period should be 1.0 seconds. The tuning of both flow loops is not critical. Use the following tuning parameters: $K_P = 5.0$, $T_I = 0.10$ min., and $T_D = 0.0$. The loop sample period should be 0.25 seconds.

Assume the following physical input, physical output, and internal memory assignments:

Variable	Description
TT1401	Temperature measurement, see range above.
FT1402	Chilled water flow measurement, see range above.
FT1403	Steam flow measurement, see range above.
FY1402	Commanded chilled water valve position, see range above.
FY1403	Commanded steam valve position, see range above.
RJACT_EN	Reactor temperature control enable; **on** to control jacket temperature (and enable cascade control).
FLWCN_EN	Flow control enable; **on** to control flows only.
TIC1401_SP	Desired reactor temperature, set by operator/program.
FIC1402_SP	Desired chilled water flow, set by operator/program when FLWCN_EN is **on**. It should just mimic the current chilled water flow setpoint when RJACT_EN is **on**.
FIC1403_SP	Desired steam flow, set by operator/program when FLWCN_EN is **on**. It should just mimic the current steam flow setpoint when RJACT_EN is **on**.
FY1402_CV	Desired chilled water valve position, set by operator/program when both RJACT_EN and FLWCN_EN are **off**. Otherwise, it should just mimic the current valve position.
FY1403_CV	Desired steam valve position, set by operator/program when both RJACT_EN and FLWCN_EN are **off**. Otherwise, it should just mimic the current valve position.

The addresses associated with the physical inputs and outputs are:

Variable	Modicon	PLC-5	ControlLogix	Siemens	GE Fanuc
TT1401	300001	N11:4	Local:4:I.Ch0Data	IW304	%AI1
FT1402	300002	N11:5	Local:4:I.Ch1Data	IW305	%AI2
FT1403	300003	N11:6	Local:4:I.Ch2Data	IW306	%AI3
FY1402	400002	N11:21	Local:5:O.Ch0Data	QW316	%AQ1
FY1403	400003	N11:22	Local:5:O.Ch1Data	QW317	%AQ2

The addresses or data types associated with the internal variables are:

Variable	Modicon Data Type	PLC-5 Addr.	Logix Data Type	Siemens Addr.	GE Fanuc Addr.
RJACT_EN	BOOL	B3/121	BOOL	M15.1	%M121
FLWCN_EN	BOOL	B3/122	BOOL	M15.2	%M122
TIC1401_SP	REAL	F8:45	REAL	MW102	%R102
FIC1402_SP	REAL	F8:46	REAL	MW104	%R104
FIC1403_SP	REAL	F8:47	REAL	MW106	%R106
FY1402_CV	REAL	F8:48	REAL	MW108	%R108
FY1403_CV	REAL	F8:49	REAL	MW110	%R110

P10-18. Override Control for Peak Shaving System. Implement the override control for the peak shaving system of Figure 10.62. The system is described in Example 10.7 and in the scenario at the beginning of the chapter. This problem is concerned with the PID control only. The interface from the other parts of the program consists of the following internal variables, all set by other parts of the program:

PSHAV_AU – Peak shaving control in automatic mode.

PEAK_DMND – Desired peak demand, in kW. Setpoint of load controller.

MIN_2400 – Minimum 2400-volt bus demand in kW. Setpoint of step-down controller.

Both power transducers (TIE12_DMND and TIE24_DMND) are calibrated to measure from 0 to 9600 kW and are connected to an analog input module having an ADC whose output values correspond to the lowest and highest power as specified before problem P10-15. The generator #3 load control command (LD_CNTRL) sent to the analog output module has a range of 0 – 100 which corresponds to the lowest and highest values of the output device control as specified before problem P10-15.

The tuning parameters for both loops should be: $K_P = 0.50$, $T_I = 3.0$ sec., and $T_D = 0.0$.The loop sample periods should be 1.0 second.

Assume the following physical input, physical output, and internal memory assignments:

Variable	Description
TIE12_DMND	12.47 kV bus demand, see range above.
TIE24_DMND	2400 V bus demand, see range above.
LD_CNTRL	Command to generator #3 load control, see range above.
PSHAV_AU	Peak shave load control enable; **on** to place both controllers in automatic, **off** places both controller in manual.
PEAK_DMND	Desired peak demand, in kW.

MIN_2400	Minimum 2400-volt bus demand in kW.

The addresses associated with the physical inputs and output are:

Variable	Modicon	PLC-5	ControlLogix	Siemens	GE Fanuc
TIE12_DMND	300001	N11:4	Local:4:I.Ch0Data	IW304	%AI1
TIE24_DMND	300002	N11:5	Local:4:I.Ch1Data	IW305	%AI2
LD_CNTRL	400002	N11:21	Local:5:O.Ch0Data	QW316	%AQ1

The addresses or data types associated with the internal variables:

	Modicon	PLC-5	Logix	Siemens	GE Fanuc
Variable	Data Type	Addr.	Data Type	Addr.	Addr.
PSHAV_AU	BOOL	B3/121	BOOL	M15.1	%M121
PEAK_DMND	INT	N7:51	INT	MW102	%R102
MIN_2400	INT	N7:52	INT	MW103	%R103

P10-19. Setpoint for Ramp/Soak Cycle. Generate the setpoint for an aluminum processing furnace. The profile is shown in Figure P10.19. When the DO_CYCLE Boolean transitions **on**, the value of TIC327_SP should follow the profile. While DO_CYCLE is **on**, the profile should be generated as shown. If DO_CYCLE turns **off** in the middle of the cycle, TIC327_SP should be set to 30. The TIC327_SP internal variable is the setpoint to a temperature controller. At the end of the 20-hour period, the CYCLE_FIN internal variable is turned **on** and stays **on** until DO_CYCLE is turned **off**. TIC327_SP and CYCLE_FIN are controlled by your program.

Assume the following internal memory assignments:

Variable	Description
DO_CYCLE	Setpoint profile generation enable. A positive transition starts the cycle. Set by another part of the ladder.
TIC327_SP	Setpoint. Value should follow profile while DO_CYCLE is **on**.
CYCLE_FIN	Cycle finish indication. Turn **on** at the end of the cycle.

The addresses or data types associated with the internal variables are:

	Modicon	PLC-5	Logix	Siemens	GE Fanuc
Variable	Data Type	Addr.	Data Type	Addr.	Addr.
DO_CYCLE	BOOL	B3/121	BOOL	M15.1	%M121
CYCLE_FIN	BOOL	B3/152	BOOL	M20.3	%M152
TIC327_SP	REAL	F8:43	REAL	MW102	%R102

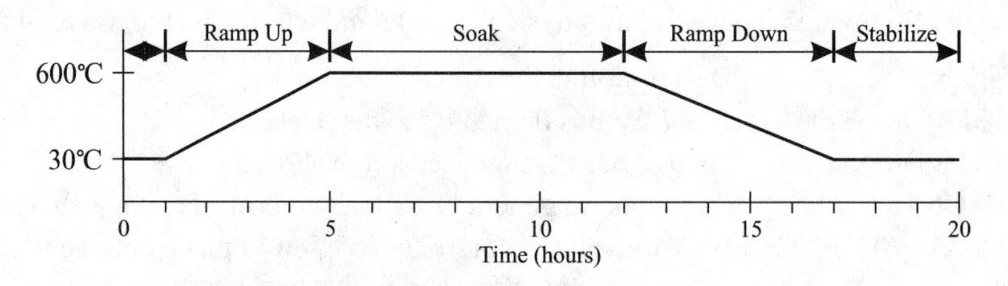

Figure P10.19. Temperature profile for heat-treat cycle.

11 Function Block Diagram

Chapter Topics:

- Function block diagram for PLCs
- Derived function blocks
- Function block diagram applications

OBJECTIVES

Upon completion of this chapter, you will be able to:

- Understand function block diagrams and their differences from ladder logic diagrams.
- Understand and program a derived function block (DFB)
- Implement PID control with function block diagrams.

Scenario: Retentive on-delay timer for Modicon.

You want a retentive on-delay timer block with the same signals as for a TON, but with the addition of an input to reset the timer accumulator.

Solution: The IEC 61131-3 standard allows one to extend the set of standard function blocks and define derived function blocks (DFBs). The inputs and outputs of an RTO DFB are shown in Figure 11.1*a*. The Modicon ladder logic code used to implement the retentive on-delay timer function block is shown in Figure 11.1*b*. The function is implemented as a more sophisticated version of the ladder logic in Figure 5.15*a*. The variable and block input/output definitions are as follows:

Variable Name	Var. Type	Data Type	Default Value
CtrCV	VAR	INT	
CtrPV	VAR	INT	
T_Tic	VAR	BOOL	
In	IN	BOOL	0
R	IN	BOOL	0
PT	IN	TIME	t#0s
Q	OUT	BOOL	
ET	OUT	TIME	

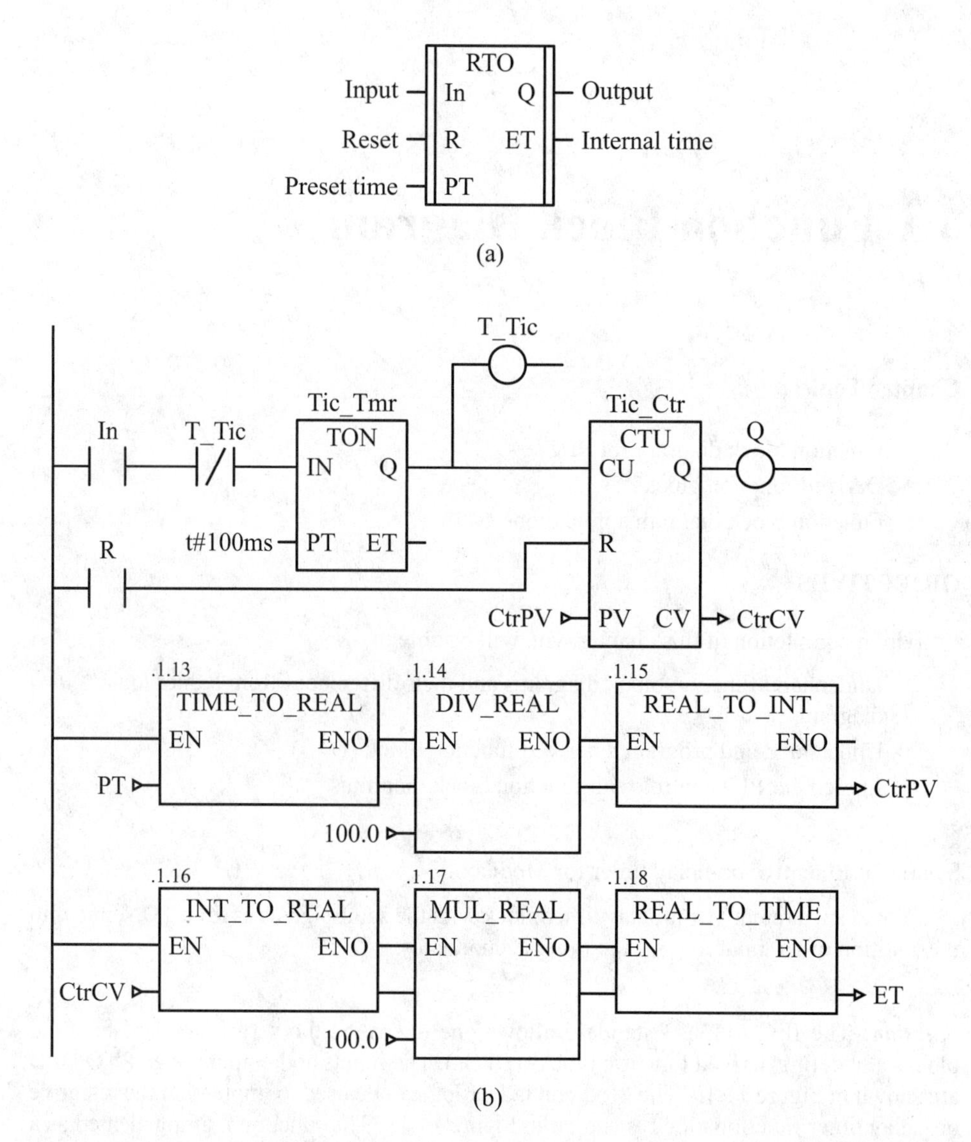

Figure 11.1. Retentive timer block: *(a)* block definition; *(b)* ladder logic implementation.

The resolution on the preset time is 100 ms, since that is the preset time for the timer that generates the pulses that are counted. Note that the PT time (in milliseconds) must be divided by 100 to obtain the preset value for the counter and the counter accumulator value must be multiplied by 100 to obtain the elapsed time in milliseconds.

11.1 INTRODUCTION

The function block diagram (FBD) language is another graphical programming language, an alternative to ladder logic. Its roots can be traced to the typical distributed control system of the 1970's which used this type of language to program the PID loops and associated logic. In general, translation between ladder logic and FBD is relatively straightforward.

As explained in Chapter 3, under the IEC 61131-3 standard, function blocks are the main program organization unit in a program. The standard also allows one to program *derived function blocks* in any of the standard languages except for sequential function chart. This concept is powerful for large programs because it allows one to encapsulate standard code segments as derived function blocks and then invoke a particular function block multiple times in a program without actually duplicating the code.

This chapter describes the FBD language for the PLCs covered by this text. For the most part, the function blocks themselves have already been introduced in conjunction with ladder logic program. However, since the FBD has no contacts or coils, function blocks must be used to provide logical functions. The timer, counter, comparison, and computation function blocks described for the Modicon and Siemens PLCs are all valid for a function block diagram. The ControlLogix function blocks for a FBD are modified from the ladder logic function blocks to accommodate multiple inputs. In addition, the ControlLogix PLC has several new function blocks only for a FBD. The PLC-5, SLC-500, and GE Fanuc PLCs do not support the FBD programming language. As done in previous chapters, the FBD programming language for a particular PLC is described in a separate section. That is, only the section(s) pertaining to the PLC(s) of interest need to be studied. Following these descriptions, examples are used to illustrate their application.

11.2 IEC 61131-3 FUNCTION BLOCK DIAGRAM

The function block diagram (FBD) language defined by the IEC 61131-3 standard is closest to the FBD language defined for the Siemens PLCs, though the Modicon Concept implementation is very close. Rather than giving a detailed explanation of the elements of the IEC 61131-3 FBD language, it is introduced in this section and detailed in the subsequent sections.

A function block diagram is a set of interconnected blocks and is based on viewing the system in terms of the flow of signals between blocks. It is similar to a ladder logic diagram, except that function blocks replace the interconnection of contacts and the coils are simply Boolean outputs of function blocks. Also, there are no power rails.

In Figure 11.2, a start/stop function illustrates the differences between logical functions as ladder logic and as function blocks. A start/stop control for a motor with one permissive and one lockout is shown in Figure 11.2*a*. An equivalent function block diagram is shown in Figure 11.2*b*. The "&" block is a logical AND block and the ">=1" block is a logical OR block. The number of inputs for each block can be increased. The circle at the lower input of the rightmost "&" block is a logical inversion, equivalent to the N.C. relay contact. This FBD has an *implicit feedback path*, since the MOTOR output of the rightmost "&" block is also an input to the leftmost "&" block. The MOTOR variable is called the *feedback variable*. An alternative FBD is shown in Figure 11.2*c*. This FBD has an *explicit feedback path*, where there is an explicit path from the MOTOR output to an input of the first "&" block. On this path, the value of MOTOR passes from right to left, which is opposite to the normal left-to-right flow. Some vendors do not allow explicit feedback paths.

The execution of the function blocks can be controlled with the optional EN input. When the EN input is **on**, the block executes. When the EN input is **off**, the block does not execute. For example, in Figure 11.3, the constant 3.5 is moved (":=" block) into

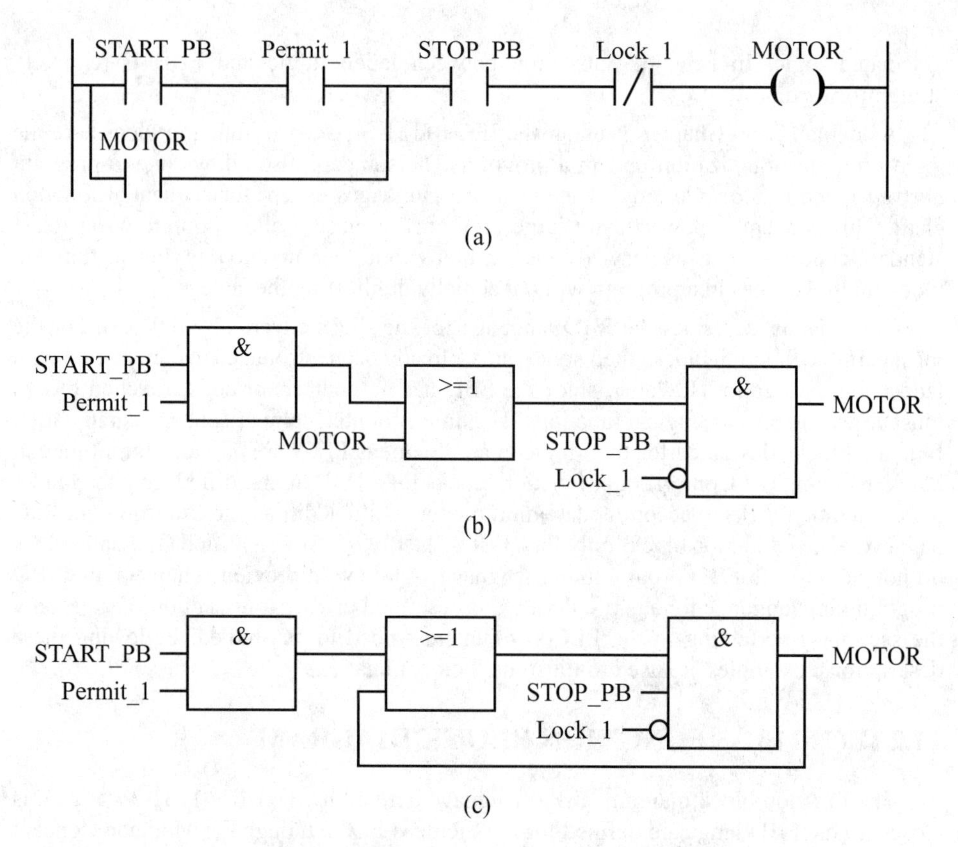

Figure 11.2. Start/stop logic: *(a)* ladder logic; *(b)* equivalent FBD with implicit feedback; *(c)* equivalent FBD with explicit feedback.

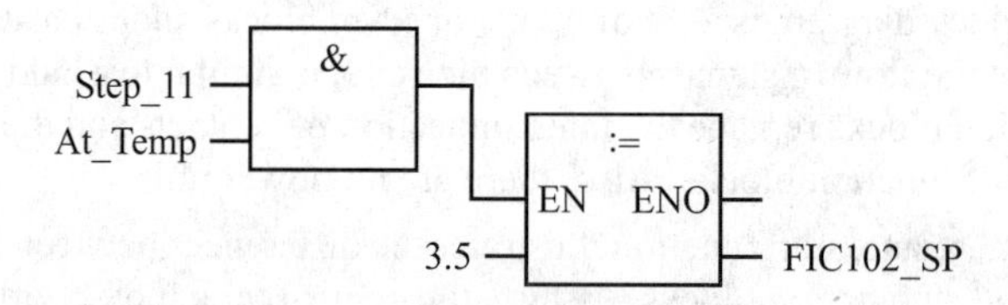

Figure 11.3. Example of EN for FBD execution control.

FIC102_SP when both Step_11 and At_Temp are true. The EN/ENO connections are completely optional in the FBD language.

The IEC 61131-3 standard does not specify a strict order of network evaluation. However, most function block diagrams are portrayed so that execution generally proceeds from left to right and top to bottom, like ladder logic. The only real exception to this generality is an explicit feedback path. The IEC 61131-3 standard (IEC, 1993) specifies that network evaluation obey the following rules:

1. "No element of a network shall be evaluated until the states of all of its inputs have been evaluated." If the input to a function block is the output from another function

block then it should be executed after the other function block. In Figure 11.2*b*, the execution order is: the leftmost "&", the ">=1", and then the rightmost "&".

2. "The evaluation of a network element shall not be complete until the states of all of its outputs have been evaluated." The outputs of a function block should not be available to other blocks until all outputs are calculated.
3. "The evaluation of a network is not complete until the outputs of all of its elements have been evaluated…" The execution of a FBD network is not complete until all outputs of all function blocks are determined.
4. "Within a program organization unit written in the FBD language, the order of network evaluation shall follow the rule that the evaluation of a network shall be complete before starting the evaluation of another network which uses one or more of the outputs of the preceding evaluated network." When data is transferred from one FBD to another, the second FBD should not be evaluated until the values from the first FBD are available.

When the FBD contains an implicit or explicit feedback path, it is handled in the following manner:

1. "Feedback variables shall be initialized by one of the mechanisms defined in clause 2. The initial value shall be used during the first evaluation of the network." Clause 2 of IEC 61131-3 defines possible variable initialization mechanisms.
2. "Once the element with a feedback variable as output has been evaluated, the new value of the feedback variable shall be used until the next evaluation of the element."

As for ladder logic, IEC 61131-3 defines the ability to skip a section of the FBD using jumps. Jumps are shown by a Boolean signal line terminated in a double arrowhead. The signal line for a jump condition originates at the Boolean output of a function block. Program control is transferred to the designated network label when the Boolean value of the signal line is true. For example, in Figure 11.4 when LS_101 and LS_102 are both **on**, the second function block is skipped and Check_LS_202 is always turned **on**. If LS_101

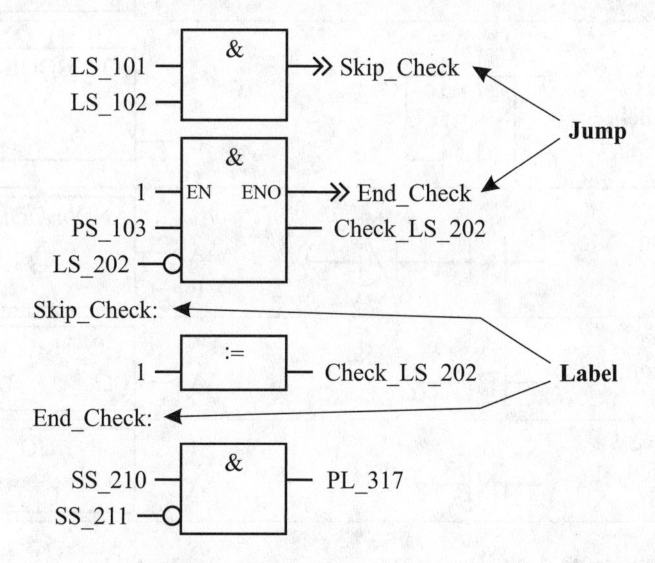

Figure 11.4. Example FBD jump.

and LS_102 are not both **on**, then the state of Check_LS_202 is determined by the logic of the second block and the unconditional jump at the ENO output causes program execution to skip to the fourth block. A jump and its target (label) must occur in the same FBD.

Unfortunately, IEC 61131-3 does not specify what happens to the network between the jump and label when the jump is executed. The interpretation in Figure 11.4 assumes that network evaluation ceases immediately and network evaluation starts at the specified label. An alternative interpretation is that all linked blocks in a network are evaluated before the jump is executed. Because of these alternate interpretations, the IEC guideline on using IEC 61131-3 now recommends that jumps in a FBD should not be used (Lewis, 1998).

11.3 MODICON FUNCTION BLOCK DIAGRAM

In general, the Modicon PLC FBD implementation closely follows the IEC 61131-3 standard. However, the Modicon FBD language does not allow explicit feedback loops and does not implement jumps. Aside from these restrictions, the major difference lies in the name of the **logic** function blocks. All of the timer, counter, comparison, computation, and advanced function blocks are identical for ladder logic and function block diagram. Thus, this section will concentrate on those function blocks that replace the contact and coil ladder logic elements.

Function block execution can be controlled with the optional EN input. If not used, this input is assumed to be a logical TRUE, which means the function block is executed on every program scan. There is also an optional ENO output connection.

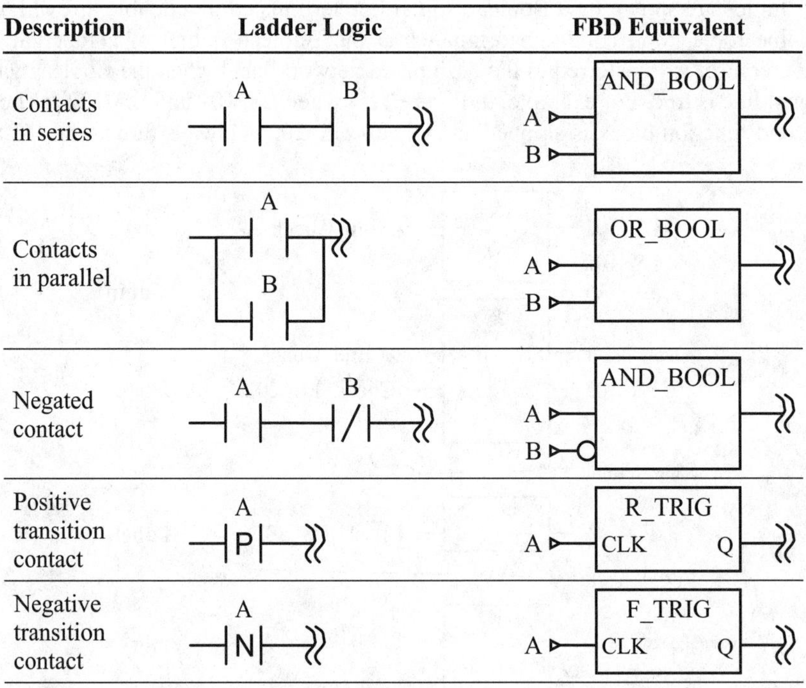

Description	**Ladder Logic**	**FBD Equivalent**
Contacts in series	A B	AND_BOOL; inputs A, B
Contacts in parallel	A; B	OR_BOOL; inputs A, B
Negated contact	A B	AND_BOOL; inputs A, B (negated)
Positive transition contact	A; P	R_TRIG; A → CLK, Q
Negative transition contact	A; N	F_TRIG; A → CLK, Q

Figure 11.5. Modicon FBD equivalents to ladder logic contacts.

Figure 11.5 shows the function block diagram equivalents to ladder logic contacts. The AND_BOOL and OR_BOOL function blocks can have up to 32 inputs. The circle at the input to an AND_BOOL or OR_BOOL block is a logical inversion, equivalent to the N.C. relay contact. The negated contact is shown in the third row of Figure 11.5 as part of a series connection of two contacts. The NOT_BOOL function block can also be used to invert a Boolean signal. Transitional contacts are implemented with the R_TRIG or F_TRIG function blocks. All of the function blocks shown in Figure 11.5 are only available for a FBD section. They may not be used in a ladder logic section.

The function block diagram equivalents to ladder logic coils are shown in Figure 11.6. An ordinary coil is simply a Boolean connection to a function block. The NOT_BOOL must be used to implement a logic inversion. A circle cannot be placed at the output of a function block to invert the output. The SR or RS function blocks can be used to implement the set coil and reset coils for a particular Boolean output. The SR function block is a set-dominant flip-flop, that is, the output is **on** if both S1 and R are **on**. The RS function block is a reset-dominant flip-flop, that is, the output is **off** if both S and R1 are **on**. The RS and SR function blocks may also be used in a ladder logic section. Transitional coils are implemented with the R_TRIG or F_TRIG function blocks. The R_TRIG and F_TRIG function blocks are only available for a FBD section.

In Figure 11.7, a start/stop function illustrates the differences between logical functions as ladder logic and as function blocks. A start/stop control for a motor with one permissive

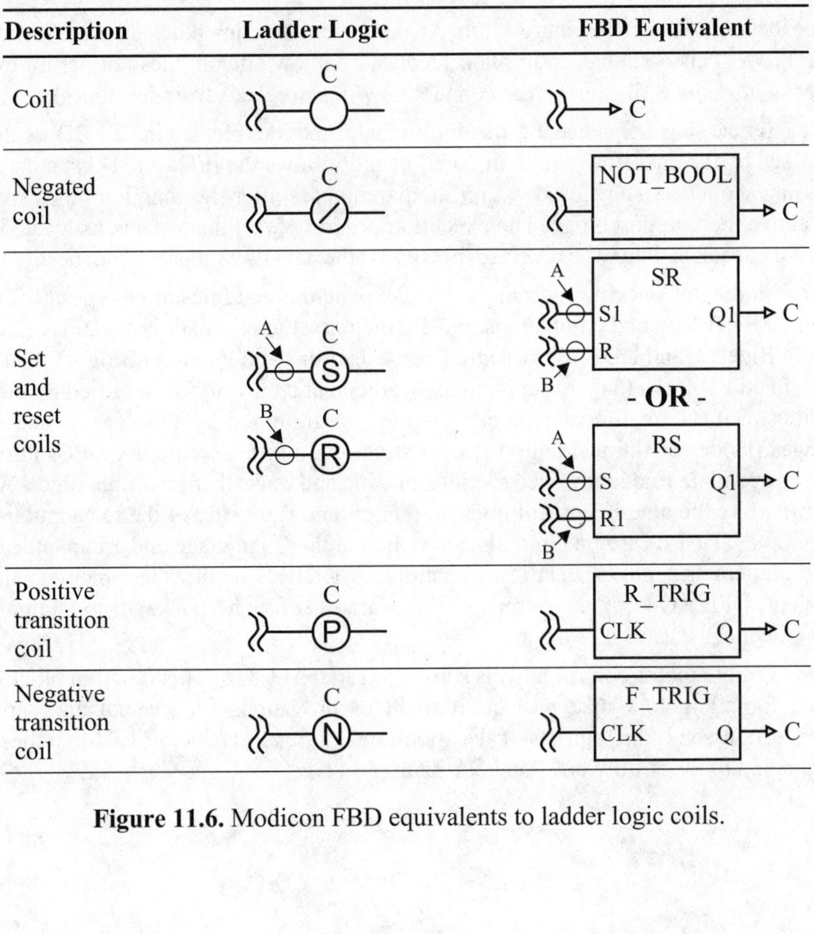

Description	**Ladder Logic**	**FBD Equivalent**
Coil	C	C
Negated coil	C	NOT_BOOL, C
Set and reset coils	A, C, S; B, C, R	A, SR, S1, Q1, C, R, B **- OR -** A, RS, S, Q1, C, R1, B
Positive transition coil	C, P	R_TRIG, CLK, Q, C
Negative transition coil	C, N	F_TRIG, CLK, Q, C

Figure 11.6. Modicon FBD equivalents to ladder logic coils.

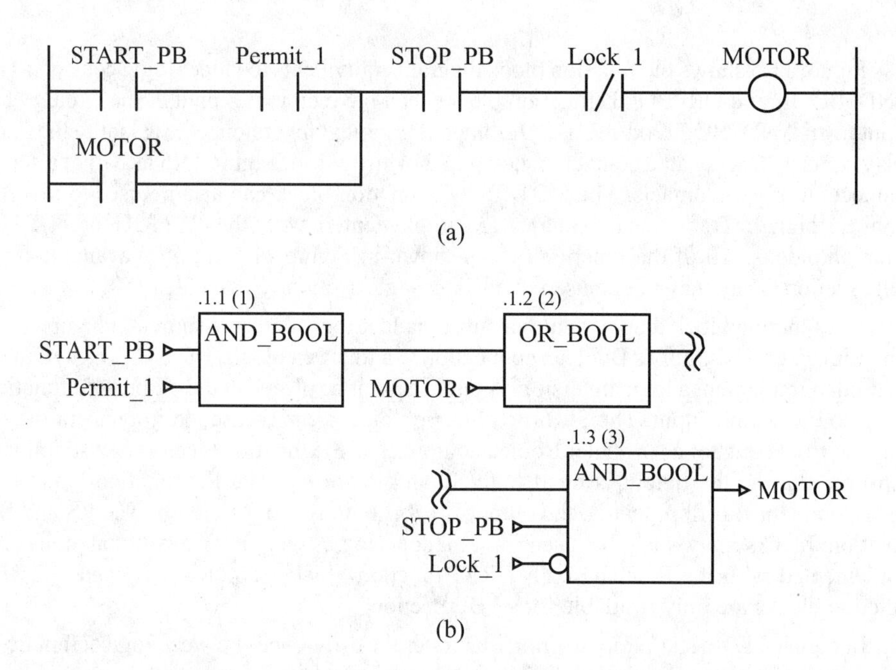

Figure 11.7. Start/stop logic for Modicon: *(a)* ladder logic; *(b)* equivalent FBD.

and one lockout is shown in Figure 11.7*a*. An equivalent function block diagram is shown in Figure 11.7*b*. This FBD has an implicit feedback path. Modicon does not permit explicit feedback paths since all flow on the connection wires proceeds from left to right.

The processing sequence of the individual function blocks in a FBD section is determined by the data flow within the section and follows the IEC 61131-3 standard. The processing sequence is enclosed within the parentheses after the function block instance name above the function block. The execution order of two function blocks located in an implicit feedback path may be reversed, but only if the data flow rules will not be violated.

The Modicon Concept programming package actually defines three types of function blocks: EFBs (Elementary Functions and Elementary Function Blocks), DFBs (Derived Function Blocks), and UDEFBs (User defined Functions and Function Blocks). The EFBs are the function blocks that are supplied by Modicon and may not be modified by the user. In contrast, DFBs are function blocks that are programmed by the user in one of the languages (ladder, FBD, instruction list, or structured text). Essentially, DFBs allow the user to encapsulate frequently used sections of code and reuse them multiple times. A DFB is identified by the double vertical lines on the left and right side of the rectangular block symbol. The UDEFBs are function blocks written in the C language and are intended to be used to implement highly specialized functions. A UDEFB requires less memory than an equivalent DFB. One must purchase a separate software package to support the development of UDEFBs.

An example motor control DFB is shown in Figure 11.31*b*. This function block could be used for all motors in a project. It includes provisions for manual and sequence (automatic) start and stop requests. It also monitors failures and generates alarm indications. This function block is fully developed in Example 11.1.

11.4 CONTROLLOGIX FUNCTION BLOCK DIAGRAM

The Allen-Bradley ControlLogix FBD implementation is compliant with the IEC 61131-3 standard. However, the names of logic, timer, and counter function blocks differ significantly from the standard and also from the corresponding ladder logic function blocks. Also, the FBD allows several new function blocks related to process control. Lastly, the ControlLogix FBD language does not implement derived function blocks and jumps within a diagram, but does implement jumps to a subroutine. Thus, this section will briefly survey the function blocks that may be used in a FBD routine. The FBD language became available with release 6 of the RSLogix 5000 programming software.

Function block execution can be controlled with the optional EnableIn input that corresponds to the EN input of the IEC 61131-3 function blocks. If not used, this input is assumed to be a logical TRUE, which means the function block is executed on every program scan. There is also an optional EnableOut output connection that corresponds to the ENO output of the IEC 61131-3 blocks.

Connections between function blocks and database tags are accomplished with IREF and OREF symbols (Figure 11.8). The OCON and ICON symbols are used to program connections between function blocks that are widely separated or on separate sheets. Like ordinary coils, an OREF or OCON symbol can refer to a particular output tag only once. There is no restriction on the number of IREF or ICON references to a particular tag. Boolean signals are shown as dashed lines, and Boolean block connections are shown with a dot on the tab. Numerical signals are shown as solid lines. Figure 11.9 is a sample FBD showing the connector symbols. The signal value appears above each output connection.

The processing sequence of the individual function blocks in a FBD program is determined by the data flow within the section and generally follows the IEC 61131-3 standard. The processing sequence is shown as part of the block properties. A function block routine executes in the following order:

1. Latch the data values of all tags in the IREF symbols.
2. Execute the function blocks in the order determined by their wiring. Feedback loops are handled as a special case, detailed below.
3. Write values to the tags in the OREF symbols.

When a group of blocks are in a loop, the execution order is not automatically determined. Instead, the user must mark the input wire that creates the loop with the *Assume Data*

FBD Symbol	Name	Purpose
A	IREF (Input reference)	Assigns tag value to function block input.
A	OREF (Output reference)	Assigns function block output value to tag.
A	ICON (Input connector)	Together, the OCON and ICON connect function blocks widely separated or on different sheets.
A	OCON (Output connector)	

Figure 11.8. ControlLogix FBD input/output connection symbols.

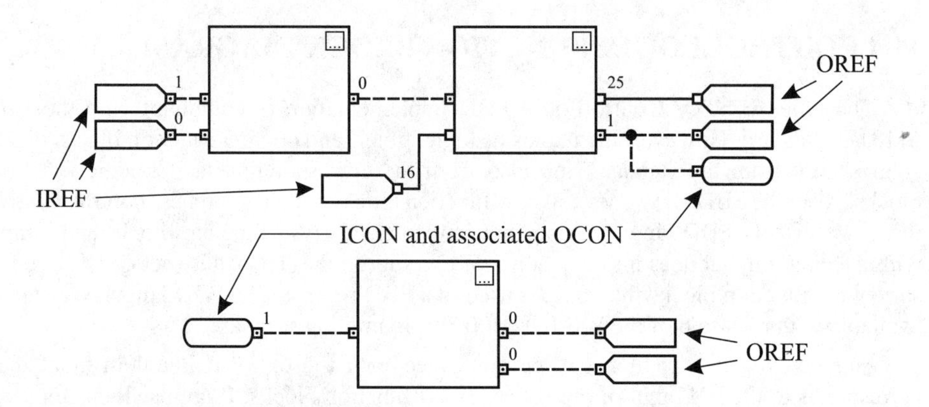

Figure 11.9. ControlLogix FBD showing use of input/output connections.

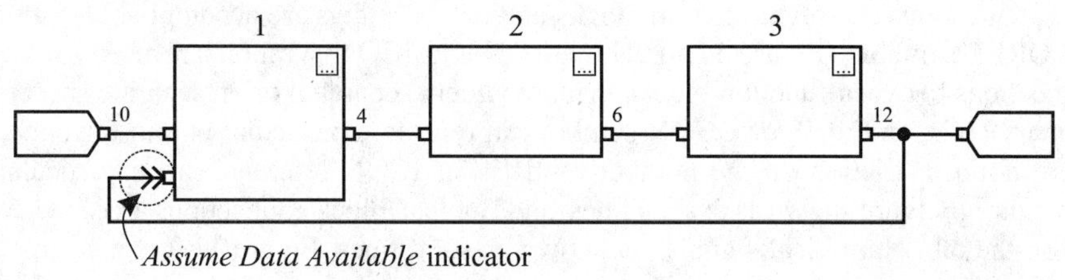

Figure 11.10. Using Assume Data Available indicator to resolve feedback loop execution.

Available indicator (double arrow), as shown in Figure 11.10. In Figure 11.10, block 1 uses the output of block 3 that was produced in the previous execution of the function block routine. Only the input to one of the blocks in the loop can have the Assume Data Available indicator.

11.4.1 Equivalents to Ladder Logic Contacts and Coils

Figure 11.11 shows the function block diagram equivalents to ladder logic contacts. The BAND and BOR function blocks can have up to 8 inputs. The BNOT block is a logical inversion, equivalent to the N.C. relay contact. The negated contact is shown in the third row of Figure 11.11 as part of a series connection of two contacts. One-shot (transitional) contacts are implemented with the OSRI or OSFI function blocks. All of the function blocks shown in Figure 11.11 are not available for a ladder logic routine.

The function block diagram equivalents to ladder logic coils are shown in Figure 11.12. An ordinary coil is simply a Boolean connection to an OREF. The SETD or RESD function blocks implement the latch coil and unlatch coils for a particular Boolean output. The SETD function block is a set-dominant flip-flop, that is, the "Out" output is **on** if both "Set" and "Reset" inputs are **on**. The RESD function block is a reset-dominant flip-flop, that is, the output is **off** if both "Set" and "Reset" inputs are **on**. One-shot (transitional) outputs are implemented with the OSRI or OSFI function blocks. The SETD, RESD, OSRI, and OSFI function blocks are only available for FBD and structured text programs.

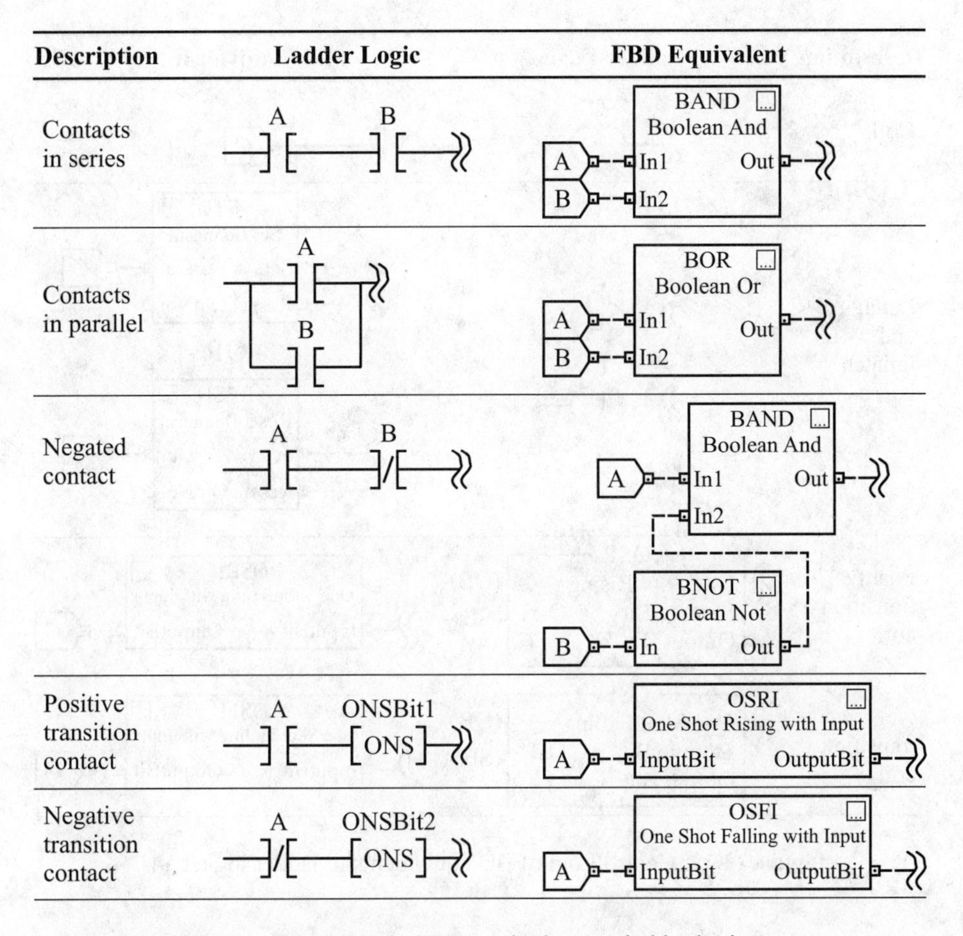

Figure 11.11. ControlLogix FBD equivalents to ladder logic contacts.

The ladder logic for a start/stop control for a motor with one permissive and one lockout is shown in Figure 11.13*a*. An equivalent function block with implicit feedback is shown in Figure 11.13*b*. The ICON/OCON provides the implicit feedback. The lower input to block BOR_01 is set to have the Assume Data Available indicator. An equivalent function block with explicit feedback is shown in Figure 11.13*c*.

11.4.2 Timer and Counter Function Blocks

The timer and counter function blocks are shown in Figures 11.14 and 11.15. For the most part, they are analogous to a combination of ladder logic function blocks:

FBD Block	Ladder Logic Equivalent
TONR	TON + RES
TOFR	TOF + RES
RTOR	RTO + RES
CTUD	CTU + CTD + RES

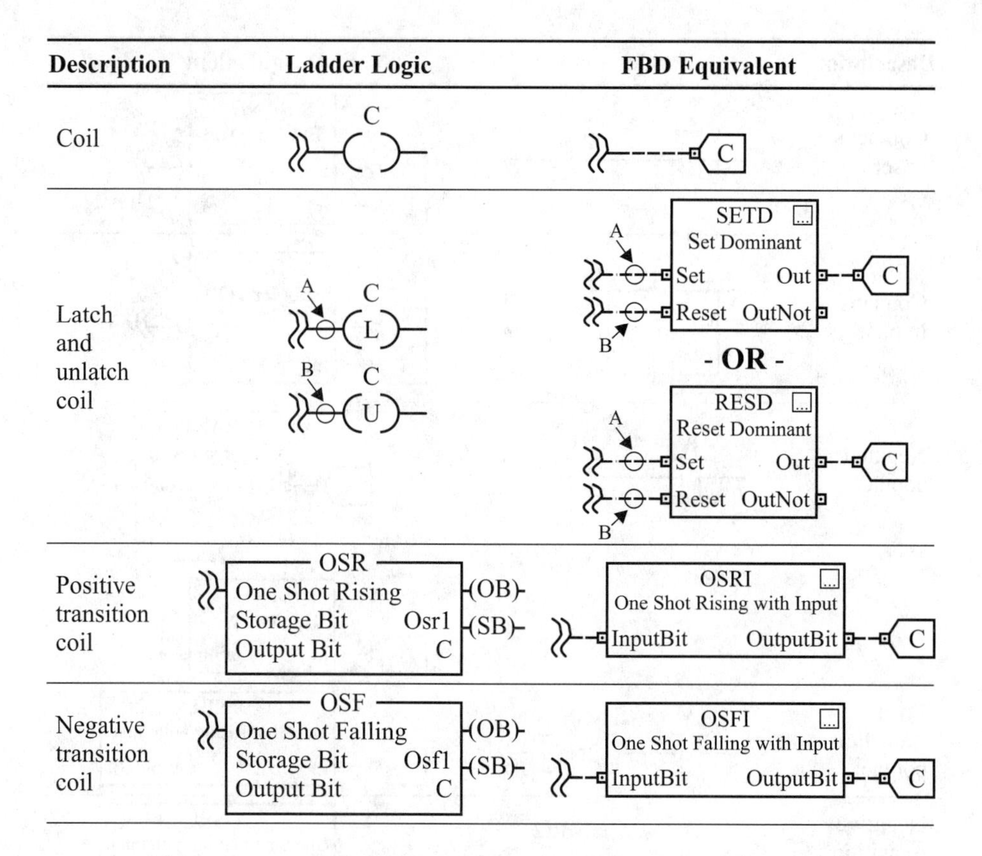

Figure 11.12. ControlLogix FBD equivalents to ladder logic coils.

The FBD timer function blocks basically add input connections for the preset (PRE) and timer reset (Reset) to the ladder logic function block. They also add the accumulator (ACC) and the done indication (DN) output connections. The other timer status bits (e.g., TT and EN) are available as outputs but are not shown in these examples. The example TONR on-delay timer in Figure 11.14*a* implements the same ladder logic example shown in Figure 5.17. The TOFR off-delay example in Figure 11.14*b* implements the TOF ladder logic example of Figure 5.19. Similarly, the retentive on-delay ladder logic example of Figure 5.21 is implemented as a RTOR shown in Figure 11.14*c*.

The CTUD FBD function block is approximately a combination of the ladder logic up-counter (CTU) and down-counter (CTD). The example CTUD in Figure 11.15*a* implements the same up-counter ladder logic example of Figure 5.23. Though not shown in this example, the user can also show the CU, CD, OV, and UN Booleans of the counter structure as block outputs. When used to count both up and down, the implementation appears as in Figure 11.15*b*. The function block diagram of Figure 11.15*b* is an incomplete implementation of the ladder logic example of Figure 5.26. Unfortunately, the ControlLogix CTUD function block when used in a FBD routine has no provision to set the accumulator to a non-zero initial value. If a ladder logic MOV function block is used to set the accumulator (like the fifth rung in Figure 5.26), it is overridden when the function block is next executed.

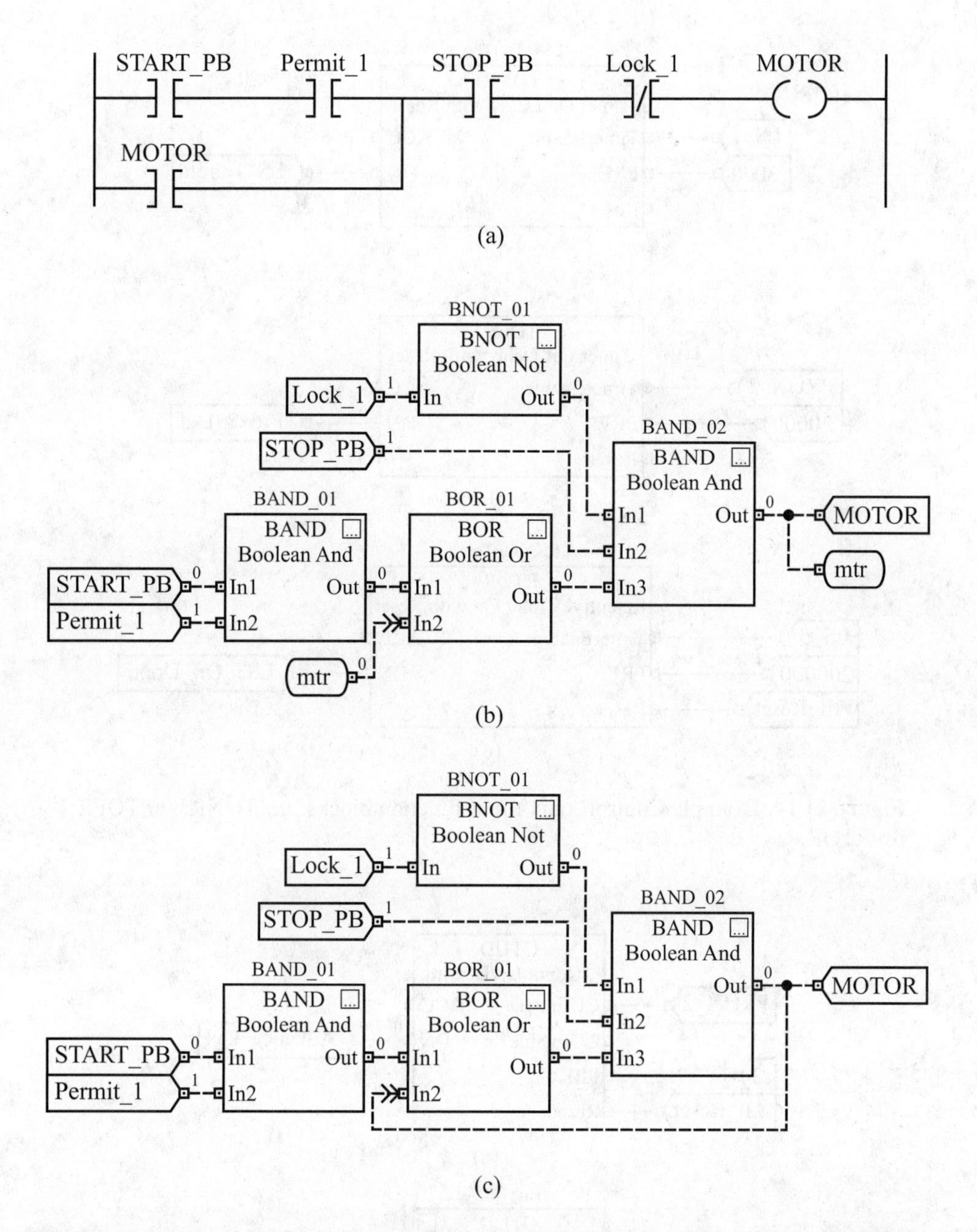

Figure 11.13. Start/stop logic for ControlLogix: *(a)* ladder logic; *(b)* equivalent FBD with implicit feedback; *(c)* equivalent FBD with explicit feedback.

11.4.3 Comparison and Computation Function Blocks

The available comparison function blocks correspond to the ladder logic comparison function blocks. The only basic difference is that the operands in the ladder logic blocks are replaced by FBD block inputs. However, the CMP ladder logic function block is not valid in a FBD routine. Example FBD comparison function blocks are shown in Figure 11.16. Both

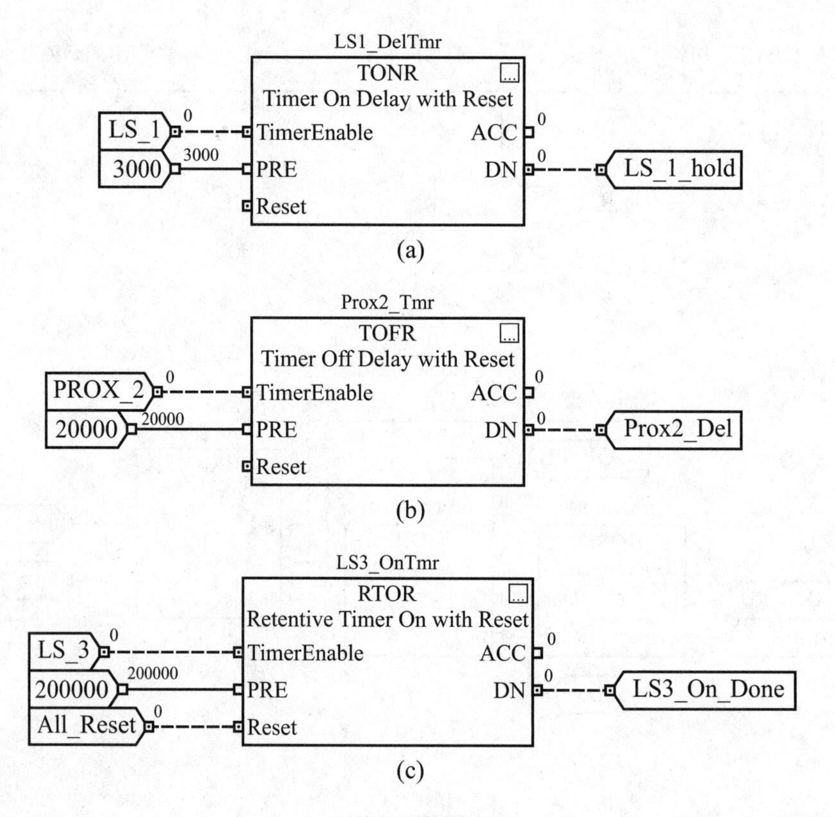

Figure 11.14. Example ControlLogix timer function blocks: *(a)* TONR; *(b)* TOFR; *(c)* RTOR.

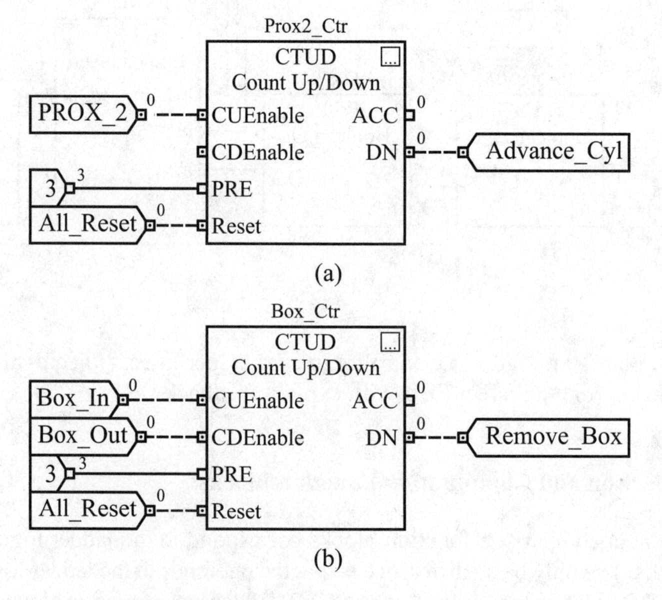

Figure 11.15. Example ControlLogix CTUD counter function block: *(a)* up counter; *(b)* up and down counter.

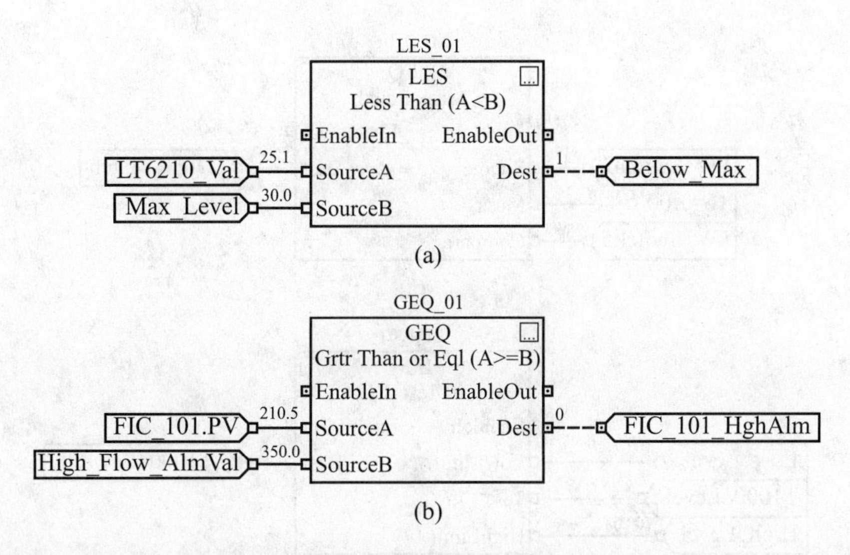

Figure 11.16. Example ControlLogix FBD comparison function blocks: *(a)* less than; *(b)* greater than or equal.

of the function blocks in Figure 11.16 are shown with the optional EnableIn and EnableOut connections. The possible comparison function blocks and the condition that turns on the Dest output are:

Block Name	Dest is On if:
EQU	SourceA = SourceB
GEQ	SourceA ≥ SourceB
GRT	SourceA > SourceB
LEQ	SourceA ≤ SourceB
LES	SourceA < SourceB
LIM	Test value within Low Limit and High Limit
MEQ	Mask(SourceA) = Mask(SourceB)
NEQ	SourceA ≠ SourceB

The LIM and MEQ function blocks have more inputs (Figure 11.17) and operate identically to the corresponding ladder logic function blocks of the same name (Section 7.5.1).

As for the comparison function blocks, the available computation function blocks correspond to the ladder logic computation function blocks. The only basic difference is that the operands in the ladder logic blocks are replaced by FBD block inputs. However, the CPT ladder logic function block is not valid in a FBD routine. Example FBD computation function blocks are shown in Figure 11.18. The possible basic arithmetic function blocks are:

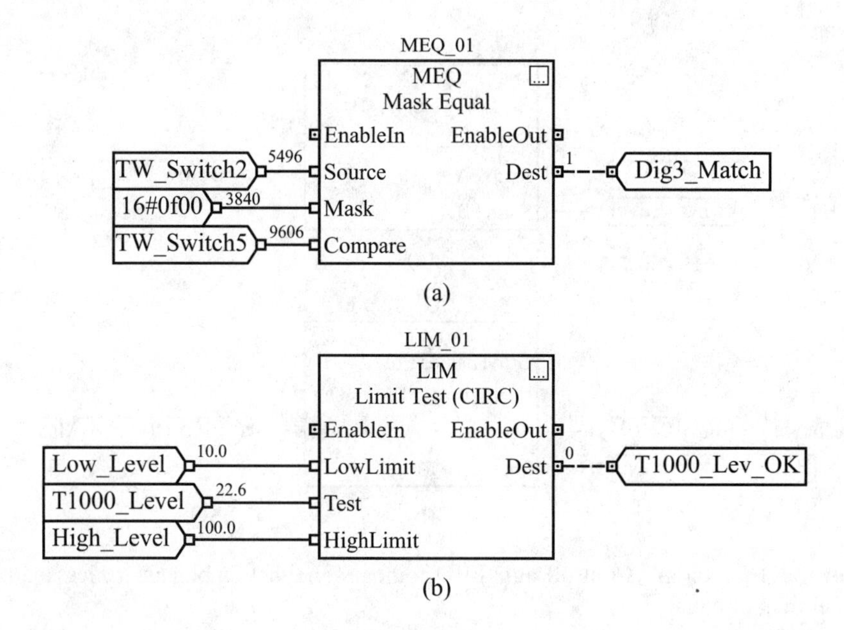

Figure 11.17. Example ControlLogix FBD advanced comparison function blocks: *(a)* mask equal; *(b)* limit test.

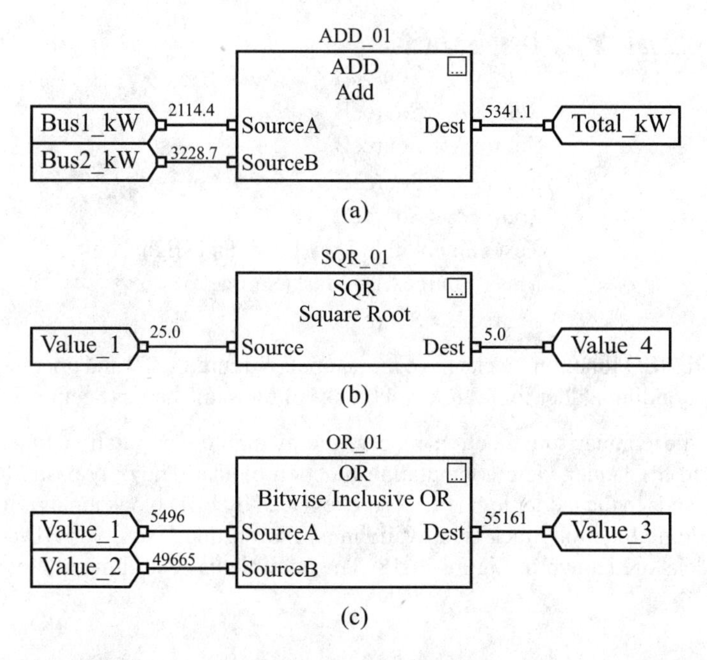

Figure 11.18. Example ControlLogix FBD computation function blocks: *(a)* addition; *(b)* square root; *(c)* inclusive-OR.

Block Name	Calculation:
ABS	Dest = Absolute value of Source (|Source|)
ADD	Dest = SourceA + SourceB
DIV	Dest = SourceA ÷ SourceB
MOD	Dest = SourceA modulo SourceB
MUL	Dest = SourceA × SourceB
NEG	Dest = – Source
SQR	Dest = Square root of Source
SUB	Dest = SourceA – SourceB

The names of the advanced math function blocks and the calculation that occurs for each one are:

Block Name	Calculation Result
ACS	Dest = Arc cosine of Source (Dest in radians)
ASN	Dest = Arc sine of Source (Dest in radians)
ATN	Dest = Arctangent of Source (Dest in radians)
COS	Dest = Cosine of Source (Source in radians)
LN	Dest = Natural logarithm of Source
LOG	Dest = Common logarithm of Source
SIN	Dest = Sine of Source (Source in radians)
TAN	Dest = Tangent of Source (Source in radians)
XPY	Dest = $(\text{Source A})^{\text{Source B}}$

The logical function blocks and the calculation that occurs for each one are:

Block Name	Calculation Result
AND	Bitwise logical AND of Source A and Source B integers
NOT	Invert all bits of Source
OR	Bitwise logical OR of Source A and Source B integers
XOR	Bitwise exclusive-OR of Source A and Source A integers

The names of the conversion function blocks and the conversion that occurs for each one are:

Block Name	Description
DEG	Convert source in radians to degrees.
RAD	Convert source in degrees to radians.
FRD	Convert source BCD value to integer.
TOD	Convert source integer value to BCD.
TRN	Truncate (remove) fractional part of source

The FBD move function blocks are different from the ladder logic move function blocks. The names and descriptions of the FBD move function blocks are:

Block Name	Description
BTDT	Move bits within an integer or between integers
MVMT	Copy source integer to destination integer, allowing portions of the integer to be masked

The CLR and MOV ladder function blocks are not available for use in a FBD routine.

The BTDT function block (Figure 11.19*a*) is useful for moving a group of bits between words and operates similarly to the BTD ladder logic function block. The only difference is that the Target is copied to the Dest before the bit move operation occurs. If the Target and Dest are identical tags, then the BTDT block functions identically as the ladder logic BTD block. The actual transfer for the BTDT block in Figure 11.19*a* is illustrated in Figure 11.19*b*. After Tmp_Out is copied to Out_Int, the lower 4 bits of (BCD) BCD_Value are copied into bits 12 to 15 of Out_Int. Out_Int is eventually copied to a 16-channel discrete output module. The four bits, Out_Int.12 to Out_Int.15, are connected to a 7 segment display that displays the (BCD) number represented by the 4 bits.

The MVMT function block is illustrated in Figure 11.20 and operates very similarly to the ladder logic MVM function block. The only difference is that the Target is copied to the Dest before the masked move operation occurs. If the Target and Dest are identical tags, then the MVMT block functions identically as the ladder logic MVM block. The example in Figure 11.20 transfers the third digit of a thumbwheel switch; the mask isolates the third digit.

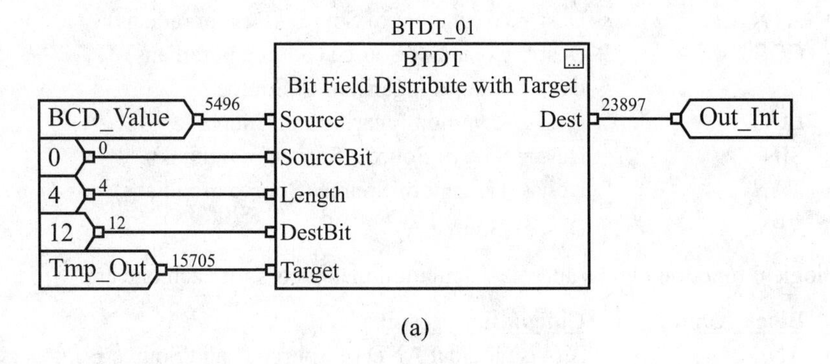

(a)

Step 1: Copy Target to Dest.

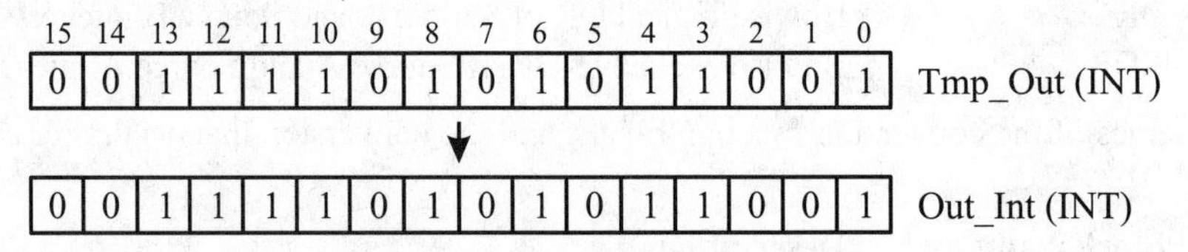

Step 2: Copy appropriate Source bits to Dest bits.

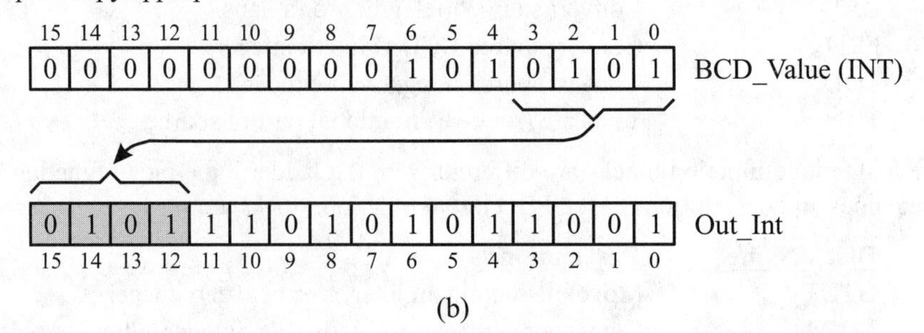

(b)

Figure 11.19. Example ControlLogix FBD bit field distribute: *(a)* function block; *(b)* operation.

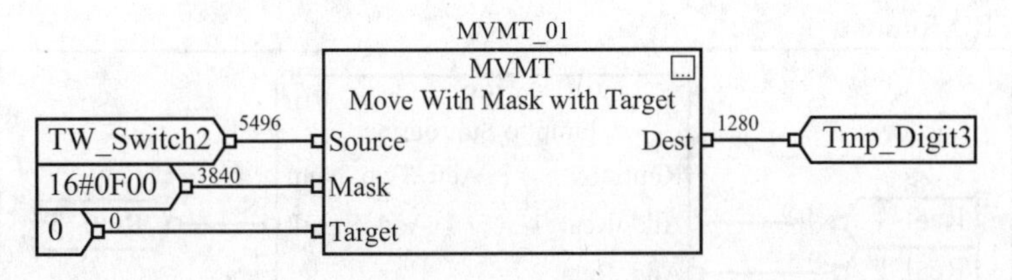

Figure 11.20. Example ControlLogix FBD masked move function block.

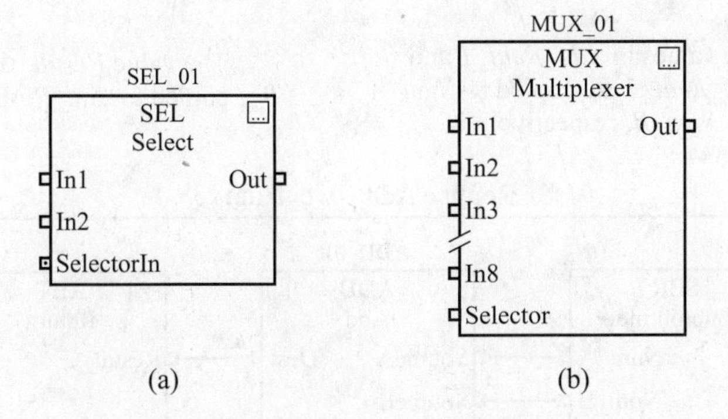

Figure 11.21. ControlLogix FBD selection function blocks: *(a)* select; *(b)* multiplexer.

Since an OREF or OCON symbol can refer to a particular output tag only once, there must be some provision to assign the results of two or more different calculations to the same tag. The SEL and MUX (Figure 11.21) function blocks provide this capability. The SEL block selects one of two inputs to be copied to the Out output. If the SelectorIn Boolean is **off**, In1 is copied to Out. If SelectorIn is **on**, In2 is copied to Out. The MUX block selects one of eight inputs to be copied to the output. The value (1 – 8) of the Selector DINT input selects the In*x* input to be copied to Out.

11.4.4 Program Control Function Blocks

The JSR (jump to subroutine), SBR (subroutine), and RET (return) function blocks are used to execute routines other than the main program routine. These FBD function blocks operate in the same manner as for the ladder logic function blocks of the same name. When enabled, the JSR function block directs program execution to the specified routine, and if needed, passes parameters to the routine. If parameters are passed to the subroutine, it must have a SBR function block. The subroutine is executed as follows:

1. If the routine contains an SBR function block, execute it first.
2. Latch all data values in IREF blocks.
3. Execute the other function blocks as specified by the wiring order (including any JSR blocks)
4. Write outputs in OREF blocks.
5. If the routine contains a RET block, execute it last.

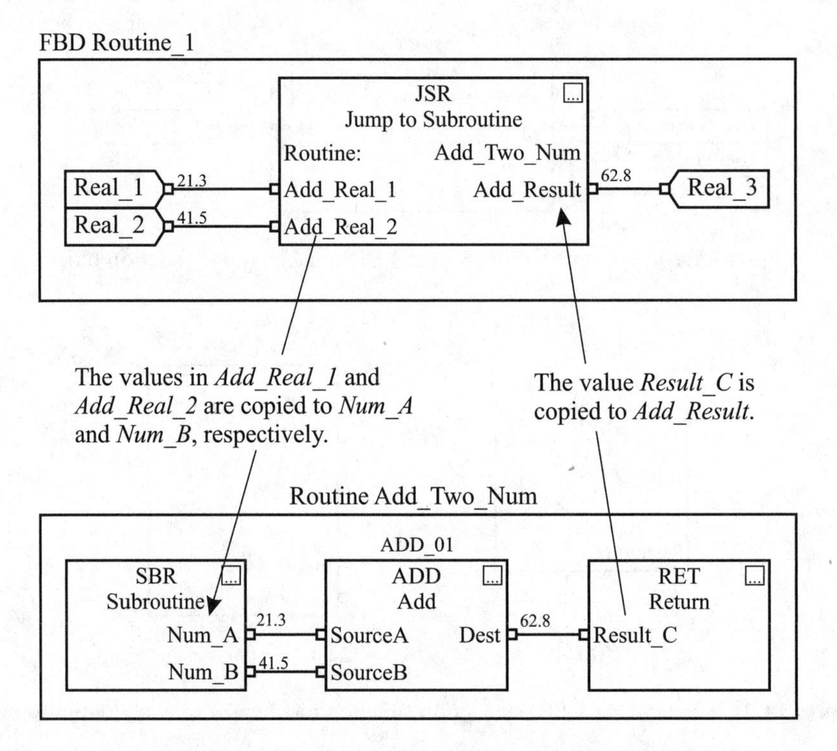

Figure 11.22. Example use of ControlLogix FBD JSR/SBR/RET function blocks.

Figure 11.22 shows an example use of a subroutine. The FBD routine named Routine_1 calls the Add_Two_Num subroutine, passing two values, Real_1 and Real_2. The Add_Two_Num subroutine receives the two values and places them into Num_A and Num_B. The result of the calculation is placed in Result_C. The RET block then passes the value in Result_C back to the main routine, which places the value into Real_3.

11.4.5 Process Control Function Blocks

The ControlLogix PIDE FBD function block implements the PID control algorithm and includes anti-reset windup and accommodations for cascade, feedforward, and ratio control strategies. The ladder logic PID function block is not available in FBD nor is the PIDE block available for ladder logic. An example PIDE loop is shown in Figure 11.23.

In this example, the FBD routine is in a periodic task and the scan rate of the task is the execution rate of the PIDE block. Alternatively, one can use a timer to trigger execution of the PIDE block. In this case, the TimingMode = 1 and the OversampleDT = timer preset in seconds. In either case, the analog input module should be producing the process variable tag five to ten times faster than the loop sample period. The real time sampling (RTS) feature of the analog input modules is another way to execute a PIDE block (TimingMode = 2). In this case, the real time sampling rate becomes the loop update rate, and the sample period is the difference between successive time stamps.

The PIDE block has 79 inputs and 40 outputs. In contrast to the PID ladder logic block, all of the configuration information appears as an input to the block, and all of the information stored internally appears as an output. Therefore, rather than list all of the

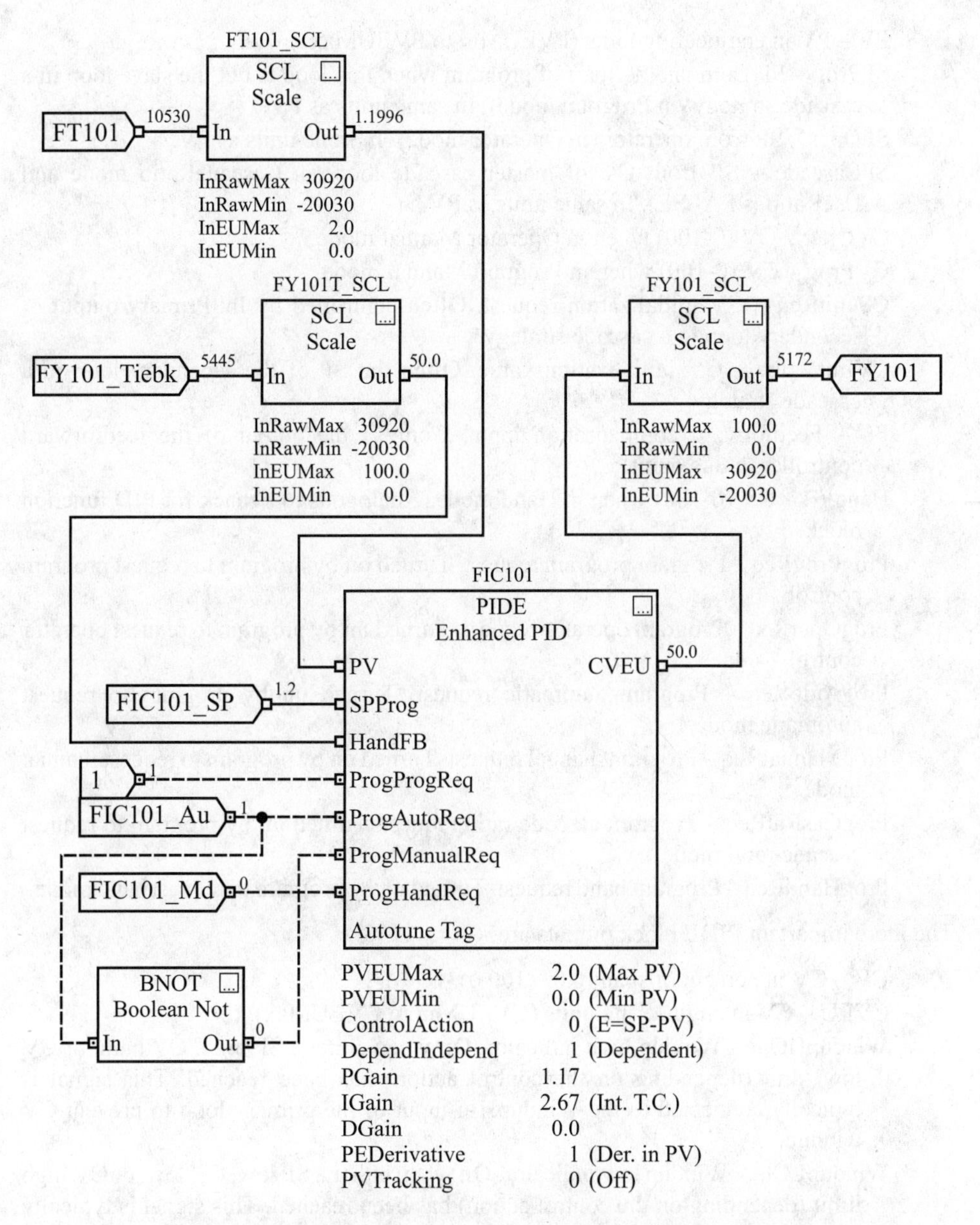

Figure 11.23. Example ControlLogix PIDE function block.

inputs, only the ones pertinent to the examples in this text are listed. More details can be found in the Rockwell Automation documentation (Rockwell Automation, 2002b). In addition, the inputs and outputs can be selectively displayed so it is not necessary to show all of the possible block inputs and outputs. The values of unconnected or hidden inputs are specified by the block configuration. The more important block inputs are:

PV – PV in engineering units (PVEUMin to PVEUMax).

SPProg – SP from another part of program when this loop is not the slave loop in a cascade strategy (in Program mode). In same units as PV.

SPOper – SP from operator (in Operator mode). In same units as PV.

SPCascade – SP from CV of master cascade loop (in CascadeRatio mode and UseRatio is FALSE). In same units as PV.

CVOper – CV (0-100) when in Operator Manual mode.

CVProg – CV (0-100) when in Program Manual mode.

CVInitReq – CV initialization request. Often controlled by InitPrimary output of secondary loop in a cascade strategy.

CVInitValue – CV initialization value. Often the SP of the secondary loop in a cascade strategy.

FF – Feedforward compensation input. Connect the output of the feedforward controller to this input.

HandFB – CV (0-100) when in Hand mode. Analogous to tieback for PID function block.

ProgProgReq – Program program request. Turned **on** by program to request program control.

ProgOperReq – Program operator request. Turned **on** by program to request operator control.

ProgAutoReq – Program automatic request. Turned **on** by program to request automatic mode.

ProgManualReq – Program manual request. Turned **on** by program to request manual mode.

ProgCasRatReq – Program cascade/ratio request. Turned **on** by program to request cascade/ratio mode.

ProgHandReq – Program hand request. Turned **on** by program to request hand mode.

The more important PIDE block outputs are:

CV – CV in percent of span (0.0 – 100.0).

CVEU – CV in engineering units (CVEUMin to CVEUMax).

WindupHOut – Windup high indicator. **On** when either a SP high, CV high, or CV low limit (depending on the control action) has been reached. This signal is typically connected to the WindupHIn input of the primary loop to prevent CV windup.

WindupLOut – Windup low indicator. **On** when either a SP low, CV low, or CV high limit (depending on the control action) has been reached. This signal is typically connected to the WindupLIn input of the primary loop to prevent CV windup.

ProgOper – Program/operator control mode indicator. **On** when in program control. **Off** when in operator control.

CasRat – Cascade/ratio mode indicator. **On** when in cascade/ratio mode.

Auto – Auto mode indicator. **On** when in automatic mode.

Manual – Manual mode indicator. **On** when in manual mode.

Hand – Hand mode indicator. **On** when in hand mode.

The PIDE block has a number of operating modes. There are basically two sets of modes, one set for operator control and one set for program control. In addition, an Override mode has a priority higher than the operator or program modes. The highest priority is the

Hand mode, which is generally set from an operator manual station. The modes, the source of the setpoint and control variable, as well as their relative priority are:

Mode	SP	CV	Priority
Hand		HandFB	1 (highest)
Override		CVOverride	2
Oper. Manual		CVOper	3
Prog. Manual		CVProg	3
Oper. Auto.	SPOper		4
Prog. Auto.	SPProg		4
Oper. Casc./Rat.	SPCascade or SPCascade×Ratio		5
Prog. Casc./Rat.	SPCascade or SPCascade×Ratio		5 (lowest)

For the example shown in Figure 11.23, the controller is completely under program control. The connection to an operator manual station (Figure 10.70) is also shown.

Example values of those PIDE inputs for configuration are shown in Figure 11.23. The tuning parameters are those for the PI controller of Example 10.4. The configuration inputs include:

Upper and lower bounds of the PV, SP, and CV
Upper and lower limits of the CV calculation
CV velocity limit
Upper and lower bounds of ratio
Reverse/direct action
Interacting or noninteracting form of the algorithm
K_P, T_I, and T_D or K_P, K_I, and K_D
Derivative on PV/error
Deviation deadband
Alarms: PV high, PV low, and deviation

The actual algorithms used to calculate the CV are very similar to the PID algorithm equations in section 10.3.2. The velocity form of the algorithm is used. The user may select either the dependent gains (interacting) or independent gains (noninteracting) form of the algorithm. For the dependent gains, the tuning parameters are K_P, T_I, and T_D, and for the independent gains form of the algorithm, the tuning parameters are K_C, K_I, and K_D. For both forms of the algorithm, time is measured in minutes.

With release 10 of the RSLogix 5000 programming software, autotuning capability was added to the PIDE function block. The user must purchase an additional activation key in order to configure this capability. The user defines a tag of the PID_AUTOTUNE data type and associates it with a PIDE block. The PID_AUTOTUNE tag holds the autotuning information. When autotuning is started, the PIDE block must already be in the manual mode. The autotuner steps the CV by a user-specified amount and monitors the PV response. The model is first-order-plus-deadtime with or without an integrator. Based on the model, the user is presented with three sets of tuning parameters:

Fast response – Fastest rise time and potentially significant overshoot.
Medium response – Fast rise time with minimal overshoot.
Slow response – No overshoot.

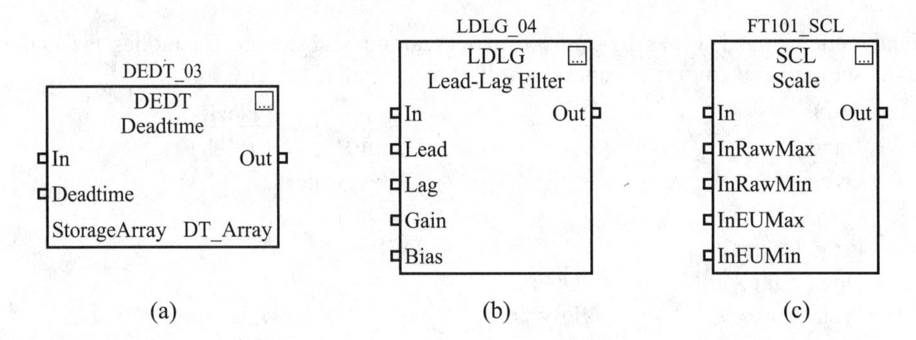

Figure 11.24. Signal conditioning blocks *(a)* time delay; *(b)* lead/lag; *(c)* scaling.

The appropriate set of parameters can then be transferred to the PIDE block configuration. The reader is referred to the autotuner documentation (Rockwell Software, 2002) for further details. In practice, automatic tuning of the PID controller is mainly used when commissioning a process. Operators are generally wary of automatic tuning since it introduces a "bump" into the process and there is a period of time in which the loop is not being controlled.

Three of the signal conditioning blocks are shown in Figure 11.24. The DEDT block delays the In signal by Deadtime (in seconds) and then transfers the value to the Out output. The time delay can be a variable. The delay buffer length is the number of elements in the StorageArray array. The LDLG function block implements a lead/lag transfer function block of (10.9). The In connection is the input, and Out is the calculation result. The Gain, Lead, and Lag inputs correspond to K, τ_1, and τ_2, respectively of (10.9). The DEDT and LDLG blocks must be executed on a periodic basis. The SCL function block changes the scale of a raw analog input value into appropriate units. The In connection is the input, and Out is the calculation result. The InRawMax and InRawMin are the maximum and minimum limits of the input signal. The InEUMax input is the scaled output that corresponds to InRawMax and InEUMin is the scaled output that corresponds to InRawMin.

Other conditioning function blocks that are available are:

- ALM – Generates alarms for an analog signal.
- DERV – Takes derivative of a signal. There is no filtering.
- FGEN – Linearizes a signal using a piecewise linear table.
- HPF – High-pass filters a signal. Frequencies below a cutoff are attenuated.
- HLL – Limits a signal between two values.
- LDL2 – Implements a second-order lead/lag, allowing complex poles and zeroes.
- LPF – Low-pass filters a signal. Frequencies above a cutoff are attenuated.
- NTCH – Notch-filters a signal. Frequencies around a notch frequency are attenuated.
- TOT – Integrates a flow rate to calculate the volume of material that has passed through the flow meter.

The RMPS function block (Figure 11.25) generates sophisticated ramp/soak profiles. The profile is determined by the information in the RampValue, SoakValue, and SoakTime arrays. This block has operational modes that are almost as sophisticated as the PIDE block.

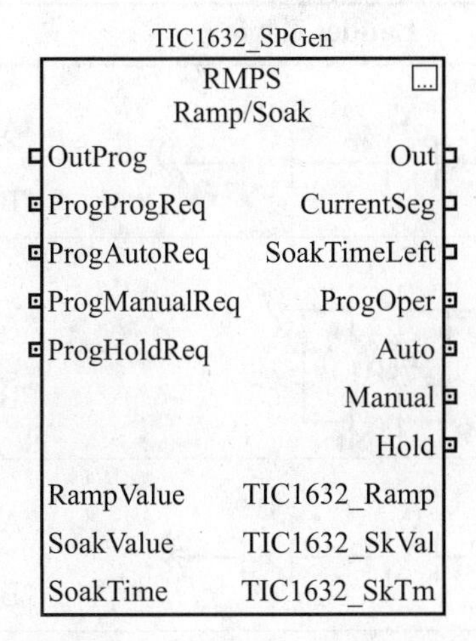

Figure 11.25. Example ControlLogix RMPS function block.

Function blocks that modify the controller output for certain applications are briefly described as:

ESEL – Selects the output signal among up to six signals. Can be configured to do high-select, low-select, median-select, mean-select, or manual select.

RLIM – Limits the rate of change of the signal. The PIDE has CV rate limiting, but this block has more features.

POSP – Generates the raise/lower logic outputs for a valve controlled by an electric servomotor

SRTP – Combines pulse-width modulation with split-ranging for two digital actuators. The pulse width of each actuator signal is proportional to a maximum cycle time.

11.5 SIEMENS S7 FUNCTION BLOCK DIAGRAM

In general, the Siemens S7 FBD implementation closely follows the IEC 61131-3 standard. However, the S7 FBD language does not allow explicit feedback loops. All of the timer, counter, comparison, computation, and advanced function blocks are identical for ladder logic and function block diagram. Thus, this section will concentrate on those function blocks that replace the contact and coil ladder logic elements.

If a particular function block has an EN input, this input can be used to control its execution. If the EN is not used or is absent, the function block is executed on every program scan. If a block has an EN input, there is also an ENO output connection. In a FBD network, the ENO output appears in the lower right of the block.

Figure 11.26 shows the function block diagram equivalents to ladder logic contacts. The & and >= function blocks can have an unlimited number of inputs and do not have an EN input. There is also an exclusive-or (XOR) function block. The circle at the input to these bit logic blocks is a logical inversion, equivalent to the N.C. relay contact. The

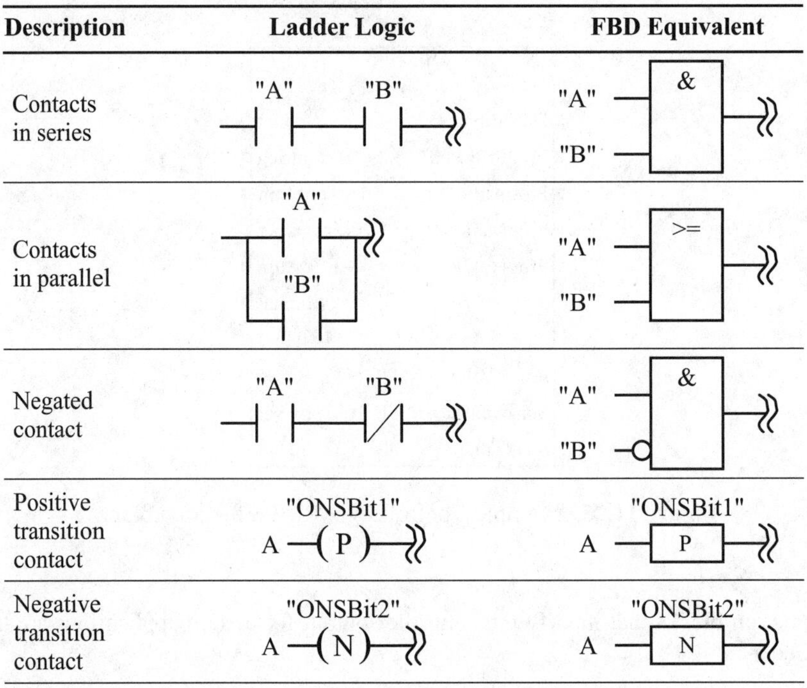

Description	Ladder Logic	FBD Equivalent
Contacts in series	"A" "B"	& "A" "B"
Contacts in parallel	"A" "B"	>= "A" "B"
Negated contact	"A" "B"	& "A" "B"
Positive transition contact	"ONSBit1" A (P)	"ONSBit1" A P
Negative transition contact	"ONSBit2" A (N)	"ONSBit2" A N

Figure 11.26. S7 FBD equivalents to ladder logic contacts.

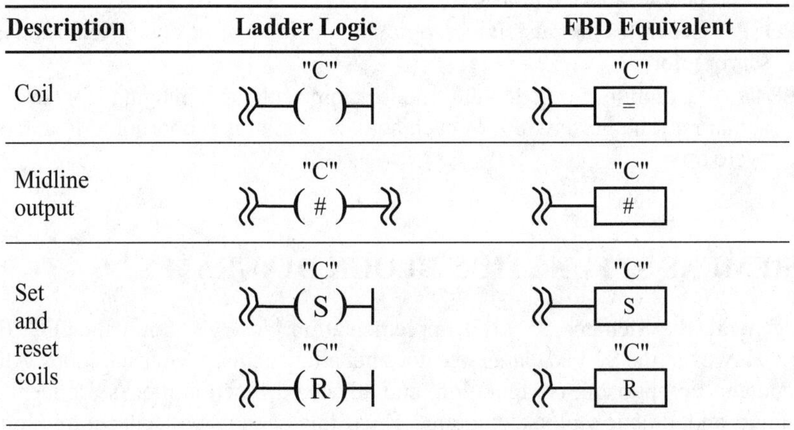

Description	Ladder Logic	FBD Equivalent
Coil	"C" ( )	"C" =
Midline output	"C" (#)	"C" #
Set and reset coils	"C" (S) "C" (R)	"C" S "C" R

Figure 11.27. S7 FBD equivalents to ladder logic coils.

negated contact is shown in the third row of Figure 11.26 as part of a series connection of two contacts. Only inputs to bit logic blocks can be inverted. Transitional contacts are implemented with the P or N function blocks. All of the function blocks shown in Figure 11.26 are only available for a FBD section. They may not be used in a ladder logic section.

The function block diagram equivalents to ladder logic coils are shown in Figure 11.27. An ordinary coil is simply an assignment to a variable. The midline output is a special coil

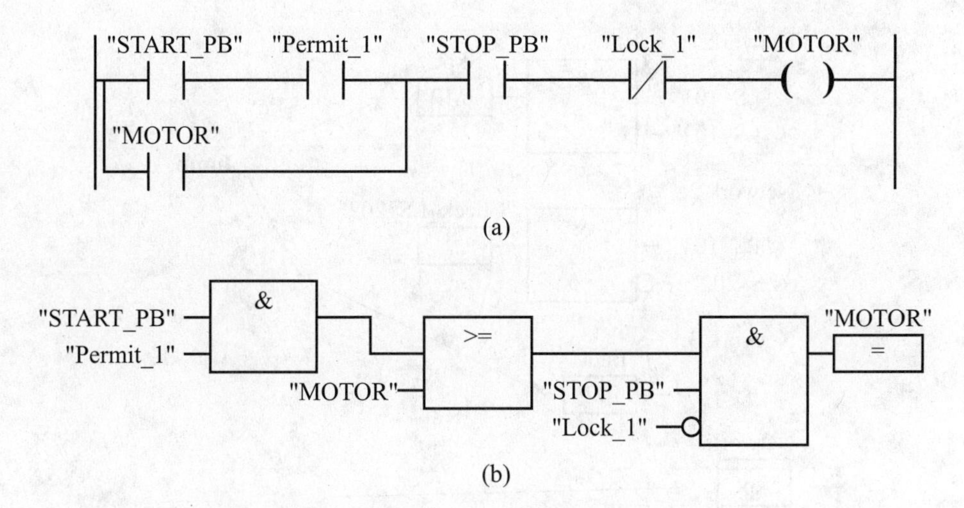

Figure 11.28. Start/stop logic for S7: *(a)* ladder logic; *(b)* equivalent FBD.

that does not terminate the branch. Other logic can occur after this coil. The S and R function blocks implement the set coil and reset coils, respectively. Transitional coils are implemented with the P or N function blocks followed by an assignment (=) block.

Figure 11.28 implements a start/stop function and also illustrates the differences between logical functions as ladder logic and as function blocks. A start/stop control for a motor with one permissive and one lockout is shown in Figure 11.28*a*. An equivalent function block diagram is shown in Figure 11.28*b*. This FBD has an implicit feedback path. S7 does not permit explicit feedback paths since all flow on the connection wires proceeds from left to right.

The processing sequence of the individual function blocks in a FBD network is determined by the data flow within the network and follows the IEC 61131-3 standard.

Jumps are shown by a Boolean signal line terminated in a JMP block. The signal line for a jump condition originates at the Boolean output of a function block. If there is no connection to the JMP block, it is an unconditional jump. Program control is transferred to the designated network label (box with upper and lower double lines) when the Boolean value of the signal line is true. If a jump is executed, the networks between the jump and its destination are not executed. A JMPN block transfers control to the label when the Boolean value of the signal is false. A label can have no more than 4 characters and the first character must be a letter. Figure 11.29 shows the S7 implementation of Figure 11.4.

The Step 7 programming package defines four types of function blocks: FBs (function blocks), FCs (functions), SFCs (system functions), and SFBs (system function blocks). A FB has local variables contained in an instance data block. A FC does not have any local storage. FBs and FCs are function blocks that are programmed by the user in one of the languages (ladder, FBD, instruction list, S7-Graph, and so on). Essentially, FBs and FCs allow the user to encapsulate frequently used sections of code and reuse them multiple times. The SFCs and SFBs are built-in functions and function blocks.

Local storage for a FB is placed in an instance data block (DB) that is associated with the FB or OB (organization block). For example, if a user creates FB10, then a data block of type FB10 must be created in order for that function block to be called.

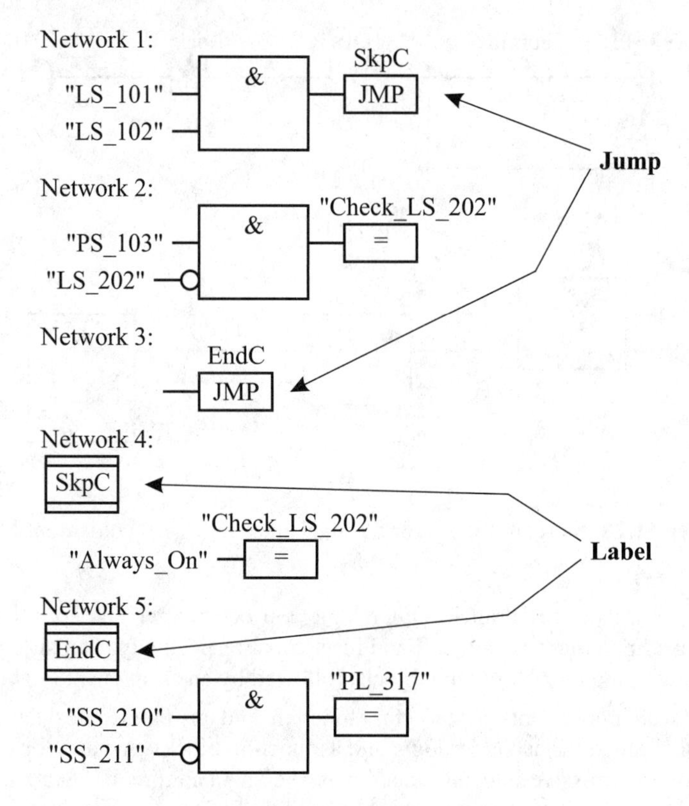

Figure 11.29. Example S7 FBD jump.

Figure 11.30. S7 save coil: *(a)* ladder logic; *(b)* DFB.

An example motor control FB is shown in Figure 11.31*c*. This function block could be used for all motors in a project. It includes provisions for manual and sequence (automatic) start and stop requests. It also monitors failures and generates alarm indications. This function block is fully developed in Example 11.1.

When implementing a function block, it is sometimes useful to pass status information through the ENO block output. The SAVE function provides this function. The ladder logic coil and the FBD block versions of the SAVE function are shown in Figure 11.30. The Boolean input to the SAVE function is transferred to the function block ENO. In order to set the ENO properly, the SAVE must be in the last network of the function block program.

11.6 EXAMPLES

Example 11.1. Motor control function block. Program a function block to handle motor control. The specifications are as follows.

The block controls a motor starter through a discrete output. There is a Hand-Off-Auto switch between the discrete output and the motor starter (Figure 4.23) that allows the operator to override the PLC control. The block operates in two modes: manual and automatic. When in the manual mode, the motor is started and stopped with "Manual Start" and "Manual Stop" commands. When in the automatic mode, the motor is controlled by "Sequence Start" and "Sequence Stop" commands. In the automatic mode, the motor is controlled by sequences. When switching between the two modes, the motor control discrete output should not change.

The block must monitor and report the following faults:

Motor fails to start within 10 seconds.
Motor overload.
Hand-Off-Auto switch not in "Auto" position.
Any fault (**on** when any of the above 3 are **on**)

The "Fail to Start" fault must be latched when it occurs. An "Alarm Reset" input must be provided that when **on**, resets the "Fail to Start" fault indication. The other fault indications track the appropriate status. For example, the "Overload Fault" is **on** when the overload is detected and **off** when the overload has been cleared. When any fault indication is **on**, the discrete output to the motor starter should be turned **off** and remain **off** until all faults are cleared. In addition, a "Manual Start" or "Sequence Start" must be used to start the motor after a fault has cleared. In order to detect these faults, the following discrete inputs are available:

Motor auxiliary switch.
Overload indication from motor starter.
Hand-Off-Auto switch position indication.

The connections to the motor control block are shown in Figure 11.31*a*, and are explained as follows:

Auxiliary contact – Closes when motor is running at proper speed.
Hand-Off-Auto switch – Closes when Hand-Off-Auto switch in "auto" position.
Overload contact – Overload indication from motor starter; **on** when overloaded.
Alarm reset – **On** to clear "auxiliary contact fail to close" failure indication.
Manual mode enable – **On** for manual mode; **off** for automatic mode.
Manual start request – **On** to start motor when in manual mode; ignored in automatic.
Manual stop request – **On** to stop motor when in manual mode; ignored in automatic.
Sequence start request – **On** to start motor when in automatic mode; ignored in manual mode.
Sequence stop request – **On** to start motor when in automatic mode; ignored in manual mode.
Motor start contact – Command to motor starter; **on** to start and run motor; **off** to stop motor.
Any failure – **On** when any failure indication is **on**.
Auxiliary contact fail to close – **On** when auxiliary contact failed to close 10 seconds after motor started.
Motor overload – **On** when motor is overloaded.
H-O-A switch in hand or off – **On** when hand-off-auto switch not in "auto" position, indicating that PLC does not control motor.

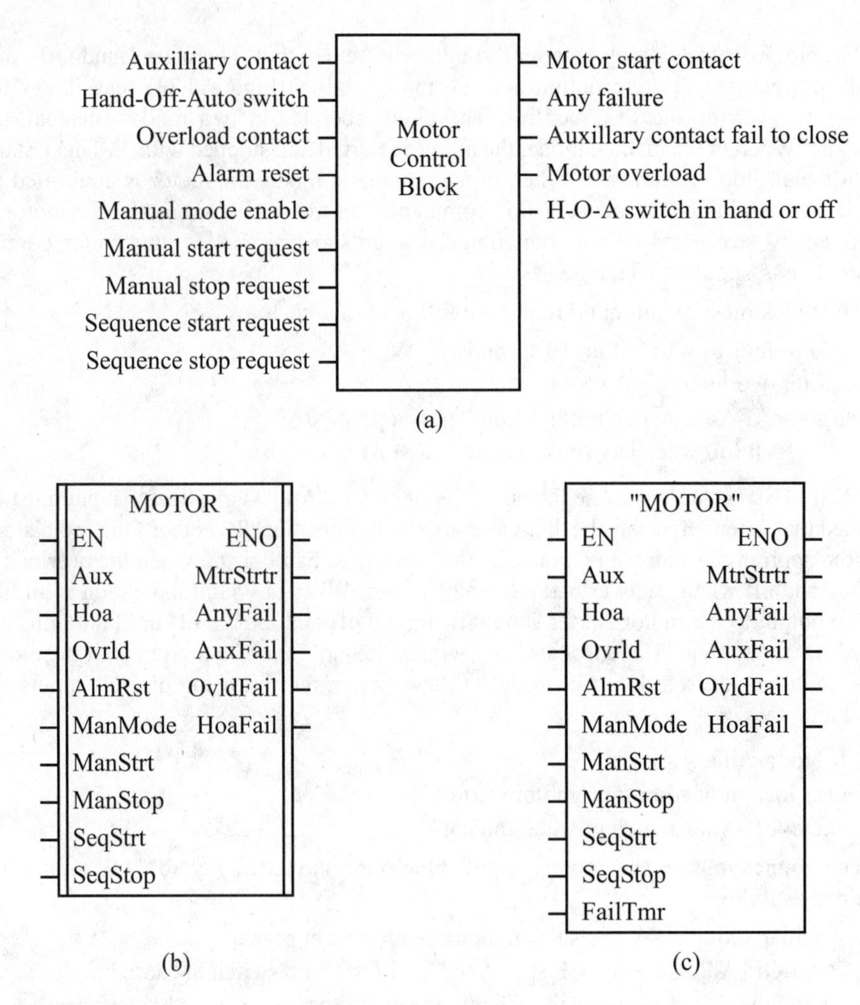

Figure 11.31. Motor control function block: *(a)* definitions of input and outputs; *(b)* as Modicon DFB; *(c)* as S7 FB.

Solution. Of the PLCs covered by this text, only the Modicon and S7 can program a function block. The Modicon DFB appears as shown in Figure 11.31*b* and the S7 FB appears as shown in Figure 11.31*c*.

The ladder logic code to implement the Modicon DFB is shown in Figure 11.32. The variable and block input/output definitions are as follows:

Variable Name	Var. Type	Data Type	Default Value
Motor_Start_Req	VAR	BOOL	
Motor_Stop_Req	VAR	BOOL	
Aux	IN	BOOL	0
Hoa	IN	BOOL	0
Ovrld	IN	BOOL	1

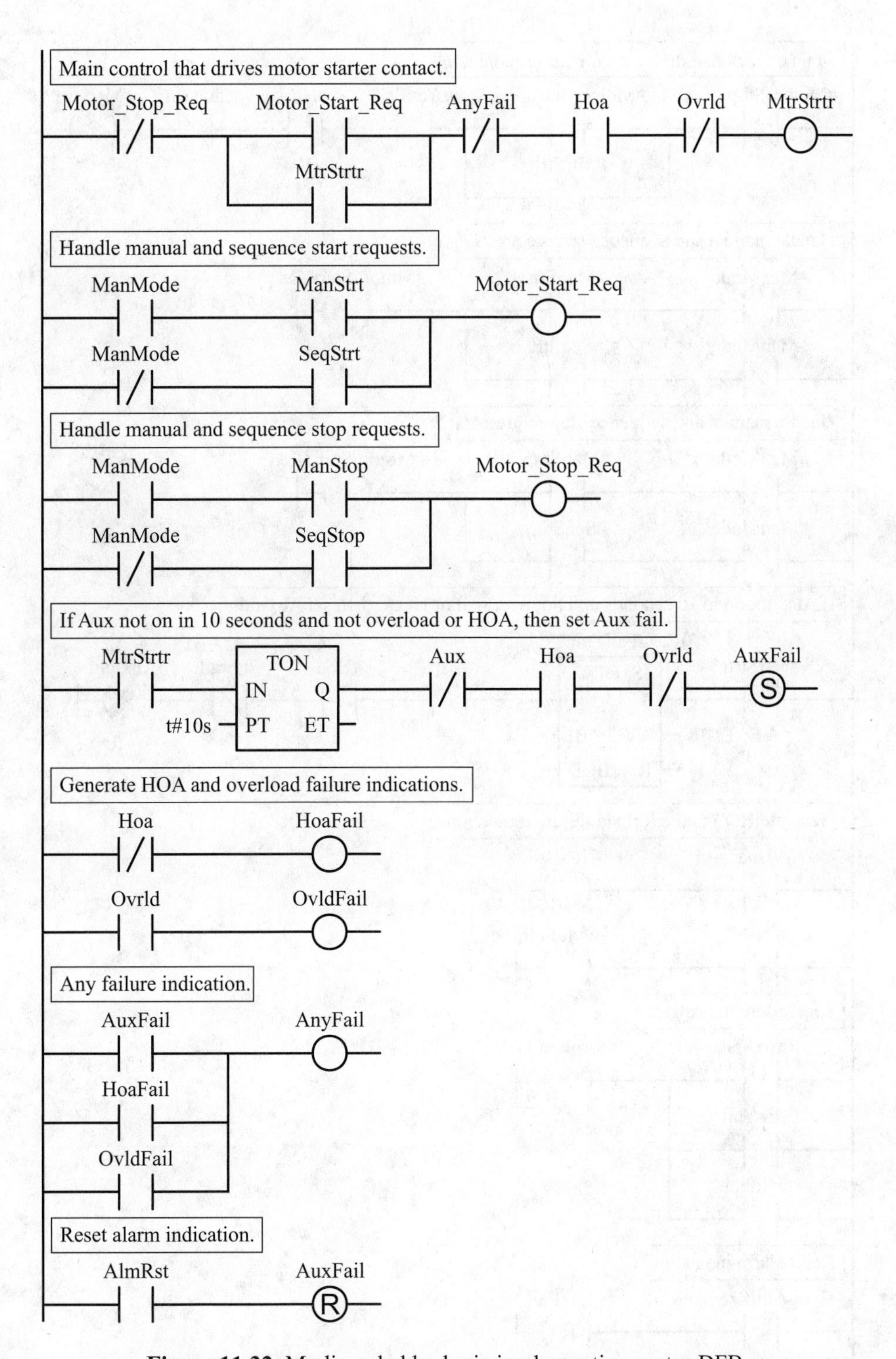

Figure 11.32. Modicon ladder logic implementing motor DFB.

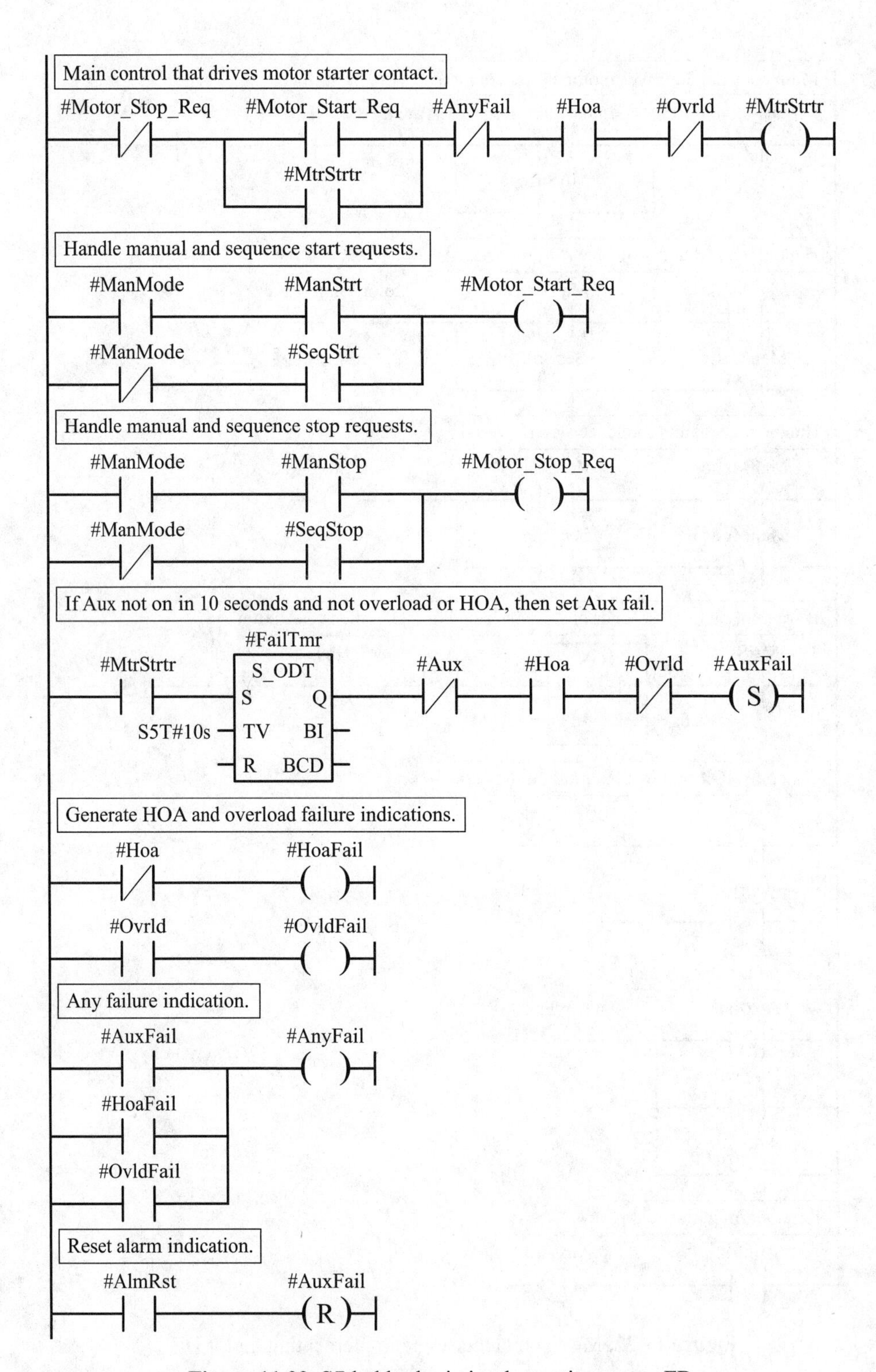

Figure 11.33. S7 ladder logic implementing motor FB.

AlrmRst	IN	BOOL	0
ManMode	IN	BOOL	1
ManStrt	IN	BOOL	0
ManStop	IN	BOOL	0
SeqStrt	IN	BOOL	0
SeqStop	IN	BOOL	0
MtrStrtr	OUT	BOOL	
AnyFail	OUT	BOOL	
AuxFail	OUT	BOOL	
OvldFail	OUT	BOOL	
HoaFail	OUT	BOOL	

The "Default Value" is the value of the input if it is unconnected. Note that the motor cannot be started if either the Aux, Ovrld, or Hoa inputs are not connected.

For the S7, the variable and block input/output definitions are as follows:

Variable Name	**Var. Type**	**Data Type**	**Default Value**
Motor_Start_Req	STAT	BOOL	
Motor_Stop_Req	STAT	BOOL	
Aux	IN	BOOL	False
Hoa	IN	BOOL	False
Ovrld	IN	BOOL	True
AlrmRst	IN	BOOL	False
ManMode	IN	BOOL	True
ManStrt	IN	BOOL	False
ManStop	IN	BOOL	False
SeqStrt	IN	BOOL	False
SeqStop	IN	BOOL	False
FailTmr	IN	TIMER	False
MtrStrtr	OUT	BOOL	
AnyFail	OUT	BOOL	
AuxFail	OUT	BOOL	
OvldFail	OUT	BOOL	
HoaFail	OUT	BOOL	

The ladder logic that implements the motor FB is shown in Figure 11.33. Note that the symbols local to the function block are prefixed with a "#." Since this FB has local storage (STAT type), a DB must be created with the FBx type, where "x" is the motor FB number.

Example 11.2. Cascade PID Control. Implement Example 10.8 using the FBD language for the Modicon and ControlLogix PLCs.

Solution. The Modicon solution is shown in Figure 11.34. The only two basic differences between this solution and the one with ladder logic (Figure 10.76) are: (1) EN/ENO used only when necessary, and (2) no contacts or coils. Only the EN for the PIDFF blocks needs to be retained. Any Boolean block inputs or outputs are treated as regular signals and either connected to another block or connected to a variable. Also, the Boolean logic blocks must be used to handle the individual controller modes.

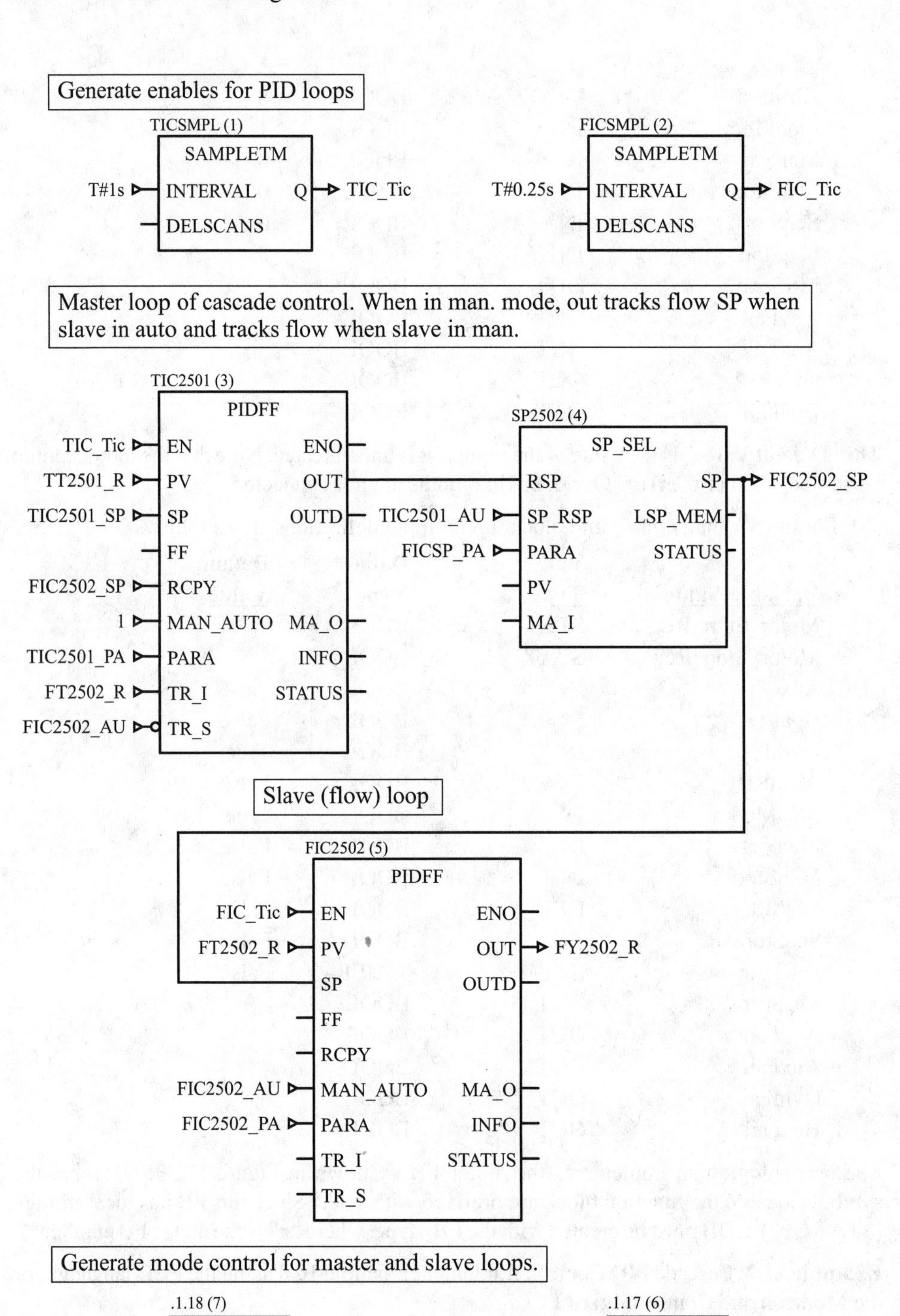

Figure 11.34. Modicon FBD cascade control. *(continued)*

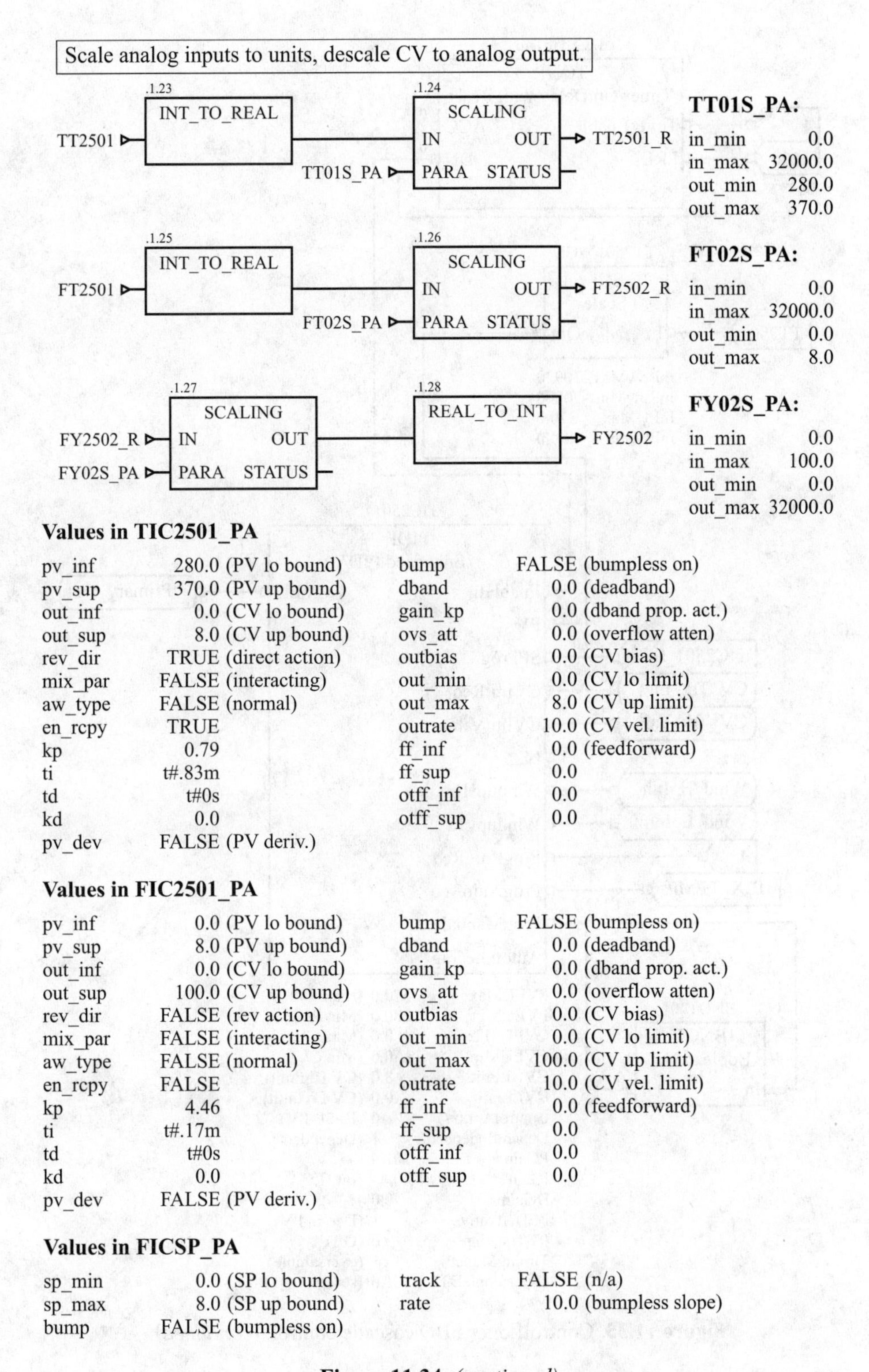

Figure 11.34. *(continued)*

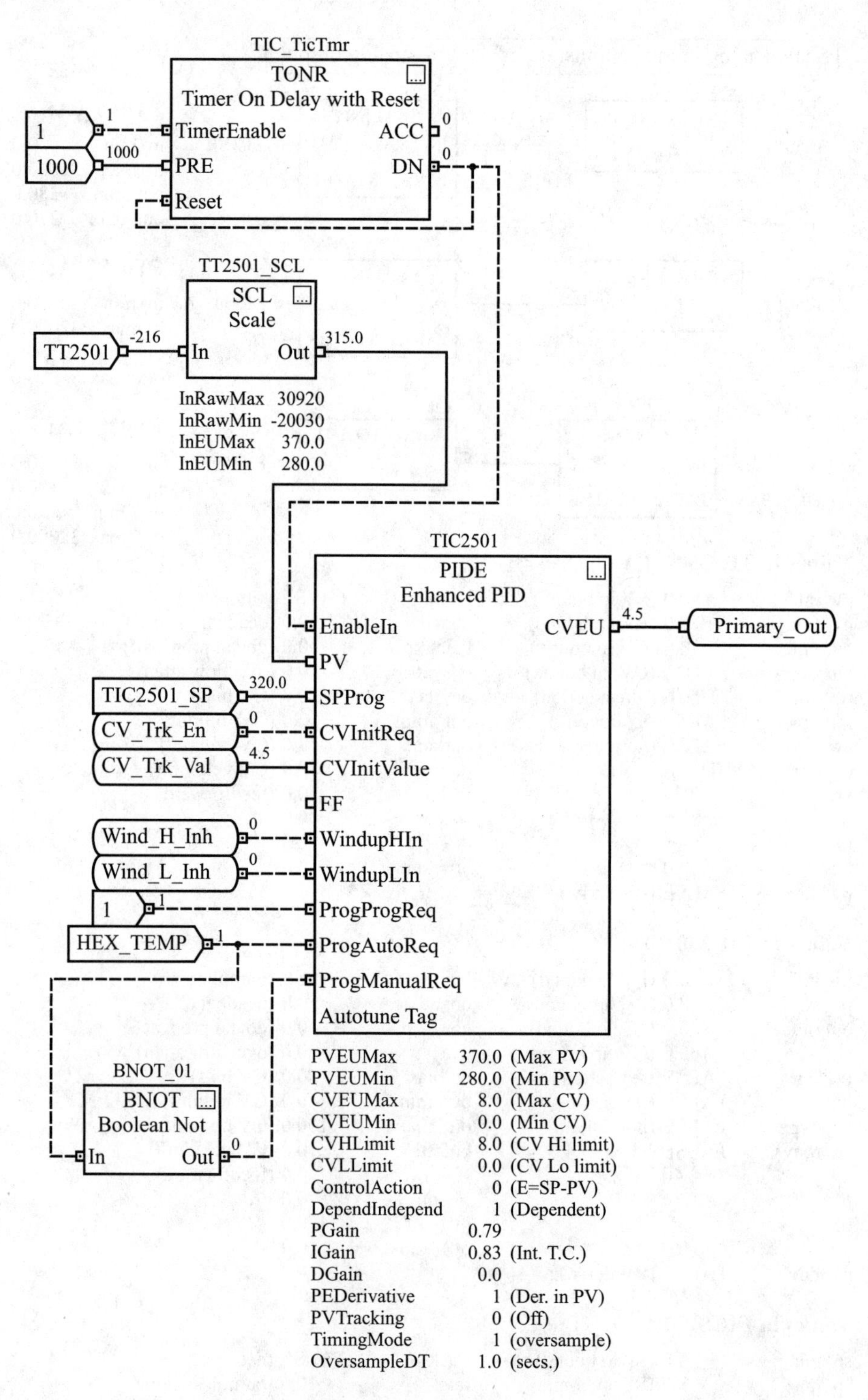

Figure 11.35. ControlLogix FBD cascade control. *(continued)*

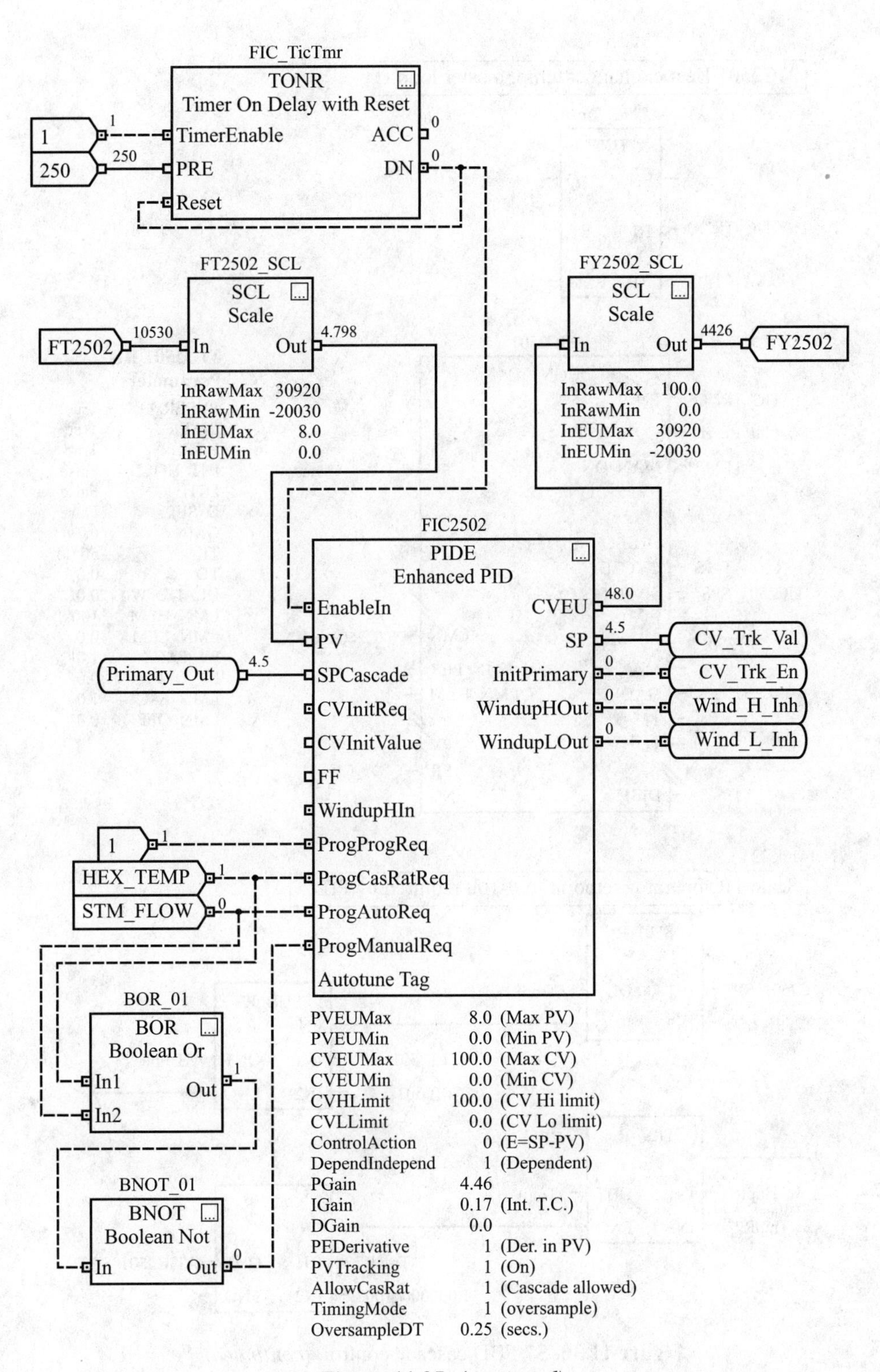

Figure 11.35. *(continued)*

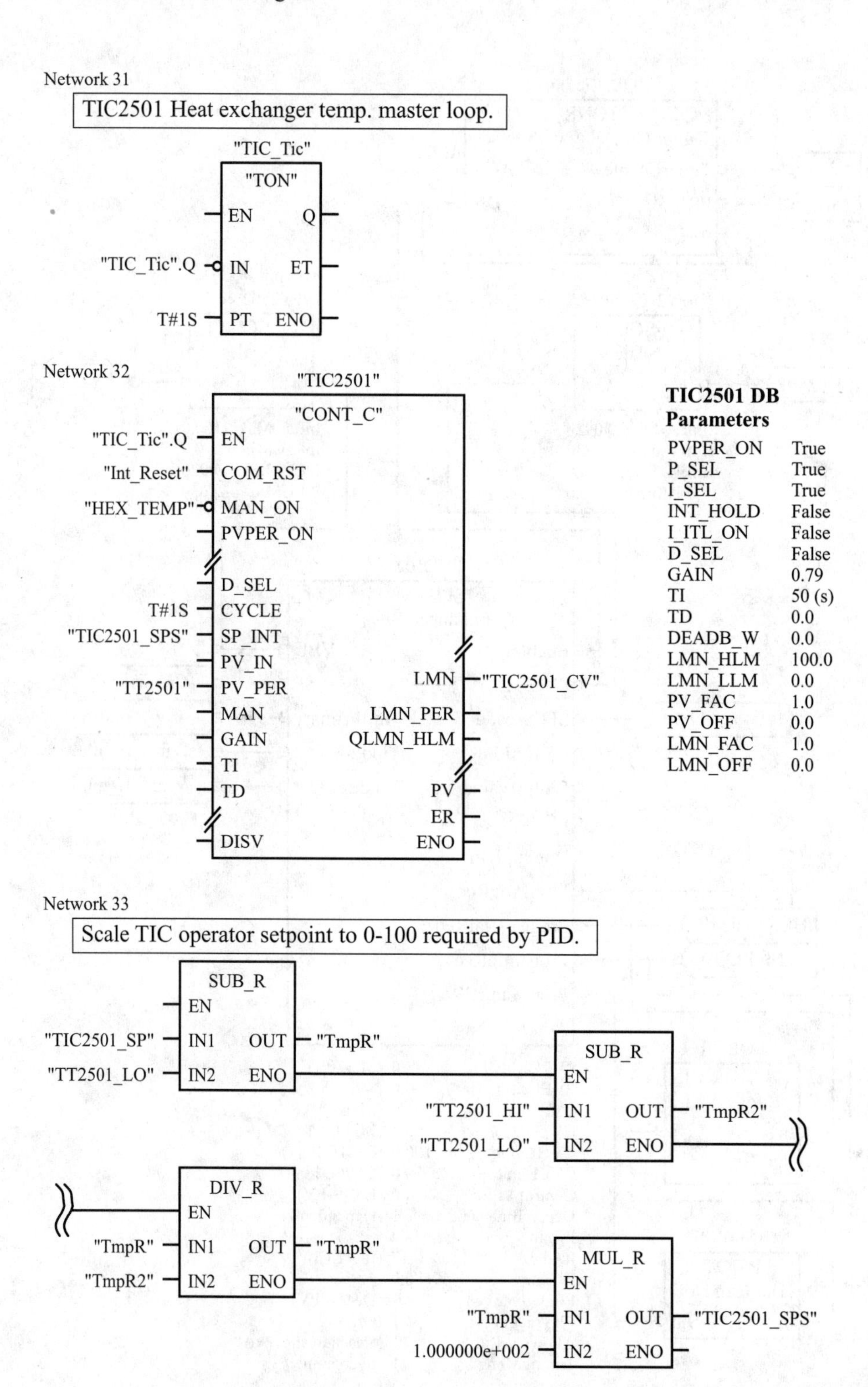

Figure 11.36. S7 FBD cascade control. *(continued)*

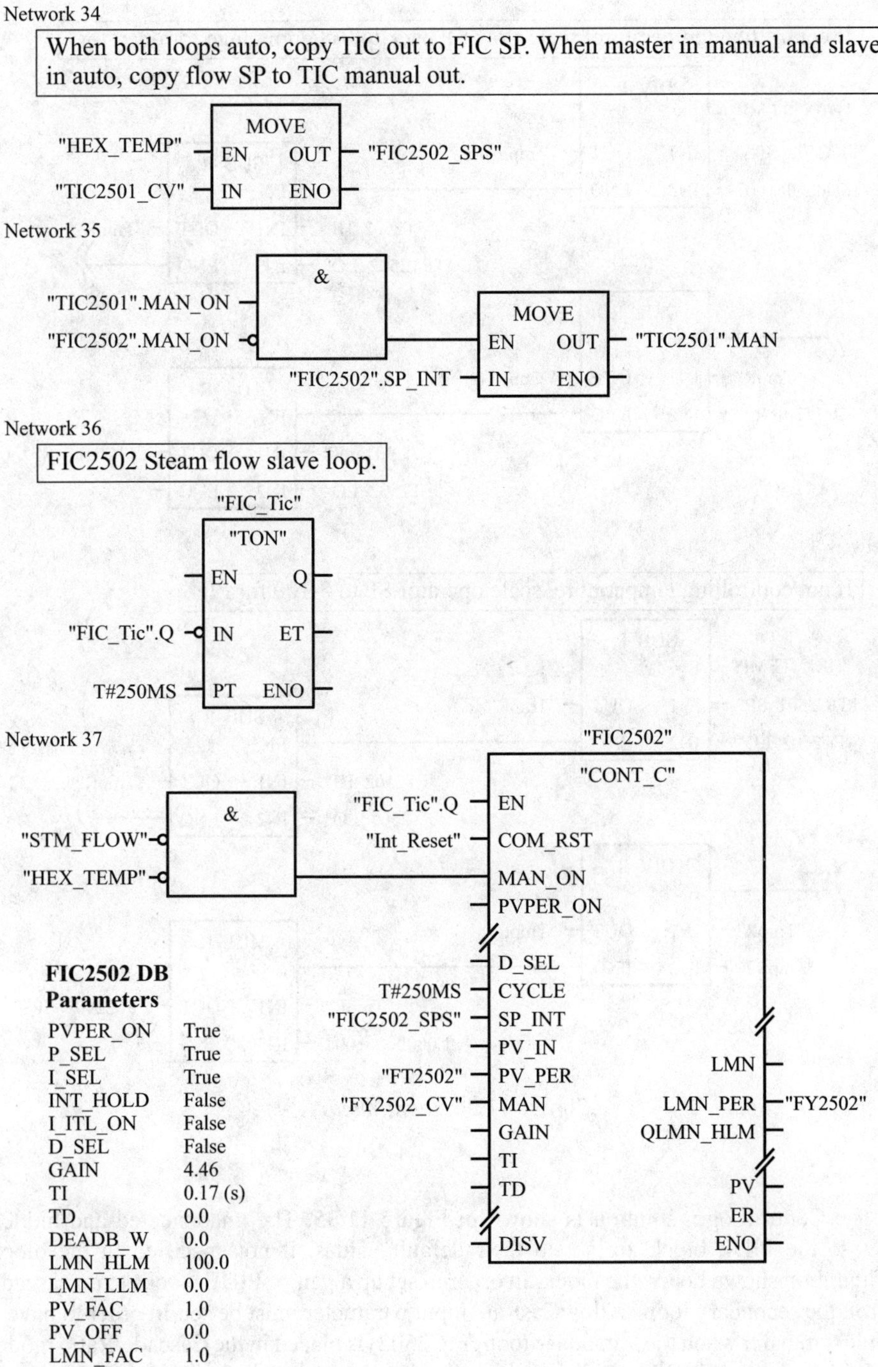

Network 34

When both loops auto, copy TIC out to FIC SP. When master in manual and slave in auto, copy flow SP to TIC manual out.

MOVE: EN = "HEX_TEMP"; IN = "TIC2501_CV"; OUT = "FIC2502_SPS"; ENO

Network 35

& : "TIC2501".MAN_ON; NOT "FIC2502".MAN_ON → MOVE EN; IN = "FIC2502".SP_INT; OUT = "TIC2501".MAN; ENO

Network 36

FIC2502 Steam flow slave loop.

"FIC_Tic" "TON": EN; IN = NOT "FIC_Tic".Q; PT = T#250MS; Q; ET; ENO

Network 37

& : NOT "STM_FLOW"; NOT "HEX_TEMP" → MAN_ON

"FIC2502" "CONT_C": EN = "FIC_Tic".Q; COM_RST = "Int_Reset"; MAN_ON; PVPER_ON; D_SEL; CYCLE = T#250MS; SP_INT = "FIC2502_SPS"; PV_IN; PV_PER = "FT2502"; MAN = "FY2502_CV"; GAIN; TI; TD; DISV; LMN; LMN_PER = "FY2502"; QLMN_HLM; PV; ER; ENO

FIC2502 DB Parameters

PVPER_ON	True
P_SEL	True
I_SEL	True
INT_HOLD	False
I_ITL_ON	False
D_SEL	False
GAIN	4.46
TI	0.17 (s)
TD	0.0
DEADB_W	0.0
LMN_HLM	100.0
LMN_LLM	0.0
PV_FAC	1.0
PV_OFF	0.0
LMN_FAC	1.0
LMN_OFF	0.0

Figure 11.36. *(continued)*

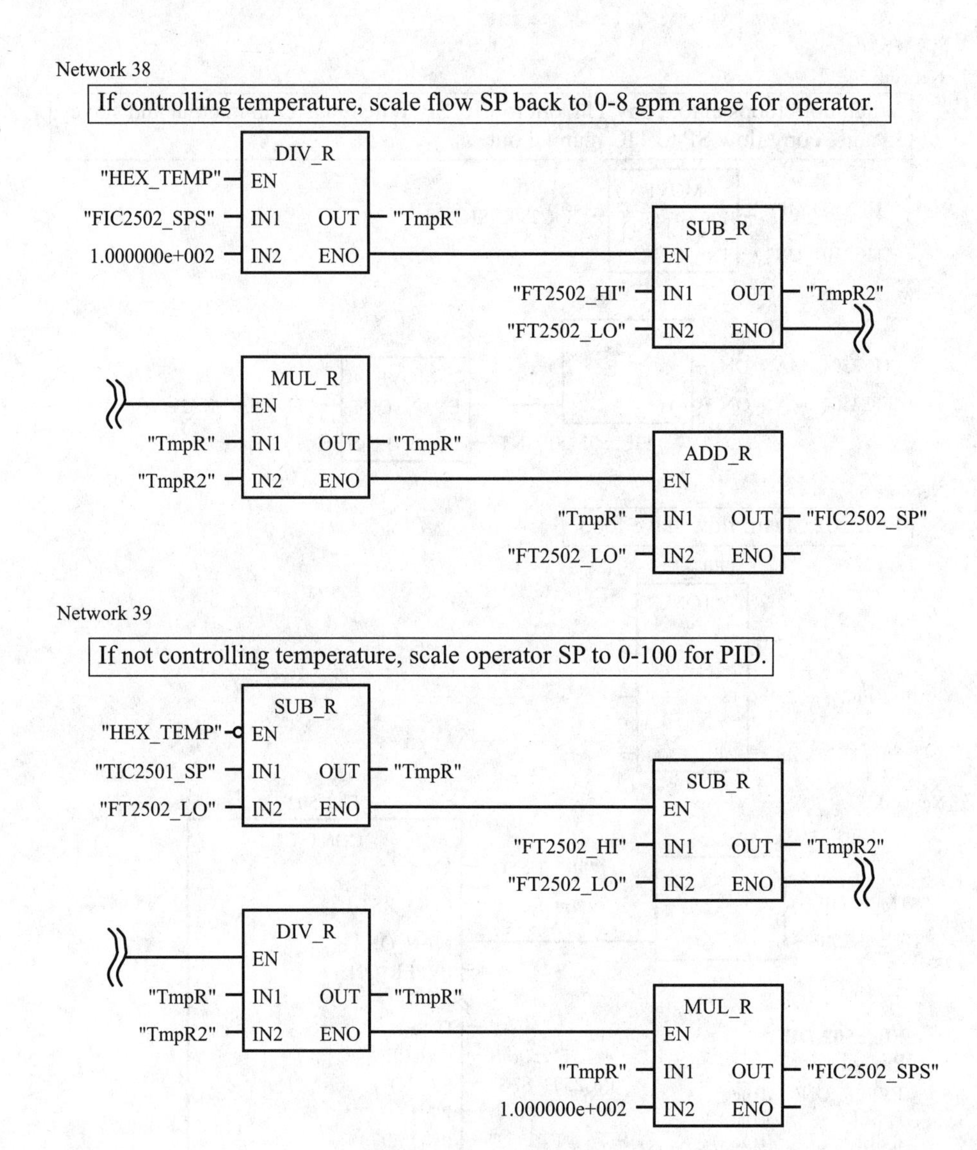

Figure 11.36. *(continued)*

The ControlLogix solution is shown in Figure 11.35. The unconnected and hidden inputs to the PIDE block are set to their default values, if not specified in the block configuration shown below the block. In order to set up a pair of PIDE blocks to do cascade control, the secondary loop "AllowCasRat" input parameter must be set. In order to have a bumpless transfer when the secondary loop (FIC2502) is placed in the Cascade/Ratio mode, the "InitPrimary" and "SP" outputs of the secondary loop are wired into the "CVInitReq" and "CVInitValue" inputs to the primary loop, respectively. Also, "WindupHOut" and "WindupLOut" outputs of the secondary loop are wired to the "WindupHIn" and "WindupLIn" inputs of the primary loop. These two discrete signals prevent primary loop windup if the secondary loop hits a CV limit. Also, note that the "PV Tracking" in the secondary loop is **on** so the secondary loop setpoint tracks the CV when it is in the manual mode. For this particular example, the FBD is one routine in the continuous task and timers are used to execute the loops at their proper sample period.

The S7 solution is shown in Figure 11.36. The unconnected CONT_C inputs are set to their default value specified by the DB parameters. The only two basic differences between this solution and the one with ladder logic (Figure 10.79) are: (1) EN/ENO used only when necessary, (2) ENO is in bottom right corner, and (3) no contacts or coils. Only the EN for the CONT_C and MOVE blocks needs to be retained. The EN for the computation blocks allows one to put the calculation in one network. Any Boolean inputs or output to blocks are treated as regular signals and either connected to another block or connected to a variable. Also, the Boolean logic blocks must be used to handle the individual controller modes.

Example 11.3. Feedforward Control. Implement Example 10.9 using the FBD language for the Modicon and ControlLogix PLCs.

Solution. The Modicon solution is shown in Figure 11.37. The only difference between this solution and the one with ladder logic (Figure 10.82) is the lack of the EN/ENO connections.

Figure 11.38 shows the modifications to the ControlLogix cascade control of Figure 11.35. After scaling and limiting the flow measurement, the feedforward correction is calculated and attached to the "FF" input of the TIC2501 PIDE block. As an alternative to the ADD and MUL blocks, the LDLG block can be used where the "Lead" and "Lag" inputs are both set to zero, "Gain" = 10.29, and "Bias" = -5.0. The only drawback is that the timing mode for the LDLG block must be configured.

The S7 solution is shown in Figure 11.39. The only differences between this solution and the one with ladder logic (Figure 10.84) are the absence of a power rail and the appearance of the connections.

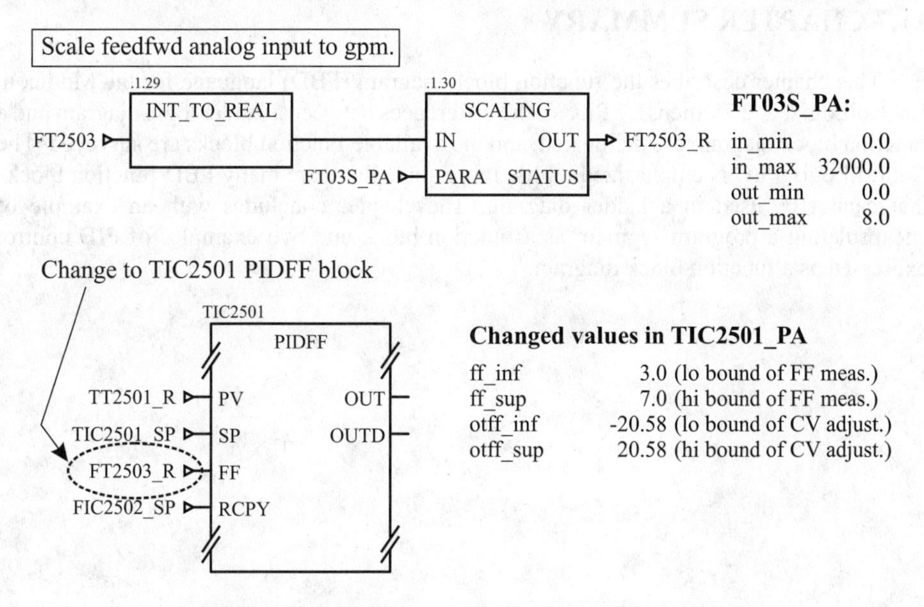

Figure 11.37. Modicon FBD feedforward control.

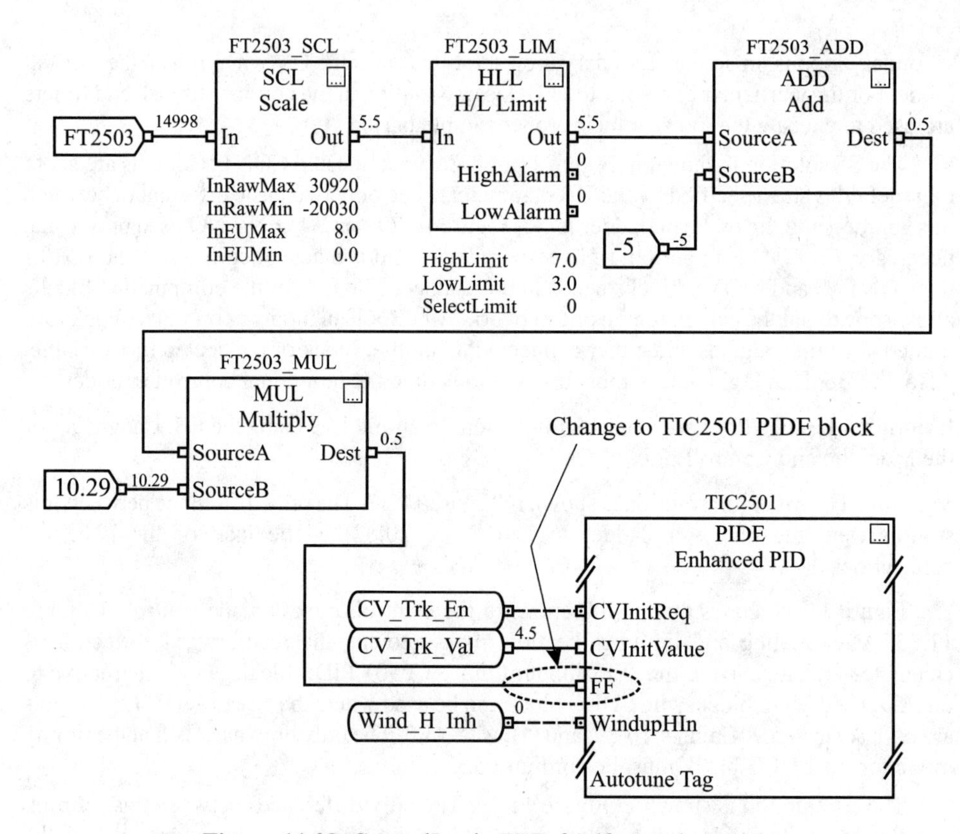

Figure 11.38. ControlLogix FBD feedforward control.

11.7 CHAPTER SUMMARY

This chapter describes the function block diagram (FBD) language for the Modicon, ControlLogix, and Siemens S7 PLCs. The differences between a ladder logic diagram and a function block diagram are delineated, and the available function blocks are surveyed. The ControlLogix PLC is emphasized a little more since there are many FBD function blocks that cannot be used in a ladder diagram. The chapter concludes with an example of encapsulating a program segment as a function block and two examples of PID control expressed as a function block diagram.

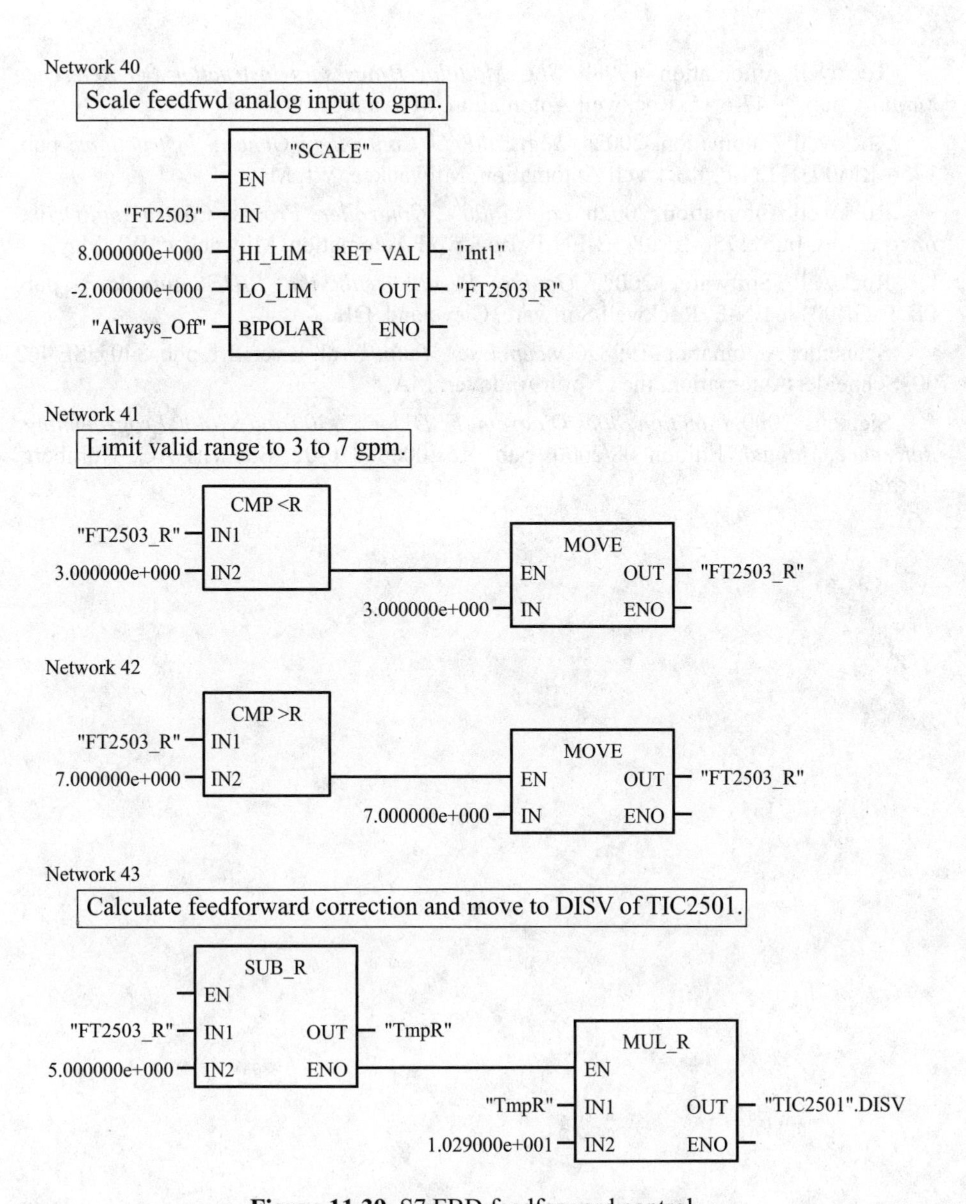

Figure 11.39. S7 FBD feedforward control.

REFERENCES

IEC, 1993. *IEC 1131-3: Programmable Logic Controllers - Part 3: Programming Languages*, International Electrotechnical Commission, Geneva, Switzerland.

Lewis, R. W., 1998. *Programming Industrial Control Systems Using IEC 1131-3*, Revised Ed., The Institution of Electrical Engineers.

Rockwell Automation, 1998a. *PLC-5 Family Instruction Set Reference Manual*, pub. 1785-6.1, Rockwell Automation, Milwaukee, WI.

Rockwell Automation, 1998b. *SLC Modular Processors Instruction Set Reference Manual*, pub. 1747-6.15, Rockwell Automation, Milwaukee, WI.

Rockwell Automation, 2002a. *Logix5000™ Controllers General Instructions*, pub. 1756-RM003F-EN-P, Rockwell Automation, Milwaukee, WI, May.

Rockwell Automation, 2002b. *Logix5000™ Controllers Process Control and Drives Instructions*, pub. 1756-RM006B-EN-P, Rockwell Automation, Milwaukee, WI, May.

Rockwell Software, 2002. *Getting Results with the PIDE Autotuner*, pub. PIDE-GR001A-EN-E, Rockwell Software, Cleveland, OH.

Schneider Automation, 1998. *Concept User Manual,* vol. 1, ver. 2.1, pub. 840 USE 462 00, Schneider Automation, Inc., North Andover, MA.

Siemens, 2000. *Function Block Diagram (FBD) for S7-300 and S7-400 Programming: Reference Manual,* Edition 08/2000, pub. A5E00068870-02, Siemens AG, Nürnberg, Germany.

PROBLEMS

P11-1. Improved Retentive On-delay Timer. Add another input to the RTO function block of Figure 11.1 labeled "Intrvl" and call this improved timer block "RTOI." The "Intvrl" input defines the timing interval, the preset time of the timer that generates the pulses to counter. The "Intrvl" input is a TIME data type.

P11-2. Changes to Motor FB. The motor control FB of Example 11.1 needs to be changed to reflect how it is controlled in manual mode.

The operator panel (Figure P11.2*a*) for manual control shows all of the motor and valve devices in one area of the process. All of the devices in an area share the same Start/Open and Stop/Close commands, activated by the buttons in the lower right of the display. There is also a button that changes the operational mode, which is also shared by all of the devices in the area. To open/close/start/stop a valve/pump device, the operator first changes the mode to manual if it is not already in manual mode. Secondly, the operator presses the "Select" button for the device. Then the operator presses either the "Start/Open" or "Stop/Close" buttons to command the device.

Two more inputs need to be provided to the standard motor block, shown in P11.2*b* or P11.2*c* (depending on the PLC being used for implementation). These two inputs are described as follows:

SelctDev – The selected motor to be started/stopped
ThisDev – The constant representing this motor

Every device in the area has a unique integer that is used to identify it for manual control. For the display in Figure P11.2*a*, some example device integers are:

Device	ID Integer
P-2170	1
P-2171	2
P-2172	3
P-2173	4
XV2174	11
XV2175	12

For a particular motor FB the "ThisDev" input is the ID integer constant for that motor. For example, the motor FB used to control the P-2172 motor has the "ThisDev" input set to 3.

When the "Select" button for a particular device is pressed on the screen, the "ReacA_Sel_Device" variable in the PLC is set to the appropriate ID integer for that valve/pump. For example, if the operator presses the P-2171 "Select" button, the "ReacA_Sel_Device" in the PLC is set to 2. The "ReacA _Sel_Device" is connected to the "SelctDev" input of all the devices in the area.

When the "Start/Open" button is pressed, the "ReacA _Man_DevStart" bit is turned **on**. When the "Stop/Close" button is pressed, the "ReacA _Man_DevStop" bit is turned **on**. The "ReacA _Man_DevStart" is connected to the "ManStrt" input of all the motors in the area. The "ReacA _Man_DevStop" is connected to the "ManStop" input of all the motors in the area.

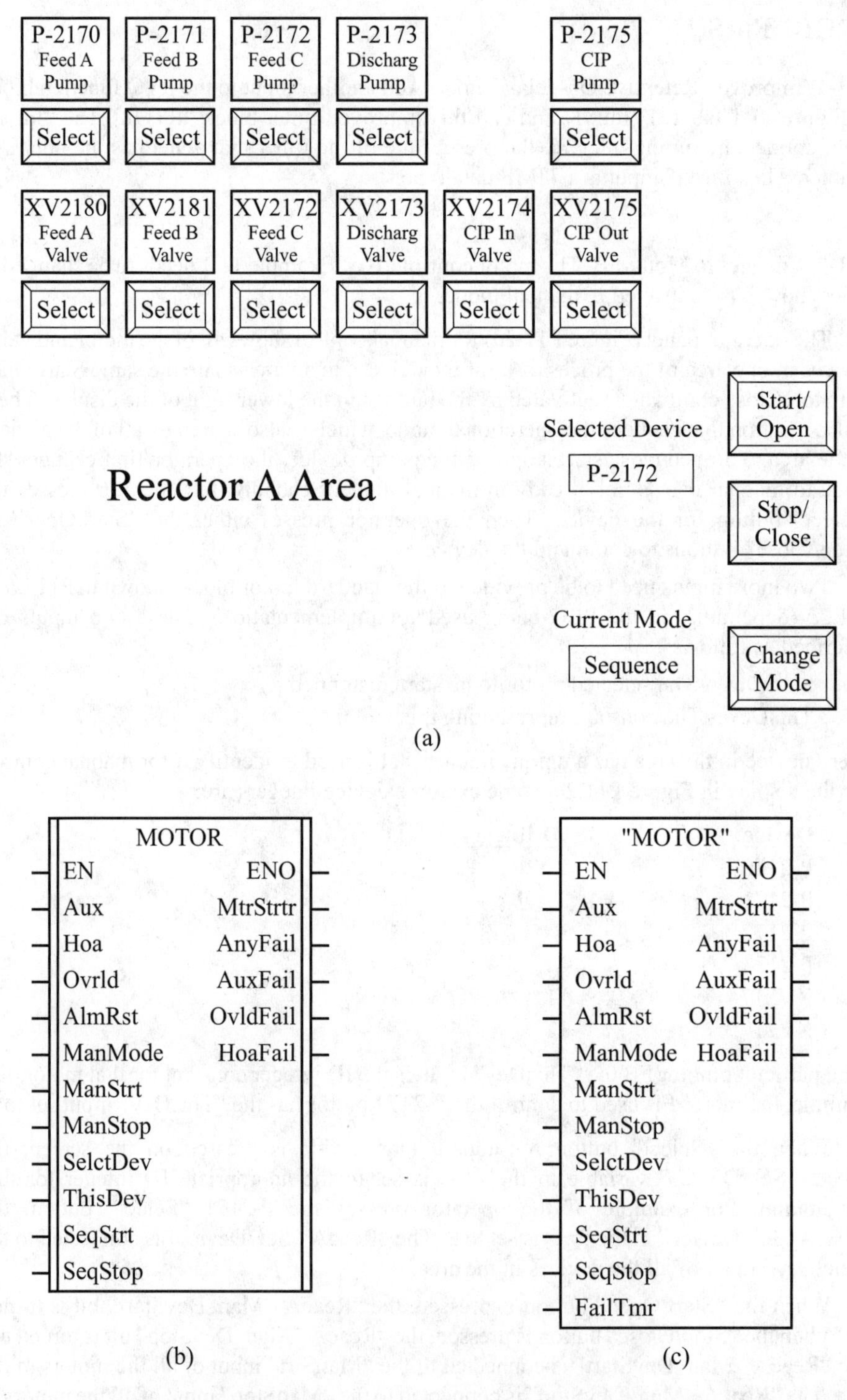

Figure P11.2. Area device operator control: *(a)* operator display; *(b)* modified Modicon motor control DFB; *(c)* modified S7 motor control FB.

P11-3. Discrete Valve Control Function Block. Program a function block (Modicon DFB or S7 FB) called "VALVE" to handle discrete (on/off control) valves. The specifications follow and are similar to the specifications for the motor control function block of Example 11.1.

The block controls a valve through a discrete output. There is no Hand-Off-Auto switch as for the motor control. The block operates in two modes: manual and automatic. When in the manual mode, the valve is opened and closed with the "ManOpen" and "ManClos" inputs. When in the automatic mode, the valve is controlled by "SeqOpen" and "SeqClos" commands. In the automatic mode, the valve is controlled by sequences. When switching between the two modes, the valve control discrete output should not change.

The open and close commands should be considered momentary. That is, once the valve has been commanded to open, the valve solenoid should be latched **on** and remain **on** until a close command unlatches the valve solenoid.

Each valve has two limit switches that indicate the state of the valve: (1) Open limit switch, (2) Close limit switch. The block must monitor for the following faults:

Both limit switches **off** for 10 seconds.
Both limit switches **on** for 10 seconds.
Valve commanded to open and open limit switch **off** after 10 seconds.
Valve commanded to close and close limit switch **off** after 10 seconds.

The faults are reported with three indications:

Any fault (**on** when any of the above 4 faults are detected).
"Fail to Open" – Valve commanded to open and any fault detected.
"Fail to Close" – Valve commanded to close and any fault detected.

The "Fail to Open" and "Fail to Close" faults must be latched when they occur. An "alarm reset" input must be provided that when **on**, resets the "Fail to Open" and "Fail to Close" fault indications. When any fault indication is **on**, the discrete output to the valve solenoid **should not be changed**.

The connections to the valve control block are shown in Figure P11.3, and are explained as follows:

OpenLS – Connected to limit switch that is **on** when valve is open.
ClsdLS – Connected to limit switch that is **on** when valve is closed.
AlmRst – **On** to clear FailTOpn and FailTCls failure indications.
ManMode – **On** for manual mode; **off** for automatic mode.
ManOpen – **On** to open valve when in manual mode; ignored in automatic mode.
ManClos – **On** to close valve when in manual mode; ignored in automatic mode.
SeqOpen – **On** to open valve when in automatic mode; ignored in manual mode.
SeqClos – **On** to close valve when in automatic mode; ignored in manual mode.
FailTmr – Timer for failure checking (S7 only); of type TIMER.
VlvSol – Command to valve solenoid; **on** to open valve; **off** to close valve.
AnyFail – **On** when FailTOpn or FailTCls is **on**.
FailTOpn – **On** when one of 4 faults detected when valve has been commanded to open.
FailTCls – **On** when one of 4 faults detected when valve has been commanded to close.

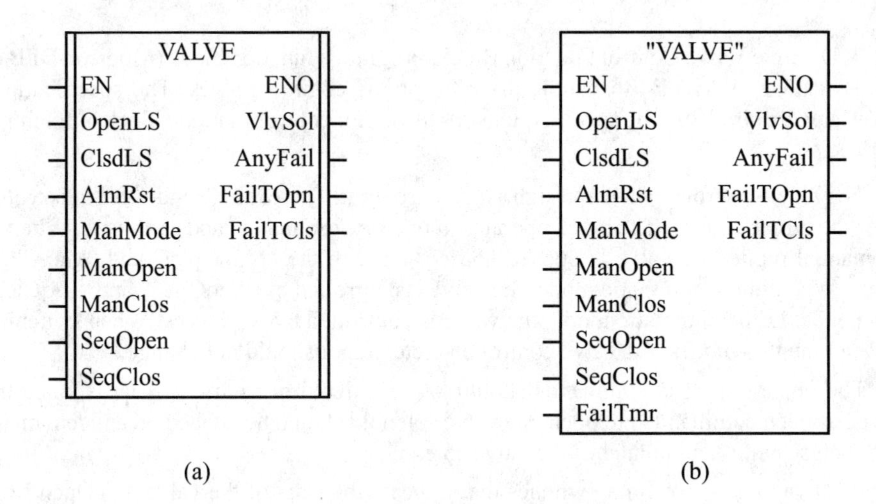

Figure P11.3. Valve control function block: *(a)* Modicon DFB; *(b)* S7 FB.

P11-4. Changes to Valve FB. Change the valve control FB of problem P11-3 in a similar manner to how the motor control FB is changed in problem P11-2.

The operator panel (Figure P11.2*a*) for manual control shows all of the motor and valve devices in one area of the process. All of the devices in an area share the same Start/Open and Stop/Close commands, activated by the buttons in the lower right of the display. There is also a button that changes the operational mode, which is also shared by all of the devices in the area. To open/close/start/stop a valve/pump device, the operator first changes the mode to manual if it is not already in manual mode. Secondly, the operator presses the "Select" button for the device. Then the operator presses either the "Start/Open" or "Stop/Close" buttons to command the device.

Two more inputs need to be provided to the standard valve block, shown in Figure P11.4. These two inputs are described as follows:

SelctDev – The selected valve to be opened/closed

ThisDev – The constant representing this valve

Every device in the area has a unique integer that is used to identify it for manual control. For the display in Figure P11.2*a*, some example device integers are:

Device	ID Integer
P-2170	1
P-2171	2
P-2172	3
P-2173	4
XV2174	11
XV2175	12

For a particular valve FB the "ThisDev" input is the ID integer constant for that valve. For example, the valve FB used to control the XV2174 valve has the "ThisDev" input set to 11.

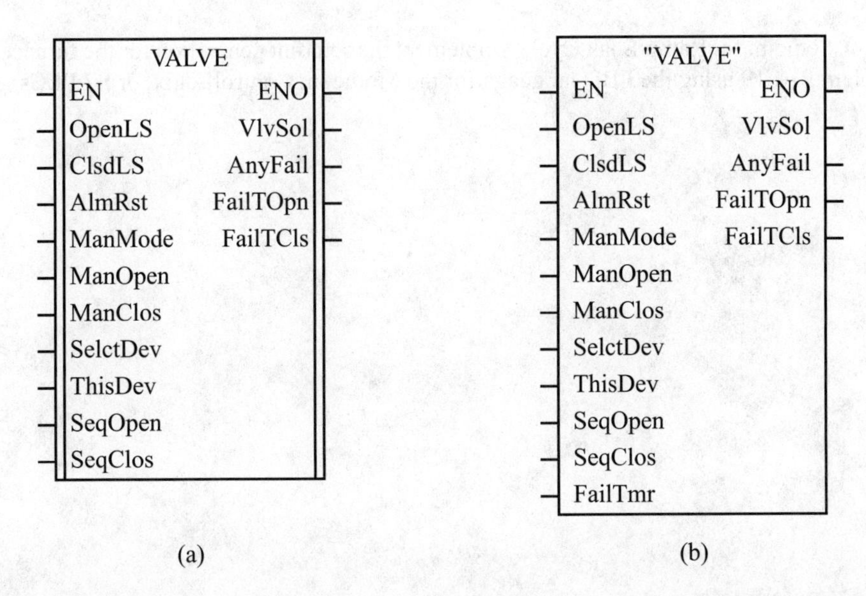

Figure P11.4. Modified valve control function block: *(a)* Modicon DFB; *(b)* S7 FB.

When the "Select" button for a particular device is pressed on the screen, the "ReacA_Sel_Device" variable in the PLC is set to the appropriate ID integer for that valve/pump. For example, if the operator presses the XV2175 "Select" button, the "ReacA_Sel_Device" in the PLC is set to 12. The "ReacA _Sel_Device" is connected to the "SelctDev" input of all the devices in the area.

When the "Start/Open" button is pressed, the "ReacA _Man_DevStart" bit is turned **on**. When the "Stop/Close" button is pressed, the "ReacA_Man_DevStop" bit is turned **on**. The "ReacA _Man_DevStart" is connected to the "ManOpen" input of all the valves in the area. The "ReacA _Man_DevStop" is connected to the "ManClos" input of all the valves in the area.

P11-5. Split-range Control of pH. Implement the split-range control of problem P10-15 using the FBD language for the Modicon, ControlLogix, or S7 PLCs.

P11-6. Split-range Control of pH With Cascade. Implement the split-range control of problem P10-16 using the FBD language for the Modicon, ControlLogix, or S7 PLCs.

P11-7. Split-range Control of Reactor Jacket. Implement the split-range control of problem P10-17 using the FBD language for the Modicon, ControlLogix, or S7 PLCs.

P11-8. Override Control for Peak Shaving System. Implement the override control of problem P10-18 using the FBD language for the Modicon, ControlLogix, or S7 PLCs.

P11-9. Setpoint for Ramp/Soak Cycle. Implement the setpoint generation for the furnace of problem P10-19 using the FBD language for the Modicon, ControlLogix, or S7 PLCs.

12 Structured Text

Chapter Topics:

- Structured text language
- Structured text applications

OBJECTIVES

Upon completion of this chapter, you will be able to:

- Understand the structured text language.
- Use the structured text language in applications.

Scenario: BCD-to-integer conversion for Modicon.

The Modicon Concept software does not include a BCD-to-integer converter function block. Program a DFB to do this function.

Solution: The inputs and outputs of the BCD_INT DFB are shown in Figure 12.1. The variable and block input/output definitions are as follows:

Variable Name	**Var. Type**	**Data Type**
dig	VAR	INT
djunkin	VAR	DINT
errflg	VAR	BOOL
i	VAR	INT
mult	VAR	INT
In_BCD	IN	WORD
Out_Int	OUT	INT

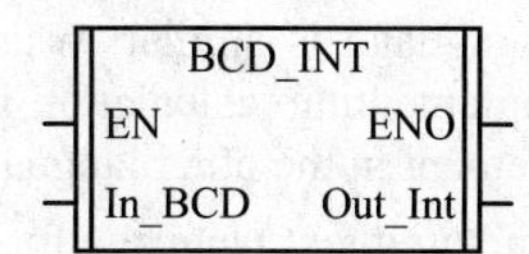

Figure 12.1. BCD-to-integer conversion function block.

The structured text code to implement this function block is shown below.

```
(*  BCD to integer conversion. Converts the WORD in In_BCD
    to INT Out_Int.  If any digit is greater than 9, then
    the result integer is set to zero. Variables:
      djunkin DINT  holds BCD number while being converted.
                     must be DINT in order to handle word > 32,767
                     which will happen if thousands digit > 7.
      dig     INT   current digit
      mult    INT   digit multiplier to put it in result
      i       INT   iteration counter to process 3 digits.
      errflg  BOOL  set when digit greater than 9 detected.

    Conversion uses the MOD operation to strip each digit and
    multiply it by the multiplier and add it to the intermediate
    result. The BCD number is shifted right 4 positions and
    the operation is repeated.    *)

djunkin := WORD_TO_DINT(In_BCD);
mult := 1;
Out_Int := 0;
errflg  := FALSE;
FOR i := 1 TO 3 DO
  dig := DINT_TO_INT(djunkin MOD 16);
  IF dig > 9 THEN
     errflg := TRUE;
  END_IF;
  Out_Int := Out_Int + dig*mult;
  djunkin := djunkin / 16;
  mult := mult * 10;
END_FOR;

(* djunkin has most sig digit *)
IF djunkin > 9 THEN
  errflg := TRUE;
END_IF;

IF errflg THEN
  Out_Int := 0;
ELSE
  Out_Int := Out_Int + DINT_TO_INT(djunkin) * mult;
END_IF;
```

12.1 INTRODUCTION

The structured text (ST) language is one of the two textual PLC programming languages, the other being instruction list. Of the two, ST is the easiest to troubleshoot and understand. The instruction list language is similar to assembly language. In general, structured text is useful for implementing calculation-intensive functions and other functions that are difficult to implement in the other languages.

This chapter describes the structured text language for the PLCs covered by this text. The SLC-500 and GE Fanuc PLCs do not support the ST programming language. Most ST implementations closely follow the IEC 61131-3 standard. Hence, this chapter is organized differently than most of the other chapters. The next section describes the IEC 61131-3 structured text. Subsequent sections describe the differences between the ST language for a particular PLC and the IEC 61131-3 standard. Following these descriptions, examples are used to illustrate ST applications.

12.2 IEC 61131-3 STRUCTURED TEXT

The structured text (ST) language defined by the IEC 61131-3 standard is a high-level language whose syntax appears similar to Pascal. The ST language has a complete set of constructs to handle variable assignment, conditional statements, iteration, and function block calling.

Structured text statements are written in a fairly free style. Statements must close with a semicolon, though a line may contain multiple statements (separated by semicolons). A lone semicolon character indicates an empty statement. The normal space character between keywords and identifiers can be replaced by a tab, end-of-line, or comment. Comments begin with the "(*" character string and end with the "*)" character string.

The IEC 61131-3 standard does not include variable declarations as part of the ST language. However, some vendors allow variable declarations as part of the ST program and so that syntax is also described here.

12.2.1 Variables and Data Types

The symbolic name (identifier) of a variable can be any string of letters, digits, and underlines provided that:

1. The first character is not a digit.
2. There are not two or more consecutive underline characters.

There is no distinction between upper and lower case. The symbolic name must be unique throughout the entire program. Any variables local to a FB are not subject to this rule. The standard states that the first six characters of an identifier should be unique. Most vendors do not enforce this restriction, though the number of characters in an identifier may be limited. If developing software that must be ported to multiple vendors, one should make sure the first six characters are unique.

The elementary variable types are as listed in Table 12.1. Structured and array variable types are also possible. Variables defined as part of a ST program or function block are declared using the VAR keyword. For example,

```
VAR
      Serial_Num: UDINT;
      Up_Time:    TIME;
END_VAR
```

Direct physical PLC addresses are represented by "%" followed by two letters, defined as in Table 12.2. Example direct addresses are:

```
%I14        (* Input bit 14 *)
%IX20       (* Input bit 20 *)
%IW41       (* Input word 41 *)
%Q23        (* Output bit 23 *)
%QB85       (* Output byte 85 *)
%MW102      (* Internal memory word 102 *)
```

Table 12.1 Elementary Data Types

Name	Description	Range of Values
BOOL	1-bit Boolean	0=cleared, 1=set
BYTE	8-bit	0 to FF hexadecimal
WORD	16-bit	0 to FFFF hexadecimal
SINT	1-byte integer	–128 to 127
USINT	1-byte integer	0 to 255
INT	2-byte integer	–32,768 to 32,767
UINT	2-byte integer	0 to 65,535
DINT	4-byte integer	-2^{31} to $2^{31}-1$
UDINT	4-byte integer	0 to $2^{32}-1$
LINT	8-byte integer	-2^{63} to $2^{63}-1$
ULINT	8-byte integer	0 to $2^{64}-1$
REAL	4-byte float. pt.	$\pm 8.4310^{37}$ to $\pm 3.3610^{+38}$
LREAL	8-byte float. pt.	$\pm 10^{\pm 308}$
TIME	4-byte	0 to $2^{32}-1$milliseconds (>49 days)

Table 12.2 Directly Represented Variable Codes

First letter	Interpretation
I	Input channel (discrete or analog)
Q	Output channel (discrete or analog)
M	Internal memory
Second letter	**Interpretation**
none	Boolean (bit)
X	Boolean (bit)
B	Byte (8 bits)
W	Word (16 bits)
D	Double word (32 bits)
L	Long word (64 bits)

The AT keyword is used to fix the PLC memory location for a particular variable. The AT keyword can only be used with global variables and are not for variables local to a function block. Some example uses are:

```
VAR
      ANA_INS AT %IW1: ARRAY[1..8] OF INT;
      DIG_OUTS AT %QX101: ARRAY[1..16] OF BOOL;
END_VAR
```

12.2.2 Assignment Statements

An assignment statement changes the value stored in a variable. The assignment operator is ":=", and an example statement is:

```
C := A;
```

In the above statement, the contents of C are replaced by the value of A. Both A and C are the same data type. The variable A in the above statement can be replaced by a literal (constant) or an expression.

Structured text has strong type-checking. The assignment above is only valid if A and C are the same data type. If A is not the same type as C, then a type conversion function must be used to convert A to the proper data type.

Whether the assignment operator is retentive or non-retentive depends on the PLC vendor. For a retentive assignment, the destination of the assignment keeps its value when the PLC does a warm start (e.g., change to run mode). For a non-retentive assignment, the destination is set to zero when the PLC does a warm start.

12.2.3 Expressions

An expression consists of operands and operators. An operand is a literal, a variable, a structured variable, a component of a structured variable, a function call, or a direct address. An operator is the symbol for an arithmetic or logic operation. The standard operators are listed in Table 12.3. Some examples of operator usage:

```
Real_Power := Volt * Current * PF;
Circle_Area := PI * Rad ** 2.0;
PV_Alarm := ( FIC_101.PV >= High_Flow_AlmVal );
Stat := ( (TW_Switch2 AND TW_Digit3) = TW_Switch5 );
```

Expressions are evaluated in the order dictated by the precedence of the operators (Table 12.3). Parenthesized parts of the expression have the highest priority, followed by function calls, and then by the arithmetic and logic operators. Operators of the highest precedence are evaluated first, followed by lower precedence operators, down to the lowest precedence. If the operators in an expression have the same precedence, they are evaluated from left to right. For example, consider the following assignment statement:

```
DTmp := Fs*rho*Cs*(Tso-Tsexit)**1.2*FFact;
```

The expression is evaluated in the following order (intermediate results are indicated by R*x*):

1. Tso - Tsexit ⇒ R1
2. R1 ** 1.2 ⇒ R2
3. Fs * rho ⇒ R3
4. R3 * Cs ⇒ R4
5. R4 * R2 ⇒ R5
6. R5 * FFact ⇒ DTmp

Table 12.3 Structured Text Operators

Operator	Description	Precedence
( )	Parentheses around expression	1 (highest)
FUNCNAME(parameter list)	Function call	2
**	Exponentiation (raising to a power)	3
–	Negation	4
NOT	Boolean complement	4
*, /	Multiplication, Division	5
MOD	Modulus operation	5
+, –	Addition, subtraction	6
<, >, <=, >=	Comparison	7
=, <>	Equality, Inequality	8
&, AND	Boolean AND	9
XOR	Boolean exclusive OR	10
OR	Boolean inclusive OR	11 (lowest)

12.2.4 Calling Functions and Function Blocks

In structured text, there is a distinction between functions and function blocks. A *function* yields exactly one data element and has no internal state information. Multiple calls to the same function with the same input parameter values will always yield the same output values. A function appears on a ladder logic diagram as a block, but with only one, unnamed output. All comparison, all data type conversion, and most arithmetic operations are classified as functions. In contrast, a *function block* has an associated algorithm and embedded data and named outputs. Multiple calls to the same function block may yield different results. All timers, counters, and DFBs are function blocks.

In order to use a function block in ST, an instance of the function block must be declared in the ST program. A function can be used without being declared.

A function can be executed by calling the function name with suitable input parameter values and placing the result in a variable. If parameters are not supplied, then default values are used. The general form of executing a function is

```
Out:=FName(InPara1:=Value1, InPara2:=Value2, . . .);
```

As an example, the ladder logic in Figure 12.2*a* can be done in ST with the statement in Figure 12.2*b*. In this case, the order of the parameters is not significant. If the input parameters are listed in the same order as the connections to the function block, then the names do not need to be listed. This format is used in Figure 12.2*c*. If the LIMIT block is called without specifying the MN and MX parameters, then the default values will be used. For example,

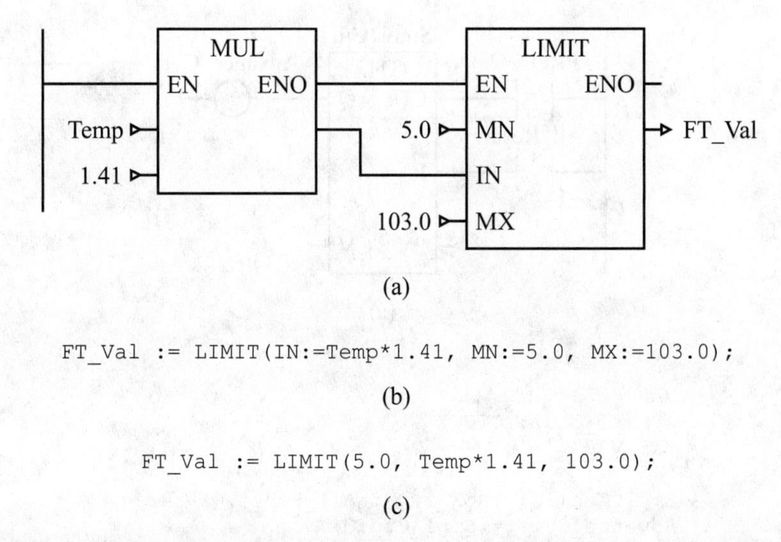

(a)

```
FT_Val := LIMIT(IN:=Temp*1.41, MN:=5.0, MX:=103.0);
```

(b)

```
FT_Val := LIMIT(5.0, Temp*1.41, 103.0);
```

(c)

Figure 12.2. Example functions: *(a)* ladder logic; *(b)* equivalent ST naming parameters; *(c)* equivalent ST without parameter names.

```
LT_Val := LIMIT(IN:=Temp2);
```

The LT_Val result is zero (assuming the default MN and MX limits are zero).

A function block is executed by calling the function block name with suitable input parameter values. If parameters are not supplied, then the input parameters from the last invocation are used. If the function block has not been executed yet, any input parameters that are not supplied will take default values (usually zero). The general form of executing a function block is

```
FBName(InPara1:= Value1, InPara2:=Value2, . . .);
```

assuming that FBName has been declared (using VAR…END_VAR). Invoking a function block does not return a value. The outputs must be referenced in subsequent statements. As an example, a CTU ladder logic rung is shown in Figure 12.3*a* and the ST equivalent is shown in Figure 12.3*b*. Note that the Q counter output is assigned to Advance_Cyl in the last statement.

12.2.5 Conditional Statements

Conditional statements allow selected statements to be executed when certain conditions are true. The two types of conditional statements are (1) IF … THEN … ELSE and (2) CASE.

The general form of an IF … THEN … ELSE statement is:

```
IF <Boolean expression> THEN
  <statements>
ELSE
  <statements>
END_IF;
```

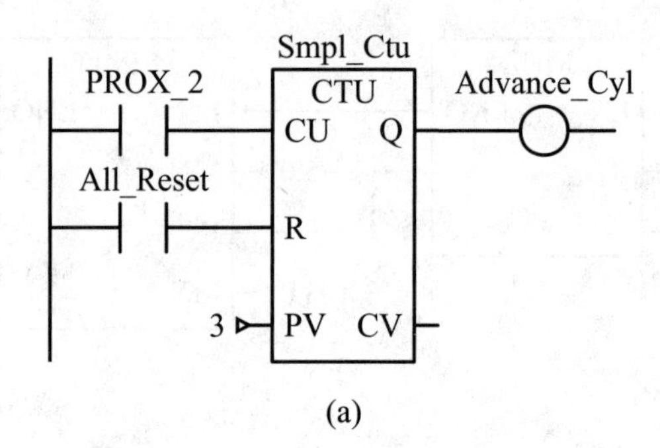

(a)

```
VAR
   Smpl_Ctu : CTU;
END_VAR

Smpl_Ctu(CU:=PROX_2, R:=All_Reset, PV:=3);
Advance_Cyl := Smpl_Ctu.Q;
```

(b)

Figure 12.3. Sample counter function block: *(a)* ladder logic; *(b)* equivalent ST.

The <Boolean expression> is any expression that returns a true or false Boolean result. It can be a single Boolean variable or a complex expression involving many variables and comparison operations. If the <Boolean expression> is true, the statements between THEN and ELSE are executed. Otherwise the statements between ELSE and END_IF are executed. If there is no need for an ELSE, the IF … THEN statement is:

```
IF <Boolean expression> THEN
  <statements>
END_IF;
```

Since the IF … THEN … ELSE construct is a statement, they can be nested within other conditional statements. Some example IF…THEN…ELSE statements follow.

```
IF Position > 0.0 THEN
  Correction := SIN( Position);
END_IF;

IF (Var1 >= 5.0) AND (Var1 < 45.0) AND (Var2 <= 100.0) THEN
  ALM := TRUE;
ELSE
  ALM := FALSE;
END_IF;

LT1000_LOALM := FALSE;
LT1000_LOLOALM := FALSE;
LT1000_HIALM := FALSE;
LT1000_HIHIALM := FALSE;
IF LT1000 >= HiLevel THEN
  IF LT1000 < HiHiLevel THEN
    LT1000_HIALM := TRUE;
```

```
    ELSE
      LT1000_HIHIALM := TRUE;
    END_IF;
  ELSE
    IF LT1000 <= LoLevel THEN
      IF LT1000 > LoLoLevel THEN
        LT1000_LOALM := TRUE;
      ELSE
        LT1000_LOLOALM := TRUE;
      END_IF;
    END_IF;
  END_IF;
```

If there are multiple ELSE conditions, then ELSIF … THEN … ELSE can be used as follows:

```
IF <Boolean expression> THEN
  <statements>
ELSIF <Boolean expression> THEN
  <statements>
ELSIF <Boolean expression> THEN
  <statements>
ELSE
  <statements>
END_IF;
```

The CASE conditional construct allows selected statements to be executed depending on the value of an INT integer:

```
CASE <integer expression> OF
  <case list 1>: <statements>
  <case list 2>: <statements>
  <case list 3>: <statements>
ELSE
  <statements>
END_CASE;
```

The <integer expression> result must be an INT data type. The set of statements that have a <case list> value that matches the value of the <integer expression> is executed. If no match is found, the statements after the "ELSE" are executed. The "ELSE <statements>" part of the construct is optional, but recommended. Each <case list> can be a single value, several values, or a range of values:

```
2:          (* single value: 2 *)
1,3,7:      (* three values: 1, 3 and 7 *)
10..20:     (* range of values: 10 to 20 inclusive *)
```

As an example, the following CASE statement sets recipe parameters.

```
CASE Recipe_Num OF
  1:    IngA_Amount := 35.2;
        IngB_Amount := 56.9;
        Mix_Tempera := 182.0;
  2:    IngA_Amount := 30.0;
        IngB_Amount := 62.3;
        Mix_Tempera := 194.0;
  3..4: IngA_Amount := 29.4;
        IngB_Amount := 47.2;
```

```
        Mix_Tempera := 175.0;
ELSE
  Illegal_Recipe := 1;
END_CASE;
```

12.2.6 Iteration Statements

Iteration statements allow selected statements to be repeatedly executed depending on the state of a variable or condition. When using iteration statements, one should avoid situations that result in infinite loops. The three types of iteration statements are (1) FOR … DO, (2) WHILE … DO, and (3) REPEAT … UNTIL. An EXIT statement is provided for all of these iteration statements to allow a premature exit from the loop.

The FOR … DO construct allows a set of statements to be repeated depending on the value of an integer iteration variable. The general form is:

```
FOR <integer variable> := <initial value exp.>
  TO <final value exp.> BY <increment> DO
    <statements>
END_FOR;
```

Basically, the <integer variable> is initially set to the <initial value exp.>, the loop statements are executed, and the <integer variable> is changed by the <increment>. If the <final value exp.> has not been reached, then the loop statements are repeated. In reality, the <integer variable> is checked against the <final value exp.> before executing the loop statements. Therefore, it is possible that no loop statements are executed. The <initial value exp.>, <final value exp.>, and <increment> can be constants or integer expressions and should not be modified by any statement in the loop. Iterations can be counted up or down, depending on the sign of <increment>. If "BY <increment>" is omitted, the iteration variable increases by one.

```
FOR i := 0 TO FIFOSize-1 DO
    Conv1Part[i] := 0;
END_FOR;
FOR i := Max TO 1 BY -1 DO
    Shift[i] := Shift[i-1];
END_FOR;
```

The WHILE … DO construct allows a set of statements to be repeated while a Boolean expression is true. The Boolean expression is tested before executing the loop statements. If false, the loop statements are not executed. Therefore, it is possible that no loop statements are executed. The general form is:

```
WHILE <Boolean expression> DO
    <statements>
END_WHILE;
```

For example, the following WHILE … DO construct finds the maximum value in an array.

```
max := NumAry[1];
i := 2;
WHILE ( i <= Max_Num ) DO
    IF ( NumAry[i] > max ) THEN
        max := NumAry[i];
    END_IF;
    i := i + 1;
```

```
END_WHILE;
```

The REPEAT … UNTIL construct allows a set of statements to be repeated while a Boolean expression is true. The Boolean expression is tested after executing the loop statements. If false, the loop statements are not repeated. The loop statements are executed at least once. The general form is:

```
REPEAT
    <statements>
UNTIL <Boolean expression>
END_REPEAT;
```

The following example finds the array index for a matching part number.

```
found := FALSE;
i := 1;
REPEAT
    IF Part_Array[i] := Part_Query THEN
        found := TRUE;
    ELSE
        i := i + 1;
    END_IF;
UNTIL (found) OR (i > Max_Num);
END_REPEAT;
```

The EXIT statement is used within an iteration statement and allows one to abort loop execution. When the EXIT statement is executed, execution continues after the end of the iteration statement. The following example finds the first bit set in an array of Booleans.

```
FOR i := 1 TO MaxStepNum DO
    IF StepBit[i] THEN
        EXIT;
    END_IF;
END_FOR;
```

12.3 MODICON STRUCTURED TEXT

The differences between the Modicon implementation of the ST language and the IEC 61131-3 standard definition of the ST language mainly concern the variable declarations. Modicon ST has the following limitations:

No SINT, LINT, USINT, ULINT, and LREAL data types.

Derived data types must be defined within a *.DTY file.

No M and L directly represented variable codes.

Limited use of VAR … END_VAR construct.

The VAR … END_VAR construct can only be used to assign non-default data types to physical memory locations and to declare function block instances. An example valid structured text VAR declaration is:

```
VAR
    Pulse: TON;   (* Instance of on-delay timer *)
    Ctr:   CTUD;  (* Instance of up/down counter *)
    %QW1:  UINT;  (* directly represented address *)
END_VAR
```

Table 12.4 Modicon Directly Represented Addresses

IEC Address	Modicon Address	Default Data Type	Other Possible Data Types
%IX*n*	1:*n*	BOOL	
%IB*n*	3:*n*	BYTE	
%IW*n*	3:*n*	INT	UINT, WORD
%ID*n*	3:*n*	REAL	DINT, UDINT, TIME
%QX*n*	0:*n*	BOOL	
%QB*n*	4:*n*	BYTE	
%QW*n*	4:*n*	INT	UNIT, WORD
%QD*n*	4:*n*	REAL	DINT, UDINT, TIME

Variables are normally defined as part of the project and not as structured text. Direct physical PLC addresses are supported in a ST section or DFB, but only as part of a statement. The IEC direct addresses that are supported, their equivalent Modicon state RAM representation, and their default data type are shown in Table 12.4. The IEC format of direct addresses is only supported in structured text and instruction list. For the other languages, the Modicon format of direct addressing is employed.

The assignment operator is retentive, though if the PLC memory does not have a battery back-up, all memory contents are lost when power fails.

12.4 CONTROLLOGIX STRUCTURED TEXT

The ST language became available with release 10 of the RSLogix 5000 programming software. The differences between the ControlLogix implementation of the ST language and the IEC 61131-3 standard are the following:

No LINT, USINT, UINT, UDINT, ULINT, LREAL, and TIME data types.
No directly represented addresses and variables in IEC format.
No variable or function block instance definitions.
Non-retentive assignment allowed.
Alternate other ways of showing comments.
Different names for timer and counter function blocks.
Different method of executing function blocks.
Mixed-mode arithmetic is allowed.

Variables are normally defined as part of the tag database for a controller or program and not as structured text. Derived data types are considered part of the project and not programmed in structured text.

The "[:=]" character string is the non-retentive assignment operator (":=" is the retentive assignment). The destination of the non-retentive assignment is set to zero when the PLC enters the run mode or leaves a sequential function chart (SFC) step when that action is programmed in ST and the SFC is configured for automatic reset.

There are two other ways of indicating comments. In addition to "(*" and "*)" delimiting a comment, "/*" and "*/" can also delimit a comment. If "//" precedes the comment, then the end-of-line terminates the comment.

The names of the timer and counter function blocks are identical to the FBD function block names:

Func. Block	**Description**
TONR	On-delay timer
TOFR	Off-delay timer
RTOR	Retentive on-delay timer
CTUD	Up/down counter

In addition, the way of executing function blocks is different. With the IEC 61131-3 ST format, the instance of the function block is invoked, passing the input values as parameters. With the ControlLogix ST, the input values are specified as elements of the function block instance (structure) before executing the function block. Invoking the general name of the function block and passing the structure as the parameter executes the function block. For example, the on-delay timer ladder logic of Figure 12.4*a* is equivalent to the FBD in Figure 12.4*b* and the structured text in Figure 12.4*c*.

For both the FBD and ST renditions, the LS1_DelTmr is defined as a FBD_TIMER type in the tag database. In IEC 61131-3 ST format, the program in Figure 12.4*c* would be:

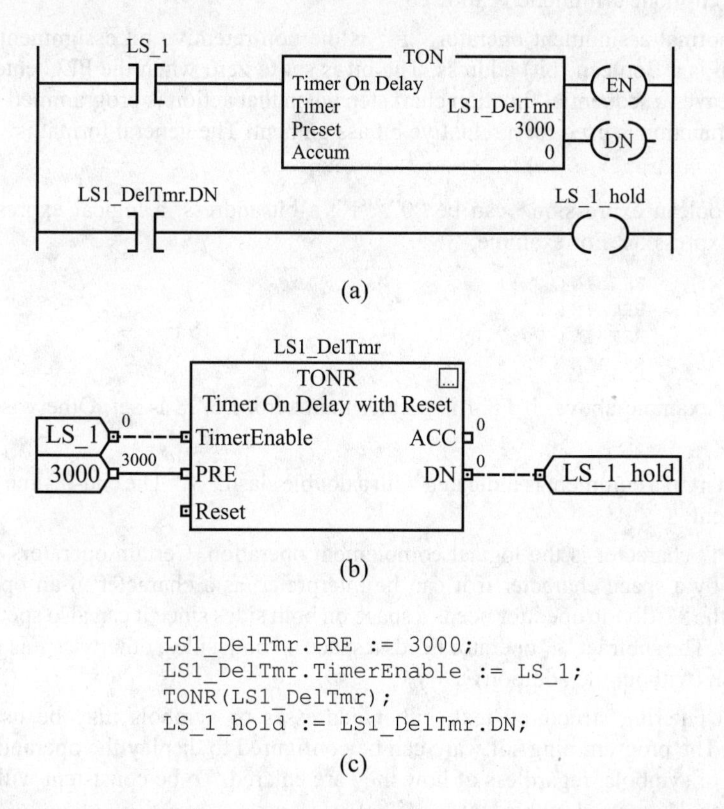

Figure 12.4. Sample ControlLogix on-delay timer: *(a)* ladder logic; *(b)* equivalent FBD; *(c)* equivalent ST.

```
VAR
  LS1_DelTmr : FBD_TIMER;
END_VAR

LS1_DelTmr(TimerEnable:=LS_1, PRE:=3000);
LS_1_hold := LS1_DelTmr.DN;
```

12.5 PLC-5 STRUCTURED TEXT

Structured text is only supported by the Enhanced PLC-5 processors that are series C, revision C and later. The differences between the PLC-5 implementation of the ST language and the IEC 61131-3 standard are as follows:

No data type definition. The data type is determined by the address.

Directly represented addresses follow the PLC-5 convention.

No variable or function block instance definitions.

Retentive and non-retentive bit assignment.

Different format of comment.

Different logical complement operator.

Different format for function block invocation.

Mixed-mode arithmetic is allowed.

The normal assignment operator, ":=" is the non-retentive bit assignment when the destination is a Boolean (bit) address. The bit is set to zero when the PLC enters the run mode or leaves a sequential function chart step when that action is programmed in ST. The RETAIN function is used for a retentive bit assignment. The general format is

```
<bit address> := RETAIN(<Boolean expression>);
```

where <Boolean expression> can be "0", "1", a bit address, a logical expression, or a compare expression. For example,

```
B3/25 := RETAIN( 0 );
B3/26 := RETAIN( 1 );
B3/27 := RETAIN( T4:7.DN );
B3/28 := RETAIN( F8:4 > 0.0 );
```

In the last example above, if F8:4 is greater than zero, B3/28 is set. Otherwise B3/28 is cleared.

The start of a comment is indicated with a double slash, "//." The end-of-line terminates the comment.

The "!" character is the logical complement operation. Certain operators need to be separated by a space character if it can be interpreted as a character in an operand. For example, the "/" divide operator needs a space on both sides since it can also specify a bit in an address. The subtract "-" operator needs a space on both sides, otherwise it is interpreted as negation (without the addition).

When entering structured text, either addresses or symbols may be used for the operands. The programming software can be configured to display the operands either as addresses or symbols, regardless of how they are entered. To be consistent with the other PLCs, symbols are used in this text.

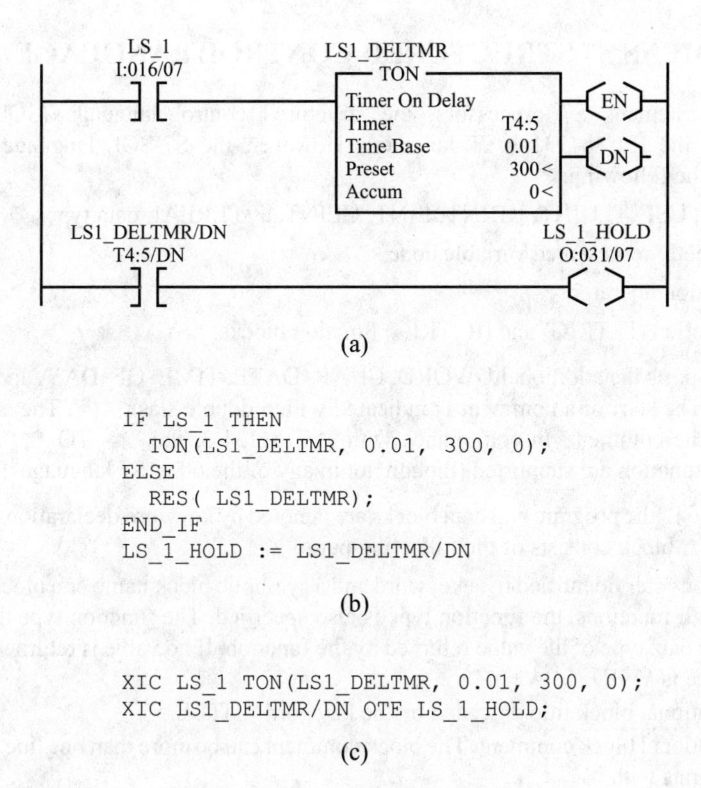
LS_1
I:016/07
LS1_DELTMR
TON
Timer On Delay
Timer T4:5
Time Base 0.01
Preset 300<
Accum 0<
EN
DN
LS1_DELTMR/DN
T4:5/DN
LS_1_HOLD
O:031/07
(a)
IF LS_1 THEN
TON(LS1_DELTMR, 0.01, 300, 0);
ELSE
RES(LS1_DELTMR);
END_IF
LS_1_HOLD := LS1_DELTMR/DN
(b)
XIC LS_1 TON(LS1_DELTMR, 0.01, 300, 0);
XIC LS1_DELTMR/DN OTE LS_1_HOLD;
(c)

Figure 12.5. Sample PLC-5 on-delay timer: *(a)* ladder logic; *(b)* equivalent ST; *(c)* shortened ST.

Ladder logic function blocks may also be used in structured text. The format is similar to the ASCII text format of entering ladder logic instructions (which is one method provided by the programming software to enter ladder logic) with the following differences:

Operands are enclosed in parentheses

Operands are separated by commas

Only one input function block in a statement

Branching is not allowed

An example use of the TON on-delay timer is shown in Figure 12.5. The general format for output function blocks is:

```
<FB name>(Operand1, Operand2, …);
```

Two examples of this format are shown in the second and fourth lines of Figure 12.5*b*. An input expression can be placed before output instruction, as shown in the first line of Figure 12.5*c*. In this case, the "XIC," which refers to the N.O. contact is optional and may be omitted. An input expression can also be a comparison operation, such as "TEMP1 < TEMP2." An input function block or instruction must be followed by an output function block or output coil, as shown in the second line of Figure 12.5*c*.

A complete list of the supported function blocks and the operands may be found in Allen-Bradley (1995).

12.6 SIEMENS S7 STRUCTURED CONTROL LANGUAGE

In the Siemens S7 processors, the structured control language (SCL) mostly implements the IEC 61131-3 ST language. However, the S7-SCL language does not implement the following:

SINT, USINT, UINT, UDINT, LINT, ULINT, and LREAL data types.

L directly represented variable code.

Negation operator.

Transition (F_TRIG) and (R_TRIG) function blocks.

S7-SCL supports the additional DWORD, CHAR, DATE, TIME_OF_DAY, and S5TIME data types. The start of a comment is indicated with a double slash, "//". The end-of-line terminates the comment. In compliance with IEC 61131-3, the ***_TO_*** data type conversion function are supported (though not in any of the other S7 languages).

In S7-SCL, the program and data blocks are denoted by keyword declarations shown in Table 12.5. A block consists of the following parts:

1. Block start identified by a keyword and a symbolic block name or a block number. With functions, the function type is also specified. The function type determines the data type of the value returned by the function. If no value is returned, the data type is VOID.
2. Optional block title preceded by the keyword "TITLE =".
3. Optional block comment. The block comment can be more than one line. Each line begins with "//".
4. Optional block attributes.
5. Optional block system attributes.
6. Declaration section (depending on the block type)

Table 12.5 S7-SCL Program and Data Block Keyword Declarations

Block Type	Designator	Block Start and End Syntax
Function Block	FB	FUNCTION_BLOCK fb_name . . . END_FUNCTION_BLOCK
Function	FC	FUNCTION fc_name: data_type . . . END_FUNCTION
Organization Block	OB	ORGANIZATION_BLOCK ob_name . . . END_ORGANIZATION_BLOCK
Data Block	DB	DATA_BLOCK db_name . . . END_DATA_BLOCK
Shared Data Type	UDT	TYPE udt_name . . . END_TYPE

7. Statement section in program blocks or assignment of actual values in data blocks.
8. Block end indicated by "END_***."

To retain compatibility with IEC 61131-3, S7-SCL allows the keyword pair PROGRAM-END_PROGRAM to substitute for the keyword pair FUNCTION_BLOCK-END_FUNCTION_BLOCK. For details on the block attributes and system attributes, see Siemens (2000).

A declaration section is divided into subsections, each indicated by a pair of keywords. The types of subsections and their format are shown in Table 12.6. The subsections can be placed in any order. Static variables for a FB or OB are placed in an instance data block (DB) that is associated with the FB or OB. For example, if a user creates FB10, then a data block of type FB10 must be created in order for that function block to be called. Temporary variables are allocated space when the function block is called and then that space is deleted when exiting the function block. In DB and UDT blocks, STRUCT ... END_STRUCT is used in place of the VAR … END_VAR declaration.

Table 12.6 S7-SCL Declaration Section Keywords

Data	Syntax	Permitted in: FB	FC	OB
Constants	CONST ... END_CONST	x	x	x
Labels	LABEL ... END_LABEL	x	x	x
Temporary Variables	VAR_TEMP ... END_VAR	x	x	x
Static Variables	VAR ... END_VAR	x	x[1]	
Input Parameters	VAR_INPUT ... END_VAR	x	x	
Output Parameters	VAR_OUTPUT ... END_VAR	x	x	
In/Out Parameters	VAR_IN_OUT ... END_VAR	x	x	

Notes:
1. Though permitted in functions, when compiled, static variables are moved to the temporary area.

The ANY data type is useful for the formal block parameters (input, in/out, or FC output). When a formal block parameter is declared as ANY, then an actual parameter of any type may be used when the block is called. The ANY data type can also be used for temporary variables. When a variable of the ANY type is on the left side of an assignment statement, the right side can be:

Local and shared variables

Variables in the DB (addressed absolutely or symbolically)

Variables in the local instance (addressed absolutely or symbolically)

NIL constant (specifying a nil pointer)

ANY data type

Timers, counters, and blocks (for example, T5, C14 or FB7).

The ANY data type is generally used for formal input parameters, in/out parameters of FBs and FCs and for output parameters of FCs. There are some restrictions on the use of the ANY data type:

1. Constants are not permitted on the right-hand side of an assignment (with the exception of the NIL constant).
2. A temporary variable of type ANY cannot be passed to another block as a formal parameter.
3. The ANY type cannot be used as a component type in a structure or as an element type for an array.

In S7-SCL program blocks, a special local variable, called the OK flag may be used to indicate the correct or incorrect execution of a block. The OK flag is a BOOL with the predefined name "OK". At the beginning of the block, the OK flag is true. It can be queried at any point in the block or can be set to true or false with SCL statements. If a called function has an error, (for example division by zero), the OK flag is set to FALSE. When the block is exited, the value of the OK flag is saved in the output parameter ENO and can be evaluated by the calling block. The OK flag does not need to be declared. However, the compiler "Set OK flag" option must be enabled before compilation in order to use the OK flag.

12.7 EXAMPLES

Example 12.1. Scaling of analog input values. The TT573 transducer measures temperature in the range of 90 to 700 °C and is connected to an analog input module having a 16-bit ADC whose output integer value corresponds to the lowest and highest sensor value as:

Value	Modicon	Logix	PLC-5	Siemens
Lowest	0	-20,030	0	5530
Highest	32,000	30,920	4095	27,648

Convert the ADC output integer (TT573_MEAS) to the temperature, in °C and store the result in TT573_DEGC. Also, the ADC output integer should be limited to the proper range before doing the conversion.

Assume the following physical input and internal variable.

Variable	Description
TT573_MEAS	Raw temperature measurement, represents 90-700 °C; ADC integer range listed above.
TT573_DEGC	Current temperature, in °C.

The address associated with the physical input is:

Variable	Modicon	PLC-5	ControlLogix	Siemens
TT573_MEAS	300001	N10:4	Local:3:I.Ch0Data	IW288

For the Modicon and Siemens PLCs, TT573_MEAS is declared an INT. For the ControlLogix, it is declared a DINT. The address or data type associated with the internal variable:

Variable	Modicon Data Type	PLC-5 Addr.	Logix Data Type	Siemens Addr.
TT573_DEGC	REAL	F12:0	REAL	MD100 (REAL)

Solution. This example is a simple application of structured text. The formulas for the various conversions are shown as the ST code.

Since an analog input is read-only, the Modicon, ControlLogix, and Siemens PLCs must use a temporary variable to hold the result of limiting the ADC output integer. For these three PLCs, the following internal variable is declared:

Variable	Modicon Data Type	Logix Data Type	Siemens Addr.
TmpInt	INT	INT	MW51 (INT)

For the PLC-5, the analog input ADC has already been transferred to a regular memory location.

The Modicon solution is:

```
TmpInt := TT573_MEAS;
IF (TmpInt < 0) THEN
  TmpInt := 0;
END_IF;
IF (TmpInt > 32000) THEN
  TmpInt:= 32000;
END_IF;
TT573_DEGC := ((INT_TO_REAL(IN:=TmpInt)) / 32000.0) * (700.0 - 90.0)
  + 90.0;
```

Note that the Modicon uses strong type-checking in the arithmetic statements. If the LIMIT function is used to check the ADC integer, the solution becomes shorter:

```
TmpInt := LIMIT_INT( IN:=TT573_MEAS, MN:=0. MX:=32000);
TT573_DEGC := ((INT_TO_REAL(IN:=TmpInt)) / 32000.0) * (700.0 - 90.0)
  + 90.0;
```

The ControlLogix solution is:

```
TmpInt := TT573_MEAS;
IF (TmpInt < -20030) THEN
  TmpInt := -20030;
```

```
END_IF;
IF (TmpInt > 30920) THEN
  TmpInt := 30920;
END_IF;
TT573_DEGC := ((TmpInt + 20030) / 50950.0) * (700.0 - 90.0)
  + 90.0;
```

For both the ControlLogix and PLC-5 processors, there is no available limiting function in structured text.

The PLC-5 solution is:

```
IF (TT573_MEAS < 0) THEN
  TT573_MEAS := 0;
END_IF;
IF (TT573_MEAS > 4095) THEN
  TT573_MEAS := 4095;
END_IF;
TT573_DEGC := (TT573_MEAS / 4095.0) * (700.0 - 90.0) + 90.0;
```

Implemented as a function, the S7-SCL solution is:

```
FUNCTION TT573_CONV VOID
VAR_TEMP
  TmpInt : INT;
END_VAR

BEGIN
  TmpInt := TT573_MEAS
  IF (TmpInt < 5530) THEN
    TmpInt := 5530;
  END_IF;
  IF (TmpInt > 27648) THEN
    TmpInt := 27648;
  END_IF;
  TT573_DEGC := ((TmpInt - 5530) / 22118.0) * (700.0 - 90.0)
    + 90.0;
END_FUNCTION
```

Note that the “22118.0” must contain a decimal point to force a floating-point divide.The LIMIT function may be used, but constants cannot be used as parameters. In this case, the function is:

```
FUNCTION TT573_CONV VOID
VAR_TEMP
  MinAI   : INT;
  MaxAI   : INT;
  TmpInt : INT;
END_VAR

BEGIN
  MinAI := 5530;
  MaxAI := 27648;
  TmpInt := LIMIT( IN:=TT573_MEAS, MN:=MinAI, MX:=MaxAI);
  TT573_DEGC := ((TmpInt - MinAI) / 22118.0) * (700.0 - 90.0)
    + 90.0;
END_FUNCTION
```

Example 12.2. Marking defective parts. Implement Example 5.4 using the ST language.

Solution. The Modicon ladder logic solution is shown in Figure 5.73. The structured text equivalent is:

```
VAR
    St_Delay,
    Pls_Tmr   : TON;
END_VAR

IF NOT P_Seal THEN
  IF ( (PDEFECT AND NOT PROX5) AND NOT S_Done ) THEN
    P_Seal := TRUE;
  END_IF;
ELSE
  IF S_Done THEN P_Seal := FALSE;
  END_IF;
END_IF;
St_Delay(IN:=P_Seal, PT:=T#5.5s);
SPRAY := St_Delay.Q;
Pls_Tmr(IN:=SPRAY, PT:=T#1s);
S_Done := Pls_Tmr.Q;
```

Assuming that the St_Delay and Pls_Tmr variables are defined to be FBD_TIMER, the ControlLogix ST statements are:

```
IF NOT St_Delay.TimerEnable THEN
  IF ( (PDEFECT AND NOT PROX5) AND NOT Pls_Tmr.DN ) THEN
    St_Delay.TimerEnable := 1;
  END_IF;
ELSE
  IF Pls_Tmr.DN THEN St_Delay.TimerEnable := 0;
  END_IF;
END_IF;
St_Delay.PRE := 5500;  St_Delay.EnableIn :=1;
TONR(St_Delay);
SPRAY := St_Delay.DN;
Pls_Tmr.EnableIn := St_Delay.DN;
Pls_Tmr.PRE := 1000;  Pls_Tmr.EnableIn := 1;
TONR(Pls_Tmr);
```

The PLC-5 ladder logic is shown in Figure 5.74. The equivalent structured text is:

```
IF !P_SEAL THEN
  IF ( (PDEFECT AND !PROX5) AND !PLS_TMR/DN ) THEN
    P_SEAL := TRUE;
  END_IF;
ELSE
  IF PLS_TMR/DN THEN P_SEAL := FALSE;
  END_IF;
END_IF;
IF P_SEAL THEN
    TON(ST_DELAY, 0.01, 550, 0);
ELSE
    RES(ST_DELAY);
END_IF;
SPRAY := ST_DELAY/DN;
```

```
IF SPRAY THEN
    TON(PLS_TMR, 0.01, 100, 0);
ELSE
    RES(PLS_TMR);
END_IF;
```

In a more compact (and less readable) form:

```
(((PDEFECT AND !PROX5) OR ST_DELAY/EN ) AND
   !PLS_TMR/DN) TON(ST_DELAY, 0.01, 550, 0);
SPRAY := ST_DELAY/DN;
SPRAY TON(PLS_TMR, 0.01, 100, 0);
```

The S7-SCL solution of the ladder logic in Figure 5.75 is implemented as the function block FB1, "Mark_Def." An instance data block must be created with type FB1 in order for this function block to be called by another program block (for example, OB1). The code for this function block is:

```
FUNCTION_BLOCK Mark_Def

VAR
    P_Seal : BOOL := FALSE;
    S_Done : BOOL;
    St_Delay,
    Pls_Tmr: TON;

END_VAR

BEGIN
    IF NOT P_Seal THEN
      IF ( (PDEFECT AND (NOT PROX5)) AND (NOT S_Done) ) THEN
        P_Seal := TRUE;
      END_IF;
    ELSE
      IF S_Done THEN P_Seal := FALSE;
      END_IF;
    END_IF;
    St_Delay(IN:=P_Seal, PT:=T#5.5s);
    SPRAY := St_Delay.Q;
    Pls_Tmr(IN:=SPRAY, PT:=T#1s);
    S_Done := Pls_Tmr.Q;

END_FUNCTION_BLOCK;
```

Note that the data blocks required for the two timers is included in the instance data block for this function block.

Example 12.3. Using the structured text language, implement the SET_STEP and GET_STEP derived function blocks that were used in Chapter 9 to implement a counter-based sequencer for the Modicon and S7 PLCs.

Solution. The Modicon DFBs are shown in Figure 12.6. The GET_STEP function block copies an element of a StepArray50 Boolean array to the output. The input signals to this block are described as follows:

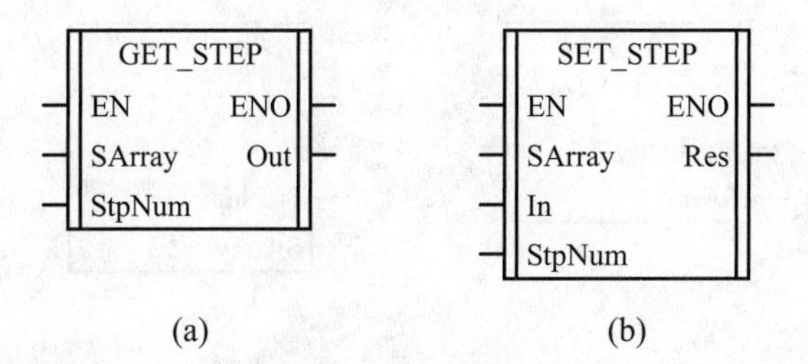

Figure 12.6. Modicon DFBs for counter-based sequencer: *(a)* GET_STEP; *(b)* SET_STEP.

SArray – Array of step-in-progress bits (of type StepArray50).
StpNum – Index of array element to reset or set.

The only output of this block, Out, is the value of SArray[StpNum]: TRUE or FALSE.

The SET_STEP function block either clears or sets an element of a StepArray50 Boolean array. The input signals to this block are described as follows:

SArray – Array of step-in-progress bits (of type StepArray50).
In – New value of element; 0 resets and 1 sets.
StpNum – Index of array element to reset or set.

The output signal of this block, Res, is the updated array of step-in-progress bits.

For the GET_STEP function block, the variable and block input/output definitions are as follows:

Variable Name	Var. Type	Data Type
SArray	IN	SArray
StepNum	IN	INT
Out	OUT	BOOL

The code in the structured text section is:

```
(* Return status of bit in step-in-prog. or step-done bit array *)
Out := SArray[StpNum];
```

For the SET_STEP function block, the variable and block input/output definitions are as follows:

Variable Name	Var. Type	Data Type
SArray	IN	SArray
In	IN	BOOL
StepNum	IN	INT
Res	OUT	SArray

The code in the structured text section is:

```
(* Set/clear bit in step-in-progress or step-done bit array *)
Res := SArray;
Res[StpNum]:=In;
```

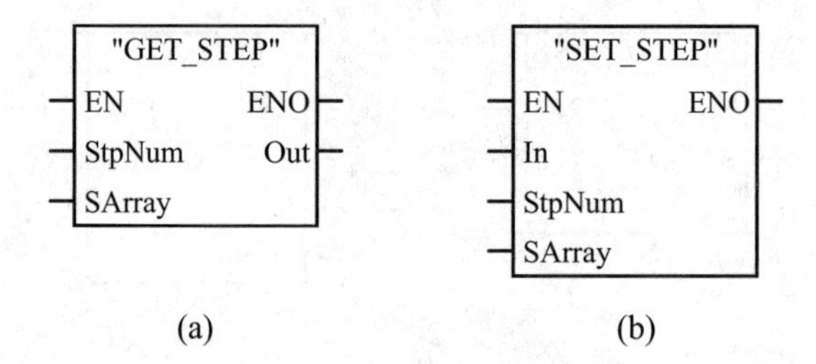

Figure 12.7. S7 functions (FCs) for counter-based sequencer: *(a)* GET_STEP; *(b)* SET_STEP.

The S7 functions (FCs) are shown in Figure 12.7. The GET_STEP function block copies an element of an ARRAY[0..50] of BOOL to the output. The input signals to this block are described as follows:

SArray – Array of step-in-progress bits.
StpNum – Index of array element to reset or set.

The output signal of this block, Out, is the value of SArray[StpNum]: TRUE or FALSE.

The SET_STEP function block either clears or sets an element of an ARRAY[0..50] of BOOL. The input signals to this block are described as follows:

SArray – Array of step-in-progress bits.
In – New value of element; 0 resets and 1 sets.
StpNum – Index of array element to reset or set.

There is no output of this block since SArray is declared as an IN_OUT parameter. The S7-SCL that implements these two functions is:

```
FUNCTION Get_Step: VOID
VAR_INPUT
    StpNum: INT;
    SArray: ARRAY[0..50] OF BOOL;
END_VAR
VAR_OUTPUT
    Out: BOOL;
END_VAR
BEGIN
  Out := SArray[StpNum];
END_FUNCTION

FUNCTION Set_Step: VOID
VAR_INPUT
    In: BOOL;
    StpNum: INT;
END_VAR
VAR_IN_OUT
    SArray: ARRAY[0..50] OF BOOL;
END_VAR
BEGIN
    SArray[StpNum] := In;
END_FUNCTION
```

Example 12.4. Simple tank level control. Implement Example 7.4 using the ST language.

Solution. The Modicon ladder logic solution is shown in Figure 7.66. The structured text equivalent is:

```
(* Convert analog input to level *)
LT428_VAL := (INT_TO_REAL(WORD_TO_INT(LT428_RAW)))
   *(15.0-1.0)/32000.0 + 1.0;

(* Level control: turn on when low, turn off when *)
(*   high. If not enabled, always turn off       *)
IF T428_CNTRL THEN
    IF (LT428_VAL < LT428_MIN) THEN
        XV427_OPEN := TRUE;
    END_IF;
    IF (LT428_VAL > LT428_MAX) THEN
        XV427_OPEN := FALSE;
    END_IF;
ELSE
    XV427_OPEN := FALSE;
END_IF;
```

The ControlLogix ladder logic is shown in Figure 7.67 and the ControlLogix ST statements are:

```
(* Get tank level *)
LT428_VAL := LT428_RAW;

(* Level control: turn on when low, turn off when *)
(*   high. If not enabled, always turn off       *)
IF T428_CNTRL THEN
    IF (LT428_VAL < LT428_MIN) THEN
        XV427_OPEN := 1;
    END_IF;
    IF (LT428_VAL > LT428_MAX) THEN
        XV427_OPEN := 0;
    END_IF;
ELSE
    XV427_OPEN := 0;
END_IF;
```

The PLC-5 ladder logic is shown in Figure 7.68. The equivalent structured text is:

```
(* Convert analog input to level *)
LT428_VAL := (LT428_RAW)*(15.0-1.0)/4095.0 + 1.0;

(* Level control: turn on when low, turn off when *)
(*   high. If not enabled, always turn off       *)
IF T428_CNTRL THEN
    IF (LT428_VAL < LT428_MIN) THEN
        XV427_OPEN := TRUE;
    END_IF;
    IF (LT428_VAL > LT428_MAX) THEN
        XV427_OPEN := FALSE;
    END_IF;
ELSE
    XV427_OPEN := FALSE;
END_IF;
```

The S7 ladder logic is shown in Figure 7.70. Implemented as a function (FC), the equivalent structured text is:

```
FUNCTION_BLOCK LT428_Ctl VOID

BEGIN
  // Convert analog input to level
  LT428_VAL := ((LT428_RAW - 5530)/(22118.0))*(15.0-1.0) + 1.0;

  // Level control: turn on when low, turn off when
  //   high. If not enabled, always turn off
  IF T428_CNTRL THEN
      IF (LT428_VAL < LT428_MIN) THEN
          XV427_OPEN := TRUE;
      END_IF;
      IF (LT428_VAL > LT428_MAX) THEN
          XV427_OPEN := FALSE;
      END_IF;
  ELSE
      XV427_OPEN := FALSE;
  END_IF;
END_FUNCTION
```

Example 12.5. Simple operator interface/alarm system for tank. Implement Example 7.5 using the ST language.

Solution. The Modicon ladder logic solution is shown in Figure 7.72. Using the INT_BCD and BCD_INT derived function blocks, the structured text equivalent is:

```
VAR
    DispConv : INT_BCD;
    TWConv   : BCD_INT;
    HrnTrig  : R_TRIG;
    Ack_Tmr  : TON;
END_VAR;

(* Display current level in lower 12 bits of LEVEL_DISP *)
DispConv( REAL_TO_INT( LT428_VAL*10.0));
Temp := AND_WORD( DispConv.Out_BCD, 16#0FFF);
LEVEL_DISP := AND_WORD(LEVEL_DISP, 16#F000);
LEVEL_DISP := OR_WORD(Temp, LEVEL_DISP);

(* Read minimum level from TW *)
Temp := TWConv( AND_WORD(MIN_TW, 16#0FFF));
T428_MIN := INT_TO_REAL( Temp )/10.0;

(* Calculate max level *)
T428_MAX := T428_MIN + 1.5;

(* Low level alarms *)
T428_LOLA := (LT428_VAL < 4.0);
T428_Hrn_Act := (LT428_VAL < 2.0);

(* Trigger horn when level drops below 2.0 or *)
(*  stays below 2 for 5 minutes after ack'ed. *)
HrnTrig(T428_Hrn_Act);
```

```
IF (HrnTrig.Q) OR (Ack_Tmr.Q) THEN
    T428_HORN := TRUE;
ELSE
    IF ALM_ACK THEN
        T428_HORN := FALSE;
    END_IF;
END_IF;

(* Time level staying below 2 after ack *)
IF (ALM_ACK AND T428_Hrn_Act) THEN
    Ack_Tmr_En := TRUE;
END_IF;
IF Ack_Tmr_En AND (NOT T428_Hrn_Act OR Ack_Tmr.Q ) THEN
    Ack_Tmr_En := FALSE;
END_IF;
Ack_Tmr( Ack_Tmr_En, T#5m);
```

Note that HrnTrig (an instance of the R_TRIG function block) is used in place of the positive transitional contact.

As of this writing, the ControlLogix structured text does not implement the BCD-to-integer or integer-to-BCD conversions. So, this implementation assumes that ladder logic or FBD has been utilized to place the thumbwheel switch reading, in tenths of feet in T428_Mint and that by placing the current feet (in tenths of feet) in the LT428_Tenths, the value is displayed on the LED display. With these assumptions, the ST statements are:

```
(* Display current level in lower 12 bits of LEVEL_DISP *)
LT428_Tenths := LT428_Val * 10;

(* Ladder logic does conv. to BCD *)
(* Ladder logic reads min. level from TW *)
T428_Min := T428_Mint / 10;

(* Calculate max level *)
T428_Max := T428_Min + 1.5;

(* Low level alarms *)
T428_LOLA := (LT428_Val < 4.0);
T428_Hrn_Act := (LT428_Val < 2.0);

(* Generate trigger when level falls below 2.0 *)
HrnOns.InputBit := T428_Hrn_Act;
OSRI( HrnOns);
Horn_Trig := HrnOns.OutputBit;

(* Trigger horn when level drops below 2.0 or *)
(*  stays below 2 for 5 minutes after ack'ed. *)
IF (Horn_Trig) OR (Ack_Tmr.DN) THEN
    T428_Horn := 1;
ELSE
    IF ALM_Ack THEN
        T428_Horn := 0;
    END_IF;
END_IF;

(* Time level staying below 2 after ack *)
```

```
IF (ALM_ACK AND T428_Hrn_Act) THEN
    Ack_Tmr_En := 1;
END_IF;
IF Ack_Tmr_En AND (NOT T428_Hrn_Act OR Ack_Tmr.DN) THEN
    Ack_Tmr_En := 0;
END_IF
Ack_Tmr.TimerEnable := Ack_Tmr_En;
Ack_Tmr.PRE := 300000;  Ack_Tmr.EnableIn := 1;
TONR( Ack_Tmr);
```

Note that the OSRI function block is used for a positive transitional contact. The following additional tags have been defined:

```
Ack_Tmr     FBD_TIMER
HrnOns      FBD_ONESHOT
Horn_Trig   BOOL
```

The PLC-5 ladder logic is shown in Figure 7.73. The equivalent structured text is:

```
(* Display current level in lower 12 bits of LEVEL_DISP *)
LT428_TENTHS := LT428_VAL * 10;
TOD( LT428_TENTHS, LT428_BCD);
BTD( LT428_BCD, 0, LEVEL_DISP, 0, 12);

(* Read minimum level from TW *)
BTD( MIN_TW, 0, MIN_LVL_BCD, 0, 12);
FRD( MIN_LVL_BCD, T428_MINT);
T428_MIN := T428_MINT / 10;

(* Calculate max level *)
T428_MAX := T428_MIN + 1.5;

(* Low level alarms *)
T428_LOLA := (LT428_VAL < 4.0);
T428_HRN_ACT := (LT428_VAL < 2.0);

(* Trigger when level falls below 2.0 *)
T428_HRN_ACT ONS HORN_ONS OTE HORN_TRIG;

(* Trigger horn when level drops below 2.0 or *)
(*  stays below 2 for 5 minutes after ack'ed. *)
IF (HORN_TRIG) OR (ACK_TMR/DN) THEN
    T428_HORN := TRUE;
ELSE
    IF ALM_ACK THEN
        T428_HORN := FALSE;
    END_IF;
END_IF;

(* Time level staying below 2 after ack *)
IF (ALM_ACK AND T428_HRN_ACT) THEN
    ACK_TMR_EN := TRUE;
END_IF;
IF ACK_TMR_EN AND (!T428_HRN_ACT OR ACK_TMR/DN) THEN
    ACK_TMR_EN := FALSE;
END_IF
ACK_TMR_EN TON(ACK_TMR, 1, 300, 0);
```

Note how the ONS is used to trigger the horn to be turned on. The HORN_TRIG symbol is associated with the B3/124 address.

The S7 ladder logic solution is shown in Figure 7.74. The I_BCD and BCD_I functions are not available in S7-SCL, so the FCs INT_BCD and BCD_INT (Figure 12.8*a*,*b*) are programmed to do these functions. Also, the R_TRIG function block (Figure 12.8c) provides the positive trigger needed for this solution. Implemented as a function block (FB), the structured text solution for this example is:

```
FUNCTION_BLOCK Tank_Intf

VAR
    TmpI          : INT;
    HrnTrig       : R_TRIG;
    T428_Hrn_Act,
    HrnTrip       : BOOL;
    Ack_Tmr       : TON;
    Ack_Tmr_En,
    Ack_Tmr_Dn    : BOOL;
END_VAR

BEGIN
    // Display current level in lower 12 bits of LEVEL_DISP
    TmpI := REAL_TO_INT( LT428_VAL * 10.0);
    Int_BCD(In_Int:=TmpI, Out_BCD:=LEVEL_DISP);
    // Read minimum level from TW
    BCD_INT( In_BCD:=( MIN_TW AND Word#16#0FFF), Out_Int:=TmpI);
    T428_MIN := TmpI / 10.0;
    // Calculate max level
    T428_MAX := T428_MIN + 1.5;
    // Low level alarms
    T428_LOLA := (LT428_VAL < 4.0);
    T428_Hrn_Act := (LT428_VAL < 2.0);
    // Trigger horn when level drops below 2.0 or
    //  stays below 2 for 5 minutes after ack'ed.
    HrnTrig(CLK:=T428_Hrn_Act);
    IF ((HrnTrig.Q) OR (Ack_Tmr.Q)) THEN
        T428_HORN := TRUE;
    ELSE
        IF ALM_ACK THEN
            T428_HORN := FALSE;
        END_IF;
    END_IF;
    // Time level staying below 2 after ack
    IF (ALM_ACK AND T428_Hrn_Act) THEN
        Ack_Tmr_En := TRUE;
    END_IF;
    IF Ack_Tmr_En AND (NOT T428_Hrn_Act OR Ack_Tmr.Q ) THEN
        Ack_Tmr_En := FALSE;
    END_IF;
    Ack_Tmr( IN:=Ack_Tmr_En, PT:=T#5m);

END_FUNCTION_BLOCK
```

Note that HrnTrig (an instance of the R_TRIG function block) is used in place of the positive transitional contact.

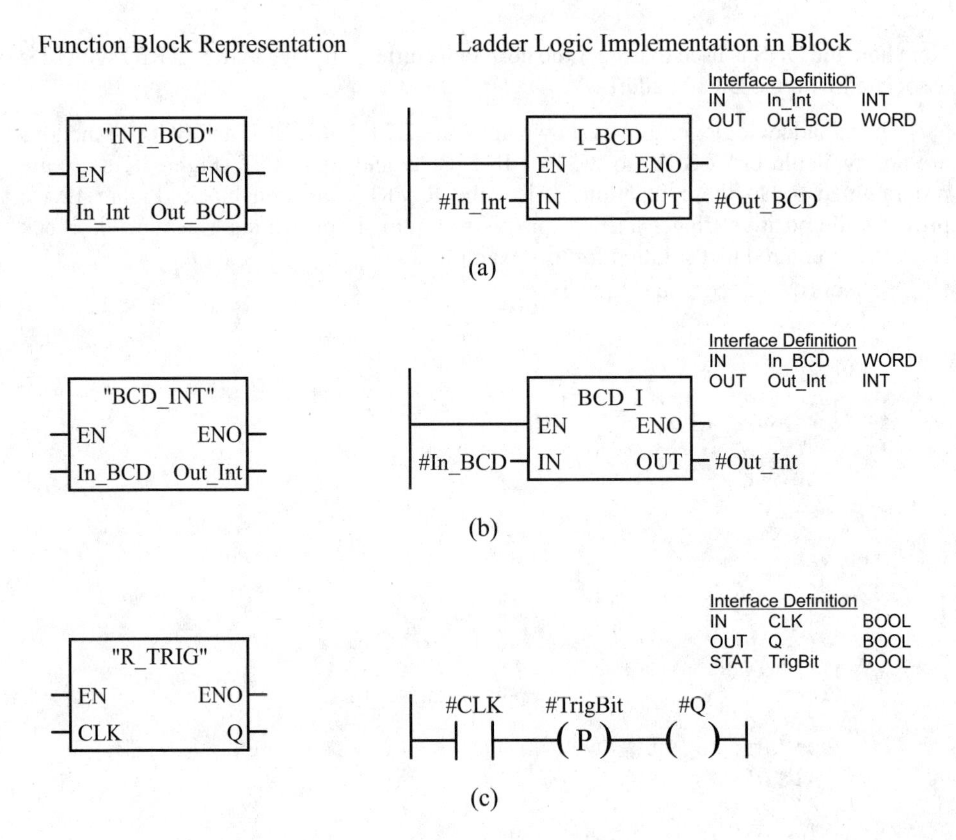

Figure 12.8. S7 functions and function blocks for Example 12.5 solution: *(a)* INT_BCD; *(b)* BCD_INT; *(c)* R_TRIG.

12.8 CHAPTER SUMMARY

This chapter describes the structured text (ST) language for the Modicon, ControlLogix, PLC-5, and Siemens S7 PLCs. The IEC 61131-3 ST language is surveyed first, and then the differences between each implementation and the standard are surveyed. The chapter concludes with examples of structured text implementations of examples already expressed in ladder logic.

REFERENCES

Allen-Bradley, 1995. *PLC-5 Structured Text User Manual*, pub. 6200-6.4.18, Rockwell Allen-Bradley Company, Milwaukee, WI.

Berger, Hans, 2000. *Automating with STEP 7 in STL and SCL: Programmable Controllers SIMATIC S7-300/400*, Publisis MCD Verlag, Erlangen, Germany.

IEC, 1993. *IEC 1131-3: Programmable Logic Controllers - Part 3: Programming Languages*, International Electrotechnical Commission, Geneva, Switzerland.

Rockwell Automation, 1998. *PLC-5 Family Instruction Set Reference Manual*, pub. 1785-6.1, Rockwell Automation, Milwaukee, WI.

Rockwell Automation, 2002. *Logix5000™ Controllers Process Control and Drives Instructions*, pub. 1756-RM006B-EN-P, Rockwell Automation, Milwaukee, WI, May.

Rockwell Automation, 2004. *Logix5000™ Controllers Common Procedures: Programming Manual*, pub. 1756-PM001G-EN-P, Rockwell Automation, Milwaukee, WI, March.

Schneider Automation, 1998. *Concept User Manual,* vol. 2, ver. 2.1, pub. 840 USE 461 00, Schneider Automation, Inc., North Andover, MA.

Siemens, 2000. *S7-SCL V5.1 for S7-300/S7-400: Manual,* Edition 09/2000, pub. A5E00059543-01, Siemens AG, Nürnberg, Germany.

PROBLEMS

P12-1. Integer-to-BCD Conversion for Modicon. The Modicon Concept software does not include an integer-to-BCD converter function block. Program a DFB to do this function. The inputs and outputs of the INT_BCD DFB are shown in Figure P12.1. The variable and block input/output definitions are as follows:

Variable Name	Var. Type	Data Type
In_Int	IN	INT
Out_BCD	OUT	WORD

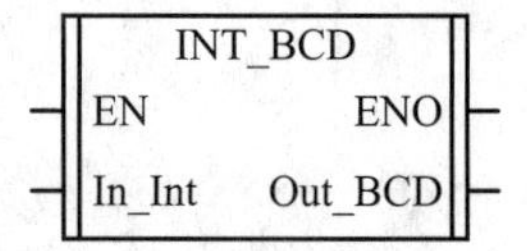

Figure P12.1. Integer-to-BCD conversion function block.

P12-2. Using the structured text language, implement the ladder logic on rung 2 of Figure 9.2 as one FB called UPD_STEP. This FB is shown in Figure P12.2. The UPD_STEP block updates the step-in-progress bits for a counter-based sequencer. Implement this for either (a) Modicon PLCs, or (b) Siemens S7 PLCs.

For the Modicon PLC, the input signals to this DFB block are described as follows:

CrtAcc – Current counter accumulator.

StpNum – Current step number (index into step-in-progress bits).

SArray – Array of step-in-progress bits (of type StepArray50).

The output signals of this block is described as follows:

StpNumO – Updated current step number.

SArrayO – Updated array of step-in-progress bits.

For the Siemens S7, implement this FB block without the output signals.

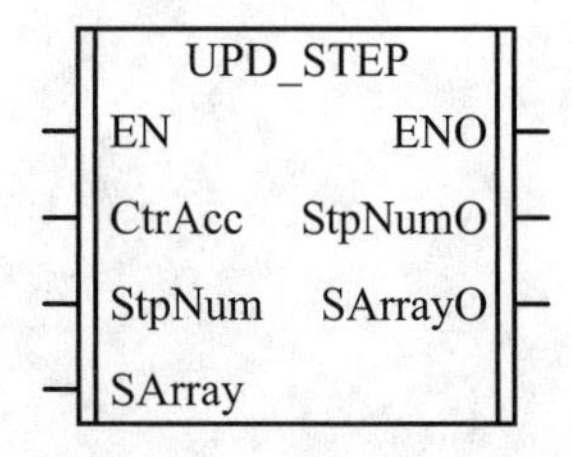

Figure P12.2. UPD_STEP function block.

General instructions for problems P12-3 to P12-11:

Write a structured text program for the application and implement it for one of the following PLCs:

Modicon Concept, **or**

Allen-Bradley ControlLogix, **or**

Allen-Bradley PLC-5, **or**

Siemens S7

If any part of the operation is ambiguous, write down your additional assumptions. The physical inputs, physical outputs, and internal variables for each situation are given in the problem. **DO NOT** assign any more physical inputs!

Unless otherwise specified, assume the ADC in the analog input module has an output integer value that corresponds to the lowest and highest sensor value as:

Value	Modicon	Logix	PLC-5	SLC-500	Siemens
Lowest	0	-20,030	0	3277	5530
Highest	32,000	30,920	4095	16,384	27,648

In the case of the ControlLogix PLC, the instructor may choose to specify that the output of the ADC is a real number configured to be in the sensor units, for example, level in feet or temperature in °C.

Also, unless otherwise specified, assume the input integer to the DAC of an analog output module corresponds to the lowest and highest values of the output device control as:

Value	Modicon	Logix	PLC-5	SLC-500	Siemens
Lowest	0	-20,030	0	6242	5530
Highest	32,000	30,920	4095	31,208	27,648

In the case of the ControlLogix PLC, the instructor may choose to specify that the input to the DAC is a real number configured to be in the actual units of the output device, for example, speed in rpm or valve position in percent of span.

Your solution should include the following:

1. Specify the PLC processor used.
2. Structured text program (with comments). For consistency among the different PLCs, use only variables/symbols/tags in the program. Use instructions and function blocks consistent with the PLC processor.
3. Table listing additional internal memory (variables/symbols/tags) used and a brief description of their use. For the Allen-Bradley ControlLogix and the Modicon Quantum/Momentum processors, list the internal variables/tags and the data type. For the other processors, list the internal variables/symbols and the associated memory address.

P12-3. Flashing Lamps. Implement the flashing lamps of problem P5-6 using the ST language.

P12-4. Level Indicator and Alarm. Implement the level indicator and alarm of problem P5-8 using the ST language.

P12-5. Bunker Alarm. Implement the low bunker alarm of problem P5-10 using the ST language.

P12-6. Alarm for Generator Room Cooling Fans. Implement the alarm of problem P5-11 using the ST language.

P12-7. Bar Classifier. Implement the bar classifier station of problem P5-14 using the ST language.

P12-8. Parking Lot Sign Controller. Implement the parking lot sign controller of problem P5-15 using the ST language.

P12-9. Simple Pressure Control. Implement the pressure controller of problem P7-15 using the ST language.

P12-10. Tank Level Indicator. Implement the tank level indicator and alarm of problem P7-17 using the ST language.

P12-11. Flow Meter Accumulator. Implement the accumulator of problem P7-18 using the ST language.

13 Instruction List

Chapter Topics:

- Instruction list language
- Instruction list applications

OBJECTIVES

Upon completion of this chapter, you will be able to:

- Understand the instruction list language.
- Use the instruction list language in applications.

13.1 INTRODUCTION

The instruction list (IL) language is the other textual PLC programming language, the first being structured text. The instruction list language is similar to assembly language. From the standpoint of the PLC designer, the IL language is very easy to implement. However, from the standpoint of the PLC user, IL is best suited for small uncomplicated problems. In addition, instruction list is useful for implementing older PLC programs already written in IL or for other functions that are difficult to implement in the other languages. For example, indirect addressing can be done in S7-STL and is not available in the other S7 languages.

This chapter describes the instruction list language for the Modicon, Siemens S7, and GE Fanuc PLCs. The Allen-Bradley PLCs do not support the IL programming language. Of the three PLC families that implement IL, the Modicon and GE Fanuc processors more closely follow the IEC 61131-3 standard. This chapter is organized similarly to Chapter 12. The next section describes the IEC 61131-3 instruction list language. Subsequent sections describe the differences between the IL language for a particular PLC and the IEC 61131-3 standard. Following these descriptions, examples are used to illustrate IL applications.

13.2 IEC 61131-3 INSTRUCTION LIST

The instruction list (IL) language defined by the IEC 61131-3 standard is a low-level language. It is comparable to assembly language programming of microprocessors. Most programming is done today with high-level languages (for example, C++). However, some situations arise in which assembly-language programming is appropriate, for example, when writing special hardware drivers. The IL language has a set of instructions to handle variable assignment, conditional statements, simple arithmetic, and function block calling.

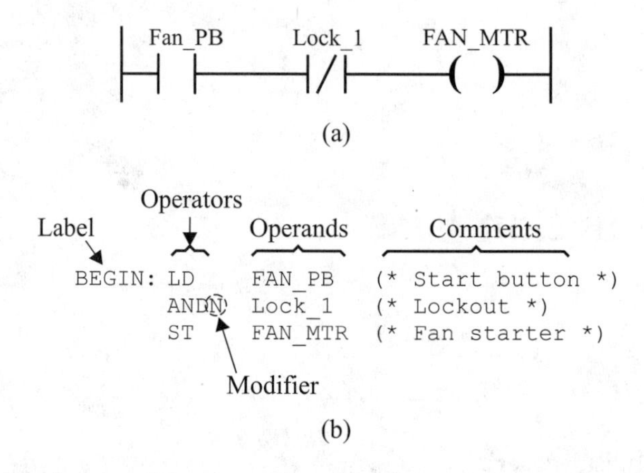

Figure 13.1. Instruction list example: *(a)* ladder logic; *(b)* equivalent IL.

The IL and ST languages share many of the same elements. Namely, the definition of variables and direct physical PLC addresses are identical for both languages (section 12.2.1).

13.2.1 IL Statements

An *instruction list* consists of a series of *instructions*. Each instruction begins on a new line and contains an *operator* with optional *modifiers*, and, if necessary for the particular operation, one or more *operands* separated by commas. The instruction can be preceded by an identifying *label* followed by a colon (":"). If present, comments are the last element on a line, begin with the "(*" character string, and end with the "*)" character string. Blank lines can be placed between instructions. The normal space character between keywords and identifiers can be replaced by a tab. Figure 13.1 shows an example list of IL instructions, illustrating the various parts.

The standard operators with their allowed modifiers and operands are listed in Table 13.1. The modifiers are summarized in Table 13.2. IL is an accumulator-oriented language, that is, each instruction uses or changes the current accumulator contents. The accumulator is a type of temporary storage and adjusts its data type according to the operand loaded into it. Unless otherwise indicated in Table 13.1, each instruction is executed according to

accumulator := accumulator OP operand

where "OP" is the operator. The value of the accumulator is replaced by the result of the accumulator operated upon by the operator with respect to the operand. IEC 61131-3 calls this accumulator the "result." For example, the instruction "`OR START_PB`" is interpreted as

accumulator := accumulator `OR START_PB`

In this case, the accumulator and START_PB are both BOOL types.

The comparison operator is interpreted with the current accumulator to the left of the comparison and the operand to the right. The Boolean result of the comparison is placed in the accumulator. For example, the instruction "`LT 40`" will place a Boolean "1" in the accumulator if the accumulator is less than 40 and a Boolean "0" otherwise.

Table 13.1 Instruction List Operators

Operator	Modifiers	Operand	Operation
LD	N	ANY[1]	Load accumulator with operand
ST	N	ANY[1]	Store accumulator to operand location
S		BOOL	If accum. is 1, set Boolean operand location to 1
R		BOOL	If accum. is 1, reset Boolean operand location to 0
AND	N, (	BOOL	Boolean AND
&	N, (	BOOL	Boolean AND
OR	N, (	BOOL	Boolean OR
XOR	N, (	BOOL	Boolean exclusive OR
ADD	(	ANY[1]	Addition
SUB	(	ANY[1]	Subtraction
MUL	(	ANY[1]	Multiplication
DIV	(	ANY[1]	Division
GT	(	ANY[1]	Compare: >
GE	(	ANY[1]	Compare: >=
EQ	(	ANY[1]	Compare: =
NE	(	ANY[1]	Compare: not =
LE	(	ANY[1]	Compare: <=
LT	(	ANY[1]	Compare: <
JMP	C, CN	LABEL	Jump to label
CAL	C, CN	NAME	Call function or function block
RET	C, CN		Return from called function or function block
)			Evaluate deferred operation

Notes:
1. Operand can be any type or operator can have type suffix in name.

Table 13.2 Instruction List Modifiers

Modifier	Effect on Execution of Previous Operator
(	Defer evaluation of operand until ")" appears
N	Invert value of operand
C	Execute operand if accumulator is "1" (true)
CN	Execute operand if accumulator is "0" (false)

The modifier "N" does a Boolean negation of the operator. For example, the instruction "`ANDN Lock_1`" is interpreted as

accumulator := accumulator `AND (NOT Lock_1)`

The left parenthesis modifier "(" indicates that the evaluation of the operator shall be deferred until a right parenthesis operator ")" is encountered. For example, an IL implementation of the start/stop rung of Figure 13.2 is

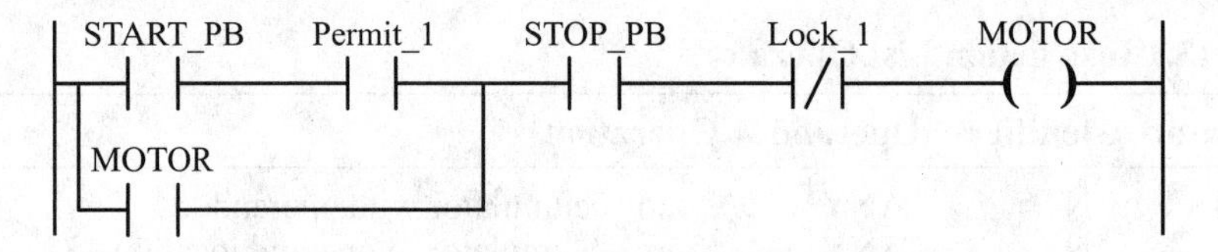

Figure 13.2. Start/stop rung in ladder logic.

```
LD    MOTOR     (* Seal *)
OR(   START_PB  (* Start button *)
AND   Permit_1  (* Permission satisfied *)
)
AND   STOP_PB   (* Stop button *)
ANDN  Lock_1    (* Lockout *)
ST    MOTOR     (* Fan starter *)
```

Note that the OR represented by the parallel branch is deferred until the START_PB and Permit_1 are ANDed.

The "C" modifier indicates that the instruction is executed if the accumulator is "1" and the "CN" modifier indicates that the instruction is executed if the accumulator is "0."

13.2.2 Calling Functions and Function Blocks

Functions can be invoked by placing the function name in the operator field. The current value of the accumulator is the first parameter of the function. Additional parameters, if required, are placed in the operand field.

As in the ST language, in order to use a function block in IL, an instance of the function block must be declared in the IL program. Function blocks may be invoked in one of three ways: (1) CAL with input parameter list; (2) CAL with load/store of input parameters; and (3) use input operators. In all three cases, invoking a function block does not return a value. The outputs must be referenced in subsequent statements.

The general form of a CAL with an input parameter list is

```
CAL FName(InPara1:=Value1, InPara2:=Value2, . . .)
```

where "FName" has been declared as the appropriate function block type. Alternatively, the input parameters can be listed on separate lines

```
CAL FName(
InPara1:=Value1
InPara2:=Value2
. . .
)
```

An example IL invocation of the ladder logic counter of Figure 13.3 using an input parameter list is

```
VAR
  Smpl_Ctu : CTU;
END_VAR

CAL Smpl_Ctu(CU:=PROX_2, R:=All_Reset, PV:=3)
LD  Smpl_Ctu.Q
ST  Advance_Cyl
```

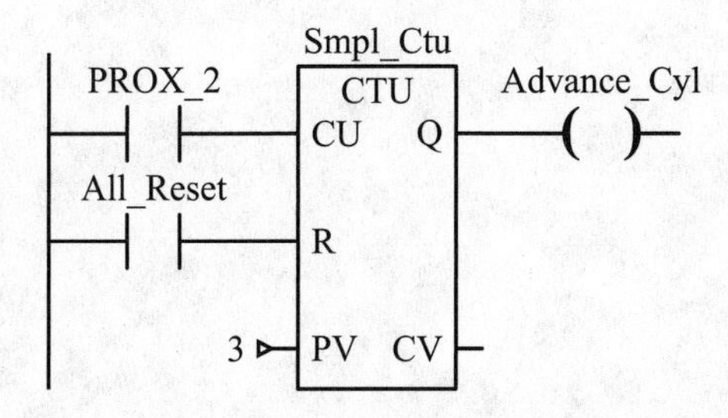

Figure 13.3. Sample ladder logic counter function block.

If an input to a function block is not assigned a value, a default value is used. When using the load/store method of assigning input parameters, values of the input parameters are stored to the input references to the invoked function block. With the load/store method, the ladder logic of Figure 13.3 in IL is

```
VAR
  Smpl_Ctu : CTU;
END_VAR

LD  PROX_2
ST  Smpl_Ctu.CU
LD  All_Reset
ST  Smpl_Ctu.R
LD  3
ST  Smpl_Ctu.PV
CAL Smpl_Ctu
LD  Smpl_Ctu.Q
ST  Advance_Cyl
```

Calling function blocks with input operators only works with some of the standard function blocks. Table 13.3 lists the IL input operators for these standard function blocks. The input operator sets the function block input signal corresponding to the name of the operator to the current value in the accumulator and then calls the operand (the function block instance). With the input operator method, the ladder logic of Figure 13.3 in IL is

Table 13.3 IL Function Block Input Operators

FB Type	Input Operators
SR	S1, R
RS	S, R1
R_TRIG	CLK
F_TRIG	CLK
CTU	CU, R, PV
CTD	CD, LD, PV
CTUD	CU, CD, R, LD, PV
TON	IN, PT
TOF	IN, PT
TP	IN, PT

```
VAR
  Smpl_Ctu : CTU;
END_VAR

LD  All_Reset
R   Smpl_Ctu
LD  3
PV  Smpl_Ctu
LD  PROX_2
CU  Smpl_Ctu
LD  Smpl_Ctu.Q
ST  Advance_Cyl
```

The CU or R operators effectively execute the counter since changes in this input cause the counter accumulator to change. The PV operator only sets the PV input. Block input parameters that are not assigned a value will either use the previous assignment value or use the default initialization value.

13.3 MODICON INSTRUCTION LIST

The differences between the Modicon implementation of the IL language and the IEC 61131-3 standard definition of the IL language mainly concern the variable declarations. Modicon IL has the following limitations:

No SINT, LINT, USINT, ULINT, and LREAL data types.
No "&" operator.
No M and L directly represented variable codes.
Limited use of VAR … END_VAR construct.
Restrictions on the use of input operators when calling function blocks.

As for the structured text language, the VAR … END_VAR construct can only be used to declare function block instances and to assign non-default data types to physical memory locations. Variables are normally defined as part of the project. Direct physical PLC addresses are supported in an IL section or DFB, but only as part of a statement. The IEC direct addresses that are supported, their equivalent Modicon state RAM representation, and their default data type are shown in Table 12.4. The IEC format of direct addresses is only supported in the instruction list and structured text languages.

There are some differences from the IEC standard when using input operators to call the function blocks in Table 13.3. The input operator may only be used once. Invoking an input operator finishes the assignment of the input parameters. Therefore, use LD/ST to load the other parameters before the input operator is invoked. As another departure from the standard, the counter function blocks using input operators (CTU, CTD, CTUD) must be suffixed with an integer data type (_INT, _DINT, _UINT, or _UDINT).

13.4 SIEMENS S7 STATEMENT LIST LANGUAGE

In the Siemens S7 processors, the statement list (STL) corresponds to the IEC 61131-3 IL language. However, there are substantial differences. The S7-STL language has different command syntax in order to remain compatible with the STL of the earlier S5 processors.

The S7-STL language does not implement the following:

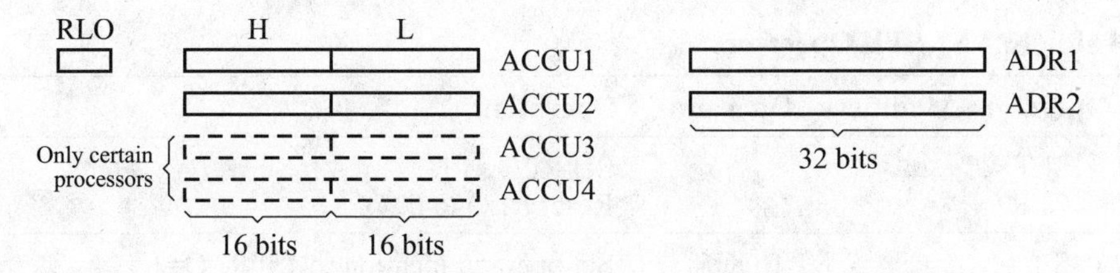

Figure 13.4. S7-STL regsiters.

SINT, USINT, UINT, UDINT, LINT, ULINT, and LREAL data types.
L directly represented variable code.

S7-STL differs from the IEC IL language in the following:

Supports the additional DWORD, CHAR, DATE, TIME_OF_DAY, and S5TIME data types.
Comment starts with a double slash, "//," and terminates at the end-of-line.

In addition, S7-STL includes more instructions than defined in the basic command set of the IEC 61131-3 standard (Siemens, 2000).

In contrast to the IEC 61131-3 IL language that has only one accumulator, the S7-STL language has several (Figure 13.4). The RLO bit is the "result of logic operation" and is essentially a Boolean register. The ACCUx registers may be used as any data type, depending on what is loaded into them and the operation performed on them. Integer (INT) operations manipulate the lower 16 bits of the accumulators ("L" in Figure 13.4). All of the S7 processors have two ACCU registers. Some of the processors have four. The ADRx registers are used for indirect addressing.

The S7-STL language can be used in two different ways:

1. Like a ladder logic or FBD network. In this case, the RLO register is initially loaded with a logical "1" (like the left power rail) and the instructions are executed. The declaration of variables is handled the same as for ladder logic.
2. Like a S7-SCL program. In this case, the STL source text is constructed like that for a SCL block (section 12.6), except STL instructions replace SCL statements.

The general format of STL instructions is basically the same as for the IEC 61131-3 IL language. However, the operators have different mnemonics. The operators that correspond to the IEC standard operators are listed in Table 13.4. There are many other instructions not listed here (Siemens, 2000).

All of the Boolean-type instructions are executed according to

RLO := RLO OP operand

where "OP" is the operator. For these instructions, the RLO is analogous to the IEC 61131-3 "result." For example, an STL implementation of the start/stop rung of Figure 13.2 is

```
A(
A     "START_PB"  // Start button
A     "Permit_1"  // Permission satisfied
O     "MOTOR"     // Seal
)
A     "STOP_PB"   // Stop button
```

Table 13.4 S7-STL Operators

Operator	Modifiers	Operand	Operation
SET			Set RLO to 1
CLR			Reset RLO to 0
S		BOOL	Set operand location to 1 if RLO=1
R		BOOL	Reset operand location to 0 if RLO=0
A	N, (	BOOL	Boolean AND of RLO with operand
O	N, (	BOOL	Boolean OR of RLO with operand
X	N, (	BOOL	Boolean exclusive OR of RLO with operand
)			Evaluate deferred operation
NOT			Invert value of RLO
=		BOOL	Store value of RLO to operand location
FP		BOOL[1]	Positive transition; RLO changes from 0 to 1
FN		BOOL[1]	Negative transition; RLO changes from 1 to 0
L		B,W,D[2]	Load ACCU1 with operand
T		B,W,D[2]	Store ACCU1 to operand location
+	I, D, R	I,D,R[3]	ACCU2 + ACCU1
-	I, D, R	I,D,R[3]	ACCU2 - ACCU1
*	I, D, R	I,D,R[3]	ACCU2 × ACCU1
/	I, D, R	I,D,R[3]	ACCU2 ÷ ACCU1
>	I, D, R	I,D,R[3]	Compare: ACCU1 > ACCU2
>=	I, D, R	I,D,R[3]	Compare: ACCU1 >= ACCU2
==	I, D, R	I,D,R[3]	Compare: ACCU1 = ACCU2
<>	I, D, R	I,D,R[3]	Compare: ACCU1 not equal ACCU2
<=	I, D, R	I,D,R[3]	Compare: ACCU1 <= ACCU2
<	I, D, R	I,D,R[3]	Compare: ACCU1 < ACCU2
JU		LABEL	Jump to label
J	C, CN	LABEL	Conditional jump to label
CALL		NAME[,db]	Call function or function block
UC		NAME	Unconditional call (no parameters)
CC		NAME	Conditional call (no parameters)
BE, BEU			Return from called function or function block
BEC			Return from called function if RLO=1

Notes:
1. Operand stores previous RLO to sense transition.
2. Operand can be BYTE, WORD, or DWORD.
3. Operand can be INT, DINT, or REAL (compatible with modifier).

```
AN    "Lock_1"     // Lockout
=     "MOTOR"      // Fan starter
```

The load and store instructions operate differently from the 61131-3 IL language. The basic load instruction, "L," loads ACCU1. However, before it loads ACCU1, the current contents of ACCU1 are moved to ACCU2 and ACCU1 is cleared. If the processor has four ACCU's, ACCU3 is moved to ACCU4, ACCU2 is moved to ACCU3, and ACCU1 is

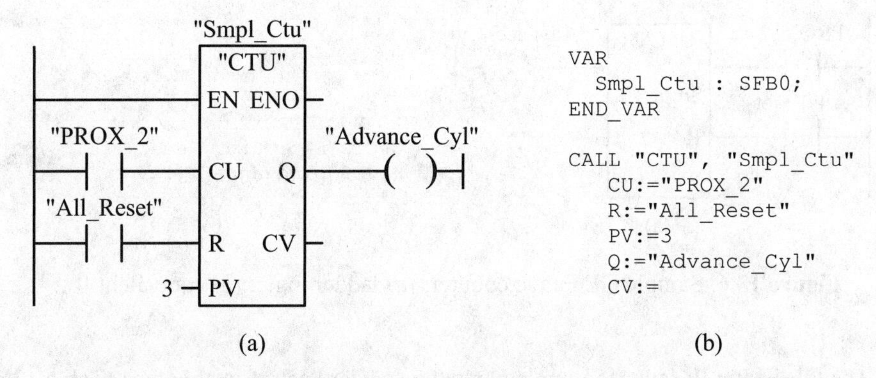

Figure 13.5. Sample S7 counter: *(a)* ladder logic; *(b)* equivalent STL.

moved to ACCU2 before loading ACCU1. The basic store instruction, "T," moves the contents of ACCU1 to the operand. There are many other load and store instructions that operate on the address registers (ADRx) and the accumulators (Siemens, 2000).

All of the arithmetic and comparison operations listed in Table 13.4 use ACCU1 and ACCU2. The result is placed in ACCU1. If the processor has two accumulators, ACCU2 remains unchanged. However, if the processor has four accumulators, ACCU3 is moved to ACCU2 and ACCU4 is moved to ACCU3. The arithmetic instructions do not change the RLO. However, they change the other status bits (such as CC1, positive result). For both the arithmetic and comparison instructions, the modifier is not optional and defines the data type of the two accumulators. The result of a comparison is placed in the RLO.

The invocation of functions or function blocks is different from IEC 61131-3. The instance data block must be specified with a call to any function block (FB, SFB). In addition, all input and output parameters are specified on the lines after the "CALL" instruction. For example, a S7-STL implementation of the counter of Figure 13.5*a* is shown in Figure 13.5*b*.

S7-STL does not support input operators. If an input to a function block (FB, SFB) is not assigned, the previous value assigned to that input is used. All inputs to a function (FC, SFC) must be assigned.

13.5 GE FANUC INSTRUCTION LIST

Compared with the IEC 61131-3 standard definition of the IL language, the GE Fanuc IL has the following limitations:

No SINT, LINT, USINT, ULINT, LREAL, and TIME data types.

No B, W, D, and L directly represented variable codes.

No use of VAR … END_VAR construct.

Nonstandard method of calling functions and blocks.

Variables are defined as part of the project and associated with a physical address when they are defined. Direct physical PLC addresses are not allowed in an IL block. The method of calling functions is outlined below. IL logic is not supported on Series 90™-70 processors.

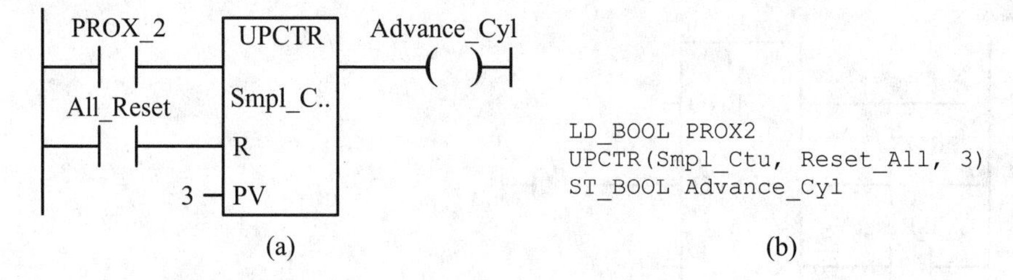

Figure 13.6. Sample GE Fanuc counter: *(a)* ladder logic; *(b)* equivalent IL.

The GE Fanuc IL language implements the standard set of instructions (Table 13.1) with the following differences:

The LD/ST instructions have a data type suffix.
One cannot LD a DINT or REAL (but ST_DINT and ST_REAL are valid)
No "&" operator.
The standard arithmetic and comparison instructions only operate on INTs

The GE Fanuc IL has the following additional instructions

NOT - inverts the current value of the Boolean accumulator.
NT - stores the Boolean accumulator to a negative transition coil.
PT - stores the Boolean accumulator to a positive transition coil.

There are also master control relay instructions (GE Fanuc, 2002a) not discussed here.

The GE Fanuc processor has two types of accumulators: (1) one 32-bit accumulator for arithmetic and comparison operations, and (2) eight Boolean accumulators for discrete logic. Only one of the eight Boolean accumulators is accessible, the others are used to support nested Boolean expressions.

There is another set of arithmetic and comparison functions that operate on INT, DINT, and REAL data types. The name of the function is suffixed with the data type and these functions have two operands. For arithmetic operations, the result is placed in the 32-bit accumulator. For comparison instructions, the result of the comparison is placed in the Boolean accumulator. The examples in this chapter show the use of these functions.

The CAL statement is reserved for invoking other IL or LD blocks. Timers, counters, and other ladder logic function blocks are invoked with their name, passing the appropriate parameters. The timer and counter functions store their output in the Boolean accumulator. A ladder logic counter and its IL equivalent are shown in Figure 13.6.

13.6 EXAMPLES

Example 13.1. Scaling of analog input values. The TT573 transducer measures temperature in the range of 90 to 700 °C and is connected to an analog input module having a 16-bit ADC whose output integer value corresponds to the lowest and highest sensor value as:

Value	Modicon	Siemens	GE Fanuc
Lowest	0	5530	0
Highest	32,000	27,648	32,000

Convert the ADC output integer (TT573_MEAS) to the temperature, in °C and store the result in TT573_DEGC. Also, the ADC output integer should be limited to the proper range before doing the conversion.

Assume the following physical input and internal variable.

Variable	Description
TT573_MEAS	Raw temperature measurement, represents 90-700 °C; ADC integer range listed above.
TT573_DEGC	Current temperature, in °C.

The address associated with the physical input is:

Variable	Modicon	Siemens	GE Fanuc
TT573_MEAS	300001	IW288	%AI0001

For the Modicon and Siemens PLCs, TT573_MEAS is declared an INT. For the GE Fanuc, it is declared a WORD. The address and/or data type associated with the internal variable:

Variable	Modicon Data Type	Siemens Addr.	GE Fanuc Addr.
TT573_DEGC	REAL	MW100 (REAL)	%R201 (REAL)

Solution. This example is a simple application of instruction list that is identical to Example 12.1. The formulas for the various conversions are shown as the IL code.

Since an analog input is read-only, the PLCs must use a temporary variable to hold the result of limiting the ADC output integer. Therefore, the following internal variable is declared:

Variable	Modicon Data Type	Siemens Addr.	GE Fanuc Addr.
TmpInt	INT	MW51 (INT)	%R3 (INT)

The Modicon solution is:

```
           LD TT273_MEAS
           ST TmpInt
(* Ensure value not below zero *)
           LT 0
           JMPCN TstUpr
           LD 0
           ST TmpInt
(* Ensure value not above 32000 *)
TstUpr:    LD TmpInt
           GT 32000
           JMPCN DoCvrt
           LD 32000
           ST TmpInt
(* Convert to degrees C          *)
(* INT_TO_REAL(TmpInt)/32000)*(700-90)+90 *)
DoCvrt:    LD 700.0
           SUB 90.0
```

```
ST TmpReal
LD TmpInt
INT_TO_REAL
DIV 32000.0
MUL TmpReal
ADD 90.0
ST TT273_DEGC
```

Implemented as part of a FB or OB, the S7-STL solution is:

```
// Save transducer reading for min and max checks
      L     "TT273_MEAS"
      T     "TmpInt"
// Check for greater than minimum
      L     5530
      <I
      JCN   TUpr
      L     5530
      T     "TmpInt"
// Check for less than maximum
TUpr: L     "TmpInt"
      L     27648
      >I
      JCN   DoCv
      L     27648
      T     "TmpInt"
//  Do conversion of transducer reading to temp. in degrees C
//  (INT-TO-REAL(TmpInt)-5530)/22118)*(700-90)+90
DoCv: L     "TmpInt"
      ITD                              // Int to double
      DTR                              // double to real
      L     5.530000e+003
      -R                               // subtract 5530
      L     2.211800e+004
      /R                               // divide by 22118
      T     "TmpR"                     // Save for later multiply
      L     7.000000e+002
      L     9.000000e+001
      -R                               // do 700 - 90
      L     "TmpR"
      *R                               // mult by result of 1st divide
      L     9.000000e+001
      +R                               // add 90
      T     "TT273_DEGC"
```

The GE Fanuc IL solution is:

```
          LD_INT TT273_MEAS
          ST_INT TmpInt
(* Ensure value not below zero *)
          LT 0
          JMPCN TstUpr
          LD_INT 0
```

```
            ST_INT TmpInt
(* Ensure value not above 32000 *)
TstUpr:     LD_INT TmpInt
            GT 32000
            JMPCN DoCvrt
            LD_INT 32000
            ST_INT TmpInt
(* Convert to degrees C         *)
(* INT_TO_REAL(TmpInt)/32000)*(700-90)+90 *)
DoCvrt:     INT_TO_REAL(TmpInt)
            ST_REAL TmpReal
            DIV_REAL( TmpReal, 32000.0)
            ST_REAL TmpReal
            SUB_REAL( 700.0, 90.0)
            ST_REAL TmpReal2
            MUL_REAL(TmpReal, TmpReal2)
            ST_REAL TmpReal
            ADD_REAL( TmpReal, 90.0)
            ST_REAL TT273_DEGC
```

Example 13.2. Marking defective parts. Implement Example 5.4 using the IL language.

Solution. The Modicon ladder logic solution is shown in Figure 5.73. Implemented as an IL section, the instruction list equivalent is:

```
VAR
    St_Delay,
    Pls_Tmr   : TON;
END_VAR

      LD    PDEFECT
      ANDN  PROX5
      OR    P_Seal
      ANDN  S_Done
      ST    P_Seal
      CAL   St_Delay(IN:=P_Seal, PT:=T#5.5s)
      LD    St_Delay.Q
      ST    SPRAY
      CAL   Pls_Tmr(IN:=SPRAY, PT:=T#1s)
      LD    Pls_Tmr.Q
      ST    S_Done
```

The S7-STL solution of the ladder logic in Figure 5.75 is implemented as part of a FB or OB. The code is:

```
// Start and seal for pulse
      A      "PDEFECT"
      AN     "PROX5"
      O      "P_Seal"
      AN     "Pls_Tmr".Q
      =      "P_Seal"
//Timers
```

```
CALL   "TON" , "St_Delay"
 IN:="P_Seal"
 PT:=T#5S500MS
 Q :="SPRAY"
 ET:=
CALL   "TON" , "Pls_Tmr"
 IN:="SPRAY"
 PT:=T#1S
 Q :=
 ET:=
```

The ladder logic for the GE Fanuc solution is similar to the Modicon solution shown in Figure 5.73. The instruction list equivalent is:

```
(* Seal Logic *)
     LD_BOOL      PDEFECT
     ANDN         PROX5
     OR           P_Seal
     ANDN         S_Done
     ST_BOOL      P_Seal
(* Cascaded timers *)
     TMR_HUNDS( St_Delay, 550)
     ST_BOOL      SPRAY
     TMR_HUNDS( Pls_Tmr, 100)
     ST_BOOL      S_Done
```

Example 13.3. Simple tank level control. Implement Example 7.4 using the IL language.

Solution. The Modicon ladder logic solution is shown in Figure 7.66. The instruction list equivalent is:

```
(* Convert analog input to level *)
LD          15.0
SUB_REAL    1.0
ST          TmpR
LD          LT428_RAW
INT_TO_REAL
MUL_REAL    TmpR
DIV_REAL    32000.0
ADD_REAL    1.0
ST          LT428_VAL

(* Level control: turn on when low, turn off when *)
(*   high. If not enabled, always turn off        *)
LD          LT428_VAL
LT          T428_MIN
OR          XV427_OPEN
AND(
LD          LT428_VAL
LE          T428_MAX
```

```
)
AND          T428_CNTRL
ST           XV427_OPEN
```

The S7 ladder logic is shown in Figure 7.70. Implemented as part of a FB or OB, the equivalent S7-STL is:

```
// Do conversion of transducer reading to level in feet.
      L      "LT428_RAW"
      ITD                              // Int to double
      DTR                              // double to real
      L      5.530000e+003
      -R                               // subtract 5530
      L      2.211800e+004
      /R                               // divide by 22118
      T      "TmpR"                    // Save for later multiply
      L      1.500000e+001
      L      1.000000e+000
      -R                               // do 15 - 1
      L      "TmpR"
      *R                               // mult by result of 1st divide
      L      1.000000e+000
      +R                               // add 1
      T      "LT428_VAL"
// Control of tank level
      L      "LT428_VAL"
      L      "T428_MIN"
      <R                               // On when drop below minimum
      O      "XV427_OPEN"
      A(
      L      "LT428_VAL"
      L      "T428_MAX"
      <=R                              // Keep on while <= maximum
      )
      A      "T428_CNTRL"
      =      "XV427_OPEN"
```

The GE Fanuc ladder logic solution is shown in Figure 7.71. Implemented as an IL block, the instruction list solution for this example is:

```
(* Convert analog input to level       *)
     INT_TO_REAL(LT428_RAW)
     ST_REAL TmpR
     DIV_REAL( TmpR, 32000.0)
     ST_REAL TmpR
     SUB_REAL( 15.0, 1.0)
     ST_REAL TmpR2
     MUL_REAL(TmpR, TmpR2)
     ST_REAL TmpR
     ADD_REAL( TmpR, 1.0)
     ST_REAL LT428_VAL
(* Comparisons for low and high levels *)
     LT_REAL(LT428_VAL,T428_MIN)
```

```
        ST_BOOL T428_Low
        GT_REAL(LT428_VAL, T428_MAX)
        ST_BOOL T428_High
    (* Control of tank level *)
        LD_BOOL T428_Low
        OR     XV427_OPEN
        ANDN  T428_High
        AND    T428_CNTRL
        ST_BOOL     XV427_OPEN
```

Example 13.4. Simple operator interface/alarm system for tank. Implement Example 7.5 using the IL language.

Solution. The Modicon ladder logic solution is shown in Figure 7.72. Using the INT_BCD and BCD_INT derived function blocks, the instruction list equivalent is:

```
VAR
    DispConv  : INT_BCD;
    TWConv    : BCD_INT;
    HrnTrig   : R_TRIG;
    Ack_Tmr   : TON;
END_VAR

(* Display current level in lower 12 bits of LEVEL_DISP *)
LD          LT428_VAL
MUL         10.0
REAL_TO_INT
ST          TmpI
CAL         DispConv( In_Int:=TmpI)
LD          DispConv.Out_BCD
AND_WORD    16#0FFF
ST          Temp
LD          LEVEL_DISP
AND_WORD    16#F000
OR_WORD     Temp
ST          LEVEL_DISP

(* Read minimum level from TW *)
LD          MIN_TW
AND_WORD    16#0FFF
ST          Temp
CAL         TWConv( In_BCD:=Temp)
LD          TWConv.Out_Int
INT_TO_REAL
DIV         10.0
ST          T428_MIN

(* Calculate max level *)
ADD         1.5
ST          T428_MAX

(* Low level alarms *)
LD          LT428_VAL
LT          4.0
```

```
ST          T428_LOLA
LD          LT428_VAL
LT          2.0
ST          T428_Hrn_Act

(* Trigger horn when level drops below 2.0 or *)
(*  stays below 2 for 5 minutes after ack'ed. *)
LD          T428_Hrn_Act
CAL         HrnTrig(CLK:=T428_Hrn_Act)
LD          HrnTrig.Q
OR          Ack_Tmr.Q
OR(
LD          T428_HORN
ANDN        ALM_ACK
)
ST          T428_HORN

(* Time level staying below 2 after ack *)
LD          ALM_ACK
OR          Ack_Tmr_En
AND         T428_Hrn_Act
ANDN        Ack_Tmr.Q
ST          Ack_Tmr_En
CAL         Ack_Tmr(IN:=Ack_Tmr_En, PT:=T#5m)
```

Note that HrnTrig (an instance of the R_TRIG function block) is used in place of the positive transitional contact.

The S7 ladder logic solution is shown in Figure 7.74. The I_BCD and BCD_I ladder logic functions are called ITB and BTI, respectively, in S7-STL. Also, the FP instruction provides the positive trigger needed for this solution. Implemented as part of a FB or OB, the S7-STL solution for this example is:

```
// Display T428 level on 7-segment LED's
      L      "LT428_VAL"
      L      1.000000e+001
      *R                                    // Multiply by 10
      RND                                   // Round
      T      "TmpI"                         // Convert to Int
      L      "TmpI"
      ITB                                   // Int to BCD
      T      "LEVEL_DISP"
// Read minimum level from thumbwheel switches.
      L      "MIN_TW"
      L      W#16#FFF
      AW                                    // And with FFF
      BTI                                   // BCD to Int
      ITD                                   // to double int
      DTR                                   // to real
      L      1.000000e+001
      /R                                    // divide by 10
      T      "T428_MIN"
// Max level is min level + 1.5
      L      "T428_MIN"
      L      1.500000e+000
      +R
```

```
      T      "T428_MAX"
// Low alarm lamp when level < 4
      L      "LT428_VAL"
      L      4.000000e+000
      <R
      =      "T428_LOLA"
// Level below 2.0 causes horn to be activated
      L      "LT428_VAL"
      L      2.000000e+000
      <R
      =      "T428_Hrn_Act"
// Horn activated when level drops below 2.0 or has remained below 2.0
// for 5 minutes. Acknowledge button silences it.
      FP     "Hrn_Ons"
      O      "Ack_Tmr".Q
      O(
      A      "T428_HORN"
      AN     "ALM_ACK"
      )
      =      "T428_HORN"
// Time level stays below 2.0 after horn acknowledged
      A      "ALM_ACK"
      O      "Ack_Tmr_En"
      A      "T428_Hrn_Act"
      AN     "Ack_Tmr".Q
      =      "Ack_Tmr_En"
      CALL   "TON" , "Ack_Tmr"
       IN:="Ack_Tmr_En"
       PT:=T#5M
       Q :=
       ET:=
```

The GE Fanuc ladder logic solution is shown in Figure 7.75. The PT instruction provides the positive trigger needed for this solution. Implemented as a IL block, the instruction list solution for this example is:

```
(* Display T428 level on 7-segment LED's*)
     MUL_REAL(LT428_VAL, 10.0)
     ST_REAL     TmpR
     REAL_TO_INT(TmpR)
     ST_INT      TmpI
     INT_TO_BCD4(TmpI)
     ST_WORD     LEVEL_DISP
(* Read minimum level from thumwheel switches *)
     AND_WORD(MIN_TW, 16#0fff)
     ST_WORD     TmpW
     BCD4_TO_INT(TmpW)
     ST_INT      TmpI
     INT_TO_REAL(TmpI)
     ST_REAL     TmpR
     DIV_REAL( TmpR, 10.0)
     ST_REAL     T428_MIN
(* Max level is min level +1.5 *)
     ADD_REAL( T428_MIN, 1.5)
     ST_REAL     T428_MAX
```

```
(* Low level lamp when level < 4 feet *)
    LT_REAL( LT428_VAL, 4.0)
    ST_BOOL     T428_LOLA
(* Level below 2.0 activates horn *)
    LT_REAL( LT428_VAL, 2.0)
    ST_BOOL     T428_Hrn_Act
    PT          Hrn_Ons
(* Horn activated when level drops below 2.0 or has
   remained below 2.0 for 5 minutes. Acknowledge button
   silences it. *)
    LD_BOOL     Hrn_Ons
    OR          Ack_Tmr_Dn
    OR(
    LD_BOOL     T428_HORN
    ANDN        ALM_ACK
    )
    ST_BOOL     T428_HORN
(* Time 5 minutes level stays below 2.0 after horn ackd *)
    LD_BOOL     ALM_ACK
    OR          Ack_Tmr_En
    AND         T428_Hrn_Act
    ANDN        Ack_Tmr_Dn
    ST_BOOL     Ack_Tmr_En
    TMR_TENTHS(Ack_Tmr, 3000)
    ST_BOOL     Ack_Tmr_Dn
```

13.7 CHAPTER SUMMARY

This chapter describes the instruction list (IL) language for the Modicon, Siemens S7, and GE Fanuc PLCs. The IEC 61131-3 IL language is surveyed first, and then the differences between each implementation and the standard are surveyed. The chapter concludes with examples of instruction list implementations of examples already expressed in ladder logic.

REFERENCES

Berger, Hans, 2000. *Automating with STEP 7 in STL and SCL: Programmable Controllers SIMATIC S7-300/400*, Publisis MCD Verlag, Erlangen, Germany.

GE Fanuc Automation, 2002a. *CIMplicity Machine Edition™ Help File*, version 3.0, GE Fanuc Automation North America, Inc., Charlottesville, VA.

GE Fanuc Automation, 2002b. *Logic Developer – PLC; PLC Programming Software: Getting Started,* pub. GFK-1918C, version 3.00, GE Fanuc Automation North America, Inc., Charlottesville, VA.

IEC, 1993. *IEC 1131-3: Programmable Logic Controllers - Part 3: Programming Languages*, International Electrotechnical Commission, Geneva, Switzerland.

Siemens, 2000. *Statement List (STL) for S7-300 and S7-400 Programming: Reference Manual,* Edition 12/2000, pub. A5E00171232-01, Siemens AG, Nürnberg, Germany.

Schneider Automation, 1998. *Concept User Manual,* vol. 2, ver. 2.1, pub. 840 USE 461 00, Schneider Automation, Inc., North Andover, MA.

PROBLEMS

General instructions for the problems:

Write an instruction list program for the application and implement it for one of the following PLCs:

Modicon Concept, **or**

Siemens S7, **or**

GE Fanuc 90-30 (with floating point)

If any part of the operation is ambiguous, write down your additional assumptions.

The physical inputs, physical outputs, and internal variables for each problem are given in the problem. **DO NOT** assign any more physical inputs!

Unless otherwise specified, assume the ADC in the analog input module has an output integer value that corresponds to the lowest and highest sensor value as:

Value	Modicon	Siemens	GE Fanuc
Lowest	0	5530	0
Highest	32,000	27,648	32,000

Also, unless otherwise specified, assume the input integer to the DAC of an analog output module corresponds to the lowest and highest values of the output device control as:

Value	Modicon	Siemens	GE Fanuc
Lowest	0	5530	0
Highest	32,000	27,648	32,000

Your solution should include the following:

1. Specify the PLC processor used.
2. Instruction list program (with comments). For consistency among the different PLCs, use only variables/symbols/tags in the program. Use the syntax and function blocks consistent with the PLC processor.
3. Table listing additional internal memory (variables/symbols/tags) used and a brief description of their use. For the Quantum/Momentum processors, list the internal variables and the data type. For the other processors, list the internal variables/symbols and the associated memory address.

P13-1. Implement the simple logic of problem P2-1 using the IL language.

P13-2. Implement the simple logic of problem P2-2 using the IL language.

P13-3. Implement the simple logic of problem P2-3 using the IL language.

P13-4. Implement the simple logic of problem P2-4 using the IL language.

P13-5. High Level Indicator and Alarm. Implement the high level indicator and alarm of problem P2-8 using the IL language.

P13-6. Low Level Indicator and Alarm. Implement the low level indicator and alarm of problem P2-9 using the IL language.

P13-7. First Failure Indicator. Implement the first failure indicator of problem P2-10 using the IL language.

P13-8. Implement the cascaded timers of problem P5-1 using the IL language.

P13-9. Implement the cascaded timers of problem P5-2 using the IL language.

P13-10. Implement the cascaded timers of problem P5-3 using the IL language.

P13-11. Implement the cascaded timers of problem P5-4 using the IL language.

P13-12. One-shot pulse. Implement the one-shot pulse of problem P5-5 using the IL language.

P13-13. Flashing Lamps. Implement the flashing lamps of problem P5-6 using the IL language.

P13-14. Level Indicator and Alarm. Implement the level indicator and alarm of problem P5-8 using the IL language.

P13-15. Bunker Alarm. Implement the low bunker alarm of problem P5-10 using the IL language.

P13-16. Alarm for Generator Room Cooling Fans. Implement the alarm of problem P5-11 using the IL language.

P13-17. Bar Classifier. Implement the bar classifier station of problem P5-14 using the IL language.

P13-18. Parking Lot Sign Controller. Implement the parking log sign controller of problem P5-15 using the IL language.

P13-19. Tank Volume Alarm System. Implement the tank volume alarm of problem P5-17 using the IL language.

P13-20. Modified Tank Volume Alarm System. Implement the tank volume alarm of problem P5-18 using the IL language.

P13-21. Simple Tank Level Control. Implement the tank level control of problem P5-20 using the IL language.

P13-22. Automatic Plant waterer. Implement the plant waterer of problem P5-21 using the IL language.

P13-23. Proportional Level Control. Implement the level controller of problem P7-14 using the IL language.

P13-24. Simple Pressure Control. Implement the pressure controller of problem P7-15 using the IL language.

P13-25. Tank Level Indicator. Implement the tank level indicator and alarm of problem P7-17 using the IL language.

P13-26. Flow Meter Accumulator. Implement the accumulator of problem P7-18 using the IL language.

14 Sequential Function Chart

Chapter Topics:

- IEC 61131-3 sequential function chart (SFC) language
- Modicon SFC language
- Allen-Bradley ControlLogix and PLC-5 SFC language
- Siemens S7-Graph language

OBJECTIVES

Upon completion of this chapter, you will be able to:

- Understand the IEC 61131-3 standard sequential function chart language
- Understand the Modicon, Allen-Bradley, and Siemens S7 implementations of the SFC language
- Write SFCs for sequential applications

Scenario: Figure 14.1 shows the side view of a station that checks the height of a part. When the piece is in position, the height check pneumatic cylinder is extended to cause the probe to contact the top of the piece. The final position of the probe is measured by a height check variable resistor, which is converted into a voltage read by a PLC analog input. The analog input value is then converted into a height in mm. After retracting the height check cylinder, pieces that are too high are lowered and ejected into a reject bin. Pieces that are not

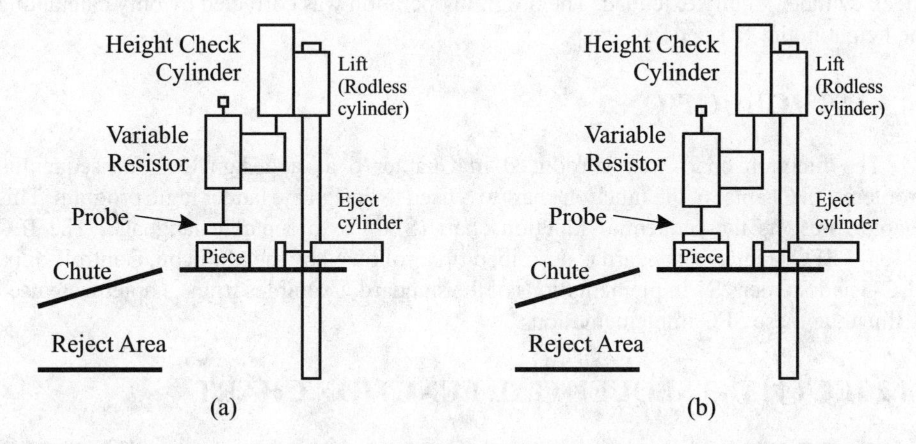

Figure 14.1. Height checking station: *(a)* height check cylinder retracted; *(b)* height check cylinder extended.

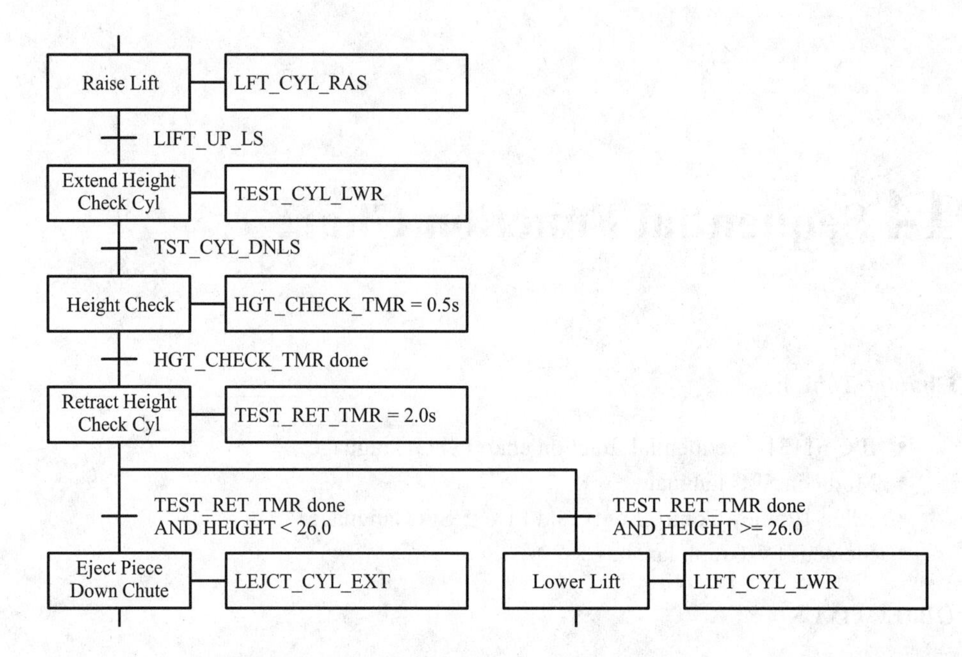

Figure 14.2. Partial function chart for height check station.

too high are pushed onto a chute that conveys the piece to the next station that drills a hole in the piece. A function chart for the operation of this station is shown in Figure 14.2. When the program was initially tested, all pieces that were too high were accepted instead of being rejected.

Solution: First, the analog input was tested by observing the analog input channel value when the probe position is changed. The value was correct, as well as the calculation of the height in mm. However, when the program was paused in the "Retract Height Check" step, the value of the height was 0 mm. Further examination of the program revealed that the height was calculated continuously. The height calculation is only valid when the height check cylinder is fully extended. The program operation was corrected by only calculating the height in the "2 sec delay" step.

14.1 INTRODUCTION

The function chart was introduced in Chapter 6 as a design tool for sequential problems. In Chapter 6, the function chart was used to design the ladder logic program. This chapter presents the sequential function chart (SFC) as a separate language. The IEC 61131-3 SFC language standard is described first, followed by the Modicon, ControlLogix, PLC-5 and Siemens S7 implementations of the standard. Examples from Chapter 6 are used to illustrate these SFC implementations.

14.2 IEC 61131-3 SEQUENTIAL FUNCTION CHART

The IEC 61131-3 sequential function chart (SFC) language is derived from the IEC 848 function chart standard (IEC, 1988) that has been used to define sequence control logic. The

IEC 61131-3 SFC language elements are derived from IEC 848 with the changes necessary to convert the representations from a documentation standard to a set of execution control elements for a programmable controller program organization unit. This format has emerged as a major programming tool in modern control systems, especially batch control systems.

The roots of the SFC language can be found in Petri nets. In a Petri net, circles and arcs depict states and transitions, respectively. Petri nets are commonly used in computer systems design. Grafcet evolved from Petri nets as an industrial form of the methodology applied to sequence control logic. Grafcet was codified as the IEC 848 function chart standard (IEC, 1988).

IEC 61131-3 defines a graphical, semi-graphical, and textual format for a SFC. Only the graphical format is explained in this chapter since this is the form most commonly provided by the vendors.

The SFC is a diagram of interconnected steps, actions, and transitions as illustrated in Figure 14.3. A SFC diagram begins with an initial step (a box enclosed in a double line) followed by an ordered set of labeled steps configured to perform the desired sequential control scheme. A vertical line attached to the top of the step represents the path into the step. A vertical line attached to the bottom of the step represents the path out of the step. A horizontal line across the vertical line represents the transition condition that causes control to pass from the step preceding the transition to the step succeeding the transition. If the step is active and the transition condition below the step is true, the logic advances to the next step. The step-wise flow (called step evolution) generally goes from top to bottom. Branching is allowed to cause the step evolution to lead back to an earlier step and to allow multiple paths. A step without a vertical line below represents the last step of the sequence.

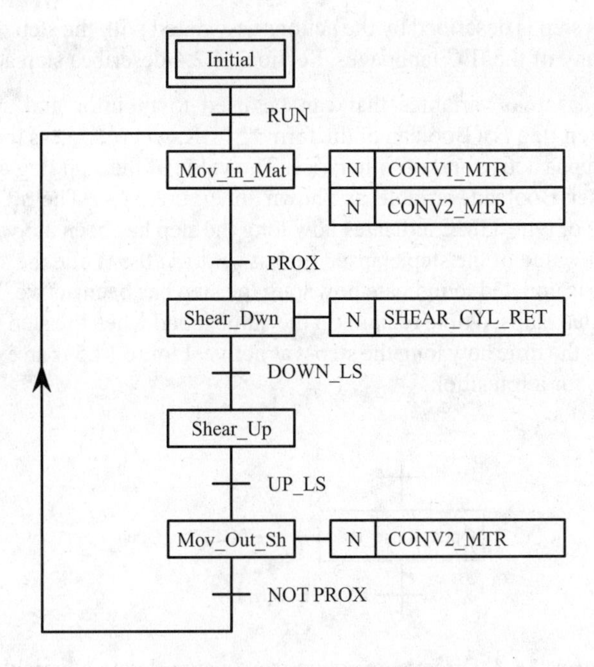

Figure 14.3. Example SFC.

IEC 61131-3 does not define a standard way to reset the SFC to its initial state, so the particular implementation of this function varies among the vendors.

The SFC in Figure 14.3 is the control for the metal shear of Examples 6.1 and 6.2. The program starts in the Initial step. When START_PB is pressed, control is passed to the Move_In_Mat step. The two conveyor motors run, moving the metal strip. In contrast to the generalized function chart defined in Chapter 6, each IEC 61131-3 action is shown separately. The "N" indicates the action is non-stored, that is, active (**on**) when the step is active. When PROX is **on**, control is passed to the Shear_Dwn step, causing the SHEAR_CYL_RET output to be turned **on**. The steps evolve in this manner until the Mov_Out_Sh step is active and PROX turns **off**. In this case, the next step is the Move_In_Mat step, and the operation repeats. The disabling (turning off) of actions when the operation is paused and the reset of the SFC to the initial step is not defined by IEC 61131-3. These aspects of the problem will be discussed when considering a particular vendor's implementation of SFCs.

The various aspects of sequential function charts are now described.

14.2.1 Steps

Each step within a sequential function chart has a unique name and should only appear once in a SFC. There are two forms of a step, both shown in Figure 14.3:

1. Normal step, depicted as a rectangle with the step name in the center of the rectangle;
2. Initial step, depicted as a double rectangle ("Initial" in Figure 14.3). Alternatively, the initial step may be depicted as a rectangle with double vertical lines. Each SFC has only one initial step, and this is the step that will be activated when the SFC is executed for the first time.

The behavior of a step is described by the actions associated with the step. Each action may be described by any of the IEC languages. Section 14.2.4 describes step actions.

Every step has two variables that can be used to monitor and synchronize step activation. The **step flag** is a Boolean of the form ****.X, where **** is the step name, that is **on** while the step is active and **off** otherwise. The value of the step flag can be connected directly to another Boolean variable as shown in Figure 14.4. The **step elapsed time** (****.T) variable of type TIME indicates how long the step has been active. When a step is first activated, the value of the step elapsed time is set to T#0s. While the step is active, the step elapsed time is updated to indicate how long the step has been active. When the step is deactivated, the step elapsed time remains at the value it had when the step was deactivated, that is, it indicates the time how long the step was active. Figure 14.5 is an example using the step elapsed time for a transition.

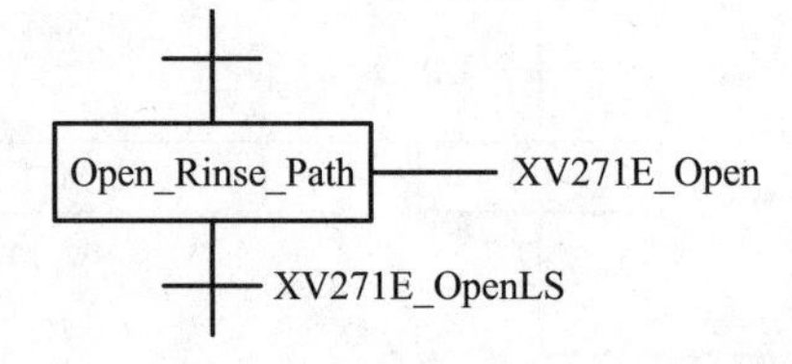

Figure 14.4. Direct connection from a step flag to a variable.

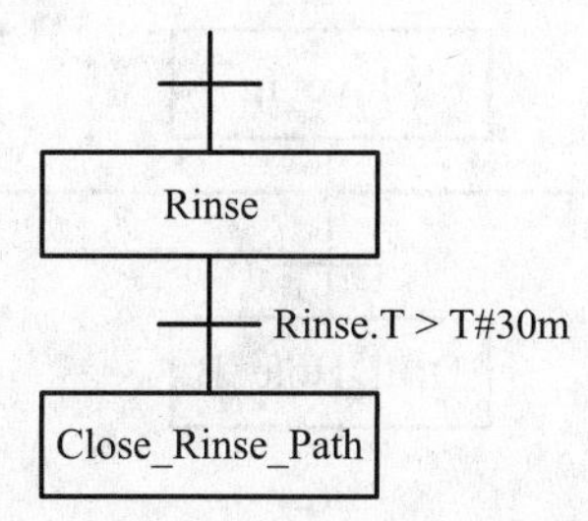

Figure 14.5. Example use of step elapsed time variable in transtion.

14.2.2 Step Evolution Rules

The flow of active steps in a SFC is called *step evolution* and generally starts with the initial step and proceeds downward. The steps and transitions alternate, that is,

Two steps are never directly linked; they are always separated by a transition.

Two transitions are never directly linked; they are always separated by a step.

Figure 14.3 shows a simple single sequence, illustrating the alternation of steps and transitions.

Sequence selection is also possible, causing the step evolution to choose between two or more different paths. An example sequence selection divergence, and its corresponding convergence, is shown in Figure 14.6. The transition conditions must be mutually exclusive, that is, no more than one can be true. Alternative forms of the divergence are shown in Figure 14.7. An asterisk at the divergence junction denotes left-to-right evaluation of the transition conditions (Figure 14.7*a*). Only one path is selected, even if more than one transition condition is true. For example, in Figure 14.7*a*, if the Move_In step is active and Trans_1 and Trans_3 are true simultaneously, the Drill_Hole_A step becomes active. The

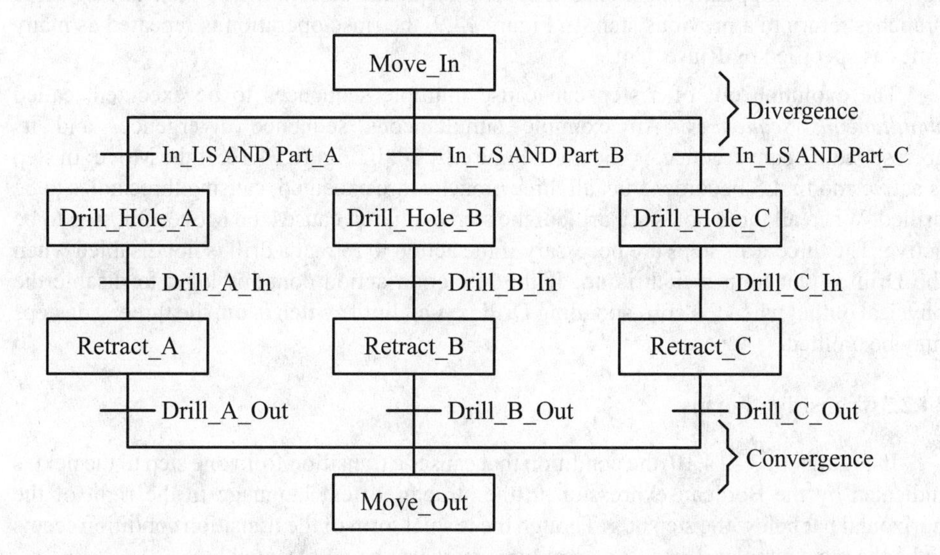

Figure 14.6. Example sequence selection divergence and convergence.

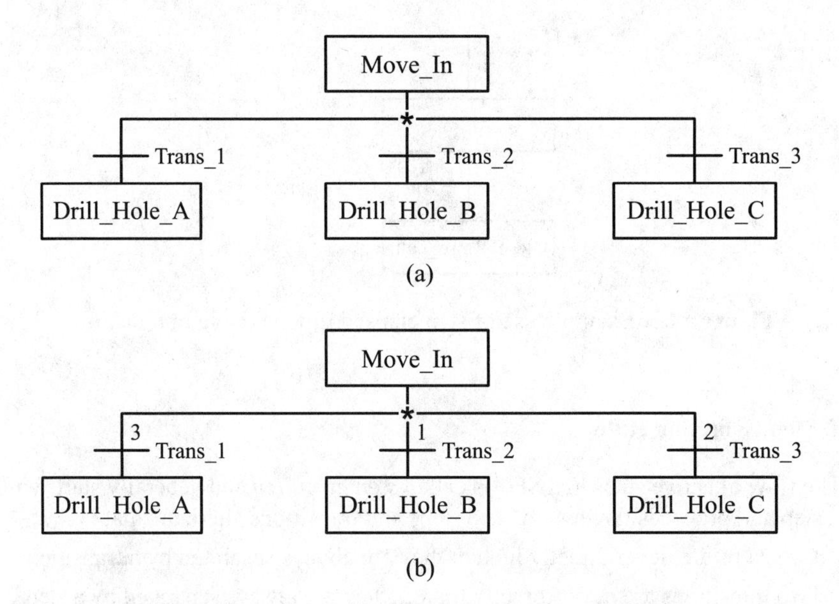

Figure 14.7. Alternate forms of sequence selection divergence: *(a)* right-to-left evaluation; *(b)* ordered evaluation.

evaluation order may be specified by numbering the branches. The lowest-numbered branch is examined first. For example, in Figure 14.7*b* , if the Move_In step is active and Trans_1 and Trans_3 are true simultaneously, the Drill_Hole_C step becomes active.

There are two special cases of sequence selection. In a *sequence skip* one or more branches contain no steps. In Figure 14.8, the steps to start up the conveying system are executed only if the conveying system is not running. Otherwise, the steps to start the conveyors are skipped. A *sequence loop* is a sequence selection in which one or more branches return to a previous step. In Figure 14.9, the rinse operation is repeated as many times as specified by Rinse_Cnt.

The evolution out of a step can cause multiple sequences to be executed, called *simultaneous sequences*. An example simultaneous sequence divergence, and its corresponding convergence, is shown in Figure 14.10. In Figure 14.10, if the Move_In step is active and In_LS becomes true, all three branches are executed, causing three holes to be drilled. When all three holes are drilled, the step evolution causes the Move_Out step to be active. The three wait steps are necessary if the action to retract a drill is not disabled when the Drill_x_Out limit switch is **on**. If the retraction action contains logic to disable the physical output when the corresponding Drill_x_Out limit switch is **on**, the three wait steps may be omitted.

14.2.3 Transition Forms

In Figures 14.3 - 14.10, the condition that causes a transition from one step to the next is indicated by the Boolean expression in the structured text language to the right of the horizontal bar below the step box. Though the textual form of the transition condition seems to be the most popular, transition conditions may also be represented by:

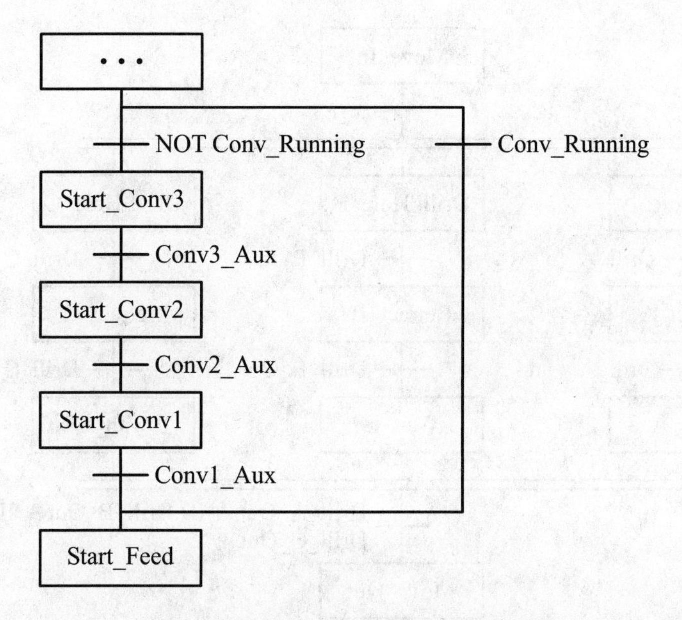

Figure 14.8. Example sequence skip.

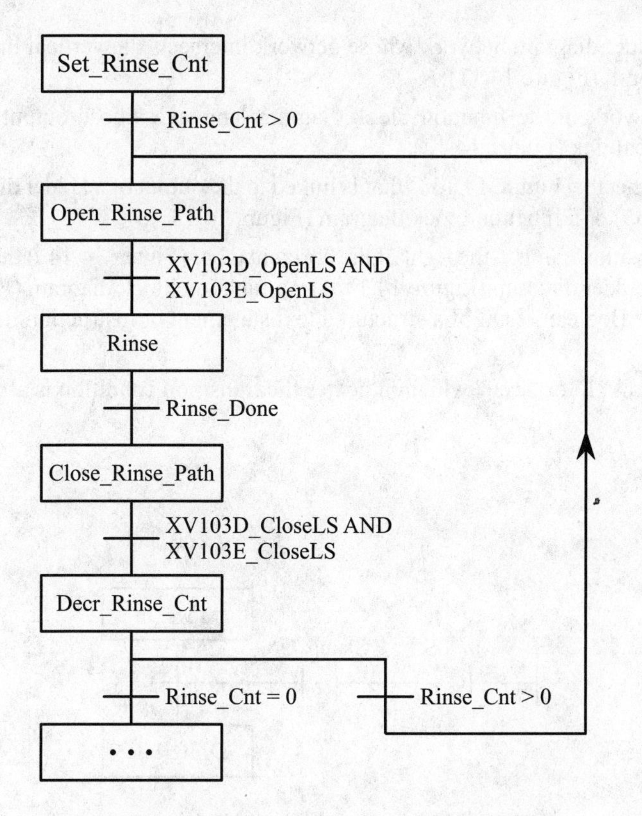

Figure 14.9. Example loop sequence.

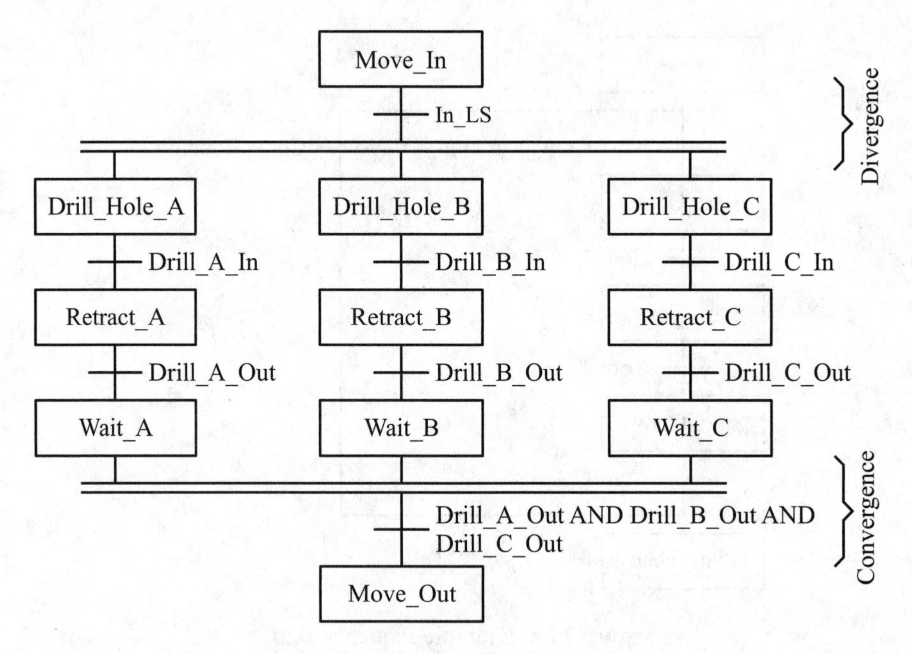

Figure 14.10. Example simultaneous sequence divergence and convergence.

1. a ladder diagram network whose network intersects the vertical link instead of a right rail (Figure 14.11);
2. a network in the function block diagram language whose output intersects the vertical link (Figure 14.12);
3. a connector (Figure 14.13*a*) that is linked to the output of a ladder diagram (Figure 14.13*b*) or a function block diagram (Figure 14.13*c*);
4. a transition name to the right of the horizontal bar (Figure 14.14*a*) that is the output of a ladder diagram (Figure 14.14*b*) or a function block diagram (Figure 14.14*c*); or the Boolean result of a structured text statement or instruction list instructions; or
5. a literal "1" or "true" which indicates the transition condition is always true.

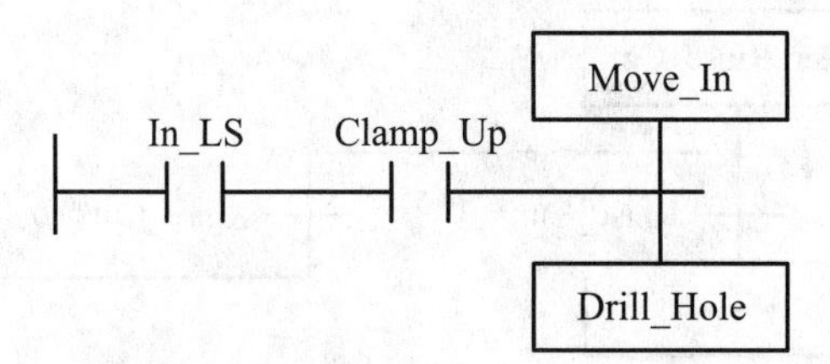

Figure 14.11. Transition as LD language.

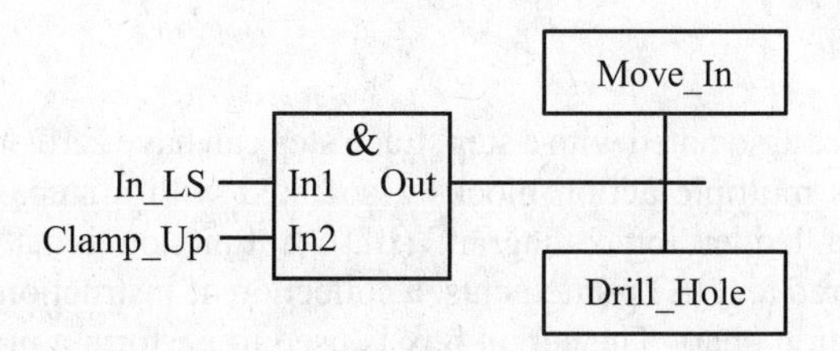

Figure 14.12. Transition condition as FBD language.

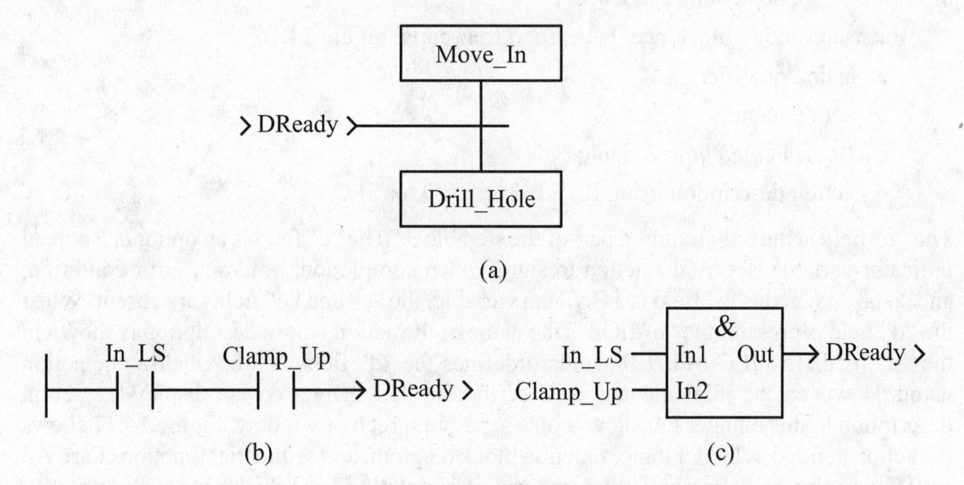

Figure 14.13. Transition connector: *(a)* connector in SFC; *(b)* connector using LD language; *(c)* connector using FBD language.

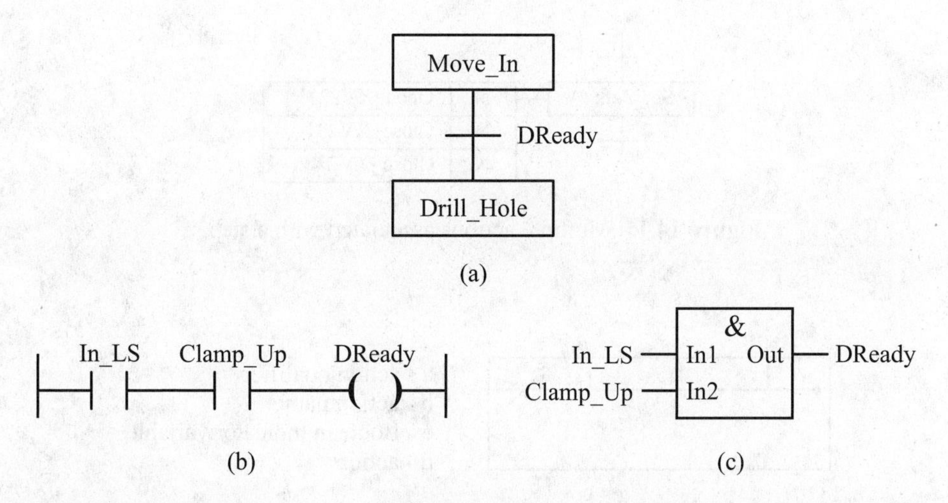

Figure 14.14. Transition name: *(a)* in SFC; *(b)* defined with LD language; *(c)* defined with FBD language.

14.2.4 Action Blocks

Action blocks are associated with a step. Each step can have zero or more action blocks. Figure 14.15 shows multiple action blocks associated with a step. An action can be a Boolean variable, a ladder logic diagram (LD), a function block diagram (FBD), a collection of structured text (ST) statements, a collection of instruction list (IL) statements, or a sequential function chart. The action box is used to perform a process action such as opening a valve, starting a motor or calculating an endpoint for the transition condition. Generally, each step issues a command although in cases where a step is only waiting for a transition (e. g., waiting for a limit switch to close) or executing a time delay (Shear_Up step of Figure 14.3), no action is attached.

Each step action block may have up to four parts, Figure 14.16:

a - action qualifier

b - action name

c - Boolean *indicator* variable

d - action description using IL, ST, LD, FBD, or SFC

The "b" field is the only required part of the step block. The "c" field is an optional Boolean indicator variable, set by the action to signify step completion, time-out, error condition, and so on. When the "b" field is a Boolean variable, the "c" and "d" fields are absent. When the "d" field is present, the "b" field is the name of the action whose description is shown in the "d" field. The IEC 61131-3 standard defines the "d" field as a box below the action name. However, the implementations described in this chapter do not display the action description in this manner but show it on a separate screen or window. Figure 14.17 shows the action defined as ladder logic, function block diagram, and sequential function chart. An action may also be defined as structured text or instruction list, which are not shown.

The action qualifier is a letter or a combination of letters describing how the step action is processed. If the action qualifier is absent, it is assumed to be "N." Possible action qualifiers are defined in Table 14.1 and described in the following paragraphs.

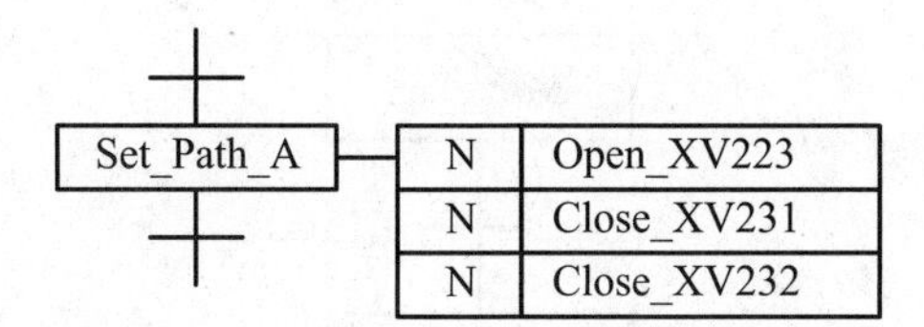

Figure 14.15. Multiple actions associated with a step.

a	b	c
	d	

a - action qualifier
b - action name
c - Boolean indicator variable
d - action

Figure 14.16. General format of action block.

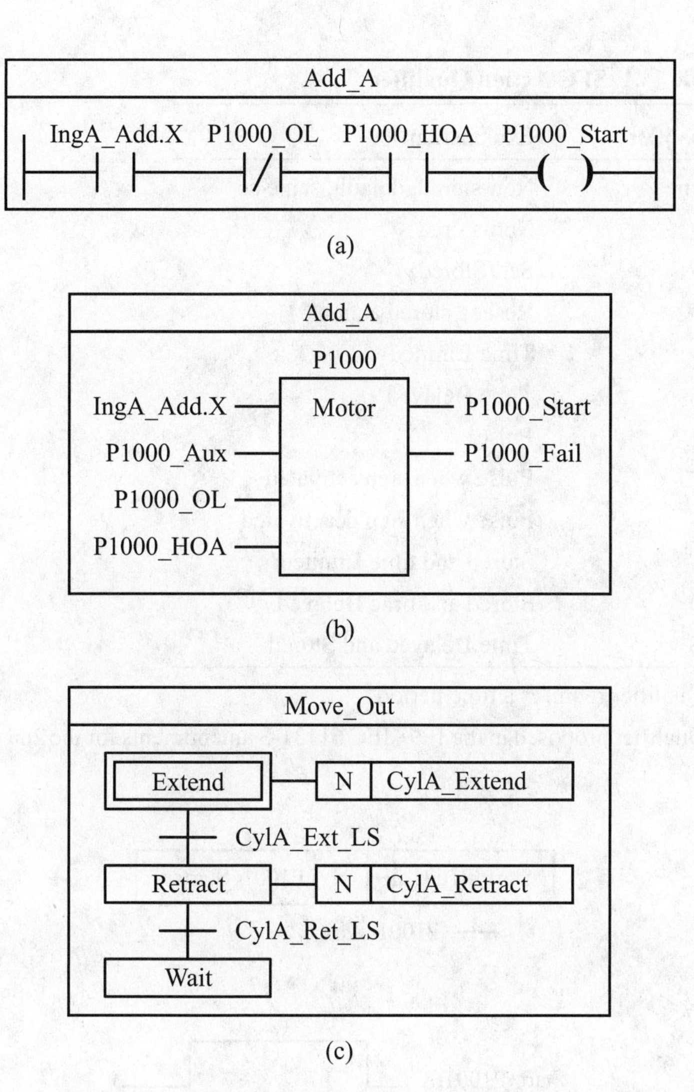

Figure 14.17. Action description: *(a)* defined with LD language; *(b)* defined with FBD language; *(c)* defined with SFC.

N – Non-stored action qualifier

A non stored action is active only when the step is active. In Figure 14.18, the action P1001_Starter executes continuously while the Start_P1001 step is active, that is, while Start_P1001.X flag is **on**. When the transition P1001_Aux turns **on**, the Start_P1001 step becomes inactive, and the P1001_Starter is turned **off** if P1001_Starter is a Boolean variable. If P1001_Starter is an action described in one of the IEC 61131-3 languages, deactivation of the step causes the action to execute one last time (often called postscan) in order to deactivate outputs and to reset action logic.

Table 14.1 SFC Action Qualifiers

Qualifier	Explanation
None	Non-stored, default, same as "N"
N	**N**on-stored
S	**S**et (**S**tored)
R	**R**eset a stored action
L[1]	Time **L**imited
D[1]	Time **D**elayed
P	**P**ulse
P1[2]	**P**ulse when step activated
P0[2]	**P**ulse when step deactivated
SL[1]	**S**tored and time **L**imited
SD[1]	**S**tored and time **D**elayed
DS[1]	Time **D**elayed and **S**tored

[1] Qualifier requires a time period

[2] Qualifier proposed in the 1998 IEC 61131-3 amendments for the 2nd ed.

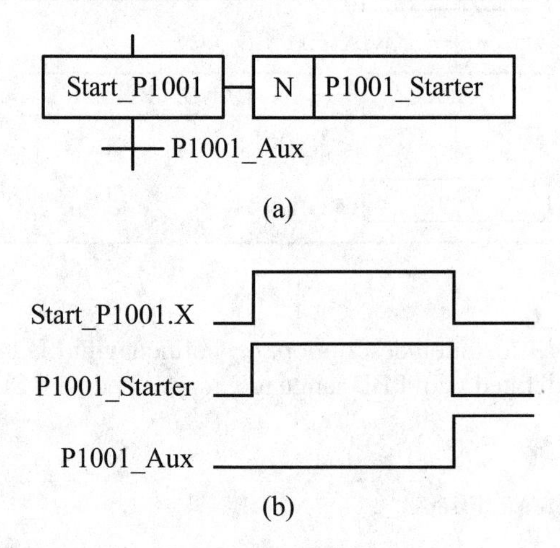

Figure 14.18. Non-stored action qualifier: *(a)* example; *(b)* timing diagram.

S and R – Stored (set) and Reset action qualifiers

A stored action becomes active when the step becomes active. The action continues to be executed even after the step is inactive. In order to stop the action, another step must have an R qualifier that references the same action. Figure 14.19 is an example use of the S and R qualifiers. The S qualifier on the action for the Open_Rinse step causes the XV2103_Sol to

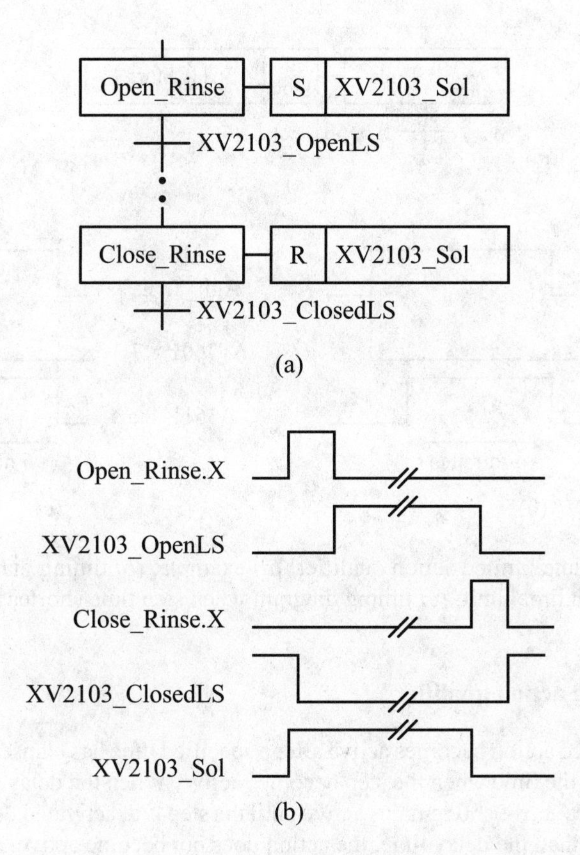

Figure 14.19. Stored (set) and reset action qualifiers: *(a)* example; *(b)* timing diagram.

be turned **on** immediately after the Open_Rinse step becomes active. The XV2103_Sol remains on until the Close_Rinse step, which has an R qualifier on the XV2103_Sol action. As soon as the Close_Rinse step becomes active, the XV2103_Sol is turned **off**. If XV2013_Sol is an action described in one of the IEC 61131-3 languages, activation of Close_Rinse causes the action to execute one last time in order to deactivate outputs and/or reset action logic.

L – time Limited action qualifier

A time limited action becomes active when the step becomes active. The action becomes inactive when a set length of time elapses or the step becomes inactive, whichever happens first. In Figure 14.20*a*, the L qualifier on the action for the Agit_Tank step causes the A3611_Start to be turned **on** immediately after the Agit_Tank step becomes active. If the step elapsed time is longer than 6 minutes, A3611_Start remains on for 6 minutes (Figure 14.20*b*). If the step elapsed time is less than 6 minutes, A3611_Start turns **off** when the step becomes inactive (Figure 14.20*c*). If A3611_Start is an action described one of the IEC 61131-3 languages, deactivation of the action causes the action to execute one more time in order to deactivate outputs and to reset action logic.

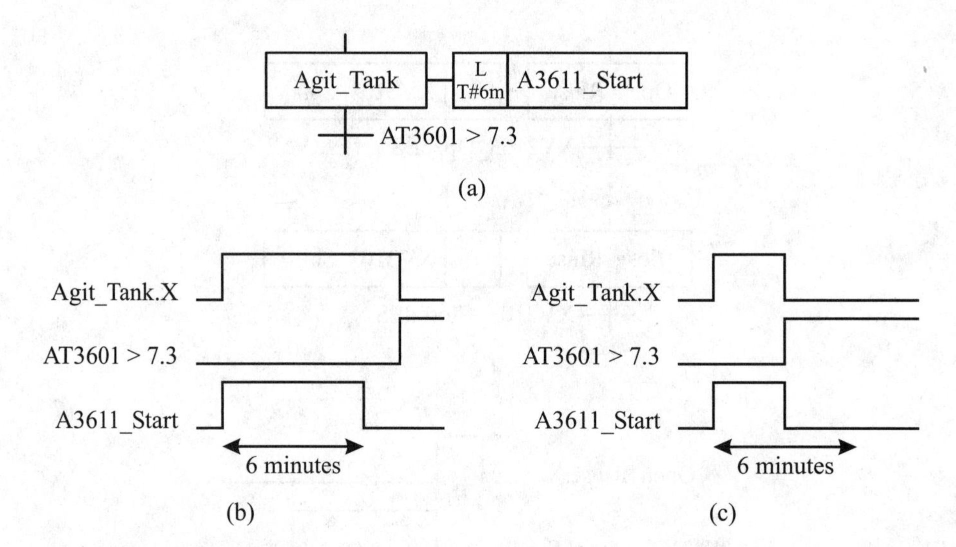

Figure 14.20. Time limited action qualifier: *(a)* example; *(b)* timing diagram when step time longer than time limit; *(c)* timing diagram when step time shorter than time limit.

D – time Delayed action qualifier

A time delayed action becomes active after a specified time has elapsed. The delay time is measured from the time when the step becomes active. When the delay time has elapsed, the action becomes active and remains active until the step is deactivated. If the elapsed time in the step is less than the delay time, the action does not become active. In Figure 14.21*a*, the Set_Alarm action is executed if the step time for Move_Out is longer than 2 seconds (Figure 14.21*b*). If the Move_Out step time is less than 2 seconds, then Set_Alarm is not executed (Figure 14.21*c*).

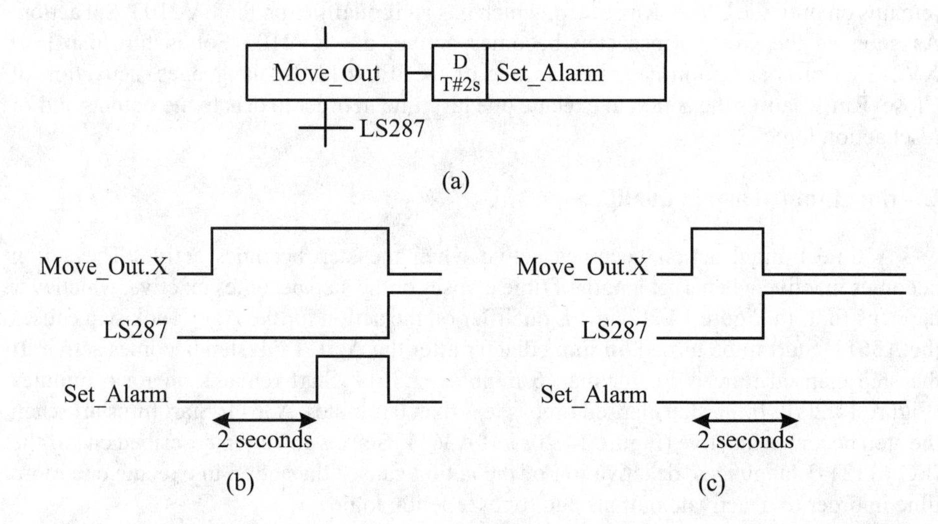

Figure 14.21. Time delayed action qualifier: *(a)* example; *(b)* timing when step time longer than time delay; *(c)* timing when step time shorter than time delay.

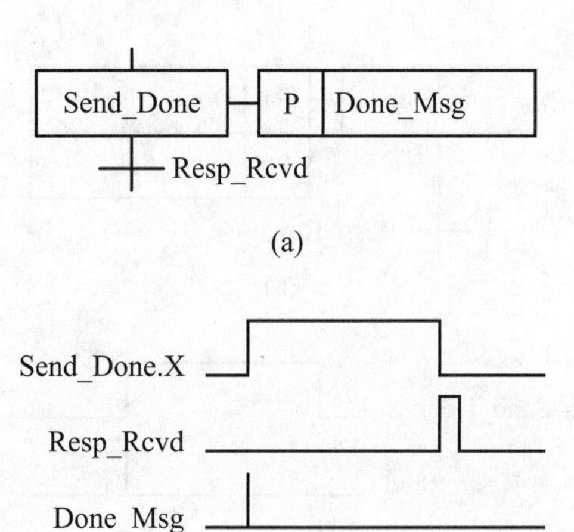

Figure 14.22. Pulse action qualifier: *(a)* example; *(b)* timing diagram.

P – Pulse action qualifier

For a P qualifer the action becomes active for the single scan in which the step becomes active. If the action is described in one of the IEC 61131-3 languages, the action executes once. In Figure 14.22, the Send_Msg action is executed once when the Send_Done step becomes active. Even if the step time is zero (the transition condition is already satisfied when the step becomes active), an action with a P qualifier is executed once. If the IEC 61131-3 standard is implemented exactly, an action with a P qualifier executes a second time from the rule that action statements or networks are executed one final time after the action deactivation. In some 61131-3 implementations, the pulse action is not executed a second time. Therefore, a step action with the P qualifier may behave differently when ported to a different system. When available, the P1 and P0 qualifiers are a better choice.

P1 and P0 – Pulse action qualifiers

For a P1 qualifer the action becomes active for the single scan in which the step becomes active. For a P0 qualifer the action becomes active for the single scan in which the step becomes inactive. If the action is described in one of the IEC 61131-3 languages, the action executes exactly once. In Figure 14.23, the Send_Msg action is executed once when the Send_Done step becomes active. The Save_Ack action is executed once when the Send_Done step becomes inactive. Even if the step time is zero (the transition condition is already satisfied when the step becomes active), an action with a P1 or P0 qualifier is executed once. For both of these qualifiers, there is no second execution when the step action deactivates. When available, the P1 and P0 qualifiers are preferred to the P qualifier.

SL – Stored and time Limited action qualifier

With the SL qualifier the action becomes active when the step becomes active. The action is deactivated after a set length of time elapses or an R qualified action block references the same action. The action remains active after the step becomes inactive, if the step time is shorter than the limit time. A step with an R qualified action block must refer to

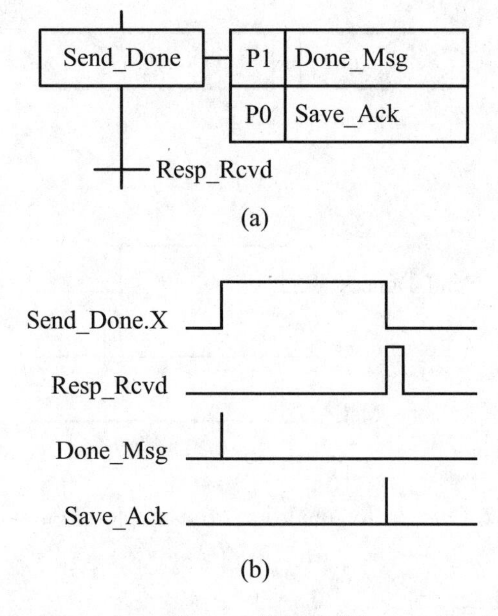

Figure 14.23. P1 and P0 pulse action qualifiers: *(a)* example; *(b)* timing diagram.

this action before this action can be used again. In Figure 14.24*a*, the SL qualifier on the action for the Agit_Tank step causes the A3611_Start to be turned **on** immediately after the

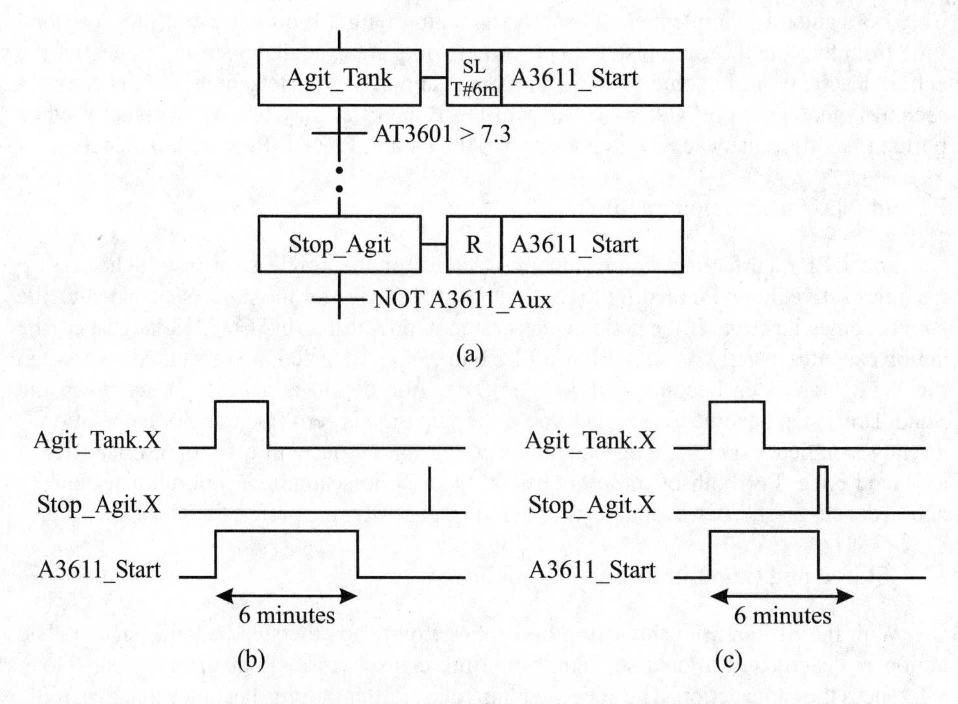

Figure 14.24. Stored and time limited action qualifier: *(a)* example; *(b)* timing when step time shorter than time limit; *(c)* timing when reset before time limit.

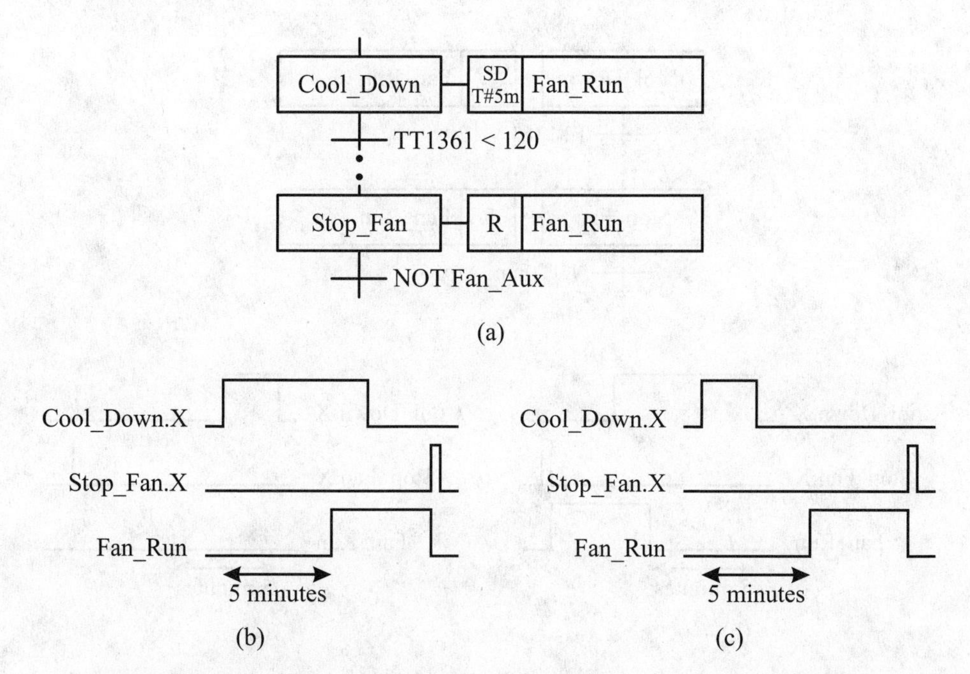

Figure 14.25. Stored and time delayed action qualifier: *(a)* example; *(b)* timing when step time longer than time delay; *(c)* timing when step time shorter than time delay.

Agit_Tank step becomes active. Even if the step elapsed time is less than 6 minutes, A3611_Start turns **off** after 6 minutes (Figure 14.24*b*). The A3611_Start is **on** for less than 6 minutes only if the Stop_Agit step becomes active during this 6 minute interval (Figure 14.24*c*). If A3611_Start is an action described in one of the IEC 61131-3 languages, deactivation of the action causes the action to execute one last time in order to deactivate outputs and to reset action logic.

SD – Stored and time Delayed action qualifier

If the action is qualified with SD, the activation of the action is delayed for a set time after the step becomes active. The action is stored after the time delay even if the step that has the SD qualifier for this action becomes inactive. After the time delay, the action is activated and remains active until another step with an R qualified action block references the same action. Figure 14.25*a* shows an example use of the SD qualifier. The Fan_Run action is activated 5 minutes after the Cool_Down step becomes active. The Cool_Down step time can be longer than 5 minutes (Figure 14.25*b*) or shorter than 5 minutes (Figure 14.25*c*). In either case, when the Stop_Fan step becomes active, the Fan_Run action is deactivated.

DS – time Delayed and Stored action qualifier

With the DS qualifier, activation of the action is delayed for a set time after the step becomes active, only if the step is still active after the time delay has elapsed. After the action is activated, another step with an R qualified block that references the same action

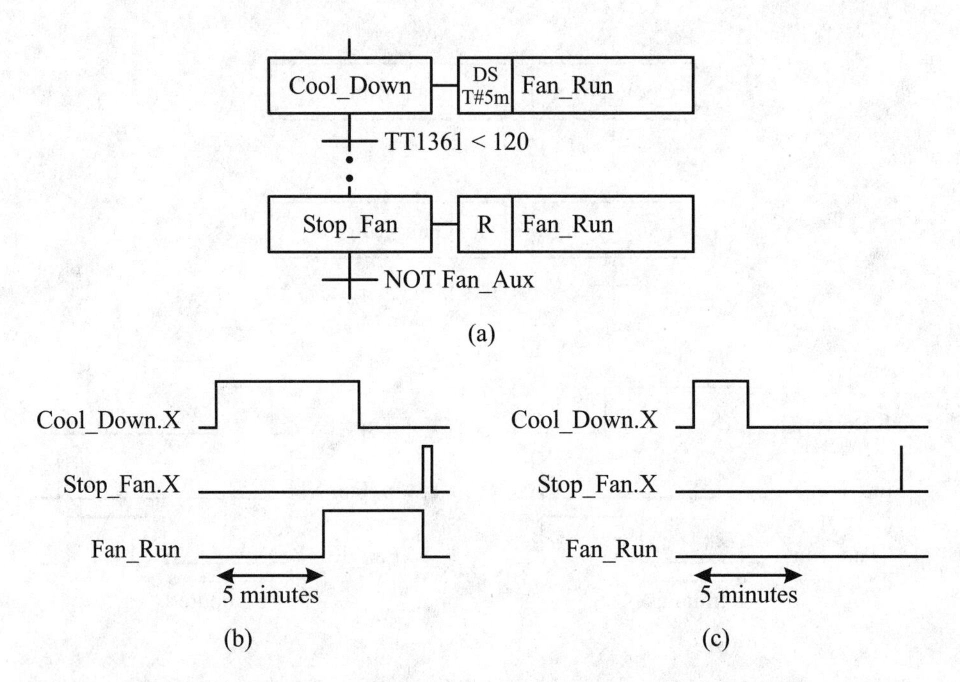

Figure 14.26. Time delayed and stored action qualifier: *(a)* example; *(b)* timing when step time longer than time delay; *(c)* timing when step time shorter than time delay.

must deactivate the action. In Figure 14.26*a*, the Fan_Run action is executed if the step time for Cool_Down is longer than 5 minutes (Figure 14.26*b*). When the Stop_Fan step becomes active, the Fan_Run action is deactivated. If the Cool_Down step time is less than 5 minutes, then Fan_Run is not executed (Figure 14.26*c*).

The IEC 61131-3 SFC language allows the use of action blocks in ladder diagrams and function block diagrams. As an example, Figure 14.27 shows an action in a ladder diagram. The action to start the motor is activated when permitted and an internal start is on. The action is time limited and turns on M705_Started while it is active. The equivalent example in the function block diagram language is shown in Figure 14.28.

A more complicated SFC example is shown in Figure 14.29. This SFC controls a batch process. The reaction vessel is heated to a desired initial temperature and then the appropriate ingredients are added, depending on the desired product. The reactor

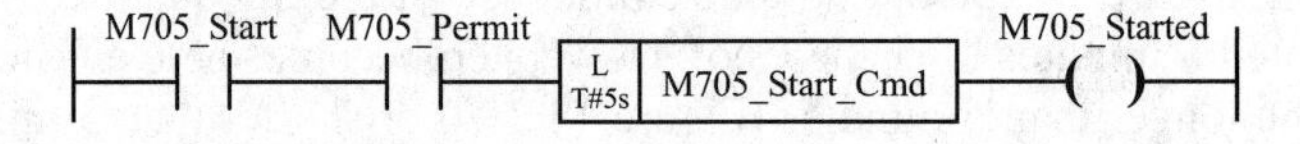

Figure 14.27. SFC action used in ladder diagram.

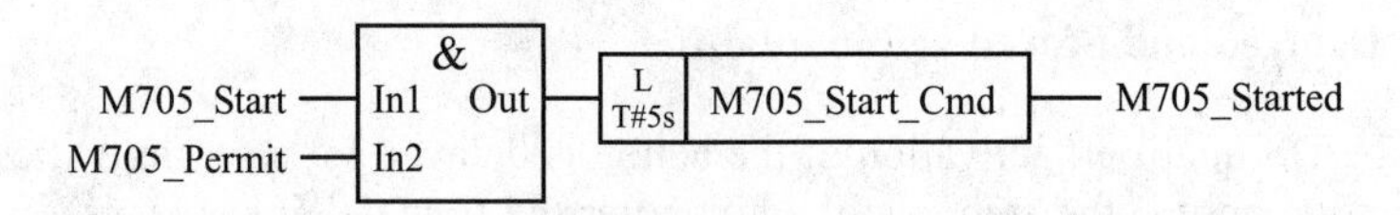

Figure 14.28. SFC action used in function block diagram.

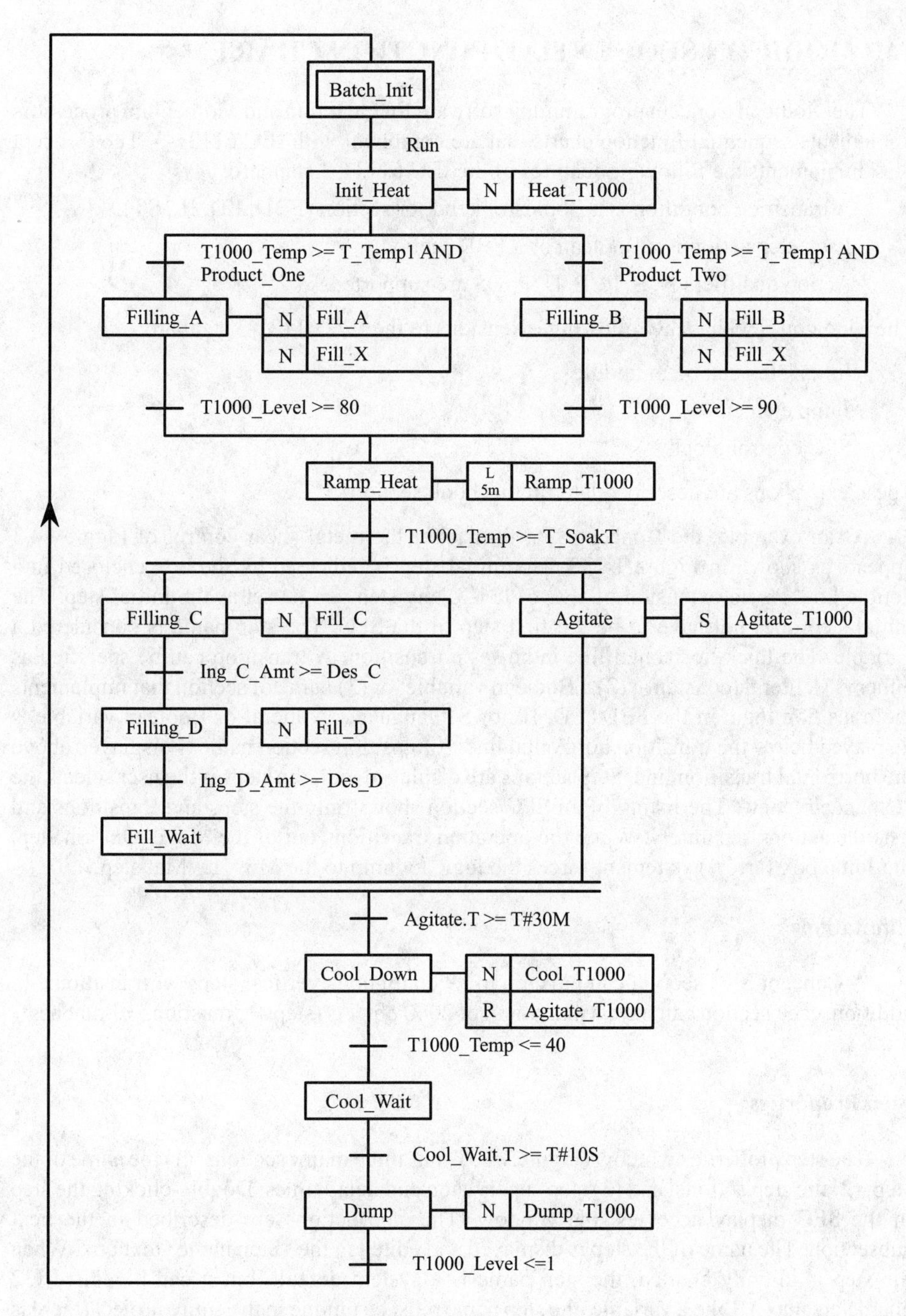

Figure 14.29. More complicated SFC showing action qualifiers.

temperature is raised to the soak temperature and then two more ingredients are added while agitating. The vessel is cooled and then dumped.

14.3 MODICON SEQUENTIAL FUNCTION CHART

The Modicon Concept programming software for Quantum and Momentum processors implements sequential function charts that are compliant with IEC 61131-3. The Concept SFC implements the following features of the IEC 61131-3 standard:

A transition condition is a Boolean, literal, or section (FBD, LD, IL, ST).

Each step action is a Boolean or a FBD section.

Action qualifiers N, S, R, L, D, P, DS are supported.

The Modicon SFC has the following extensions to the IEC 61131-3 standard:

Initial step can be in middle

Jump element

SFC control block

These extensions are described later in this book section.

As an example, the Concept SFC format for the metal shear control of Figure 14.3 appears as shown in Figure 14.30. The initial step is indicated by the box enclosed in a double line. As an extension of IEC 61131-3, any step can be set as the initial step. The initial step does not have to be the first step in the SFC. The step name is considered a variable. The thick horizontal line indicates a transition. A transition can be specified as either (1) a literal (constant); (2) a Boolean variable; or (3) name of section that implements the transition logic in the FBD, LD, IL, or ST language. A literal or Boolean variable is displayed below the transition horizontal line. A transition section name is displayed above the horizontal transition line. Step actions are displayed with the steps if the user selects the "expanded" view. The listing of an SFC section shows only the steps and transitions and lists the actions separately. When the operation transitions out of the Move_Out_Sh step, the Jump box (arrow) statement forces the logic to jump to the Mov_In_Mat step.

Limitations

A Concept SFC section can have up to 99 contiguous vertical steps w/ transitions. In addition, each section can have a maximum of 2000 objects (steps + transtions + branches + joints).

Step Properties

The step properties window (Figure 14.31) has three major sections: (1) the name of the step; (2) the step actions; and (3) step supervision and delay times. Double-clicking the step in the SFC display accesses this window. The step actions are described in the next subsection. The name of the step is displayed and edited in the "Step name" text box. When the step is initially created, the step name is a system default, but it can be edited (32 characters max.). Like a variable, the step name must be unique in the entire project (there is no distinction between upper/lower case). If this step is an initial step, the "Initial Step" box is checked.

The step delay time ("Delay" field) is the minimum length of time a step should be active. When defined, the minimum supervision time ("Minimum" field) and maximum supervision time ("Maximum" field) monitor the step time and indicate an error if the actual

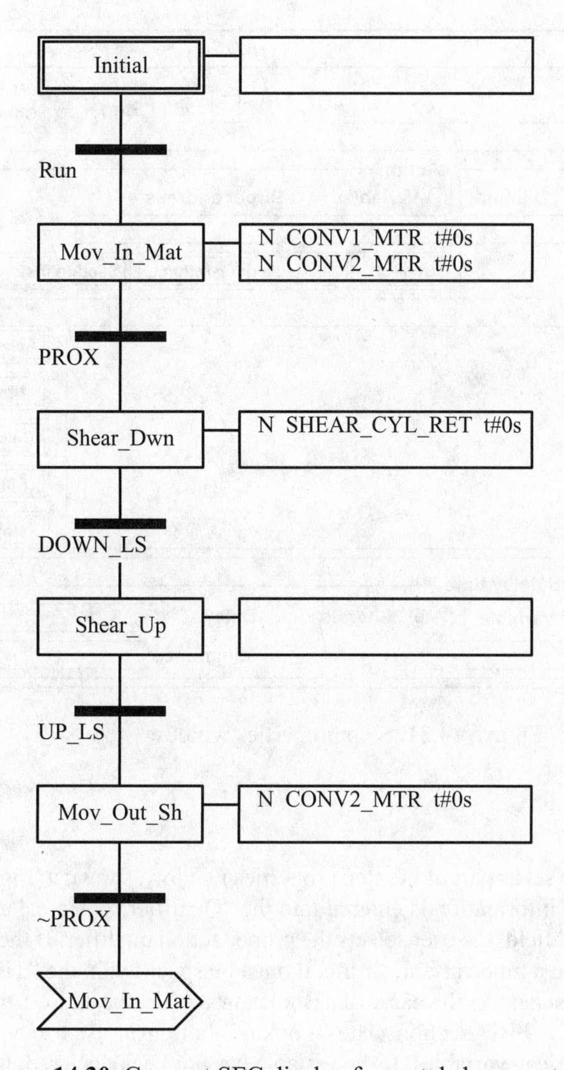

Figure 14.30. Concept SFC display for metal shear control.

step time falls outside these values. The error indications are described as part of the step status. Note that

Delay time ≤ Minimum supervision time < Maximum supervision time.

If the "Literals" button is selected, the maximum supervision time, the minimum supervision time, and the delay time can be entered in the text boxes as a time literal. If the "'SFCSTEP_TIMES' variable" button is selected, the bottom part of the step properties window is replaced by a field that allows one to specify the name of a variable of type SFCSTEP_TIMES. A variable named "varname" of type SFCSTEP_TIMES has the following components:

varname.delay - step delay time (of type TIME)
varname.min - minumum supervision time (of type TIME)
varname.max - maximum supervision time (of type TIME)

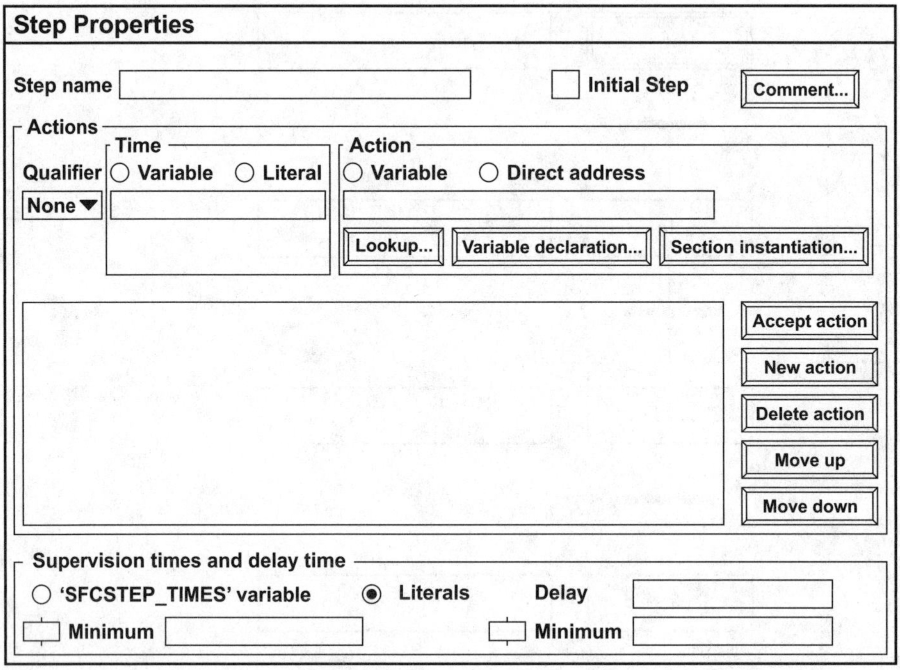

Figure 14.31. Step properties window.

Step Actions

The step actions are set as part of the step properties window, shown in Figure 14.31. If an action is desired, the information is entered into the "Qualifier," "Time," and "Action" fields. In the "Qualifier" field, the user selects the proper action qualifier. If the L, D, or DS qualifier is selected, then a time variable or literal must be specified in the "Time" field. In the "Action" field, the user enters the name of a Boolean variable, the address of a hardware output, or the name of a FBD section. The "Lookup" button is used to view a list of previously declared Boolean variables. If the variable has not been declared, the "Variable declaration" button is used to invoke the variable editor. If the action is a macro (FBD section) that has not been inserted into a section, the "Section instantiation" allows one to do so.

The "Accept action," "New action," and "Delete action" buttons are used to create/modify/delete step actions. If the step contains no actions, the proper fields for the action are defined, and then "New action" is selected. If the step contains at least one action, the selected action fields are displayed in the upper part of the "Actions" portion of the window. To modify the fields for a selected action, change the desired fields and select "Accept action" when done. To add a new action, select the "New action" button, change the action fields and select "Accept action." Use the "Delete action" button to delete the selected action. The "Move up," and "Move down" buttons are used to move the selected action up or down, respectively, in the list of actions. Figure 14.32 shows an example step properties window with three actions. Note that the selected action is displayed in two places in the window.

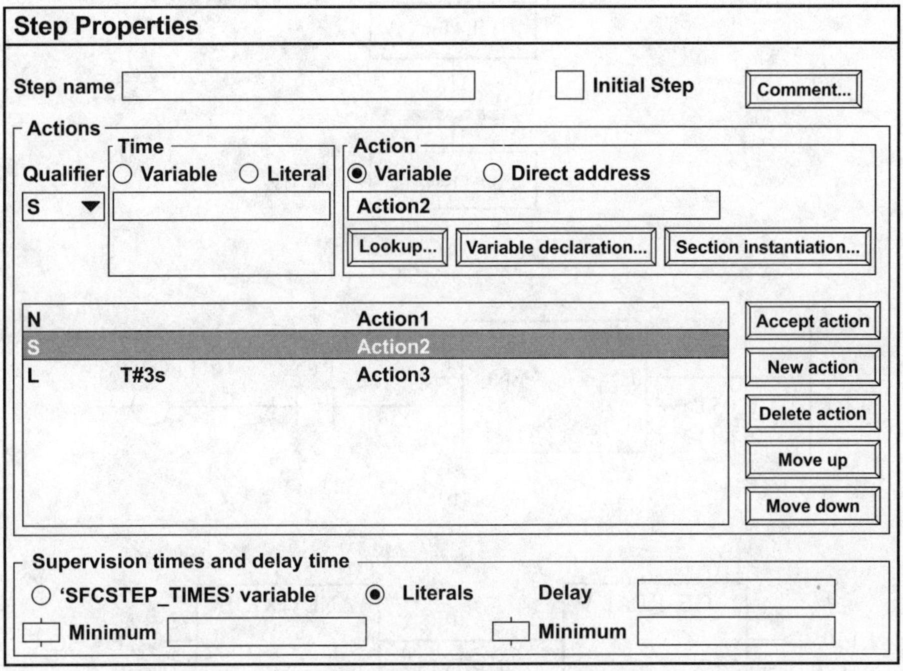

Figure 14.32. Sample actions in step properties window.

Step Status

The step status information is accessed as components of a variable whose name is the name of the step. The status information associated with a step is:

Name	Description
.t	Length of time step has been active (TIME type)
.x	**On** when step is active (Boolean)
.tminErr	**On** when step duration is less than the minimum supervision time (Boolean), **off** otherwise.
.tmaxErr	**On** when step duration is greater than the maximum supervision time (Boolean), **off** otherwise.

For example, to access the step flag of the Shear_Up step of Figure 14.30, the variable is "Shear_Up.x." To access the step elapsed time of the same step, the variable is "Shear_Up.t."

Transitions

A step transition can be assigned to a Boolean variable, to a Boolean literal, to a direct hardware address (input or output), or to a transition section. A variable, literal, or direct address is displayed below the transition line. If the transition is defined as a transition section, the name of the transition section is displayed above the transition line. A transition section is the same as the named transition of IEC 61131-3 (Figure 14.14) and may be written in the FBD, LD, IL, or ST languages. An example transition section appears on the SFC as shown in Figure 14.33*a*. Alternate forms of the transition section are shown in

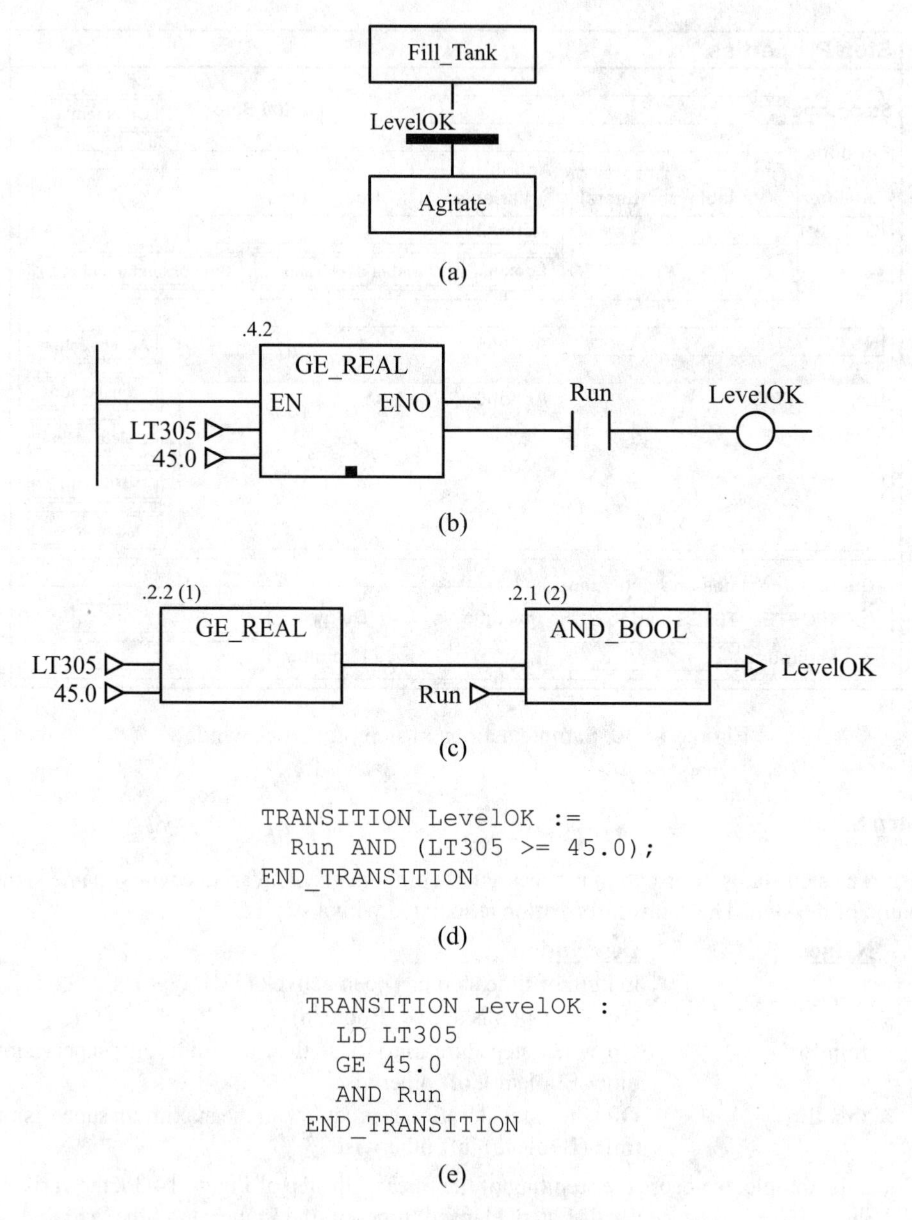

Figure 14.33. Transition section: *(a)* in SFC; *(b)* defined with LD; *(c)* defined as FBD; *(d)* defined as ST; *(e)* defined in IL.

Figure 14.33*b-e*. Note that the name of the transition section is the output variable of the rung, function block, structured text statement, or the result of the last instruction list statement.

Jump

A Jump lets the SFC skip steps and resume execution at the specified step in the SFC. For example, a Jump can be used to repeat execution of the SFC.

Figure 14.30 shows a Jump implementing a repeat of the SFC operation. The Jump occurs as the last part of the SFC and is shown as a box in the shape of an arrow pointing right. The name in the Jump box is the name of the jump destination. In Figure 14.30, when the "Mov_Out_Mat" step is active, and the "~Prox" transition is true, the jump forces the "Mov_In_Mat" step to become active.

A sequence skip, shown in Figure 14.34*a*, allows one to skip certain SFC steps. It is implemented as a sequence selection divergence and a jump to a step below the divergence. In Figure 14.34*a* (the Modicon implementation of Figure 14.8), the steps to start the conveyors are executed only if the conveying system is not running.

A sequence loop is constructed similarly to a sequence skip. The only difference is that the jump destination is above the selection divergence. For example, in Figure 14.34*b* (the Modicon implementation of Figure 14.9), the rinse operation is repeated as many times as specified.

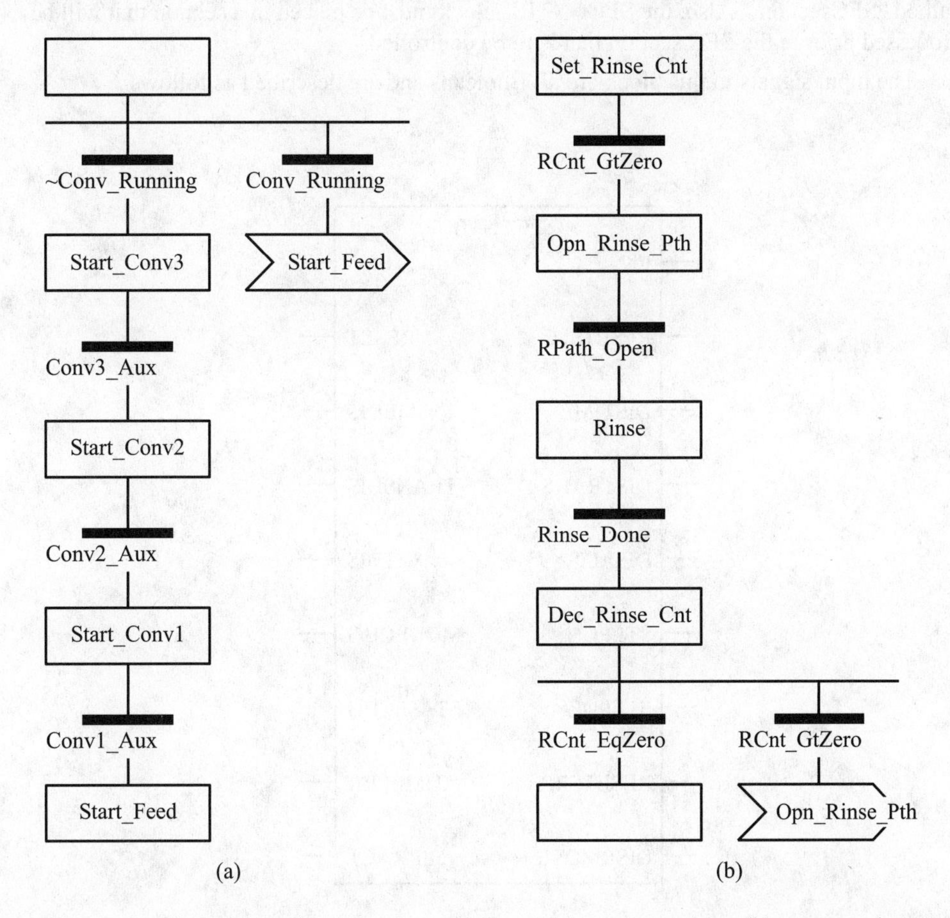

Figure 14.34. Modicon jump implementations: *(a)* sequence skip; *(b)* sequence loop.

There are some restrictions as to where the Jump may be placed in the SFC. A Jump may not be in a simultaneous sequence. Also, the destination of a jump statement may not be in a simultaneous sequence.

In order to avoid confusing the flow of the SFC, jumps should be used sparingly.

SFC Control

The SFCCNTRL and XSFCCNTRL function blocks are available to control the execution of a SFC. The SFCCNTRL function block, shown in Figure 14.35, allows programmatic manipulation of the processing of a SFC section. For example, step actions can be disabled, transition conditions can be overridden, or the sequence can be reset to the initial step. The SFCCNTRL block offers the same control actions that are available through the online menu and the animation panel. In addition, the function block has an input that can prevent the modification of the operating mode from the online animation screen. The XSFCCNTRL block has three additional inputs.

In order to assign the function block to a specific SFC section, the name of the SFC section MUST be entered as the name of the instance of the SFCCNTRL function block. For example, in Figure 14.35, the SFCCNTTRL controls the SFC contained in the section named "SFCsection." Also, the SFCCNTRL block must be placed in a section that will be processed prior to the SFC section that is to be controlled.

The input signals to this block are all Booleans and are described as follows:

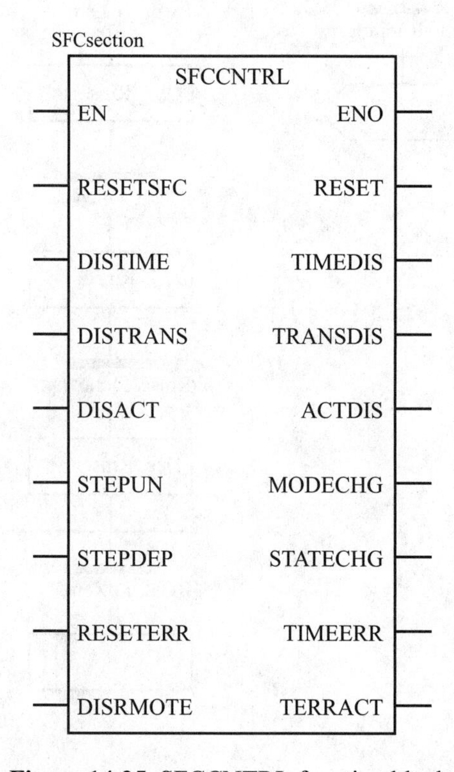

Figure 14.35. SFCCNTRL function block.

RESETSFC - SFC reset and standardized start. A change from false (0) to true (1) at the input stops the sequence and all actions are reset. There is no option for operator actions. A change from true to false at the input activates the initial step.

DISTIME (DISable TIME check) - A true condition at the input disables the checking for the minimum and maximum supervision times. This SFC control input does not disable the update of the step elapsed time.

DISTRANS (DISable TRANSitions) - A true condition at the input disables evaluation of the transitions. The sequence remains in the current step(s), independent of the signals at the transitions and the operation of the sequence is only possible through the RESETSFC, STEPUN, STEPDEP control commands.

DISACT (DISableACTions) - A true condition at the input disables processing of all step actions. Any actions that are set with the S or DS qualifiers are **reset** when DISACT is **on**. When actions are reenabled (DISACT = false), actions set with S or DS in a step prior to the step when actions are disabled, **remain reset**. Therefore, any logic that must remain **on** when actions are disabled must be set/reset in another program section. This SFC control input does not disable the update of the step elapsed time.

STEPUN (STEP UNconditional) - A change from false to true at the input activates the next step independent of the transition state, but not until the step delay time of the current step has terminated. In a simultaneous divergence, this command always activates all branches, in a selection divergence, the left branch is always activated.

STEPDEP (STEP transition DEPendent) - A change from false to true at the input and a satisfied transition condition will activate the next step. This command is executed only if there is a true condition at the DISTRANS input. By freezing the transitions (with DISTRANS = true) this control command allows one to manually move through the steps in a sequential fashion.

RESETERR (RESET ERRor display) - A change from false to true at this input will reset the display of the error messages generated by the supervisory times.

DISRMOTE (DISable ReMOTE) - A true condition at the input inhibits the control of the SFC with the online animation screen (Set Reset Flag, Disable Time Check, Disable Transition, Disable Actions). Nevertheless, the SFCCNTRL function block can still control the SFC.

Modicon warns the user that the RESETSFC, DISTRANS, DISACT, STEPUN and STEPDEP inputs are not recommended for troubleshooting with controllers of machine tools, processes or materials maintenance systems while they are running. The use of these inputs may result in unsafe, dangerous, and destructive operations of the tools or processes that are connected to the controller.

The output signals of the SFCCNTRL block are all Booleans and are described as follows:

RESET (mode of RESET) - The output becomes 1 if the sequence is stopped with the RESETSFC input of the SFCCNTRL or through the SFC online commands. Therefore, this output may have a different value than the RESETSFC input.

TIMEDIS (execution mode TIME supervision DISabled) - The output becomes 1 if the display of the time errors is disabled with the DISTIME input or through the

SFC online commands. Therefore, this output may have a different value than the DISTIME input.

TRANSDIS (execution mode TRANSitions DISabled) - The output becomes 1 if the evaluation of transitions has stopped with the DISTRANS input or through the SFC online commands. Therefore, this output may have a different value than the DISTRANS input.

ACTDIS (execution mode ACTions DISabled) - The output becomes 1 if the output of actions has stopped because of the DISACT input or through the SFC online commands. Therefore, this output may have a different value than the DISACT input.

MODECHG (execution MODE CHanGe) - The output becomes 1 for one cycle if one or several operating modes of the sequence have been changed. It does not matter whether the change was performed by the function block input (RESESTSFC, DISTIME, DISACT or DISTRANS) or through the SFC online commands.

STATECHG (sfc STATE CHanGe) - The output becomes 1 for one program scan if the state (step) of the sequence has been changed. This change may be caused by the processing of the sequence, by the SFCCNTRL function block, or through the SFC online commands.

TIMEERR (supervision TIME ERRor) - The output becomes 1 for one program scan if a step time violates either the minimum or maximum supervision time.

TERRACT (supervision Time ERRor ACTive) - The output remains 1 as long as there is at least one step time violating either the minimum or maximum supervision time.

Design Tip

When using SFCCNTRL to pause the SFC operation, remember the following:

1. If the DISACT input to the SFCCNTRL block is used to turn off SFC actions, any logic that must remain **on** when actions are disabled **must** be set/reset in another program section (e.g., ladder diagram or structured text). When DISACT input is true, ***all*** step actions are turned **off**.
2. If the DISTRANS input to the SFCCNTRL block is used to disable SFC transitions, the "Run" contact does not need to appear in series with any of the transition condition logic.
3. If the step elapsed timer (****.t) must be suspended when the SFC operation is paused, a separate retentive timer must be used to track the step time.

The XSFCCNTRL function block is the same as the SFCCNTRL function block with three additional inputs:

STATION - Drop number for transition diagnosis.

ALLTRANS (Scan ALL TRANSitions) – When this input is true, all transition sections are scanned to determine the condition of all transitions. The sections are scanned even if the associated step is inactive. Obviously, the program scan time will increase.

RESSTEPT (RESest STEP Time) - A true condition at the input deactivates the step time calculation. All step times, all time supervision errors, and the TERRACT output will be reset as long as this input is true.

On-line Animation

When online with a processor, a SFC section may be animated to show the state of the steps and transitions. When in animation mode, the state of a step is indicated as follows:

Step symbol white	Step inactive
Step symbol green	Step active
Step symbol magenta	Maximum supervision time exceeded. Step color reverts to white when step becomes inactive.
Step symbol yellow	Minimum supervision time not reached. Step color remains yellow when step becomes inactive.

In addition, the step elapsed time is displayed in the step rectangle. After the step becomes inactive, the time shows the time duration of the step. With each activation of the step, the time display is set to zero and is updated while the step is active.

When the SFC is animated, the state of a transition defined by a Boolean variable is indicated as follows:

Transition line red	Transition is false
Transition line green	Transition is true

The state is always shown whether the transition is being scanned (the previous step active) or not. If a transition is defined by a transition section, the line remains black.

14.4 CONTROLLOGIX SEQUENTIAL FUNCTION CHART

The Allen-Bradley ControlLogix processors implement sequential function charts that are compliant with IEC 61131-3. The SFC language was introduced with release 10 of the RSLogix 5000 programming software. The ControlLogix SFC implements the following features of the IEC 61131-3 standard:

A transition condition is a Boolean expression or a call to a subroutine.

Each step action block is a Boolean, structured text, or a call to a subroutine. The subroutine can be implemented in any of the supported languages.

Action qualifiers N, S, R, L, D, P, P1, P0, SL, SD, and DS are supported.

However, the ControlLogix SFC does not implement the step ****.T variable in the same manner as set forth in the IEC 61131-3 standard. The ControlLogix SFC has the following extensions to the standard:

Initial step can be in middle

SFC reset and pause

These extensions are described later in this section.

As an example, the ControlLogix SFC format for the metal shear control of Figure 14.3 appears as shown in Figure 14.36. The initial step is indicated by the box enclosed in a

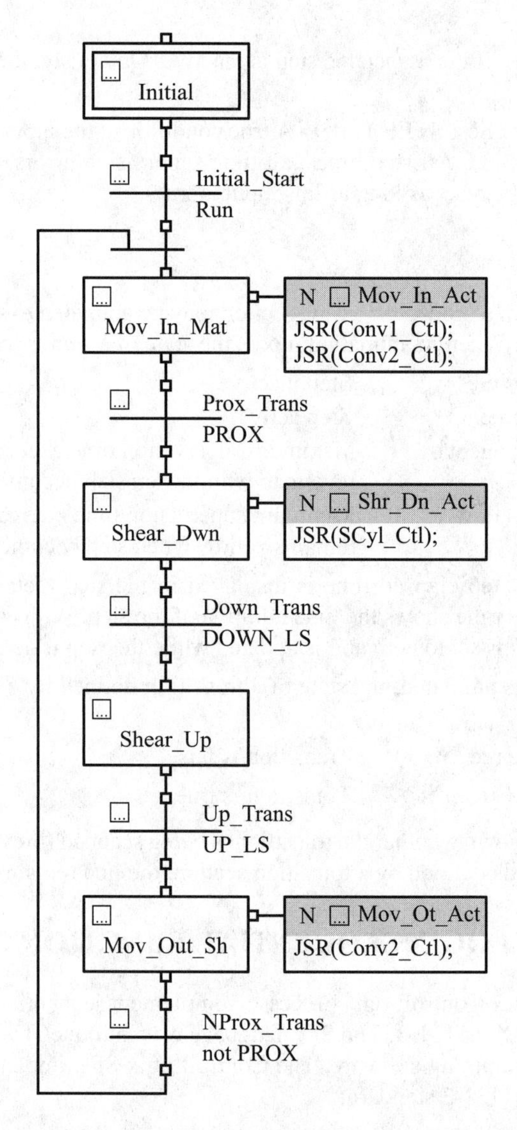

Figure 14.36. ControlLogix SFC for metal shear control.

double line. As an extension of IEC 61131-3, any step can be set as the initial step. The initial step does not have to be the first step in the SFC. The step name is considered a variable. The name of the transition is placed above the horizontal line and is a Boolean variable. The transition condition is displayed below the transition horizontal line. A transition can be specified as either (1) a constant; (2) a Boolean expression; or (3) a JSR to another routine. The user can choose whether or not the step actions are displayed with the steps. In Figure 14.36, the step actions are implemented as subroutines, written as ladder logic in Figure 14.37. When the operation transitions out of the Move_Out_Sh step, it branches back to the Mov_In_Mat step.

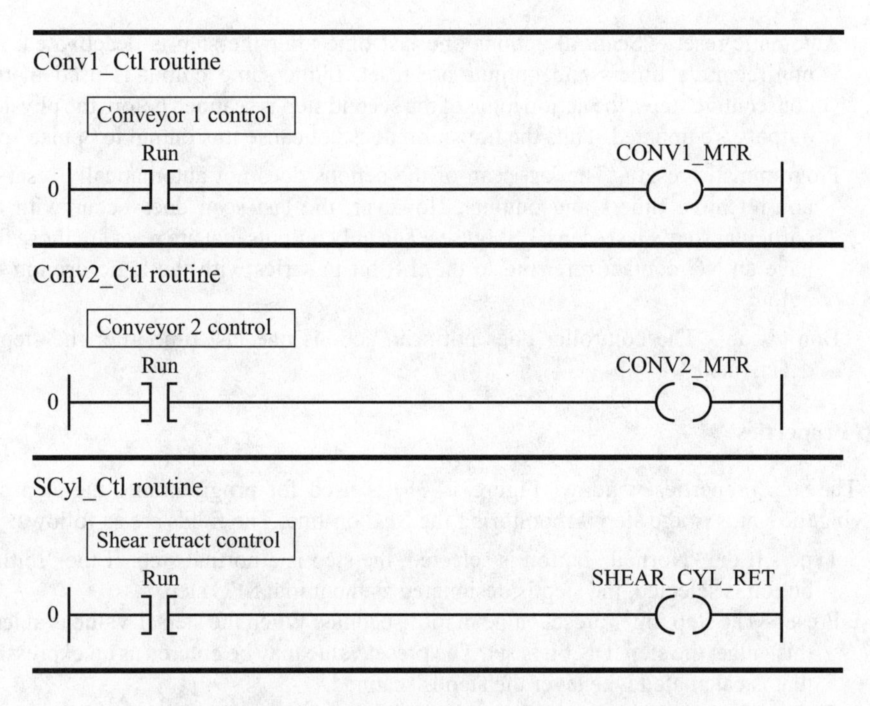

Figure 14.37. Action routines for metal shear control.

SFC Configuration

The operation of all SFCs in the controller can be configured as part of the controller properties. The following can be specified: (1) execution control, (2) restart position, and (3) last scan of active steps. The execution control determines the overall operation of the SFC when it is scanned:

Execute current active steps only - scan the currently active step(s) and then return to the calling routine. Any transitions that are true are noted, but the last scan of the current step(s) does not happen until the next scan of the SFC.

Execute until FALSE transition - scan the currently active step(s). As long as the transitions are true, continue scanning the next step(s). When a false transition condition is encountered, return to the calling routine. This operation mode can reduce the scan time of the SFC, but it can also lead to a watchdog timeout since the SFC may scan many steps before encountering a false transition.

The restart position configuration specifies where the SFC scan will begin after a transition from program mode to run mode:

Restart at most recently executed step – begin the SFC scan at the step(s) that was executing when the controller was switched out of run mode.

Restart at initial step – start the scan with the initial step, regardless of what step(s) was executing when the controller was switched out of run mode.

When a particular step transitions from active to inactive, the last scan of active steps can be specified as one of three possibilities:

Automatic reset – Scan all actions one last time after the step is deactivated. All non-retentive timers and outputs are reset. If the same output is used in two consecutive steps, the action logic of the second step is scanned before the physical outputs are updated. Thus the transition does not cause this output to “pulse” off.

Programmatic reset – The last scan of the actions does not automatically reset all non-retentive timers and outputs. However, the last scan does occur with the particular step’s last scan (.LS) bit set. The only outputs that are reset are those that have an NC contact referring to the .LS bit in series with the logic driving the output.

Don’t scan - The controller does not scan actions one last time after the step is deactivated.

Step Properties

The step properties window (Figure 14.38) is used for programming the step and showing the status of the step if monitoring the SFC on-line. The fields are as follows:

Type - If the “Normal” button is selected, the step is a normal step. If the “Initial” button is selected, the step is designated as the initial SFC step.

Preset - The step timer preset value in milliseconds. When the step .T value is at least this value, the step .DN bit is set. The preset value may be entered as an expression that is calculated whenever the step is scanned.

Timer - The current value of the step timer accumulator (.T value) in milliseconds. This value indicates how long the step has been active during this execution. When the step is first activated, this value is reset to 0. When the step is inactive, the elapsed time is retained. This field is for monitoring only.

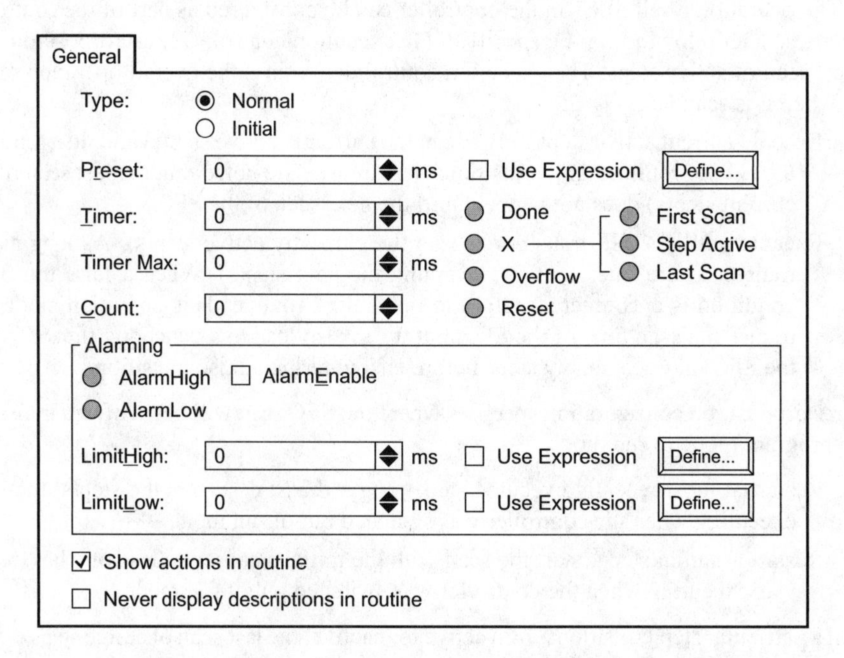

Figure 14.38. ControlLogix step properties window.

Timer Max - The highest value reached by the step execution timer in milliseconds. If the step timer accumulator value exceeds this value, this value is changed to equal the step timer. This field is for monitoring only since it is cleared when the SFC is reset.

Count - The number of times the step has been active since this count was last reset. If this counter reaches its upper limit, it resets to 0 and continues counting. This field is for monitoring only since it is cleared when the SFC is reset.

Done - Indicator is blue when the step .DN bit is set.

X - Indicator is blue when step .X is on, indicating the step is active.

First Scan - Indicator is blue when step is being scanned for the first time.

Step Active - Indicator is blue when step is active, except during the first and last scan of the step.

Last Scan - Indicator is blue when step actions are being scanned for last time because step has transitioned to inactive.

Overflow - Indicator is blue if .T has reached its maximum and reset to zero.

Reset - Indicator is blue when SFC is reset and this step is the step at which the SFC will resume execution.

AlarmEnable - If checked, the High and Low alarms are enabled.

LimitHigh - If AlarmEnable is checked and the step timer accumulator is at least this value, the step .AlarmHigh bit is set and the AlarmHigh indicator changes to blue. Once set, this bit remains set until the user or program resets it. This time value can also be entered as an expression that it is calculated when the step is scanned.

LimitLow - If AlarmEnable is checked and the step timer accumulator is less than this value when the step deactivates, the step .AlarmLow bit is set and the AlarmLow indicator changes to blue. This time value can also be entered as an expression that it is calculated when the step is scanned.

Show actions in routine - If checked the actions are displayed next to the step.

Never display description in routine - If checked, the description for the step tag is not displayed in the SFC.

Step Status

The step status is stored as part of the step tag which is a SFC_STEP structured data type. The more important information fields are:

Field	Name	Description
.X	Step flag	**On** when step is active
.DN	Timer done	**On** when step timer accumulator exceeds preset
.PRE	Preset value	Timer preset value (ms)
.T	Step accum.	Timer accumulator value (ms). Timer continues to run after reaching the preset value. This is a DINT, which deviates from IEC 61131-3.

Other fields are described in Rockwell Automation (2004). For example, to access the step flag of the Shear_Up step of Figure 14.36, the tag is Shear_Up.X. To access the step elapsed time of the same step, the reference is Shear_Up.T.

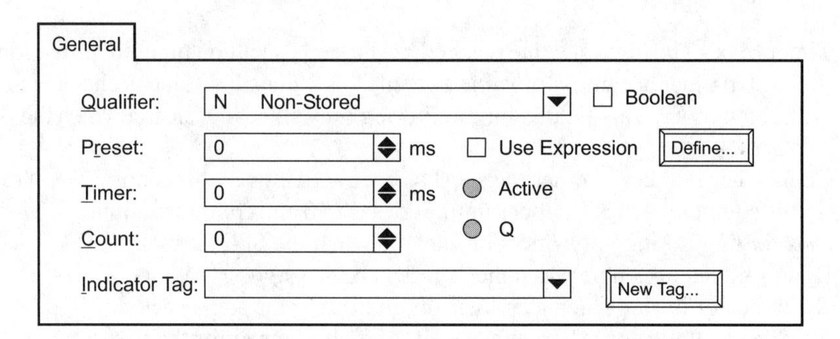

Figure 14.39. ControlLogix action properties window.

Step Actions

The step actions are added to the step and the step action properties window (Figure 14.39) is used for specifying the general properties of the step action and showing the status of the action if monitoring the SFC on-line. The fields are as follows:

Qualifier - One of the IEC 61131-3 action qualifiers.

Boolean - If checked, the action .Q bit is set when the step is active. Structured text cannot appear in the SFC action.

Preset - Specifies the time (in ms) for one of the action time-based qualifiers (L, D, SL, SD, DS). As for the step properties, this time value may be entered as an expression such that it is calculated when the action is scanned.

Timer - The current value of the action timer accumulator (.T value) in milliseconds. If the action qualifier is not one of the time-based qualifiers (L, D, SL, SD, DS), the accumulator is not changed. This field is for monitoring only.

Count - The number of times the action has been active since this count was last reset. If this counter reaches its upper limit, it resets to 0 and continues counting. This field is for monitoring only since it is cleared when the SFC is reset.

Active - Indicator is blue when the action is active.

Q - Indicator is blue when action is active, except during the last scan of the action when the action is non-Boolean.

Indicator Tag - Name of tag to be displayed while monitoring the SFC. The name of the tag and its value is shown to the right of the action name. This is useful for displaying data values relevant to the SFC application (for example, the value of a flow accumulator when filling a tank).

Actions execute in the order shown in the diagram. The execution order can be changed by dragging the action to its correct position, or by changing the order in the step properties or action properties window.

A non-Boolean step action can have structured text within the body of the action. Often, the structured text is one or more JSR's to other routines (Figure 14.36). However, any set of structured text statements may be used. Note that if a retentive assignment ":=" is used to set a Boolean to a "1," the Boolean remains set after the action becomes inactive.

Design Tip

Be careful about use of the retentive assignment operator (:=) with Booleans in the structured text in an action. The Boolean is **not** reset when the step becomes inactive. Use the non-retentive assignment ([:=]) with Booleans and configure the SFC for automatic reset on the last scan to ensure they are reset when the step becomes inactive.

Action Status

The action status is stored as part of the action tag which is a SFC_ACTION structured data type. The status information fields are:

Field	Name	Description
.Q	First scan	**On** when action is active, except during the last scan of the action when the action is non-Boolean
.A	Action flag	**On** when step is active
.PRE	Preset value	Timer preset value
.T	Accumulator	Action timer accumulator value for time-based qualifiers.

For example, to access the action flag of the Mov_In_Act action of Figure 14.36, the reference is Mov_In_Act.Q.

Transitions

Transitions may be specified as a structured text Boolean expression or a JSR to a subroutine. The subroutine language must be either ladder logic or structured text and must include an EOT (end of transition). For example, a transition with multiple conditions can be implemented in structured text as shown in Figure 14.40*a*. Implemented as a subroutine,

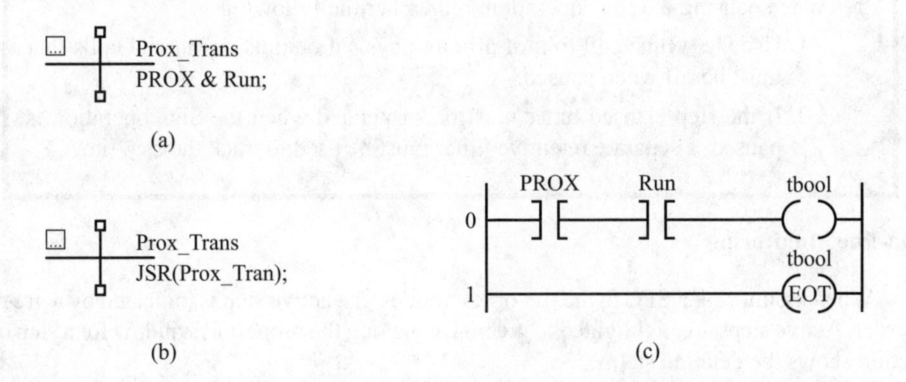

Figure 14.40. ControlLogix transitions: *(a)* as structured text; *(b)* as subroutine call; *(c)* subroutine as ladder logic.

the same transition and associated ladder logic subroutine is shown in Figure 14.40*b* and 14.40*c*, respectively . The structured text implementation of the subroutine is:

```
tbool := PROX & Run;
EOT(tbool);
```

By default, the transitions for the start of a selection branch are checked from left to right. The order can be specified by assigning a priority to each path of the selection branch, similar to the ordered evaluation in Figure 14.7*b*.

SFC Control

The SFR (sequential function reset) and SFP (sequential function pause) function blocks are used to control a SFC. They are available in the ladder logic and structured text languages.

The SFR instruction resets the logic in a sequential function chart. This instruction is shown in Figure 14.41*a*. When the input condition to the ladder logic SFR block instruction changes to true, the processor performs a post scan on all active steps and actions in the selected SFC routine. All stored actions are reset. Then the processor resets the active step to the step specified in the SFR instruction, and the SFC starts execution at that step. The SFR instruction (Figure 14.41*a*) has two parameters. The "SFC Routine Name" is the name of the SFC routine, and the "Step Name" is the step at which the SFC should restart. For example, for the shear SFC shown in Figure 14.36, the SFR instruction could be used to reset the SFC and start it at the Initial step.

The SFP instruction pauses a sequential function chart. This instruction is shown in Figure 14.41*b*. The SFP has two parameters. The "SFC Routine Name" is the name of the SFC routine and the "Target State" is the desired action. When the input condition to the ladder logic SFP block instruction changes to true, the selected SFC is either paused (target state is "Paused") or resumes execution (target state is "Executing"). Separate SFP blocks must be used to pause and then resume a particular SFC. When the SFC is paused, only the transitions are disabled. The step timers continue to increment (though not updated in the step properties window), and the step actions continue to be enabled.

Design Tip

When pausing the SFC operation, remember the following:

1. Use the "Run" coil to turn off any physical outputs or internal coils that must be off when paused.
2. If the step elapsed timer must be suspended when the SFC operation is paused, a separate retentive timer must be used to track the step time.

On-line Monitoring

When monitoring a SFC in the run or test modes, the active step is indicated by a green border. Active steps are highlighted in green. Displaying the properties window for a step or action shows the detailed status.

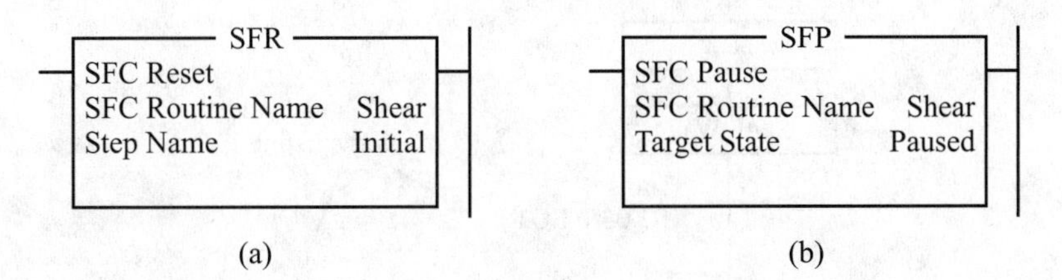

Figure 14.41. ControlLogix SFC control: *(a)* SFC reset; *(b)* SFC pause.

14.5 PLC-5 SEQUENTIAL FUNCTION CHART

The Allen-Bradley PLC-5 implements sequential function charts that are compliant with IEC 61131-3. The SFC language was introduced with the original PLC-5 processors and improved for the enhanced PLC-5 processors. The implementation for the enhanced PLC-5 processors is emphasized in this chapter, though the major differences from the original PLC-5 are outlined in this section.

The PLC-5 SFC implements the following features of the IEC 61131-3 standard:

Transition condition is implemented as a ladder program file.

Each step action block is a program file (ladder, structured text, or a SFC). Each step may have up to 8 action blocks.

Action qualifiers N, S, R, L, D, P1, P0, SL, SD, DS are supported.

The PLC-5 SFC does not implement the step ****.X and ****.T variables of IEC 61131-3 in the same manner as set forth in the standard. These are explained with the step status below. The PLC-5 SFC has the following extensions to the IEC 61131-3 standard:

Jump

SFC reset

Macro (for display/print)

These extensions are described later in this section.

The SFC language for the original PLC-5 processors have the following limitations:

Only one action block per step.

Actions cannot be described in ST or SFC languages. Only the N (None) action qualifier is supported.

Step time is not implemented automatically.

Only one SFC per processor.

Maximum of 24 steps active simultaneously.

SFC reset not supported.

SFC scan operation cannot be configured.

As an example, the enhanced PLC-5 SFC format for the metal shear control of Figure 14.3 appears as shown in Figure 14.42. The start and end of the SFC are labeled as such and are each shown as a rectangle with two extra horizontal bars. The start and end cannot be edited, so the step below the "Start" box is really the initial step. The name to the left of the horizontal transition line is the name of the transition (for documentation purposes). The name to the right to the horizontal transition line is the name of the program file that

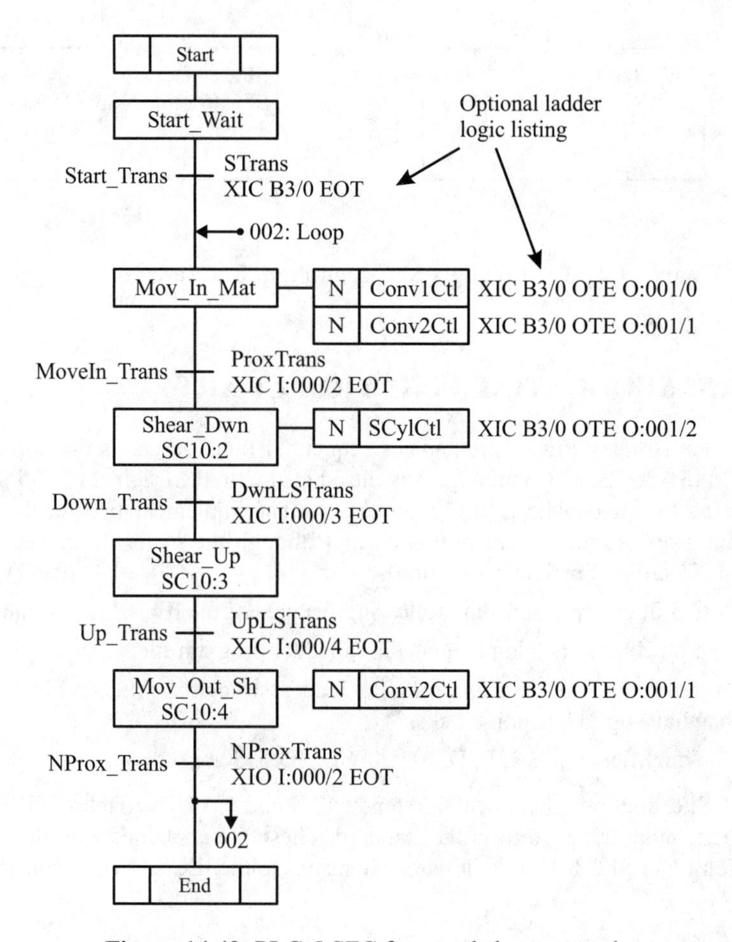

Figure 14.42. PLC-5 SFC for metal shear control.

implements the transition (If the file is not named, the number of the file is shown). The line below the program file name is the ladder logic in the program file (in PLC-5 ladder text). The action is the name of the program file that implements the action (if the action program file is not named, the number of the file is shown). Optionally, the ladder logic code in the action and transition program files can be displayed in the ASCII text format. Within the step box, the name is listed, as well as the symbol of the timer that stores the step time. When the operation transitions out of the Move_Out_Sh step, the Goto statement forces the logic to jump to the label before the Mov_In_Mat step. If the "End" step is reached, the SFC automatically re-commences operation at "Start."

The display and print formats of the SFC are controlled by the SFC Options tab of the View Properties window (display) and SFC Report View Options (printing). The SFC diagram in Figure 14.42 has the "ProgFile logic", "Step Timers", "Progfile Names", and "Element Names" options selected.

The original PLC-5 processors support only one SFC (in file 1). For the enhanced PLC-5 processors one can define more than one SFC file, but any main SFC must be specified as a main control program if it is not in program file 1.

Limitations

Because the maximum number of program files in the PLC-5 is 998, if the PLC-5 has only one SFC, it can have a maximum of 997 action blocks and transitions, minus any ladder logic or structured text files not a part of the SFC. Also, there is a maximum of 16 selection or simultaneous parallel branches (seven for the original PLC-5).

SFC Configuration

For the enhanced PLC-5, the scan and post scan operation can be configured as part of the SFC properties. Also, one can specify the data file numbers for the step timers and the timers for those action qualifiers that need timers (L, D, SL, SD, and DS). The post scan configuration can be set to one of two possibilities:

Auto Reset - Reset all non-retentive timers and outputs during the post scan (extra execution of action logic when the step is deactivated). If the same output is used in two consecutive steps, the action logic of the second step is scanned before the physical outputs are updated. Thus the transition does not cause this output to "pulse" off.

Manual Reset - The post scan of the action logic does not automatically reset all non-retentive timers and outputs. However, the post scan does occur with the last scan flag set in the controller status (S:1/14). The only outputs that are reset are those that have an NC contact referring to S:1/14 (XIO S:1/14) instruction in series with the logic driving the output.

The scan configuration for simultaneous branches can be set to one of two possibilities:

Standard - In a simultaneous branch, the I/O and the convergence transition are scanned between simultaneous steps when all of the last steps in the simultaneous branches are active. The original PLC-5 processor scans simultaneous steps in this manner.

Advanced - In a simultaneous branch, the I/O is scanned and then all active steps are scanned (no I/O scan between steps). The convergence transition is only checked after the right-most active step of the converge is scanned.

If one enters a non-zero number for the step timer file, a data file of type SC is created to hold the step timers. A zero step timer file number disables the step timers. If one enters a non-zero number for the action timer file, a data file of type T is created to hold the timers required by the L, D, LS, DS, and SD action qualifiers. A zero action timer file number disables the action timers. For both of these timer files, it is best to assign data file numbers that are unique to the particular SFC.

Step Actions

The step actions are set as part of the step properties window, shown in Figure 14.43 (accessed by selecting the step and clicking the right-mouse button). If an action block is desired, the box on the left side is checked and the corresponding fields on that row are specified. In the "Program File" column, the user enters the number of the file implementing that action, or a file type (Ladder Logic, SFC Sub Chart, or Structured Text). If one of the file types is selected, the programming software will create a file of the specified type for the step action when the SFC is verified. In the "Action Qualifier"

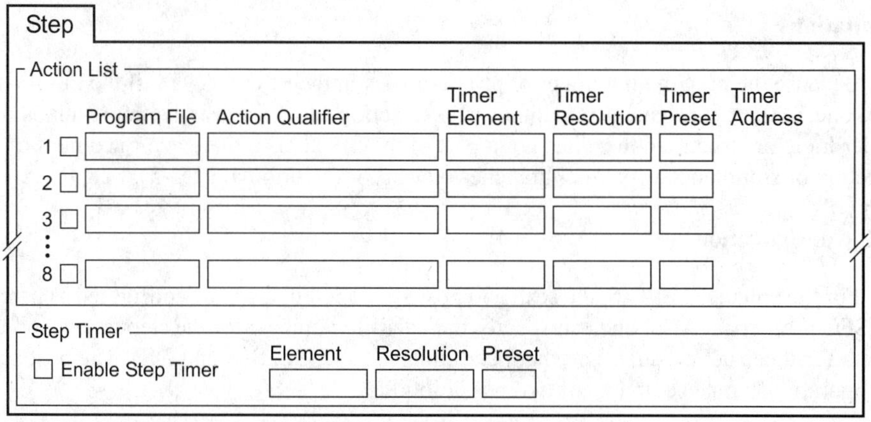

Figure 14.43. PLC-5 Step properties window.

column, the user selects the proper action qualifier. If the L, D, SL, SD, or DS qualifier is selected, then the timer element, resolution, and preset values must be specified. The software displays the timer address and preset time. The action timer file must already have been specified as part of the SFC configuration.

If a step timer is desired, the "Enable Step Timer" box is checked, and the timer information is filled in. The step timer file must already have been specified as part of the SFC configuration. The step timer accumulator may be used to track how long a step is active in order to monitor the timing of the SFC. The step timer done bit could be used to set an alarm if the step time is too long.

Action files can be used in multiple steps. Also, action files associated with a step are scanned only when the step is active.

Figure 14.44 shows an example step properties window with three actions and the corresponding SFC display for this step. Example action files for these step actions are shown in Figure 14.45.

Step Status

The step status is stored as part of the step timer, and is only active if the "Enable Step Timer" box is checked in the step actions window. If no step timer is defined for a step, the status for that step cannot be accessed. The more important status information associated with a step timer is:

Field	Name	Description
.SA	Step flag	**On** when step is active
.DN	Timer done	**On** when step timer is done
.PRE	Preset value	Timer preset value
.TIM	Accumulator	Timer accumulator value. Timer continues to run after reaching the preset value. Multiply by time base (0.01 or 1 second) to obtain step elapsed time.

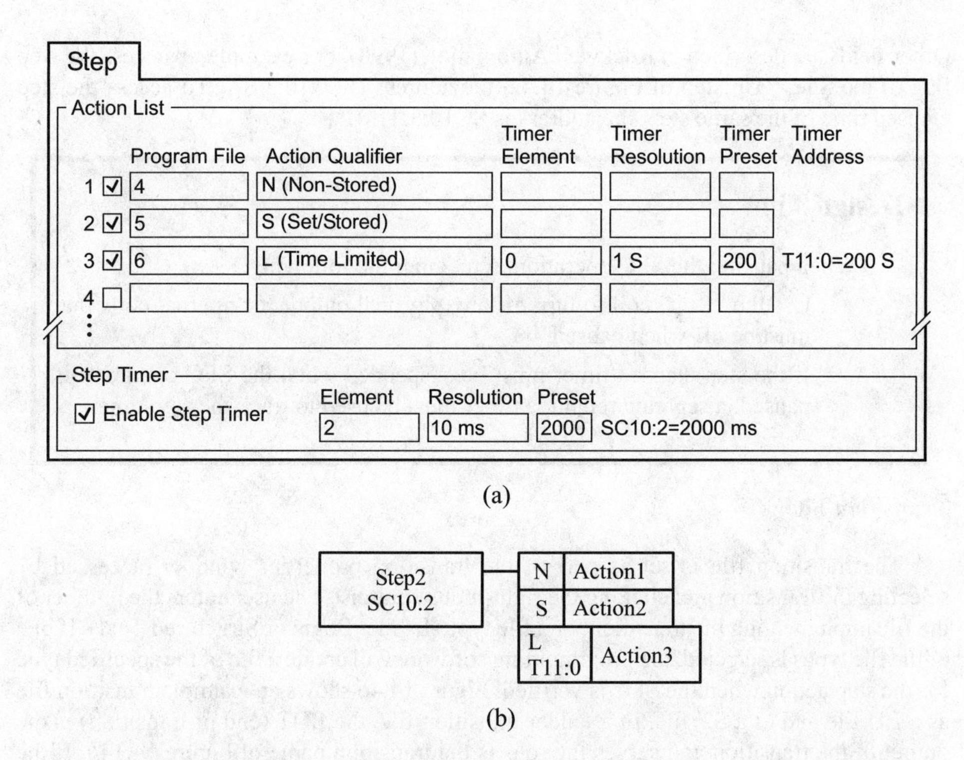

Figure 14.44. Example PLC-5 step actions: *(a)* step properties window; *(b)* step display.

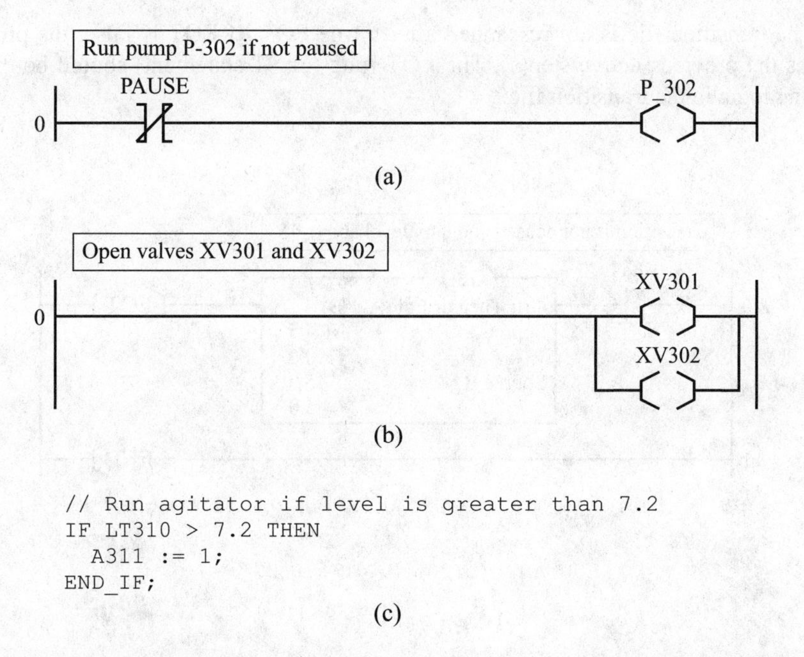


```
// Run agitator if level is greater than 7.2
IF LT310 > 7.2 THEN
  A311 := 1;
END_IF;
```

(c)

Figure 14.45. Example PLC-5 action ladder logic files: *(a)* Action1 ladder file; *(b)* Action2 ladder file; *(c)* Action3 structured text file.

Other fields are described in Rockwell Automation (1998). For example, to access the step flag of the Shear_Up step of Figure 14.42, the address is SC10:3.SA. To access the step elapsed time of the same step, the address is SC10:3.TIM.

Design Tip

When pausing the SFC operation, remember the following:

1. Use the "Run" coil to turn **off** any physical outputs or internal coils that must be **off** when paused.
2. If the step elapsed timer must be suspended when the SFC operation is paused, a separate retentive timer must be used to track the step time.

Transition File

The transition file is set as part of the transition properties window (accessed by selecting the transition and clicking the right-mouse button). The user enters the number of the file implementing the transition, or a file type (Ladder Logic or Structured Text). If one of the file types is selected, the programming software will create a file of the specified type for the step action when the SFC is verified. Figure 14.46 shows an example transition file as a LD file and as a ST file. In a ladder transition file, the EOT (end of transition) is the output of the transition and serves the role as the transition name of Figure 14.14*b*. If the EOT is true, the processor post scans the preceding active step(s) to reset all non-retentive timer and output instructions. The processor will then continue on to the next step(s) in the path.

The transition file is not rescanned after a true EOT. If EOT is false, the processor rescans the previous active step(s). The EOT rung (or ST statement) should be the only working logic in the transition file.

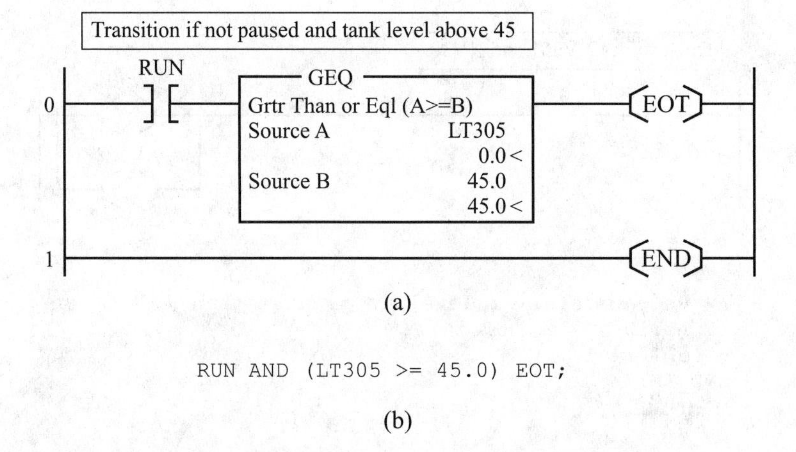

(a)

```
RUN AND (LT305 >= 45.0) EOT;
```

(b)

Figure 14.46. Example PLC-5 transition file: *(a)* ladder logic; *(b)* structured text.

Goto and Label

A Goto instruction lets the SFC skip steps and resume execution at the specified label in the SFC. For example, a Goto can be used to repeat execution of the SFC or to execute certain steps when an error condition occurs.

Figure 14.42 shows a Goto and Label implementing a sequence loop that repeats the SFC operation. The Goto statement occurs before the End block and is shown as an arrow extending out to the right and down. The number (002) below the arrow end is the Label. The Label is defined before the Mov_In_Mat step. The Label definition is shown as an arrow entering the SFC from the right. The label number along with the name of the loop (if defined) appears to the right of the arrow. Each Label must be assigned a unique 3-digit number in the range of 001 - 250.

A Goto can be used to construct a sequence skip. Figure 14.47*a* shows a sequence skip implemented with a sequence selection, and Figure 14.47*b* shows the same skip implemented with a Goto and a Label.

There are some restrictions as to where the Goto statements and labels may be placed in the SFC. A Goto statement may be placed only at the end of the SFC (after the last transition) or at the end of a path in a sequence selection. Labels may be placed before a step or before a simultaneous sequence divergence.

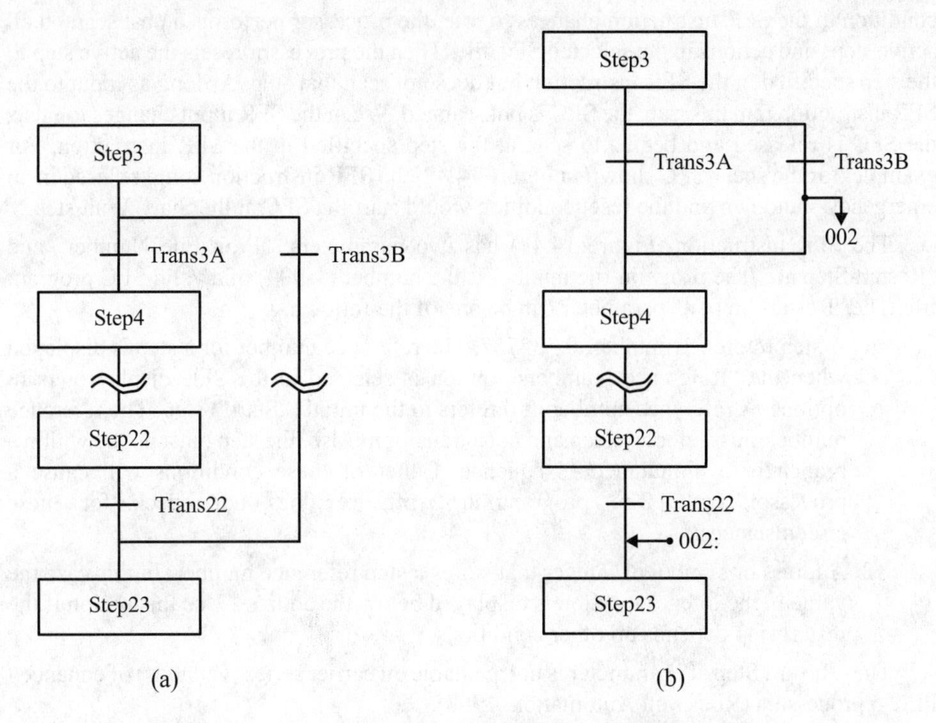

Figure 14.47. Example PLC-5 sequence skip: *(a)* using sequence selection; *(b)* using Goto.

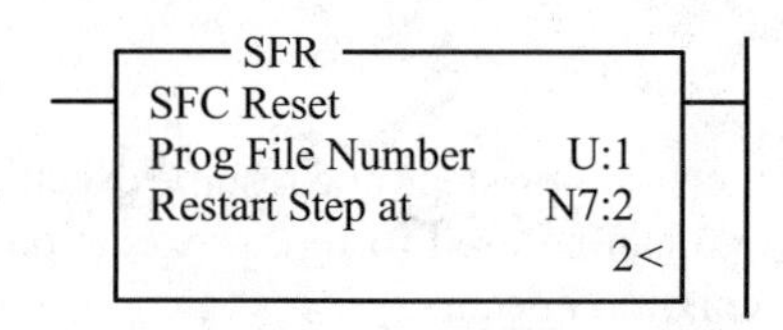

Figure 14.48. PLC-5 sequential function chart reset (SFR) instruction.

Other rules for Goto statements and labels:

Up to 250 labels in one SFC, numbered 001 - 250

More than one Goto statement can jump to the same label.

Cannot jump into, out of, or between branches of simultaneous sequences.

In order to avoid confusing the flow of the SFC, Gotos should be used sparingly.

SFC Control

The only available external SFC control is the SFR (sequential function reset) ladder logic instruction that resets the logic in a sequential function chart. This instruction is only supported on enhanced PLC-5 processors and is shown in Figure 14.48. When the input condition to the SFR instruction changes to true, the processor performs a post scan on all active steps and actions in the selected SFC file. Then the processor resets the active step to the step specified in the SFR instruction but does not scan that step. As long as input to the SFR instruction remains true, the SFC is not scanned. When the SFR input changes to false, the SFC is released and begins to scan at the step specified in the SFR instruction. For example, for the shear SFC shown in Figure 14.42, the SFR instruction could be used in an emergency shutdown and the reset condition would start the SFC at the Start_Wait step.

The SFR instruction (Figure 14.48) has two parameters: "Prog File Number" and "Restart Step at." The program file number is the number (1-999) of a valid SFC program file. The "Restart Step at" parameter can be one of the following:

1. A step reference number, 0 - 32767. The reference number for a step is displayed when the "Reference Numbers" option is selected in the SFC display or print options. A reference number of 0 refers to the initial ("Start") step. The reference number must refer to a step and not a transition. Also, the step must not be within a branch of a simultaneous sequence. Either of these conditions will cause a processor fault. The programming software does not check for these circumstances.
2. Address or symbol of integer that stores a step reference number. In this case the value in the integer location is displayed below the address. Use this option if the restart step depends on other conditions.

The "Restart Step at" parameter is not available on earlier series (versions) of enhanced PLC-5 processors (Rockwell Automation, 1998).

Macro

A macro is a condensed portion of a sequential function chart. A macro can contain an entire branch structure (sequence selection or simultaneous sequences) or a step/transition

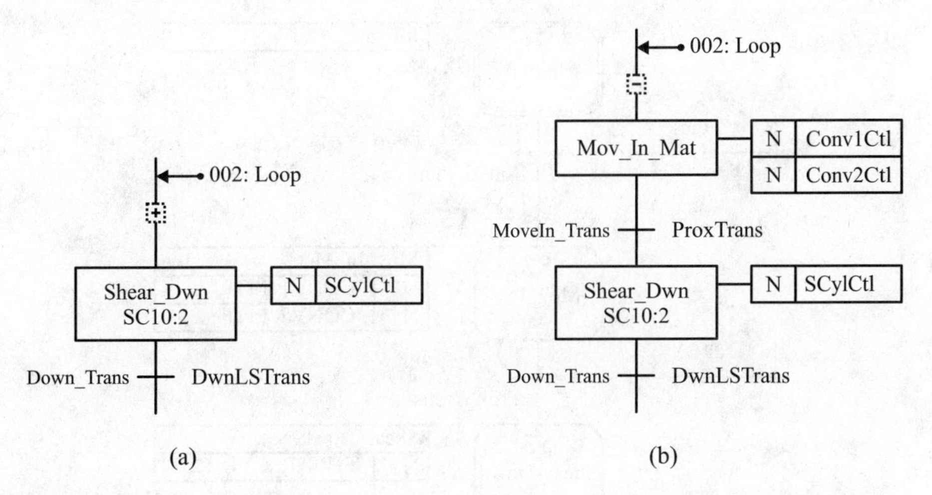

Figure 14.49. Mov_In_Mat step/transition of Figure 14.42 as macro: *(a)* contracted; *(b)* expanded.

pair. Macros are used to condense portions of the SFC so that more can fit on one screen or page. A macro appears as a box with a plus sign in it when contracted (Figure 14.49*a*). When expanded, the macro appears as a box with a minus sign above the step/transition pair or branch structure (Figure 14.49*b*).

On-line Monitoring

When monitoring a SFC in the run or test modes, the active step is indicated by a contrasting rectangle surrounding the step.

14.6 SIEMENS S7 SEQUENTIAL FUNCTION CHART

The S7-Graph programming language implements sequential function charts that are compliant with IEC 61131-3. The S7-Graph SFC implements the following features of the IEC 61131-3 standard:

A transition condition is a ladder diagram or FBD network intersecting the vertical link.

Each step action block is a Boolean, simple arithmetic, or a call to a function block. The function block can be a system function or user-programmed in any of the supported languages.

Action qualifiers N, S, R, L, and D are supported.

As a deviation from the standard, the IEC P0 and P1 action qualifiers are handled as the S0 and S1 events which are combined with one of the standard action qualifiers. The S7-Graph SFC has the following extensions to the IEC 61131-3 standard:

Event-dependent actions (for example, interlocks and supervision errors)

Initial step can be in middle

SFC control through the function block interface

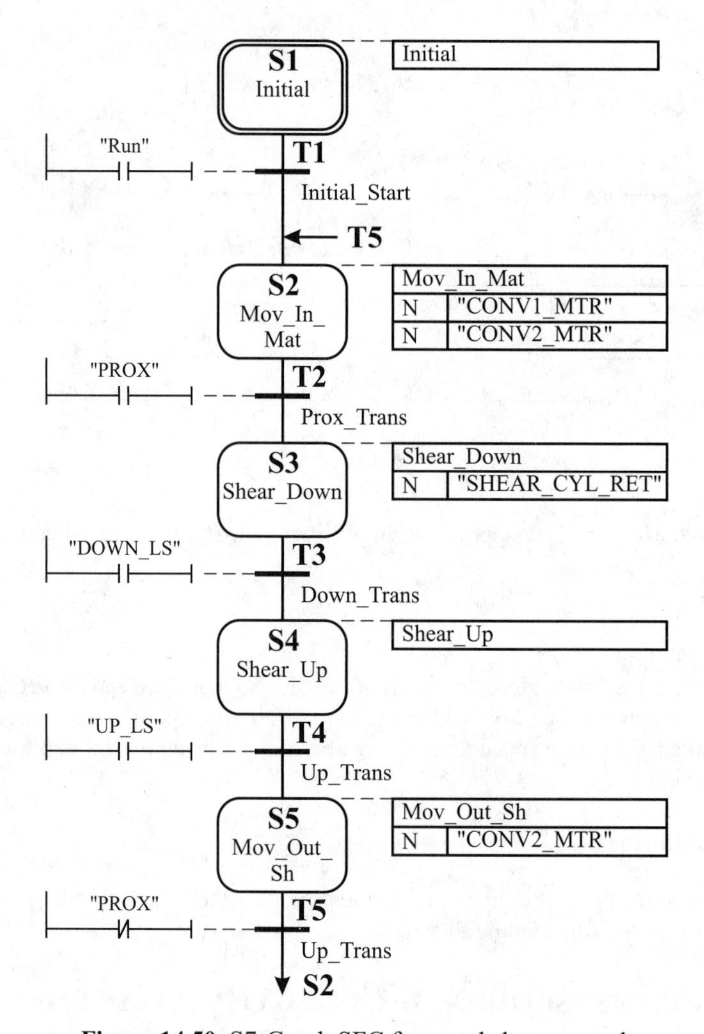

Figure 14.50. S7-Graph SFC for metal shear control.

As an example, the S7-Graph format for the metal shear control of Figure 14.3 appears as shown in Figure 14.50. The initial step is indicated by the rounded rectangle enclosed in a double line. As an extension of IEC 61131-3, any step can be set as the initial step. The initial step does not have to be the first step in the SFC. The step name is considered a variable. The step number follows the "S" in the step rounded rectangle. Step actions are displayed with the steps. The thick horizontal line indicates a transition. The transitions in Figure 14.50 are shown as a ladder diagram network whose right power rail is connected to the transition line. When the operation transitions out of the Move_Out_Sh step, the arrow (jump) forces the logic to jump to the Mov_In_Mat step.

Limitations

A function block implemented with S7-Graph can contain up to 8 sequencers (SFCs) and have a maximum of 250 steps and transitions. A sequencer can contain up to 256 branches with up to 125 paths in sequence selection branches or up to 249 paths in simultaneous sequence branches. To avoid extremely long execution times, no more than 20 to 40 paths are advisable.

Step Properties

The major step properties that are accessed by a properties window are: (1) the step number; (2) the step name; (3) a step comment; and (4) whether this is the initial step. The step number and step name can also be changed on the SFC diagram. When the steps are initially created, the step name and number are set to defaults which can be changed. Like a variable, the step name must be unique in the entire project (there is no distinction between upper/lower case). Any step supervision, such as, a step minimum duration and/or maximum duration is programmed external to the step as a supervision condition.

Step Actions

The step actions are normally programmed on the SFC diagram. When an action is added, the qualifier is placed in the left portion and the action is placed in the right portion. The L and D qualifiers require a time and in this case, the right portion of the action is divided into an upper and lower rectangle. The action is in the upper portion and the time constant is placed in the lower portion.

S7-Graph adds the CALL action qualifier to the standard N, S, R, L, and D qualifiers. When the CALL action qualifier is used, the name of a specified block (FB, FC, SFB, or SFC) is placed in the right portion of the step action. S7-Graph also adds timer and counter qualifiers. Unfortunately, they only work on the timer/counter addressable memory and are not IEC-compliant. The interested reader is referred to Siemens (1999).

S7-Graph adds interlock and supervision modifiers to the step qualifiers. An interlock is a condition that can alter the execution of individual actions. A supervision is a condition that can alter the normal step sequence. The interlock and supervision for a step is only accessible when the display is set to view the individual step/transition pairs. An example step with a programmed interlock and supervision is shown in Figure 14.51.

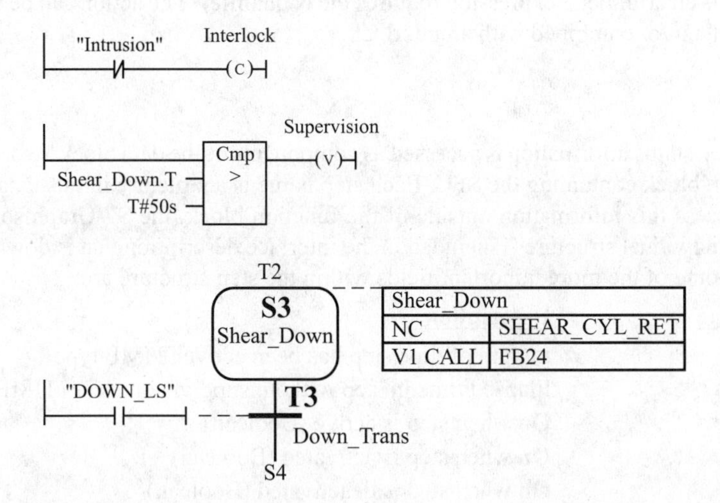

Figure 14.51. S7-Graph step with programmed interlock and supervision.

The letter "C" following any of the N, S, R, or CALL qualifiers indicates that an interlock must be satisfied in order to activate the action. For example, in Figure 14.51, the action that activates the SHEAR_CYL_RET is not started until there is no intrusion into the workcell ("Intrusion" is off). However, once this action is initiated, the interlock is not checked again and a subsequent intrusion does not stop the shear. The SFC interlocks do not substitute for interlocks that protect personnel.

With S7-Graph, a step action can be combined with an event. An event is usually associated with the change in the state of a step, supervision, or interlock. However, the acknowledgment of a message and the setting of a registration are also events. The possible events are:

Event	Description
S1	Transition to step becoming active
S0	Transition to step becoming inactive
L0	Transition to interlock becoming true
L1	Transition to interlock becoming false
V1	Transition to supervision condition becoming true
V0	Transition to supervision condition becoming false
A1	Message is acknowledged
R1	Registration is set

Note that the S1 and S0 events are equivalent to the IEC P1 and P0 action qualifiers. The event is placed before the action qualifier. These events may not be used with the L and D action qualifiers. If an action is combined with an event, the action is executed only in the scan in which the event took place. For example, in Figure 14.51 FB24 is executed when the step time exceeds 50 seconds (the supervision).

The events can be combined with two special event dependent actions, ON and OFF. The ON and OFF actions are used to activate and deactivate, respectively, other steps. The ON and OFF actions can be combined with an interlock.

An action can also be a simple arithmetic expression. The types of arithmetic statements that are permitted are in the form A:=B, A:=func(B) and A:=B<operator>C. An action that is an arithmetic expression requires the N qualifier. The action can be dependent on an event and/or combined with an interlock.

Step Status

The step status information is accessed as components of the data block associated with the function block containing the SFC. Each step name is a structure in this data block. In order to access this information outside of the function block, the S7-Graph source must have the "Individual structures" included in the interface description that is downloaded to the PLC. Some of the more important fields within the step structure are:

Name	Description
.T	Length of time step has been active (TIME type)
.U	Elapsed time in step without supervision error (TIME type)
.X	**On** when step is active (Boolean)
.S1	**On** when step is activated (Boolean)
.S0	**On** when step is deactivated (Boolean)

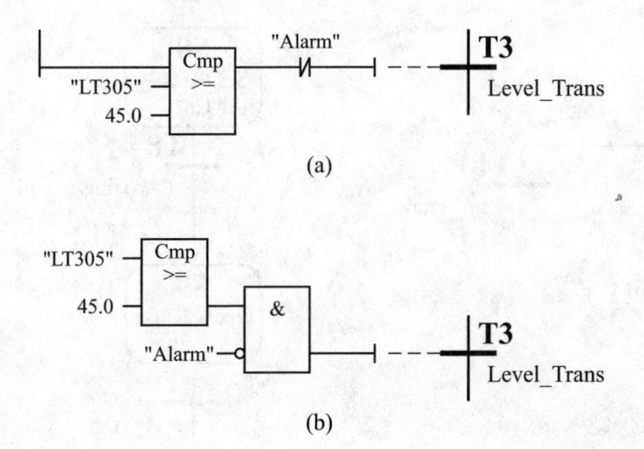

Figure 14.52. S7-Graph transition logic: *(a)* ladder logic; *(b)* FBD network.

For example, to access the step flag of the Shear_Up step of Figure 14.50, the variable is "Shear_Up.X." To access the step elapsed time of the same step, the variable is "Shear_Up.T." Other fields in the step structure are listed in Siemens (1999).

Transitions

A transition can be specified as either (1) a ladder diagram (LD) network whose right power rail is connected to the transition line; or (2) a function block diagram (FBD) network whose output connects to the transition line. Figure 14.52 shows the same transition as an LD network and a FBD network. For both languages, a restricted set of elements is available. For the LD language, only normally open contacts, normally closed contacts, and CMP blocks are allowed in the transition. For the FBD language, only AND, OR, and CMP blocks are allowed.

If more than one transition at the start of a selection branch is satisfied, the leftmost transition is checked first. If it is not satisfied, the priority of the other transitions is determined by their transition numbers. The transition with the lowest number has the highest priority and is checked next.

Permanent Instructions

Ladder logic or function block logic can be programmed as part of the S7-Graph function block. This logic is called *permanent instructions* and they may be executed before or after the sequence is executed. This logic is executed once per scan of the function block regardless of the state of the SFC. For the LD language, a combination of normally open contacts, normally closed contacts, and CMP blocks terminated in one coil is allowed in each permanent instruction. For the FBD language, a network of AND, OR, and CMP blocks terminated in an assignment block is allowed. Any number of permanent instructions may be programmed, however each LD/FBD network is limited to 32 elements.

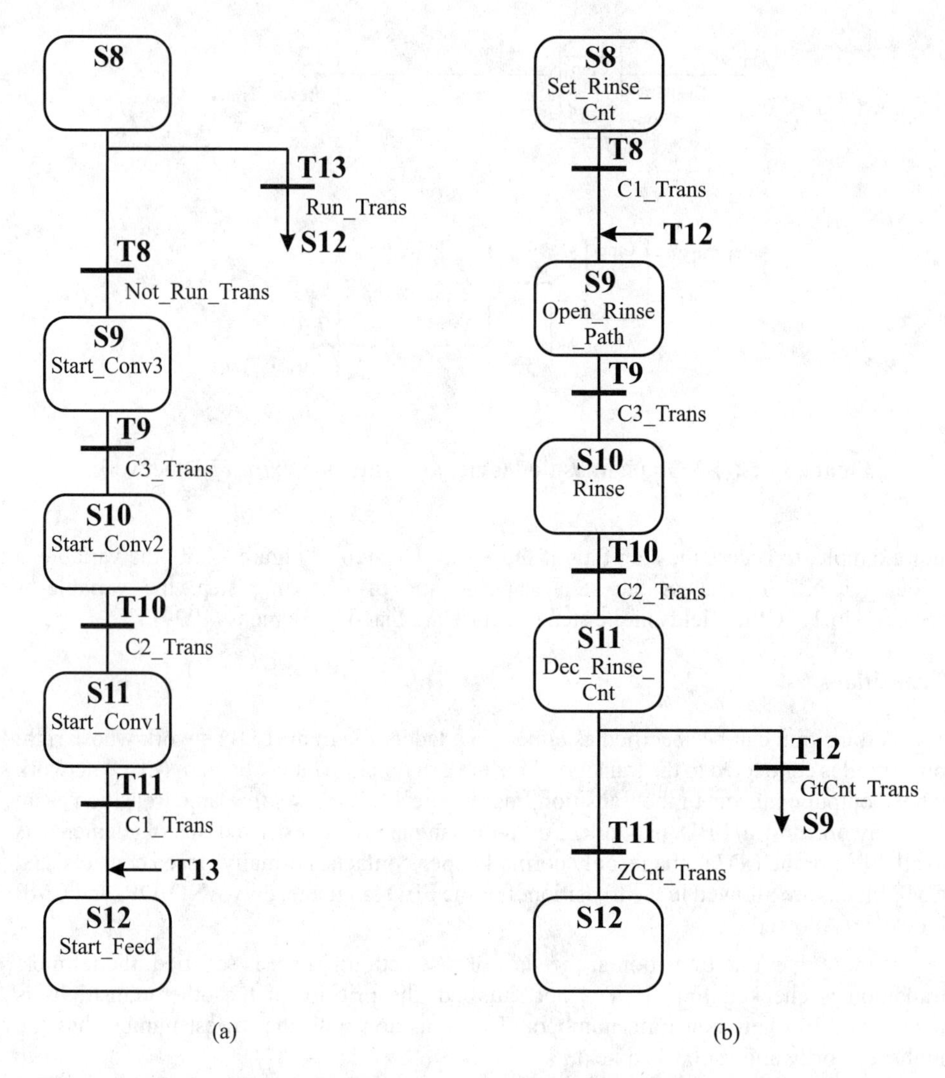

Figure 14.53. S7-Graph jump implementations: *(a)* sequence skip; *(b)* sequence loop.

Jump

A Jump lets the sequence skip steps and resume execution at the specified step. For example, a Jump can be used to repeat the sequence.

Figure 14.50 shows a Jump implementing a repeat of the SFC operation. The Jump occurs as the last part of the SFC and is shown as an arrow pointing down with a reference to the step number that is the destination of the jump. When the operation transitions out of the Move_Out_Sh step, the arrow (jump) forces the logic to jump to step S2 (Mov_In_Mat).

A sequence skip, shown in Figure 14.53*a*, allows one to skip certain SFC steps. It is implemented as a sequence selection divergence and a jump to a step below the divergence. In Figure 14.53*a* (the S7-Graph implementation of Figure 14.8), the steps to start the conveyors are executed only if the conveying system is not running.

A sequence loop is constructed similarly to a sequence skip. The only difference is that the jump destination is above the selection divergence. For example, in Figure 14.53*b* (the S7-Graph implementation of Figure 14.9), the rinse operation is repeated as many times as specified. For both of these examples, only the overall structure is shown without the transition logic and step actions.

There are some restrictions as to where the Jump may be placed in the sequence. A Jump source or destination should not be in a simultaneous sequence. In order to avoid confusing the flow of the sequence, jumps should be used sparingly.

SFC Control

The external connections to the function block containing the S7-Graph sequence are available to control the execution of the sequences. The standard set of interface connections is shown in Figure 14.54. The entire set consists of 29 inputs and 32 outputs. The standard set, described below, allows some programmatic manipulation of the processing of a SFC section. When used in the examples, the standard set is supplemented by three other inputs and outputs that disable step actions, pause timers, and pause the sequence.

Unless otherwise stated, the input signals to the S7-Graph function block are all Booleans and are described as follows:

OFF_SQ - Turn off the sequencer. A change to true (1) at the input deactivates all steps. The INIT_SQ must be used to start the sequence at the initial step. Any actions that are active with the S qualifier are not reset.

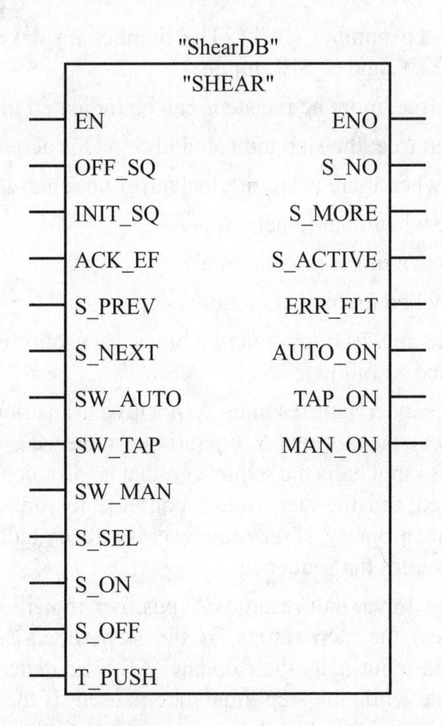

Figure 14.54. S7-Graph standard function block connections.

INIT_SQ - Initialize the sequencer. A true at this input activates the initial step. Any actions that are active with the S qualifier are not reset.

ACK_EF - Acknowledge error or fault. A positive transition also forces transition to next step.

S_PREV - Indicate previous step in S_NO output.

S_NEXT - Indicate next step in S_NO output.

SW_AUTO - Switch mode to automatic. A true at this input forces the sequencer to the automatic mode: the next step is activated when its transition is satisfied.

SW_TAP - Switch mode to inching. A true at this input forces the sequencer to the inching mode: the next step is activated when its transition is satisfied and there is a positive transition on the T_PUSH input.

SW_MAN - Switch mode to manual. A true at this input forces the sequencer to the manual mode: the next step is not activated when its transition is satisfied. The steps are selected and deselected manually.

S_SEL - Select a specific step (INT). When nonzero, S_NO is set to the specific step. The S_ON and S_OFF inputs are used to activate/deactivate the step in the manual mode.

S_ON - Activate the step indicated in the S_NO output (manual mode).

S_OFF - Deactivate the step indicated in the S_NO output (manual mode).

T_PUSH - Force transition when the condition is satisfied and there is a positive transition on this input. Applicable in inching mode.

The standard outputs of the function block are described as follows:

S_NO - Display step number (INT). The number displayed is controlled by the S_PREV, S_NEXT, and S_SEL inputs.

S_MORE - When true, more active steps can be indicated in S_NO.

S_ACTIVE - When true, the step indicated in S_NO is active.

ERR_FLT - True when there is an interlock error or supervision error.

AUTO_ON - True when in automatic mode.

TAP_ON - True when in the inching mode.

MAN_ON - True when in manual mode.

Three input signals to an S7-Graph function block are useful for pausing the operation of a SFC and are described as follows:

HALT_SQ – Sequencer halt/resume. A positive transition at the input toggles (stops/reactivates) the sequencer operation. If the SFC is running, a positive transition on this input halts the sequencer, that is, disables the transitions. Actions are still executed and the step timers continue to run. Actions with L and D qualifiers execute properly. If the sequencer is already halted, a positive transition on this input resumes the sequence.

HALT_TM – Step timer halt/resume. A positive transition at the input toggles (stops/reactivates) the step timers. If the step timers are running, a positive transition on this input halts their update. All time-dependent actions remain at their current state while the step timers are paused. If the step timers are already paused, a positive transition on this input resumes the update of the step timers.

ZERO_OP – Step action disable/enable. A positive transition at the input toggles (disables/enables) processing of all step actions. If actions are enabled, a positive transition on this input disables all actions. Any CALLs are not executed. Any actions that are set with the S qualifier remain **on**. If actions are disabled, a positive transition on this input reenables all actions. This input does not disable the update of the step elapsed time, nor does it disable transitions. If the sequencer contains S/R actions, the sequence should also be halted to disable the transitions. If actions are disabled after a set action is **on** and the sequencer logic transitions into and executes the step that resets that action, the action remains **on**.

Three outputs from a S7-Graph block that are useful for monitoring the status of a SFC pause are:

SQ_HALTED - True when SFC is halted.

TM_HALTED - True when update of step times is paused.

OP_ZEROED - True when step actions are disabled.

Design Tip

When using the inputs to the S7-Graph function block to pause the SFC operation, remember the following:

1. The OFF_SQ and INIT_SQ inputs do not reset any active actions that have the S qualifier.
2. The HALT_SQ, HALT_TM, and ZERO_OP inputs are all toggles. Therefore, one must be careful in constructing the logic to change to the desired state.
3. If the HALT_SQ input to the block is used to pause the SFC, the "Run" contact does not need to appear in series with any of the transition condition logic. However, if certain steps must continue to operate when the SFC is paused, HALT_SQ should not be toggled until the SFC is at a step where it can be paused.
4. The HALT_TM input to the block is useful to suspend the step elapsed timer (****.T).
5. If the sequencer contains S/R actions, the transitions should be disabled whenever the step actions are disabled.

On-line Monitoring

When online with a processor, a S7_Graph SFC may be monitored to show the state of the steps and transitions. When monitoring, the state of a step is indicated as follows:

Step symbol white	Step inactive
Step symbol green	Step active

In addition, the step elapsed time (T) and the elapsed time without supervision error (U) are displayed above the step actions. After the step becomes inactive, the times remain at their value when the step deactivated. With each step activation, the times are set to zero and updated while the step is active. The state of each action is indicated to the right as a "0" for inactive and "1" for active.

When the SFC is monitored, the state of the transition for active steps is indicated as follows:

Transition line black	Transition is false
Transition line green	Transition is true

The transitions for inactive steps are always black. The transition logic for active steps is displayed in the same manner as when monitoring a ladder or function block program on-line. The transition logic for inactive steps are shown in light gray.

14.7 EXAMPLES

These examples provide SFC solutions to examples from Chapter 6. These examples are implemented for Concept, ControlLogix, PLC-5 and Siemens S7 processors.

Example 14.1. Tub Loader Control. Use the SFC language to implement the control of the tub loader described in Example 6.3 (Figure 14.55).

Solution. The Modicon solution is shown in Figures 14.56 - 14.58. The SFC section (named Part_Tub_Sect) is shown in Figure 14.56, and the step actions and transition sections are shown in Figure 14.57. Comparing the SFC with the function chart of Figure 6.15 and the ladder logic code of Figure 6.16, there are three major differences:

1. An extra step to check for tub movement is added before the time delays that continue holding the gates open.
2. The P action qualifier is used to reset the parts counter and the retentive timer.

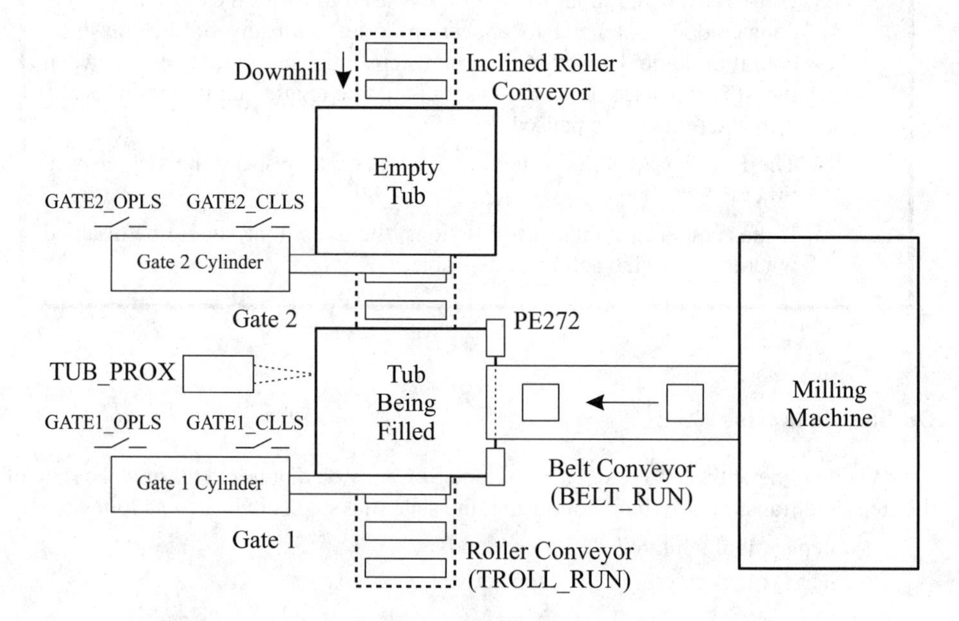

Figure 14.55. Parts tub loader station.

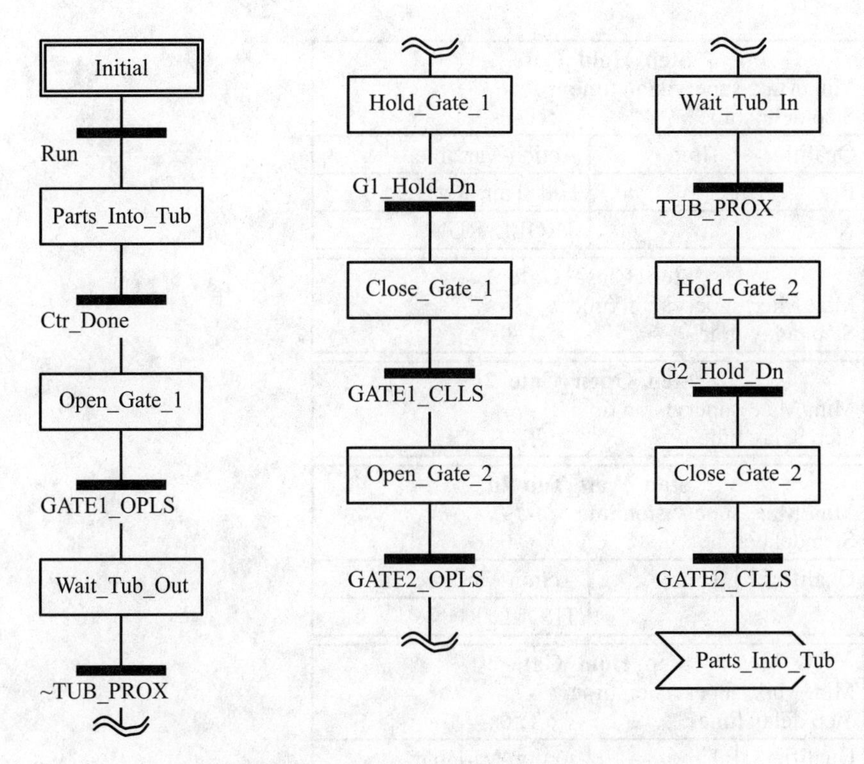

Figure 14.56. Modicon SFC section for parts tub loader.

Step Initial (Initial-Step)		
Min./Max. supervision time : - / -		
Step delay time : T#0s		

Step Parts_Into_Tub		
Min./Max. supervision time : - / -		
Step delay time : T#0s		
Qualifier	Time	Action-Variable
P		Ctr_Reset
N		BELT_RUN
N		Tub_Permissive

Step Open_Gate_1		
Min./Max. supervision time : - / -		
Step delay time : T#0s		

Step Wait_Tub_Out		
Min./Max. supervision time : - / -		
Step delay time : T#0s		
Qualifier	Time	Action-Variable
N		TROLL_RUN

Figure 14.57. Modicon parts tub loader actions and transition sections. *(continued)*

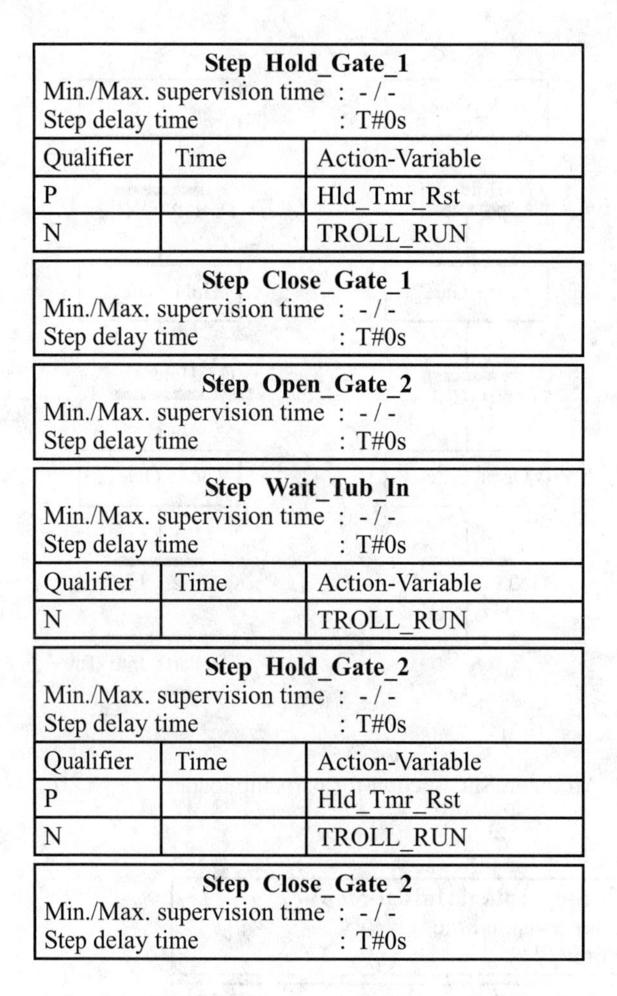

Step Hold_Gate_1
Min./Max. supervision time : - / -
Step delay time : T#0s

Qualifier	Time	Action-Variable
P		Hld_Tmr_Rst
N		TROLL_RUN

Step Close_Gate_1
Min./Max. supervision time : - / -
Step delay time : T#0s

Step Open_Gate_2
Min./Max. supervision time : - / -
Step delay time : T#0s

Step Wait_Tub_In
Min./Max. supervision time : - / -
Step delay time : T#0s

Qualifier	Time	Action-Variable
N		TROLL_RUN

Step Hold_Gate_2
Min./Max. supervision time : - / -
Step delay time : T#0s

Qualifier	Time	Action-Variable
P		Hld_Tmr_Rst
N		TROLL_RUN

Step Close_Gate_2
Min./Max. supervision time : - / -
Step delay time : T#0s

Section G1_Hold_Dn

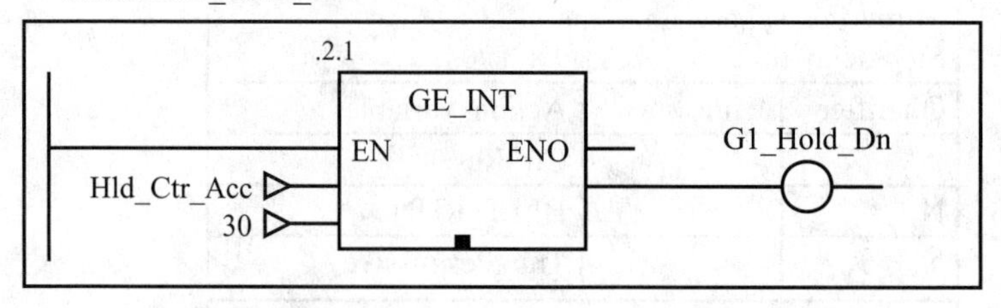

Section G2_Hold_Dn

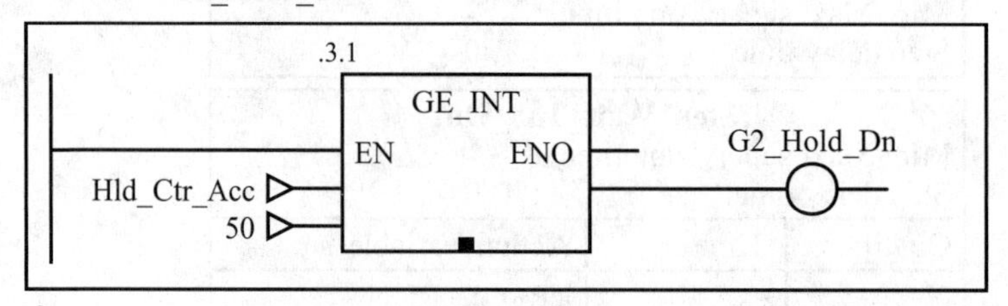

Figure 14.57. *(continued)*

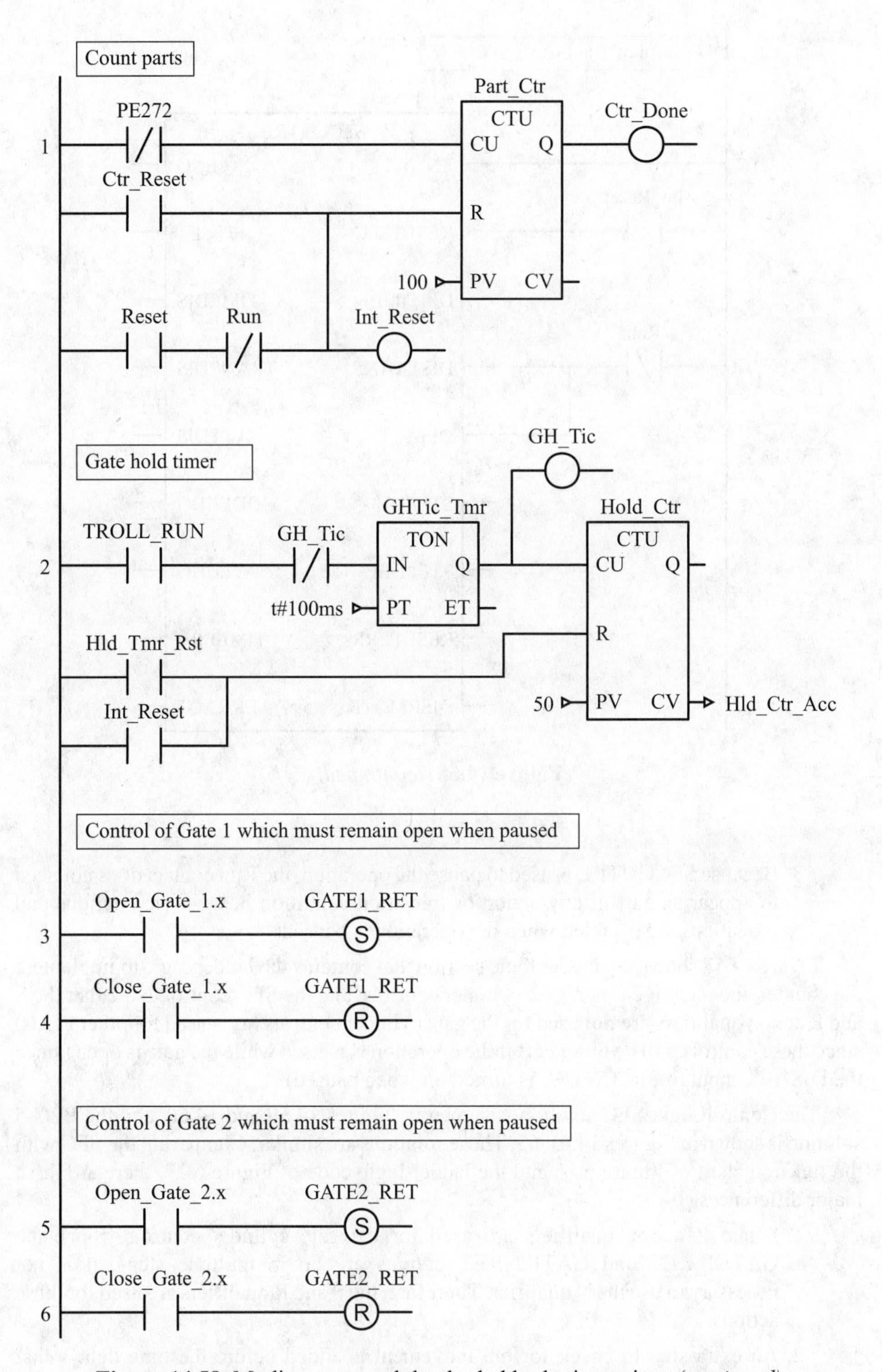

Figure 14.58. Modicon parts tub loader ladder logic section. *(continued)*

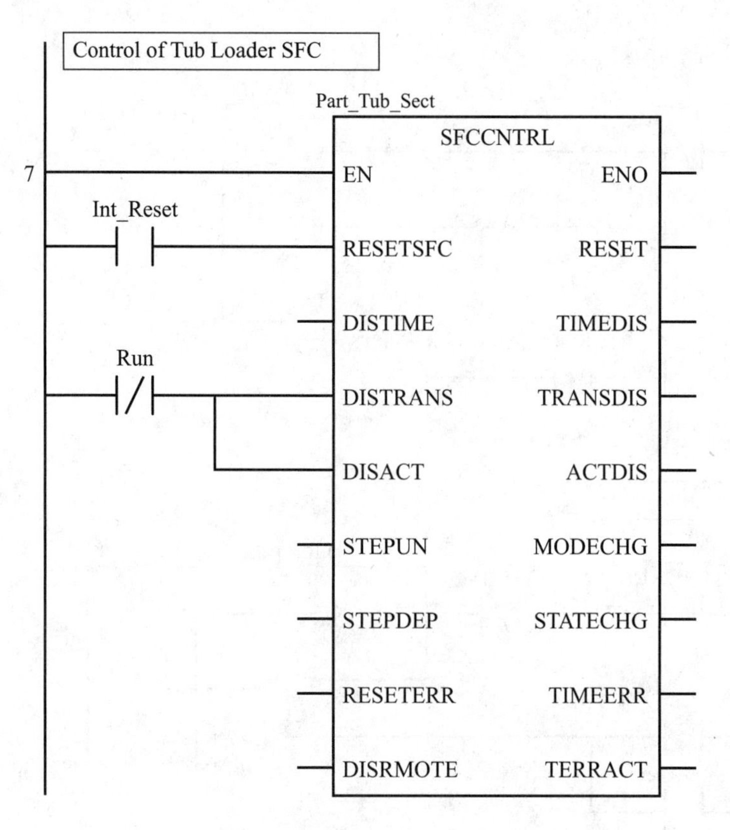

Figure 14.58. *(continued)*

3. Because SFCCNTRL is used to pause the operation, the Run contact does not need to appear as part of any action or transition condition because step actions and transitions are disabled when the operation is paused.

Figure 14.58 shows the ladder logic section that contains the ladder logic to implement the counter, the retentive timer, gate cylinder controls, and the SFC control. Note that the S and R action qualifiers are **not** used for the gate cylinder controls (as is used for other PLCs) since these controls will be turned **off** if the operation is paused while the gate is open (since the DISACT input to SFCCNTRL is turned **on** when paused).

The ControlLogix SFC solution is shown in Figures 14.59 and 14.60, and the PLC-5 solution is shown in Figures 14.61-63. These solutions are similar. Comparing the SFC with the function chart of Figure 6.15 and the ladder logic code of Figure 6.17, there are three major differences:

1. S and R action qualifiers are used for the gate cylinder controls. Since the GATE1_RET and GATE2_RET outputs are on in multiple steps, it is not necessary to use the N qualifier. Therefore, the S and R qualifiers are used for these actions.
2. An extra step to check for tub movement is added before the time delays that continue holding the gates open.
3. The P1 action qualifier is used to reset the parts counter and the hold timer.

For both solutions, note that the same timer is used for the steps that hold the gate open. Since this timer must retain the accumulator value when the operation is paused, a retentive timer must be used. Therefore, the timer must be placed in an action file since the SFC step timers cannot be paused.

For the ControlLogix, the SFC in routine Part_Tub is shown in Figure 14.59. The path from the transition out of the Close_Gate_2 step to the Parts_Into_Tub step is hidden. Only the start and end of this path is shown. Figure 14.60 shows the MainRoutine that calls the Part_Tub SFC and the other routines that support the operation.

For the PLC-5, the SFC (in program file 1) is shown in Figure 14.61. The numbers in parentheses are the program file for the action or transition. Figure 14.62 has the ladder logic in program file 2, which is executed all the time. The program files containing the transitions and actions in ladder logic are shown in Figure 14.63. For each of these files, the END rung is omitted.

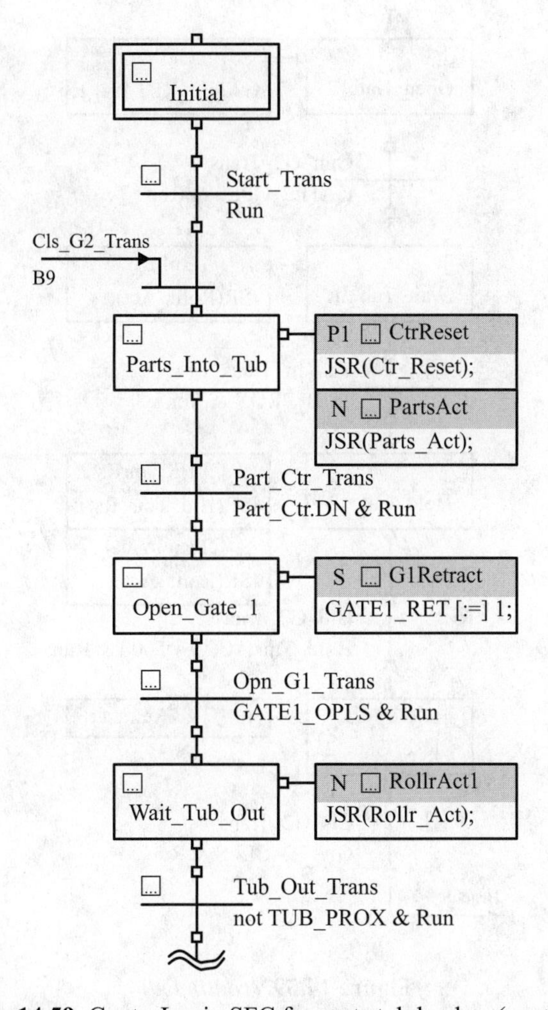

Figure 14.59. ControLogix SFC for parts tub loader. *(continued)*

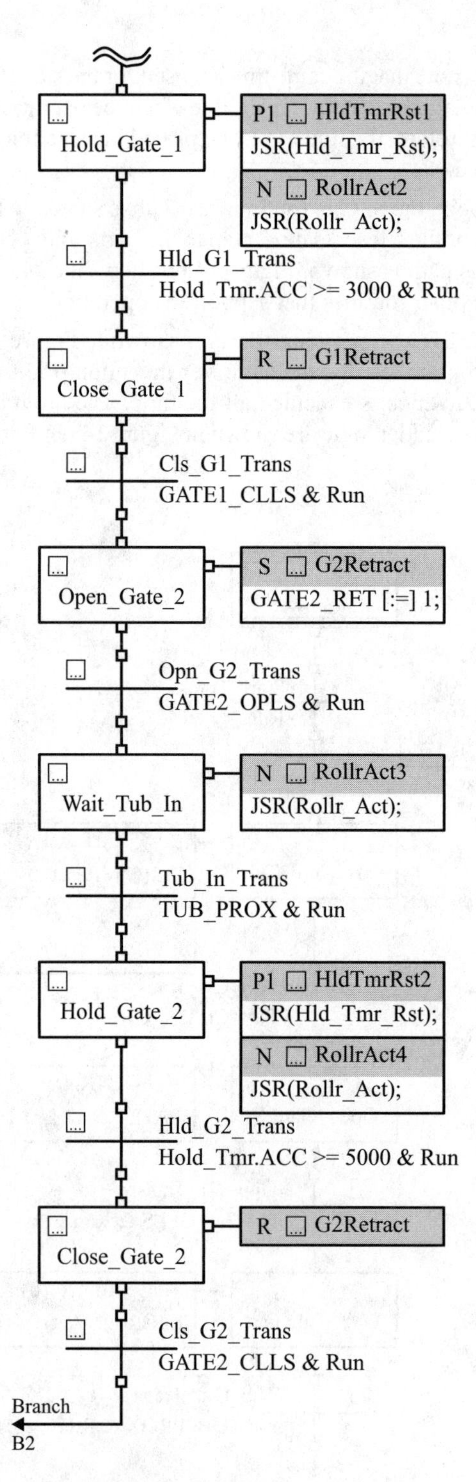

Figure 14.59. *(continued)*

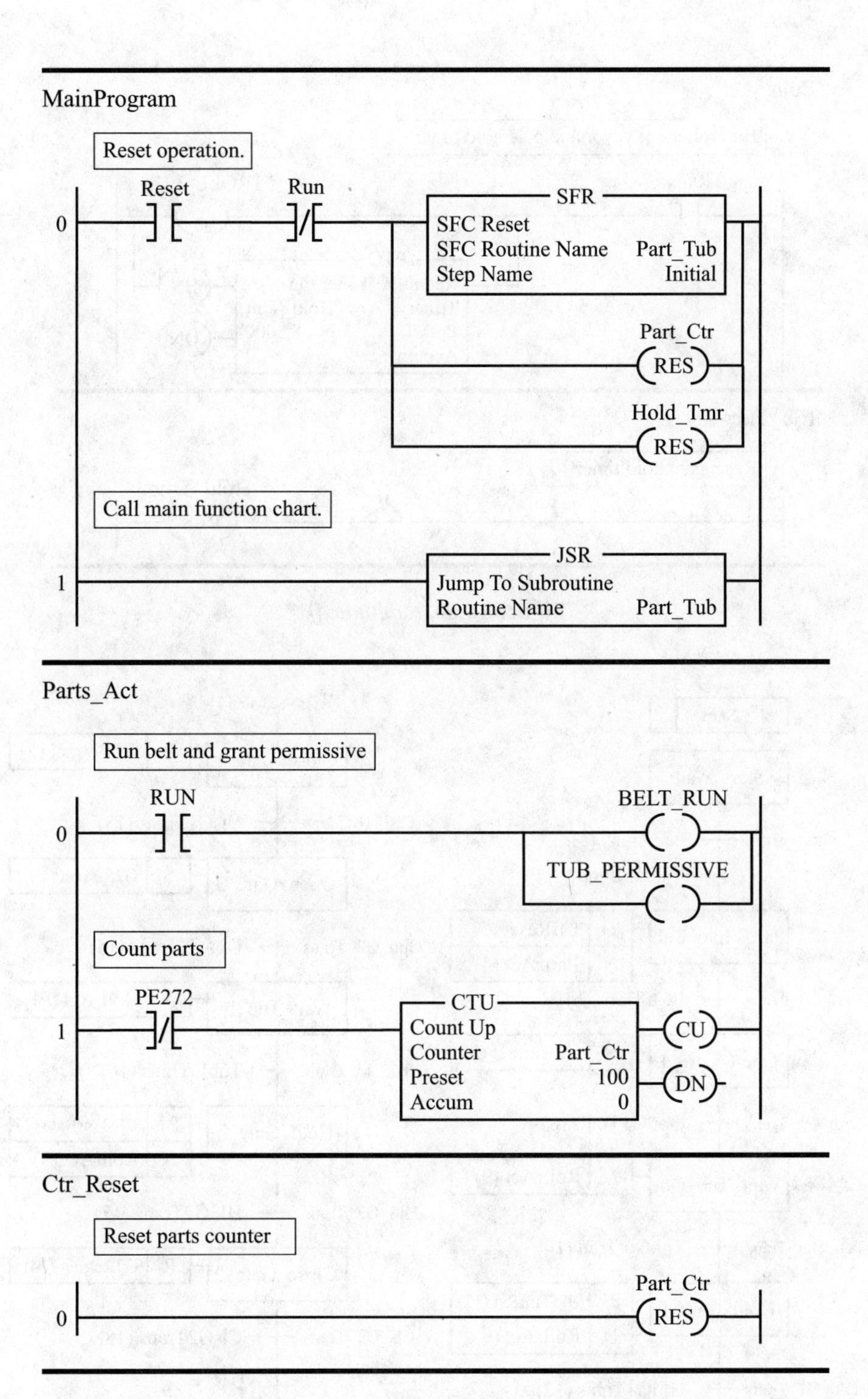

Figure 14.60. ControLogix ladder logic routines for parts tub loader. *(continued)*

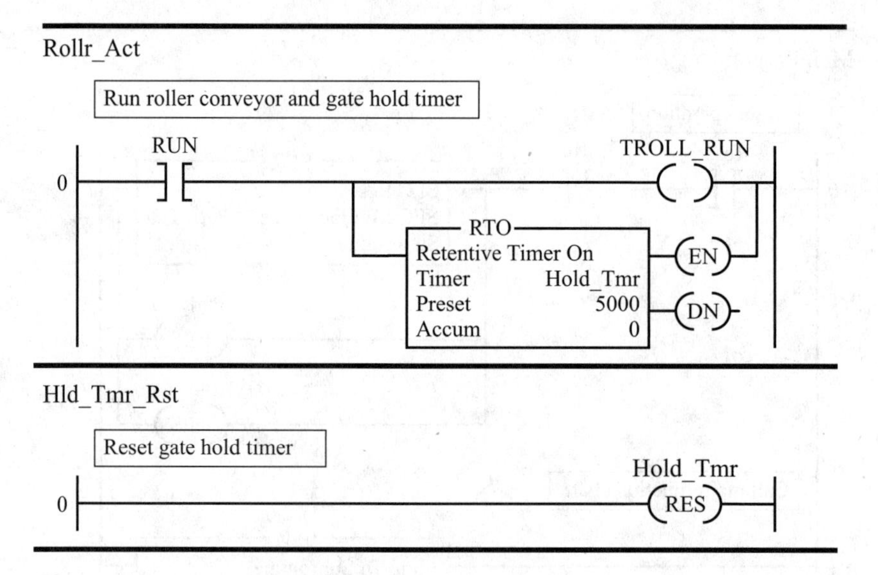

Figure 14.60. *(continued)*

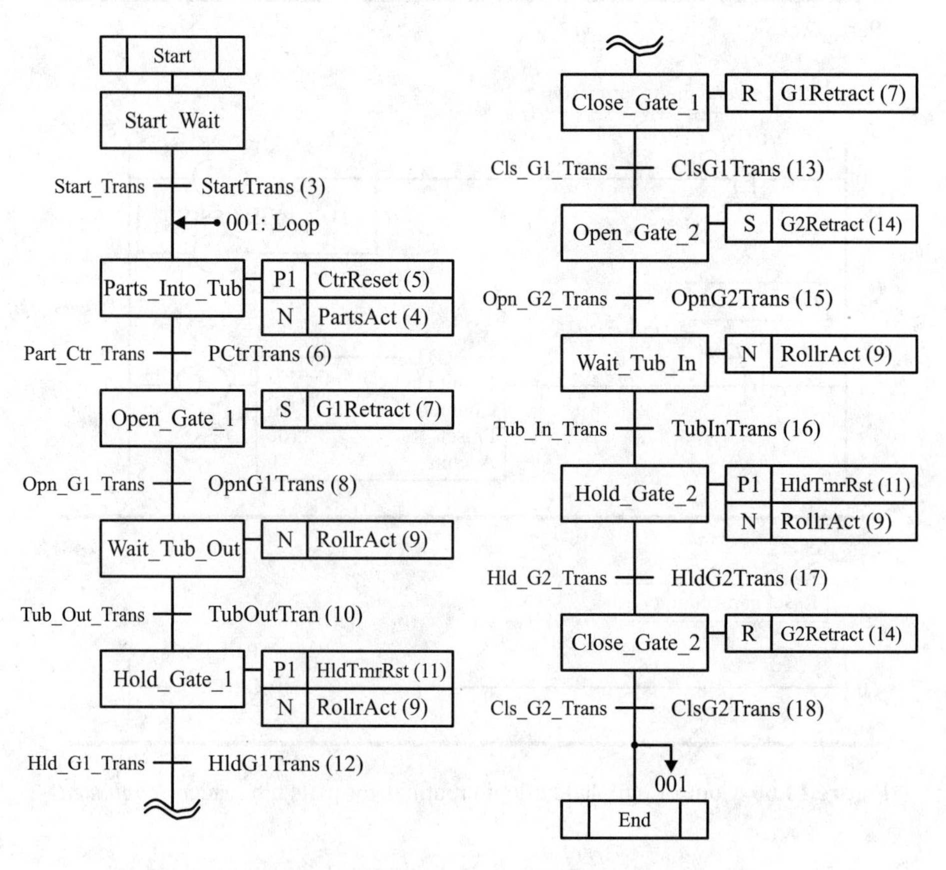

Figure 14.61. PLC-5 SFC file for parts tub loader.

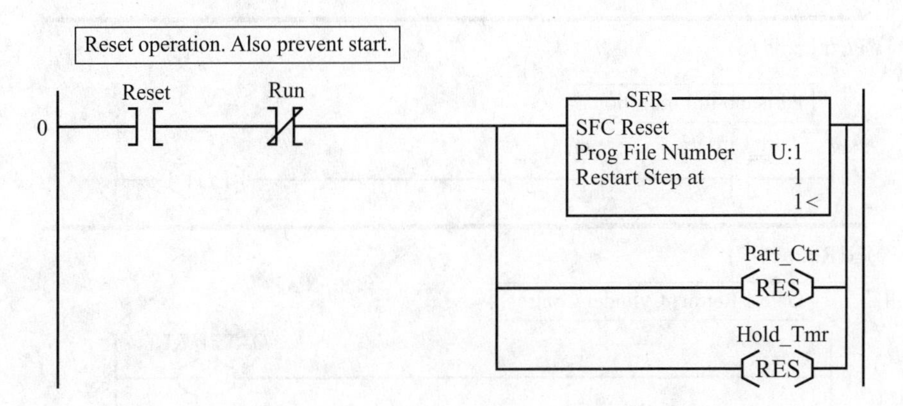

Figure 14.62. PLC-5 parts tub loader ladder logic in program file 2.

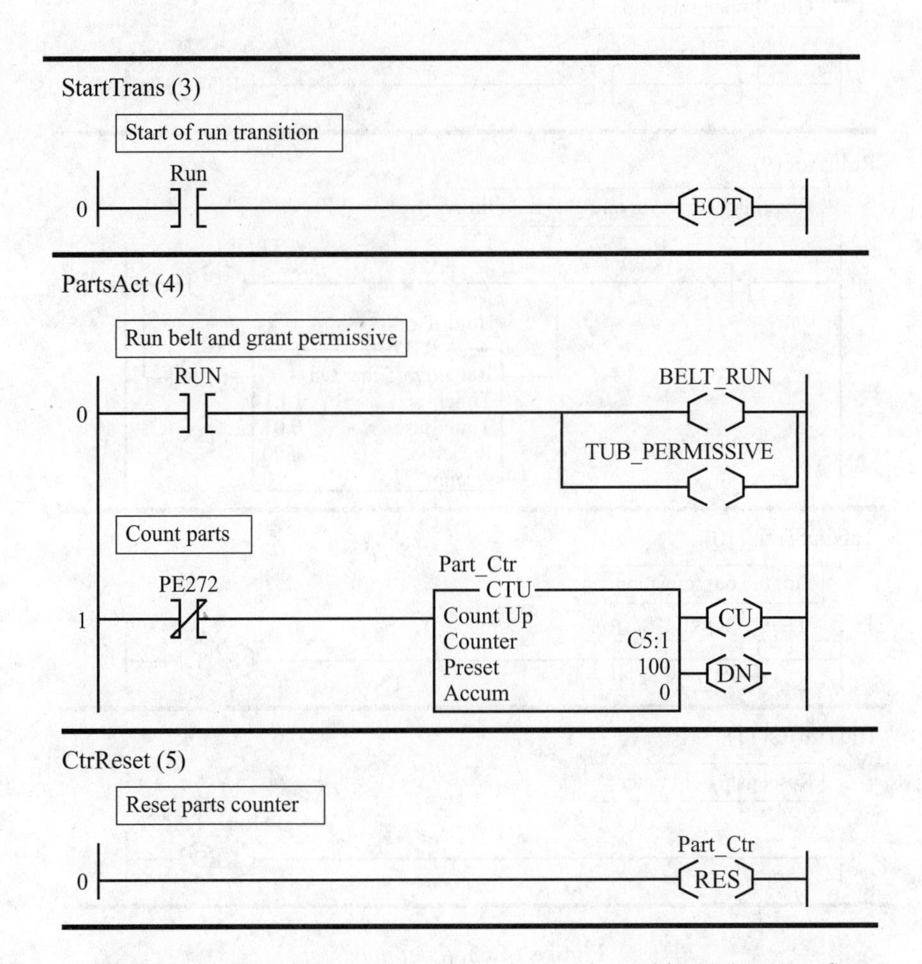

Figure 14.63. PLC-5 parts tub loader actions and transitions. *(continued)*

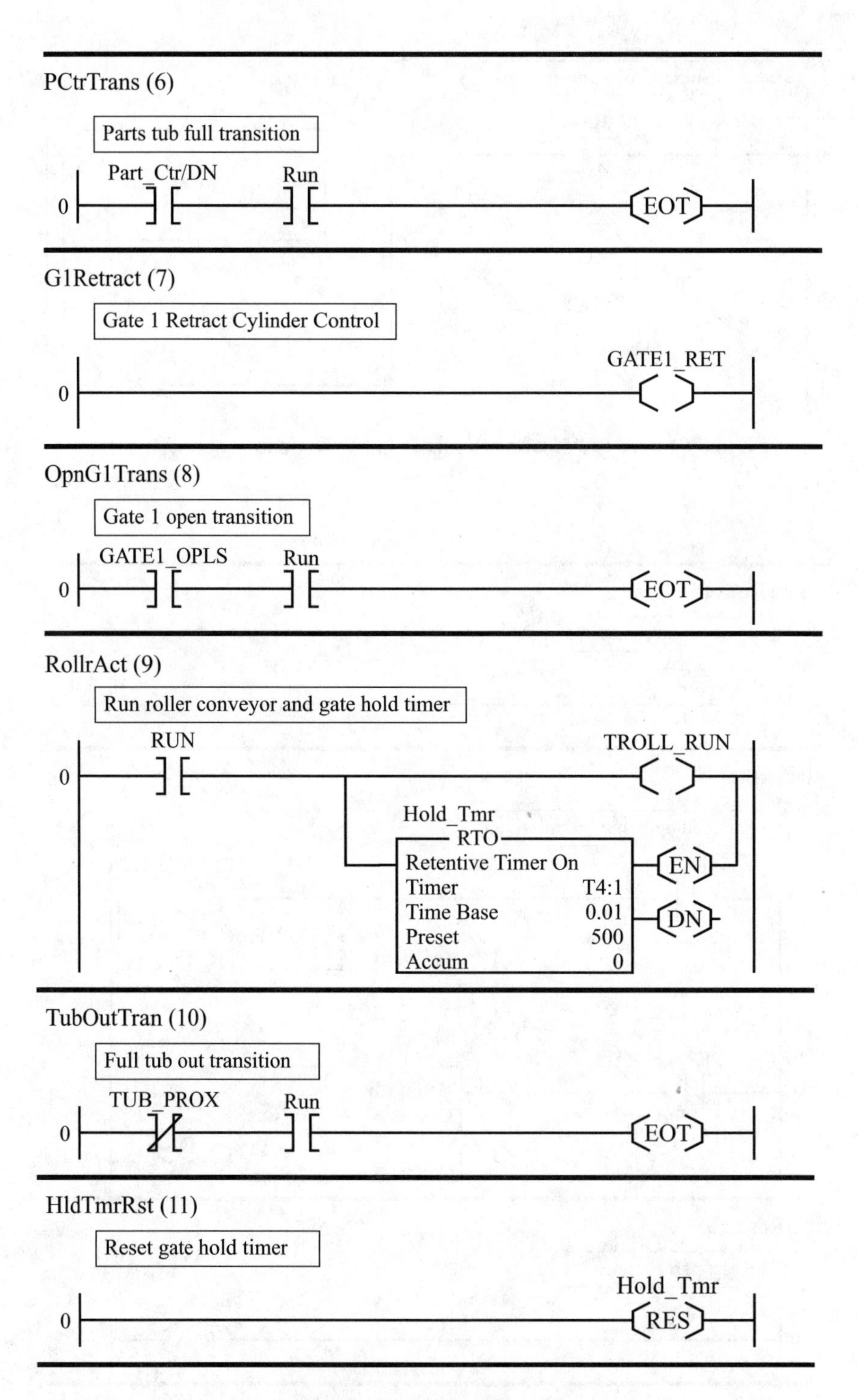

Figure 14.63. *(continued)*

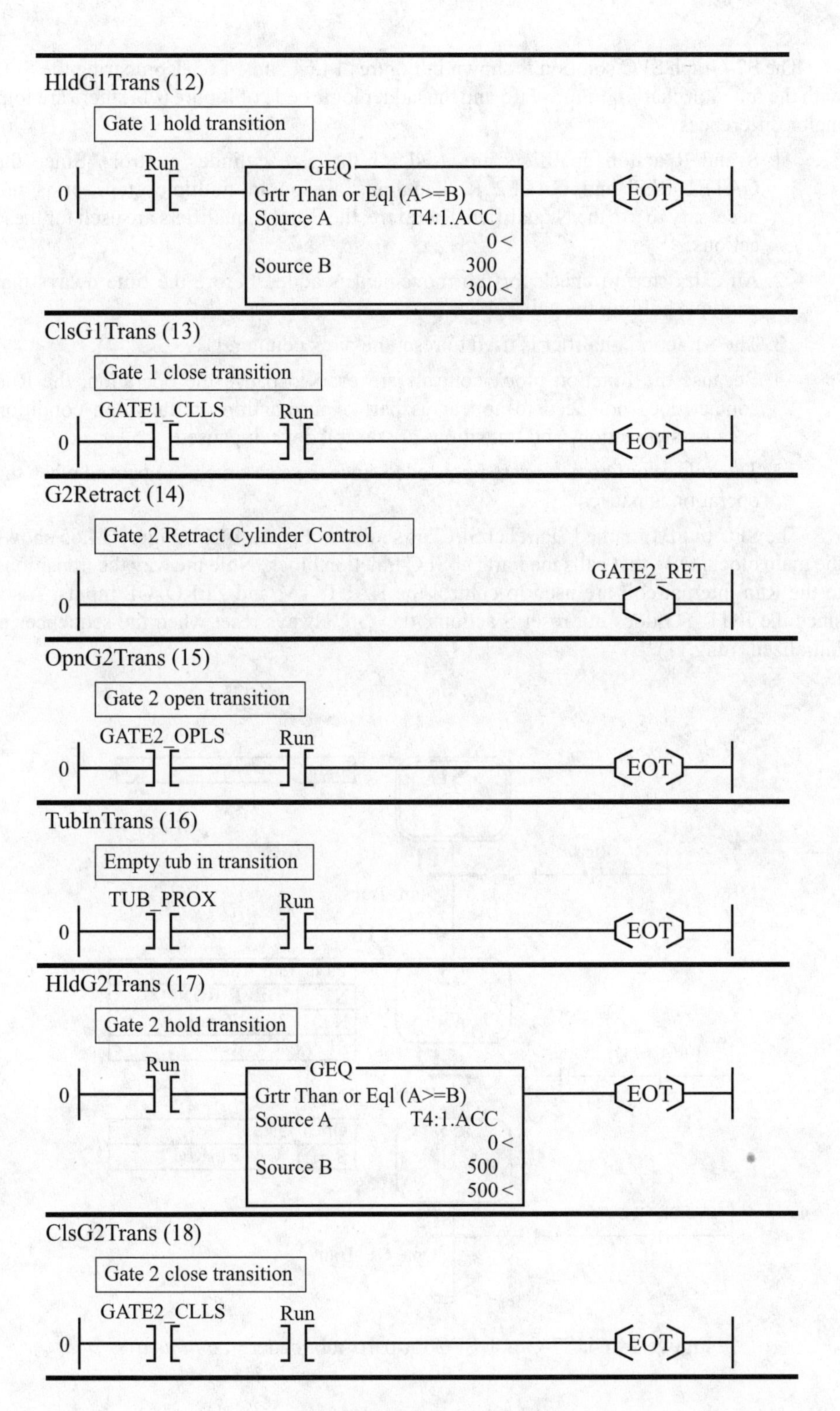

Figure 14.63. *(continued)*

The S7-Graph SFC solution is shown in Figures 14.64 and 14.65. Comparing the SFC with the function chart of Figure 6.15 and the ladder logic code of Figure 6.17, there are four major differences:

1. S and R action qualifiers are used for the gate cylinder controls. Since the GATE1_RET and GATE2_RET outputs are on in multiple steps, it is not necessary to use the N qualifier. Therefore, the S and R qualifiers are used for these actions.
2. An extra step to check for tub movement is added before the time delays that continue holding the gates open.
3. The S1 action qualifier is used to reset the parts counter.
4. Because the function block controls are used to pause the operation, the Run contact does not need to appear as part of any action or transition condition because step actions and transitions are disabled when paused.
5. The hold retentive timers are not needed since the step timers are paused when the operation is paused.

The SFC in FB1, named "PartTubSFC" is shown in Figure 14.64. Figure 14.65 shows the main block, OB1 that calls the PartTubSFC function block. Note the way the transitions in the Run internal coil are used to control the HALT_TM and ZERO_OP inputs. Also, since the INIT_SQ does not reset S actions, they are always reset when the sequencer is initialized (rung 11).

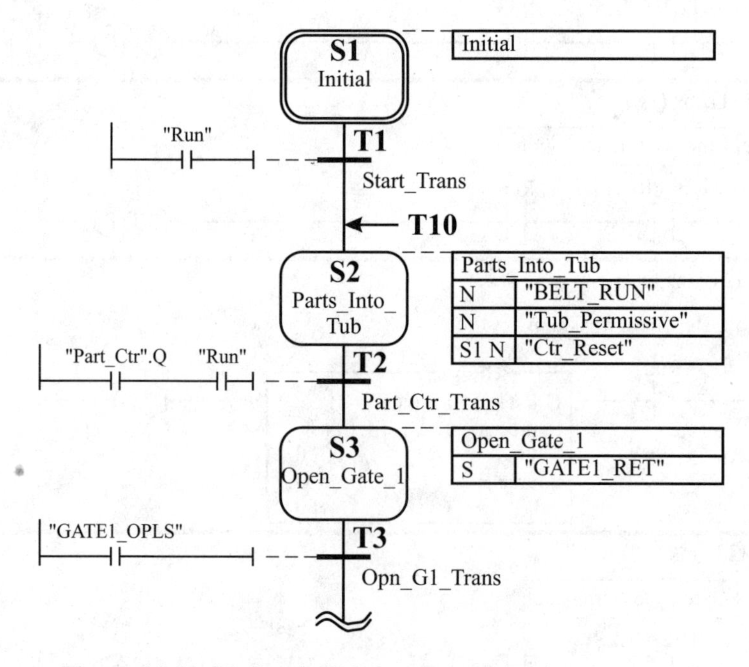

Figure 14.64. S7-Graph SFC for parts tub loader. *(continued)*

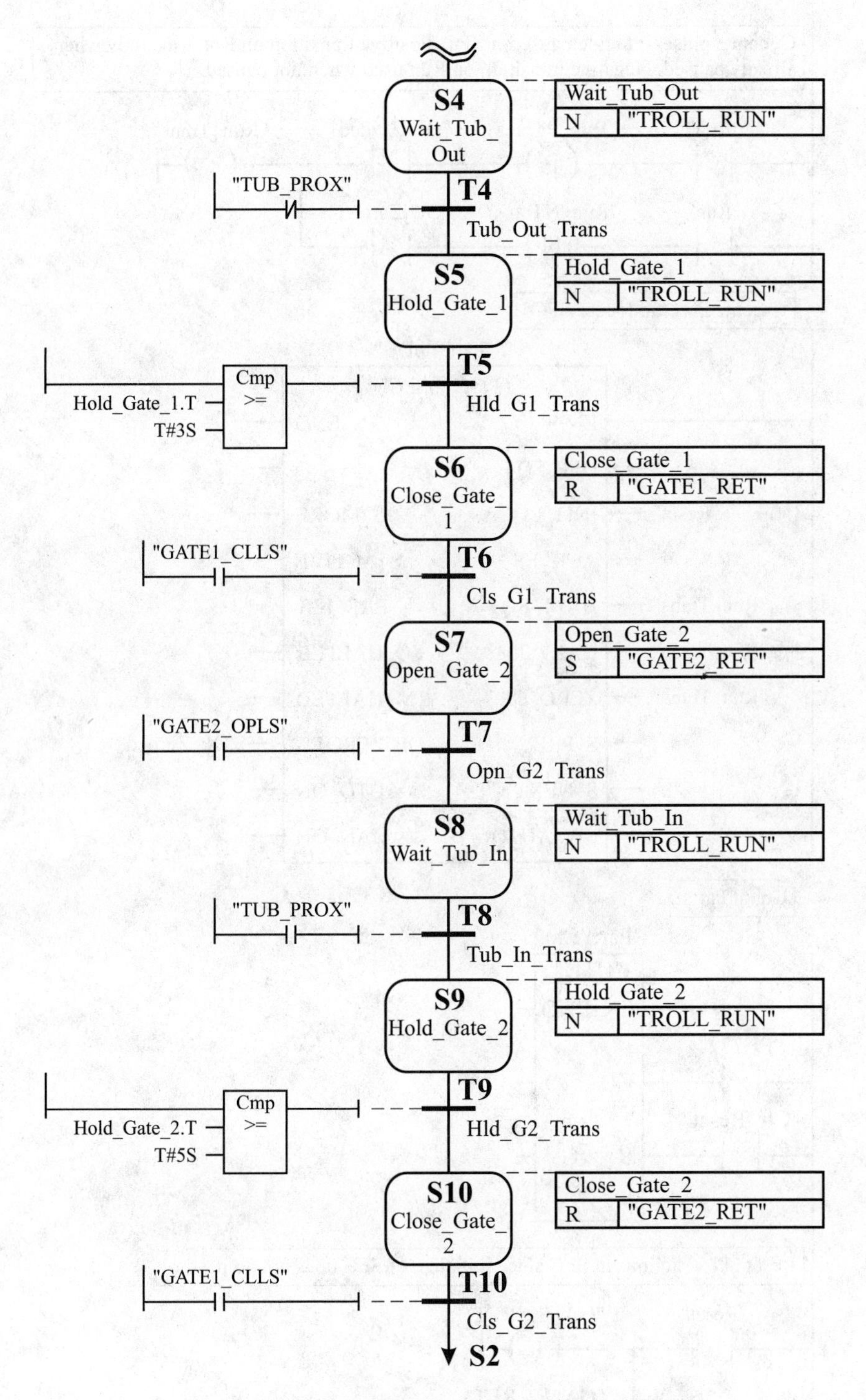

Figure 14.64. *(continued)*

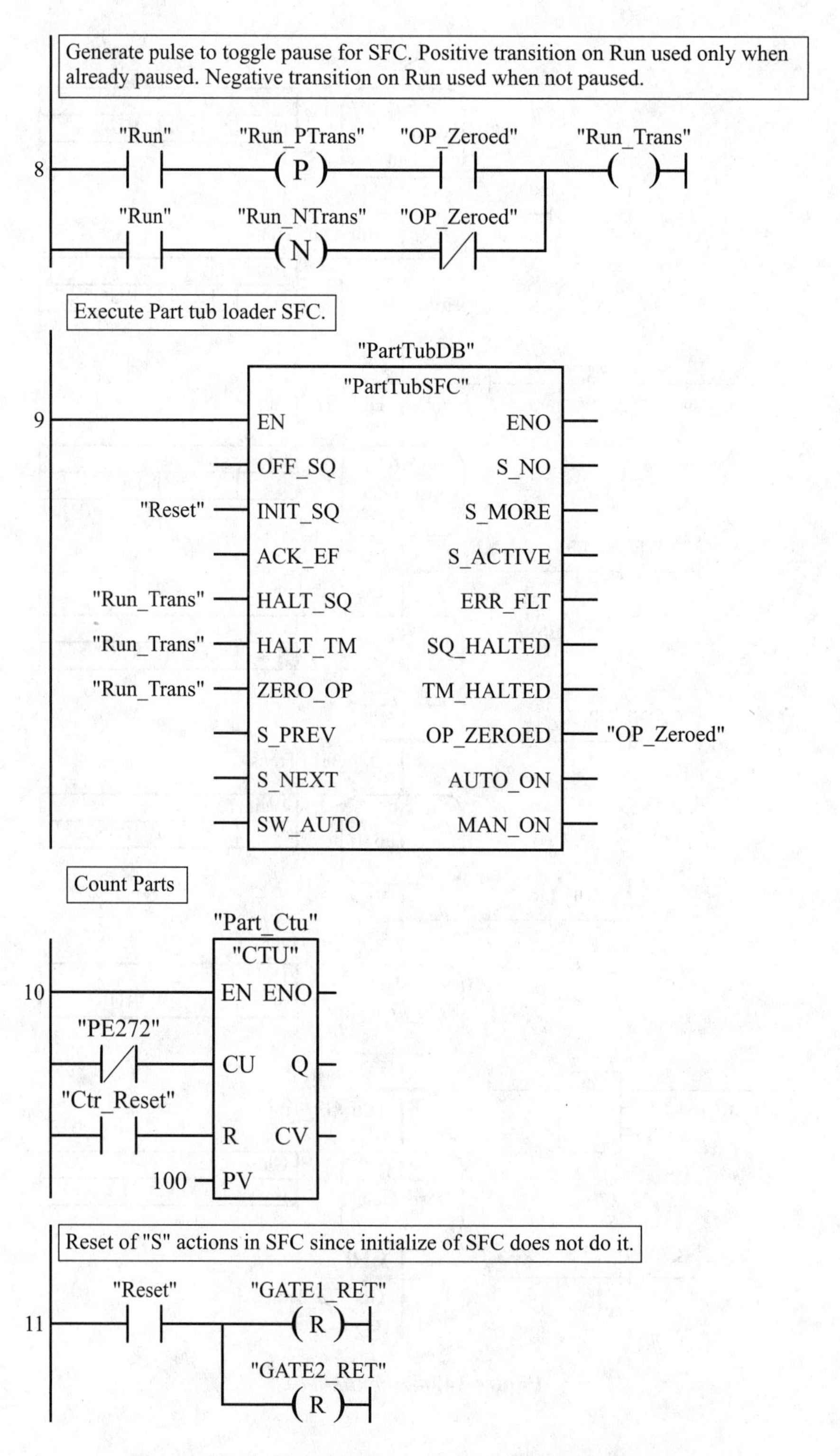

Figure 14.65. S7 ladder logic in OB1 for parts tub loader.

Example 14.2. Engine Inverter Station Control. Use the SFC language to implement the control of the engine inverter of Example 6.5 (Figure 14.66).

Solution. For the Modicon, the SFC section (named Invert_Normal) for the normal operation is shown in Figure 14.67, and the step actions and transition sections are shown in Figure 14.68. The transition sections use the ST language. Comparing the SFC with the function chart of Figure 6.33, the only major difference is that the "raise pallet" and "lower rotator" steps are combined into one step with two actions. Note that in order for the steps that control the engaging hooks to function properly, SFCCNTRL cannot disable transitions when paused. When paused in the middle of these steps, the step must complete. Therefore the Run contact does need to appear as part of many of the transition conditions.

The SFC section (named Invert_Reset) for the reset operation is shown in Figure 14.69 and the step actions and transition sections are shown in Figure 14.70. Since transitional functions are not allowed in transitions, the transition out of the last step waits for the RESET_PB to be released before waiting for it to be pressed. Figure 14.71 shows the ladder logic section that contains the ladder logic to implement the pallet retainer control, the gripper control, and the SFC controls. Note that the S and R action qualifiers are **not** used for the pallet retainer and gripper cylinder controls (as is used for other processors) since these controls will be turned **off** if the operation is paused.

The ControlLogix SFC solution is shown in Figures 14.72-74, and the PLC-5 solution is shown in Figures 14.75-78. These solutions are similar. Comparing the normal operation SFC with the function chart of Figure 6.33, there are two major differences:

1. S and R action qualifiers are used for the pallet retainer (PALL_UPCTL) and the gripper cylinder (GRIP_CLOS) controls.
2. The "raise pallet" and the "lower rotator" steps are combined into one step with two actions.

For the ControlLogix, the SFC for the normal station operation (routine Invert_Normal) is shown in Figure 14.72 and the SFC for the reset operation (routine Invert_Reset) is shown in Figure 14.73. Figure 14.74 shows the MainRoutine that calls the Part_Tub SFC and the structured text routines that support the operation. Note the use of a JSR for the initial transition out of the initial reset step. The OSRI function is used in the ResetPB_Trans routine as a one-shot to detect the rising edge of the RESET_PB. Compared with the PLC-5 solution, the ControlLogix solution is much more compact and many of the step actions are handled as structured text in the SFC.

For the PLC-5, the SFC (in program file 1) for the normal station operation is shown in Figure 14.75. Data file SC10 is the step timer file and T11 is the action timer file for this SFC. The configuration for the step and action timers are shown below the action boxes, for the step but does not appear in the actual SFC display. The numbers in parentheses are the program file for the action or transition. The SFC (in program file 3) for the reset operation is shown in Figure 14.76. The step timer file is SC12. Figure 14.77 has the ladder logic in program file 2, which is executed all the time. The program files containing the transitions and actions in structured text are shown in Figure 14.78.

The S7-Graph SFC solution is shown in Figures 14.79-81. Comparing the normal operation SFC with the function chart of Figure 6.33, there are three major differences:

1. S and R action qualifiers are used for the pallet retainer (PALL_UPCTL) and the gripper cylinder (GRIP_CLOS) controls.

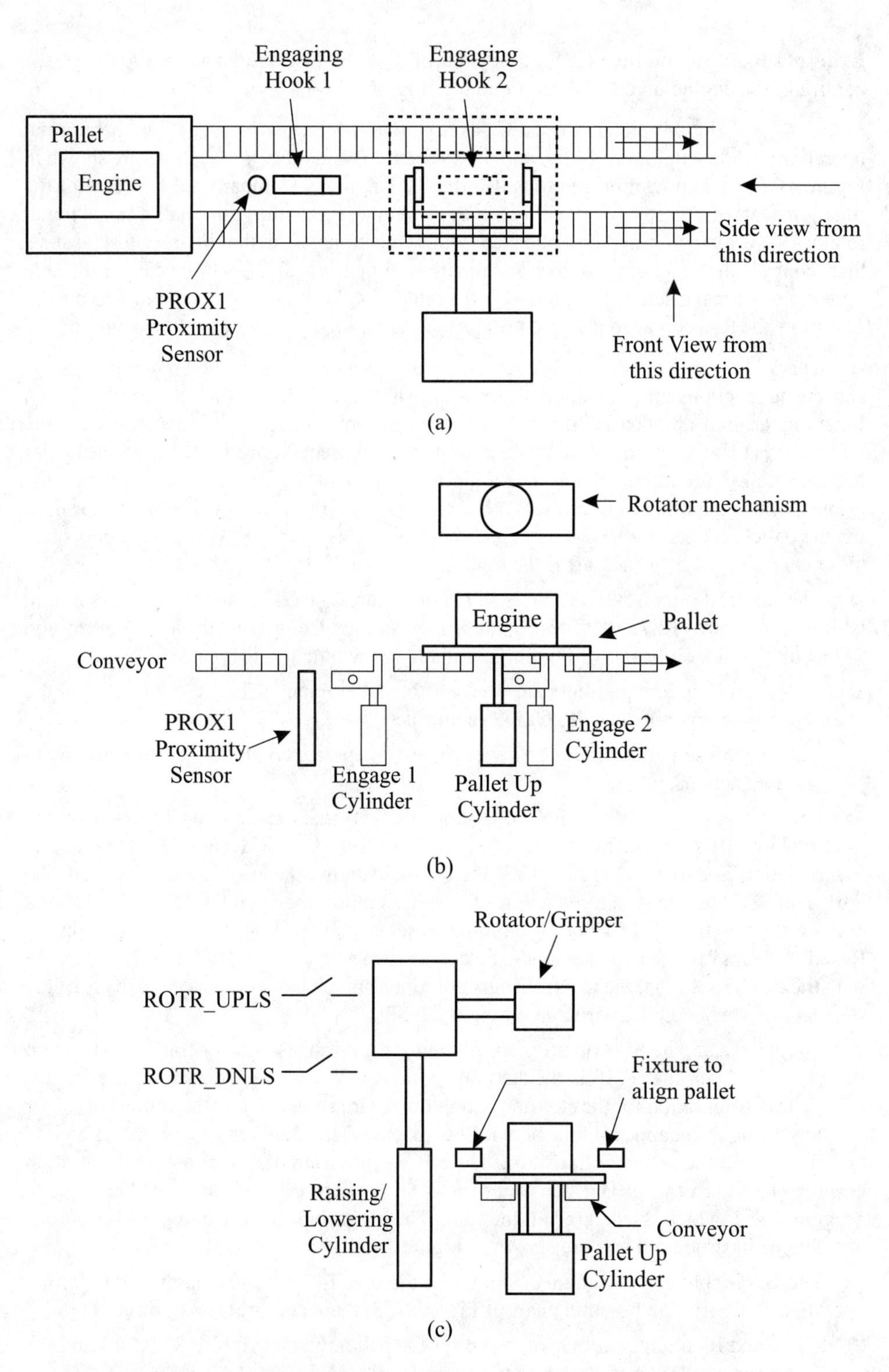

Figure 14.66. Engine inverter station: *(a)* top view; *(b)* front view; *(c)* side view.

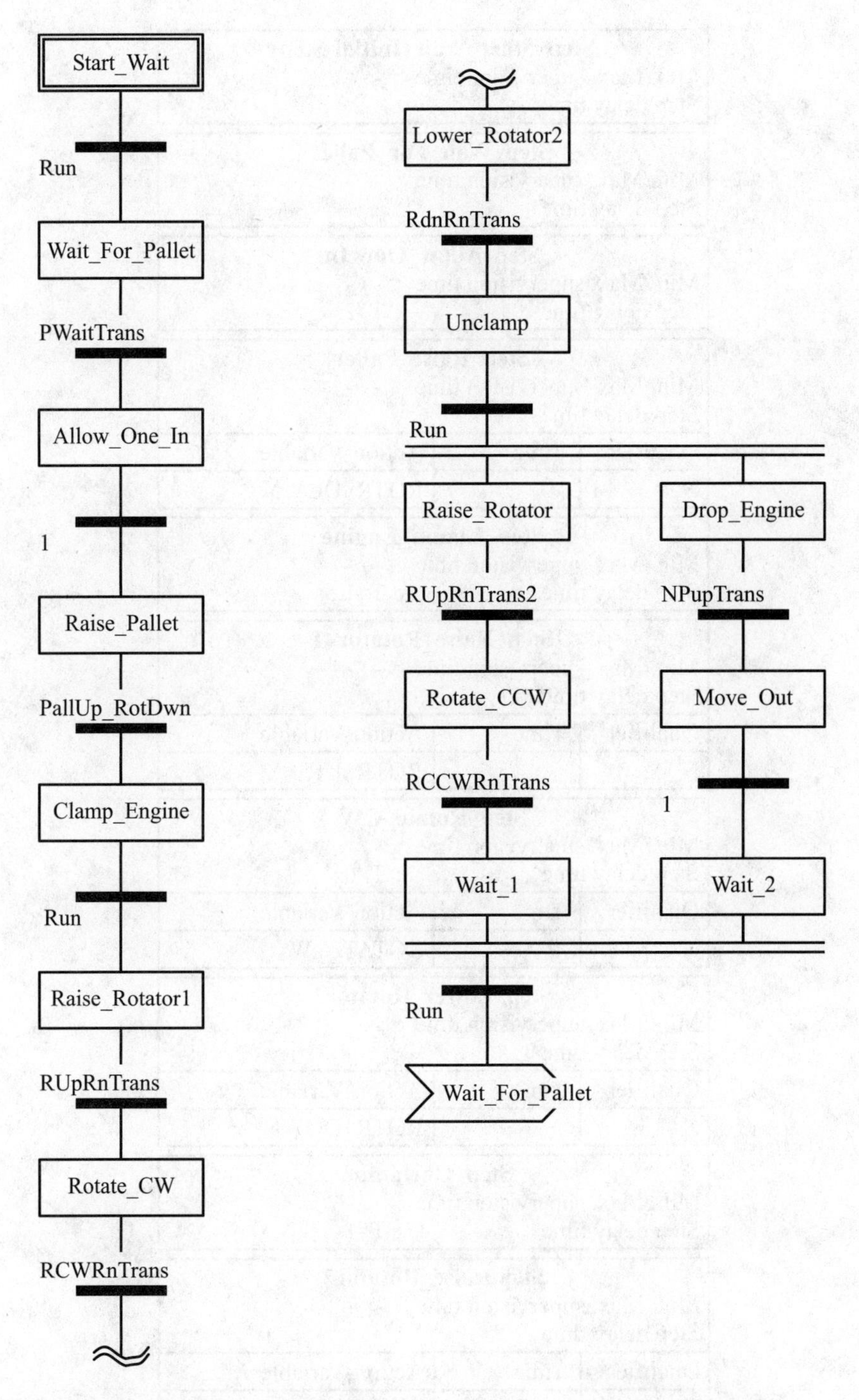

Figure 14.67. Modicon SFC section for engine inverter normal operation (named "Invert_Normal").

Step Start_Wait (Initial-Step)
Min./Max. supervision time : - / -
Step delay time :

Step Wait_For_Pallet
Min./Max. supervision time : - / -
Step delay time :

Step Allow_One_In
Min./Max. supervision time : - / -
Step delay time : T#2s

Step Raise_Pallet		
Min./Max. supervision time : - / -		
Step delay time :		
Qualifier	Time	Action-Variable
N		ROTR_DOWN

Step Clamp_Engine
Min./Max. supervision time : - / -
Step delay time : T#1.5s

Step Raise_Rotator_1		
Min./Max. supervision time : - / -		
Step delay time :		
Qualifier	Time	Action-Variable
N		ROTR_UP

Step Rotate_CW		
Min./Max. supervision time : - / -		
Step delay time : T#0s		
Qualifier	Time	Action-Variable
N		ROTAT_CW

Step Lower_Rotator2		
Min./Max. supervision time : - / -		
Step delay time :		
Qualifier	Time	Action-Variable
N		ROTR_DOWN

Step Unclamp
Min./Max. supervision time : - / -
Step delay time : T#1s

Step Raise_Rotator2		
Min./Max. supervision time : - / -		
Step delay time :		
Qualifier	Time	Action-Variable
N		ROTR_UP

Figure 14.68. Modicon "Invert Normal" SFC actions and transition sections. *(continued)*

Step Rotate_CCW		
Min./Max. supervision time : - / -		
Step delay time :		
Qualifier	Time	Action-Variable
N		ROTAT_CCW

Step Wait_1
Min./Max. supervision time : - / -
Step delay time :

Step Drop_Engine
Min./Max. supervision time : - / -
Step delay time :

Step Move_Out
Min./Max. supervision time : - / -
Step delay time : T#3s

Step Wait_2
Min./Max. supervision time : - / -
Step delay time :

Section NPupTrans

```
TRANSITION NPupTrans :=
  (NOT PALL_UPLS) AND Run;
END_TRANSITION
```

Section PallUp_RotDwn

```
TRANSITION PallUp_RotDwn :=
  PALL_UPLS AND ROTR_DNLS AND Run;
END_TRANSITION
```

Section PWaitTrans

```
TRANSITION PWaitTrans :=
  PROX1 AND Run;
END_TRANSITION
```

Section RCCWRnTans

```
TRANSITION RCCWRnTrns :=
  ROTR_CCWLS AND Run;
END_TRANSITION
```

Section RCWRnTans

```
TRANSITION RCWRnTrns :=
  ROTR_CWLS AND Run;
END_TRANSITION
```

Figure 14.68. *(continued)*

Section RdnRnTrans

```
TRANSITION RdnRnTrans :=
  ROTR_DNLS AND Run;
END_TRANSITION
```

Section RUpRnTrans

```
TRANSITION RUpRnTrans :=
  PALL_UPLS AND Run;
END_TRANSITION
```

Section RUpRnTrans2

```
TRANSITION RUpRnTrans2 :=
  PALL_UPLS AND Run;
END_TRANSITION
```

Figure 14.68. *(continued)*

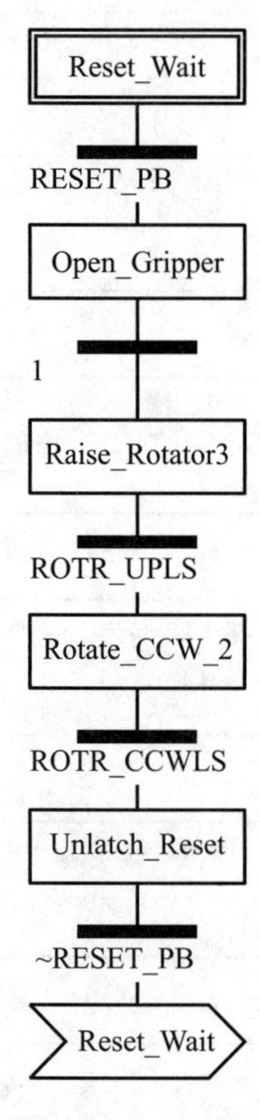

Figure 14.69. Modicon SFC section for engine inverter reset operation (named "Invert_Reset").

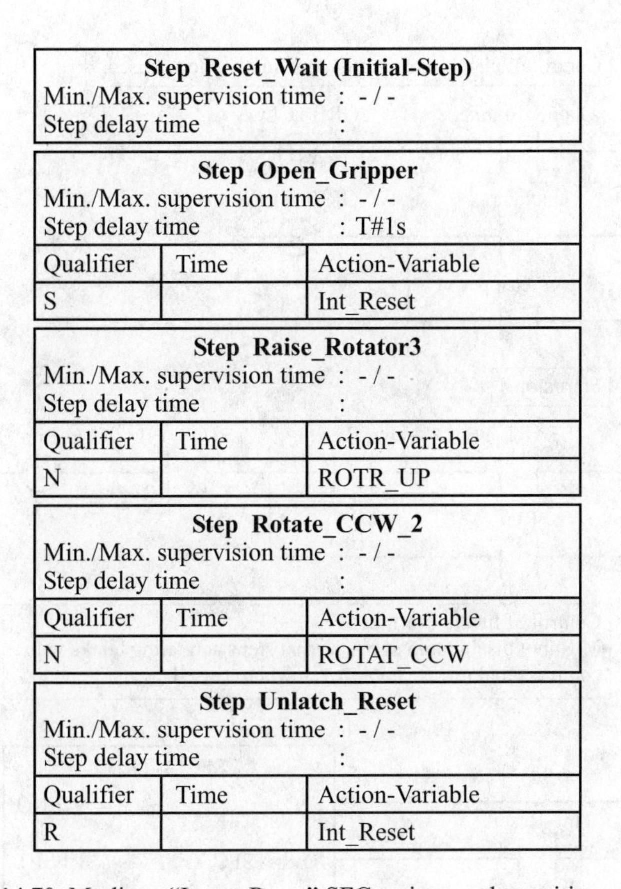

Step Reset_Wait (Initial-Step)
Min./Max. supervision time : - / -
Step delay time :

Step Open_Gripper
Min./Max. supervision time : - / -
Step delay time : T#1s

Qualifier	Time	Action-Variable
S		Int_Reset

Step Raise_Rotator3
Min./Max. supervision time : - / -
Step delay time :

Qualifier	Time	Action-Variable
N		ROTR_UP

Step Rotate_CCW_2
Min./Max. supervision time : - / -
Step delay time :

Qualifier	Time	Action-Variable
N		ROTAT_CCW

Step Unlatch_Reset
Min./Max. supervision time : - / -
Step delay time :

Qualifier	Time	Action-Variable
R		Int_Reset

Figure 14.70. Modicon "Invert Reset" SFC actions and transition sections.

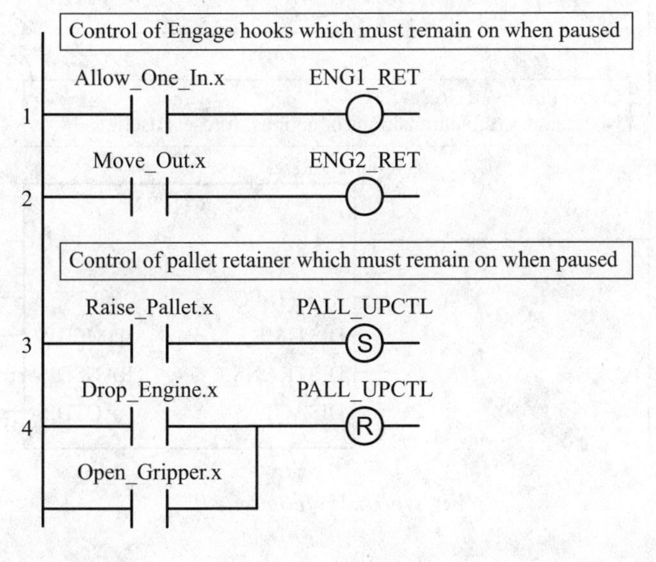

Figure 14.71. Modicon engine inverter ladder logic section. *(continued)*

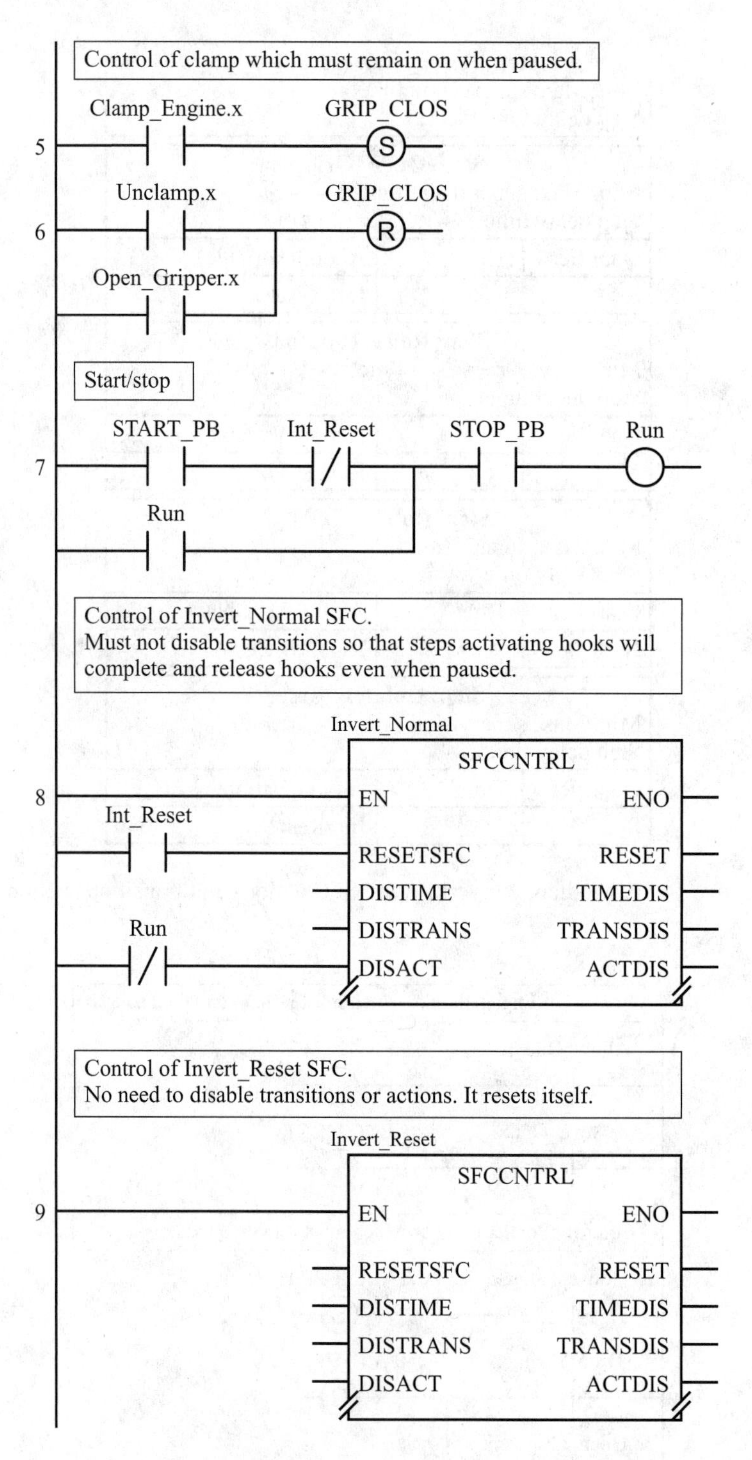

Figure 14.71. *(continued)*

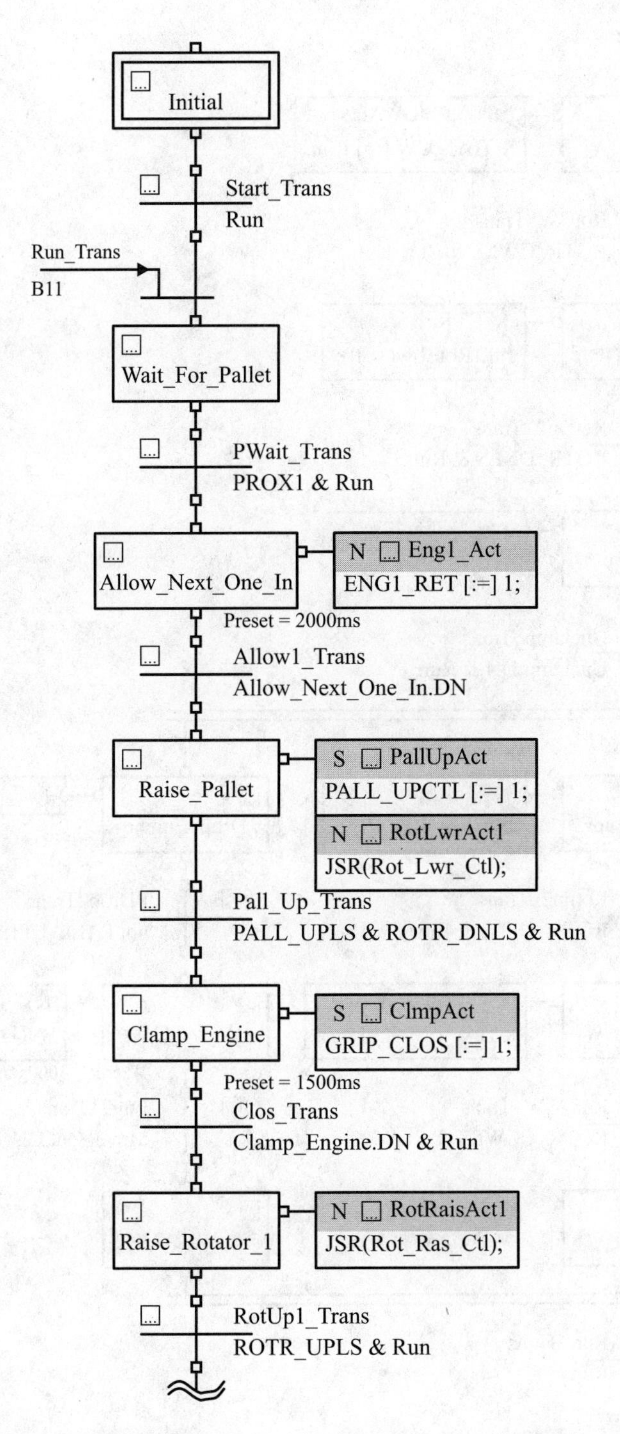

Figure 14.72. ControLogix SFC for engine inverter normal operation. *(continued)*

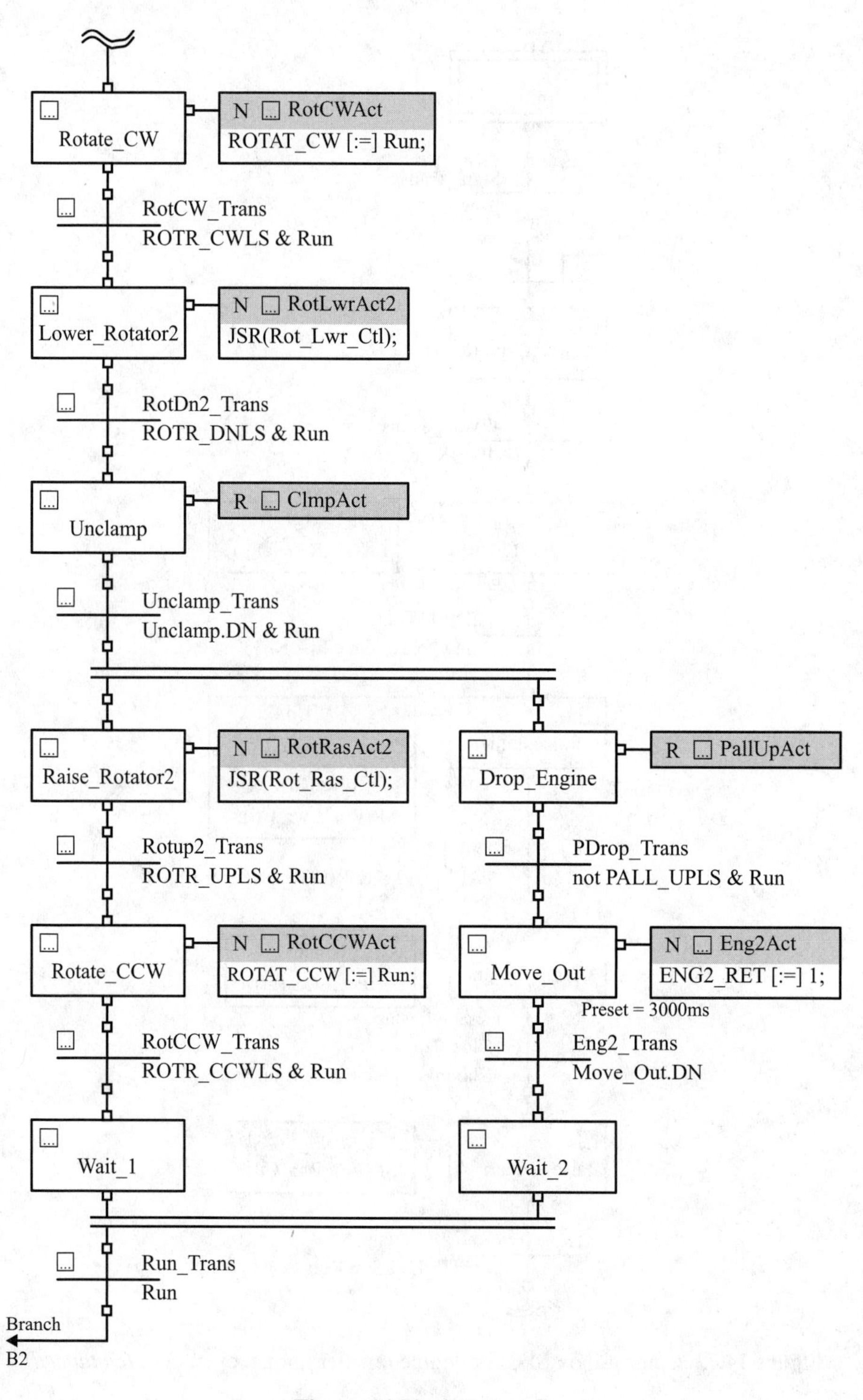

Figure 14.72. *(continued)*

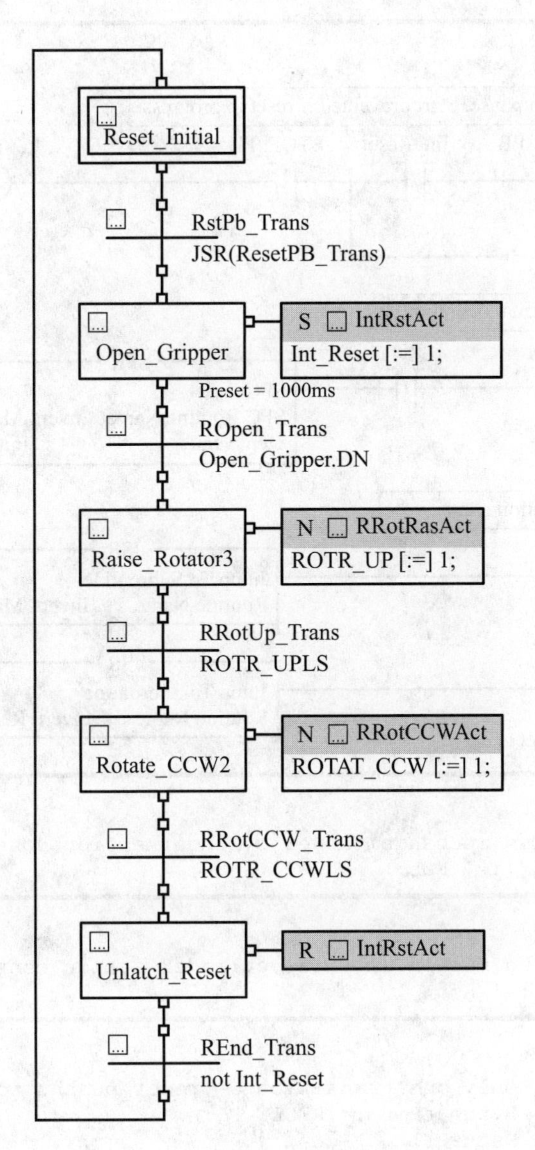

Figure 14.73. ControLogix SFC for engine inverter reset operation.

MainProgram

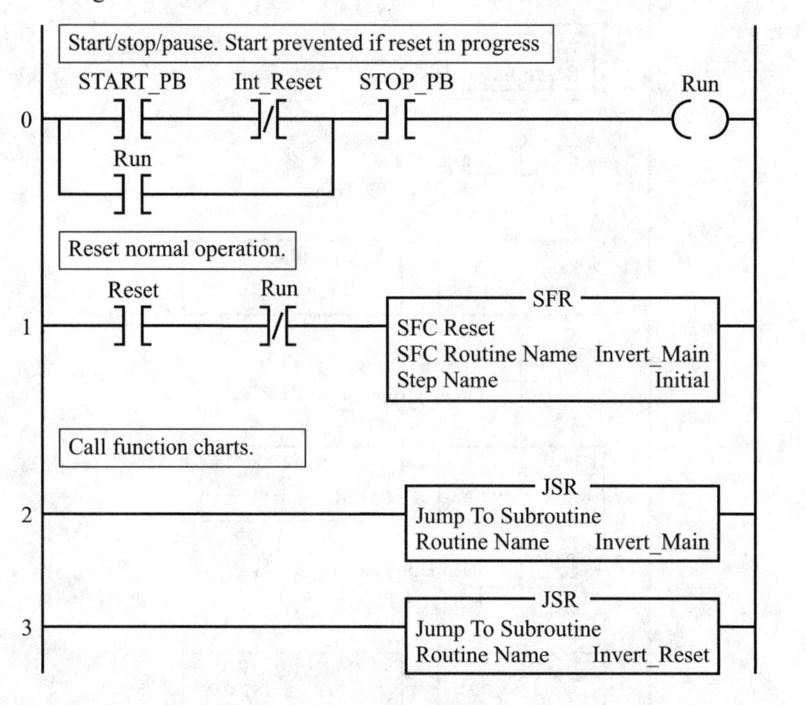

Rot_Lwr_Ctl

```
// Rotating mechanism lower cylinder action control
ROTR_DOWN [:=] Run;
```

Rot_Ras_Ctl

```
// Rotating mechanism raise cylinder action control
ROTR_UP [:=] Run;
```

ResetPB_Trans

```
// Detect only one transition of reset pushbutton
OSRI_Rst_PB.InputBit := RESET_PB;
OSRI(OSRI_Rst_PB);
TmpBit := OSRI_Rst_PB.OutputBit & not Run;
EOT(TmpBit);
```

Figure 14.74. ControLogix routines for engine inverter.

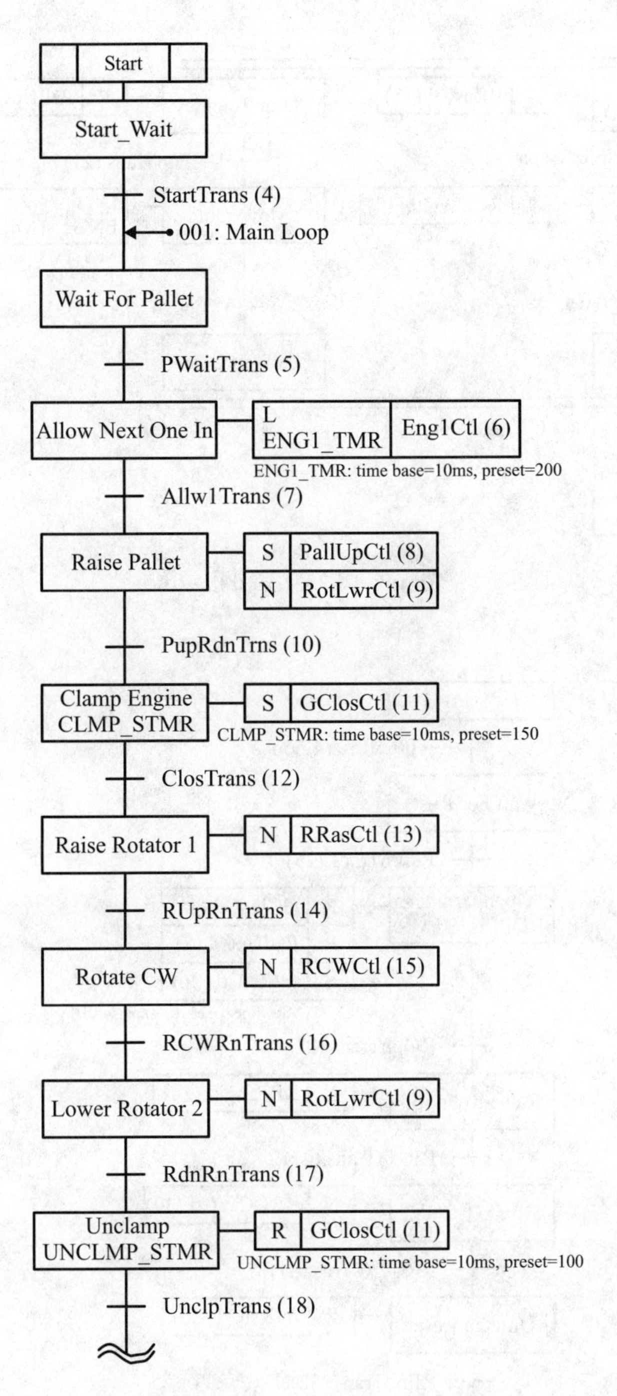

Figure 14.75. PLC-5 SFC file for engine inverter station normal operation. *(continued)*

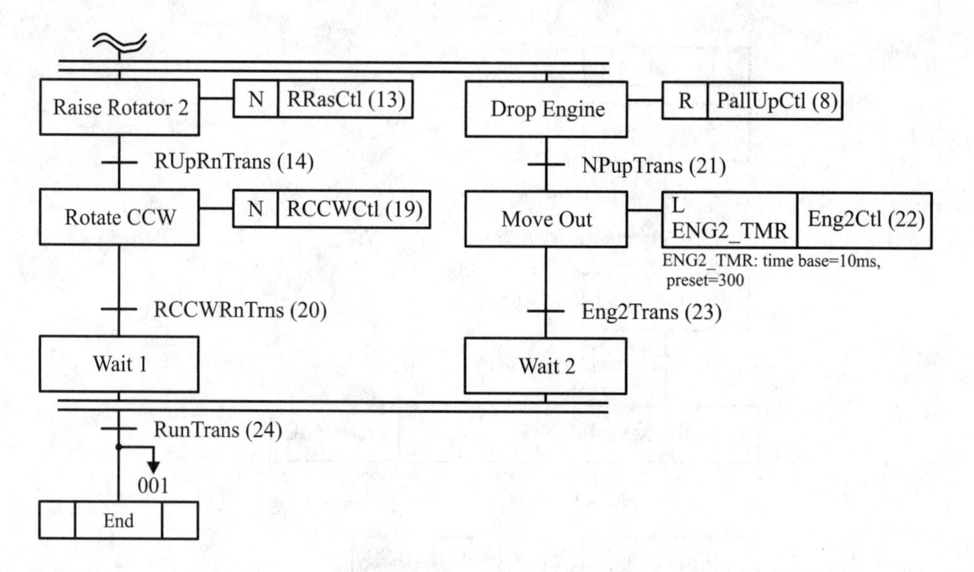

Figure 14.75. *(continued)*

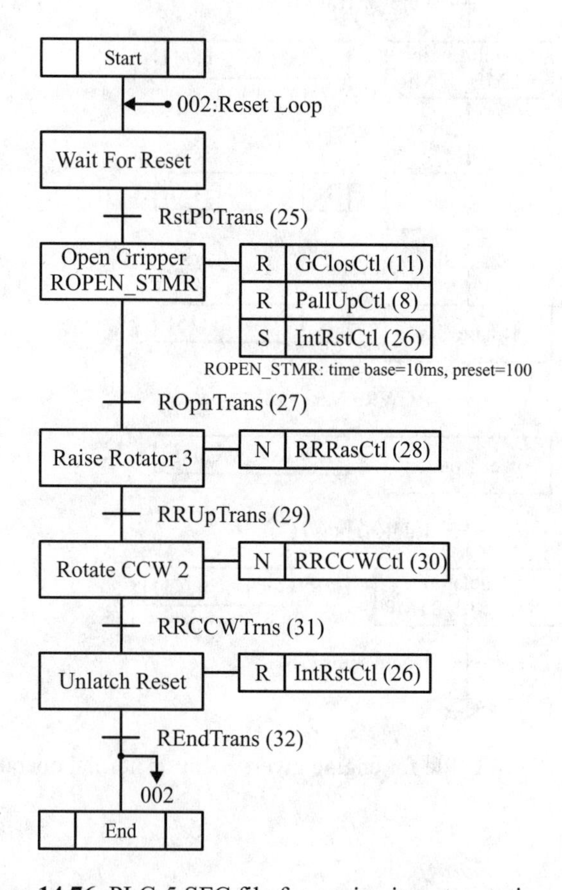

Figure 14.76. PLC-5 SFC file for engine inverter station reset.

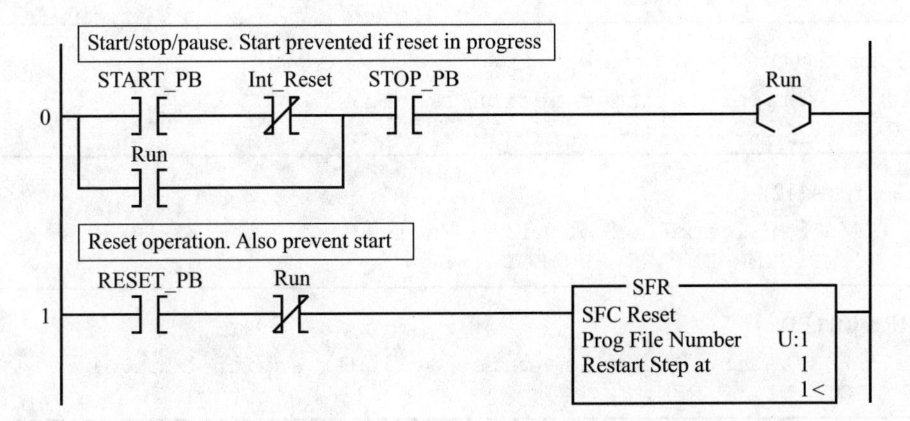

Figure 14.77. PLC-5 engine inverter ladder logic in program file 2.

StartTrans (4)

```
// Transition out of Wait for Start
RUN EOT ();
```

PWaitTrans (5)

```
// Transition out of Wait for Pallet
PROX1 AND RUN EOT ();
```

Eng1Ctl (6)

```
// Engage 1 hook action control
ENG1_RET := 1;
```

Allw1Trans (7)

```
// Transition out of Allow One In
ENG1_TMR/DN EOT ();
```

PallUpCtl (8)

```
// Pallet retainer cylinder action control
PALL_UPCTL := 1;
```

RotLwrCtl (9)

```
// Rotating mechanism lower cylinder action control
ROTR_DOWN := RUN;
```

PupRdnTrns (10)

```
// Transition out of Raise Pallet
PALL_UPLS AND ROTR_DNLS AND RUN EOT ();
```

Figure 14.78. PLC-5 engine inverter station actions and transitions. *(continued)*

GClosCtl (11)

```
// Gripper cylinder action control
GRIP_CLOS := 1;
```

ClosTrans (12)

```
// Transition out of Clamp Engine
CLMP_STMR/DN AND RUN EOT ();
```

RRasCtl (13)

```
// Rotating mechanism raise cylinder action control
ROTR_UP := RUN;
```

RUpRnTrans (14)

```
// Transition out of Raise Rotator
ROTR_UPLS AND RUN EOT ();
```

RCWCtl (15)

```
// Clockwise rotary cylinder action control
ROTAT_CW := RUN;
```

RCWRnTrans (16)

```
// Transition out of Rotate CW
ROTR_CWLS AND RUN EOT ();
```

RdnRnTrans (17)

```
// Transition out of Lower Rotator
ROTR_DNLS AND RUN EOT ();
```

UnclpTrans (18)

```
// Transition out of Unclamp
UNCLMP_STMR/DN AND RUN EOT ();
```

RCCWCtl (19)

```
// Counterclockwise rotary cylinder action control
ROTAT_CCW := RUN;
```

RCCWRnTrns (20)

```
// Transition out of Rotate CCW
ROTR_CCWLS AND RUN EOT ();
```

PupRdnTrns (21)

```
// Transition out of Drop Engine
!PALL_UPLS AND RUN EOT ();
```

Figure 14.78. *(continued)*

Eng2Ctl (22)

```
// Engage 2 hook action control
ENG2_RET := 1;
```

Eng2Trans (23)

```
// Transition out of Move Out
ENG2_TMR/DN EOT ();
```

RunTrans (24)

```
//Transition out of simultaneous convergence
RUN EOT ();
```

RstPBTrans (25)

```
// Transition out of Wait for Reset
//  ONS allows one execution of SFC if PB held down
RESET_PB AND !RUN AND ONS (B3/0) EOT ();
```

IntRstCtl (26)

```
// Internal reset control
INT_RESET := 1;
```

ROpnTrans (27)

```
// Transition out of Open Gripper (Reset SFC)
ROPEN_STMR/DN EOT ();
```

RRRasCtl (28)

```
// Rotating mechanism raise cylinder action control
ROTR_UP := 1;
```

RRupTrans (29)

```
// Transition out of Raise Rotator (Reset SFC)
ROTR_UP EOT ();
```

RRCCWCtl (30)

```
// Counterclockwise rotary cylinder action control (Rst)
ROTAT_CCW := 1;
```

RRCCWTrns (31)

```
// Transition out of Rotate CCW in reset SFC
ROTR_CCWLS EOT ();
```

REndTrans (32)

```
// Transition out of Unlatch Reset (Reset SFC)
!INT_RESET EOT ();
```

Figure 14.78. *(continued)*

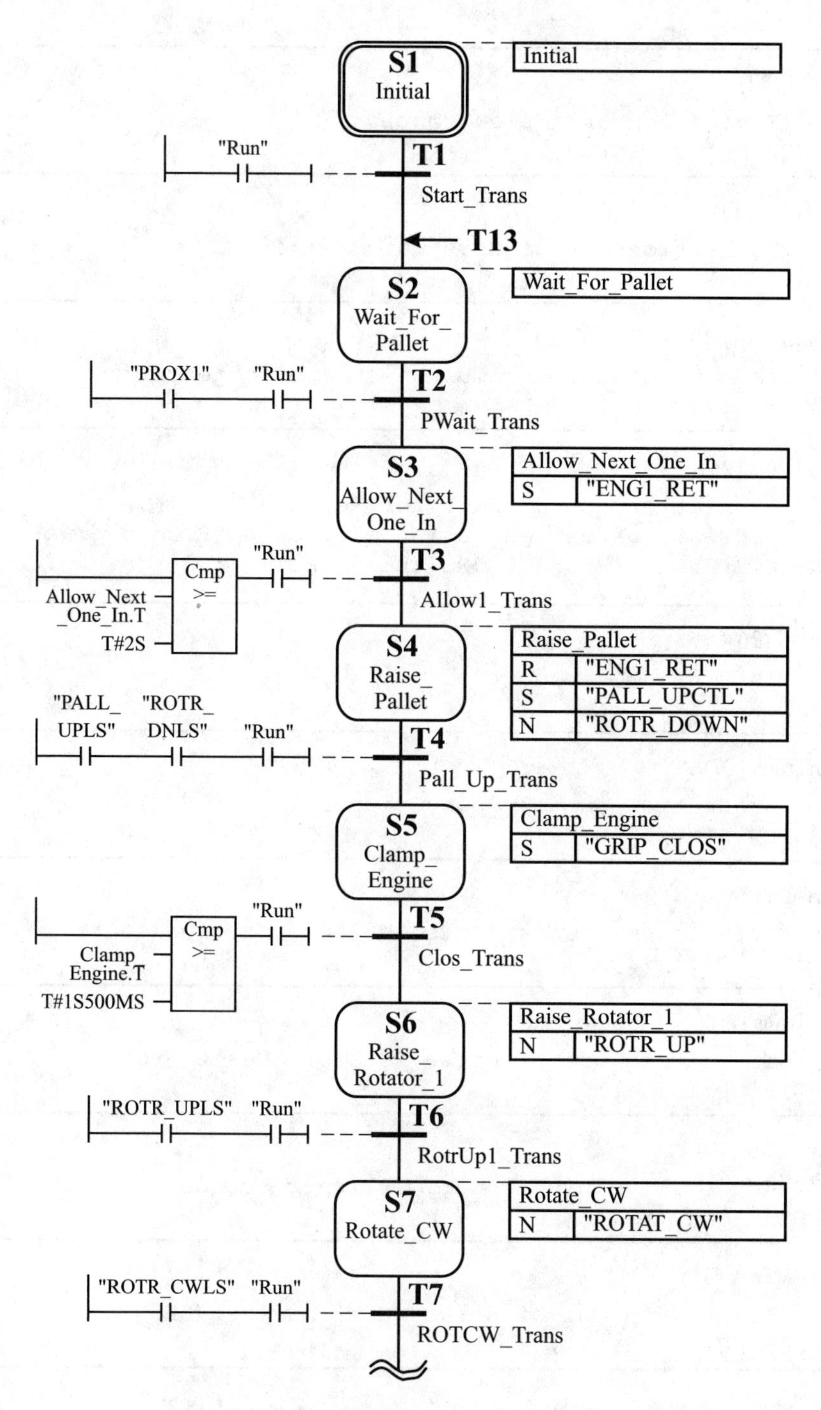

Figure 14.79. S7-Graph SFC for engine inverter station normal operation. *(continued)*

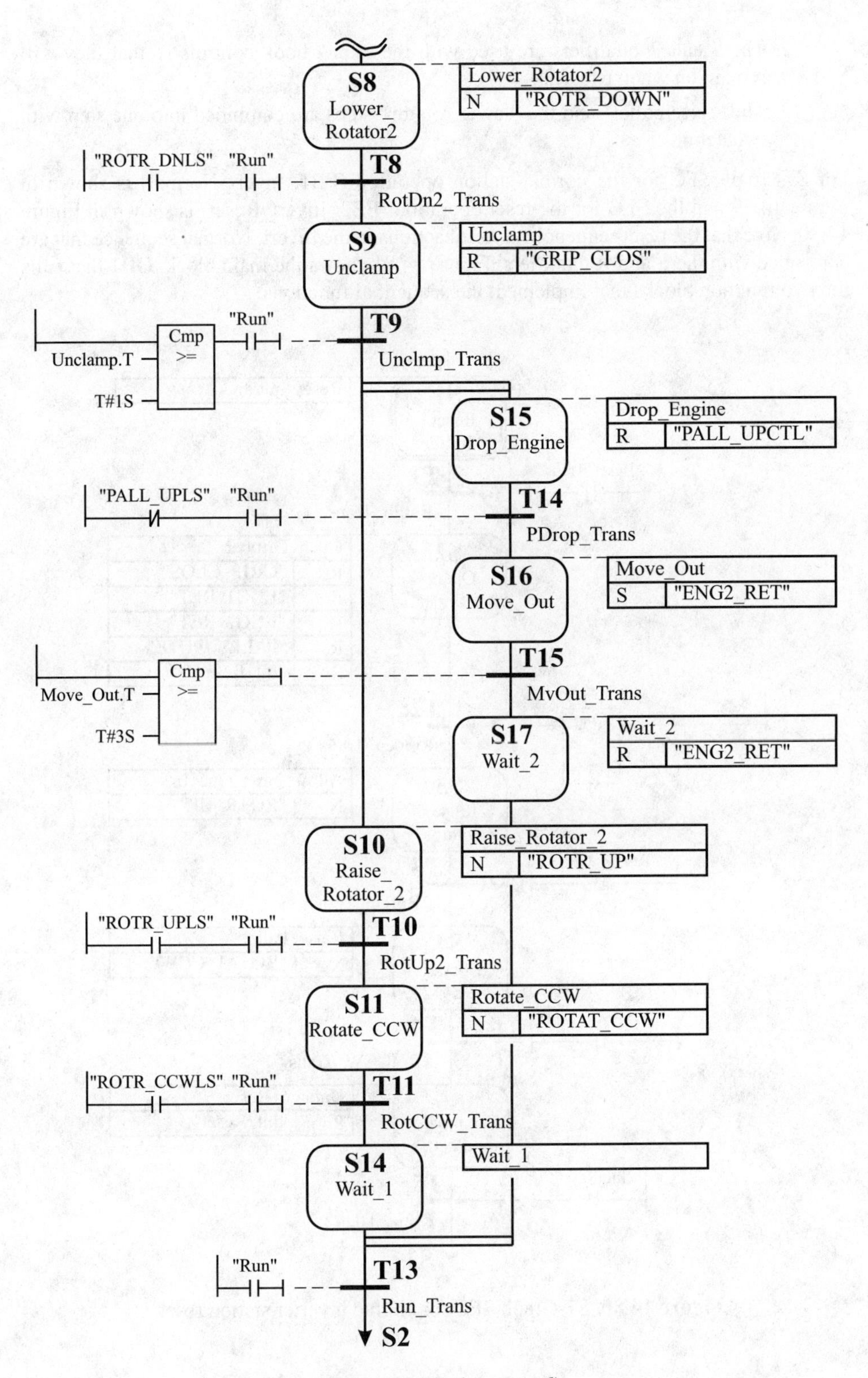

Figure 14.79. *(continued)*

2. The S and R qualifiers are used with the retract hook controls so that they will remain on when paused.
3. The “raise pallet” and the “lower rotator” steps are combined into one step with two actions.

For S7-Graph SFC for the normal station operation (FB1, Invert_Normal) is shown in Figure 14.79 and the SFC for the reset operation (FB2, Invert_Reset) is shown in Figure 14.80. Note that the reset sequence resets all actions in the Invert_Normal sequence that are controlled with the S and R qualifiers. Figure 14.81 shows the main block, OB1 that calls the two function blocks that implement the sequential functions.

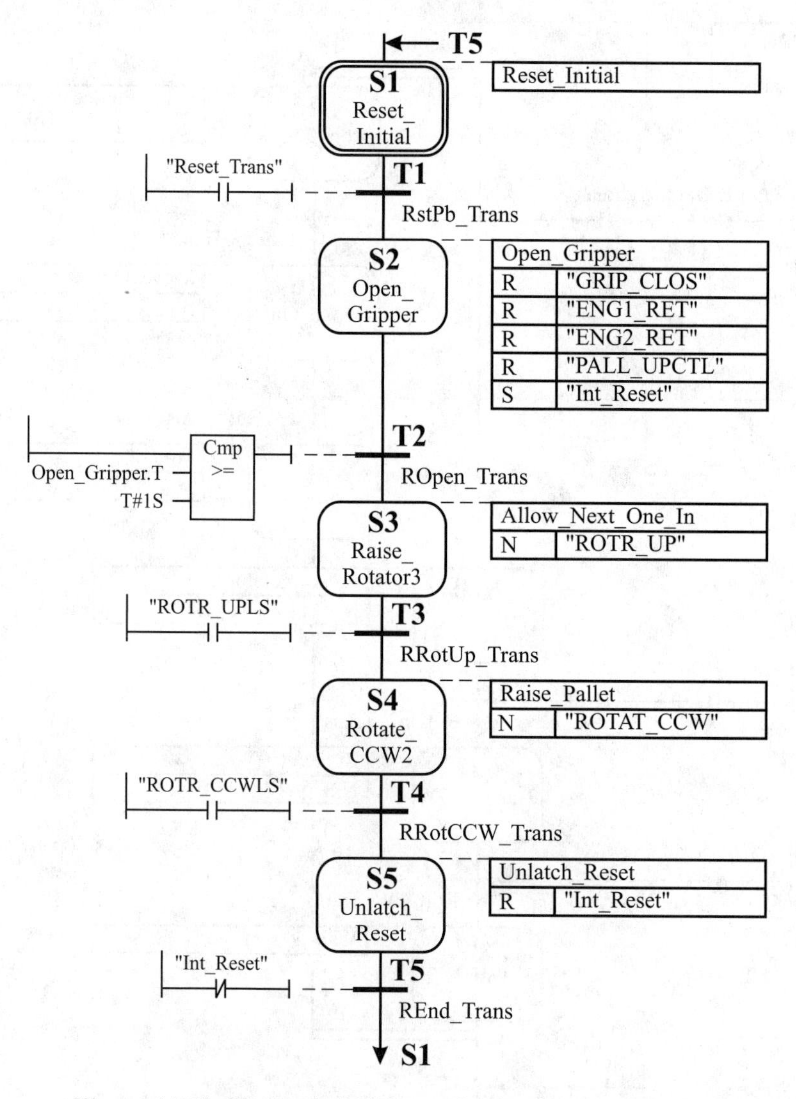

Figure 14.80. S7-Graph SFC for engine inverter station reset.

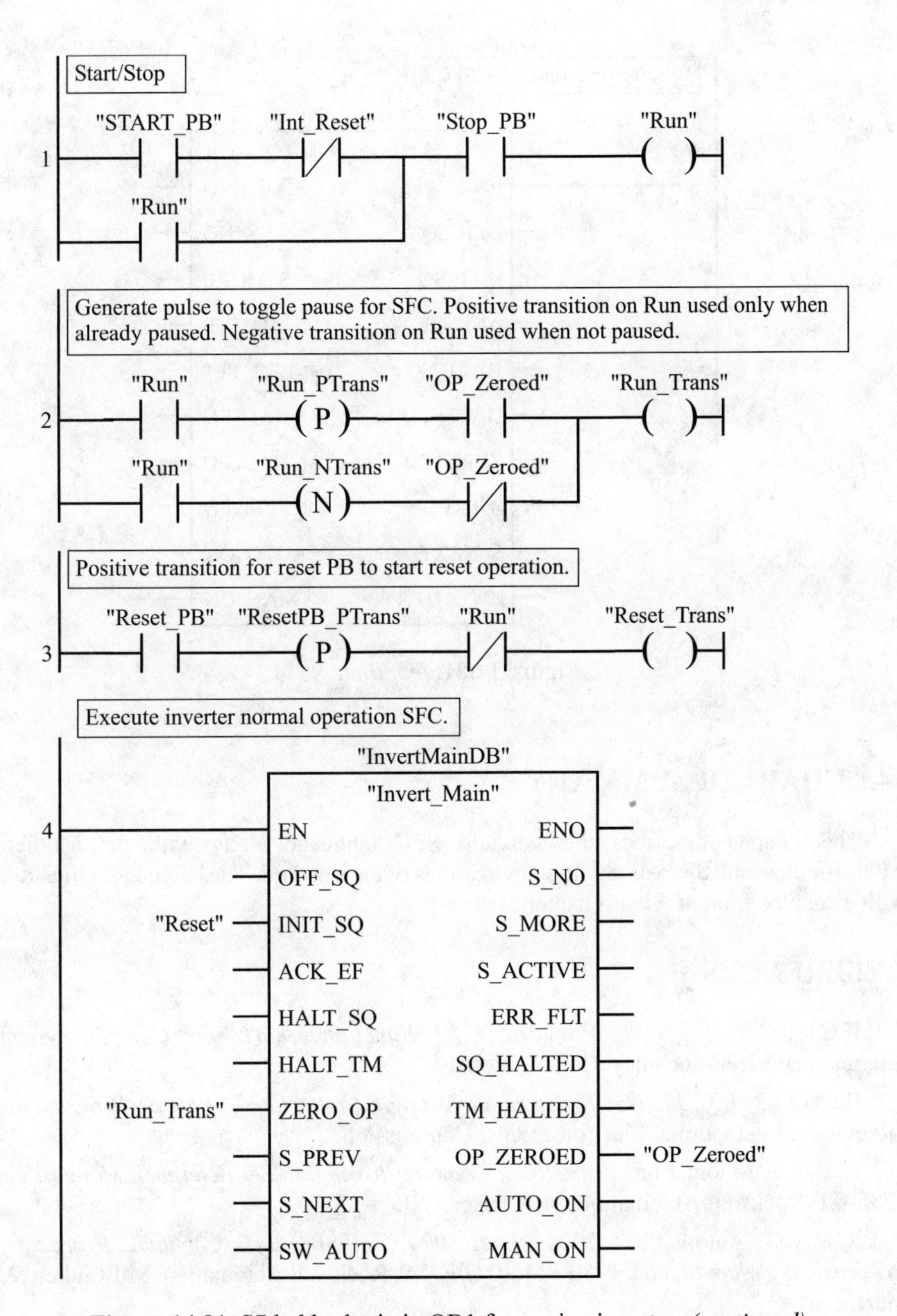

Figure 14.81. S7 ladder logic in OB1 for engine inverter. *(continued)*

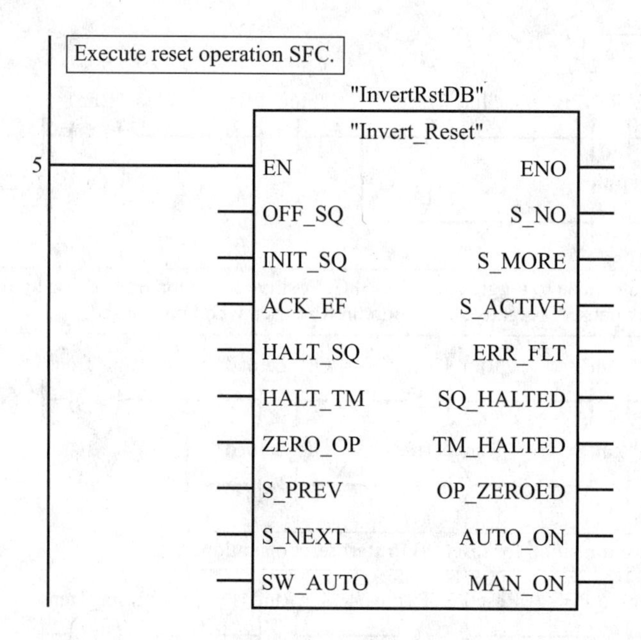

Figure 14.81. *(continued)*

14.8 CHAPTER SUMMARY

This chapter describes the standard SFC language along with the Modicon, Allen-Bradley, and Siemens S7 implementations of the standard. The language is illustrated with examples from previous chapters.

REFERENCES

IEC, 1988. *IEC 848: Preparation of Function Charts for Control Systems*, International Electrotechnical Commission.

IEC, 1993. *IEC 1131-3: Programmable Logic Controllers - Part 3: Programming Languages*, International Electrotechnical Commission.

Rockwell Automation, 1998. *PLC-5 Family Instruction Set Reference Manual*, pub. 1785-6.1, Rockwell Automation, Milwaukee, WI.

Rockwell Automation, 2004. *Logix5000™ Controllers Common Procedures: Programming Manual*, pub. 1756-PM001G-EN-P, Rockwell Automation, Milwaukee, WI, March.

Schneider Automation, 1998. *Concept User Manual,* vol. 1, ver. 2.1, pub. 840 USE 461 00, Schneider Automation, Inc., North Andover, MA.

Siemens, 1999. *S7-Graph for S7-300/400 Programming Sequential Control Systems: Manual,* Edition 01, 5/99, pub. C79000-G7076-C526-01, Siemens AG, Nürnberg, Germany.

PROBLEMS

General instructions for the problems:

Write a sequential function chart program for the application and implement it for one of the following PLC ladder logic languages:

Modicon Concept, **or**
Allen-Bradley ControlLogix, **or**
Allen-Bradley PLC-5/SLC-500, **or**
Siemens STEP 7

If any part of the operation is ambiguous, write down your additional assumptions. The physical inputs, physical outputs, and internal variables for each situation are given in the problem. **DO NOT** assign any more physical inputs!

Unless otherwise specified, assume the ADC in the analog input module has an output integer value that corresponds to the lowest and highest sensor value as:

Value	Modicon	CLogix	PLC-5	Siemens
Lowest	0	-20,030	0	5530
Highest	32,000	30,920	4095	27,648

In the case of the ControlLogix PLC, the instructor may choose to specify that the output of the ADC is a real number configured to be in the sensor units, for example, level in feet or temperature in °C.

Also, unless otherwise specified, assume the input integer to the DAC of an analog output module corresponds to the lowest and highest values of the output device control as:

Value	Modicon	CLogix	PLC-5	Siemens
Lowest	0	-20,030	0	5530
Highest	32,000	30,920	4095	27,648

In the case of the ControlLogix PLC, the instructor may choose to specify that the input to the DAC is a real number configured to be in the actual units of the output device, for example, speed in rpm or valve position in percent of span.

Your solution should include the following:

1. Specify the PLC processor used.
2. SFC program (with comments, if possible). For consistency among the different PLCs, use only variables/symbols/tags. Use format consistent with the PLC processor. Include other sections/files/FBs that support the SFC.
3. Table listing additional internal memory (variables/symbols/tags) used and a brief description of their use. For the Allen-Bradley ControlLogix and the Modicon Quantum/Momentum processors, list the internal variables/tags and the data type. For the other processors, list the internal variables/symbols and the associated memory address.

P14-1. Carton Sealer Control. Implement the carton sealing control of problem P6-1.

P14-2. Batch Process Control. Implement the batch control of problem P6-2.

P14-3. Bag Sealing Control. Implement the ladder logic for the bag sealer of problem P6-4.

P14-4. Erbia Elevator Control. Implement the erbia elevator control of problem P6-5.

P14-5. Transfer Station Control. Implement the transfer station control of problem P6-6.

P14-6. Hole Drilling Station 1 Control. Implement the drilling station control of problem P6-8.

P14-7. Oiler Station Control. Implement the oiler station control of problem P6-9.

P14-8. Pressing Station Control. Implement the pressing station control of problem P6-10.

P14-9. Case Erector Control. Implement the case erector control of problem P6-11.

P14-10. Batch Process Control. Implement the batch control system of problem P6-12.

P14-11. Erbia Can Tipper/Rotator Control. Implement the station of problem P6-15.

P14-12. Bagging Machine Control. Implement the bagging machine control of problem P6-17.

P14-13. Drilling Station Control. Implement the drilling station control of problem P6-18.

P14-14. Bolt Driving Station Control. Implement the bolt-driving station control of problem P6-19.

P14-15. Palletizing Station Control. Implement the palletizer control of problem P6-20.

P14-16. Drilling Station Control. Implement the drilling station control of problem P6-22.

P14-17. Bolt Driving Station Control. Implement the bolt-driving station control of problem P6-23.

P14-18. Weigh Scale Station Control. Implement the weigh scale station control of problem P7-20.

P14-19. Width Check Station Control. Implement the width check station control of problem P7-21.

P14-20. Stamping Station Control. Implement the stamping station control of problem P7-22.

P14-21. Leak Check Station Control. Implement the valve leak check station control of problem P7-23.

P14-22. Hole-drilling Station 2 Control. Implement the drilling station control of problem P7-24.

P14-23. Hole-drilling Station 3 Control. Implement the drilling station control of problem P7-25.

P14-24. Batch Reactor Control. Implement the batch reactor control of problem P7-28.

P14-25. Multi-tank Batch Control. Implement the batch process control of problem P7-29.

15 Troubleshooting

Chapter Topics:

- General fault diagnosis techniques
- Diagnosing input/output problems
- PLC processor status indications
- Finding programming errors
- Diagnosing PC-to-PLC communication errors

OBJECTIVES

Upon completion of this chapter, you will be able to:

- Understand the general fault diagnosis method
- Diagnose problems with the PLC hardware and program
- Diagnose PC-to-PLC communication problems

Scenario: Problem when installing new program.

A small production system is controlled by a Modicon PLC. Basically, the system removes a part from a magazine, inspects the part, drills a hole in the part, checks for the presence of the hole, and then conveys the piece to the next station. The program also tracks the number of defective parts and the number of good parts produced. When first tested, the program did not run when the start push button was pressed. However, holding down the push button allows the program to run, but the pneumatic control valves "buzz", indicating that they were being rapidly turned on and off.

Solution: The problem appeared to be with the rung that controls the Run internal coil, rung 1 in Figure 15.1. When examining the operation of the program, the Run internal coil "flashes" on and off. First, the operation of the start and stop pushbuttons was examined. Both of these discrete inputs are on a remote I/O module connected to the PLC by Modbus+. The Peer Cop is properly configured to communicate with the I/O module and the START_PB and STOP_PB coils appear to remain **on** when the Run internal coil briefly flashes **off**. The program is searched for other places where START_PB and STOP_PB are being used as output coils and none are found. The HMI screen programming software has a reference to STOP_PB, but is not used on any screens. It is deleted from the HMI database anyway and the problem still occurs.

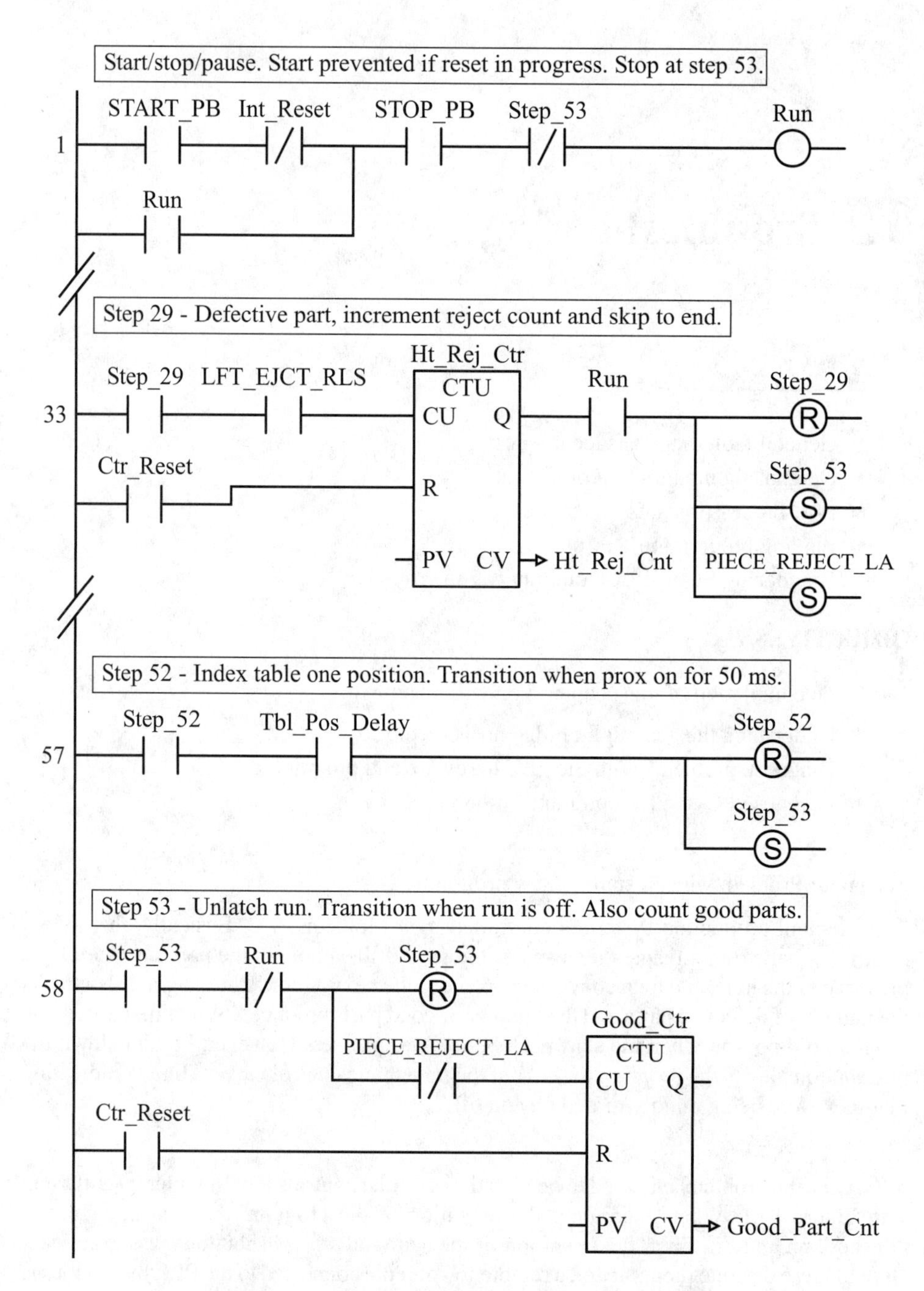

Figure 15.1. Portions of ladder logic with problems.

Since START_PB and STOP_PB have been eliminated from consideration, the problem must be connected with either the Int_Reset or Step_53 internal coils. Int_Reset would not stop the operation; it only prevents it from being restarted. So the program is searched for the rungs where Step_53 is used as an output coil. Rungs 33, 57, and 58 of

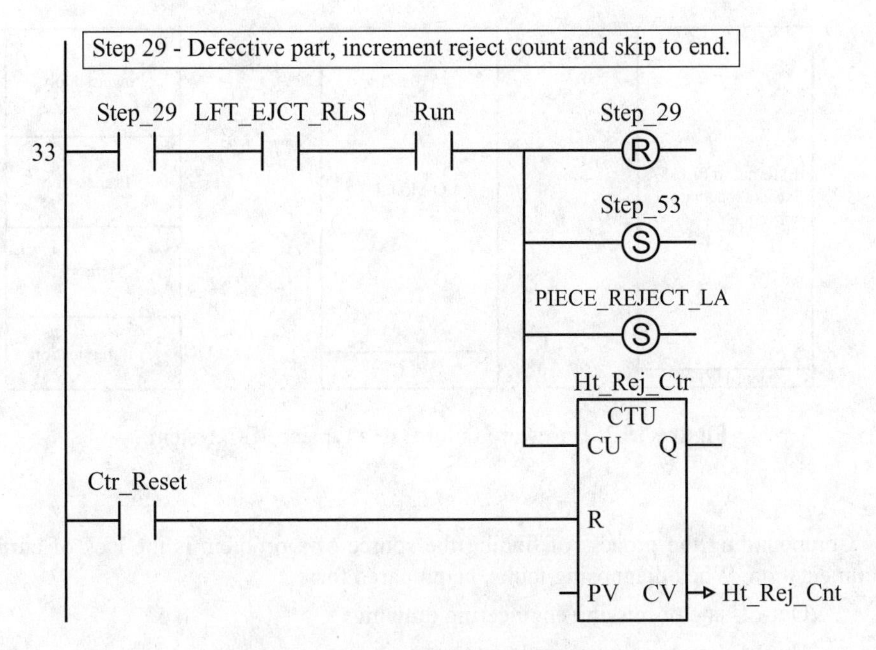

Figure 15.2. Corrected step 29 transition.

Figure 15.1 show three of the other four references. The fourth reference is a reset coil that is part of the internal reset. Examining rung 33 while the program is running shows the source of the error. The counter Q output is always **on**, and so when Run is **on**, Step_53 is set, which causes the Run coil to be unlatched on the next program scan (in rung 1). The PV counter input is unconnected, setting the counter preset value to zero, explaining why the Q output is always **on**. The counter is not part of the transition condition and so the problem is corrected by placing the counter in parallel with the outputs, as shown in Figure 15.2.

15.1 INTRODUCTION

Troubleshooting is the process of locating and eliminating the source of trouble in a system. Furthermore, the source of the problem must be found and fixed in a minimum amount of time. This chapter provides an introduction to troubleshooting methods and provides general troubleshooting information for PLC systems. In the area of troubleshooting, one needs (1) good analytical skills, and (2) experience. With good analytical skills, one becomes an expert after years of experience.

One knack of finding faults quickly is knowing where to look first. Given a number of possible sources of the failure, one should know the most likely places and eliminate them first. Figure 15.3 shows the failure probability of the different parts of the PLC system hardware (Parr, 2001). This figure shows that the majority of hardware faults in a PLC system are actually a failure in the field devices and not in the PLC. Within the PLC itself, the majority of failures are in the I/O modules. Program errors should be found and fixed before the system is commissioned. After commissioning, the number of failures due to a program error should be small.

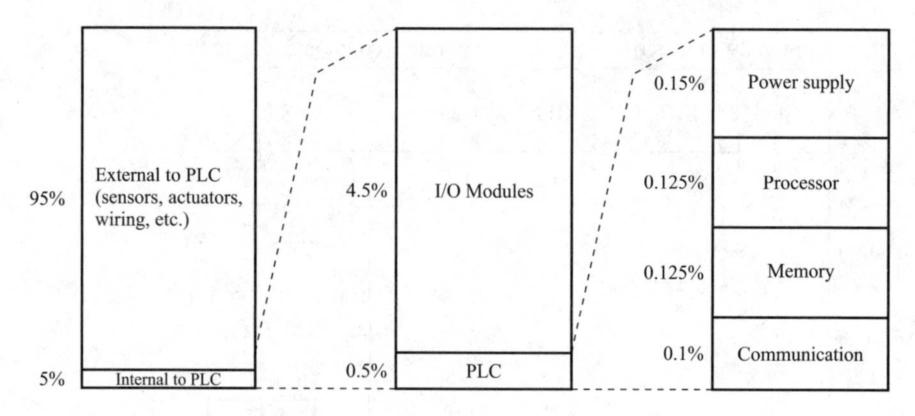

Figure 15.3. Hardware failures in a typical PLC system.

Compounding the process of finding the source of a problem is the lack of current documentation. When diagnosing faults, be prepared for:

Out-of-date or missing engineering drawings

Out-of-date or no program listings

Obsolete equipment (no documentation)

Most companies keep a set of documentation that was complete when the equipment was installed. However, as changes are made to the system, the documentation (or at least all copies of it) may not be kept current. Also, manufacturer's manuals may be inadvertently lost or destroyed.

After presenting the general procedure to find and correct problems in the system, more specific information is presented for faults in the I/O devices, the PLC hardware, the PLC program, and the PC-to-PLC communications link. Finally, troubleshooting aids that can be designed into a system are suggested.

15.2 GENERAL TROUBLESHOOTING PROCEDURES

The general procedure for finding and correcting faults is shown in Figure 15.4. With the evidence and other information about the fault, one constructs a hypothesis, or guess, about the source of the problem. In order to verify the source of the problem, one must test the hypothesis. If the test does not confirm the hypothesis, then more information may need to be gathered. If the test corroborates the hypothesis, then the source has been found and then the fault can be corrected or repaired. If the source of the fault is a PLC hardware module, then the module is replaced. Usually, the faulty module is identified and not the actual component within the module. The module is replaced with a spare module and the faulty module is sent to the manufacturer or service depot for repair. Simple programming problems are usually corrected while the processor is still in the run mode and with minimum disruption. More extensive program modifications may require waiting to download the changed program until the next scheduled downtime.

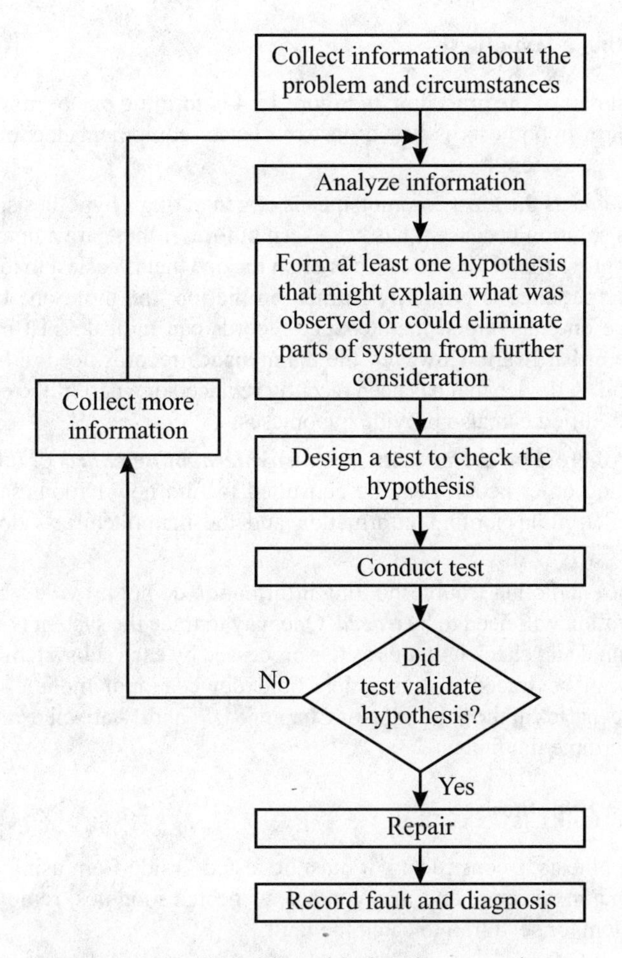

Figure 15.4. General troubleshooting procedure.

15.2.1 Gathering Information About the Fault

Often, experience is the best source of the type of information that should be gathered. At a minimum, the following should be known:

- What happened?
- Where is the problem?
- What time did it occur? Does another event happen at the same time?
- When does the problem occur? Does it repeat?

It is also important to eliminate irrelevant information. However, knowing what is relevant often comes with experience.

15.2.2 Generating a Hypothesis

The hardest part of the procedure in Figure 15.4 is forming one or more hypotheses to test. Composing a hypothesis is based on experience, equipment documentation, or by tracing through the system.

Past ***experience*** is the most common means of generating a hypothesis. One knows the problem and its solution because it has been seen before. If there are a number of possible hypotheses, the guess that is first checked is often the one that is easiest to test or is the most probable one. Experience is primarily learned on the job: the more one has worked, the more experience one has. Good maintenance records can indicate past problems with a particular piece of hardware. However, the maintenance records need to be searchable in order to be useful. A device that has been recently replaced or a part of the program that has been recently modified can also provide hypotheses.

If the type of problem is a new one, then ***troubleshooting charts*** or other information sources (including other people) can be consulted to find new hypotheses. This chapter contains general troubleshooting information and the manufacturer's documentation is another source.

If experience and other troubleshooting information do not provide a hypothesis, then the system operation will need to be ***traced***. One way to trace the system is to start from the source of the signal and check its status as it is processed by each subsystem. For example, a discrete input can be traced in this order: field device, input module, processor, and program. The scenarios at the beginning of Chapters 4, 7, and 14 are all examples of tracing a system to determine the fault.

15.2.3 Testing a Hypothesis

After a hypothesis is constructed, it must be tested. Aside from using a multimeter to test voltages and/or currents, one may replace suspected modules, remove questionable parts of the system, or set a trap to catch the fault.

When diagnosing discrete and analog input/output modules, a digital multimeter is often adequate to find the fault. However, for more complicated modules, such as motion controllers, a multimeter may be inadequate. In this case, one often ***substitutes*** a known good module and verifies that the problem has disappeared. One of the disadvantages with this method of testing is that the system operation may be disrupted. For example, in order to replace a suspected defective motion control module when one axis fails, all of the other axis controls on that module must be temporarily disabled when the module is replaced. Normally, this is not an operation that is attempted while the system is operating.

In a loosely coupled system, ***removing*** the suspected module is another way of testing the hypothesis. Several PLCs communicating with each other is a common example of a loosely coupled system. An incorrect message in one of the PLCs in such a system can cause data corruption in the other PLCs. In this case, the suspected PLC is disconnected from the network to test the hypothesis.

For a spurious or transient problem, setting a trap is often the only effective method of testing its existence and checking for other conditions. Even when the system logs and archives data, it may not be sampled frequently enough to catch the event. In this case, the PLC program is often modified to monitor for the suspected event and record other conditions when it occurs. In certain systems, the processor can be halted when the event occurs so that all of the PLC data can be examined. The scenario at the beginning of Chapter

7 is an example of an event that caused an automatic halt of the processor and then the PLC data was examined to determine the actual cause of the fault and the subsequent changes in the PLC program to prevent future faults.

15.2.4 Erratic Behavior

If the PLC system exhibits a large number of failures or erratic behavior, the most likely cause is a problem with the power supply. Another cause is the presence of electro-magnetic interference.

First, the integrity of the power and ground connection to the PLC should be checked. One should visually check the power and ground wiring for loose or corroded connections and cracked insulation. The ground integrity can be checked by verifying that the voltage between the PLC ground terminal and a known ground is zero.

Second, the source to the power supply should be checked. The power supply input voltages should be within the recommended range. If the source to the power supply is AC voltage and is lower than required (often called "voltage sag"), then the source of the problem should be identified. If the low voltage is a recurrent problem, then a constant-voltage transformer may need to be inserted between the AC power supply and the PLC power supply connection. If the PLC power supply input voltage is DC, then the power supply that generates this voltage should be checked for problems. In this case, the AC ripple of the DC voltage should also be small.

Thirdly, the outputs of the PLC power supply should be checked that the voltages are within the recommended ranges. Unfortunately, these outputs may be difficult to check due to the inability to connect a meter to the power supply outputs.

Another cause of erratic behavior is the presence of electromagnetic interference (EMI) or radio frequency interference (RFI). Unfortunately, it may be difficult to determine the source since one must correlate the problem with an EMI or RFI event. Possible EMI or RFI events are (1) a large motor starting, (2) an unshielded electric solenoid actuating, (3) arc welding nearby, (4) a lightening strike, or (5) use of a handheld radio transmitter. Solutions to EMI or RFI problems usually involve properly grounding, shielding, or conditioning the PLC power source.

15.3 TROUBLESHOOTING I/O MODULES

The most common troubleshooting problem in a PLC system has to do with the inputs and outputs. When troubleshooting I/O problems, the primary goal is to determine why the internal status of the PLC memory does not agree with the external device. The mapping of the status/value of an I/O channel to the internal PLC memory is covered in Chapter 3 and is not repeated here. A problem with an I/O channel is due to a failure in one of four places:

1. the device,
2. the PLC I/O module, or
3. the power supply for the I/O module or device, or
4. the wiring between the device and the PLC I/O module.

An internal failure of the PLC processor generally affects the values from multiple I/O modules and/or more serious problems and is covered in the next section of this chapter. If the problem appears to occur in multiple I/O modules and these modules are connected to the processor by some communication link, then check the communication link for failures.

When diagnosing I/O failures, a meter that can accurately measure voltage, current, and resistance is often essential. Also, a device (e.g., a notebook computer) that can be used to monitor the PLC memory is necessary.

Discrete I/O modules generally have status indicators on the module, one for each channel, as shown in the circuit diagrams in Chapter 4. Whether the status indicator is on the device side of the module isolation or on the PLC side of the isolation barrier is relevant only to those finding the failed component in the module. If the failure is in the I/O module, the troubleshooting information here will allow one to isolate the failure to a particular module. The failed module is then repaired by the manufacturer or by a service center.

A troubleshooting chart for discrete input and output modules are shown in Table 15.1 and Table 15.2. Since the most likely cause of a failure is the I/O device the charts starts with the state of the I/O device, checking the state of the channel indicator, and then the PLC on-line status of the I/O channel. For example, if the discrete input device is off/open/deactivated, the channel status indicator on the discrete input module is **on**, and the PLC on-line status of the channel is **on**, then the most likely cause is one of three possibilities:

1. Off-state leakage current of the input device is high enough to trigger the threshold detector in the module (AC types only), or
2. Input device is damaged, or
3. Input module circuit is damaged.

The "recommended action" column contains information in order to confirm or eliminate the probable cause.

Troubleshooting analog modules is usually more difficult than for discrete modules because the modules generally have no indication of the analog channel voltage or current. One can connect small panel meters to the analog channels to monitor the voltage/current, but these are generally not used for voltage signals since a voltmeter can easily be connected without disturbing the wiring. However, when current loops are used, these small panel meters will greatly hasten the troubleshooting process because one will not need to break the loop in order to connect and disconnect a meter. Breaking an analog output loop causes the device to sense a zero current, which may lead to disastrous consequences. At the very least, a small (100 ohm) resistor should be inserted in the loop so that the loop current can be measured without disturbing the wiring.

Troubleshooting charts for analog modules are shown in Table 15.3 and Table 15.4. Both of these troubleshooting charts start from a valid source of the analog value. For an analog input, the physical quantity must be in the valid range and then the PLC value is checked. If the PLC value is "pegged" at the minimum or maximum value, then the channel voltage/current must be checked to find the source of the problem. If the value in the PLC is in the valid range, but is inconsistent with a panel meter indication (e.g., the physical quantity is about 30 gpm and the PLC value is 20 gpm), then the most likely causes are incorrect configuration and/or calibration of the I/O module or sensor. For an analog output, the PLC value must be in the valid range and then the actuator response is checked. If the actuator is "pegged" at the minimum or maximum, then the channel voltage/current must be checked to find the source of the problem. If the actuator response is in the valid range, but is inconsistent with the PLC value (e.g., the PLC value for a value is 60% and the valve is 40%

Table 15.1. Discrete Input Diagnosis Guide.

Input Device is On/Closed/Activated			
Channel LED is	And	Probable Cause	Recommended Action
On	On-line status shows the input as **off** or ladder program operates as though it is **off**.	Input is forced off in program	Remove input force for channel.
		Input circuit is damaged	Verify proper wiring. Try another input channel. Replace module.
	Input device will not turn **off**.	Device is shorted or damaged	Verify device operation. Replace device.
	Program operates as though device is momentarily **off**.	Momentary dip in power supply voltage	Increase DC power supply wattage rating.
Off	On-line status shows the input as **off** or the ladder program operates as though it is **off** and/or the input circuit will not turn **on**.	Low voltage across the input	Check voltage between input channel and common. Check source voltage.
		Incorrect wiring or open circuit	Check wiring and common connections.
		Input signal turn-on time too fast for input circuit	Check module and device timing specifications.
		Input circuit is incompatible	Check specification and sink/source compatibility (if DC input).
		Input circuit is damaged	Verify proper wiring. If possible, try other input channel. Replace module.

Input Device is Off/Open/Deactivated			
Channel LED is	And	Probable Cause	Recommended Action
On	On-line status shows the input as **on** or the ladder program operates as though it is **on** and/or the input circuit will not turn **off**.	Input device off-state leakage current exceeds specification (AC inputs)	Check device and input circuit specifications. Use load resistor to bleed-off circuit.
		Input device is shorted or damaged	Verify device operation. Replace device.
		Input circuit is damaged	Verify proper wiring. If possible, try other input channel. Replace module.
Off	On-line status shows the input as **on** or ladder program operates as though it is **on**.	Input is forced on in program	Remove input force for channel.
		Input circuit is damaged	Verify proper wiring. If possible, try another input channel. Replace module.
	Input device will not turn **on**.	Device is shorted or damaged	Verify device operation. Replace device.

Table 15.2. Discrete Output Diagnosis Guide.

Output Device is On/Energized			
Channel LED is	And	Probable Cause	Recommended Action
On	On-line status shows the output as **off** and the output circuit will not turn **off**.	Programming error	Check for duplicate output coils using the search function.
		Output is forced on in program	Remove output force for channel.
		Output circuit is damaged	Use the force function to force output off. If the output device does not turn off, the output circuit is damaged. Try another output channel. Replace module.
Off	On-line status shows the output as **off** and the output device will not turn **off**.	Output circuit off-state leakage current may exceed output device specification.	Check device and output circuit specifications. Use load resistor to bleed-off current. Neon lamps as load on 120v output modules need a bleed resistor.
		Incorrect wiring	Check wiring. Disconnect from PLC and verify device operation.
		Output device is shorted or damaged	Verify device operation. Replace device.
		Output device is incompatible	Check specification and sink/source compatibility (if DC input).
		Output circuit is damaged	Verify proper wiring. Try other output channel. Replace module.

Output Device is Off/De-energized			
Channel LED is	And	Probable Cause	Recommended Action
On	On-line status shows the output as **on** and the output device will not turn **on**.	Low voltage across the load	Measure the source voltage and check specifications.
		Incorrect wiring or open circuit	Check wiring and COMMON connections.
		Output device is incompatible	Check specification and sink/source compatibility (if DC input).
		Output circuit is damaged	Verify proper wiring. Try other output channel. Replace module.
Off	On-line status shows the output as **on** and the output device will not turn **on**.	Programming error	Check for duplicate output coils using the search function.
		Output is forced off in program	Remove output force for channel.
		Output circuit is damaged	Use the force function to force output off. If the output device does not turn off, the output circuit is damaged. Try another output channel. Replace module.

Table 15.3. Analog Input Diagnosis Guide.

Value of physical quantity is in the normal range			
PLC value is	And	Probable Cause	Recommended Action
Min.	Measurement of voltage or current at module channel is zero	Bad sensor power supply	Check sensor power supply. Replace if necessary.
		Inadequate power supply voltage (current meas.)	Loop power supply voltage should be at least (number of loop devices)x5V + wire resistance voltage drop at 20 mA.
		Broken wire	Check wiring between sensor and module.
	Measurement of voltage or current at module is consistent with sensor value.	Input circuit is damaged	If possible, try another input channel Replace module.
Max.	Measurement of voltage or current at module is at or above maximum value for channel	Incorrect wiring or short circuit to power supply.	Check wiring for proper module connections and shorts.
		Incorrect voltage/ current selection	Check voltage/current selection jumpers or module configuration.
	Measurement of voltage or current at module is consistent with sensor value.	Incorrect voltage/ current selection	Check voltage/current selection jumpers or module configuration.
		Input circuit is damaged	If possible, try another input channel Replace module.
In Range	Value in PLC memory inconsistent with sensor measurement.	Incorrect module configuration	Check channel range, channel min. and max. scaling range values.
		Incorrect resistor value	Check resistor used to convert current to voltage for input channel.
		Module or sensor not calibrated.	Disconnect sensor wiring from module. Connect a known good voltage/current source to module channel and set it to min., max., and mid-range channel values. If PLC values correct, recalibrate sensor. Otherwise, recalibrate module.
	Value in PLC memory varying while sensor is constant (differential voltage input).	Common mode voltage too high.	Check voltage between both differential voltage connections and module common. If higher than allowed, check power supply and sensor grounding.

Table 15.4. Analog Output Diagnosis Guide.

PLC value is in the normal range			
Actuator acts as if value is	And	Probable Cause	Recommended Action
Min.	Measurement of voltage at module channel is zero (voltage output)	Short circuit in wiring or sensor	Disconnect wiring from output channel and recheck voltage. If not zero, check wiring for short.
	Measurement of current at module channel is zero (current output)	Broken wire to sensor	Disconnect wiring from output channel, install 250 ohm resistor across channel. If current not zero, check for broken wire.
		Inadequate power supply voltage	Check loop power supply voltage (may not be possible, depending on module).
	Measurement of voltage or current at module is zero.	Incorrect voltage/ current selection	Check voltage/current selection jumpers or module configuration.
		Output circuit is damaged	If possible, try another output channel Replace module.
	Measurement of voltage/ current at module is consistent with sensor value.	Actuator circuit is damaged	Test actuator response to different voltages/currents. Replace actuator.
Max.	Measurement of voltage or current at module is at or above maximum value for channel	Incorrect wiring or short circuit to power supply.	Check wiring for proper module connections and shorts.
		Output circuit is damaged	If possible, try another output channel Replace module.
	Measurement of voltage/ current at module is consistent with sensor value.	Actuator circuit is damaged	Test actuator response to different voltages/currents. Replace actuator.
In Range	Actuator response inconsistent with value in PLC memory.	Incorrect module configuration	Check channel range, channel min. and max. scaling range values.
		Module or actuator not calibrated.	Disconnect actuator wiring from module. Measure voltage/current at channel for min., max., and mid-range PLC values. If values correct, recalibrate actuator. Otherwise, recalibrate module.
		Actuator not calibrated.	Test actuator response to different voltages/currents. Replace actuator.

open), then the most likely causes are configuration and calibration of the I/O module or sensor. Further testing is necessary to isolate calibration problems.

The ability to override the status of a physical discrete input or to override the logic driving a physical output coil and force the output to a desired status is useful for testing. Although there are few exceptions, this override function only applies to physical discrete inputs and physical discrete outputs. In addition, this function is called by different names. In Modicon PLCs this function is called input/output disabling. In Allen-Bradley and Siemens PLCs, it is called input/output forcing and in GE Fanuc PLCs, it is called override. The Modicon I/O disabling and GE Fanuc overrides operate in a similar manner. The

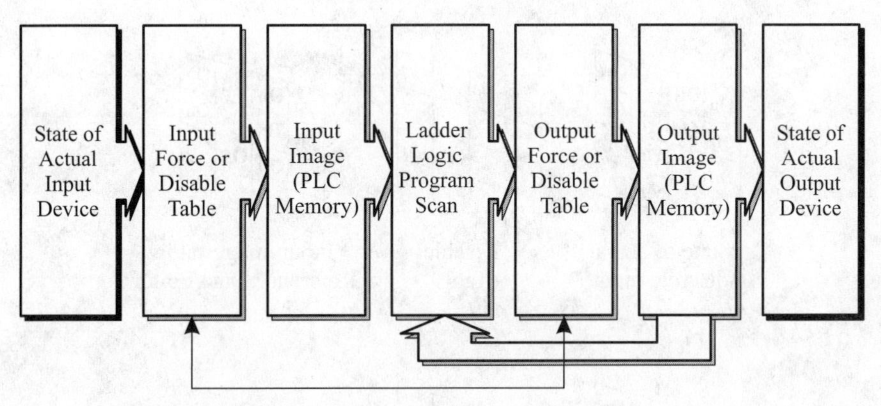

Figure 15.5. Relationship of forcing/disabling with PLC program scan.

Allen-Bradley and Siemens forcing functions operate slightly differently and are described separately.

The force/disable function modifies the PLC program scan as shown in Figure 15.5. For discrete inputs, the force/disable function acts like a mask (Modicon disable and GE Fanuc override) or a filter (Allen-Bradley and Siemens forcing). For discrete outputs, the forcing/disable function acts like a mask.

An output force/disable/override is useful for troubleshooting discrete outputs. Forcing an output to the **on** and/or **off** state can be used to test that particular output. Otherwise, output forces should not be used. Using an output force to override the PLC logic should be used only temporarily until the logic can be corrected. An input force/disable/override is often useful for testing a PLC program. If the PLC is not connected to physical I/O, the forces allow one to simulate the inputs. Other ways of simulating the system without having any physical I/O are described in Chapter 21. An input force can also be used to temporarily bypass a failed discrete input device so that operation may continue while the device is being repaired. However, overriding safety devices in this manner is not recommended.

Safety Caution

Note: Enabling or disabling forces can result in sudden machine movement, possibly injuring personnel. While forces are enabled, a new force value is applied immediately, with no prompt for confirmation. **USE EXTREME CAUTION WHEN USING FORCES!**

The operation of Modicon input/output disabling is shown in Figure 15.6. The disable table functions as a mask. A particular discrete input or output is disabled in the Reference Data Editor by "checking" the "Disable" column for that input/output. When the disable table entry for a particular physical discrete input (1*x* address) is disabled (depicted as "D" in Figure 15.6*a*), the input is disabled and the state of that particular input is not written to the input image memory. When disabled, the user changes the discrete input value with the

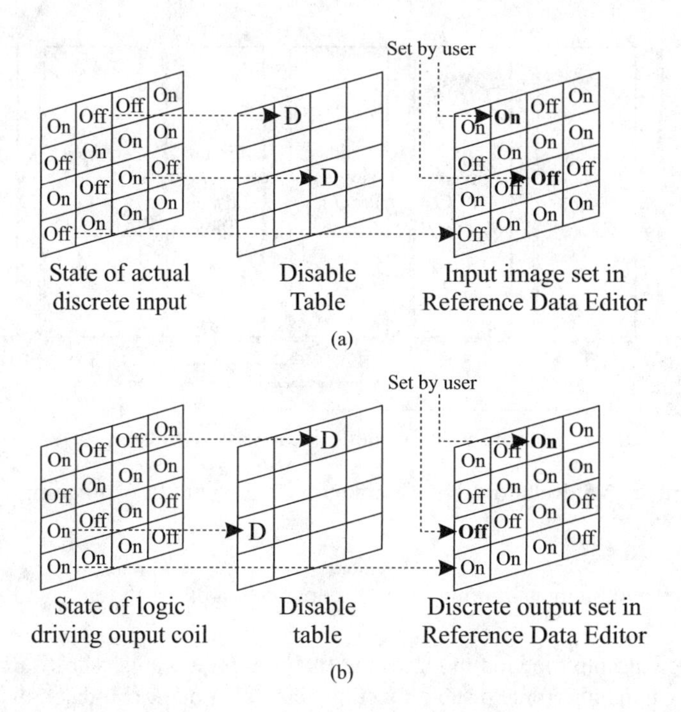

Figure 15.6. Modicon disable function: *(a)* discrete inputs; *(b)* discrete outputs.

Reference Data Editor. When a particular physical discrete output (0*x* address) is disabled (Figure 15.6*b*), the result of the logic that determines state of the output coil (ordinary, inverted, set, or reset) is not written to the output image and the user changes the value with the Reference Data Editor. Any contact that refers to the physical output uses the value in the output image. Disabling outputs only applies to 0*x* addresses connected to discrete module channels. Any other 0*x* addresses cannot be disabled.

Allen-Bradley discrete input/output forcing is shown in Figure 15.7. The force table functions as a filter. The force table entry for a particular physical discrete input or output can be one of three characters:

. Not forced

1 Forced **on**

0 Forced **off**

When a physical discrete input is forced (Figure 15.7*a*), the value in the force table overrides the actual input device status with the value in the force table. When a particular physical discrete output is forced (Figure 15.7*b*), the value in the force table overrides the value determined by the result of the logic that drives the output coil (ordinary, latch, or unlatch). Any contact that refers to the physical output uses the value in the output image.

For the Allen-Bradley PLCs, it requires two steps to actually implement a force. First, the particular inputs/outputs are forced to the desired values and secondly all of the forces are enabled. The forces are not actually applied until they are enabled.

For PLC-5 and SLC-500 processors the size of the force tables corresponds to the size of the discrete input and discrete output image files. For series E and later PLC-5

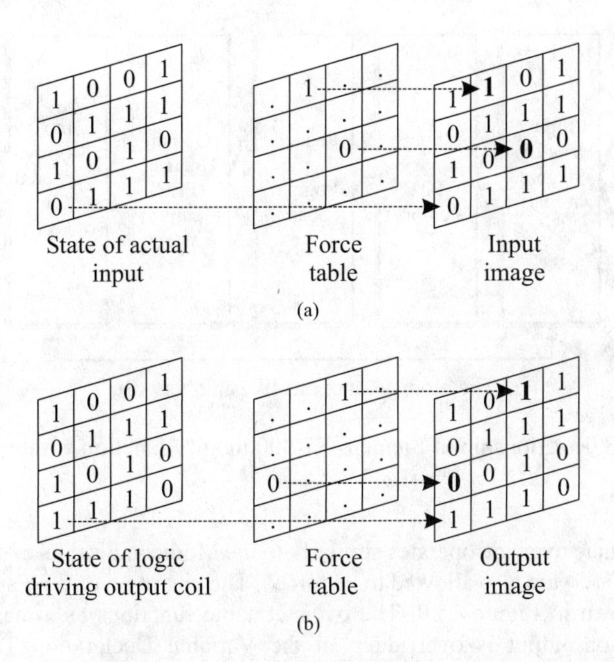

Figure 15.7. Allen-Bradley force function: *(a)* discrete inputs; *(b)* discrete outputs.

processors, one can force integers in a data file used for a block transfer (BTR and BTW) function block by defining an extended force file. The extended force file for the block transfer acts like the force table for discrete inputs and outputs.

For ControlLogix processors, the force table for each discrete I/O module resides in the processor. Therefore, if one controller is forcing a particular input module, other controllers monitoring the input module are not affected. In contrast, output modules are "owned" by a particular processor and the owner processor is the only processor allowed to write values to the module. If the owner forces an output module channel, other processors monitoring the output module will also monitor the forced value.

Forcing for the Siemens S7-400 processors works similarly to the Allen-Bradley processors. The user defines those variables that are forced with a "Force Values" window. Bit memory (M addresses) and peripheral I/O (PIB , PIW, PID, PQB, PQW, or PQD addresses) can be forced in addition to the discrete I/O. A particular symbol or address is added to the force values window and its force value is also indicated. The force is actually implemented when the force flag is turned on. When the force flag is on for a particular discrete input address (I, IB, IW, or ID) or peripheral input, the force value overrides the actual input status. When a particular discrete output address (Q, QB, QW, or QD), internal bit memory, or peripheral output is forced, the force value overrides the value determined by the logic that writes to that variable.

For the Siemens S7-300 processors, forcing only applies to discrete inputs. Discrete outputs can be forced but any program logic that writes to that output will overwrite the force values. One can modify the discrete outputs with a variable table and program the modifications to apply the values at the end of every program scan. This method does not override the value determined by the user program logic, but does override the value when transferring the discrete output image to the physical outputs (Figure 15.8).

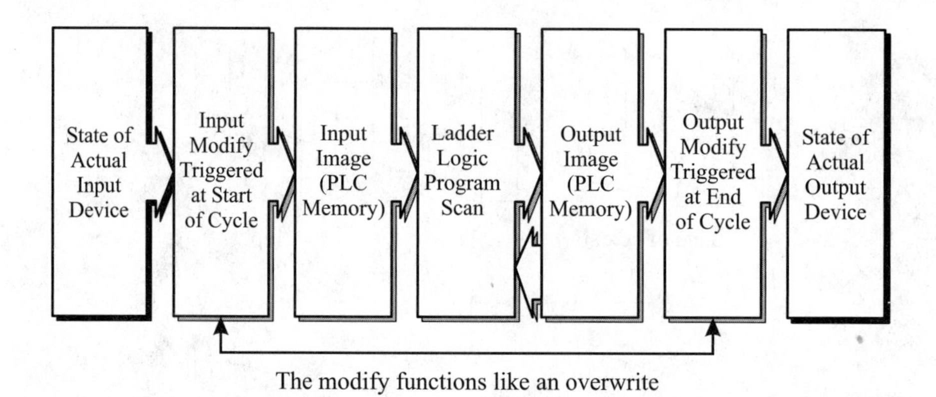

Figure 15.8. Relationship of Siemens S7-300 modify function with program scan.

The GE Fanuc override operates similarly to the Modicon disable, except that internal coils (%M and %G) are also allowed to be forced. The operation of GE Fanuc input/output override is shown in Figure 15.9. The override table functions as a mask. A particular discrete input or output is overridden in the Variable Declaration Table (VDT) by "checking" the "Ovr" column for that input/output. When the VDT entry for a particular physical discrete input (%I address) is overridden (depicted as "Ovr" in Figure 15.9*a*), the input is effectively disabled and the value of that particular input is not written to the input

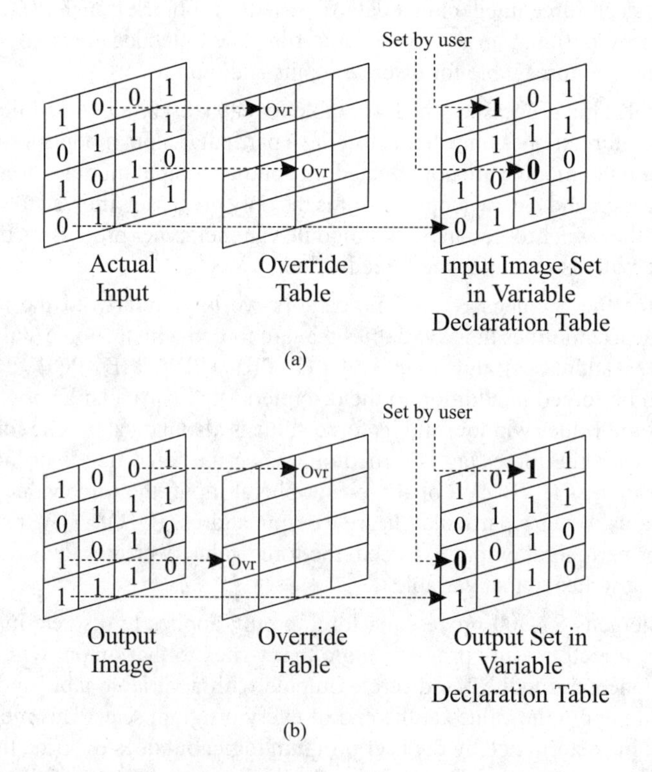

Figure 15.9. GE Fanuc override function: *(a)* discrete inputs; *(b)* discrete outputs.

image memory. When overridden, the user changes the discrete input value with the VDT. When a particular physical or internal discrete output (%Q, %M, or %G address) is disabled (Figure 15.9*b*), the result of the logic that determines the state of the output coil (ordinary, negated, set, or reset) is not written to the address and the user changes the value with the VDT.

15.4 PROCESSOR STATUS INDICATORS

Most PLC processors have a series of status lights on the front panel of the module. Detailed information about the status lights and the information they convey is found in the manufacturer's manual. A sampling of the status indicators for the PLCs covered by this text are described in this section.

The common Quantum processor indicators are shown in Figure 15.10*a* and mean the following:

Indicator	**Description**
Ready	Green when power-up diagnostics passed
Run	Steady green when processor in RUN mode
	Flashing green indicates error code
Modbus	Green when activity on Modbus (serial) port
Modbus+	Green when activity on Modbus Plus port
Mem Prt	Amber when memory is write-protected
Bat Low	Red when battery needs replacing
Error A	Red when error on Modbus Plus port

The common ControlLogix processor indicators are shown in Figure 15.10*b* and are described as:

Indicator	**Description**
RUN	Green when processor in RUN mode
FORCE	Amber when I/O forces enabled and/or active
BAT	Red when battery has low voltage or is missing
I/O	Green when communicating with I/O
	Flashing red when faulted
RS232	Green when communicating with PC on serial link
OK	Green when controller OK
	Red when faulted

The indicators on a PLC-5 processor vary by the specific processor. The common indicators are shown in Figure 15.10*c* and signify:

Indicator	**Description**
BATT	Red when battery has low voltage or is missing
PROC	Green when processor in RUN mode
	Red when faulted
FORCE	Amber when I/O forces enabled and/or active
COMM	Green when channel is communicating

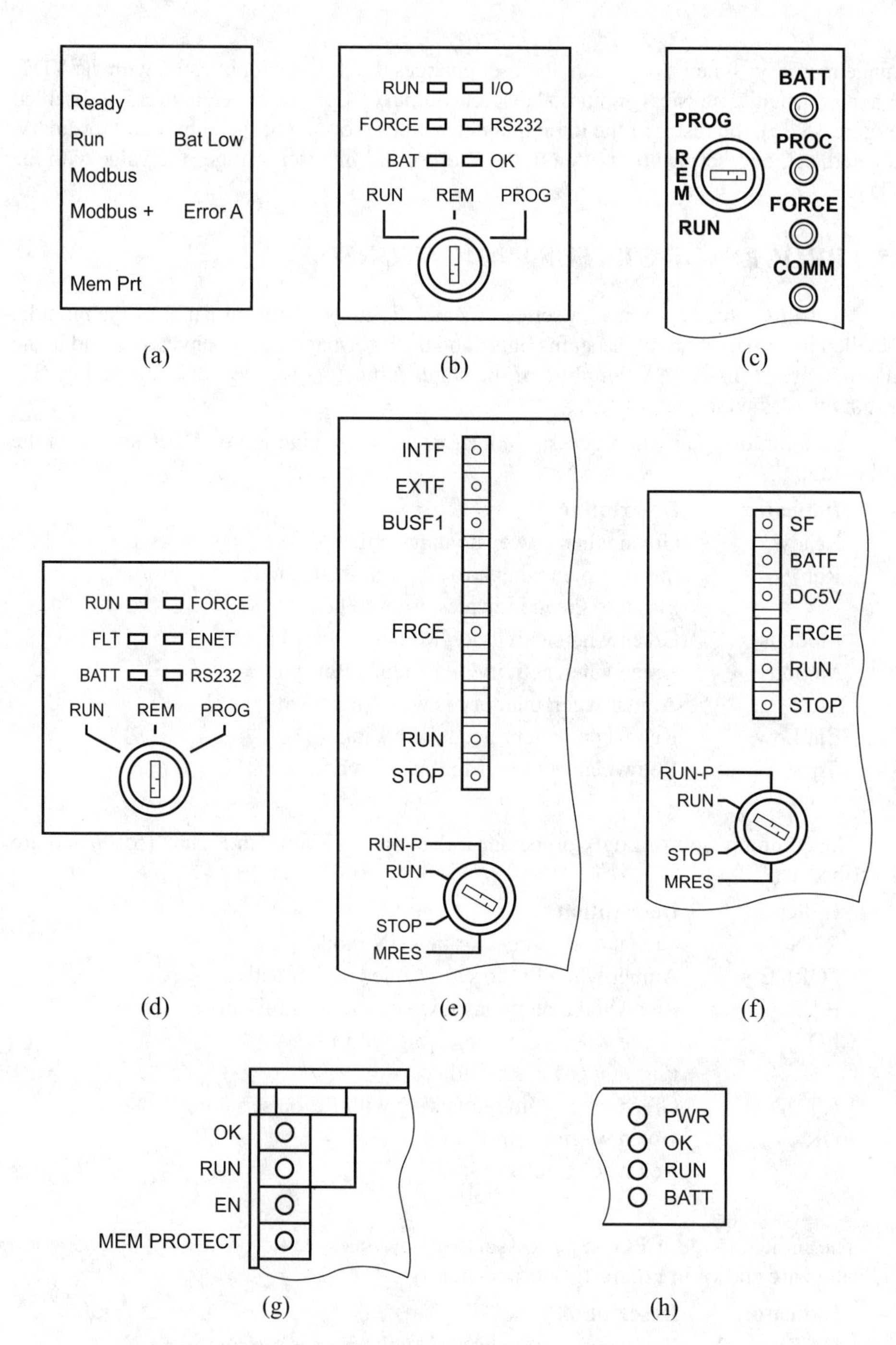

Figure 15.10. Processor diagnostic indicators: *(a)* Quantum; *(b)* ControlLogix; *(c)* PLC-5; *(d)* SLC-5/05; *(e)* S7-400; *(f)* S7-300; *(g)* 90-70; *(h)* 90-30.

Depending on the processor, the COMM indicator shows the status of the serial port or the DH+ channel. Other processor indicators show the activity and faulted status of other communication channels (e.g., Ethernet, ControlNet, DH+, remote I/O).

The indicators on a SLC-5/05 processor are shown in Figure 15.10*d* and are described as:

Indicator	**Description**
RUN	Green when processor in RUN mode
FLT	Flashing red when controller has fault
	Steady red when fatal error (no communications)
BATT	Red when battery has low voltage or is missing
FORCE	Amber when I/O forces enabled and/or active
ENET	Green when communicating on Ethernet
	Flashing red when faulted
RS232	Green when communicating with PC on serial link

For the SLC-5/03, the ENET indicator is replaced by a DH485 indicator for the DH-485 network and for the SLC-5/04, the ENET indicator is replaced by DH+ for the DH+ network. The other SLC processors have similar indicators.

Figure 15.10*e* shows the common processor status indicators for a Siemens S7-400 and are described as:

Indicator	**Description**
INTF	Red when internal software fault
EXTF	Red when external hardware fault
FRCE	Amber when I/O forces active
RUN	Green when processor in RUN mode
STOP	Amber when processor in STOP, HALT, or start-up
BUSF 1	Red when fault on PROFIBUS-DP interface 1
BUSF 2	Red when fault on PROFIBUS-DP interface 2

When the processor has a major fault (defective state), the INTF, EXTF, FRCE, RUN, and STOP indicators all flash. Depending on the specific processor, there may be other status indicators.

The common S7-300 processor indicators are shown in Figure 15.10*f* and signify the following:

Indicator	**Description**
SF	Red when hardware or software fault
BATF	Red when battery low or missing
DC5V	Green when CPU has 5 volts DC
FRCE	Amber when I/O forces active
RUN	Green when processor in RUN mode
STOP	Amber when processor in STOP, HALT, or start-up

If the particular processor has a Profibus interface, a BUSF indicator is present that is red when there is a fault on the communication channel.

For the GE Fanuc 90-70 PLC, the system status indicators on the processor (Figure 15.10g) are as follows:

Indicator	Description
OK	Green when PLC operating properly
RUN	Green when processor in RUN mode
EN	On when outputs enabled
MEM PT	On when memory protect keyswitch is on

Some processors have a second vertical column of LED status indicators that show whether a particular serial port is enabled and active.

For the GE Fanuc 90-30 processor, the system status indicators are on the power supply module (Figure 15.10*h*) and indicate:

Indicator	Description
PWR	Green when no faults in the power supply
OK	Green when PLC operating properly
RUN	Green when processor in RUN mode
BATT	Red when battery voltage low

The indicators on the GE Fanuc 90-30 processors show whether a particular communication channel is active.

To diagnose processor faults or to access more detailed information about the processor; one must access the processor status through the programming software. In many PLC processors, the status indicators and fault information is accessible to the PLC programs and the PLC program can be programmed to take certain actions. For example, the ControlLogix and PLC-5 processors can be programmed to execute a fault routine when a fault is detected. Normally, the processor will halt when a major fault is detected. For these processors, a fault routine can record the fault, clear the fault and restart the processor so that operation can be continued without interruption.

15.5 PROGRAM PROBLEMS

In order to aid in troubleshooting program problems, PLC programming software packages provide two useful tools: (1) data monitor, and (2) cross reference. Data monitoring functions allow one to monitor and/or modify specified program variables. A program cross reference provides a list of the program variables and for each variable indicates where it is used and how it is used (contact, coil, block, etc.).

The data monitoring functions vary among the vendors from a primitive display of the data tables to a graphical display similar to a human-machine interface (HMI). Most vendors provide a data monitor that allows the user to specify the variables/tags/symbols to be monitored and/or modified. Table 15.5 summarizes the various data monitoring functions.

When troubleshooting, the cross reference information is very useful when it is searched while online with the processor. References to a particular variable can easily be determined and then the user can jump to other parts of the program that use that variable. The user can trace the operation backwards by finding the places where the variable is written (coil, move, etc.). Alternatively, a user can trace the operation forward by finding the places where a particular output coil or calculation result is used in the program. An example cross reference is shown in Figure 15.11. In this cross-reference, the ASR symbol is used in the program in seven places: once as an ordinary output coil (OTE) and the other

Table 15.5. Data Monitoring Functions.

Processor	Name of Data Monitoring Function	Display Format
Modicon	Reference Data Editor	User specifies variables in table.
ControlLogix	Data Monitor	All program or routine tags displayed in table.
PLC-5/SLC-500	Data file monitoring	Display of data file contents in table.
	Custom Data Monitor	User specifies symbols in table.
	Custom Graphical Monitor[1]	HMI-like graphical display.
Siemens S7	Variable table	User specifies variables in table.
GE Fanuc	Variable Declaration Table	User specifies variables in table.

[1]Only available in professional versions of programming software.

six times as a normally open contact (XIC) in three program files. For the Modicon processors, the entire cross reference is not displayed from within the Concept programming software, though the cross reference for a particular variable is displayed with the search function.

A troubleshooting chart for common programming problems is shown in Table 15.6. Before checking for programming errors, first verify that it is not a problem with a physical input/output. Use Tables 15.1 to 15.4 to eliminate that possibility. For beginning programmers, a repeated ordinary coil is a common programming problem.

```
ASR        {B40/121} Auto Start Relay
                OTE - File #2 AUT/MAN - 6
                XIC - File #4 RE/UN FDR - 0, 7
                      File #5 BUCK ELEV - 0
                      File #7 CONV 1,2,3 - 0, 7, 14
B1FLL      {O:12/14} Bunker 1 Full Level Lamp
                OTE - File #7 CONV 1,2,3 - 26
B1FLLW     {B44/23} Bunker 1 Full Level Lamp - Wonderware
                OTE - File #7 CONV 1,2,3 - 26
B1FLP      {I:7/14} Bunker 1 Full Level Probe
                XIC - File #7 CONV 1,2,3 - 24
B1FLR      {B40/159} Bunker 1 Full Level Relay
                OTE - File #7 CONV 1,2,3 - 25
                XIC - File #2 AUT/MAN - 8
                XIO - File #2 AUT/MAN - 7
                      File #7 CONV 1,2,3 - 26
B1FLT      {T4:32} Bunker 1 Full Level Timer
                TOF - File #7 CONV 1,2,3 - 24
B1HLL      {O:12/13} Bunker 1 High Level Lamp
                OTE - File #7 CONV 1,2,3 - 23
```

Figure 15.11. Sample cross reference (PLC-5/SLC-500).

Table 15.6. Program Diagnosis Guide.

Symptom	Probable Cause	Recommended Action
Discrete input seems to intermittently change.	Problem with physical input	Follow Table 15.1 diagnosis guide.
	Discrete input used as coil	Use cross reference to verify that output coil does not refer to input.
	HMI writing to discrete input.	Check for reference to input in HMI. Verify that HMI only reads variable.
Discrete output or internal coil does not turn **on** when it should.	Repeated coil output (not set/reset)	Use cross reference to check that coil or negated coil does not refer to same variable..
	Rung not being executed	Verify that jump-to-subroutine is being executed. Check for jumps.
	Problem in logic that determines state of contacts	Use cross reference to find coils referring to contacts in the rung being examined. Check logic driving these coils.
Timing interval too short or non-existant	Timer preset is zero	Check timer preset.
	Retentive timer not being reset	Check timer reset logic (may be missing).
	Timer preset equal to 1 (PLC-5/SLC)	Timer preset equal to 1 may actually time-out immediately.
Items not being counted	Incorrect preset	Check counter preset. Some counters do not count beyond the preset value. Check any logic that loads the preset value.
	Counter not allowed to count	Check counter reset and/or enable logic.
	Counter input not transitioning	Check counter input logic. Most counters count transitions at the input.
Counter seems to count more items than expected	Incorrect counter input logic	Counter is counting extra transitions. For A-B counters, also check for logic turning off CU bit in counter structure.

It may also be possible that the controller does not behave properly in a given situation because the situation was unforeseen in the original program. In this case, the program needs to be modified to detect the new conditions and control the process accordingly.

For a spurious or transient problem, setting a trap is often the only effective method of testing its existence and checking for other conditions. In this case, the PLC program is modified to monitor for the suspected event. When the suspected event occurs, an internal coil can be latched and other conditions can be stored. In extreme conditions, the processor can be halted, though this will obviously disrupt the operation of other parts of the process.

Depending on the particular PLC, there may be ladder logic (or other language) instructions useful for troubleshooting program problems. All of the processors covered by this text, except for Modicon have jump instructions that can be used to skip sections of code. The ControlLogix and PLC-5 processors have an AFI ladder logic contact that disables the logic on a particular rung. These instructions are covered in Chapter 8.

15.6 COMMUNICATION PROBLEMS

This section focuses on diagnosing communication problems between a personal computer and a PLC. Troubleshooting communication problems between two PLCs or to remote I/O is vendor-dependent and is not covered in this text. A personal computer is connected to a PLC in one of two ways: (1) directly through the computer serial port (Figure 15.12), or (2) through a communication network (Figure 15.13).

A personal computer (PC) is often directly connected to a PLC with a serial (usually RS-232) cable. However, depending on the vendor, the software connection between the programming software to the PC serial port may be direct (Figure 15.12*a*) or through a communication server (Figure 15.12*b*). The use of a separate software package (called RSLinx) to manage the connection between the programming software and the PLC is common to Rockwell Automation products. In either case, most problems involve either the serial cable or the configuration of the PC serial port. Assuming the serial cable has the correct connections, the cable should be checked for:

Bad solder or crimp connections

Bent or pushed-in connector pins

Faulty grounding connection (for long cables)

The serial port should be checked for the correct:

Baud rate

Parity (even, odd, or none)

Number of stop bits

Error checking method

Duplex (full-duplex or half-duplex)

Flow control (Xon/Xoff, etc.)

With the RSLinx software one can auto-configure the serial connection and thus automatically find the proper serial port configuration (assuming the PLC serial port exists and is properly configured).

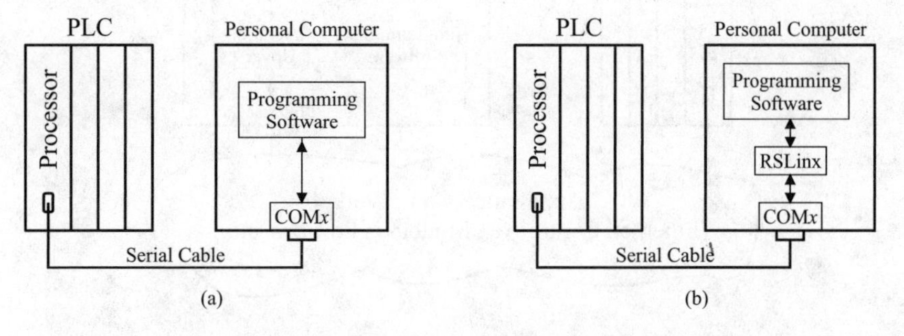

Figure 15.12. Direct PC-to-PLC communications: *(a)* General connection; *(b)* Rockwell Automation software connection.

A common problem when downloading a program to the PLC for the first time is that the programmer forgets to set the PLC serial port baud rate in the PLC program configuration to match the baud rate of the PC serial port. When that happens, the program will generally download without error, but communications between the PC and the PLC will terminate at the end of the download. This problem is common when programming PLC-5 processors because the default PLC serial port baud rate of 2400 bits/sec. is much slower than most users want to communicate with the PLC. In addition, the programming software does not detect that the new program has a different PLC serial port configuration. For a SLC-500, the problem of downloading a program with different serial port parameters is less prevalent since the programming software detects the changed communication parameters and displays a warning message.

A less common problem is that the PLC or PC serial port may be defective or the PLC serial port may have been accidentally disabled. To test the PC serial port, check that it can communicate with another PLC. To check for a disabled port, try communication to the PLC through another communication port (e.g., Ethernet). As a last resort, setting the PLC to a default state will determine if the PLC serial port is defective. Unfortunately, this method will interrupt the operation of whatever the PLC is controlling and the PLC program will need to be restored. To set the PLC to its default state, power must be disconnected to the PLC and the processor battery must be removed. Depending on the vendor, one may need to also use a temporary jumper to discharge a hold-up capacitor that maintains the voltage to the PLC volatile memory. In the default state, the PLC serial port parameters are set to a default configuration as documented by the manufacturer.

When the connection between the PLC and the PC is not via a serial cable, but through a communication network (Figure 15.13), diagnosing a problem becomes more complex. In this case, the PC usually also serves as an operator interface and the same communication network is used for the PLC programming and the operator interface. The problem can occur in any of the numbered connections in Figure 15.13. Usually, one must check each "link" in the communication chain by examining each of the software drivers in the communication path.

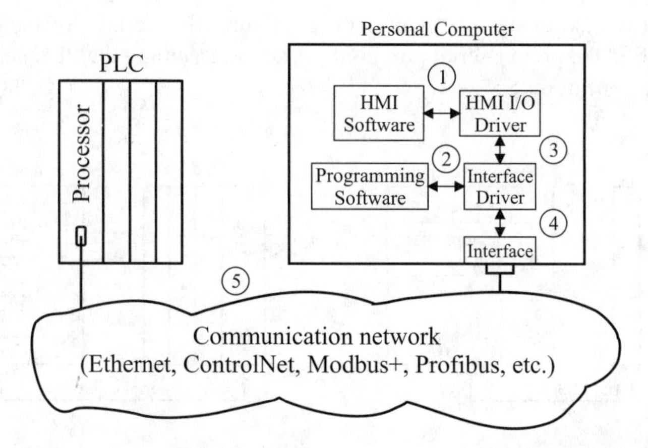

Figure 15.13. PC-to-PLC connection through communication network.

15.7 DESIGNING FOR FAULT DIAGNOSIS

Since most equipment will fail at some time, the designer should add indicators and fault information to the operator interface to allow common faults to be diagnosed quickly. For example, a simple conveyor motor starter requires two discrete inputs (start and stop push buttons) and one output (motor contactor). However, when a fault occurs, maintenance personnel may spend excessive time tracing the source of the fault. With a few additional inputs and some indicator lamps, the time to repair will be reduced. For this conveyor motor control, the total number of inputs and outputs could be:

Inputs	Outputs
Start push button	Motor running
Stop push button	Motor stopped
Contactor auxiliary contact	Conveyor running
Motor overload contact	Conveyor fault
440 volt supply on	
Conveyor drive speed switch	
Conveyor follower speed switch	
Motor current	

The speed switches on the drive and follower conveyor shafts allow quick diagnosis of the major conveyor mechanical problems. The motor current measurement can be used to indicate a potential problem with the conveyor before the motor overheats or a shaft breaks. The fault lamp only indicates that a fault has been detected. The specific fault can be identified by the PLC and indicated on an operator interface screen. For example, the above inputs could be used to indicate the following specific faults:

Auxiliary contact not closed in 10 seconds after start
Motor overload
440 volt supply fault
Motor current excessive (precursor to eventual overload)
Conveyor drive failure (auxiliary contact closed, drive speed switch off)
Conveyor belt failure (drive speed switch on, follower speed switch off)

15.8 CHAPTER SUMMARY

This chapter provides an introduction to troubleshooting methods and provides general troubleshooting information for PLC systems. Troubleshooting information is presented for the I/O devices, the PLC hardware, the PLC program, and the PC-to-PLC communications link.

REFERENCES

Allen-Bradley, 1995. *SLC 500 TM Modular Hardware Style – Installation and Operation Manual*, pub. 1746-6.2, Allen-Bradley Company, Inc, Milwaukee, WI.

Allen-Bradley, 1996a. *Classic 1785 PLC-5 Programmable Controllers: User Manual*, pub. 1785-6.2.1, Allen-Bradley Company, Inc., Milwaukee, WI.

Allen-Bradley, 1996b. *SLC 500 TM Analog I/O Modules: User Manual*, pub. 1746-6.4, Allen-Bradley Company, Inc, Milwaukee, WI.

Allen-Bradley, 1998. *Analog Output Module: User Manual*, pub. 1771-6.5.30, Allen-Bradley Company, Inc, Milwaukee, WI.

Allen-Bradley, 1999. *Analog Input Module: User Manual*, pub. 1771-6.5.115, Allen-Bradley Company, Inc, Milwaukee, WI.

GE Fanuc Automation, 1999a. *Series 90TM-30 Installation and Hardware Manual,* pub. GFK-0356P, GE Fanuc Automation North America, Inc., Charlottesville, VA.

GE Fanuc Automation, 1999b. *Series 90TM-70 Programmable Controller Installation Manual,* pub. GFK-0262G, GE Fanuc Automation North America, Inc., Charlottesville, VA, 1999.

GE Fanuc Automation, 2000. *Series 90TM-30 PLC I/O Module Sepcifications,* pub. GFK-0898F, GE Fanuc Automation North America, Inc., Charlottesville, VA.

Rockwell Automation, 1998a. *ControlLogix Analog I/O Modules: User Manual*, pub. 1756-6.5.9, Rockwell Automation, Inc., Milwaukee, WI.

Rockwell Automation, 1998b. *Enhanced and Ethernet PLC-5 Programmable Controllers: User Manual*, pub. 1785-6.5.12, Rockwell Automation, Inc., Milwaukee, WI.

Rockwell Automation, 1998c. *Industrial Automation Wiring and Grounding Guidelines*, pub. 1770-4.1, Rockwell Automation, Inc., Milwaukee, WI.

Rockwell Automation, 1998d. *Logix5550 Controller: User Manual*, pub. 1756-6.5.12, Rockwell Automation, Inc., Milwaukee, WI.

Rockwell Automation, 2001. *SLC 500TM Modular Hardware Style: User Manual*, pub. 1747-UM011C-EN-P, Rockwell Automation, Inc., Milwaukee, WI.

Rockwell Automation, 2002. *ControlLogixTM Controller and Memory Board: Installation Instructions*, pub. 1756-IN101G-EN-P, Rockwell Automation, Inc., Milwaukee, WI.

Schneider Automation, 2002. *Modicon Quantum Automation Series Hardware Reference Guide,* ver. 10.0, pub. 840 USE 100 00, Schneider Automation, Inc., North Andover, MA.

Siemens, 1998. *S7-400, M7-400 Programmable Controllers Module Specifications: Reference manual,* July, 2000 edition, pub. A5E00069467-03, Siemens AG, Nürnberg, Germany.

Siemens, 1999. *S7-300 Programmable Controller Hardware and Installation Manual,* Ed. 2, pub. EWA 4NEB 710 6084-02 01, Siemens AG, Nürnberg, Germany.

16 Sensors and Actuators

Chapter Topics:

- Discrete and analog sensors
- Discrete and analog actuators

OBJECTIVES

Upon completion of this chapter, you will be able to understand:

- The types of sensors and their applications
- The types of actuators

Scenario 1: Using photoelectric proximity sensors to detect silicon wafer cassettes. A particular application processes "cassettes" of 150 mm silicon wafers in a series of chemical baths. Each cassette holds up to 20 wafers and two cassettes are processed simultaneously. A gantry is used to move the cassettes from the loading station to the first of a series of chemical baths. Figure 16.1 shows the major steps to extract the cassettes from a bath. In this figure, the second cassette is behind the cassette shown. The cassettes remain in a chemical bath for a certain amount of time and then they are moved to the next bath. Eventually, they are moved from the last chemical bath to an unloading station, where they are removed by an operator.

As part of the failure handling, the system needs to verify that cassettes are properly being removed from a bath. There is a reliability problem with this type of end effecter. Occasionally, it will not pick up one or both of the cassettes. A similar system using this type of end effecter has two sensors in each bath. A sensor beneath each cassette position is used to verify that cassettes are being picked up. However, this method cannot be used in this system because of the chemicals in the baths. So, diffuse reflective photoelectric proximity sensors are mounted on one of the end effecter paddles (Figure 16.1*d*). However, this application has significant background reflections from the liquid in the baths and from the white plastic beneath the cassettes in the loading and unloading stations. Before mounting the photoelectric sensors, you test a sensor and find that it can be adjusted to be insensitive to the liquid background, as long as the sensor is only checked when the gantry is fully up. It is still sensitive to the white plastic bench top at the loading and unloading stations. However, placing a gray pad at the loading and unloading stations solved that problem. Encouraged, both sensors are mounted and adjusted. However, when operating the system, you note that it now appears to be sensitive to the liquid background when the gantry is above a bath. The sensor indicates a cassette in the end effecter when there is no cassette.

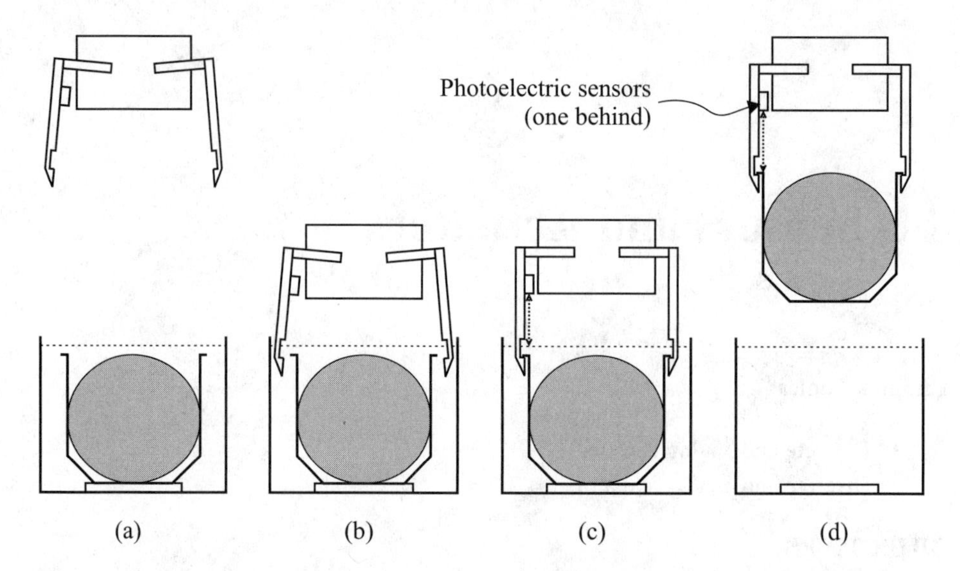

Figure 16.1. Gantry picking up cassettes: (a) up with clamp open; (b) down, ready to clamp cassettes; (c) cassettes clamped; (d) up with cassettes.

***Solution*:** Obviously, a different sensor must be used. After researching diffuse photoelectric sensors, you discover that there are certain diffuse reflective photoelectric sensors that suppress background reflections with triangulation. You purchase and install these sensors. These sensors work reliably. The presence/absence of a cassette must still be checked when the gantry is in the up position since the cassette must be out of the bath for the sensor to detect the cassette.

Scenario 2: Thermocouple measurements in an aluminum heat-treating furnace. Heating an aluminum plate to a temperature just below the melting temperature in order to alter the alloy grain structure is a common operation in aluminum production. When examining the aluminum plates in a certain batch, the metal grain structure is not correct, indicating a problem with the furnace temperature.

***Solution*:** Obviously, something is wrong with the furnace temperature control. Examining the temperature logs for that batch of aluminum plates processed by the furnace reveals no anomalies. The furnace zone temperatures are monitored by thermocouples mounted in the furnace ducts that supply the heated air. To verify the operation of the furnace temperature control, a furnace survey is performed. Thermocouples mounted on a steel plate are placed inside the furnace and these thermocouples monitor the temperatures in the various parts of the furnace during a normal heat-treating operation. The actual temperatures, as determined by the thermocouples mounted on the steel plate, are about 10 °F higher than the temperatures reported by the control system. Investigating the thermocouple measurement system, you find that there is no cold-junction compensation, but all of the thermocouple junctions with the thermocouple input modules are at an isothermal block. The temperature of the isothermal block is about 40 °F, and it should be 32 °F. It is then that someone notices that the temperature of the equipment room where the thermocouple input modules are located is about 10 °F higher than normal. It is normally around 60 °F and someone had set the thermostat to 72 °F, which is more amenable to working in the room. The control signal for the isothermal block cooling control is at its maximum, indicating that it is not able to maintain the isothermal block at its proper temperature of 32 °F. The equipment room thermostat is changed to 60 °F. After about an hour, the isothermal block temperature is back at 32 °F. A subsequent survey of the furnace reveals no temperature measurement problems. A locking cover is placed over the room thermostat to prevent this problem in the future.

16.1 INTRODUCTION

In order for the PLC to be useful, it must be connected to the process. Sensors are inputs to the PLC and actuators are the outputs that manipulate the process. A typical PLC system has connections to both discrete and analog devices. Discrete and analog sensors are described first since there are a large number of possible sensors. Lastly, discrete and analog actuators are explained.

16.2 DISCRETE SENSORS

The output of a discrete sensor has two states: off/on, open/closed, or 0/1. The most common application of a discrete sensor is to sense the presence or absence of an object. Limit switches and proximity sensors fulfill this role. Many motion control applications use encoders to sense the position and/or velocity of an object. Other discrete sensors detect the value of a physical quantity such as a high temperature or a low pressure. Although all of these types of sensors are described, proximity sensors are emphasized due to their wide variety of implementation technologies.

16.2.1 Limit switches

Limit switches are generally contact sensors; in other words, the object to be sensed comes in contact with the sensor and moves a lever arm. Two example limit switches are shown in Figure 16.2. The roller lever actuator shown in Figure 16.2*a* is often used to detect large objects that are widely spaced, for example, boxes moving down a conveyor belt. This

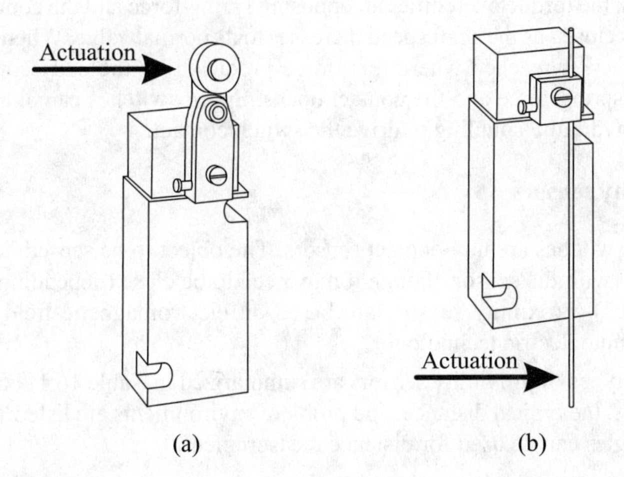

Figure 16.2. Example limit switches: *(a)* roller lever-actuated; *(b)* gravity return.

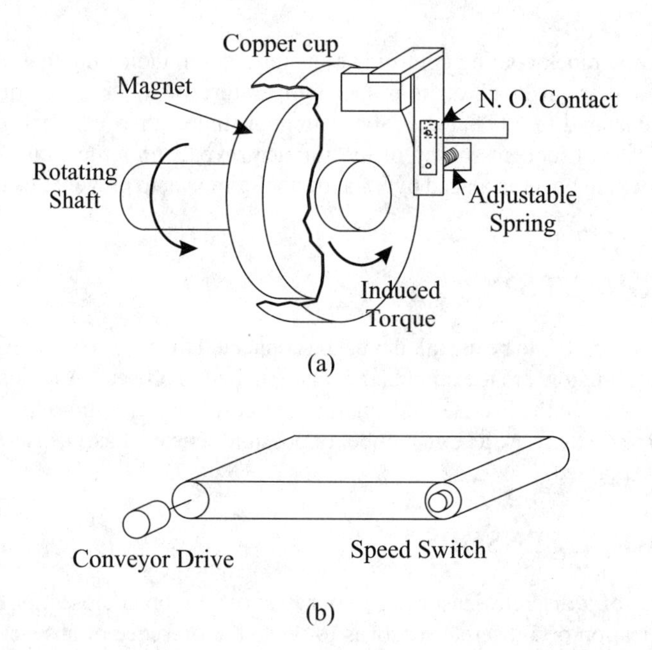

Figure 16.3. Speed switch: *(a)* mechanism; *(b)* typical placement.

type of limit switch is mounted so that the object pushes the lever right (or left) to change the contact. The gravity return actuation in Figure 16.2*b* is often used to detect light objects moving down a conveyor. This type of limit switch is mounted above the conveyor.

One special form of a limit switch is a speed switch. A speed switch detects the speed or direction of a rotating shaft. When mounted on the non-driven shaft of a conveyor belt, the speed switch detects both a broken belt or a broken drive shaft. The magnetic induction type of operating mechanism is illustrated in Figure 6.3*a*. When the shaft rotates, the rotating magnet induces eddy currents in the copper cup. These eddy currents produce a torque proportional to the shaft speed. The cup rotates a lever that operates a contact. As the shaft speed increases, the torque overcomes an opposing spring force and the contact closes. The contact remains closed as the shaft speed increases to its normal value. When the shaft speed decreases, a speed is reached where the torque produced by the eddy current no longer overcomes the spring force and the contact opens. Speed switches can alternatively use a mechanical or hydraulic coupling to drive the switch contact.

16.2.2 Proximity sensors

Proximity switches are non-contact sensors. The object to be sensed does not need to come in contact with the sensor, though it may need to be close (depending on the type of proximity switch). Proximity sensors are based on electromagnetic field, electric field, ultrasonic, or photoelectric technologies.

The major types of proximity sensors are summarized in Table 16.1. For each one, the sensed materials, the typical distance, and problem environments are listed. Note that some of the technologies can be used for distance measurement.

Table 16.1 Comparison of Discrete Proximity Sensors

Sensor Type	Sensed Materials	Maximum Distance	Measure Distance?	Problem Environments
Inductive	Metal	15 mm	yes, nonlinear	
Capacitive	Metal, Nonmetal	30 mm	yes, nonlinear	dirty, wet
Hall effect	Magnetic	3 mm	no	dirty, wet
Reed switch	Magnetic	60 mm	no	
Ultrasonic	Any	10 m	yes	
Photoelectric	Any	0.3m-100 m[1]	yes	dusty

Notes:

1. Depends on sensing mode (through-beam, retro-reflective, diffuse)

Inductive

Inductive proximity switches detect ferrous and nonferrous metallic objects. They operate on the principle that metals interact with an electromagnetic field. Inductive proximity switches are either unshielded (Figure 16.4*a*) or shielded (Figure 16.4*b*). Shielded sensors are used when the sensor is mounted flush in surrounding metal without causing the mount to trigger the sensor. The electromagnetic field is generated by a coil of wire on a ferrite core. The coil is part of an oscillator circuit.

The operation of an inductive proximity switch is shown in Figure 16.5. As a metal object enters the electromagnetic field, eddy currents are induced in the metal object. These eddy currents absorb some of the electromagnetic energy, causing the oscillator amplitude

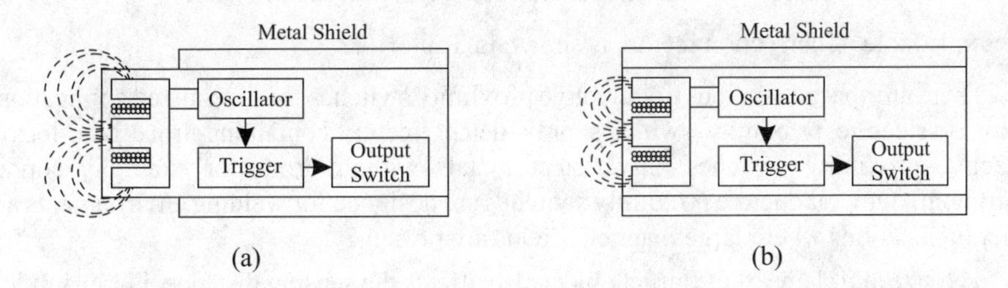

Figure 16.4. Inductive proximity switch block diagram: *(a)* unshielded; *(b)* shielded.

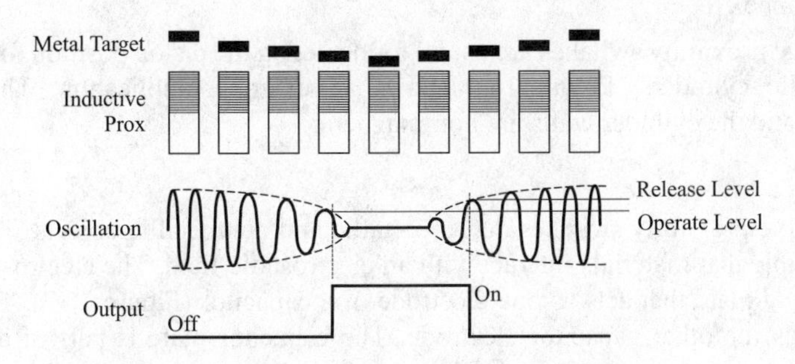

Figure 16.5. Inductive proximity switch operation.

Table 16.2 Inductive Proximity Correction Factors

Target Material	Correction Factor
Mild Steel	1.0
Stainless Steel	0.85
Brass	0.50
Aluminum	0.45
Copper	0.40

to decrease. A trigger circuit senses the decreased oscillation amplitude and changes the state of the output to **on**. When the oscillation amplitude then increases beyond the release level, the state of the output is changed to **off**. Note that the operate and release levels are different, called the hysteresis. Hysteresis helps prevent "chattering" (output rapidly turning **on** and **off**) when the sensor is vibrated or when the object is stationary at the nominal sensing distance.

The sensing distance is a function of the object size and material, the area of the electromagnetic field, which is determined by the face area of the sensor, and whether the sensor is shielded or unshielded. For example, an unshielded cylindrical inductive proximity switch with an 18 mm diameter from a certain vendor has a nominal sensing distance of 8 mm for a mild steel object that is 18 mm square. If this sensor is shielded, the nominal sensing distance drops to 5 mm. If the unshielded sensor has a diameter of 12 mm, the nominal sensing distance decreases to 4 mm and if the unshielded sensor has a diameter of 30 mm, the nominal sensing distance increases to 15 mm. To determine the sensing distance for materials other than mild steel, a correction factor must be used to determine the actual sensing range.

$$\text{Sensing Range} = (\text{Nominal Sensing Range})\times(\text{Correction Factor})$$

A sample table of correction factors is shown in Table 16.2.

There are special versions of inductive proximity switches for specialized applications. Ferrous-selective proximity switches only detect metals containing iron. Non-ferrous selective proximity switches only detect metals without iron (for example, copper, aluminum). Other inductive proximity switches are designed for welding environments and other applications where large magnetic fields are present.

The size and shape of the target object also affects the sensing distance. For example, a rounded target usually reduces the sensing distance. An object smaller than the sensor face area reduces the sensing distance and an object larger than the face area increases the sensing distance.

Inductive proximity switches are useful for detecting the piston position for pneumatic and hydraulic cylinders. Figure 16.6 shows an example application. The piston is magnetized and the cylinder walls are non-magnetic.

Capacitive

Capacitive proximity switches detect metallic and nonmetallic objects. They operate on the principle that materials interact with an electrostatic field. The electrostatic field is generated by a plate that acts as one electrode of a capacitor (Figure 16.7). The detected object acts as the other capacitor electrode. The capacitor plate is part of an oscillator circuit.

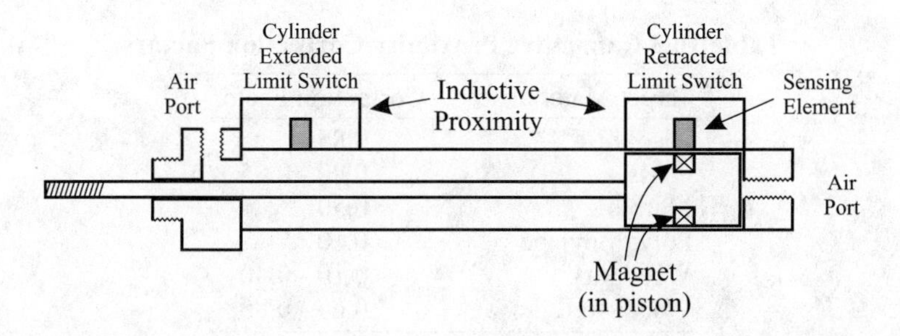

Figure 16.6. Inductive proximity sensor as cylinder piston limit switches.

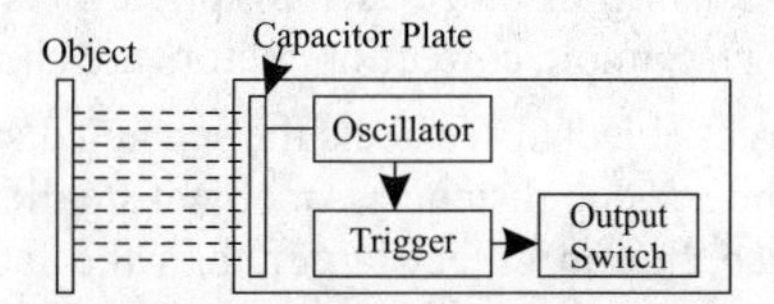

Figure 16.7. Capacitive proximity switch block diagram.

The operation of a capacitive proximity switch is shown in Figure 16.8. As an object enters the electrostatic field, the capacitance increases, causing the oscillator to start oscillating and the amplitude to increase. A trigger circuit senses the increased oscillation amplitude and changes the state of the output to **on** when the amplitude is at the operate level. When the oscillation amplitude then decreases below the release level, the state of the output is changed to **off**. Note that the operate and release levels are different, called the hysteresis. Hysteresis helps prevent "chattering" (output rapidly turning **on** and **off**) when the sensor is vibrated or when the object is stationary at the nominal sensing distance.

The sensing distance is a function of the object size and material; and the area of the electrostatic field, which is determined by the face area of the sensor. For example, a cylindrical capacitive proximity switch with an 18 mm diameter from a certain vendor has a nominal sensing distance of 1 mm for a glass object that is 18 mm square. If the object is polypropylene, the nominal sensing distance is 0.5 mm. If the sensor has a diameter of 12 mm, the nominal sensing distance decreases to 0.5 mm and if the sensor has a diameter of 30 mm, the nominal sensing distance increases to 2 mm. To determine the sensing distance for

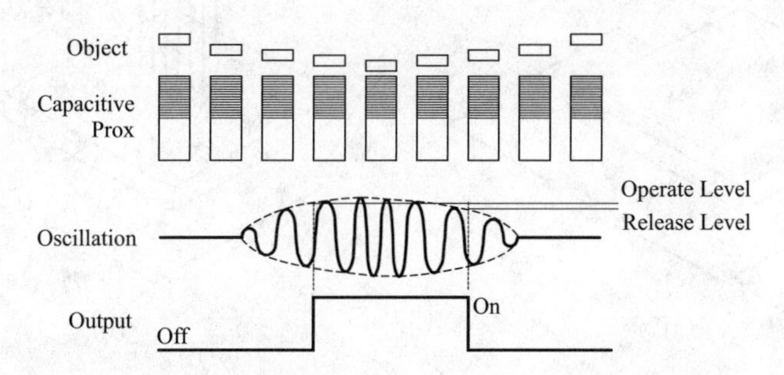

Figure 16.8. Capacitive proximity switch operation.

Table 16.3 Capacitive Proximity Correction Factors

Target Material	Correction Factor
Alcohol	0.85
Glass	0.20 - 0.55
Marble	0.50
Polypropylene	0.10
Wood, dry	0.10 - 0.40
Wood, wet	0.60 - 0.85

various materials, the nominal sensing distance is multiplied by a correction factor to determine the actual sensing range. Sample correction factors are shown in Table 16.3.

The size and shape of the target object also affects the sensing distance. For example, a rounded target usually reduces the sensing distance. An object smaller than the sensor face area reduces the sensing distance and an object larger than the face area increases the sensing distance.

Although capacitive proximity sensors are not sensitive to the target material magnetic properties, they are sensitive to the medium in the gap between the sensor and the target. Anything that affects the dielectric constant of the gap will change the proximity detection. Thus, capacitive proximity sensors are not recommended for applications that have excessive dust, water, or machining fluids.

Hall Effect

Hall effect sensors are used to detect magnetic materials. If a magnetic field is applied perpendicular to a current-carrying conductor, it generates a voltage perpendicular to the current flow. The sensor is manufactured as a plate of a semiconductor material because the Hall effect is more prominent in semiconductors. The operation of a Hall sensor is illustrated in Figure 16.9. When a DC current flows through the semiconductor plate, no transverse voltage is generated (Figure 16.9*a*). However, when a magnetic field is applied perpendicular to the plate current flow, the current flow curves toward one edge of the plate, generating a small voltage (Figure 16.9*b*). This small voltage is amplified, and then when

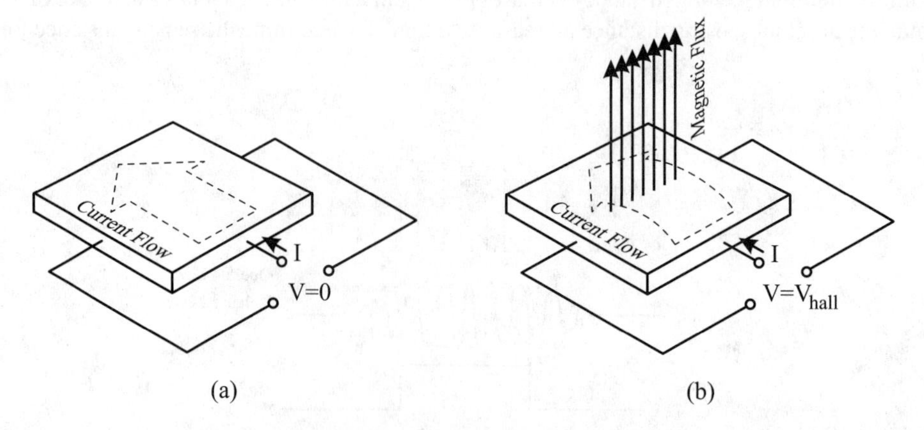

Figure 16.9. Hall effect principle: *(a)* no magnetic field; *(b)* magnetic field present.

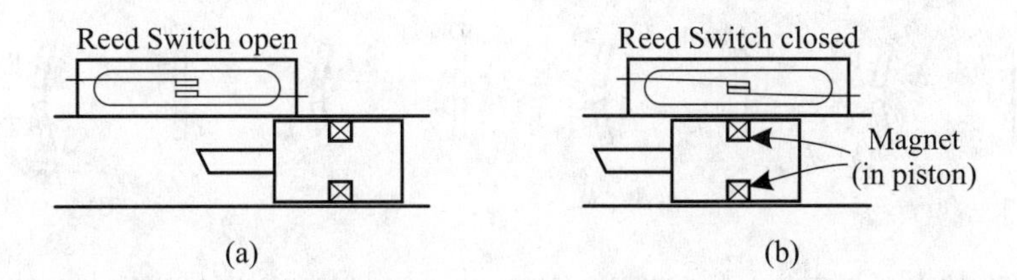

Figure 16.10. Magnetic reed switch operation: *(a)* no magnetic field; *(b)* magnetic field present.

above a threshold, the magnetic object is detected. As for the inductive and capacitive proximity switches, Hall effect proximity switches have hysteresis. The magnetic field strength needed to turn on the switch is higher than the field strength required to sustain the on switch indication. Hall sensors are frequently used to detect the position of a cylinder piston, as for inductive proximity sensors (Figure 16.7).

Magnetic Reed Switch

As an alternative the Hall effect sensor, a magnetic reed switch can also be used to detect the position of a magnetic cylinder piston. Operation of a magnetic reed switch is illustrated in Figure 16.10. A reed switch contains hermetically-sealed contacts. When the piston magnet moves close to the switch, the contacts are magnetized and pull together (Figure 16.10*b*). When the magnet moves away from the contacts, they open. The advantage of the reed switch is that it can handle AC signals.

Ultrasonic

Ultrasonic transducers use sound waves to detect an object. They can be used to measure distance or proximity. The basic principle is to emit a sound wave "pulse" and then measure the time for the pulse to be detected by the receiver. There are two basic configurations as shown in Figure 16.11. The transmitter and receiver can be separate piezo-electric elements focused on the same point, Figure 16.11*a*. In this case, the operation is shown in Figure 16.12. The wave pulse is generated by the transmitter, reflected by the object and detected by the receiver. The alternative configuration of an ultrasonic transducer (Figure 16.11*b*) combines the transmitter and receiver. In this case, the transmitter and receiver do not need to be focused on the same point. The operation of the combined transmitter and receiver ultrasonic transducer is shown in Figure 16.13. The wave pulse is generated by the piezo-electric element, and then the element is switched to its

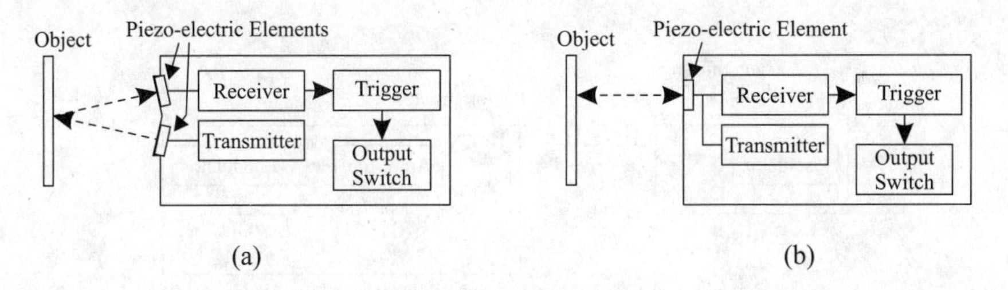

Figure 16.11. Ultrasonic proximity switch block diagram: *(a)* separate transmitter and receiver element; *(b)* combined transmitter/receiver element.

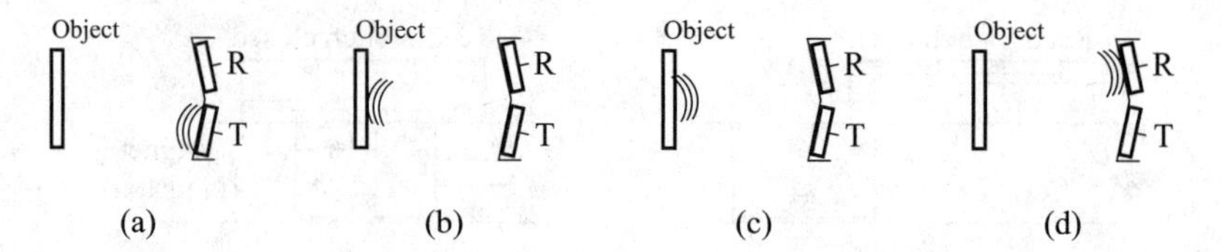

Figure 16.12. Operation of separate transmitter and receiver: *(a)* wave launched; *(b)* wave impinges object; *(c)* wave reflected; *(d)* wave impinges receiver.

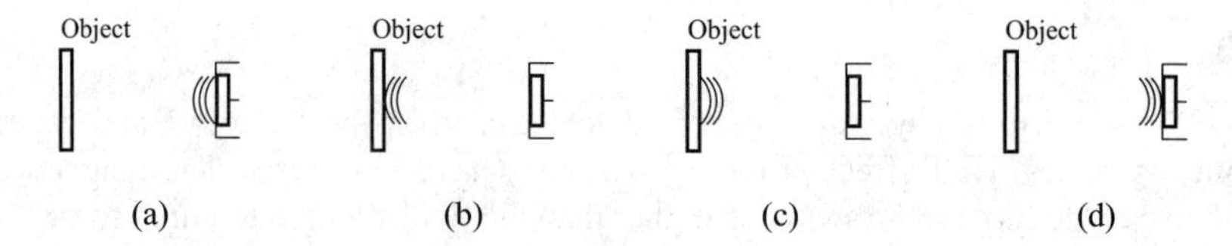

Figure 16.13. Operation of combined transmitter/receiver: *(a)* wave launched; *(b)* wave impinges object; *(c)* wave reflected; *(d)* wave impinges receiver.

receiving mode. The wave is reflected by the object and then detected by the element. In this type of ultrasonic transducer, there is a minimum sensing distance. The trailing edge of the pulse must leave the transducer before the leading edge of the reflected pulse can be detected. If the target is too close, the leading edge of the reflected wave pulse will be impinging on the transducer before it has completely transmitted the wave pulse.

Because ultrasonic sensors depend on receiving a reflected sound wave for proper operation, the target must be a good reflector of sound waves. Preferably, the target should be a smooth, flat surface. Rounded or uneven objects may be detected, but at a reduced maximum sensing distance. Soft materials, such as foam rubber and fabric are difficult to detect since they are not strong sound reflectors.

Ultrasonic proximity switches have a longer sensing range than inductive or capacitive proximity switches. Typical sensing ranges are from 30 cm to 100 cm.

Photoelectric Sensors

Most photoelectric sensors operate in the same basic manner, shown in Figure 16.14. An oscillator drives a light-emitting diode (LED) to generate a modulated light beam. The modulation frequency is typically several kilohertz. A phototransistor responds to this light beam, and its response is amplified. The demodulator essentially responds only to the

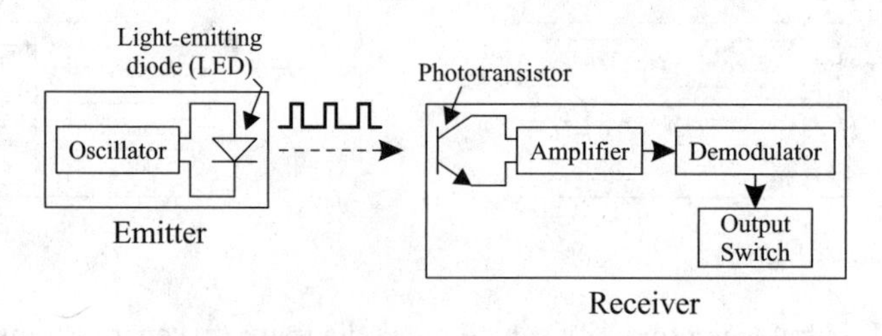

Figure 16.14. Photoelectric sensor block diagram.

modulated light beam, effectively blocking any ambient light. Phototransistors are more sensitive in the infrared or visible red range of light frequencies and so the emitter LED is typically in this range. Photoelectric sensors that differentiate between colors require a visible light source. For certain applications, a visible LED may be used and for others that sense a wide range of colors, an incandescent light source is required.

There are some applications where only ambient light is sensed. Hot metal or glass objects emit infrared light. When the infrared light is more intense than the surrounding light level, a receiver with a filter that only admits infrared light can be used. No emitter is required for these applications.

Photoelectric sensors operate in one of two ways: light-operate or dark-operate. A light-operate photoelectric sensor energizes its output when the received light intensity increases above a threshold. A dark-operate sensor energizes its output when the received light intensity decreases below a threshold.

The major difference between types of photoelectric sensors is the way the emitter and receiver are packaged. The major types are: through-beam, retroreflective, and diffuse reflective. Polarizing and convergent-beam photoelectric sensors are used for special applications.

Through-beam. In the through-beam configuration, the emitter and receiver are positioned opposite to each other so that the beam from the emitter is aimed directly at the receiver (Figure 16.15). An object is detected when it interrupts the beam. As long as the sensed object is opaque, the through-beam configuration is the most reliable method of using photoelectric sensors. The distance between the emitter and receiver can be more than 100 meters. Through-beam sensors are best for sensing non-metallic objects through heavy dirt, dust, moisture, and condensation.

There are few applications where the through-beam configuration is not the best. It is generally not recommended when detecting clear films or containers. If the object does not completely interrupt the beam, then apertures, lenses, or fiber optics may be used to shape the beam to match the part profile. If the part is small and passes at a predictable distance from the sensor, then a convergent-beam reflective sensor works better. If the emitter and receiver are close, an infrared beam tends to pass through thin opaque materials like paper, cloth, and plastics. In this case, the light beam is attenuated with apertures or the emitter and receiver are intentionally misaligned. Alternatively, the material may be opaque to a visible LED emitter.

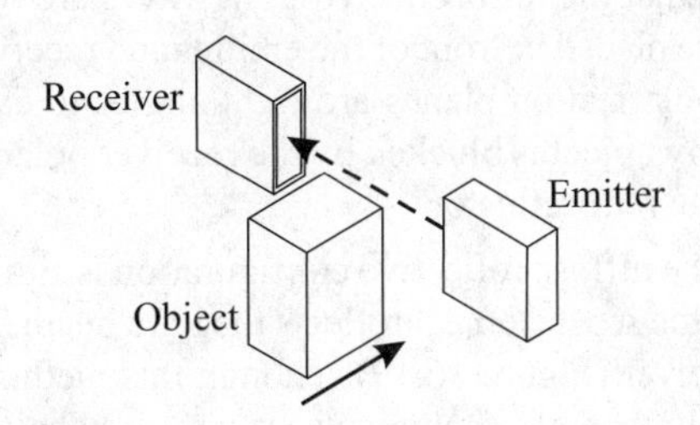

Figure 16.15. Through-beam photoelectric sensor operation.

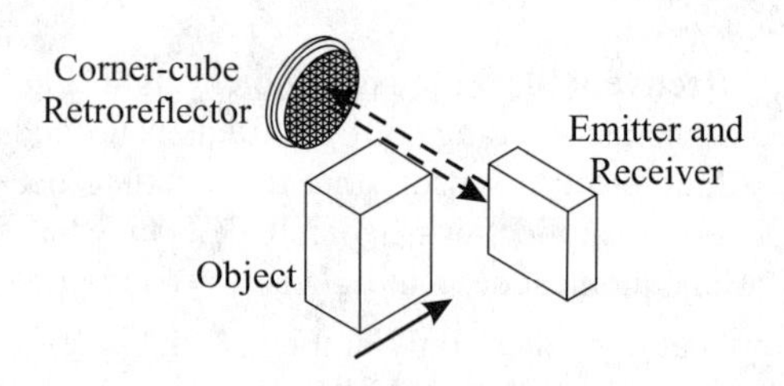

Figure 16.16. Retroreflective photoelectric sensor operation.

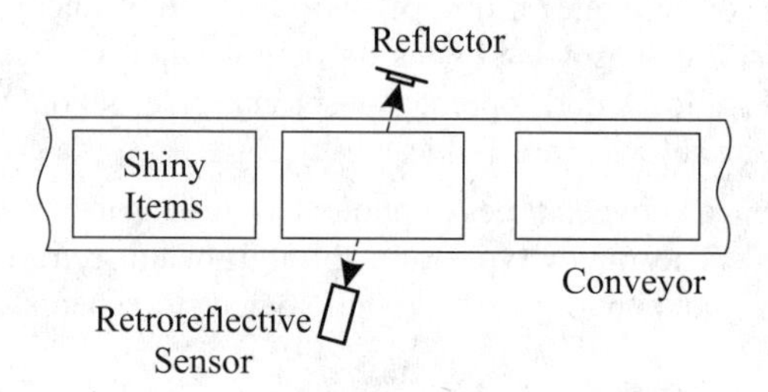

Figure 16.17. Skewing retroreflective photoelectric sensor.

Retro-reflective. In the retro-reflective configuration, the emitter and receiver are in the same package and a reflector is used to return light to the receiver (Figure 16.16). An object is detected when it interrupts the beam. The retro-reflective configuration is used instead of the through-beam configuration when sensing is possible from only one side. The reflector is generally constructed of corner-cube prisms (like a bicycle reflector) that reflect the light parallel to the incident beam. This configuration is most popular in conveyor application where the objects are large (for example, cartons) and where the environment is relatively clean. The sensing distance is typically less than 5 meters, significantly less than the distance for the through-beam configuration. The retro-reflective configuration does not work for those applications that are a challenge for the through-beam configuration.

If the sensed objects are shiny and flat (for example, a shrink-wrapped box), the sensor is skewed so that light reflected from the object does not reach the receiver (Figure 16.17). For shiny rounded objects, (for example, an aluminum can), a special type of retro-reflective sensor is used to ignore reflections from the object. A corner-cube prism reflector has the property that the retroreflected light waves are rotated 90° to the incident wave. Polarizing filters are placed in front of the emitter and receiver lenses. The two filters are oriented so that the polarization planes are right angles to each other (Figure 16.18). Light reflected by the shiny object is blocked by the receiver polarizing filter because it has not been rotated 90° by the retroreflector.

Diffuse reflective. The diffuse reflective configuration is similar to the retro-reflective configuration except that the sensed object reflects the light beam. An object is sensed when it reflects light to the receiver (Figure 16.19). Though this method of sensing is attractive since it has the fewest number of components, it may be challenging to make it sense reliably and consistently. To use the diffuse reflective photoelectric sensor, the reflective properties of the sensed object must be drastically different than the background. It will be a challenge to sense a shiny object in front of a reflective background. As a general rule, the

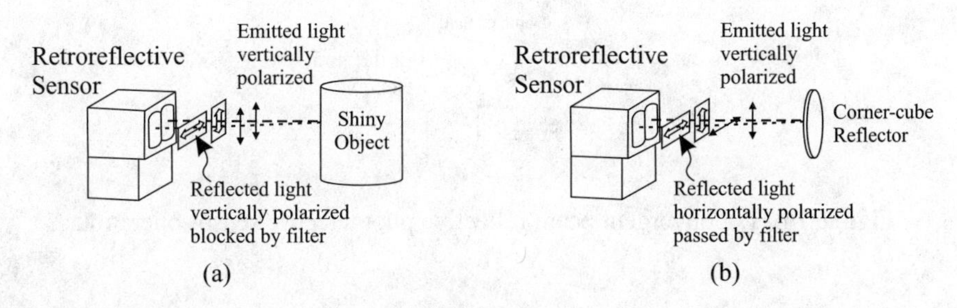

Figure 16.18. Polarized retroreflective photoelectric sensor: *(a)* shiny object in path; *(b)* no object in path.

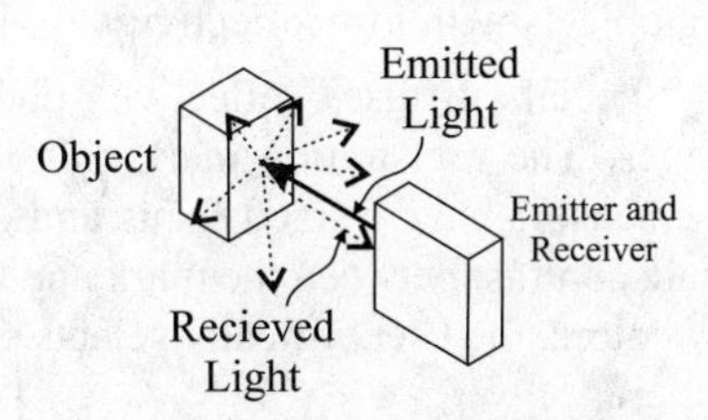

Figure 16.19. Diffuse reflective photoelectric sensor operation.

distance from the diffuse reflective sensor to the background should be at least four times the distance to the sensed object (Banner Engineering, 1994). This rule assumes that the background is less reflective than the sensed object. Any attempt to adjust the amplifier gain in order to suppress the background will not improve the situation. In this case, an alternative sensor configuration is the only viable alternative.

Diffuse reflective photoelectric sensors can suppress background reflections with triangulation. In this arrangement, there are two receivers, each aimed at a different target distance (Figure 16.20). Receiver R1 is aimed at the sensed target and R2 is aimed at the background. The focusing lens is adjusted for R1. When the reflected light intensity sensed by R1 is greater than the intensity sensed by R2, the target object is recognized. Triangulation ignores objects beyond the target.

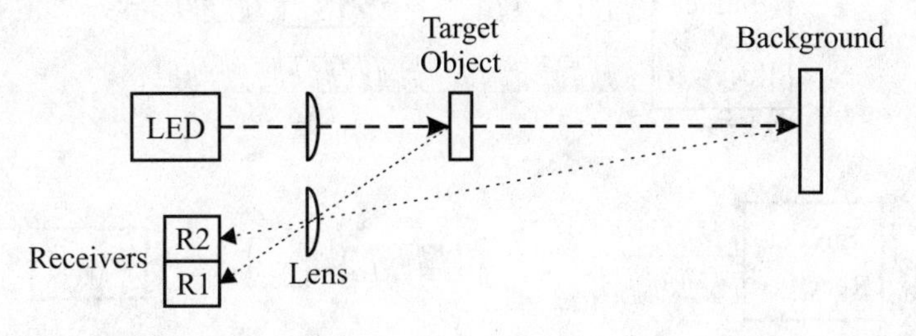

Figure 16.20. Diffuse reflective photoelectric sensor operation using triangulation to suppress background.

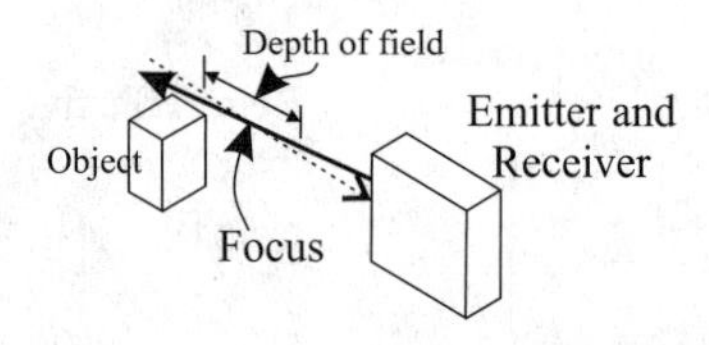

Figure 16.21. Convergent beam reflective photoelectric sensor operation.

Convergent-beam. A convergent-beam configuration uses lenses to focus both the emitter and receiver to the same point (Figure 16.21). This configuration produces a small, intense area at a fixed distance from the sensor lens. This configuration is useful for sensing small objects and for sensing objects with low reflectivity.

Registration marks. Special diffuse reflective photoelectric sensors detect registration marks on packages. The registration mark aids in aligning the material for printing or packaging. These sensors have a fixed focus and detect the registration color mark by sensing the gray-scale contrast between the mark and the background. Depending on the background and mark colors, the user typically selects either a red or green LED as the emitter.

Clear objects. Sensing clear materials, such as clear plastic films or clear glass bottles is a challenging application for photoelectric sensors. Photoelectric diffuse reflective sensors without lenses can detect clear materials at short distances (up to 50 mm). Without the lenses, the receiver is less dependent on receiving light reflected parallel to the emitted beam. One vendor uses coaxial optics and circular polarization to maximize the contrast between the object and the background.

Fiber optics. In certain situations, space may be too restrictive or the environment too hostile for the photoelectric sensor components. In these situations, fiber optic cables are used to couple the photoelectric sensor to the sensing situation (Figure 16.22). For the through-beam configuration, two separate fiber optic cables are used – one to transmit the

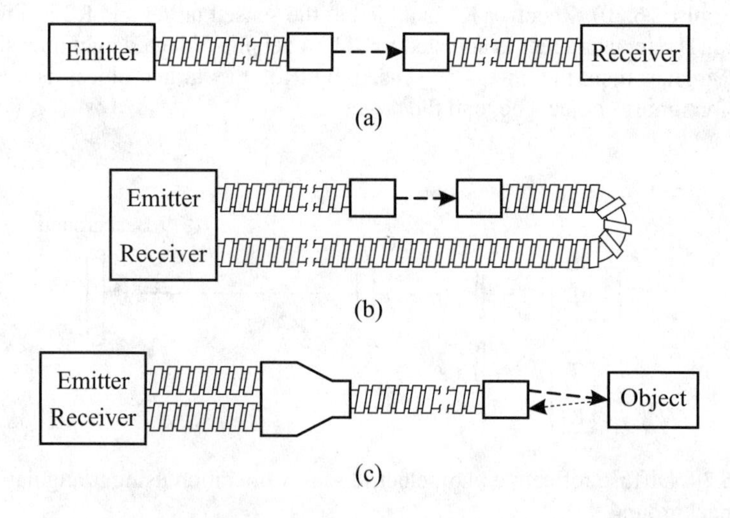

Figure 16.22. Photoelectric sensors with fiber optics: *(a)* individual emitter and receiver; *(b)* combined emitter and receiver; *(c)* bifurcated fiber for reflective operation.

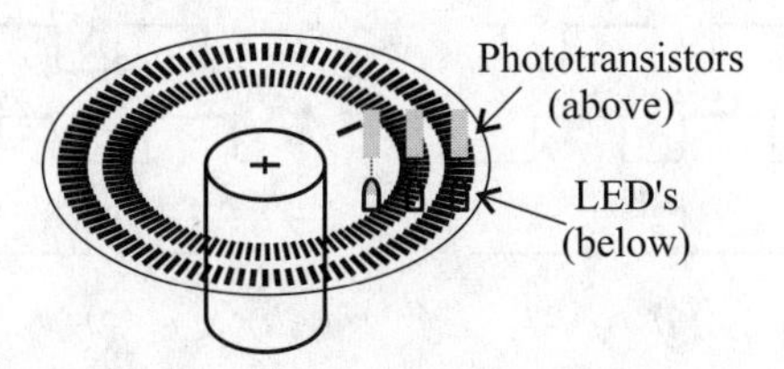

Figure 16.23. Simplified encoder.

emitted beam and the other to conduct the received beam (Figure 16.22*a, b*). For diffuse or retroreflective configurations, a single fiber optic cable is split into two cables, called a bifurcated cable (Figure 16.22*c*). Half of the fiber optic cable strands conduct the emitted light and the other half of the strands conduct the reflected light.

16.2.3 Encoders

Motion applications use encoders to determine the position and/or velocity of a rotary shaft. An encoder consists of a disk with lines in one or more bands or tracks (Figure 16.23). For each band there is a miniature through-beam photoelectric sensor that senses the lines passing as the disk rotates. The number of lines on the encoder disk determines the encoder resolution. Encoders with more than 1000 lines per track are common.

There are two basic types of encoders: incremental and absolute. Incremental encoders are the more common since they require fewer disk tracks and fewer interface signals to the input module.

The two basic types of incremental encoder disks are shown in Figure 16.24. A single-track encoder has only one output signal that is a square wave (Figure 16.24*a*). The direction of travel cannot be determined with this type of encoder. The travel distance is determined by counting the pulses and the velocity is determined by measuring the frequency of the square wave signal. A two-phase quadrature encoder has three tracks (Figure 16.24*b*). The relative phasing of the A and B signals indicate the direction of encoder rotation. If the positive edge of A leads the positive edge of B, the encoder is rotating clockwise (Figure 16.25*a*). For counterclockwise rotation, the positive edge of A

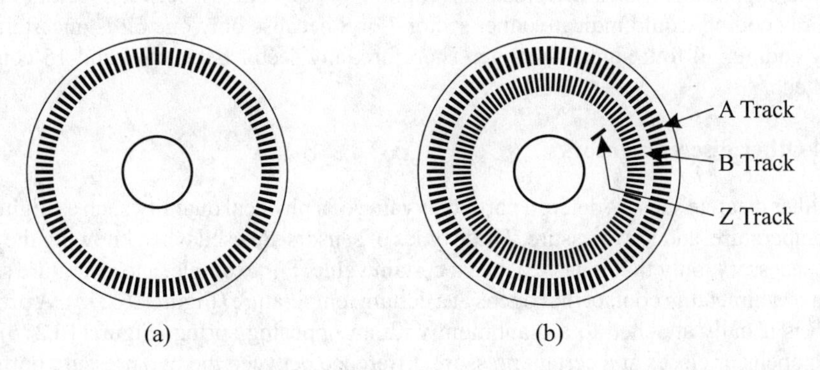

Figure 16.24. Incremental encoder disk: *(a)* single track; *(b)* two-phase quadrature encoder tracks.

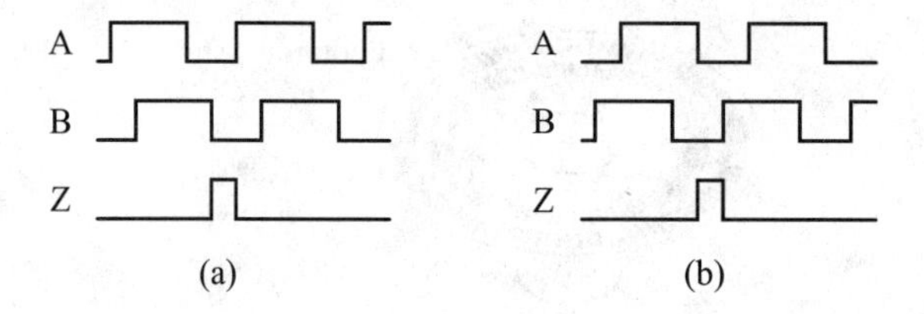

Figure 16.25. Quadrature encoder signals: *(a)* clockwise rotation; *(b)* counterclockwise rotation.

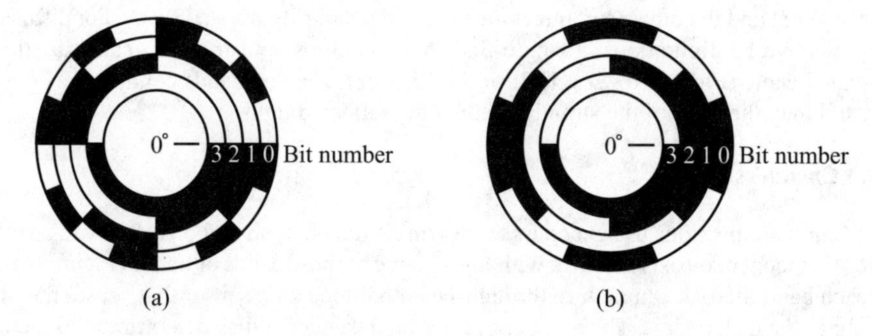

Figure 16.26. Absolute encoder disks: *(a)* binary code; *(b)* Gray code.

lags the positive edge of B (Figure 16.25*b*). The Z signal is the index pulse, which pulses once for each encoder revolution.

An absolute encoder provides multiple outputs, usually eight or sixteen, that provide the position of the disk relative to a zero point. Example absolute encoders that provide a 4-bit output are shown in Figure 16.26. These encoders provide the position of the disk relative to the zero position shown in the figure. Binary and Gray code representations of the position are the most popular coding schemes. The binary and Gray code representations of the disk positions are shown in Table 16.4. Gray code has the advantage that only one track changes during any transition. If there is any ambiguity because the phototransistor is reading the "edge" of one of the bands, the indicated position is in error by only one. For example, suppose the disk is at a clockwise rotation of 180 degrees, between sectors 7 and 8. The Gray coding would indicate either sector 7 or 8 because only one bit is uncertain. For binary coding, all four signals change. Therefore, any sector between 0 and 15 could be indicated.

16.2.4 Other discrete sensors

Other discrete sensors detect a particular value of a physical quantity such as high level, low temperature, and low pressure. These types of sensors are used when knowing the value is not necessary, only that it has reached a certain value. For example, a temperature switch can have a bimetallic contact that opens at a certain temperature (Figure 16.27*a*). A pressure switch is usually attached to a diaphragm with an opposing spring (Figure 16.27*b*). The switch opens or closes at a certain pressure difference between the two pressure ports.

Table 16.4 Absolute Encoder Outputs

Clockwise rotation angle (degrees)	Sector number	Binary code	Gray code
0.0 - 22.5	0	0000	0000
22.5 - 45.0	1	0001	0001
45.0 - 67.5	2	0010	0011
67.5 - 90.0	3	0011	0010
90.0 - 112.5	4	0100	0110
112.5 - 135.0	5	0101	0111
135.0 - 157.5	6	0110	0101
157.5 - 180.0	7	0111	0100
180.0 - 202.5	8	1000	1100
202.5 - 225.0	9	1001	1101
225.0 - 247.5	10	1010	1111
247.5 - 270.0	11	1011	1110
270.0 - 292.0	12	1100	1010
292.5 - 315.0	13	1101	1011
315.0 - 337.5	14	1110	1001
337.5 - 360.0	15	1111	1000

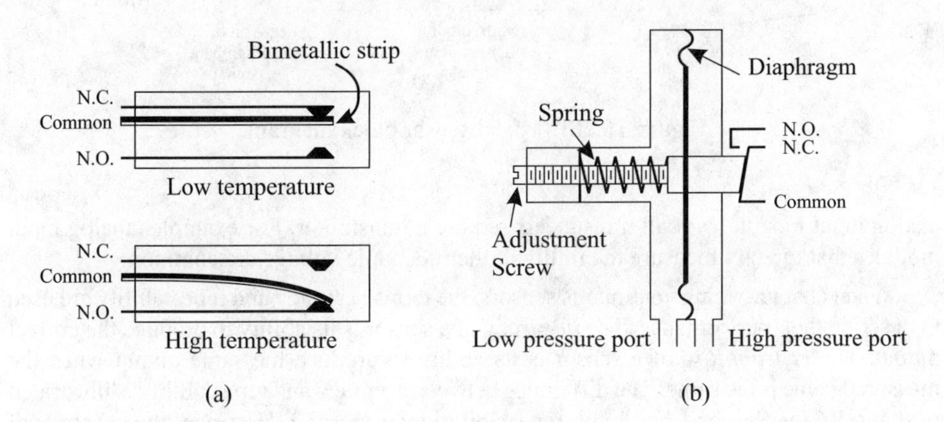

Figure 16.27. Other discrete sensors: *(a)* high temperature switch; *(b)* high pressure switch.

16.3 ANALOG SENSORS

An analog sensor measures the value of a physical quantity than can have an infinite number of values. Table 16.5 lists the most common physical quantities and the prevalent type of sensor technology used to measure the quantity. A sensor converts the physical phenomenon to an appropriate signal that is connected to an analog input channel. Many sensors contain both a transducer and a transmitter (Figure 16.28). In general terms, a transducer is a device that converts energy from one form to another. In the context of PLCs, a transducer converts a physical phenomenon (for example, temperature, flow, pressure, level. etc.) to a low-level electrical signal. The transmitter amplifies the millivolt or microampere signal from the transducer to the volt or milliampere signal required by the

Table 16.5 Common Transducer Types

Physical Quantity	Transducer
Temperature	Thermocouple Resistance Temperature Detector (RTD) Thermistor
Displacement	Potentiometer Linear Variable Differential Transformer (LVDT)
Force, Weight	Strain Gauge
Pressure	Force on diaphragm Capacitance
Flow	Pressure drop across orifice Coriolis

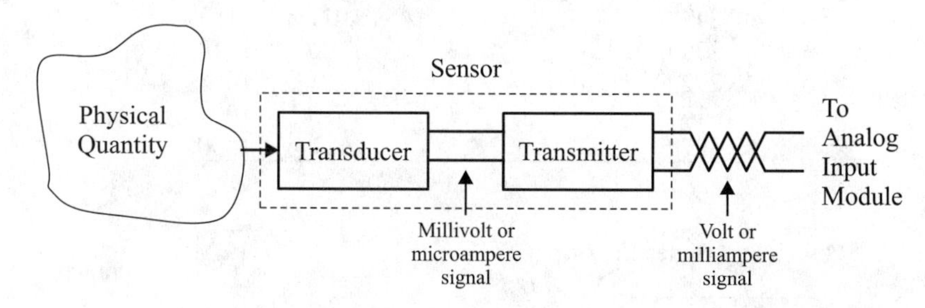

Figure 16.28. Typical sensor block diagram.

analog input module. Not all transducers require a transmitter. For example, analog input modules that directly measure the millivolt thermocouple voltage are common.

When characterizing continuous sensors, the terms accuracy and repeatability are used to describe their performance. The *accuracy* of a sensor is its ability to produce the correct output. The *repeatibility* of a sensor is its ability to produce the same output when the measured value is the same. The difference between accuracy and repeatability is illustrated in Figure 16.29. Sensor 1 has better repeatability than sensor 2. However, the accuracy of sensor 2 is better than sensor 1 since its range of values is closer to the true value.

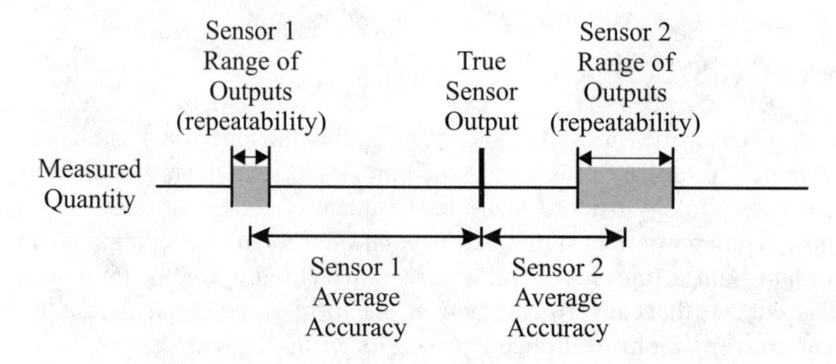

Figure 16.29. Difference between accuracy and repeatability.

After introducing the bridge circuit which is common in transducer circuitry, the various types of transducers used to measure temperature, displacement, force, pressure, flow, and level are described.

16.3.1 Bridge circuit

Many of the transducers listed in Table 16.5 rely on a bridge circuit to convert resistance changes to voltage changes. One may well ask why one cannot measure the resistance directly with an ohmmeter. There are two main reasons resistance is typically not directly measured:

1. Temperature compensation
2. Typical resistance changes are small

Temperature compensation is an important consideration. Often the resistance changes due to temperature can be as significant as the resistance changes due to the measured phenomenon.

A voltage sensitive bridge is shown in Figure 16.30. The resistances are typically in the 1000's of ohms. A current sensitive bridge is very similar, except that resistances are typically around 10 ohms. If R_S approaches zero (a perfect source) and R_D approaches infinity (a perfect detector) then,

$$V_a = V_S \frac{R_3}{R_1 + R_3} \text{ and } V_b = V_S \frac{R_4}{R_2 + R_4}$$

$$V = V_a - V_b = V_S \left[\frac{R_3}{R_1 + R_3} - \frac{R_4}{R_2 + R_4} \right]$$

$$= V_S \left[\frac{R_3 (R_2 + R_4) - R_4 (R_1 + R_3)}{(R_1 + R_3)(R_2 + R_4)} \right]$$

$$= V_S \left[\frac{R_2 R_3 - R_1 R_4}{(R_1 + R_3)(R_2 + R_4)} \right] \qquad (16.1)$$

If the bridge is balanced, $V = 0$, and

$$R_2 R_3 - R_1 R_4 = 0 \text{ and } \frac{R_1}{R_2} = \frac{R_3}{R_4}$$

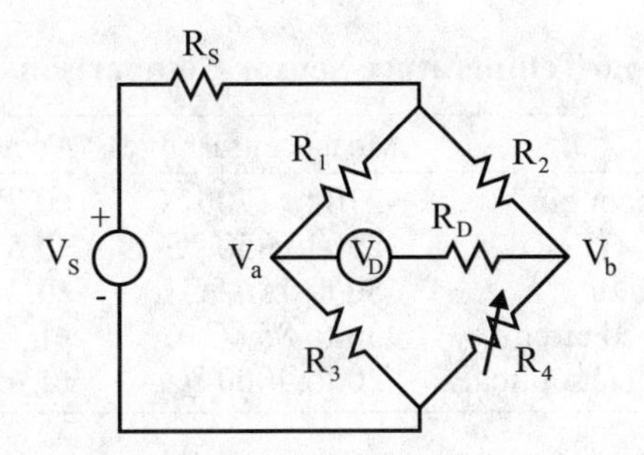

Figure 16.30. Voltage sensitive bridge.

Typically, $R_1 = R_2$, and so $R_3 = R_4$ when the bridge is balanced. When the bridge is balanced, what happens when R_4 (the transducer) changes to unbalance the bridge?

Let $R_1 = R_2$, and $R_4 = R_3 + \Delta R$

$$V = V_S\left[\frac{R_1R_3 - R_1(R_3 + \Delta R)}{(R_1 + R_3)(R_1 + R_3 + \Delta R)}\right] = V_S\left[\frac{-R_1(\Delta R)}{(R_1 + R_3)(R_1 + R_3 + \Delta R)}\right] \qquad (16.2)$$

If $R_1 + R_3 >> \Delta R$

$$V \approx V_S\left[\frac{-R_1(\Delta R)}{(R_1 + R_3)^2}\right] \qquad (16.3)$$

If one is interested in measuring changes in the resistance of R_4 (ΔR),

$$\Delta R \approx -V\left[\frac{(R_1 + R_3)^2}{V_S R_1}\right] \qquad (16.4)$$

16.3.2 Temperature sensors

The five most common temperature sensors are the thermocouple, resistance temperature device (RTD), thermistor, integrated circuit, and optical pyrometer. The temperature ranges of these five sensors and their relative accuracy are compared in Table 16.6. For the thermocouple, RTD, and thermistor, a typical device spans part of the entire range specified in Table 16.6. The relative advantages and disadvantages of these sensors is shown in Table 16.7. The basic responses of each sensor type are compared in Figure 16.31.

Regardless of the temperature sensor, most applications require the sensor be mounted inside a thermowell (Figure 16.32) that protects the sensor from the process chemicals. The thermowell also allows the temperature sensor to be replaced without interrupting the process stream. When measuring the temperature of a chemical stream or the chemical inside a process vessel, thermowells are required. Thermowells are not utilized when the space is limited (for example, motor bearings and compressor internals), when a fast response is needed, when measuring the air temperature, or when measuring surface temperature. The thermowell does introduce a measurement lag into the process. For example, a thermowell may add a 5 second lag into the process which translates into an effective time delay of 20 to 25 seconds.

Table 16.6 Temperature Sensor Comparison

Sensor	Measuring Range	Accuracy
Thermocouple	-270 to 1700 °C[1]	±0.75%[1]
RTD	-250 to 750 °C	±0.5%
Thermistor	-80 to 150 °C	±0.2 °C
Integrated circuit	-30 to 85 °C	±1°C
Noncontact optical	-20 to 4000 °C	±1 to 2%[2]

Notes:

1. Depends on thermocouple type
2. Percentage of full scale

Table 16.7 Temperature Sensor Advantages and Disadvantages

Sensor	Advantages	Disadvantages
Thermocouple	Self-powered Simple Rugged Inexpensive Wide temperature range	Nonlinear Low voltage Needs reference Least stable Least sensitive
RTD	Most stable Most accurate More linear than thermocouple	Expensive Requires power source Small ΔR Self-heating
Thermistor	High output Fast	Nonlinear Limited temperature range Fragile Requires power source
Integrated circuit	Most linear Highest output Inexpensive	Low temperature range Requires power source Slow Self-heating
Optical pyrometer	Non-contact Highest maximum temperature	Expensive Many mechanical parts

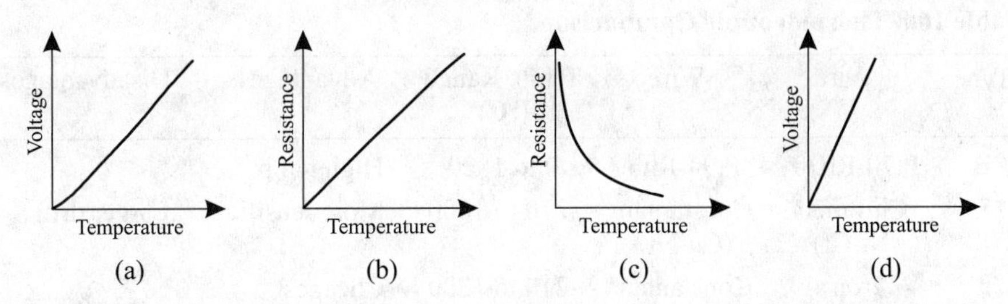

Figure 16.31. Typical response curves: *(a)* thermocouple; *(b)* RTD; *(c)* thermistor; *(d)* integrated circuit.

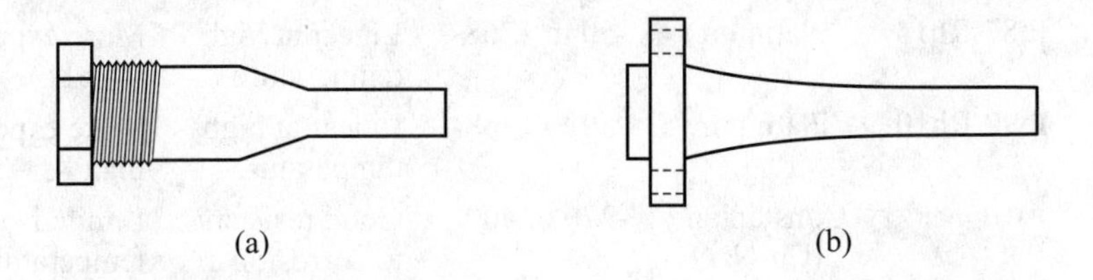

Figure 16.32. Thermowell: (a) threaded well; (b) flanged well.

Thermocouple

Thermocouples are the most versatile temperature-measuring element. They can be used over a wide temperature range. They are much more rugged than the other types of sensors and are often welded to a metal part or clamped under a screw. They can be manufactured on-site by soldering or welding. The only major drawback is the low voltage measurement and so one must be careful when the thermocouple is a long distance from the analog input module.

The operation of a thermocouple is based on the Seebeck effect which is a property of junctions of dissimilar metals. When two wires that are different metals are joined at both ends and one end is heated, an electromotive force (emf) is generated. For example, in Figure 16.33*a*, as $T_1 - T_2$ increases, the emf also increases. If the circuit is broken at the cold end (Figure 16.33*b*), the open circuit voltage, v_{ab}, is a function of the temperature difference between T_1 and T_2.

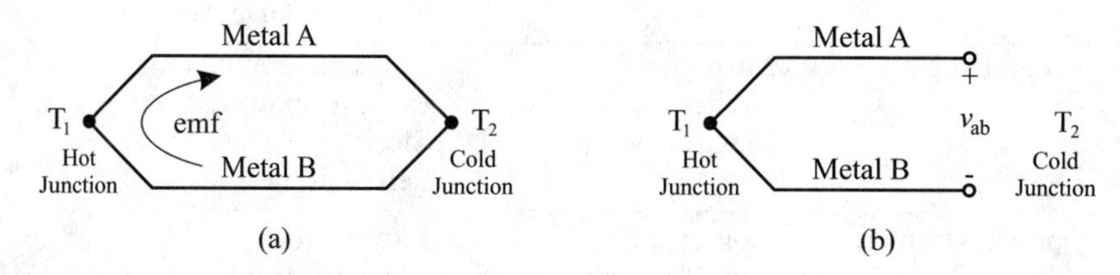

Figure 16.33. Basic thermocouple operation: *(a)* Seebeck effect; *(b)* Seebeck voltage.

Table 16.8 Thermocouple Comparison

Type	+ Wire	- Wire	Temp. Range (°C)	Advantages	Disadvantages
B	Pt70-Rh30	Pt94-Rh6	0 to 1820	High temp.	
E	Chromel (Ni-Cr)	Constantan (Cu-Ni)	-270 to 1000	Most sensitive	Larger drift
J	Iron	Constantan[1] (Cu-Ni)	-210 to 1200	Cheapest	
K	Chromel (Ni-Cr)	Alumel (Ni-Al)	-270 to 1372	Stability	
N	Nicrosil (Ni-Cr-Si)	Nisil (Ni-Si-Mn)	-270 to 1300	More stable than K	
R	Pt87-Rh13	Platinum	-50 to 1768	Linear at high temperature	More expensive than K
S	Pt90-Rh10	Platinum	-50 to 1768	Linear at high temperature	More expensive than K
T	Copper	Constantan (Cu-Ni)	-270 to 400	Good resistance to corrosion from moisture	Limited temperature range

Note:
1. Not the same copper-nickel alloy as for the E and T thermocouples.

Table 16.8 lists the most common thermocouple types and the materials used to make the junction. The letter designations follow the recommendations of the Instrumentation, Systems, and Automation (ISA) organization and the American Society for Testing and Materials (ASTM). The letter type, for example, type J, identifies a specific temperature-voltage relationship and not a particular composition of the two wires. The wires for thermocouples of a given type are allowed to have variations in composition as long as the temperature-voltage relationship remains within specified tolerances (Burns, et. al., 1993). The voltage generated by these thermocouples as a function of temperature is shown in Figure 16.34*a* (Burns, et. al, 1993). The Seebeck coefficient, shown in Figure 16.34*b* is the slope of the temperature-voltage curves in Figure 16.34*a*. The Seebeck coefficient clearly shows the nonlinear nature of thermocouples. The K, R, and S thermocouples are reasonably linear for temperatures greater than 0 °C.

In practice, the junction voltage cannot be measured directly because the voltmeter leads introduce additional thermocouple junctions (Figure 16.35). In the case of the K thermocouple in Figure 16.35, there exist chromel-copper and alumel-copper junctions in addition to the chromel-alumel junction. The two new junctions introduced by the measurement process produce their own voltage, dependent on the temperature of the junctions. The standard thermocouple voltage-to-temperature conversions specify that the reference junctions are at 0 °C. In the past, an ice bath was used to keep the reference junctions at 0 °C. However, with *cold-junction compensation* the temperature of the cold

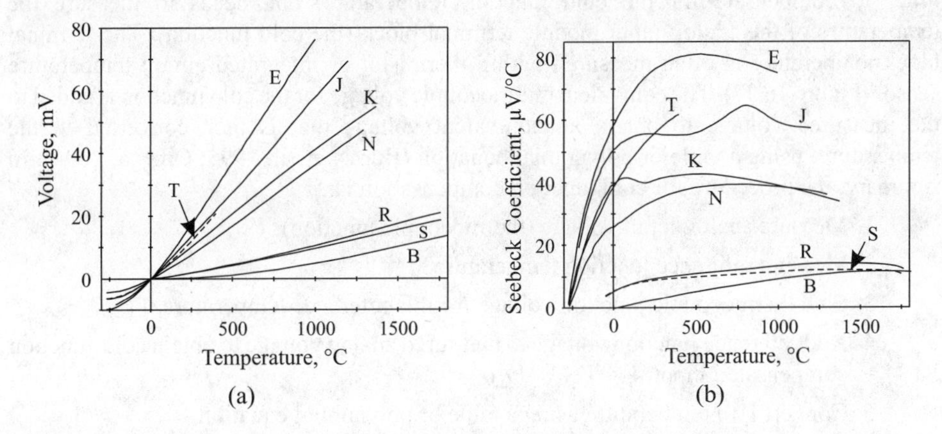

Figure 16.34. Thermocouple characteristics as a function of temperature: *(a)* voltage; *(b)* Seebeck coefficient.

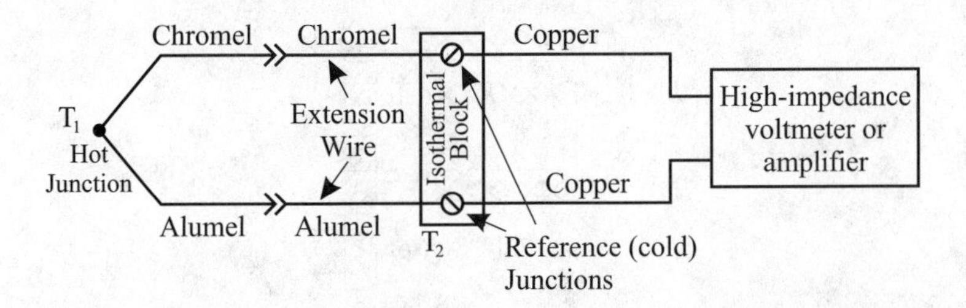

Figure 16.35. Thermocouple voltage measurement.

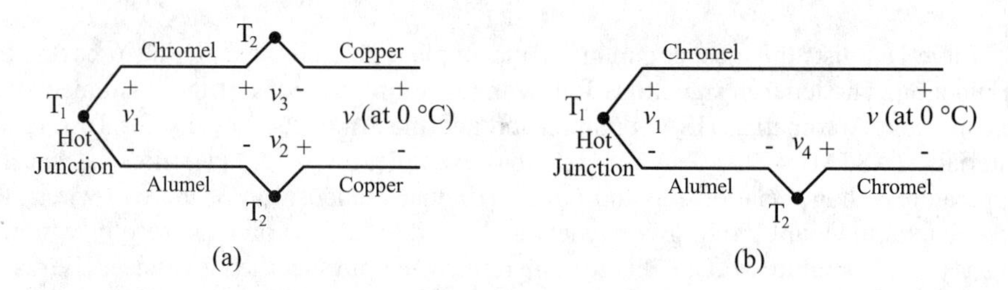

Figure 16.36. Cold junction temperature effects: *(a)* cold junction thermocouples; *(b)* equivalent circuit.

junction is measured and then used to adjust the measured voltage. With the advent of microprocessor-based analog input modules, the ice bath is not necessary because the microprocessor can implement the cold-junction compensation.

If the reference (cold) junction is not at 0 °C, the effect of thermocouple junctions at the isothermal block of Figure 16.35 is shown in Figure 16.36*a*. Both of these junctions produce a voltage which alters the measured voltage. Since the copper-copper connections inside the voltmeter do not produce any thermocouple junctions, the equivalent thermocouple circuit is shown in Figure 16.36*b*. The effect of a cold junction is essentially another thermocouple (of the same type) wired in opposition to the thermocouple being used for measurement. In order to compensate for the cold junction temperature, one needs to measure the temperature of the analog input module terminal block (the cold junction). The terminal block temperature is often measured with a thermistor or integrated circuit temperature sensor (Figure 16.37). The equivalent thermocouple voltage for the cold junction is added to the measured voltage to obtain an equivalent voltage that is then converted to the temperature, using a table or polynomial equation (Burns, et. al, 1993; Omega, 2004). In summary, the procedure for cold junction compensation is:

1. Measure analog input voltage (thermocouple junction), V_{TC} .
2. Measure reference junction temperature.
3. Find thermocouple junction voltage for this reference temperature, V_{CJ} .
4. Add reference junction voltage to measured analog voltage to obtain cold-junction compensated input, $V = V_{TC} + V_{CJ}$.
5. Convert V to temperature using a table or polynomial equation.

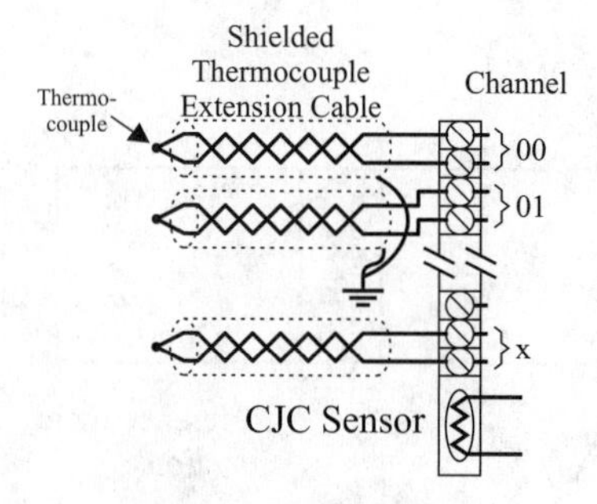

Figure 16.37. Typical thermocouple input module with cold-junction compensation.

This procedure will be illustrated by two examples, but first the conversion of the junction voltage to temperature will be explained. The voltage generated by these thermocouples as a function of temperature is presented in tabular form in Burns et. al. (1993). Given a measured voltage, one can look up the temperature, using interpolation to calculate the temperature when the voltage falls between two temperature entries. The linear interpolation formula is developed as follows. If V_1 is the voltage for temperature T_1 and V_2 is the voltage for temperature T_2, and V falls between V_1 and V_2 then T, the temperature that corresponds to V, is calculated as

$$T = \frac{V - V_1}{V_2 - V_1}(T_2 - T_1) + T_1 \tag{16.5}$$

The standard thermocouple tables are quite large since they report the voltage for every degree in the temperature range. For this reason, Burns et al (1993) also provide approximate polynomial functions that can calculate the temperature, given the voltage. The general equation for the polynomial is

$$T = c_0 + c_1 V + c_2 V^2 + c_3 V^3 + c_4 V^4 + \ldots + c_n V^n \tag{16.6}$$

where V is the voltage in mV and n is the polynomial order. There are also polynomials that can calculate the thermocouple voltage for a given temperature of the form

$$V = c_0 + c_1 T + c_2 T^2 + c_3 T^3 + c_4 T^4 + \ldots + c_n T^n \tag{16.7}$$

For example, for a J thermocouple producing a voltage between 0.0 and 42.919 mV, the coefficients of the 7th order polynomial to convert the voltage to the temperature, in °C, are:

$c_0 = 0.0$	$c_4 = -2.549687 \times 10^{-4}$
$c_1 = 1.978425 \times 10^{1}$	$c_5 = 3.585153 \times 10^{-6}$
$c_2 = -2.001204 \times 10^{-1}$	$c_6 = -5.344285 \times 10^{-8}$
$c_3 = 1.036969 \times 10^{-2}$	$c_7 = 5.09890 \times 10^{-10}$

The error in the calculated temperature value is between –0.04 to 0.04 °C. The chapter appendix contains other conversion polynomials. The amount of computation is a major drawback to using polynomial functions for the conversion. If one does not need a small error range, a lookup table can be constructed from selected points from the standard. The temperature is obtained by interpolating between the entries. For example, one control equipment vendor used a table of 40 entries to obtain a maximum error of 1 °C.

Example 16.1. The wiring diagram of a T thermocouple is shown in Figure 16.38. The voltage across the thermocouple wires, measured at the terminals of the analog input channel is 14.420 mV. The temperature of the cold junction is 24 °C. What is the temperature (in °C) of the hot junction? Find your answers to the nearest one-hundredth of a degree. Do the voltage-to-temperature conversion using:

(a) the T thermocouple table

(b) the National Institute of Standards and Technology (NIST) polynomial coefficients:

Solution. (a) A partial T thermocouple reference table is shown in Figure 16.39. Note that for positive temperatures, the temperature increases by one degree as one proceeds across the row.

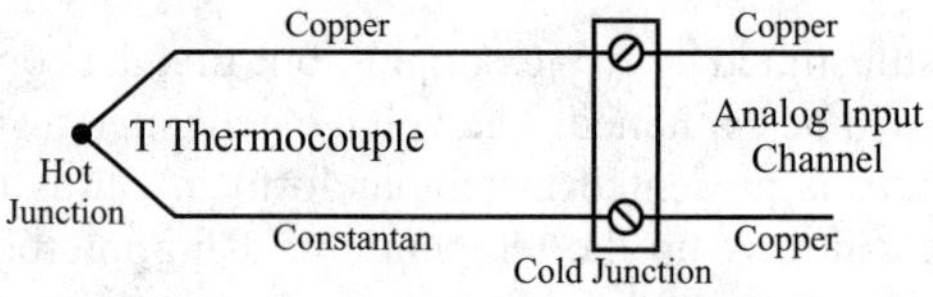

Copper
Copper
T Thermocouple
Analog Input Channel
Hot Junction
Constantan
Copper
Cold Junction

Figure 16.38. T thermocouple measurement example.

ITS-90 Table for type T thermocouple

Thermoelectric Voltage in mV

°C	0	-1	-2	-3	-4	-5	-6	-7	-8	-9	-10
-270	-6.258										
-260	-6.232	-6.236	-6.239	-6.242	-6.245	-6.248	-6.251	-6.253	-6.255	-6.256	-6.258
...											
-140	-4.419	-4.443	-4.466	-4.489	-4.512	-4.535	-4.558	-4.581	-4.604	-4.626	-4.648
-130	-4.177	-4.202	-4.226	-4.251	-4.275	-4.300	-4.324	-4.348	-4.372	-4.395	-4.419
-120	-3.923	-3.949	-3.975	-4.000	-4.026	-4.052	-4.077	-4.102	-4.127	-4.152	-4.177
-110	-3.657	-3.684	-3.711	-3.738	-3.765	-3.791	-3.818	-3.844	-3.871	-3.897	-3.923
-100	-3.379	-3.407	-3.435	-3.463	-3.491	-3.519	-3.547	-3.574	-3.602	-3.629	-3.657
...											
-10	-0.383	-0.421	-0.459	-0.496	-0.534	-0.571	-0.608	-0.646	-0.683	-0.720	-0.757
0	0.000	-0.039	-0.077	-0.116	-0.154	-0.193	-0.231	-0.269	-0.307	-0.345	-0.383
°C	0	-1	-2	-3	-4	-5	-6	-7	-8	-9	-10

ITS-90 Table for type T thermocouple

Thermoelectric Voltage in mV

°C	0	1	2	3	4	5	6	7	8	9	10
0	0.000	0.039	0.078	0.117	0.156	0.195	0.234	0.273	0.312	0.352	0.391
10	0.391	0.431	0.470	0.510	0.549	0.589	0.629	0.669	0.709	0.749	0.790
20	0.790	0.830	0.870	0.911	0.951	0.992	1.033	1.074	1.114	1.155	1.196
30	1.196	1.238	1.279	1.320	1.362	1.403	1.445	1.486	1.528	1.570	1.612
40	1.612	1.654	1.696	1.738	1.780	1.823	1.865	1.908	1.950	1.993	2.036
...											
290	14.283	14.341	14.399	14.456	14.514	14.572	14.630	14.688	14.746	14.804	14.862
300	14.862	14.920	14.978	15.036	15.095	15.153	15.211	15.270	15.328	15.386	15.445
310	15.445	15.503	15.562	15.621	15.679	15.738	15.797	15.856	15.914	15.973	16.032
320	16.032	16.091	16.150	16.209	16.268	16.327	16.387	16.446	16.505	16.564	16.624
...											
400	20.872										
°C	0	1	2	3	4	5	6	7	8	9	10

Figure 16.39. T thermocouple temperature-voltage table (partial).

From the problem, $V_{TC} = 14.42$ mV. The cold junction temperature is 24 °C, and the corresponding thermocouple voltage is read from the table as 0.951 mV, meaning $V_{CJ} = 0.951$ mV. Therefore, $V = V_{TC} + V_{CJ} = 15.371$ mV.

Reading the table, the temperature that corresponds to this junction voltage is between 308 and 309 C. The temperatures and corresponding junction voltages are

Temperature	Voltage
308 °C	15.326 mV
309 °C	15.386 mV

To use the formula in equation (16.5), $T_1 = 308$, $T_2 = 309$, $V_1 = 15.326$, and $V_2 = 15.386$.

$$T(°\text{C}) = \frac{15.371 - 15.326}{15.386 - 15.326}(309 - 308) + 308 = \frac{0.045}{0.06}(1) + 308 = 308.75\ °\text{C}$$

(b) For the T thermocouple, the NIST polynomial coefficients for converting temperature in the range of 0 to 400 °C to junction voltage (in mV) are

$c_0 = 0.0$ $\qquad c_5 = 1.0996880928\times10^{-11}$
$c_1 = 3.8748106364\times10^{-2}$ $\qquad c_6 = -3.0815758772\times10^{-14}$
$c_2 = 3.3292227880\times10^{-5}$ $\qquad c_7 = 4.5479135290\times10^{-17}$
$c_3 = 2.0618243404\times10^{-7}$ $\qquad c_8 = -2.7512901673\times10^{-20}$
$c_4 = -2.1882256846\times10^{-9}$

Using these coefficients in equation (16.7), the cold junction voltage for 24 °C is 0.951 mV, meaning $V_{CJ} = 0.9513$ mV. Therefore, $V = V_{TC} + V_{CJ} = 15.371$ mV.

The NIST polynomial coefficients for converting junction voltage in the range of 0 to 20.872 mV to the temperature (in °C) are

$c_0 = 0.0$ $\qquad c_4 = -2.165394\times10^{-3}$
$c_1 = 2.592800\times10^{1}$ $\qquad c_5 = 6.048144\times10^{-5}$
$c_2 = -7.602961\times10^{-1}$ $\qquad c_6 = -7.293422\times10^{-7}$
$c_3 = 4.637791\times10^{-2}$

The conversion error is ±0.03 °C. Using equation (16.6), the conversion of V into the temperature is

$$\begin{aligned} T(^\circ\mathrm{C}) &= c_0 + c_1V + c_2V^2 + c_3V^3 + c_4V^4 + c_5V^5 + c_6V^6 \\ &= 0.0 + 398.5393 - 179.6334 + 168.4293 - 120.8775 + 51.8959 - 9.6193 \\ &= 308.7343\ ^\circ\mathrm{C} \end{aligned}$$

Rounded to hundredths, $T = 308.73$ °C, which is within the error tolerance, as compared to the value obtained from the table in part (a).

Example 16.2. The wiring diagram of a T thermocouple is shown in Figure 16.38. The voltage across the thermocouple wires, measured at the terminals of the analog input channel is –4.790 mV. The temperature of the cold junction is 21 °C. What is the temperature (in °C) of the "hot" junction? Find your answers to the nearest one-hundredth of a degree. Do the voltage-to-temperature conversion using:

(a) the T thermocouple table
(b) the National Institute of Standards and Technology (NIST) polynomial coefficients:

Solution. (a) A partial T thermocouple reference table is shown in Figure 16.39. Note that for negative temperatures, the temperature *decreases* by one degree as one proceeds across the row.

From the problem, $V_{TC} = -4.790$ mV. The cold junction temperature is 21 °C, and the corresponding thermocouple voltage is read from the table as 0.830 mV, meaning $V_{CJ} = 0.830$ mV. Therefore, $V = V_{TC} + V_{CJ} = -3.960$ mV.

Reading the table, the temperature that corresponds to this junction voltage is between –121 and –122 °C. The temperatures and corresponding junction voltages are

Temperature	Voltage
–122 °C	–3.975 mV
–121 °C	–3.949 mV

To use the formula in equation (16.5), $T_1 = -122$, $T_2 = -121$, $V_1 = -3.975$, and $V_2 = -3.949$.

$$T(°\mathrm{C}) = \frac{-3.960 - (-3.975)}{-3.949 - (-3.975)}(-121 - (-122)) + (-122) = \frac{0.015}{0.026}(1) - 122 = -121.42\ °\mathrm{C}$$

(b) For the T thermocouple, the NIST polynomial coefficients for converting temperature in the range of 0 to 400 °C to junction voltage (in mV) are given in Example 16.1. Using these coefficients in equation (16.7), the cold junction voltage for 21 °C is 0.8299 mV, meaning $V_{CJ} = 0.8299$ mV. Therefore, $V = V_{TC} + V_{CJ} = -3.9601$ mV.

The NIST polynomial coefficients for converting junction voltage in the range of –5.603 to 0 mV to the temperature (in °C) are

$c_0 = 0.0$ $\quad c_4 = 4.2527777\times10^{-1}$
$c_1 = 2.5949192\times10^{1}$ $\quad c_5 = 1.3304473\times10^{-1}$
$c_2 = -2.1316967\times10^{-1}$ $\quad c_6 = 2.0241446\times10^{-2}$
$c_3 = 7.9018692\times10^{-1}$ $\quad c_7 = 1.2668171\times10^{-3}$

The conversion error is –0.02 to +0.04 °C. Using equation (16.6), the conversion of V into the temperature is

$$\begin{aligned} T(°\mathrm{C}) &= c_0 + c_1V + c_2V^2 + c_3V^3 + c_4V^4 + c_5V^5 + c_6V^6 + c_7V^7 \\ &= 0.0 - 102.7588 - 3.3428 - 49.0699 + 104.5812 - 129.5608 + 78.0571 - 19.3455 \\ &= -121.4496\ °\mathrm{C} \end{aligned}$$

Rounded to hundredths, $T = -121.44$ °C, which is within the error tolerance, as compared to the value obtained from the table in part (a).

Other thermocouple configurations are shown in Figure 16.40. When multiple thermocouples are connected in parallel (Figure 16.40*a*), the net voltage measured at the cold junction is indicative of the *average* of the measured temperatures. When two thermocouples are connected in series, but in opposite polarities, the net voltage measured at the cold junction indicates the *difference* of the two hot junction temperatures. For example, in Figure 16.40*b*, the voltage at the cold junction measures $T_1 - T_2$. A *thermopile* (Figure 16.40*c*) is a series connection of thermocouples. All hot junctions are at the same temperature and all cold junctions are at the same temperature. This arrangement effectively amplifies the thermocouple voltage. For the arrangement in Figure 16.40*c*, the measurement is three times the voltage of one thermocouple. However, cold-junction

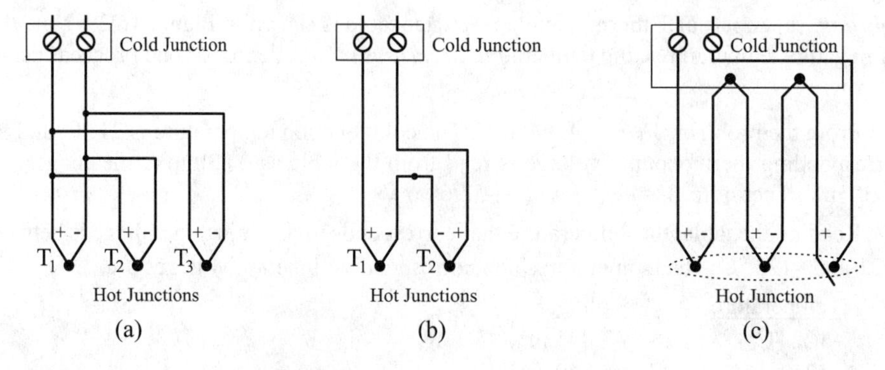

Figure 16.40. Other thermocouple configurations: *(a)* temperature average; *(b)* temperature difference; *(c)* thermopile.

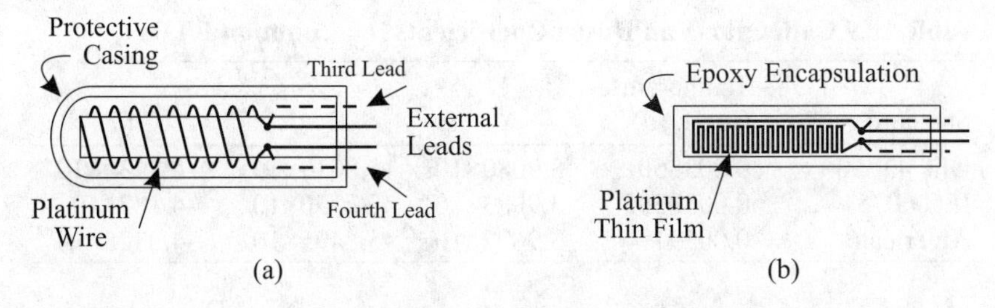

Figure 16.41. Typical RTD construction: *(a)* wire wound; *(b)* thin film.

compensation is slightly more complicated since for each thermocouple in series, one must also add the cold-junction compensation voltage to obtain the correct voltage for the voltage-to-temperature conversion. Thermopiles are used as the detector in some infrared radiation pyrometers.

Resistance Temperature Device (RTD)

A resistance temperature device (RTD) is somewhat less versatile than a thermocouple due to its smaller temperature range. However, it is more linear and more stable than a thermocouple.

The operation of a RTD is based on the temperature dependence of wire resistance. The resistance of a metal wire changes with temperature. Figure 16.41 shows two typical methods of RTD construction. In Figure 16.41*a*, the platimum wire is wrapped around a support and then encapsulated inside a ceramic or glass casing. Since platinum is expensive, most RTDs are now constructed as a thin film deposited on a small ceramic substrate and then encapsulated (Figure 16.41*b*). Platinum is the metal of choice for RTDs due to its stability and relatively large change in resistance with temperature changes. Copper and nickel are other common RTD metals. Balco (a nickel-iron alloy) and tungsten are also used to construct RTD, though rarely used. A typical RTD resistance versus temperature is shown in Figure 16.42.

RTDs are commonly classified by their nominal resistance at 0 °C. Platinum wire RTDs are typically 100 ohms at 0 °C. The nominal resistance of platinum thin film RTDs

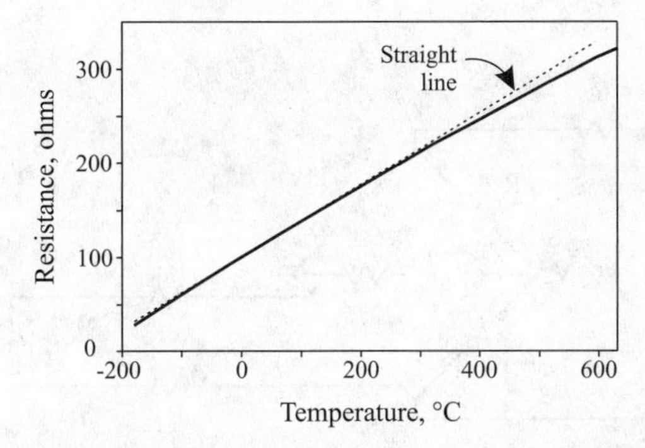

Figure 16.42. Typical RTD resistance characteristic as a function of temperature.

Table 16.9 Callendar-Van Dusen Coefficients for Common RTDs

Standard	Temperature Coeff. (α)	A	B	C (T < 0)
DIN 43760	0.003850	3.9080×10^{-3}	-5.8019×10^{-7}	-4.2735×10^{-12}
IEC 60751	0.0038505	3.9083×10^{-3}	-5.7750×10^{-7}	-4.183×10^{-12}
American	0.003911	3.9692×10^{-3}	-5.8495×10^{-7}	-4.2325×10^{-12}

range from 200 to 1000 ohms at 0 °C. One common method of expressing the relationship between temperature (T) and resistance (R_{RTD}) is the Callendar-Van Dusen equation:

$$R_{RTD} = R_0 + R_0\alpha\left[T - \delta(0.01T-1)(0.01T) - \beta(0.01T-1)(0.01T)^3\right]$$

where R_0 is the resistance at 0 °C, T is the temperature in °C, and α, β, and δ are constants. The constant α is the temperature coefficient in units of ohms/ohms/°C. This relationship is typically expressed as the cubic equation

$$R_{RTD} = R_0\left[1 + AT + BT^2 + C(T-100)^3\right] \tag{16.8}$$

This equation is valid over the range of -183 °C to 630 °C. The coefficients for common RTDs are shown in Table 16.9. Note that the C coefficient is zero for temperatures above 0 °C. The different standards specify different wire purity and composition. The DIN 43760 and IEC 60751 standard thermocouples are more prevalent than the older American standard. Since the C coefficient in equation (16.8) is zero for temperatures above 0 °C, the resulting quadratic equation can be solved for the temperature given a measurement of the RTD resistance. In this situation, the temperature can be calculated as

$$T = \frac{1}{2}\left[-\frac{A}{B} - \sqrt{\left(\frac{A}{B}\right)^2 - 4\left(\frac{R_0 - R_{RTD}}{BR_0}\right)}\right] \tag{16.9}$$

When used with a bridge circuit, RTD resistance can be measured as in Figure 16.43. However, if the RTD is far from the bridge, then the lead resistance can be significant, leading to errors in the resistance measurement. To compensate for lead resistance, a 3-wire RTD can be used where a third wire is connected to one lead of the RTD element. A bridge with a 3-wire RTD is shown in Figure 16.44. The value of R_{L3} is irrelevant since the current through it is very small.

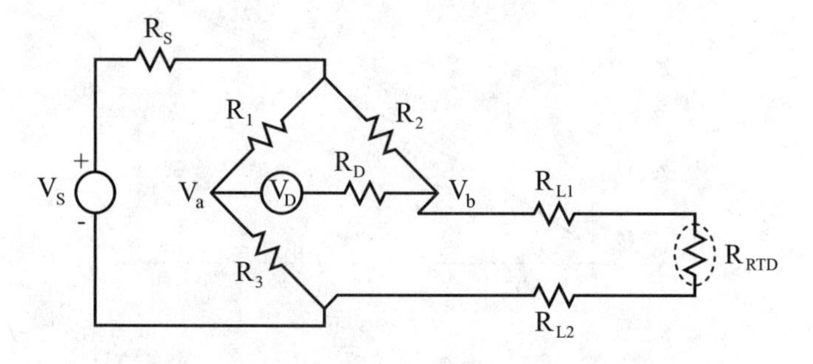

Figure 16.43. Wheatstone bridge with two-wire RTD.

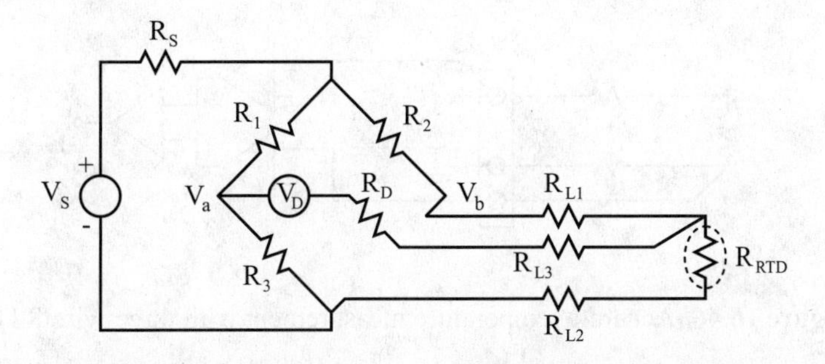

Figure 16.44. Wheatstone bridge with three-wire RTD.

The main problem with measuring RTD resistances is that the bridge circuit only works well with small changes in temperature. An RTD whose resistance is 100 ohms at 0 °C will have a resistance of 175.86 ohms at 200 °C. This resistance change violates the assumption of relatively small resistance changes in order to use equation (16.4) to calculate the resistance. One must use equation (16.2) which means there is a nonlinear relationship between resistance changes (ΔR) and the measured voltage, V_D.

The most accurate method of measuring RTD resistance uses a current source with either a 3-wire or 4-wire RTD. Figure 16.45 illustrates the method for a four-wire RTD. A current source establishes a constant current through the RTD. Since the amplifier has high input impedance, the current through the sense wires is very small and hence the effect of the sense wire resistances, R_{L3} and R_{L4}, is negligible. Note that the lead wire resistances, R_{L1} and R_{L2}, have no effect on the measurement. The RTD resistance is then

$$R_{RTD} = \frac{V}{I_{RTD}}$$

A current source can be used with a three-wire RTD to produce an accurate measurement of RTD resistance as shown in Figure 16.46 (Rockwell Automation, 2003). The sense lead is used to subtract the effect of both lead resistances. The amplifier outputs are

$$V_1 = I_{RTD}\left(R_{RTD} + 2R_L\right)$$
$$V_2 = 2I_{RTD}R_L$$
$$V = V_1 - V_2 = I_{RTD}R_{RTD}$$

and the RTD resistance is calculated with the same equation as for the four-wire RTD.

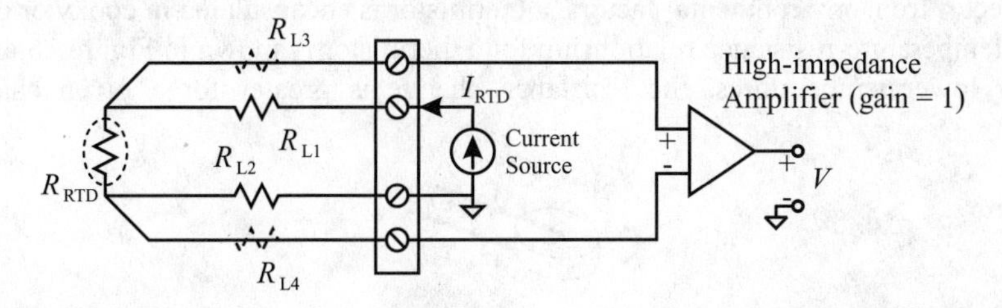

Figure 16.45. Accurate temperature measurement with four-wire RTD.

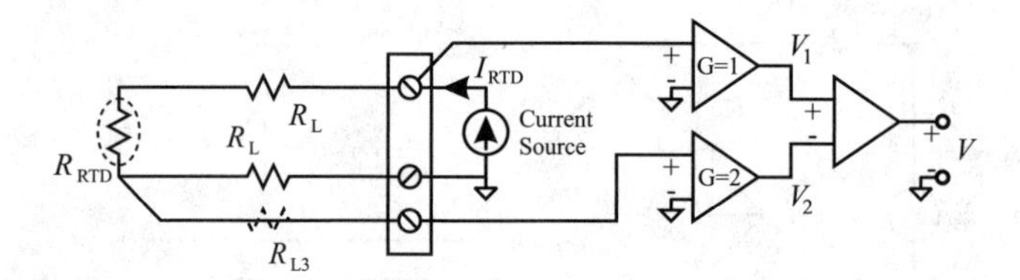

Figure 16.46. Accurate temperature measurement with three-wire RTD.

The accuracy of a RTD is affected by the magnitude of the current through it. Because the RTD is a resistance, current through it produces a small amount of heat, called the *self-heating effect*. The current through the RTD needs to be small (less than 1 mA) to minimize self-heating.

Example 16.3. A three-wire RTD measures temperature and the analog input uses the circuit of Figure 16.46 to measure the resistance. The RTD is a platinum RTD whose nominal resistance (R_0) is 100 ohms at 0 °C. The RTD has been manufactured according to the IEC 60751 standard. The measured RTD resistance is 180 ohms. What is the temperature of the RTD? Find your answers to the nearest one-hundredth of a degree. Do the voltage-to-temperature conversion using the Callendar-Van Dusen equation.

Solution. Since the measured resistance is greater than 100 ohms, the RTD temperature is greater than 0 C. R_0 = 100 and R_{RTD} = 180. The RTD temperature is calculated using equation (16.9) with the appropriate coefficients in Table 16.9 that correspond to the IEC 60751 standard

$$T = \frac{1}{2}\left[-\frac{3.9083\times10^{-3}}{-5.775\times10^{-7}} - \sqrt{\left(\frac{3.9083\times10^{-3}}{-5.775\times10^{-7}}\right)^2 - 4\left(\frac{100-180}{\left(-5.775\times10^{-7}\right)100}\right)}\right]$$

and T = 211.29 °C.

Thermistor

A thermistor is also a temperature-sensitive resistor. However, the thermistor differs from the RTD in one important feature – it is more sensitive to temperature changes. Over a narrow temperature range, the thermistor resistance can change as much as a few percent. Most thermistors are made from a semiconductor material that exhibits a negative temperature coefficient, that is, its resistance decreases with temperature.

Most thermistors are constructed as a ceramic bead with two lead wires (Figure 16.47). To protect it from environmental factors, a thermistor is encapsulated in epoxy or glass. A typical temperature-resistance relationship for a thermistor is shown in Figure 16.48. Note that for lower temperatures, the resistance change is greater for a given change in

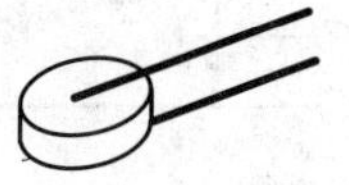

Figure 16.47. Typical thermistor construction.

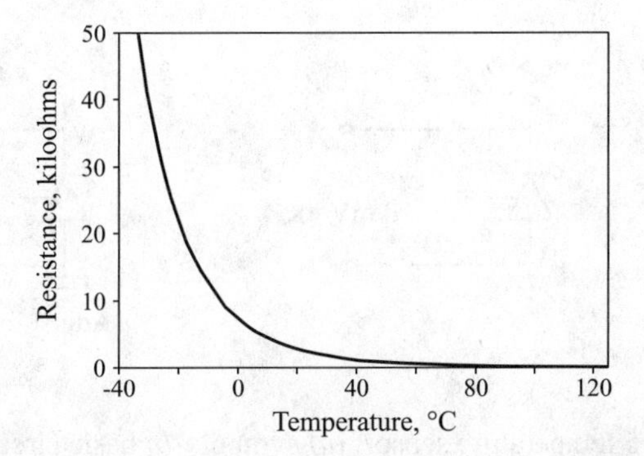

Figure 16.48. Typical thermistor resistance characteristic as a function of temperature.

temperature. The Steinhart-Hart equation is a common method of expressing the relationship between the resistance and temperature:

$$\frac{1}{T} = a + b(\ln R) + c(\ln R)^3$$

where a, b, and c are constants, R is the resistance in ohms, and T is the temperature in Kelvins (K = °C+273.15). The manufacturer specifies the Steinhart-Hart constants since thermistor curves have not been standardized to the same extent as for thermocouples and RTDs.

The circuits used to measure thermistor resistance are basically the same as for an RTD. However, compensation for lead resistance is generally not necessary since the lead resistance is very small compared to the thermistor resistance changes.

Integrated Circuit Temperature Sensor

Two temperature sensors that are integrated circuits are described here. The National Semiconductor LM335 device produces a voltage proportional to temperature and the Analog Devices AD590 produces a current proportional to temperature. Both devices are based on the property that the base-emitter voltage of a bipolar transistor is proportional to temperature. In contrast to the thermocouple and thermistor, the temperature range of the integrated circuit temperature sensors is limited to the range of -55 °C to 150 °C.

The LM335 temperature sensor (National Semiconductor, 2000) operates as a two-terminal zener diode with a breakdown voltage directly proportional to its absolute temperature. Figure 16.49*a* shows the symbol and connections to the device. The ADJ terminal is used to calibrate the sensor and increase the accuracy. The LM335 is used as a basic temperature sensor as shown in Figure 16.49*b*. If smaller error is desired, then the ADJ terminal is used as in Figure 16.49*c*. Depending on the device within the LM335 series, the uncalibrated device error can be as high as 9 °C. Calibration reduces this error to 1 °C. The R_1 resistor determines the bias current which must be within the range 0.4 to 5 mA. The bias current should be low to prevent self-heating errors.

The AD590 temperature sensor (Analog Devices, 2003) is a two-terminal device that produces an output current proportional to the absolute temperature. With a supply voltage between 4 to 30 volts, the device acts like a high-impedance constant current regulator producing 1 μA/K. Figure 16.50*a* shows the symbol and connections to the device. The

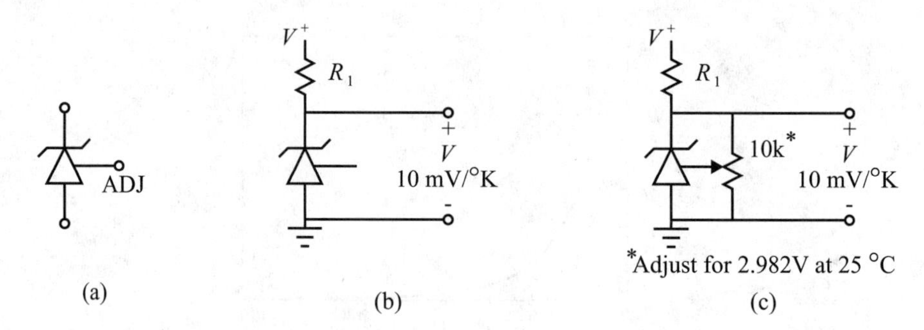

Figure 16.49. LM335 temperature sensor: *(a)* symbol; *(b)* basic circuit; *(c)* calibrated output.

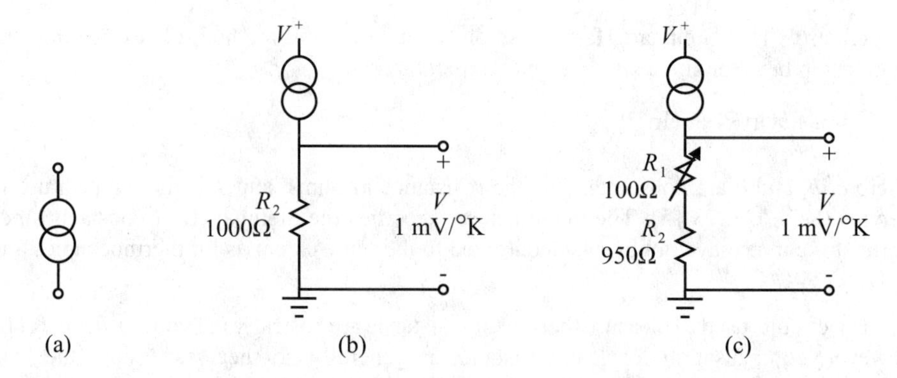

Figure 16.50. AD590 temperature sensor: *(a)* symbol; *(b)* basic circuit; *(c)* calibrated output.

AD590 is used as a basic temperature sensor as shown in Figure 16.50*b*. If smaller error is desired, then a variable resistor is added as in Figure 16.50*c*. The R_1 resistor is adjusted to produce the proper voltage at the output. Depending on the particular AD590 device, the uncalibrated device error ranges from 1.7 °C to 5.5 °C. Calibration reduces this error to 1.0 °C to 2.0 °C.

Noncontact Temperature Measurement

A pyrometer is a noncontact method of temperature measurement. It is commonly used when measuring the temperature of a target that is inaccessible or in a hostile environment. Common applications are measuring flame temperature or the temperature of a moving strip of hot metal. There are two basic types of noncontact temperature measurement devices. The first is infrared thermometers that measure the infrared radiation (wavelength 0.7 to 80 μm) emitted from the hot object. The second type, optical pyrometers, measure temperature in the visible light spectrum (wavelength 0.4 to 0.7 μm).

Both of these types of noncontact temperature measurement utilize the property that all materials having a temperature above absolute zero (-273 °C) emit radiant energy. Noncontact temperature measurement devices measure this radiant energy by comparing it to an ideal target, called a *blackbody*. A blackbody emits all of its energy. Emissivity is defined as the ratio between the actual energy emitted from a target and the energy emitted from a blackbody.

$$\text{Emissivity} = \frac{\text{Energy emitted from target}}{\text{Energy emitted from blackbody}}$$

Emissivity is dependent on both wavelength and temperature. So, in order to measure the temperature of an object, its emissivity must be known. However, for many materials, the emissivity changes rapidly as the target temperature changes. This phenomenon complicates the temperature measurement and is an inherent weakness in noncontact temperature measurement.

For a given application, physical factors other than the temperature of the target influence the measured radiation. These factors include: target material, target size, target distance, interfering gases, interfering film (for example, glass or plastic), and the ambient temperature. All noncontact thermometers measure all of the energy in their field of view within the specified spectral band. Additional reflected energy sources in the field of view are measured along with the target energy source.

A typical infrared thermometer is shown in Figure 16.51. Using infrared filters, an optical lens system focuses energy onto an infrared detector, which converts the energy to an electrical voltage. Fiber optics are typically used to separate the electronics from the application. Single-color infrared thermometers are the most common noncontact measurement device. These devices measure temperature within a narrow or wide segment of the infrared spectrum. Multicolor infrared thermometers measure the temperature at two or more segments of the infrared spectrum. If the emissivity values at the two segments are the same, the temperature can be accurately measured.

One of the major drawbacks to earlier infrared thermometers is that the operator must estimate the target emissivity in order to determine the target temperature. Recent instruments add a pulsed laser to a narrow bandwidth single-color infrared thermometer to determine the emissivity. The pulsed laser wavelength is within the same radiation bandwidth used to measure the target temperature. At the detector, the pulsed laser radiation (square wave) is superimposed on the relatively constant target radiation. With signal processing, the two components are separated and the pulsed laser radiation provides a measurement of the emissivity.

In a typical optical pyrometer (Figure 16.52), the unknown intensity of the light radiated from the hot target at 0.655 μm is compared with the brightness of the lamp filament. The temperature is determined by manually (or automatically) adjusting the lamp current until the brightness of the filament matches the brightness of the target (Figure 16.53). Optical pyrometers are better suited for manual operation or for applications that do not require fast sample rates.

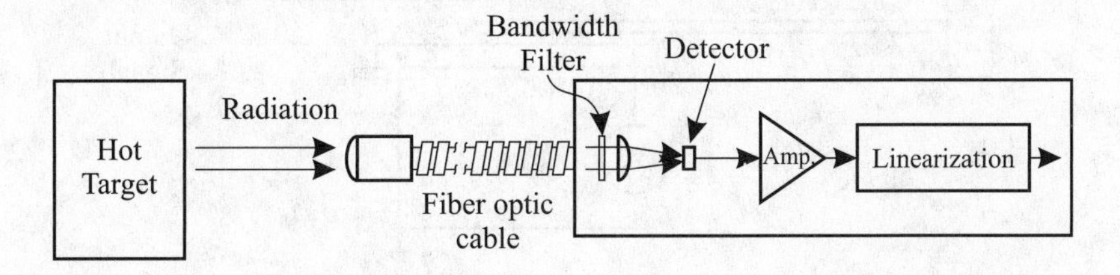

Figure 16.51. Infrared radiation detector.

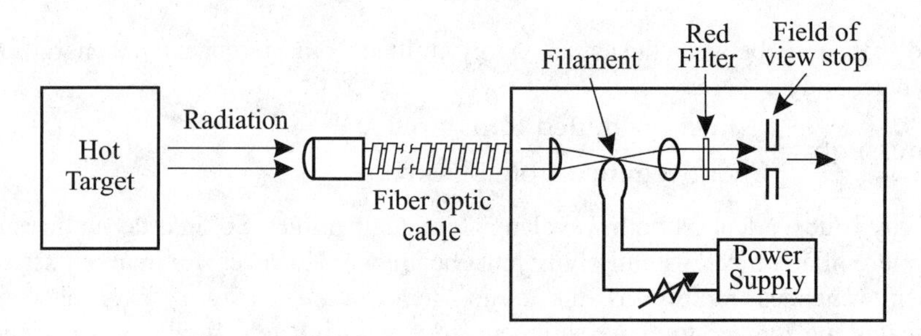

Figure 16.52. Optical pyrometer.

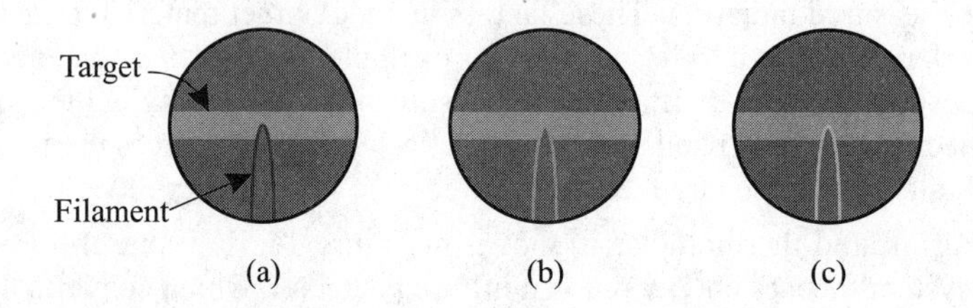

Figure 16.53. Disappearing-filament pyrometer: *(a)* filament cooler; *(b)* filament same temperature; *(c)* filament hotter.

16.3.3 Displacement Sensors

One of the easiest ways to measure linear displacement is with a potentiometer, as shown in Figure 16.54. It is relatively inexpensive, though less accurate than other ways to measure displacement. A rotary potentiometer can be used to measure rotary position.

A linear variable differential transformer (LVDT) is the most common method of measuring accurate linear position. As shown in Figure 16.55*a*, a LVDT is a transformer with two secondary windings and a moveable core. The two secondary windings are separated along the core and are connected in such a way that one secondary (secondary A) is in phase with the primary and the other secondary winding (secondary B) is out of phase with the primary. When the two secondary voltages are added and rectified, the output voltage, V, is proportional to the position of the moveable core. This relationship is shown in Figure 16.55*b*. When the core is in the middle position, the two secondary voltages exactly

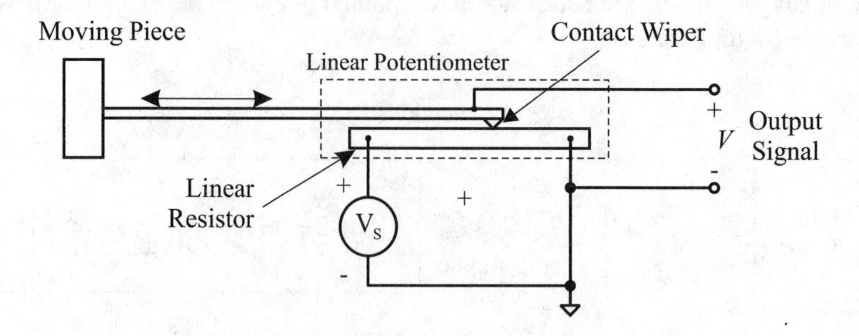

Figure 16.54. Linear potentiometer position sensor.

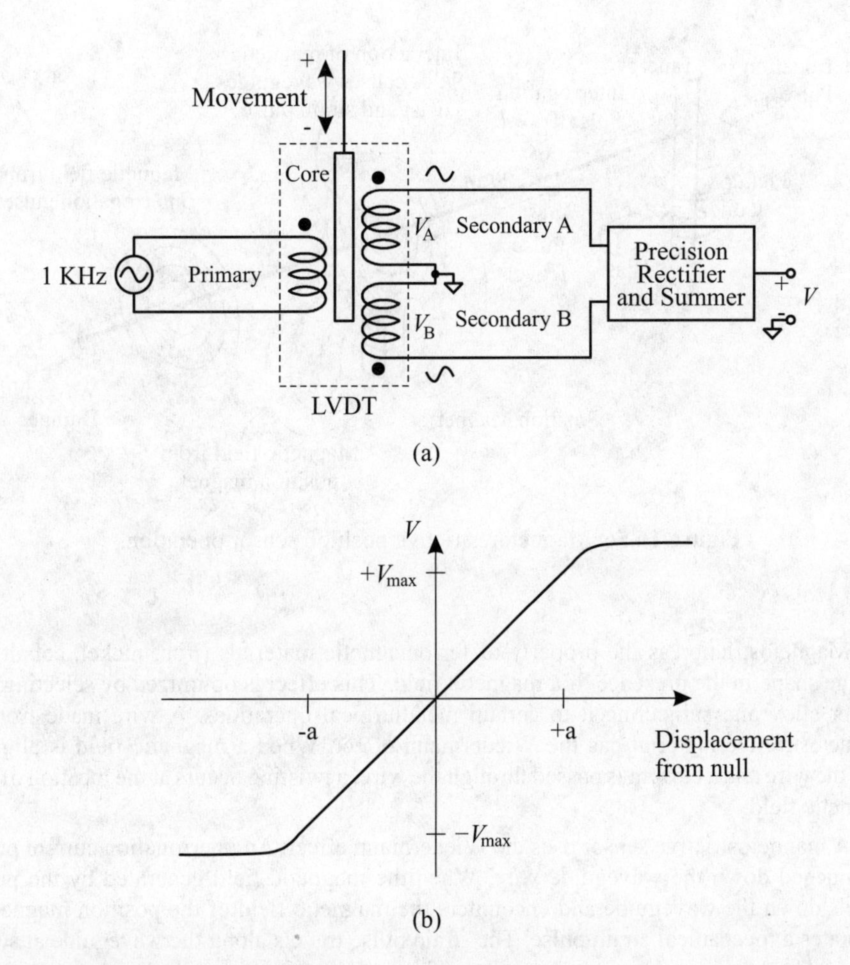

Figure 16.55. Linear variable differential transformer (LVDT): *(a)* general circuit; *(b)* output as function of position.

balance each other and the output voltage is zero. This position is also called the null position. When the core is moved up from the null (Figure 16.55*a*), the coupling between the primary and secondary A is stronger and thus the output voltage is positive. When the core is moved down from the null, the coupling between the primary and secondary B is stronger and thus the output voltage is negative. In reality, the linear relationship between the position and the output voltage is only valid over a certain range (Figure 16.55*b*).

The typical accuracy of a LVDT is 0.025%. Though generally used for small displacements (< 5 cm), stroke lengths of up to 60 cm are possible. For larger displacements, a LVDT is prohibitively expensive.

A magnetostrictive position sensor uses the interaction between a magnet and a waveguide to determine the position of the magnet. It is a noncontact method of measuring position, that is, the object being sensed does not contact the sensor. Figure 16.56 illustrates the operation of a magnetostrictive position sensor.

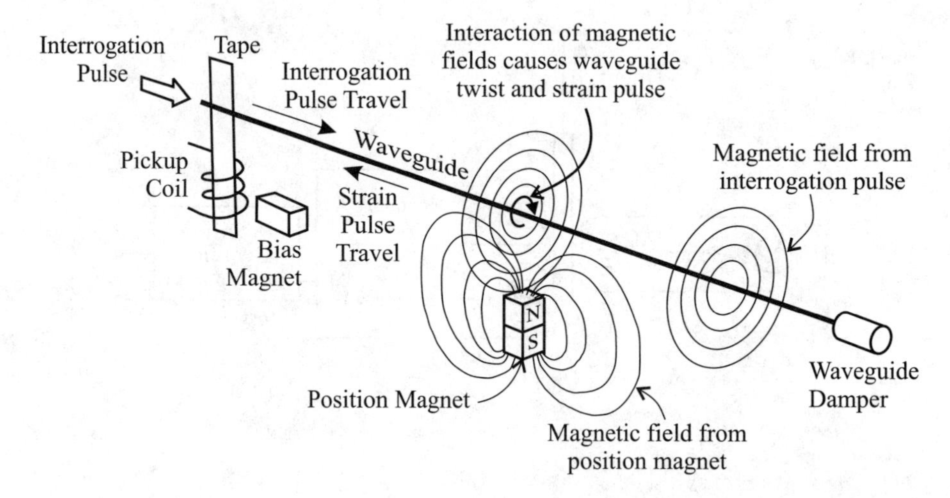

Figure 16.56. Magnetorestrictive position sensor operation.

Magnetostriction is the property of ferromagnetic materials (iron, nickel, cobalt) to change shape in the presence of a magnetic field. This effect is optimized by selecting the proper alloy and subjecting it to certain metallurgical operations. A wire made from a magnetostrictive material has the Wiedermann effect. When a magnetic field is aligned with the wire and a current is passed through the wire, a twisting occurs at the location of the magnetic field.

A magnetostrictive sensor uses the Wiedermann effect. An interrogation current pulse is launched down the waveguide wire. When the magnetic field generated by the pulse travels down the waveguide and encounters the magnetic field of the position magnet, it generates a mechanical strain pulse. The strain pulse travels along the waveguide at sonic speed. The strain pulse is sensed through the Villari effect: applying stress to a magnetostrictive material changes its magnetic permeability. A small piece of magnetostrictive material, called the tape, is welded to the waveguide at the same end that the interrogation pulse is generated. A pickup coil is wrapped around the tape and a biasing magnet is placed next to this coil. The sonic strain pulse from the waveguide passes down the tape, changing its magnetic permeability and inducing a pulse in the pickup coil. The elapsed time between the launch of the interrogation pulse and the arrival of the pulse at the pickup coil indicates the magnetic position. Since the strain pulse travels in both directions along the waveguide, it must be damped at the waveguide end opposite the pickup.

Ultrasonic transducers (Figure 16.11) are generally used when sensing long distances. The distance is the time difference between the transmitted and received "ping" divided by the velocity of sound in the medium (usually air).

Rotary encoders can also be used to measure linear position. In this case, there must be a mechanical mechanism to convert the linear motion into rotary motion.

16.3.4 Force Sensors

Force transducers are frequently used to measure weight. Strain gauges are the most common way to measure force along an axis. Strain gauges are based on the principle that

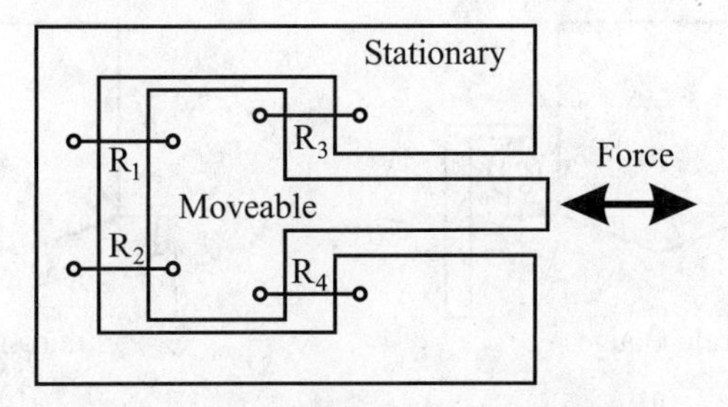

Figure 16.57. Unbonded strain gauge.

the resistance of a conductor changes as it is stretched. There are two types of strain gauges: unbonded and bonded.

An unbonded strain gauge is shown in Figure 16.57. The moveable part is attached to a stationary part with four wires, labeled $R_1 - R_4$. Actually, each "wire" consists of a length of wire wrapped around the pair of nonconductive posts multiple times in order to increase the resistance change. As the moveable part moves right or left, one pair of wires stretches (increasing the resistance) and the other pair contracts (decreasing the resistance). The resistance changes are converted to voltage change with a voltage sensitive bridge (Figure 16.30).

More commonly, force is measured with a bonded strain gauge (Figure 16.58*a*). The strain gauge is composed of wire or foil mounted on a flexible backing which is then bonded to the material whose strain is being measured. The tensile or compressive force along the material causes it to stretch or shrink. The strain gauge is subject to the same movement and

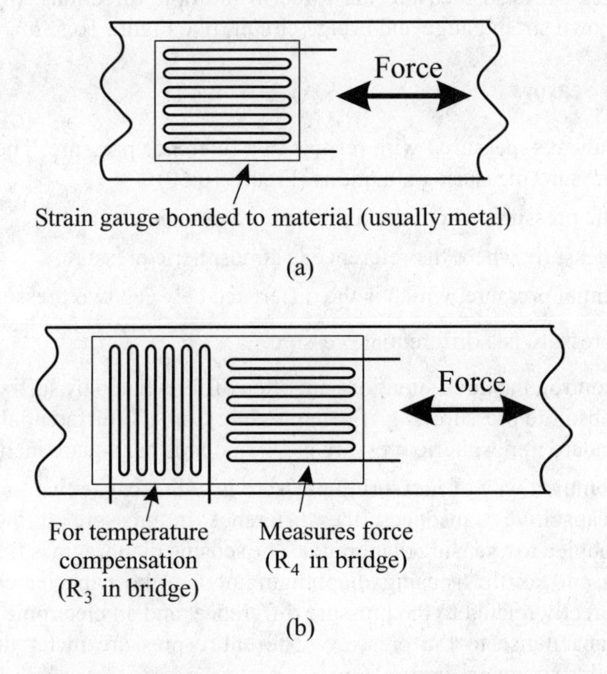

Figure 16.58. Bonded strain gauge: *(a)* element; *(b)* with temperature compensation.

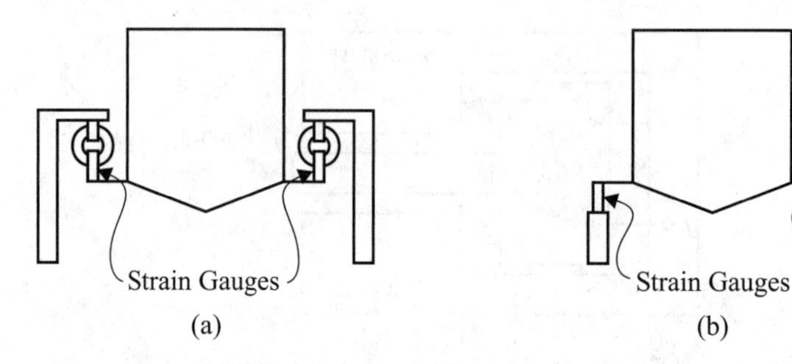

Figure 16.59. Vessel weight measurement with strain gauge: *(a)* tension; *(b)* compression.

stretches or shrinks along the axis of the wire path. This movement changes the resistance of the strain gauge. This resistance change is small, and so a Wheatstone bridge (Figure 16.30) converts the resistance change into a voltage change.

The strain gauge resistance is also dependent on the temperature, so to compensate for temperature changes, another strain gauge is mounted with its axis perpendicular to the force being measured. Since the foil of this strain gauge has very little material oriented in the direction of the measured force, its resistance is dependent on the temperature. This second strain gauge is connected as R_3 in Figure 16.30.

Strain gauges are commonly used to measure the weight of vessels, as shown in Figure 16.59. Though only two strain gauges are shown, the vessel will have three or four gauges measuring the weight. The sum of the weights is the weight of the vessel.

Strain gauges can also measure the force in multiple directions. In this case, each direction has its own strain gauge and bridge circuit, like Figure 16.58*b*.

16.3.5 Pressure Sensors

Pressure is always measured with respect to a reference pressure. There are basically three types of pressure-measuring situations (Figure 16.60):

1. Absolute pressure, where the reference is a complete vacuum.
2. Gage pressure, where the reference is atmospheric pressure.
3. Differential pressure, which is the difference between two pressures.

Note that gage pressure is a differential pressure.

In process control, the three situations are often differentiated by suffixing the pressure units with "a" (absolute pressure), "g" (gage pressure), or "d" (differential pressure). Also note that the standard atmospheric pressure is 14.7 pounds per square inch (psi).

The most common way of measuring pressure is with a capacitive transducer (Figure 16.61*a*). In a capacitive transducer, the difference in pressure at the two isolating diaphragms is coupled to a sensing diaphragm. The sensing diaphragm is fixed between two capacitor plates and as the sensing diaphragm moves, the capacitance changes. The capacitance is directly related to the pressure difference, and an electronic circuit converts the measured capacitance to the pressure. The entire pressure meter that contains the measurement cell is shown in Figure 16.61*b*.

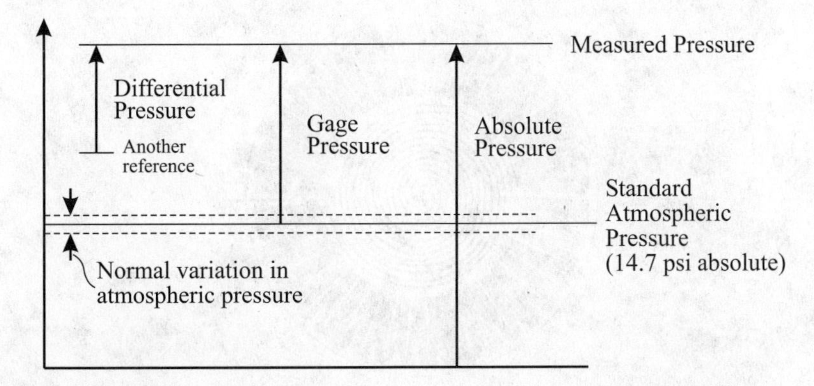

Figure 16.60. Relationship of absolute, gage, and differential pressures.

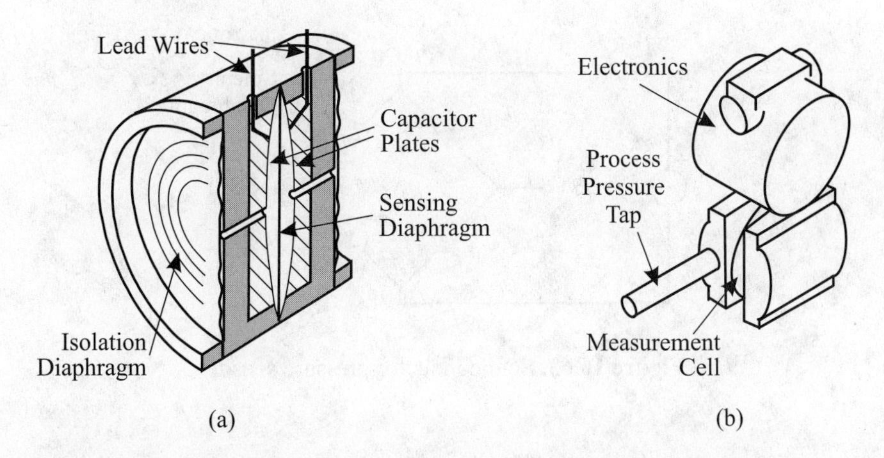

Figure 16.61. Capacitive pressure measurement: *(a)* measurement cell; *(b)* differential pressure meter.

Alternatively, a strain gauge can be bonded directly to the diaphragm (Figure 16.62) to measure pressure. The spiral foil in the center measures the tangential strain and the radial foil around the outside measures the radial strain. The measured force divided by the diaphragm area is the pressure.

Another method of measuring pressure involves a piezoresistive bridge mounted on a thin silicon diaphragm (Figure 16.63). Each of the bridge resistors is a resistor constructed from silicon. The bridge resistors are arranged so that when pressure is applied to the diaphragm, R_{P1} and R_{P2} increase in value and R_{V1} and R_{V2} decrease in value. These changes cause a millivolt output across the S+ and S- terminals.

Regardless of the particular method of measuring the pressure, one side of the diaphragm is coupled to the process fluid. How the other side of the diaphragm is handled determines the type of measurement. If a chamber on the other side of the diaphragm is completely evacuated, the sensor measures absolute pressure. If the other side of the

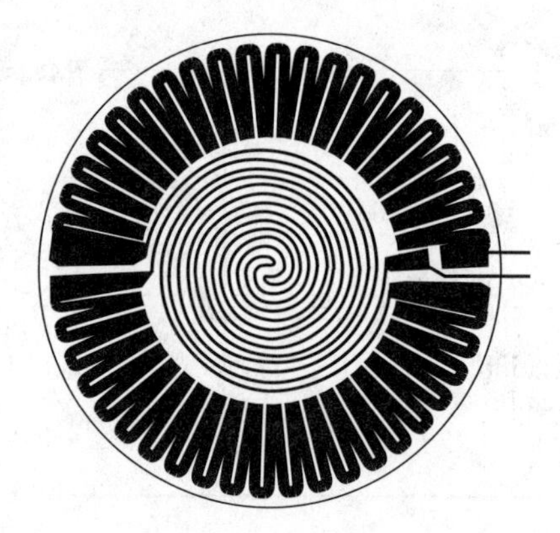

Figure 16.62. Pressure measurement with strain gauge on diaphragm.

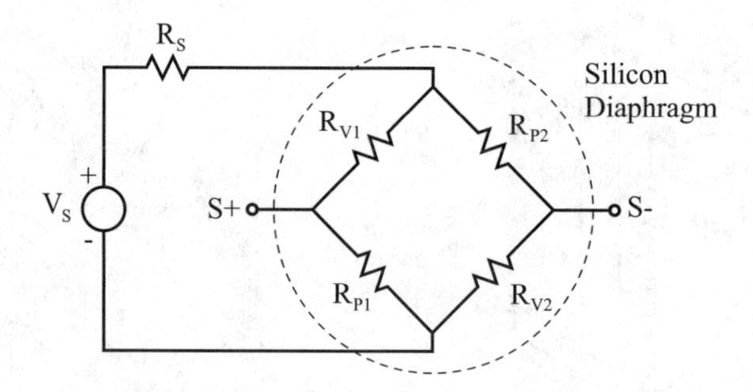

Figure 16.63. Semiconductor pressure sensor.

diaphragm is exposed to the atmosphere, the sensor measures gage pressure. A differential pressure sensor connects the other side of the diaphragm to the reference pressure.

16.3.6 Flow Sensors

There are many methods of measuring the flow of gases, liquids, and solids. Only the most common methods are described here. Gas and fluid flow is emphasized because of the larger variety of measuring methods.Table 16.10 compares common flow sensors.

Fluid and gas flow sensors can be categorized by the manner in which they measure flow:

1. *Flow sensors with wetted moving parts* (such as turbine meters). These sensors have precision-machined moving parts that are in the process stream. For this reason, they are generally only applicable to clean fluids.
2. *Flow sensors with no wetted moving parts* (such as orifice and vortex). The lack of moving parts is an advantage, though they are subject to excessive wear if measuring the flow of a very dirty or abrasive stream. These sensors require an obstruction that is inserted in the flow stream.

Table 16.10 Flow Sensor Comparison

Sensor Type	Accuracy[1]	Gas[3]	Liquids	Slurries[3]	Comments
Orifice Plate	3%	Y	Y	N	Clean liquids
Venturi Tube	3%	Y	Y	S	Clean liquids
Pitot Tube	4%	Y	Y	N	Air and water
Turbine	0.5% [2]	S	Y	N	Clean liquids
Magnetic	0.5% [2]	N	Y	Y	
Vortex	1% [2]	Y	Y	N	Clean liquids
Transit Ultrasonic	4%	S	Y	N	Clean liquids
Doppler Ultrasonic	4%	N	Y	S	Dirty liquids
Coriolis	0.4% [2]	S	Y	S	

Notes:
1. Percentage of full scale.
2. Percentage of flow rate.
3. Y=yes; N=no; S=sometimes, suitable under certain conditions.

3. *Flow sensors that do not obstruct the stream* (such as magnetic and Coriolis). These sensors are suitable for dirty and abrasive fluids. They are also suitable for very viscous fluids.
4. *Flow sensors mounted externally to the stream* (such as a clamp-on ultrasonic). These sensors do not come in contact with the stream, but because of their limitations, they are not used in many applications.

Fluid and gas flow sensors may also be categorized as to what they measure directly:

1. *Velocity*, such as turbine and orifice meters. The volumetric flow is determined by multiplying the velocity by the cross-section area.
2. *Volumetric*, such a positive-displacement meter. These types of meters are not discussed here.
3. *Mass*, such as Coriolis mass flow meters.

Differential Pressure Flowmeters

A very common method of measuring fluid or gas flow is to measure the pressure drop across an orifice plate or venturi tube inserted into the stream (Figure 16.64). The orifice plate or venturi tube is called the primary element and the differential pressure (DP) meter is called the secondary element.

The orifice plate (Figure 16.64*a*) is a flat piece of metal with a hole of a certain size bored in it. The hole is sharp-edged in order to obtain the sharpest drop in pressure. The orifice diameter is typically around one-half of the pipe diameter. The most common location for the two DP meter pressure taps are 25 mm to either side of the orifice plate. Another common location for the pressure taps, called vena contracta taps, are located one pipe diameter upstream and at the vena contracta (point of minimum pressure) 0.3 to 0.8 pipe diameters downstream of the orifice. Orifice plates are easy to install, have no moving parts, and application data is generally more extensive than for other differential pressure flow meters.

The venturi tube (Figure 16.64*b*) consists of a section of pipe with a conical entrance, a short straight throat, and a conical outlet. The DP meter taps are upstream of the inlet and at

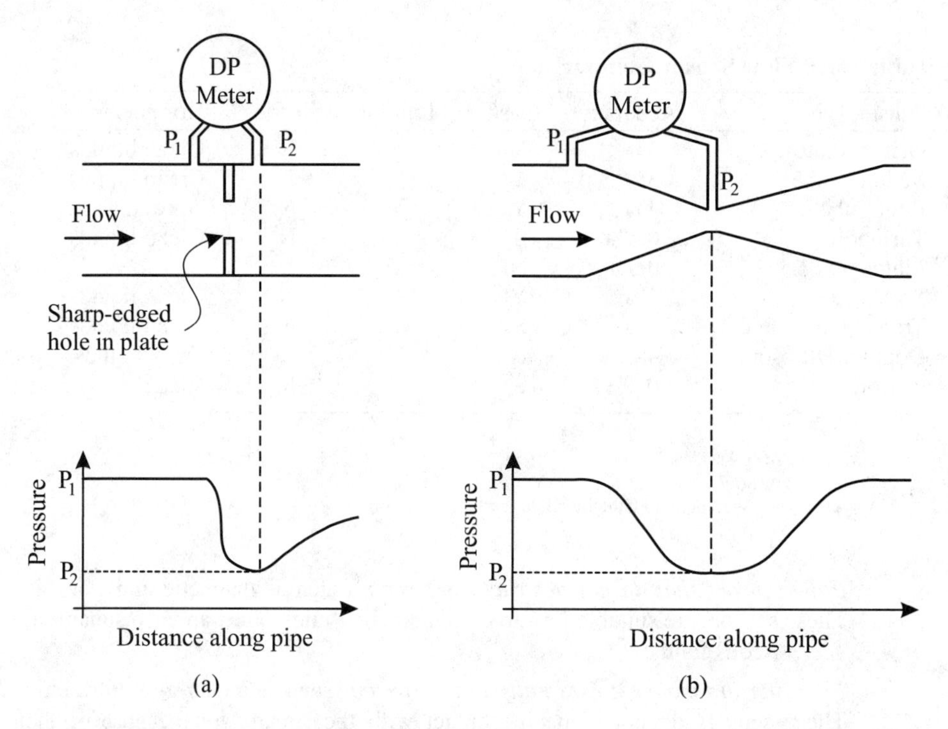

Figure 16.64. Flow measurement with differential pressure sensors: *(a)* orifice plate; *(b)* venturi tube.

the throat. A venturi tube will measure more flow than a comparable orifice plate, but is larger and more expensive than an orifice plate.

When measuring the flow through large air or gas ducts, a pitot tube (Figure 16.65) is used. The probe consists of two parts. The impact pressure is sensed with a tube bent toward the flow, and the static pressure is sensed by another closed tube with a hole in the side away from the flow. Since the velocity is not evenly distributed across the duct, a more accurate measurement of velocity is obtained with an averaging pitot tube. An averaging pitot tube

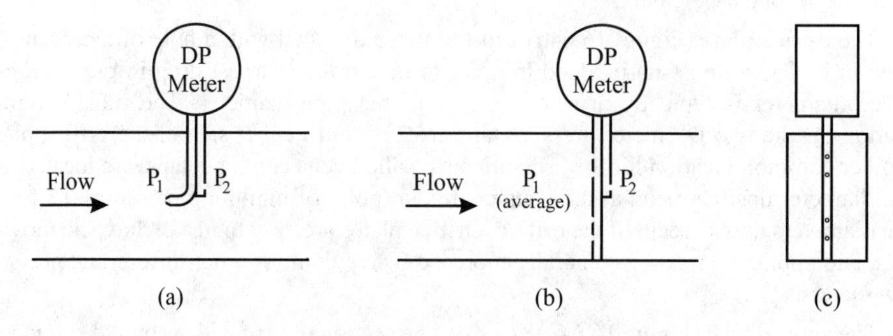

Figure 16.65. Flow measurement with pitot tube: *(a)* non averaging tube; *(b)* averaging tube; *(c)* end view of averaging tube.

has four or more impact pressure taps located at mathematically defined locations (Figure 16.65*b*).

One of the disadvantages of all differential pressure flow meters is their low accuracy (typically 3% of full scale) and low turndown ratio. The turndown ratio is the maximum flow rate divided by the minimum flow rate. The turndown ratio for differential flow meters is 4:1 at best.

For all of the differential pressure flow measurement techniques,

$$\text{Velocity of fluid (or gas)} = k\sqrt{\Delta P} = k\sqrt{P_2 - P_1}$$

The volumetric flow rate, Q, is thus

$$Q = \text{velocity} \times \text{area} = Ak\sqrt{\Delta P} = K\sqrt{\Delta P}$$

For this reason, square-root conversions are common in process control applications.

When measuring gas flow rates, temperature and pressure compensation is required if the temperature and pressures change from their original design values (Battikha, 1997). Liquids are incompressible, but will require temperature compensation for accurate measurements.

All differential pressure flow meters measure volumetric flow rate, that is, volume/time. For gases, the volumetric flow rate can be converted to mass flow rate using the ideal gas law:

$$PV = nRT$$

Converting to flow rates,

$$P\frac{dV}{dt} = \frac{dn}{dt}RT \tag{16.10}$$

where dV/dt is the volumetric flow rate, dn/dt is the mass flow rate, R is the gas constant, P is pressure and T is temperature. Using Q for the volumetric flow rate, equation (16.10) can be rearranged to calculate the mass flow rate, given the volumetric flow rate

$$\frac{dn}{dt} = \frac{P}{RT}Q \tag{16.11}$$

For liquids, one needs to know the liquid density, ρ, to calculate the mass flow rate from the volumetric flow rate

$$\frac{dn}{dt} = \rho Q \tag{16.12}$$

Turbine Flowmeters

A turbine flowmeter (Figure 16.66) has a rotor immersed in the liquid stream that turns as the fluid moves through it. A magnetic pickup mounted above the turbine senses the passage of each rotor blade, generating a pulse waveform. Since each pulse represents the passage of a certain amount of fluid, the volumetric flow rate is proportional to the frequency of the pulses. Pelton wheel and paddlewheel flow meters are similar to a turbine flow meter except that the rotor is only partially submerged in the flow stream.

Turbine flowmeters are good for low flow rates and are not sensitive to changes in fluid density. In addition, by counting the pulses, the amount of fluid passing through the turbine can be determined. However, they are not suitable for dirty or viscous fluids. In addition,

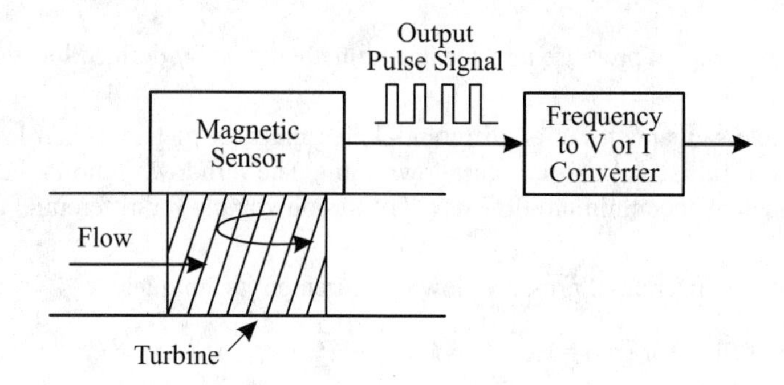

Figure 16.66. Turbine flowmeter.

they are affected by any entrained gas in the fluid. Because they have moving parts, turbine flowmeters are more susceptible to wear.

Magnetic Flowmeters

A magnetic flowmeter is based on Faraday's law. When a conductor is moved perpendicular through a magnetic field, a voltage is induced in the conductor that is proportional to the velocity of the conductor. In a magnetic flowmeter (Figure 16.67), the flow is perpendicular to a magnetic field. The voltage induced by the moving fluid is sensed by two electrodes that are aligned perpendicular to both the flow and the magnetic field. The voltage is proportional to the average velocity of the fluid. The fluid must be electrically conductive. However, the magnetic meter has no moving parts and is unaffected by changes in the fluid viscosity and pressure.

Vortex Flowmeters

In a vortex flowmeter (Figure 16.68) an obstruction, called a bluff body, is placed in the flow stream. This obstruction is a particular shape and sets up vortices in the flow stream. The frequency of the vortices is proportional to the volumetric flow rate. Vortex vibrations are often sensed by strain gauges, capacitive sensors, or magnetic pickups. The vibration frequency is then converted to a volumetric flow rate. The vortex flow meter is suitable for fluids that are not too viscous and that do not contain a significant amount of solids.

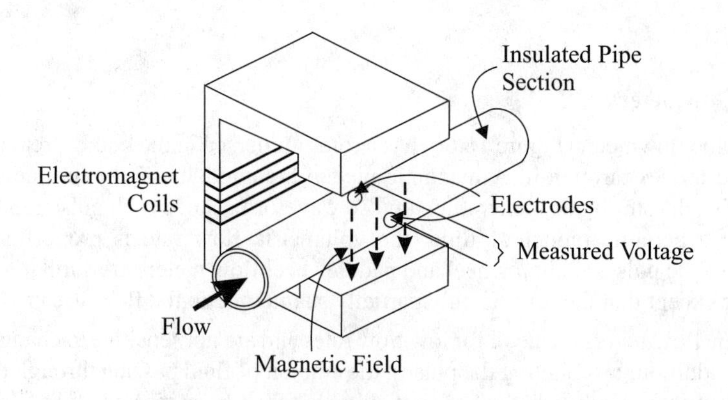

Figure 16.67. Magnetic flowmeter.

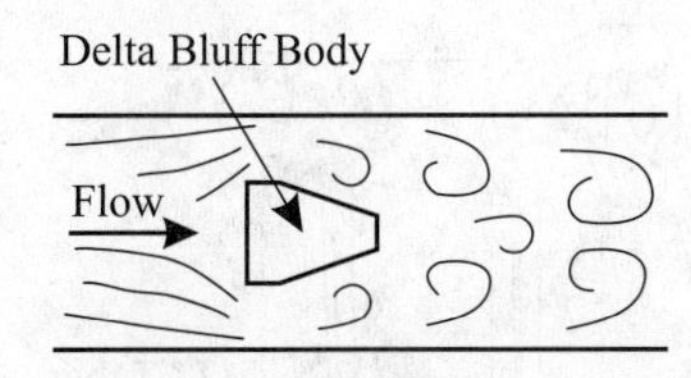

Figure 16.68. Vortex flowmeter.

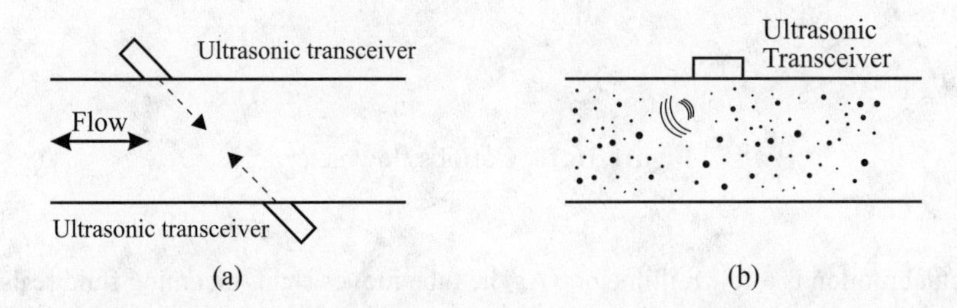

Figure 16.69. Ultrasonic flowmeters: *(a)* transit-time; *(b)* Doppler.

Ultrasonic Flowmeters

There are two types of ultrasonic flowmeters. Both the transit-time and Doppler ultrasonic flowmeters do not obstruct the flow and can measure flow in either direction. Both of them can be clamped to the outside of a pipe which is an advantage when adding a flowmeter to an existing application.

The transit-time flowmeter (Figure 16.69*a*) uses two ultrasonic transceivers placed at a 45 degree angle to the flow stream. Both send out ultrasonic pulses that are detected by the other. The difference in transit time between the two beams is proportional to the flow rate. The ultrasonic pulses that are traveling in the direction of the flow travel faster than the pulses that are traveling against the flow. This type of flowmeter cannot be used with porous pipes (such as cast iron or cement pipes).

The ultrasonic Doppler flowmeter (Figure 16.69*b*) transmits ultrasonic pulses into the flow stream. Bubbles and other foreign matter in the flow stream reflect the pulses which are received by the transceiver. The velocity of the particles change the frequency of the reflected pulses. This frequency shift is proportional to the flow rate. The reflected pulses are averaged to obtain an average flow rate. In order for this type of flowmeter to operate, the flow stream must have entrained gas or other particles.

Coriolis Flowmeter

The previous flowmeters measured either the stream velocity or volumetric flow rate. By also measuring the temperature (and pressure for gas streams), one can calculate the mass flow rate. The Coriolis flow meter measures the mass flow rate directly.

In its most common configuration, a Coriolis flowmeter consists of two U-shaped tubes through which the fluid flows (Figure 16.70). Note that the full flow of the fluid travels through the tubes. The "pipe" at the top of the flowmeter is for support. Figure 16.71 illustrates the operation of this flowmeter. Each tube is forced to oscillate at its natural frequency (on the order of 80 times a second). The motion in Figure 16.71*a* is exaggerated.

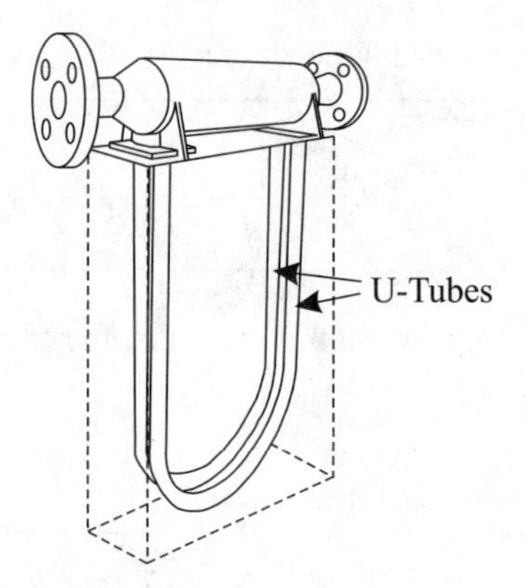

Figure 16.70. Coriolis flowmeter.

The actual motion is a few millimeters. As the tube moves right, incoming fluid resists by pushing left. Outgoing fluid pushes right because it resists being moved left and out. These forces set up a twist in the tube. When the tube moves left in the second half of the vibration cycle, the twist is in the opposite direction. This combination of forces that causes the tube twist is called the Coriolis effect. The mass flow is proportional to the maximum twist angle.

The Coriolis flow meter measures most streams, including viscous and abrasive streams. However, gas pockets in the stream affect the measurement. Since it measures mass flow rate directly and fairly accurately, the Coriolis flowmeter is becoming popular in blending applications. It is relatively costly, the only real reason its use is not more widespread.

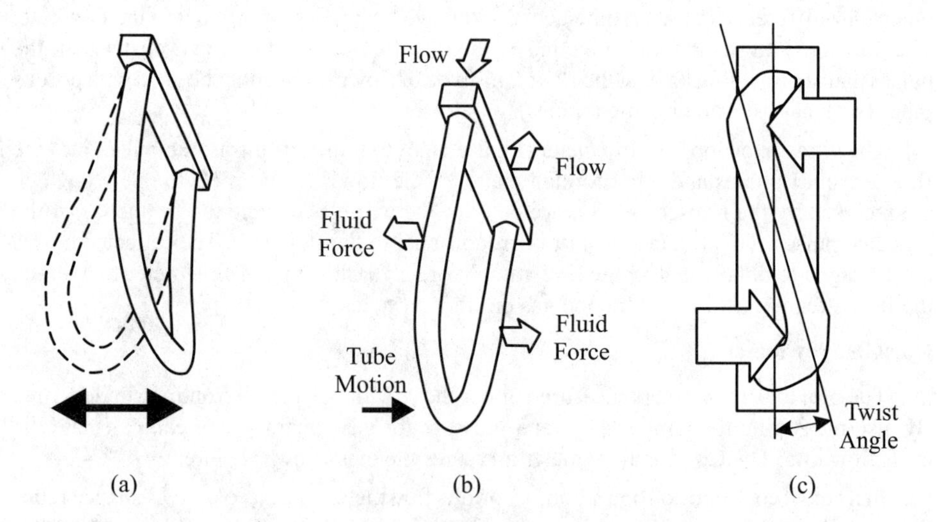

Figure 16.71. Coriolis flowmeter operation: (a) tube vibration; (b) forces on tube; (c) resultant tube twist.

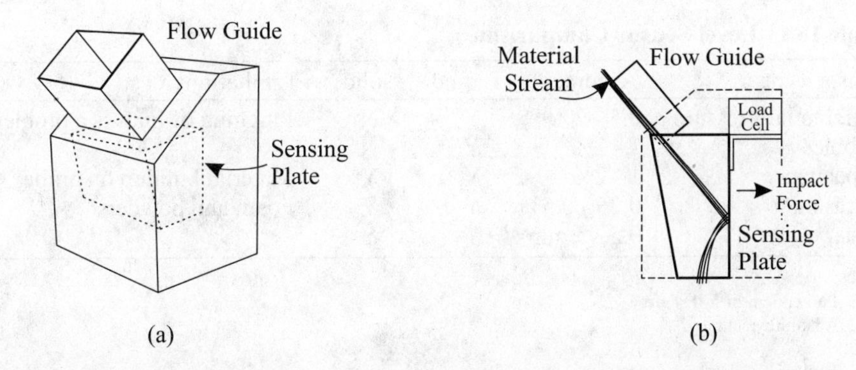

Figure 16.72. Dry solids flowmeter: *(a)* overall view; *(b)* principle of operation.

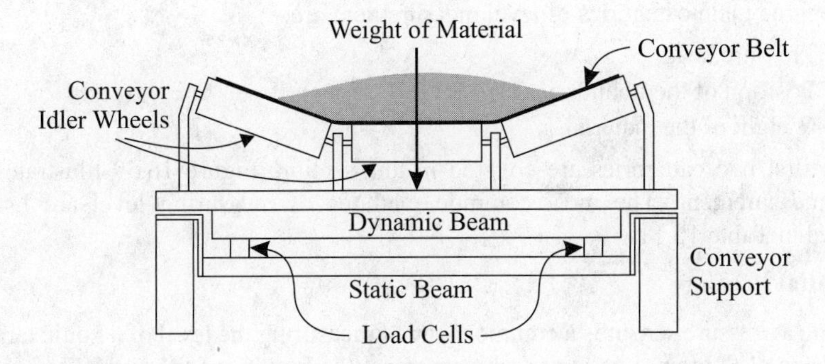

Figure 16.73. Conveyor belt scale for solid flow measurement.

Solid Flow

There are two common ways of measuring the flow of solid material. Figure 16.72 shows a flow sensor that measures material being gravity-fed. The material passes down a flow guide at a certain angle and then impinges on a sensing plate. The force on the sensing plate, measured by the load cell, is proportional to the flow rate.

When the material is being conveyed on a belt, an easy method of measuring the material flow is to place a weigh scale below one of the idler assemblies (Figure 16.73). In this case, the weight on the idler wheels is transferred to a dynamic beam. Strain-gauge load cells between the dynamic beam and the static beam measure the weight. The weigh scale is calibrated to "factor out" the belt weight, so the weight is zero when the belt contains no material. Multiplying the weight by the belt speed (sensed by an encoder mounted on an idler wheel) calculates the solid flow rate.

16.3.7 Level Sensors

Level measurements are key indicators of material inventory within a system. Technically, level sensors are used to measure the position of the boundary between two materials. Commonly, the interface is between air and a solid or between air and a liquid.

Table 16.11 Level Sensor Comparison

Sensor Type	Accuracy[1]	Liquid	Solid	Limitations
Differential Pressure	0.5 - 2%	Y	N	Plugging of lines is a problem
Bubbler	1 - 2%	Y	N	
Capacitance	1 - 2%	Y	Y	Material buildup on probe
Ultrasonic	0.25 - 0.5%	Y	Y	Foam and powders
Radar	0.5 - 5 mm[2]	Y	Y	

Notes:
1. Percentage of full scale.
2. Absolute accuracy.

However, there are some applications where the interface between two liquids (for example, water and oil) is of interest.

The three main categories of level measurement are:

1. Pressure head
2. Position of the boundary
3. Weight of the material

The first two categories are covered in this section. Figure 16.59 illustrates vessel weight measurement. The most common methods of measuring level are listed and compared in Table 16.11.

Differential Pressure

Using a pressure sensor is a common way of measuring the level of a liquid tank. If the tank is open at the top, a gage pressure sensor at the bottom of the tank (Figure 16.74*a*) measures the *hydrostatic* head, the pressure exerted by the fluid. If the tank is closed, then the differential pressure relative to the pressure of the atmosphere on top of the liquid must be used (Figure 16.74*b*). The pressure divided by the density is the height, though the pressure transmitter can be calibrated to produce an output in height units. Since it is usually difficult to perfectly align the sensor element with the tank bottom, the zero point of the pressure transmitter is often adjusted in order to measure the height of the fluid relative to the tank bottom.

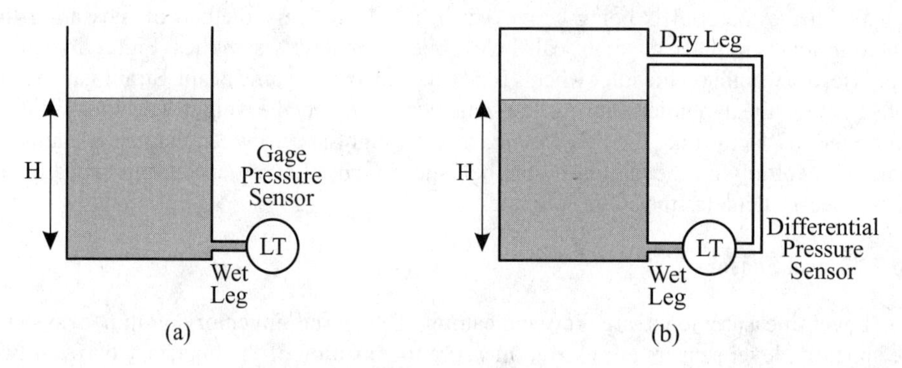

Figure 16.74. Liquid level measurement with pressure sensor: *(a)* open tank; *(b)* closed tank.

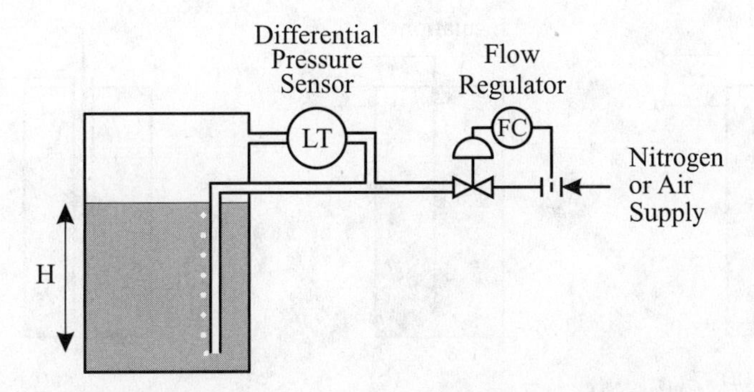

Figure 16.75. Liquid level measurement with bubbler tube.

This type of level measurement is easy to install and has a wide range of measurement. The pressure sensor diaphragm material must be compatible with the fluid in the tank. Also, small diameter piping between the pressure meter and the tank is susceptible to plugging. This type of level measurement assumes the fluid density remains constant.

Bubbler Tube

When the fluid in the tank is highly corrosive, an alternate method of measuring liquid height involves a bubbler tube. In this method (Figure 16.75), a small amount of air or inert gas is forced through a tube that extends nearly to the bottom of the tank. The end of the tube is notched to produce uniform small bubbles. The pressure required to force air bubbles from the bottom of the tube is the hydrostatic pressure exerted by the fluid level. A flow controller provides a constant air flow (5 to 50 m^3/hr.) to the bubbler tube. The pressure of the air supply should be at least 10 psi greater than the maximum hydrostatic pressure when the tank is full.

Overall, this scheme costs more than a simple differential pressure meter. If an inert gas is required, then it must be provided. The additional flow controller adds to the cost. In some cases, a pressure regulator must be added to the air supply to the flow controller to provide smoother level measurements.

Capacitance

A capacitance level probe measures the electrical capacitance between the probe and the vessel wall (Figure 16.76). This capacitance varies as the tank level varies. Capacitance level probes are often called RF probes due to their use of radio-frequency signals (a few MHz) to measure the capacitance. Capacitance probes can be used for both liquids and solids. There are three basic configurations. If the tank is metal and the tank contents are non-conductive, the probe consists of a metal rod (Figure 16.76*a*). In this case, the rod and the tank wall are the capacitor plates and the material in the tank is the dielectric. If the tank contents are conductive, then the probe is insulated (Figure 16.76*b*). In this case, the probe and the tank contents are the capacitor plates and the insulation is the dielectric. If the tank is an irregular shape (not a vertical cylinder) or constructed of plastic, the probe consists of a rod surrounded by a cylinder (Figure 16.76*c*). The outer cylinder serves as the other capacitor plate. This configuration has the advantage that the probe electronics can be calibrated before the probe is placed inside the tank.

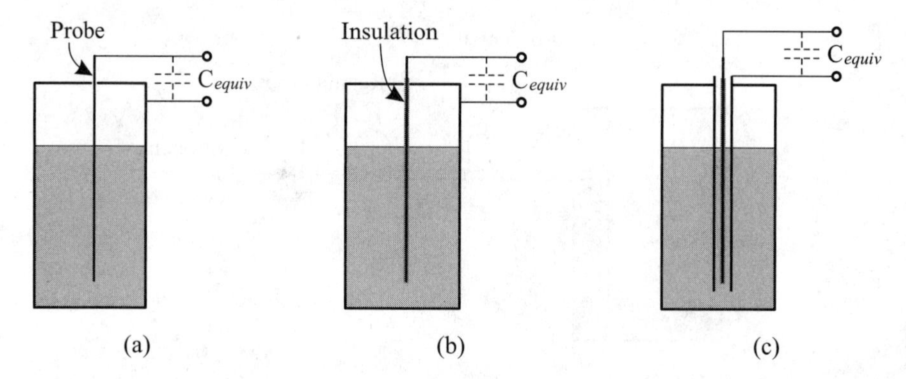

Figure 16.76. Capacitance level measurement: *(a)* non-conductive material; *(b)* conductive material; *(c)* nonmetallic tank.

Capacitance probes are relatively easy to install though calibration may be time consuming. The buildup of conductive material on the outside surface of the insulated probe has the most detrimental effect on the accuracy of a capacitance level sensor. Materials that produce conductive coatings include latex, carbon black, and fine metal powders.

Ultrasonic

Ultrasonic level sensors use sound waves to detect an object. The basic principle is to emit a "pulse" of a frequency slightly above the normal range of audible sound and then measure the time for the pulse to be detected by the receiver. The sensor usually combines the transmitter and receiver in one piezo-electric element. The operation of ultrasonic level sensor is shown in Figure 16.77. The wave pulse is generated by the piezo-electric element and then the element is switched to its receiving mode. The wave is reflected by the object and then detected by the element. The drawback to this approach is that there is a minimum sensing distance. The trailing edge of the pulse must leave the transducer before the leading edge of the reflected pulse can be detected. Note that with the sensor configuration in Figure 16.77, the distance measured is the air space over the material. The distance must be subtracted from the tank height to obtain the material height. Many sensors are calibrated to

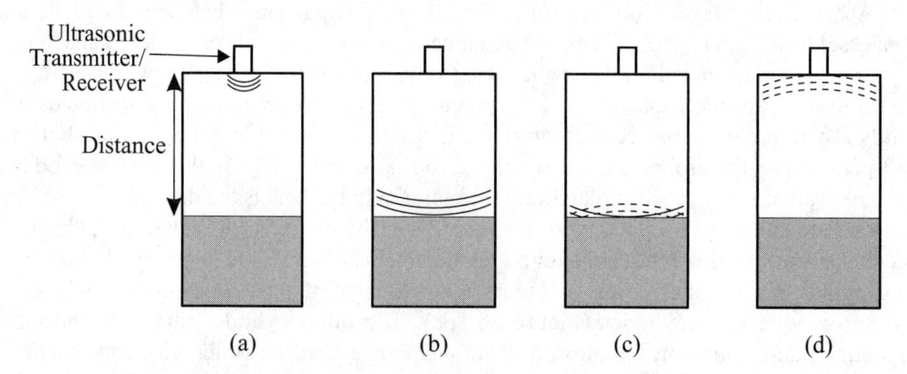

Figure 16.77. Ultrasonic level measurement: *(a)* wave launched; *(b)* wave impinges surface; *(c)* wave reflected; *(d)* wave impinges receiver.

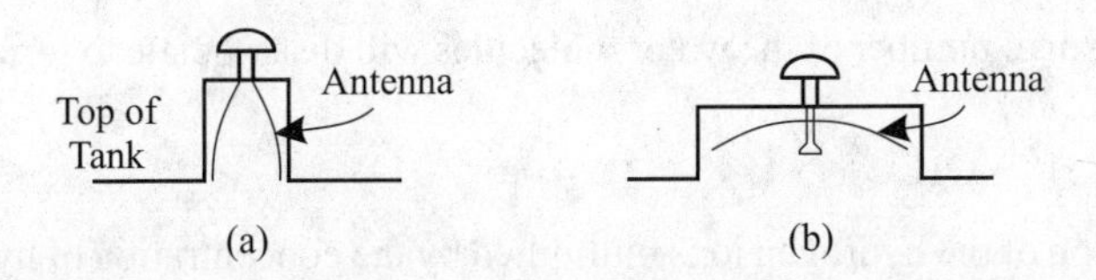

Figure 16.78. Radar level sensors: *(a)* horn antenna; *(b)* parabolic antenna.

do this conversion automatically. The sensor can be mounted at the bottom of the tank, but this configuration exposes the sensor to the material.

Because ultrasonic sensors depend on receiving a reflected sound wave for proper operation, the material top surface should be a good reflector of sound waves. Preferably, the material should have a smooth and flat surface, that is, liquid. However, most solid materials are fine, but at a reduced maximum sensing distance. This type of sensor has problems when the liquid has foam on top or the solid is powdery. Also, since the speed of sound is dependent on temperature, an accurate measurement requires temperature compensation.

Radar

Radar level sensors are similar in operation to ultrasonic level sensors except that the frequency is typically around 10 GHz. Radar level sensors either "pulse" the wave or frequency-modulate a continuous wave. The operation of the "pulse" type radar sensor is similar to the ultrasonic level sensors described previously. The continuous wave radar sensor sends out a frequency modulated signal, usually in successive linear ramps. The frequency difference between the transmitted and received signals indicates the distance. Radar level sensors are mounted on top of the tank and measure the distance of the air space over the material. Sample radar transmitter/receiver antennas are shown in Figure 16.78.

As for the ultrasonic sensors, the reflective properties of the material surface affect the strength of the received radar signal. Liquids are good reflectors and solids are not good reflectors. In contrast to ultrasonic level sensors, radar can detect the liquid level beneath airy foam or dust. However, if the foam or dust is thick, its level will be detected instead of the underlying liquid. Compared with ultrasonic level sensors, the composition of the air space does not affect the performance of radar sensors. However, ultrasonic sensors work better in dirty applications or with solids whose grain size is greater than 20 mm.

16.3.8 Chemical Sensors

Chemical sensors measure some chemical property aspect of a process control material. The three most common chemical measurements are pH, oxidation-reduction potential (ORP), and conductivity. All three of these types of measurements are briefly described in this section.

pH

pH is a measure of the acidity or alkalinity of a water solution. The relative number of hydrogen (H^+) and hydroxide (OH^-) ions determines the acidity or alkalinity of a water solution. If the number of hydrogen ions is higher, the solution is acidic. If the number of hydroxide ions is higher, the solution is alkaline (also called basic). If the number of hydrogen and hydroxide ions is the same, the solution is neutral. In any water-based solution a very small number of the water molecules will disassociate to form hydrogen and hydroxide ions:

$$H_2O = H^+ + OH^-$$

The concentration of the hydrogen ions multiplied by the concentration of hydroxide ions is a constant. Expressed as an equation,

$$K_W = [H^+]\,[OH^-]$$

where the brackets signify molar concentration and K_W is the dissociation constant for water. The value of K_W is dependent on temperature and is 1.00×10^{-14} at 25 °C. In its strict definition, pH is the negative logarithm of the hydrogen ion activity. In practice, the pH is another way of expressing the hydrogen ion concentration, defined as

$$pH = -\log[H^+] \tag{16.13}$$

For example, if the hydrogen ion concentration is 1.00×10^{-5} moles/liter, the pH is 5.00. A neutral solution has a pH of 7.0, if the temperature is 25 °C. An acidic solution has a pH greater than 0.0 and less than 7.0. A smaller pH value indicates a stronger acid. A basic solution has a pH greater than 7.0 and less than 14.0. A larger pH value indicates a stronger base.

Using equation (16.13) as a basis for measuring pH means that one measures the hydrogen ion concentration over 15 decades, which is not practical. Instead, the measurement of pH is based on the use of a pH-sensitive electrode, a reference electrode, and a temperature sensor.

A simplified pH measurement cell is shown in Figure 16.79. The potential difference is measured between the pH-sensitive electrode (called the measuring electrode) and the reference electrode. The temperature sensor, usually an RTD or thermistor, is used for temperature compensation. The measuring electrode, the reference electrode, and the temperature sensor are often packaged together, as shown in Figure 16.80. The measuring electrode and the reference electrode are both electrochemical half-cells. The measuring electrode consists of a silver wire coated with silver chloride immersed in a chloride solution of fixed concentration and thus fixed pH. The chloride solution is contained in a bulb of pH-sensitive glass that allows hydrogen ions to diffuse into the chloride solution.

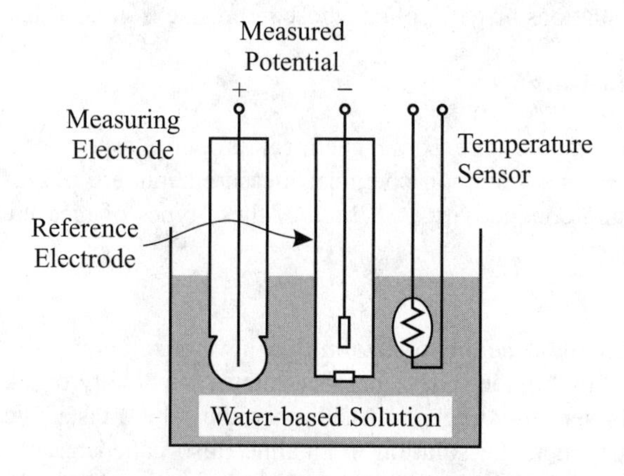

Figure 16.79. Simplified pH measurement cell.

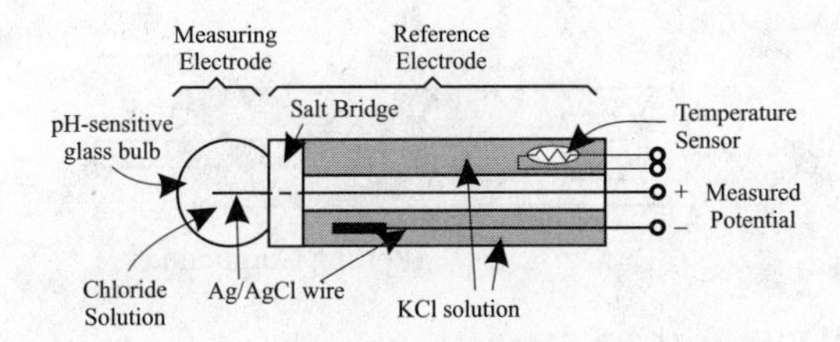

Figure 16.80. Combination pH probe construction.

Electric potentials are developed at the interfaces between the wire and the filling solution, the filling solution and the glass, and the glass and the liquid whose pH is being measured. The potential developed on the outside of the bulb depends on the pH of the test liquid. Since the other two potentials are fixed, the overall potential developed by the measuring electrode half-cell is dependent on the test liquid pH. The reference electrode consists of a silver wire coated with silver chloride immersed in a potassium chloride solution within a glass tube. For most industrial pH probes, the reference solution is a gel. The salt bridge consists of a porous material and it provides the electrical contact between the liquid whose pH is being measured and the reference electrode. Electric potentials are developed at the interfaces between the wire and the potassium chloride solution and across the salt bridge. The electric potentials of both of these interfaces are constant and hence the potential developed by the reference half-cell is constant.

Although the value of pH can range from 0 to 14, solutions whose pH is near either end of the range are better measured with a conductivity sensor (Rosemount Analytical, 2001). Solutions with high pH (>13) quickly destroy glass probes. Since the salt bridge allows ion exchange between the reference cell and the measured liquid, certain chemicals, such as bisulfites and ammonia, can poison the reference cell. Multiple junction reference electrodes can counteract this effect. Undissolved solids in the measured liquid can plug the salt bridge or coat the sensor. In this case, on-line or manual cleaning may be needed.

Oxidation-Reduction Potential (ORP)

In certain applications, the oxidizing or reducing nature of a chemical is of importance. In drinking water and wastewater treatment, the oxidizing or reducing nature of water measures the ability of the water to support (or not support) life. In a metal plating application, the oxidation-reduction potential measures the metal depletion in the plating bath.

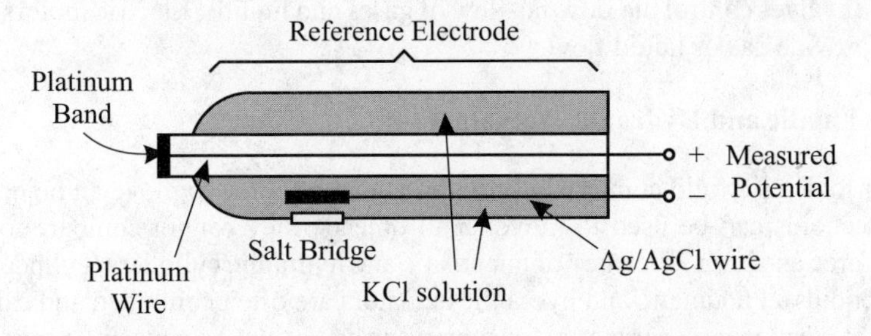

Figure 16.81. Combination ORP probe construction.

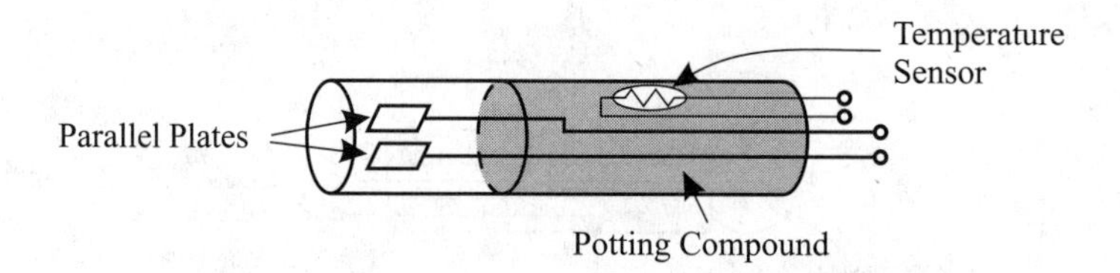

Figure 16.82. Conductivity probe construction.

An oxidation-reduction potential (ORP) sensor measures the ratio of concentrations of oxidized and reduced substances. An ORP measurement sensor is an electrochemical cell similar to a pH sensor; the basic difference is the measurement electrode (Figure 16.81). The measurement electrode consists of a band or disk of a noble metal (usually platinum or gold) attached to the base of a sealed glass tube. A wire of the same metal is welded to the band to provide a connection to the electrode lead. The glass tube is not filled. The cell voltage is the ORP of the measured solution.

Conductivity

Conductivity is the ability of a solution to conduct an electric current between two electrodes. The current between the two probes is conducted by ions in the solution. When the solution has a larger number of ions, the conductivity is higher. The electric current is an alternating current to prevent complete ion migration to the two electrodes. Conductivity is the reciprocal of resistivity and is usually measured in a unit of measurement called the "Siemen/cm", abbreviated as "S." For many solutions, the conductivity is in the range of μS or mS.

An example conductivity probe is shown in Figure 16.82. The electrodes are insulated by the potting compound and the surface and spacing of the electrodes determines the cell constant. A cell constant of 1.0 implies two electrodes spaced one centimeter apart with each electrode one square centimeter in area. Since the conductivity of common solutions varies as much as 1-3% per °C, a temperature sensor must be included to provide accurate conductivity measurements.

16.4 DISCRETE ACTUATORS

Discrete actuators convert the on/off PLC output signals into physical phenomena. Cylinders, motors, and valves are described in this section. In mechanical systems, the physical phenomenon is most often motion. Cylinders provide linear or rotary motion. Electric motors also control rotary or linear motion. Only rotating motors are described here. On/off valves control the flow/no-flow of gases and liquids. Electric motors also drive pumps to provide gas or liquid flow.

16.4.1 Pneumatic and Hydraulic Actuators

Air or hydraulic fluid commonly provides actuation force to move an object. Though electric solenoids can be used to move small objects, they cannot compare to the large actuation force and high efficiency of pneumatic and hydraulic cylinders (cylinders are also called solenoids). Pneumatic and hydraulic actuators are often combined and called "fluid power." This section concentrates on pneumatic systems, but the concepts apply equally to hydraulic systems. In general, pneumatic actuators are for low force applications and

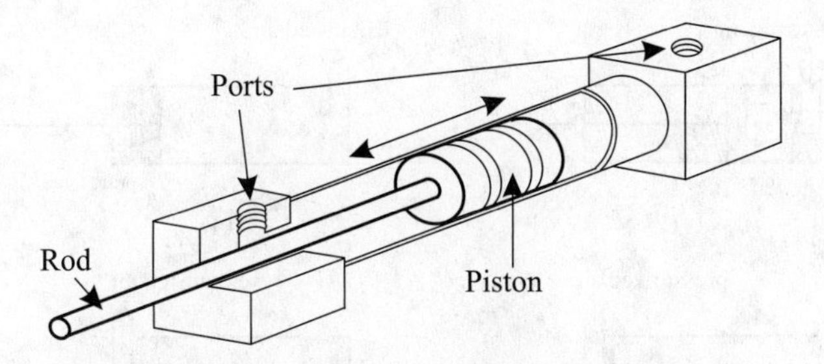

Figure 16.83. Typical linear cylinder construction.

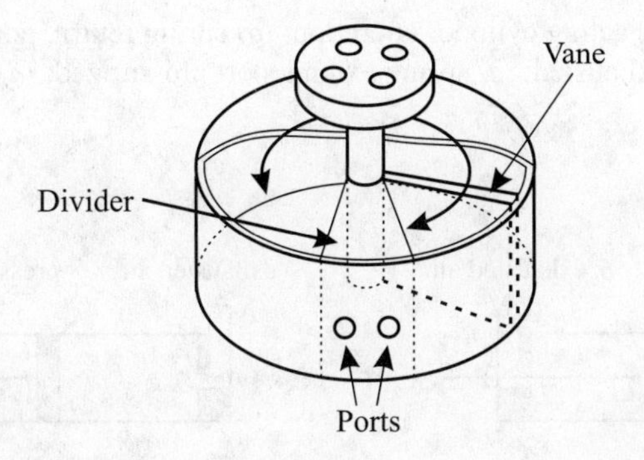

Figure 16.84. Typical rotary cylinder construction.

hydraulic actuators are for high force applications. Since the actuation force is pressure times the cylinder area, larger cylinders are needed for larger actuation force.

There are two major components in a fluid power actuator: a cylinder and a control valve. The cylinder provides the actuation movement and the control valve directs the flow of air or hydraulic fluid to the cylinder. The major categories of cylinders are discussed first, followed by the types of control valves.

Cylinders are classified in two ways: (1) linear vs. rotary, and (2) the number of control ports. A linear cylinder provides straight-line motion and a rotary cylinder provides rotational motion. A typical linear cylinder is shown in Figure 16.83. A piston slides within a metal cylinder and is attached to a rod. Pressurized air (or hydraulic fluid) is admitted to a port to move the piston and hence the rod. Unfortunately, the piston is free to twist. So-called nonrotating cylinders have a square or hexagonal rod. A rotary cylinder (Figure 16.84) consists of a vane attached to a shaft that is free to rotate within a wide, short cylinder. Pressurized air enters one of the two ports to move the vane in either the clockwise or counterclockwise direction. Because of the placement of the two ports and the divider, the maximum rotation is about 270°.

Cylinders are also classified as to whether they have one control port (single-acting) or two control ports (double-acting). When pressure is applied to the port of a single-acting spring-return cylinder (Figure 16.85*a*), the piston moves right, extending the rod and compressing the spring. When the port is exhausted to the atmosphere (Figure 16.85*b*), the spring forces the piston to the left, retracting the rod. When pressure is applied to the port of

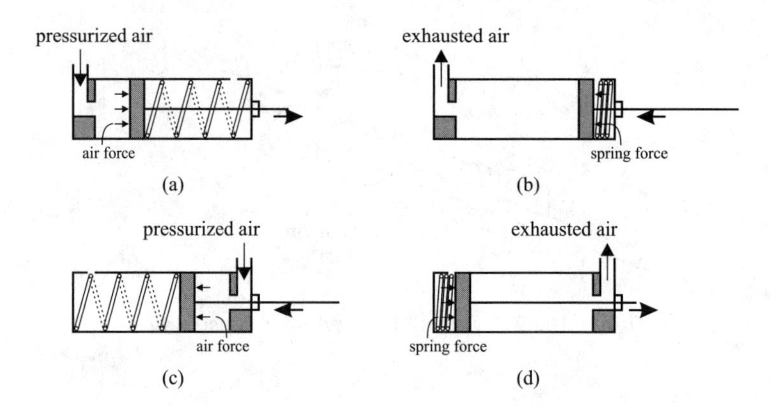

Figure 16.85. Single acting cylinder operation: *(a)* spring return, port pressurized; *(b)* spring return, port exhausted; *(c)* spring extend, port pressurized; *(d)* spring extend, port exhausted.

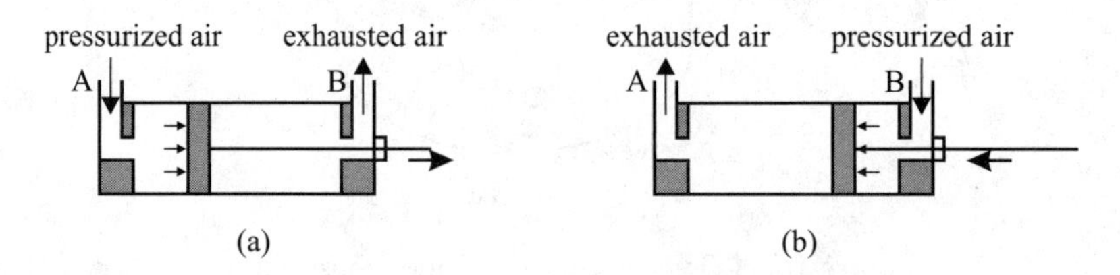

Figure 16.86. Double acting cylinder operation: *(a)* port A pressurized and port B exhausted; *(b)* port A exhausted and port B pressurized.

a single-acting spring extend cylinder (Figure 16.85*c*), the piston moves left, retracting the rod and compressing the spring. When the port is exhausted (Figure 16.85*d*), the spring causes the piston to move right and extend the rod. Note that the spring defines the default position of the cylinder. A double-acting cylinder (Figure 16.86) has two control ports, labeled A and B. When port A is pressurized and port B is exhausted, the piston moves right. If port A is exhausted and port B is pressurized, the piston moves left. Rotary cylinders are almost always double-acting due to the complications in mounting a spring. In this case, if one port is pressurized and the other is exhausted, the shaft moves clockwise. If the port connections are reversed, the shaft moves counterclockwise.

A double-acting cylinder opens up other control possibilities. Ports A and B can both be exhausted (freeing the piston), both pressurized, or both closed. The latter two possibilities allow the piston to be held at an intermediate position, allowing position control. In addition, the piston extension and retraction velocities can be controlled with separate speed control valves.

A single-acting cylinder with spring return/retract will not impart as much actuating force since a portion of the force required to move the piston must overcome the opposing spring force. The control valves for single-acting cylinders are simpler. However, control valves for double-acting cylinders can also be used for single action cylinders.

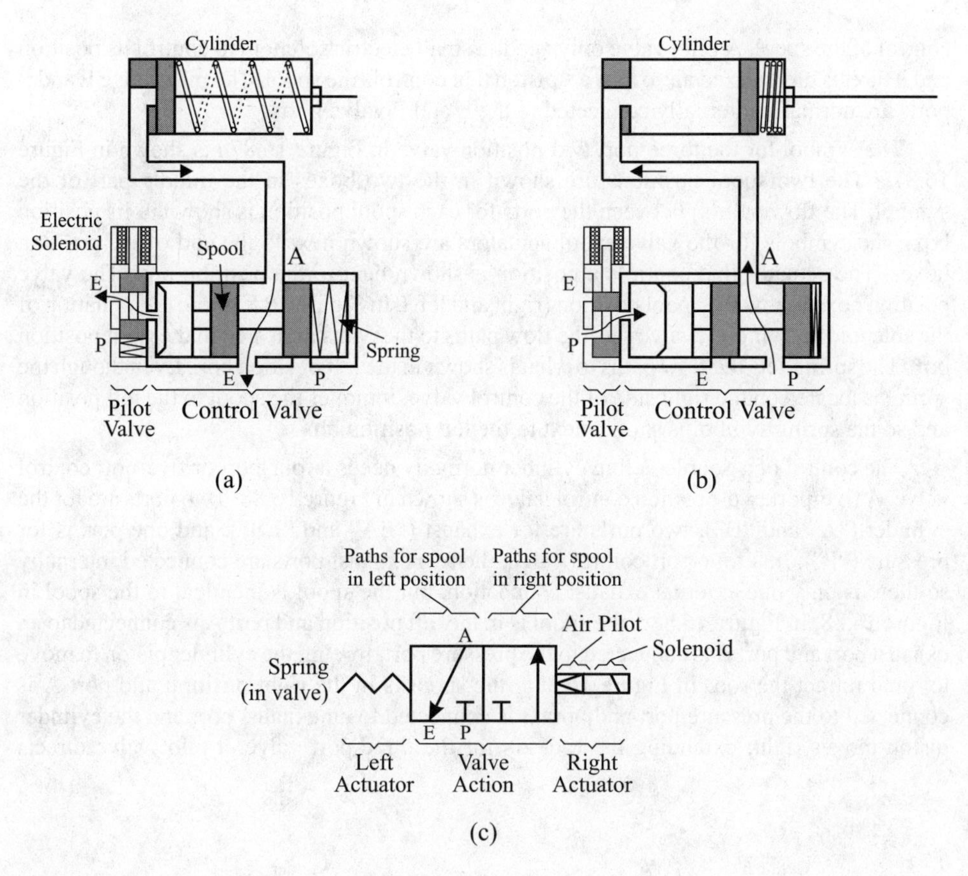

Figure 16.87. Three port directional valve: *(a)* port A exhausted; *(b)* port A pressurized; *(c)* valve symbol.

Directional control valves are classified as to the number of ports and the number of positions. The number of ports refers to the number of air (or hydraulic) connections to the valve and the number of positions is the number of distinct states of the valve. Each position defines one set of flow paths.

The control of a single-acting cylinder normally requires a three-port two-position control valve, illustrated in Figure 16.87. The three ports are the port for the cylinder ("A"), the pressure port ("P"), and the exhaust port ("E"). The pressure port is connected to a source of pressurized air and the exhaust port is connected to the atmosphere. The spool is the main component of the control valve and its position determines the flow paths. In Figure 16.87*a*, the spool is in the left position and port A is connected to the exhaust port. Therefore, the cylinder spring causes the cylinder piston to move left and retract the rod. In Figure 16.87*b*, the spool is in the right position and port A is connected to the pressure port. In this case, the cylinder piston moves right, extending the rod. The control valve has a pilot valve (controlled by an electric solenoid) which directs pressurized air to provide the force to move the spool to the right position. When the electric solenoid is de-energized, the spool piston is exhausted and a spring provides the force to move the spool to the left position. Using a pilot valve to control the spool position is a common technique. The force required to move the spool can be surprisingly large and requires a larger electric solenoid for direct control of the spool. A pilot valve only needs a small electric solenoid to control its position and it directs pressurized air to move a piston that controls the spool. The pilot valve E and P ports are normally internally connected to the E and P valve ports.

The symbol for the three-port two-position valve in Figure 16.87*a* is shown in Figure 16.87*c*. The two spool positions are shown in the two boxes in the middle part of the symbol. The flow path(s) between the ports for each spool position is shown in its position box. The symbols for the valve spool actuators are shown next to the end of the position boxes. The actuator that controls a position is shown next to the position box. The valve position boxes show the spool position (right and left). In Figure 16.87*c*, the combination of the solenoid and air pilot valve sets the flow paths to the paths indicated in the right position box. The spring sets the flow paths to what is shown in the left position box. Even though the spring is located on the right side of the control valve, it moves the spool to the left position and so the spring symbol is shown next to the left position box.

The control of a double-acting cylinder normally needs a four-port or five-port control valve. A five-port two-position control valve is shown in Figure 16.88. Two ports are for the cylinder ("A" and "B"), two ports are for exhaust ("EA" and "EB"), and one port is for pressure ("P"). In a four-port control valve, the two exhaust ports are connected internally so there is only one external exhaust connection, but the spool is identical to the spool in Figure 16.88. In Figure 16.88*a*, the spool is in the left position and port A is connected to an exhaust port and port B is connected to the pressure port, forcing the cylinder piston to move left and retract the rod. In Figure 16.88*b*, the spool is in the right position and port A is connected to the pressure port and port B is connected to an exhaust port and the cylinder piston moves right, extending the rod. As for the three-port valve, a pilot valve directs

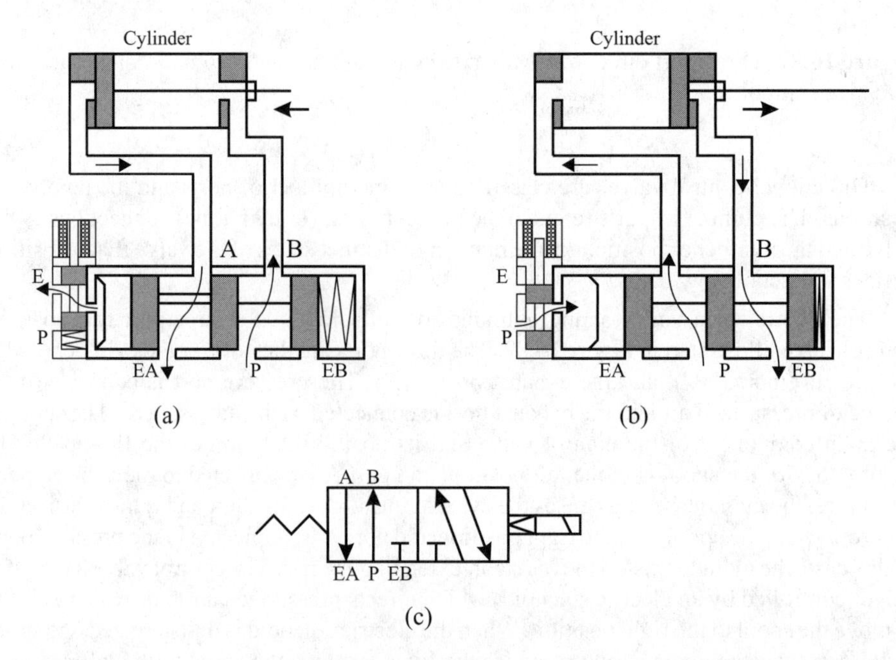

Figure 16.88. Five port two-position directional valve: *(a)* port A exhausted and port B pressurized; *(b)* port A pressurized and port B exhausted; *(c)* valve symbol.

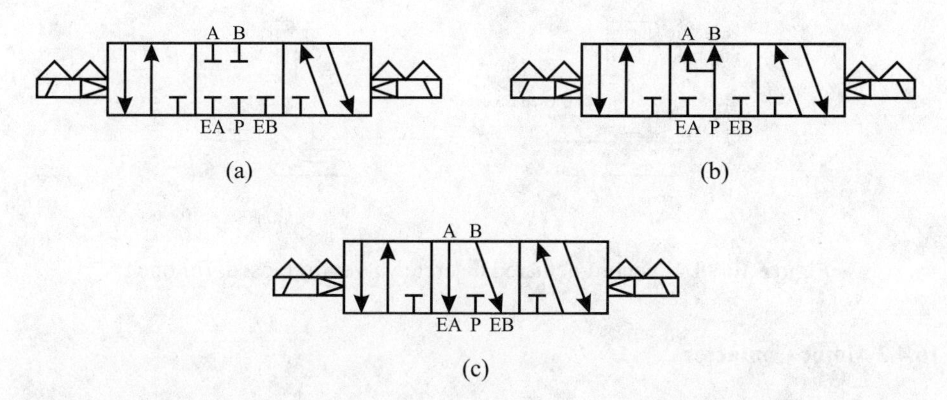

Figure 16.89. Five port three-position directional valve: *(a)* closed center; *(b)* pressure center; *(c)* exhaust center.

pressurized air to provide the force to move the spool to the right position. The symbolic representation for this five-port two-position valve appears in Figure 16.88*c*.

Five-port three-position valves provide other control options for double-acting cylinders. The three different types are shown symbolically in Figure 16.89. All of these valves have two control solenoids. The center position shows the flow paths when neither control solenoid is energized. When the right solenoid is energized, the rightmost position shows the flow paths. When the right solenoid is then deenergized, a spring returns the spool to the center position. When the left solenoid is energized, the leftmost position shows the flow paths. If both solenoids are energized, the spool position is undefined. Typically, the spool assumes the center position in this circumstance. For all three valves shown in Figure 16.89, an electric solenoid controls a pilot valve. The differences between the valves shown in Figure 16.89 are the paths when the valve is in the center position. Both ports A and B can be closed (Figure 16.89*a*), pressurized (Figure 16.89*b*), or exhausted (Figure 16.89*c*). When both ports A and B are exhausted, the cylinder piston is free to move. When both ports are pressurized, the cylinder piston will stop immediately. When both ports are closed, the cylinder piston also ceases motion, though it may continue to move a small distance if the load is light.

PLC discrete outputs are used to operate the directional control valves. A two-position valve requires only a single discrete output channel. A three-position valve needs two discrete output channels. The logic to control a three-position valve should include logic that prevents both outputs from being energized simultaneously.

16.4.2 Discrete Valves

Discrete valves provide on-off control of liquid and gas flows. A typical electric-solenoid valve is shown in Figure 16.90. When the solenoid is energized, it moves a valve stem and a plug off a seat, allowing the process fluid or gas to flow. Depending on the situation, the valve may contain limit switches indicating that the valve is open and/or closed. If the valve is large, a pilot valve may be used to provide a larger actuating force. Alternatively, a reversing motor with gearing can provide more actuating force.

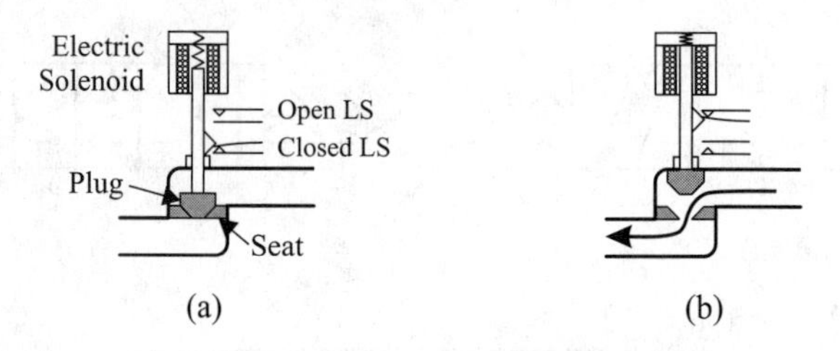

Figure 16.90. Solenoid-actuated discrete valve: *(a)* closed; *(b)* open.

16.4.3 Motor Contactors

Single-speed motors are often controlled with a motor contactor as shown in Figure 16.91. The example shown is for a three-phase AC motor. A PLC relay output channel is used to control the contactor coil since the coil power source is derived from the 440-volt bus and is isolated from the PLC. The contactor often has a fourth contact, called the auxiliary contact. This contact provides a discrete input feedback to the PLC that indicates the motor contactor is closed. Note that the auxiliary contact also opens when there is an overload. Contactors can also provide a normally-closed overload contact to the PLC to detect overload problems.

A contactor for a reversing motor is shown in Figure 16.92. In this case, there are two discrete outputs from the PLC, one for each direction. To reverse the motor, the A and C phases are switched. The contactor also has protection to prevent both forward and reverse directions being energized simultaneously since this action would result in a short between the A and C phases. Each direction has its own auxiliary contact.

To provide an operator override for a motor, a hand-off-auto (HOA) switch is often used in conjunction with PLC control. Hand-off-auto switches and their use with motor contactors are discussed in section 4.2.2 and an example is shown in Figure 4.23.

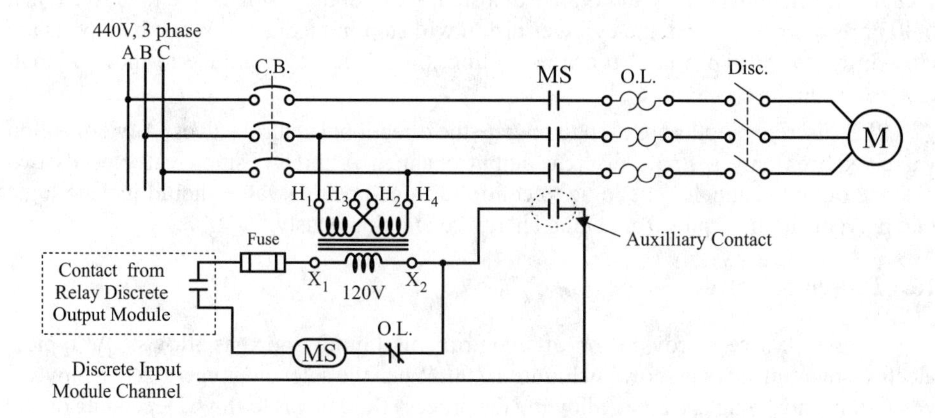

Figure 16.91. Motor contactor.

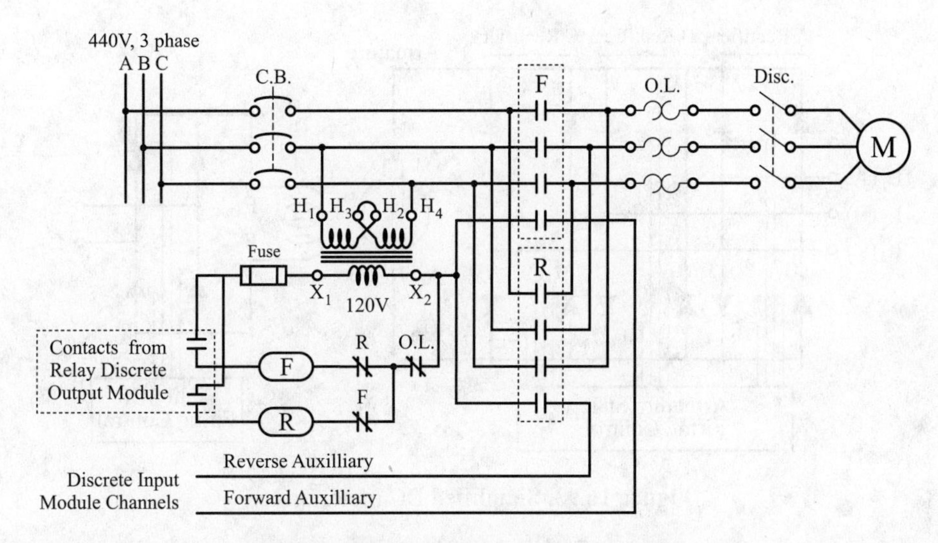

Figure 16.92. Reversing motor contactor.

16.5 ANALOG ACTUATORS

Instead of just on/off control, there are many situations where a physical quantity must be regulated. In this case, the PLC has an analog output channel connected to an actuator. The most common actuators are an electric motor or a control valve. These are described first, followed by a survey of devices to control the feed rate of solid materials.

16.5.1 Electric Motors

Electric motors often provide the power to move mechanical systems, to pump process fluids, to compress gases, and to pneumatically convey powders. Before modern electronic motor controllers, most applications that required a variable-speed motor used a DC motor. However, AC motors are typically more reliable (no brushes to wear out) and are less expensive. Modern solid-state drive electronics have allowed the AC motor to basically supplant the DC motor in many variable-speed applications. Most modern motor controllers (called *motor drives*, or just *drives*) use electronics to provide efficient control of the motor speed and/or torque.

Variable-speed DC drives are described first, followed by variable-speed AC drives. The drive for a stepper motor, a special kind of brushless motor, is described next. This section on motor drives concludes with the control of servomotors, a specially-designed DC or AC motor.

Variable-Speed DC Drives

Traditionally, DC motors have been used in variable-speed applications. The speed of a DC motor is easily regulated by changing the armature current while holding the field current constant. The torque is controlled by changing the field current with a constant armature current. Before electronics, the speed of a DC motor was regulated by placing a variable resistor in series with the armature power supply. This method is inefficient because of the power loss in the resistor, especially under heavy mechanical loads.

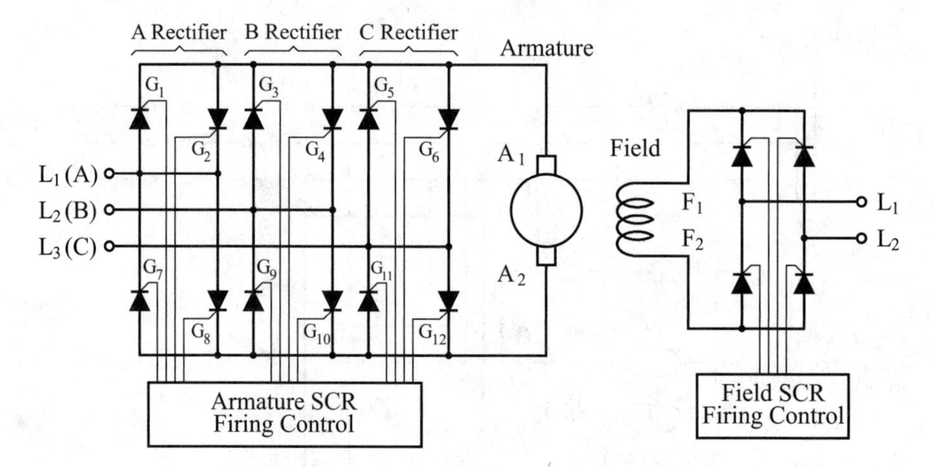

Figure 16.93. Simplified DC motor drive.

A simplified DC motor drive is shown in Figure 16.93. The three-phase power is rectified into a DC voltage that drives the armature. One phase is rectified to produce the field voltage. The rectifiers are silicon-controlled rectifiers (SCRs). An SCR has the property that when a positive pulse is applied to the gate terminal (labeled G_x in Figure 16.93) and there is a positive anode-to-cathode voltage, the rectifier conducts as long as the anode-to-cathode voltage remains positive. When used in a bridge configuration to rectify an AC voltage, the SCR conducts during one half-cycle of the AC waveform. The application of the gate pulse is often called "firing" the gate. If the gate pulse is delayed so that the SCR conducts during only part of the AC half-cycle, then only that portion is conducted to the DC load. The result of delaying the gate pulse is a reduction in the average DC voltage. In this manner, the armature voltage can be varied from zero to the maximum. SCRs can conduct high currents with little loss and so are much more efficient than variable resistors when controlling the armature voltage.

The operation of the three-phase rectifier in Figure 16.93 is illustrated in Figure 16.94. The odd-numbered SCRs are used to provide a positive voltage to the armature (where A_1 is considered the positive terminal) and the even-numbered SCRs are used to provide a negative voltage to the armature. For the sake of describing the operation, only the odd-numbered SCRs are considered. The SCR firing delay (called the *firing delay*) is expressed in degrees starting from the beginning of the AC waveform. One AC cycle is 360 degrees. When the appropriate SCRs are fired at the beginning of each AC half-cycle (Figure 16.94*a*), the resultant armature voltage is at its maximum, $1.65 \times V_p$, where V_p is the peak phase voltage (Fitzgerald, Kingsley, and Umas, 2003). If all three phases are summed, the waveform is "rippled." However, the large inductance of the armature smoothes out these variations, producing a nearly constant (over a few AC cycles) average voltage. Note that within each phase bridge, the firing of the lower SCR is delayed 180 degrees from the upper SCR to steer the negative portion of the AC waveform. When the SCR firing angles are delayed 90 degrees (Figure 16.94*b*), only half of the AC waveform is conducted to the armature, halving the average voltage and halving the speed. When the SCR firing angles are delayed 135 degrees (Figure 16.94*c*), the average voltage is less than 15% of the maximum.

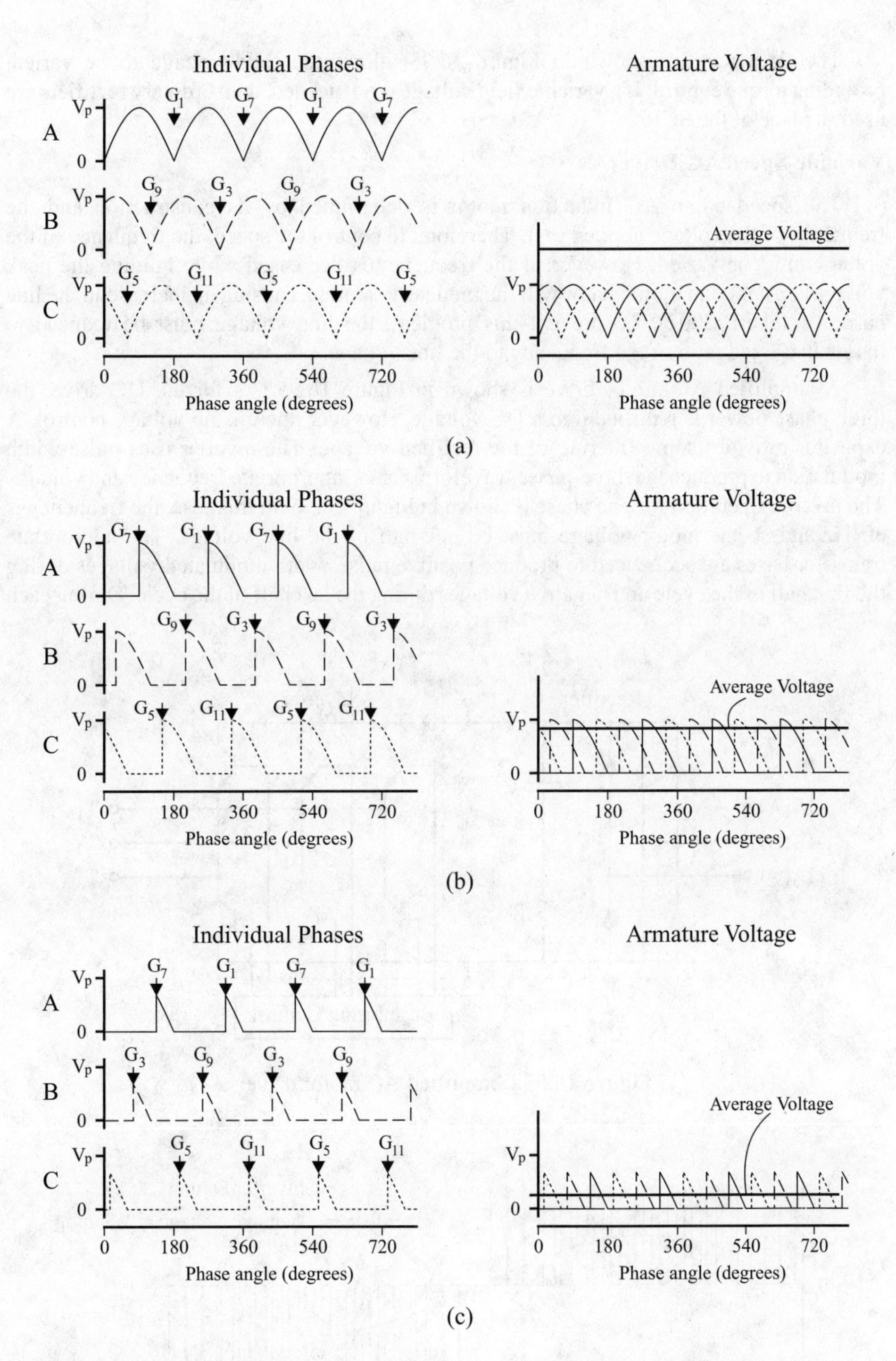

Figure 16.94. DC armature voltage as a function of SCR firing angle: *(a)* zero degrees; *(b)* 90 degrees; *(c)* 135 degrees.

The field rectifier shown in Figure 16.93 allows the field voltage to be varied, providing torque control. If a variable field voltage is not needed, then ordinary rectifiers are used in place of the SCRs.

Variable-Speed AC Drives

The speed of an AC induction motor is determined by its construction and the frequency of the voltage applied to it. Therefore, to control the speed, the frequency of the voltage must be varied. However, if the frequency is decreased while holding the peak voltage constant, the motor stator will magnetically saturate, causing an increase in the line current (Hubert, 2002). To prevent this problem, the line voltage must be reduced to maintain a fixed ratio of the frequency to the line voltage.

A simplified AC motor drive is shown in Figure 16.95. As for the DC drive, the three-phase power is rectified into a DC voltage. However, there is no voltage control. A capacitor provides some filtering of the rectified voltage. The inverter uses pulse-width modulation to produce the three-phase waveforms at the appropriate frequency and voltage. The inverter operation for one phase is shown in Figure 16.96. In this case, the frequency is 30 Hz and so the motor voltage must be one-half of the line voltage. The appropriate transistor bases are sequenced to produce positive pulse-width modulated voltages during the first half of the cycle and negative voltages during the last half of the cycle. During each

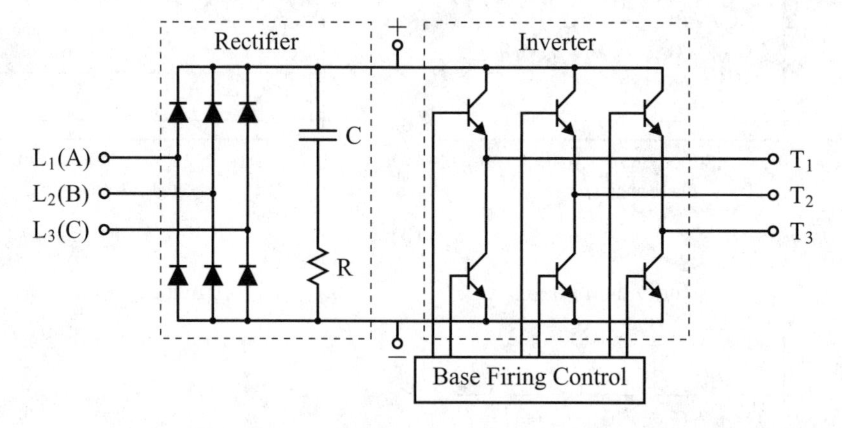

Figure 16.95. Simplified AC motor drive.

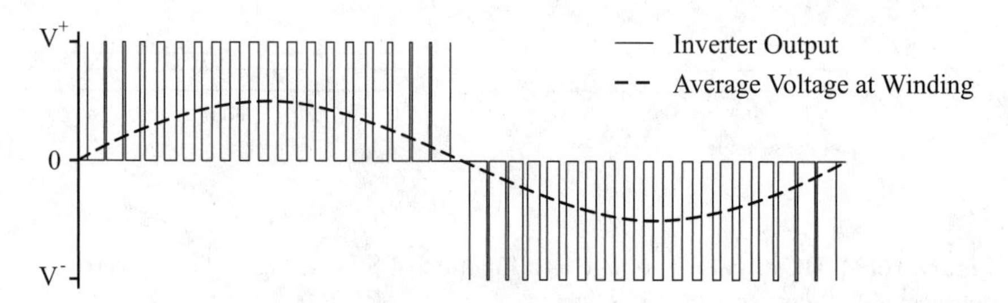

Figure 16.96. Pulse-width modulation to produce AC voltage and frequency for one phase.

half cycle, the duty cycle of the pulses start at zero, increase to 50%, and then decrease to zero. The duty cycle is defined to be the percent of time the pulse is nonzero during its period. Since the maximum duty cycle is 50%, the peak voltage is 50% of the line voltage.

Stepper Motor Drives

A stepper motor is a brushless permanent-magnet type motor that translates incoming pulses into mechanical motion. Because the stepper motor makes a fixed angular motion in response to the pulses, stepper motors are often used in an open-loop configuration. In this case, the motion is controlled by generating the proper pulses to the motor, and encoders are not used. Figure 16.97 shows a simplified stepper driver and stepper motor. The stepper driver is similar to the inverter section of an AC motor drive. In this case, the stepper has four phases. Typical pulses for this stepper motor when driven in the half-step mode are shown in Figure 16.98. The overlapping phase pulses provide the ability to position the motor between poles. In the example shown, the motor turns clockwise for 18 half-steps and then reverses direction.

Stepper motors have two disadvantages. First, if the stepper motor encounters a torque load higher than its rating, the motor "cogs" and does not move. For this reason, position feedback is provided by encoders in high-performance motion applications. Second, one must be careful when using encoders in a stepper motor application. Because the motor is driven with pulses, the actual shaft rotational motion is also "pulsed" and not smooth as for a servomotor. If the stepper motor is driving a flexible load (for example, a belt), the pulsed shaft motion is magnified and causes false encoder pulses. For this reason, servomotors are often a better choice.

Servomotor Drives

A servomotor is a specially-designed brushed DC motor or brushless AC motor. The traditional servomotor is a brushed DC motor, where the coil is wound on the armature and the stator is a permanent magnet. Though the motor controller of Figure 16.93 can be used, servomotor applications are typically lower power. In this case, the variable armature voltage is often provided by a variable-output DC power supply whose voltage is automatically adjusted to maintain a desired speed (measured by a tachometer). A brushless

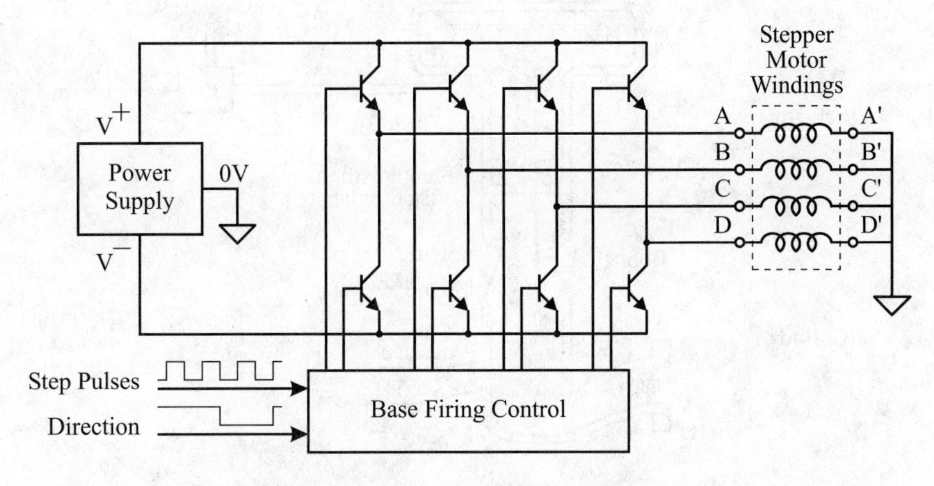

Figure 16.97. Simplified stepper motor drive.

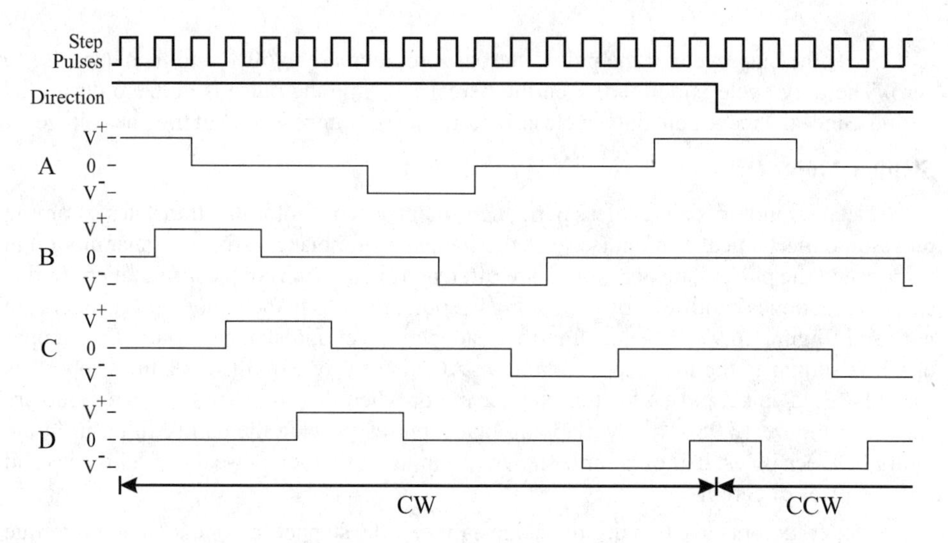

Figure 16.98. Phase signals for stepper motor operation.

AC servomotor is a smaller version of larger AC motors. Hence, the drive electronics are basically the same as for the variable-speed AC drive of Figure 16.95.

16.5.2 Control Valves

In chemical process control systems, control valves regulate the flow of fluids or gases. The typical parts of a globe valve are shown in Figure 16.99. The two basic components of a control valve are the valve body and the actuator. The valve may have other accessory components such as a current-to-pneumatic converter, a positioner, a position sensor, and limit switches.

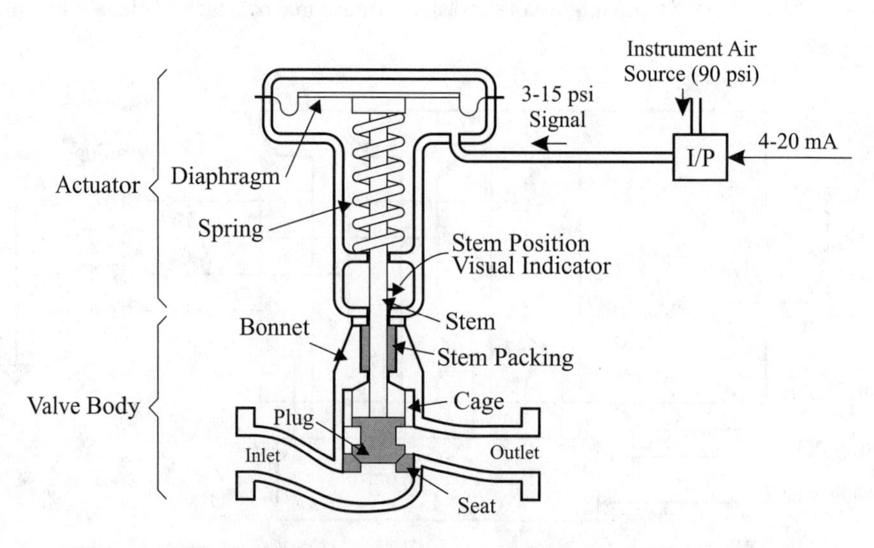

Figure 16.99. Typical pneumatic-actuated control valve (air-to-open).

The valve shown in Figure 16.99 has linear control motion, that is, the stem moves up and down to change the position of the plug and thus vary the flow opening. When the plug is down against the seat, the valve is closed. A cage guides the plug movement. The bonnet contains the stem packing which prevents process fluid leakage from around the stem, and yet allows the stem to move. The actuator in Figure 16.99 is a pneumatic diaphragm. Pressurized air admitted to the lower chamber moves the diaphragm up and thus raises the valve stem. A current-to-pneumatic (I/P) converter changes the 4-20 mA signal from the PLC to a 3-15 psi "signal" to the valve actuator.

The actuator for the control valve in Figure 16.99 is commonly called an *air-to-open* or *fail-close* actuator. If air pressure is lost, the valve automatically closes. Whether a valve should fail in the open or closed position is usually dictated by safety considerations. An *air-to-close* or *fail-open* actuator is shown in Figure 16.100. Note that its basic difference with the air-to-open actuator is that the pressurized air is admitted to the upper chamber and lowers the valve stem in response to increasing pressure.

A fail-close type of actuator is used when the fluid is a fuel or a material input to a exothermic (heat-producing) reaction. Most valves that handle chemicals are the fail-close type. A fail-open type of actuator is appropriate when the manipulated stream is cooling fluid to a reactor or other type of system. Generally, one must ask the question, "If the air pressure to this valve is lost, what is the safe position of this valve?"

Though the globe valve is common, other types of valves may be appropriate. Two common rotary-action valves, ball and butterfly valves are shown in Figure 16.101. Both of these valves have less turbulence at maximum flow. In addition, the actuator must supply a rotary action for these valves. Rotary valves are generally less costly than globe valves in normal applications (Baumann, 1998).

The valve is sized appropriately for the given application. The valve sizing coefficient, C_V, is defined to be

$$C_v = q\sqrt{G_f / \Delta P}$$

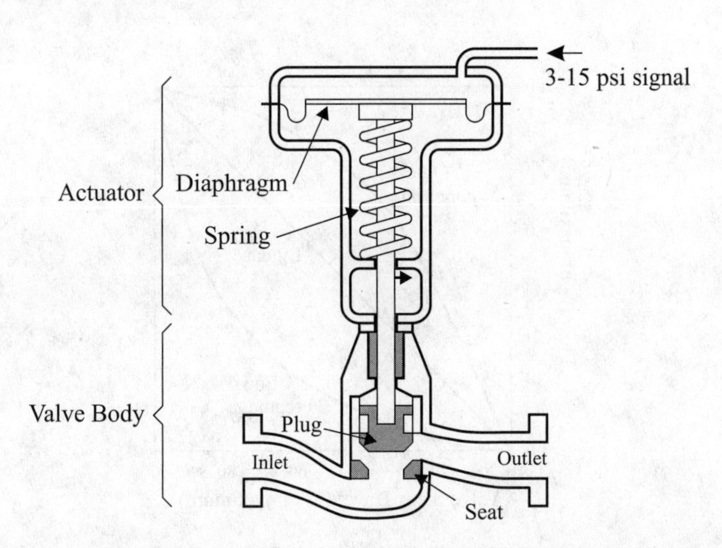

Figure 16.100. Typical pneumatic-actuated air-to-close control valve.

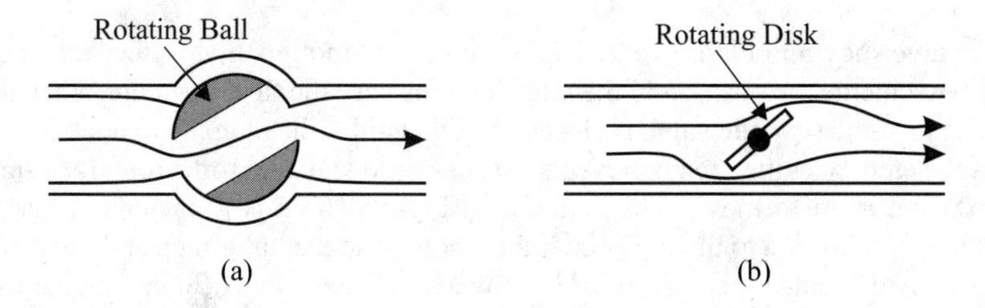

Figure 16.101. Rotary-actuated valves: *(a)* ball valve; *(b)* butterfly valve.

where q is the flow rate, G_f is the specific gravity of the process fluid, and ΔP is the pressure drop across the valve (Baumann, 1998). Calculating the required C_v for the maximum flow often requires guesswork since the inlet pressure may unknown. The usual result is an oversized valve and its maximum opening is less than 50% at the maximum flow rate (Baumann, 1998).

Besides calculating the valve C_v, choosing the valve flow characteristic is another important design decision. A valve's flow characteristic is the flow rate through the valve body as a function of the position as it changes from 0% to 100%. The *inherent* flow characteristics are theoretical and are determined for a constant pressure drop across the valve. The *installed* flow characteristics are the actual flow characteristics when the valve is in the actual system. In general, the installed flow characteristic is not the same as the inherent flow characteristic. There are three flow characteristics: (1) linear, (2) equal percentage, and (3) quick opening. The flow rate through the valve as a function of the stem travel for each of these characteristics is shown in Figure 16.102. For a *linear* flow characteristic, the flow rate is directly proportional to the valve stem travel. An *equal percentage* flow characteristic has the property that equal increments of stem travel result in equal percentage changes in the flow. For example, if the flow doubles as the stem moves from 30% to 40%, the flow will also double as the stem moves from 50% to 60%. A *quick opening* characteristic has large flow changes with minimal changes in the stem position

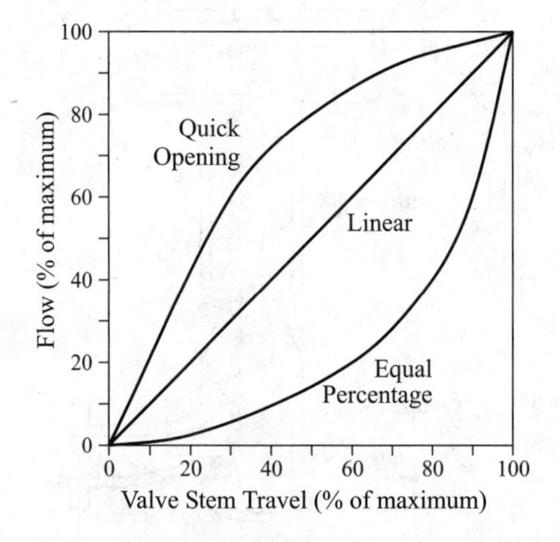

Figure 16.102. Valve flow characteristics.

when the valve is nearly closed. As the valve opens, the effect of increases in the stem position lessens. This type of flow characteristic is not suitable for regulatory control.

Baumann (1998) uses the following rule of thumb when deciding whether to choose a valve with an inherent linear or equal percentage flow characteristic. Find the ratio between the pressure drop across the valve at its minimum flow and the pressure drop at its maximum flow. If this ratio is less than 2:1, choose a linear inherent valve characteristic. Otherwise, use an equal percentage flow characteristic. Baumann cites two other reasons why an equal percentage valve is often a better choice:

1. Better utilization of the available valve control range. Since most valves are oversized, the typically flow is around 40% of the maximum valve flow. At this flow, the stem position for a linear valve is about 40% and the stem position for an equal percentage valve is about 75%.
2. Better response at low flows. The minimum flow is usually around 5% of the maximum. A small process upset at this flow for a linear valve characteristic may cause the plug to bump against the seat. However, for an equal percentage characteristic, the stem position is around 15%, and a small process upset will not cause a problem.

Ideally, one wants a linear installed flow characteristic. If the stem position changes by 10% of its travel, the flow should also change by 10% of the maximum. However, this situation is unusual over the full range of the flow. Since most control loops operate within a narrower range, it is only necessary that the relationship between the stem position and flow is "reasonably linear" over the range of interest. Most PID tuning rules will tolerate a change in the "valve gain" of ±50%.

The control valve is often the critical component in a process control loop and has a major influence on loop stability. The major problem is dead time, that is, the time required for the actuator/valve to respond to a change in the PLC analog output signal. This characteristic is often called the "dead band" or "stiction" of the actuator/valve combination. The biggest problem is the friction in the valve stem movement due to the packing. The packing must provide a good seal. But if too tight, the stem will not move until the pressure to the actuator builds up enough to overcome the friction. The ideal valve has an operating dead band of less than 1% of the maximum travel (Baumann, 1998).

A motor is an alternate valve actuator. There are two major types: (1) AC motor gear drive, and (2) stepper motor. In the AC motor drive actuator, the motor speed is reduced by a set of gears to a few revolutions per minute. A stepper motor provides more accurate positioning, but its torque is limited. Both types of motor actuators provide more precise positioning, but both often have slower dynamics when compared with pneumatic actuators. In addition, motor actuators do not have fail-close or fail-open capability.

When controlling the flow of a liquid, there are two possible basic control configurations. Conventionally, a fixed-speed motor driving a pump provides the pressure head and a control valve provides the throttling to control the flow. This scheme is shown in Figure 16.103*a*. With the introduction of variable-speed AC motor drives, using a variable-speed motor driving a pump to control liquid flow became possible (Figure 16.103*b*). The throttling action of a valve is thermodynamically irreversible and thus the pressure drop across the valve is wasted energy. The perceived energy savings is a rationale for using a variable-speed drive instead of a valve to control the flow. However, the energy savings can only be justified when the pump is deliberately oversized (Baumann, 1981). There are some applications where a speed-controlled pump is clearly the best choice.

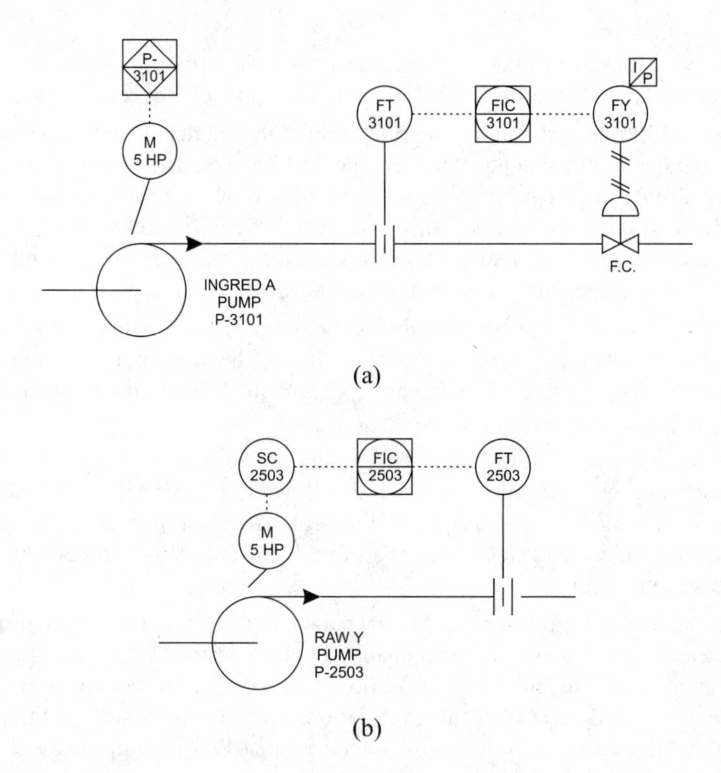

Figure 16.103. Flow control: *(a)* fixed-speed pump; *(b)* variable-speed pump.

When pumping a highly corrosive fluid, a speed-controlled pump avoids the expense of a special alloy valve. If valve dead band is a problem, a speed-controlled pump can improve the control.

16.5.3 Solid Material Feeders

Controlling the feed rate of solid material is a little more difficult than controlling the flow of a liquid or gas. Common methods of solid material flow include weigh belt feeders, vibratory feeders, rotary valves, and loss-in-weight feeders.

A conveyor belt scale (Figure 16.73) forms the basis for a weigh belt feeder, illustrated in Figure 16.104. A bed of material is formed on the conveyor belt as it is discharged from a

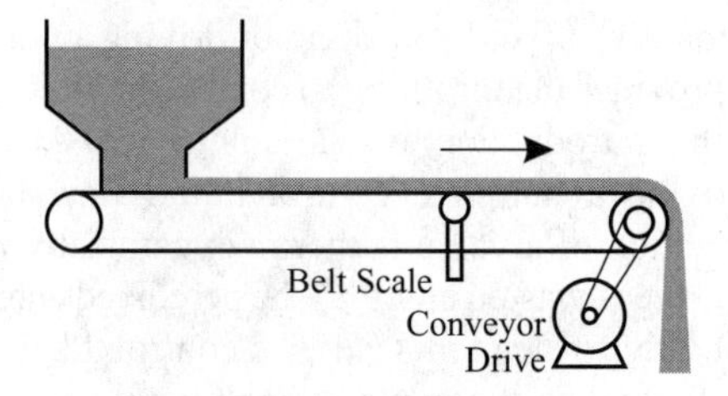

Figure 16.104. Weigh belt feeder.

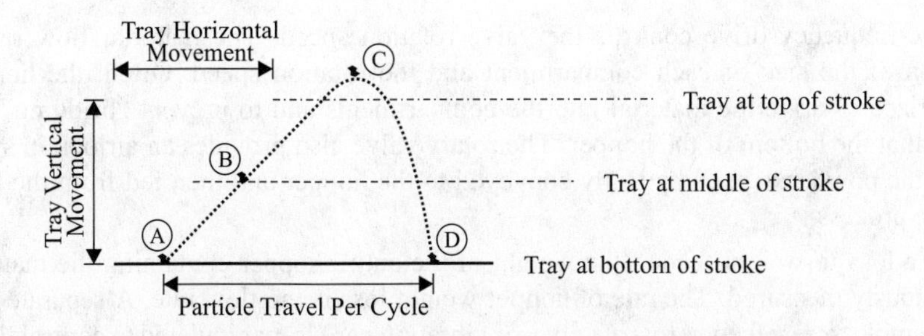

Figure 16.105. Vibratory feeder operation.

hopper and the belt speed is controlled in order to maintain the desired flow rate. Weigh belt feeders are typically used for granular materials that do not generate much dust.

A vibratory feeder replaces the conveyor belt of Figure 16.104 with a vibrating tray. A vibrating tray is more efficient when moving mid-sized materials (0.3 to 50 mm in diameter). On a vibratory feeder, particles are "thrown" up and forward so that the particles drop further down the surface. Figure 16.105 illustrates how a vibrating tray moves one particle (Eriez, 2003). During one cycle of the vibrating tray, the tray surface travels horizontally and vertically from the bottom of the stroke to the top of the stroke and then returns to its starting position. An individual particle starts at position "A" on the tray. At position "B," the particle leaves the tray with a trajectory that goes through "C" and then drops to "D." When the tray is at the top part of the stroke, the particle is in position "C" and the tray is back at the bottom part of the stroke when the particle drops to "D."

The vibration amplitude, frequency and angle of deflection are chosen to move a certain material at a specific rate. The actual vibrations are often generated by an electric motor driving an eccentric (out-of-balance) shaft. The vibration created by the eccentric is amplified through a system of springs. An alternative, more efficient design uses a vibrating electromagnet to generate the vibrations (Eriez, 2003).

Rotary valves are a common way to control the flow of powders from a bulk tank. A rotary valve (Figure 16.106) consists of a series of vanes contained within a cylinder. Material enters a wedge-shaped compartment from the top, is rotated 180 degrees and then drops from the inverted compartment. An attached motor whose speed is controlled by a

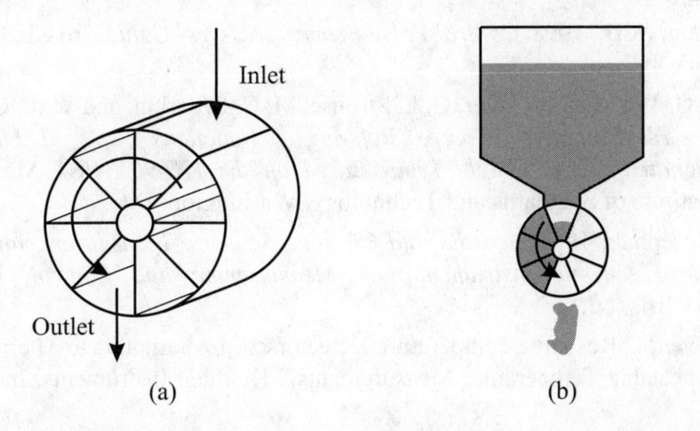

Figure 16.106. Rotary valve: *(a)* vanes of valve; *(b)* feeding material from hopper.

variable-frequency drive controls the valve rotation speed. The material flow rate is a function of the size of each compartment and the rotation speed. Often, the hopper is pressurized to drive the material into the compartments and to prevent "bridging" of the material at the bottom of the hopper. The rotary valve also provides an airlock in systems where the powder is pneumatically conveyed to the hopper and then fed from the hopper into the process.

In a loss-in-weight feeder, the weight of the entire hopper containing the material is continuously measured. The rate of hopper weight loss is the flow rate. A separate device (for example, screw feeder, rotary valve, or vibrating pan) is manipulated to control the feed rate. The disadvantage of this type of feeder is that the hopper must be periodically refilled. When the hopper is being refilled, the calculation for the weight loss rate must be suspended. If an accurate measurement of material leaving the hopped is desired, then material feeding must be stopped while the material is being refilled.

16.6 CHAPTER SUMMARY

This chapter describes common sensors and actuators that appear in PLC-controlled systems. Both discrete and analog devices are covered.

REFERENCES

Allen-Bradley, 1988. *Bulletin 1333 Series B Adjustable Frequency AC Motor Drives: Instruction Manual*, pub. 1395-5.1, Allen-Bradley Company, Inc., Milwaukee, WI, August.

Analog Devices, 2003. *Two Terminal IC Temperature Transducer, AD590*, Analog Devices, Inc., Norwood, MA, http://www.analog.com.

Anderson, M., and J. Herdan, 1999. "Oxidation-reduction Potential," International Scientific Communications, Inc., , (December).

Banner Engineering, 1994. *Handbook of Photoelectric Sensing*, 2nd ed., part number 03190, Banner Engineering Corp., Minneapolis, MN.

Battikha, N. E., 1997. *The Condensed Handbook of Measurement and Control*, ISA, Research Triangle Park, NC.

Baumann, H. D., 1981. "Control Valve vs. Variable-Speed Pump," *Chemical Engineering* (June 29): 81-84.

Baumann, H. D., 1998. *Control Valve Primer: A Users' Guide*, 3rd ed., ISA, Research Triangle Park, NC.

Burns, G. W., M. G. Scroger, G. F. Strouse, M. C. Croarkin, and W. F. Guthrie, 1993. *Temperature-Electromotive Force Reference Functions and Tables for the Letter-Designated Thermocouple Types Based on the ITS-90*, NIST Monograph 175, National Institute of Standards and Technology, Washington, D.C.

Carr, Joseph J., 1993. *Sensors and Circuits: Sensors, Transducers, and Supporting Circuits for Electronic Instrumentation, Measurement and Control*, Prentice-Hall, Englewood Cliffs, NJ.

Cejer, Mark. "Resistive Temperature Detectors: An Alternative to Thermocouples for Precise, Repeatable Temperature Measurements," Keithley Instruments, Inc., Cleveland, Ohio.

Eriez, 2003. *How to Choose and Use Vibratory Feeders and Conveyors*, Eriez Magnetics.

Fitzgerald, A. E., Charles Kingsley, Jr., and Stephen D. Umans. 2003. *Electric Machines*, 6th ed., McGraw-Hill, New York, NY.

GLI International. n. d. "Electrolytic (Contacting) Conductivity Measurement," Technical Bulletin TB-C1, Rev. 2-201, GLI International, Inc., Milwaukee, WI.

Hubert, Charles I., 2002. *Electric Machines: Theory, Operation, Applications, Adjustment, and Control*, 2nd ed., Prentice-Hall, Upper Saddle River, NJ.

Maron, Jeffrey, 1999. "Selecting Noncontact Pyrometers and Thermometers," *Process Heating*, Business News Publishing Co., September.

Milltronics, 2002. *L-300 Dry Solids FLowmeter Instruction Manual*, Siemens Milltronics Process Instruments Inc., Peterborough, ON, April.

Milltronics, 2003. *Milltronics MSI Belt Scale Instruction Manual*, Siemens Milltronics Process Instruments Inc., Peterborough, ON, August.

National Semiconductor, 2000. *LM135/LM235/LM335, LM135A/LM235A/LM335A Precision Temperature Sensors*, National Semiconductor Corporation, http://www.national.com.

Omega Engineering, 2004. *OMEGA Complete Temperature Measurement Handbook and Encyclopedia*®, Volume MMV™ 5th Edition, Omega Engineering, Inc., Stamford, CT.

Prisciandaro, J., Butchko, D., 2004. *Introduction to Pneumatics and Pneumatic Circuit Problems for FPEF Trainer*, Fluid Power Education Foundation, Milwaukee, WI.

Rockwell Automation, 2003. *ControlLogix Analog I/O Modules: User Manual*, pub. 1756-UM009B-EN-P, Rockwell Automation, Milwaukee, WI, November.

Rockwell Automation, 2004. *Bulletin 1395 Digital DC Drive: User Manual*, pub. 1395-5.40, Rockwell Automation, Milwaukee, WI, February.

Rosemount Analytical, 1999. *Theory and Practice of pH Measurement*, pub. PN 44-6033, Rosemount Analytical, Inc., Irvine, CA, September.

Rosemount Analytical, 2001. *The Theory of pH Measurement*, pub. ADS 43-002, Rosemount Analytical, Inc., Irvine, CA, August.

Schultz, Warren, 1997. "Interfacing Semiconductor Pressure Sensors to Microcomputers," *Motorola Application Note AN1318*, Motorola, Inc.

PROBLEMS

Note: Thermocouple tables may be found in Omega Engineering (2004).

P16-1. The wiring diagram of a J thermocouple is shown in Figure P16.1. The voltage across the thermocouple wires, measured at the terminals of the analog input channel is 9.310 mV. The temperature of the reference (cold) junction is 21 °C. What is the temperature (in °C) of the hot junction? Find your answers to the nearest one-hundredth of a degree. Do the voltage-to-temperature conversion using:

(a) the J thermocouple table

(b) the National Institute of Standards and Technology (NIST) polynomial coefficients:

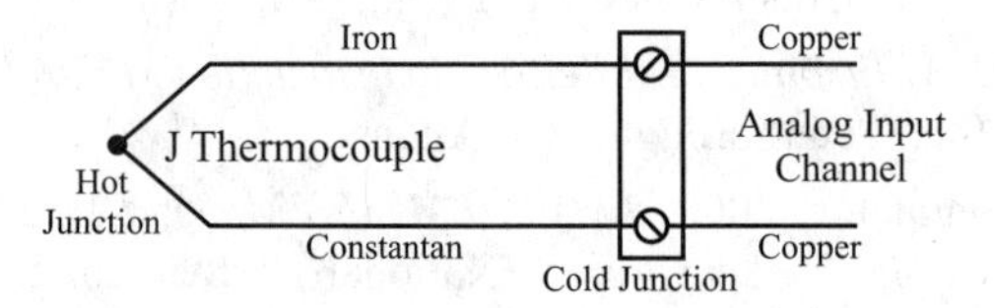

Figure P16.1. J thermocouple measurement.

P16-2. The wiring diagram of a J thermocouple is shown in Figure P16.1. The voltage across the thermocouple wires, measured at the terminals of the analog input channel is 11.120 mV. The temperature of the reference (cold) junction is 20 °C. What is the temperature (in °C) of the hot junction? Find your answers to the nearest one-hundredth of a degree. Do the voltage-to-temperature conversion using:

(a) the J thermocouple table

(b) the National Institute of Standards and Technology (NIST) polynomial coefficients:

P16-3. The wiring diagram of a J thermocouple is shown in Figure P16.1. The voltage across the thermocouple wires, measured at the terminals of the analog input channel is 11.570 mV. The temperature of the reference (cold) junction is 24 °C. What is the temperature (in °C) of the hot junction? Find your answers to the nearest one-hundredth of a degree. Do the voltage-to-temperature conversion using:

(a) the J thermocouple table

(b) the National Institute of Standards and Technology (NIST) polynomial coefficients:

P16-4. The wiring diagram of a J thermocouple is shown in Figure P16.1. The voltage across the thermocouple wires, measured at the terminals of the analog input channel is 13.460 mV. The temperature of the reference (cold) junction is 25 °C. What is the temperature (in °C) of the hot junction? Find your answers to the nearest one-hundredth of a degree. Do the voltage-to-temperature conversion using:

(a) the J thermocouple table

(b) the National Institute of Standards and Technology (NIST) polynomial coefficients:

P16-5. The wiring diagram of a J thermocouple is shown in Figure P16.1. The voltage across the thermocouple wires, measured at the terminals of the analog input channel is 15.434 mV. The temperature of the reference (cold) junction is 24 °C. What is the temperature (in °C) of the hot junction? Find your answers to the nearest one-hundredth of a degree. Do the voltage-to-temperature conversion using:

(a) the J thermocouple table

(b) the National Institute of Standards and Technology (NIST) polynomial coefficients:

P16-6. The wiring diagram of a J thermocouple is shown in Figure P16.1. The voltage across the thermocouple wires, measured at the terminals of the analog input channel is 28.230 mV. The temperature of the reference (cold) junction is 24 °C. What is the temperature (in °C) of the hot junction? Find your answers to the nearest one-hundredth of a degree. Do the voltage-to-temperature conversion using:

(a) the J thermocouple table

(b) the National Institute of Standards and Technology (NIST) polynomial coefficients:

P16-7. The wiring diagram of a J thermocouple is shown in Figure P16.1. The voltage across the thermocouple wires, measured at the terminals of the analog input channel is –5.330 mV. The temperature of the reference junction is 21 °C. What is the temperature (in °C) of the "hot" junction? Find your answers to the nearest one-hundredth of a degree. Do the voltage-to-temperature conversion using:

(a) the J thermocouple table

(b) the National Institute of Standards and Technology (NIST) polynomial coefficients:

P16-8. The wiring diagram of a J thermocouple is shown in Figure P16.1. The voltage across the thermocouple wires, measured at the terminals of the analog input channel is –8.085 mV. The temperature of the reference junction is 24 °C. What is the temperature (in °C) of the "hot" junction? Find your answers to the nearest one-hundredth of a degree. Do the voltage-to-temperature conversion using:

(a) the J thermocouple table

(b) the National Institute of Standards and Technology (NIST) polynomial coefficients:

P16-9. The wiring diagram of a K thermocouple is shown in Figure P16.9. The voltage across the thermocouple wires, measured at the terminals of the analog input channel is 9.890 mV. The temperature of the reference (cold) junction is 25 °C. What is the temperature (in °C) of the hot junction? Find your answers to the nearest one-hundredth of a degree. Do the voltage-to-temperature conversion using:

(a) the K thermocouple table

(b) the National Institute of Standards and Technology (NIST) polynomial coefficients:

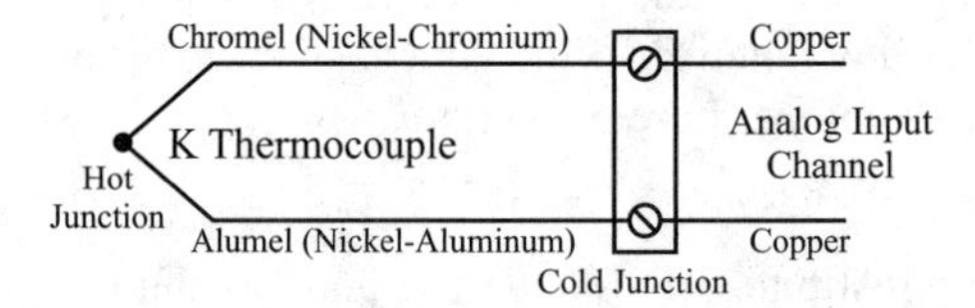

Figure P16.9. K thermocouple measurement.

P16-10. The wiring diagram of a K thermocouple is shown in Figure P16.9. The voltage across the thermocouple wires, measured at the terminals of the analog input channel is 27.350 mV. The temperature of the reference (cold) junction is 24 °C. What is the temperature (in °C) of the hot junction? Find your answers to the nearest one-hundredth of a degree. Do the voltage-to-temperature conversion using:

(a) the K thermocouple table

(b) the National Institute of Standards and Technology (NIST) polynomial coefficients:

P16-11. The wiring diagram of a K thermocouple is shown in Figure P16.9. The voltage across the thermocouple wires, measured at the terminals of the analog input channel is 27.413 mV. The temperature of the reference (cold) junction is 22 °C. What is the temperature (in °C) of the hot junction? Find your answers to the nearest one-hundredth of a degree. Do the voltage-to-temperature conversion using:

(a) the K thermocouple table

(b) the National Institute of Standards and Technology (NIST) polynomial coefficients:

P16-12. The wiring diagram of a K thermocouple is shown in Figure P16.9. The voltage across the thermocouple wires, measured at the terminals of the analog input channel is 33.430 mV. The temperature of the reference (cold) junction is 28 °C. What is the temperature (in °C) of the hot junction? Find your answers to the nearest one-hundredth of a degree. Do the voltage-to-temperature conversion using:

(a) the K thermocouple table

(b) the National Institute of Standards and Technology (NIST) polynomial coefficients:

P16-13. The wiring diagram of an R thermocouple is shown in Figure P16.13. The voltage across the thermocouple wires, measured at the terminals of the analog input channel is

9.910 mV. The temperature of the reference (cold) junction is 23 °C. What is the temperature (in °C) of the hot junction? Find your answers to the nearest one-hundredth of a degree. Do the voltage-to-temperature conversion using:

(a) the R thermocouple table

(b) the National Institute of Standards and Technology (NIST) polynomial coefficients:

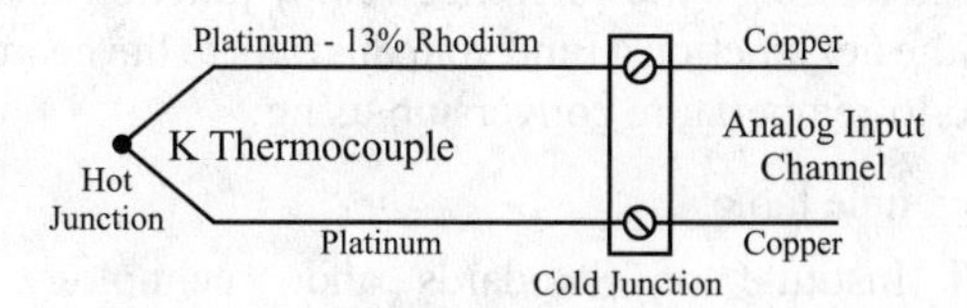

Figure P16.13. R thermocouple measurement.

P16-14. The wiring diagram of an R thermocouple is shown in Figure P16.13. The voltage across the thermocouple wires, measured at the terminals of the analog input channel is 12.394 mV. The temperature of the reference (cold) junction is 25 °C. What is the temperature (in °C) of the hot junction? Find your answers to the nearest one-hundredth of a degree. Do the voltage-to-temperature conversion using:

(a) the R thermocouple table

(b) the National Institute of Standards and Technology (NIST) polynomial coefficients:

P16-15. The wiring diagram of a T thermocouple is shown in Figure P16.15. The voltage across the thermocouple wires, measured at the terminals of the analog input channel is 12.421 mV. The temperature of the reference (cold) junction is 23 °C. What is the temperature (in °C) of the hot junction? Find your answers to the nearest one-hundredth of a degree. Do the voltage-to-temperature conversion using:

(a) the T thermocouple table

(b) the National Institute of Standards and Technology (NIST) polynomial coefficients:

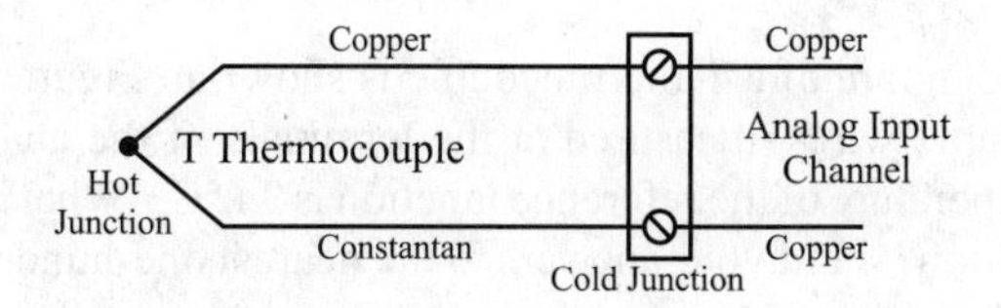

Figure P16.15. T thermocouple measurement.

P16-16. The wiring diagram of a T thermocouple is shown in Figure P16.15. The voltage across the thermocouple wires, measured at the terminals of the analog input channel is 14.420 mV. The temperature of the reference (cold) junction is 24 °C. What is the temperature (in °C) of the hot junction? Find your answers to the nearest one-hundredth of a degree. Do the voltage-to-temperature conversion using:

(a) the T thermocouple table

(b) the National Institute of Standards and Technology (NIST) polynomial coefficients:

P16-17. The wiring diagram of a T thermocouple is shown in Figure P16.15. The voltage across the thermocouple wires, measured at the terminals of the analog input channel is 15.830 mV. The temperature of the reference (cold) junction is 25 °C. What is the temperature (in °C) of the hot junction? Find your answers to the nearest one-hundredth of a degree. Do the voltage-to-temperature conversion using:

(a) the T thermocouple table

(b) the National Institute of Standards and Technology (NIST) polynomial coefficients:

P16-18. The wiring diagram of a T thermocouple is shown in Figure P16.15. The voltage across the thermocouple wires, measured at the terminals of the analog input channel is 17.420 mV. The temperature of the reference (cold) junction is 25 °C. What is the temperature (in °C) of the hot junction? Find your answers to the nearest one-hundredth of a degree. Do the voltage-to-temperature conversion using:

(a) the T thermocouple table

(b) the National Institute of Standards and Technology (NIST) polynomial coefficients:

P16-19. The wiring diagram of a T thermocouple is shown in Figure P16.15. The voltage across the thermocouple wires, measured at the terminals of the analog input channel is -3.690 mV. The temperature of the reference junction is 23 °C. What is the temperature (in °C) of the "hot" junction? Find your answers to the nearest one-hundredth of a degree. Do the voltage-to-temperature conversion using:

(a) the T thermocouple table

(b) the National Institute of Standards and Technology (NIST) polynomial coefficients:

P16-20. The wiring diagram of a T thermocouple is shown in Figure P16.15. The voltage across the thermocouple wires, measured at the terminals of the analog input channel is –3.780 mV. The temperature of the reference junction is 24 °C. What is the temperature (in °C) of the "hot" junction? Find your answers to the nearest one-hundredth of a degree. Do the voltage-to-temperature conversion using:

(a) the T thermocouple table

(b) the National Institute of Standards and Technology (NIST) polynomial coefficients:

P16-21. The wiring diagram of a T thermocouple is shown in Figure P16.15. The voltage across the thermocouple wires, measured at the terminals of the analog input channel is

–4.790 mV. The temperature of the reference junction is 21 °C. What is the temperature (in °C) of the "hot" junction? Find your answers to the nearest one-hundredth of a degree. Do the voltage-to-temperature conversion using:

(a) the T thermocouple table

(b) the National Institute of Standards and Technology (NIST) polynomial coefficients:

P16-22. A three-wire RTD measures temperature and the analog input uses the circuit of Figure 16.46 to measure the resistance. The RTD is a platinum RTD whose nominal resistance (R_0) is 100 ohms at 0 °C. The RTD has been manufactured according to the IEC 60751 standard. The measured RTD resistance is 150 ohms. What is the temperature of the RTD? Find your answers to the nearest one-hundredth of a degree. Do the voltage-to-temperature conversion using the Callendar-Van Dusen equation.

P16-23. A three-wire RTD measures temperature and the analog input uses the circuit of Figure 16.46 to measure the resistance. The RTD is a platinum RTD whose nominal resistance (R_0) is 100 ohms at 0 °C. The RTD has been manufactured according to the IEC 60751 standard. The measured RTD resistance is 200 ohms. What is the temperature of the RTD? Find your answers to the nearest one-hundredth of a degree. Do the voltage-to-temperature conversion using the Callendar-Van Dusen equation.

P16-24. A three-wire RTD measures temperature and the analog input uses the circuit of Figure 16.46 to measure the resistance. The RTD is a platinum RTD whose nominal resistance (R_0) is 100 ohms at 0 °C. The RTD has been manufactured according to the IEC 60751 standard. The measured RTD resistance is 160 ohms. What is the temperature of the RTD? Find your answers to the nearest one-hundredth of a degree. Do the voltage-to-temperature conversion using the Callendar-Van Dusen equation.

P16-25. A three-wire RTD measures temperature and the analog input uses the circuit of Figure 16.46 to measure the resistance. The RTD is a platinum RTD whose nominal resistance (R_0) is 100 ohms at 0 °C. The RTD has been manufactured according to the IEC 60751 standard. The measured RTD resistance is 80 ohms. What is the temperature of the RTD? Find your answers to the nearest one-hundredth of a degree. Do the voltage-to-temperature conversion using the Callendar-Van Dusen equation.

P16-26. A three-wire RTD measures temperature and the analog input uses the circuit of Figure 16.46 to measure the resistance. The RTD is a platinum RTD whose nominal resistance (R_0) is 100 ohms at 0 °C. The RTD has been manufactured according to the IEC 60751 standard. The measured RTD resistance is 70 ohms. What is the temperature of the RTD? Find your answers to the nearest one-hundredth of a degree. Do the voltage-to-temperature conversion using the Callendar-Van Dusen equation.

APPENDIX

THERMOCOUPLE CONVERSION POLYNOMIAL COEFFICIENTS

The standard thermocouple tables are quite large since they report the voltage for every degree in the temperature range. For this reason, Burns et al (1993) also provide approximate polynomial functions that can calculate the temperature, given the voltage. The general equation for the polynomial is

$$T = c_0 + c_1 V + c_2 V^2 + c_3 V^3 + c_4 V^4 + \ldots + c_n V^n$$

where V is the voltage in mV and n is the polynomial order. There are also polynomials that can calculate the thermocouple voltage for a given temperature of the form

$$V = c_0 + c_1 T + c_2 T^2 + c_3 T^3 + c_4 T^4 + \ldots + c_n T^n$$

In the following tables, the coefficients for the temperature-to-voltage conversions have been rounded to eight significant figures. The original coefficients are reported in Burns et al (1993) to 12 significant figures. Since the effect of rounding the coefficients has not been investigated, the conversion error range is not given in the tables. In the following tables, the coefficients for the voltage-to-temperature conversions have not been altered from Burns et al (1993).

For the K thermocouple, the conversion from temperature to voltage has an additional exponential term when the temperature is above 0 °C. The equation for this conversion is

$$V = c_0 + c_1 T + c_2 T^2 + c_3 T^3 + c_4 T^4 + \ldots + c_9 T^9 + a_0 e^{a_1 (T - a_2)^2}$$

Table 16A.1 B Thermocouple Conversion Polynomial Coefficients

Range / Coeff.	*Conversion of Temperature to Voltage*		*Conversion of Voltage to Temperature*	
	0 to 630.615 °C	630.615 to 1820 °C	0.291 to 2.431 mV	2.431 to 13.820 mV
c_0	0.0000000E+00	-3.8938169E+00	9.8423321E+01	2.1315071E+02
c_1	-2.4650818E-04	2.8571747E-02	6.9971500E+02	2.8510504E+02
c_2	5.9040421E-06	-8.4885105E-05	-8.4765304E+02	-5.2742887E+01
c_3	-1.3257932E-09	1.5785280E-07	1.0052644E+03	9.9160804E+00
c_4	1.5668292E-12	-1.6835345E-10	-8.3345952E+02	-1.2965303E+00
c_5	-1.6944529E-15	1.1109794E-13	4.5508542E+02	1.1195870E-01
c_6	6.2990347E-19	-4.4515431E-17	-1.5523037E+02	-6.0625199E-03
c_7		9.8975641E-21	2.9886750E+01	1.8661696E-04
c_8		-9.3791330E-25	-2.4742860E+00	-2.4878585E-06
Error			-0.02 to 0.03 °C	-0.01 to 0.02 °C

Table 16A.2 E Thermocouple Conversion Polynomial Coefficients

Range / Coeff.	*Conversion of Temperature to Voltage*		*Conversion of Voltage to Temperature*	
	-270 to 0 °C	0 to 1000 °C	-8.825 to 0 mV	0 to 76.373 mV
c_0	0.0000000E+00	0.0000000E+00	0.0000000E+00	0.0000000E+00
c_1	5.8665509E-02	5.8665509E-02	1.6977288E+01	1.7057035E+01
c_2	4.5410977E-05	4.5032276E-05	-4.3514970E-01	-2.3301759E-01
c_3	-7.7998049E-07	2.8908407E-08	-1.5859697E-01	6.5435585E-03
c_4	-2.5800161E-08	-3.3056897E-10	-9.2502871E-02	-7.3562749E-05
c_5	-5.9452583E-10	6.5024403E-13	-2.6084314E-02	-1.7896001E-06
c_6	-9.3214059E-12	-1.9197496E-16	-4.1360199E-03	8.4036165E-08
c_7	-1.0287606E-13	-1.2536600E-18	-3.4034030E-04	-1.3735879E-09
c_8	-8.0370124E-16	2.1489218E-21	-1.1564890E-05	1.0629823E-11
c_9	-4.3979497E-18	-1.4388042E-24		-3.2447087E-14
c_{10}	-1.6414776E-20	3.5960899E-28		
c_{11}	-3.9673620E-23			
c_{12}	-5.5827329E-26			
c_{13}	-3.4657842E-29			
Error			-0.01 to 0.03 °C	-0.02 to 0.02 °C

Table 16A.3 J Thermocouple Conversion Polynomial Coefficients

Range / Coeff.	*Conversion of Temperature to Voltage*	
	-210 to 760 °C	760 to 1200 °C
c_0	0.0000000E+00	2.9645626E+02
c_1	5.0381188E-02	-1.4976128E+00
c_2	3.0475837E-05	3.1787104E-03
c_3	-8.5681066E-08	-3.1847687E-06
c_4	1.3228195E-10	1.5720819E-09
c_5	-1.7052958E-13	-3.0691369E-13
c_6	2.0948091E-16	
c_7	-1.2538395E-19	
c_8	1.5631726E-23	

Range / Coeff.	*Conversion of Voltage to Temperature*		
	-8.095 to0 mV	0 to 42.919 mV	42.919 to 69.553 mV
c_0	0.0000000E+00	0.000000E+00	-3.11358187E+03
c_1	1.9528268E+01	1.978425E+01	3.00543684E+02
c_2	-1.2286185E+00	-2.001204E-01	-9.94773230E+00
c_3	-1.0752178E+00	1.036969E-02	1.70276630E-01
c_4	-5.9086933E-01	-2.549687E-04	-1.43033468E-03
c_5	-1.7256713E-01	3.585153E-06	4.73886084E-06
c_6	-2.8131513E-02	-5.344285E-08	
c_7	-2.3963370E-03	5.099890E-10	
c_8	-8.3823321E-05		
Error	-0.05 to 0.03 °C	-0.04 to 0.04 °C	-0.04 to 0.03 °C

Table 16A.4 K Thermocouple Conversion Polynomial Coefficients

Range / Coeff.	*Conversion of Temperature to Voltage* -270 to 0 °C	0 to 1372 °C
c_0	0.0000000E+00	-1.7600414E-02
c_1	3.9450128E-02	3.8921205E-02
c_2	2.3622374E-05	1.8558770E-05
c_3	-3.2858907E-07	-9.9457593E-08
c_4	-4.9904829E-09	3.1840946E-10
c_5	-6.7509059E-11	-5.6072845E-13
c_6	-5.7410327E-13	5.6075059E-16
c_7	-3.1088873E-15	-3.2020720E-19
c_8	-1.0451609E-17	9.7151147E-23
c_9	-1.9889267E-20	-1.2104721E-26
c_{10}	-1.6322697E-23	
c_{11}		
c_{12}		
c_{13}		

Exponential Coeffecients (0 to 1372 °C only)

a_0	1.1859760E-01
a_1	-1.1834320E-04
a_2	1.2696860E+02

Range / Coeff.	*Conversion of Voltage to Temperature* -5.891 to 0 mV	0 to 20.644 mV	20.644 to 54.886 mV
c_0	0.0000000E+00	0.000000E+00	-1.318058E+02
c_1	2.5173462E+01	2.508355E+01	4.830222E+01
c_2	-1.1662878E+00	7.860106E-02	-1.646031E+00
c_3	-1.0833638E+00	-2.503131E-01	5.464731E-02
c_4	-8.9773540E-01	8.315270E-02	-9.650715E-04
c_5	-3.7342377E-01	-1.228034E-02	8.802193E-06
c_6	-8.6632643E-02	9.804036E-04	-3.110810E-08
c_7	-1.0450598E-02	-4.413030E-05	
c_8	-5.1920577E-04	1.057734E-06	
c_9		-1.052755E-08	
Error	-0.02 to 0.04 °C	-0.05 to 0.04 °C	-0.05 to 0.06 °C

Table 16A.5 N Thermocouple Conversion Polynomial Coefficients

Range / Coeff.	*Conversion of Temperature to Voltage* -270 to 0 °C	0 to 1300 °C
c_0	0.0000000E+00	0.0000000E+00
c_1	2.6159106E-02	2.5929395E-02
c_2	1.0957484E-05	1.5710142E-05
c_3	-9.3841112E-08	4.3825627E-08
c_4	-4.6412040E-11	-2.5261170E-10
c_5	-2.6303358E-12	6.4311819E-13
c_6	-2.2653438E-14	-1.0063472E-15
c_7	-7.6089300E-17	9.9745339E-19
c_8	-9.3419668E-20	-6.0863246E-22
c_9		2.0849229E-25
c_{10}		-3.0682196E-29

Range / Coeff.	*Conversion of Voltage to Temperature* -3.990 to 0 mV	0 to 20.613 mV	20.613 to 47.513 mV
c_0	0.0000000E+00	0.00000E+00	1.972485E+01
c_1	3.8436847E+01	3.86896E+01	3.300943E+01
c_2	1.1010485E+00	-1.08267E+00	-3.915159E-01
c_3	5.2229312E+00	4.70205E-02	9.855391E-03
c_4	7.2060525E+00	-2.12169E-06	-1.274371E-04
c_5	5.8488586E+00	-1.17272E-04	7.767022E-07
c_6	2.7754916E+00	5.39280E-06	
c_7	7.7075166E-01	-7.98156E-08	
c_8	1.1582665E-01		
c_9	7.3138868E-03		
Error	-0.02 to 0.03 °C	-0.02 to 0.03 °C	-0.04 to 0.02 °C

Table 16A.6 R Thermocouple Conversion Polynomial Coefficients

Coeff. \ Range	Conversion of Temperature to Voltage		
	-50 to 1064.18 °C	1064.18 to 1664.5 °C	1664.5 to 1768.1 °C
c_0	0.0000000E+00	2.9515793E+00	1.5223212E+02
c_1	5.2896173E-03	-2.5206125E-03	-2.6881989E-01
c_2	1.3916659E-05	1.5956450E-05	1.7128028E-04
c_3	-2.3885569E-08	-7.6408595E-09	-3.4589571E-08
c_4	3.5691600E-11	2.0530529E-12	-9.3463397E-15
c_5	-4.6234767E-14	-2.9335967E-16	
c_6	5.0077744E-17		
c_7	-3.7310589E-20		
c_8	1.5771648E-23		
c_9	-2.8103863E-27		

Coeff. \ Range	Conversion of Voltage to Temperature			
	-0.226 to 1.923 mV	1.923 to 13.228 mV	11.361 to 19.739 mV	19.739 to 21.103 mV
c_0	0.0000000E+00	1.334584505E+01	-8.199599416E+01	3.406177836E+04
c_1	1.8891380E+02	1.472644573E+02	1.553962042E+02	-7.023729171E+03
c_2	-9.3835290E+01	-1.844024844E+01	-8.342197663E+00	5.582903813E+02
c_3	1.3068619E+02	4.031129726E+00	4.279433549E-01	-1.952394635E+01
c_4	-2.2703580E+02	-6.249428360E-01	-1.191577910E-02	2.560740231E-01
c_5	3.5145659E+02	6.468412046E-02	1.492290091E-04	
c_6	-3.8953900E+02	-4.458750426E-03		
c_7	2.8239471E+02	1.994710149E-04		
c_8	-1.2607281E+02	-5.313401790E-06		
c_9	3.1353611E+01	6.481976217E-08		
c_{10}	-3.3187769E+00			
Error	-0.02 to 0.02 °C	-0.005 to 0.005 °C	-0.0005 to 0.001 °C	-0.001 to 0.002 °C

Table 16A.7 S Thermocouple Conversion Polynomial Coefficients

Coeff. \ Range	*Conversion of Temperature to Voltage* -50 to 1064.18 °C	1064.18 to 1664.5 °C	1664.5 to 1768.1 °C
c_0	0.0000000E+00	1.3290044E+00	1.4662823E+02
c_1	5.4031331E-03	3.3450931E-03	-2.5843052E-01
c_2	1.2593429E-05	6.5480519E-06	1.6369357E-04
c_3	-2.3247797E-08	-1.6485626E-09	-3.3043905E-08
c_4	3.2202882E-11	1.2998961E-14	-9.4322369E-15
c_5	-3.3146520E-14		
c_6	2.5574425E-17		
c_7	-1.2506887E-20		
c_8	2.7144318E-24		

Conversion of Voltage to Temperature

Coeff. \ Range	-0.235 to 1.874 mV	1.874 to 11.950 mV	10.332 to 17.536 mV	17.536 to 18.693 mV
c_0	0.00000000E+00	1.291507177E+01	-8.087801117E+01	5.333875126E+04
c_1	1.84949460E+02	1.466298863E+02	1.621573104E+02	-1.235892298E+04
c_2	-8.00504062E+01	-1.534713402E+01	-8.536869453E+00	1.092657613E+03
c_3	1.02237430E+02	3.145945973E+00	4.719686976E-01	-4.265693686E+01
c_4	-1.52248592E+02	-4.163257839E-01	-1.441693666E-02	6.247205420E-01
c_5	1.88821343E+02	3.187963771E-02	2.081618890E-04	
c_6	-1.59085941E+02	-1.291637500E-03		
c_7	8.23027880E+01	2.183475087E-05		
c_8	-2.34181944E+01	-1.447379511E-07		
c_9	2.79786260E+00	8.211272125E-09		
Error	-0.02 to 0.02 °C	-0.01 to 0.01 °C	-0.0002 to 0.0002 °C	-0.002 to 0.002 °C

Table 16A.8 T Thermocouple Conversion Polynomial Coefficients

Range / Coeff.	*Conversion of Temperature to Voltage*		*Conversion of Voltage to Temperature*	
	-270 to 0 °C	0 to 400 °C	-5.603 to 0 mV	0 to 20.872 mV
c_0	0.0000000E+00	0.0000000E+00	0.0000000E+00	0.000000E+00
c_1	3.8748106E-02	3.8748106E-02	2.5949192E+01	2.592800E+01
c_2	4.4194434E-05	3.3292228E-05	-2.1316967E-01	-7.602961E-01
c_3	1.1844323E-07	2.0618243E-07	7.9018692E-01	4.637791E-02
c_4	2.0032974E-08	-2.1882257E-09	4.2527777E-01	-2.165394E-03
c_5	9.0138020E-10	1.0996881E-11	1.3304473E-01	6.048144E-05
c_6	2.2651157E-11	-3.0815759E-14	2.0241446E-02	-7.293422E-07
c_7	3.6071154E-13	4.5479135E-17	1.2668171E-03	
c_8	3.8493940E-15	-2.7512902E-20		
c_9	2.8213522E-17			
c_{10}	1.4251595E-19			
c_{11}	4.8768662E-22			
c_{12}	1.0795539E-24			
c_{13}	1.3945027E-27			
c_{14}	7.9795154E-31			
Error			-0.02 to 0.04 °C	-0.03 to 0.03 °C

17 Communication Networks

Chapter Topics:

- General communication network concepts
- Standard and proprietary factory networks
- PLC-to-PLC communication function blocks

OBJECTIVES

Upon completion of this chapter, you will be able to understand:

- Typical communication networks
- Major features of standard and proprietary factory networks
- Implementation of PLC-to-PLC communications with the PLCs covered by this text

Scenario: Detecting a failure in a remote I/O module

A particular application processes "cassettes" of 150 mm silicon wafers in a series of chemical baths (Figure 17.1). The current system uses a Modicon Compact 984 PLC to control a gantry that moves the cassettes between the baths. The operator places a pair of cassettes into the loading station and the gantry moves the cassettes to the first of a series of chemical baths. The cassettes remain in a chemical bath for a certain amount of time and then they are moved to the next bath. Eventually, they are moved from the last chemical bath to an unloading station, where they are removed by an operator. The operator places

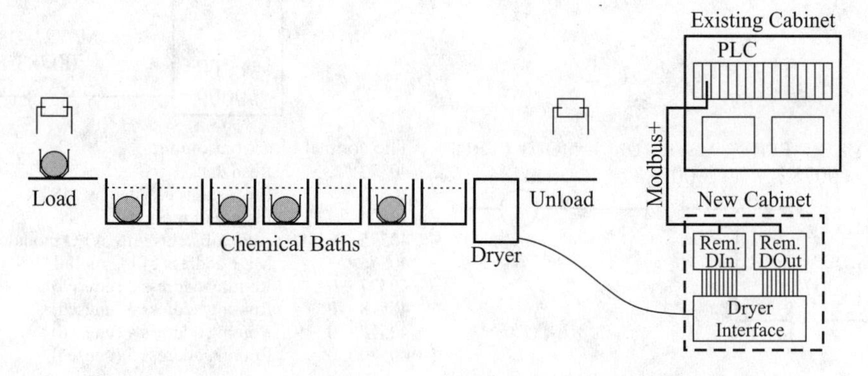

Figure 17.1. Silicon wafer processing system.

the cassettes into a "spin" dryer and spins the cassettes for 3 minutes to remove any water remaining on the surface of the wafers. When the drying cycle is finished, the operator removes the cassettes from the dryer.

As an improvement to the process, the PLC is upgraded to load and unload the cassettes from the dryer and to control the dryer operation. You purchase a special PLC interface module for the dryer that presents 10 discrete inputs and 6 discrete output signals to the PLC. There are not enough spare discrete I/O channels to handle the dryer. In addition, there is no room in the cabinet for more I/O modules. This particular PLC has a built-in Modbus+ interface for communication with remote I/O. So, this type of system is installed. A Modbus+ network cable is fed to another cabinet that houses the remote I/O modules, dryer interface module, and a power supply (Figure 17.1). This particular PLC uses "Peer Cop" to map registers from the Modbus+ remote modules to PLC internal discrete addresses. No special PLC block instructions are required to read from the discrete input module and write to the discrete output module.

The system is installed as designed. The PLC dryer control works as it should. However, during your testing of changes in the motion control, you need to hit the E-stop button. When power is restored, the PLC cannot seem to control the dryer. After some troubleshooting, you discover a blown fuse for the remote discrete input module. The PLC has not detected a lack of communication with the module.

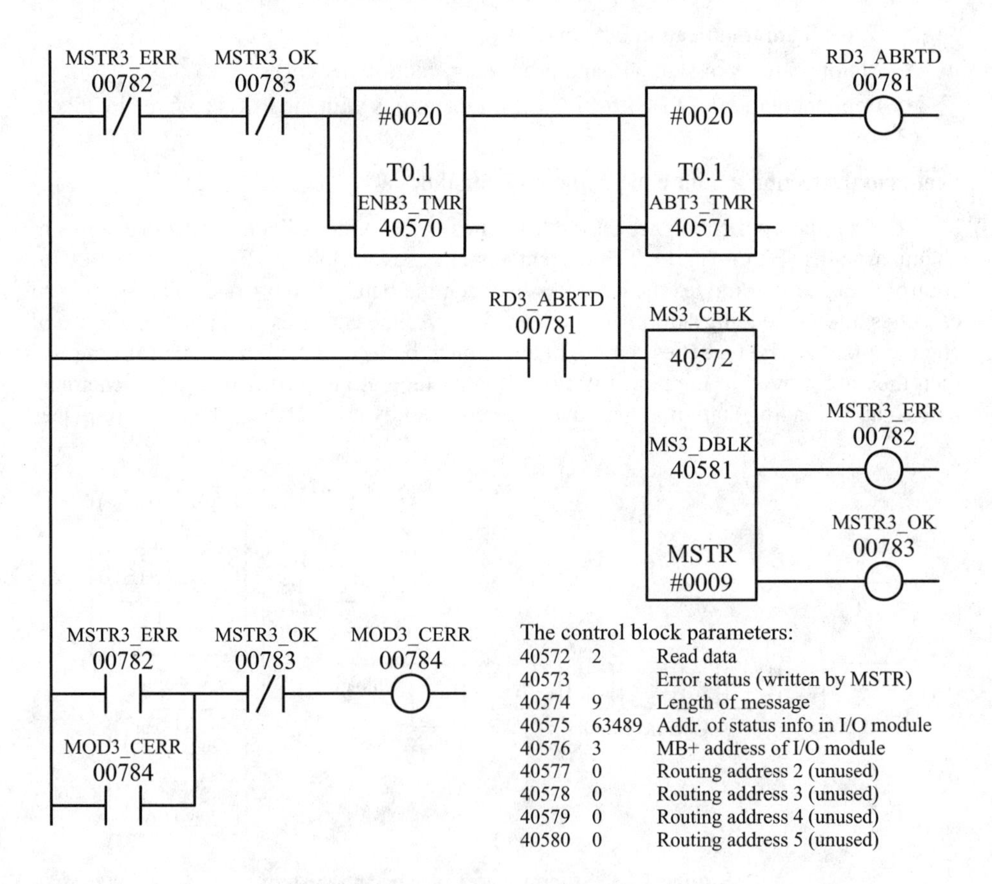

Figure 17.2. Ladder logic to check for presence of remote module.

Solution: After more investigation, you discover that Peer Cop in this PLC does not report communication errors. So, you add ladder logic (Figure 17.2) to read the status of a remote I/O module every 2 seconds. If the MSTR block fails due to a communication error or there is no response within 2 seconds, then a communication error indication is set for the module.

17.1 INTRODUCTION

This chapter is an overview of communication networks available for use in PLC systems. A *local area network* (LAN) is a high-speed medium-distance communication system linking multiple devices. Each device on a LAN is often called a *node*. In most factory automation systems there are multiple communication networks, often connected in a hierarchical manner (Figure 17.3). The backbone network is generally Ethernet and connects the business and office computers. A gateway device connects an automation network to the backbone. Most systems have multiple automation networks, though only one is shown in Figure 17.3. An automation network is optimized for the needs of automation: short messages and fast response. The automation network links PLCs and operator terminals (HMI). The gateway provides the business-related function access to the PLCs and their information. Below the PLCs, the third level of the hierarchy contains the input/output (I/O) networks. These networks range from remote I/O networks to distributed I/O networks. A remote I/O network is basically a proprietary extension of the normal chassis-based I/O where a chassis of I/O modules is located remotely from the processor. A distributed I/O network is one in which the individual discrete I/O or analog I/O devices are connected to a standard fieldbus network.

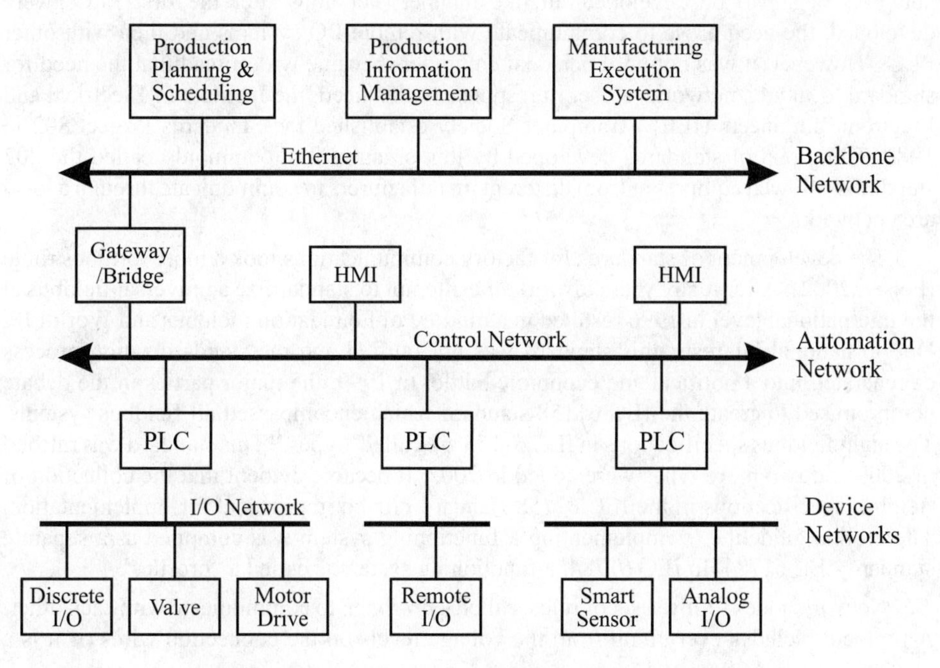

Figure 17.3. Factory communications hierarchy.

Table 17.1 Categorization of Networks

Backbone Network	Automation Network	Device Network
Ethernet	ControlNet	AS-i
Ethernet/IP	DH+	DeviceNet
Modbus/TCP	FF HSE	FF H1
PROFInet	Modbus+	INTERBUS
	P-Net	PROFIBUS-DP
	SwiftNet	PROFIBUS-PA
	WorldFIP	Seriplex

The various networks described in this chapter generally fit into the hierarchy as listed in Table 17.1. However, note that Ethernet is often used as the networking technology for all levels of the hierarchy, even down to the I/O network. Standard network protocols are covered first, generally starting from the top of the hierarchy and proceeding to the bottom. Then proprietary Modicon, Allen-Bradley, and GE Fanuc protocols are described. Lastly, the function blocks that implement PLC-to-PLC communication are explained. This chapter does not cover proprietary remote I/O protocols, nor does it cover the SDS (smart distributed system) and HART (highway addressable remote transducer) network protocols.

17.2 NETWORK PROTOCOLS

With the advent of computers and the need to interconnect them, communication networks began to be developed. In like manner, not long after the first PLCs were developed, the need arose to communicate with remote I/O systems and then with other PLCs. However, it was not until personal computers became widespread that the need for standard local area networks arose. In response to this need, the Institute of Electrical and Electronic Engineers (IEEE) Computer Society established the Standards Project 802 in 1980. The group of standards developed by this organization, commonly called the 802 standards, allowed equipment from different manufacturers to communicate through a local area network.

The development of standards for factory communications took a more tortuous route (Felser, 2002). After many years of work, the attempt to standardize a universal fieldbus at the international level in 1996 resulted in a mixture of Foundation Fieldbus and WorldFIP. Due to national interests, this standard was not ratified and the standardization process degenerated into a political and economic battle. In 1999, the major parties in the debate compromised to create the IEC 61158 standard which encompassed all fieldbus systems. The eight fieldbus specifications in IEC 61158 are called "types." This standard was ratified in 2000 and two more types were added in 2002. It became evident that the collection of fieldbus specifications in the IEC 61158 standard proved impractical for implementation. Therefore a guideline to implementing a functioning system was compiled as a separate standard, IEC 61784. In IEC 61784, a functioning system is called a "profile."

Network nodes follow a set of rules, called a *protocol*, to communicate with each other. A protocol includes everything from the voltage levels on the connection wires (if it is a

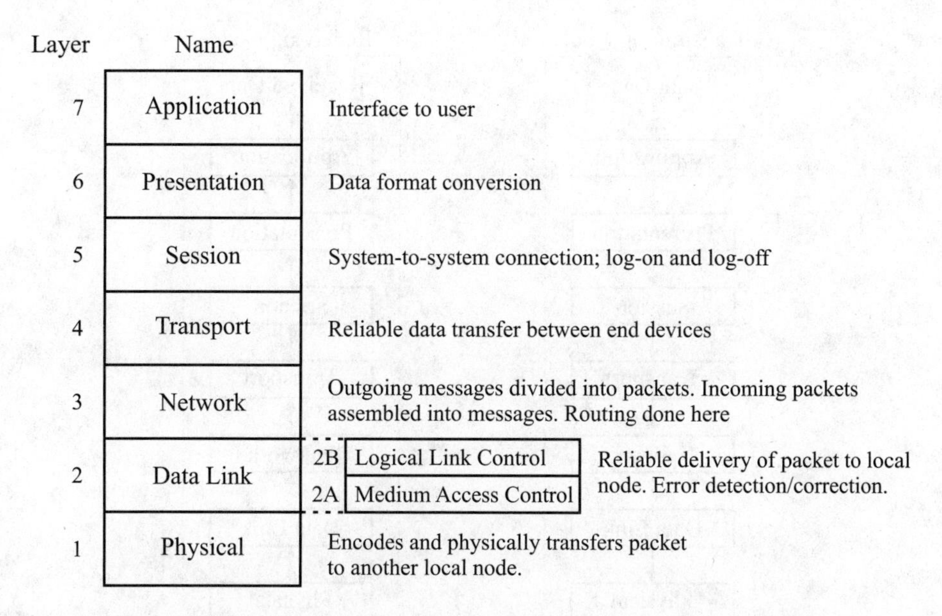

Figure 17.4. Open Systems Interconnection (ISO) reference model.

wired network) to the interpretation of the data packets by an application program. A protocol often includes:

Network medium
Access to the medium by multiple nodes
Handling communication errors
Information encoding
Message interpretation

To provide a guideline to protocol development, the International Standards Organization (ISO) published the Open Systems Interconnection (OSI) reference model in 1979. The OSI reference model divides the protocol functions into seven hierarchical layers (called a protocol "stack"), as shown in Figure 17.4. The data link layer is divided into two sublayers, medium access control (MAC) and logical link control (LLC). Each of these layers performs some function of the protocol. For efficiency, most factory automation networks use only layers 1, 2, and 7. The other layers add unnecessary complexity and delay.

In operation, the use of the OSI model appears as in Figure 17.5. A program sends a message to the application layer of the protocol in its node. The message proceeds downward through the protocol stack, is placed on the network medium by the physical layer, is received by the physical layer of the destination node, and then proceeds up the protocol stack of the destination node. The operation of a protocol is analogous to the process of sending a letter. The letter is typed (application, presentation), sealed into an addressed envelope (session, transport), picked up by the mail carrier and placed in a mail sack going to the appropriate destination (network, data link), and transported to destination post office (physical). At the destination city, the process is reversed.

The IEEE 802 protocols cover the lower two layers of the OSI model. Some of the parts of the 802 standard are shown in Figure 17.6. The 802.2 standard specifies a common

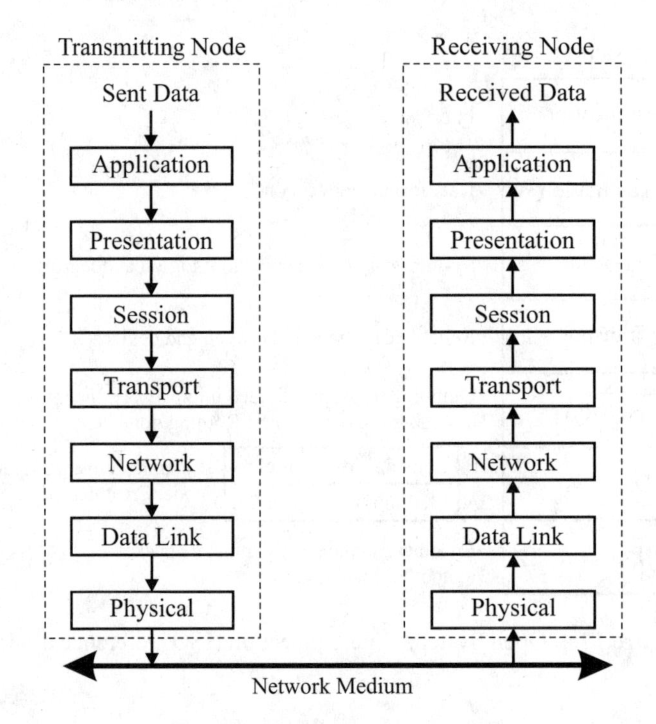

Figure 17.5. Protocol operation.

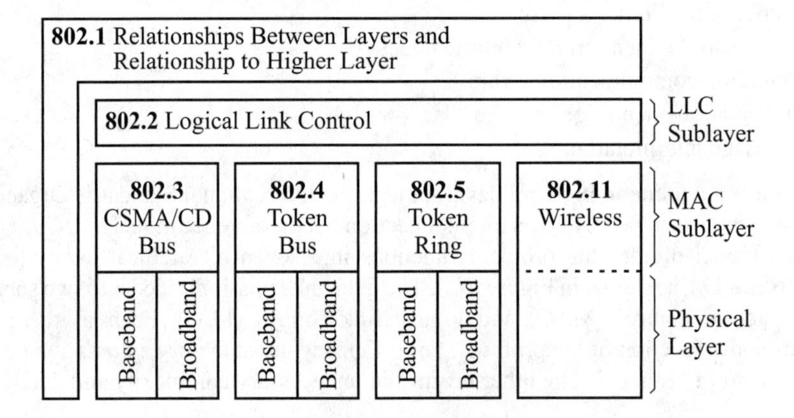

Figure 17.6. IEEE 802 standards.

logical link control (LLC) sublayer for the other parts of the standard. The most common standards for office networks are 802.3, which defines the Ethernet protocol, and 802.11, which defines wireless networks. The token bus (802.4) protocol was developed for factory communications. Though this standard was later withdrawn, many of its concepts were used in the Foundation Fieldbus standard. The token ring (802.5) protocol was adopted by IBM, but not currently used since Ethernet was extended to use fiber optic media.

Table 17.2. IEC 61784 Profiles and IEC 61158 Protocols

IEC 61784 Profile	IEC 61158 Protocols			Protocol Name
	Physical	Data Link	Application	
CPF-1/1	Type 1	Type 1	Type 9	Foundation Fieldbus (H1)
CPF-1/2	Ethernet	TCP/UDP/IP	Type 5	Foundation Fieldbus (HSE)
CPF-1/3	Type 1	Type 1	Type 9	Foundation Fieldbus (H2)
CPF-2/1	Type 2	Type 2	Type 2	ControlNet
CPF-2/2	Ethernet	TCP/UDP/IP	Type 2	Ethernet/IP
CPF-3/1	Type 3	Type 3	Type 3	PROFIBUS-DP
CPF-3/2	Type 1	Type 3	Type 3	PROFIBUS-PA
CPF-3/3	Ethernet	TCP/UDP/IP	Type 10	PROFInet
CPF-4/1	Type 4	Type 4	Type 4	P-Net RS-485
CPF-5/1	Type 1	Type 7	Type 7	WorldFIP (MPS, MCS)
CPF-5/2	Type 1	Type 7	Type 7	WorldFIP (MPS, MCS, SubMMS)
CPF-5/3	Type 1	Type 7	Type 7	WorldFIP (MPS)
CPF-6/1	Type 8	Type 8	Type 8	INTERBUS
CPF-6/2	Type 8	Type 8	Type 8	INTERBUS TCP/IP
CPF-6/3	Type 8	Type 8	Type 8	INTERBUS Subset
CPF-7/1	Type 6	Type 6	-	Swiftnet transport
CPF-7/2	Type 6	Type 6	Type 6	Swiftnet full stack

The ten protocols in the IEC 61158 standard cover the physical, data link, and application layers of the OSI model. The IEC standard is organized by these layers. The individual types are thus described for each layer. In order to guide practical implementations of the protocols, guidelines were compiled into IEC 61784 as *profiles*. The relationship between the IEC 61784 profiles, the IEC 61158 types, and the protocol names is shown in Table 17.2. There are basically seven different main profiles. Before describing the individual networks, general topologies, media access methodologies, and network media need to be discussed.

17.2.1 Network Topologies

When constructing a local area network, there are three main network topologies, that is, how devices are physically connected. The bus topology (Figure 17.7*a*) is by far the most common topology in factory automation communications. In a bus network, the devices are all connected to the same media and theoretically every PLC can communicate with any other PLC. The network connection is commonly called a "tap." Depending on the particular network, the tap may be a simple BNC "T" connector, a terminal strip, or a multi-pin connector. In some networks, the cable may be "daisy-chained" between PLCs. The star topology, shown in Figure 17.7*b* is used in some older, proprietary networks. In this case, each PLC is connected to a central network controller and any PLC-to-PLC messages pass through the network controller. The ring topology (Figure 17.7*c*) was developed for early fiber-optic networks. In a ring topology, each PLC is connected to and

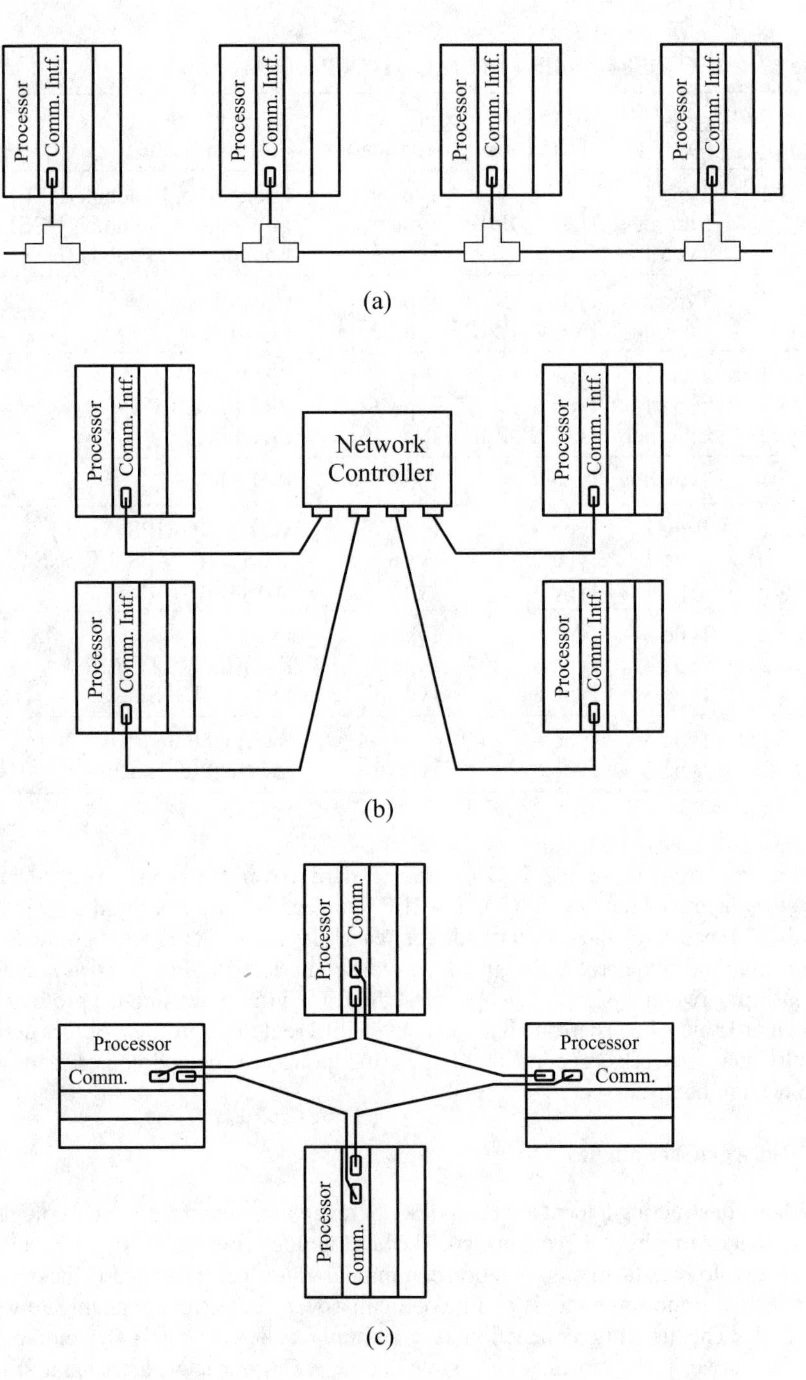

Figure 17.7. Network topologies: *(a)* bus; *(b)* star; *(c)* ring.

communicates with its two neighbors. An individual PLC-to-PLC message may have to make multiple "hops" in order to reach its destination.

The star topology is still used in Ethernet networks. In this case, the "network controller" is a hub or switch. Even though the Ethernet physical topology is most like a multi-level star, it logically acts like a bus connection, that is, each network device communicates with another network device and is not cognizant of any intervening hardware. The ring topology has basically been supplanted by the fiber optic version of Ethernet. In addition, some of the bus networks allow fiber optics to replace cable segments.

17.2.2 Media Access

With a bus topology, one must have some method of controlling a particular device's access to the bus. There are three main methods of bus arbitration:

1. Master/slave
2. Carrier sense multiple access with collision detection
3. Token passing

Though the bus arbitration for a particular network is often not one of these three, it has elements of at least one of them.

With master/slave arbitration, one of the network nodes is the designated master. The master polls each network node to check its presence (or node status, "health") and to allow the node to transmit messages to other nodes. Master/slave is the simplest arbitration method. However, if the master node fails, then the network fails. A backup master will solve this problem. This method of bus arbitration was common in the earlier distributed process control systems. Though not used for PLC-to-PLC communications, master/slave bus arbitration is still utilized in I/O networks.

Carrier sense multiple access with collision detection (CSMA/CD) is a masterless arbitration scheme. When a node wants to send a message, it waits for no network traffic and then attempts to send a message. If two nodes transmit simultaneously, then a *collision* occurs and each of the offending nodes waits a random amount of time before checking for no network traffic in an attempt to resend the message. Ethernet uses CSMA/CD as its basic bus access method. While CSMA/CD is a simple masterless protocol, performance rapidly deteriorates if the network traffic is heavy. With the original Ethernet specification, when the attempted network transmissions exceed about 60% of the available capacity, the transmission delay increases dramatically (Ciminiera et al, 1988). Higher baud rate and the use of Ethernet switches in place of hubs have overcome this disadvantage (Lian et al, 2001).

In token-passing arbitration, a special message, called the *token*, is circulated among the network nodes. Possessing the token grants the node access to the network and the node can transmit messages. When finished with the transmissions, the station passes the token to the next station in the list. The token is analogous to the baton that is passed from one runner to the next in a relay race. The runner possessing the baton is the one racing. Token passing is illustrated in Figure 17.8. The token rotation is 2-1-3. The steps to generate the initial token and rotation list are not shown. The token starts in node 2. When node 2 finishes transmitting messages, it sends a special message to node 1, granting it the token. Node 1 transmits its messages and then passes the token to node 3. When node 3 finishes its message transmission, it passes the token to node 2 and the cycle recommences. Token passing guarantees delivery of some messages under high network traffic, even beyond the

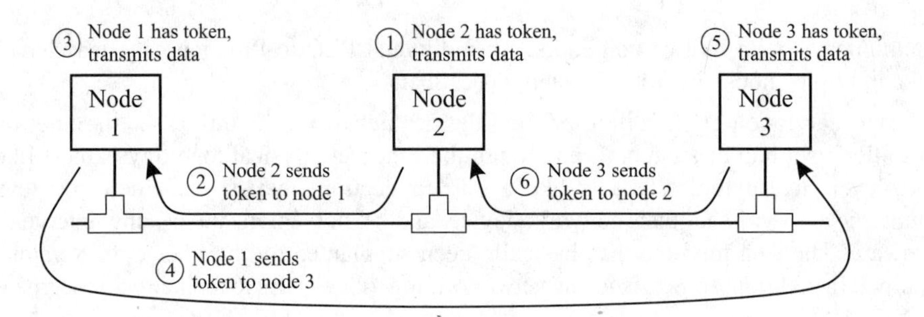

Figure 17.8. Token passing operation.

available capacity. This arbitration is the most complicated, having to deal with such issues as generating the initial token and allowing stations to leave and enter the rotation.

When the Ethernet (CSMA/CD) and token bus protocols were being developed in the 1980's as the IEEE 802.3 and 802.4 standards, there was a fierce debate as to which one was more suitable for factory communications. Ethernet was generally viewed as not acceptable since message delivery could not be guaranteed under high network loads. When things "go wrong" in a factory, the network traffic is substantial due to the alarm messages being transmitted from the PLCs to the operator terminals. The debate has largely subsided because of three reasons:

1. The cost of an Ethernet connection declined faster than the cost of a token bus connection.
2. The baud rate of the Ethernet network increased 100-fold.
3. The development of Ethernet switches

However, the token bus arbitration method still survives in the Foundation Fieldbus, ControlNet and Profibus networks.

17.2.3 Network Media

There are five main categories of network media:

Twisted pair
Baseband coaxial cable
Broadband coaxial cable
Fiber optic
Radio frequency

As its name implies, a twisted pair cable consists of pairs of wires twisted around each other. The twisting provides some noise immunity. Shielding the cable further increases the noise immunity. Figure 17.9*a* shows the construction of an example shielded twisted pair cable. Twisted pair cables are generally used for lower speed networks. A baseband coaxial cable is a flexible cable having a shield around a single conductor (Figure 17.9*b*). Baseband coaxial cable can handle higher data rates and longer distances than twisted pair cable. Broadband RG-59 coaxial cable is the medium commonly used for cable TV. It is a rigid coaxial cable and the shield forms the outside of the cable (Figure 17.9*c*). For each channel, there is a transmitting frequency and a receiving frequency. One end of the cable is called the head end. All nodes transmit to the head end, which retransmits the signal at the

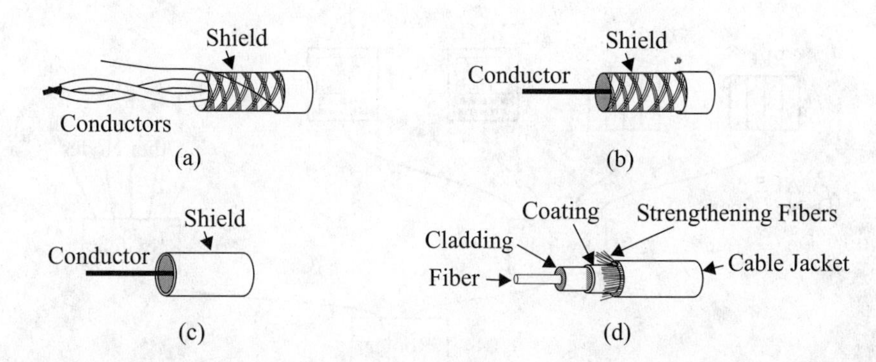

Figure 17.9. Network media: *(a)* twisted pair; *(b)* baseband coaxial; *(c)* broadband coaxial; *(d)* fiber optics.

receiving frequency. This medium supports multiple channels on the same physical medium and thus each channel is its own LAN. With repeaters, a network with this medium can be extended up to 30 miles. Though it can support very large networks, the connection cost for each node is relatively high due to the high-frequency modulators and demodulators. Fiber optic cable (Figure 17.9*d*) is immune to electrical interference and so is used in very noisy industrial environments. Though initially this medium was costly, its cost is now comparable to wired media. However, it is still more complex to install since it cannot be easily spliced. In manufacturing, it is typically used to extend wired busses long distances and through electrically noisy areas. Wireless communication networks rely on radio frequency transmission. This type of medium is becoming popular since it lowers the installation cost. However, it is only useful for short distances and objects in the transmission path can disrupt communications. In addition, there are security concerns since the signal can be monitored remotely.

17.2.4 Redundancy

Having a redundant system means that one can tolerate failures. Redundant network media is fairly common, but it only protects against a cut cable or fiber. Redundant network cables with redundant communication modules protects against more failures, but at the expense of more complexity. Those automation networks that support redundancy are indicated in the following sections.

17.3 ETHERNET

Ethernet is by far the most prevalent backbone network. In the early 1980's, General Motors spearheaded the development of GM MAP (General Motors Manufacturing Automation Protocol), which at the time was expected to be the backbone network for factory communications. The medium was broadband coaxial cable. A few systems were installed, but the connection cost for each node was high. The cost of Ethernet network connections continued to decline, essentially making GM MAP prohibitively expensive.

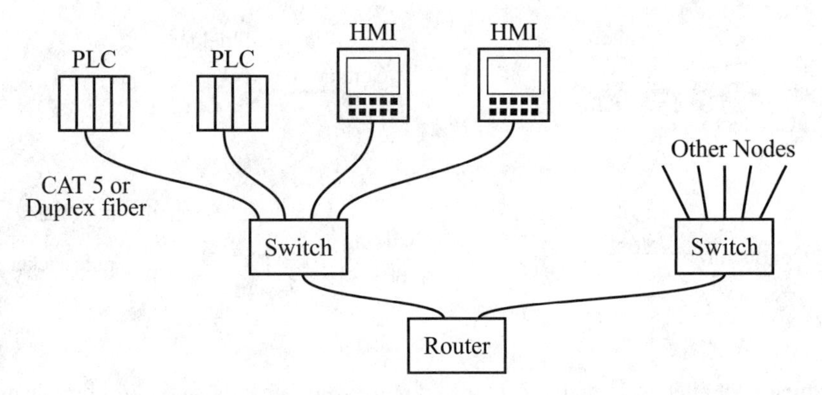

Figure 17.10. Ethernet topology.

Physical Layer

The original 802.3 specification called for two types of physical media, thin coaxial cable (RG-8) and thick coaxial cable (RG-58). The most popular media today is CAT-5 (category 5) unshielded twisted pair cable with 4 twisted pairs or duplex fiber. Wireless modems are also available. The general structure of an Ethernet network is that of a tree/star (Figure 17.10). At the switch (or hub), the network resembles a star topology. However, further up the hierarchy, the network looks more like a tree with routers connecting to multiple switches.

Data Link Layer

Logically, the Ethernet network more resembles a bus. As described earlier, CSMA/CD (carrier-sense multiple access with collision detection) is the bus access method.

Application Layer

Multiple application protocols have been built on top of the Ethernet data link and physical layers. Foundation Fieldbus HSE, Ethernet/IP, and PROFINET are described in later sections. Even earlier protocols, like Modbus, have been implemented with Ethernet (and called Modbus/TCP).

17.4 FOUNDATION FIELDBUS

The Foundation Fieldbus (FF) network has three versions: H1, H2, and high-speed Ethernet (HSE). FF H1 is basically a network for devices at the base level of factory automation networks and FF HSE is a higher-level network connecting controllers. The H2 version is a remainder of an older Foundation Fieldbus draft (Felser, 2002). Since no products are likely to be available, it is not covered here. One of the unique characteristics of Foundation Fieldbus is a fully specified application layer based on function blocks. The communication model of the FF protocols is shown in Figure 17.11. Both H1 and HSE share the same application layer and user application definitions. The differences between the two versions are in the data link and physical layers. Note that layers 3 – 6 in the OSI model are not used. The HSE physical and data link layers are the same as for 100-MHz

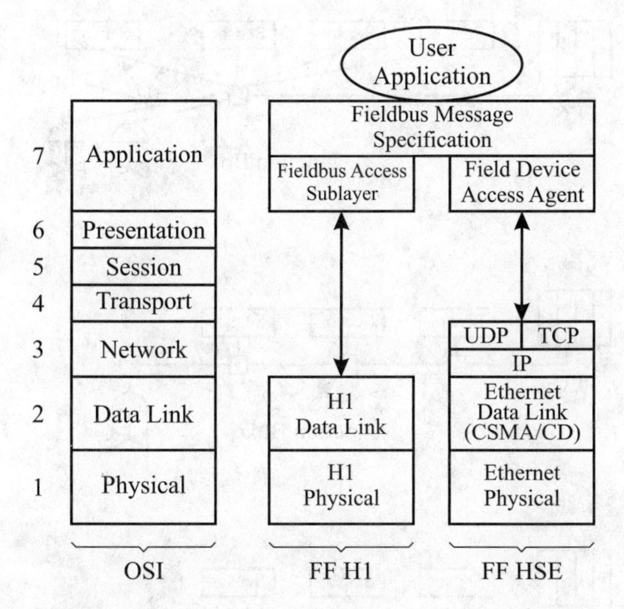

Figure 17.11. Fieldbus communication model.

Ethernet. The physical and data link layers of H1 are described here, followed by a brief description of the user application layer, which is common to both H1 and HSE.

Development of the FF H1 protocol started in the mid-1980's under the auspices of the ISA S50 committee. Many of the industrial companies that helped develop IEEE 802.4 joined this committee and turned their attention to standardizing a process control field network. The FF H1 network was designed as a substitute for 4-20 mA and HART (highway addressable remote transducer) signal transmission in process control applications. Eventually, the HSE version was added in the late-1990's.

17.4.1 H1 Physical Layer

The FF H1 medium is twisted pair #16 AWG for the trunk cable and #18 AWG wire for the spurs, which is basically the same cabling used for 4-20 mA wiring to analog sensors or actuators. Shielding is not required, though it does reduce noise susceptibility. Possible network topologies are shown in Figure 17.12. The tree or "chicken foot" topology (Figure 17.12*a*) consists of a single fieldbus segment (trunk) connected to a common junction box to form a network. The connections from the devices to the junction box are called spurs. The tree topology is best when retrofitting existing 4-20 mA analog sensors/actuators since at the most, only a new trunk cable needs to be installed. Though spurs can be up to 200 meters long, the recommended length is 30 meters or less. The bus with spurs topology (Figure 17.12*b*) consists of devices connected to a multi-drop trunk segment through a spur. This topology is generally more costly than the tree topology. The daisy chain topology (Figure 17.12*c*) eliminates the junction boxes, but is not recommended since adding new devices to the network disrupts network communication. The possible network topologies can also be combined.

Without repeaters, a FF H1 segment can have up to 32 devices and be no more than 1900 meters long. The total segment length is calculated by adding length of the spurs to the

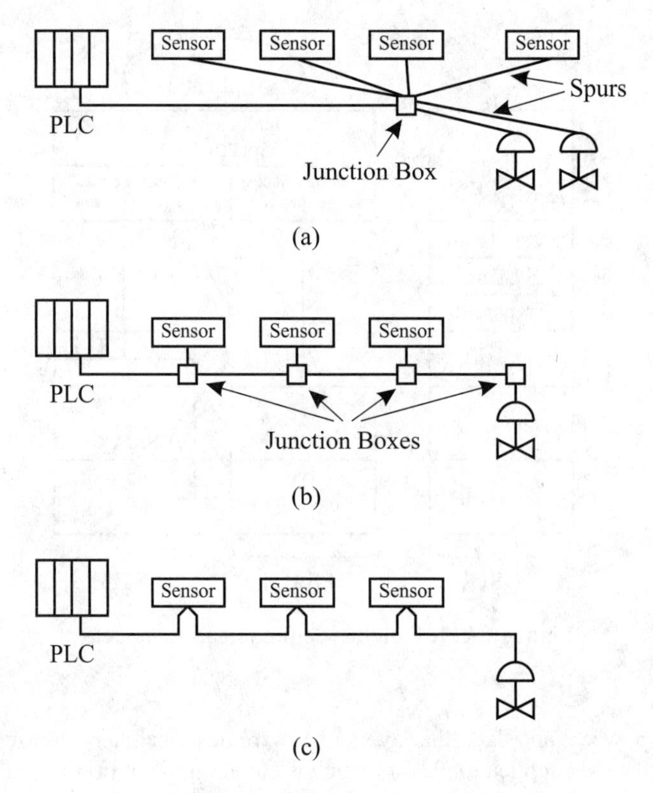

Figure 17.12. Foundation Fieldbus topologies: *(a)* tree; *(b)* bus with spurs; *(c)* daisy chain.

length of the main trunk line. When multiple segments are connected with repeaters the number of devices on a segment can be increased to a maximum of 240 devices. In FF terminology, a link consists of one or more segments interconnected with repeaters. All of the devices on a link share a common schedule, which is explained in the data link layer.

Data is transmitted at the rate of 31.25 Kbit/s and is Manchester encoded. The transmitting device delivers ±10 mA into a 50 ohm equivalent impedance to create a 1 volt peak-to-peak voltage modulated on the network DC power. Devices may be powered from the network, which explains the limit on the number of devices on a segment.

Redundant media is not supported. However, for applications that require high availability, basically everything else should be redundant.

17.4.2 H1 Data Link Layer

FF H1 uses a centralized scheduler, called a link active scheduler (LAS). The link master (LM) is the device on a link containing the LAS. There must be at least one LM per link. Redundant link masters are supported, but only one of them is functioning as the LAS at any time. The LAS maintains a list of transmission times for all data buffers in all devices that need to be transmitted cyclically. The LAS issues a compel data (CD) message to a device when it is time for it to broadcast its data. Upon receipt of a CD message, a device "publishes" (broadcasts) its data buffer to all devices on the link. Any device configured as a "subscriber" (receiver) of the data extracts the data from the message. The LAS must take into account publisher/subscriber relationships when scheduling CD messages. An example LAS schedule is shown in Figure 17.13*b* and explained along with the application layer.

During those periods when there is no scheduled transmission, the LAS may issue a pass token (PT) message to a device, which gives it permission to send messages to another node. Unscheduled exchanges between devices are handled with a client/server type of exchange. In this type of exchange, a device (the client) requests data from another device (the server) when the client receives a PT. When the server receives its PT from the LAS, it responds with the data requested by the client.

17.4.3 User Application Layer

The user application layer in a device is basically a set of blocks. There are three types of blocks: resource block, transducer block, and function block. Each device has only one resource block which describes the characteristics of the fieldbus device such as the device name, manufacturer, and serial number. A transducer block (TB) decouples the local I/O from the function blocks. There is typically one TB for each I/O channel. A TB contains information such as calibration data and sensor type. The function blocks define the behavior of a device and are similar to IEC 61131-3 function blocks. The input and output parameters of function blocks can be linked over the fieldbus. The Fieldbus Foundation has defined sets of standard function blocks (Fieldbus Foundation, 2003). For example, the ten basic standard function blocks are:

Function Block Name	Symbol
Analog Input	AI
Analog Output	AO
Bias/Gain	BG
Control Selector	CS
Discrete Input	DI
Discrete Output	DO
Manual Loader	ML
Proportional/Derivative	PD
Proportional/Integral/Derivative	PID
Ratio	RA

The user can also define a flexible function block (FFB) which is basically an encapsulation of a 61131-3 function block.

The execution of the function blocks is scheduled along with the fieldbus communications. The function block schedules contain the start time offset (called the DL) from the beginning of the link schedule. A *macrocycle* is a single iteration of a schedule within a device. The LAS and each device have a macrocycle. All devices are synchronized to the start of the link schedule.

For example, given the system in Figure 17.13*a*, a possible scheduling of messages and function block execution is shown in Figure 17.13*b*. This system consists of a flow sensor (AI), a PID block, and a valve (AO). Since the PID block needs a current flow sensor reading before it is executed, the AI block execution is scheduled first (DL=0), followed by the transmission of its data buffer (DL=10, initiated by a CD from the LAS). The PID block

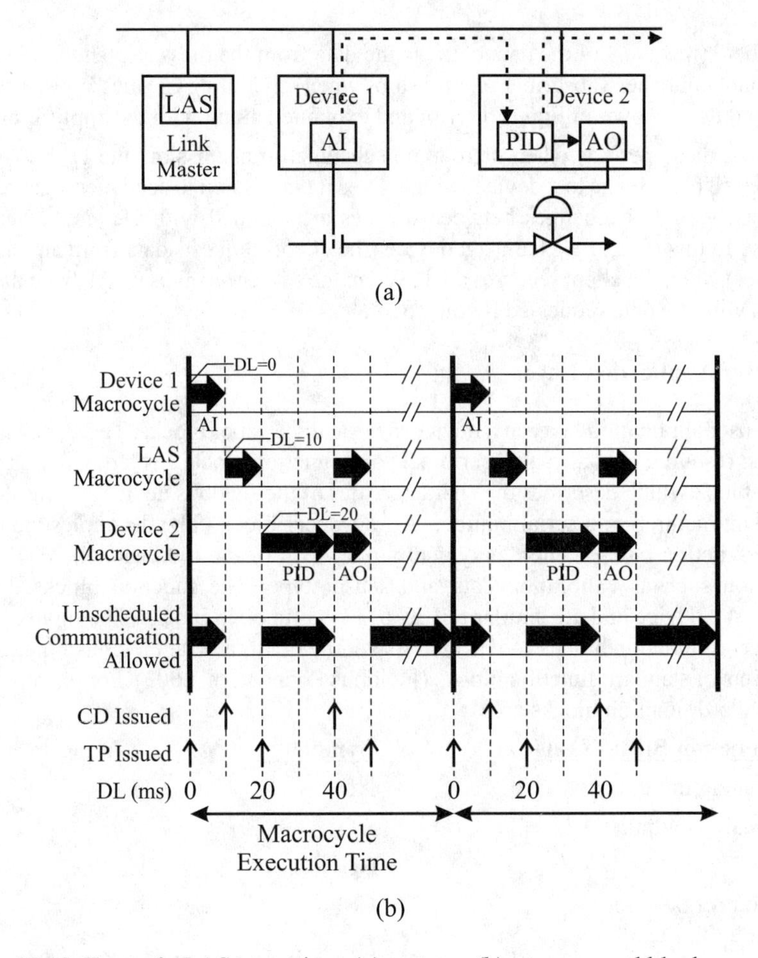

Figure 17.13. Example LAS operation: *(a)* system; *(b)* message and block execution timing.

executes next (DL=20), followed by the AO block (DL=40) to transmit the appropriate value to the valve. Simultaneous to the AO block execution, the PID data buffer is broadcast on the network (DL=40). PT messages are issued at the start of those intervals where unscheduled messages may be transmitted. The execution of the function blocks is controlled by the system management function in a device.

For the HSE fieldbus, there is no LAS and so the communication is immediate instead of scheduled. However, the function blocks execute in the same manner as for the H1 fieldbus.

17.5 CIP-RELATED PROTOCOLS

The DeviceNet, ControlNet, and Ethernet Industrial Protocol (Ethernet/IP) protocols are all related because they share the Control and Information Protocol (CIP) for the upper

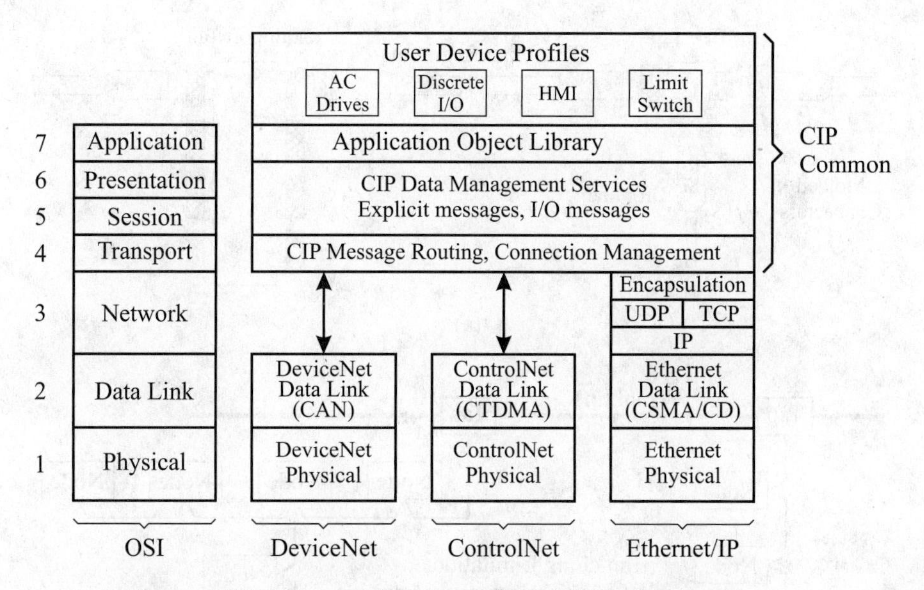

Figure 17.14. Communication model for CIP-related protocols.

layers (Figure 17.14). The differences between these protocols are at layers 1, 2, and 3 of the OSI model.

ControlNet was originally developed by Allen-Bradley and Honeywell in the early 1990's to transmit time-critical I/O and peer-to-peer data. In parallel with this effort, Allen-Bradley also developed the DeviceNet protocol for device communications. Both of these protocol specifications were published in the mid-1990's. In 1997, the administration of the ControlNet protocol was transferred to ControlNet International, a multi-vendor association. Adminstration of the DeviceNet protocol was turned over to the Open DeviceNet Vendors Association in 1995. Ethernet/IP was developed recently to provide an acceptable application layer and industrially-hardened connectivity built on top of standard Ethernet.

The DeviceNet and ControlNet physical and data link layers are described first, followed by a brief introduction to the CIP layers.

17.5.1 DeviceNet

The DeviceNet protocol was developed for device networks. It is relatively low speed but efficient at handling the short messages to/from I/O modules.

Physical Layer

The physical layer of DeviceNet is the same as the Controller Area Network (CAN) developed by Bosch in the early 1980's as an automotive network standard. The DeviceNet medium is a 5 conductor shielded cable, two twisted pairs plus a shield drain. One twisted pair carries the signal and the other twisted pair carries the power. The network topology is trunkline/dropline (Figure 17.15). A trunkline tap can be for one or multiple drop lines (Figure 17.15*a*). In addition, a dropline can be daisy-chained between devices, as shown in Figure 17.15*b*. A DeviceNet network can have up to 64 nodes. There are three data transmission rates: 125, 250, and 500 Kbit/s. The maximum trunkline length depends on the

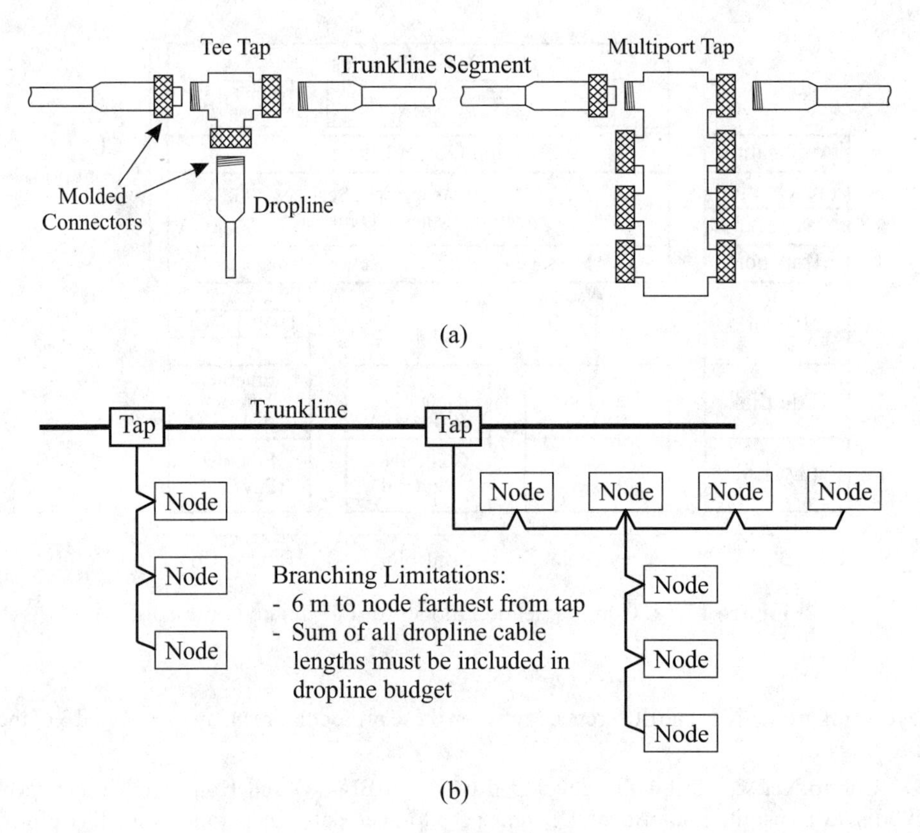

Figure 17.15. DeviceNet network topology: *(a)* trunkline taps; *(b)* daisy-chained drop lines.

data rate. For the thick trunkline cable the maximum distance is 500 m for the 125 Kbit/s data rate down to 100 m for the 500 Kbit/s data rate. If the thin (drop line) cable is used for the trunkline, the maximum length of the trunkline is 100 m. The maximum drop length is 6 m and the sum of all drop cable lengths must not exceed a maximum.

Several different connector types can be used on DeviceNet. Both sealed and unsealed connectors are available. For devices installed on the factory floor, mini-style and micro-style pluggable, sealed connectors are used. For nodes installed inside cabinets, open-style connectors can be used.

Devices are ordinarily powered from the DeviceNet cable. Since the trunkline current rating is 8 amps, the power supply conductor is broken into segments, each segment powered by a separate power supply.

Data Link Layer

The method of bus arbitration is similar to the CSMA/CD used on Ethernet, but without the collisions. If two or more nodes start transmitting simultaneously, the bus conflict is resolved by a bit-wise arbitration. A logical “0” is dominant on the wire and overrides a logical “1.” When a node transmits a “1,” but hears a “0,” it immediately stops transmitting. The “winning” node continues to transmit its message to completion. With this method of arbitration, neither information nor time is lost. Since the first data in a DeviceNet message is an 11-bit identifier, the winning node is the one with the lowest-numbered identifier. The message contains at most 8 bytes of data, though there is a fragmentation protocol that permits larger amounts of data to be broken into multiple messages.

Network and Transport

In accordance with CIP, a connection must be established between two devices before data can be exchanged. The 11-bit CAN identifier is used to define the connection identifier. The uniqueness of connection identifiers is required to take full advantage of producer/consumer capabilities.

DeviceNet devices may be clients or servers or both. For a typical client device, its connection produces requests and consumes responses. For a typical server device, its connections consume requests and produce responses. However, a client or server connection may only consume messages. These connections would be the destination for Cyclic or Change-of-State messages. Similarly, a client or server connection may only produce messages. These connections would be the source for Cyclic or Change-of-State messages.

DeviceNet provides for a simplified communication scheme based on a master/slave relationship. This connection scheme called the Predefined Master/Slave Connection Set, simplifies the movement of the I/O messages most often used in device-level networks. Most sensors and actuators perform some predetermined function in which the type and amount of data produced and/or consumed by the device is known. The Predefined Master/Slave Connection Set provides connections that are almost entirely configured when the device is added to the network or after the network is powered up. In this case, a "master" device must claim ownership of this predefined connection set within its "slave" to start the data flow. Multiple masters cannot share slave devices. The slave devices produce data in one of the following manners:

Polled - Slave receives "output" data from the master device in an order defined by the scan list in the master. For a given system configuration, the polled method produces deterministic behavior.

Cyclic - Slave device produces its data at a precisely defined interval. Depending on the application this method of data production can reduce the amount of traffic on the wire and more efficiently use the available bandwidth.

Change-of-state - Slave produces data whenever it changes, or at a base heartbeat rate. With the heartbeat, the consuming device knows that the producer is still alive and active.

17.5.2 ControlNet

The ControlNet protocol was developed as an automation network (Figure 17.3). It is designed to efficiently handle time-critical data transfers between PLCs.

Physical Layer

The ControlNet medium can either be RG-6 coaxial cable or fiber optic cable. The usual network topology is trunkline/dropline (Figure 17.16) using RG-6 coaxial cable. Fiber optic cables are used as point-to-point links to extend the network. ControlNet also supports tree and star topologies with fiber optic repeaters. Both coaxial cable and fiber optic systems can be designed to meet the requirements of intrinsic safety environments. A

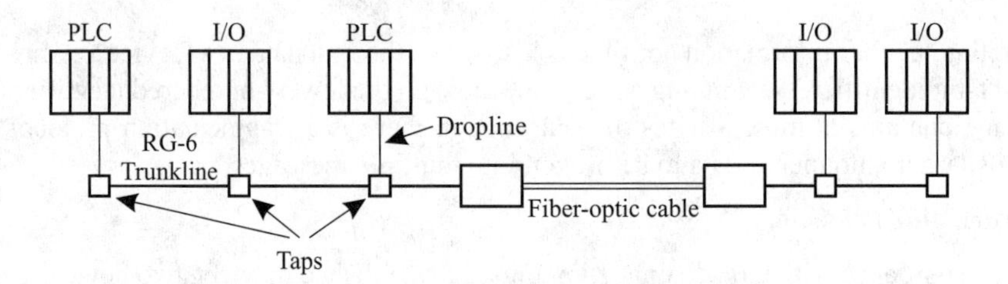

Figure 17.16. ControlNet trunkline/dropline topology.

ControlNet network can have up to 99 nodes. Without signal repeaters, it can extend to 1000 m with two nodes and 250 m with 48 nodes. With repeaters, the trunk can extend up to 25 km. ControlNet supports redundant media. If redundant media is used, nodes transmit on both cables and listen continuously to both cables. When listening, each node independently decides which cable has the best signal. Data is transmitted at the rate of 5 Mbit/s and is Manchester encoded.

Data Link Layer

ControlNet uses Concurrent Time Domain Multiple Access (CTDMA) to control node access to the bus. CDTMA is designed so that time-critical data transfer, such as I/O or peer-to-peer inter-locking data, is not hindered by other data transfers such as PLC programming. The operation of CDTMA is shown in Figure 17.17. Time is divided into network update times (NUTs). The duration of a NUT is configured to be between 2 ms and 100 ms. Within the first part of each NUT, an implicit token rotation algorithm grants media access. The token rotation starts from the lowest configured node address and proceeds to the highest configured node address. There is no centralized bus scheduler. All nodes are continuously synchronized so that they exactly know when they may access the media to

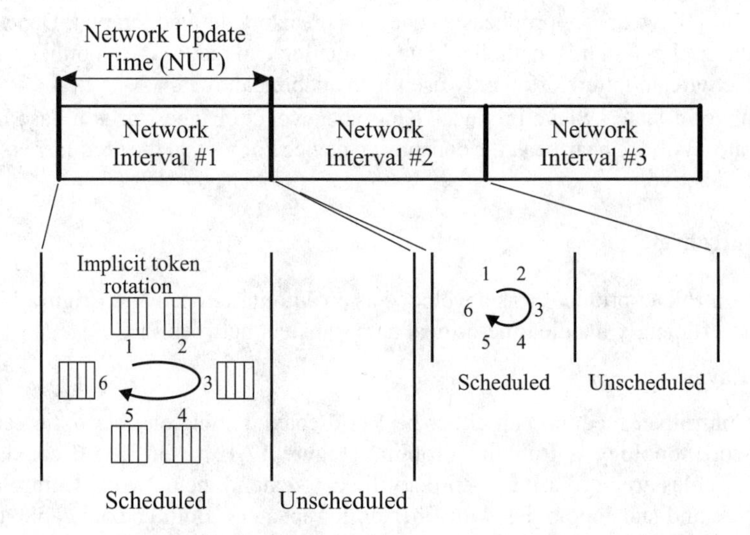

Figure 17.17. ControlNet bus arbitration.

broadcast their data. Transmission time for real-time data is also allocated in the NUT. The remaining transmission time within a NUT supports non-time-critical data.

Though CDTMA does not have a centralized scheduler, the network must be configured by some network management device. The biggest drawback to this method of bus arbitration is that the entire network must be reconfigured when any node adds a new scheduled transmission. During network configuration all running PLC programs must be stopped.

Network and Transport Layers

ControlNet requires a formal connection to be established between application entities before information can be transferred. A connection defines a path or virtual circuit between application end points for data transfer. Connections can be either peer-to-peer or multicast (multiple destination nodes read the same data packet). Data may be transmitted based on "cyclic", "change-of-state" or "application" triggers.

17.5.3 Ethernet/IP

EtherNet/IP uses standard Ethernet and TCP/IP (transport control protocol/Internet protocol) protocols to transport CIP messages. As for both DeviceNet and ControlNet, EtherNet/IP provides a producer/consumer model for the exchange of time-critical control data. EtherNet/IP uses IP multicast so that many EtherNet/IP devices can receive the same produced information from a single producing device. EtherNet/IP uses standard IEEE 802.3 technology. To improve determinism, EtherNet/IP recommends the use of commercial Ethernet switches with 100 Mbps transmission rate and full-duplex operation.

As shown in Figure 17.14, CIP messages are encapsulated into either a Transport Control Protocol (TCP) or a User Datagram Protocol (UDP) connection. The encapsulation protocol defines a reserved TCP port number and a reserved UDP port number that is supported by all EtherNet/IP devices. Depending on the particular message, it may be sent by either UDP or TCP. Some encapsulated messages can only be sent by TCP. Other messages may be sent by either UDP or TCP (ControlNet Int., 2001b).

On Ethernet, it is possible for a data packet to be lost, for example due to excessive collisions. Ethernet does not guarantee the delivery of a packet. Producers continue to send data at the specified rate and the consumers receive the next packet after the lost packet. The degree to which lost packets can be tolerated is application-specific. Ethernet is unsuitable for those applications that cannot tolerate lost packets.

17.5.4 CIP Application Layer

The Control and Information Protocol (CIP) provides common communication protocol layers on top of DeviceNet, ControlNet, and Ethernet/IP (Figure 17.14). CIP has two primary purposes:

Transport of control-oriented data

Transport of other information, such as configuration, PLC program, and diagnostics.

The CIP is object-oriented. Both communication and application entities are referenced as objects. The general CIP object model is shown in Figure 17.18 (ControlNet Int., 2001a). The objects in this model are:

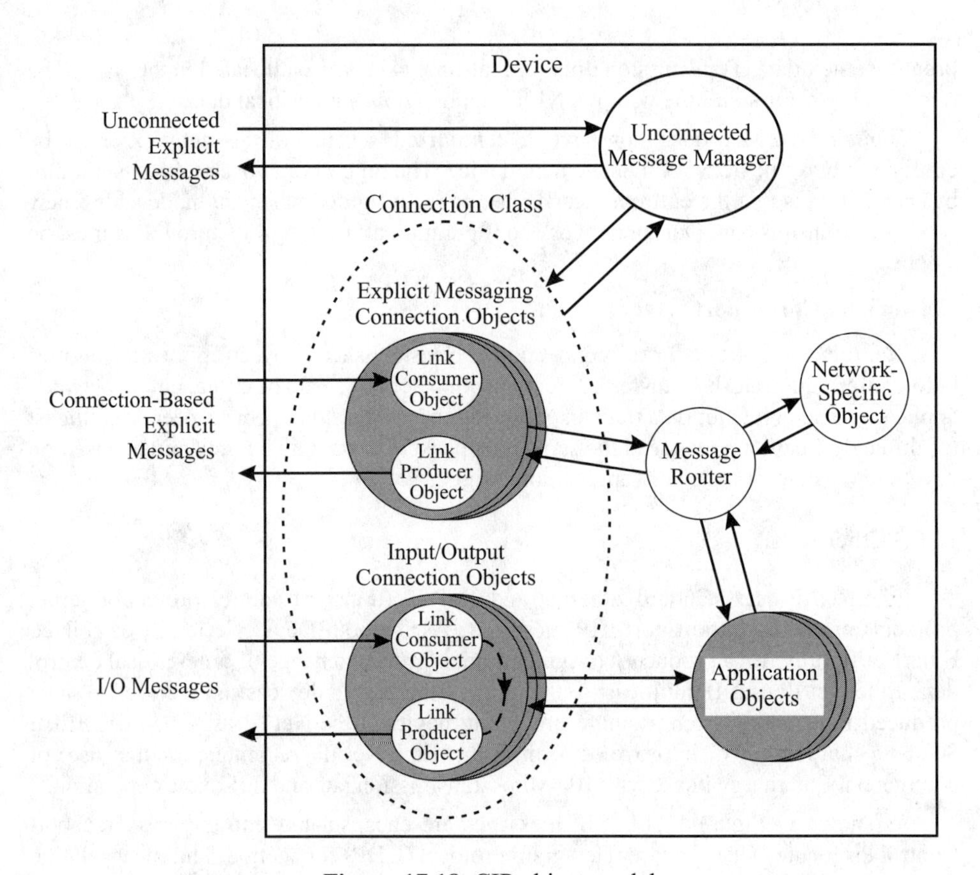

Figure 17.18. CIP object model.

Unconnected Message Manager - Processes CIP unconnected explicit messages.

Connection Class - Allocates and manages internal resources associated with both Explicit and Input/Output messaging connections.

Connection Object - Manages the communication-specific aspects associated with a particular application-to-application network relationship.

Network-Specific Link Object - Provides the configuration and status of a physical CIP network connection (DeviceNet, ControlNet, and Ethernet/IP objects).

Message Router - Distributes Explicit Request Messages to the appropriate handler.

Application Objects - Implement the intended purpose of the product.

The Unconnected Message Manager (UCMM) is responsible for processing the messages that establish both explicit messaging and I/O connections. Explicit messaging connections are point-to-point, that is exist between only two devices. I/O connections can be either point-to-point or *multicast*. Multicast connections allow a single transmission to be heard by many nodes.

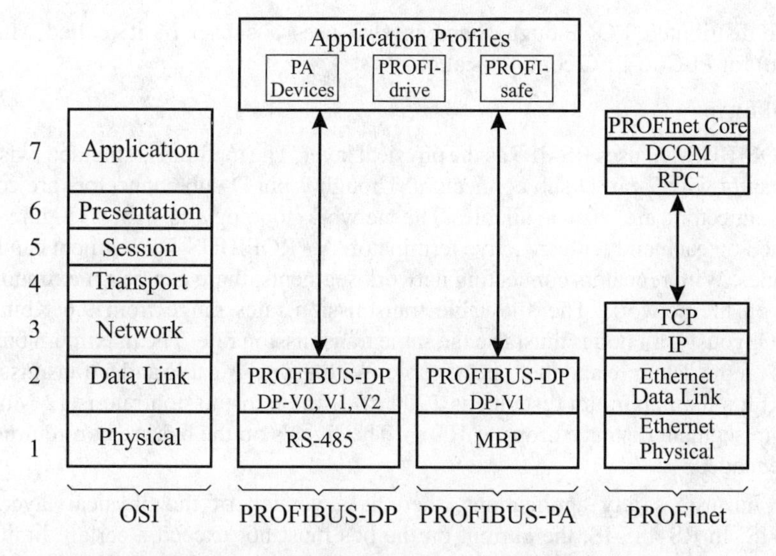

Figure 17.19. Communication model for PROFIBUS protocols.

17.6 PROFIBUS (DP, PA, PROFINET)

The PROFIBUS (PROcess FIeld BUS) protocol is the result of an effort funded by the German Federal Ministry for Research and Technology in 1987-1990 to build a process automation digital field bus. PROFIBUS has three parts:

1. PROFIBUS-DP (decentral periphery)
2. PROFIBUS-PA (process automation)
3. PROFIBUS-FMS (fieldbus message specification)

PROFIBUS-FMS and PROFIBUS-PA were published as the DIN 19245 standard, parts 1 and 2. In 1993, PROFIBUS-DP was added to this standard as part 3. PROFIBUS became a part of the EN 50170 standard in 1996. Though PROFIBUS-FMS was the first PROFIBUS communication protocol, it was omitted from the IEC 61158 standard and so it is not discussed here. PROFInet is a more recent development by the PROFIBUS trade organization, PNO (PROFIBUS Nutzerorganisation) to answer the trend toward increasing utilization of Ethernet in factory automation.

The relationship between PROFIBUS-DP, PROFIBUS-PA, and PROFInet are shown in Figure 17.19. PROFIBUS-PA is essentially a subset of the data link layer of PROFIBUS-DP with a different physical layer. PROFInet is not the PROFIBUS application layer on top of Ethenet. It basically uses standard information technology functions.

The PROFIBUS-DP network is described first, followed by PROFIBUS-PA. Lastly, PROFInet is discussed.

17.6.1 PROFIBUS-DP

The PROFIBUS-DP communication protocol is widely used in PLC automation in Europe. It was developed for a mix of discrete and analog devices. It appears to be primarily used for distributed I/O, though Siemens also uses a subset of it (called Multipoint Interface) for PLC-to-PLC communication.

Physical Layer

PROFIBUS-DP uses RS-485 as the physical layer. The medium is shielded twisted pair cable usually with 9-pin D-sub connectors. Though 9-pin D-sub connectors are common, sealed connectors are also available. The network topology is a bus (Figure 17.7*a*), terminated on each end with an active terminator. A PROFIBUS-DP segment can have up to 32 nodes. With repeaters connecting network segments, there can be a maximum of 126 devices on the network. The allowable transmission rates range from 9.6 Kbit/s to 12 Mbit/s. Obvously, all nodes must use the same transmission rate. The maximum bus length depends on the data rate and the type of cable. With a type-A cable and a transmission rate of 9.6 Kbit/s the maximum distance is 1200 m. If the transmission rate is 12 Mbit/s, the maximum segment distance drops to 100 m. The signals on the bus are non-return-to-zero (NRZ) encoded.

For intrinsic safety applications, there is a version of the physical layer, called RS-485-IS. In RS-485-IS, the current on the bus must not exceed a certain limit, which depends on the voltage level. For RS-485-IS, the medium is a shielded twisted 4-wire cable and its maximum transmission rate is 1.5 Mbit/s. Fiber optic cabling options are also available. The fiber can replace a network point-to-point cable, can allow a star and ring configurations (Siemens, 1999a).

Data Link Layer

PROFIBUS-DP defines three versions of its data link layer:

DP-V0: Basic DP functions
DP-V1: Enhancements for process automation
DP-V2: Enhancements for motion control

DP-V0 is the original PROFIBUS data link layer and the enhancements are recent additions. DP-V0 is described first and then the enhancements are discussed.

DP-V0 supports both master/slave and peer-to-peer communications. There are three classes of network devices:

DP Master Class 1 (DPM1)
DP Master Class 2 (DPM2)
DP Slave

A DPM1 device cyclically exchanges information with slaves at a specified message cycle. PLCs are typically DPM1 devices. A DPM2 device is also a bus master, but is usually an engineering or configuration device. A DPM2 does not exchange information with a slave device. A slave device is typically a remote I/O device (for example, discrete I/O or variable-speed drive), but can be HMI devices.

In a mono-master system, there is only one master and it controls the bus. In a multi-master system (Figure 17.20*a*), multiple masters share the bus. Since only one master can control the bus, a token is circulated among the masters. The master that possesses the token controls the bus and communicates with its slaves, or with one of the other masters. Slaves respond only to direct queries from a master device. Though all masters can read the input and output images of any slave, only one DPM1 device can write to a slave's output image. This master is assigned during configuration. In Figure 17.20*a*, PLC 1 is the master

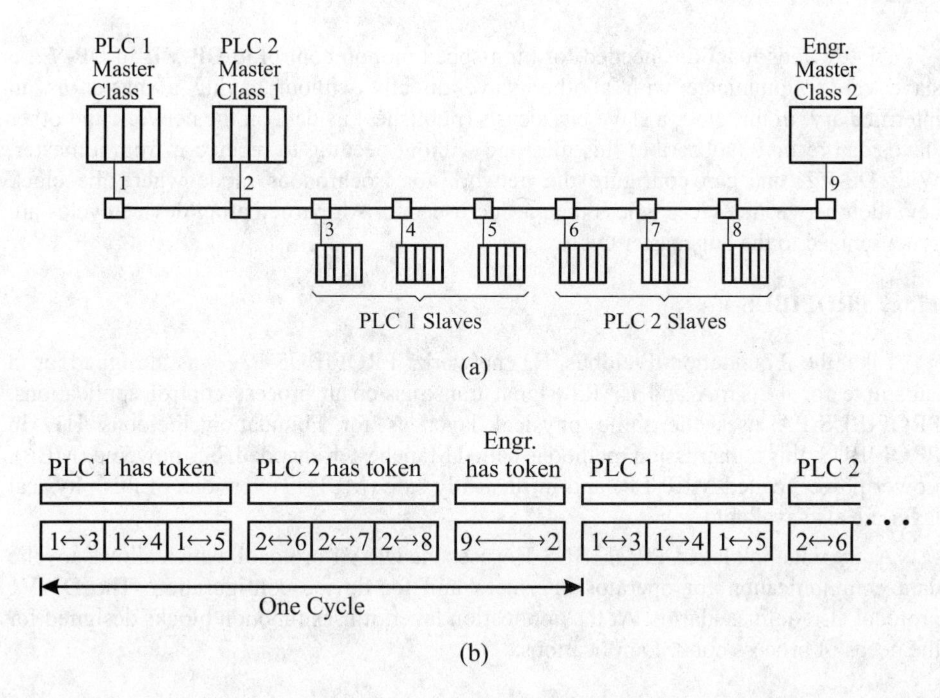

Figure 17.20. Example DP-V0 operation: *(a)* system; *(b)* message timing.

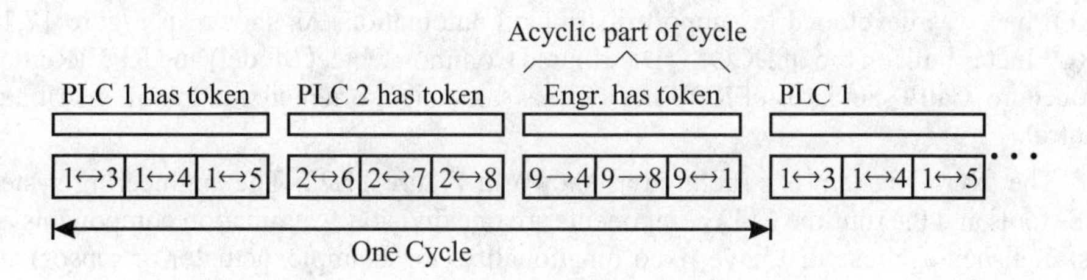

Figure 17.21. Example DP-V1 operation timing.

of slave devices 3 - 5 and PLC 2 is the master of slaves 6 - 8. When a particular PLC has the token, it communicates with its slaves, checking their configuration and then transferring the data (Figure 17.20*b*). When the engineering device (DPM2) has the token, it communicates peer-to-peer with one of the PLCs.

DP-V1 adds acyclic capability to DP-V0. Transmission of any acyclic data is done between the last cyclic exchange with a slave and the end of a cycle. When a DPM2 device has the token during this period, it can transmit data to any other master or slave. At the end of the cycle, the token is always returned to the first DPM1 device. If there is a large amount of acyclic data, its transmission may span multiple cycles. The total cycle time in DP-V1 is longer than in DP-V0. In DP-V1, a DPM2 master can communicate to any slave. For example, a DP-V1 timing of the system in Figure 17.20*a* is shown in Figure 17.21. In this case, during the acyclic part of the period, station 9 (DPM2) sends information to two slaves and has a short exchange with PLC 1. DP-V1 also defines alarms and portable IEC 61131-3 function blocks.

DP-V2 adds functions needed for high-speed motion control to DP-V1. In DP-V2, a slave can communicate with another slave directly without having a master as an intermediary. In this case, a slave broadcasts (publishes) its data on the network and other slaves can receive (subscribe) this message without needing to receive it from a master. With DP-V2, one can configure the network for isochronous mode where the clock deviation between devices is less than a microsecond. All participating device cycles are synchronized to the bus master cycle.

17.6.2 PROFIBUS-PA

Like the Foundation Fieldbus H1 network, PROFIBUS-PA was designed as a substitute for 4-20 mA and HART signal transmission in process control applications. PROFIBUS-PA uses the same physical layer as for Foundation Fieldbus H1. In PROFIBUS, this transmission method is called Manchester-encoded, bus powered (MBP). Lower power (called MBP-LP) and intrinsically safe (MBP-IS) versions of this physical layer are also available.

At the data link layer, PROFIBUS-PA uses the DP-V1 protocol, which allows acyclic data communication for operator interfaces and for device configuration. The DP-V1 protocol also defines alarms. At the application layer, it uses function blocks designed for the needs of process control applications.

17.6.3 PROFInet

PROFInet is related to PROFBUS in that it was developed by the same organization. PROFInet was developed to support distributed automation. As shown in Figure 17.19, PROFInet is built on top of DCOM (Distributed Common Object Model) and RPC (Remote Procedure Call) standards. PROFInet defines an object-oriented model of distributed control.

The overall system is structured as shown in Figure 17.22. The engineering system (ES) tools and the runtime (RT) components are one division. Automation components are distinguished as those that have fixed functionality (for example, actuator or sensor) and those that have programmable functionality (a PLC). The RT-Auto objects are the automation objects in the factory automation component that may be seen or accessed by another component. Each RT-Auto object has an associated ES-Auto object for the

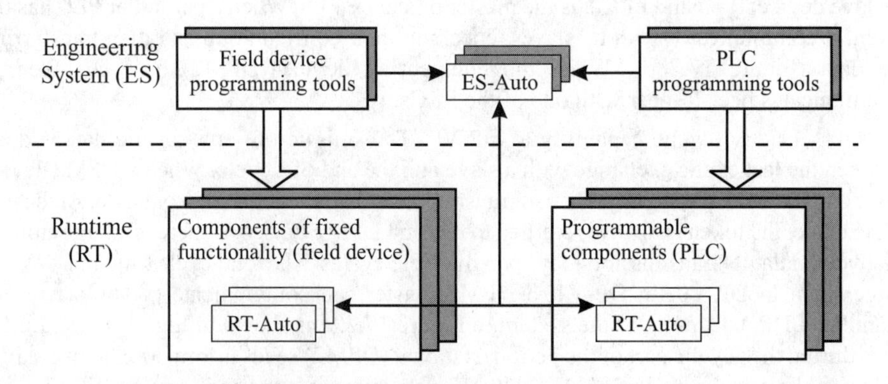

Figure 17.22. PROFInet overall view.

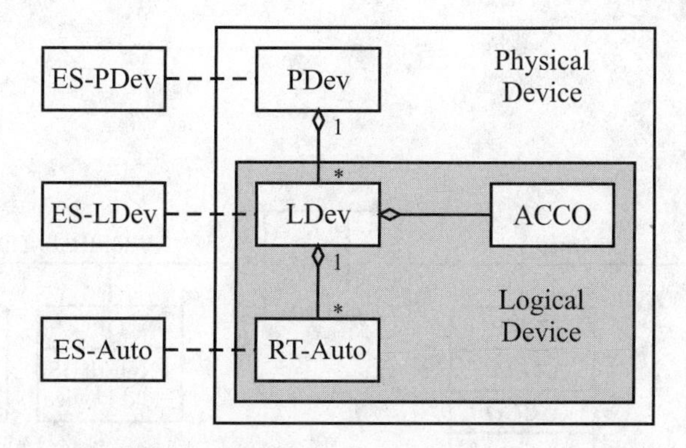

Figure 17.23. PROFInet runtime object model.

engineering tools. The RT-Auto objects provide their functionality through well-defined COM (Common Object Model) interfaces. The automation objects are connected through the DCOM object bus.

The PROFInet runtime object model (Figure 17.23) represents the objects in a device together with the interfaces and methods that are externally accessible (Profibus, 2003). The Physical Device (PDev) represents a physical component having at least one Internet protocol interface. The PDev object exposes the properties of the device. Each hardware component has only one PDev object. A PDev contains one or more logical devices (LDev). An LDev is a software or firmware package as an autonomous entity. The LDev participates as a sensor, actuator, controller, and so on, to solve one part of the automation system. Each LDev has an ACCO (active control connection object) and one or more RT-Auto's. The ACCO is responsible for the exchange of data/events between RT-Auto objects. The tasks of the ACCO include:

- Establishing configured or dynamically created connections.
- Transport of data and events along these connections
- Ensuring the transparency of the connections between the RT-Auto's (whether the connection is local or remote is transparent to the RT-Auto's)
- Implementing failure strategies

The RT-Auto (runtime automation) object represents the automation functionality in the form of a process-related component. They are self-contained modules. One can think of an LDev as a function block diagram and each RT-Auto object as a function block.

Each RT-Auto device has one associated ES-Auto (engineering system automation) object that hides the internal object structure. The ES-Auto object is like a Modicon derived function block or S7 function block. When invoked in the function block editor, the block with the named connections is displayed, but the underlying implementation is not. The LDev and PDev objects also have associated engineering system objects.

Note that since PROFInet is not PROFIBUS on Ethernet, a PROFInet device cannot communicate directly with PROFIBUS devices. Instead, a proxy device, which functions like a gateway, provides RT-Auto objects that do the mapping between the slave devices on PROFIBUS and the PROFInet objects that use them (Figure 17.24).

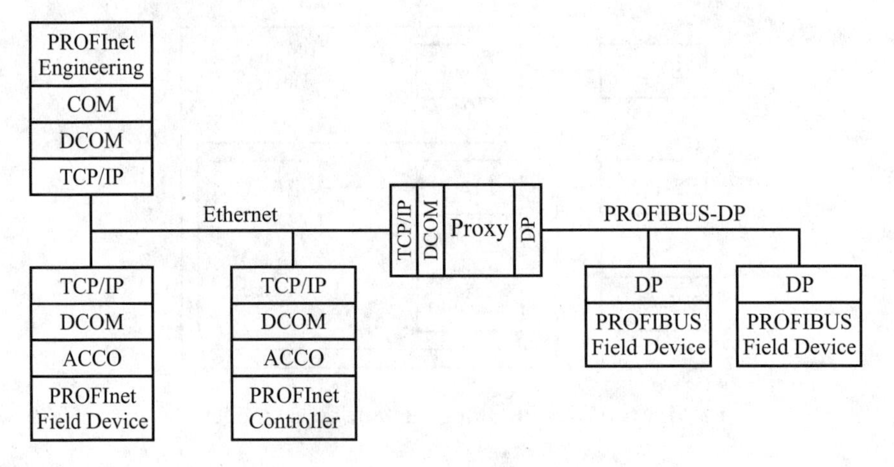

Figure 17.24. PROFBUS connection to PROFInet.

17.7 P-NET

The P-NET protocol was developed in 1983 by Proces-Data A/S in Denmark and the first product to use this field bus was introduced in 1984. The protocol was enhanced to add multi-network and multi-port functions in 1986. The P-NET standard became part of the CENELEC (European Committee for Electrotechnical Standardization) EN 50170 standard in 1996. P-NET implements layers 1 - 4 and 7 of the OSI model (Figure 17.25).

Physical Layer

Like PROFIBUS, P-NET uses RS-485 as the physical layer. The medium is shielded twisted pair cable. The network topology is a ring, a bus, or a redundant bus (Figure 17.26). One can also use a cable with two twisted pairs for 4-wire P-NET. The additional pair supplies 24-volt power. A P-NET segment can have up to 125 nodes. The transmission rate

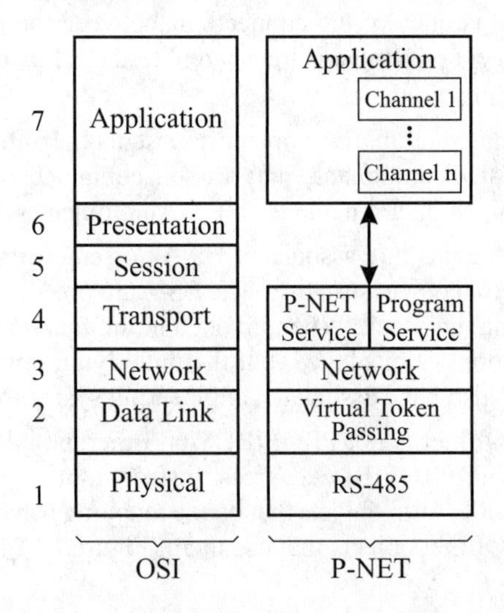

Figure 17.25. P-NET communication model.

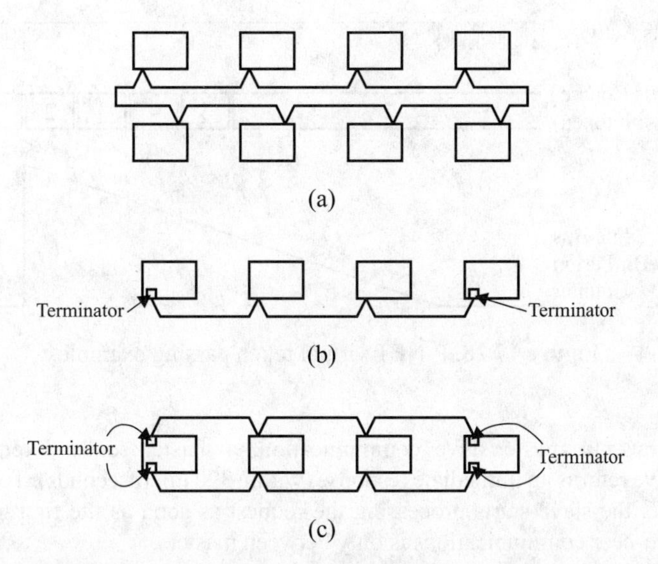

Figure 17.26. P-NET network topologies: *(a)* ring; *(b)* bus; *(c)* redundant bus.

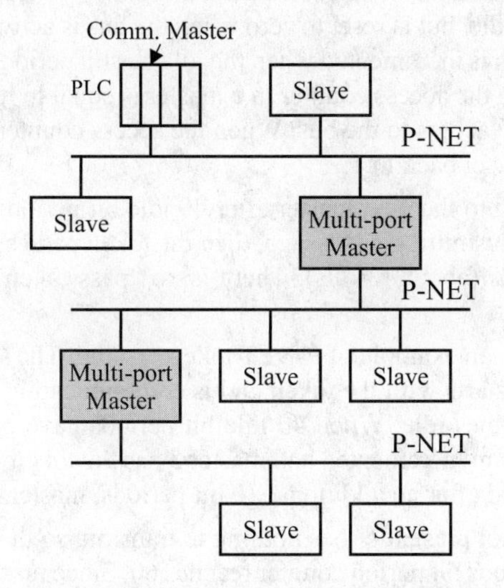

Figure 17.27. P-NET multi-net structure.

is 76.8 Kbit/s. The maximum bus length is 1200 m. The signals on the bus are non-return-to-zero (NRZ) encoded. Larger networks can be constructed by connecting segments with multi-port masters (Figure 17.27). Direct addressing between segments is handled with layer 3.

Data Link Layer

P-NET has basically two types of devices: master and slave. A master is typically a PLC, HMI, or engineering workstation. There can be up to 32 masters per bus segment. A slave is typically an I/O interface module. P-NET supports master/slave and peer-to-peer

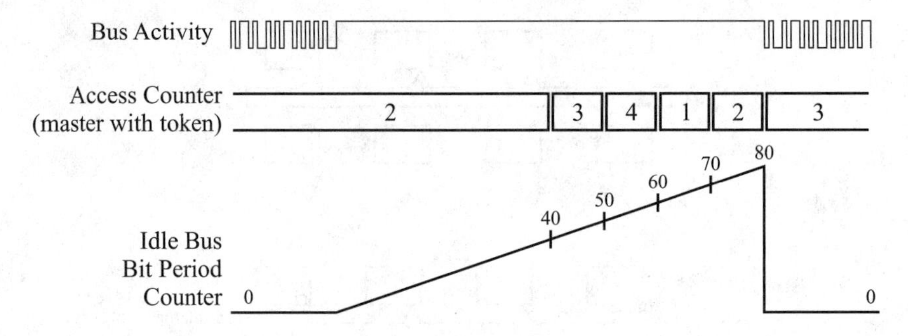

Figure 17.28. P-NET virtual token passing example.

communications. In master/slave communication, a master sends a request and the addressed slave returns an immediate response (within 390 microseconds). To meet this fast response time, the slave starts processing the request as soon as the first message bytes arrive. Peer-to-peer communications is only between masters.

Virtual token passing is used to control access of the masters to the bus. Each P-NET master is given a node address (NA), between 1 and the number of expected masters on the segment. All masters contain an "idle bus bit period counter" which increments for each bit period when the bus is idle, but is reset to zero when the bus is active. Each master also has an access counter, which is incremented when the idle bus bit period counter reaches 40, 50, 60, 70, and so on. When the access counter in a master is equal to its node address, it holds the token and is allowed access to the bus. When the access counter exceeds the maximum number of masters, it is set back to 1.

The token is passed to the next master after 40 idle bit periods (about 520 μs). If that master does not start transmitting a message, then the token passes to the next master after 10 more idle bit periods (about 130 μs). There is no "pass token" message between the masters.

Figure 17.28 shows an example of P-NET token passing. The system is configured for four masters. Master 2 starts with the token and is communicating with a slave. After this exchange, the bus becomes idle. When 40 idle bit periods have been counted, all access counters in the masters are incremented and master 3 has the token. Master 3 does not have anything to transmit, and after an additional 10 bit periods, master 4 has the token.

Master 4 is either not present or has nothing to transmit, so the virtual token passes to master 1, when the idle bus bit period counter reaches 60. Since masters 1 and 2 do not need access, the token is eventually passed to master 3, when the idle bus bit period counter is equal to 80. This time, master 3 needs to communicate with a slave. Since data appears on the bus, all idle bus bit period counters are reset.

To ensure real time data collection, each frame transmitted on the network is a maximum of 56 data bytes. If the requested data length is higher than 56 bytes, the response is automatically divided into several successive transmissions.

Network and Service Layers

The network layer handles the routing of messages from one segment in a multi-net system (Figure 17.27). The multi-masters do the bulk of the work, though the originator of a message does need to specify the routing in the message.

Channel: Digital I/O			
SWNo	**Value**		**Description**
x0	----		FlagReg
x1	5.3	s	OutTimer
x2	0		Counter
x3 *	0.4	A	OutCurrent
x4 *	200.5	s	OperatingTime
x5 *	----		UserByteArray
x6 *	5.9	s	FBTimer
x7 *	8.0	s	FBPreset
x8 *	2.0	s	OutPreset
x9	----		ChConfig
xA *	0.25	A	MinCurrent
xB *	0.81	A	MaxCurrent
xC *	----		UserRealArray
xD	----		Maintenance
xE	----		ChType
xF	----		ChError

* Optional, may be declared unused

Figure 17.29. Example P-NET digital I/O channel object.

Layer 4, the service layer, deviates from the OSI model (Figure 17.25). The function of this layer is twofold. When the device is a master, this layer handles the messaging requests from the application program. The program service breaks the message into packets (if the request is more than 56 bytes), transmitting them in order. The response to the request is passed back to the application. When the device is a slave, layer 4 provides the P-NET service which reads or writes data to internal memory via the "softwire" table. The softwire table is a list of the global variables in the node and their information. Each global variable in the node has an entry in the softwire table and the softwire number is the table index. An softwire table entry holds information on the variable. If the variable is in another slave, the softwire table entry holds the node address of the other slave and the appropriate softwire index.

Application

The application layer consists of one or more process objects. Each object is called a "channel." A channel can be a discrete input point, an analog output, a PID controller, and so on. A channel contains the data necessary to support the control function and to support maintenance. A channel is structured as 16 registers, each having its own relative logical address, called a softwire number (SwNo). An example digital I/O channel is shown in Figure 17.29 (P-Net, 1996). This channel can be configured for various functions, such as input, output, one shot output, timer output, and so on. Placing an appropriate value in the ChConfig register selects the function.

17.8 WORLDFIP

The FIP (Flux Information Processbus) protocol was developed in the early 1980's and published as a French standard in the late 1980's. This standard used a producer/consumer model of communication. The client/server communication method was added in the early 1990's and the protocol was renamed WorldFIP. WorldFIP was then included in the

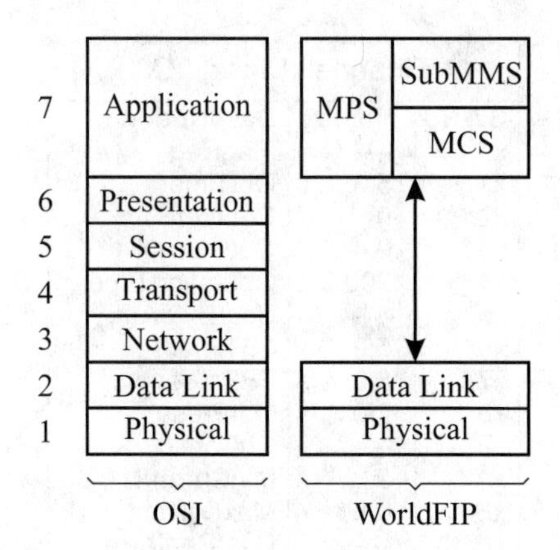

Figure 17.30. WorldFIP communication model.

European EN 50170-3. The communication model of the WorldFIP protocol is shown in Figure 17.30.

Physical Layer

WorldFIP often uses shielded twisted pair cable as the medium cable usually with 9-pin D-sub connectors. When using wire, the network topology is a bus or tree (Figure 17.31*a*). A WorldFIP segment can have up to 32 nodes. A maximum of four repeaters can connect network segments, allowing a maximum of 152 devices on the network. The allowable transmission rates are 31.25 kbit/s, 1 Mbit/s, and 2.5 Mbit/s. For these three transmission rates, the maximum segment length is 1900m, 1000m, and 500m, respectively. The standard transmission rate is 1 Mbit/s. The signals on the bus are Manchester encoded.

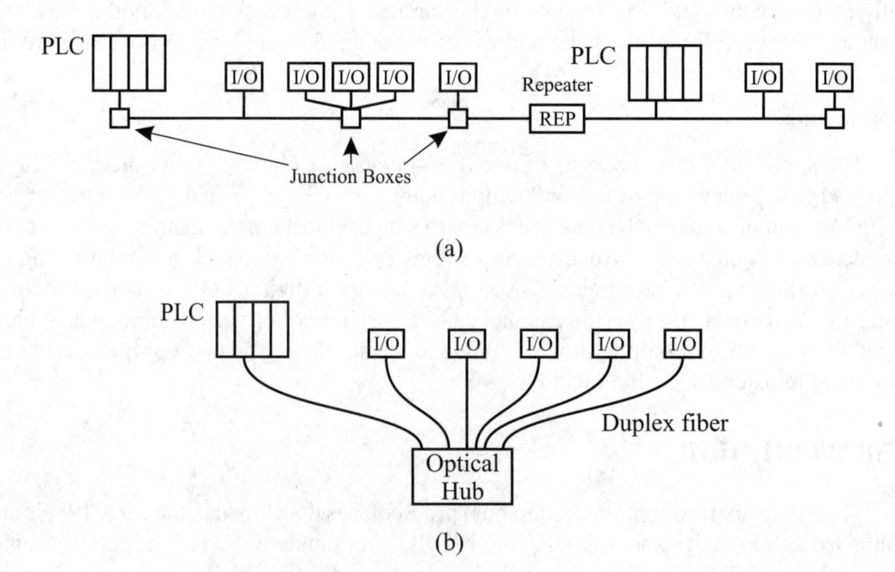

Figure 17.31. WorldFIP network topology: *(a)* wire; *(b)* fiber optics.

Alternatively, optical fiber can be used as the physical medium. In this case the network topology is a star (Figure 17.31*b*). Also, a pair of fiber optic cables can serve as a bus extended between two repeaters. With the optical fiber, the transmission rate is 5 Mb/s, though most vendors use the same speeds as for the copper wire so that optical fiber and copper wire can be mixed in the same system.

WorldFIP supports medium redundancy. When the station transmits a frame, the frame is simultaneously transmitted on both cables and each receiver receives the frame on both cables. Though the station listens to the cable with the first carrier detection, the station network management can force it to listen or transmit on one cable if, for example, too many errors have been detected on one of the cables.

Data Link Layer

WorldFIP uses a centralized scheduler, called the bus arbitrator (BA) to control access to the medium. The BA device coordinates the exchange of identified variables (producer/consumer) and message transfers. The BA handles these types of network traffic:

1. Cyclic - Transmitted at a fixed period (for example, closed-loop control).
2. Events - Transmitted when occurs (for example, alarms).
3. Messages - Transmitted when required and at a lower priority (for example, program download, upload of diagnostics).

Time is divided into macrocycles, which is based on the period of the slowest periodic variable and elementary cycles, which is the period of the fastest periodic variable. During each elementary cycle, network transmissions are allocated in the following priority order:

1. Periodic variables
2. Aperiodic variables
3. Messages (non-critical)

The configuration of the elementary cycles and macrocycles for periodic variables is described first, followed by a description of the other types of transmissions.

When the system is configured the bus arbitrator (BA) is given the list of variables to be scanned periodically and their scan periods. Based on this list, the BA generates a schedule of these transmissions. The length of the schedule is called a macrocycle. The macrocycle is divided into elementary cycles, the length of the smallest period. An example schedule is shown in Figure 17.32*a*. For this example, the scan periods of the variables are as follows:

Variable	Period
A	5ms
B	10ms
C	15ms
D	20ms
E	20ms
F	30ms

The vertical axis corresponds to the scan time within an elementary cycle. The horizontal axis shows the elementary cycles that constitute a macrocycle. In the first elementary cycle, all six variables are transmitted. In the second elementary cycle, only variable A is transmitted. The macrocycle repeats after 12 elementary cycles, or 60 ms. For this example, a more uniform distribution of the load is shown in Figure 17.32*b*.

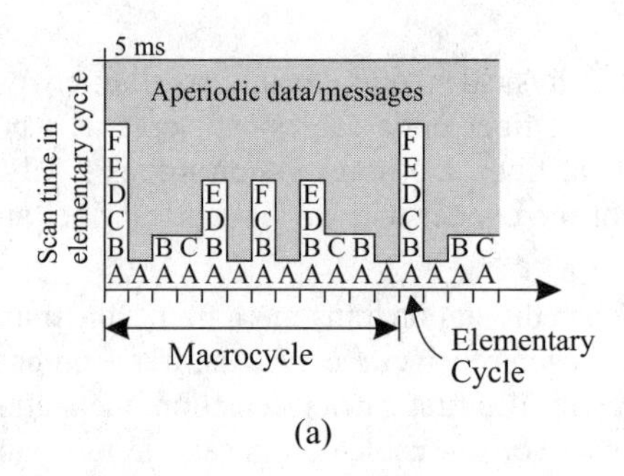

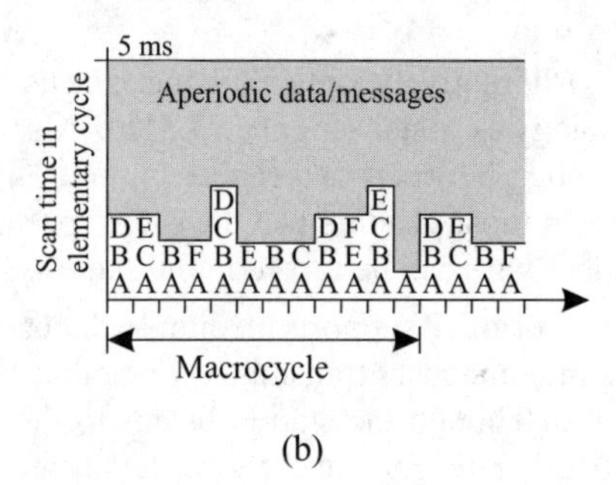

Figure 17.32. WorldFIP macrocycle example: *(a)* simple scheduling; *(b)* uniform load distribution.

To start a producer/consumer exchange for a particular identifier, the BA issues an ID_DAT frame with the 16-bit identifier for that variable on the network. The producer of that identifier broadcasts a RP_DAT frame with the data. This frame is received by the BA and any other device on the segment that is a consumer of that identifier.

After the last periodic producer/consumer exchange in an elementary cycle, the BA can use the remaining time to fulfill requests for aperiodic transfers. A producer signals that it has event-initiated data to send by setting a certain bit in the RP_DAT frame in response to an ID_DAT frame transmitted during the periodic part of the elementary cycle. When the BA has finished the last periodic transfer in an elementary cycle, it polls each producer that indicated a need to send event data. Each polled producer responds with a list of identifiers. The BA places these identifiers in a queue and when all event-related identifiers have been collected, it initiates a producer/consumer exchange for each of these identifiers.

After the periodic and aperiodic variables have been transmitted, the remaining time in the elementary cycle is used for other messages. Non-critical messages, such as upload/download and diagnostic reads, fill in the rest of the elementary cycle.

The WorldFIP protocol has two distinct types of addresses:

1. Variable addresses - Each variable in the system has a 16-bit integer (identifier) that identifies it in the producer/consumer transfer
2. Node addressing - Each node in the system has a 24-bit integer that identifies the network segment and the address of the node in the segment.

Redundant bus arbitrators are supported. Only one bus arbitrator may be active at any given instant. The others monitor the activity of the active bus arbitrator. When the backup BA detects silence on the network of a certain period (depending on its station number) it elects itself as arbitrator. If there are multiple backup arbitrators, the one with the lowest station number wins.

Application Layer

In the application layer, three services provide the interface to the application program. The MPS (manufacturing periodical/aperiodical services) layer provides the user with:

Local and remote read/write services
Variable transmission/reception indications
Information on the freshness of information consumed
Information on the spatial and temporal consistency of data

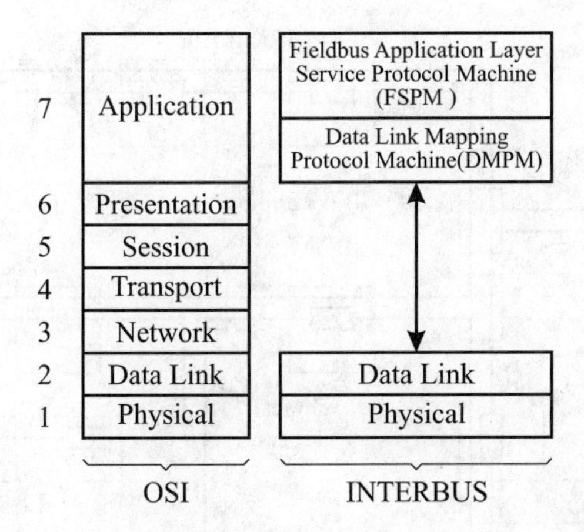

Figure 17.33. INTERBUS communication model.

SubMMS (subset of manufacturing messaging services) is basically a subset of the MMS application layer as a part of the GM MAP standardization effort. The subMMS service is typically used for application commission, network supervision, and integration with higher-level systems (WorldFIP, 1994). The subMMS service recognizes six device classes: (1) sensor, (2) actuator, (3) I/O multiplexer, (4) operator console, (5) programming console, and (6) PLC. The MCS (message control services) sublayer provides the interface between SubMMS and the data link layer.

17.9 INTERBUS

The INTERBUS, or INTERBUS-S, protocol was initially developed in the mid-1980's by Phoenix Contact and several German technical institutions. This protocol was initially developed as a proprietary protocol, but was eventually adopted as a European standard EN 50254-3 in 1998. The INTERBUS communication model and it relationship to the OSI model is shown in Figure 17.33.

Physical Layer

INTERBUS uses the same medium as RS-485, unshielded twisted pair. The topology (Figure 17.34) is basically a ring, that is, all devices are integrated into the transmission path. Each device in the loop receives and retransmits the signal allowing long loop distances. The physical appearance is like a tree structure. A bus terminal (BT) module "opens" the ring allowing a branch. Branch subnetworks can be up to 16 levels deep. There can be a maximum of 63 devices in a loop segment and up to 512 devices in the total network. The maximum length between two devices on a bus is 400 m and the maximum length between two devices on a loop is 20 m. The transmission rate is a fixed 500 kbit/s. The signals on the bus are NRZ encoded.

Regular cable is three twisted pairs. Two twisted pairs for both sides of the loop and the other twisted pair for common. One version of INTERBUS cable transmits power, adding three wires for power, common, and ground. Because of the ring structure, INTERBUS also supports optical fiber, radio, and infrared media.

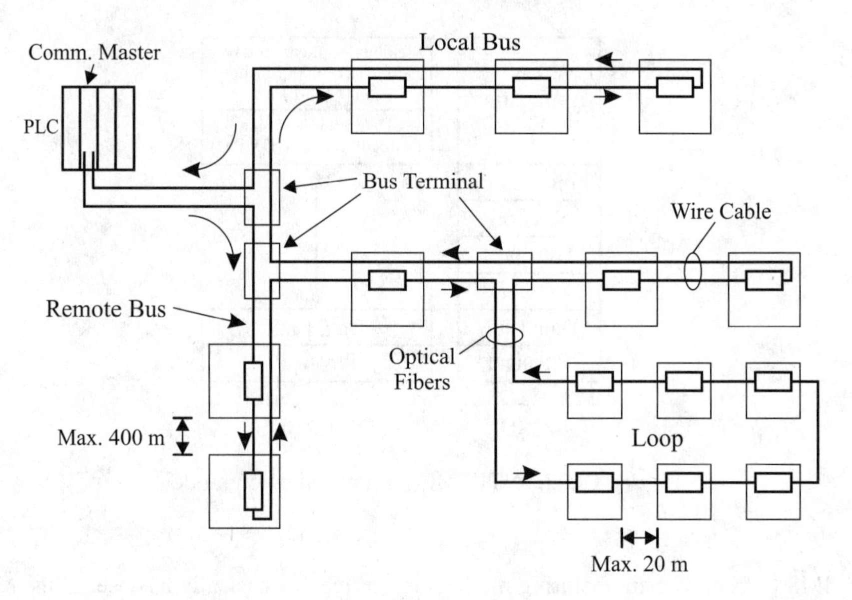

Figure 17.34. INTERBUS network topology.

The address of a device is fixed by its position on the loop. The first device is assigned address 1, the second device is address 2, and so on. The addresses are assigned when the loop is initially configured.

Data Link Layer

INTERBUS uses a master/slave method to communicate to devices on the ring. The physical transmission of messages on the ring is achieved with a summation-frame protocol. Figure 17.35 shows an example message transmission on an INTERBUS network with four slave devices. One of the devices is a discrete output module. The master sends

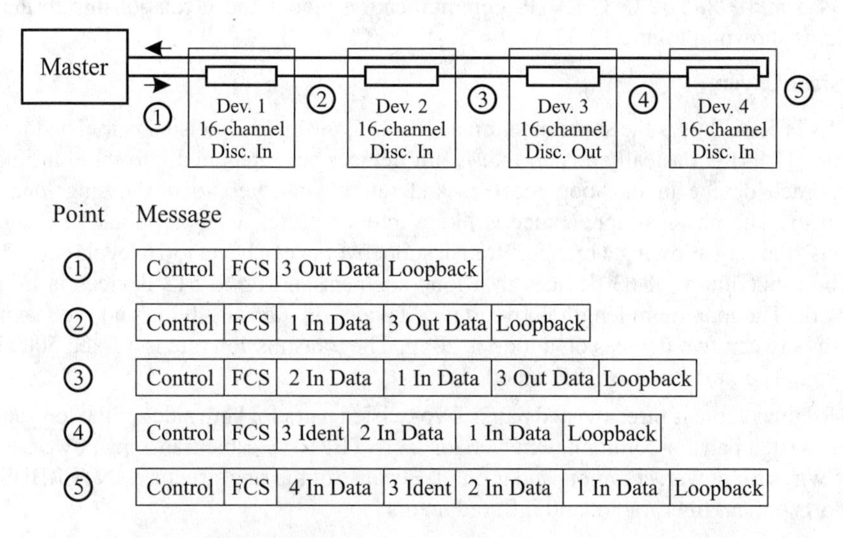

Figure 17.35. INTERBUS summation-frame protocol example.

out a message frame starting with a loopback header, the discrete output data, frame-check-sequence (FCS), and ending control word. When the message passes through the first device, it adds its data to the frame, modifying the FCS, and then sends the frame to the next device. Each input module adds its data and identification information to the frame. The discrete output module extracts its data from the frame and adds its identification information. When the message leaves the last device in the loop and is transmitted back to the master, the frame contains all of the discrete input data and identification information from each device. The summation-frame protocol is very efficient for cyclic data since the overhead associated with a request-response is eliminated.

A message transfer to one of the devices in the network is handled in a manner similar to how discrete output was transmitted in the example (Figure 17.35). The message is fragmented and each part is inserted into the message slot for that device. The destination slave recombines the fragments to form the entire message.

Application Layer

The FSPM (Fieldbus application layer Service Protocol Machine) layer provides the communication interface to the application program. For cyclic transmission/reception of process data, it uses a push producer/consumer mechanism. For non-cyclic communication, the mechanism is client/server. Master and slave can act as a client or server. The DMPM (Datalink Mapping Protocol Machine) provides the interface between the FSPM and the data link layer.

17.10 SWIFTNET

SwiftNet was developed to satisfy the need of an aircraft manufacturer for a synchronous and very high speed (up to 120 000 samples/sec) flight data bus. SwiftNet implements layers 1, 2, and 7 of the OSI model (Figure 17.4).

Physical Layer

SwiftNet uses RS-485 as the physical layer. The medium is shielded twisted pair cable usually with 9-pin D-sub connectors. The network topology may be a linear bus, tree, star, or some combination of the three (Figure 17.36). A Swiftnet segment can have up to 32 nodes. With repeaters connecting network segments, there can be a maximum of 122

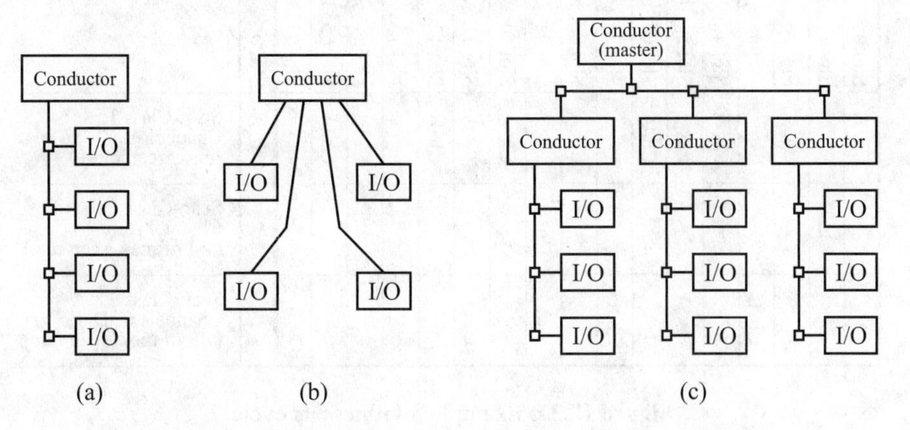

Figure 17.36. Swiftnet topology: *(a)* bus; *(b)* star; *(c)* tree.

devices for a linear bus. For a star topology, there may be a maximum of 922 devices on the network. The allowable transmission rates range from 78.125 Kbit/s to 5 Mbit/s. Obviously, all nodes must use the same transmission rate. The maximum segment length depends on the data rate and the type of cable. With a transmission rate of 78.125 Kbit/s the maximum distance is 4800 m. If the transmission rate is 5 Mbit/s, the maximum segment distance drops to 400 m. The signals on the bus are Manchester encoded.

Data Link Layer

SwiftNet uses a tightly synchronized Time Domain Multiple Access (TDMA) protocol to control node access to the bus. This protocol uses "silent" frame addresses and "silent" control fields to minimize overhead. Time is divided into bus cycles and each bus cycle is divided into equal-length slots. A typical bus cycle has 65,536 (2^{16}) slots. The slots at intervals of 2, 4, 8, 16, and so on, are allocated as channels. Each channel is assigned one data item, which may be a scanned (short) variable, a part of a longer data item, or part of an FMS message. Channels scanned at the same rate are assigned into a "scan class." A typical bus cycle has 15 scan classes.

The operation of a bus cycle is shown in Figure 17.37. Channel A is scanned at the maximum scan rate supported by the bus. Channel B is scanned at one-fourth of the maximum and channels C, D, and E are scanned at one-eighth of the maximum. Only three scan classes are shown. Channels C, D, and E are assigned to the same scan class.

One node on a segment must be designated as the Conductor to synchronize the other nodes. Redundant Conductors are supported. The Conductor of the top segment of a tree topology synchronizes the entire network. In this topology, the bridges pass the synchronization signal to the other segments.

SwiftNet supports producer/consumer and peer-to-peer communications. Real-time variable transfers use the producer/consumer so that multiple nodes may receive the same data. The identifier of the data item is implicit, identified by its slot(s) in a bus cycle. Non-critical messages use peer-to-peer communications and are broken into smaller fragments and the fragments are transmitted during bus slots dedicated for these messages.

Bus Cycle 1																	Bus Cycle 2	
Slot 0	Slot 1	Slot 2	Slot 3	Slot 4	Slot 5	Slot 6	Slot 7	Slot 8	Slot 9	Slot 10	Slot 11	Slot 12	Slot 13	//	Slot 65534	Slot 65535	Slot 0	
Ch. A		Ch. A		Ch. A		Ch. A		Ch. A		Ch. A		Ch. A		//	Ch. A	Bus Sync.	Ch. A	Scan-Class 1, Channel A (max. scan rate)
	Ch. B								Ch. B					//		Bus Sync.		Scan-Class 2, Channel B (1/4 of max. scan rate)
			Ch. C				Ch. D				Ch. E			//		Bus Sync.		Scan-Class 3, Channels C, D, E (1/8 of max. scan rate)

Figure 17.37. Example Swiftnet bus cycle.

Application Layer

The SwiftNet application layer provides the following types of application services:

Virtual Field Device - Status, unsolicited status and identification.

Object Dictionary - Get and put object descriptions.

Context Management - Initiate, abort and reject services.

Application Relationship - Unconfirmed send, confirmed send, abort, establish, get buffered message, status and XON/OFF services.

Variable Access - Read, write and information reports of simple, array and structured variables and variable lists.

Event - Notification, acknowledging, altering condition monitoring and time-stamping of events.

Load Region - Upload/download of load regions.

Function Invocation - Start, stop, resume, reset, kill, creation and deletion of function invocations.

17.11 AS-I

The actuator sensor interface (AS-i) network was developed in the early 1990's by a consortium of European companies. It was developed as a low-level bus to interface discrete sensors and actuators. It was later extended to include analog sensors and actuators. It was ratified as EN 50295-2 in 1998 and IEC 62026-2 in 2000. The AS-i protocol covers layers 1, 2, and 7 of the OSI model, though only the physical and data link layers are described here.

Physical Layer

AS-i uses a two-wire unshielded cable as the medium. The usual cable is yellow and has a trapezoidal cross-section (Figure 17.38), though a conventional round cable is also available. The network topology may be a linear bus, tree, star, or some combination of the three (Figure 17.39), as for Foundation Fieldbus H1. An AS-i network can have a maximum of 31 slave devices. If the master supports extended addressing, there may be up to 62 slave devices. The total cable length is 100 m, though with repeaters the cable length can be extended to 300 m. The transmission rate is a fixed 167 Kbit/s. The two-conductor cable supplies both power and signal, though if a device draws more than 200 mA a separate two-conductor black cable with the same trapezoidal cross-section supplies additional 24-volt DC power. A red version of the cable supplies 240-volt AC power.

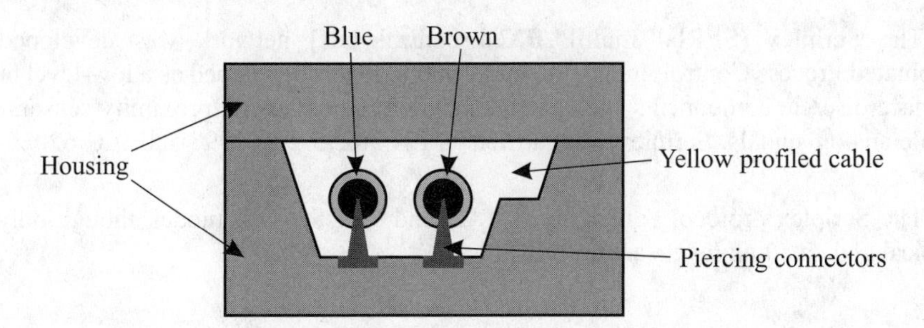

Figure 17.38. AS-i network cable.

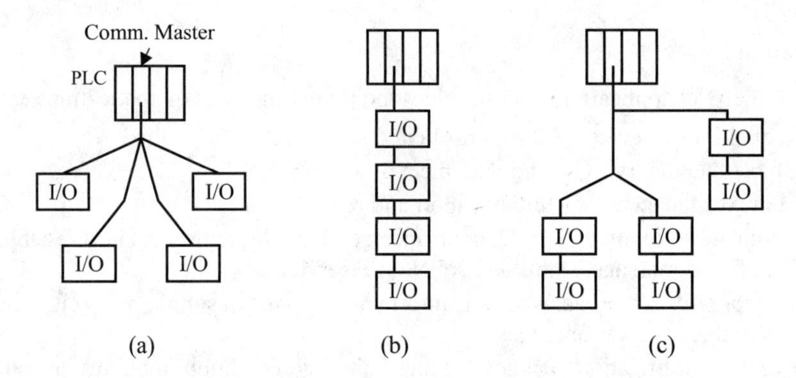

Figure 17.39. AS-i topologies: *(a)* star; *(b)* linear bus; *(c)* tree.

There are two versions of AS-i. The original AS-i specification (V1) allowed 31 slave devices. Each device can have a maximum of 4 discrete inputs and 4 discrete outputs and so the network can support 124 discrete inputs and 124 discrete outputs. Version 2.1 of the AS-i specification introduced extended addressing and the ability to handle analog inputs and outputs. In V2.1, there can be a maximum of 62 slaves, addressed as 31 A slaves and 31 B slaves. However, AS-i V2.1, the maximum number of discrete outputs per device decreases to 3, so the network can support a maximum of 248 discrete inputs and 186 discrete outputs.

Data Link Layer

The AS-i protocol is a master/slave protocol. The master polls the slaves and receives a response. The master sends a request message to a slave with the four output bits and the slave responds with a message containing the four discrete input bits. A fully loaded (31 slaves) V1 network scans all slaves within 5 ms.

For an AS-i V2.1 network, the master scans each slave in the A mode and then in the B mode using the fourth output bit as a switch. A fully loaded (62 slaves) V2.1 network scans all slaves within 10 ms.

Analog signals are handled by an AS-i V2.1 master by using multiple scans to transmit parts of the analog data. Five cycles are required to transmit 12-bit data and seven cycles are needed for 16-bit data.

17.12 SERIPLEX

The Seriplex (SERIal multiPLEXed control bus) network was developed by Automated Process Control, Inc. in the mid-1980's. It was developed as a low-level bus to interface discrete components such as panel switches, contactors, proximity sensors, and simple analog signals. Seriplex was ratified as EN 50295-2 in 1998 and IEC 62026-6 in 2001.

The Seriplex protocol covers layers 1, 2, and 7 of the OSI model, though only the physical and data link layers are described here.

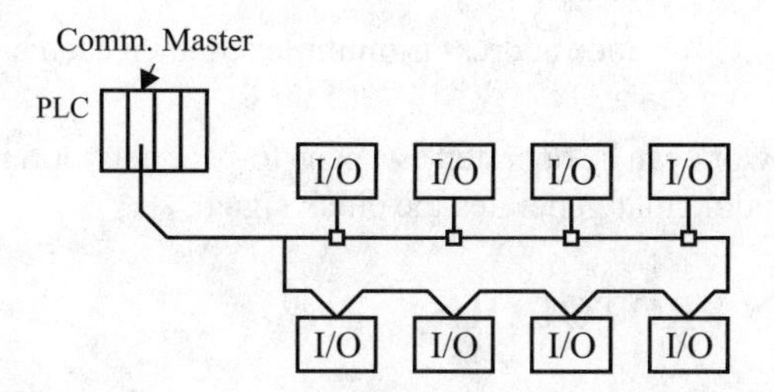

Figure 17.40. Seriplex loop topology.

Physical Layer

Seriplex uses a five-conductor shielded cable, two twisted pairs plus a shield drain. One twisted pair carries the power and the other twisted pair carries the clock signal and data signal. The network topology can be either a daisy-chain, trunkline/dropline, loop (Figure 17.40), or combination of the three. A Seriplex network can have up to 255 nodes. The transmission rate ranges from 10 kbit/s to 192 kbit/s. The maximum cable length depends on the data rate. For a 10 kbit/sec data rate, the maximum total distance of the cable (in any topology) is 1700 m.

Several different connector types can be used on Seriplex. Both sealed and unsealed connectors are available. For devices installed on the factory floor, mini-style and micro-style pluggable, sealed connectors are used. For nodes installed inside cabinets, open-style connectors can be used.

Devices are powered from the Seriplex cable. Since the cable current rating is 4 amps, the power supply conductor is broken into segments, each segment powered by a separate power supply.

Nodes can be operated in a multiplexed or non-multiplexed mode. When a node is non-multiplexed, each address can have one discrete input and one discrete output. In this case, the system can have a maximum of 255 discrete inputs and 255 discrete outputs. When a node is multiplexed, each address has one word (16 bits) of input data and output data. The word can be either an analog value or multiple discrete channels. In a multiplexed configuration, the system can have a maximum of 3840 discrete input and 3840 discrete outputs or 240 analog inputs and 240 analog outputs. The host is configured as to which node addresses are multiplexed.

Seriplex supports redundant cables and redundant I/O devices. The redundant cable can be in the form of a loop wiring configuration that can handle a single wire break, or the second cable can be totally separate. The "wire-OR" capability of nodes allows multiple nodes with identical functions to share the same node address.

Data Link Layer

The Seriplex network is usually operated in a master/slave configuration where the master controls the clock signal. At the start of a scan cycle, the master sends a synchronization pulse on the clock signal and then generates clock pulses. Each Seriplex node counts the clock pulses. When the number of clock pulses is equal to the node address, then a discrete signal is exchanged between the data signal and the node. If the node is a discrete output, the node reads the data line. If the node is a discrete input, then it transmits

its value on the data line. If a node address is multiplexed, then each bit of the 16-bit word is transferred on successive scans.

The Seriplex network can be operated as a peer-to-peer network. In this case, a network must have a clock module that generates the clock signal.

17.13 MODICON PROTOCOLS

The Modbus protocol was introduced by Modicon in 1979 as one of the first PLC-to-PLC protocols. It quickly became a de facto industry standard. It was originally developed for a multi-drop network of PLCs. However, it is also implemented on top of a token bus network (Modbus Plus or Modbus+) and on top of Ethernet (Modbus/TCP). These three implementations are related as shown in Figure 17.41. Modbus remains a popular protocol for SCADA (supervisory control and data acquisition) since it works over any serial medium (telephone, radio, satellite). The Modbus serial and TCP versions were eventually transferred to the Modbus Organization and so the standard is openly available. The lower layers of Modbus Plus are still proprietary.

17.13.1 Modbus Serial

There are two types of physical layers for the Modbus serial. The RS-232 physical layer is intended for a connection between two devices, most often a programming terminal and the PLC. The RS-485 physical layer is for a multi-drop network.

The RS-485 medium is shielded twisted pair cable usually with 9-pin D-sub or RJ-45 connectors. The RS-485 may be implemented in a 2-wire or 4-wire configuration. The network topology is a daisy-chained or trunkline/dropline linear bus terminated at both ends. Each segment can have up to 32 nodes, though with repeaters connecting network segments, there can be a maximum of 248 devices. The allowable transmission rates range

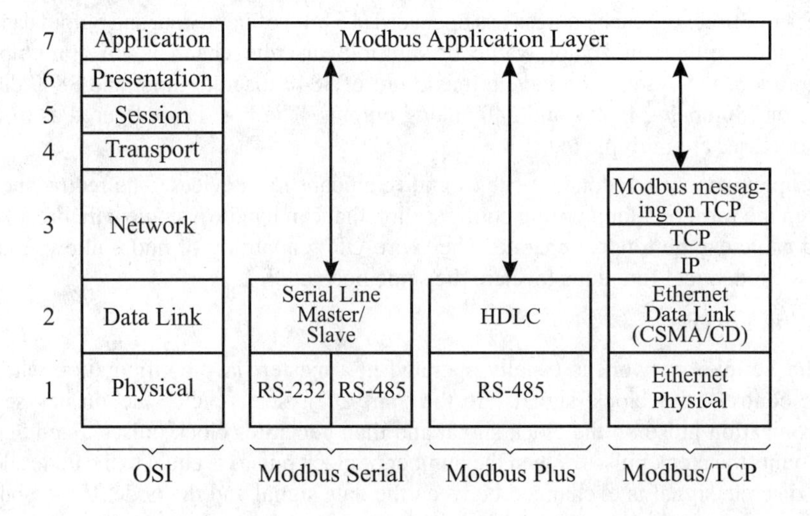

Figure 17.41. Communication model for Modicon protocols.

from 1200 bit/s to 115 kbit/s. The default transmission rate is normally 9600 or 19200 bit/s. The maximum segment length is dependent on the baud rate. For 9600 bit/s, the maximum length is 1000 m.

There are two serial transmission modes: ASCII and RTU. In the RTU (Remote Terminal Unit) mode of transmission, each message byte is transmitted unmodified. In the ASCII (American Standard Code for Information Interchange) mode of transmission, each message byte is transmitted as two ASCII characters. This mode is used when the communication link or device cannot meet the timing requirements of the RTU mode.

The data link layer implements a master/slave protocol. The network contains only one master, which sends requests to the other nodes and receives their responses. The slave nodes never transmit data without receiving a request from the master. The slave nodes do not communicate with each other. The master can initiate a request to an individual slave node (node 1 - 247) in the unicast mode and receives one response message. In broadcast mode, the master addresses the message to node 0 and all slaves receive the message. There is no response to a broadcast message.

17.13.2 Modbus Plus

The RS-485 medium is shielded twisted pair cable usually with 9-pin D-sub connectors. The network topology is a daisy-chained or trunkline/dropline linear bus terminated at both ends. Each segment can have up to 32 nodes, though with repeaters connecting network segments, there can be a maximum of 64 devices. The transmission rate is a fixed 1 Mbit/s. The maximum segment length is 450 m. Modbus Plus supports redundant cables.

Networks can be joined by bridges to form larger networks (Figure 17.42). The routing of the message is not automatic. The application layer (ladder logic program) must specify the routing path in the message.

The data link layer implements a token passing protocol. When passing the token, a node can transmit global data (up to 32 words) to all network nodes. Although only one

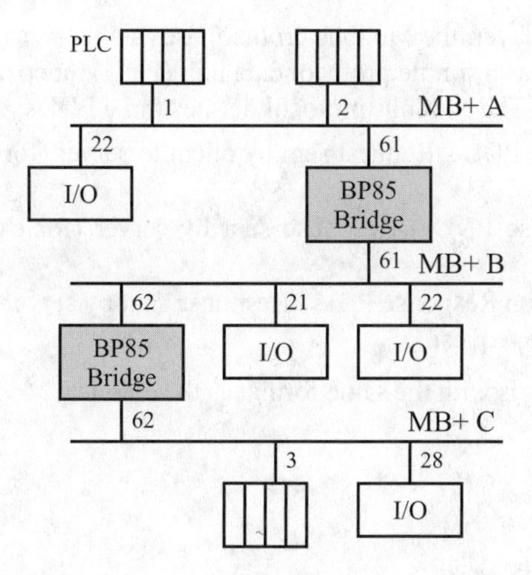

Figure 17.42. Modbus Plus multi-net structure.

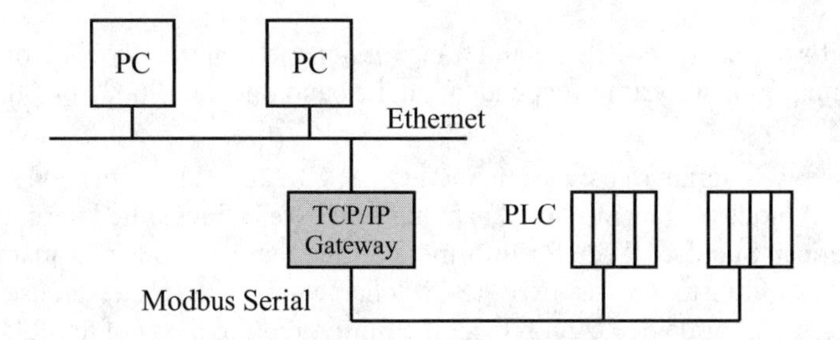

Figure 17.43. Modbus/TCP with serial device.

node accepts the token pass, all nodes receive the global data. The passing of global data is similar to the producer/consumer model.

17.13.3 Modbus/TCP

Modbus/TCP uses standard Ethernet and TCP/IP protocols to transport a Modbus message. The Modbus messaging service provides client/server communications between devices connected on an Ethernet TCP/IP network. Client/server communications use four types of messages:

Modbus Request - message sent by client to initiate exchange.
Modbus Indication - request message received by server.
Modbus Response - response message sent by server.
Modbus Confirmation - response message received by client.

One common way of using Modbus/TCP is to use a gateway device to communicate with older PLCs that do not have an Ethernet interface (Figure 17.43). The gateway also allows multiple Modbus networks to be linked together across Ethernet. This capability allows a master on any Modbus network to access slave devices on another network.

17.13.4 Modbus Application Layer

At the application layer, the Modbus protocol uses a client/server model. At this level, the message is defined as a simple protocol data unit (PDU) independent of the underlying communication layers. The Modbus protocol defines three PDUs:

Modbus Request PDU - Request sent by client to server (for example, to read/write data values)

Modbus Response PDU - Response sent by server (for example, requested data values)

Modbus Exception Response PDU - Response sent by server if there was an error in processing the request.

Addressing of variables is with the same format as the classical Modicon PLCs (0x, 1x, 3x, 4x memory locations).

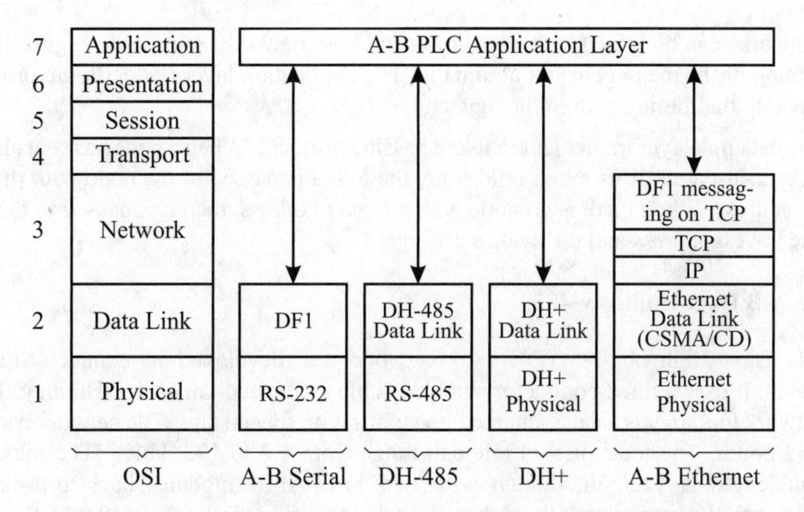

Figure 17.44. Communication model for Allen-Bradley protocols.

17.14 ALLEN-BRADLEY PROPRIETARY NETWORKS

Allen-Bradley introduced its first peer-to-peer network, Data Highway, in 1979, for a multi-drop network of PLCs. Later, it was enhanced and named Data Highway+ (DH+). This network became the standard network between PLC-5 processors. At about the same time, the DH485 network was developed for the SLC-500 processors. When PLC-5 Ethernet processors became available, the same messaging was implemented on top of Ethernet. These four implementations are related as shown in Figure 17.44. All of these protocols are considered proprietary, though the DF1 protocol and message structure are openly available (Allen-Bradley, 1996). For all four of these protocols, the structure of the messages is the same.

17.14.1 A-B Serial

Communications over a serial link with any Allen-Bradley ControlLogix, PLC-5, or SLC-500 processor uses the DF1 protocol. The DF1 protocol is a data-link layer protocol that combines features of subcategories D1 (data transparency) and F1 (two-way simultaneous transmission with embedded responses) of the ANSI x3.28 specification (ANSI, 1976). The DF1 protocol has two categories:

half-duplex for master/slave communication, and
full-duplex for peer-to-peer communication.

17.14.2 A-B Data Highway Plus

The Data Highway Plus (DH+) medium is shielded twisted pair cable. The network topology is a daisy-chained or trunkline/dropline linear bus terminated at both ends (Allen-Bradley, 1994). Each trunkline can have up to 64 nodes. The transmission rate may be 57.6, 115.2, or 230.4 kbit/s. Earlier processors only supported the lowest transmission rate. The maximum trunkline length is 3050 m. The DH+ cables can be redundant, but there is no built-in function to switch between cables when one of them fails.

Networks can be joined by bridges to form larger networks (similar to Figure 17.42). The routing of the message is not automatic. The application layer (ladder logic program) must specify the routing path in the message.

The data link layer implements a token passing protocol. When a node has sent all of its messages or used all of its token-hold time, the token is passed to the node with the next highest address. When there is no node with a higher address, then it is passed to the node with the lowest address and the cycle starts again.

17.14.3 A-B Data Highway-485

The Data Highway-485 (DH-485) network was developed to connect SLC-500 processors. It uses a three-conductor shielded cable as its medium (Allen-Bradley, 1994). The network topology is a daisy-chained linear bus with special taps. The network can have up to 32 nodes. The transmission rate can range from 1.2 to 19.2 kbit/s. The maximum segment length is 1220 m, though with two 1747-AIC+ modules back-to-back, two segments can be connected to make a total network length of 2440 m (Rockwell Automation, 1998a).

The data link layer implements a token passing protocol. Certain low-level devices (for example, a bar-code reader) are respond-only nodes and do not participate in the token passing.

17.15 GE FANUC PROPRIETARY NETWORKS

The GE Fanuc PLCs use a multi-drop RS-485/RS-422 network to connect processors. Depending on the configuration, the medium is one of three possibilities: (1) single twisted pair, (2) two twisted pairs, or (3) four twisted pairs. Each of these is shielded cable with an additional wire for common. The network topology is a daisy-chained linear bus with special taps. The network can have up to 63 nodes. The transmission rate can range from 300 to 19200 bit/s. The maximum segment length is 1220 m, though with an isolated repeater/converter, two segments can be connected to make a total network length of 2440 m.

The data link protocol can be configured to be CCM, SNP, SNP-X, or RTU. The CCM and SNP-X protocols are unavailable for the Versamax processors.

The CCM (communication control module) protocol is available with certain communication modules. It supports both master/slave and peer-to-peer communications. When used in peer-to-peer communications, it uses a form of CSMA/CD to control access and detect collisions.

The SNP (Series Ninety Protocol) protocol is a proprietary protocol developed by GE Fanuc (GE Fanuc, 2000a). It is the built-in communications protocol for Series 90 processors. It is a master/slave protocol. Only one device on the network is the master. While a programming device is normally the master, one of the PLC processors can be a master.

The SNP-X protocol is an optimized extension of SNP. It provides a performance improvement over SNP, but it does not support processor programming or configuration operations.

The RTU (remote terminal unit) protocol is the same as the Modbus RTU protocol. However, the GE Fanuc PLCs can only serve as a RTU slave device.

The GE Fanuc Ethernet communication modules support the Ethernet global data (EGD) exchange protocol. This method of communication over Ethernet is described in section 17.16.4.

17.16 LADDER LOGIC COMMUNICATION BLOCKS

For each of the PLCs covered by this text, the supported standard networks are listed. For the standard I/O networks, the method of device access is discussed. In addition, the function blocks required to implement PLC-to-PLC communication are described and illustrated with examples.

17.16.1 Modicon

Modicon Quantum interface modules for AS-i, INTERBUS, PROFIBUS, and DeviceNet map directly into the processor input/output image. For AS-i, INTERBUS, and DeviceNet master modules, the table is a fixed length and a portion of that image is dedicated to each slave device on the network. For the PROFIBUS module, the concept is the same, but there is an additional step. The PROFIBUS-DP network configuration is specified with a separate software package and then loaded into the PROFIBUS-DP master module. This configuration is used to produce the processor I/O mapping.

Certain Ethernet modules can function as I/O scanners for I/O modules connected directly to Ethernet. In this case, the Ethernet scanner is configured separately from the other I/O modules, but the concept is still the same. The registers on the I/O modules are mapped to the processor I/O image. I/O modules connected to Modbus Plus are configured with the Peer Cop.

Function blocks are provided to communicate with other processors and modules on Modbus Plus and Ethernet networks. The MBP_MSTR block works for both networks and a variety of operations can be specified. Function blocks are also provided to read and write registers from another node on these networks. These are described first, followed by a description of the MBP_MSTR block.

The function blocks to read and write registers from other nodes on an Ethernet or Modbus Plus network are shown in Figure 17.45. The blocks are:

CREAD_REG - Continuously read registers from another node.

CWRITE_REG - Continuously write registers to another node.

READ_REG - Read registers from another node when there is a positive transition on the REQ input.

WRITE_REG - Write registers to another node when there is a positive transition on the REQ input.

The common input connections to these blocks are described as follows:

SLAVEREG - Offset to the first 4x register in the other node to read from/write to. If the first register is 40154, then this input should be 154.

NO_REG - Number of registers to read from/write to

AddrFld - Address of other node (data type WordArr5). Use TCP_IP_ADDR or ModbusP_ADDR blocks to form this array.

REQ - A false-to-true transition on this input starts the operation (READ_REG and WRITE_REG blocks).

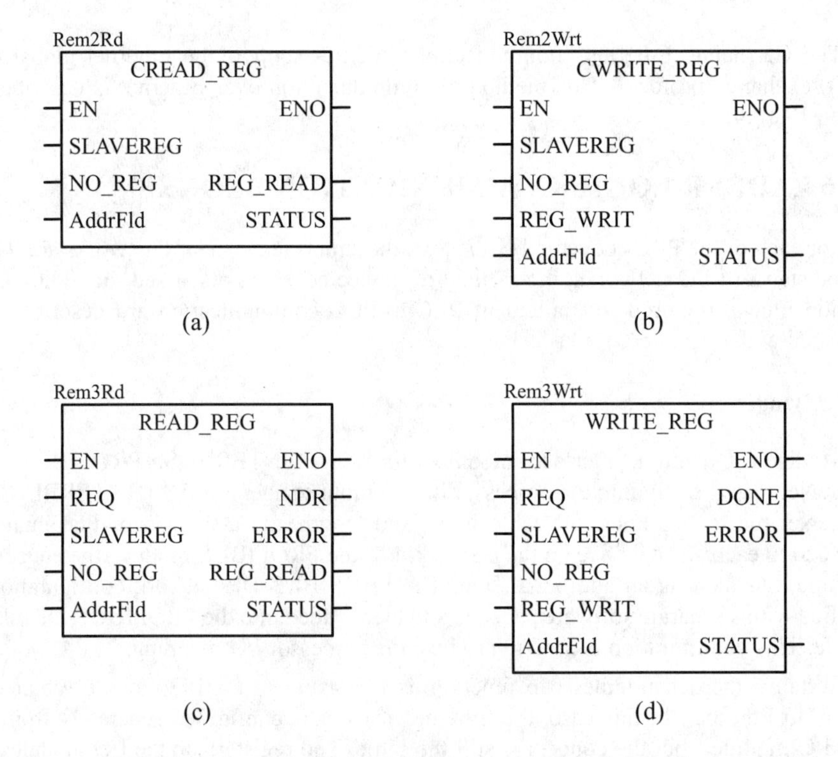

Figure 17.45. Concept communication function blocks: *(a)* continuous read; *(b)* continuous write; *(c)* read; *(d)* write.

REG_WRIT - First register of array to be written to other node (CWRITE_REG and WRITE_REG only)

The output connections are:

READ_REG - First register of array that receives result of reading the registers from the other node (CREAD_REG and READ_REG blocks).

STATUS - Error status of operation.

ERROR - True for one scan when the block has an error (READ_REG and WRITE_REG blocks)

NDR - True for one scan when new data read (READ_REG block).

DONE - True for one scan when data written (WRITE_REG block).

The ERROR output connection cannot be used for checking whether the communication is successful. If the other node is disconnected, there is no error reported. In order to determine if the communication link is operational, a register in the node must be read on a periodic basis. If the data is not received (sensed by the NDR output) within a certain time, then the link is not operational.

The two blocks used to construct the AddrFld input for the communication blocks are shown in Figure 17.46. The TCP_IP_ADDR (Figure 17.46*a*) block is for forming the AddrFld when communicating over Ethernet. The Slot_ID input is the backplane slot in which the Ethernet module resides. When the destination node is an Ethernet node, the

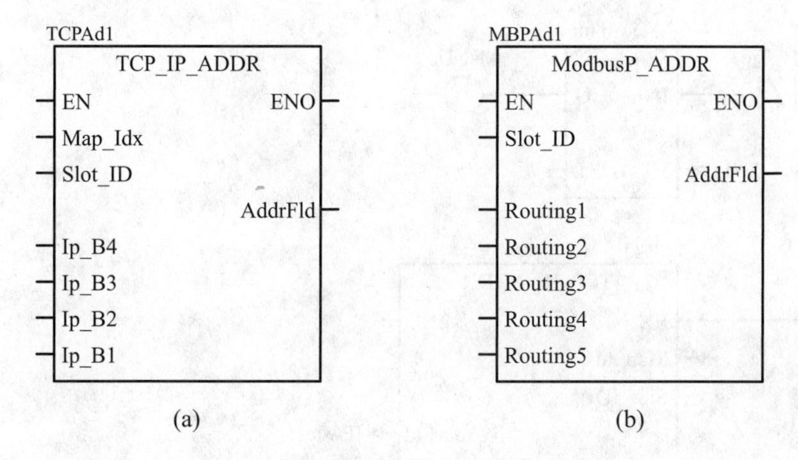

Figure 17.46. Concept node address blocks: *(a)* Ethernet; *(b)* Modbus Plus.

Map_Idx input is not used and the Ip_B1 to Ip_B4 inputs are the four bytes of the Ethernet IP address. Ip_B4 is the most significant byte. The Map_Idx input is used when the destination node is on a Modbus Plus network connected through a Modbus-Plus-to-Ethernet-Bridge (MBPET) module. The Map_Idx is the path index in the MBPET that identifies the destination Modbus Plus node. In this case, the Ip_B1 to Ip_B4 inputs are the Ethernet IP address of the MBPET.

The ModbusP_ADDR block (Figure 17.46*b*) constructs an AddrFld variable when communicating over Modbus Plus. The Slot_ID input is the backplane slot in which the Modbus port resides. If the Modbus Plus port on the processor is used, this is the slot for the processor. The Routing1 to Routing5 inputs specify the path to the destination node. If the destination node is on the same Modbus Plus segment, only Routing1 is used and it is the address of the destination node. If the destination is on another network segment, then the routing inputs specify the route to the destination. For example, if the PLC at address 1 in Figure 17.42 needs to communicate with the I/O module at address 28 on network C, the inputs to the ModbusP_ADDR block are Routing1=61, Routing2=62, Routing3=28, Routing4=0, and Routing5=0. If the destination is another processor, the backplane slot that contains the Modbus Plus interface must be specified as the upper byte of the Routing1 input. For example, if the PLC at address 1 in Figure 17.42 needs to communicate with the processor at address 3 (Modbus Plus port on slot 3) on network C, the inputs to the ModbusP_ADDR block are Routing1=829(61+256*3), Routing2=62, Routing3=3, Routing4=0, and Routing5=0.

An example program that communicates with a remote I/O module connected to Ethernet is shown in Figure 17.47. The I/O module has 16 discrete input channels and 16 discrete output channels. The IP address of the module is 101.126.43.200. The read and write of the module is done every second. If the new read data is not received within 0.5 seconds of the request, then a communication error Boolean is set.

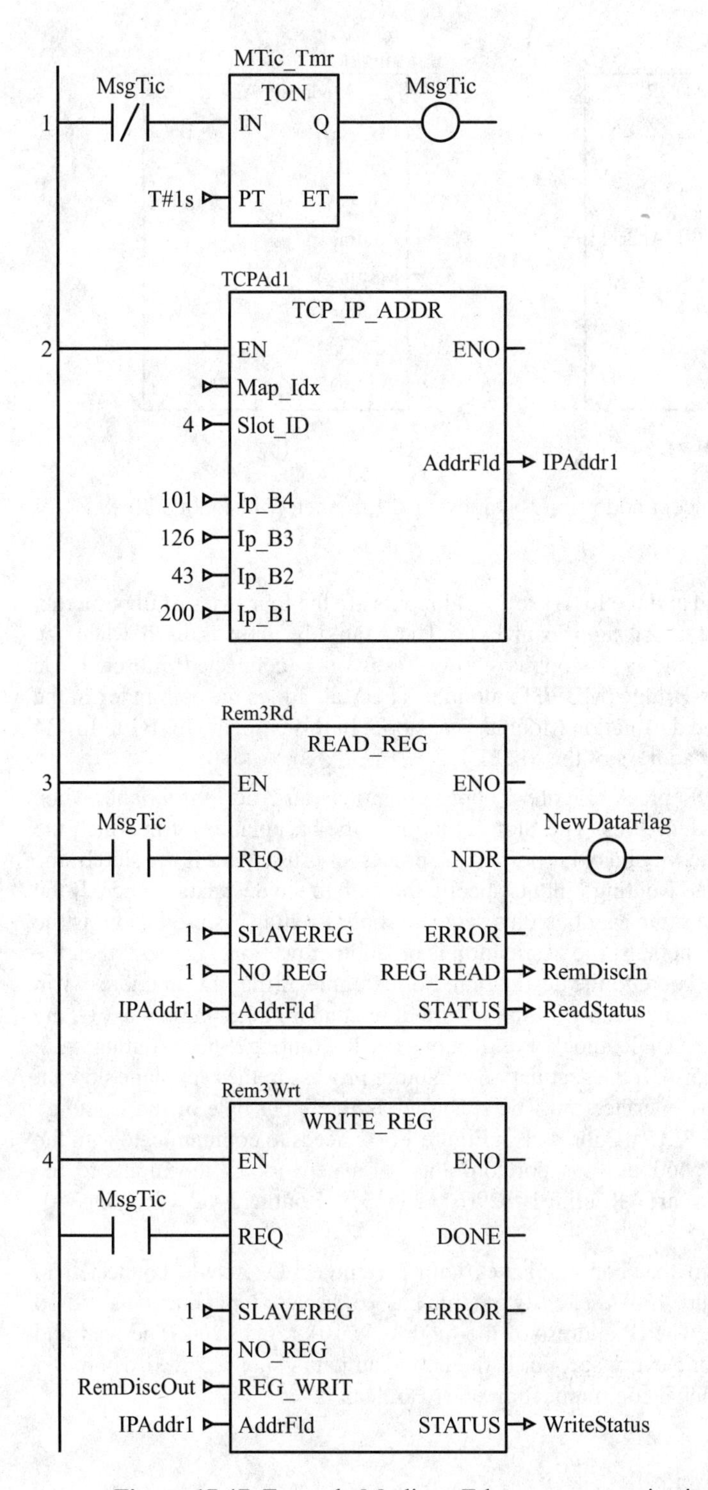

Figure 17.47. Example Modicon Ethernet communications. *(continued)*

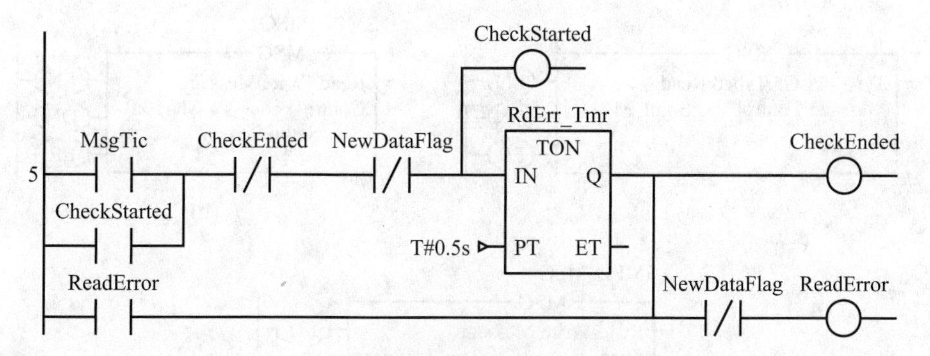

Figure 17.47. *(continued)*

17.16.2 Allen-Bradley

Ethernet, ControlNet, DeviceNet, and Data Highway Plus interface modules are available for most of the Allen-Bradley PLCs, though CompactLogix processors only support Ethernet, DeviceNet, and DH-485. There are two available gateways to Foundation Fieldbus H1: Ethernet/IP-to-H1 and ControlNet-to-H1. PROFIBUS-DP master modules are available for ControlLogix, PLC-5, and SLC-500 processors. INTERBUS and AS-i master modules are available for ControlLogix and SLC-500 processors. Most of the modules that interface to the sensor networks (DeviceNet, PROFIBUS, INTERBUS, and AS-i) map directly into the processor input/output image. The table is a fixed length and a portion of that image is dedicated to each slave device on the network. The PLC-5 PROFIBUS-DP master module is not handled like an I/O module. It is a coprocessor that interacts directly with the processor integer data files to produce a data image similar to the analog I/O modules. A portion of that image is dedicated to each slave device on the network.

The MSG block provides the peer-to-peer communications function for Allen-Bradley PLCs. This block is described and then the procedure for setting up the producer/consumer interaction for ControlLogix processors is illustrated.

MSG Block

The various forms of the MSG block are shown in Figure 17.48. The MSG operation is triggered on the false-to-true transition of its input. In general, the MSG block allows data to be exchanged between processors on any of the peer-to-peer networks (Ethernet, ControlNet, DH+, DH-485) for which the processor has an interface. The network used to illustrate the configuration of the MSG block is shown in Figure 17.49. It contains an Ethernet network, a ControlNet network, two DH+ networks, and interfaces that allow connection between the various networks. No I/O modules are shown so that the examples can concentrate on the PLC-to-PLC communication.

For the ControlLogix PLC, the MSG block allows one to read/write tags in another ControlLogix processor or to read/write data addresses in the PLC-5, PLC-3, and PLC-2 processors. Assuming the processor being programmed is named Reactor1 (slot 0 of the CLogix1 backplane), the I/O configuration is set up as shown in Figure 17.50. The I/O modules are not shown. Note that the communication interface modules are shown in the tree structure. A module resides in the backplane slot indicated by the bracketed number. The module name is after the module catalog number. Devices attached to the ControlNet

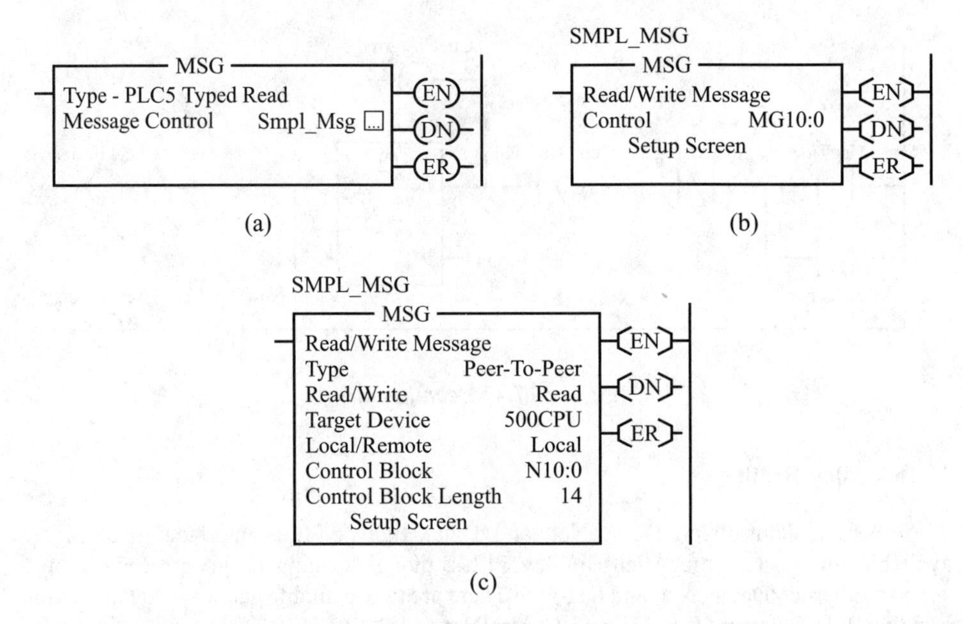

Figure 17.48. MSG blocks: *(a)* ControLogix; *(b)* PLC-5; *(c)* SLC-500.

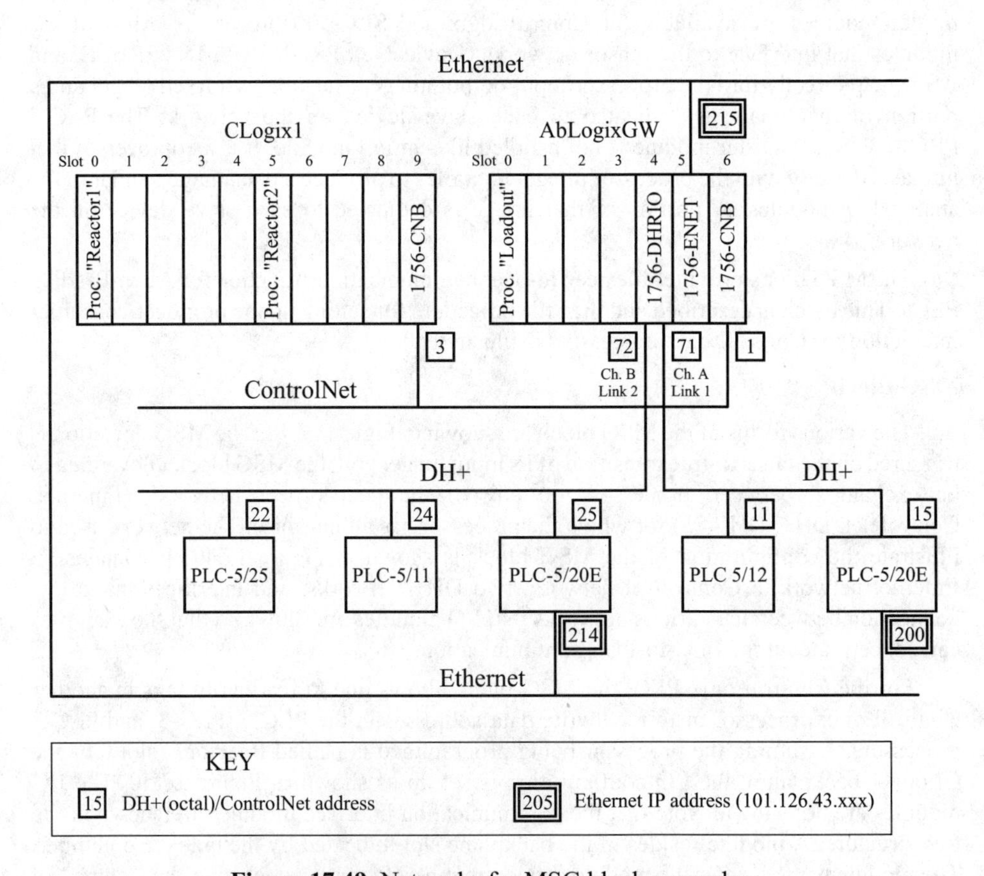

Figure 17.49. Networks for MSG block examples.

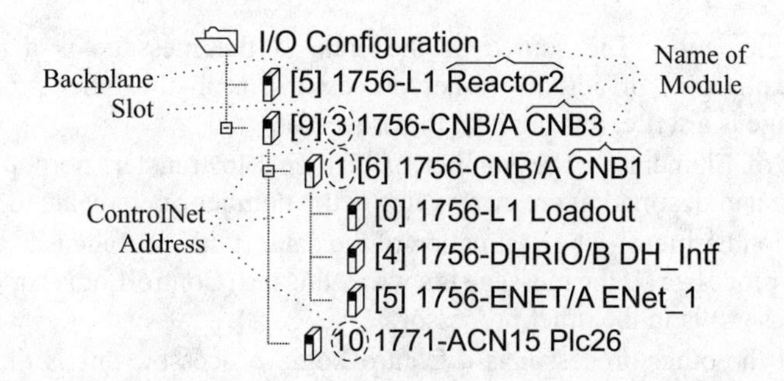

Figure 17.50. ControlLogix I/O configuration tree for Reactor1 processor.

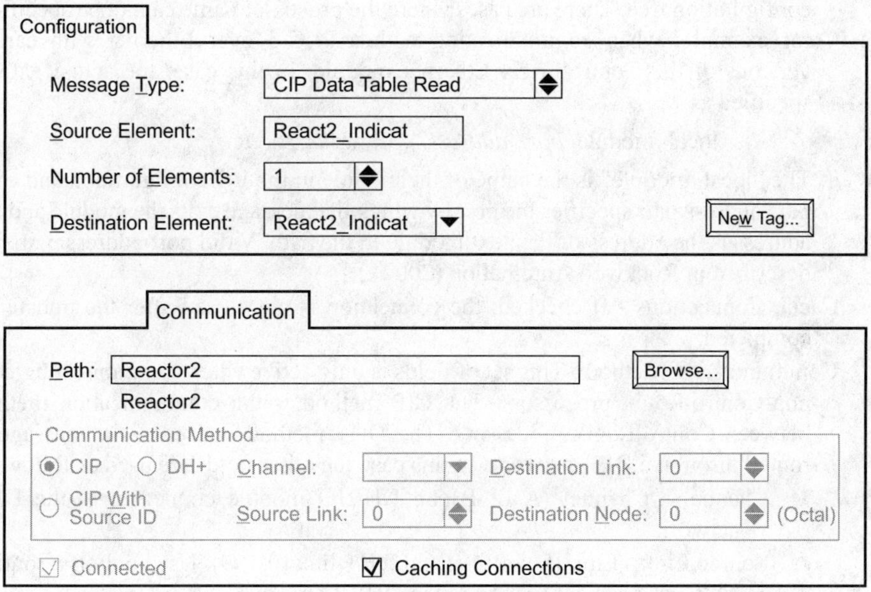

Configuration

Message Type: CIP Data Table Read
Source Element: React2_Indicat
Number of Elements: 1
Destination Element: React2_Indicat
New Tag...

Communication

Path: Reactor2
Reactor2
Browse...
Communication Method
CIP DH+ Channel: Destination Link: 0
CIP With Source ID Source Link: 0 Destination Node: 0 (Octal)
Connected Caching Connections

Figure 17.51. ControlLogix MSG configuration for reading from Reactor2 processor.

have their ControlNet address indicated after the slot number for the ControlNet bridge (CNB) in the same chassis as the processor and before the slot number for CNB modules in other chassis. Any ControlLogix processors for which communications is desired must appear in the I/O configuration tree.

The Message Control tag specifies the messaging details. The fields in the MSG configuration (Figure 17.51) are as follows:

Message Type - The three main categories of messages are data table read/write, CIP generic and block transfer read/write. The data table messages transfer information between processors and the other processor is specified as a CIP (ControlLogix), PLC-5, SLC-500, PLC-3 or PLC-2. The block transfer messages are used to communicate with a block-transfer I/O module (for example, a PLC-5 analog input module) and the CIP generic messages are for configuring and testing I/O modules.

Source Element - The source of the data. If the message is a read, this tag (ControlLogix) or address (other processors) is in the other processor. If the message is a write, this tag is in the processor.

Number of Elements - The number of elements to transfer, normally one. If the source and destination are arrays, this is the number of elements to read/write.

Destination Element - The destination of the data. If the message is a read, this tag is in the processor. If the message is a write, this tag (ControlLogix) or address (other processors) is in the other processor.

Path - If the other processor is a ControlLogix processor, this is the name of the processor as specified in the I/O configuration tree. If the other processor is not a ControlLogix processor, this is the name of the module that is the gateway to the other network. The actual path to the remote processor is specified by the I/O configuration tree. There are cases where the processor name cannot be specified, for example, when communicating with a PLC-5 over Ethernet with earlier versions of the ControlLogix Ethernet module. In this case, the actual path is specified as

local_module*, port, address, port, address,* etc.

The "local_module" is the name of the module in the I/O configuration and each port-address pair specifies the port by which the message exits the module and the address is the address of the next module in the path. Valid port-address pairs are described in Rockwell Automation (2002).

Cache Connections - If checked, the connection is not closed after the transfer is completed.

Communication Method - This set of fields is only active when communicating with non-ControlLogix processors. The CIP method is the communication method between ControlLogix processors. The DH+ method is used if the message is routed through a DH+ network. In this case the other fields are used as follows:

Channel - Channel (A or B) on DHRIO module connected to the DH+ network.

Source Link - Link ID for the local DH+ link (0-199). Used only if a routing table has been configured in the DHRIO module.

Destination Link - Link ID for the remote DH+ link where the target device resides (0 - 199). Used only if a routing table has been configured in the DHRIO module.

Destination Node - DH+ address of remote processor (0-77 octal).

The CIP with Source ID method is used for an unsolicited message that is routed through an Ethernet network or a ControlNet network to an operator interface that requires the source link to identify the data. The use of the other fields is described in Rockwell Automation (2002).

When reading a tag named React2_Indicat in the processor named Reactor2 into the React2_Indicat tag of the processor, the MSG configuration appears as shown in Figure 17.51. The name of the other processor (Reactor2) appears in the Path field. If the same information was read from the processor named Loadout, the only change would be that the path is set to "Loadout." An example writing data to a PLC-5 processor is shown in Figure 17.52. In this case, an integer (R1_Cmd) is written to N7:10 in the PLC-5. The PLC-5 is address 25 on the left-side DH+ network. The Ethernet connection to this processor can also be used. In this case, path to the PLC-5 processor cannot be specified in the I/O

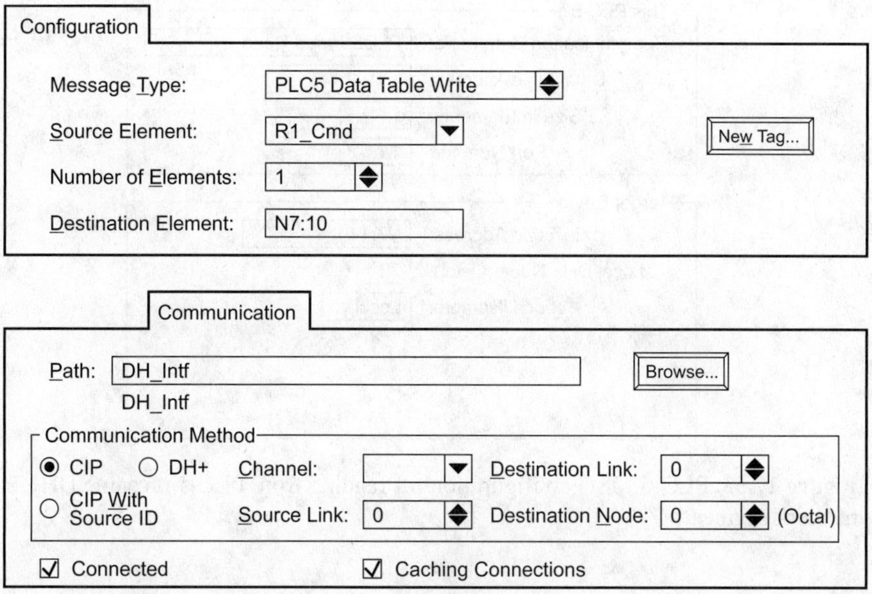

Figure 17.52. ControlLogix MSG configuration for writing to PLC-5 on DH+ network.

configuration tree. The path is "Enet_1,2,101.126.43.214" and the Communication Method is set to "CIP."

In PLC-5 processors, the MSG block allows one to read/write data addresses in another PLC-5, SLC-500, PLC-3, or PLC-2 processor. Later versions of the Ethernet and ControlNet PLC-5 processors allow the MSG block to read/write tags in a ControLogix processor. The Control address contains the messaging details. For original PLC-5 processors, the control address is the start of an integer block. The MG file type is applicable for the newer PLC-5 processors and its fields (Figure 17.53) are described as follows. The fields for this (local) PLC are:

Communication Command - Specifies the type of transfer (read/write) and the type of the other processor (PLC-5, SLC-500, PLC-3 or PLC-2).

Data Table Address - Address of the data in this processor. If the message is a read, this address is the destination of the data. If the message is a write, this address is the source of the data.

Size in Elements - The number of elements to transfer, starting with the given data table address.

Port Number - The processor communication port. The possible port numbers are:

0 - Serial

1A, 1B, 2A, 2B - DH+ (if configured for DH+)

2 - Ethernet (PLC-5/xxE) or ControlNet (PLC-5/xxC)

3A - "Sidecar" module attached to processor. Ethernet (1785-ENET)or ControlNet (1771-ACN).

The available ports depend on the particular processor. The fields for the other processor (target device) are:

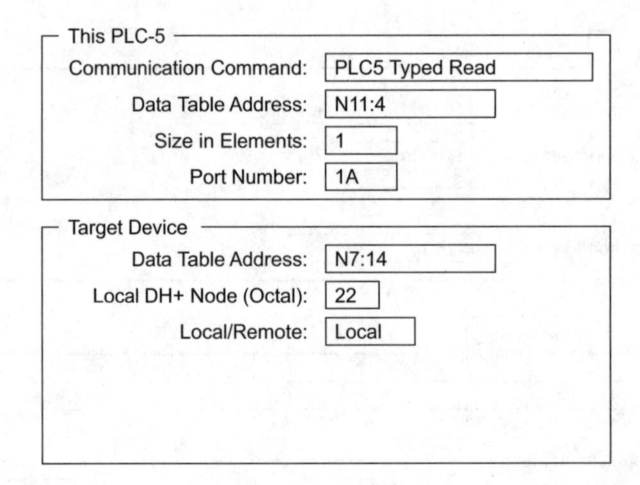

Figure 17.53. PLC-5 MSG configuration for reading from PLC-5 on same DH+ network segment.

Data Table Address - Address of the data in the other processor. If the message is a read, this address is the source of the data. If the message is a write, this address is the destination of the data.

Local DH+ Node - If the target processor is on the same DH+ segment as this processor, this is the DH+ address of the remote processor (0-77 octal). If the target device is on another DH+ segment, this is the address of the bridge, the first device in the path to the target node.

Local/Remote - Set to "Local" if the target processor is on the same DH+ segment as this processor. Set to "Remote" if the target device is on another DH+ segment.

If the target device is on a remote DH+ network, additional fields must be specified (Figure 17.54):

Remote Link Type - The type of network connected to the other side of the bridge module, "Data Highway" or "Data Highway II" (DH+).

Node - the DH+ address of the remote processor (0-77 octal).

User - User number of target node. Normally set to one.

Remote Bridge Link ID - Link ID for the connection on the bridge device that specifies the DH+ segment where the target device resides.

If the port number is an Ethernet port, the target device information appears as shown in Figure 17.55. The "Ethernet (IP) Address" field contains the IP address of the other processor. The "Multihop" field is set to "Yes" if the target device must be reached through a ControlLogix Ethernet module. The target device can be a ControlLogix, PLC-5, or SLC-500 processor. The path to the target is specified in a table (Rockwell Automation, 1998b). Multihop messaging is only available for recent PLC-5 Ethernet processors.

For the PLC-5/11 at DH+ address 24 reading N7:14 from the PLC-5/25 at address 22 and placing it in N11:4, the MSG configuration appears as shown in Figure 17.53. If the same information was read from the PLC-5/12 processor at DH+ node 11 on the other DH+ segment, the MSG configuration is shown in Figure 17.54. The target device local node

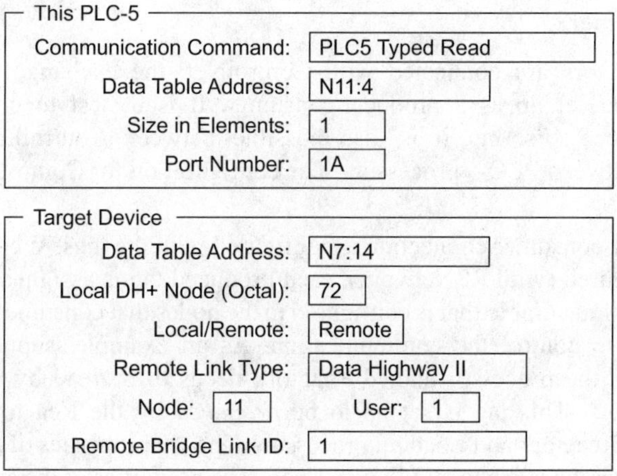

This PLC-5
Communication Command: PLC5 Typed Read
Data Table Address: N11:4
Size in Elements: 1
Port Number: 1A

Target Device
Data Table Address: N7:14
Local DH+ Node (Octal): 72
Local/Remote: Remote
Remote Link Type: Data Highway II
Node: 11 User: 1
Remote Bridge Link ID: 1

Figure 17.54. PLC-5 MSG configuration for reading from PLC-5 on linked DH+ network segment.

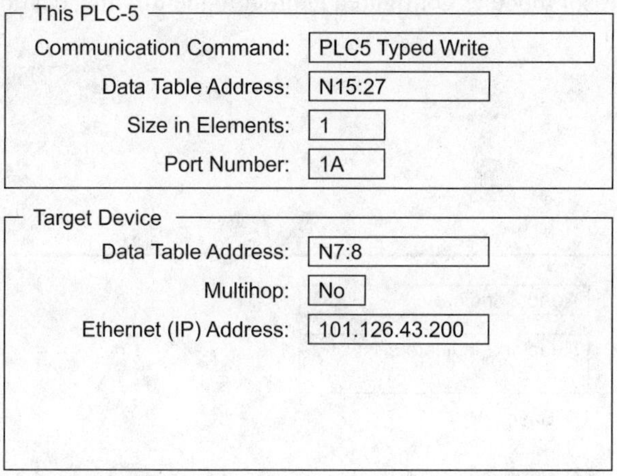

This PLC-5
Communication Command: PLC5 Typed Write
Data Table Address: N15:27
Size in Elements: 1
Port Number: 1A

Target Device
Data Table Address: N7:8
Multihop: No
Ethernet (IP) Address: 101.126.43.200

Figure 17.55. PLC-5 MSG configuration for writing to PLC-5 over Ethernet.

address is set to the address of the DHRIO, which is functioning as a bridge between the two DH+ segments. The node address of the PLC-5/12 processor is placed in the "Node" field below the "Remote Link Type" and the Link number is the DHRIO link number connected to the right DH+ network. If the two PLC-5/20E processors wanted to exchange information, they could do it over DH+ or over Ethernet. A sample MSG configuration for the PLC-5/20E at IP 101.126.43.214 to write a location to the PLC-5/20E at IP 101.126.43.200 is shown in Figure 17.55.

The configuration of the MSG block for a SLC-500 processor (Figure 17.48*c*) is similar to the configuration of the PLC-5 MSG block. There are two basic differences: (1) a SLC-500 can only communicate with another SLC-500 or PLC-5 processor, and (2) the control block must be in an integer data file.

Producer/Consumer

When processors are connected with ControlNet, the exchange of data between processors can be set up as a producer/consumer. It is easiest to configure between ControlLogix processors, but it is also possible between ControlLogix and PLC-5 processors and between PLC-5 processors. The configuration for ControlLogix processors is described here.

The producer/consumer connection is configured with the tags. When the ControlNet network is configured (with RSNetworx), each produced tag is assigned a time slot to be sent and a connection number that is configured in the nodes that consume that tag. No MSG block is needed to control the communication. As an example, suppose a tag named React2_Indicat in the processor named Reactor2 needs to be read by the Reactor1 and Loadout processors. This tag is set up to be *produced* by the Reactor2 processor and *consumed* by the Reactor1 and Loadout processors. The tag properties of React2_Indicat in the Reactor2 processor are shown in Figure 17.56. The properties of the consumed tag, also called React2_Indicat in the Reactor1 processor are shown in Figure 17.57. The Reactor1 I/O configuration has the tree of Figure 17.50 in order to identify the Producer. The properties of the consumed tag in the Loadout processor will appear identical to Figure 17.57, except that the scope is "Loadout". The I/O configuration will need to have the network and processor modules configured in order to identify the location of the Reactor2 processor.

General

Name: React2_Indicat

Description: Reactor 2 indicators

Tag Type: ○ Base ○ Alias ◉ Produced ○ Consumed

Data Type: DINT

Scope: Reactor2

Style: Decimal

Connection

Maximum Consumers: 10

☐ Programmatically (IOT Instruction) Send Event Trigger to Consumers

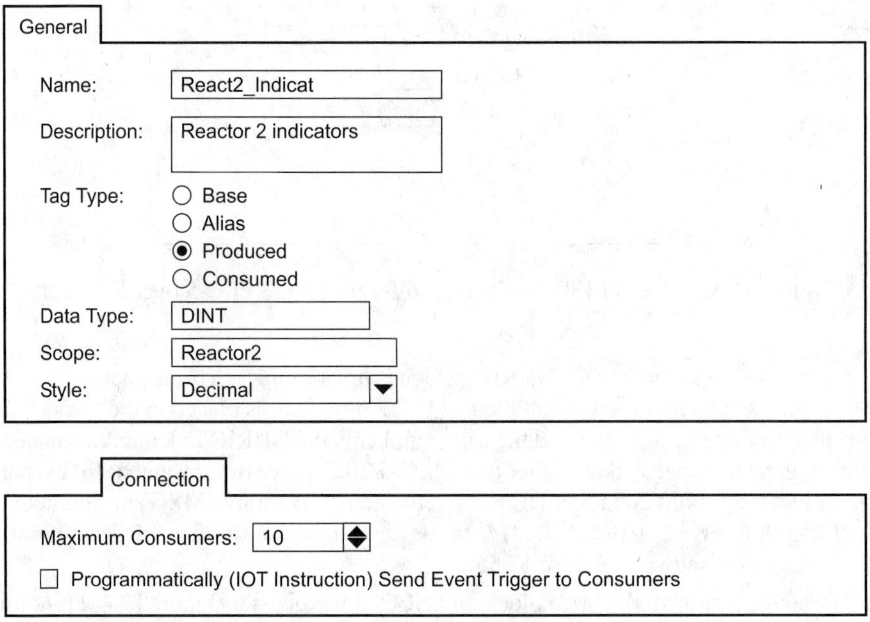

Figure 17.56. ControlLogix tag configuration for producer.

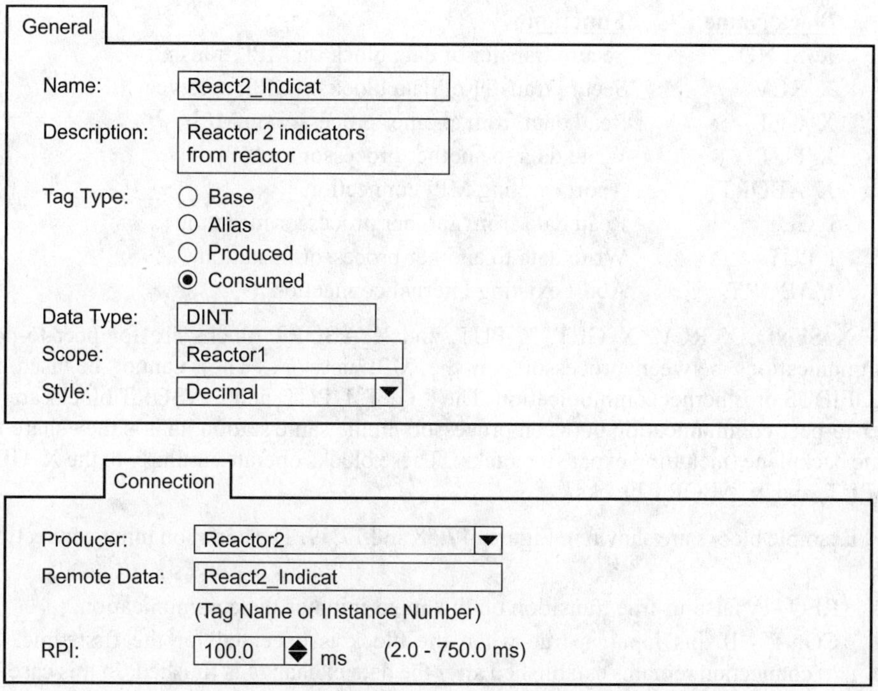

General

Name: React2_Indicat

Description: Reactor 2 indicators from reactor

Tag Type: ○ Base ○ Alias ○ Produced ◉ Consumed

Data Type: DINT

Scope: Reactor1

Style: Decimal

Connection

Producer: Reactor2

Remote Data: React2_Indicat

(Tag Name or Instance Number)

RPI: 100.0 ms (2.0 - 750.0 ms)

Figure 17.57. ControlLogix tag configuration for consumer.

17.16.3 S7

PROFIBUS DP, and AS-i master interface modules are available for the S7-300 processors. The AS-i master module maps directly into the processor input/output image. The table is a fixed length and a portion of that image is dedicated to each slave device on the network. When the PROFIBUS module is configured, the slave modules are mapped into the processor I/O image. The available Ethernet modules support peer-to-peer communications with recent processors.

Peer-to-peer communication may also be done on a PROFIBUS segment called the Multipoint Interface (MPI) subnet. The structure of an MPI subnet is basically the same as a PROFIBUS subnet. In general, the same network components are used to set up both networks. However, different components are used for a PROFIBUS network for a transmission rate greater than 1.5 Mbps.

There are two methods provided to transfer data between processors. A set of function blocks provides peer-to-peer communication between processors. Alternatively, global data communications may also be configured. The function blocks for peer-to-peer communication are illustrated first and then setting up the global data communications is described.

Peer-to-Peer

There are two methods of peer-to-peer (PLC-to-PLC) communication with S7 processors: (1) configured connections and (2) non-configured. All S7-300 and S7-400 processors support non-configured connections. The available blocks are:

Block Name	Function
X_SEND	Secure transfer of data block on MPI, transmit
X_RCV	Secure transfer of data block on MPI, receive
X_GET	Read data from another processor on MPI
X_PUT	Write data to another processor on MPI
X_ABORT	Abort existing MPI connection
I_GET	Read data from another processor in station
I_PUT	Write data to another processor in station
I_ABORT	Abort existing internal connection

The X_SEND, X_RCV, X_GET, X_PUT, and X_ABORT blocks are for peer-to-peer communications between processors on the MPI network. They cannot be used for PROFIBUS or Ethernet communication. The I_GET, I_PUT, and I_ABORT blocks are for peer-to-peer communication between processors in the same station, that is they share the same backplane (including expansion racks). These blocks operate similarly to the X_GET, X_PUT, and X_ABORT blocks.

Example blocks are shown in Figures 17.58 and 17.59. The common input connections are:

REQ - A false-to-true transition on this input initiates the communication.

CONT - If this input is true when the block is executed for the first time, the connection remains established after the data exchange is finished. In this case, an X_ABORT block must terminate this connection. If this input is false, the connection is terminated after the data exchange is finished.

DEST_ID - MPI address (node number) of the other processor.

Common output connections are:

RET_VAL - Zero is the block executed without error. Otherwise, it contains an error code (Siemens, 2000)

BUSY - True as long as exchange has not completed. False when the exchange is complete.

Only one connection between two processors can be active. So, if there are multiple blocks of data that must be exchanged between two processors, one exchange must finish before the next one is initiated.

The X_SEND and X_RCV blocks are used together. The X_SEND block is in the processor that initiates the transfer and the X_RCV block is in the processor that receives the transfer. An example X_SEND block is shown in Figure 17.58*a* and the corresponding X_RCV block in the other processor is shown in Figure 17.58*b*. For the X_SEND block, the SD input is the data block to be sent. The REQ_ID input is the job identifier (DWORD) that will be used in the other processor to discriminate this message from others in the queue. All messages initiated by X_SEND blocks to a particular processor appear in one queue and so the message identifier should be used by X_RCV blocks in that processor to transfer the proper data to its data block (RD output). The EN_DT input is set to true in order to transfer the oldest data block in the queue to the RD output. The NDA (new data arrived) output is true when there is any data block in the queue and the REQ_ID output is the job identifier for this data block. The second network (in Figure 17.58*b*) sets Cpy_Rcv1 true when new data has arrived and its job identifier is the one desired. On the next program scan, the received data block is copied to the "Rcv_Data".Data location.The MOVE blocks are used

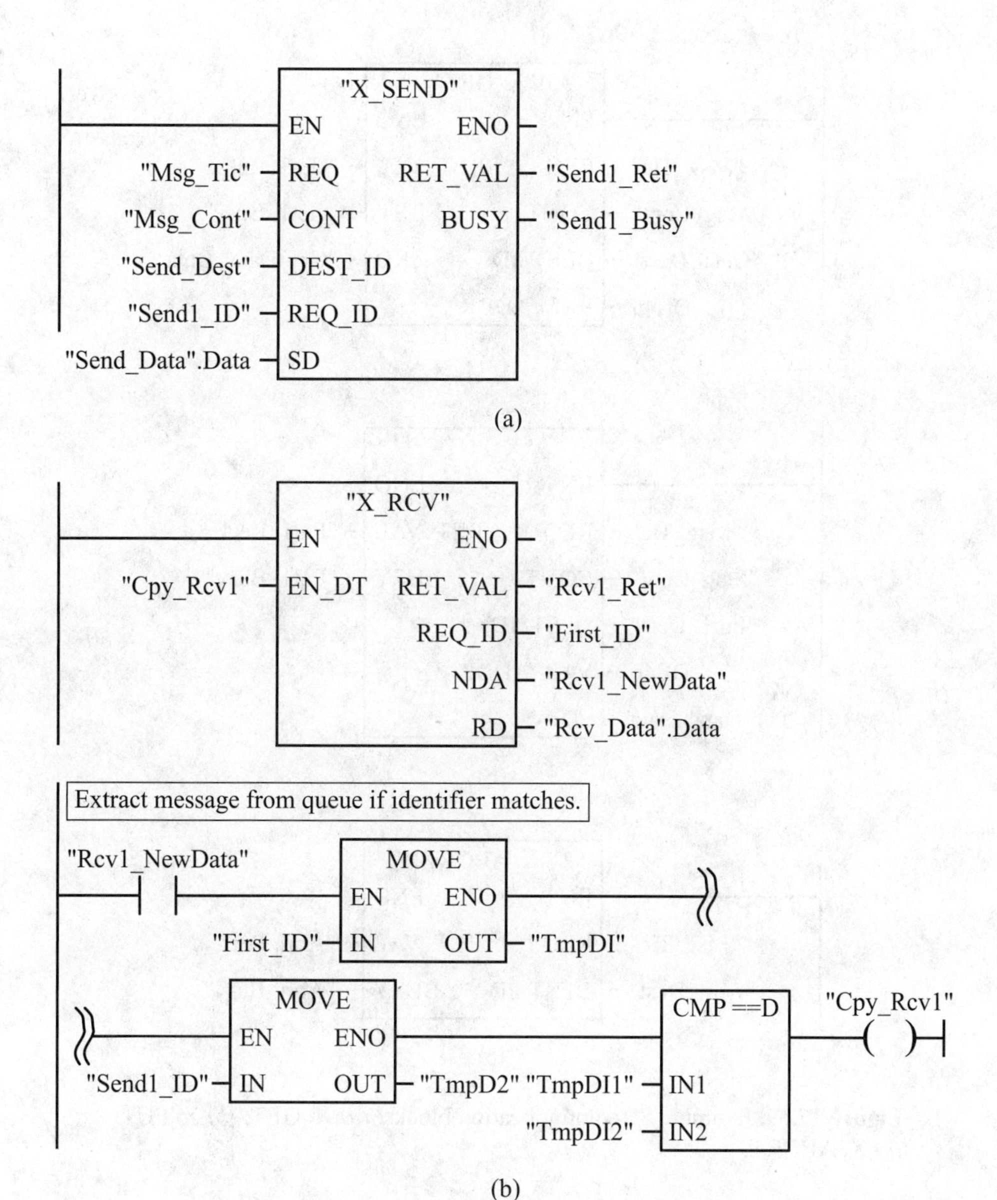

Figure 17.58. Example S7 X_SEND/X_RCV pair: *(a)* X_SEND block; *(b)* corresponding X_RCV in other processor.

to convert the job identifiers (DWORD) to DINTs in order to do the comparison. The "Send1_ID" variables in both processors are assumed to be the same value.

The other communication blocks are shown in Figure 17.59. For the X_GET block (Figure 17.59*a*), the VAR_ADDR input is the reference to the source data in the remote processor (DEST_ID node number) and the RD output is the reference to the destination in this processor. For the example in Figure 17.59*a*, the entire data block DB45 in the Get1_Dest node is transferred to the Get_Data block in this processor. The Get_Data block

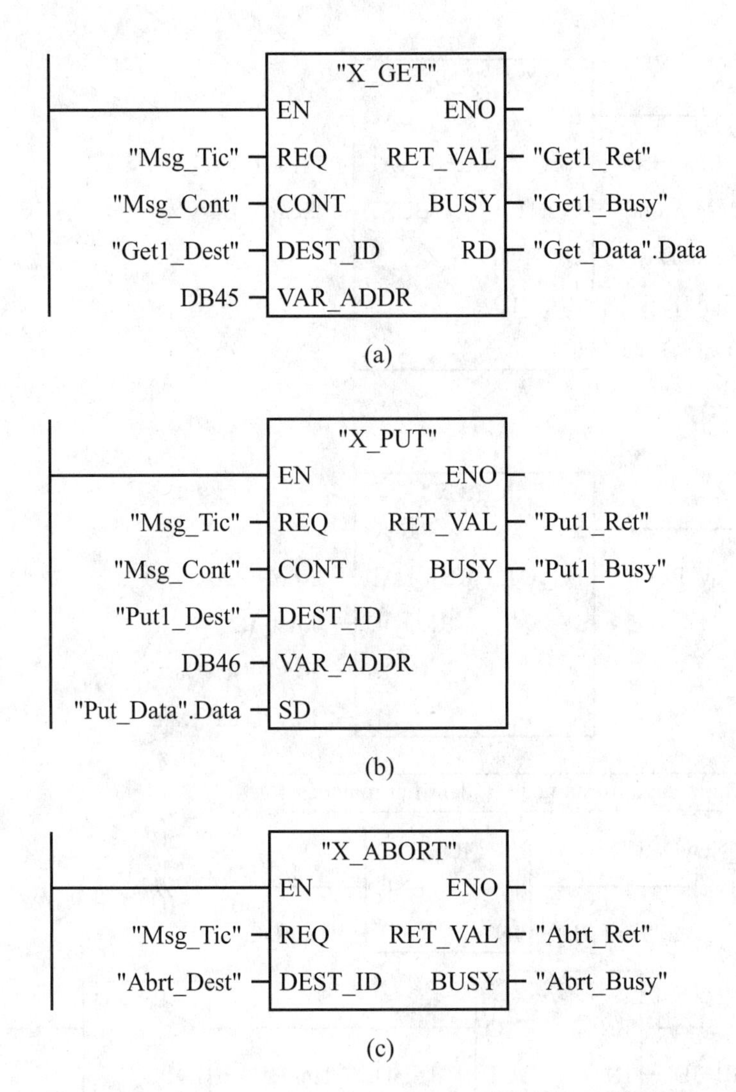

Figure 17.59. Example S7 communication blocks: *(a)* X_GET; *(b)* X_PUT; *(c)* X_ABORT.

is an array of INTs. For the X_PUT block (Figure 17.59*b*), the VAR_ADDR input is the reference to the destination in the remote processor (DEST_ID node number) and the SD input is the source data in this processor. For the example in Figure 17.59*b*, the Put_Data.Data array in this processor is transferred to the DB46 data block in the Put1_Dest node. The Put_Data block is an array of INTs. The X_ABORT block in Figure 17.59*c* terminates the active connection between this processor and the Abrt_Dest node.

For S7-400 processors and recent S7-300 processors, communications over Ethernet is provided by configured connections using the following blocks:

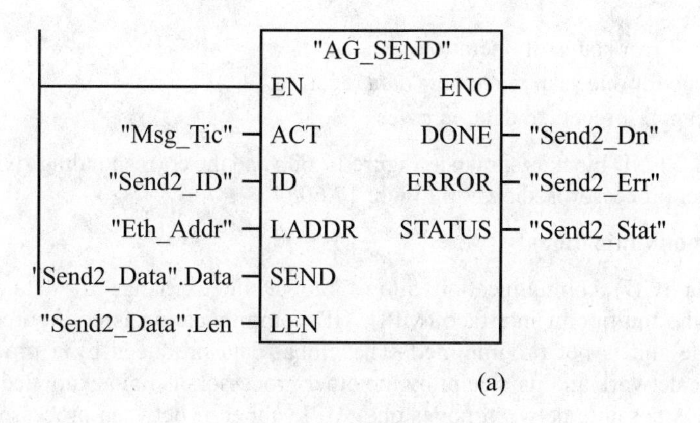

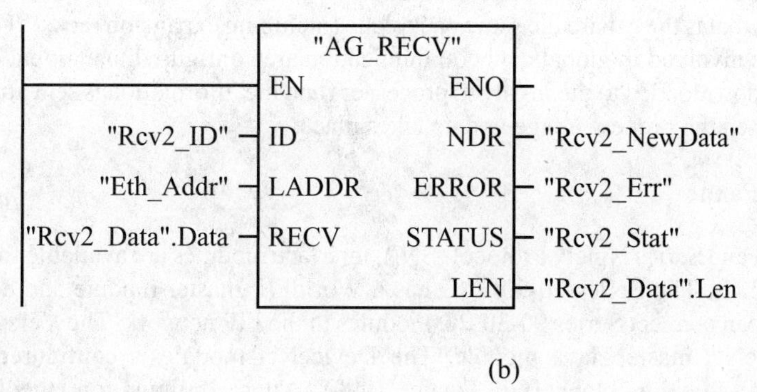

Figure 17.60. Example S7 AG_SEND/AG_RECV pair: *(a)* AG_SEND block; *(b)* corresponding AG_RECV in other processor.

Block Name	**Function**
AG_SEND	Transfer of data block (<240 bytes), transmit
AG_RECV	Transfer of data block (<240 bytes), receive
AG_LSEND	Transfer of data block (>240 bytes), transmit
AG_LRECV	Transfer of data block (>240 bytes), receive

Like X_SEND and X_RCV, the AG_SEND and AG_RECV blocks (and AG_LSEND and AG_LRECV) are used together.

Example blocks are shown in Figure 17.60. The input connections are:

ACT - A false-to-true transition on this input initiates the communication.

ID - Connection identifier. Defined in the network configuration.

LADDR - Ethernet module start address. Defined in the module configuration.

SEND - Data block to be sent.

RECV - Received data block placed in this area.

LEN - Length of transmitted data, in bytes.

The output connections are:

DONE - True for one scan when send successfully completed.

ERROR - True when the block has an error.

STATUS - Error status of operation.
NDR - True for one scan when new data received.
LEN - Length of received data, in bytes.

An example AG_SEND block is shown in Figure 17.60*a* and the corresponding AG_RECV block in the other processor is shown in Figure 17.60*b*.

Global Data Communications

Global data (GD) communication allows the cyclic exchange of data between processors via the multipoint interface (MPI). GD communication is configured with a global data table and is not programmed. The global data produced by a processor is broadcast on the network and its receipt by the other processors is not acknowledged. GD communication is possible between nodes on a MPI subnet or between processors in the same station, that is they share the same backplane (including expansion racks). The address areas that are involved in global data communication are configured in a global data table. This table is downloaded to the involved processors and the information is sent and received cyclically when the process image update takes place.

17.16.4 GE Fanuc

Ethernet and Series Ninety Protocol (SNP) interface modules are available for all of the GE Fanuc PLCs. The Series 90-70 PLC has a WorldFIP master module and a FIP slave module that can connect Series 90-30 I/O modules to the FIP network. The VersaMax PLC has a DeviceNet master/slave module. The DeviceNet module is configured with the COMM_REQ function block (GE Fanuc, 1999). After configuration, the DeviceNet modules map directly into the processor input/output image. A VersaMax PLC can also function as a PROFIBUS-DP slave.

Processor-to-processor communication is available two ways over Ethernet. Peer-to-peer communications is available through the COMM_REQ block. Alternatively, producer/consumer relationships can be set up over Ethernet using the Ethernet global data exchange. The use of the COMM_REQ block is illustrated first, followed by a description of Ethernet global data exchange.

Peer-to-Peer

Peer-to-peer (PLC-to-PLC) communications is set up through the COMM_REQ block, shown in Figure 17.61. The input connections are as follows:

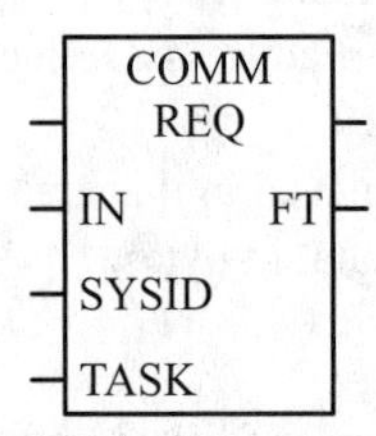

Figure 17.61. GE Fanuc COMM_REQ block.

IN - The starting address of a block containing the command block that specifies the communication parameters (SYSID=256*rack_number+slot_number).

SYSID - The rack and slot of the communications module. The high byte of the word is the rack number and the low byte is the slot number.

TASK - The mailbox task identifier for the communications module. For most Ethernet modules, the value should be zero.

The FT output is turned on if there is a problem sending the command block to the communications module or there is an error in one of the parameters. If there is a problem with the communication network, then error information is contained in the communications module status indicators and in the COMM_REQ status word (CRS) and in the Detailed Channel Status (DCS) words. The location of the CRS is specified as part of the command block and the DCS words are contained in the command block.

Rather than detail the contents of the command block (GE Fanuc 2002), two examples are presented that illustrate the operation of the COMM_REQ block to set up a read channel and a write channel. Figure 17.62 shows an example COMM_REQ block and the other ladder logic that sets up a read channel. When the read is to be initiated, the CRS is cleared, the fault bit is cleared, four BLKMOV function blocks load the command block, and then the COMM_REQ is executed. The details of the command block values are shown in Figure 17.63. This example sets up a channel to read registers %R201 - %R220 in the PLC at IP address 101.126.43.120 and place them in registers %R251 - %R270 in the current

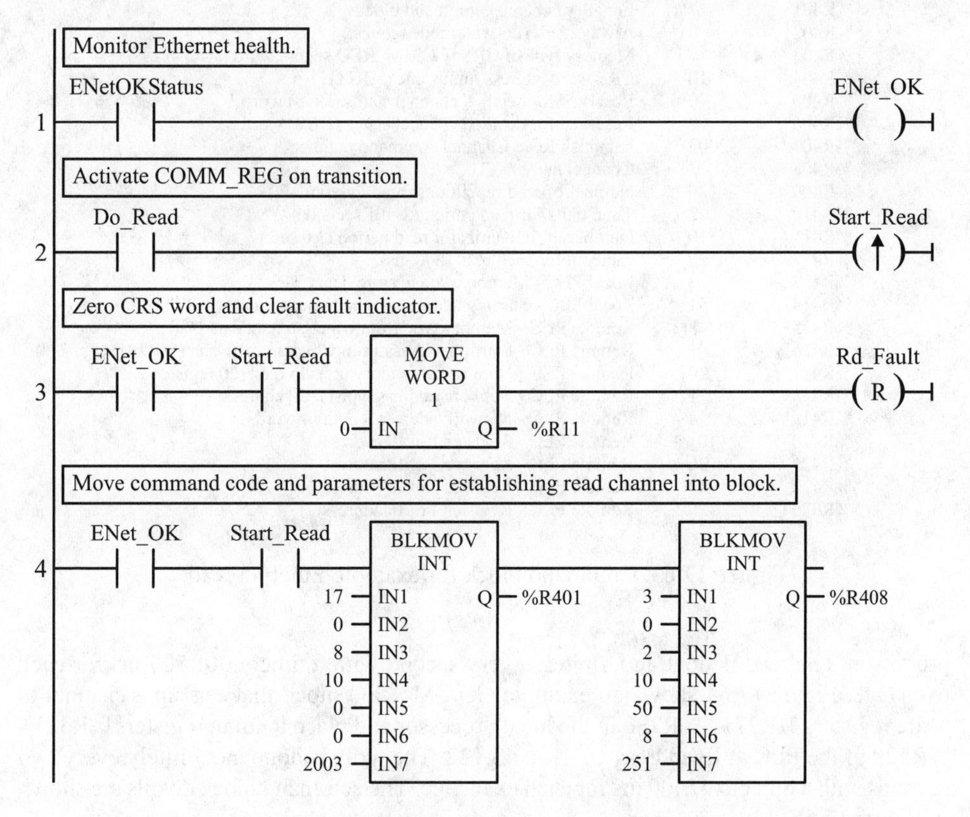

Figure 17.62. Example GE Fanuc Ethernet read command. *(continued)*

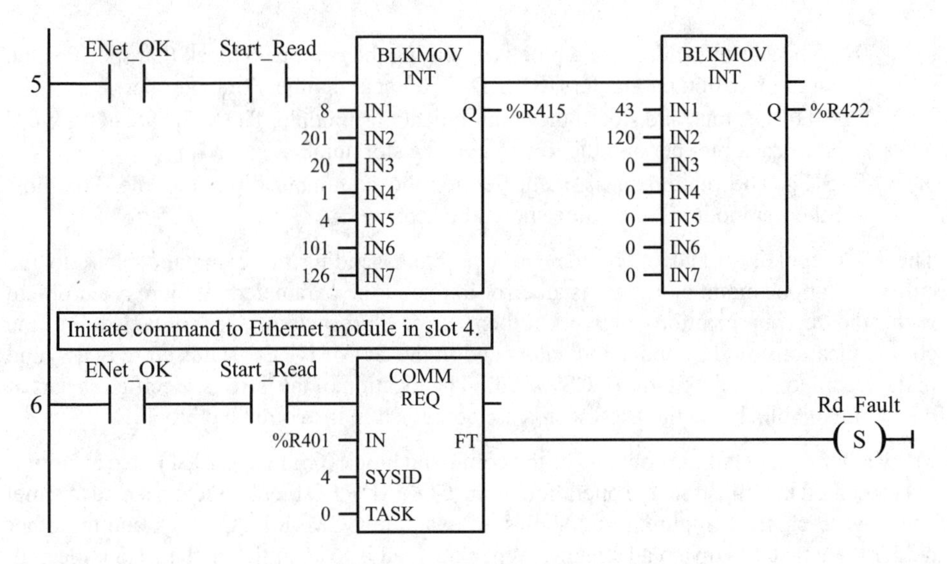

Figure 17.62. *(continued)*

Command Block:

Addr.	Contents	Description
%R401	17	Length of channel command block
%R402	0	Always zero (no-wait mode request)
%R403	8	Memory type of CRS (COMM_REQ status) word (%R)
%R404	10	CRS word address minus one (%R11)
%R405	0	Reserved for detailed channel status (DCS) word 1
%R406	0	Reserved for detailed channel status (DCS) word 2
%R407	2003	Establish Read Channel command number
%R408	3	Channel number (3)
%R409	0	Number of read repetitions (read indefinitely)
%R410	2	Time units for read period (2=0.1 seconds)
%R411	10	Number of time units for read period (1.0 sec.)
%R412	50	Timeout for each read (500 ms)
%R413	8	Local PLC - Memory type to store data (%R)
%R414	251	Local PLC - Starting address at which to store data (%R251)
%R415	8	Remote PLC - Memory type from which to read data (%R)
%R416	201	Remote PLC - Starting address from which to read data (%R201)
%R417	20	Remote PLC - Number of memory units to read (20 registers)
%R418	1	Remote PLC - Network address type (1=IP address)
%R419	4	Remote PLC - Network address length (4 words)
%R420	101	Remote PLC - Register 1 of IP address
%R421	126	Remote PLC - Register 2 of IP address
%R422	43	Remote PLC - Register 3 of IP address
%R423	120	Remote PLC - Register 4 of IP address

Figure 17.63. Command block for example Ethernet read.

processor. The read is done indefinitely every second with a timeout of 500 ms for each exchange. Figure 17.64 shows an example COMM_REQ block that sets up a channel to write registers %R271 - %R280 in the local processor and place them in registers %R321 - %R329 of the PLC at IP address 101.126.43.122. The write is done indefinitely every two seconds with a timeout of 500 ms for each exchange. The command block details are shown in Figure 17.65.

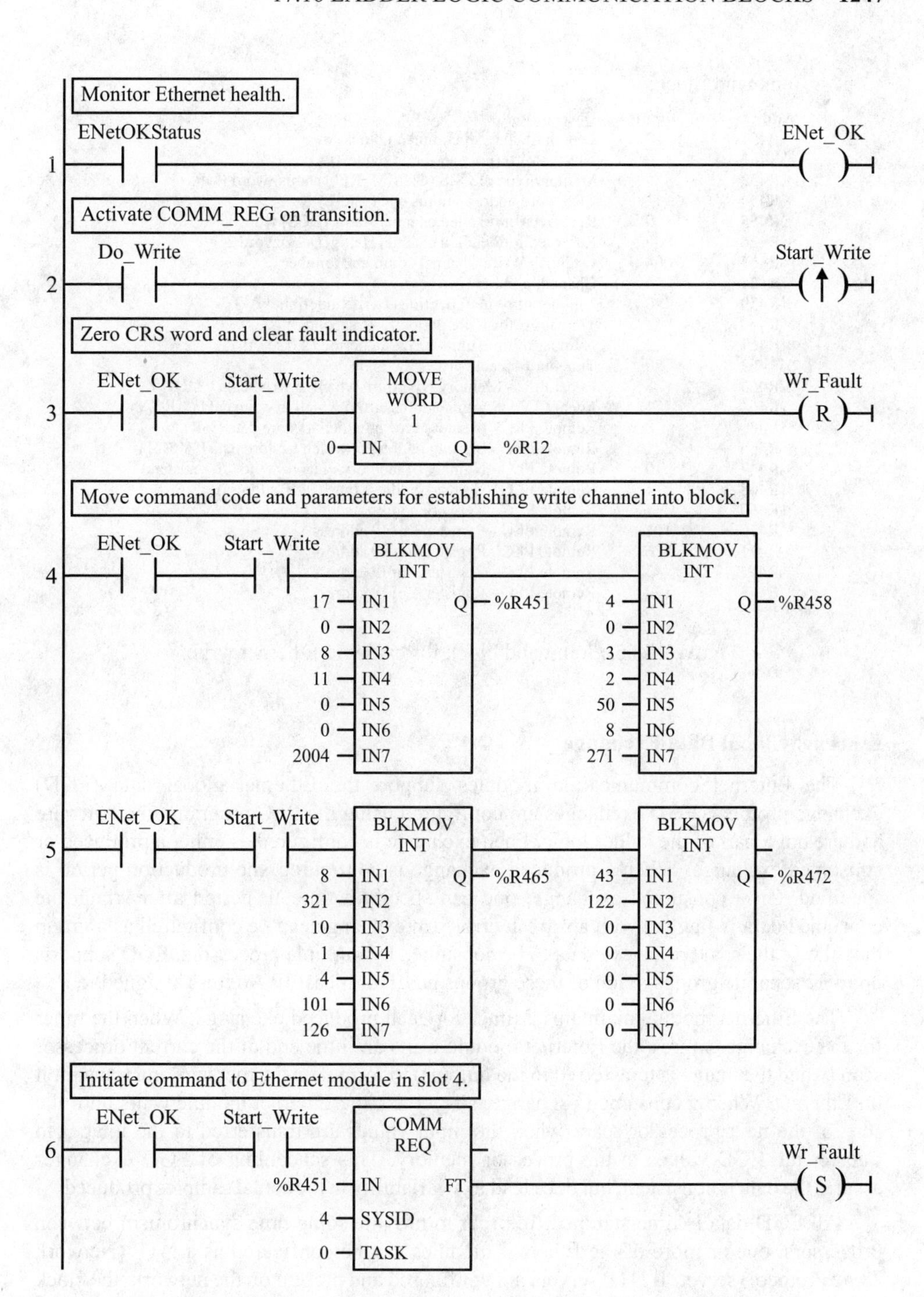

Figure 17.64. Example GE Fanuc Ethernet write command.

Command Block:

Addr.	Contents	Description
%R451	17	Length of channel command block
%R452	0	Always zero (no-wait mode request)
%R453	8	Memory type of CRS (COMM_REQ status) word (%R)
%R454	11	CRS word address minus one (%R12)
%R455	0	Reserved for detailed channel status (DCS) word 1
%R456	0	Reserved for detailed channel status (DCS) word 2
%R457	2004	Establish Write Channel command number
%R458	4	Channel number (4)
%R459	0	Number of write repetitions (write indefinitely)
%R460	3	Time units for write period (3=1 second)
%R461	2	Number of time units for write period (2.0 sec.)
%R462	50	Timeout for each write (500 ms)
%R463	8	Local PLC - Memory type from which to write data (%R)
%R464	271	Local PLC - Starting address from which to write data (%R271)
%R465	8	Remote PLC - Memory type at which to store data (%R)
%R466	321	Remote PLC - Starting address at which to store data (%R321)
%R467	10	Remote PLC - Number of memory units to write (10 registers)
%R468	1	Remote PLC - Network address type (1=IP address)
%R469	4	Remote PLC - Network address length (4 words)
%R470	101	Remote PLC - Register 1 of IP address
%R471	126	Remote PLC - Register 2 of IP address
%R472	43	Remote PLC - Register 3 of IP address
%R473	122	Remote PLC - Register 4 of IP address

Figure 17.65. Command block for example Ethernet write.

Ethernet Global Data Exchange

The Ethernet communication modules support the Ethernet global data (EGD) exchange protocol. EGD exchanges are configured using the PLC programming software and are not a part of the ladder logic. Each exchange is configured as either a produced or consumed exchange. When a produced exchange is configured, the production period is specified. On a consumed exchange, one can specify a timeout period after which the consumed data is flagged with a refresh error. An exchange can be configured as a group that allows the same produced data to be consumed by multiple processors. EGD supports up to 32 separate groups. Each of these groups has a multicast IP Address assigned to it.

The Ethernet module maintains a timer for each produced exchange. When the timer for the exchange expires, the Ethernet module waits until the end of the current processor scan (when the image is transferred to the outputs) to formulate the message and transmit it on Ethernet. When a consumed exchange is received, the Ethernet module waits until the start of the next processor scan (when the input values are transferred to the image) to transfer the EGD values to the processor memory. This scheduling of EGD exchanges assures the data is consistent, but does lead to a variability in the actual samples produced.

All EGD data is time-stamped. In order to provide some time synchronism between processors, one or more of the Ethernet modules can be configured as a NTP (Network Time Protocol) server. If NTP servers are configured and present on the network, the clock on each Ethernet module is periodically synchronized to the clock from one to three NTP servers. To do this synchronization, the Ethernet module periodically requests the time from the servers and uses the time from the most accurate server, based on the NTP stratum number.

When a 90-70 system has redundant processors, the EGD exchanges may be copied from the primary processor to the secondary processor.

17.17 CHAPTER SUMMARY

This chapter reviews standard and proprietary factory communication networks available for PLC systems. Standard network protocols are covered first and then proprietary Modicon, Allen-Bradley, and GE Fanuc protocols are described. Lastly, the function blocks that implement PLC-to-PLC communication are explained.

REFERENCES

Allen-Bradley, 1994. *Data Highway/Data Highway Plus/Data Highway II/Data Highway-485 Cable: Installation Manual*, pub. 1770-6.2.2, Allen-Bradley Company, Inc., Milwaukee, WI, April.

Allen-Bradley, 1996. *DF1 Protocol and Command Set: Reference Manual*, pub. 1770-6.5.16, Allen-Bradley Company, Inc., Milwaukee, WI, October.

ANSI, 1976. *Procedures for the Use of the Communication Control Characters of American National Standard Code for Information Interchange in Specified Data Communication Links*, ANSI.X3-28.1976, American National Standards Institute, Washington, D.C.

Ciminiera, Luigi, Claudio DeMartini, and Adriano Valenzano, 1988. "Industrial IEEE 802.3 Networks with Short Delivery Time for Urgent Messages," *IEEE Transactions on Industrial Electronics*, vol. 35, no.1 (February): 18-25.

ControlNet Int., 2001a. *Ethernet/IP Specification - Vol. 1: CIP Common Specification*, Release 1.0, ControlNet Int., Inc. and Open DeviceNet Vendor Assoc., Ann Arbor, MI, June 5.

ControlNet Int., 2001b. *Ethernet/IP Specification - Vol. 2: Ethernet/IP Adaptation of CIP*, Release 1.0, ControlNet Int., Inc. and Open DeviceNet Vendor Assoc., Ann Arbor, MI, June 5.

Crowder, Robert, n.d. "Type 8 SwiftNet," Deutsche Kommission Elektrotechnik, .

Felser, M., 2002. "The Fieldbus Standard: History and Structure," Technology Leadership Day 2002, organized by MICROSWISS Network, HTA Luzern, Oct. 10.

Fieldbus Foundation, 2003. *Foundation Fieldbus Technical Overview*, pub. FD-043, Rev. 3.0, Fieldbus Foundation, Austin, TX.

GE Fanuc Automation, 1999a. *Series 90^{TM}-30 PLC: Installation and Hardware Manual*, pub. GFK-0356P, GE Fanuc Automation North America, Inc., Charlottesville, VA.

GE Fanuc Automation, 1999b. *Series 90^{TM}-70 PLC: Installation Manual*, pub. GFK-0262G, GE Fanuc Automation North America, Inc., Charlottesville, VA.

GE Fanuc Automation, 1999c. *VersaMax^{TM} System DeviceNet Communications Modules: User's Manual*, pub. GFK-1533, GE Fanuc Automation North America, Inc., Charlottesville, VA, June.

GE Fanuc Automation, 2000a. *Series 90^{TM} PLC Serial Communications: User's Manual*, pub. GFK-0582D, GE Fanuc Automation North America, Inc., Charlottesville, VA, November.

GE Fanuc Automation, 2000b. *VersaMax^{TM} System Profibus Network Modules: User's Manual*, pub. GFK-1534B, GE Fanuc Automation North America, Inc., Charlottesville, VA, November.

GE Fanuc Automation, 2002. *TCP/IP Ethernet Communications for the Series 90^{TM} PLC: User's Manual*, pub. GFK-1541B, GE Fanuc Automation North America, Inc., Charlottesville, VA, May.

IEC, 2000. *Low-Voltage Switchgear and Controlgear - Controller-Device Interfaces (CDIs) - Part 2: Actuator Sensor Interface (AS-I)*, IEC 62026-2, Ed. 1.0, International Electrotechnical Commission, Geneva, Switzerland.

IEC, 2001. *Low-Voltage Switchgear and Controlgear - Controller-Device Interfaces (CDIs) - Part 6: Seriplex (Serial Multiplexed Control Bus)*, IEC 62026-6, Ed. 1.0, International Electrotechnical Commission, Geneva, Switzerland.

IEC, 2003a. *Digital Data Communications for Measurement and Control - Fieldbus for Use in Industrial Control Systems - Part 1: Overview and Guidance for the IEC 61158 Series*, IEC 61158-1, Ed. 1.0, International Electrotechnical Commission, Geneva, Switzerland.

IEC, 2003b. *Digital Data Communications for Measurement and Control - Fieldbus for Use in Industrial Control Systems - Part 2: Physical Layer Specification and Service Definition*, IEC 61158-2, Ed. 3.0, International Electrotechnical Commission, Geneva, Switzerland.

IEC, 2003c. *Digital Data Communications for Measurement and Control - Fieldbus for Use in Industrial Control Systems - Part 3: Data Link Service Definition*, IEC 61158-3, Ed. 3.0, International Electrotechnical Commission, Geneva, Switzerland.

IEC, 2003d. *Digital Data Communications for Measurement and Control - Fieldbus for Use in Industrial Control Systems - Part 4: Data Link Protocol Specification*, IEC 61158-4, Ed. 3.0, International Electrotechnical Commission, Geneva, Switzerland.

IEC, 2003e. *Digital Data Communications for Measurement and Control - Fieldbus for Use in Industrial Control Systems - Part 5: Application Layer Service Definition*, IEC 61158-5, Ed. 3.0, International Electrotechnical Commission, Geneva, Switzerland.

IEC, 2003f. *Digital Data Communications for Measurement and Control - Fieldbus for Use in Industrial Control Systems - Part 6: Application Layer Protocol Specification*, IEC 61158-6, Ed. 3.0, International Electrotechnical Commission, Geneva, Switzerland.

IEC, 2003g. *Digital Data Communications for Measurement and Control - Part 1: Profile Sets for Continuous and Discrete Manufacturing Relative to Fieldbus Use in Industrial Control Systems*, IEC 61784-1, Ed. 1.0, International Electrotechnical Commission, Geneva, Switzerland.

IEEE, 1990. *IEEE Standard for Information technology—Telecommunications and information exchange between systems—Local and metropolitan area networks—Common specifications—Part4: Token-Passing Bus Access Method and Physical Layer Specifications*, ISO/IEC 8802-4-1990, Institute of Electrical and Electronics Engineers, New York, NY.

IEEE, 2002. *IEEE Standard for Information technology—Telecommunications and information exchange between systems—Local and metropolitan area networks—Common specifications—Part3: Carrier-Sense Multiple Access with Collision Detection (CSMA/CD) Access Method and Physical Layer Specifications*, IEEE 802.3^{TM}-2002, Institute of Electrical and Electronics Engineers, New York, NY.

Klemm, Eckehardt, n.d. "Type 8 Interbus," Deutsche Kommission Elektrotechnik, .

Lian, Feng-Li, James R. Moyne, and Dawn M. Tilbury, 2001. "Performance Evaulation of Control Networks: Ethernet, ControlNet, and DeviceNet," *IEEE Control Systems Magazine*, (February): 66-83.

Modbus, 2002a. *MODBUS Application Protocol Specification*, Modbus Organization, Hopkinton, MA, May 8.

Modbus, 2002b. *MODBUS Messaging on TCP/IP: Implementation Guide*, Rev 1.0, Modbus Organization, Hopkinton, MA, May 8.

Modbus, 2002c. *MODBUS Over Serial Line: Specification & Implementation Guide*, Rev. 1.0, Modbus Organization, Hopkinton, MA, Dec. 2.

P-Net, 1996. *The P-NET® Fieldbus for Process Automation*, International P-NET User Organization, Silkeborg, Denmark.

Profibus, 2002. *PROFIBUS Technology and Application: System Description*, PROFIBUS Nutzerorganisation, e.V., Karlsruhe, Germany, October.

Profibus, 2003. *PROFInet Architecture Description and Specification*, Ver. 2.01, PROFIBUS Nutzerorganisation, e.V., Karlsruhe, Germany, August.

Rinaldi, J., 2003. "An Overview of PROFInet®: An Innovative Distributed Automation Solution," Real Time Automation, Wauwatosa, WI.

Rockwell Automation, 1998a. *AIC+ Advanced Interface Converter: User Manual*, pub. 1761-6.4, Rockwell Automation, Milwaukee, WI, April.

Rockwell Automation, 1998b. *PLC-5 Family Instruction Set Reference Manual*, pub. 1785-6.1, Rockwell Automation, Milwaukee, WI.

Rockwell Automation, 2002. *Logix5000™ Controllers General Instructions: Reference Manual*, pub. 1756-RM003F-EN-P, Rockwell Automation, Milwaukee, WI, May.

Rockwell Automation, 2003. *SLC 500™ Instruction Set: Reference Manual*, pub. 1756-RM0010D-EN-P, Rockwell Automation, Milwaukee, WI, November.

Rockwell Automation, 2004a. *ControlNet to Foundation Fieldbus H1 Linking Device: Installation Instructions*, pub. 1788-IN051D-EN-P, Rockwell Automation, Milwaukee, WI, February.

Rockwell Automation, 2004b. *FOUNDATION Fieldbus Linking Device: Installation Instructions*, pub. 1757-IN021C-EN-P, Rockwell Automation, Milwaukee, WI, April.

Rockwell Automation, 2004c. *Logix5000™ Controllers Common Procedures: Programming Manual*, pub. 1756-PM001G-EN-P, Rockwell Automation, Milwaukee, WI, March.

Schneider Automation, 1998. *Concept Block Library IEC,* vol. 3, ver. 2.1, pub. 840 USE 462 00, Schneider Automation, Inc., North Andover, MA.

Siemens, 1999a. *Fiber Optic Solutions with PROFIBUS System*, pub. 6ZB5 310-0GP02-0BA2, Siemens AG, Nuernberg, Germany.

Siemens, 1999b. *S7-300 Programmable Controller Hardware and Installation: Manual,* Ed. 2, 10/99, pub. EWA 4NEB 710 6084-02 01, Siemens AG, Nuernberg, Germany.

Siemens, 2000a. *SIMATIC NET PROFIBUS Networks Manual*, Edition 05/2000, pub. 6GK1970-5CA20-0AA1, Siemens AG, Nuernberg, Germany.

Siemens, 2000b. *System Software for S7-300/400 System and Standard Functions: Reference Manual*, Edition 08/2000, pub. A5E00069892-02, Siemens AG, Nuernberg, Germany.

WorldFIP, 1994. "Fieldbus Guide Part II: Application Layer," WorldFIP International, Meudon-la-Foret, France, December.

WorldFIP, 1998. *The WorldFIP Protocol*, Ver. 2, WorldFIP International, Meudon-la-Foret, France, February.

18 Human-Machine Interface

Chapter Topics:

- General operator interface concepts
- Operator panel and screen design

OBJECTIVES

Upon completion of this chapter, you will be able to understand

- Operator interface types
- Good operator panel design
- Good operator computer screen design

Scenario 1: Operator-initiated starts with permissives.

A certain batch control process is started from a touch-screen HMI (human-machine interface). However, the process does not start because not all of the permissives are met. When a detailed status screen is displayed, the operator discovers that two cooling valves are open. They should have been closed in the last step of the previous batch. Maintenance personnel determine that the valves are being commanded closed, but the valves are still in the open position. One valve is quickly repaired, but the other one needs to be replaced. The process cannot be operated without this valve, so they wait a day for a new valve to be received from the vendor and replaced. However, as soon as power is restored to the valve limit switches, the batch process immediately starts filling the initial ingredient. The operator has not initiated the batch. Nothing is hurt by this action. However, this action is unexpected, and you are called in to find the reason for the unexpected start.

Solution: At first, you are puzzled by the cause. After interviewing the maintenance personnel who handled the valve repair and the operator who reported the valve problem, your suspect a problem with the batch start. When questioned, the operator does not remember stopping the batch after reporting the problem with the two cooling valves. An initial check of the PLC program uncovers no problem. Next, you examine the touch-screen programming. The start button is set to be a latching button, that is, when the button icon is depressed, a bit is set in the PLC. This bit remains set when the button icon is released. The stop button is configured to be an unlatching button. The batch started unexpectedly because the operator start request was still active when the power was restored to the valve limit switch. The PLC detected a closed valve (all permissives met), and the first step of the batch process was initiated. The operator start and stop requests are changed to act like momentary push buttons. The operator start is changed to a momentary switch that sets a bit in the PLC as long as the button icon is pressed. Otherwise, the bit is cleared. The operator stop is changed to a momentary switch that clears a bit in the PLC as long as the button icon is pressed. Otherwise, the bit is set. Also, the batch start/stop logic is changed to be more like Figure 2.31. To prevent this problem in the future, the programming standard is changed to require all HMI operator starts to be momentary push buttons. In addition, a small project is initiated to correct this problem in all processes operated with a touch-screen HMI.

Scenario 2: Hydrofluoric acid spill.

A certain process contains a hydrofluoric (HF) acid bath (Figure 18.1). The tank contains a high level switch and a high-high level switch. The PLC control maintains the HF tank level between the high level switch and the high-high level switch. When the tank level drops below the high level switch (switch turns **on**), the HF fill valve is turned **on** to fill the tank until the high-high level switch turns **off**. The operator can override the automatic HF fill valve control and add acid to the tank, but not beyond the high-high level switch. If the high-high level switch is **off**, the HF fill valve is closed.

The system that places and removes items in the HF bath is upgraded. During the testing of this upgrade, this bath is empty. The high-high level switch is not working, so it is removed from the tank, but still connected to the PLC discrete input module. One night, the HF acid monitor on the plant sewer discharge sounds, indicating excess HF acid in the sewer discharge. Only a few units in the plant use HF acid and so the source is quickly located to this process. When the personnel arrive, HF acid has overflowed the tank, covering part of the floor and flowing into the floor drain. The HF lockout valve is quickly closed to prevent further loss and the area is cleaned up.

Solution: There are three faults here. The obvious one is the absence of the high-high level switch. In addition, the HF lockout valve should have been closed since HF acid was not necessary for the testing and the high-high level switch was not operational. The third fault was the operator-initiated HF tank fill. No operator opened the HF fill valve since it was still being tested and not operational. The most likely cause was an HF tank fill initiated by a person cleaning the touch screen. In order to help prevent this problem in the future, the HMI is changed to add a confirmation pop-up window whenever the operator attempts to open the HF fill valve by touching its icon on the screen. This change will at least prevent

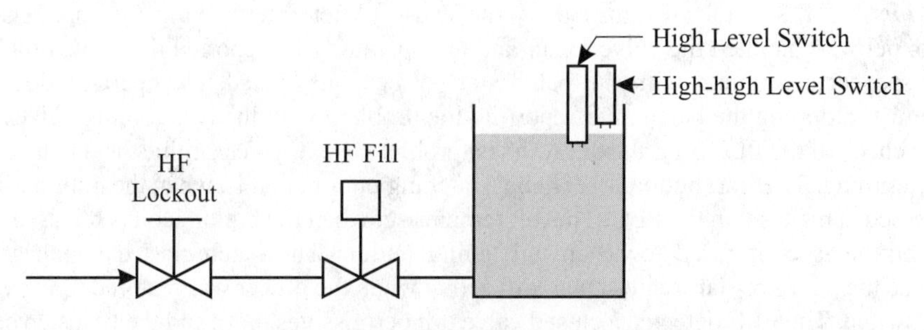

Figure 18.1. Hydrofluoric acid tank.

inadvertent addition of HF acid, and could have prevented this accident in spite of the other failures.

18.1 INTRODUCTION

In the not-too-distant past, the typical user interface to a control system consisted of a panel with industrial-sized switches, push buttons, panel lamps, gauges, PID controllers, and strip chart recorders. The size ranged from a small panel with a few switches and lamps to a panel along one or more walls of a room. The larger panels typically had a graphical representation of the process with the switches and lamps in appropriate locations. All of the panel devices were hard wired to the field devices and to PLC modules. With the advent of low-cost personal computers, the larger hard-wired panels were replaced by a computer screen with process graphics and operator commands entered via a keyboard. Today, a typical user interface is a color graphic touch screen. Panel displays have not disappeared entirely, though. They are sometimes still used as a hot backup if the computer system fails. In addition, some equipment has local operator control panels. For example, a conveyor motor may have a hand-off-auto (HOA) switch located close to the motor that allows maintenance personnel to override the action of the control system.

The human-machine interface (HMI) is a window to the process and is called by various other names:

- operator interface (OI)
- man-machine interface (MMI)
- touch panel

In this chapter, the general structure and functions of a user interface are reviewed. Good design practice for operator panels and operator screens is also discussed. The discussion is general though some examples are presented.

18.2 HMI TYPES

Depending on the application, an operator interface may be:

Mechanical buttons/switches and panel lamps
Stack lights
Small text displays (one to four lines)
Large scrolling text displays
Proprietary graphic displays
Proprietary HMI software on a personal computer
Open software-based systems (for example, Visual Basic) on a personal computer
Web servers embedded in a PLC

Mechanical switches and lights are used for simple applications. For example, a wood chip truck dump station and its local control panel are shown in Figure 18.2. The trailer is raised with a hydraulic cylinder, and the wood chips are conveyed to the storage bin. The panel has start/stop switches for the hydraulic pump and the conveying system and a joy stick to control the up/down of the lift. There are "running" indicators for the hydraulic pump and the conveying system. In addition, there is an individual "running" indicator for each of the conveyors in the conveying system.

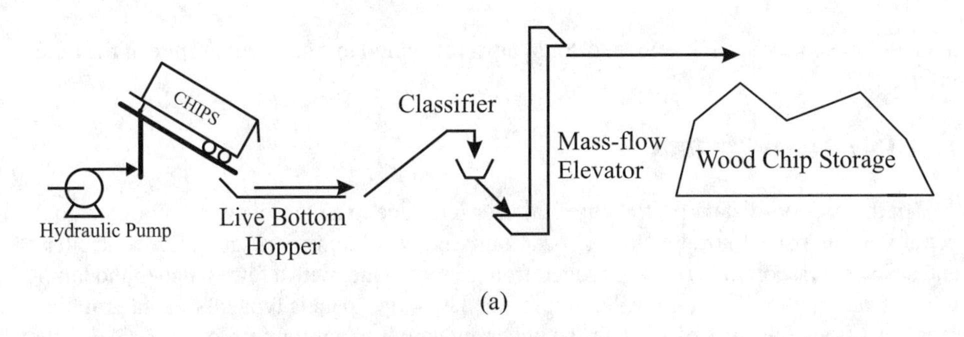

(a)

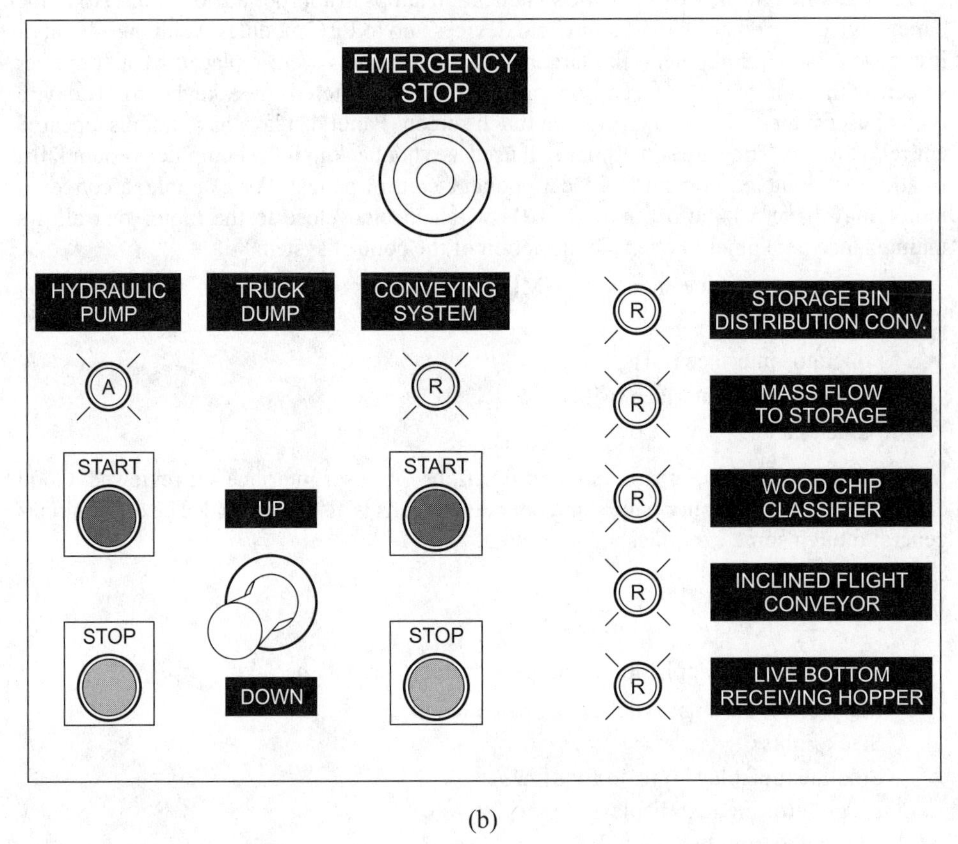

(b)

Figure 18.2. Wood chip truck dump: *(a)* system; *(b)* local control panel.

Stack lights consist of cylindrical lamps 50-70 mm diameter and 60-70 mm high stacked on top of one another (Figure 18.3). The lamps can be steady, flashing, or strobed. In addition, horn or siren modules can be in the stack. Stack lights are typically used on machine applications to allow an operator to quickly assess the overall status of a machine or process. For example, green could indicate a normally running machine. Yellow could indicate that a part feeder is low and needs refilling, and red flashing could indicate a stopped machine. Typically, a touch screen or text display is used in conjunction with a stack light for more detailed status information.

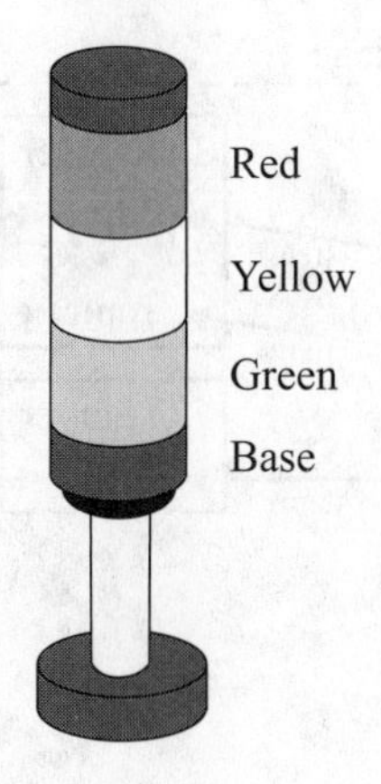

Figure 18.3. Stack light.

Text displays range from simple one- or two-line displays to large scrolling-text displays. The small displays are typically used to display status and error information for a machine or portion of the process. The small text displays are less expensive than comparable-sized touch screens. The large scrolling-text displays are often used on assembly lines to display messages for the line personnel, for example, current production rate or problems with certain stations. Text displays operate in one of two basic methods. The PLC can send the text message or a message number to the display device. In the latter method, the display device is programmed with a table that contains the text message for each corresponding number.

Proprietary graphic displays are prepackaged systems that have a monochrome or color CRT (cathode-ray tube) or LCD (liquid-crystal display) screen. The screen may or may not be touch-sensitive. If not touch-sensitive, the screen is often surrounded by function keys or other buttons allowing operator input. These systems often communicate directly with the PLC to read and write memory locations. One of the drawbacks of this type of display is that they only work with the PLCs of the vendor.

Proprietary HMI software running on a personal computer is generally more complicated than the proprietary graphic displays. However, they have more capabilities and can tie into other applications, for example, batch control and the storage of production data in a SQL database. Most of these HMI packages can be used with the PLCs of many vendors. The advantage of these systems is that the platform (a personal computer) is relatively inexpensive. Many of these systems are placed in control rooms. However, if the system must be deployed in the industrial environment where computer hard-disk drives will often fail, there are alternatives. The proprietary HMI system can be implemented with distributed clients (a diskless personal computer) communicating back to a centralized server using terminal services, sockets, or a web browser.

The general structure of proprietary HMI's is shown in Figure 18.4. There are three major components of the HMI package: a database, one or more graphics screens, and one or more I/O servers. The database is the heart of the HMI software. The graphic screen objects are programmed to interact with the data base variables, and the database variables interact with the I/O servers. In general, a different I/O server is required for each type of PLC and communication network. For example, for a particular PLC, there is one I/O server for communicating through its serial port and another I/O server when communicating

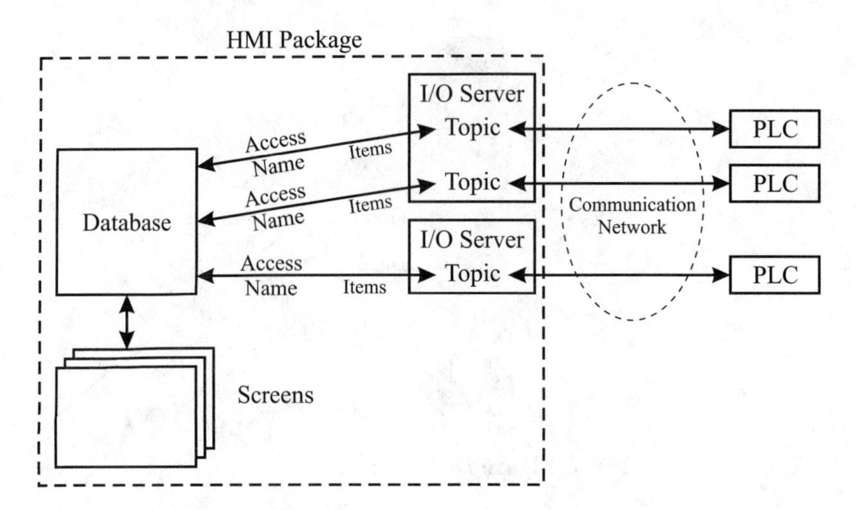

Figure 18.4. General structure of HMI software.

through its Ethernet port. Within the I/O server, a "topic name" is basically the communication channel defined for a particular PLC. One can define multiple topics for one PLC, especially if some of the PLC data needs to be acquired frequently and most of the data can be acquired at a much slower rate. Communication between the database and the I/O server is generally modeled on the dynamic data exchange (DDE) or object linking and embedding (OLE) method of data exchange. For each PLC, the communication between the database and the I/O server is often called an "access name." The access name defines the I/O server and the topic in the server. The current value of the database variables are acquired from the I/O server which communicates with the PLC. If the operator changes a variable in the database, its value is sent to the I/O server, which writes it to the PLC.

Open software-based systems (for example, Visual Basic) on a personal computer can be used in place of the proprietary HMI software. One still needs to construct a database and either write or purchase PLC communication drivers (I/O servers). These types of systems can have an overall lower cost since one does not need to pay for an annual license fee for every computer that is running the HMI. However, the initial development costs tend to be higher. Like the proprietary HMI, open software-based systems can be implemented with distributed clients.

An alternate operator interface that is gaining acceptance is the use of an embedded web server in the PLC (Figure 18.5). The web server is part of the Ethernet interface module, and its pages are stored either within the Ethernet interface module or within the PLC data memory. The web server provides an alternate path to view and/or modify the PLC data memory. The types of web pages that can be constructed range from text displays to graphical displays.

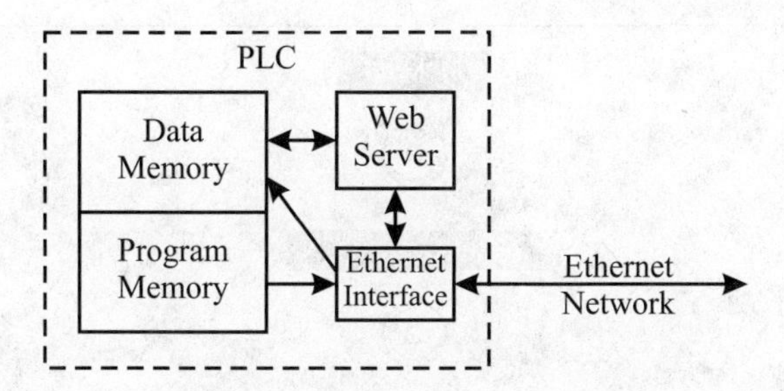

Figure 18.5. Embedded web server.

18.3 HMI PANEL DESIGN

When the operator interface is a panel consisting of simple switches and indicators, they should be laid out in an orderly and consistent manner. The example in Figure 18.2*b* shows a simple panel with 6 controls: emergency stop, two start push buttons, two stop push buttons, and a two-position joy stick. This particular panel also shows the "running" status of the hydraulic pump and the conveying system. Additionally, the "running" status of each part of the conveying system is displayed on the right side. Another simple panel is shown in Figure 18.6. This is a control for a cooling water sump system. There is an overall on/off rotary switch, individual rotary switches for the three system pumps, and three keyed switches for the three cooling tower pumps. There are also various alarm and other indicator lamps, as well as an alarm acknowledgement push button.

The intuitive placement and operation of various controls (often called *operators*) is shown in Figure 18.7. Pushbuttons should be placed in a position corresponding to the desired action (Figure 18.7*a*). According to the NFPA 79 standard (NFPA, 2002), start pushbuttons should be mounted above or to the left of their associated stop pushbutton. Up is also the intuitive direction for forward and increasing speed. For sideways directions, the push buttons should mimic the expected motion. For rotating switches, the intuitive direction for start is in the clockwise direction (Figure 18.7*b*). For a rotating knob control (for example, to adjust a desired speed), the clockwise direction is the intuitive one to increase the quantity (Figure 18.7*c*). On a toggle operator control, the up direction should be used for raising or increasing (Figure 18.7*d*).

According to the NFPA 79 standard (NFPA, 2002), panel operators and indicators should be color coded in accordance with Table 18.1. In general, red and amber indicators signify that a potential hazardous condition exists. Emergency stop switches should have a red-colored palm or mushroom head. In addition, the background around the switch should be yellow. For any panel indicator, some method of testing the indicator should be provided. Some indicators are "push-to-test," that is, whenever they are pushed, the lamp is lit. For indicators that are not "push-to-test" and for illuminated pushbuttons, the panel should have a lamp test pushbutton.

The distance between panel operators should be large enough so that a gloved hand or finger used to actuate one button/switch does not accidentally trigger another button/switch. The minimum distance between buttons is typically 40 to 50 mm.

In most manufacturing control panels, a red pilot light indicates an abnormal condition. However, in power plants or power systems, the opposite is generally true. Closed circuit

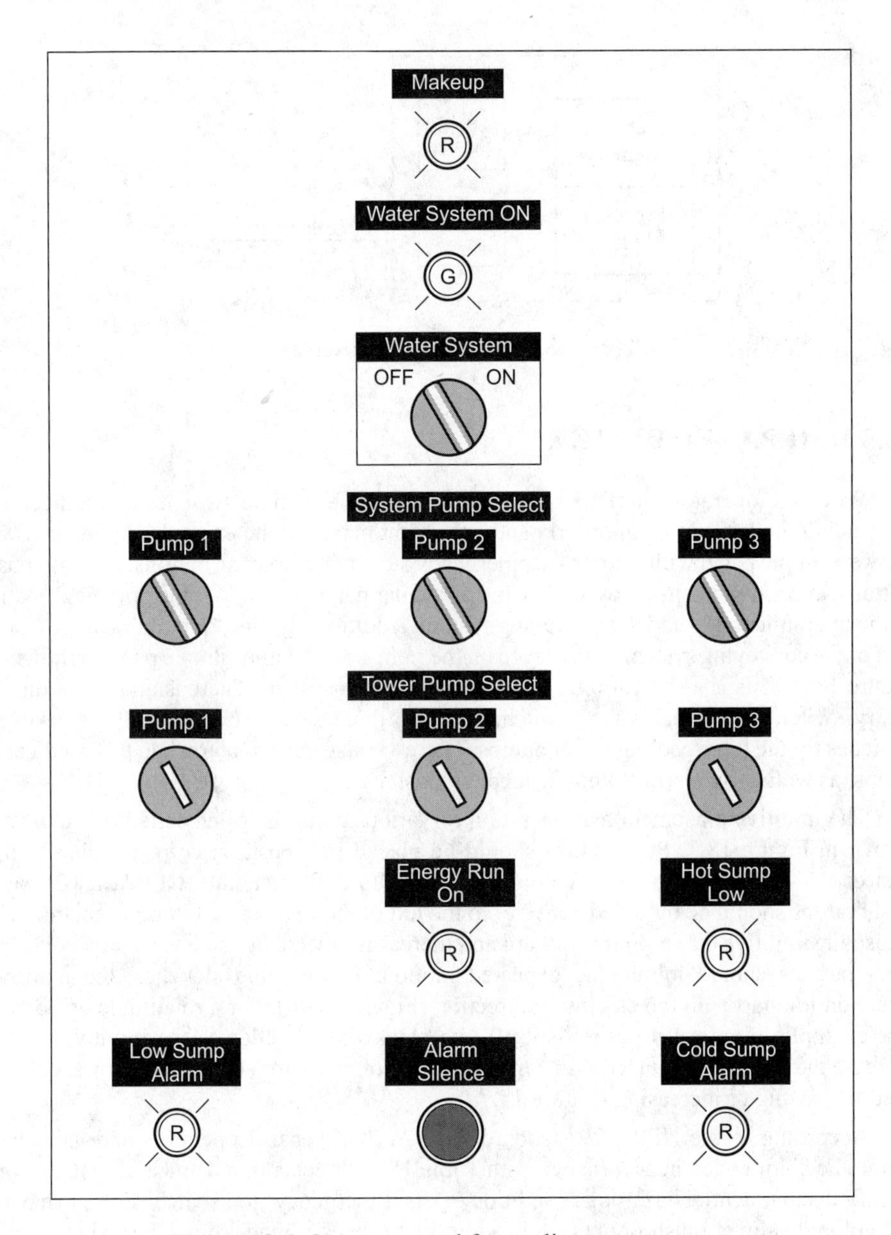

Figure 18.6. Operator panel for cooling water system.

breakers are indicated by red pilot lights and open circuit breakers are indicated by green pilot lights.

Operators expect some kind of feedback to their actions. If the result cannot be heard or seen by some movement, then a panel indication should be turned on.

Panels can also have analog indications, for example, flows, temperatures, and pressures. These can be displayed with digital or analog meters and there are advantages for each one. Digital meters can display a value with a smaller resolution. For example, a

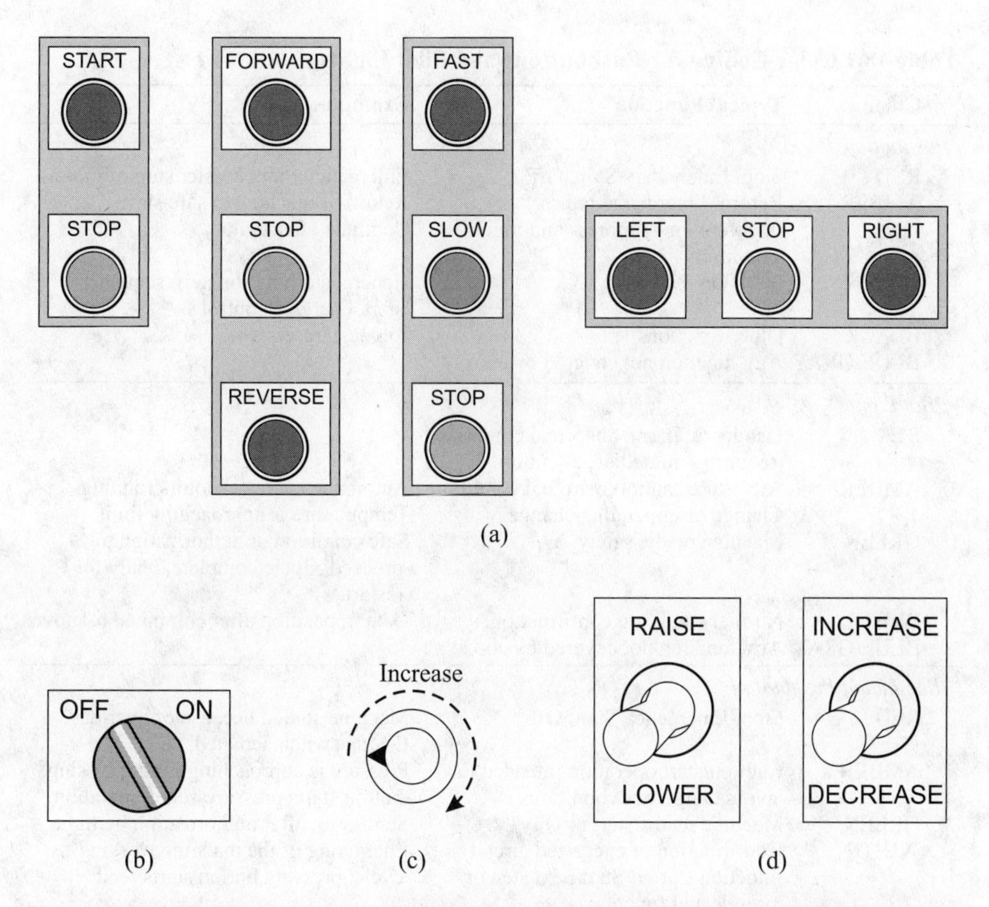

Figure 18.7. Intuitive operators: *(a)* push buttons; *(b)* selector switch; *(c)* rotating knob; *(d)* toggle.

4-digit meter has a resolution of 0.1% full-scale. An analog meter has a resolution of about 1%, regardless of the signal accuracy. However, an operator can more easily detect abnormal patterns from an analog meter. For example, one can quickly scan a row of pressure dial indicators and pick out the one or two that are approaching an abnormal condition before an alarm sounds. If a panel requires many analog indicators, it is usually more cost-effective to display them on a CRT or LCD display.

Table 18.1 Color Coding for Pushbuttons and Pilot Lights

Color	Typical Function	Examples
Pushbutton		
RED	Stop, Emergency Stop, Off	Emergency Stop, Master stop of motors
AMBER	Return, Emergency return, Intervention - suppress abnormal condition	Return of machine to safe state. Continue after fault
GREEN	Start, On	General start, motor start, sequence start, energize control
BLACK	Other functions	Jog, test, reset
BLUE/GRAY	Any function not covered by above	
Pilot Light		
RED	Danger or alarm, abnormal condition requiring immediate attention	
AMBER	Attention, caution/marginal condition Change or impending change	Automatic cycle or motors running. Temperature is approaching limit.
GREEN	Machine ready, safety	Safe condition or authorization to proceed. Cycle complete, ready for restart.
WHITE	Normal condition confirmation	Gate in position after command to move.
BLUE/GRAY	Any function not covered by above	
Illuminated Pushbutton[1]		
RED	Stop, Emergency Stop, Off	Machine stalled because of overload. E-Stop switch actuated.
AMBER	Caution/start operation intended to avoid dangerous conditions	Pressure is approaching limit; pressing. button starts pressure-relief operation..
GREEN	Machine ready/Start or On	Start or on after authorization by light.
WHITE	Confirmation of energized circuit or function started/Start next step or preselected function	Energizing of the machine working cycle; pressing button starts feed
BLUE/GRAY	Any function not covered by above	

Notes:
1. Function(s) of the light is separated from the function(s) of the button by slash (/).

18.4 GRAPHICAL HMI DESIGN

Many PLC-based control systems use graphical displays as the primary operator interface. Guidelines for their design are presented after describing the general types of graphical displays.

18.4.1 Graphical Screen Types

The type of screen is often very different for the various levels of the control hierarchy. At the lowest level the display is very simple touch screen with graphical representations of the switches and indicators. In a control room, a graphical representation of the process presents overall status information about the unit. Detailed information about an object is accessed by touching the object. At the higher levels, managers are more interested in overall operation of the plant, and the HMI typically consists of numbers and graphs of production information, such as production rate, percent rejects, utilization rates, material flow between plant units, and so on.

The basic types of graphical displays are as follows:

1. *Operational Summary*. These are the displays one uses to monitor a process. They present summary information and usually display some graphic representation of the process. The amount and level of detail depend on the level in the hierarchy that one finds the display. For example, a machine display could have an on/off indication for every motor, bearing temperatures, and the dwell time for various parts of the machine. A machining center display may only display the production rate for that machine. Alarms — indications of abnormal conditions — are displayed as indicators. For example, a failed motor may be indicated by changing its color to red. Detailed alarm information is usually presented on the alarm summary screen.

2. *Configuration/Setu*p. Detailed process command parameters and parameters used to set up and/or configure control modules occur on this type of display. For example, PID loop tuning parameters are displayed and modified on this type of display. This type of display tends to be more textual. Also, security measures are often attached to this screen so that only lead operators or engineers can change the parameters.

3. *Alarm Summary*. The alarm summary presents a complete list of time-stamped active alarms. It includes alarms that have been acknowledged by an operator as well as those that have not been acknowledged by an operator. An alarm remains in the alarm summary until the condition causing the alarm has cleared and an operator has acknowledged it. The three possible states of an alarm in this summary are thus (1) active, not acknowledged; (2) active, acknowledged; and (3) no longer active, but not acknowledged. Generally, a different text/background color or blinking/not blinking is used to distinguish the three categories of alarms. Alarms may also be prioritized. The alarm summary list may be arranged by priority (highest at top), by the time stamp (most recent at top), by the acknowledgment status (unacknowledged alarms at top), or in some combination of these groupings.

4. *Event History*. An event history presents a time-stamped list of all significant events that have occurred in the process. Besides alarms, events such as motors starting/stopping, operators logging in/out, and changes in configuration parameters are recorded. The type of information that may be logged depends on the user interface vendor. Generally, the event history is maintained in more permanent storage and eventually copied to an archival device.

5. *Trend*. Values of pertinent process variables, such as flow, temperature, and production rate, over a period of time are shown by this type of display. This type of screen provides the ability to chart the progress of the process in real time. Generally, more than one variable may be plotted on the same screen. This type of display replaces the strip chart recorder. Trended data kept for archival purposes is often called *historical trend* data.

6. *Manual Control*. Displays used to manually control a device are generally only available to maintenance personnel. Depending on the process, they may be accessed only from a screen near the equipment rather than from a centrally located control room. These screens are meant to bypass the automatic control system when conditions preclude the control system from working. Generally, these displays are used cautiously, and permission is granted only when the process is in a safe state.

7. *Diagnostic*. These screens are used by maintenance personnel to diagnose equipment failures and usually contain information more detailed than alarms. For example, most variable-speed motor drives (controllers) have a wealth of diagnostic information. A diagnostic display could be set up to display this information when requested. For example,

with this display an operator could diagnose a drive fault as an "overcurrent fault on acceleration" without needing to walk to the physical drive and access the information from the drive front panel.

Security issues are often overlooked when designing a user interface. The computer-based user interface allows access to a large amount of process information and parameters. Thus, it is necessary to restrict access to certain functions. Typically, a user logs on to the system with a *user name* and *password,* which grants him or her an *access level.* A higher access level permits greater access to the restricted functions. For example, an operator generally is not permitted to change recipes or PID tuning parameters. However, an engineer logging onto the same system can access these functions provided his or her access level is high enough.

18.4.2 Screen Design Guidelines

Display clarity is very important in the control room where there are multiple graphical displays, each one showing some aspect of the plant. The operator must be able to easily scan the displays from a distance and notice if any problems are present. The ability to note problems from a distance also applies to the operator screens present on the plant floor. This section presents some guidelines for screen design (Hexatec, 2002). These design guidelines apply to graphical screens in the control room as well as local operator panels out in the process or mounted on a machine.

Screen Layout

Screens should be arranged to facilitate easy scanning. Generally, operators scan a screen like they would scan a newspaper or magazine. In the U.S. and Europe, one starts in the upper left corner, proceeds to the upper right corner, and then on down the page. Since a graphical screen does not have lines, most operators will only do a few incomplete scans of the screen (Figure 18.8). With this consideration, important items should be positioned along the top and right sides of the display. Alarms are best positioned along the top of the screen, important data should be in the right center, and buttons and controls in the lower right of the screen.

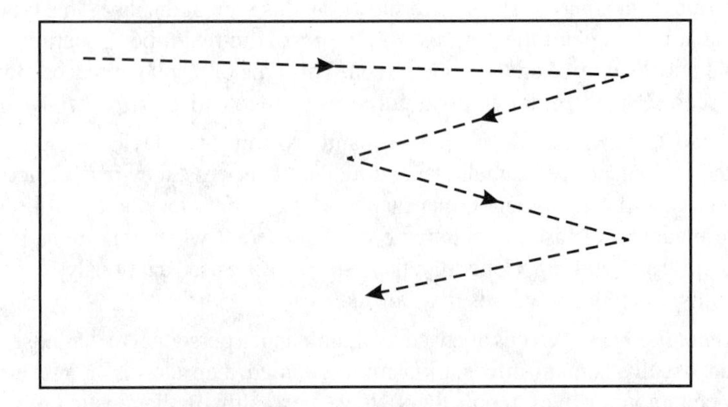

Figure 18.8. Typical scan of operator interface screen.

When the screen contains a graphical representation of the process, it should be a simplified version of the P&ID diagrams. Material flow should mimic the P&ID diagram and is usually left-to-right and/or top-to-bottom.

Color

Color is a powerful tool for enhancing the visibility of key data, but excessive use of color can be confusing or overwhelming. Therefore, the number of colors should be kept to a minimum. Twenty years ago, most HMI systems had only four colors, and the operators were happy with that!

The color convention for status and alarms should follow the same convention as for panel indicator lights, namely,

Red	alarm, danger, stop
Yellow	caution, marginal condition, risk of danger
Green	running, ready, safe condition

These key safety colors should be used sparingly for other purposes.

Large areas of primary colors (for example, red) should be avoided because they will cause a color-vision effect called *successive contrast*. If one looks at a bright-red image for about 30 seconds and then looks at a white surface, an *afterimage* consisting of the same image but in a green color is perceived. In addition, about 8% of men have some degree of color blindness. For these people, there is some confusion in the perception of reds and greens (also yellows, oranges, and browns). Therefore, one should not solely rely on color to indicate plant condition.

Because the center of the human retina cannot easily sense blue (Murch, 1984), blue should be avoided for small objects and thin lines. However, blue is a good background color.

Background Colors

Although black and white provide good color contrast for text, they are not good screen backgrounds since they are not suitable for a range of colors. Muted tones, such as grays and blues, are the best background colors. These colors provide good contrast for the green, yellow, and red key safety colors. Avoid bright colors for a background. These colors are very tiring on the eyes. Different background colors can be used to immediately identify groups of screens. For example, light gray may be used for the top level process screen, very light brown for the raw ingredients, light green for the reactors, and light blue for the water treatment unit. However, keep the number of background colors to a minimum. The use of subtle shading to create the illusion of raised or lowered panels on the screen is an effective way to differentiate areas of the display.

Static Graphics

Many operator interface screens contain a graphical representation of the process plant. The graphical representation helps the operator to visualize the process and the measurement locations. However, there is a tendency to place too much detail on the display and therefore make it difficult to discern important dynamic information. Therefore, keep the displays simple. Instead of putting the entire process on one screen, important overall information belongs on the top level screen, and then the operator selects the appropriate unit-level screen display.

Muted tones are best for process equipment representations. Large areas of strong colors are distracting. Outlining an object in black will make it noticeable. Many HMI packages have graphical object libraries that contain three-dimensional objects such as tanks conveyors, towers, and so on. These can be used effectively, but can be overused.

Though photographs are sometimes used as backgrounds, they generally produce cluttered backgrounds that do not have enough contrast with the foreground colors. Photographs are appropriate for maintenance and diagnostic displays, providing useful information for the personnel without having to find the manual for a piece of equipment.

Text and Data Values

The text on a display is an important way of communicating information to the operator. Unfortunately, a common complaint about displays is that the text is difficult to read. There are many text fonts available, but the following guidelines will avoid problems:

1. Select a common font that will exist on all computers, such as Arial. This guideline is especially important if the HMI is being developed for the Windows operating system. If the screens are developed with an unusual font, the screen font may be mapped to a different font when it is transferred to the operator station PC.
2. Use a sans-serif type of font, such as Arial. Fonts are classified as serif or sans-serif. A serif refers to the extra decorative lines at the ends and corners of each letter. Books, magazine, and newspapers are normally set in a serif font because a serif font is easier to read. However, because computer screens do not clearly render the detail of a serif font, it is better to use a sans-serif font.
3. Select a font size large enough for most operators. Remember that many operators are older than 40 and need reading glasses for small text. A 16-point font is a good starting point. Up to two larger point sizes (for example, 20-point and 24-point) should be selected for labels and headings.
4. Avoid the temptation to use more than one font and more than three point sizes. If more detail is needed, use a "pop-up" window selected by the operator to view the additional text.
5. Reserve upper-case text for headings. TOO MUCH UPPER-CASE TEXT CAUSES EYE STRAIN AND CAN BE DIFFICULT TO READ, ESPECIALLY IF IT IS UNDERLINED.
6. Most text should be in lower case, with the first letter of each word capitalized, like a book title. Some people favor capitalizing only the first letter of the leading word. Whether "Boiler Stack Temperature" is preferred over "Boiler stack temperature" is the user's choice. However, whichever one is chosen, be consistent. Using only lower case text is distracting to the operator.

Data values should be logically grouped on the screen. An operator will find it difficult to scan a random distribution of data values around a process graphic. If the operator needs to compare values, they should be next to each other. Units should be displayed sparingly. For example, if flows are displayed in pounds/hour, placing a "lbs/hr" next to each flow value clutters the display. It is also important to use the same set of units throughout. For example, one should decide whether temperatures should be displayed in °C, °K, °F, or °R and then maintain those units throughout. The displayed data resolution should be appropriate for the measurement. For example, displaying decimal digits for a temperature (e.g., 104.23 °C) is often unnecessary since the measurement accuracy is often greater than +/- 1 °C.

Alarms

Alarm status for the overall machine or process should be organized into groups and should be visible on every screen. Preferably, they should be placed along the top of the screen. There should be a simple method to access a screen displaying additional alarm details. The alarm colors should follow the safety convention:

Red	alarm, danger, stop
Yellow	caution, marginal condition, risk of danger
Blue	mandatory action.

In order to accommodate color-blind operators, any color change must be supplemented with a pictorial change. The shape or position of the object can change or additional text or object can appear on the screen. The object could also flash, but once the alarm is acknowledged, the flashing must stop. Unnecessary flashing objects are irritating. Similarly, an alarm should not cause the display to change to another display or cause a pop-up window to appear. Having a page disappear or a pop-up window to appear over a page when changing a value is aggravating. In extreme cases, cascading alarms can effectively lock out the operator from the system.

If the alarm is critical, an audible alert should sound. Audible alerts impart importance since they are heard by multiple personnel. A system that can create multiple horn pitches and tones can transmit the importance of the alarm. A high-pitch, fast-pulsing sound conveys urgency, whereas a low-pitch, slow-pulsing sound is less urgent (Hexatec, 2002).

Plant Status Animation

Color coding conventions for process status are generally not as well-defined as for alarms. Alarm logic suggests that red should indicate a running (dangerous) process and green for a stopped (safe) process. In fact, this is the convention used in the power industry. However, most process and machinery indications are green for running and red for stopped. To avoid misunderstandings and to account for color blindness, it is better to use a "hollow" symbol filled with the background color when the device is stopped, and filled with a contrasting color when the device is running. Alternatively, the equipment status can be indicated by text ("Running" or "Stopped"), but text is not conducive to easy screen scanning. If there is a risk of confusing a red status indicator for an alarm, then another color should be used, for example, magenta.

Navigation

To use a system that has multiple screens, the operator must be able to change between screens quickly and easily. In the manufacturing environment, touch screens are the preferred method since they eliminate the less-reliable keyboard. In a control room, the pointing device is often a mouse.

Regardless of the pointing device, the screen "hotspot" (touch area) must be obvious and large enough to be hit easily. There are two main ways of denoting a hotspot. A button on the display is an obvious hotspot. The button should be clearly labeled to indicate the effect of "pressing" the button. Alternatively, the hotspot can be embedded in the graphical picture. For example, in a process overview display showing a schematic layout of the process, "pressing" on an area will change the screen to a more detailed display of the area.

The displays are normally organized in a hierarchical, or tree, structure. The top-level display is the overview of the process. Moving between the displays should be simple and obvious. The lower right hand part of the screen is a good place for the "Next lower display" button. It should also be possible to backtrack and return to the previous screen. All displays should have a button that displays the overview screen and a button that accesses the detailed alarm screen.

If possible, the navigation buttons should be grouped together so the operator can move between screens with little movement of the pointing device. If the operator is expected to routinely switch between two or more screens, the button for the next screen in the sequence should be located at same point on each screen, so that the operator can quickly change displays without moving the pointing device.

Device Control

When buttons are used for device control, then a pop-up window should be used to confirm the action selected, for example, "Open XV103 Valve — OK or Cancel." As shown in scenario 2 at the start of this chapter, the confirmation avoids accidentally activating the device.

When using a touch screen, one must be careful that hotspots are not too close to prevent accidentally selecting an adjacent hotspot. When the HMI is in the field and the operators have gloves, hotspots may need to be spaced 50 mm or more center-to-center.

18.5 GRAPHICAL HMI DEVELOPMENT

To develop an HMI application, there are four major tasks:

1. Set up the communication with the PLCs.
2. Create the tag database.
3. Draw the graphical objects on the windows.
4. Animate the objects.

Setting up the communication with the PLCs often involves configuring the access names, I/O servers, and topics shown in Figure 18.4. However, for a simple graphical HMI package designed to interface with a limited set of PLCs, the communication setup is usually uncomplicated and may consist of only specifying the type of interface to the PLC.

When initially programming an HMI application, it is helpful to verify the communication configuration. Configure a few tags (for example, one Boolean, one integer, and one real), draw and animate a few objects with these tags, and then test for proper operation. When using an HMI package for the first time, this step may save you many hours of correcting mistakes due to a minor configuration error.

The tag database is the heart of the HMI software. To ease the task of building the database, most HMI packages provide a way to export and import the database. One can configure the database entries with a spreadsheet program and then import the database into the HMI application. Most HMI vendors also provide a way to import tags from the PLC programming software.

The graphical drawing tools available in most HMI packages are generally simple. More complicated objects are generally imported from a drawing package, or imported from a library of objects.

Object animation is basically the process of attaching properties to a screen object that allow it to react to an operator touch or to change its color, shape, and so on, dependent on a tag value. The types of animation are described below.

Most people develop an application by doing the tasks in the order above. However, one can draw each graphical object first, and then animate it, letting the system prompt the user to define any undefined tag. This process is known as creating a tag "on the fly."

18.5.1 Animation Types

There are two basic types of animation: (1) user input, and (2) display. A user input type of animation allows an operator to change tag values. A display animation allows a value to be displayed as well as allow an object to change shape, position, color, and so on.

User Inputs

Touch-sensitive. This type of object animation allows an operator to input data into the system. For example, the operator may open or close a valve, enter a new alarm setpoint, or type a password for access to maintenance functions. These objects are identified with a frame or highlight around the object when the mouse cursor passes over it. There are generally three types of touch-sensitive inputs:

1. Discrete - Controls the value of a Boolean tag. When touched, a dialog box appears, prompting the operator to select one of two commands, for example, "Open Valve" or "Close Valve."
2. Analog - Used to input the value of an analog (integer or real) tag. When activated, an input box appears, prompting the operator to enter a value. The value may be entered from the standard keyboard or from an optional on-screen keypad.
3. String - Used to input the value of a text string type of tag. When touched, an input box appears, prompting the operator to enter the string. The characters may be entered from the standard keyboard or from an optional on-screen keyboard.

Slider. This type of object is a symbol that can be moved around the window with a finger on a touch screen or a mouse cursor. As the object "handle" is moved, it alters the value of the tag attached to it. The slider provides an alternative way to input analog values into the system albeit with less precision than a touch-sensitive user input.

The slider may be horizontal or vertical. In Figure 18.9*a*, the slider object is the "handle." Some HMI packages allow one to define both a horizontal and vertical slider user input as shown in Figure 18.9*b*. In this case, the slider is inside a rectangle and its position determines the value of two variables, for example, a x-position and a y-position.

Pushbutton. Perform an operation when the object is touched (touch-screen display) or when clicked with the mouse. The most common operations are:

1. Discrete value change - The object acts like a pushbutton that controls the state of a Boolean tag. Available pushbutton actions include set (latch), reset (unlatch), toggle (change state), momentary on, and momentary off.
2. Execute script - Allows a small program to be executed when the object is touched. Depending in the HMI package, there may be up to three different scripts: "When

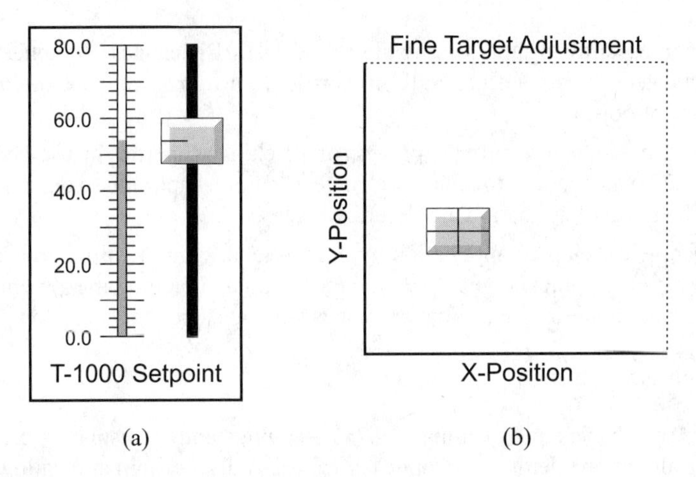

Figure 18.9. Slider user input: *(a)* one dimension; *(b)* two dimensions.

Pressed," "When Released," and "While Down." A "When Pressed" script executes once when the object is pressed and a "When Released" script executes once when the object is released. A "While Down" script executes continuously on a set time interval as long as the object continues to be pressed. This type of script waits one time interval before executing, so if the script must start execution immediately, create a duplicate "When Pressed" script. Scripts are generally written in Visual Basic, or another similar language. Scripts can be used to set tags to specific values, show and/or hide screens, start and control other applications, print the screen, and so on.

Display Animation

Value Display. Displays the value of a tag or expression on the screen. If the tag is a Boolean, then one user-defined text message is displayed if the tag is true and another user-defined text message is displayed if the tag is false.

Line, Fill and Text Color. Changes the line color, fill color, or text color attributes of an object. There are four types of color animation:

1. Discrete - The color is linked to a Boolean tag or expression. In this case, the color can be one of two values.
2. Analog - The color is linked to a real or integer tag or expression. The HMI may allow a continuous color gradation, or may define a fixed number of value ranges defined by breakpoints. In the latter case, each range has a different color.
3. Alarm - The color of an object can be linked to the alarm state of a tag or group of alarms. If the alarm state is a Boolean, the color can be one of two values; one for the normal state and one for the alarm state. If the tag has multiple alarm conditions (for example, low-low, low, high, high-high), then the normal state and each alarm condition can have a different color.

Object Size. Varies the height and/or width of an object, depending on the value of an integer or real expression.

Object Location. Changes the location of an object, depending on the value of an integer or real expression. This type of animation is useful for displaying items moving on a conveyor or the movement of a gantry crane.

Object Percent Fill. Varies the fill level of a filled shape according to the value of an integer or real expression. The fill can be vertical or horizontal. This type of animation is often used to indicate the level of a liquid in a vessel, though it can also be used to build a horizontal bar graph.

Visibility. Controls the visibility (whether it is shown or not) of an object according the value of a Boolean tag or expression.

Blink. Makes an object blink based on the value of a Boolean tag or expression.

Rotation. Makes an object rotate based on the value of an integer or real tag or expression.

Disable. Disables the touch functionality of an object based on the value of a Boolean tag or expression. The disable animation is very useful for security features. For example, a touch-sensitive or pushbutton input can be disabled based upon the logged-on operator's access level or name.

18.5.2 Helpful Hints

When defining a tag, one should make sure to select the correct data type. After one has saved a tag definition or attached the tag to a screen object, some HMI packages will not allow one to easily change the basic type. For example, if one incorrectly defines an integer as a discrete data type, it may not be easy to correct the data type. In some HMI packages, the process to delete a tag involves a few steps. If one needs to correct the data type for a tag already attached to one or more screen objects, then these screen objects will need to be modified to remove all references to the tag. Then the tag can be deleted and redefined.

Any tag that refers to a physical input may need to be set to "Read Only" (depending on the HMI package and PLC).

When working with Modicon PLCs using IEC programming (Concept or Unity), in order to change and/or display a variable, it must be associated with an address (0x or 4x). Unlocated variables cannot be accessed.

Complex objects are assembled from many simple objects (lines, filled shapes, and text) that are either combined or grouped together. When simple objects are *combined*, the assemblage is treated as a single object. Any changes in object attributes (for example, fill color or line color) are applied to all of the components in the combination. When simple objects are *grouped*, each object retains its attributes and animation. Object grouping is useful for creating PID or discrete controller faceplates. Once a set of objects is grouped, the attributes and animation of the individual objects cannot be changed. To change the appearance or operation of a grouping, it must be "ungrouped" and the individual object(s) changed before regrouping. When a group is duplicated, one generally just needs to change the tags associated with the animation.

Multiple status indicators for the same device can be "stacked" on top of each other, each one having a different visibility animation. For example, a motion servomotor object could have a yellow "yield" triangle, representing a warning condition, placed over the motor. A "frown face" on top of the triangle representing an error condition and a "stop sign" could be placed on top of the "frown face" to represent a over-travel fault. The visibility animation for each object is programmed so that at most one of these indicators is displayed. The three indicators "travel" with the servo and so their location animation must be identical to the servomotor object. The drawback to stacking objects is when an object's animation needs to be changed. The objects on top will need to be "unstacked" before the bottom objects can be altered.

Frequently used objects (including their animation) should be placed in libraries. When these objects are imported, only the tag references need to be changed.

18.5.3 Sample HMI Screens

Figure 18.10 shows an operator screen for a power plant coal handling system. This screen is normally used to only monitor the system. To control the system, the operator uses a six-foot wide panel with a process graphic and with the switches and indicators arranged in a manner similar to what is shown in Figure 18.10. The system is currently moving coal from the unloading feeder to bunker 5. The unloading feeder, bucket elevator, conveyor 1, conveyor 2, and conveyor 3 are all running. These indicators are all red, but shown up as dark gray in the figure. The gate position indicators are white when lit. All three gates are in the left position. All of the "plugged chute" indicators are yellow when lit. In the scenario shown in Figure 18.10, all of the plug indicators are off. All of the bunker level indicators are red when on. Bunker 5 is being filled, and the level is between the low and the full (middle) position.

The operator screen for a batch reactor is shown in Figure 18.11. The running status of each motor and the open status of each valve is shown in green. In addition, a pipe is shown in green when material is flowing through it. When the device control object is touched, a popup screen is displayed as shown in Figure 18.12. The operator can then manually open/close the valve, provided he/she has permission. Alarms are shown in the upper right. The operator can be scroll through the alarms, or access the entire alarm summary display (by pressing the "Alarm Summary" button). The displays for the other units are accessed by pressing the appropriate button. An overview display for the entire process may be access from any of the unit screens by pressing the "Overview" button.

Typical "faceplate" pop-up windows for discrete (on/off) control of a motor and a valve are shown in Figure 18.13. A typical faceplate for a variable-speed drive is shown in Figure 18.14. In addition to the start and stop buttons, the operator can adjust the desired speed by moving the arrow. The actual speed is shown as a vertical bar and as a value below the bar. The motor current is also displayed.

A typical faceplate for a PID control loop is shown in Figure 18.15. The process variable and setpoint values are shown as vertical bars whose height indicates the value. The units are typically shown along the side and the numeric value is shown somewhere close to the bars; here they are shown below. The controller output is displayed as a horizontal bar along the bottom of the faceplate. This bar may also be displayed vertically, usually as the rightmost bar. The mode (Auto or Manual) is displayed and the Aut/Man button provides a way to change the mode. Since this faceplate indicates the mode is Auto, the setpoint may be changed, which is indicated by the arrow between the PV and SP bars. For a touch-screen display, the operator changes the setpoint by pressing and sliding the arrow. The setpoint may also be changed by touching the setpoint value, which causes a keypad window to pop up, and keying in a new value. In the Manual mode, the operator changes the controller output in a similar manner. Other tuning parameters are accessed by touching the Param button, which causes another window to pop up, displaying the other parameters (tuning parameters, alarm limits, output velocity limits, etc.). When the Trend button is touched, a

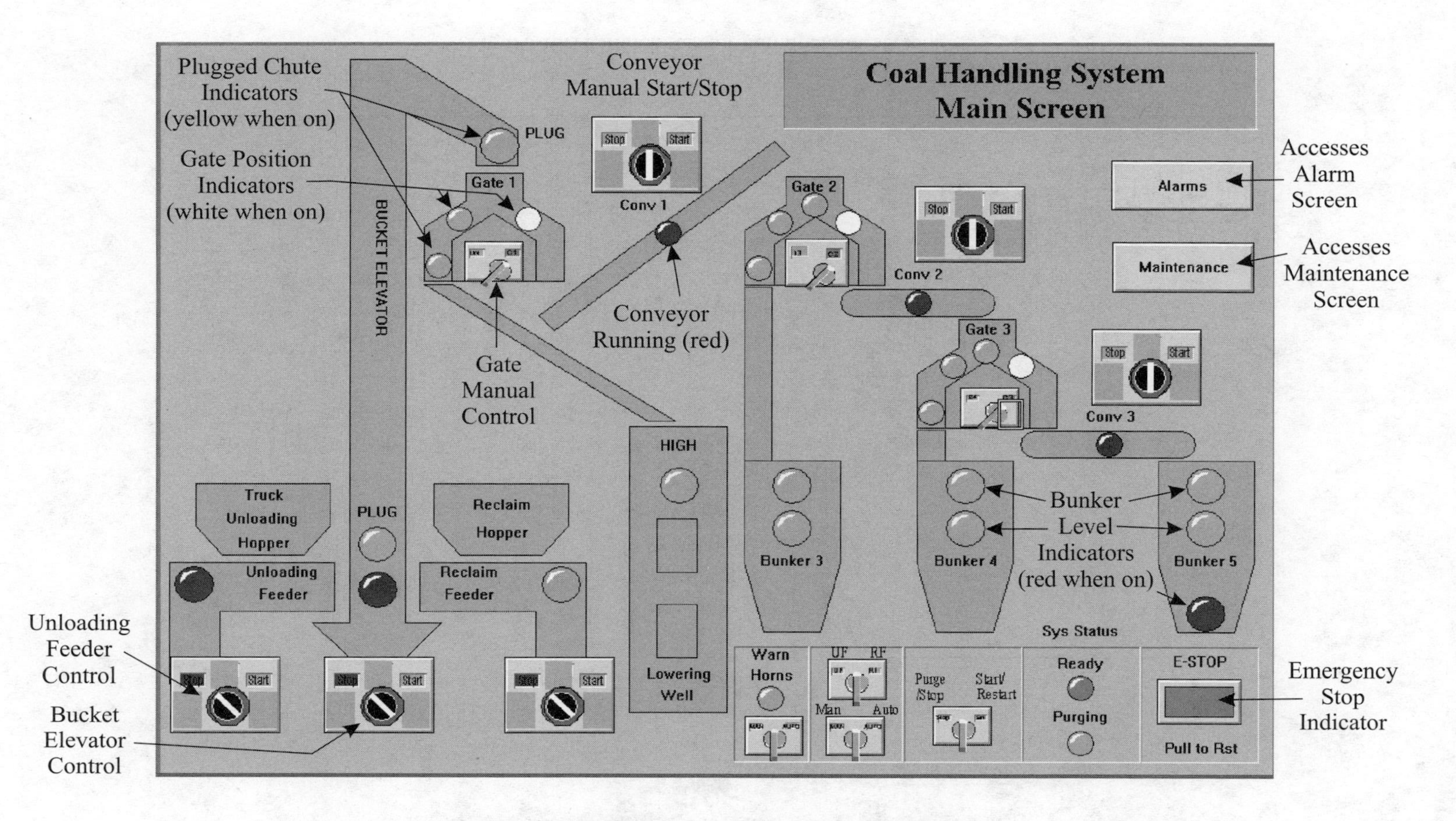

Figure 18.10. Coal handler main operator screen.

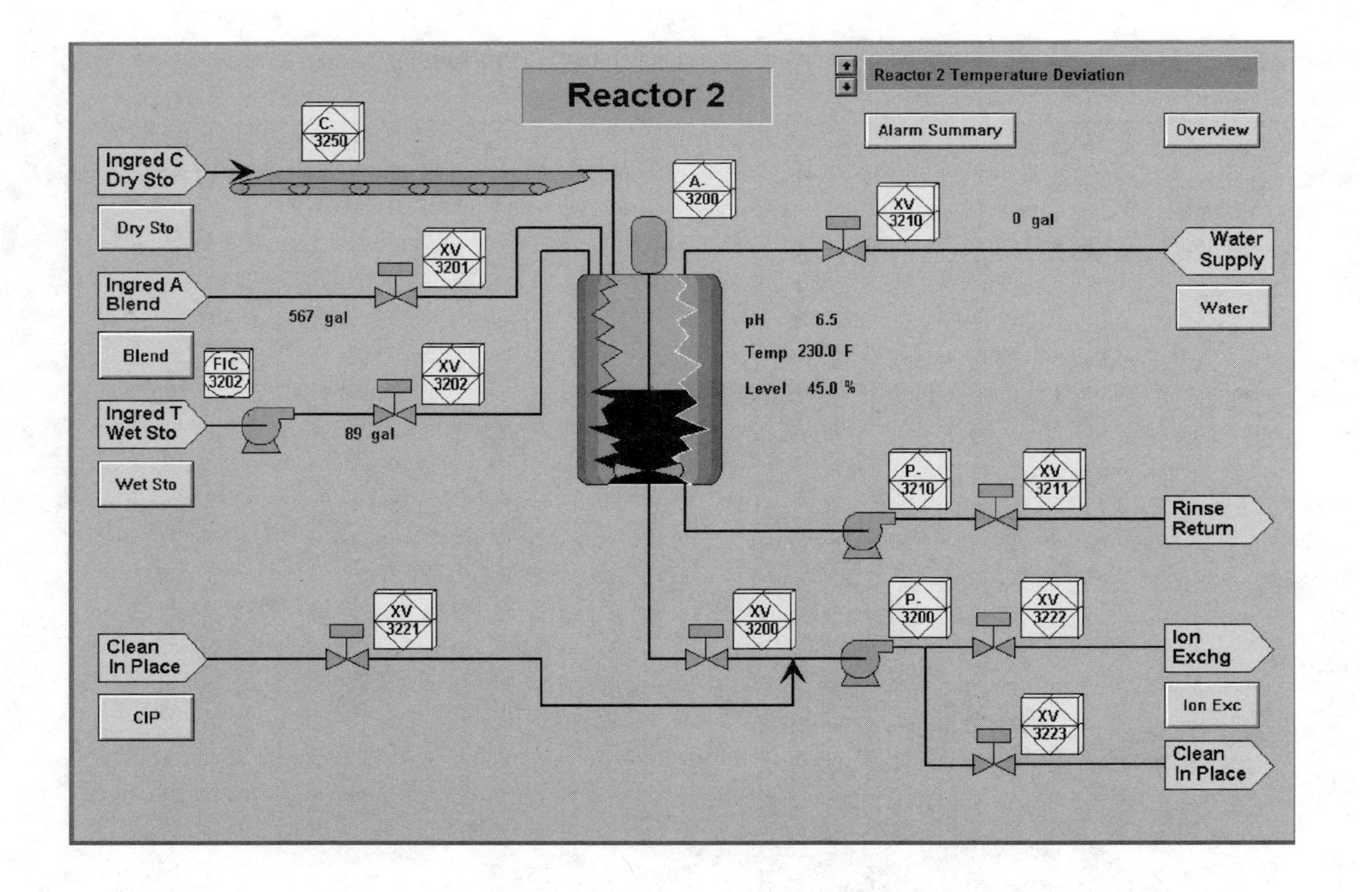

Figure 18.11. Batch reactor unit operator screen.

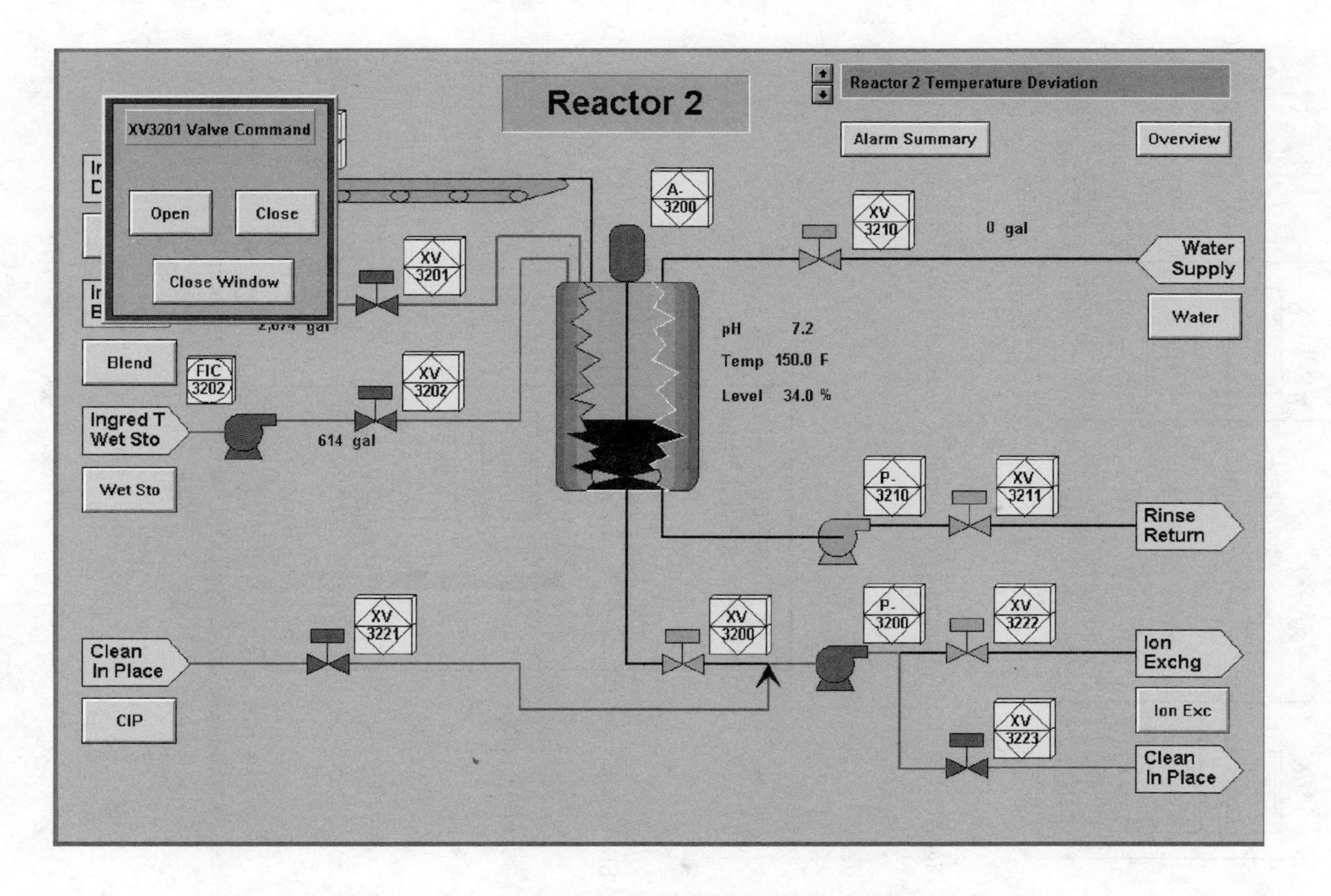

Figure 18.12. Device control pop-up on batch reactor unit operator screen.

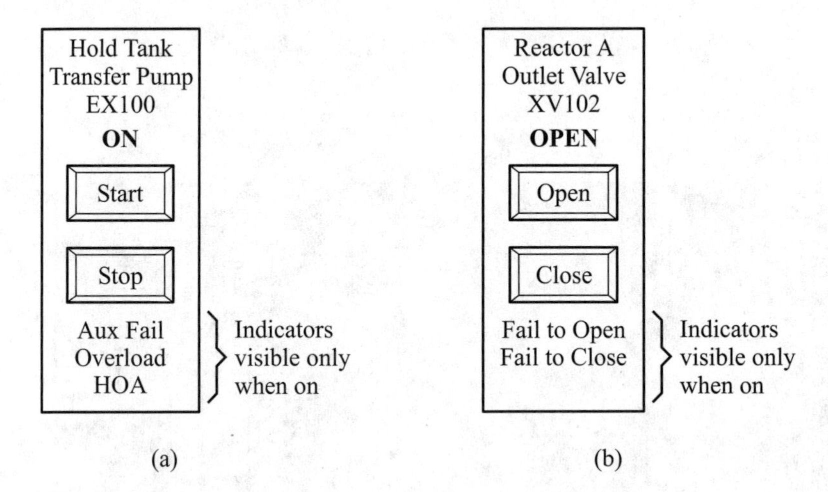

Figure 18.13. Typical discrete device control faceplates: *(a)* motor; *(b)* valve.

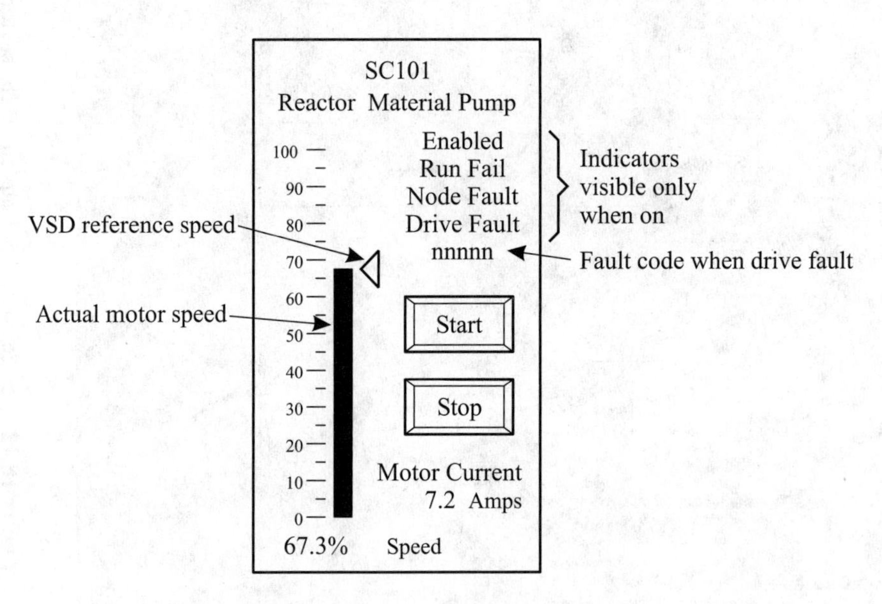

Figure 18.14. Typical variable-speed drive faceplate.

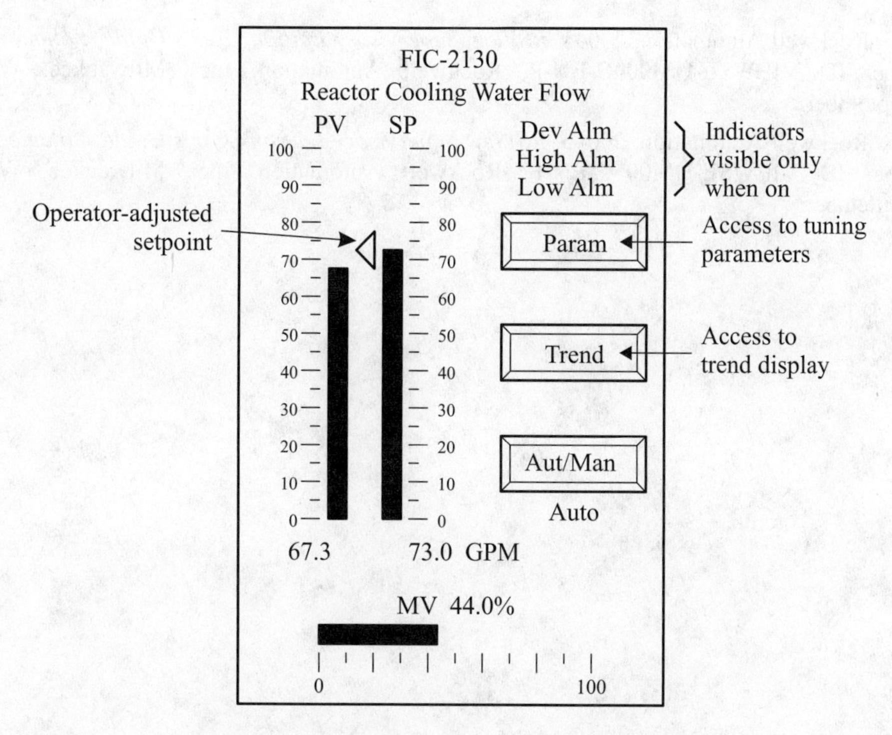

Figure 18.15. Typical PID control loop faceplate.

trend window pops up to the side of the faceplate and displays a plot of the process variable, setpoint, and controller, similar to a strip chart recorder.

18.6 CHAPTER SUMMARY

This chapter reviews the general structure and functions of a user interface. Design guidelines for operator panels and operator screens are also presented. The guidelines are illustrated with examples.

REFERENCES

Hexatec, 2002. *Operator Screen (HMI) Guidelines*, Hexatec, Inc, Northumberland, UK.

Invensys Systems, Inc., 2002. *Wonderware® FactorySuite™ InTouch™ User's Guide*, Doc. ID 9399-SECSRVGR-JAN00, Invensys Systems, Inc., Foxboro, MA, September.

Murch, Gerald, 1984. " Physiological Principles for the Effective Use of Color," *IEEE Computer Graphics and Applications*, vol. 4, no.11 (November): 49-54.

National Fire Protection Association, 2002. *NFPA 79 – Electrical Standard for Industrial Machinery*, 2002 Edition, National Fire Protection Association, Quincy, MA.

Rockwell Automation, 2004a. *RSView Supervisory Edition User's Guide, Volume 1*, Doc. ID VIEWSE-UM004C-EN-P, Rockwell Automation, Inc., Milwaukee, WI, September.

Rockwell Automation, 2004b. *RSView Supervisory Edition User's Guide, Volume 2*, Doc. ID VIEWSE-UM005C-EN-P, Rockwell Automation, Inc., Milwaukee, WI, September.

19 Control System Security

Chapter Topics:

- Factory automation network security
- PLC processor program and data security

OBJECTIVES

Upon completion of this chapter, you will be able to understand:

- Security threats to a factory automation system
- Methods of control network protection
- Methods of PLC program and data protection

Scenario: A security breach.

Your consulting firm is contracted to put in control system for a sewage system for the local municipality. Since the system is spread out over a geographical area, radio modems are used to link pumping stations with the central control room. After a few months, you start getting reports of equipment malfunctions. Raw sewage is pumped into rivers and parks, places where it should not go. In one incident, up to one million liters of raw sewage flowed onto the grounds of a Hyatt Regency Resort. The cleanup costs are not trivial. The municipality is quite concerned because your firm installed and commissioned the system. The system operation logs are checked and the operators are interviewed. There is no record of the control system causing these events. You suspect someone is sabotaging the system with malicious intent. The police launch a criminal investigation. About an hour after a report of a system malfunction is received, one of your former employees is detained by the police. He was one of the engineers that commissioned the system. In his vehicle, there is a radio modem and a laptop computer with the software that allows one to access the pumping station controllers.

Solution: Security is installed on the system to prevent this type of attack in the future. The former employee spends some time in prison (Green, 2001).

19.1 INTRODUCTION

With the proliferation of computer networks in the manufacturing enterprise, the security of manufacturing control systems has become more of a concern. Many security concerns arise because of the connection of the manufacturing control systems to corporate communication networks. Historically, firewalls have been used to isolate a corporate network from public networks, like the Internet. However, as corporate communication networks become more like the Internet, it will become harder to completely isolate the corporate network infrastructure from the public Internet.

In order to mitigate the risk to the control system, the interdependency of the manufacturing process, policies, procedures, and people must be managed and then combined with the appropriate security technology. The key security questions are (Falkenau, 2003a, 2003b):

- What are the security risks with the physical connections between the manufacturing control system and the rest of the world?
- How do we handle those people and applications that need to access the control system from outside the control system?
- How do those people inside the control system (operators, engineers) access resources outside the control system (for example, Internet and intranet)?

This chapter is primarily concerned with handling the security risks of accessing the controller programs and data from both inside and outside the control system. General communication network protection strategies are discussed first. Then, the security mechanisms for specific PLCs are reviewed.

19.2 FACTORY AUTOMATION NEWORK SECURITY

One of the main security threats to a PLC system is through its communication connections. At the very least, one must connect to the PLC processor in order to program it. This is usually done through a serial interface. Most security threats are through a peer-to-peer network where the PLC processors, personal computers, and communication gateways are connected. The security threat from I/O networks is minimal since they are operated in a master/slave configuration where the PLC processor or I/O scanner controls the network.

The security threats to PLC systems can be categorized as:

1. Inside the control system by unauthorized users
2. Outside the control system by unauthorized or malicious users

Table 19.1 summarizes the types of security threats through the various communication networks. All PLC systems are subject to inside threats. An inside threat is often from an inexperienced employee that does something like connect to the wrong PLC on a network. Less often, a disgruntled employee can also be a security threat. Communication connections are subject to outside threats if there is a gateway or some other connection to a public Ethernet network. Note that a relatively safe serial port connection is subject to outside threats if the serial port is connected to a modem that may be accessed with a telephone connection (Figure 19.1). At a minimum, a modem connection should be

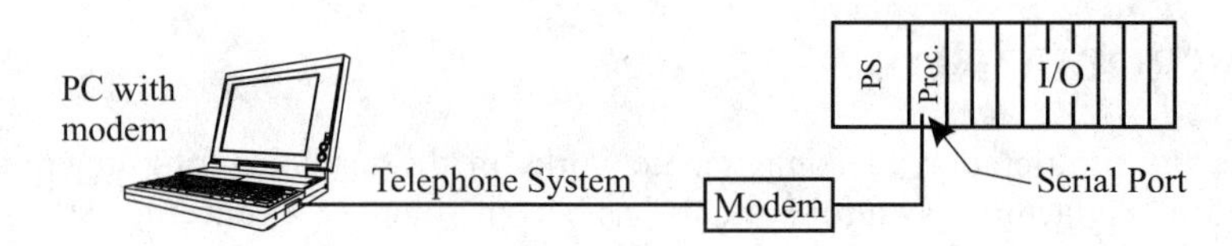

Figure 19.1. Modem connection to processor.

Table 19.1 Security Threats to PLC

Network Connection	Threats	
	Inside	Outside
ControlNet	Yes	Yes, if Ethernet gateway on network connected to public network.
DH+ (PLC-5/SLC-500)	Yes	Yes, if 1771-KF2 on network connected to modem or if Ethernet gateway on network connected to public network.
DH-485 (SLC-500)	Yes	Yes, if Ethernet gateway on network connected to public network.
Ethernet	Yes	Yes, if connected to public network.
Genius (GE Fanuc)	Yes	Yes, if modem on multidrop network.
Modbus (Modicon)	Yes	Yes, if connected to modem.
Modbus+ (Modicon)	Yes	Yes, if Ethernet gateway on network is connected to public network.
MPI (Siemens)	Yes	Yes, if connected to Ethernet gateway that is connected to public network.
PPI (S7-200)	Yes	Yes, if connected to modem.
Profibus-DP	Yes	Yes, if Ethernet gateway on network is connected to public network.
Serial port	Yes	Yes, if connected to modem.
SNP (GE Fanuc)	Yes	Yes, if modem on multidrop network.

protected with a processor password. For better security, the modem should be a callback modem. When the modem answers, it prompts for a password. Upon receipt of a valid password, the modem calls the associated number to establish a connection.

There are three main protection mechanisms:

1. **Isolate system**. Either a stand-alone PLC or an isolated network. Key access to cabinet containing the PLC processors.
2. **Passwords**. A correct password must be supplied in order to gain access to the processor and/or its data.
3. **Firewall**. Interposed between the control network and the corporate network.

In the past, system isolation was the more typical method of control system security. The PLC equipment was placed in locked cabinets that only engineers and maintenance technicians could access. Even if the PLCs were connected on a network, the network was a proprietary network not accessible from the outside.

However, the manufacturing control system now connects to a corporate network, generally Ethernet, in order to allow access to the control system by corporate functions such as production management and manufacturing execution systems. To provide protection against outside threats, Falkenau (2003a) recommends that a firewall be interposed between the manufacturing control system and the remainder of the corporate network, shown in Figure 19.2. The firewall must have an integral hardened operating system and must interoperate with external authentication servers. In addition, any data traversing public networks should be encrypted.

According to Falkenau (2003a, 2003b), the firewall should be part of a robust security policy that protects the manufacturing control systems and networks:

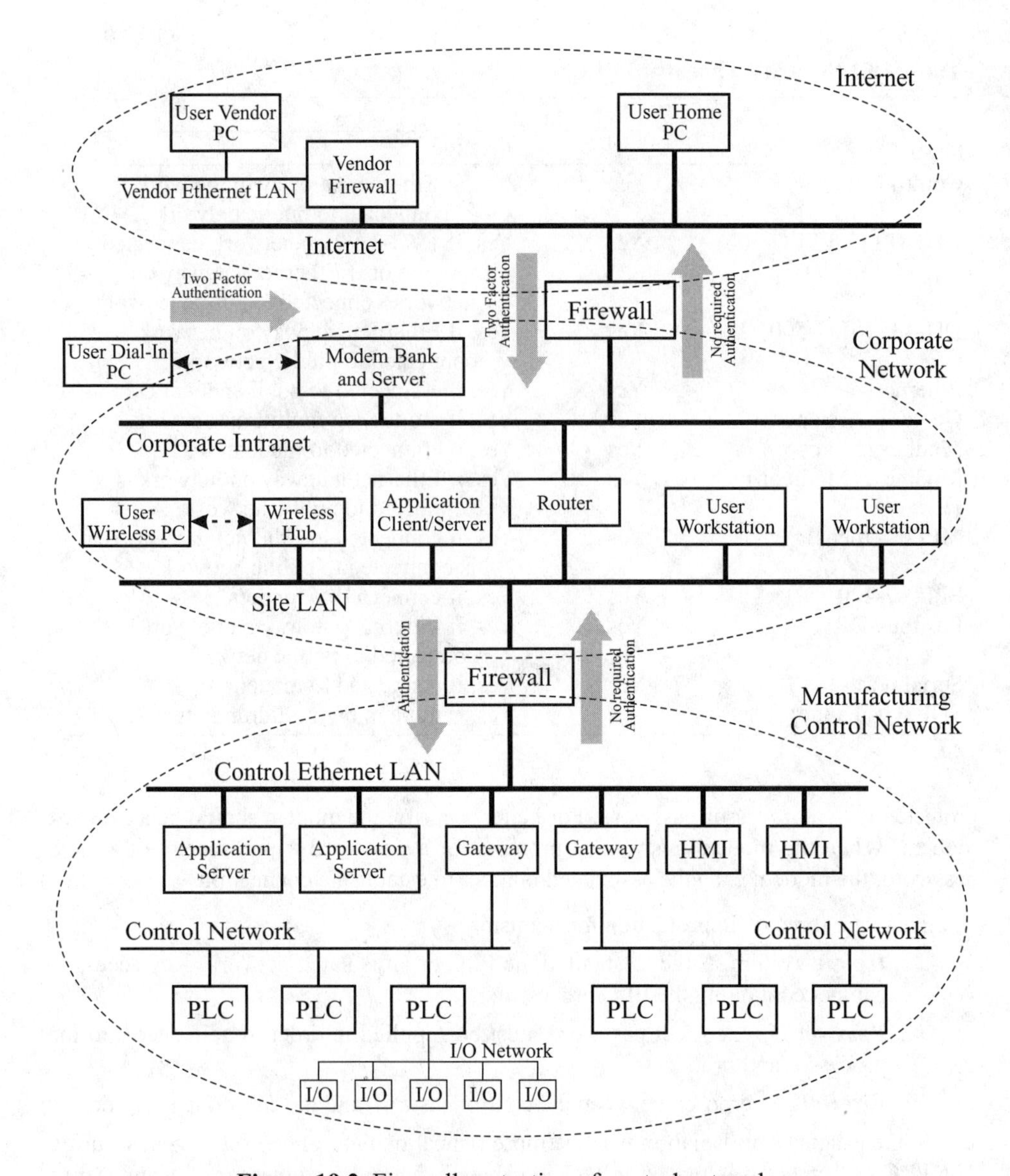

Figure 19.2. Firewall protection of control networks.

- A firewall shall separate the process control network from any external network (local-area network, wide-area network, Internet). Disconnection from the external network is the most secure, but often not an option.
- Any interactive access to the control network shall require two-factor authentication and authorization.
- Any noninteractive access to the control network shall be controlled using static rules for the source-destination pair based on Internet protocol addresses and services.
- Any data traversing public networks shall be encrypted.

- All control computers, servers, and HMI interfaces shall have virus-protection software.
- All control firewalls shall be centrally monitored and supported.
- All control firewalls shall be co-managed by manufacturing and information technology personnel.
- The policies, procedures, and firewall configurations shall be periodically reviewed for compliance.

Two-factor authentication is more secure than the traditional password access mechanism. A widely-used form of two-factor authentication is the bank ATM card. The combination of a personal identification number (PIN) and a valid ATM card provides a sufficient level of security to support access to bank services. For use in an enterprise, authorized users are issued a device (for example, key fob, card, software token) that generates a single-use token code that changes periodically (for example, once every minute). When a user accesses the system with a valid login, the correct PIN and token must also be provided in order to actually access the system.

The same security threats to a factory automation system are also present in supervisory control and data acquisition (SCADA) networks that are an integral part of any nation's infrastructure (electric power, oil and gas pipelines, transportation, and so on). To address these security concerns, the Office of Energy Assurance within the U. S. Dept. of Energy formulated a series of steps to help improve the security of supervisory control and data acquisition (SCADA) networks (U.S. Dept. of Energy, 2002). The steps that are specific actions to increase security are as follows:

1. Identify all connections to SCADA networks.
2. Disconnect unnecessary connections to the SCADA network.
3. Evaluate and strengthen the security of any remaining connections to the SCADA network.
4. Harden SCADA networks by removing or disabling unnecessary services.
5. Do not rely on proprietary protocols to protect your system.
6. Implement the security features provided by device and system vendors.
7. Establish strong controls over any medium that is used as a backdoor into the SCADA network.
8. Implement internal and external intrusion detection systems and establish 24-hour-a-day incident monitoring.
9. Perform technical audits of SCADA devices and networks, and any other connected networks, to identify security concerns
10. Conduct physical security surveys and assess all remote sites connected to the SCADA network to evaluate their security.
11. Establish SCADA "Red Teams" to identify and evaluate possible attack scenarios.

Another ten steps focus on the management actions that establish an effective security program:

1. Clearly define cyber security roles, responsibilities, and authorities for managers, system administrators, and users.
2. Document network architecture and identify systems that serve critical functions or contain sensitive information that require additional levels of protection.
3. Establish a rigorous, ongoing risk management process.
4. Establish a network protection strategy based on the principle of defense-in-depth.
5. Clearly identify cyber security requirements.
6. Establish effective configuration management processes.
7. Conduct routine self-assessments.
8. Establish system backups and disaster recovery plans.
9. Senior organizational leadership should establish expectations for cyber security performance and hold individuals accountable for their performance.
10. Establish policies and conduct training to minimize the likelihood that organizational personnel will inadvertently disclose sensitive information regarding SCADA system design, operations, or security controls.From within and without the control system, passwords are often used to control access to the program for an individual PLC. However, most processors do not have any protection for access to the data.

19.3 PLC PROCESSOR SECURITY

The security protection offered by the PLCs covered by this text is summarized in Table 19.2. The options range from only restricting access to the programming software to protecting access to individual data locations. As of this writing, only the PLC-5 and SLC-500 processors offer write-access protection to processor data. The following sections outline the security options that are available for each of the processors covered by this text.

19.3.1 Modicon Concept Security

The security system in Concept is not for the processor or for individual projects. It is only used to restrict the functionality of the Concept software and its utilities. Concept defines nine access level privileges (lowest to highest):

1. ReadOnly	Can view projects offline and online, but cannot change. Can connect to processor and view variables online.
2. SFC Panel	Allow user to reset SFC
3. ChangeData	Can change literals online
4. ForceControl	Can force steps and variables
5. Download	Can download program and configuration
6. ChangeProgram	Can make program changes, but not in DFBs or EFBs
7. ChangeConfig	Can change PLC configuration
8. Tools	Can use DFB, EFB, and converter tools
9. Supervisor	Can work with security

When security is activated, the supervisor defines each user name and associated password and access level. Access to a level also includes privileges for all levels below that level. Other features of the Concept security are:

Table 19.2 PLC Processor Security Methods

PLC	Available Security
Modicon Concept	Password access to Concept and utilities FactoryCast has password access to data
ControlLogix	Password access to project Password access to routine source code
PLC-5	Password access to project Password and privileges access to program and data files Individual data file element protection on protected processors
SLC-500	Password access to project Password access to program in PLC Program OEM lock Data file write access protection
S7	Password access to PLC on-line functions
GE Fanuc	Password access to PLC on-line functions Block lock settings to restrict access to individual program blocks Password access to write data

- One can always get ReadOnly access, even if all user names and/or passwords are fogotten.
- The supervisor can activate/deactivate security.
- The security information must be copied to each computer on which Concept is installed.
- For a particular user name, a password is not required. Though, when a password is assigned, it must be at least 6 and no more than 12 characters.
- The security system does not prevent copying project files.

There is protection from unauthorized users accessing the program in a Quantum/Momentum processor. Only the processor configuration, data values, and the 984 ladder logic sections can be uploaded. The IEC 61131-3 program sections can only be downloaded to a processor.

The Modicon 140 NOE 77110 module for the Quantum controllers is an embedded web server that allows access to the processor configuration and the processor data. However access to the PLC variables is controlled with a password. The FactoryCast software package is used to define the user names and associated read- and write-permission passwords. Unfortunately, this particular module has some security flaws (Rutenkroger, 2003).

19.3.2 Rockwell Software Security Server

For recent versions of all Allen-Bradley PLC programming software packages, the Rockwell Software Security Server is a centralized system for governing access to resources. A resource can be either an application (for example, RSLogix 5000, RSLogix 5)

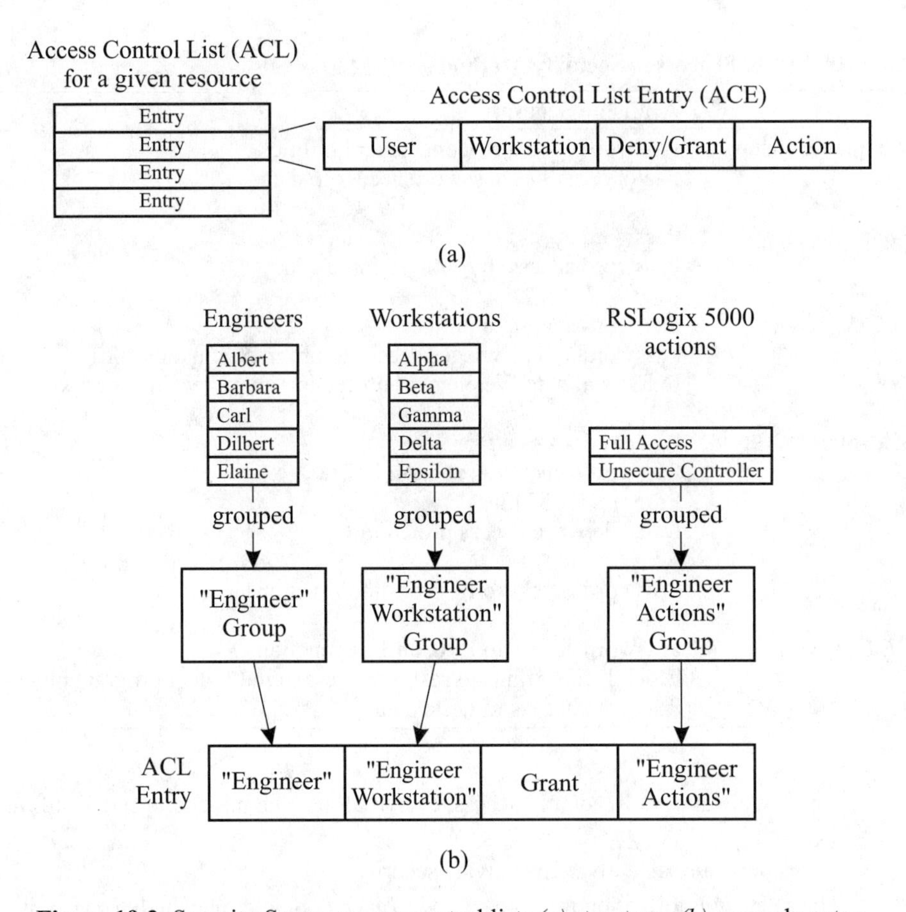

Figure 19.3. Security Server access control list: *(a)* structure; *(b)* example entry.

or a specific PLC processor, designated by its communication path. For each resource, an access control list (ACL) is constructed, as illustrated in Figure 19.3*a*. Each entry in the ACL has four parts:

User – a particular user or group of users.

Workstation – the network name of the computer (network version of Security Server).

Action – action that can be performed on a resource (for example, download/upload, modify data).

Deny/grant – whether the user is not allowed to do the action (deny) or allowed to do the action (grant).

An example ACL entry is shown in Figure 19.3*b*. In this entry, a group of engineers at a particular set of workstations is granted the "full access" and "unsecure controller" actions. This entry could be associated with a certain processor or with all RSLogix 5000 projects. A group of maintenance personnel may be granted the "maintain project" action, but denied the "update firmware" action. These particular examples are for the RSLogix 5000 software. The set of available actions is specific to each programming package.

The Security Server can grant/deny read and write access to processor data from the programming software. However, it cannot control access to processor data from an operator interface that communicates directly with the processor. This type of security is part of the processor configuration.

User names and their associated passwords are defined as part of the Windows operating system.

19.3.3 ControlLogix Security

The security system for the ControlLogix processors is part of the programming software. One can define Routine Source Protection to prevent access to the logic within one or more routines of a project. Separately, the RSI Security Server protects a project. One may use either or both of these security options.

Routine source protection is a part of the RSLogix 5000 programming software. One must activate this feature before it can be used. In order to protect a routine, the user defines a **source key**. A source key is an alphanumeric string that follows the same rules as a tag, except it is not case-sensitive. All source keys are stored unencrypted in the "sk.dat" file. A source key can be reused. The number of source keys reflects a tradeoff between the need for protection and the number of source keys to manage:

Source Keys	Level of Protection
One for all projects	Less protection (less keys to manage)
One for each project	
One for each routine in each project	More protection (more keys to manage)

Typically, one would define source keys for selected routines because of trade secrets or to protect critical control functions from modification.

When a source key is defined for a routine, one also specifies whether the routine may be viewed (displayed) when the source key is absent. The allowable user actions on a protected routine depend on whether the source key is contained in the key file and whether viewing is allowed:

Source Key in "sk.dat"	Viewing Allowed	Protection
Yes	Yes	Full access to the routine
No	Yes	Source may be displayed/printed, but not modified
No	No	Source cannot be displayed/printed or modified

The user is still allowed to download a project and execute all routines, regardless of whether the source keys are available for all protected routines.

Access to a protected routine from a specific computer can be recovered by (1) adding the source key(s) to the existing "sk.dat" file, (2) copying the "sk.dat" file and linking it to RSLogix 5000, or (3) creating a new source key file ("sk.dat") and manually add the source key(s). The "sk.dat" file is an unencrypted text file with each line containing one source key.

Note that routine source protection does not restrict access to the processor data.

With the Security Server, introduced in section 19.3.2, a user can be granted the following global actions that are not related to a particular project:

Secure Controller – Can secure an unsecured controller.
New Project – Can create project or translate a PLC-5/SLC-500 project.
Update Firmware – Can update controller firmware

The following actions are granted/denied for a specific processor or group of processors:

View Project – Can view a project offline.
Go Online – Can view a project offline and online.
Maintain Project – Can view project offline and online, save project, upload/download project, update firmware, change controller mode.
Full Access – Perform all actions available through the programming software except unsecuring a secured controller.
Unsecure Controller – Unsecure a secured controller.
Update Firmware – Can update controller firmware.

19.3.4 PLC-5 Security

The PLC-5 processors offer three types of security: (1) the Security Server, (2) original and enhanced PLC-5 processor-based security, and (3) PLC-5 protected processors. The Security Server is part of the programming software and is described in section 19.3.2. The other two security methods are a function of the processor model and revision level. The PLC-5 protected processors add data table element protection to the security of the enhanced PLC-5 processors. The Security Server can be used in conjunction with both processor-based security methods.

With the Security Server, the following actions can be granted/denied globally (not related to a particular project) or they can be granted/denied for a specific processor or group of processors:

Data Table Value Modification – Can change data file elements.
Description Editing – Can modify address/symbol database descriptions.
Downloading Program to PLC-5 – Can download program to processor.
Forcing Functions – Can force discrete I/O.
Offline Monitoring – Can view a project offline.
Offline Programming – Can change program when offline.
Online Monitoring – Can view a project online.
Online Processor Mode Changes – Can change processor mode when online.
Online Programming – Can change program when online.
Updating Program from PLC-5 – Can upload program from processor.

For the original PLC-5 processors and the earliest versions of certain enhanced PLC-5 processors (Rockwell Automation, 1998; Rockwell Software, 2000), one may define a **master password** that limits access to the program files for a given processor. The password must be specified before one is allowed to go online with the processor or before a program can be uploaded from or downloaded to the processor. However, the password is not needed to access the data files. Read and write access to the data files does not need a password. So, this method does not protect the processor data.

For later versions of the enhanced PLC-5 processors (Rockwell Automation, 1998; Rockwell Software, 2000), the **passwords and privileges** method of processor protection is offered (Figure 19.4). In this scheme, the processor has four **privilege classes**. Each class

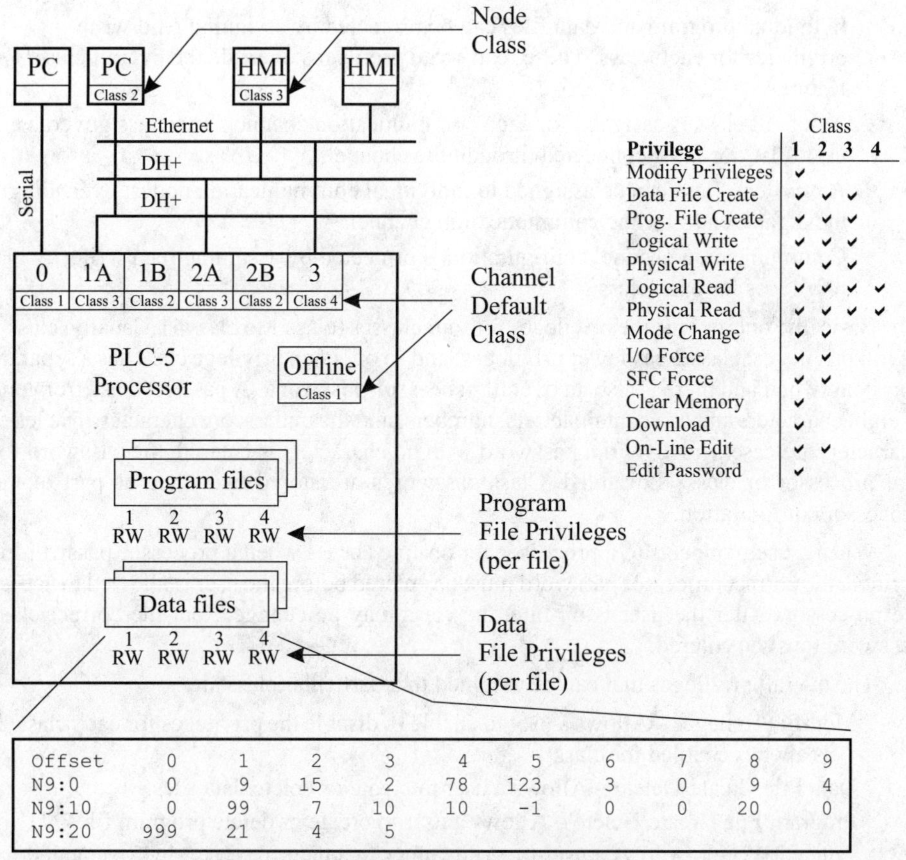

Offset	0	1	2	3	4	5	6	7	8	9
N9:0	0	9	15	2	78	123	3	0	9	4
N9:10	0	99	7	10	10	-1	0	0	20	0
N9:20	999	21	4	5						

Data Table Element Protection (DTEP) File
(Protected PLC-5 processors only)

Figure 19.4. PLC-5 passwords and privileges security.

has a set of privileges that define how a user may interact with the processor. For example, the classes could be defined as:

Class 1: Engineer
Class 2: Maintenance
Class 3: PLC-to-PLC communications
Class 4: HMI (restricted write access)

Note that a class can be defined for a user that is not a person interacting with the processor using the programming software. The features of this method of processor protection are:

- Each of the four privilege classes has a different password and a different set of privileges.
- Each class has a set of overall privileges, such as, overall read/write privileges for program and data files and whether on-line editing is allowed.

- Individual program and data files can be protected by assigning read/write privileges for each class. These read/write privileges override the overall class features.
- A default class is assigned for each communication channel. The class governs a user, PLC, or HMI connected through the channel.
- A privilege class can be assigned to individual communication nodes, overriding the default class for the communication channel.
- Communication channel configuration is protected by assigning read/write privileges for each class.

Basically, one assigns the privileges for four classes (class 1 to class 4). Usually, class 1 has all privileges; class 2 has fewer privileges; and so on. Each privilege class has a separate **class password** and there is also an overall **processor password**. A password has from one to eight characters and can contain letters, numbers, and the underscore character. The letter characters are case-sensitive. If a password with no characters is entered, the password for that processor or class is disabled. Class passwords are stored encrypted as part of the processor configuration.

When a user connects to a processor for on-line access when a processor password is defined, the correct processor password must be entered before the user is allowed to access the processor. After the user is on-line, the class may be changed, but the correct class password must be entered.

The overall privileges that can be assigned to a particular class are:

Modify Privileges – Allows a user to enable or disable the privileges for each class. It is always enabled for class 1.

Data File Create/Delete – Allows a user to create or delete data files.

Program File Create/Delete – Allows a user to create or delete program files.

Logical Write – Allows a user to write values to a data file. It is always enabled for class 1.

Physical Write – Allows data table write requests from messages coming from non-programming DH+ nodes (for example, MSG write commands from another PLC).

Logical Read – Allows a user to read program and data files. This privilege is required in order to upload to or go online with the processor. It is always enabled for class 1.

Physical Read – Allows data table read requests from non-programming DH+ nodes (for example, MSG read commands from another PLC). It is always enabled for class 1.

Mode Change – Allows a user to change the processor mode when the processor key switch is in the "REM" (remote) position.

I/O Force – Allows a user to enable or disable I/O forces in the processor, or to clear all I/O forces.

SFC Force – Allows a user to enable or disable sequential function chart (SFC) forces, force individual transitions on or off, or clear all SFC forces.

Clear Memory – Allows a user to clear the processor memory.

Restore (Download) – Allows a user to download or partial download a processor.

On-Line Editing – Allows a user to change a program file in any processor mode.

Edit Password – Allows a user to edit a password for classes 1 to 4.

Table 19.3 Example Data File Classes

Name	File	Type	Class 1	Class 2	Class 3	Class 4
TIMER	4	T	RW	R	R	
COUNTER	5	C	RW	R	R	
CONTROL	6	R	RW	R	R	
INTEGER	7	N	RW	RW	RW	RW
FLOAT	8	F	RW	RW	RW	

Table 19.4 Example Channel Default Classes

		Default User Class
Offline:		Class 1
Channel 0:	<DF1>	Class 1
Channel 1A:	<DH+>	Class 4
Channel 1B:	<I/O Scanner>	Class 4
Channel 2A:	<Ethernet>	Class 3

The read and write privileges for individual program and data files are assigned for each class (Figure 19.4). The individual file privileges override the logical write, logical read, physical write, and physical read privileges for a particular class. For example, even if class 3 is allowed physical writes, data file 7 could be set to disable write access for class 3. For example, a portion of the data file privileges could be as shown in Table 19.3. Note that the timer, counter, and control files can only be changed if the device or user is logged in as class 1. Here, class 4 is assumed to be an operator interface. If timer or counter accumulators need to be displayed, the processor program will need to move them to the N7 file and they can be accessed from there. The read/write privileges do not affect the processor program access to the data files set by the global/local data file property.

Each communication channel has a default user class (Figure 19.4). When an external device communicates with the processor through a channel, the class for that channel defines the privileges. The default class for offline programming is also defined along with the communication channels. In order to connect to the processor or to access the project with the RSLogix 5 programming software, the user must know the processor password. If the user wants to change the class, he/she will need to know the appropriate class password. For example, the channel privileges for a PLC-5/40E processor could be as shown in Table 19.4. Channel 0 is the serial port on the processor and so assigning the highest class is relatively safe since one needs physical access to the processor to connect to this port. However, if channel 0 is connected to a dial-up modem, then the default class should not be class 1. Once a user is logged into the processor, the class can be changed (if one knows the class password).

The channel class password also applies to recent Ethernet PLC-5 processors with the embedded web server (Rockwell Automation, 2002). The embedded web server allows one to access the Ethernet configuration and the data tables. However, a user cannot change the configuration or data tables. Also, if the Ethernet channel does not have the privilege to read a data table, it cannot be monitored.

Table 19.5 Example Node Privileges

Channel	Remote Station Address	Remote Bridge Link ID	Class
DH+ 1A	20	0	Class 2
DH+ 1A	21	0	Class 3

Default class privileges cannot be assigned to a channel configured as an I/O scanner or adapter. Whatever class is assigned in this case is ignored. The read/write privileges to each communication channel status file is determined by the read/write privileges of the data file.

The default class defined for a DH+ communication channel can be overridden by individual node privileges (Figure 19.4). Normally, all nodes on the network connected to a DH+ channel have the default privilege class of the communication channel. Table 19.5 shows an example node privilege table. The "Remote Bridge Link ID" column is used when the node is connected to another DH+ network. In this case, the "Remote Station Address" is the address of the bridge device and the "Remote Bridge Link ID" is the link number in the bridge that identifies the location of the node on the remote network. For nodes on the same network as the processor, the "Remote Bridge Link ID" is zero. The two entries in Table 19.5 allow more privileges than the default class of Table 19.4. If the individual data file privileges are as given in Table 19.3, the node privileges of Table 19.5 allow read/write access of data file F8.

When considering restricting access to program and data files, the privilege hierarchy is as follows:

1. Data/program file privileges (highest priority)
2. Node privileges
3. Channel privileges (lowest priority)

Read and write privileges for the configuration information of each communication channel is assigned to each class. Though they are called "Channel Privileges," they are not the same as the default classes assigned to each communication channel. The channel privileges only govern whether a particular class is allowed to access and/or change the configuration of a particular communication channel. For example, one would probably want to limit the ability to change the configuration for the Ethernet channel to class 1. All other classes could only read the information.

The protected PLC-5 processors (PLC-5/16, -5/26, -5/46, and -5/86) add data-table element protection (DTEP) to the passwords and privileges method of the enhanced PLC-5 processors (Allen-Bradley, 1995). The DTEP method allows one to define data-file locations that can only be changed by a class-1 user (assuming only class 1 has the "modify privileges" privilege). While DTEP is primarily intended to protect certain data locations from being modified when a user is online with the processor, it can also prevent an operator interface from modifying certain data memory locations.

The system administrator is assumed to be the only user with class-1 privileges and class 1 is the only class that has the "modify privileges" privilege. In order to set up DTEP, the system administrator:

1. Defines an integer data file, called the DTEP file.
2. Writes the DTEP file number in the S:63 status file location
3. Enters the data-file protection ranges into the DTEP file.

Contents of data file N9

```
Offset      0     1     2     3     4     5     6     7     8     9
N9:0        0     9    15     2    78   123     3     0     9     4
N9:10       0    99     7    10    10    -1     0     0    20     0
N9:20     999    21     4     5
```

Processor Status File

S:63 9

Explanation of DTEP file

Data File Number	Starting Element Number	Ending Element Number	Explanation
0	9	15	Output image O:11 to O:17
2	78	123	MCP configuration in status file
3	0	9	B3:0 to B3:9
4	0	99	T4:0 to T4:99
7	10	10	N7:10 only
-1	0	0	Skip this range
20	0	999	All of file 20
21	4	5	Elements 4 and 5 of file 21

Figure 19.5. Sample DTEP file.

In the DTEP file, each address range is specified by three integers: (1) the data file number, (2) the starting element number, and (3) the ending element number. Figure 19.5 shows an example DTEP file with an explanation of the contents. The DTEP file address ranges must follow these rules:

- The first range starts at element 0 of the DTEP file, the second range starts at element 3, and so on.
- The ending element number must be equal to or greater than the starting element number.
- A starting element number of 0 and an ending element number of 999 protects an entire data file, regardless of length.
- A "-1" data file number indicates an unused protection range.

The DTEP security is enabled when:

The user communicating with the processor is not allowed to modify privileges (typically, class 2, 3, or 4),

Word S:63 of the status file contains the number of a DTEP file.

When DTEP is in effect, writes to the specific data file ranges in the DTEP file are prevented. One is also prevented from adding or modifying ladder logic instructions that can reference these data file ranges. A download to a protected processor is also screened for violations. Bit S:17/11 in the status file is set whenever a user attempts to modify a protected memory location.

There are a few caveats when working with a protected processor project in RSLogix 5. A protected processor project cannot be converted to a non-protected processor. However, a non-protected processor can always be converted to a protected processor. Also, a protected processor project cannot be exported. There are also some restrictions on the use of indirect and indexed addressing in protected processors (Allen-Bradley, 1995).

19.3.5 SLC-500 Security

The SLC-500 processors offer three types of security: (1) the Security Server, (2) password protection of the processor, (3) program OEM lock, and (4) data file access protection. The Security Server for the SLC-500 programming software is similar to the Security Server for the PLC-5 programming software. The particular types of data file protection that are available are a function of the processor model. All three security methods can be used independently of each other.

All of the SLC-500 processors have two processor passwords: the **password** and the **master password** (Rockwell Automation, 2002b). The passwords restrict online access to the processor by the programming software. One of the passwords must be specified before one is allowed to go online with the processor or before a program can be uploaded from or downloaded to the processor. However, a password is not needed to access the data files. This method does not protect the processor data. The two passwords allow all the processors in a project to have the same Master Password and different Passwords. This method allows one to restrict access to specific processors for some users and yet allow other users access to all processors without having to divulge all individual passwords. Each password is a numeric value of up to 10 digits.

Access to the program can also be denied by setting the **OEM lock** bit (S:1/14). When this status bit is set, the programming software must have a matching copy of the project file in order to monitor the ladder logic. While the protection is limited, it does prevent someone from "reverse engineering" the program by simply uploading it without having the address/symbol database. To program this feature, one deselects "Allow Future Access" in the compiler options for the processor. This feature can also be selected by unconditionally setting the S:1/14 bit in the ladder logic.

There are two types of data file access protection. With **static protection**, the data file values cannot be changed by any of the communication channels. Changes to the data file are allowed by the program only. **Constant protection** does not allow any changes to the data file by the communication channels or by the ladder program. Constants can only be changed offline and then downloaded to the processor. For the SLC-5/03, -5/04, and -5/05 processors, the protection for each data file can be specified. The SLC-5/02 processor allows the user to specify static protection for the output files, all files, or no files. For the SLC-5/01 processor, the output files always have static protection and all other data files are unprotected.

Communication channel write protection is offered for the SLC-5/03, -5/04, and -5/05 processors. When this feature is enabled, a user connected to the processor by that channel cannot change the mode, force I/O, change data files, change program files, clear memory, download a program, or configure the channel. This protection is permanent and not recommended unless the other channel remains unprotected.

19.3.6 S7 Security

The security system for both the S7-300/400 and S7-200 processors is based on defining the protection level for a processor. Depending on the protection level, a password may be required to access certain on-line programming functions. Only one protection level can be defined for a given processor. The protection level basically defines which on-line functions can be accessed without knowing the password. When the correct password is entered, the user has unrestricted access to the on-line processor functions. This security

Table 19.6 S7-200 Security Levels

<table>
<tr><th>Function</th><th>Level 3</th><th>Level 2</th><th>Level 1</th></tr>
<tr><td>Read/write data</td><td rowspan="3">Access Allowed</td><td rowspan="4">Access Allowed</td><td rowspan="10">Access Allowed</td></tr>
<tr><td>Start/stop processor</td></tr>
<tr><td>Read/write time-of-day clock</td></tr>
<tr><td>Upload processor</td><td rowspan="7">Password Required</td></tr>
<tr><td>Download processor</td><td rowspan="6">Password Required</td></tr>
<tr><td>Delete program block, data block, or system block</td></tr>
<tr><td>Force I/O</td></tr>
<tr><td>Write output in STOP mode</td></tr>
<tr><td>Read execution status</td></tr>
<tr><td>Copy to memory cartridge</td></tr>
</table>

scheme does not protect processor data from access by other processors or by operator interfaces. The protection levels for the two types of processors are different and so are described separately.

The protection levels for S7-300/400 processors restrict read/write access for on-line functions (for example, upload, download, modify data). There are three protection levels:

Level 1 – Read/write permission determined by processor keyswitch position. If RUN-P or STOP : no restrictions. If RUN: read only access. User can optionally define a password that can override the RUN position.

Level 2 – Read access only, regardless of keyswitch position.

Level 3 – No read/write access, regardless of keyswitch position.

The password consists of up to eight ASCII characters. The password is case-sensitive.

The protection levels for S7-200 processors restrict access to certain on-line functions. The S7-200 processor offers three levels of protection, shown in Table 19.6. Level 1 offers no protection. Level 2 requires a password in order to modify the program and force I/O. Level 3 is the most restrictive and requires a password to upload the program, in addition to the restrictions for Level 2. The password is not case-sensitive and consists of up to eight ASCII characters.

19.3.7 GE Fanuc Security

There are two types of security for GE Fanuc PLCs: (1) processor security, and (2) block lock settings. The processor security can be used to restrict the online access to the entire PLC program and data. The block lock settings can be used to restrict access to individual ladder logic (LD) and instruction list (IL) blocks.

The processor security system for the GE Fanuc processors is based on four access levels for a processor. Each access level may have a password associated with it. There are four access levels:

Level 1 – Read access only to PLC data memory. This level does not have a password and so is always available.

Level 2 – Read/write access to PLC data, except that discrete I/O cannot be forced. The PLC can be started or stopped. The PLC and I/O fault tables can be cleared.

Level 3 – Read/write access to PLC data, program, and hardware configuration; discrete I/O forcing.

Level 4 – Read/write access to PLC data, program, hardware configuration, and passwords. OEM protection can be locked or unlocked.

The default access level is the highest level that does not have a password. If no passwords are defined, the default access level is level 4. If passwords are defined for levels 2, 3, and 4, then any operator interface will not be able to change any PLC data. Each password consists of up to six ASCII characters and is case-sensitive.

Access level 4 has an OEM protection feature. When OEM protection is locked, the user is prevented from uploading the program from the processor or downloading over the locked program. This feature is useful for an Original Equipment Manufacturer (OEM) to further restrict access to the program and configuration. The OEM key consists of up to six ASCII characters and is stored in the PLC. One must supply the correct password when locking/unlocking OEM protection.

The processor security features can be completely disabled by setting the processor Password property in the hardware configuration to "Disabled." If the processor security features are disabled, the program can be downloaded and uploaded, but a hardware configuration that has the Password property enabled cannot be downloaded. If the processor security features are disabled, they can be restored by completely clearing the processor memory but this also clears the processor program and data. The processor memory is cleared by removing the power from the power supply, disconnecting the battery, and possibly shorting the battery connection terminals. Consult the appropriate manufacturer's documentation for the appropriate procedure.

The block lock settings restrict access to individual program blocks. Each program block has a lock setting property. The possible lock settings are:

Unlocked – The block may be edited and viewed.

Edit Lock – The block cannot be edited, but it can be viewed. A password should be defined for this lock setting. In order to change to another lock setting, the correct password must be entered.

View Lock – The block cannot be edited or viewed. A password should be defined for this lock setting. In order to change to another lock setting, the correct password must be entered.

Permanent Edit Lock – The block can never be edited, but it can be viewed. This setting can only be changed to Permanent View Lock. **Warning**: once a block is permanently locked, it can never be unlocked. A password should be defined for this lock setting. In order to change to another lock setting, the correct password must be entered.

Permanent View Lock – The block can never be edited or viewed. A password is not necessary since this setting can never be changed. **Warning**: once a block is permanently locked, it can never be unlocked.

Though not necessary, a password should be specified with any locked block. A user must then provide the correct password in order to unlock the block. The password contains from four to sixteen ASCII characters.

19.4 CHAPTER SUMMARY

This chapter described various methods of restricting access to controller programs and data from both inside and outside the control system. General communication network protection strategies were discussed and then the available security mechanisms for the PLCs covered by this text are reviewed.

REFERENCES

Allen-Bradley, 1995. *PLC-5 Protected Processors: Supplement*, pub. 1785-6.5.13, Allen-Bradley Company, Inc., Milwaukee, WI.

Falkenau, L., 2003a. "Protecting Process Control Systems and Networks from Cyber Attack" presented at the World Batch Forum North America Conference, Woodcliff Lake, NJ, April 13-16.

Falkenau, L., 2003b. "Site Networking and Beyond," *InTech*, July, 64.

GE Fanuc Automation, 1999a. *Series 90^{TM}-30 PLC: Installation and Hardware Manual*, pub. GFK-0356P, GE Fanuc Automation North America, Inc., Charlottesville, VA.

GE Fanuc Automation, 1999b. *Series 90^{TM}-70 PLC: Installation Manual*, pub. GFK-0262G, GE Fanuc Automation North America, Inc., Charlottesville, VA.

GE Fanuc Automation, 2001. *VersaMax® PLC: User Manual*, pub. GFK-1503C, GE Fanuc Automation North America, Inc., Charlottesville, VA.

Green, G., 2001. "Hacker Jailed for Sewage Sabotage," *Courier Mail (Queensland, Australia)*, 1 November.

Rockwell Automation, 1998. *Enhanced and Ethernet PLC-5 Programmable Controllers: User Manual*, pub. 1785-6.5.12, Rockwell Automation, Inc., Milwaukee, WI, November.

Rockwell Automation, 2002. *Ethernet PLC-5 Programmable Controllers: Product Release Notes; Series E, Revision F.2; Series D, Revision G.2; Series C, RevisionQ.2,*, pub. 1785-RN003D-EN-P, Rockwell Automation, Inc., Milwaukee, WI, November.

Rockwell Software, 2000. *Security Server: Getting Results Guide*, Doc. ID 9399-SECSRVGR-JAN00, Rockwell Software Inc., Milwaukee, WI.

Rockwell Software, 2002a. *RSLogix 5 ver. 5.50 Help File*, Rockwell Software Inc., Milwaukee, WI.

Rockwell Software, 2002b. *RSLogix 500 ver. 5.50 Help File*, Rockwell Software Inc., Milwaukee, WI.

Rutenkroger, H. J., 2003. "Internet Controlled Programmable Logic Controllers; A Look at Security," M. S. Thesis, University of Missouri-Rolla, August.

Schneider Automation, 1998. *Concept User Manual,* vol. 2, ver. 2.1, pub. 840 USE 461 00, Schneider Automation, Inc., North Andover, MA.

Schneider Automation, 2001. *FactoryCast User's Guide for Quantum, Premium and Micro*, Schneider Automation, Inc., North Andover, MA.

Siemens, 2002a *Programming with STEP 7 V5.2: Manual,* Edition 12/2002, pub. A5E00171230-01, Siemens AG, Nuernberg, Germany.

Siemens, 2002b. *S7-200 Programmable Controller System Manual*, Edition 04/2002, pub. A5E00157957-01, Siemens AG, Nuernberg, Germany.

Siemens, 2002c. *Step 7 ver. 5.2 Help File*, Siemens AG, Nuernberg, Germany.

U.S. Dept. of Energy, 2002. *21 Steps to Improve Cyber Security of SCADA Networks*, Washington, DC.

20 Selecting a PLC

Chapter Topics:

- General PLC selection criteria
- PLC families

OBJECTIVES

Upon completion of this chapter, you will be able to understand:

- Considerations when selecting a PLC for a given application
- The range of PLC families offered by the manufacturers represented in this text

Scenario: Expansion of power plant coal handler PLC.

In a previous project, you supervised the upgrade of a power plant coal-handling system from a relay-controlled system to a PLC-controller system. The installation is successful and they are pleased with the increased flexibility. In fact, you have been called back to the plant for a couple of minor changes to the system to alter its operation and add diagnostic information to the operator panel.

Now they want to upgrade the wood-chip handling system from a relay-controlled system to a PLC-controlled system. The coal handler PLC is using less than 20% of its available memory, but the additional I/O is a problem. The current coal handling system uses 15 I/O modules in two 10-slot chassis and you estimate that about 8 additional I/O modules will be needed. The SLC-500 can handle up to 30 I/O modules. However, the current panel layout (Figure 20.1*a*) will not permit the third chassis to be mounted within the reach of a 50-inch chassis interconnect cable. The third chassis must be mounted on the right panel of the cabinet, which will require a 12-foot interconnect cable. Is there a way out of this dilemma?

Solution: Later SLC-500 processors (which you have) permit the I/O to be expanded beyond the usual 30-slot limit by adding an I/O scanner (1747-SN) to the chassis and using a remote I/O link to another chassis with a remote I/O adapter (1747-ASB) placed in the processor slot. This arrangement (Figure 20.1*b*) allows you to design a system with no physical changes to the existing coal-handling system.

20.1 INTRODUCTION

Most of this text has been concerned with programming PLCs. Before one can program a PLC, it must first be selected. Actually, the first choice is whether to choose a PLC or a

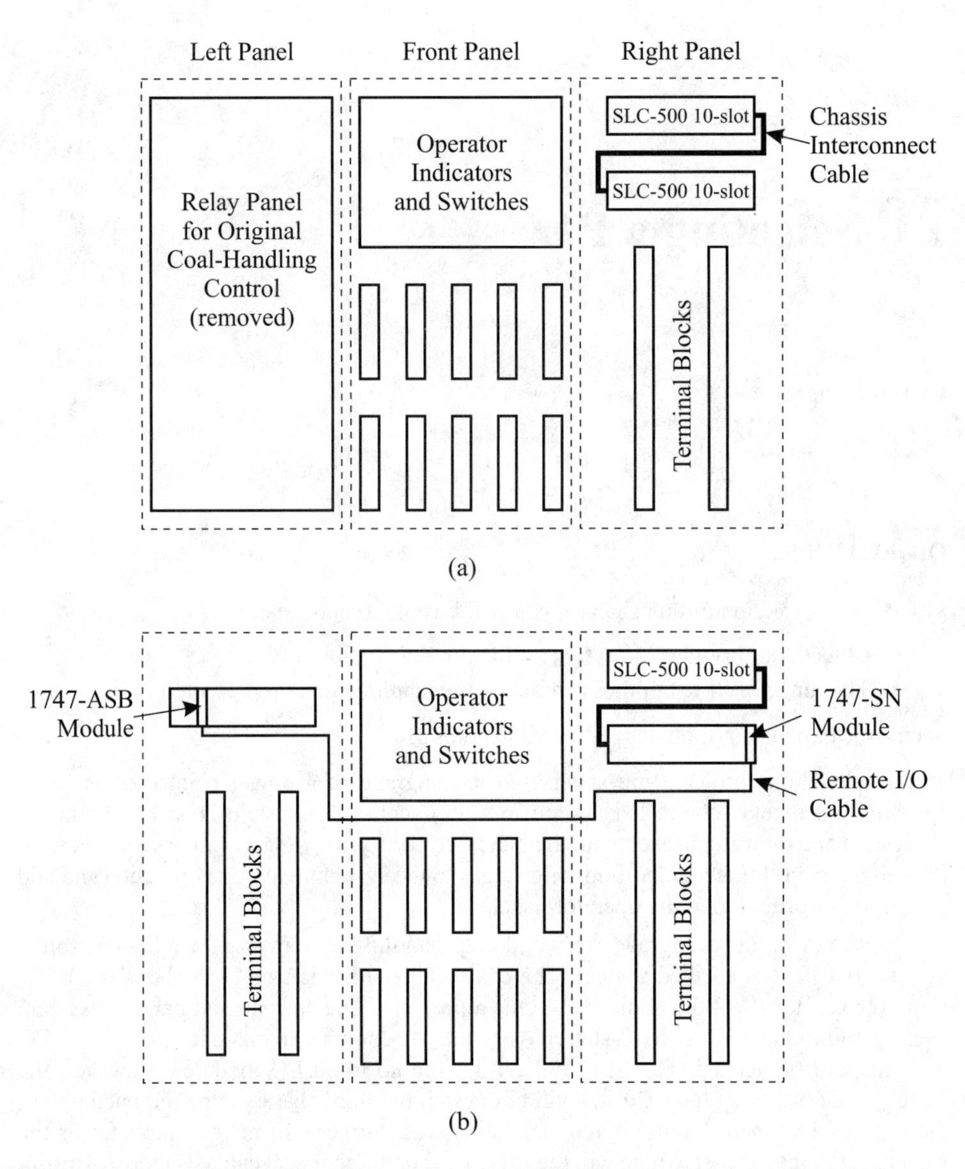

Figure 20.1. Coal-handling system panel layout: (a) before adding wood chip handler control; (b) after adding wood chip handler control.

PC-based control system. That comparison is discussed in Chapter 1 and is not addressed here. General selection factors are described first and then the PLC families of the manufacturers represented by this text are characterized.

20.2 SELECTION FACTORS

When selecting a PLC, the biggest consideration is the application, which ranges from a small stand-alone relay replacement to a large system containing hundreds of thousands of I/O points, requiring multiple PLCs and coordination among them. PLCs can be classified according to the range of I/O channels needed by the application as shown in Figure 20.2. As indicated in Figure 20.2, as the number of I/O channels that a particular PLC can handle increases, the amount of program memory and available functions also increases. The medium-sized PLCs (and larger) generally have specialized I/O modules and more communication options. A few years ago, PID control was not supported by the smaller PLCs. However, that function is now available even in the smallest PLCs. The smaller PLCs generally only support ladder logic programming whereas the larger PLCs support multiple languages.

The smallest (nano) PLCs are often a compact unit with built-in I/O channels, though some have the capability to add a few expansion I/O channels. As one progresses to larger PLCs, they progress to DIN-rail mounted modules that are connected together and then up to chassis-based systems where the modules are plugged into a backplane. The medium-sized (and larger) PLCs tend to support some kind of remote I/O, whether it is with a proprietary network and/or with a standard network.

Though the number of I/O channels is a big selection factor, other factors that determine the type of PLC chosen include:

- Specialized I/O - Does the application demand high-speed counters, motion control, TTL digital I/O, or other specialized interface?
- Remote I/O - Is some of the I/O located some distance from the processor?
- Expandability - Can more I/O be added to the system in the future?

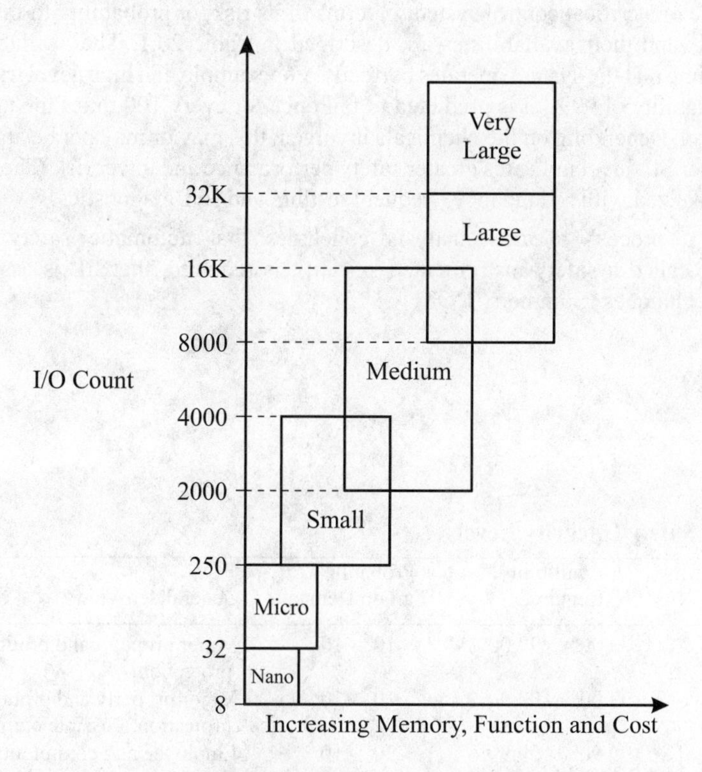

Figure 20.2. PLC system sizes.

- Networking - Does data need to be exchanged between processors or between processors and computers?
- Redundancy - Does the system need to function even when the processor fails?
- Safety - Does the system need to meet certain safety standards?
- Programming language - Does it support languages other than ladder logic?
- Manufacturer reputation - If the system fails, are replacement parts readily available?
- Standardization - Has the company standardized on PLCs from a certain manufacturer?
- Price

The cost of a PLC system is much more than just the cost of the PLC hardware. The overall cost includes programming, installation, maintenance, and training. The relatively high cost of training means that companies generally limit the allowable PLCs to those of one vendor. The $500 savings on a single PLC from a different vendor is overshadowed by the costs required to train even one technician. The maintenance cost also includes the cost of spare modules kept in stock for speedy replacement. This consideration often limits one to keep the types of I/O modules to a minimum. For example, instead of using 8-, 16-, and 32-channel 24-V discrete input modules, it is often a wiser choice to use only 16-channel modules.

When a PLC is used for automatic safety protection, it must meet certain safety standards (IEC, 1998; ISA, 1996). The safety integrity level (SIL) defines the safety performance of a critical control system in terms of its risk, or probability to fail. The four safety levels and their availabilities are described in Table 20.1. The availability is the percent of time that the system operates correctly. For example, if a high-level trip for a tank has an availability of 99%, it is predicted to fail once for every 100 times the tank reaches the high level. Depending on the chemicals involved, this may or may not be an acceptable risk. A higher SIL level indicates greater safety performance and lower risk. The higher SIL levels are realized with redundancy, frequent testing, and self-diagnostics.

When a process hazards analysis concludes that automatic safety protection (commonly called a safety instrumented system), is required, the SIL is assigned by a variety of techniques (Summers, 1998).

Table 20.1 Safety Integrity Levels

Safety Integrity Level	Availibility Required	Probability to Fail on Demand	Generalized View
1	90.00% - 99.00%	10^{-2} - 10^{-1}	Minor property and production protection.
2	99.00% - 99.90%	10^{-3} - 10^{-2}	Major property and production protection. Possible employee injury
3	99.90% - 99.99%	10^{-4} - 10^{-3}	Employee and community impact.
4	99.99% - 99.999%	10^{-5} - 10^{-4}	Catastrophic community impact.

20.3 PLC FAMILIES

Though there are a large number of vendors of PLC equipment, only the PLC families of the manufacturers represented by this text are described. In addition, this section is further limited to the PLC families available at the time of this writing. Only the major features of these families are described. More information can be obtained from the vendors.

20.3.1 Telemecanique Modicon PLC Families

The general families of Modicon PLCs, produced under the Telemecanique brand, are summarized in Table 20.2. These systems span the entire range of applications. Due to the recent introduction of the Unity hardware and software programming, there is some overlap between the older Quantum (Concept) and Premium (PL7) platforms.

The Zelio-Logic controller is basically a self-contained replacement for industrial relays. It does have some capability for expansion. It is programmed in ladder logic and has timer and counter functions. The Zelio-Logic is programmed with its built-in display and panel push buttons.

The Twido controllers are self-contained "brick" PLCs for nano- and micro-sized systems. The controllers mount on a DIN rail and have some expansion capability. They are programmed in the ladder logic, instruction list, or Grafcet (SFC) languages by the TwidoSoft programming package. They can also handle PID loops.

The TSX Micro controller is a small chassis-based controller intended for machine control application. It is has limited expansion capability though it can support I/O devices connected to an AS-i network. A TSX Micro controller can be programmed in the ladder

Table 20.2 Telemecanique Modicon PLC Families

Processor Family	Maximum Discrete Inputs	Maximum Discrete Outputs	Maximum Analog Inputs	Maximum Analog Outputs	Notes
Zelio-Logic	16+8Exp	10+6Exp	0	0	
Twido	24+192[1]Exp	16+192[1]Exp	0+14Exp	0+7Exp	Max. 7 exp. modules AS-I devices
Micro	160	160	16	8	Max 5 slots AS-I devices
Momentum	8192	8192	26,048[3]	26,048[3]	
Premium Unity	2048[1]+Exp	2048[1]+Exp	512[2]+Exp	512[2]+Exp	Specialized I/O
Premium PL7	2040[1]+Exp	2040[1]+Exp	256[2]+Exp	256[2]+Exp	Specialized I/O
Premium Atrium	1024[1]+Exp	1024[1]+Exp	128[2]+Exp	128[2]+Exp	Specialized I/O
Quantum Unity	34,336[1]+Exp	34,336[1]+Exp	2416[2]+Exp	2200[2]+Exp	Some specialized I/O
Quantum Concept	32,768[1]+Exp	32,768[1]+Exp	2048[2]+Exp	2048[2]+Exp	Some specialized I/O

Notes:
1. Maximum number total discrete inputs plus outputs.
2. Maximum number total analog inputs plus outputs.
3. Maximum total number of registers.

logic, instruction list, structured text, or Grafcet languages by the PL7 programming package.

The Momentum PLCs are basically small, single-unit "brick" processors mounted on a DIN rail. Actually, the processor is mated with an I/O module to construct a PLC. Other I/O modules can be addressed through Modbus+ or IO-Bus (a form of Interbus). Certain processors can address I/O modules connected to Ethernet. Though not originally intended for this purpose, the Momentum processors can handle medium-sized systems.

The Premium PLC has three basic versions. The Premium Unity and PL7 PLCs are modular chassis-based controllers primarily for medium-sized discrete applications. The Premium PL7 processors are programmed with the PL7 or Unity programming software and the Premium Unity processors have more memory and higher performance, but are only programmed with the newer Unity programming software. The Premium Atrium Unity and PL7 processor is a card that is inserted into a personal computer (PC) backplane slot. An external power supply maintains power independent of the PC. The Atrium processor uses the same I/O modules as the Premium Unity and PL7 processors. Though there are Unity and PL7 versions of the Atrium processor, the amounts of external I/O supported are identical.

For the Premium processors, there are a fair number of modules for specialized applications such as motion control and weighing systems. The Premium Unity and PL7 PLC system also supports redundant processors and redundant I/O modules.

The Quantum PLCs are modular chassis-based controllers primarily for large and very large applications in both the discrete and process control applications. Besides high-speed counters and motion modules, there are a few other specialized I/O modules.

There are two types of Quantum processors listed in Table 20.2. The Quantum Concept processors are programmed with the Concept or Unity programming software and the Quantum Unity processors have more memory and higher performance, but are only programmed with the newer Unity programming software. Like the Premium processors, the Quantum Unity and Concept PLC systems also support redundant processors and redundant I/O modules.

20.3.2 Rockwell Automation PLC Families

The general families of Rockwell Automation PLCs are summarized in Table 20.3. As for the other vendors, these systems span the entire range of applications. The ControlLogix and CompactLogix are the most recent platforms and will probably eventually replace the PLC-5 and SLC-500 systems. However, due to the large installed base of PLC-5 and SLC-500 systems, they will continue to be supported for many years.

The Pico controller is basically a self-contained replacement for industrial relays. It is programmed in ladder logic and has timer and counter functions. The Pico may be programmed from its display or its program may be downloaded from a PC. On some of the controllers, up to two of the input channels can be configured as either discrete inputs or analog inputs.

The MicroLogix and SLC-500 controllers are programmed in ladder logic and share the same programming package (RSLogix500). The MicroLogix controllers mount on a DIN rail and span the range from micro- to small I/O count. The MicroLogix 1000 controllers are self-contained "brick" PLCs and the MicroLogix 1200 PLCs are an expandable version of the MicroLogix 1000. All of the MicroLogix controllers can handle

Table 20.3 Rockwell Automation PLC Families

Processor Family	Maximum Discrete		Maximum Analog		
	Inputs	Outputs	Inputs	Outputs	Notes
Pico	12+12Exp	6+6Exp	2[1]	0	
MicroLogix 1000	20	12	2	1	
MicroLogix 1200	26+96Exp	16+96Exp	0+24Exp	0+24Exp	Max. 136 discrete I/O Max 24 analog I/O
MicroLogix 1500	16+512Exp	12+512Exp	0+128Exp	0+128Exp	Max 16 expansion I/O modules
SLC-500	960+Exp	960+Exp	480+Exp	240+Exp	Max 30 I/O modules Specialized I/O
PLC-5	3072	3072	3072[3]	3072[3]	Specialized I/O
CompactLogix	960	960	240	240	Max. 30 modules
ControlLogix	128K[2]	128K[2]	4000[3]	4000[3]	Some specialized I/O
GuardPLC 1200	20	8	0	0	
GuardPLC 1600	20+1024[2]Exp	8+1024[2]Exp	0	0	Max. 64 I/O modules
GuardPLC 1800	24+1024[2]Exp	8+1024[2]Exp	8	0	Max. 64 I/O modules
GuardPLC 2000	144	96	48	48	Max 6 I/O modules

Notes:
1. Uses 2 discrete input channels
2. Maximum number total discrete inputs plus outputs.
3. Maximum number total analog inputs plus outputs.

arithmetic operations and all but the MicroLogix 1000 can handle PID control. The MicroLogix 1500 controllers have a few more options and use the same expansion I/O modules as the CompactLogix controllers.

The SLC-500 controllers address medium-sized systems. The system is modular, based on chassis mounting. There are a wide range of available specialized modules, including motion control and standard communication networks. The size of the system can be expanded beyond the normal limit of 30 I/O modules with Remote I/O, DeviceNet, and ControlNet scanners.

The PLC-5 controllers were originally developed as a replacement for the single-slot PLC-2 processors and then later expanded to encompass some of the larger applications covered by the PLC-3 processors. The PLC-5 system is a chassis-based modular system. Depending on the particular processor, up to 93 chassis of I/O modules can be supported. The PLC-5 has the largest selection of specialized modules, including motion control, plastic injection molding control, and clutch/brake control. In physical size, PLC-5 modules are about twice the height of SLC-500 modules.

The PLC-5 also supports redundant processors. A redundant PLC-5 system is constructed by two PLC-5 chassis each with one PLC-5 processor and one backup communications module (BCM). The I/O modules must be remote from the two redundant controller chassis. The two BCM modules are connected with a dedicated serial link and the two processors share the DH+ and remote I/O networks.

The ControlLogix processors support the needs of very large systems. This architecture supports multiple processors in a chassis. Its only drawback is that it is relatively new and does not have the breadth of specialized modules as the PLC-5. It can still interface to the

PLC-5 I/O modules, however. The CompactLogix system addresses small systems, using the same programming software (RSLogix 5000) as the ControlLogix system. The ControlLogix hardware is a modular chassis-based system whereas the CompactLogix system is DIN rail-mountable modules. Physically, ControlLogix modules are about the same size as SLC-500 modules. The CompactLogix I/O modules are also used by the MicroLogix 1500 processors.

A redundant ControlLogix system can be configured by populating two ControlLogix chassis identically with one Logix5555 processor, up to five ControlNet bridge modules, one Ethernet module, and one System Redundancy module. The two System Redundancy modules are connected with a fiber-optic cable. All I/O modules must be in chassis remote from the two redundant controller chassis. For added redundancy, the ControlNet network can have redundant cables.

The GuardPLC processors are designed for application in systems up to SIL 3 according to IEC-61508 without restrictions. The GuardPLC 1200 processor is a self-contained system with I/O that addresses the need for nano-sized safety systems. The GuardPLC 1600 and GuardPLC 1800 processors address the need for micro- and small-sized safety systems. Both of these processors can communicate with up to 64 distributed I/O modules or other processors over a dedicated Ethernet network. The GuardPLC 1800 processor has all the features of the GuardPLC 1600 processor, adding 8 analog input channels and two high-speed counters. The GuardPLC 2000 system is a modular, chassis-based system that does not handle as many discrete I/O channels as the GuardPLC 1600/1800 processor, but will handle a larger number of analog I/O channels.

All of the GuardPLC processors have redundant microprocessors in one controller and self-test of the I/O channels during operation. Errors in an I/O channel are automatically detected and if the error affects safe operation of the channel, the respective channel is forced to the **off** state. The GuardPLC processors are programmed according to IEC 61131-3 function block language.

20.3.3 Siemens PLC Families

The general families of Siemens PLCs are summarized in Table 20.4. Though there are fewer families than other vendors, these systems span the entire range of applications. The older S5 family of PLC systems is not described, though it is still currently being sold.

The LOGO! controller is basically a replacement for industrial relays. It has expansion capability through a few expansion modules or to an AS-i network. It is programmed in ladder logic and can show text messages on its display. The LOGO! may be programmed from its display or its program may be downloaded from a PC. On some of the controllers, up to two of the input channels can be configured as either discrete inputs or analog inputs.

The S7-200 controllers are self-contained "brick" PLCs for nano- and micro-sized systems. The processor and expansion modules mount on DIN rail and all but one processor can be expanded with additional I/O modules or to devices on an AS-i network. They are programmed in the ladder logic, statement list, or function block languages. The S7-200 processors can also handle PID loops.

The C7 PLCs are an "all-in-one" package for small applications, including a S7-300 processor and an operator panel. There is some integrated I/O channels and most models can be additionally expanded by a connection to S7-300 I/O modules or with PROFIBUS-DP slaves.

Table 20.4 Siemens PLC Families

Processor Family	Maximum Discrete		Maximum Analog		
	Inputs	Outputs	Inputs	Outputs	Notes
LOGO!	8+16Exp	4+16Exp	2[1]+6Exp	0	AS-i interface
S7-200	24+112Exp	16+112Exp	0+28Exp	0+14Exp	Max. 7 expansion I/O modules AS-i interface
C7	992[2]	992[2]	248[3]	248[3]	Includes HMI
S7-300	16384[2]	16384[2]	1024[3]	1024[3]	Specialized I/O
S7-400	131K[2]	131K[2]	8192[3]	8192[3]	Specialized I/O
WinAC	131K[2]	131K[2]	8192[3]	8192[3]	Specialized I/O

Notes:
1. Two (max.) analog inputs use 2 discrete inputs on the base unit.
2. Maximum number total discrete inputs plus outputs.
3. Maximum number total analog inputs plus outputs.

The S7-300 controllers are modular PLC systems to handle small to medium-sized applications. Some of the processors have integrated I/O channels. The modules mount on wide DIN rail. There is a good range of specialized modules available that cover motion control, weighing, and intrinsic safety.

The S7-300F processors are designed for application in systems up to SIL 3 according to IEC-61508. In order to meet SIL 3, S7-300 F-series modules must also be used. These processors do not have redundant microprocessors in the controller and the safety rating is achieved by the use of fail-safe logic functions in the processor and in the I/O channel self-test and fail-safe operation. The safety functions are programmed with a special version of the ladder and function block languages. The primary differences between the special programming languages and their standard counterparts concerns limitations in the allowed functions and data types and in the allowed address areas.

The S7-400 processors support the needs of large and very large systems. It is a chassis-based modular system. It supports fewer specialized modules than the S7-300, though it can still interface to the S7-300 modules through PROFIBUS-DP. Redundant processors and redundant I/O networks are fully supported. The WinAC processor is a S7-400 series processor on a card that is inserted into a personal PC backplane slot. An external power supply maintains power independent of the PC. The WinAC processor uses PROFIBUS DP to interface to I/O modules.

20.3.4 GE Fanuc PLC Families

The GE Fanuc PLC families are summarized in Table 20.5. These systems span the entire range of applications, though until the PACSystems processors were introduced, the ability to handle very large applications was limited. The programming of the VersaMax, Series 90-30 and Series 90-70 processors is very similar, but is limited to the ladder logic and instruction list languages.

The VersaMax Nano processor is a small single-unit "brick" PLC. The VersaMax Micro PLC can handle micro-sized systems with its expansion I/O modules. The VersaMax

Table 20.5 GE Fanuc PLC Families

Processor Family	Maximum Discrete		Maximum Analog		Notes
	Inputs	Outputs	Inputs	Outputs	
VersaMax Nano	6	4	1	0	
VersaMax Micro	16+Exp	12+Exp	2+Exp	1+Exp	Max. 140 I/O points
VersaMax	2048	2048	960	768	Max 64 I/O modules
Series 90-30	2048[1]	2048[1]	32,640[2]	32,640[2]	Motion control module
Series 90-70	12,288[1]	12,288[1]	8192[2]	8192[2]	Some specialized I/O
PACSystem RX3i	32,768	32,768	32,640	32,640	
PACSystem RX7i	32,768	32,768	32,640	32,640	Uses 90-70 I/O

Notes:
1. Maximum number total discrete inputs plus outputs.
2. Maximum number total analog inputs plus outputs.

processor can handle small- to medium-sized systems. All of the VersaMax modules are mounted on DIN rail.

The Series 90-30 PLC is a modular chassis-based system that handles medium-sized systems. Beyond the normal discrete and analog I/O modules, a two-axis servo motion control module is available. The Series 90-70 PLC is also a modular chassis-based system, but it handles large applications. Physically, the 90-70 modules are physically about twice the size of the 90-30 modules. The 90-70 processor supports some specialized I/O modules, but no motion control modules. Redundant 90-70 processors are supported.

The PACSystems processors are recent additions to the GE Fanuc automation products. The RX3i PLC has a similar physical size to the Series 90-30 PLC systems though it can handle a very large system. The RX3i has its own set of I/O modules, but it can also interface to a 90-30 expansion chassis and thus can act as a replacement processor for the Series 90-30 processor. The set of available RX3i I/O modules is similar to the modules available for the Series 90-30 PLC. Though there are some limitations, the RX7i is basically a replacement processor for the Series 90-70 processor and uses the 90-70 expansion racks for its I/O. RX7i supports redundant processors. A redundant processor system contains an active processor and a backup processor synchronized with the active processor. The primary and backup processors are in the same chassis. A failure in the active processor causes the backup processor to assume control. The RX3i and RX7i processors support structured text (IEC 61131-3 compliant) language programming in addition to ladder logic compatible with earlier Series 90 PLCs.

20.4 CHAPTER SUMMARY

This chapter reviews the various factors one should consider when selecting a PLC for a particular application. After summarizing general selection criteria, the PLC families of the manufacturers represented by this text are described.

REFERENCES

GE Fanuc Automation, 2003. *VersaMax® Micro PLCs and Nano PLCs: User's Manual*, pub. GFK-1645D, GE Fanuc Automation North America, Inc., Charlottesville, VA, September.

GE Fanuc Automation, 2004a. *PACSystems™ PLC: CPU Reference Manual*, pub. GFK-2222B, GE Fanuc Automation North America, Inc., Charlottesville, VA, July.

GE Fanuc Automation, 2004b. *PACSystems RX3i System Manual*, pub. GFK-2314, GE Fanuc Automation North America, Inc., Charlottesville, VA, June.

GE Fanuc Automation, 1999a. *Series 90™-30 PLC: Installation and Hardware Manual*, pub. GFK-0356P, GE Fanuc Automation North America, Inc., Charlottesville, VA.

GE Fanuc Automation, 1999b. *Series 90™-70 Programmable Controller: Data Sheet Manual*, pub. GFK-0262G, GE Fanuc Automation North America, Inc., Charlottesville, VA, November.

GE Fanuc Automation, 2000. *Series 90™-30 PLC: I/O Module Specifications*, pub. GFK-0898F, GE Fanuc Automation North America, Inc., Charlottesville, VA, July.

GE Fanuc Automation, 2001. *VersaMax® PLC: User's Manual*, pub. GFK-1503C, GE Fanuc Automation North America, Inc., Charlottesville, VA, March.

IEC, 1998. *Functional Safety of Electrical/Electronic/Programmable Electronic Safety- Related Systems - Part 1: General Requirements*, IEC 61508-1, Ed. 1.0, International Electrotechnical Commission, Geneva, Switzerland.

IEC, 2000a. *Functional Safety of Electrical/Electronic/Programmable Electronic Safety- Related Systems - Part 2: Requirements for Electrical/Electronic/Programmable Electronic Safety-Related Systems*, IEC 61508-2, Ed. 1.0, International Electrotechnical Commission, Geneva, Switzerland.

IEC, 2000b. *Functional Safety of Electrical/Electronic/Programmable Electronic Safety- Related Systems - Part 3: Software Requirements*, IEC 61508-3, Ed. 1.0, International Electrotechnical Commission, Geneva, Switzerland.

IEC, 2000c. *Functional Safety of Electrical/Electronic/Programmable Electronic Safety- Related Systems - Part 4: Definitions and Abbreviations*, IEC 61508-4, Ed. 1.0, International Electrotechnical Commission, Geneva, Switzerland.

IEC, 2000d. *Functional Safety of Electrical/Electronic/Programmable Electronic Safety- Related Systems - Part 5: Examples of Methods for the Determination of Safety Integrity Levels*, IEC 61508-5, Ed. 1.0, International Electrotechnical Commission, Geneva, Switzerland.

IEC, 2000e. *Functional Safety of Electrical/Electronic/Programmable Electronic Safety- Related Systems - Part 6: Guidelines on the Application of IEC 61508-2 and IEC 61508-3*, IEC 61508-6, Ed. 1.0, International Electrotechnical Commission, Geneva, Switzerland.

IEC, 2000f. *Functional Safety of Electrical/Electronic/Programmable Electronic Safety- Related Systems - Part 7: Overview of Techniques and Measures*, IEC 61508-7, Ed. 1.0, International Electrotechnical Commission, Geneva, Switzerland.

ISA, 1996. *ISA-S84.01 - Application of Safety Instrumented Systems for the Process Industries-1996*, The Instrumentation, Systems, and Automation Society, Research Triangle Park, NC.

Rockwell Automation, 2004. *Allen Bradley Automation Systems Catalog*, pub. B115, Rockwell Automation, Milwaukee, WI.

Schneider Electric, 2004a. *Modicon Premium Automation Platform - Unity &PL7: Catalogue,* Art. 802625 - MKTED204072EN, Schneider Electric Industries SAS, Rueil-Malmaison, France, July.

Schneider Electric, 2004b. *Modicon Quantum Automation Platform - Unity, Concept &ProWORX 32: Catalogue,* Art. 802621 - MKTED204071EN, Schneider Electric Industries SAS, Rueil-Malmaison, France, July.

Schneider Electric, 2004c. *Programmable Controllers, Automation Platforms, Distributed I/O - The Essential Guide,* Art. 074020 - DIA6ED2040203EN, Schneider Electric Industries SAS, Rueil-Malmaison, France.

Schneider Electric, 2004d. *Twido Programmable Controllers: Software Reference Guide,* Pub. TWD USE 10AE, Ver. 2.5, Schneider Electric Industries SAS, Rueil-Malmaison, France, July.

Siemens, 2002. *Products for Totally Integrated Automation and Micro Automation: Catalog ST 70 - 2003*, Siemens AG, Nuernberg, Germany.

Summers, Angela E., 1998. "Techniques for Assigning a Target Safety Integrity Level," *ISA Transactions*, 37: 95-104.

Telemecanique, 2004e. *Zelio Logic 2 Smart Relay: User's Guide,* Pub. SR1 MAN01EN, Telemecanique, Rueil-Malmaison, France, April.

21 Control Projects

Chapter Topics:

- Phases of a typical control project
- Example control requirements
- Standard code
- Testing

OBJECTIVES

Upon completion of this chapter, you will be able to understand:

- What happens in a typical factory automation project
- The importance of a control requirements definition
- The importance of standard code
- How to test a program with a process simulation

Scenario: A successful project begins with a thorough understanding of control improvements and with the ability to use the right frame of reference.

On one project, you are confronted with a typical late design situation. The process is a waste filtration system. The control design specifies the need for 400 highly interactive interlocks. By experience, you know that this design will be very expensive to implement and commission. You need to reduce the costs of the design.

Solution: Initially, you have a hard time understanding why there are so many interlocks. After consulting with the customer you discover the problem. The original designer's frame of reference was in terms of PID loops and interlocks. For all but a handful of interlocks, the control objective is to stop the inflow if the effluent flow is stopped. By taking a different view, most of the interlocks were replaced with a control scheme that stops the appropriate inflows when the outflows stop. You are able to significantly reduce costs by focusing on the requirements rather than control details developed from the wrong frame of reference.

21.1 INTRODUCTION

A control system is designed and implemented as part of a capital project. During the lifecycle of a plant there are numerous control projects. To properly understand the role of control engineering on a capital project, a plant lifecycle view should be considered (Erickson and Hedrick, 1999). Though capturing some aspects of a lifecycle view, this chapter focuses on the control project.

Though all phases of a typical control design project are discussed in this chapter, certain aspects of a successful project are elaborated. The control requirements developed during the preliminary engineering phase are important and so an example control requirements definition is presented. During the detailed design and implementation phases, the use of standard code is an important concept. In order to shorten the installation and commissioning phases of a project, the program must be tested as early as possible. The use of process simulation is essential to this goal since it allows one to test the program without the process and I/O hardware.

21.2 TYPICAL CONTROL DESIGN PROJECT

Project teams execute control projects to build and improve manufacturing facilities. Control projects range from small equipment modification projects to large, greenfield projects; from process de-bottlenecks to new product lines.

One very important aspect of a control project is the *extent of automation*, depicted in Figure 21.1. As depicted in this figure, a plant is composed of three major areas as it relates to a capital project:

- Control and information technology
- Plant personnel
- Process technology

The "extent of automation" line is the boundary between the plant personnel and the other two major areas. All control projects must consider personnel as part of the system. The extent of automation is defined in the control requirements definition, developed in the preliminary design.

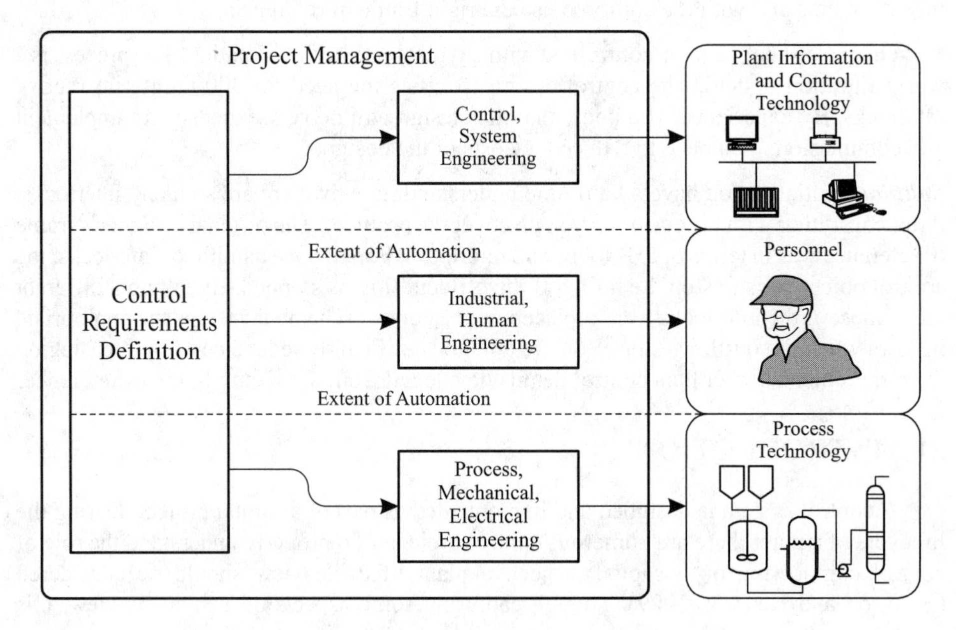

Figure 21.1. Extent of automation on control projects.

The process technology area contains the equipment that processes the materials to make product. In this area, automation provides the physical leverage to plant personnel. The extent of automation, therefore, includes mechanical and pneumatic moving equipment, such as pumps, valves, and conveyors.

The control and information technology area contains the PLCs and computers that implement the control strategy. The extent of automation here is the amount of operating activities that are performed by the PLCs and computers. The automation may be fully-automatic, replacing manual activities, or it may be semi-automatic, augmenting the manual activities.

The process technology and the control and information technology support the plant operating personnel. The technology also provides the mental and physical leverage to operate the plant effectively. The user interface lies at the boundary between the personnel and the other two major areas. Thus, the user interface is a critical consideration in capital project execution.

In the context of this text, control projects contain three major aspects:

1. PLCs – control strategy implementation,
2. HMI – interface between the operator and the automation,
3. Electrical and Instrumentation (E & I) – direct interface to the process equipment.

Regardless of the size, the eight major phases of every control project are (Figure 21.2):

Planning
Preliminary Design
Detailed Design
Implementation
Installation
Commissioning
Startup
Training

Though all phases are described in this section, the most emphasis is placed on the preliminary design phase.

21.2.1 Planning

Regardless of the size, every capital project begins with some planning. There are two major products of the planning phase:

- First draft of project requirements
- Estimate of project resources

The overall flow on a capital project begins with the definition of the project requirements. Omission of this step often leads to project failure. This step also requires a multidisciplinary team approach. The team should include plant operation experts and engineering experts familiar with the application and with the plant's current standards (equipment, documentation, etc.).

The project requirements form the basis of the first estimate of the needed project resources. This first estimate is often very rough. A more accurate estimate is often produced by the next step, preliminary engineering.

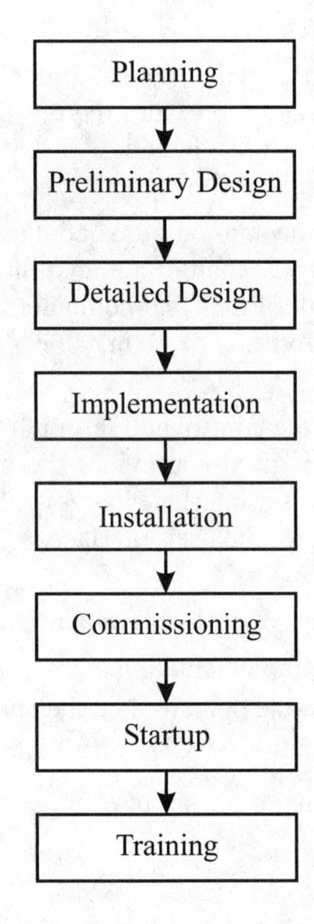

Figure 21.2. Control project steps.

Once the requirements are clearly stated, they can be distributed to the appropriate engineering disciplines for the design and implementation phases. Control engineers are involved in meeting the requirements for the control and information technology. Industrial and human engineering experts handle the plant organization requirements. Of course, the process technology is the responsibility of the process engineering experts. All of these disciplines are orchestrated by the project management.

21.2.2 Preliminary Design

During preliminary engineering, the primary objective is to first understand how to operate the process and then define the control requirements to support the operations.

There are two groups involved in the preliminary design. The process engineers are concerned with the process, that is, what is to be controlled. This group is responsible for the process technology. The control engineers are involved with the control requirements and thus are responsible for the control technology.

As depicted in Figure 21.3, the process engineer's preliminary design activities are summarized as follows:

- Prepare the conceptual process design.
- Prepare the initial process technology budget.

The conceptual process design produces the design specifications for the physical plant equipment. For a discrete-parts manufacturing process, a conceptual process design

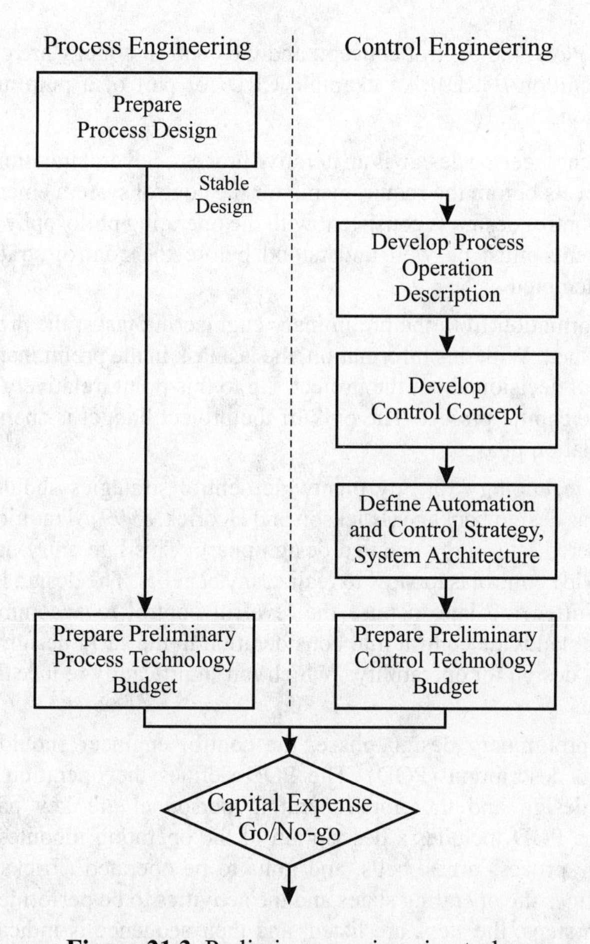

Figure 21.3. Preliminary engineering tasks.

includes production rates and material flow patterns. For a chemical process, it includes data about any chemical unit operations and material/energy flow properties. The latter are specified at various operating points in the process for the various steady-state operating conditions.

The process design is usually represented by a process flow diagram (PFD) with an associated equipment item list for the major plant systems. The process technology capital budget is determined from this information.

For the control aspects of a process design, the preliminary engineering activities for the project (Figure 21.3), in order, are as follows:

- Develop the process operation description (POD).
- Develop the control concept.
- Define the preliminary automation and control strategy.
- Define the preliminary system architecture.
- Prepare the preliminary control technology budget.

Collectively, the POD, the control concept, and the control strategy are called the control requirements definition (CRD). An example CRD for part of a pulp and paper mill is presented in section 21.3.

Preliminary engineering design is an iterative process. Several iterations are required at various review levels before the requirements for the control system emerge. This process ensures that the control design is consistent with the operating philosophy of the plant. The control requirements must be well understood before the control strategy and system architecture is attempted.

With the information from the preliminary engineering tasks, the preliminary project budget can be refined. With this information, the last task in the preliminary design stage is usually a go/no-go decision about the project. Up to this point, relatively little money has been spent on the capital project. The bulk of the project budget is spent on the detailed design and installation phases.

The control technology for any plantwide control strategies should be part of the conceptual process design package (Erickson and Hedrick, 1999). Traditionally, plantwide control is considered late in the detailed design phase. This late entry usually means the budget for plantwide control is too low to realize any benefits. The design is already "cast in CAD" and it is often too late to raise the level of control to accommodate plantwide schemes. Taking plantwide control into consideration in the early design phase forces the team to consider "design for operability," which can significantly reduce the lifecycle costs of a process plant.

Within the preliminary design phase, the control engineer should first develop a process operation description (POD). The POD defines the operating strategy for the proposed plant design and therefore operating personnel are key participants in its development. The POD includes a description of the operating modules and defines the boundaries of the process areas, cells, and units to be operated (Erickson and Hedrick, 1999). It also defines the operating states and the activities to be performed for each. If the activities contain steps, the steps are listed, and their sequence is indicated. The control objectives are identified as part of the operating state description. The POD should describe all operating activities whether or not they will be automated.

In preparing a POD, the typical questions to be addressed include (Erickson and Hedrick, 1999):

- What are the basic steps or divisions within the process operation? How is each operated?
- What are the significant process conditions and/or events that impact quality assurance, production, or protection of equipment, people, and the environment?
- What are the routine, special, and emergency response operations in each operating state?
- What types of process information must be collected and saved for performance monitoring (reports, data archiving, etc.)?
- What data must be supplied to other systems, including business data systems?

After developing the POD, the control engineers need to determine the amount of control to be implemented, captured as the control concept. The control concept contains:

- Requirements to be met by the control and information technology.
- Extent of automation required to operate the plant and achieve enterprise objectives.

The control concept forms the basis for the control system design. It defines the extent of automation in terms of control requirements for the areas, cells, and units. The control concept is also used to verify the delivered system during system testing and commissioning. It should be prepared without a particular implied implementation.

In preparing the control concept the typical questions to be considered include (Erickson and Hedrick, 1999):

- What operating module activities and control objectives will be manual and what should be automated (i.e., the extent of automation)?
- How flexible must the automation be (e.g., multiple products, frequent equipment changes)?
- How do control activities interact (e.g., concurrent operation, shared resources)?
- How do control activities and operating personnel interact (e.g., data presentation, equipment selections, control commands, data entry)?

When developing the control concept, one should not spend much time considering details such as the control logic of individual valves, blowers, pumps, and motors. While important details are often unearthed while developing the control concept, the details should be kept to a minimum. It is proper to note them and save them for later use. The overall design process is less efficient if too much detail is covered too soon (particularly if the process design is still unstable). Control details should be left for consideration during detailed design.

After the control requirements are understood and documented, the project team develops the preliminary control strategy and system architecture. The control strategy defines the control types and interrelations to fulfill the control requirements. The system architecture defines the hardware and software platform that will be required to execute the control strategies.

The control concept and control strategy are developed using the reference model described in Chapter 3 of Erickson and Hedrick (1999). Operating modules as defined by the POD help segment these documents in order to relate them to the process design.

A preliminary CRD package, containing a first pass at the POD and the control concept, should be produced as soon as practical. The level of detail is obviously limited to the information available at the time. Certain items might simply be noted as TBD (to be determined).

Likewise, the initial control strategy and system architecture based on the control concept is helpful in reviewing various control concept candidates early in the project. For both the control strategy and system architecture, the control algorithms and hardware/software requirements are very high-level or conceptual. This philosophy provides flexibility in the budgeting activity.

The CRD sections are valuable inputs in developing the preliminary P&ID in the detail design effort. Later, as the process design becomes stable and the detail design is finalized, the CRD package is updated to produce a final version. All TBD references, for instance, should be resolved. This final version becomes the final project control documentation, an important project deliverable.

The CRD documentation is only the beginning of the control design package. It is used as a design basis for preparing the other follow-on project deliverables. For example, in the detailed design phase, the control strategy must be further described and detailed prior to beginning implementation. Similarly, the control system schematics may also be influenced by items mentioned in the documents.

A CRD has many benefits, both direct and indirect. The primary benefit is the early involvement of those persons most familiar with the plant's operation in developing the control system requirements. This method forces the participants to contemplate and describe the exact process area operation. Many issues relating to basic operations will surface *prior* to the selection of the control system equipment.

There are also several secondary benefits from the process. These include:

- Identification of the extent of automation early in a project, which provides a better baseline for budget control
- Initial definition of alarm management requirements to avoid unnecessary alarms in inactive operating states
- Initial definition of operator interface span of vision and control

21.2.3 Detailed Design

The detailed design begins after project approval, either near or at the end of the preliminary engineering activity. The detailed design phase requires many times the effort spent in preliminary design. Some detailed design is usually considered when developing the control concept in the preliminary design phase. A new or unusual requirement may require a check on whether or not the requirement can be implemented.

Detailed design adds sufficient detail to the initial control strategy and system architecture to provide a firm basis for implementation. It is important that the detailed specifications fulfill the control requirements as defined by the control concept. Detailed design also includes defining the system test, education, and documentation requirements for the system.

The detailed design phase develops the following:

- Measurement and final control functional specifications
- Safety instrumented system functional specifications
- Discrete and regulatory control functional specifications
- Procedural control functional specifications
- Process information data models
- User interface functional specifications

These specifications include the control technology specifications for the system hardware, embedded software, and application software programming. These specifications should address the size, performance, reliability, and environmental conditions to be met by the technology in this application.

Many projects must also address the process and control technology considerations of package process units. These units are pre-engineered packages that supply both the process and control technology for a plant system. These systems should be required to meet the same level of detail design specifications as the project-engineered systems. How these systems interface with the rest of the control technology is important.

A detailed design is represented by several design information packages. These individual packages tend to be highly interrelated. The types of design documentation include:

- P&ID
- Loop diagrams
- Electrical schematics
- Panel layouts
- Sequence control description
- Graphical User Interface (GUI) descriptions
- Implementation standards

For chemical process control, the P&ID traditionally contained the functional specification of the plant controls. However, modern control strategies are too complex to adequately represent on the P&ID. The P&ID still represents the measurement and final control systems, but many projects use other representations for the higher level controls.

The measurement and final control systems are still largely distinct components that must be wired to the controllers. Loop diagrams and electrical schematics provide the interconnect details for implementation and installation.

If procedural control automation is required, a sequence description is prepared. This sequence description provides the instructions for programming the controllers to provide the required level of automation.

The user interface is defined by panel layout drawings if field operation is required. In current computer-based systems, a description of the GUI is prepared. The GUI description is a critical but often overlooked design statement. The user interface is the most important aspect of a control system design. The best control strategy will fail if the user interface is not utilized.

Overall, one should minimize "reinventing" the wheel. If there is a design, or part of a design, that has proven itself, do not reengineer it. More importantly, there should be a system of capturing reusable strategies that can be shared in an enterprise.

21.2.4 Implementation

The implementation phase involves the procurement of the measurement and final control hardware and the control system hardware with its embedded software. It also includes the configuration and programming of the programmable logic controllers and the graphical user interfaces according to the detail design. This activity is complete after the system is verified in system testing. As part of this system testing, the system may be "staged," or set up in a temporary facility, to more completely test the system before installation.

The implementation of the system architecture requires hardware considerations such as power, grounding, wiring, and protection. The degree of concern is a function of the actual site environment of a process plant.

Standard code to implement sequential and device control plays an important role in the implementation phase. Encapsulating standard control functions in a function block is one means to this goal. At the very least, standard ladder logic code segments should be saved in a library for reuse. Section 12.4 presents standard code examples.

The final step in the implementation activity is to verify the correct operation of the system. It begins with module testing followed by preliminary system testing by the implementation team. More detail about this testing is presented in section 21.5.

21.2.5 Installation

Installation is the activity that situates and powers the system at the plant site. This activity includes the interconnection wiring and system interconnection check-out. Each measurement and final control device is checked. The PLC system and operator interfaces are made operational to help in this effort.

After measurement and final control system wring-out, the control system performance is checked to make sure communication over the network is acceptable. Once system operation is checked and the installation is verified, the system is ready for commissioning.

21.2.6 Commissioning

For this phase, each plant system is brought on-line and the system is checked to make sure it works as required to support the operation of the process technology. The initial control settings are established and the system is readied for the first production run. At this point, the system is ready to make product. For a chemical process, this phase is usually done in conjunction with verifying the process technology. The combination is commonly called water testing or first chemical testing.

21.2.7 First Production Startup and Turnover

With the previous step, the control engineering team should have demonstrated that the control requirements have been met and the system is ready to be used. As the first production begins, at least some of the engineering team should remain with the system. The operating personnel should be running the process while the engineers monitor the performance and operation. The transition from the engineering team to the operating team is critical to the successful completion of the project. After the operating personnel take ownership, the project can be declared finished. The only activity left is to make sure the design information package is updated to an as-built state and turned over to the production and maintenance personnel.

21.2.8 Training

During the latter stages of the implementation activity, training of the plant personnel that must use the system should start. Training activities proceed from this point to the end of the project and may extend beyond the end of the project as new personnel join the organization. Engineers, operators, supervisors, management, and maintenance personnel all need to be trained to use the new system. Of course, the type of training differs according to the position and duties of the personnel. If a staged system was developed for testing, it often plays an important role in training operators since an emergency situation can be simulated on the staged system without fear of actual equipment damage or personnel injury if the operator makes a mistake.

21.3 EXAMPLE CONTROL REQUIREMENTS DEFINITION

As an example CRD (Erickson and Hedrick, 1999), consider the pulp and paper mill site shown in Figure 21.4 divided into plant areas and process cells. The woodyard cell in divided into units as shown in Figure 21.5. This example develops the process operation

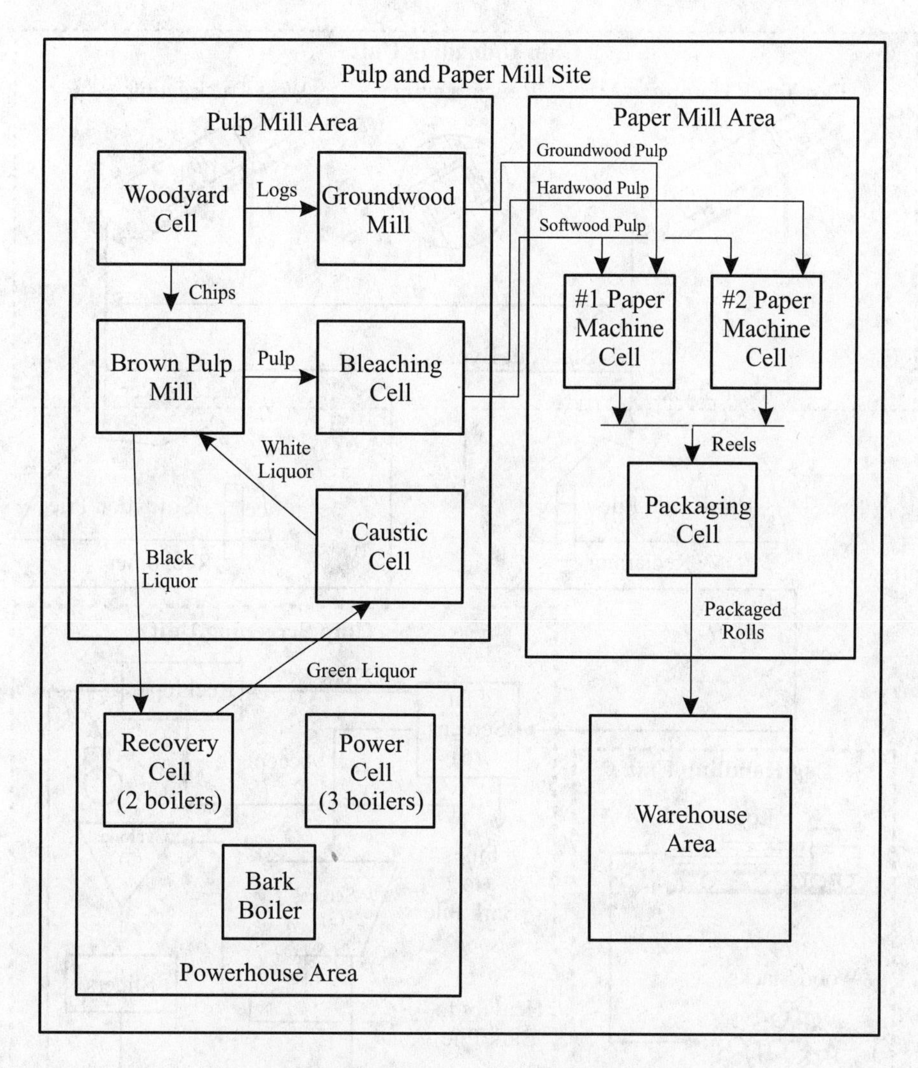

Figure 21.4. Plant areas and cells for paper plant.

description, control concept, and the control strategy for the chip unloading unit of the woodyard cell.

21.3.1 Process Operation Description

Purchased chips are unloaded from one of two truck dumps or a rail dump. The truck dumps operate by tilting the truck-trailer, allowing the chips to fall out into a hopper, where the chips are conveyed to a destination (pile or chip processing unit). The rail dump is a rotary dumper that rotates the wood chip car, causing the chips to fall into a dump pit, and the chips are conveyed to the destination. The east truck dump is used only for hardwood chips and the west truck dump is used only for softwood chips. The chips from the railcar dump can be conveyed to either chip pile. In addition, a bypass path exists for the chips to be conveyed directly to the screening unit.

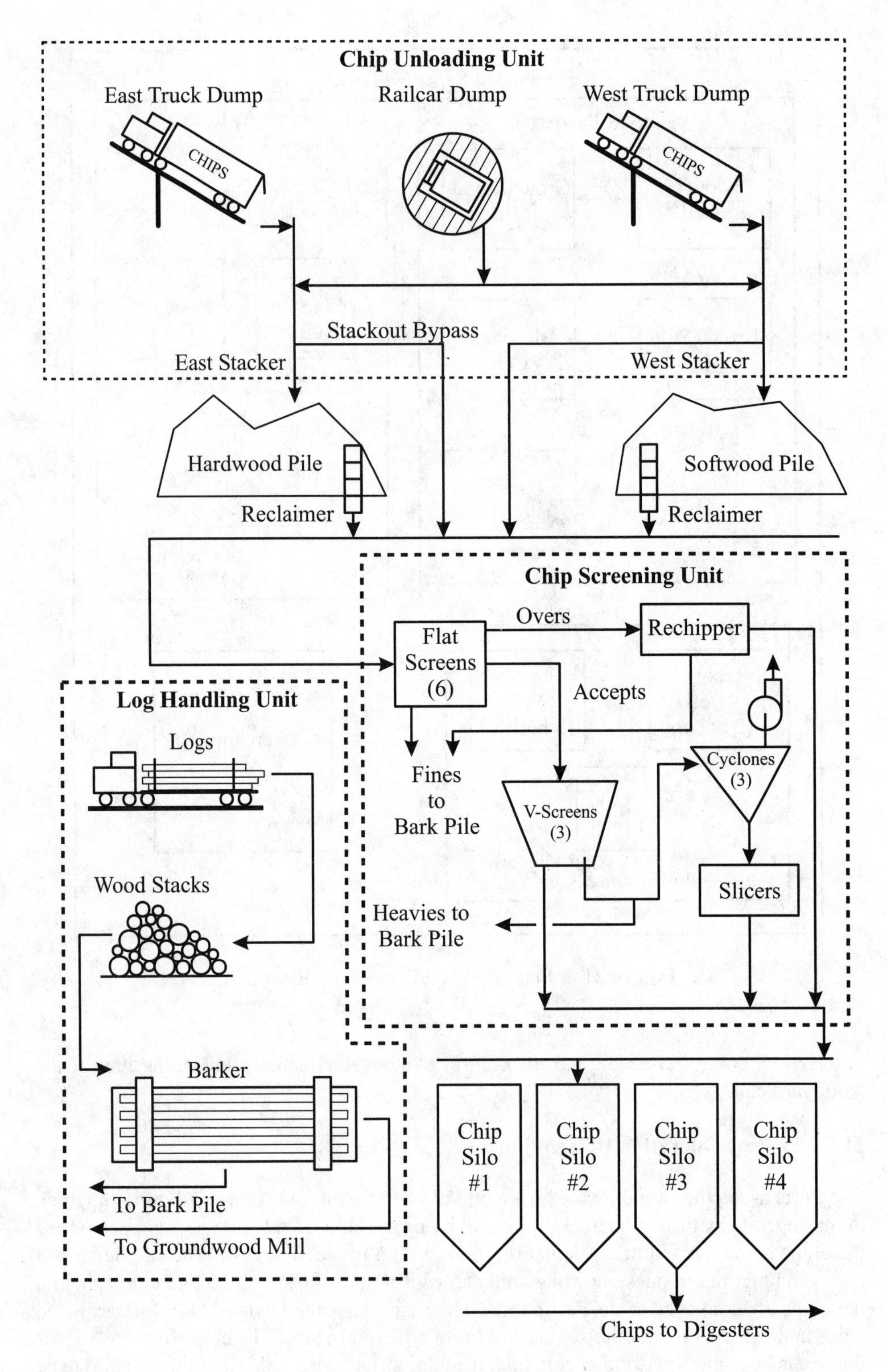

Figure 21.5. Woodyard cell.

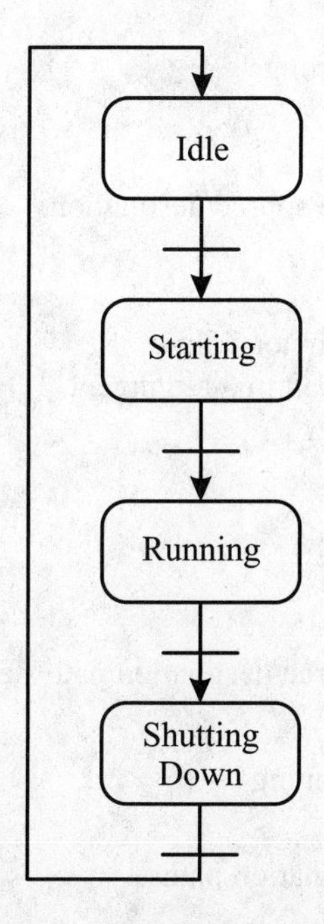

Figure 21.6. Chip unloading unit operating states.

The primary control objective of the chip unloading unit is to convey wood chips from one of three sources (east/west truck dump or rail dump) to one of three destinations (hardwood/softwood pile or screening unit). The operating states of this unit are shown in Figure 21.6:

Idle
Starting
Running
Shutting Down

Normal operation is continuous in order to supply the chip processing unit (if running) or the softwood and hardwood piles. The states are described as follows:

Operating State Name : Idle

Routine Activities
Clean equipment as needed.
Perform inspection.

Exception Handling
None.

Primary Control Objectives
None.

Performance Information
None.

State End Conditions
Startup requested.

Operating State Name : Starting

Routine Activities

Prestart checks.

Start conveyors for a source/destination.

Exception Handling

Shutdown if:

Conveyor motor failure.

Conveyor belt mis-alignment.

Primary Control Objectives

None.

Performance Information

None.

State End Conditions

Conveyors for a source/destination path started.

Operating State Name : Running

Routine Activities

Starting source/destination paths.

Exception Handling

Shutdown if:

Conveyor motor failure.

Conveyor belt mis-alignment.

High level on a dump station.

High chip pile level.

Primary Control Objectives

None.

Performance Information

Chips unloaded per shift.

State End Conditions

Shutdown requested.

Operating State Name : Shutting Down

Routine Activities

Shutdown all source/destination path conveyors.

Exception Handling

None.

Primary Control Objectives

None.

Performance Information

None.

State End Conditions

All conveyors stopped.

21.3.2 Control Concept

Chip Unloading Unit Supervision

Extent of Automation

Provide control of dump stations.

Provide automatic startup, shutdown, and path changes for the transfer of chips from the dump stations.

Collect performance data (tons of softwood and hardwood chips unloaded per shift).

Flexibility of Automation

None.

Control Activity Coordination

Path selection equipment modules will interact.

Interaction with Operating Personnel

Operators control raise/lowering of truck dump stations at the station.

Operators control rail dump stations at the station.

Chip path selection done by operator. Interlocks prevent illegal selections.

Display status information from control modules.

21.3.3 Control Strategy

The individual conveyor devices are controlled by the conveyor path equipment modules. The conveyor path equipment modules are:

1. East truck dump to hardwood pile
2. East truck dump to screening unit
3. West truck dump to softwood pile
4. West truck dump to screening unit
5. Railcar dump to hardwood pile
6. Railcar dump to softwood pile
7. Railcar dump to screening unit via east conveyor
8. Railcar dump to screening unit via west conveyor

Each conveyor path equipment module has a startup and a shutdown phase that starts/stops the individual conveyor devices. The conveyor paths share the individual conveyor devices.

When a path is started, the equipment is started in backward order. For example, the last conveyor in a path is started first. When a path is shutdown, the equipment is stopped so that all material on a conveyor is removed before that conveyor is stopped.

Certain paths are allowed to be running simultaneously. For example, when path 1 is running, paths 3, 4, 6, or 8 are allowed to be started. For a given source, its destination may be changed, but only after sufficient time has elapsed after the end of a dump to allow the material to be cleared off the conveyors of the currently selected path.

If the chip processing unit is shutdown while it is a destination, the conveyor path is immediately set to send the chips to the appropriate chip pile. For example, if path 2 is currently running, the path is immediately changed to path 1.

Devices

East truck dump table:
Raise/lower by operator.

East truck dump gate:
Open/close by operator.

East truck dump chocks:
Raise/lower by operator.

West truck dump table:
Raise/lower by operator.

West truck dump gate:
Open/close by operator.

West truck dump chocks:
Raise/lower by operator.

Railcar dump clamps:
Raise/lower by operator.

Railcar rotary dumper:
Rotate/back by operator.

East conveyor:
Start/stop by path equipment modules or operator.

West conveyor:
Start/stop by path equipment modules or operator.

Traverse conveyor:
Start/stop by path equipment modules or operator.

Railcar dump conveyor:
Start/stop by path equipment modules or operator.

East stackout bypass conveyor:
Start/stop by path equipment modules or operator.

West stackout bypass conveyor:
Start/stop by path equipment modules or operator.

Interlocks

Do not allow start of path equipment module if destination pile too high.

Do not allow start of path 2 if chip screening unit not running or running but processing softwood chips.

Do not allow start of path 4 if chip screening unit not running or running but processing hardwood chips.

Do not allow truck dump gate to open until an appropriate path is running.

Do not allow rail dump gate to open until an appropriate path is running.

Do not allow a truck dump to be raised until an appropriate path is running.

Do not allow rail dump to be rotated until an appropriate path is running.

Backward startup and forward shutdown is enforced even when manually controlled by the operator.

If a downstream conveyor is stopped because of a failure, the upstream conveyors are emergency-stopped.

21.4 STANDARDIZATION

In any project, there should be standard ways of performing many project tasks. This standardization becomes apparent in the documentation and in the PLC program. It is a sign of good engineering practice. Regardless of who actually produced one section of the POD, it should appear very similar to any other section. The sequence diagrams should also be similar in appearance. The code that implements the control of similar devices should look similar, if not nearly identical. Variable names should also follow a naming convention. The importance of standardization is apparent to those that must support an installed system. Knowing how a system is documented and how the code is structured makes the task much easier. In addition, personnel can be easily moved between projects with little loss in productivity.

Standardizing the control of common devices should be a requirement for any project. One way of standardizing control functions is to encapsulate them as a function block. This approach is illustrated in Chapter 11 with discrete valve and motor control. This approach is not currently possible with the Allen-Bradley and GE Fanuc PLCs.

For the PLC-5 and SLC-500 PLCs, one can save (export) a ladder logic code segment to an external file. For the PLC-5, the name of this file has the ".PC5" extension and for the SLC-500, this file has the ".SLC" extension. This code can then be imported into a different program or re-imported into the same program. During the import operation, one can define a *fixup table* to change the data addresses in the imported program to new addresses to avoid addressing conflicts. Using the fixup table avoids the need to do a "search and replace" on the imported ladder logic code, though the symbols and descriptions of these addresses must be imported separately.

Starting with revision 13, the ControlLogix programming software supports saving (exporting) code segments in libraries. Each library has an ".L5X" extension and is a text file. If needed, a text editor is used to modify the tags and descriptions before importing the library into a program. Earlier versions of the programming software did not support libraries, making the process of encapsulating and duplicating standard code more difficult. For the earlier versions, the ladder logic, structured text, or function block diagrams to be duplicated are saved in a separate routine in order to easily identify them. The entire project is saved as a file with the ".L5K" extension. This file is a text file and so can be modified with a text editor. With a text editor, the code to be duplicated and the associated tags are saved to another file, becoming a library. To import the code, one must use a text editor to paste the library into the project L5K file. The tags must be placed in the "tag section" of the L5K file and the routine must be placed in the appropriate program. The "search and replace" feature of the text editor must be used to change the tags of the imported code to the appropriate ones.

For the GE Fanuc PLCs, only IL and C blocks can be exported to an external file. These blocks can then be imported into a different program or re-imported into the same program. After importing the block, one must do a "search and replace" on the imported code to avoid addressing conflicts.

21.4.1 Standard Device Control

The following devices are used to illustrate standard device control:

Example 21.1	On/off motor device
Example 21.2	Variable speed drive on network
Example 21.3	Discrete (on/off) valve

Example 21.1. *Typical motor device.* The bulk of this example will concern the control aspects of this device. However, in order to present a complete picture of this device, the control objective and concept that lead to the control strategy are described.

Control Objective: To move material from tank T-110 to tank T-120.

Control Concept: Because tank T-120 is at a higher level than T-110, a pump must be employed to move the material. Figure 21.7 shows the device tag, EX100, associated with the pump. The pump needs to be started and stopped automatically by sequence steps or manually by an operator.

Control Strategy: To start and stop the motor in the manual or automatic control state. Stop the motor on failure conditions. Generate overload fail alarm, auxiliary fail alarm, and HOA-switch-not-in-Auto indications.

The device has two control states: Manual and Automatic, shown in Figure 21.8. The control state determines the source of the commands to start and stop the motor. In the Manual control state, the motor may only be started or stopped by the operator. In the Automatic control state, the motor may only be started or stopped by steps in automatic sequences. Switching between the Manual and Automatic control state should not change the operating state (running or stopped) of the motor. The operational states of the equipment are shown in Figure 21.9. The Failed state is entered from any of the other states.

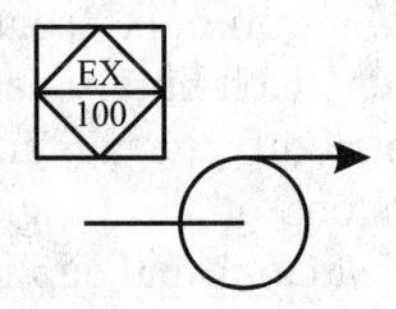

Figure 21.7. P&ID symbol for motor device control associated with pump.

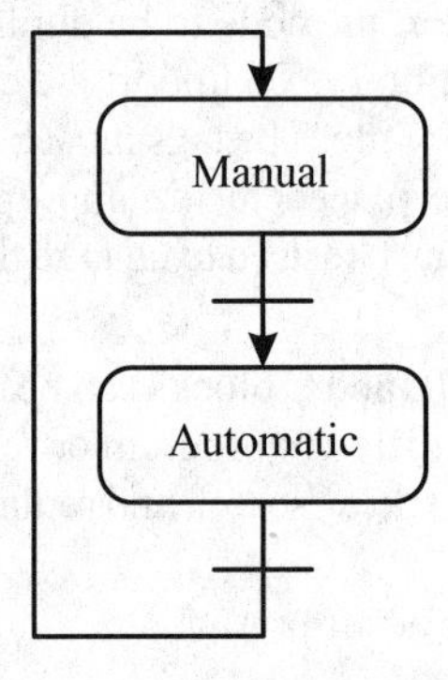

Figure 21.8. Control states of motor and valve devices.

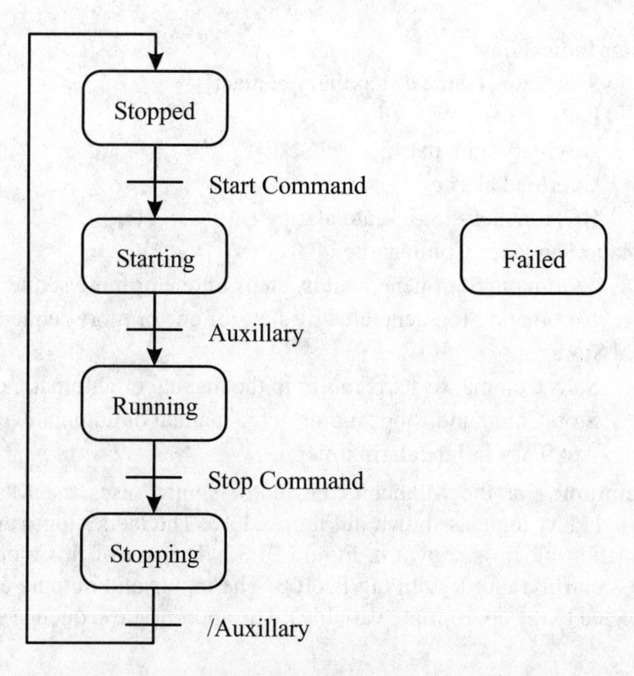

Figure 21.9. Operational states of motor device.

The auxiliary fail alarm must not be generated until 20 seconds has elapsed after the motor contactor has been closed and the auxiliary contact has not closed. Provisions must be made to allow the operator to reset the auxiliary fail alarm indication.

Process System Items

Motor Starter (contactor or motor control center)
Hand-Off-Auto (HOA) switch
Overload indicator
Auxiliary contact

Detail Design:

Physical Inputs:

Auxiliary contact (on when motor running)
Overload trip (on when motor overloaded)
HOA switch auto contact (on when auto contact is closed)

Physical Outputs:

Starter (on to start/run motor)

Operator Commands:

Manual Start
Manual Stop
Manual/Automatic control state
Reset alarm

Operator Indications:
- Run status (same as auxiliary contact)
- Failure alarm
- Auxiliary Fail alarm
- Overload alarm
- HOA-switch-not-in-auto alarm

Automatic Sequence Commands:
- Automatic Start generated by steps of one or more sequences
- Automatic Stop generated by steps of one or more sequences

Internal Storage:
- Start Command, starts motor in the manual or automatic control state
- Stop Command, stops motor in the manual or automatic control state
- Auxiliary failure alarm timer

Implementation: For the Modicon, the motor control uses the MOTOR derived function block in ladder logic as shown in Figure 21.10. The ladder logic that implements this derived function block is shown in Figure 11.32. The use of this block is shown in Figure 21.10 to control a motor with tag EX100. The inputs and outputs of the MOTOR block are connected to the appropriate variables. The appropriate sequence step latches the

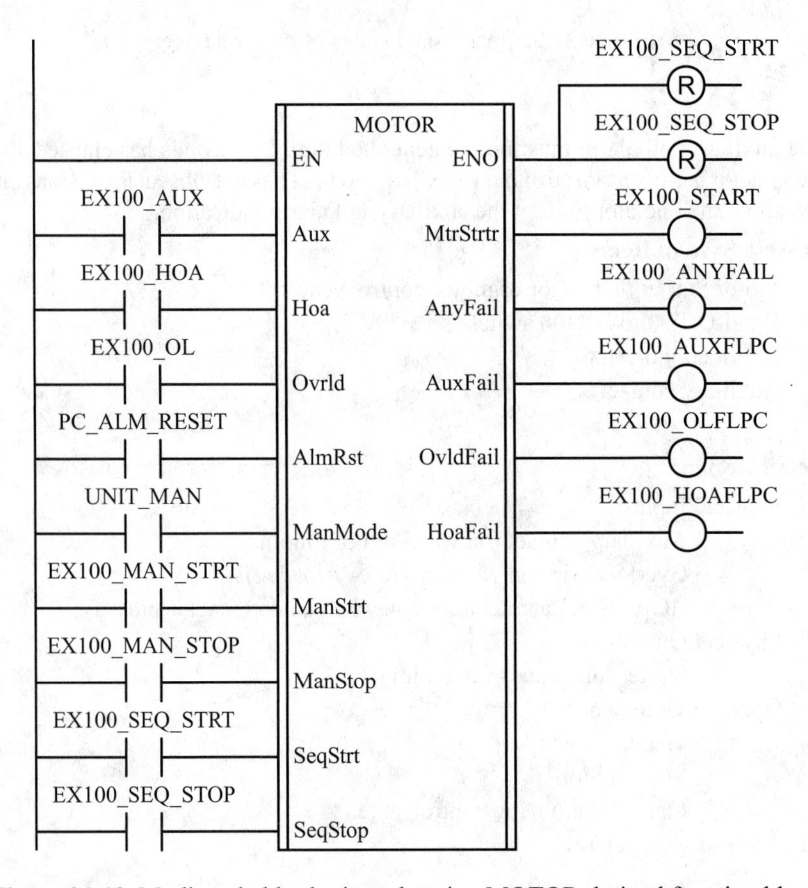

Figure 21.10. Modicon ladder logic code using MOTOR derived function block.

EX100_SEQ_STRT or EX100_SEQ_STOP internal coil to control the motor. These two internal coils are always unlatched after the block executes. Alternatively, contacts referring to the individual sequence steps that start the motor could be placed in parallel and connected to the SeqStrt input connection. However, if an additional step starts the motor, the program must be changed here as well as in the sequence. The approach used here allows one to change the steps that control a motor without having to change the logic at the motor control function block. The manual control state, shown here as specific to this motor, may be the state for a grouping of equipment. For example, the manual control state may be defined for the group of the pumps and valves associated with a reactor.

This motor control is implemented in ladder logic for the PLC-5 in Figure 21.11. The ladder logic code for a ControlLogix PLC is very similar. The first rung controls the physical output that drives the motor contactor (or motor starter). Note that the motor is turned **off** on the first scan of the ladder, when there is an overload, or when any failure occurs. Though an overload also causes the EX100_ANYFAIL to turn on, it is placed on the first rung so that an overload immediately turns **off** the motor, rather than waiting one scan for the EX100_ANYFAIL. The start and stop internal coils to drive the motor contactor are determined by the second and third rungs. In these two rungs, the operator generates the start and stop commands when the control is in the manual state. When the control is in the automatic state (not manual state), the motor is started and stopped by steps in the various sequences (function charts). The appropriate step latches the EX100_SEQ_START or EX100_SEQ_STOP internal coil to control the motor. These two internal coils are always unlatched by this ladder logic. The reason for this method of sequence-based control was explained in conjunction with the Modicon PLC. The manual control state is usually the state for a grouping of equipment. The fourth rung delays checking for the auxiliary fail alarm until 20 seconds after the motor is started. The first branch of the fifth rung generates the auxiliary fail alarm. This alarm must be latched since this failure will cause the output to the starter to be turned off, thus disabling the conditions for this alarm. The second and third branches of the fifth rung generate the overload fail alarm and the indication that the HOA switch is not in the auto position. The sixth rung generates one summary failure indication that would appear on an alarm summary screen. The seventh rung resets the auxiliary failure

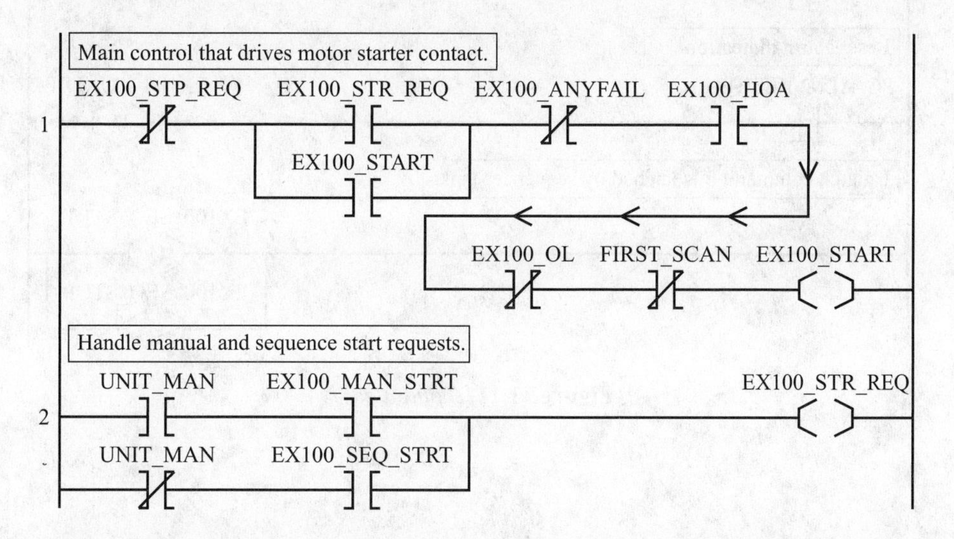

Figure 21.11. PLC-5 ladder logic code for on/off motor device control. *(continued)*

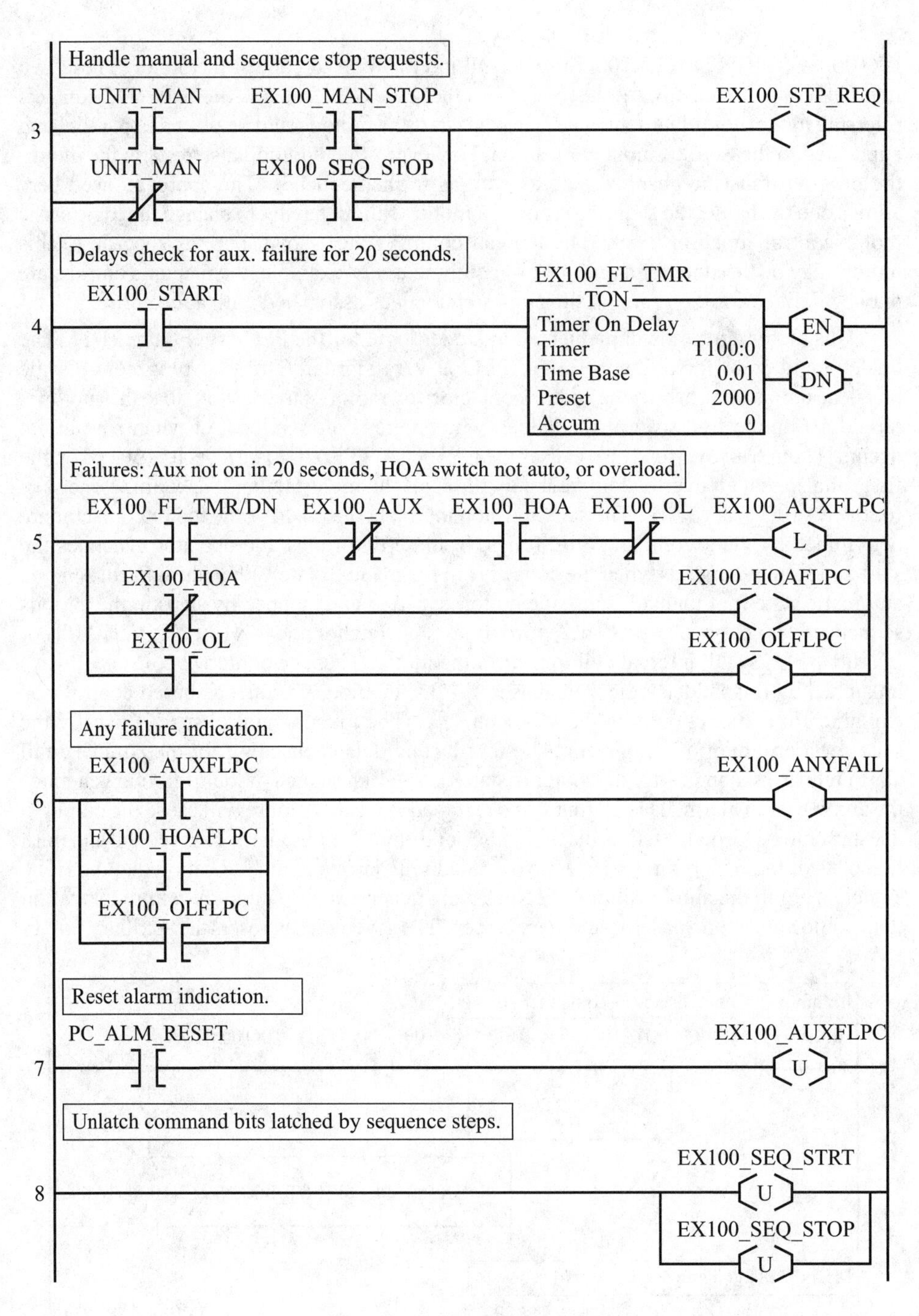

Figure 21.11. *(continued)*

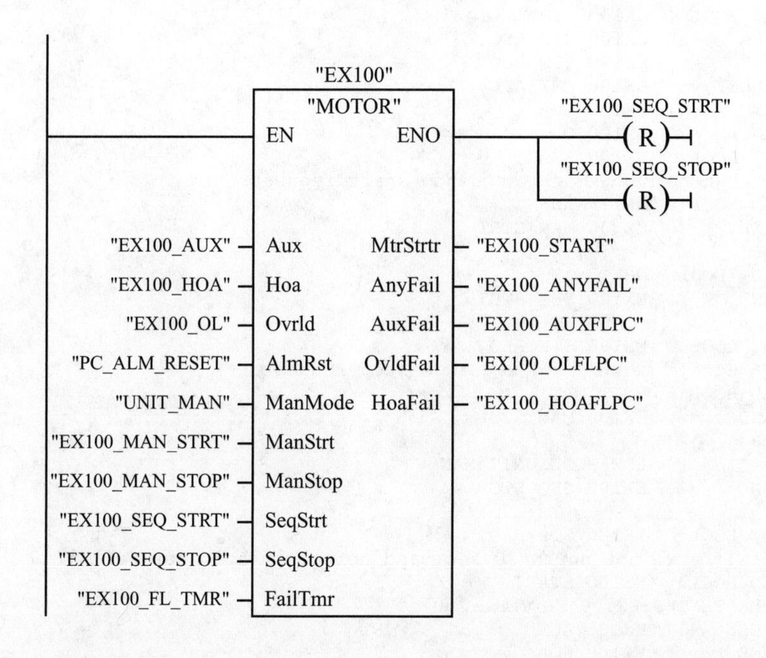

Figure 21.12. S7 ladder logic code using MOTOR function block.

alarm so that another start attempt is allowed. As for the manual/auto control state, the reset may be for a group of equipment, rather than specific to each device. The last rung unlatches the sequential control commands.

A Siemens S7 implementation (Figure 21.12) uses the MOTOR function block (FB) whose ladder logic implementation is shown in Figure 11.33. An instruction list block for a GE Fanuc PLC is shown in Figure 21.13.

A possible operator interface faceplate for this device is shown in Figure 21.14. In a typical system, this faceplate is invoked from an operator screen that shows all of the devices in a unit, for example, a packaging machine.

Assume the following input, output, and internal symbols.

Variable	Description
EX100_AUX	Auxiliary contact.
EX100_OL	Overload contact.
EX100_HOA	HOA switch auto contact.
EX100_START	Motor contactor.
EX100_MAN_STRT	Motor start request from operator.
EX100_MAN_STOP	Motor stop request from operator.
UNIT_MAN	Manual/auto control state for unit: **on** for manual, **off** for auto.
PC_ALM_RESET	Alarm reset from operator interface.
EX100_ANYFAIL	Indicates any failure to operator.
EX100_AUXFLPC	Motor auxiliary failure indication to operator interface.

```
(* Main control that drives motor starter contact *)
LD_BOOL    EX100_START
OR         EX100_STR_REQ
ANDN       EX100_STP_REQ
ANDN       EX100_ANYFAIL
AND        EX100_HOA
ANDN       EX100_OL
ST_BOOL    EX100_START
(* Handle manual and sequence start requests *)
LD_BOOL    UNIT_MAN
AND        EX100_MAN_STRT
OR(
LDN_BOOL   UNIT_MAN
AND        EX100_SEQ_STRT
)
ST_BOOL    EX100_STR_REQ
(* Handle manual and sequence stop requests *)
LD_BOOL    UNIT_MAN
AND        EX100_MAN_STOP
OR(
           LDN_BOOL UNIT_MAN
AND        EX100_SEQ_STOP
)
ST_BOOL    EX100_STP_REQ
(* If aux. not on in 20 sec. and not ol or hoa, set fail *)
LD_BOOL    EX100_START
TMR_TENTHS(EX100_FL_TMR, 200)
ANDN       EX100_AUX
AND        EX100_HOA
ANDN       EX100_OL
S          EX100_AUXFLPC
(* Generate HOA and overload fail indications *)
LDN_BOOL   EX100_HOA
ST_BOOL    EX100_HOAFLPC
LD_BOOL    EX100_OL
ST_BOOL    EX100_OLFLPC
(* Any failure indication *)
LD_BOOL    EX100_AUXFLPC
OR         EX100_HOAFLPC
OR         EX100_OLFLPC
ST_BOOL    EX100_ANYFAIL
(* Reset alarm indication *)
LD_BOOL    PC_ALM_RESET
R          EX100_AUXFLPC
(* Unlatch command bits latched by sequence steps *)
LD_BOOL    #ALW_ON
R          EX100_SEQ_STRT
R          EX100_SEQ_STOP
```

Figure 21.13. GE Fanuc instruction list code for on/off motor device control.

EX100_OLFLPC	Motor overload failure indication to operator interface.
EX100_HOAFLPC	Motor HOA-switch-not-in-auto indication to operator interface.
EX100_SEQ_STRT	Motor start request from sequence.
EX100_SEQ_STOP	Motor stop request from sequence.
EX100_STR_REQ	Motor start request.
EX100_STP_REQ	Motor stop request.
EX100_FL_TMR	Times auxiliary failure.

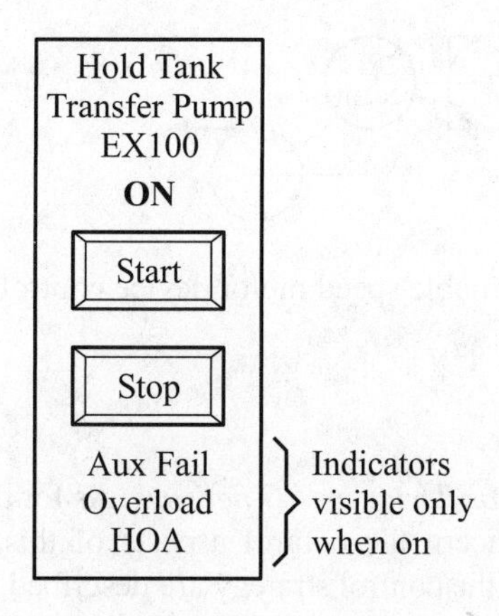

Figure 21.14. Faceplate for on/off motor device control.

The addresses associated with the physical inputs and outputs are:

Variable	Modicon	PLC-5	ControlLogix	Siemens	GE Fanuc
EX100_AUX	%100001	I:01/00	Local:1:I.Data.0	I4.0	%I1
EX100_OL	%100002	I:01/01	Local:1:I.Data.1	I4.1	%I2
EX100_HOA	%100003	I:01/02	Local:1:I.Data.2	I4.2	%I3
EX100_START	%000001	O:04/00	Local:4:O.Data.0	Q8.0	%Q1

The addresses or data types associated with the internal variables:

	Modicon	PLC-5	ControlLogix	Siemens	GE Fanuc
Variable	Data Type	Addr.	Data Type	Addr.	Addr.
EX100_MAN_STRT	BOOL	N13:1/0	BOOL	M101.0	%M217
EX100_MAN_STOP	BOOL	N13:1/1	BOOL	M101.1	%M218
UNIT_MAN	BOOL	N13:0/0	BOOL	M100.0	%M201
PC_ALM_RESET	BOOL	B44/0	BOOL	M20.1	%M50
EX100_ANYFAIL	BOOL	N21:0/0	BOOL	M201.0	%M301
EX100_AUXFLPC	BOOL	N21:0/1	BOOL	M201.1	%M302
EX100_OLFLPC	BOOL	N21:0/2	BOOL	M201.2	%M303
EX100_HOAFLPC	BOOL	N21:0/3	BOOL	M201.3	%M304
EX100_SEQ_STRT	BOOL	N13:1/2	BOOL	M101.2	%M219
EX100_SEQ_STOP	BOOL	N13:1/3	BOOL	M101.3	%M220
EX100_STR_REQ	n/a	B40/0	BOOL	DB7.DBX6.0	%M401
EX100_STP_REQ	n/a	B40/1	BOOL	DB7.DBX6.1	%M402
EX100_FL_TMR	n/a	T100:0	TIMER	T41	%R301

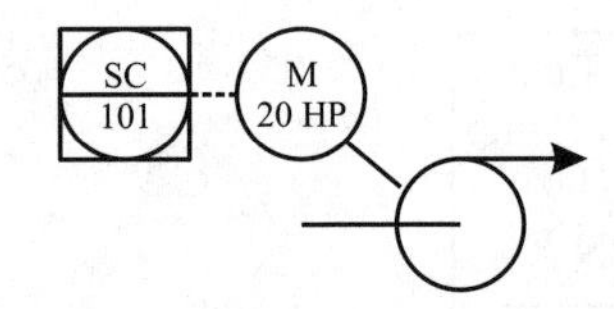

Figure 21.15. P&ID symbol for variable speed motor device control associated with pump.

Example 21.2. *Variable speed motor device on I/O network.* As for the previous example, the bulk of this example will concern the control aspects of this device. The control objective and concept that leads to the control strategy are described.

Control Objective: To feed material to reactor tank T-140.

Control Concept: In order to control feed rate, a variable-speed pump must be employed to move the material. Figure 21.15 shows the device tag, SC101, associated with the pump. The pump needs to be started and stopped automatically by sequence step or manually by the operator. The operator controls the motor speed in the manual control state. When under sequence control, the pump speed is controlled by the sequence. The variable-speed drive for the pump is a node on a DeviceNet network.

Control Strategy: To start and stop the motor in the manual or automatic control state. Set the motor speed in the manual or automatic control state. Stop the motor on failure conditions. Generate drive fault alarm, fail-to-run alarm, and DeviceNet node fault alarm indications; drive fault code; drive current; and drive speed indications.

The device has two control states: Manual and Automatic, shown in Figure 21.8. The control state determines the source of the commands to start the motor, stop the motor, and control the motor speed. In the Manual control state, the motor may only be started or stopped by the operator. In the Automatic control state, the motor may only be started or stopped by steps in automatic sequences. Switching between the Manual and Automatic control state should not change the operating state (running or stopped) of the motor. The operational states of the equipment are shown in Figure 21.9, except that the Auxiliary indication is replaced by a Running indication from the drive. The Failed state is entered from any of the other states.

The fail-to-run alarm must not be generated until 20 seconds has elapsed after the drive start command has been sent to the drive and the drive running indication has not turned on. Provisions must be made to allow the operator to reset the fail-to-run alarm indication.

Process System Items

Variable speed drive (VSD) as a DeviceNet node

Detail Design:

Inputs from VSD:

Drive enabled (on when VSD enabled)
Running (on when motor running)
Faulted (on when drive faulted)

Motor speed (0-32,767, represents 0-100%)
Motor current (0-32,767, represents 0-50 amps)
Fault code (valid when drive faulted)
DeviceNet node faulted (on when node fault)

Outputs to VSD:

Stop command (on to stop motor)
Start command (on to start/run motor)
Speed reference

Operator Commands:

Manual Start
Manual Stop
Manual/Automatic control state
Desired motor speed
Reset alarm

Operator Indications:

Run status
Failure alarm
Fail-to-run alarm
Drive fault alarm
Drive enabled
DeviceNet node fault alarm
Motor speed (0-100%)
Motor current (0-50 amps)
Drive fault code

Automatic Sequence Commands:

Automatic Start generated by steps of one or more sequences
Automatic Stop generated by steps of one or more sequences
Desired motor speed

Internal Storage:

Start Command, starts motor in the manual or automatic control state
Stop Command, stops motor in the manual or automatic control state
Motor run request
Fail-to-run alarm timer

Implementation: The motor control is implemented in ladder logic within a PLC, as shown in Figure 21.16 for the PLC-5. The ladder logic code for a ControlLogix PLC is very similar. In addition, an implementation for a Modicon or a GE Fanuc PLC is similar.

The code is similar to the code for the on/off motor with additional logic to handle the commands to the VSD and status from the VSD. A DeviceNet scanner is already set up so that addresses N23:1 to N23:4 are from the VSD and addresses N24:1 to N24:4 are to the VSD. The first rung controls the internal run request that is translated the start or stop command sent to the VSD on rungs three and four. The motor is turned off on the first scan of the ladder, or when any failure occurs. The desired speed is converted to the proper units for the VSD in rung two. The start and stop internal coils to drive the motor contactor are determined by the fifth and sixth. These two rungs function in the same manner as rungs two and three in the on/off motor control in Figure 21.11. The seventh rung delays checking for the drive fail-to-run alarm until 20 seconds after the motor is started. The first branch of the eighth rung generates the fail-to-run alarm. This alarm must be latched since this failure will cause a stop command to be issued to the motor, thus disabling the conditions for this alarm. The second and third branches of the eighth rung generate the drive fault and node fault alarms. Rung 9 generates one summary failure indication that would appear on an alarm summary screen. The tenth rung calculates the motor speed and current for display and the eleventh rung copies the drive enabled indicator for the operator display. Rung 12 displays the VSD fault code and rung 13 resets the auxiliary failure alarm so that another start attempt is allowed. The last rung unlatches the sequential control commands.

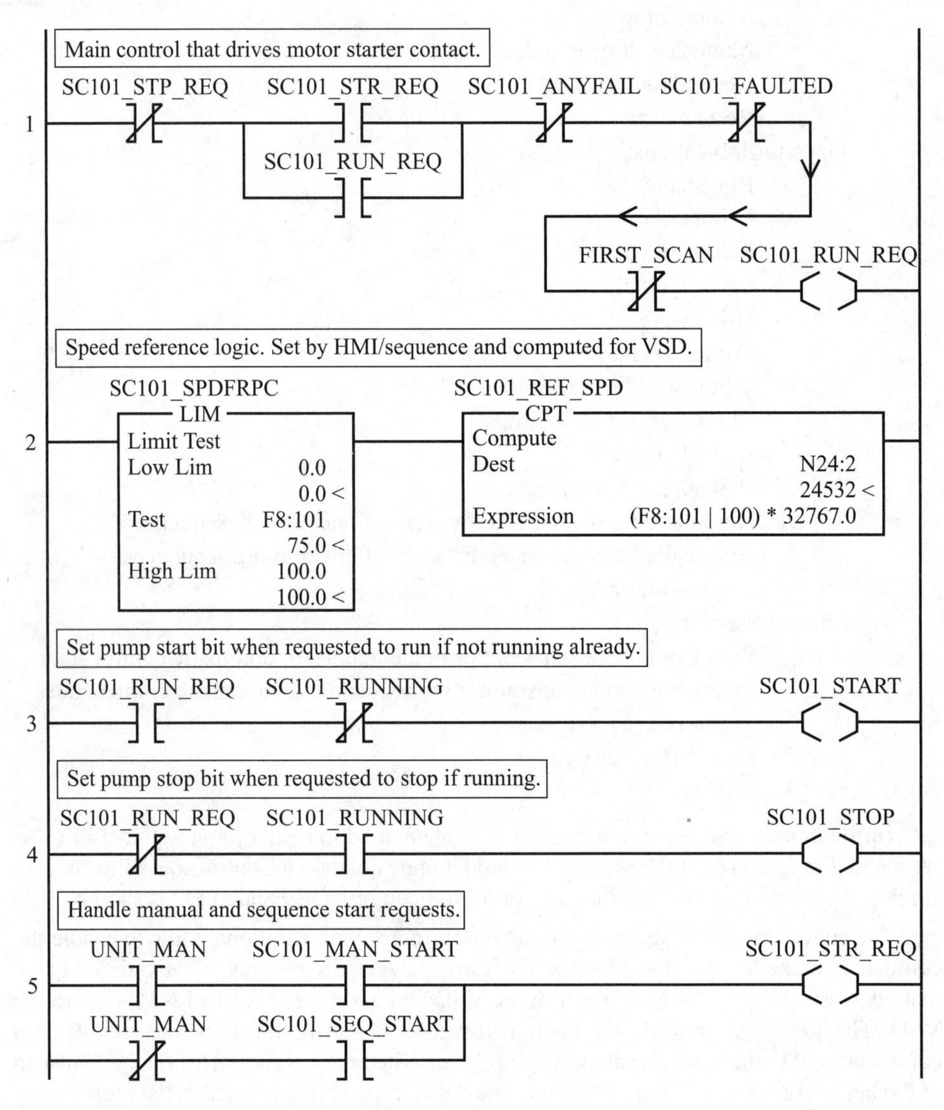

Figure 21.16. PLC-5 ladder logic code for variable speed motor device control. *(continued)*

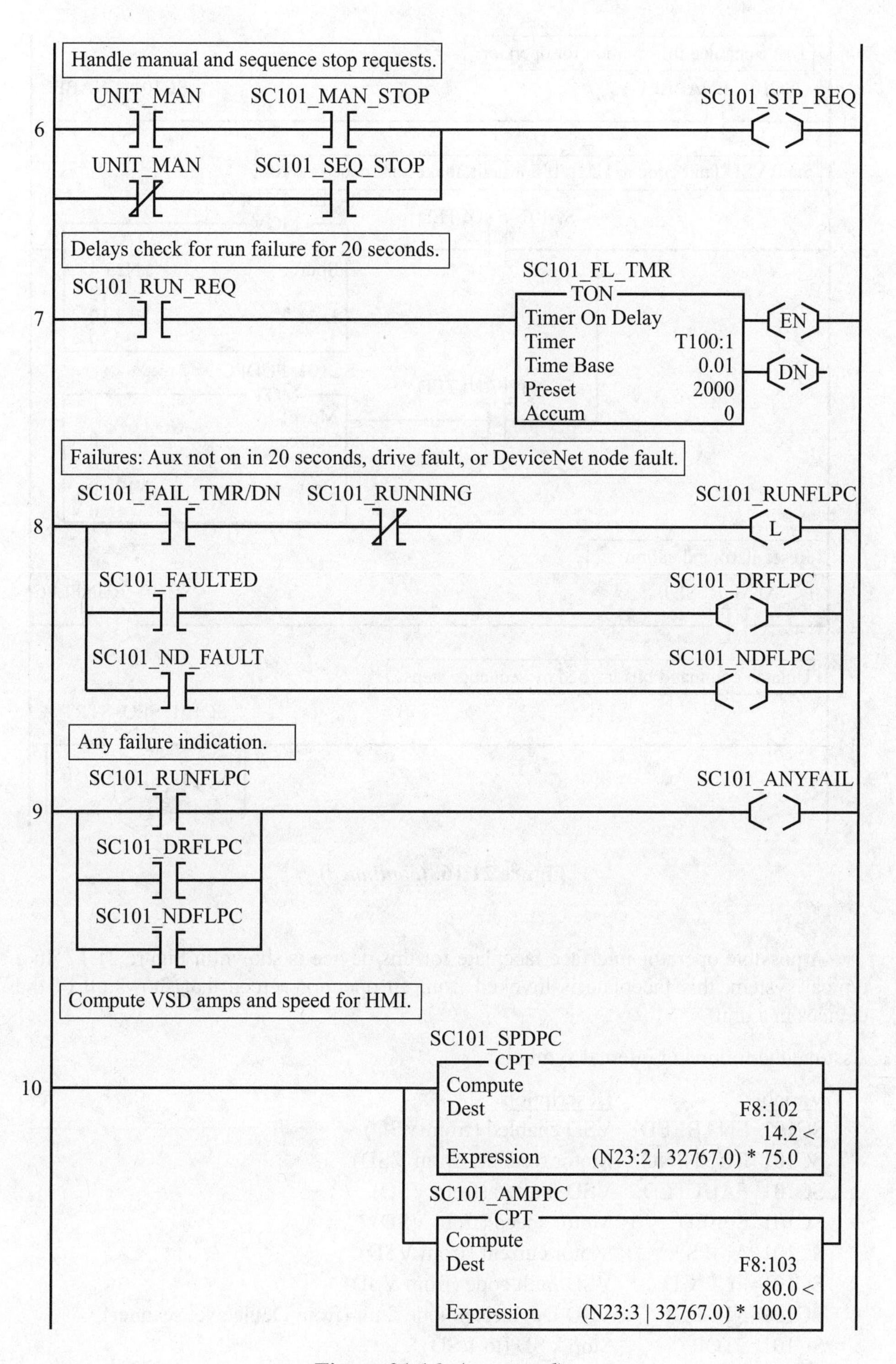

Figure 21.16. *(continued)*

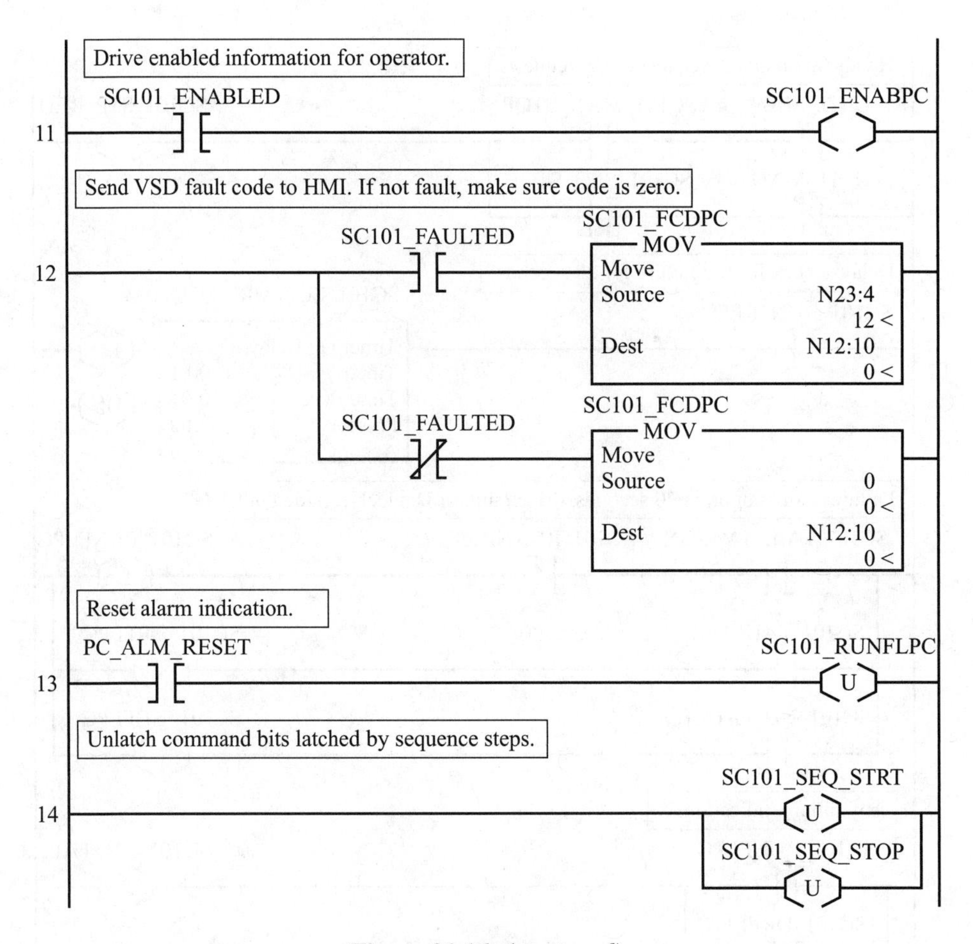

Figure 21.16. *(continued)*

A possible operator interface faceplate for this device is shown in Figure 21.17. In a typical system, this faceplate is invoked from an operator screen that shows all of the devices in a unit.

Assume the following internal symbols.

Variable	Description
SC101_ENABLED	VSD enabled (from VSD).
SC101_RUNNING	Motor running (from VSD).
SC101_FAULTED	VSD faulted (from VSD).
SC101_SPEED	Motor speed (from VSD).
SC101_AMPS	Motor current (from VSD).
SC101_FLT_CD	VSD fault code (from VSD).
SC101_ND_FLT	VSD DeviceNet node fault (from DeviceNet scanner).
SC101_STOP	Stop VSD (to VSD).
SC101_STRT	Start VSD (to VSD).
SC101_REF_SPD	VSD reference speed (to VSD).

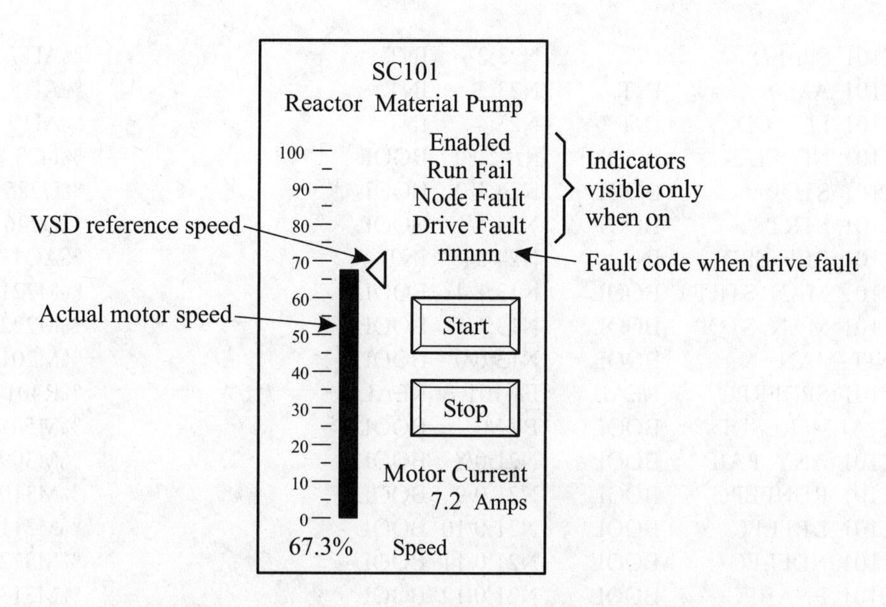

Figure 21.17. Faceplate for variable speed motor device control.

SC101_MAN_STRT	Motor start request from operator.
SC101_MAN_STOP	Motor stop request from operator.
UNIT_MAN	Manual/auto control state for unit: **on** for manual, **off** for auto.
SC101_SPDFRPC	Desired motor speed (from operator/sequence).
PC_ALM_RESET	Alarm reset from operator interface.
SC101_ANYFAIL	Indicates any failure to operator.
SC101_RUNFLPC	Motor fail-to-run failure indication to operator interface.
SC101_DRFLPC	VSD drive fault indication to operator interface.
SC101_NDFLPC	VSD DeviceNet node fault indication to operator interface.
SC101_ENABPC	VSD enabled indication to operator.
SC101_SPDPC	Motor speed to operator interface.
SC101_AMPPC	Motor current to operator interface.
SC101_FCDPC	VSD fault code to operator interface.
SC101_SEQ_STRT	Motor start request from sequence.
SC101_SEQ_STOP	Motor stop request from sequence.
SC101_STR_REQ	Motor start request.
SC101_STP_REQ	Motor stop request.
SC101_RUN_REQ	Motor run request.
SC101_FL_TMR	Times failure to run.

The addresses or data types associated with the internal variables:

Variable	Modicon Data Type	PLC-5 Addr.	ControlLogix Data Type	GE Fanuc Addr.
SC101_ENABLED	BOOL	N23:1/0	BOOL	%I225
SC101_RUNNING	BOOL	N23:1/1	BOOL	%I226
SC101_FAULTED	BOOL	N23:1/7	BOOL	%I231

SC101_SPEED	INT	N23:2	INT	%AI17
SC101_AMPS	INT	N23:3	INT	%AI18
SC101_FLT_CD	INT	N23:4	INT	%AI19
SC101_ND_FLT	BOOL	N23:248/1	BOOL	%I423
SC101_STOP	BOOL	N24:1/0	BOOL	%Q225
SC101_STRT	BOOL	N24:1/1	BOOL	%Q226
SC101_REF_SPD	INT	N24:2	INT	%AQ17
SC101_MAN_STRT	BOOL	N13:1/4	BOOL	%M221
SC101_MAN_STOP	BOOL	N13:1/5	BOOL	%M222
UNIT_MAN	BOOL	N13:0/0	BOOL	%M201
SC101_SPDFRPC	REAL	F8:101	REAL	%R401
PC_ALM_RESET	BOOL	B44/0	BOOL	%M50
SC101_ANY_FAIL	BOOL	N21:0/8	BOOL	%M309
SC101_RUNFLPC	BOOL	N21:0/9	BOOL	%M310
SC101_DRFLPC	BOOL	N21:0/10	BOOL	%M311
SC101_NDFLPC	BOOL	N21:0/11	BOOL	%M312
SC101_ENABPC	BOOL	N21:0/12	BOOL	%M313
SC101_SPDPC	REAL	F8:102	REAL	%R403
SC101_AMPPC	REAL	F8:103	REAL	%R405
SC101_FCDPC	INT	N12:10	INT	%R260
SC101_SEQ_STRT	BOOL	N13:1/6	BOOL	%M223
SC101_SEQ_STOP	BOOL	N13:1/7	BOOL	%M224
SC101_STR_REQ	BOOL	B40/8	BOOL	%M409
SC101_STP_REQ	BOOL	B40/9	BOOL	%M410
SC101_RUN_REQ	BOOL	B40/10	BOOL	%M411
SC101_FL_TMR	n/a	T100:1	TIMER	%R303

Example 21.3. *Typical discrete valve device.* As for the pumps in the two previous examples, the bulk of this example will concern the control aspects of this device. The control objective and concept that leads to the control strategy are described.

Control Objective: To drain the products from reactor, R-140, to storage tank T-150.

Control Concept: Because the reactor is vented and at a higher level than T-150, gravity will be employed to move the material. Figure 21.18 shows the device tag, XV102, associated with the valve. The valve needs to be opened and closed automatically by sequence step or manually by the operator.

Control Strategy: To open and close the valve in the manual or automatic control state. Generate fail-to-open and fail-to-close alarms.

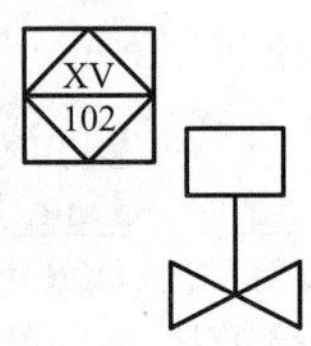

Figure 21.18. P&ID symbol for discrete-valve device control.

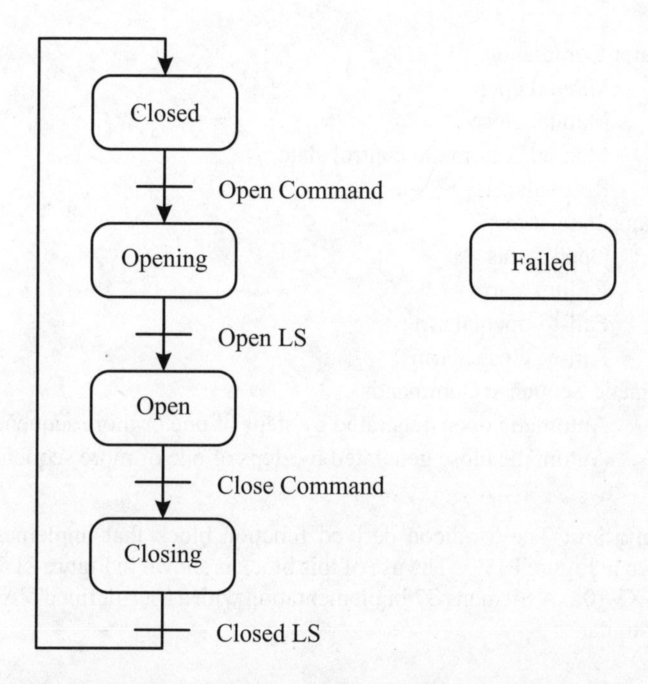

Figure 21.19. Operational states of discrete-valve device.

The device has two control states: Manual and Automatic, shown in Figure 21.8. The control state determines the source of the commands to open and close the valve. In the manual control state, the valve may only be opened or closed by the operator. In the automatic control state, the valve may only be opened or closed by steps in automatic sequences. Switching between the manual and automatic control state should not change the operating state (opened or closed) of the valve. The operational states of the valve are shown in Figure 21.19. The Failed state is entered from any of the other states.

The fail-to-open and fail-to-close alarms must not be generated until 20 seconds has elapsed after the valve has been commanded to open or close and the appropriate limit switch has not closed. Provisions must be made to allow the operator to reset the alarm indications.

Process System Items

Valve solenoid
Valve-open limit switch
Valve-closed limit switch

Detail Design

Physical Inputs:

Valve-open limit switch (**on** when valve fully open)
Valve-closed limit switch (**on** when valve fully closed)

Physical Output:

Valve solenoid (**on** to open the valve)

Operator Commands:
- Manual open
- Manual close
- Manual/Automatic control state
- Reset alarms

Operator Indications:
- Open status
- Failure alarm
- Fail-to-open alarm
- Fail-to-close alarm

Automatic Sequence Commands:
- Automatic open generated by steps of one or more sequences
- Automatic close generated by steps of one or more sequences

Implementation: The Modicon derived function block that implements this valve control is shown in Figure P11.3. The use of this block is shown in Figure 21.20 to control a valve with tag XV102. A Siemens S7 implementation with a user-defined VALVE function block (FB) is similar.

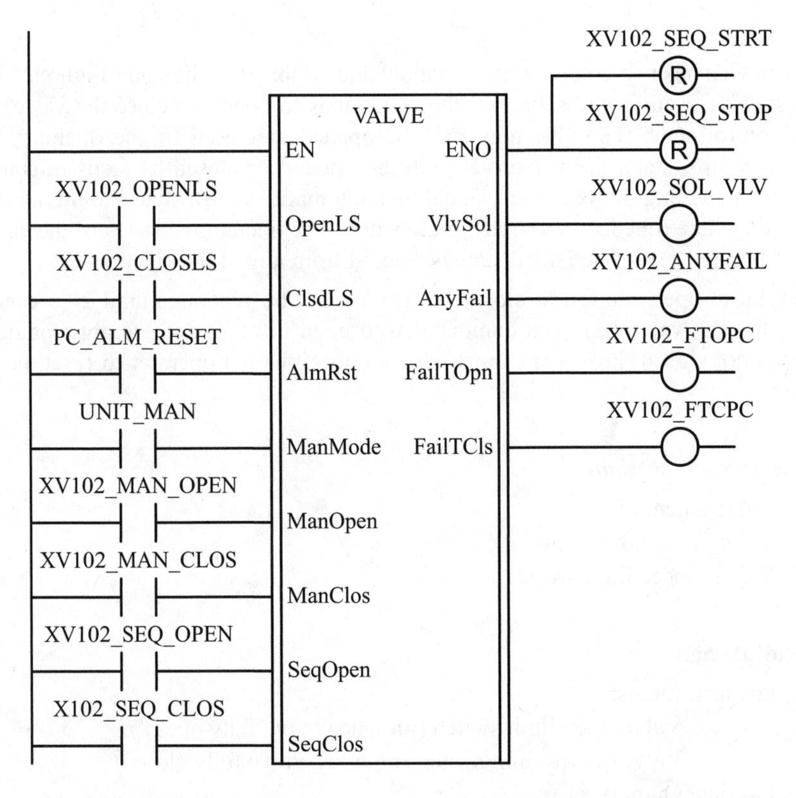

Figure 21.20. Modicon ladder logic code using VALVE derived function block.

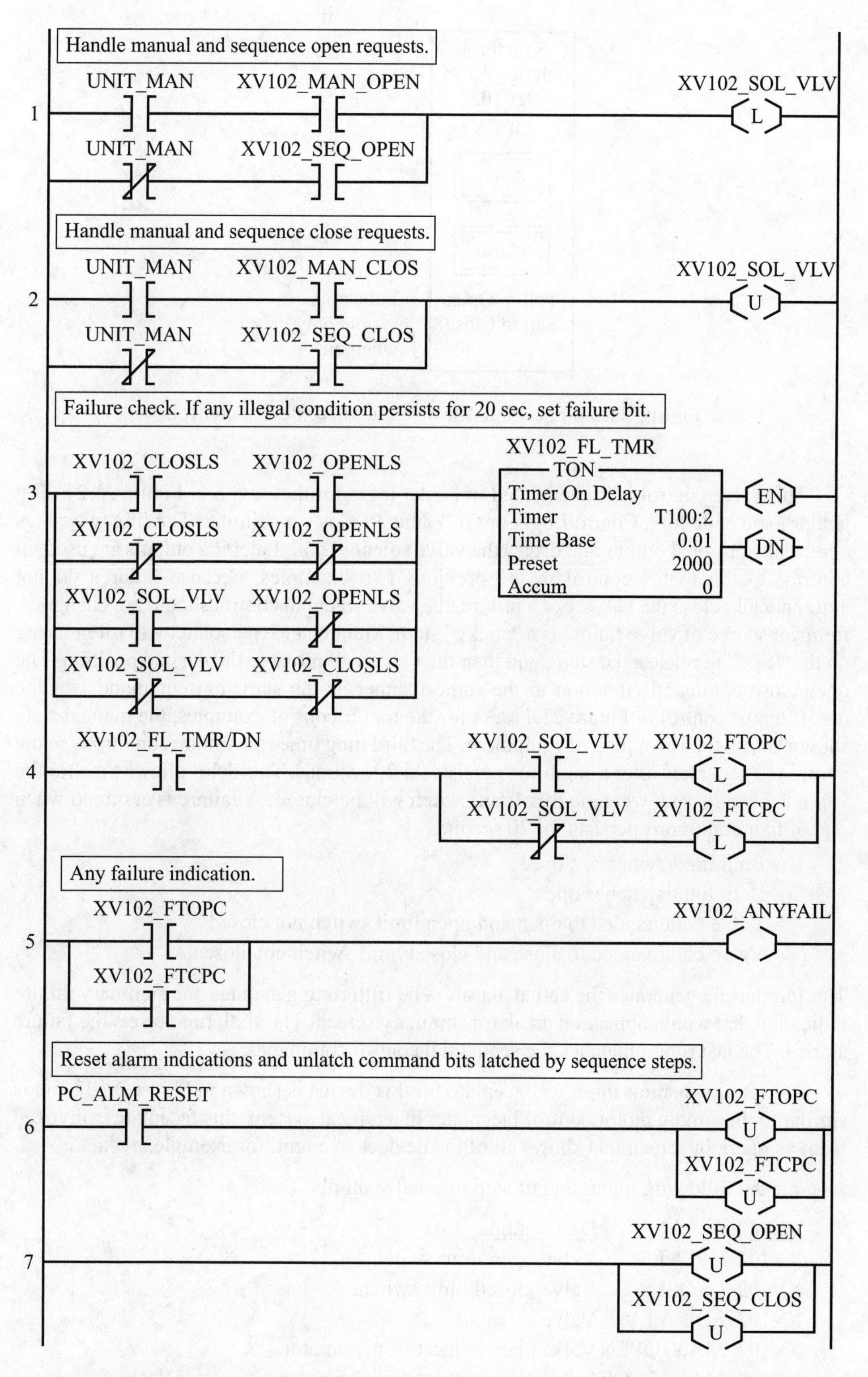

Figure 21.21. PLC-5 ladder logic code for discrete-valve device control.

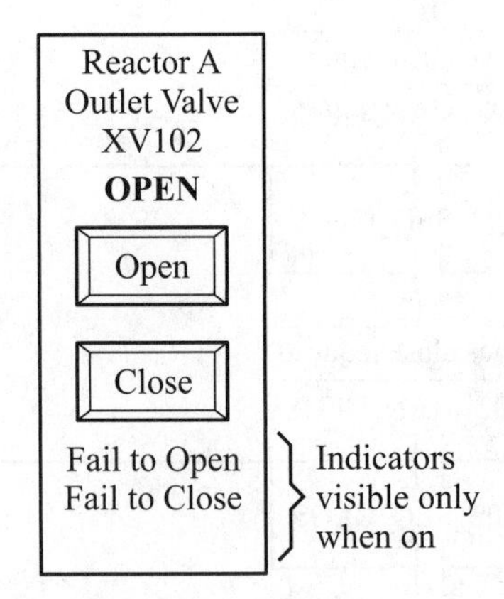

Figure 21.22. Faceplate for discrete-valve device control.

This valve control is implemented in ladder logic for the PLC-5 in Figure 21.21. The ladder logic code for a ControlLogix or GE Fanuc PLC is very similar. The first two rungs control the physical output that drives the valve solenoid coil. Latching outputs are used, in contrast to the motor control in the previous two examples, because failures do not automatically close the valve. For a failure, the valve solenoid control should not change. A frequent source of valve failure is a "sticky" stem. Maintenance personnel will often "bang on the valve" to release the stem, and then the valve will move to the desired position. The open/close commands function in the same manner as the start/stop commands for the on/off motor control in Figure 21.11. As for the motor control examples, the manual state shown here is for a grouping of equipment. The third rung times the failure conditions so the alarms are generated after a condition persists for 20 seconds. This delay allows time for the valve to change state when neither limit switch will be closed. A failure is assumed when one of four conditions persists for 20 seconds

Both limit switches closed
Both limit switches open
Valve commanded to open and open limit switch not closed
Valve commanded to close and closed limit switch not closed

The fourth rung generates the actual alarms. The fifth rung generates one summary failure indication that would appear on an alarm summary screen. The sixth rung resets the failure alarms. The last rung unlatches the sequential control commands.

A possible operator interface faceplate for this device is shown in Figure 21.22 and is similar to the simple motor control faceplate. In a typical system, this faceplate is invoked from an operator screen that shows all of the devices in a unit, for example, a reactor.

Assume the following input, output, and internal symbols.

Variable	Description
XV102_OPENLS	Valve-open limit switch.
XV102_CLOSLS	Valve-closed limit switch.
XV102_SOL_VLV	Valve solenoid.
XV102_MAN_OPEN	Valve open request from operator
XV102_MAN_CLOS	Valve close request from operator

UNIT_MAN	Manual/auto control state for unit: **on** for manual, **off** for auto
PC_ALM_RESET	Alarm reset from operator interface.
XV102_ANYFAIL	Indicates any failure to operator.
XV102_FTOPC	Valve fail-to-open failure indication to operator interface.
XV102_FTCPC	Valve fail-to-close failure indication to operator interface.
XV102_SEQ_OPEN	Valve open request from sequence
XV102_SEQ_CLOS	Valve close request from sequence
XV102_FL_TMR	Times failures

The addresses associated with the physical inputs and outputs are:

Variable	Modicon	PLC-5	ControlLogix	Siemens	GE Fanuc
XV102_OPENLS	%100005	I:01/04	Local:1:I.Data.4	I4.3	%I5
XV102_CLOSLS	%100006	I:01/05	Local:1:I.Data.5	I4.4	%I6
XV102_SOL_VLV	%000002	O:04/01	Local:4:O.Data.1	Q8.1	%Q2

The addresses or data types associated with the internal variables:

Variable	Modicon Data Type	PLC-5 Addr.	CLogix Data Type	Siemens Addr.	GE Fanuc Addr.
XV102_MAN_OPEN	BOOL	N13:1/8	BOOL	M102.0	%M225
XV102_MAN_CLOS	BOOL	N13:1/9	BOOL	M102.1	%M226
UNIT_MAN	BOOL	N13:0/0	BOOL	M100.0	%M201
PC_ALM_RESET	BOOL	B44/0	BOOL	M20.1	%M50
XV102_ANYFAIL	BOOL	N21:1/0	BOOL	M202.0	%M317
XV102_FTOPC	BOOL	N21:1/1	BOOL	M202.1	%M318
XV102_FTCPC	BOOL	N21:1/2	BOOL	M202.2	%M319
XV102_SEQ_OPEN	BOOL	N13:1/10	BOOL	M102.2	%M227
XV102_SEQ_CLOS	BOOL	N13:1/11	BOOL	M102.3	%M228
XV102_FL_TMR	n/a	T100:2	TIMER	DBW0.0	%R305

21.4.2 Unit Sequence Control

Sequence control is often discussed in the context of driving a set of process equipment in a coordinated cycle to make a batch chemical product. This type of sequence control manipulates devices, PID loop setpoints, and other parameters in order to accomplish the control objective. However, sequence control is often employed in non-batch control applications, for example, the startup and shutdown of a unit.

Figure 21.23 illustrates sequence control using the terminology of the S88 batch control standard (ISA, 1995). The process is depicted as a state diagram, and the sequence control as a simplified sequential function chart (SFC). The initial state of a process unit is Idle (that is, not making product). When it is in the Operating state, the unit is making product. The Startup state covers the sequence of steps necessary to bring the unit to the Operating state. Likewise, the Shutdown state contains the steps necessary to shut off the unit and return to the Idle state. Often because of abnormal conditions, there is a faster way to shut down the process, called the Emergency Shutdown state. The states in Figure 21.23 are nearly universal to the control of any unit. There may be other states, as well.

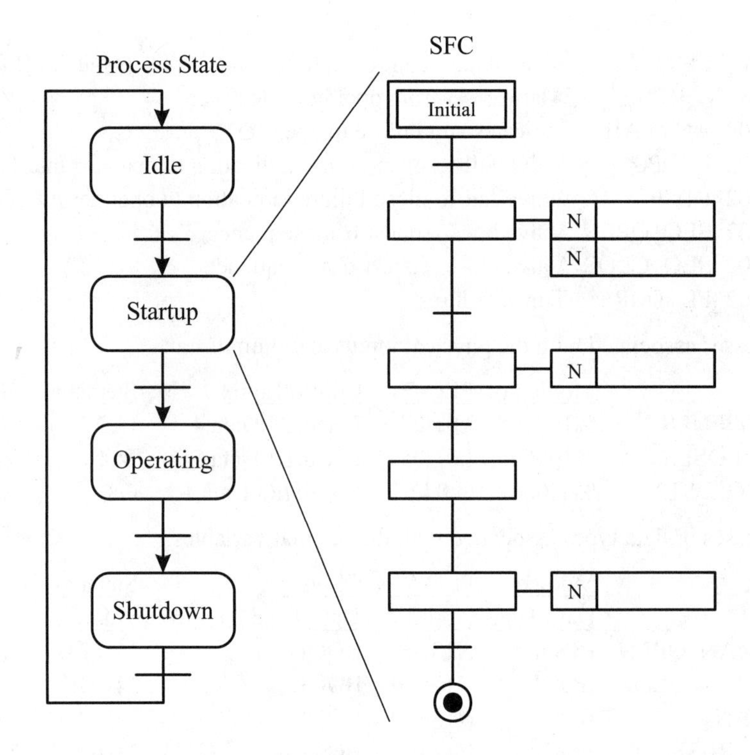

Figure 21.23. Unit sequence control.

The SFC associated with a state is in the Initial step until an automatic or manual event causes the SFC to move through its sequence logic. At the end of the sequence, the sequencer returns to the Initial step and waits for the next start command.

The coordination of the sequences associated with a set of process equipment, called a unit, is the subject of this section. Sequences may be implemented using the technique of Chapter 6 or any of the methods of Chapter 9. The emphasis will be on the coordination of the sequences such that only one is operational at any given time.

In the context of the S88 batch control standard (ISA, 1995), the set of sequences for a unit is called a *unit procedure*, and each sequence is called an *operation*. In general, each operation corresponds to one process state.

Example 21.4. *Unit supervision sequence control.* For this example, the unit procedure is assumed to have the operations shown in Figure 21.24. Only one operation can be active at any instant. Each one of the operations is expressed as a function chart (Figure 21.25), called a sequence. Some of the transition logic is shown in Figure 21.24. For example, when the Startup operation is complete, the Operate operation is automatically started. In general, the operator can request any of the operations be started. Though for this example, it is unreasonable for the operator to initiate the Operate operation.

The Hold operation is basically a one-step sequence that allows manual control (called maintenance mode) of devices in order to correct a problem. The Hold operation is often entered automatically when certain problems occur, though the operator can request it if a problem is detected.

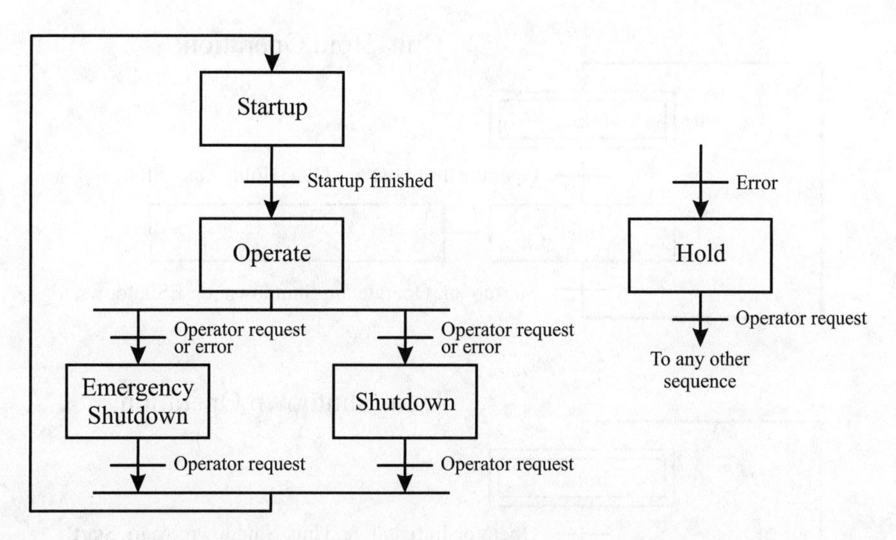

Figure 21.24. Overall view of operations for example unit.

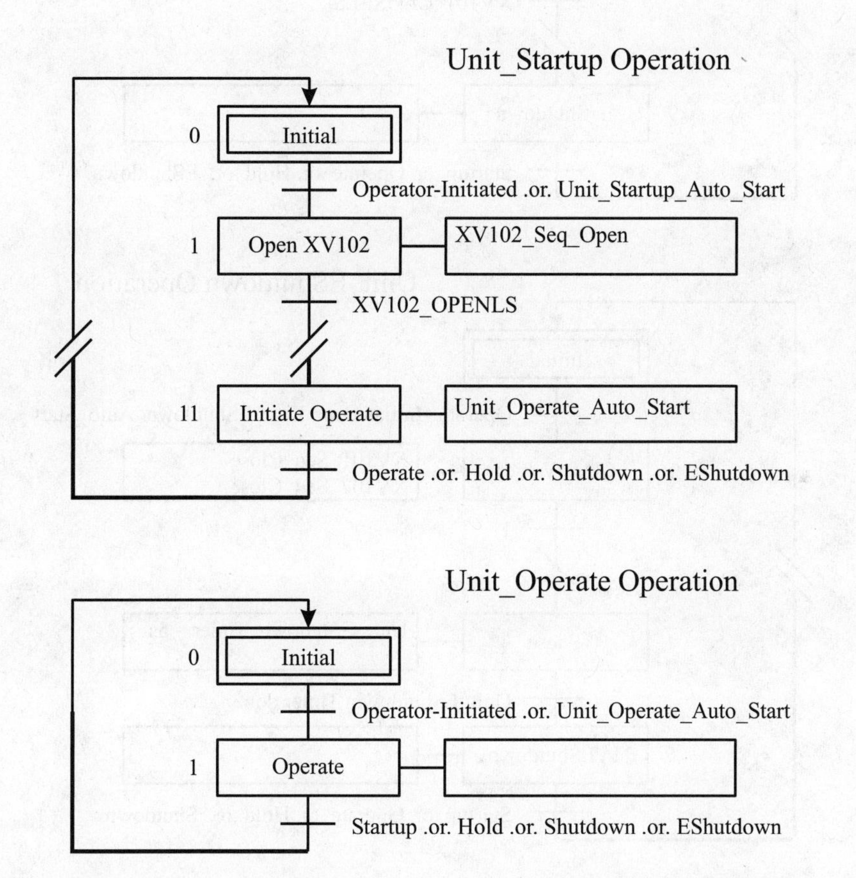

Figure 21.25. Operations (sequences) for example unit. *(continued)*

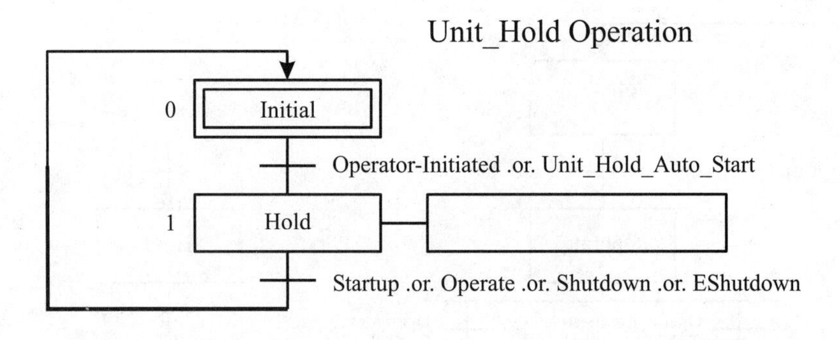

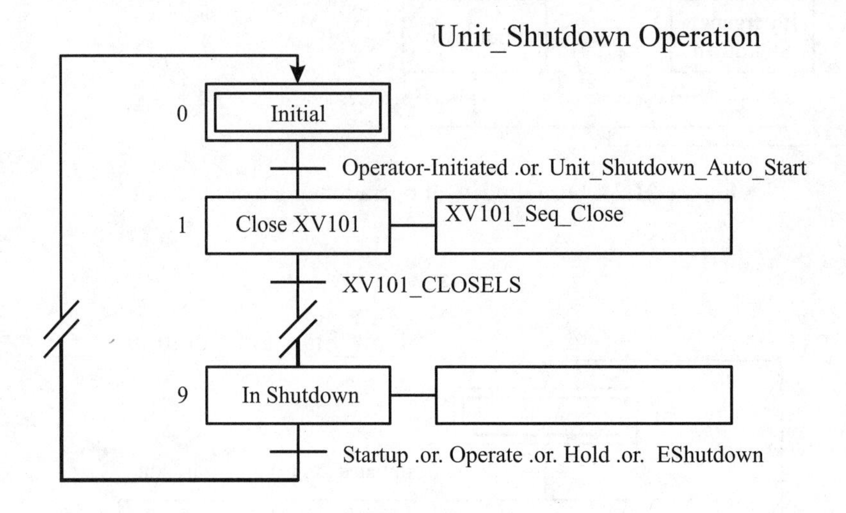

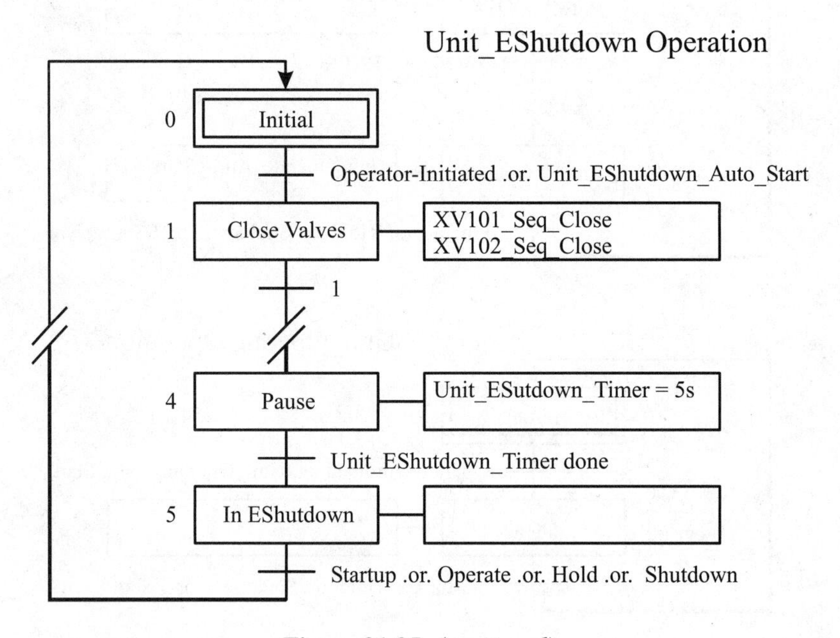

Figure 21.25. *(continued)*

The Shutdown and Emergency Shutdown (often called E-Shutdown) operations may be requested by the operator, automatically initiated at the end of the Operate operation, or automatically initiated by a device failure. The Shutdown operation is usually an orderly turn-off of the unit equipment. The E-Shutdown operation is an immediate turn-off of the unit equipment and is invoked in dire circumstances.

A sequence is initiated in one of two ways:

1. Operator request, or
2. Automatic request from another sequence or due to abnormal process conditions.

All sequenced control logic and interlocking is in the PLC. This example concerns the sequences and the coordination between them. For this example, the implementation of the SFC is the counter-based ladder-logic sequence of Chapter 9. The control of one device is shown in the implementation. Control of PID loops can also be accommodated, though not shown in this example.

In order to keep the operator abreast of unit sequence activities, an integer message number is available to an HMI. Each step in each operation has a message number unique for that unit. For this unit, Unit_Startup has message numbers 1 - 20; Unit_Operate has message numbers 21 - 40; Unit_Hold has message numbers 41 - 60; and so on.

There are six sections in a PLC sequence and these parts are standard for the different sequences implemented in the PLC:

1. Grant manual mode for unit devices.
2. Initiate sequence.
3. Handle step-in-progress bits.
4. Increment step counter
5. Transitions between steps and device control from sequence
6. Automatic start for sequence.

These sections are illustrated for each of the PLCs covered by this text in Figures 21.26 – 21.30. The variable-naming convention is explained later. The six sections are described in the following paragraphs. Though there is some variation among the processors, the implementation for GE Fanuc processors deviates significantly from the others for the third and fourth sections.

Rung 1 is the first section of the sequence. This rung appears once for the group of sequences for a unit and handles the granting of manual control to the devices in the unit (called maintenance mode). In maintenance mode, the motors and valves are started/stopped manually by an operator at a local touch panel (LTP) located close to the unit equipment rather than automatically by a sequence. The maintenance mode is granted when the Local indication is set and the "Hold", "Shutdown", or "E-Shutdown" sequences are in their last steps. Maintenance mode may be granted in other sequences, but these are nearly universal. The "Unit_Maint" bit is added as a series condition to the manual and sequence start/stop (or open/close) requests in the device control.

The second part of the sequence (rung 2; GE Fanuc rungs 2 - 5) initiates the sequence, generates the message number, and sets the indication that the sequence is in progress. The sequence is initiated one of three ways:

1. By the operator from the PC (when not in local mode), or
2. By the operator from the LTP (when in local mode), or
3. By an internal PLC start request ("auto-request").

Note the use of the GEQ to seal around the start requests. The reason for this method of sealing is explained later.

The start request is blocked if any other sequence in the group is auto-starting. When the sequence is initiated, the transition increments the counter to step 1 and resets the other counters in the group. The output logic also adds a constant to the sequence counter accumulator to calculate the message number and also generates an indication that the sequence is in progress. The message number and sequence-running indication is for the operator interface. Each sequence in a unit adds a different constant to calculate the message number such that each step in each unit sequence has a unique message number.

Note that a GEQ is used to seal the sequence start request. Using the "_Running" bit for a sequence does not work in this case. A sequence is turned off when its counter is reset due to another sequence starting. If the "_Running" bit is used for the seal, the seal is not broken if this sequence's counter is reset due to an operator request to start another sequence. The use of the GEQ to seal the sequence start request also handles the case where one counter handles multiple sequences. One common case where this is done is in material transfer from one source tank to one of multiple destination tanks. As far as the operator is concerned, each transfer is a separate sequence. Each of the transfer sequences has an individual "_Running" bit but all share the same counter. Since the only difference among these sequences is which valve is opened/closed in a few steps, it is reasonable to combine all of these transfers in one sequence and use the individual "_Running" bits to open/close the appropriate valves in the steps.

The third section (rung 3 for all but GE Fanuc) handles the Unit_Startup_Step[] (Step-in-progress) bits for the sequence. The variable Unit_Startup_StepNum is the current bit in the Unit_Startup_Step[] array that is **on**. When the counter increments (or is changed due to branching), the old Unit_Startup_Step[] bit must be cleared, the Unit_Startup_StepNum must be reconciled to it, and the new Unit_Startup_Step[] bit must be set. If the next step number is zero, the step-in-progress bit is not latched since the counter accumulator and not the step-in-progress bit determines when the sequence is in its initial step.The logic for the PLC-5/SLC-500 processors is a little different. Since all of the step-in-progress bits are in one data file (B20), a pointer to the appropriate bit number, UNIT_STRT_INP, is calculated as the step number plus a fixed constant. The UNIT_STRT_INP is also used for the array of transition bits.

The fourth section (rung 4 for all but GE Fanuc) handles the increment of the counter to the next step when one step is complete. With a counter-based sequence, one must always ensure there is an **off**-to-**on** transition at the counter input when the step number increments. Therefore, the counter input should always be turned **off** after the increment to the next step. This action will ensure a proper increment to the next step when the transition condition out of a step is already satisfied when the step is activated (or it is a spare step). Placing the logic for updating the step-in-progress bit (rung 3) ***before*** the counter increment (rung 4) satisfies this requirement concerning the counter input. When the counter increments, the index into the step-in-progress bit array changes on the next scan. When this index is changed, the step-done bit of the new step is always **off** because the rung that handles the transition out of the new step has not been scanned to turn it **on**. Hence, the counter input is **off** during the program scan after the counter accumulator changes. If the transition condition of the new step is already satisfied, then the step-done bit of the new step is turned **on** during this scan, and the counter is incremented on the next scan. If rungs 3 and 4 are swapped so that the counter increment is before the logic that updates the step-in-progress bit, the counter input will not change under certain conditions. Specifically, the counter will not increment to the next step after a step whose transition condition out of the step is already satisfied when entering the step. In this case, the following actions happen on the same scan: (1) the counter increments because the step-done bit of the current step is on, (2) the step-in-progress bit of the new step is turned **on**, and (3) the step-done bit of the new step turns **on**. Therefore, on the next program scan, the counter input is still **on**, and the counter will not increment to the next step.

The GE Fanuc implementation (rungs 6 - 9 of Figure 21.30) handles sections three and four together. The BIT_SEQ block implements most of the logic needed to change the step-in-progress bit. However, the reset of the step-in-progress bits for a sequence is handled separately.

The fifth section (rungs 5-14; GE Fanuc rungs 10-19) is the "meat" of the Startup sequence. Each rung evaluates the transition condition. If the transition condition is satisfied, then the appropriate Unit_Startup_Trans[] bit is set. Rung 5 demonstrates a step that commands XV102 to open. In general, if a step commands a valve to open/close, a motor to start/stop, then the appropriate bit is set. This bit will be cleared by the valve/motor/etc. device code.

Rungs 15 – 17 in Figures 21.26 – 21.29 are the second, third and fourth sections for the Unit_Operate sequence. For a GE Fanuc PLC, rungs 20 - 27 in Figure 21.30 implement these sections for the Unit_Operate sequence.

The next-to-last step in the E-Shutdown sequence (rung 67; GE Fanuc rung 82) delays 5 seconds before transitioning to the last step. This delay allows equipment to finish closing, stopping, etc. before maintenance mode, and therefore local control of the devices, is granted. In the E-Shutdown sequence, the steps command the devices to go to a safe state without waiting for the device to get to the safe state.

The sixth section is the logic that handles all of the "automatic start" start sequence requests. The first part (rungs 68-82; GE Fanuc rungs 83-97) has rungs that delay various failures that cause a certain sequence, commonly Hold or Shutdown, to be started.

Rung 83 (GE Fanuc rungs 98-100) is the automatic start for the Unit_Operate sequence. This sequence is automatically started when the Unit_Startup is in the last step (step 11). The series conditions at the beginning of the rung prevent the sequence from starting if another sequence in the unit is already auto-starting. There is also a condition that prevents an auto restart of the Unit_Operate if it is already running. The start condition uses a one-shot or transitional contact to turn on the auto start bit, and a timer is used to hold the auto start request bit **on** for 5 seconds (to allow time for other logic to be resolved). Rung 84 (GE Fanuc rungs 101-103) is a sample automatic start for the Unit_Shutdown sequence. The conditions that start the sequence are the parallel combination of the done bits from the device failure delay timer.

The second through fifth sections are repeated for each sequence in the group, except that "Unit_Startup" in the variables/tags/symbols is replaced by "Unit_Operate," "Unit_Hold," "Unit_Shutdown," or "Unit_EShutdown" as appropriate.

In the ladder logic code for the unit sequences, note the variable/tag/symbol name conventions. In an actual application, the "Unit" part of the name is replaced by the name of the unit; for example, Reactor1, Reactor2, LoadOut, LoadIn, Blend1, and so on. The next section further elaborates a variable naming convention.

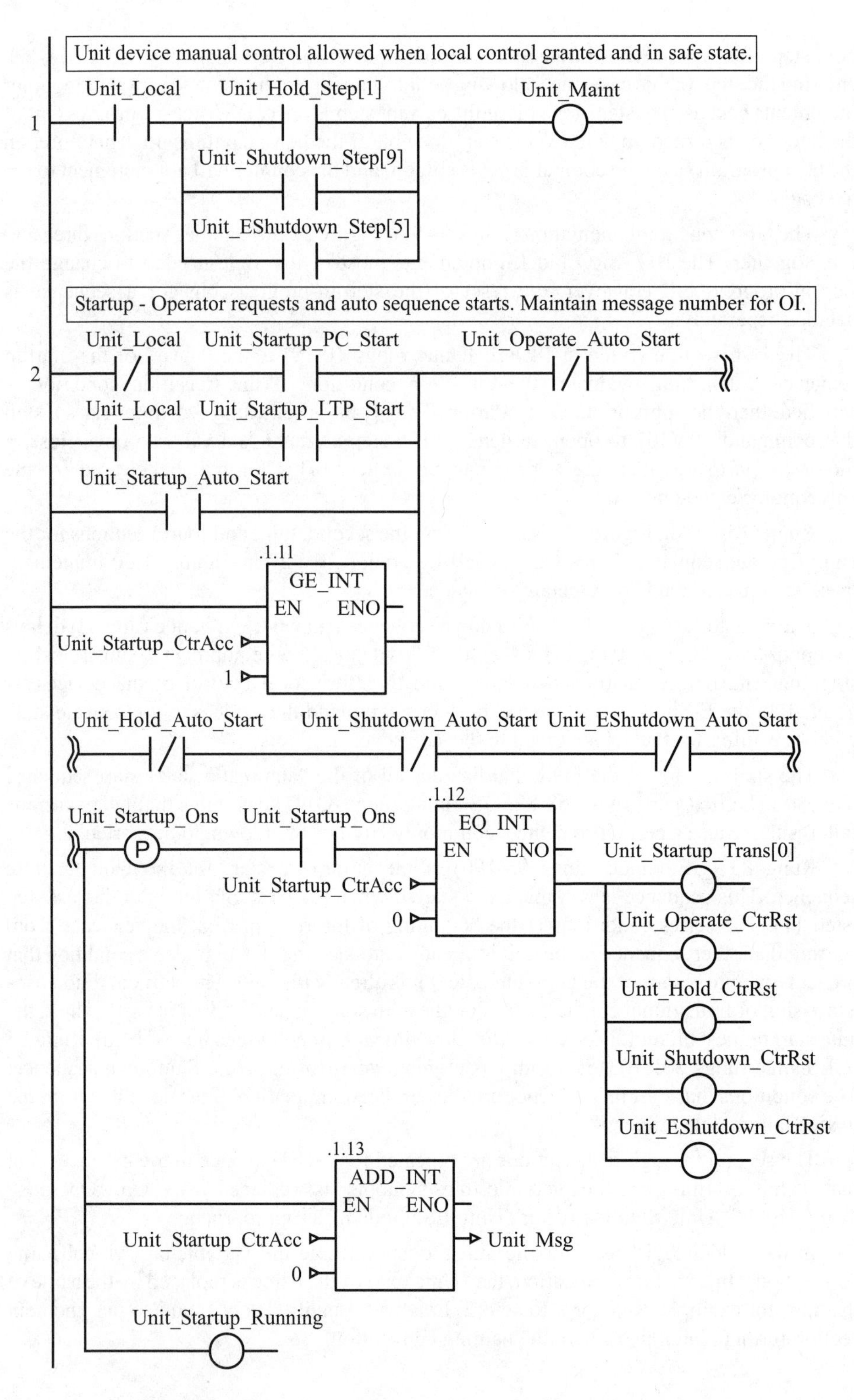

Figure 21.26. Modicon sequences for example unit. *(continued)*

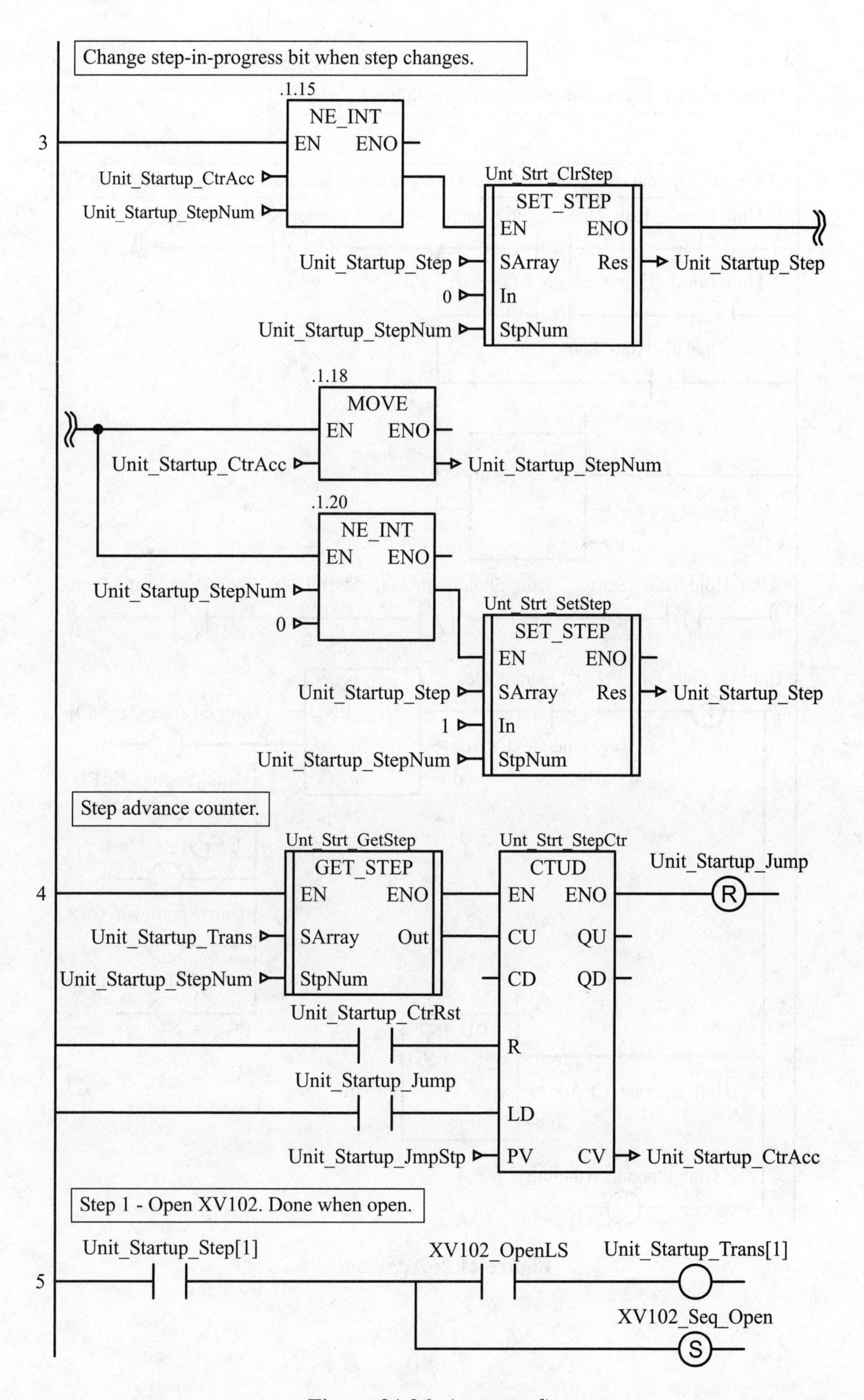

Figure 21.26. *(continued)*

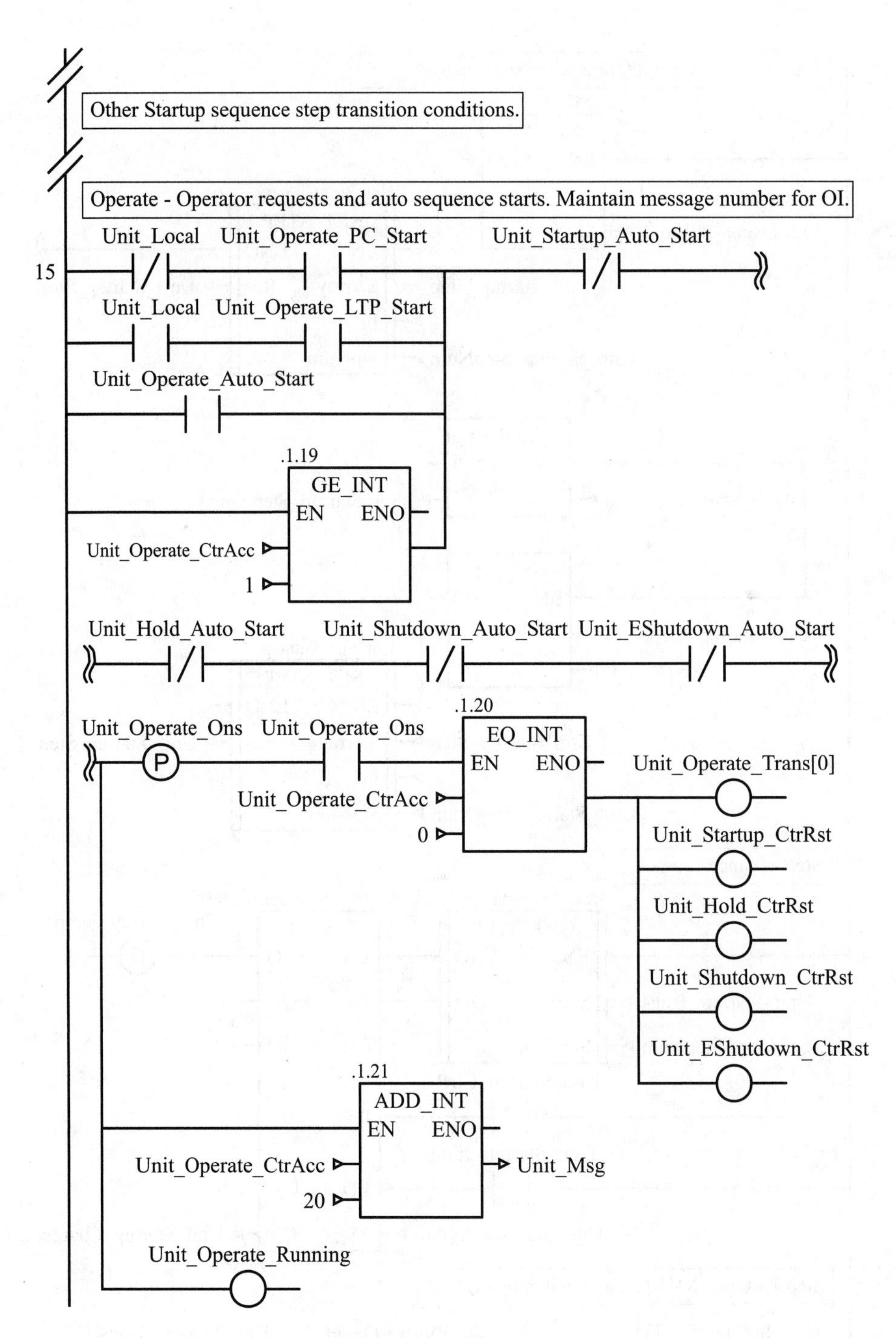

Figure 21.26. *(continued)*

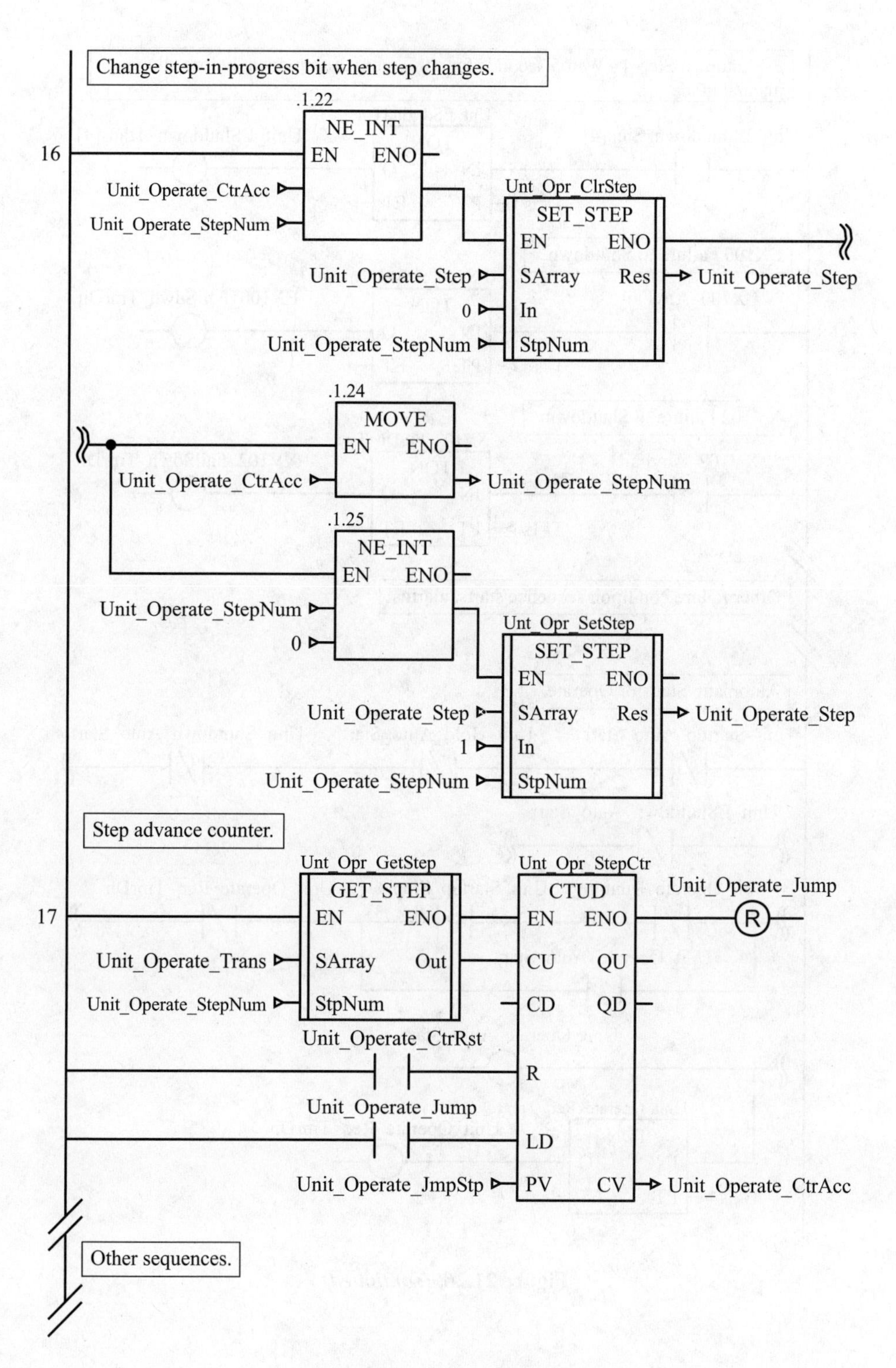

Figure 21.26. *(continued)*

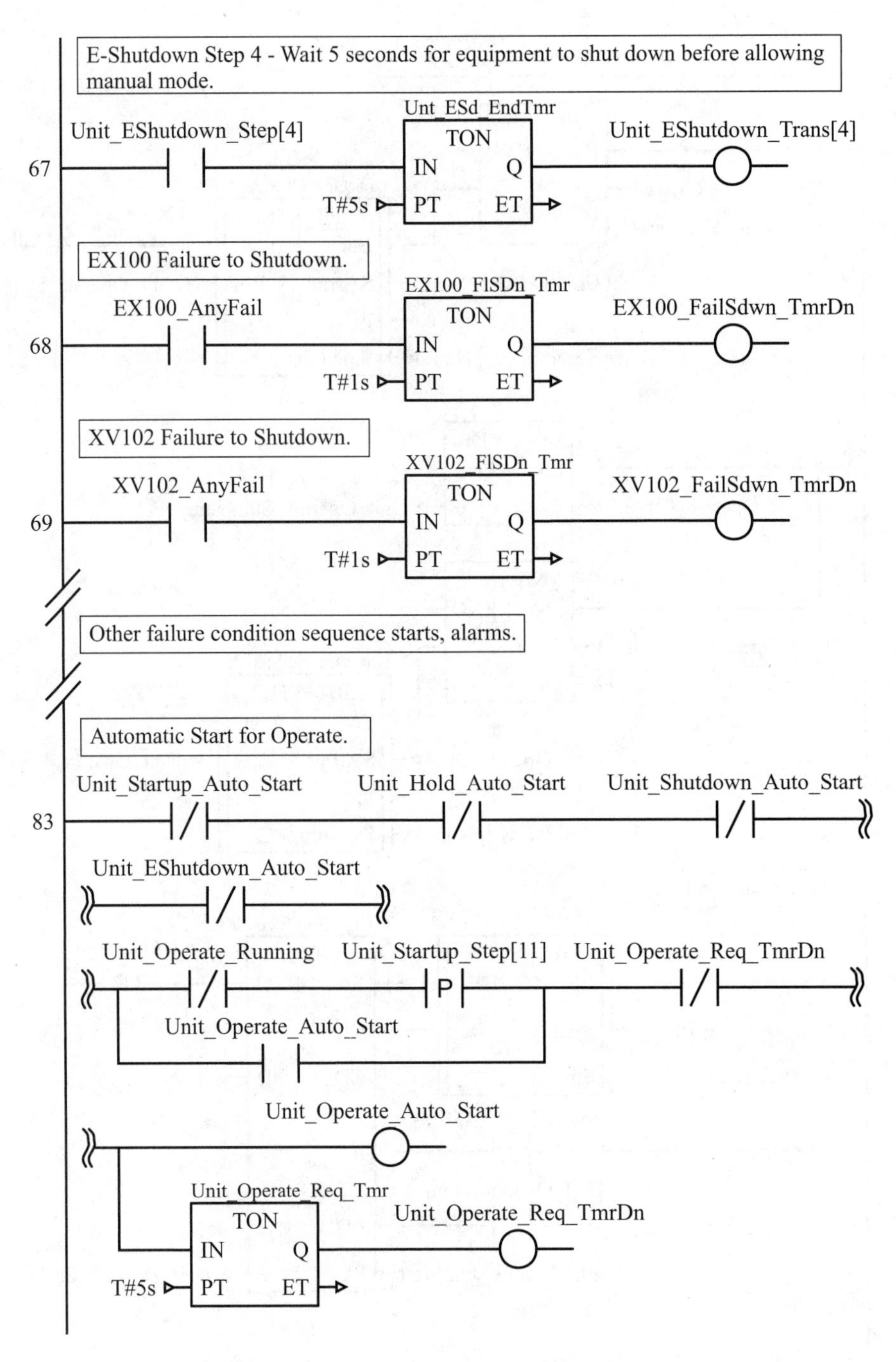

Figure 21.26. *(continued)*

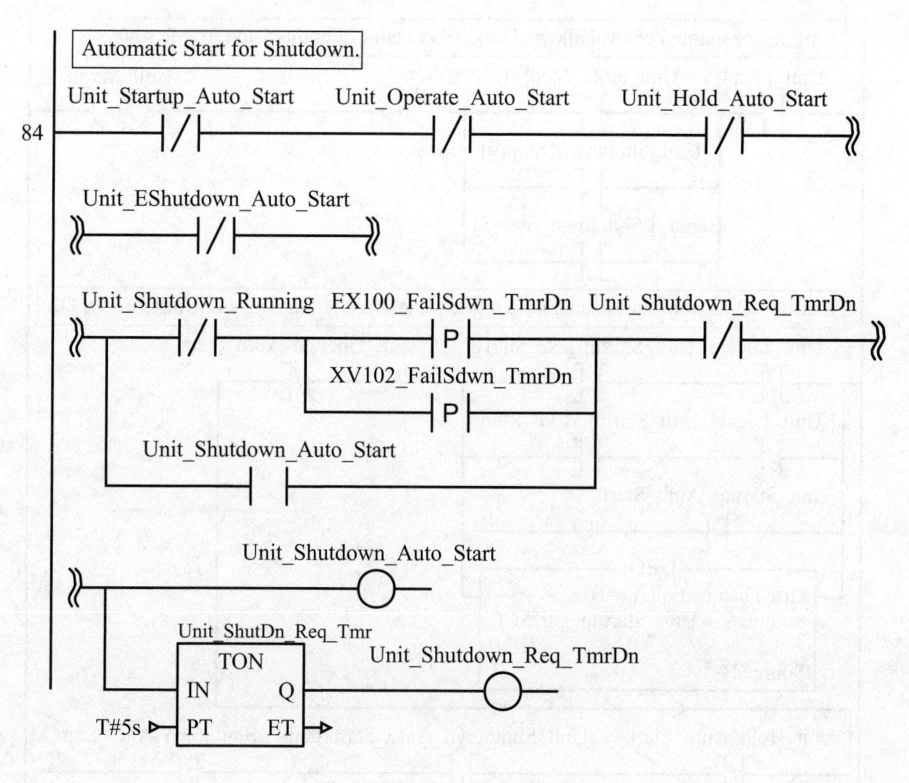

Figure 21.26. *(continued)*

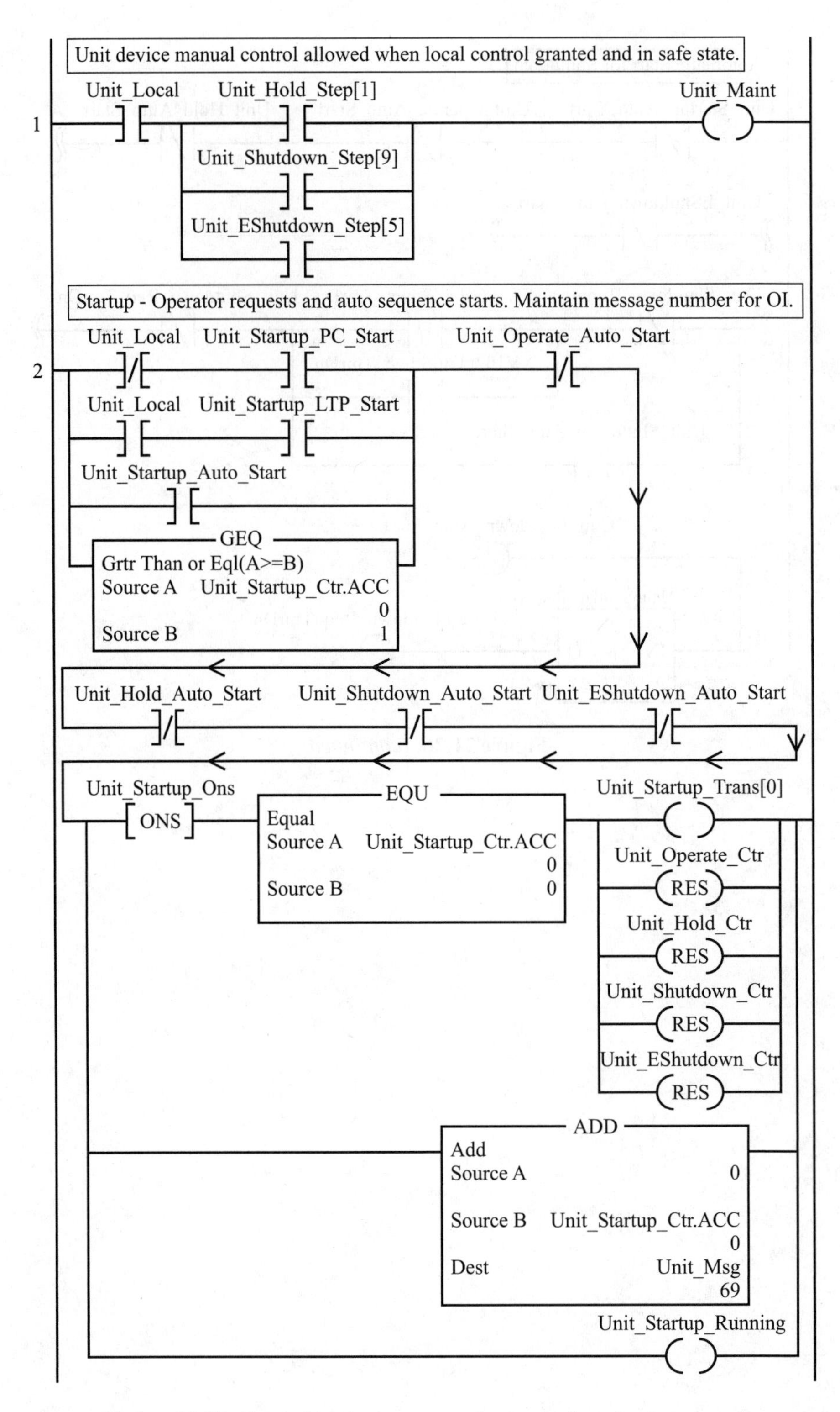

Figure 21.27. ControlLogix sequences for example unit. *(continued)*

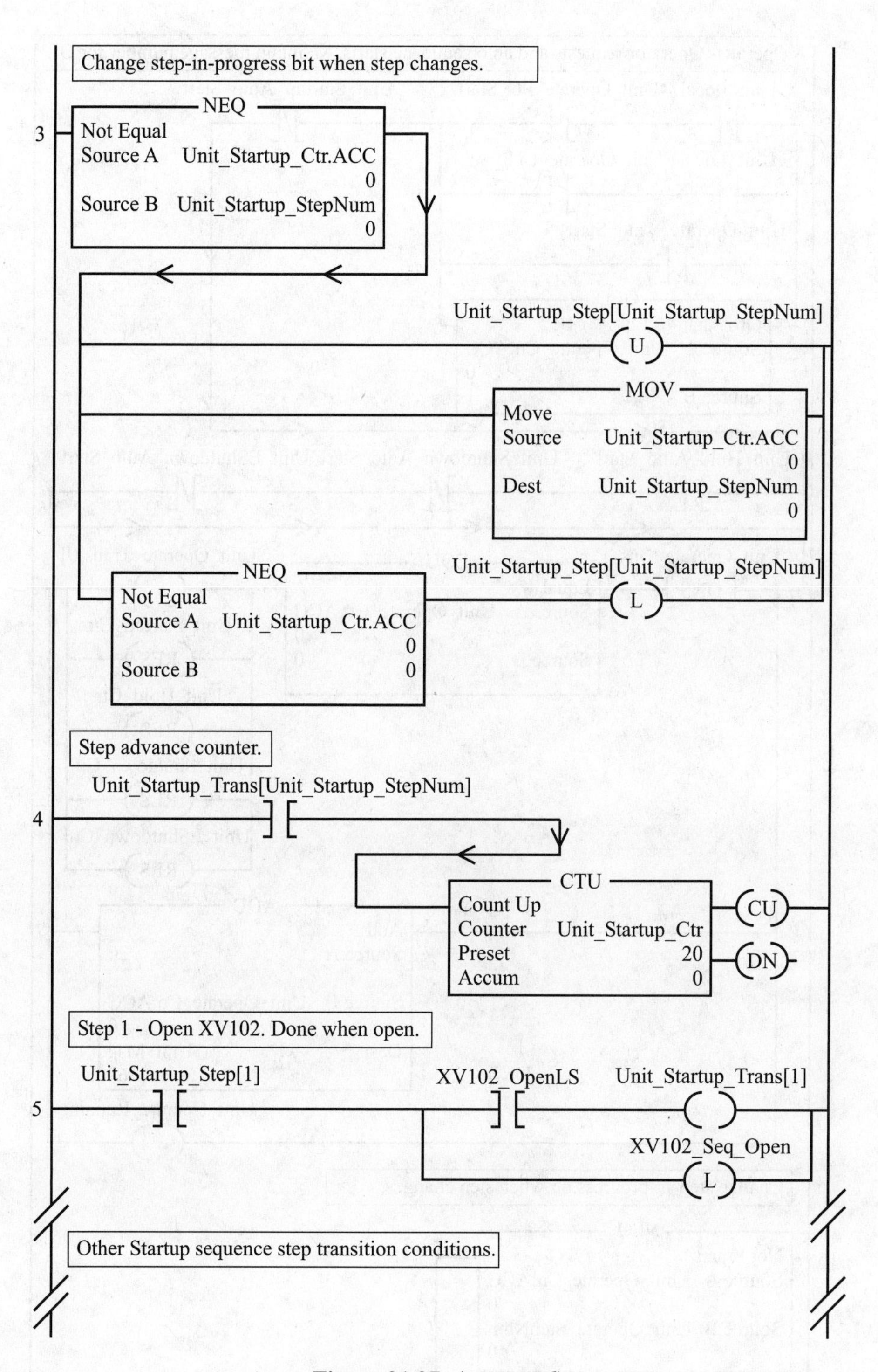

Figure 21.27. *(continued)*

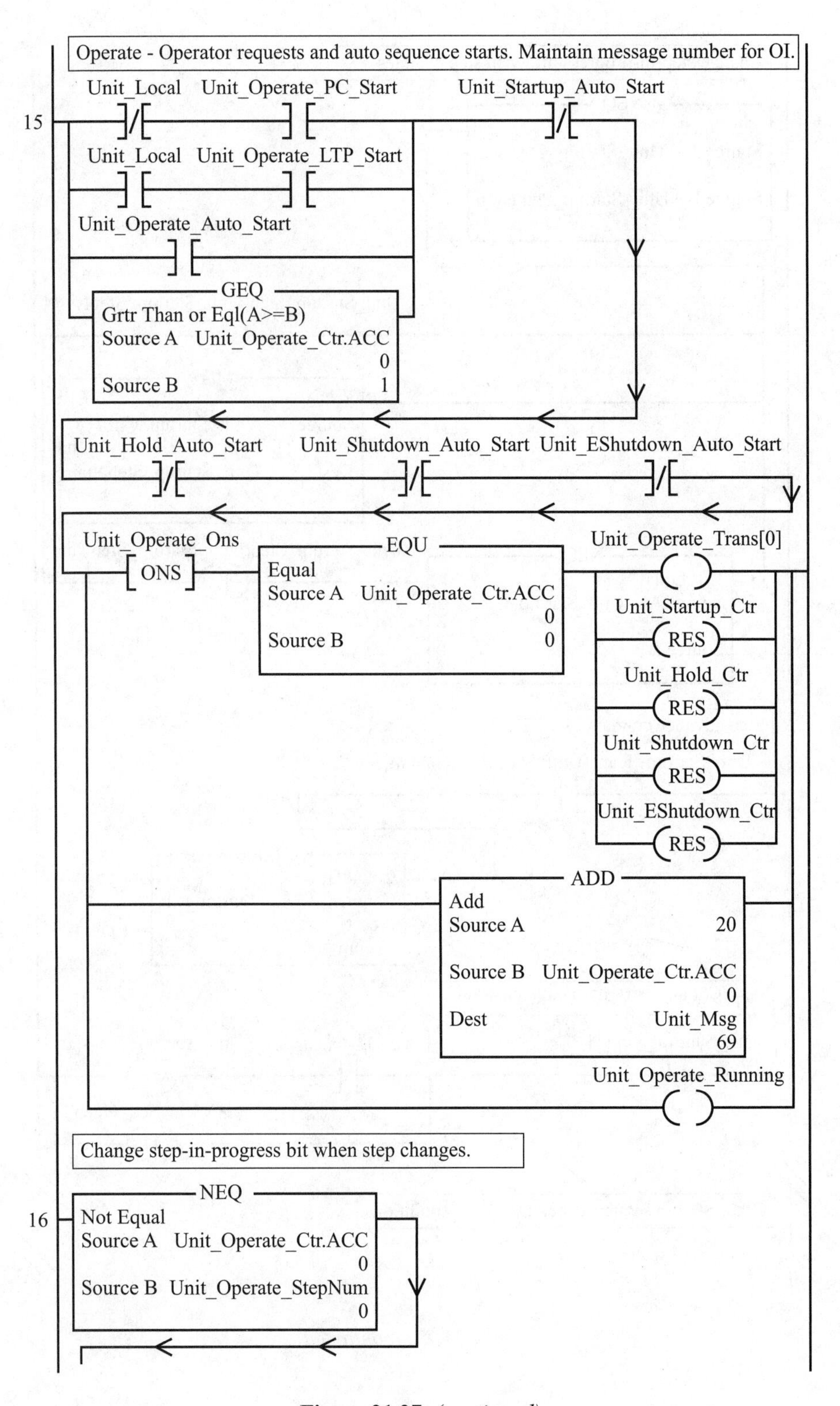

Figure 21.27. *(continued)*

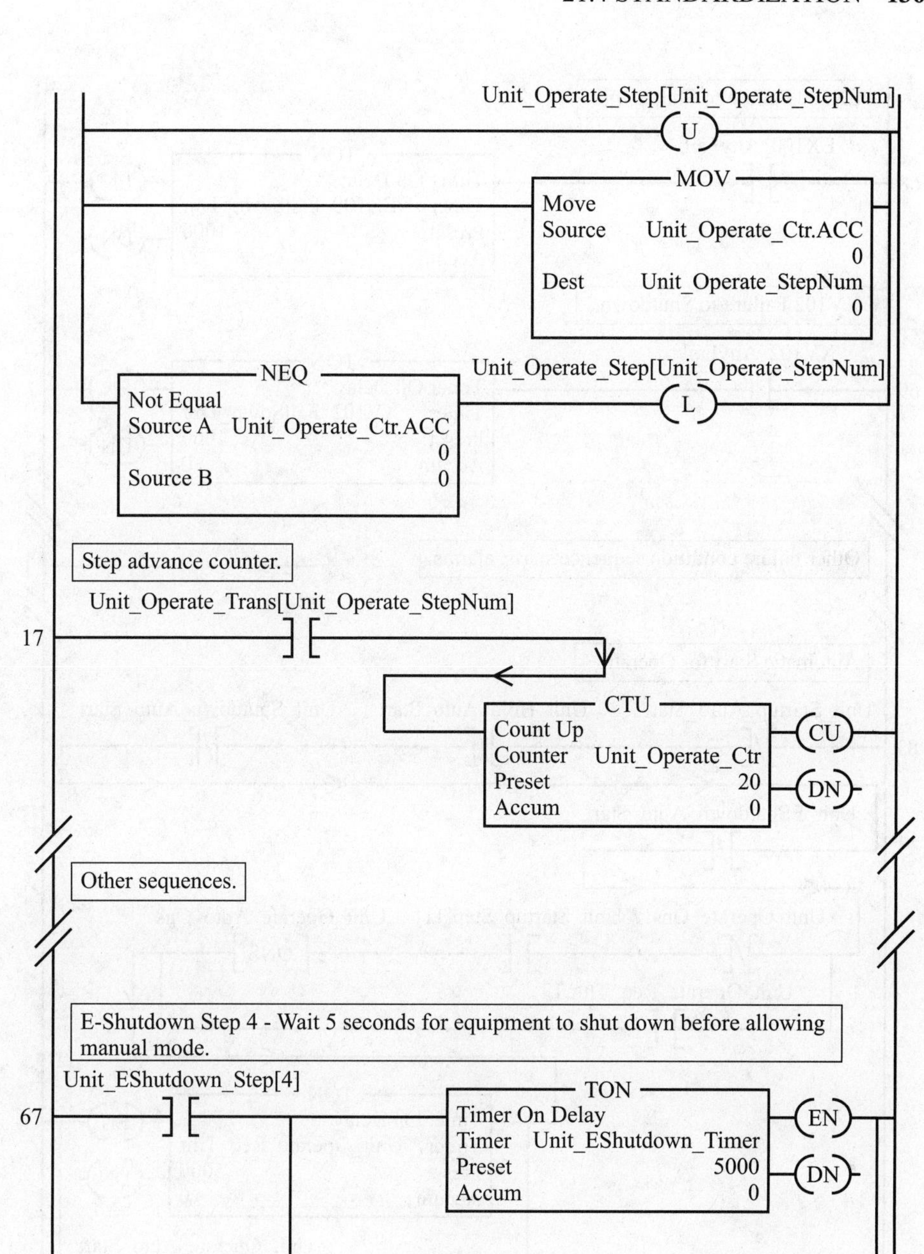

Unit_Operate_Step[Unit_Operate_StepNum]
U
MOV
Move
Source Unit_Operate_Ctr.ACC
0
Dest Unit_Operate_StepNum
0
NEQ
Not Equal
Source A Unit_Operate_Ctr.ACC
0
Source B 0
Unit_Operate_Step[Unit_Operate_StepNum]
L
Step advance counter.
Unit_Operate_Trans[Unit_Operate_StepNum]
17
CTU
Count Up
Counter Unit_Operate_Ctr
Preset 20
Accum 0
CU
DN
Other sequences.
E-Shutdown Step 4 - Wait 5 seconds for equipment to shut down before allowing manual mode.
Unit_EShutdown_Step[4]
67
TON
Timer On Delay
Timer Unit_EShutdown_Timer
Preset 5000
Accum 0
EN
DN
Unit_EShutdown_Timer.DN
Unit_EShutdown_Trans[4]

Figure 21.27. *(continued)*

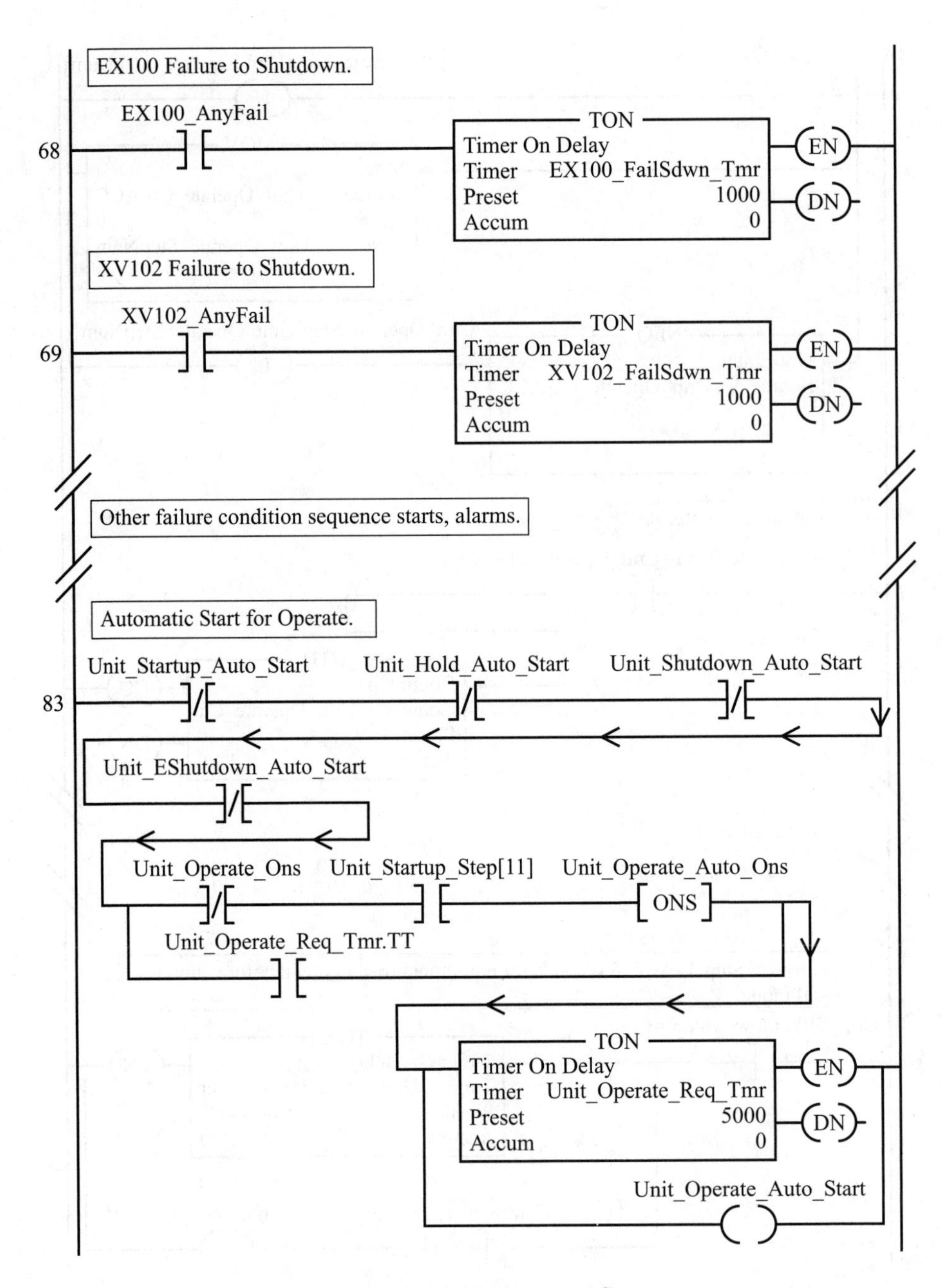

Figure 21.27. *(continued)*

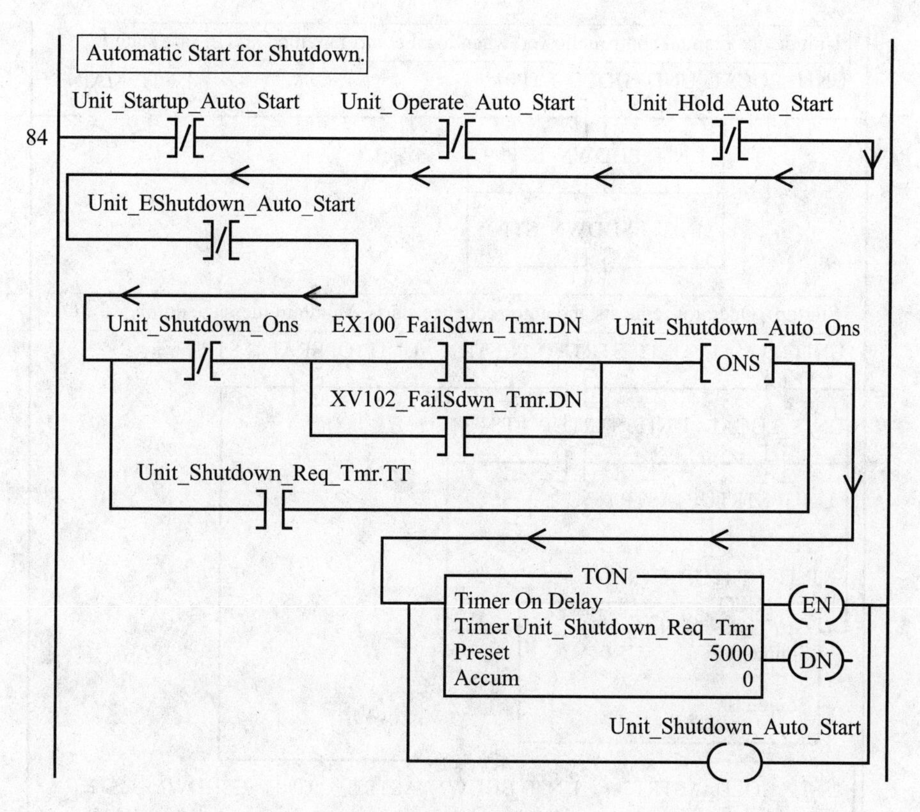

Figure 21.27. *(continued)*

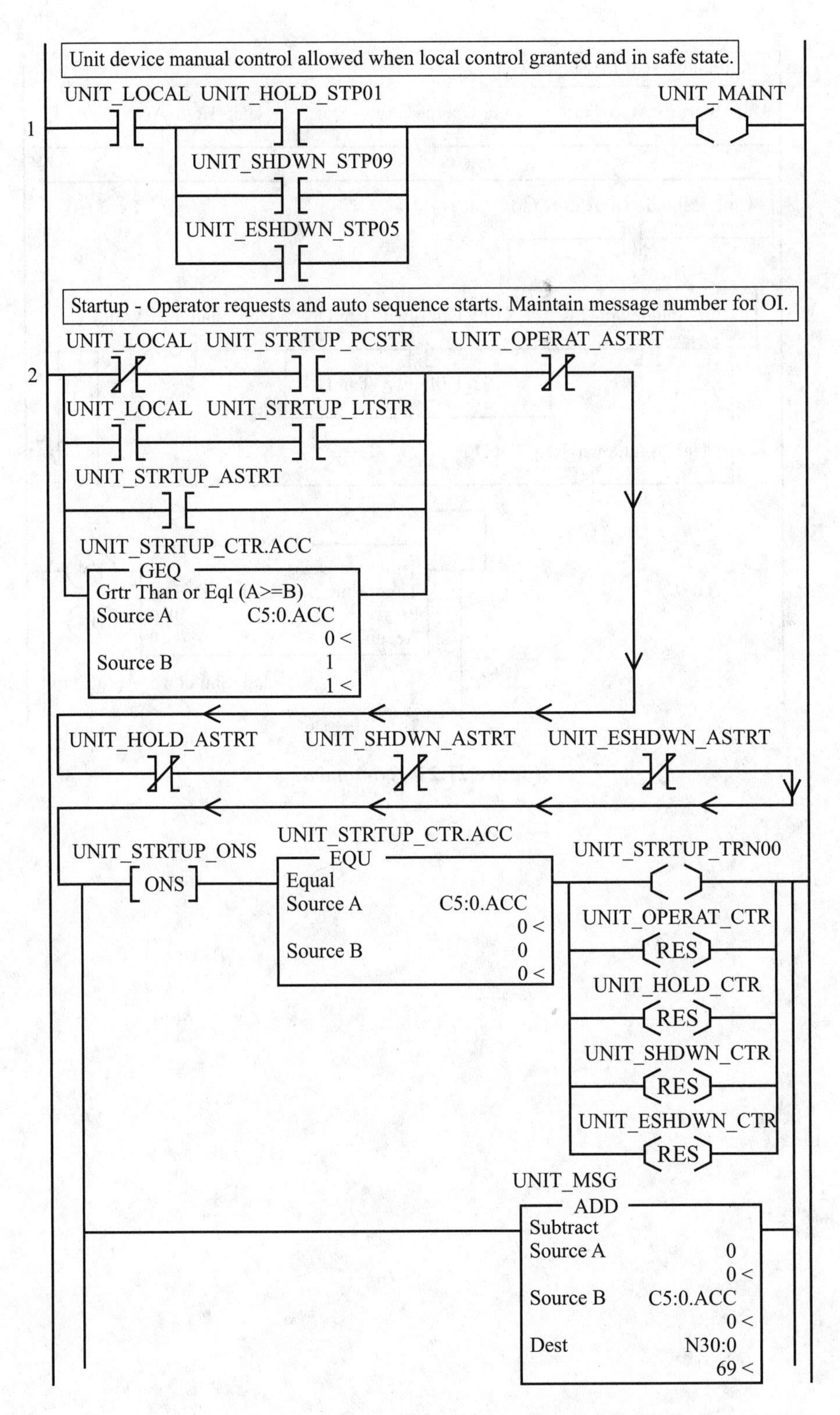

Figure 21.28. PLC-5 sequences for example unit. *(continued)*

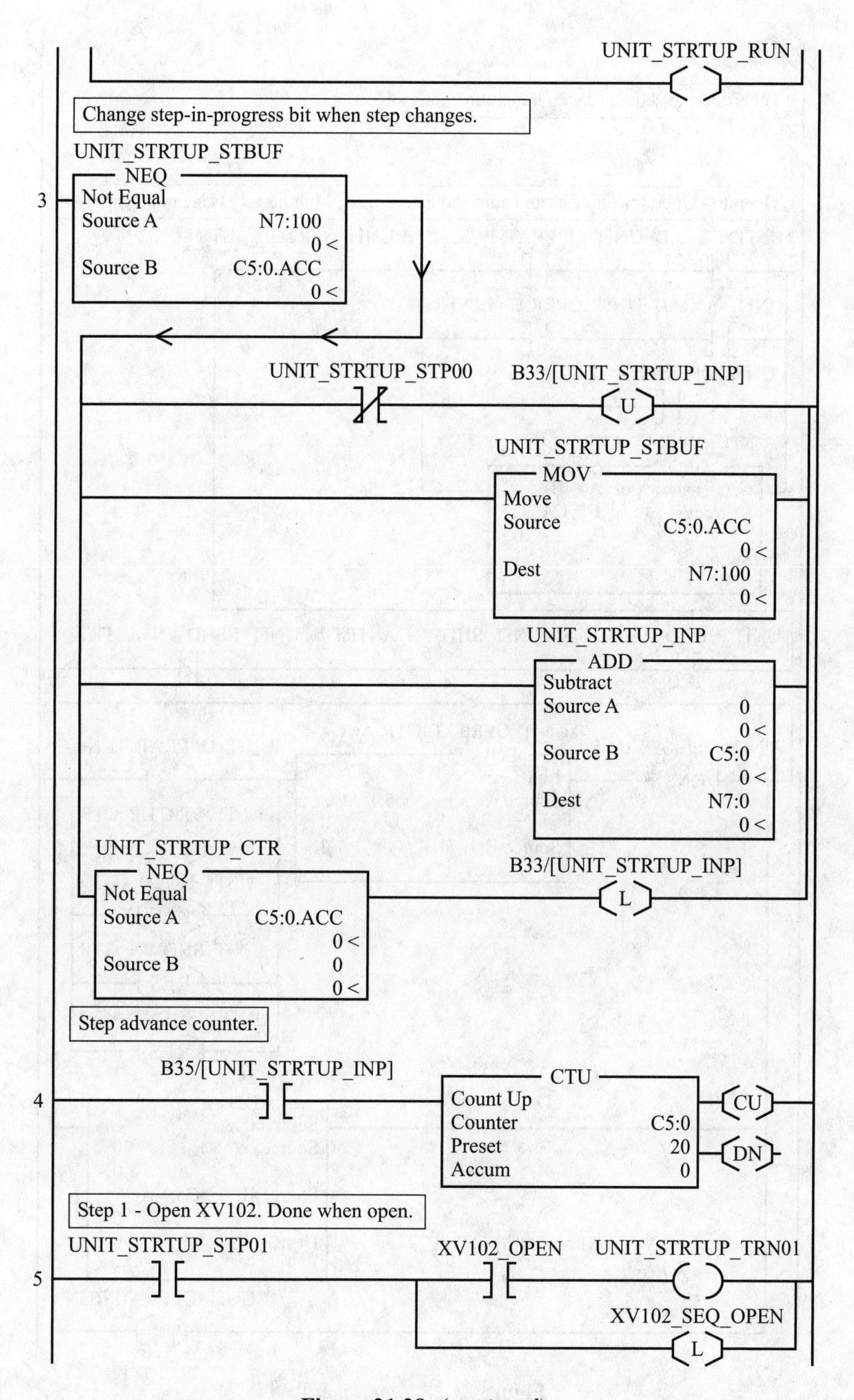

Figure 21.28. *(continued)*

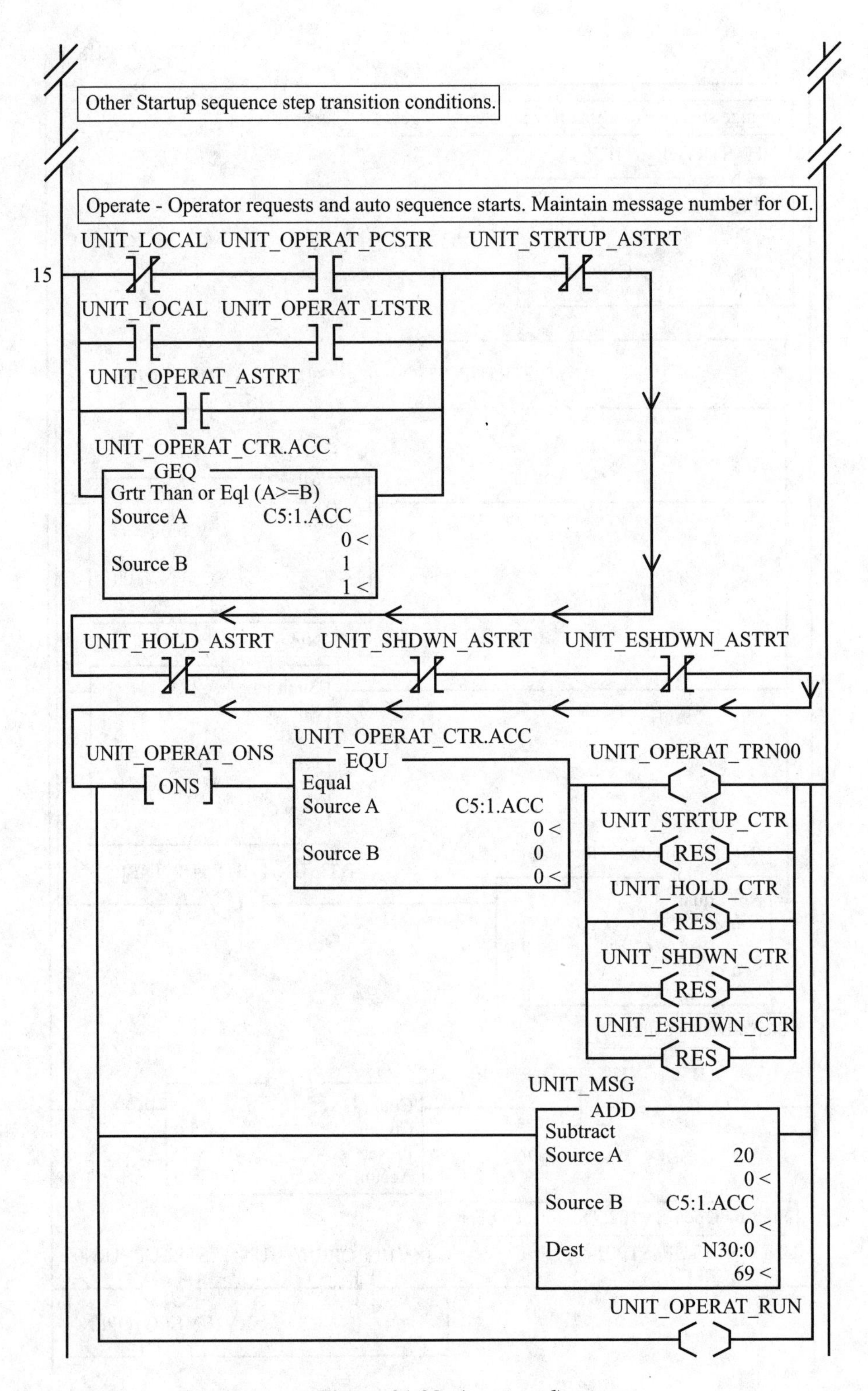

Figure 21.28. *(continued)*

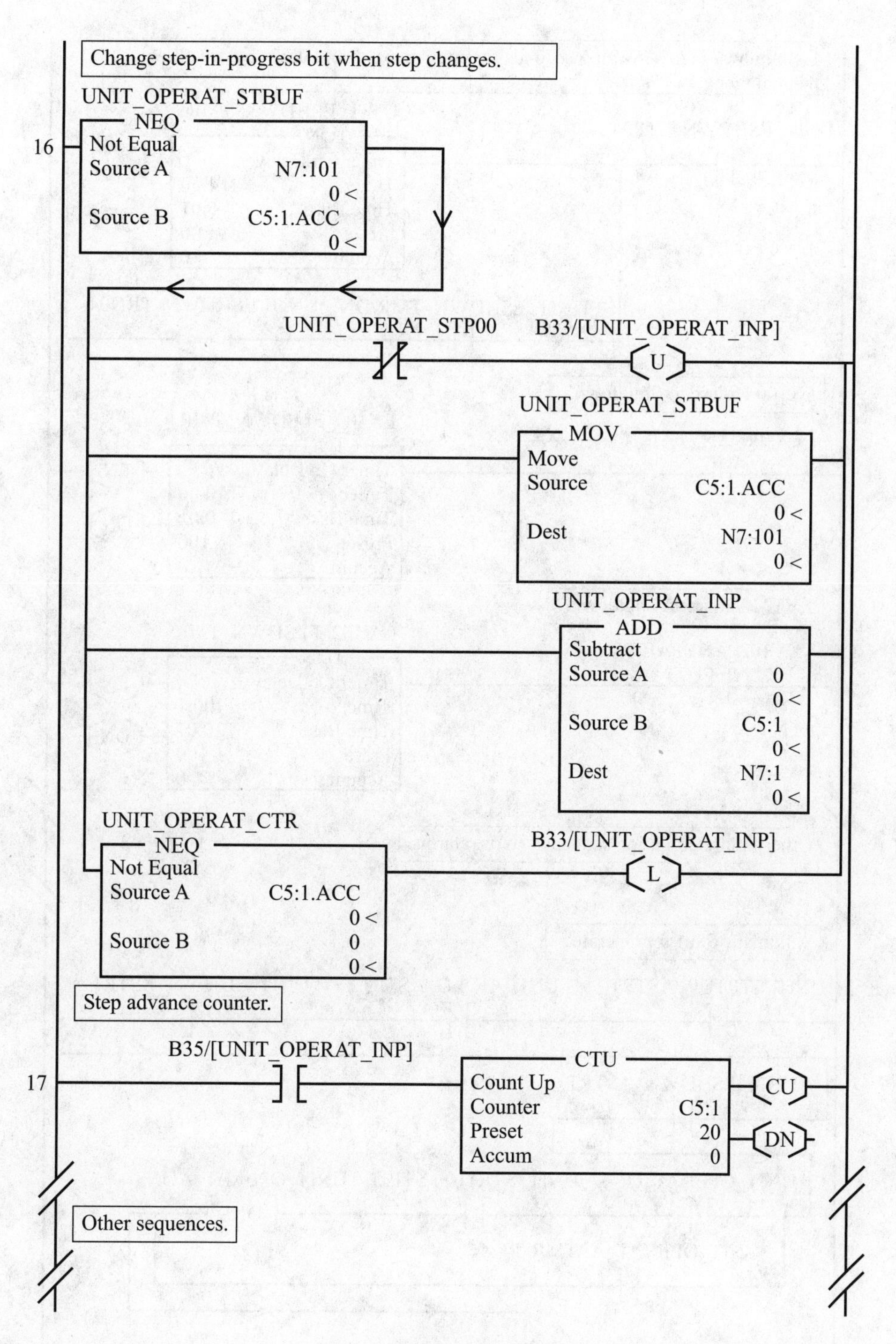

Figure 21.28. *(continued)*

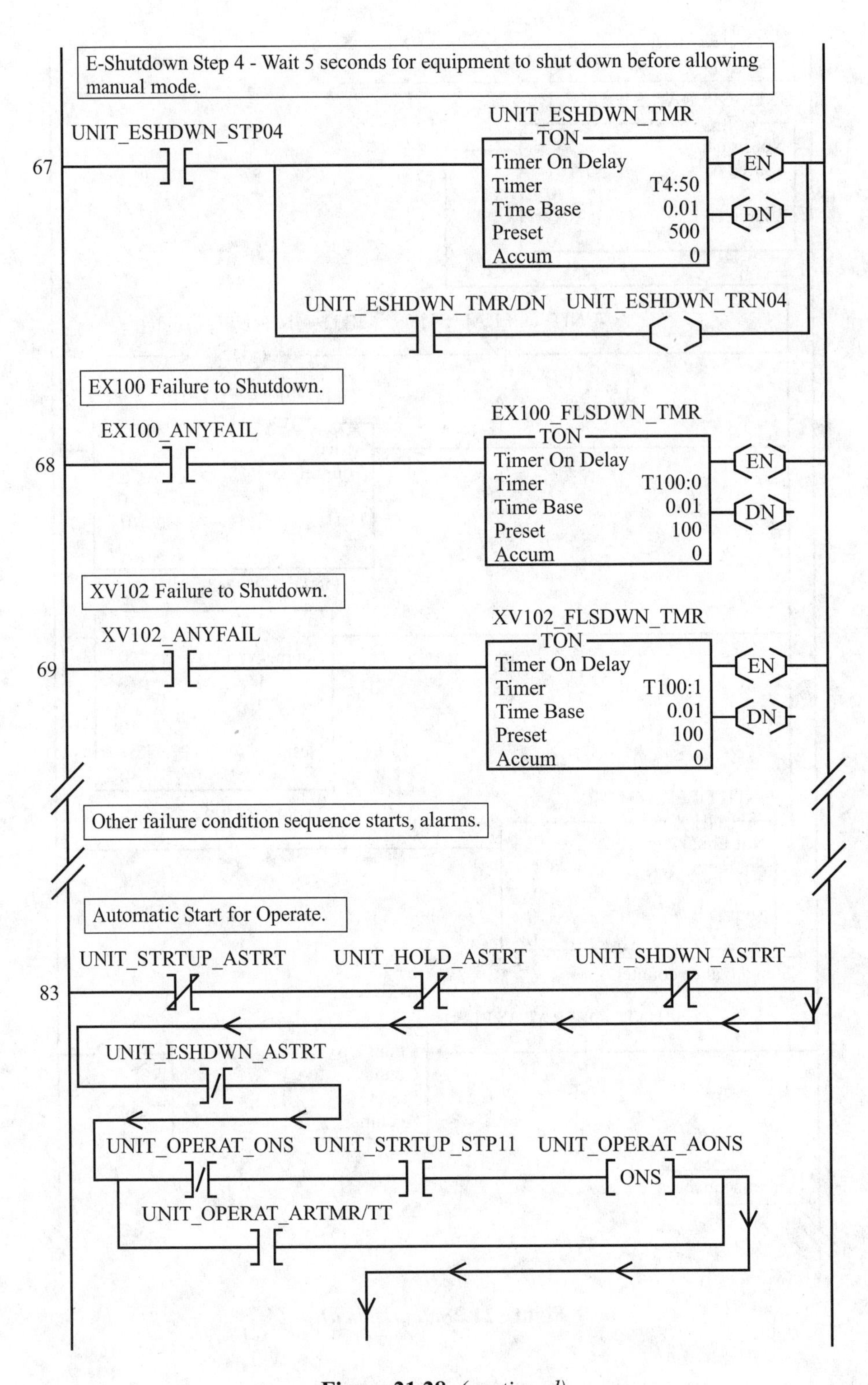

Figure 21.28. *(continued)*

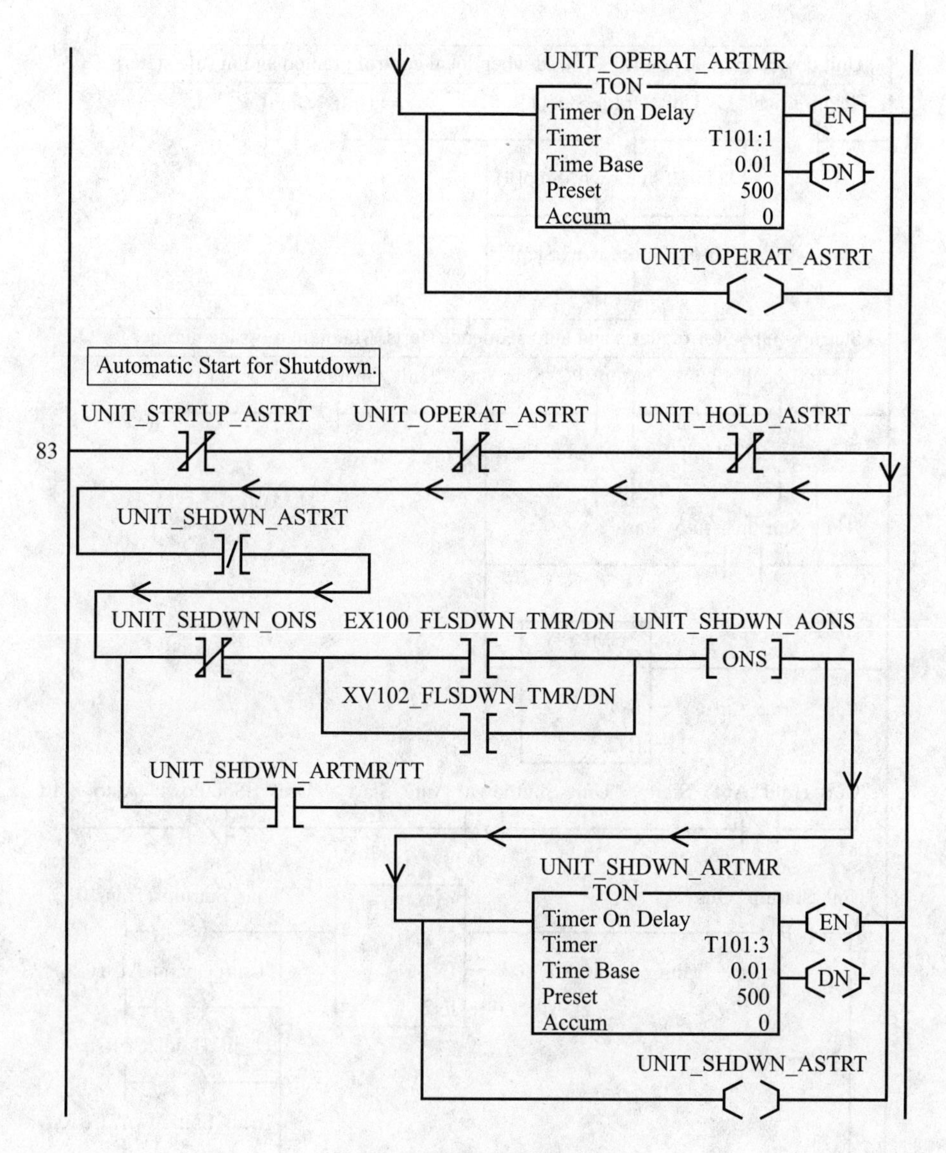

Figure 21.28. *(continued)*

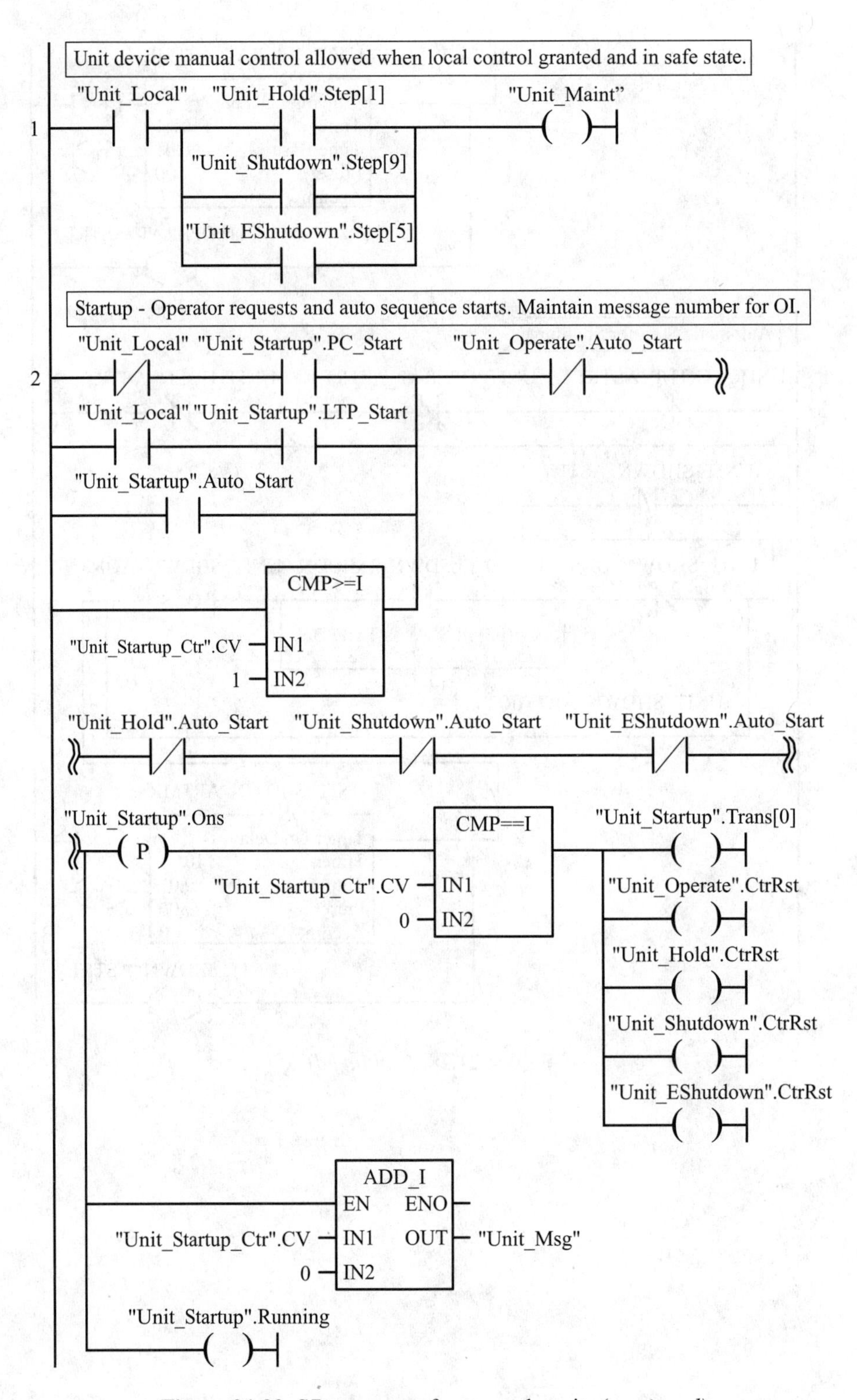

Figure 21.29. S7 sequences for example unit. *(continued)*

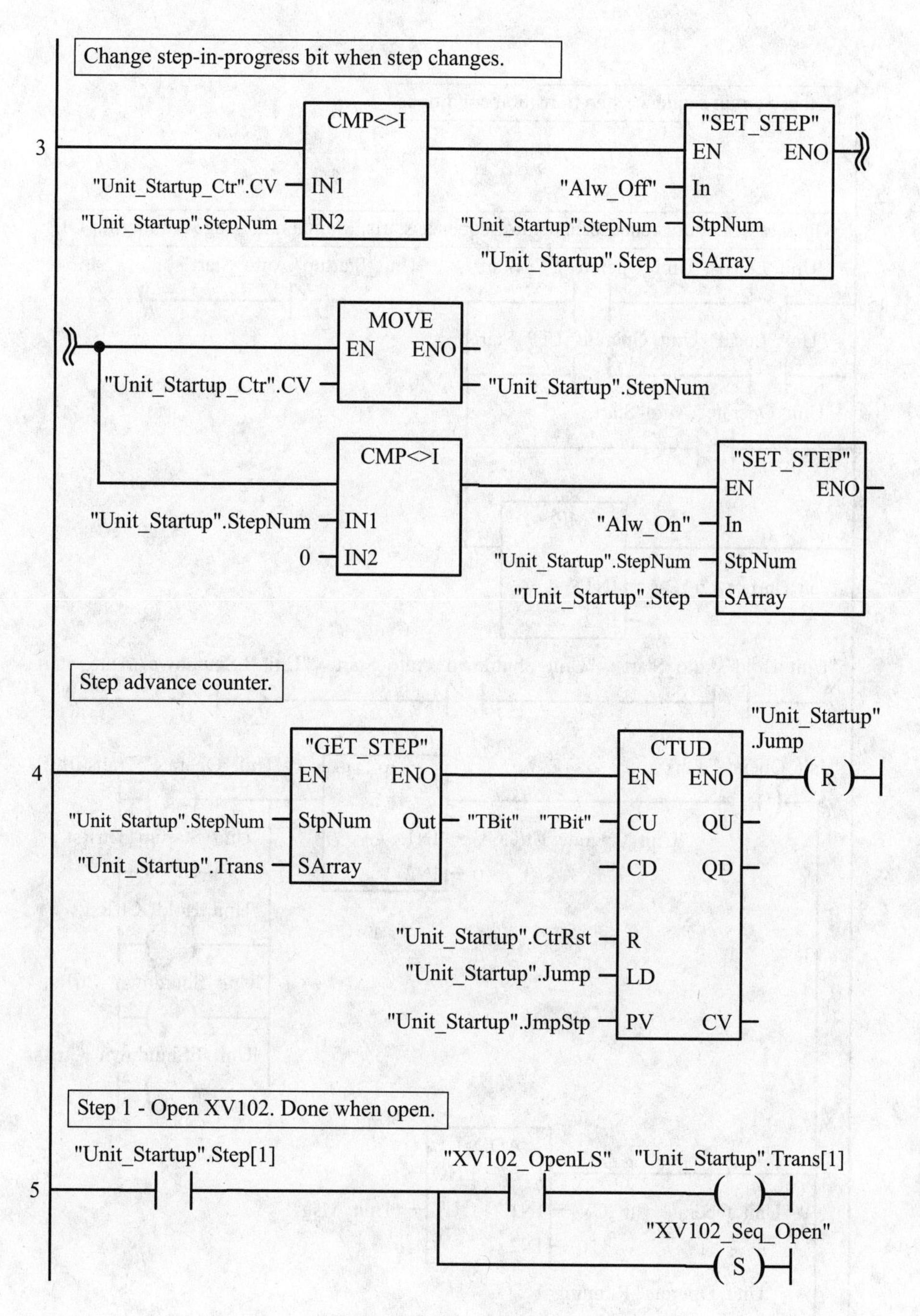

Figure 21.29. *(continued)*

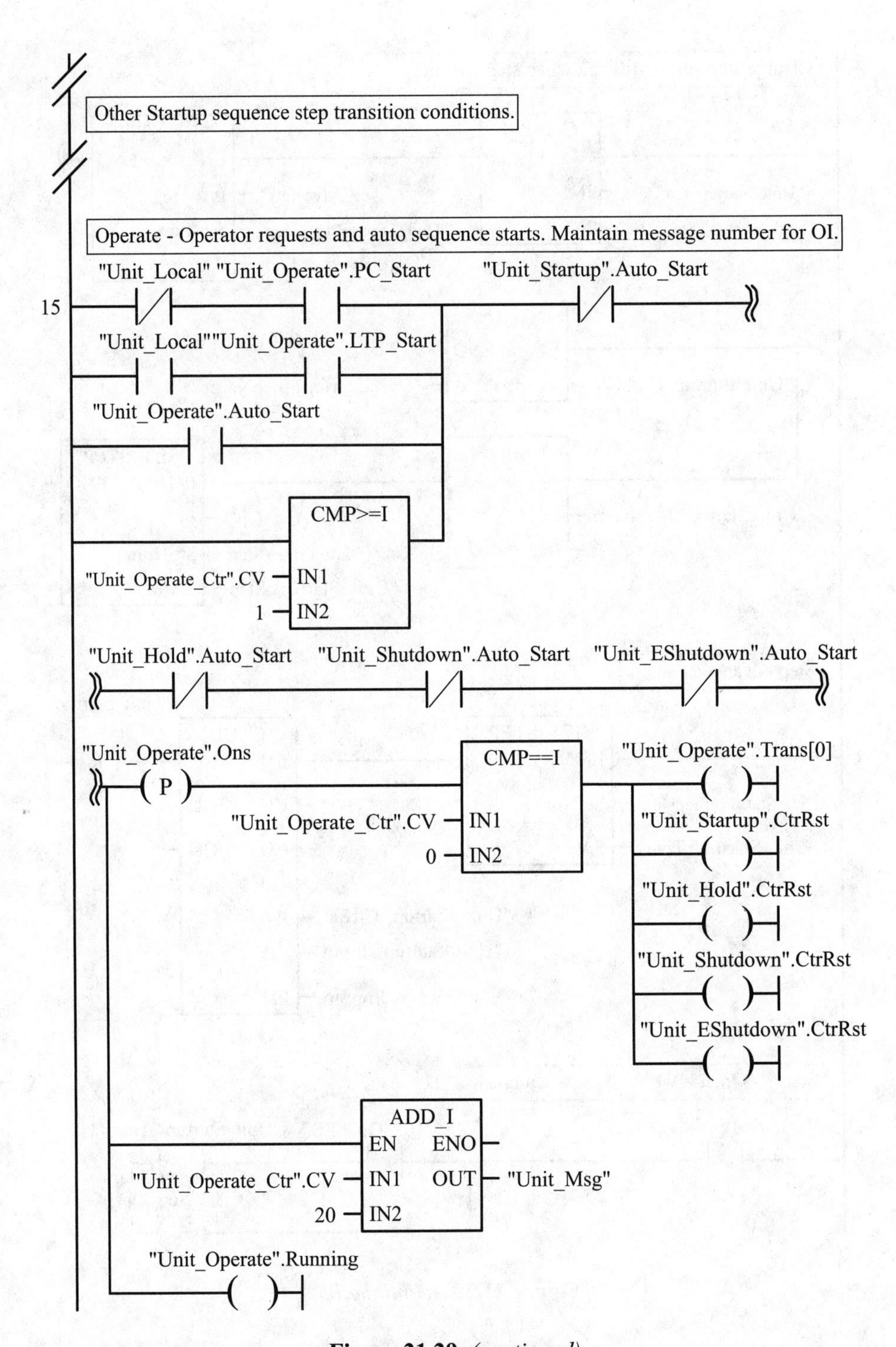

Figure 21.29. *(continued)*

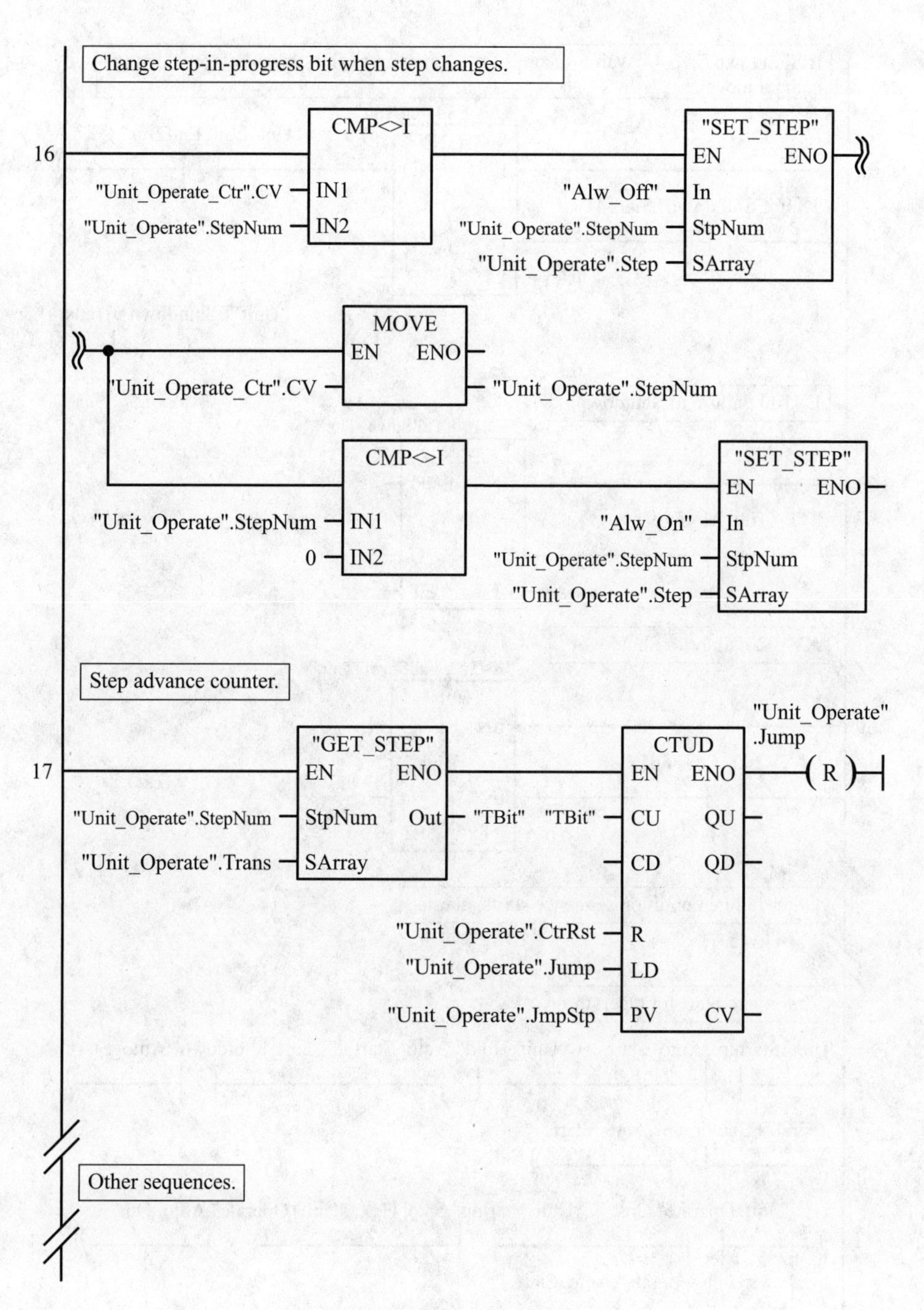

Figure 21.29. *(continued)*

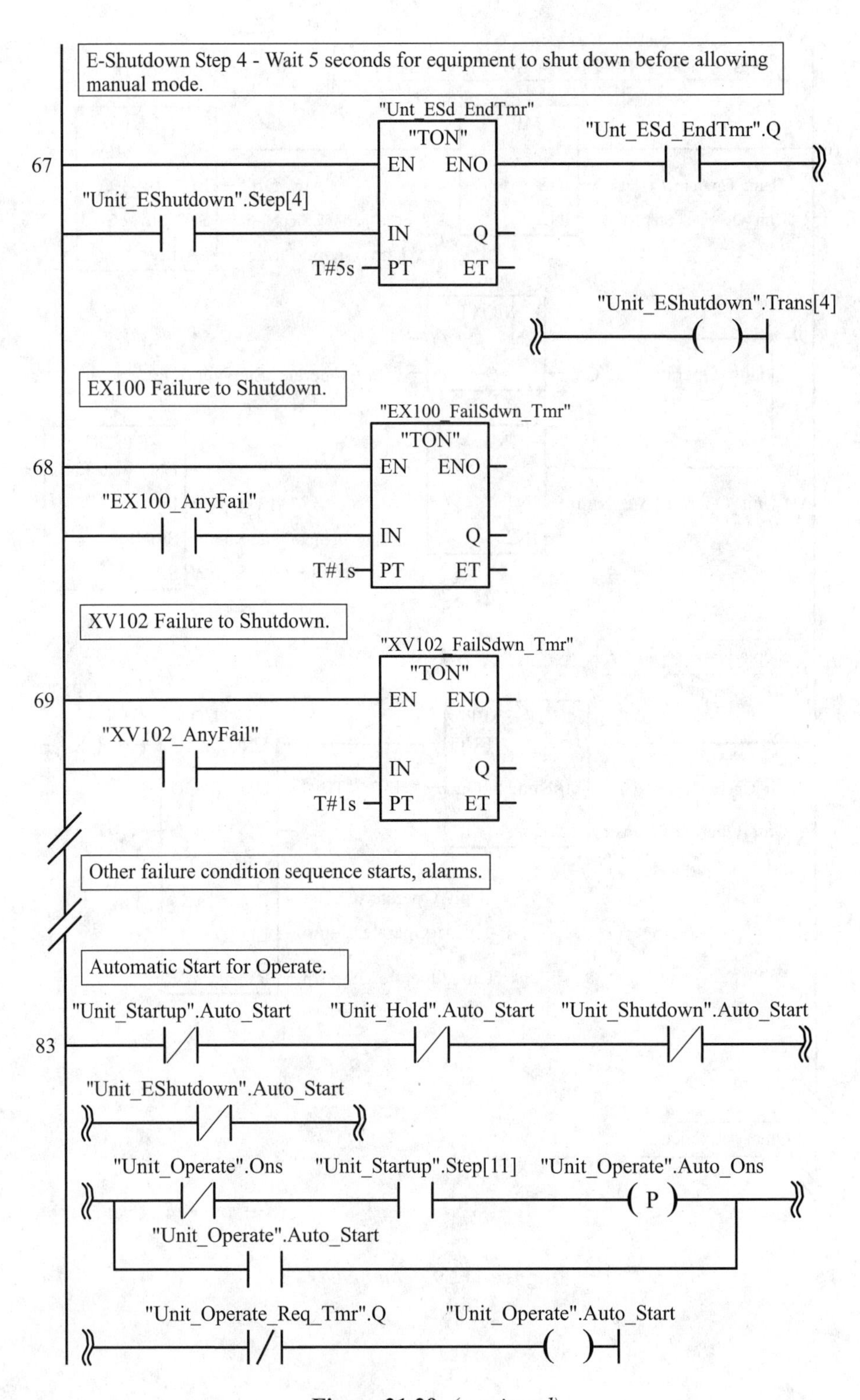

Figure 21.29. *(continued)*

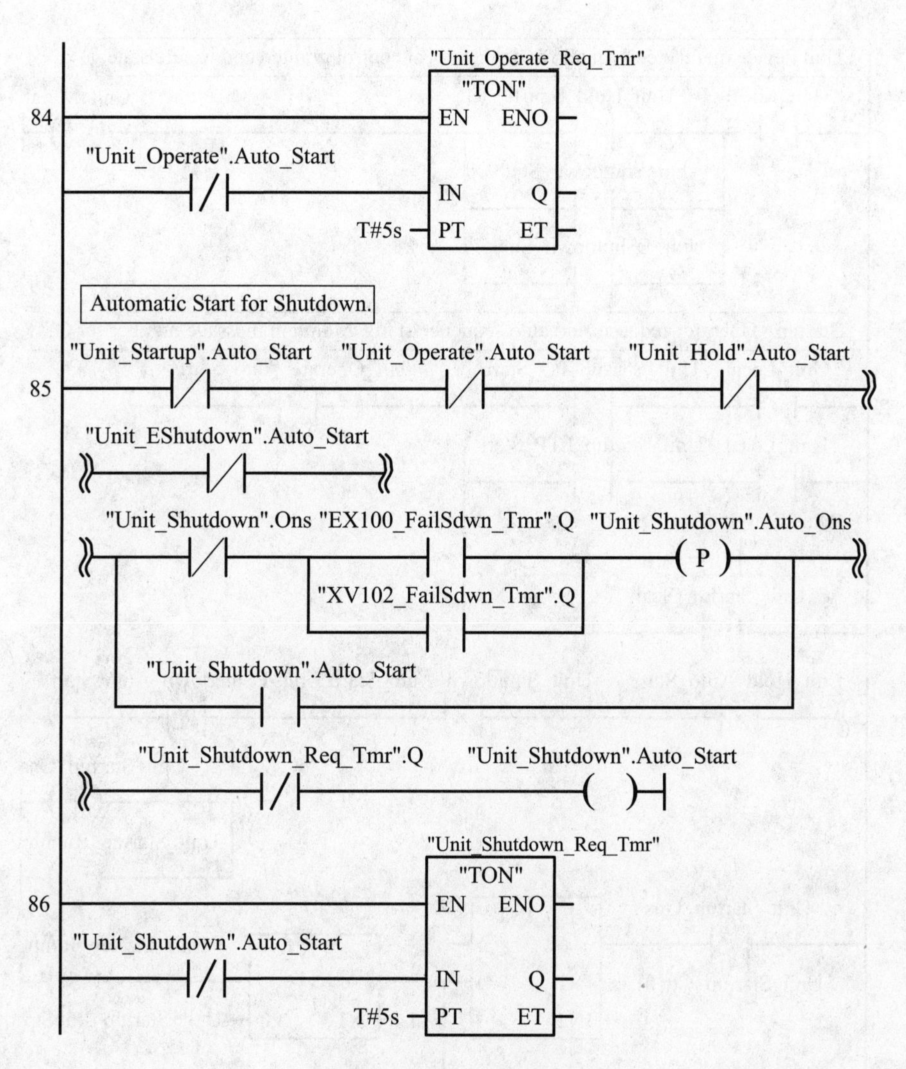

Figure 21.29. *(continued)*

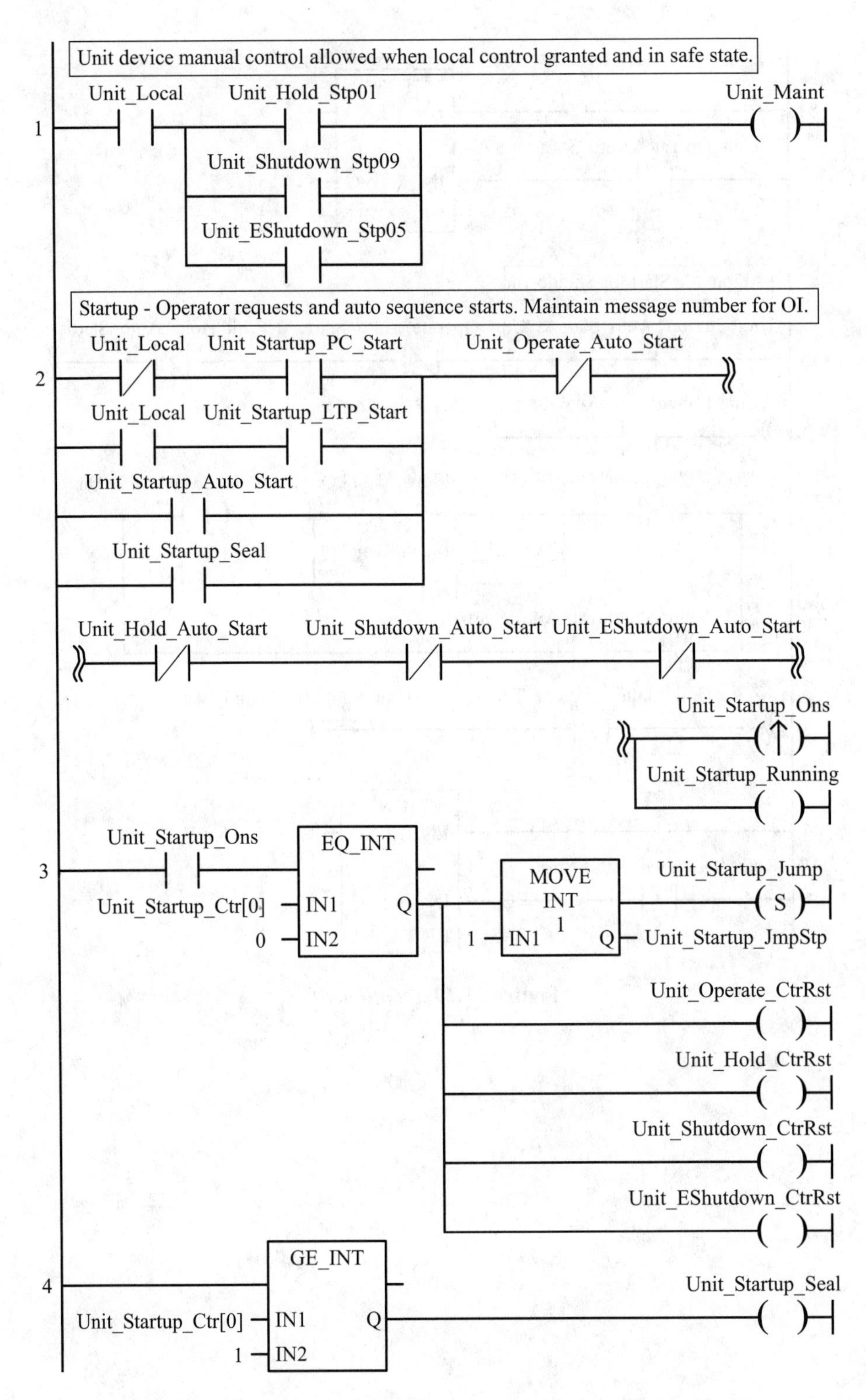

Figure 21.30. GE Fanuc sequences for example unit. *(continued)*

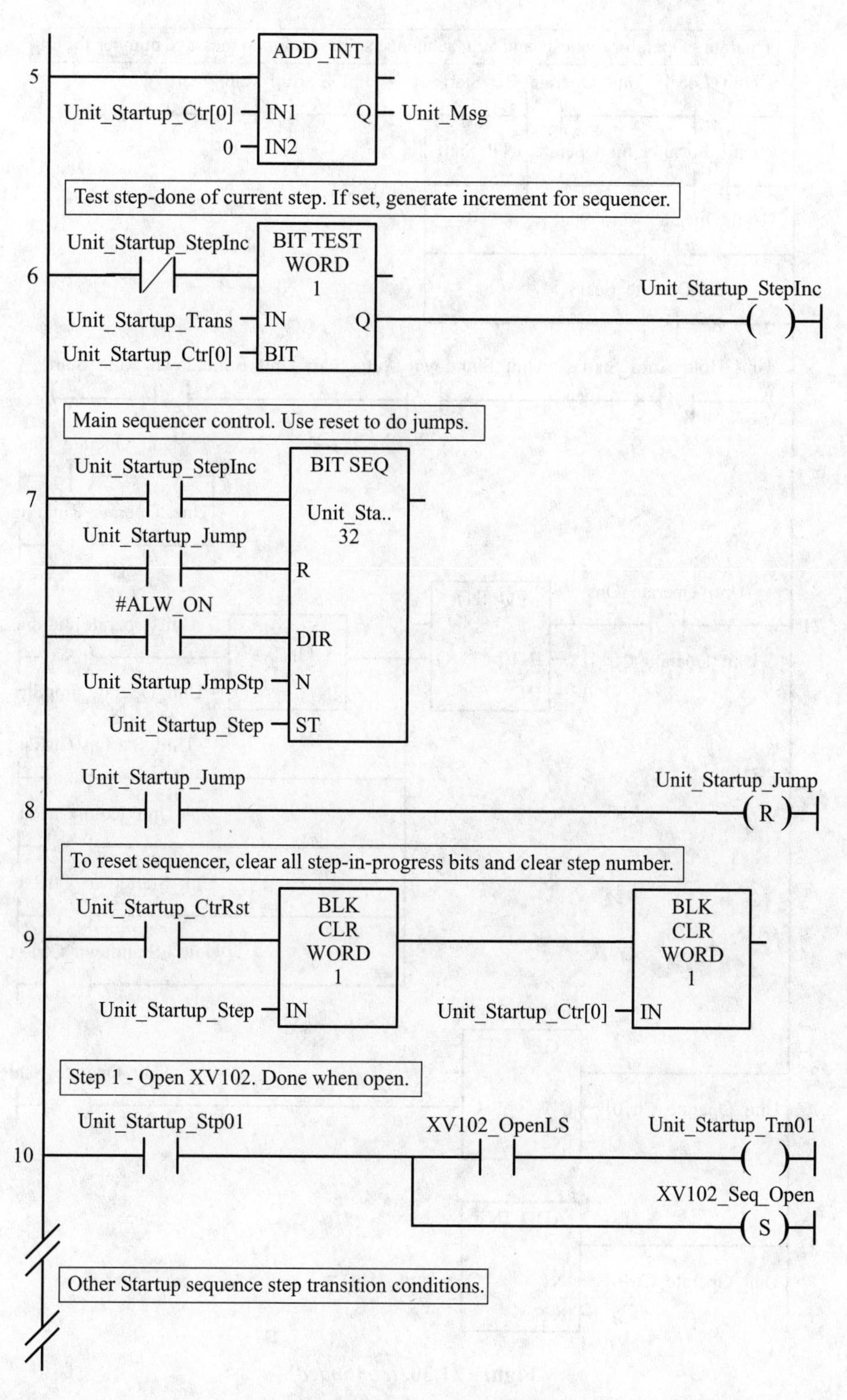

Figure 21.30. *(continued)*

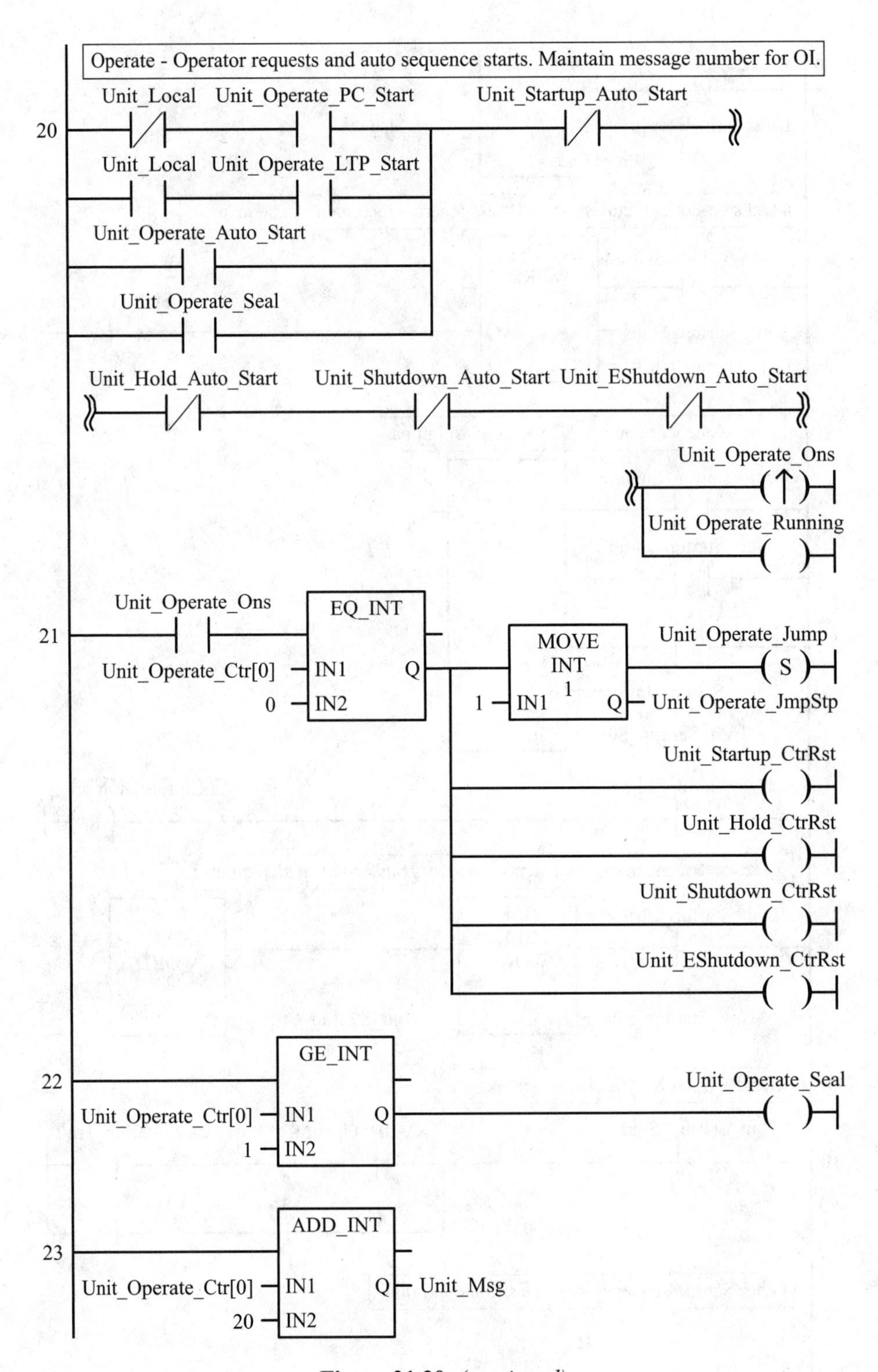

Figure 21.30. *(continued)*

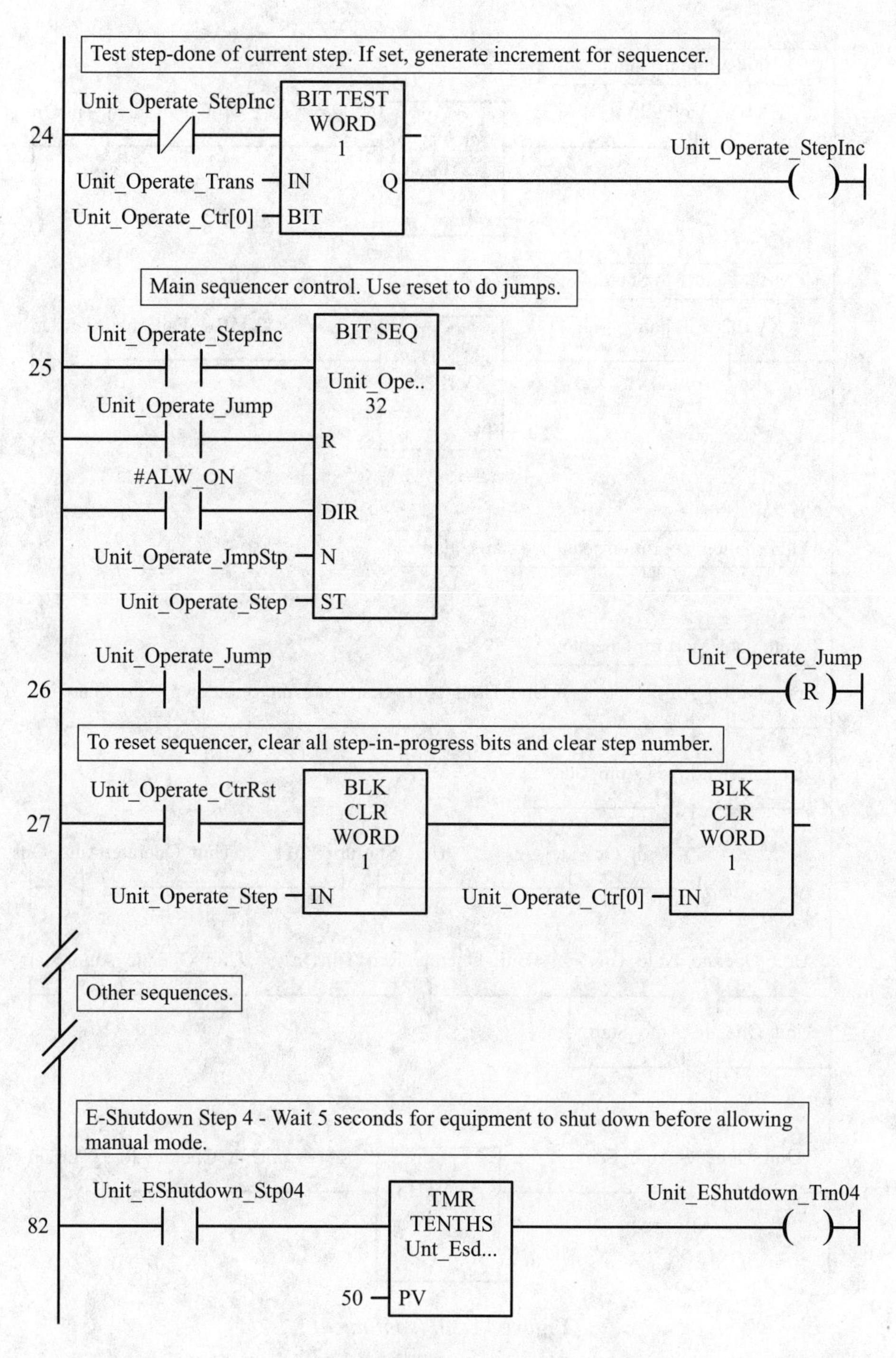

Figure 21.30. *(continued)*

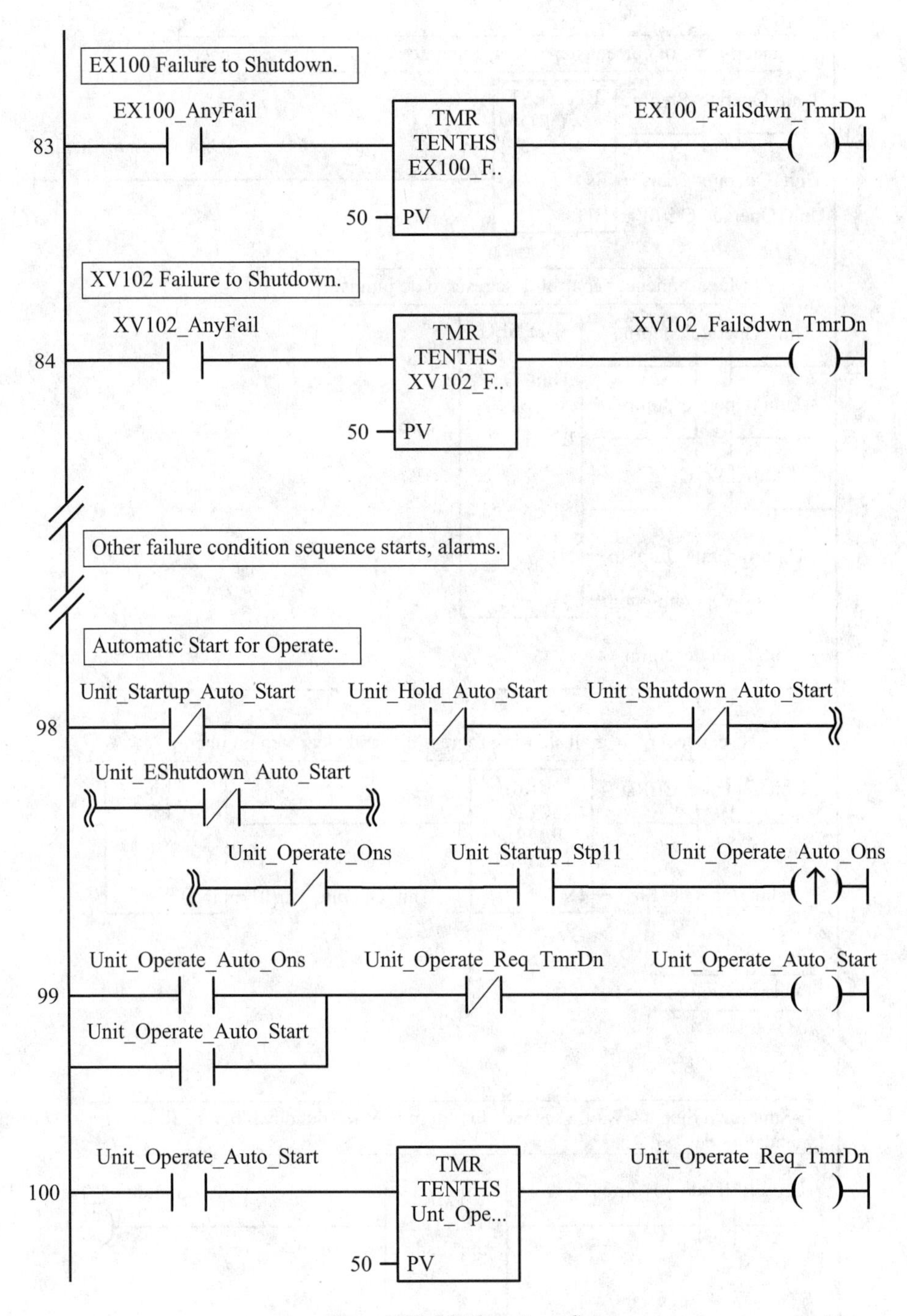

Figure 21.30. *(continued)*

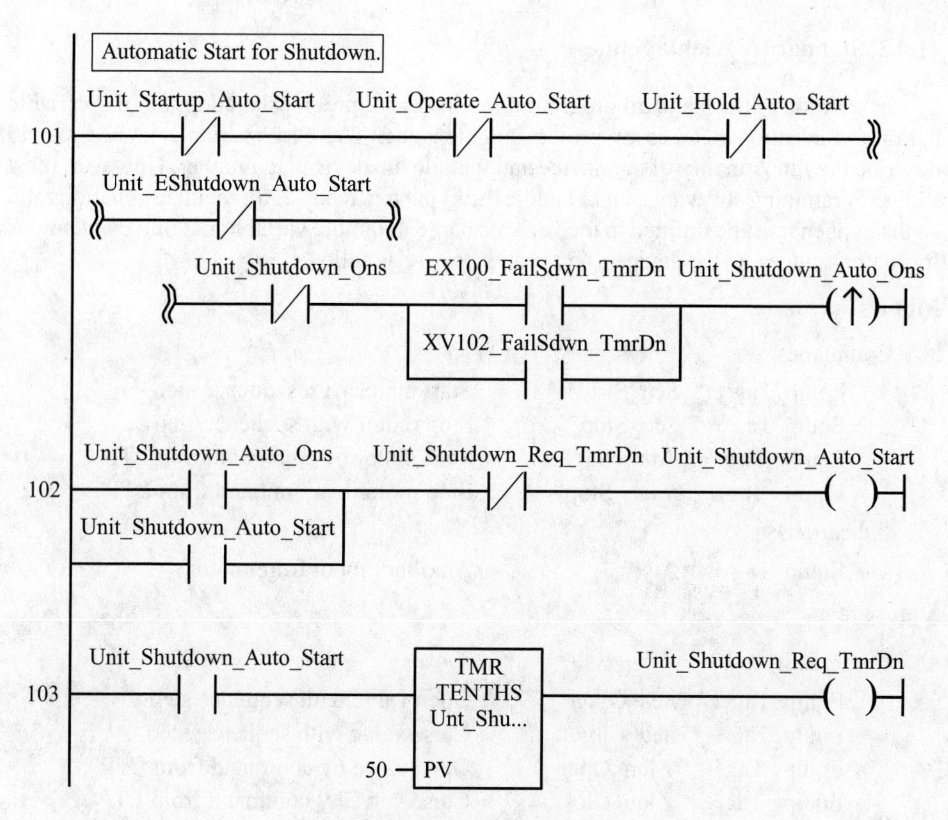

Figure 21.30. *(continued)*

21.4.3. Standard Variable Names

In addition to the standard programming illustrated previously, adoption of a variable naming convention also eases project maintenance. The PLC variable names should describe the functionality of the device and include the device tag number. However, most PLC programming software cannot handle the hyphen in many equipment designations and so the hyphen must be omitted in the variable name. Example variable-naming conventions for motor devices, valve devices, and sequences are as follows:

Motors

Commands:

Equip_Tag + “_Seq_Strt”	Start motor with sequence step
Equip_Tag + “_Seq_Stop”	Stop motor with sequence step
Equip _Tag + “_Man_Strt	Start motor by command from LTP
Equip _Tag + “_Man_Stop	Stop motor by command from LTP

Indications:

Equip_Tag + “_Aux”	Auxillary input from motor

Valves

Commands:

Equip_Tag + “_Seq_Open	Open valve with sequence step
Equip_Tag + “_Seq_Clos	Close valve with sequence step
Equip _Tag + “_Man_Open	Open valve by command from LTP
Equip _Tag + “_Man_Clos	Close valve by command from LTP

Indications:

Equip_Tag + “_OpenLS	Open limit switch for valve
Equip_Tag + “_ClosLS	Closed limit switch for valve

Sequences

Unit _Tag + “_” + Seq_Name + “_PC_Start”	Sequence start request from PC.
Unit _Tag + “_” + Seq_Name + “_LTP_Start”	Sequence start request from LTP.
Unit _Tag + “_” + Seq_Name + “_Step[]”	Sequence step in progress.
Unit _Tag + “_” + Seq_Name + “_Trans[]”	Sequence transition condition satisfied.
Unit_Tag + “_” + Seq_Name + “_Ctr”	Sequence counter.
Unit_Tag + “_” + Seq_Name + “_CtrAcc”	Sequence counter accum. (Modicon).
Unit_Tag + “_” + Seq_Name + “_CtrRst”	Sequence counter reset (Modicon, GE).
Unit_Tag + “_” + Seq_Name + “_Jump”	Jump out of normal sequence (Modicon, GE).
Unit_Tag + “_” + Seq_Name + “_JmpStp”	Jump destination (Modicon, GE).
Unit_Tag + “_” + Seq_Name + “_StepInc”	Sequence increment (GE).

Unit _Tag + "_" + Seq_Name + "_StepNum"	Sequence step bit currently set.
Unit _Tag + "_" + Seq_Name + "_Running"	Sequence running indication.
Unit_Tag + "_" + Seq_Name + "_Seal"	Sequence seal (GE).
Unit _Tag + "_" + Seq_Name + "_Ons"	Sequence one-shot storage to start.
Unit _Tag + "_" + Seq_Name + "_Auto_Start"	Sequence auto start bit.
Unit _Tag + "_" + Seq_Name + "_Auto_Ons"	Sequence auto-start one-shot storage bit.
Unit _Tag + "_" + Seq_Name + "_Req_Tmr"	Sequence auto-start hold timer.
Unit _Tag + "_Msg"	For a unit, holds the message number.
Unit _Tag + "_Local"	For a unit, On when local control, off when HMI (remote) control.
Unit _Tag + "_Maint"	For a unit, On when in maintenance mode: devices started/stopped at LTP.

The PLC-5/SLC-500 processors have a 20-character limit on the symbol name, so the symbol-naming convention for sequence-related symbols is modified to be:

Unit _Tag + "_" + Seq_Name + "_PCSTR"	Sequence start request from PC.
Unit _Tag + "_" + Seq_Name + "_LTSTR"	Sequence start request from LTP.
Unit _Tag + "_" + Seq_Name + "_STPxx"	Sequence step in progress ("xx" is the step number).
Unit _Tag + "_" + Seq_Name + "_TRNxx"	Sequence transition condition satisfied ("xx" is the step number).
Unit_Tag + "_" + Seq_Name + "_CTR"	Sequence counter.
Unit _Tag + "_" + Seq_Name + "_STNUM"	Sequence step bit currently set.
Unit _Tag + "_" + Seq_Name + "_INP"	Indirect pointer to bit arrays.
Unit _Tag + "_" + Seq_Name + "_RUN"	Sequence running indication.
Unit _Tag + "_" + Seq_Name + "_ONS"	Sequence one-shot storage to start.
Unit _Tag + "_" + Seq_Name + "_ASTRT"	Sequence auto start bit.
Unit _Tag + "_" + Seq_Name + "_AONS"	Sequence auto-start one-shot storage bit.
Unit _Tag + "_" + Seq_Name + "_ARTMR"	Sequence auto-start hold timer.
Unit _Tag + "_MSG"	For a unit, holds the message number.
Unit _Tag + "_LOCAL"	For a unit, On when local control, off when HMI (remote) control.

Unit _Tag + "_MAINT" — For a unit, On when in maintenance mode: devices started/stopped at LTP.

For the S7 implementation of sequences, a user-defined data type (UDT) named "Sequence_Type" (defined in Figure 21.31) holds all of the relevant information for one sequence. Each sequence has a variable named

Unit_Tag + "_" + Seq_Name

of "Sequence_Type." The appearance of the relevant symbols is only slightly different than for the other PLCs. For example, the symbol for the sequence start request from the LTP for the Startup sequence of Example 21.4 (Figure 21.29) is

"Unit_Startup".PC_Start

For the Allen-Bradley PLCs, each tag (symbol) has a descriptor with five description fields. As an example, the five description fields could be specified as follows:

Line 1. The device tag number
Line 2. The area name
Line 3. The unit name.
Line 4. The device description.
Line 5. Blank

For example, a pump, with a tag number P-5202, used in the feedwater unit of a boiler area could be described as:

Line 1 P-5202
Line 2 Boiler
Line 3 Feedwater
Line 4 Pump B
Line 5

Addr.	Name	Type	Init. Value	Comment
0.0		STRUCT		
+0.0	StepNum	INT	0	Current step number
+2.0	Step	ARRAY[0..50]		Step in progress bits
*0.1		BOOL		
+10.0	Trans	ARRAY[0..50]		Step transition bits
*0.1		BOOL		
+18.0	PC_Start	BOOL	FALSE	Sequence start req. from PC
+18.1	LTP_Start	BOOL	FALSE	Sequence start req. from LTP
+18.2	Ons	BOOL	FALSE	One-shot storage to start
+18.3	Running	BOOL	FALSE	Running indication
+18.4	CtrRst	BOOL	FALSE	Sequence counter reset request
+18.5	Auto_Start	BOOL	FALSE	Auto start request
+18.6	Auto_Ons	BOOL	FALSE	Auto-start one-shot storage
+18.7	Jump	BOOL	FALSE	Jump out of normal sequence
+20.0	JmpStp	INT	0	Jump destination step
=22.0		END_STRUCT		

Figure 21.31. "Sequence_Type" S7 user-defined data type.

21.5 TESTING

Before the system is installed, the PLC program should be tested for proper operation and to verify the operator interfaces. This testing is performed without any connection to the actual process. In order to appropriately test the system operation, the actual process should be simulated. For most processes, the simulation does not need to be an accurate model of the process, just enough so that the PLC operation can be verified. If the unit is a complicated chemical process, then the expense of designing a reasonably faithful dynamic model may be justified. The process simulation can also be used for operator training; both before and after the actual system is commissioned.

There are two primary ways to simulate the process:

1. External process simulator, or
2. Simulation program in the PLC processor.

The separate process simulator has the advantage that it does not require any of the PLC program memory, but has the disadvantage that it requires extra hardware (a PC and an interface card). For both of these simulation methods, the actual PLC processors are used in the testing.

For some of the PLCs covered by this text, one can purchase an *emulator* that runs the PLC program on a PC, thus not requiring a processor to verify the program operation. An emulator has the disadvantages:

- Program executes slower than the PLC processor, meaning that any critical timing issues cannot be accurately tested.
- Some processor communication interfaces may not be modeled, possibly restricting the operator interface and PLC-to-PLC communication tests.

Emulators are useful for the initial testing of short programs, for example, a new standard device, but may not be acceptable for full-scale system testing.

The operation of an external process simulator is shown in Figure 21.32. The process simulator connects to the remote I/O communication network and acts like the PLC remote I/O. The actual I/O is not used. The simulator must be configured (or programmed) to set the emulated physical inputs to their proper values in response to the physical outputs commanded by the PLC processor.

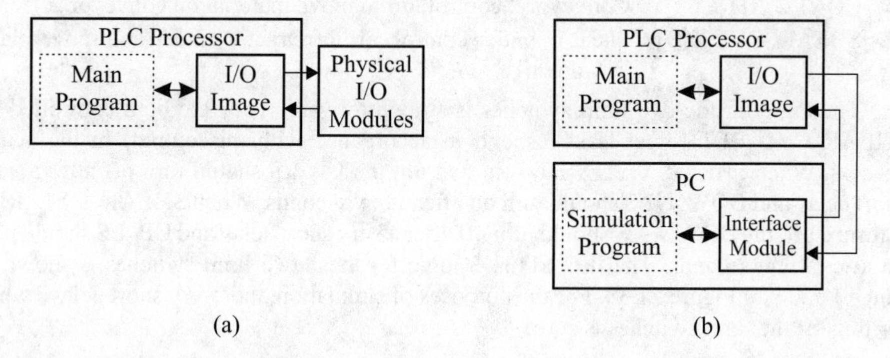

Figure 21.32. External process simulation: *(a)* normal I/O update; *(b)* PC-based simulation.

In the author's opinion, the use of the PLC to simulate the process is a powerful tool in the testing of a PLC program. It does not require separate hardware, though it uses some of the processor memory. Depending on the particular processor, this process can be very easy, to moderately difficult. In all cases, the normal I/O update is disabled or circumvented, and a simulation program in the PLC "reads" the usual physical outputs and "writes" the usual physical inputs. The physical outputs are essentially "tied back" to the physical inputs. This simulation logic is often called "tie-back logic." After explaining the general philosophy behind tie-back logic and illustrating it with some examples, the specific methods of implementing tie-back logic for each of the PLCs covered by this text are described.

21.5.1 General Simulation Concepts

The general concept behind the process simulation is that the PLC outputs are the "process" inputs and the PLC inputs are the "process" outputs. In the tie-back logic the physical inputs are thus the output coils. Only the physical PLC outputs should be used to drive the simulated physical PLC inputs. Do not use any internal variables of the program being simulated. The simulation is ***should not*** depend on a particular implementation. With this rule, the tested program could be completely rewritten, and the simulation could still be used to test it. To formulate the tie-back logic for a particular physical input one should ask the question, "In the actual process, what physical output(s) causes this input to change?" The following examples illustrate the formulation of simulation logic.

Example 21.5. *Simulation of Metal Shear of Example 6.2.* The tie-back, or simulation, logic does not include the start and stop switches. These are still assumed under operator control and can easily be forced even when the physical input modules are absent. The tie-back logic needs to drive the following inputs:

Variable	Description
PROX	Proximity sensor, **on** when strip in shearing position
DOWN_LS	Limit switch, N. O., **on** (closed) when blade fully down
UP_LS	Limit switch, N. O., **on** (closed) when blade fully up

The following outputs are available to drive the inputs:

Variable	Description
CONV1_MTR	Conveyor 1 control, **on** to move material on conveyor 1
CONV2_MTR	Conveyor 2 control, **on** to move material on conveyor 2
SHEAR_CYL_RET	Shear cylinder control, **on** to retract cylinder and move blade down

The logic for the two limit switches is straightforward. They are both controlled by SHEAR_CYL_RET (or at least respond in accordance with this output) in the actual process. When SHEAR_CYL_RET is turned **on**, the UP_LS should turn **off** after a very short delay and DOWN_LS should turn **on** after a few seconds. When SHEAR_CYL_RET is turned **off**, the DOWN_LS should turn **off** after a very short delay and UP_LS should turn **on** after a few seconds. The IEC 61131-3 logic for these two limit switches is shown in rungs 1 and 2 of Figure 21.33. For the purposes of simulation, the "very short delay" when turning **off** the limit switches is zero.

The logic for PROX requires a little more thought. Ultimately, PROX responds when one or both of the conveyors are run. PROX should turn **on** a few seconds after both

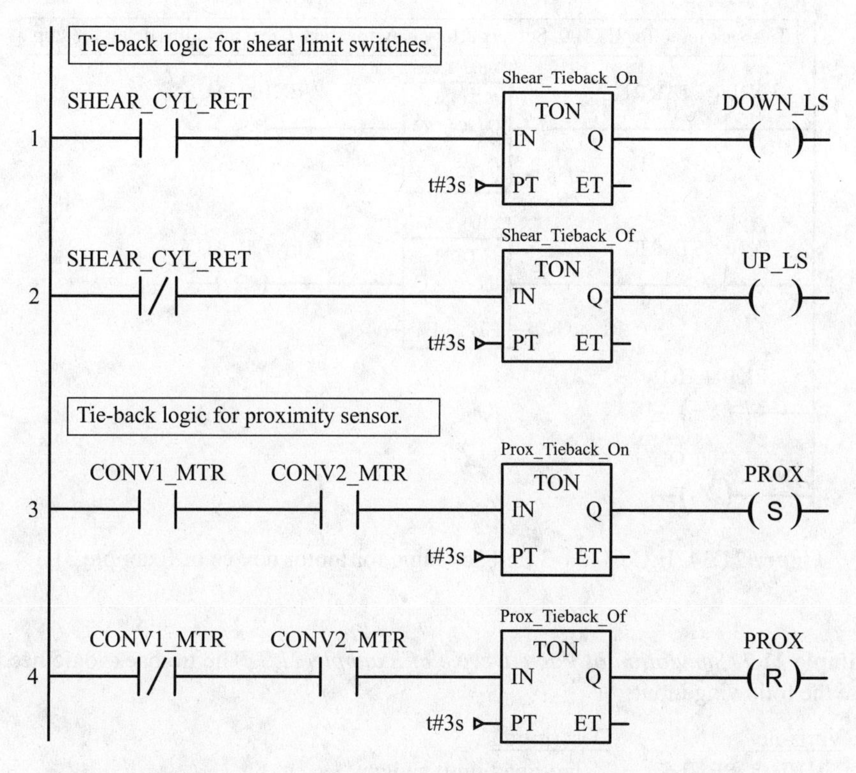

Figure 21.33. IEC 61131-3 tie-back logic for metal shear of Example 6.2.

conveyors start running. PROX should turn **off** a few seconds after only conveyor 2 is running. The IEC 61131-3 logic for PROX is shown in rungs 3 and 4 of Figure 21.33.

Example 21.6. *Simulation of Motor Device of Example 21.1.* The simulation logic needs to determine the following inputs:

Variable	Description
EX100_AUX	Auxiliary contact.
EX100_OL	Overload contact.
EX100_HOA	HOA switch auto contact.

The only output is EX100_START, the motor contactor control.

The logic for the EX100_AUX input is straightforward. When EX100_START is turned **on**, EX100_AUX should turn **on** after a few seconds. When EX100_START is turned **off**, EX100_AUX should turn **off** after a few seconds. The EX100_OL input should be forced **off**, and the EX100_HOA input should be forced **on**. The IEC 61131-3 logic for these three inputs is shown in Figure 21.34.

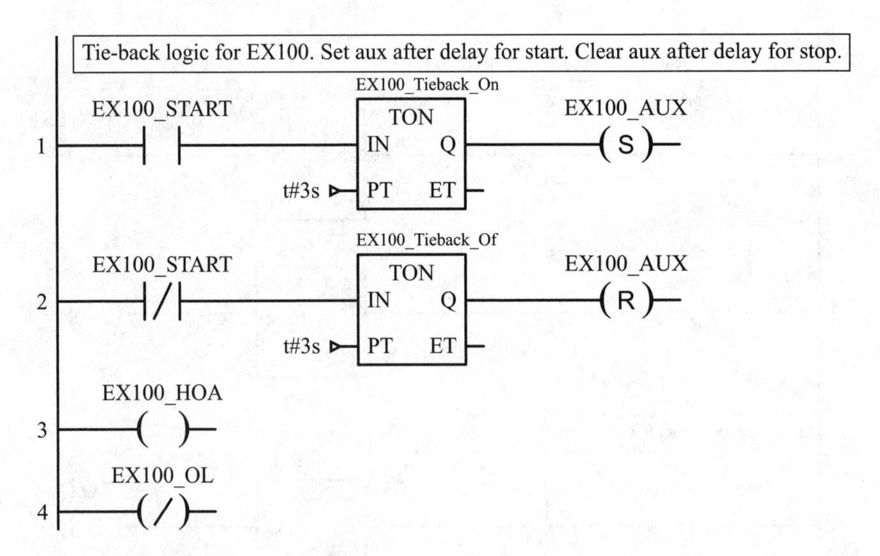

Figure 21.34. IEC 61131-3 tie-back logic for motor device of Example 21.1.

Example 21.7. *Simulation of Valve Device of Example 21.3.* The tie-back logic needs to drive the following inputs:

Variable	Description
XV102_OPENLS	Valve-open limit switch.
XV102_CLOSLS	Valve-closed limit switch.

The only output is XV102_SOL_VLV, the valve solenoid.

The logic for the two limit switches is nearly identical to the shear limit switches in Example 21.5. When XV102_SOL_VLV is turned **on**, the XV102_CLOSLS switch should turn **off** after a very short delay (Immediately) and XV102_OPENLS should turn **on** after a few seconds. When XV102_SOL_VLV is turned **off**, XV102_OPENLS should turn **off** immediately and XV102_CLOSLS should turn **on** after a few seconds. The IEC 61131-3 logic for these two limit switches is shown in Figure 21.35.

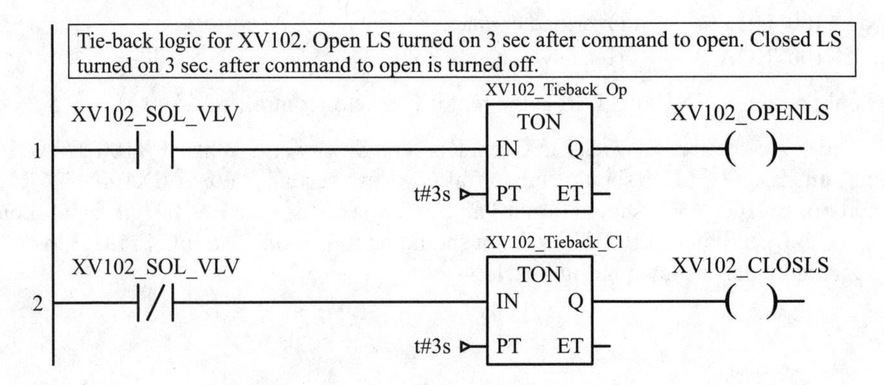

Figure 21.35. IEC 61131-3 tie-back logic for valve device of Example 21.3.

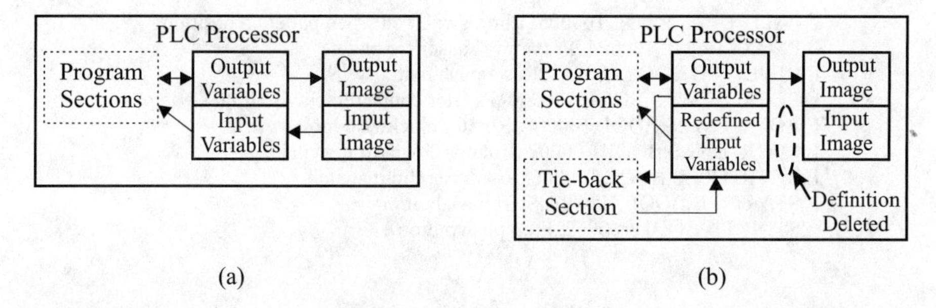

Figure 21.36. Modicon process simulation: *(a)* normal interaction with I/O image; *(b)* tie-back logic.

21.5.2 Modicon Tie-Back Logic

To implement tie-back logic in a Modicon PLC, the physical input variables are redefined as unlocated variables and a section for the tie-back logic is added to the program (Figure 21.36). The tie-back logic reads the physical output locations and writes to the redefined input variables. The tie-back logic can be disabled and therefore may remain in the project.

The I/O modules are not needed. Only a chassis with a power supply and the processor in the correct slot is required. If testing the HMI, then any required communication modules (for example, Ethernet) must be added.

The general strategy is to export the variable database as a comma-separated-value (CSV) file, delete the addresses for the physical input variables, and then import these changes into the project. To setup the tie-back logic, the procedure is as follows:

1. In the Variable Editor, check the "Exp" column for the physical input variables. This action marks these variables for export.
2. Export the variable database as "Variables: Text delimited" with a comma (",") as the separator. Also, check the "Export variables" and "Export only marked variables" options on the export filter settings. Save the variables with a ".csv" extension. This file contains the physical input definitions.
3. With a text editor or spreadsheet program, delete the I/O address definition for each variable (row) in the file saved in the previous step. Save this new file with a different name. This file contains the simulated input definitions. Note: if using a spreadsheet program to edit the file, the variables must contain a comment.
4. Import the simulated input definitions into the project to be tested as "Variables: Text delimited." When importing, set the delimiting character to "," and check the "Allow modification of existing variables" option. You will receive a warning since the import writes over existing variable definitions.
5. Program the tie-back logic in a separate program section.

An example exported physical input variable definition and the corresponding simulated input variable definition is shown in Figure 21.37. This example is for the engine inverter station of Example 6.4. The text format of the files is shown. If imported into a spreadsheet program, each comma delimits a column.

When finished with the tie-back logic testing, the tie-back section can be disabled or the tie-back logic can be saved. In either case, the original physical input variable definitions

```
E,PALL_UPLS,BOOL,100005,,Limit switch on when pallet up position
E,PROX1,BOOL,100004,,Proximity sensor for pallet
E,RESET_PB,BOOL,100003,,Reset push button
E,ROTR_CCWLS,BOOL,100009,,Rotator counterclockwise limit switch
E,ROTR_CWLS,BOOL,100008,,Rotator clockwise limit switch
E,ROTR_DNLS,BOOL,100007,,Rotator down limit switch
E,ROTR_UPLS,BOOL,100006,,Rotator up limit switch
E,START_PB,BOOL,100001,,Start push button
E,STOP_PB,BOOL,100002,,Stop push button
```

(a)

```
E,PALL_UPLS,BOOL,,,Limit switch on when pallet up position
E,PROX1,BOOL,,,Proximity sensor for pallet
E,RESET_PB,BOOL,,,Reset push button
E,ROTR_CCWLS,BOOL,,,Rotator counterclockwise limit switch
E,ROTR_CWLS,BOOL,,,Rotator clockwise limit switch
E,ROTR_DNLS,BOOL,,,Rotator down limit switch
E,ROTR_UPLS,BOOL,,,Rotator up limit switch
E,START_PB,BOOL,,,Start push button
E,STOP_PB,BOOL,,,Stop push button
```

(b)

Figure 21.37. Modicon input variable definitions for Example 6.4: *(a)* physical inputs; *(b)* simulated inputs.

must be restored. To disable the tieback section, one needs to turn **on** the "disable" Boolean in the section control. For example, if the section is named "Tieback", the "Tieback.disable" variable needs to be turned **on**. This variable may be set with logic, or directly with the Reference Data Editor. The disadvantage of this method is that the tie-back outputs (simulated inputs) cannot be modified with the original physical input definitions. To save the tie-back section, the procedure is as follows:

1. Save the project as a new name. This project will be used to keep the tie-back logic in case the program needs to be retested.
2. Open the original project and delete the tie-back logic section(s).

In either case, import the original physical input variable definitions saved in step (2) of the tie-back logic setup.

In order to use a disabled tie-back logic section,

1. Import the simulated input definitions as "Variables: Text delimited" into the original project. When importing, set the delimiting character to "," and check the "Allow modification of existing variables" option. You will receive a warning since the import writes over existing variable definitions.
2. Turn off the "disable" Boolean in the section control for the tie-back logic section (".disable").

To reuse a saved tie-back logic section, do the following:

1. Import simulated input definitions as "Variables: Text delimited" into the original project. When importing, set the delimiting character to "," and check the "Allow modification of existing variables" option. You will receive a warning since the import writes over existing variable definitions.
2. Export the tie-back logic from the project that contains the tie-back logic with the following steps. Open the project containing the tie-back logic. Start a "Program: Sections" export. Select your project and then select the tie-back section. Specify the name of the file that will contain the exported section, for example "Tieback.sec."
3. Open the original project and import the tie-back logic section. Start a "Program: Sections" import. Select the file saved in the previous step. When presented with the replacement window, just select "OK" to start the import.

21.5.3 ControlLogix Tie-Back Logic

To implement tie-back logic in a ControlLogix PLC, the aliases for the physical input variables are redefined to simulation tags and a tie-back logic routine is added to the program (Figure 21.38). The logic in the tie-back routine reads the physical output aliases and writes to the simulation tags aliased to the physical input variables. The tie-back logic routine does not need to be taken out of the processor.

The I/O modules are not needed. Only a chassis with a power supply and the processor in the correct slot is required. If testing the HMI, then any required communication modules (for example, Ethernet or ControlNet) must be added.

The general idea is to export the tag database as a comma-separated-value (CSV) file, redefine the aliases for the tags that refer to physical inputs, and then import these changes into the project. To setup the tie-back logic, the procedure is as follows:

1. Export the tags as an "RSLogix 5000 Import/Export File (*.CSV)" file. Only controller tags need to be exported.
2. With a text editor or spreadsheet program, delete all of the lines (rows) of the tags that are not the physical inputs. Keep the first seven lines of header information and save this file. This file contains the aliased physical input definitions.
3. For the file created in the previous step, define the aliases as regular tags. In the first column (spreadsheet column A), replace "ALIAS" with "TAG." Put the appropriate data type in the fifth column (column E). Delete the I/O address in the

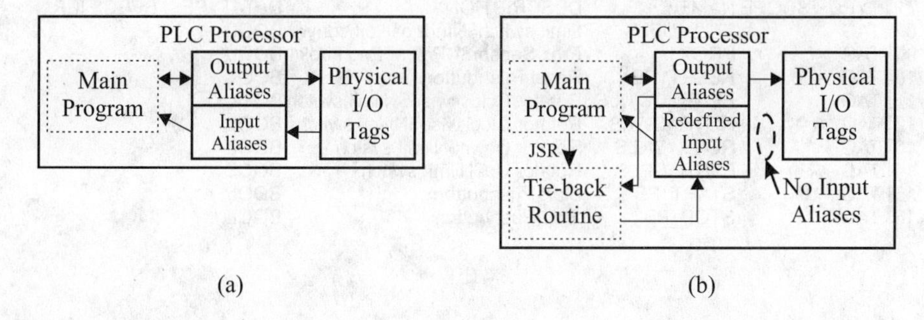

Figure 21.38. ControlLogix process simulation: *(a)* normal interaction with I/O tags; *(b)* tie-back routine.

sixth column (column F). Save this new file with a different name. This file contains the simulated input definitions.

4. Import the simulated input tags as an "RSLogix 5000 Import/Export File (*.CSV)" file. You will receive a warning since the import writes over existing variable definitions.
5. Program the tie-back logic in a separate routine.
6. Place a JSR block in the main routine that calls the tie-back logic routine.

An example exported physical input tag alias definition and the corresponding simulated input tag definition is shown in Figure 21.39. This example is for the engine inverter station of Example 6.4. The spreadsheet format of the files is shown.

When finished with the tie-back logic testing, the original physical input tag aliases are restored and the tie-back routine JSR is disabled:

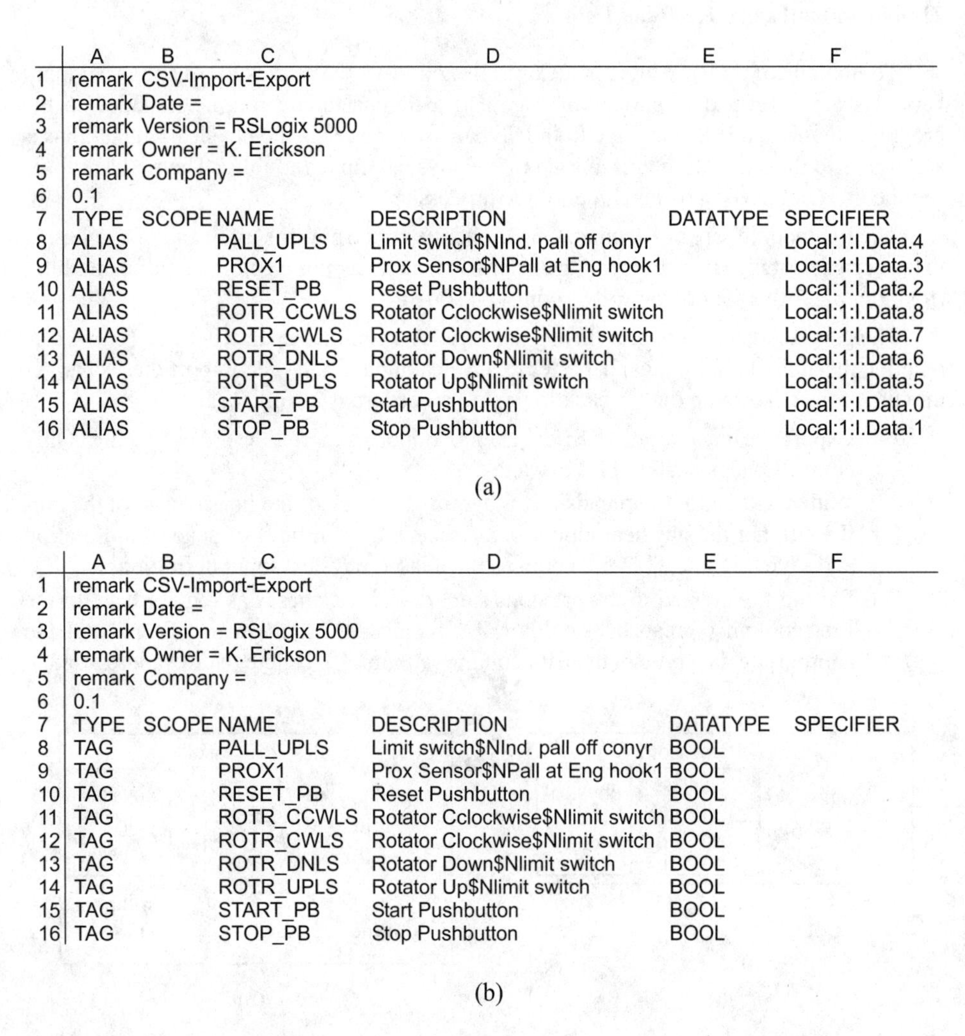

	A	B	C	D	E	F
1	remark	CSV-Import-Export				
2	remark	Date =				
3	remark	Version = RSLogix 5000				
4	remark	Owner = K. Erickson				
5	remark	Company =				
6	0.1					
7	TYPE	SCOPE	NAME	DESCRIPTION	DATATYPE	SPECIFIER
8	ALIAS		PALL_UPLS	Limit switch$NInd. pall off conyr		Local:1:I.Data.4
9	ALIAS		PROX1	Prox Sensor$NPall at Eng hook1		Local:1:I.Data.3
10	ALIAS		RESET_PB	Reset Pushbutton		Local:1:I.Data.2
11	ALIAS		ROTR_CCWLS	Rotator Cclockwise$Nlimit switch		Local:1:I.Data.8
12	ALIAS		ROTR_CWLS	Rotator Clockwise$Nlimit switch		Local:1:I.Data.7
13	ALIAS		ROTR_DNLS	Rotator Down$Nlimit switch		Local:1:I.Data.6
14	ALIAS		ROTR_UPLS	Rotator Up$Nlimit switch		Local:1:I.Data.5
15	ALIAS		START_PB	Start Pushbutton		Local:1:I.Data.0
16	ALIAS		STOP_PB	Stop Pushbutton		Local:1:I.Data.1

(a)

	A	B	C	D	E	F
1	remark	CSV-Import-Export				
2	remark	Date =				
3	remark	Version = RSLogix 5000				
4	remark	Owner = K. Erickson				
5	remark	Company =				
6	0.1					
7	TYPE	SCOPE	NAME	DESCRIPTION	DATATYPE	SPECIFIER
8	TAG		PALL_UPLS	Limit switch$NInd. pall off conyr	BOOL	
9	TAG		PROX1	Prox Sensor$NPall at Eng hook1	BOOL	
10	TAG		RESET_PB	Reset Pushbutton	BOOL	
11	TAG		ROTR_CCWLS	Rotator Cclockwise$Nlimit switch	BOOL	
12	TAG		ROTR_CWLS	Rotator Clockwise$Nlimit switch	BOOL	
13	TAG		ROTR_DNLS	Rotator Down$Nlimit switch	BOOL	
14	TAG		ROTR_UPLS	Rotator Up$Nlimit switch	BOOL	
15	TAG		START_PB	Start Pushbutton	BOOL	
16	TAG		STOP_PB	Stop Pushbutton	BOOL	

(b)

Figure 21.39. ControlLogix input variable definitions for Example 6.4: *(a)* physical input aliased tags; *(b)* simulated inputs.

1. Import the aliased physical input tags saved in step (2) of the tie-back logic setup as an "RSLogix 5000 Import/Export File (*.CSV)" file. You will receive a warning since the import writes over existing variable definitions.
2. Place an AFI (always false) instruction before the JSR block that calls the tie-back routine.

In order to re-enable the tie-back routine, import the simulated input tags and remove the AFI (always false) instruction before the JSR block that calls the tie-back routine.

For RSLogix 5000 version 13.0 and later, the tie-back routine rungs can be saved as a library file (L5X file) so that they can be removed and then imported later for more testing. For RSLogix versions prior to version 13.0, there is no easy way to save the tie-back routine so that it can be removed and then imported later for more testing. The following procedure performs that task:

1. With RSLogix 5000, save the entire project as an L5K file (File | Save As.., select "*.L5K")
2. Use a text editor to modify the L5K project file. DO NOT use a word processor since it will insert extra characters into the file.
3. Locate the tie-back routine. The name of the routine will immediately follow a "ROUTINE" keyword. The code for a routine is listed between the keywords "ROUTINE" and "END_ROUTINE".
4. Delete everything but the tie-back routine (everything before the "ROUTINE" keyword and after the "END_ROUTINE" keyword).
5. Save the tie-back routine with a different name, but with the L5K extension.
6. In the original project, delete the tie-back routine and the JSR that calls it.

To import a previously saved tie-back routine into a project,

1. Save the entire project as an L5K file.
2. Using a text editor, locate the end of the program. Find the name of the main program (usually "MainProgram" and then locate the next "END_PROGRAM" keyword to identify the end of the program.
3. Insert the previously saved tie-back routine just before the "END_PROGRAM" keyword.
4. Save this L5K file.
5. In RSLogix 5000, open the L5K file saved in the previous step, enter the desired name of the project file, and import the project.
6. In the main program file, place a JSR block that calls the tie-back logic routine.

21.5.4 PLC-5/SLC-500 Tie-Back Logic

Among the PLCs covered by this text, tie-back logic is the easiest to implement on the PLC-5 and only slightly harder on the SLC-500. To implement tie-back logic in a PLC-5 or SLC-500, the I/O scan must be inhibited and a tie-back logic routine added to the program (Figure 21.40). The logic in the tie-back routine reads the discrete output image and writes to the discrete input image. The tie-back logic routine does not need to be taken out of the processor.

For a PLC-5 and SLC-500, the I/O modules are not needed. For the PLC-5, only a chassis with a power supply and the processor in the correct slot is required. For a SLC-500, the system must contain the processor, all chassis, and all power supplies for application,

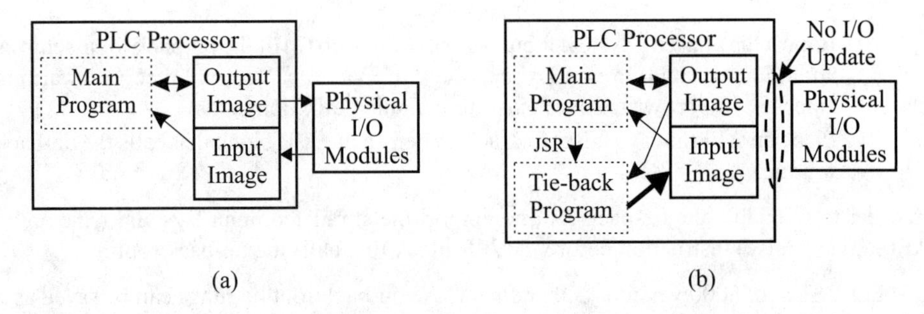

Figure 21.40. PLC-5/SLC-500 process simulation: *(a)* normal I/O update; *(b)* tie-back logic.

but the I/O modules are not necessary. When testing the HMI, then any required communication modules (for example, Ethernet or ControlNet) must be added.

The tie-back logic is set up as follows:

1. For a PLC-5 processor, open the processor status and select the "Rack" tab. Set the inhibit bit of all racks to "1." An example is shown in Figure 21.41 for a PLC that supports 24 remote racks.
2. For a SLC-500 processor, open the processor status and select the "IO" tab. Set all I/O slot enables (except for slot 0) to "0." An example is shown in Figure 21.42.
3. Program the tie-back logic in a separate program file.
4. In the main program file, place a JSR block that calls the tie-back program file.

When finished with the tie-back logic testing, the I/O scan is re-enabled and the tie-back program file JSR is disabled:

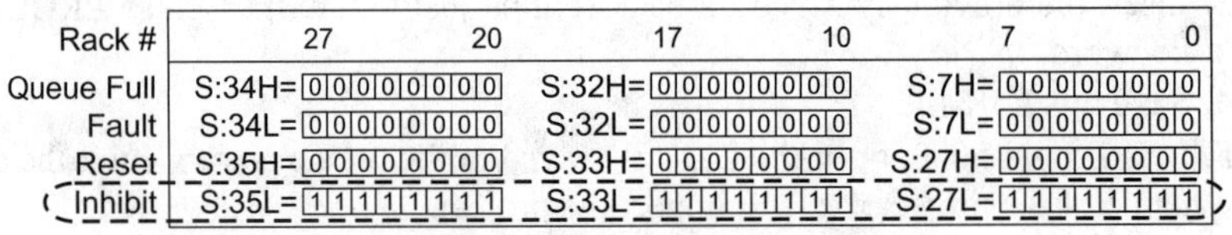

Rack #	27 … 20	17 … 10	7 … 0
Queue Full	S:34H=00000000	S:32H=00000000	S:7H=00000000
Fault	S:34L=00000000	S:32L=00000000	S:7L=00000000
Reset	S:35H=00000000	S:33H=00000000	S:27H=00000000
Inhibit	S:35L=11111111	S:33L=11111111	S:27L=11111111

Figure 21.41. PLC-5 I/O rack inhibits.

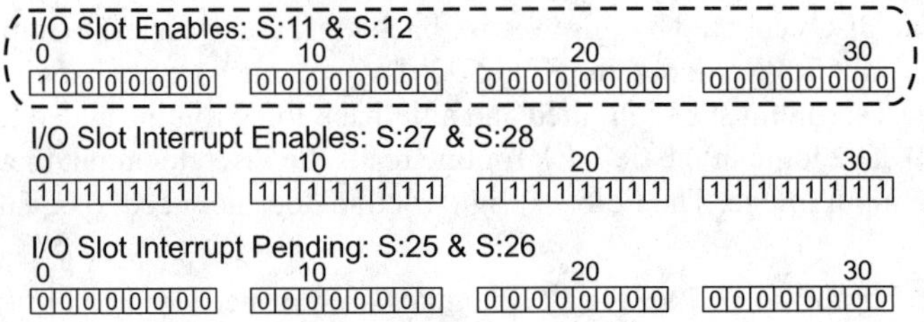

	0	10	20	30
I/O Slot Enables: S:11 & S:12	10000000	00000000	00000000	00000000
I/O Slot Interrupt Enables: S:27 & S:28	11111111	11111111	11111111	11111111
I/O Slot Interrupt Pending: S:25 & S:26	00000000	00000000	00000000	00000000

Figure 21.42. SLC-500 I/O slot enables.

1. Place an AFI (always false) instruction before the JSR block that calls the tie-back program file.
2. For a PLC-5 processor, open the processor status and select the "Rack" tab. Set the inhibit bit of all racks to "0."
2. For a SLC-500 processor, open the processor status and select the "IO" tab. Set all I/O slot enables to "1."

For the PLC-5, the tie-back routine rungs can be saved as a library file (PC5 file) so that they can be removed and then imported later for more testing. The SLC-500 does not support library files, but the tie-back ladder logic rungs can be "copied" into the paste buffer and then "pasted" into an empty project in order to save it for later use. After saving the tie-back program file, it can be deleted from the original project.

21.5.5 S7 Tie-Back Logic

The S7 processor is one of the more difficult PLCs to implement tie-back logic since the I/O scan cannot be disabled and the symbols associated with the physical inputs cannot be redefined as an internal address (like Modicon or ControlLogix). To circumvent these difficulties, the input image is transferred to a duplicate input image that is used by the program in place of the actual input image (Figure 21.43). To test the program with the tie-back logic, the transfer to the duplicate input image is disabled and the tie-back function block writes to the duplicate input image.

The I/O modules are not needed. Only a power supply and the processor are required. If testing the HMI, then any required communication modules (for example, Ethernet) must be added.

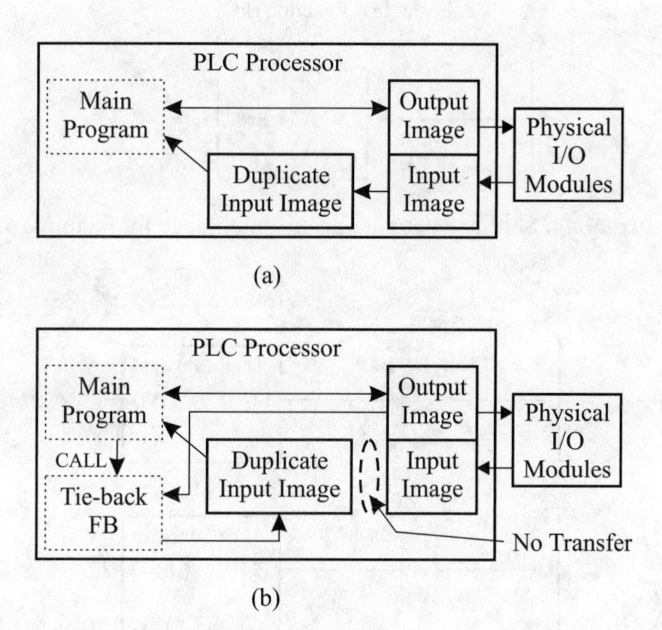

Figure 21.43. S7 process simulation: *(a)* normal transfer to duplicate input image; *(b)* tie-back logic.

In the STEP7 programming software, the symbols are for program documentation. The program code uses the addresses and not the symbols. When the address associated with a symbol is changed, the address in the program does not change. Before programming the processor, the physical input symbols must be associated with internal addresses, the duplicate input image. As an example, the addresses associated with the physical inputs for the engine inverter station of Example 6.4 are redefined as

Symbol	Duplicate Addr.	Physical Addr.
START_PB	M20.0	I0.0
STOP_PB	M20.1	I0.1
RESET_PB	M20.2	I0.2
PROX1	M20.3	I0.3
PALL_UPLS	M20.4	I0.4
ROTR_UPLS	M20.5	I0.5
ROTR_DNLS	M20.6	I0.6
ROTR_CWLS	M20.7	I0.7
ROTR_CCWLS	M21.0	I1.0

The function that copies the physical input image to the duplicate input image is shown in Figure 21.44.

The tie-back logic is programmed in a separate function block (for example, "Tie_Back" in Figure 21.45). The tie-back function and the function that copies the physical input image to the duplicate input image must be controlled so that only one of them writes to the duplicate input image. In the example shown in Figure 21.45, an internal variable "Enab_Tie_Back," controls the duplicate input image. If Enab_Tie_Back is **on**, the

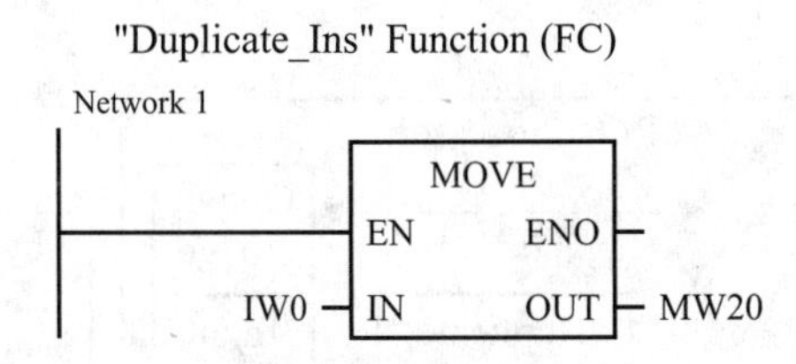

Figure 21.44. S7 function to duplicate input image for Example 6.4.

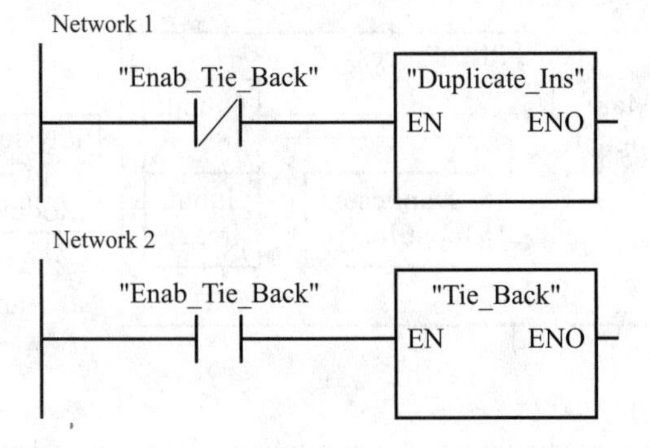

Figure 21.45. S7 control of duplicate input image and tie-back logic.

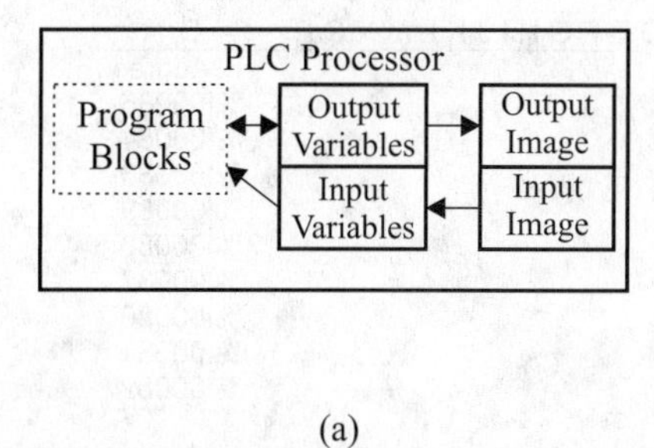

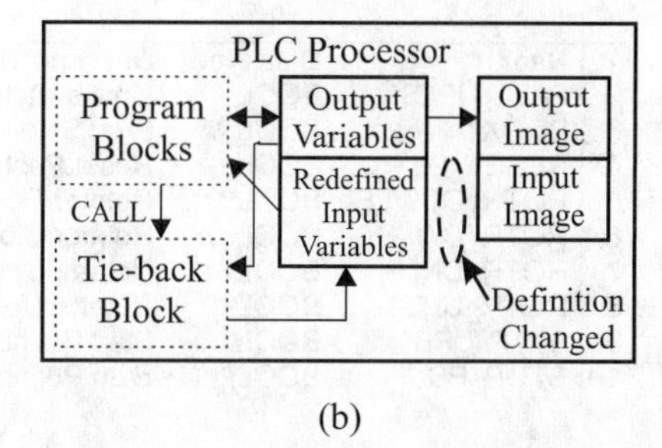

Figure 21.46. GE Fanuc process simulation: *(a)* normal interaction with I/O image; *(b)* tie-back logic.

physical input image is not copied to the duplicate input image and the tie-back function controls the duplicate input image. If Enab_Tie_Back is **off**, the physical input image is copied to the duplicate input image and the tie-back function is not called.

The tie-back function block can be saved in a library so that it can be removed and then copied back into the project later for more testing. After saving the tie-back function block, it can be deleted from the original project.

21.5.6 GE Fanuc Tie-Back Logic

To implement tie-back logic in a GE Fanuc PLC, the variables defined for physical input addresses are redefined for internal addresses and a block for the tie-back logic is added to the program (Figure 21.46). The tie-back logic reads the physical output variables and writes the redefined physical input variables.

The I/O modules are not needed. Only a chassis with a power supply and the processor in the correct slot is required. If testing the HMI, then any required communication modules (for example, Ethernet) must be added.

The general process is to export the variable database as a comma-separated-value (CSV) file, redefine the addresses for the physical input variables, and then import these changes into the project. To setup the tie-back logic, the procedure is as follows:

1. Export the variable database as "Comma Separated Values." This file contains the physical input definitions.
2. With a spreadsheet program, delete all of the lines (rows) of the variables that are not the physical inputs. Keep the first line of header information. Save this file. This file contains the physical input definitions.
3. With a spreadsheet program, redefine the physical input addresses for each variable (row) in the file saved in the previous step. Define them as internal memory locations. Save this new file with a different name. This file contains the simulated input definitions.
4. Import the simulated input definitions. On the import options screen, set the following:

    Identify variable conflict - by variable name

    If there is a conflict - overwrite existing variable properties

    Import all of the variables. You will receive warnings since the import writes over existing variable definitions.

	A	B	C	D E F G H I J K L M N O P	Q
1	Name	DataType	Description	. . . .	IOAddress
2	PALL_UPLS	BOOL	Limit switch In		%I00085
3	PROX1	BOOL	Prox Sensor Pa		%I00084
4	RESET_PB	BOOL	Reset Pushbutt		%I00083
5	ROTR_CCWLS	BOOL	Rotator Counte		%I00089
6	ROTR_CWLS	BOOL	Rotator Clockw		%I00088
7	ROTR_DNLS	BOOL	Rotator Down I		%I00087
8	ROTR_UPLS	BOOL	Rotator Up lim		%I00086
9	START_PB	BOOL	Start Pushbutto		%I00081
10	STOP_PB	BOOL	Stop Pushbutto		%I00082

(a)

	A	B	C	D E F G H I J K L M N O P	Q
1	Name	DataType	Description	. . . .	IOAddress
2	PALL_UPLS	BOOL	Limit switch In		%M00205
3	PROX1	BOOL	Prox Sensor Pa		%M00204
4	RESET_PB	BOOL	Reset Pushbutt		%M00203
5	ROTR_CCWLS	BOOL	Rotator Counte		%M00209
6	ROTR_CWLS	BOOL	Rotator Clockw		%M00208
7	ROTR_DNLS	BOOL	Rotator Down I		%M00207
8	ROTR_UPLS	BOOL	Rotator Up lim		%M00206
9	START_PB	BOOL	Start Pushbutto		%M00201
10	STOP_PB	BOOL	Stop Pushbutto		%M00202

(b)

Figure 21.47. GE Fanuc input variable definitions for Example 6.4: *(a)* physical inputs; *(b)* simulated inputs.

5. Program the tie-back logic in a separate program block.
6. In the main program block, place a CALL block to invoke the tie-back logic block.

An example exported physical input variable definition and the corresponding simulated input variable definition is shown in Figure 21.47. This example is for the engine inverter station of Example 6.4. The spreadsheet format of the files is shown. The relevant information appears in columns A and Q and so columns B - P are abbreviated and columns R - AW are not shown.

When finished with the tie-back logic testing, the original physical input definitions (saved in step 2 of the above procedure) should be imported into the project and the tie-back block and its CALL should be removed. Even if the call to the tie-back block is removed, the program will not properly validate since the tie-back block is writing to physical input locations. To save the tie-back block, it can be copied into the paste buffer and then "pasted" into an empty project in order to save it for later use. After saving the tie-back block, it can be deleted from the original project.

21.6 CHAPTER SUMMARY

This chapter described the typical phases in a control design project. The control requirements, standardization, and testing aspects of a project are elaborated.

REFERENCES

Allen-Bradley, 1996. *Classic 1785 PLC-5 Programmable Controllers: User Manual*, pub. 1785-6.2.1, Allen-Bradley Company, Inc., Milwaukee, WI, April.

Erickson, K. T. and Hedrick, J. L. *Plantwide Process Control*, John Wiley, 1999.

GE Fanuc Automation, 2002. *CIMplicity Machine Edition™ Help File*, version 3.0, GE Fanuc Automation North America, Inc., Charlottesville, VA.

Instrument Society of America, *ISA-S88.01, Batch Control, Part 1: Models and Terminology*, Instrument Society of America, Research Triangle Park, NC, 1995.

Rockwell Automation, 1998. *Enhanced and Ethernet PLC-5 Programmable Controllers: User Manual*, pub. 1785-6.5.12, Rockwell Automation, Milwaukee, WI, November.

Rockwell Automation, 2003. *SLC 500™ Instruction Set: Reference Manual*, pub. 1756-RM0010D-EN-P, Rockwell Automation, Milwaukee, WI, November.

Rockwell Automation, 2004. *Logix5000™ Controllers Common Procedures: Programming Manual*, pub. 1756-PM001G-EN-P, Rockwell Automation, Milwaukee, WI, March.

Schneider Automation, 1998. *Concept User Manual,* vol. 2, ver. 2.1, pub. 840 USE 461 00, Schneider Automation, Inc., North Andover, MA.

Siemens, 1996. *System Software for S7-300 and S7-400 Program Design: Programming Manual,* pub. C79000-G7076-C506-01, Siemens AG, Nürnberg, Germany.

PROBLEMS

General instructions for the problems:

Implement the solution and include the tie-back logic one of the following PLC processors:

Modicon Concept, **or**
Allen-Bradley ControlLogix, **or**
Allen-Bradley PLC-5/SLC-500, **or**
Siemens STEP 7, **or**
GE Fanuc 90-30 (with floating point)

Tie-back logic specifications:

1. Do not simulate START_PB, STOP_PB, and RESET_PB in your tieback logic. However, define these physical inputs as internal variables so they can be manipulated without having to force them.
2. The tie-back logic cannot use any internal logic (step internal coils, etc.) of the program being tested. You are allowed to use any of the defined physical I/O.
3. If the application contains a RESET_PB, or some other variable/tag used to reset the process, it may be used to set any initial states of the tieback logic (for example, set LS3 **on**).

When your solution is downloaded to a processor and the processor is place in Run mode, the operator will force the appropriate inputs to start the process. For most of the problems, the test is started with the following procedure:

1. The START_PB, STOP_PB, and RESET_PB are initially **off**.
2. The RESET_PB is turned **on** and then **off**.
3. The STOP_PB is turned **on**.
4. The START_PB is turned **on** and then **off**.

The application should start. If the process repeats its operation, it should continue until stopped by the operator (for example, by turning **off** the STOP_PB).

Your solution should include the following:

1. Function chart
2. Listing of program
3. Project files

Additional Specifications for a Modicon Implementation:

1. Place tie-back logic in section named "Tieback."

Additional Specifications for a ControlLogix Implementation:

1. Place tie-back logic in routine named "Tieback."

Additional Specifications for a PLC-5/SLC-500 Implementation:

1. Place tie-back logic in program file #100, named "TIEBACK."
2. Any tieback timers should go in data file T100.
3. Any internal bits for the tieback should go in data file B101.

Additional Specifications for a S7 Implementation:

1. Place tie-back logic in a function block named "Tieback."
2. The function (FC) to copy the physical input addresses to the duplicate input image is named "Duplicate_Ins."

Additional Specifications for a GE Fanuc Implementation:

1. Place tie-back logic in a block named "Tieback."

P21-1. Carton Sealer Control. Implement the carton sealing control of problem P6-1 and include the tie-back logic.

P21-2. Batch Process Control. Implement the batch control of problem P6-2 and include the tie-back logic.

P21-3. Bag Sealing Control. Implement the ladder logic for the bag sealer of problem P6-4 and include the tie-back logic.

P21-4. Erbia Elevator Control. Implement the erbia elevator control of problem P6-5 and include the tie-back logic.

P21-5. Transfer Station Control. Implement the transfer station control of problem P6-6 and include the tie-back logic.

P21-6. Hole Drilling Station 1 Control. Implement the drilling station control of problem P6-8 and include the tie-back logic.

P21-7. Oiler Station Control. Implement the oiler station control of problem P6-9 and include the tie-back logic.

P21-8. Pressing Station Control. Implement the pressing station control of problem P6-10 and include the tie-back logic.

P21-9. Case Erector Control. Implement the case erector control of problem P6-11 and include the tie-back logic.

P21-10. Batch Process Control. Implement the batch control system of problem P6-12 and include the tie-back logic.

P21-11. Erbia Can Tipper/Rotator Control. Implement the station of problem P6-15 and include the tie-back logic.

P21-12. Bagging Machine Control. Implement the bagging machine control of problem P6-17 and include the tie-back logic.

P21-13. Drilling Station Control. Implement the drilling station control of problem P6-18 and include the tie-back logic.

P21-14. Bolt Driving Station Control. Implement the bolt-driving station control of problem P6-19 and include the tie-back logic.

P21-15. Palletizing Station Control. Implement the palletizing station control of problem P6-20 and include the tie-back logic.

P21-16. Weigh Scale Station Control. Implement the weigh scale station control of problem P7-20 and include the tie-back logic.

P21-17. Width Check Station Control. Implement the width check station control of problem P7-21 and include the tie-back logic.

P21-18. Stamping Station Control. Implement the stamping station control of problem P7-22 and include the tie-back logic.

P21-19. Leak Check Station Control. Implement the valve leak check station control of problem P7-23 and include the tie-back logic.

P21-20. Hole-drilling Station 2 Control. Implement the drilling station control of problem P7-24 and include the tie-back logic.

P21-21. Hole-drilling Station 3 Control. Implement the drilling station control of problem P7-25 and include the tie-back logic.

P21-22. Batch Reactor Control. Implement the batch reactor control of problem P7-28 and include the tie-back logic.

P21-23. Multi-tank Batch Control. Implement the batch process control of problem P7-29 and include the tie-back logic.

22 Example Projects

Chapter Topics:

- Power plant coal handler control design
- Chemical process control design

OBJECTIVE

Upon completion of this chapter, you will be able to understand the design and implementation of a typical control project.

22.1 INTRODUCTION

As a culmination to this text, this chapter outlines two project case studies. The first project is the control system for a power plant coal handler and the second project is the control for a batch chemical plant. The coal handler project is typical of a small- to medium-sized application and has only discrete sensors and actuators. The design and implementation for this application is completely developed. The batch chemical project is typical of a large application involving many PLC processors that must communicate with each other. This project has both discrete and continuous sensors and actuators. The design for this application is only developed. The complete implementation is left as an exercise.

Both projects are only outlined in this chapter. The accompanying CD contains the detailed documentation for both of these projects.

22.2 COAL HANDLING SYSTEM

The coal handling system manages the transfer of coal from either a truck or the reclaim coal pile to one of three bunkers. An overall schematic of the process is shown in Figure 22.1. This section presents the control requirements definition (CRD) that contains the process operation description, the control concept, and the control strategy for the coal handling system. The accompanying CD contains the detailed design documentation.

22.2.1 Process Operation Description

Purchased coal is unloaded into a truck dump hopper. The truck trailer tilts up, allowing the coal to fall out into a hopper, where it is conveyed to the reclaim coal pile or to one of the coal bunkers inside the power plant. When the truck dump hopper is empty, the coal must come from the reclaim hopper, which is loaded from the reclaim coal pile. The primary control objective of the coal handling unit is to convey coal from one of two sources (truck

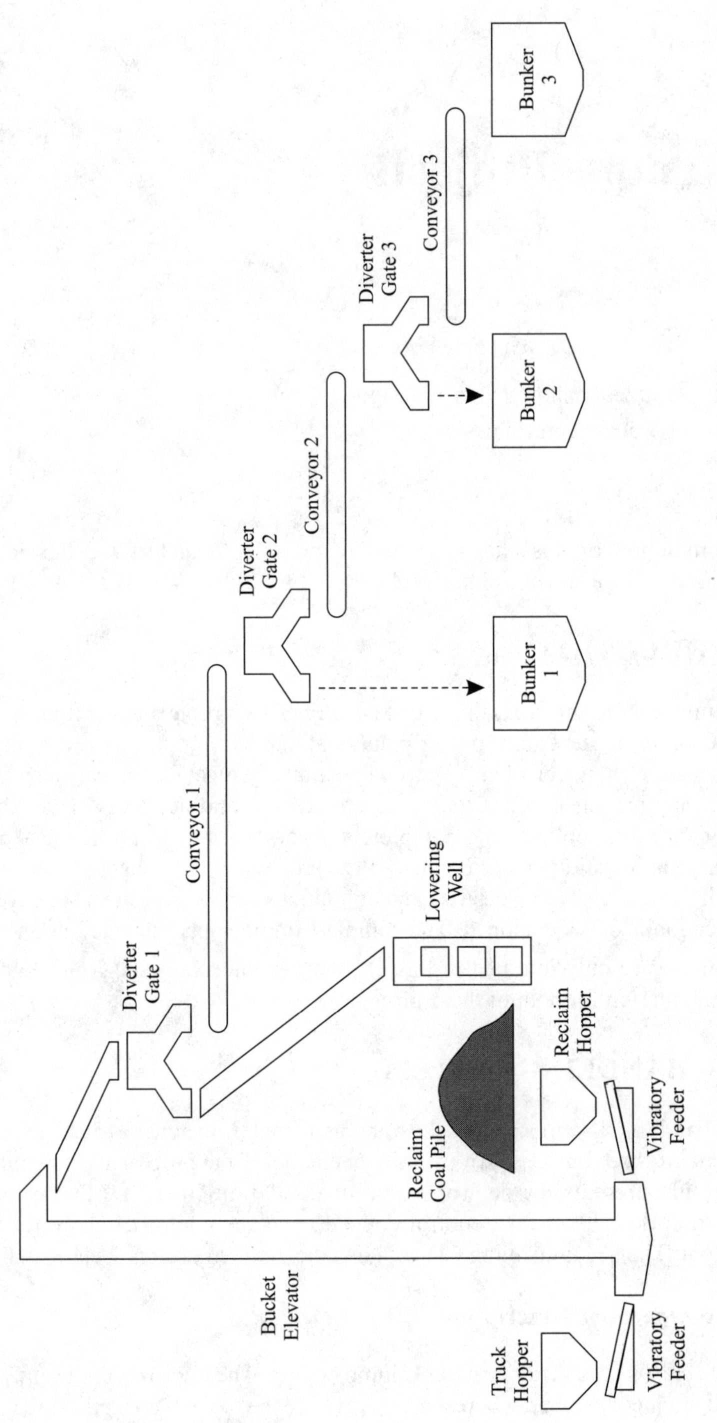

Figure 22.1. Overall process.

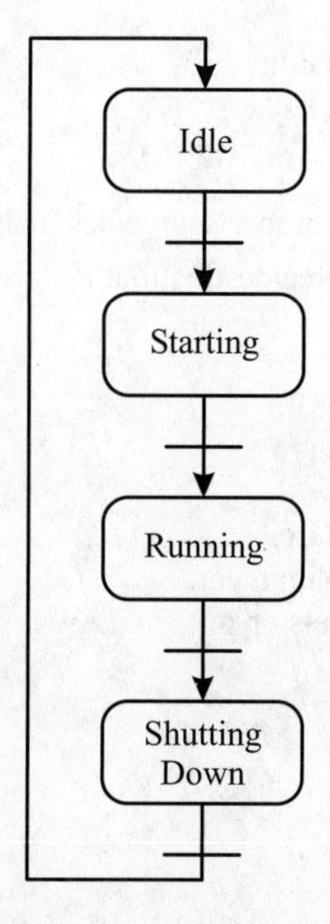

Figure 22.2. Coal handler states.

hopper or reclaim hopper) to one of four destinations (reclaim, bunker 1, bunker 2, or bunker 3). The operating states of this unit are shown in Figure 22.2. Normal operation is intermittent, running only when a truck needs to unload or a coal bunker is nearly empty. The states are described as follows:

Operating State Name: Idle

Routine Activities

Clean equipment as needed.

Perform inspection.

Exception Handling

None.

Primary Control Objectives

None.

Performance Information

None.

State End Conditions

Startup requested.

Operating State Name: Starting

Routine Activities

Set diverter gates for the proper source/destination.

Start conveyors for a source/destination.

Start bucket elevator

Start appropriate feeder

Exception Handling

Shutdown if:
- Conveyor motor failure.
- Conveyor belt mis-alignment.
- Conveyor pull cord e-stop
- Coal plug detected.

Primary Control Objectives

None.

Performance Information

None.

State End Conditions

Conveyors for a source/destination path started.

Operating State Name: Running

Routine Activities

Periodic checks of level in Bunker #1, #2, and Bunker #3 (if being filled).

Exception Handling

Shutdown if:
- Conveyor motor failure.
- Conveyor belt mis-alignment.
- Conveyor pull cord e-stop
- Coal plug detected.
- High level on a destination bunker.
- High reclaim coal pile level.

Primary Control Objectives

Level of coal in bunker.

Performance Information

None.

State End Conditions

Shutdown requested either by operator, or when bunker 3 is full.

Operating State Name: Shutting Down

Routine Activities

Shutdown all path conveyors.

Stop vibratory feeders

Exception Handling

None.

Primary Control Objectives

None.

Performance Information

None.

State End Conditions

All conveyors stopped.

22.2.2 Control Concept

Unit Supervision

Extent of Automation

Provide control of feeders, bucket elevator, conveyors, and diverter gates.

Provide automatic startup and shutdown for the transfer of coal to bunker 3.

Flexibility of Automation

None.

Control Activity Coordination

None.

Interaction with Operating Personnel

Operators can control feeders, bucket elevator, conveyors, and diverter gates.

Path selection done by operator. Interlocks prevent illegal selections.

Display alarm status information from devices.

22.2.3 Control Strategy

Two conveyor paths can be automatically controlled:

1. Unloading feeder to bunker 3
2. Reclaim feeder to bunker 3

All other paths are controlled by the operator.

When a path is started, the equipment is started in backward order. For example, the last conveyor in a path is started first. When a path is shutdown, the equipment is stopped so that all material on a conveyor is removed before that conveyor is stopped.

The operator uses switches on the control panel to manually control the conveyor and gate devices. Local control switches located near each gate and conveyor provide override control.

The operator can select “automatic mode” from the control panel. In automatic mode, the path to bunker 3 must be manually set. When the bunker 3 level is low, the conveyors, the bucket elevator, and the selected source feeder (reclaim or unload) are appropriately started. When the bunker 3 level is full, the conveyors are appropriately stopped.

Devices

Unloading feeder:

Start/stop by auto path control to bunker 3 or operator.

Reclaim feeder:

Start/stop by auto path control to bunker 3 or operator.

Bucket elevator:

Start/stop by auto path control to bunker 3 or operator.

Diverter gate 1:

Change position by operator.

Conveyor 1:

Start/stop by auto path control to bunker 3 or operator.

Diverter gate 2:

Change position by operator.

Conveyor 2:

Start/stop by auto path control to bunker 3 or operator.

Diverter gate 3:

Change position by operator.

Conveyor 3:

Start/stop by auto path control to bunker 3 or operator.

Interlocks

Do not allow start of conveyor if destination bunker level is high.

Do not allow start of bucket elevator if diverter gate set to "reclaim" and coal pile level is high.

Backward startup and forward shutdown is enforced even when manually controlled by the operator.

If a downstream conveyor is stopped because of a failure, the upstream conveyors are emergency-stopped.

22.2.4 Detailed Design

Documentation for the detailed design is in the accompanying CD. The following items are included:

Detailed control narrative which details the process operation and device control
Operation description of the OI panel that displays the alarms
Test plan
Electrical wiring diagrams
Panel layout
Operator graphical control panel design

PLC program
InTouch project screens used to test program before installation
OI panel project files

22.3 MULTI-UNIT CHEMICAL PROCESS

The K chemical process is a fictional batch chemical process and includes units to unload raw ingredients, store ingredients, blend, react, remove impurities, load the finished products, clean-in-place, and sample the product. An overall schematic of the K process is shown in Figure 22.3. This section describes the process. The accompanying CD contains the control requirements definition and the detailed design documentation.

22.3.1 Process Description

The K process is divided into loadin, production, loadout, and utility areas (Figure 22.3). The loadin area is further divided into two cells: a wet unload cell, with truck and rail units; and a dry unload cell, with rail dry unload, dry storage loadin, and dry storage loadout units. The wet ingredient storage is basically a set of tanks shared between the loadin and production areas. The truck wet and rail wet unload units control the inlet side of the tanks and the blend and reactors control the outlet side of the tanks. There is no separate control of the tanks and hence it is not defined as a unit. The production area is divided into a reactor cell and an ion exchange cell. In the future, the QA sample unit may also be used by the ion exchange cell and so it is considered a separate unit. The reactor cell contains a blend unit and two reactor units. The ion exchange cell contains only one ion exchange unit. The loadout area consists of a product storage unit and a loadout unit. The utility area contains a water treatment, steam generation, clean-in-place (CIP), and regen material storage cells. Only the CIP cell is described.

Each of the areas is briefly described. More detail about the process operation is in the CRD.

The loadin area is subdivided into wet unload and dry unload cells. This area unloads wet and dry ingredients from trucks or rail cars and transfers them to storage tanks. The truck wet unload unit transfers wet ingredients to one of six storage tanks and the rail wet unload unit transfers wet ingredients to one of the same six tanks (Figure 22.4). Note that the wet ingredient storage is shared between the loadin area and the production area. The dry unload cell is divided into rail dry unload, dry storage loadin, and dry storage loadout units (Figure 22.5). The rail dry unload and dry storage loadin units transfer grain from rail cars to one of three storage tanks. Upon request from reactor 2, the dry storage loadout unit transfers grain from one of the storage tanks to the reactor.

The production area is subdivided into reactor and ion exchange cells. This area also contains the QA sample unit, which is used by the reactors. The reactor cell has a blending unit and two reactors (Figure 22.6). The blending unit blends up to four wet ingredients from the wet storage tanks into one of the reactor ingredients. Each reactor takes appropriate ingredients from the blend unit and wet ingredient storage and produces a product according to a recipe. The reactor 2 unit also takes an additional ingredient from a dry storage tank. The ion exchange cell removes impurities from the product. Currently, the ion exchange cell has only one ion exchanger unit (Figure 22.7), though in the future, two more tanks are expected to be added. The QA sample unit (Figure 22.8) samples product from a reactor while making a batch, providing a QA value. This unit also returns product to the reactor.

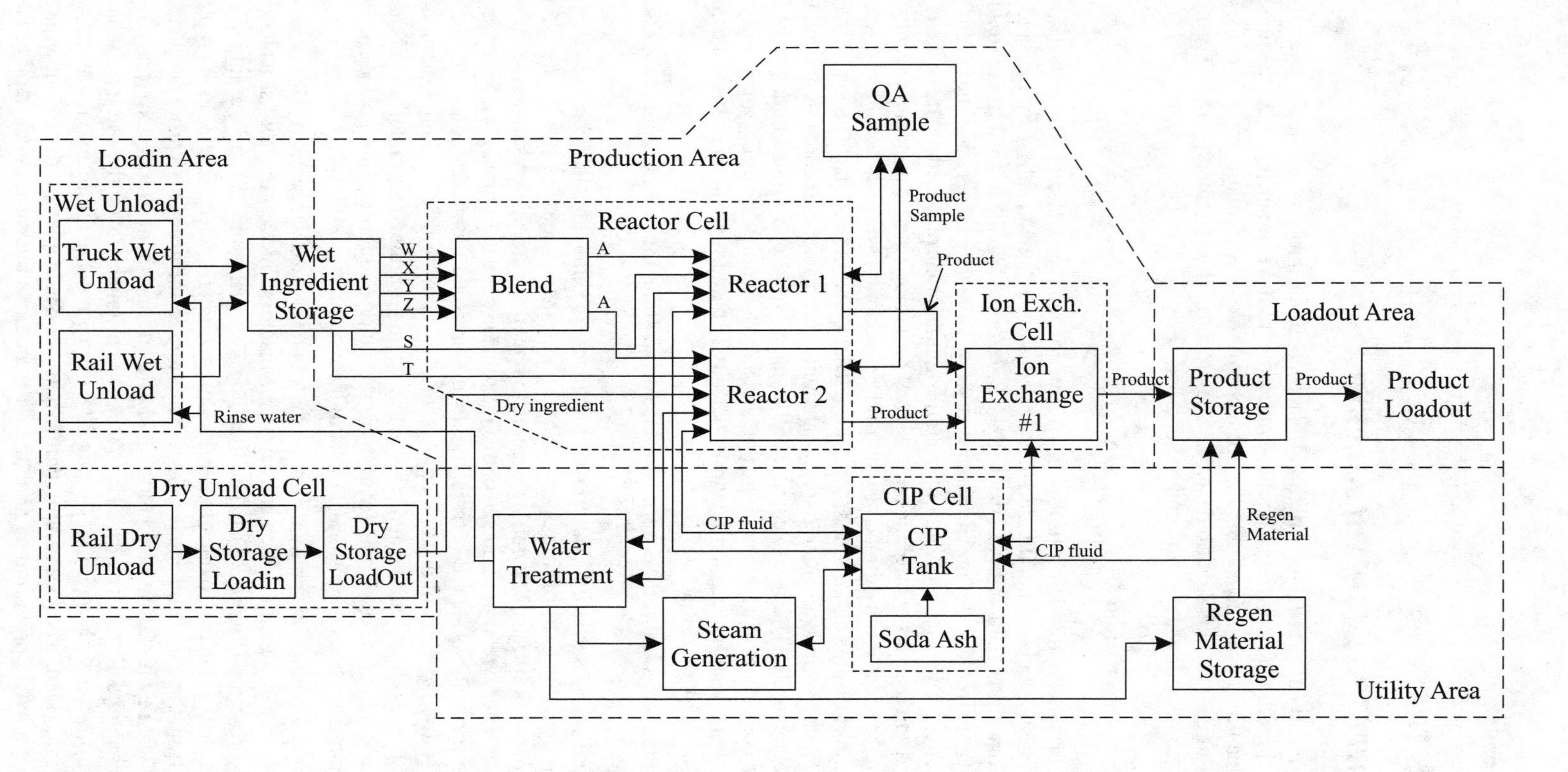

Figure 22.3. K chemical process overall process flow diagram.

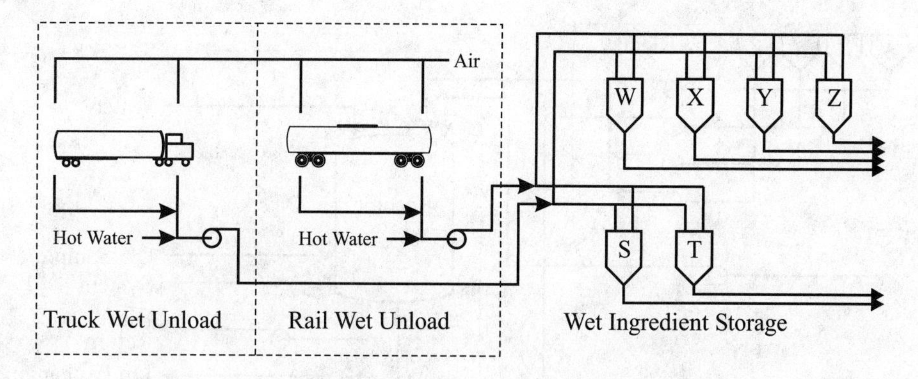

Figure 22.4. Wet unload cell.

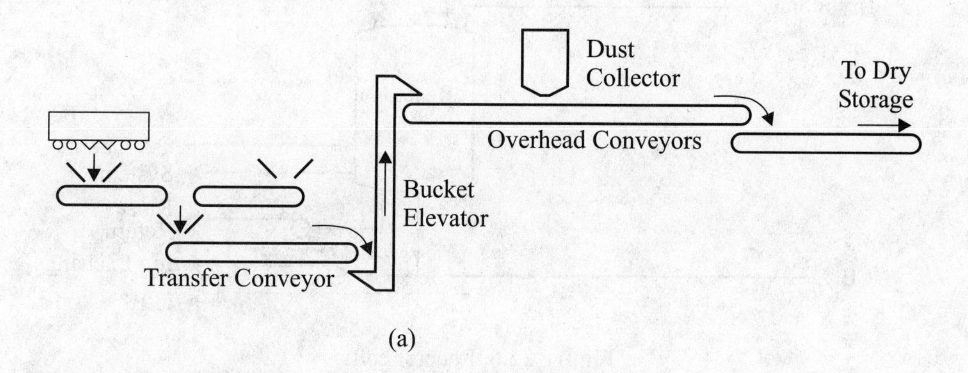

(a)

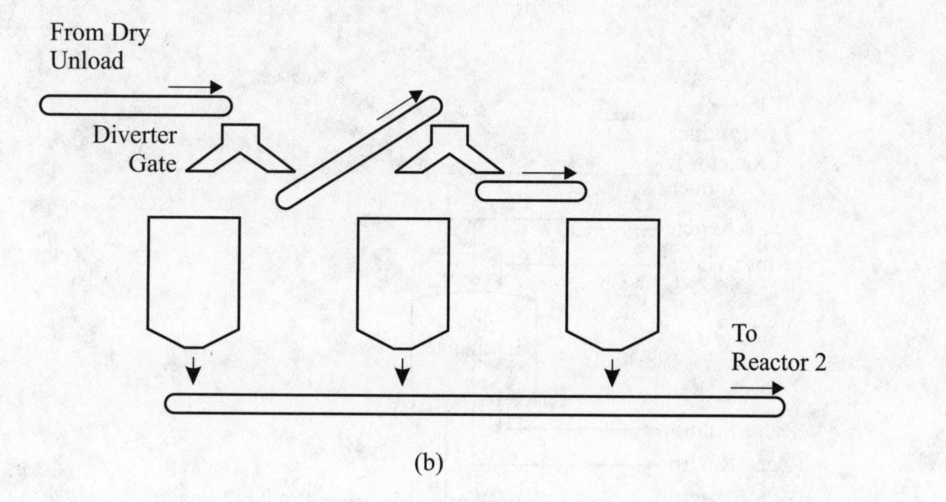

(b)

Figure 22.5. Dry unload cell: *(a)* rail dry unload unit; *(b)* dry storage load in and load out units.

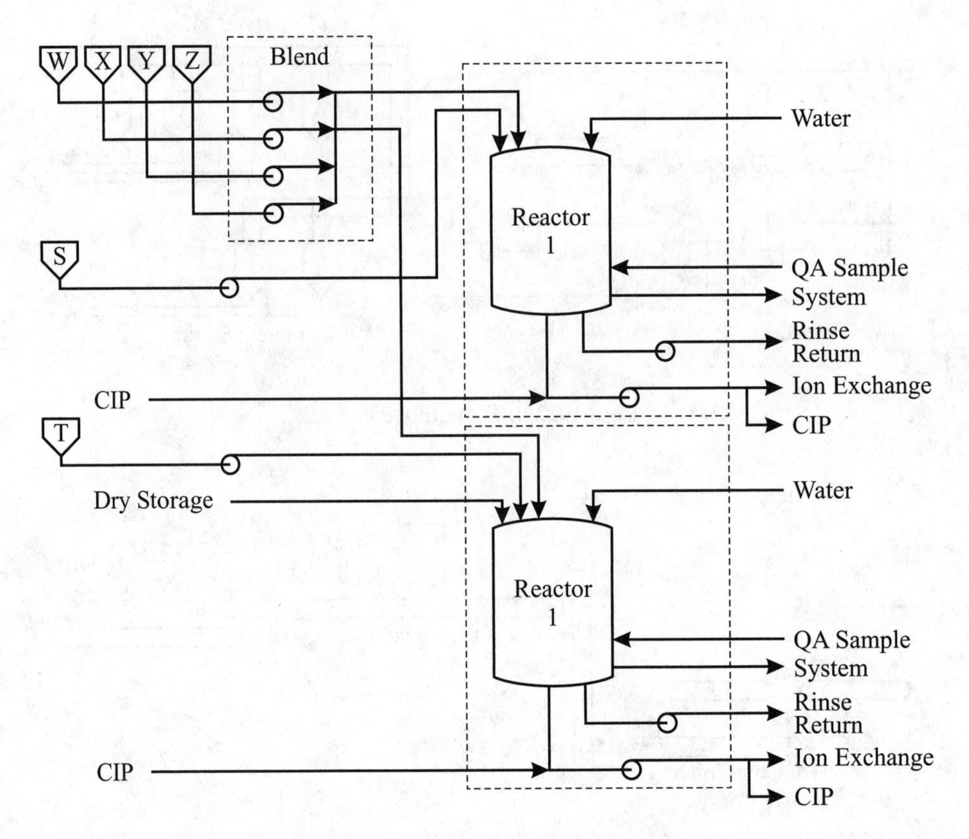

Figure 22.6. Reactor cell.

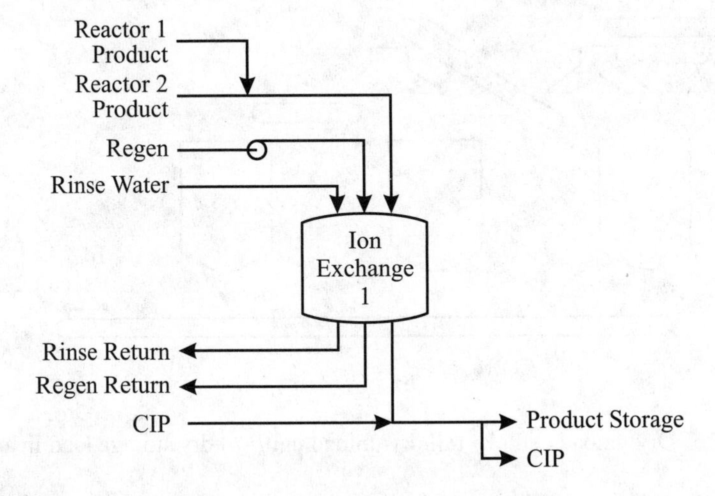

Figure 22.7. Ion exchange cell.

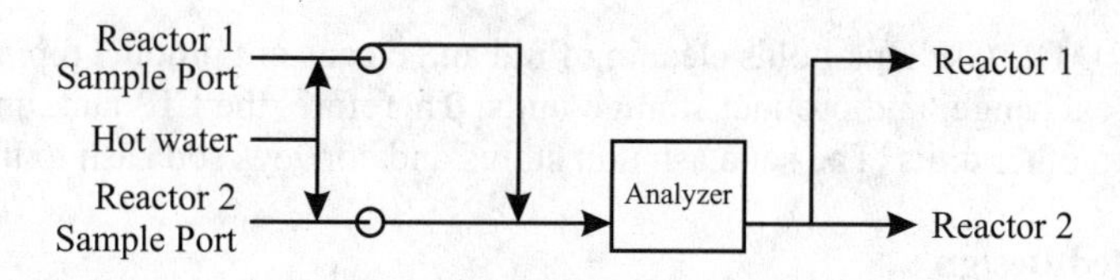

Figure 22.8. QA sample unit.

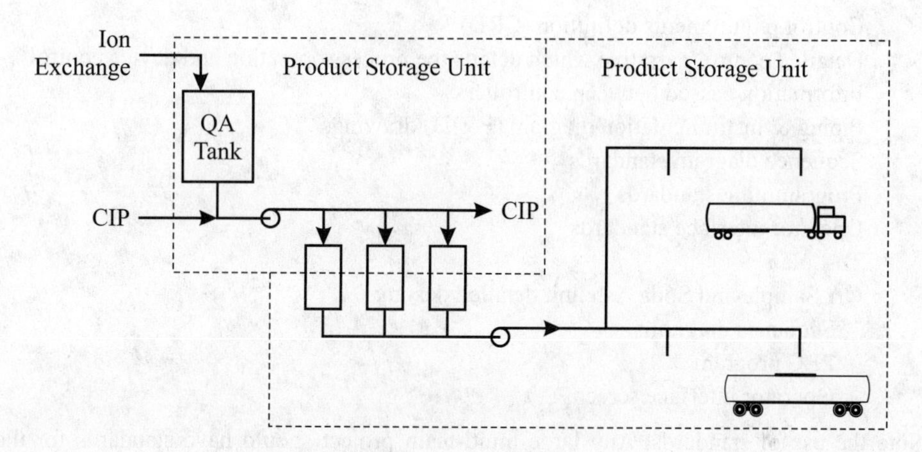

Figure 22.9. Product loadout area.

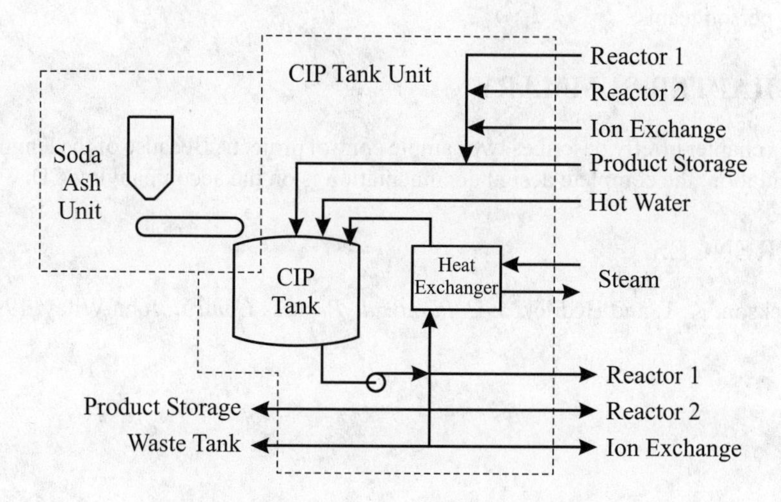

Figure 22.10. Clean-in-place (CIP) cell.

The loadout area is subdivided into product storage and product loadout units. This area transfers the product to storage tanks and also transfers the product from the storage tanks to truck trailers or rail cars (Figure 22.9). The utility area is subdivided into water treatment, steam generation, clean-in-place, and regen material cells. Only the clean-in-place cell is described here. The clean-in-place (CIP) cell consists of the CIP tank and soda ash units

(Figure 22.10). The CIP tank holds cleaning fluid and cleans out product piping in the two reactors, ion exchange, and product storage units. Therefore, the CIP tank unit has many connections to other units. The soda ash unit stores and conveys soda ash to the CIP tank.

22.3.2 Detailed Design

The detailed design documentation is in the accompanying CD. The following items are included:

- Control requirements definition (CRD)
- Detailed control narrative which details the process operation and device control
- Information passed between controllers
- Piping & instrumentation diagram (P&ID) drawings
- Sequence diagram standards
- Programming standards
- Operator interface standards
- Test plan
- QA Sample and Soda Ash unit detailed design:
  - Sequence diagrams
  - PLC program
  - Operator interface screens

Note the use of standards. Any large multi-team project should have standards for the design documentation, programs, and operator interface.

This project is intended as a class project, where the various units are assigned to two- or three-person teams.

22.4 CHAPTER SUMMARY

This chapter briefly describes two sample control projects. Because of the length of the documentation, the complete design documentation is on the accompanying CD.

REFERENCES

Erickson, K. T. and Hedrick, J. L. *Plantwide Process Control*, John Wiley, 1999.

A Number Systems and Conversions

Since PLCs are basically specialized computers, they ultimately use binary numbers for their calculations. This appendix reviews the representation of numbers in binary, octal, hexadecimal, and binary-coded decimal (BCD) formats. In addition, this appendix covers the conversion of decimal numbers into binary, octal, hexadecimal, and BCD numbers and the conversion of binary, octal, and hexadecimal numbers into decimal numbers. Only whole numbers, that is, numbers without a fractional part are considered.

Binary, octal, decimal, and hexadecimal number systems are all positional number systems. Each digit position represents a weight that is a power of the number system *base*. The value of a digit is determined by multiplying the digit by the weight for that position. In a decimal number, the base is 10. The leftmost digit has a weight of 10^0; the next digit left has a weight of 10^1, the next digit left has a weight of 10^2, and so on. For example, the decimal number 2596 means $2\times10^3 + 5\times10^2 + 9\times10^1 + 6\times10^0$.

Binary, octal, and hexadecimal numbers have a base of 2, 8, and 16, respectively. BCD numbers have a base of 10, but the individual digits are represented by the 4-bit binary pattern for the decimal digit. A subscript shows the base of a number when it is not obvious. For example, 42_{10} means the number is decimal, while 42_8 is octal and 42_{16} is hexadecimal. The "H" or "h" suffix is an alternate way of showing a hexadecimal number, such as 42H or 42h. Since 8 and 16 are powers of 2, conversions between binary and octal or between binary and hexadecimal numbers are simple.

A.1 BINARY NUMBERS

In a binary number, the only digits allowed are 0 and 1. The base is 2 and the powers of 2 increase from 0 as shown in Figure A.1. One digit in a binary number is called a *bit*, 8 bits are called a *byte*, and 16 bits are called a *word* (Figure A.2). The *least significant* bit has the smallest weight and the *most significant* bit has the smallest weight.

For signed integers, negative numbers are represented in binary most commonly in the *two's complement* representation. To negate a binary number, each digit is complemented ($1 \rightarrow 0$ and $0 \rightarrow 1$) and then one is added to the complement. In the two's complement

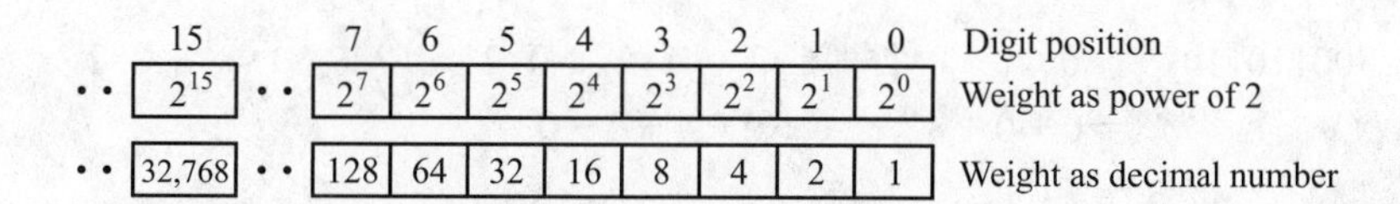

Figure A.1. Weight of binary digits.

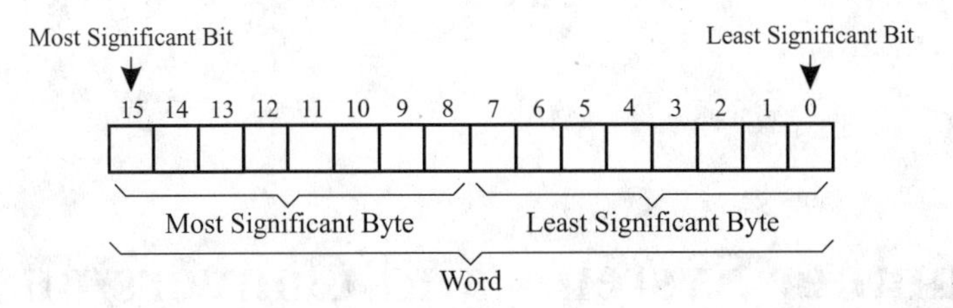

Figure A.2. Sixteen-bit binary number.

representation, a negative binary number is recognized by a 1 in the most significant (leftmost) position. For example, the 16-bit integer number 0000000001011001_2 is negated in the following manner:

0000000001011001_2 original number

↓

1111111110100110_2 each digit complemented

↓

1111111110100111_2 add one to the complement

Binary-to-Decimal Conversion Converting a positive binary number to a decimal number is easy. Each digit is multiplied by its weight and then all of the values are summed to obtain the result. This method is equivalent to adding the powers of two for which the digit is a one. For example, to convert the 8-bit number 01011001_2 to decimal,

$$
\begin{aligned}
01011001_2 &= 0\times2^7 + 1\times2^6 + 0\times2^5 + 1\times2^4 + 1\times2^3 + 0\times2^2 + 0\times2^1 + 1\times2^0 \\
&= 0 + 64 + 0 + 16 + 8 + 0 + 0 + 1 \\
&= 89_{10}
\end{aligned}
$$

If the binary number is negative, one should negate it (converting it to a positive number) and then convert the positive number to its decimal equivalent. The negative sign is then prefixed to the result. For example, to convert the 8-bit signed integer number 11001010_2 to decimal,

Since the leftmost digit is 1, this is a negative binary number. Therefore, it must first be negated

11001010_2 original (negative) number

↓

00110101_2 each digit complemented

↓

00110110_2 add one to the complement

$$
\begin{aligned}
00110110_2 &= 0\times2^7 + 0\times2^6 + 1\times2^5 + 1\times2^4 + 0\times2^3 + 1\times2^2 + 1\times2^1 + 0\times2^0 \\
&= 0 + 0 + 32 + 16 + 0 + 4 + 2 + 0 \\
&= 54_{10}
\end{aligned}
$$

So, $11001010_2 = -54_{10}$

Decimal-to-Binary Conversion Converting a decimal number to a binary number is a little more complicated. For a positive decimal number, the procedure is as follows:

1. Repeatedly divide the decimal number by 2 and note the remainders. Continue until the result is zero.
2. The binary number is formed by writing the remainders in reverse order, starting with the last remainder as the most-significant digit.
3. Prefix the result from step 2 with enough 0 digits to produce the number of digits needed in the result (usually 8, 16, or 32 digits).

For example, to convert 121_{10} to a 16-bit binary integer,

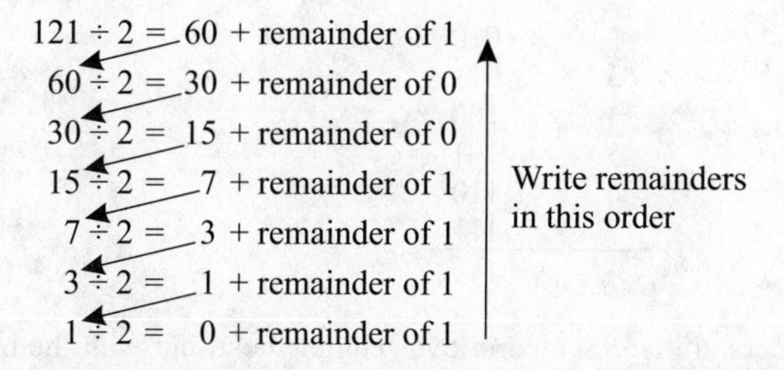

So, $121_{10} = 1111001_2$. Prefixing it with zeros to produce a 16-bit integer, the result is

$121_{10} = 0000000001111001_2$

To convert a negative decimal number to a binary number,

1. Ignoring the sign of the decimal number, convert it to a binary number.
2. Prefix the result from step 1 with enough 0 digits to produce the number of digits needed in the result (usually 8, 16, or 32 digits).
3. Take the twos complement of the binary number determined in step 2.

For example, to convert -121_{10} to a 16-bit binary integer,

From the previous example, $121_{10} = 0000000001111001_2$

0000000001111001_2 121_{10}

↓

1111111110000110_2 each digit complemented

↓

1111111110000111_2 add one to the complement

So, $-121_{10} = 1111111110000111_2$

A.2 OCTAL NUMBERS

In an octal number, only the digits 0 - 7 are allowed. The base is 8 and the powers of 8 for the digit weights increase from 0 as shown in Figure A.3. The relationship between octal numbers and binary numbers is shown in Table A.1. An octal digit represents 3 binary

	5	4	3	2	1	0	Digit position
• •	8^5	8^4	8^3	8^2	8^1	8^0	Weight as power of 8
• •	32,768	4096	512	64	8	1	Weight as decimal number

Figure A.3. Weight of octal digits.

Table A.1. Octal-Binary Number Equivalents

Octal	Binary
0	000
1	001
2	010
3	011
4	100
5	101
6	110
7	111

digits. Negative octal numbers are represented in twos complement, but with the binary digits grouped by three digits to form each octal digit.

Octal-to-Decimal Conversion Converting a positive octal number to a decimal number is easy. Each digit is multiplied by its weight and then all of the values are summed to obtain the result. For example, to convert the 6-digit number 042736_8 to decimal,

$$
\begin{aligned}
042736_8 &= 0\times8^5 + 4\times8^4 + 2\times8^3 + 7\times8^2 + 3\times8^1 + 6\times8^0 \\
&= 0 + 16384 + 1024 + 448 + 24 + 6 \\
&= 17886_{10}
\end{aligned}
$$

Decimal-to-Octal Conversion Converting a decimal number to an octal number is similar to the method used to convert a decimal number to binary. For a positive decimal number, the procedure is as follows:

1. Repeatedly divide the decimal number by 8 and note the remainders. Continue until the result is zero.

2. The octal number is formed by writing the remainders in reverse order, starting with the last remainder as the most-significant digit.

For example, to convert 12107_{10} to octal,

$$
\begin{aligned}
12107 \div 8 &= 1513 + \text{remainder of } 3 \\
1513 \div 8 &= 189 + \text{remainder of } 1 \\
189 \div 8 &= 23 + \text{remainder of } 5 \\
23 \div 8 &= 2 + \text{remainder of } 7 \\
2 \div 8 &= 0 + \text{remainder of } 2
\end{aligned}
$$

Write remainders in this order (from bottom to top)

So, $12107_{10} = 27513_8$. Alternatively, one could convert the decimal number into a binary number and then starting from the right, write the octal equivalent of each group of 3 binary digits, for example,

$$12107_{10} = 10111101001011_2$$
$$= 10\ 111\ 101\ 001\ 011_2$$
$$= 2\ \ 7\ \ 5\ \ 1\ \ 3_8$$

A.3 HEXADECIMAL NUMBERS

In a hexadecimal number, the digits 0 - 9, A - F are allowed. The base is 16 and the digit weights are powers of 16 as shown in Figure A.4. The relationship between hexadecimal numbers and binary numbers is shown in Table A.2. A hexadecimal digit represents four binary digits. Negative hexadecimal numbers are represented in twos complement, but with the binary digits grouped by four digits to form each hexadecimal digit.

Hexadecimal-to-Decimal Conversion Converting a positive hexadecimal number to a decimal number is easy. Each digit is multiplied by its weight and then all of the values are summed to obtain the result. The digits A - F need to be converted to their decimal equivalent (Table A.2) before executing the multiplication. For example, to convert the 4-digit number $4A7E_{16}$ to decimal,

$$4A7E_{16} = 4\times16^3 + A\times16^2 + 7\times16^1 + E\times16^0$$
$$= 4\times16^3 + 10\times16^2 + 7\times16^1 + 14\times16^0$$
$$= 16384 + 2560 + 112 + 14$$
$$= 19070_{10}$$

Decimal-to-Hexadecimal Conversion Converting a decimal number to a hexadecimal number is similar to the method used to convert a decimal number to binary or octal. For a positive decimal number, the procedure is as follows:

	5	4	3	2	1	0	Digit position
• •	16^5	16^4	16^3	16^2	16^1	16^0	Weight as power of 16
• •	1,048,576	65536	4096	256	16	1	Weight as decimal number

Figure A.4. Weight of hexadecimal digits.

Table A.2. Hexadecimal-Binary Number Equivalents

Hexadecimal	Binary	Decimal	Hexadecimal	Binary	Decimal
0	0000	0	8	1000	8
1	0001	1	9	1001	9
2	0010	2	A	1010	10
3	0011	3	B	1011	11
4	0100	4	C	1100	12
5	0101	5	D	1101	13
6	0110	6	E	1110	14
7	0111	7	F	1111	15

1. Repeatedly divide the decimal number by 16 and note the remainders. Convert the remainders that are greater than 9 to their hexadecimal equivalent. Continue until the result is zero.
2. The hexadecimal number is formed by writing the remainders in reverse order, starting with the last remainder as the most-significant digit.

For example, to convert 12107_{10} to hexadecimal,

$$
\begin{aligned}
12107 \div 16 &= 756 + \text{remainder of } 11 \rightarrow B \\
756 \div 16 &= 47 + \text{remainder of } 4 \rightarrow 4 \\
47 \div 16 &= 2 + \text{remainder of } 15 \rightarrow F \\
2 \div 16 &= 0 + \text{remainder of } 2 \rightarrow 2
\end{aligned}
$$

↑ Write remainders in this order

So, 12107_{10} = 2F4BH. Alternatively, one could convert the decimal number into a binary number and then starting from the right, write the hexadecimal equivalent of each group of 4 binary digits, for example,

$$
\begin{aligned}
12107_{10} &= 10111101001011_2 \\
&= 10\ 1111\ 0100\ 1011_2 \\
&= 2 \quad F \quad 4 \quad B_{16}
\end{aligned}
$$

A.3 BINARY-CODED DECIMAL NUMBERS

Many earlier PLCs stored integer numbers internally in the BCD format. This format was used because early operator display panels used thumbwheel switches to enter numeric values and the pattern of discrete inputs from a thumbwheel switch is in the BCD format. Recent PLCs internally store integer values in the binary format. Nevertheless, thumbwheel switches are still used as an inexpensive method of operator-input of numeric values and these BCD values must be converted to a normal binary number before they can be used in calculations.

BCD numbers have a base of 10, but the individual digits are represented by the 4-bit binary pattern for the decimal digit. For example, the decimal number 7395 is represented as a BCD number:

7	3	9	5
↓	↓	↓	↓
0111	0011	1001	0101

The bit pattern is the same as 0111001110010101_2 which is equivalent to $29{,}589_{10}$. Note that the display of a BCD number is the same as a hexadecimal number (except that there are no A-F digits).

To convert a BCD number into binary, the BCD number is first converted to a decimal number and then the decimal number is converted to its equivalent binary representation. Most PLCs have a function block that handles this conversion.

B Electrical Diagram Symbols

Table B.1. Selector Switches

Example Two-position Selector Switches	
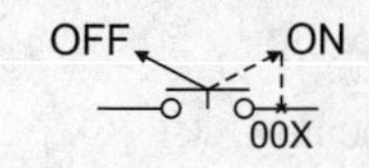	Left maintain - spring return from right Contact closed in right position, open in left
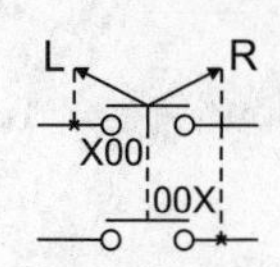	Left and right maintain Top contact closed in left position, open in right Bottom contact closed in right position, open in left
Example Three-position Selector Switches	
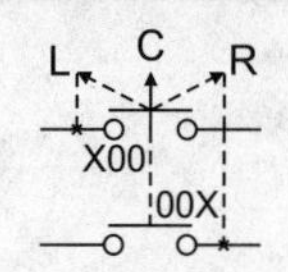	Center maintain - spring return from left and right Top contact closed in left position, open otherwise Bottom contact closed in right position, open otherwise
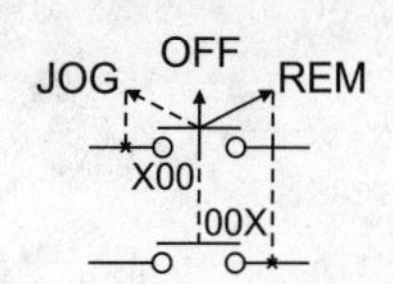	Center and right maintain - spring return from left Top contact closed in left position, open otherwise Bottom contact closed in right position, open otherwise
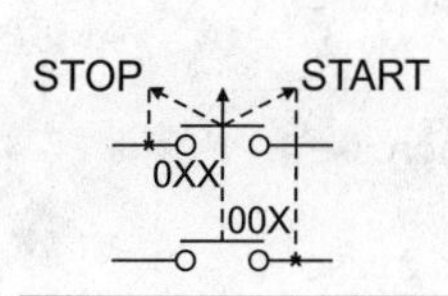	Center maintain - spring return from left and right Top contact open in left position, closed otherwise Bottom contact closed in right position, open otherwise

Table B.2. Discrete Input Devices

Input Type	Symbol	Description
Push Button	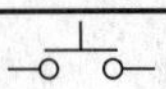	NO
	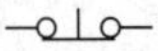	NC
	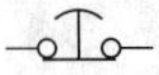	Mushroom head
	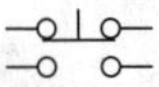	NC and NO
Limit Switch		NO
		NO - held closed
		NC
		NC - held open
Time Delay Contact	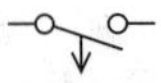	NO - delay opening
		NO - delay closing
	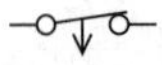	NC - delay closing
		NC - delay opening
Proximity Switch		Closes in position
		Opens in position
Speed Switch	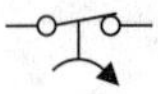	Opens on increase
		Closes on increase
Temperature Switch	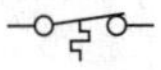	Opens on rise
	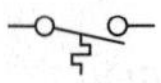	Closes on rise
Liquid Level Switch	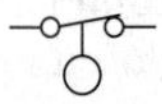	Opens on increase
	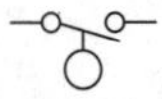	Closes on increase
Pressure Switch	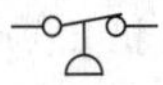	Opens on increase
		Closes on increase
Flow Switch	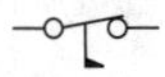	Opens on increase
		Closes on increase

Notes:
NC - Normally closed contact
NO - Normally open contact

Table B.3. Protective Devices

Symbol	Description
	Fuse
C.B.	Circuit breaker
O.L.	Motor overload
	Disconnect

Table B.4. Discrete Output Devices

Symbol	Description	
R	Pilot Light	Letter is lens color A - amber R - red B - blue W - white G - green
R	Pilot Light (Push-to-test)	
	Relay Coil	
	Solenoid	
	Three-phase motor	
	Single-phase motor	

C Piping and Instrumentation Diagram (P&ID) Symbols

The symbols used in the P&ID's in this text are explained in this appendix. For the most part, they adhere to the ISA standard, S5.1 (ISA, 1986).

Each measuring device and control equipment module on a P&ID is identified with a tag that is two or three letters followed by a number. The letter abbreviations are used to identify the various types of measuring devices and control equipment. The first letter of the tag indicates the variable type and the succeeding letter(s) provide more information about the function being performed. The abbreviations used in this text are summarized in Table C.1. The only letter that does not conform to the S5.1 standard is the letter "X", which is unclassified in S5.1. Examples of common abbreviations are:

FT	Flow transmitter
LAH	Level alarm, high level
FIC	Flow controller with the measurement indicated
XV	Discrete (on/off) valve
EX	Electric motor

Each tag is located inside a circle (regulatory entity) or a diamond (discrete entity). A square is placed around the circle or diamond if the entity performs control functions. These symbols are summarized in Figure C.1. A diamond inside a square represents a device, a discrete control object. A diamond alone represents a status, a discrete value. A circle inside a square represents a loop, a regulatory control object. A circle alone represents an indicator, an analog value, which is typically an analog transmitter.

In addition, interlock causes and actions are attached to the circles and/or diamonds. An interlock cause is indicated with by the letter "I" followed by a number within a smaller diamond. The associated interlock action uses the same identification as the cause, except within a small square. The specific interlock cause and action information is usually documented as a note the diagram or in another document.

The signal connections between control entities are indicated as different line styles, as shown in Figure C.2. Symbols for common process elements are shown in Figure C.3.

REFERENCE

Instrument Society of America, *ISA-S5.1-1984, Instrumentation Symbols and Identification*, Instrument Society of America, 1986.

Table C.1 Identification Letters

	First Letter	Suceeding Letters
A	Analyzer	Alarm
C	Concentration	Control
D	Density	
E	Voltage	
F	Flow	
H		High
I		Indicating
L	Level	Low
P	Pressure	
Q		Totalize
S	Speed, slide gate	Switch
T	Temperature	Transmitter
V		Valve
X	Discrete (on-off)	Motor
Y		Compute, convert

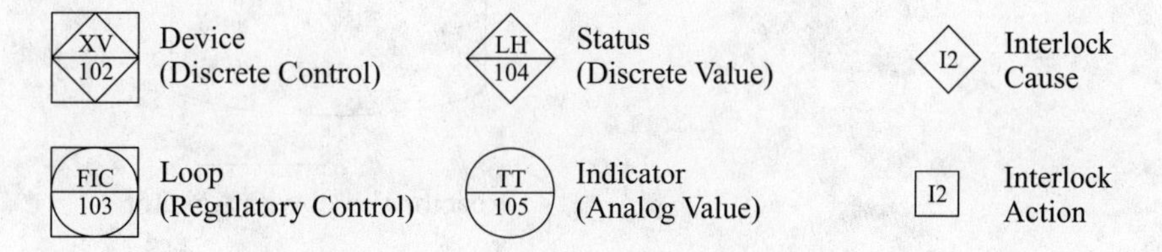

Figure C.1. Symbols for control entities.

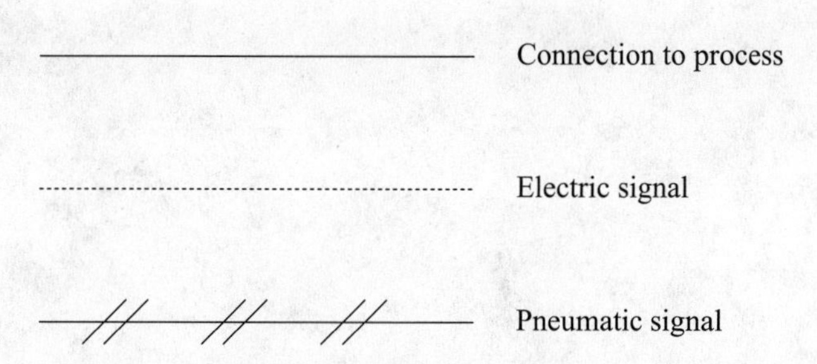

Figure C.2. Control signals.

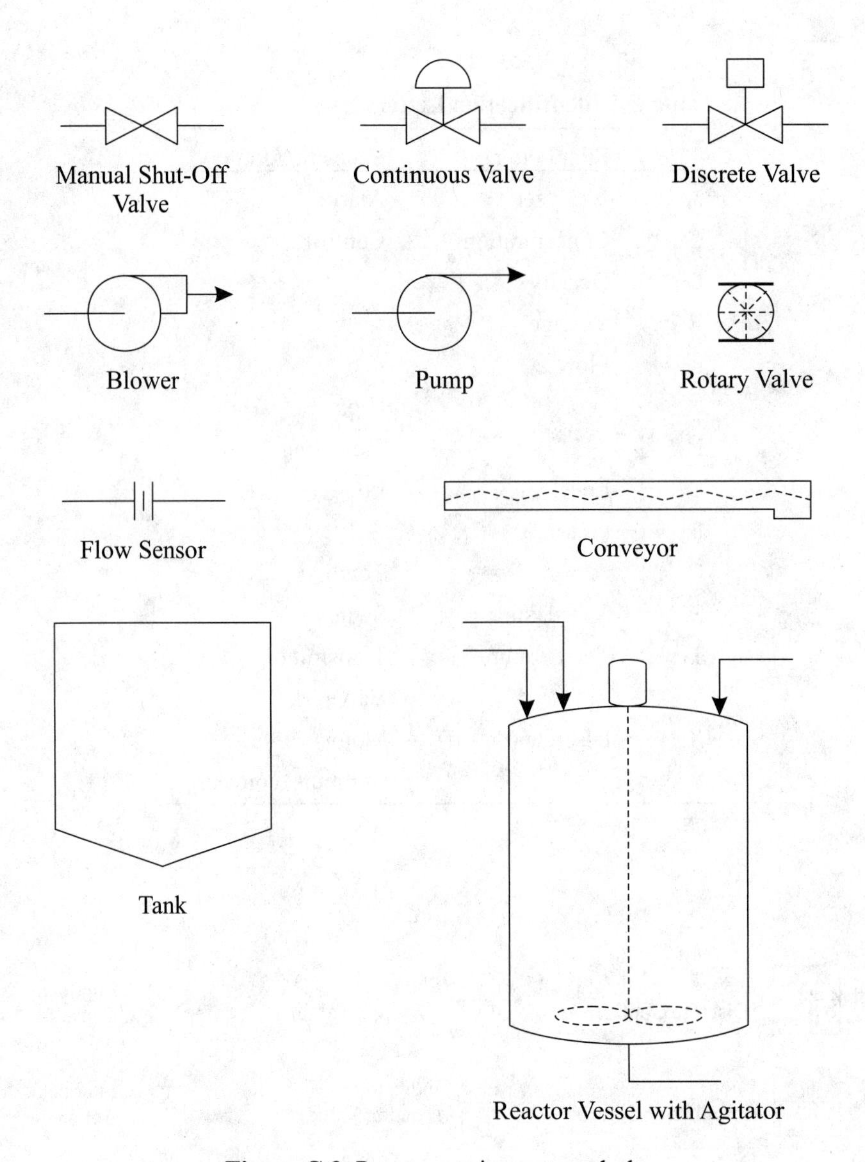

Figure C.3. Process equipment symbols.

Glossary

Note: Definitions quoted from other sources are so indicated with the source. References with similar definitions are also noted. Italicized words in a definition are defined in this glossary.

absolute pressure. The pressure of a gas or liquid measured relative to a complete vacuum.

accuracy. The ability of an *analog sensor* to produce the correct output.

action. Defines the outputs or other behaviors that are active in a *function chart* or *sequential function chart* step.

actuator. A device that manipulates a physical input to the process (for example, an air valve or a motor). Its input is connected to a PLC *output module*.

ADC. Abbreviation for *analog-to-digital converter*.

address. The alphanumeric string that defines the location of an input *channel*, output channel, or internal processor memory.

air-to-close/air-to-open. Describes control valve fail-safe action. When the air supply fails, an air-to-close valve will open so flow through the valve is unobstructed, and an air-to-open valve will close, obstructing flow though the valve.

American National Standards Institute. A private, non-profit organization that administers and coordinates voluntary standardization in the U. S.

analog actuator. An *actuator* used to regulate a physical quantity. The most common analog actuators are an electric motor or a control valve.

analog input module. Receives a measured quantity (voltage or current) from an *analog sensor* and other devices that produce *analog signals*.

analog output module. Generates a voltage or current signal that drives an *analog actuator* to manipulate a physical quantity.

analog sensor. A *sensor* that measures the value of a physical quantity than can have an infinite number of values.

analog signal. Represents a physical quantity that can have an infinite number of values.

analog-to-digital converter. A device that converts the analog voltage into an integer number, which has a finite resolution.

AND. A logical operation that requires all input signals to be true (1, on) to produce a true output.

ANSI. Abbreviation for *American National Standards Institute*.

Array. An indexed collection of data elements, all of the same data type. Each element is designated by its index, or position in the array. For example, if an array is named "Int_Ary", one of its elements is designated by "Int_Ary[4]," where "4" is the index, also called the subscript. Arrays can have more than one dimension and each dimension has its own index. A two-dimensional array of numbers is arranged as a table and has two indices. For example "Two_Ary[3,2]" refers to the element in the third row and second column.

ASCII. Abbreviation for American Standard Code for Information Interchange. A seven-bit code used to represent alphanumeric characters, punctuation marks, and control codes.

AS-i. Abbreviation for Acuator Sensor Interface. Originally developed as a low-level bus to interface to discrete sensors and actuators.

ASTM. Abbreviation for American Society for Testing and Materials.

automatic feedback control. *Feedback control* in which a controller device monitors the controlled variable of interest and commands a *manipulated variable* in order to maintain a desired value of the *controlled variable*.

automatic mode. The state of a PID controller where it calculates the *manipulated variable* according to the PID equation, and the operator changes the *setpoint*.

baseband coaxial cable. A *coaxial cable* that sends signals at one frequency.

batch. "1.) The material that is being produced or that has been produced by a single execution of a batch process. 2.) An entity that represents the production of a material at any point in the process." (ISA, 1995)

batch control. Control functions for a *batch process*.

batch process. Finite quantities (batches) of material are produced by subjecting quantities of input materials to a defined order of processing actions using one or more pieces of equipment. Batch processes are discontinuous processes from a material flow standpoint. Batch processes are neither discrete nor continuous, though they have characteristics of both.

baud rate. The number of binary bits transmitted per second over a serial communication link.

BCD. Abbreviation for *binary-coded decimal*.

binary-coded decimal. A way of representing decimal numbers in a binary format. The numbers have a base of 10, but the individual digits are represented by the 4-bit binary pattern for the decimal digit.

binary number. A number system whose base is 2 and uses only the digits 0 and 1. Proceeding from the right-most (least significant) position, the digit weights are 1, 2, 4, 8, 16, 32, and so on.

bit. The smallest unit of binary information, it can have a value of 0 or 1.

block diagram. A representation of the process where major groups of equipment are shown as rectangular blocks with the material and/or information flow between them.

block transfer. A method to move multiple *words* of data between the *I/O modules* and the PLC processor memory.

Boolean. The *data type* of a *bit*.

branch. A parallel path within a ladder logic *rung*.

bridge. A device that connects two *local area networks* that have the same or similar *protocols*.

bridge circuit. Converts *sensor* resistance changes to voltage or current changes, providing temperature compensation.

broadband coaxial cable. A *coaxial cable* that sends signals at multiple frequencies.

bubbler tube. Used to measure the height of corrosive liquids. A small amount of air or inert gas is forced through this tube. The pressure required to force air bubbles from the tube is proportional to the fluid level.

bumpless transfer. When the PID controller is switched from *manual mode* to *automatic mode*, the calculated *manipulated variable* change is either filtered, or ramped to the calculated value. This gradual change in the *manipulated variable* is better tolerated by the equipment and the process.

bus. A conductor or group of conductors serving as a common power or communication connection.

bus topology. A communication network topology where all nodes are connected to the same medium and thus share access. A node on the bus can transmit or receive data from any of the other nodes.

byte. A group of eight binary digits.

CAN. Abbreviation for *Controller Area Network*.

capacitive pressure sensor. A pressure sensor where the sensing diaphragm is fixed between two capacitor plates and as the sensing diaphragm moves with changes in pressure, the capacitance changes.

capacitive proximity sensor. A *proximity sensor* that detects metallic and nonmetallic objects by the principle that materials interact with an electrostatic field.

capital project. A project in which manufacturing facilities are constructed and/or improved.

carrier-sense multiple access with collision detection. A masterless method of controlling access to a *local area network* with bus topology.

cascade control. Control scheme where the *manipulated variable* output of one controller becomes the *setpoint* of another controller. (ISA, 1979)

cascade mode. The state of a PID controller where the *setpoint* is supplied from another controller or device (not the operator) and the PID algorithm calculates the *control variable*.

cell. A logical grouping of equipment required to process one stream or manufacture one product or group of products. A process cell is a set of cooperating *units*. (ISA, 1995)

central processing unit. The part of the PLC that interprets and executes the *firmware*.

channel. The connection of one *signal* to an I/O module. The physical connection involves one or more electrical terminals.

closed-loop control. Same as *feedback control*.

coaxial cable. A flexible or rigid cable having a shield around a single conductor.

coil. A *ladder diagram* symbol that represents a discrete output or bit in internal memory.

cold junction compensation. A method of measuring the temperature of the *thermocouple* cold junction and using it to adjust the measured thermocouple hot junction voltage.

conductivity. The ability of a solution to conduct an electric current between two electrodes.

configuration. The entire body of software (program and data) that corresponds to a PLC system. Generally, a configuration equates with the program and data for one PLC.

contact. A *ladder diagram* symbol that represents a discrete input or bit in internal memory.

continuous control. A control system whose signal inputs and outputs are *continuous-time signals*. The control devices are either analog electronic or pneumatic controllers.

continuous process. A process in which material passes in a continuous stream through the processing equipment. (ISA, 1995)

continuous-time signal. A signal whose values are defined for all time. See also *discrete-time signal*.

Control Concept. A section of the *Control Requirement Definition* that defines the extent of automation for the plant system.

control loop. See *loop*.

Control Requirement Definition. Control information package containing the *Process Operation Description*, *Control Concept*, *control strategy* and detailed control design.

control strategy. Defines the control types and interrelations to fulfill the control requirements.

control variable. A quantity varied by the controller in order to affect the *controlled variable*. Also called *manipulated variable*.

controlled variable. "In a control loop, the variable the value of which is sensed to originate a feedback signal." (ISA, 1979) Measured by the *process variable*.

Controller Area Network. The physical layer of *DeviceNet*. Originally developed as an automotive network.

ControlNet. A network originally developed for time-critical I/O and peer-to-peer data transmission.

convergent-beam photoelectric sensor. A *photoelectric sensor* that uses lenses to focus both the emitter and receiver at the same point.

Coriolis flowmeter. Measures the mass flow rate directly with the Coriolis effect. Fluid moving through a vibrating U-shaped tube sets up a twist in the tube. The mass flow is proportional to the maximum twist angle.

CPU. Abbreviation for *central processing unit*.

critically damped. The time response of the system to a step signal input has the fastest time response possible without *overshoot*. (ISA, 1979)

CRD. Abbreviation for *Control Requirement Definition.*

cross reference. A list of program variables and for each variable, indicates where it is used and how it is used.

CSMA/CD. Abbreviation for *carrier-sense multiple access with collision detection.*

current sinking. See *sinking.*

current sourcing. See *sourcing.*

CV. Abbreviation for *control variable.*

DAC. Abbreviation for *digital-to-analog converter.*

damping ratio. The ratio of the second peak to the first peak in the *process variable* response. Only defined if the process variable response is *underdamped.* (ISA, 1979)

dark-operate sensor. A *photoelectric sensor* that energizes its output when the received light intensity decreases below a threshold.

Data Highway. One of the first PLC-to-PLC communication protocols; developed by Allen-Bradley.

Data Highway +. An enhanced version of *Data Highway.*

data type. A classification that identifies data as one of various types, such as Boolean, integer, or real and states the valid range of values and its storage format.

DCS. Abbreviation for *distributed control system.*

deadtime. "The interval of time between initiation of an input change or stimulus and the start of the resulting observable response." (ISA, 1979)

decimal number. A number system whose base is 10 and uses the digits 0 - 9. Proceeding from the right-most (least significant) position, the digit weights are 1, 10, 100, 1000, and so on.

derivative action. The controller *manipulated variable* calculation is based on the rate of change of the *process variable.* Also called rate action. (ISA, 1979)

derivative gain. For a PID controller, the derivative gain is the proportionality constant relating the change in controller output to the *derivative action.*

derivative time constant. Same as the *derivative gain.*

derived function block. A function block that is programmed by the user, allowing one to encapsulate frequently-used code sections and easily reuse them.

DeviceNet. A relatively low-speed network for distributed I/O modules and other devices.

DFB. Abbreviation for *derived function block.*

DH+. Abbreviation for *Data Highway+.*

DH-485. Abbreviation for Data Highway-485, a version of *Data Highway* for the SLC-500 processors.

differential pressure. The difference between two pressure measurements.

differential pressure flowmeter. A sensor that measures fluid or gas flow by measuring the pressure drop across an *orifice plate* or *venturi tube.*

diffuse reflective photoelectric sensor. A *photoelectric sensor* where the emitter and receiver are in the same package and the sensed object returns the light beam to the receiver.

digital-to-analog converter. Converts the integer number from the PLC into a voltage signal.

digital control. A control system whose control devices are digital controllers or digital computers. Technically, PID controllers in a PLC are digital controllers, though they behave like an analog electronic controller. Also called discrete-time control, the signal inputs and outputs are *discrete-time signals.*

direct-acting. A process or controller is called direct-acting if an increase in the *input signal* causes an increase in the *output signal.*

direct action. See *direct-acting.*

directly represented variable. Address of a memory or I/O location in the PLC.

discrete actuator. Convert the on/off PLC output signal into a physical phenomena.

discrete control. Control consisting of *discrete sensors* and *discrete actuators.*

discrete input module. An *input module* that senses the status of a device that has only two states, on/off, open/closed, running/stopped, and so on.

discrete output module. An *output module* that switches a device that has only two states, on/off, open/closed, and so on.

discrete parts manufacturing process. A type of process where a specified quantity of material moves as a unit (part or group of parts) between work stations, and each unit maintains its unique identity (ISA, 1995).

discrete sensor. A *sensor* whose output has two states: off/on, open/closed, or 0/1.

discrete signal. Represents a physical quantity that has only two states, on/off, open/closed, and so on.

discrete-time control. See *digital control.*

discrete-time signal. A signal whose values are defined only at the sampling instants. Any process measurements must be converted to discrete-time signals before being used by a digital controller. See also *continuous-time signal.*

distributed control system. Developed to provide *regulatory control* functions for factory automation. See also *programmable electronic system.*

disturbance. Process influence that affects the *process variable*, but is not manipulated by the controller. (ISA, 1979)

Doppler ultrasonic flowmeter. Transmits ultrasonic pulses into the flow stream and monitors the reflected pulses. The fluid flow rate is proportional to the frequency shift of the reflected pulses.

double-acting cylinder. A pneumatic or hydraulic cylinder with two controls.

dwell time. The time a process remains halted in order for another process to occur. For example, a carousel is commonly used to move a part between machining stations. The part is loaded onto the carousel, the carousel moves the part to the individual stations, pausing while each machining operation is performed, and eventually the part is removed from the carousel. The *dwell time* is the time the carousel pauses to allow the stations to process the part.

electromagnetic interference. An electromagnetic disturbance that disrupts or degrades the performance of electronic equipment.

EMI. Abbreviation for *electromagnetic interference.*

empirical model. Mathematical model of a process based on experimental data.

encoder. A discrete sensor used in position control applications to determine the position and/or velocity of a rotary shaft.

Ethernet. A popular, inexpensive *local area network* originally developed for the office environment, but is becoming a popular network for factory automation.

Ethernet/IP. A network that provides a control application layer on top of standard *Ethernet*.

expansion chassis. A chassis containing only *I/O modules* and a communication interface, and not the PLC processor.

fail-safe. A failure in the system causes the process to assume a safe condition, normally **off**. For example, a fail-safe output channel will assume the **off** condition when there is a failure in the module, PLC processor, or power source.

fault. An internal processor error that causes the processor to halt its operation.

FBD. Abbreviation for *function block diagram.*

feedback control. Control scheme that uses knowledge of the output to take corrective action. See *automatic feedback control* and *manual feedback control*. (ISA, 1979)

feedforward control. Control scheme that eliminates or reduces the *disturbance* effect on the *process variable* by using a measurement of the *disturbance* to modify the calculation of the *manipulated variable*. (ISA, 1979)

firewall. A communication network device that filters all network packets to determine if they are legitimate requests to be passed to the destination. A firewall protects a local area network from unauthorized users.

firmware. In a PLC processor, the software that is embedded in the processor that executes the user program and handles the communication tasks. The user program cannot modify the firmware. Other modules, for example, communication interfaces or motion control modules also contain firmware. In earlier processors, the firmware was contained in read-only memory (ROM) integrated circuit chips. Most recent processors store the firmware in electrically-erasable read-only memory (EEROM) integrated circuit chips that can allow firmware updates without disassembling the module.

FODT. Abbreviation for first-order plus deadtime, a type of *empirical model.*

force. To override the status of a physical discrete input or to override the logic driving a physical output coil and make the output be a desired value.

Foundation Fieldbus H1. A *local area network* for device-level communications originally developed as a substitute for 4-20 mA signal transmission in process control applications.

Foundation Fieldbus HSE. A *local area network* that provides the Foundation Fieldbus application layer on top of standard *Ethernet.*

function block. (1) In IEC 61131-3, the basic unit of a program and may be written in any of the IEC languages, (2) in a ladder logic program, any entity that is not a contact or coil, for example, timer and counter, (3) the entities that are interconnected in a function block diagram.

function block diagram. One of the standard PLC languages. A set of interconnected *function blocks* and signal connections between the blocks.

function chart. A diagram of interconnected steps, actions, and transitions used for sequential control. A simplified version of the *sequential function chart.*

fuse. A device consisting of easily melted metal that interrupts electrical current when the current is too high.

gage pressure. The pressure of a gas or liquid measured relative to atmospheric pressure.

gain. The ratio of the change in the *steady-state* output to a step change in the input, provided the output does not saturate (ISA, 1979).

gateway. A device that connects two *local area networks* that have significantly different *protocols.*

global data table. Data that is shared between PLC processors.

global variable. A variable accessible to all elements contained in a configuration, resource, or program. For example, a global program variable is accessible to all function blocks and routines in the program.

ground. A connection made from the equipment to earth, or zero potential, for safety purposes.

group. For the PLC-5 processor, it is an addressing unit corresponding to an input-image word and an output-image word. An I/O group can contain up to 16 input channels and 16 output channels and can occupy two, one, or one-half slots in the chassis.

GUI. Abbreviation for graphical user interface. See *human-machine interface.*

Hall effect proximity sensor. A *proximity sensor* that detects magnetic materials based on the Hall effect. When a magnetic field is applied perpendicular to a DC current flowing through a semiconductor plate, a small voltage difference perpendicular to the current flow is generated. When this voltage is above a threshold, the magnetic object is detected.

hexadecimal number. A number system whose base is 16 and uses the digits 0 - 9 and letters A - F. Proceeding from the right-most (least significant) position, the digit weights are 1, 16, 256, 4096, and so on.

high-signal selector. A device that automatically compares two or more input signals and allows the signal with the higher value to be the output.

HMI. Abbreviation for *human-machine interface.*

HOA switch. Type of switch having three positions: (1) Hand, (2) Off, and (3) Auto. It is often used between the PLC and a discrete device, such as a motor. In the "Hand" position, the operator manually starts the device. In the "Off" position, the device is manually stopped. In the "Auto" position, the PLC starts and stops the device.

human-machine interface. The interface between the human operator and the control system.

hydraulic. Refers to a system or component that is moved with fluid pressure.

hydraulic actuator. A cylinder with a piston that provides the actuation force with hydraulic fluid pressure.

hysteresis. A dead band purposely introduced in the operation of discrete sensors to eliminate "chattering" when the sensed phenomenon is at the on/off boundary. For a proximity sensor, the object is sensed at a certain distance. The object must move further away to change the sensor output.

IAE. Abbreviation for the integral of the absolute error, a control loop performance measure.

IEC. Abbreviation for International Electrotechnical Commission, an international standards-making organization.

IEC 61131. Abbreviation for *IEC 1131: Programmable Logic Controllers*, International Electrotechnical Commission, 1993.

IEC 61131-3. Part 3 of the IEC 61131 (formerly 1131) standard. Defines the standard PLC languages: *ladder logic*, *sequential function chart*, *function block diagram*, *structured text*, and *instruction list*.

IEEE. Abbreviation for The Institute of Electrical and Electronics Engineers.

IEEE 802.3. The IEEE standard that defines the *Ethernet* data communication protocol, which is a *carrier sense multiple access with collision detection* type of protocol.

IEEE 802.4. The IEEE standard that defines a *token bus* communication protocol.

IL. Abbreviation for *instruction list*.

image table. The PLC processor memory that contains a copy of the input and output *channel* values.

increase close/increase open. Controller parameter provided to compensate for valve actuator action (air-to-close or air-to-open). Use increase close for an air-to-close valve and increase open for an air-to-open valve.

indexed addressing. A data addressing scheme where the value of an index register is added to the address to obtain a new address.

indirect addressing. A data addressing scheme where the contents of one memory location specify the location of another data item. For example, the integer "Ary_Idx" could specify which element in the *array* "Int_Ary" needs to be displayed for the operator.

inductive proximity sensor. A *proximity sensor* that detects ferrous and nonferrous metallic objects by the principle that metals interact with an electromagnetic field.

infrared thermometer. A noncontact temperature sensor that measures temperature by focusing the infrared radiation from the hot target onto an infrared detector, which converts the energy to an electrical voltage.

input module. Provides the physical interface between the PLC and an *input signal*.

input signal. "A *signal* applied to a device, element, or system." (ISA, 1979)

instruction. (1) In a ladder diagram, it generically refers to the contact and coil symbols as well as to the names of the function blocks, (2) a statement in an instruction list program.

instruction list. One of the standard PLC languages. A low-level textual language similar to microprocessor assembly language.

integral action. The controller *manipulated variable* calculation is based on the integrated error, the *setpoint* minus the *process variable*. (ISA, 1979)

integral gain. For PI or PID controllers, the integral gain is the proportionality constant relating the change in controller output to the *integral action*. (ISA, 1979)

integral time constant. The reciprocal of the *integral gain*. (ISA, 1979)

integral windup. When a controller has *integral action*, a persistent error will cause the integral term to increase (or decrease) to a value of large magnitude.

integrated circuit temperature sensor. A temperature sensor that is based on the property that the base-emitter voltage of a bipolar transistor is proportional to temperature.

INTERBUS. Originally developed by a German consortium, it is a *local area network* with a ring topology.

interlock. Designed to detect an abnormal process condition and take action to prevent an undesirable or hazardous event.

I/O module. A plug-in component that provides the physical interface between the PLC processor and the field devices, such as switches, lamps, and valves.

IP rating. The IEC enclosure designation consisting of the letters "IP" followed by two digits.

ISA. Abbreviation for the Instrumentation, Systems, and Automation Society.

isolation. Provides the interface between the field and PLC voltage levels, preventing ground loops and noisy electrical signals from interfering with the PLC operation. Often provided by *optical isolation.*

ITAE. Abbreviation for the integral of the product of time and the absolute error, a control loop performance measure.

jog. A momentary **on** state often used by the operator to override the automatic motion control.

jump. Program execution control that allows one to skip ladder rungs, instruction list statements, or SFC steps.

ladder diagram. One of the standard PLC languages. A graphical language resembling an electrical wiring diagram with contacts, coils and blocks.

ladder logic. A symbolic programming language traditionally used in *programmable logic controllers*. It was developed from the relay ladder logic wiring diagram.

LAN. Abbreviation for *local area network.*

latch. (1) A ladder logic output coil that is energized when any rung path passes power and remains energized when no rung path passes power, (2) an electronic or electromechanical device that energizes its output and maintains the output after the input signal is turned off.

LCD. Abbreviation for *liquid crystal display.*

LD. Abbreviation for *ladder diagram.*

LED. Abbreviation for *light-emitting diode.*

light-emitting diode. A semiconductor diode that emits light when current passes through the junction in the forward direction.

light-operate sensor. A *photoelectric sensor* that energizes its output when the received light intensity increases above a threshold.

limit switch. A *discrete sensor* that indicates the presence/absence of an object. Often, the sensed object moves a lever arm to close a switch contact.

liquid crystal display. A low-power display that uses a liquid crystal to display the graphics and text for an operator interface.

local area network. A high-speed medium-distance communication system linking multiple devices.

local variable. A variable defined at the software element (for example, function block or subroutine) that can only be accessed by the software element.

lockout. (1) Completely disabling all energy sources to a system and applying a locking device to each energy source to prevent accidental startup, (2) in a program, a condition that stops a device and does not allow it to restart until the condition is cleared.

loop. A single-input, single-output controller that monitors a transmitter and manipulates a physical quantity (usually a control valve position) in order to force a process variable to the desired setpoint. The controller is typically a *PID controller*. (ISA, 1979)

loss-in-weight feeder. A solid material feeder that infers the flow rate from the rate of hopper weight loss. A separate device (for example, screw feeder) is manipulated to control the feed rate.

low-signal selector. A device that automatically compares two or more input signals and allows the signal with the lower value to be the output.

magnetic flowmeter. Measures fluid flow based on Faraday's law. The moving fluid induces a voltage across two electrodes that are aligned perpendicular to both the flow and the magnetic field. The voltage is proportional to the average velocity of the fluid.

magnetic reed switch. A *proximity sensor* consisting of sealed contacts. When a magnet moves close to the switch, the contacts are magnetized and pull together.

man-machine interface. Same as *human-machine interface.*

manipulated variable. A quantity varied by the controller in order to affect the *controlled variable.* (ISA, 1979) Also called the *control variable.*

manual feedback control. *Feedback control* in which operating personnel monitor the *controlled variable* of interest and take corrective action in order to maintain the desired value.

manual mode. The state of a PID controller where the operator sets the *manipulated variable*, and the PID equation is not executed.

mask. A logical function that only allows only certain bits in the word to be changed or compared. For example, in a masked word move, a "1" in the mask means the particular bit is passed from the source to the destination and a "0" in the mask means the particular bit is blocked.

master. In a *master/slave* type of controlling access to a *local area network*, this node controls how the other nodes (*slave* nodes) access the network. The master polls the slave nodes, permitting them to transmit messages.

master control relay. (1) A hard-wired relay that de-energizes physical discrete control devices when an emergency-stop switch is pressed; (2) a ladder logic instruction that enables/disables non-retentive outputs within a range of rungs.

master/slave. A method of controlling access to a *local area network* with bus topology where one *node* is designated the master that controls how other nodes access the network.

MCR. Abbreviation for *master control relay.*

memory. The part of the PLC processor that stores data and program either permanently or temporarily.

memory map. The allocation of the PLC processor memory into segments for certain purposes. For example, certain segments may be allocated for data and others for program. A particular data segment may only contain one type of data (for example, bits, timers, etc.).

Modbus. One of the first PLC-to-PLC communication protocols; developed by Modicon.

Modbus Plus. The Modbus communication protocol implemented on top of a *token bus* network.

Modbus/TCP. The Modbus communication protocol implemented on top of *Ethernet.*

mode. (1) For a PLC processor, it defines how the processor scans the program (see *program mode*, *run mode*, and *test mode*); (2) for a PID controller, it indicates the state of the control algorithm (see *automatic mode*, *cascade mode*, *manual mode*, and *tracking mode*).

motor contactor. An output actuator used to control a single-speed motor that is basically a three- or four-pole relay that handles the high motor current.

motor drive. A modern motor controller that uses electronics to provide efficient control of the motor speed and/or torque.

MV. Abbreviation for *manipulated variable.*

NAND. A logical operation that requires all input signals to be true (1, on) to produce a false output.

NEMA. Abbreviation for National Electrical Manufacturers Association.

NFPA. Abbreviation for National Fire Protection Association.

node. Device on a *local area network.*

nonretentive timer. A timer that resets its accumulator value when the input signal is false (0, off).

NOR. A logical operation that requires all input signals to be false (0, off) to produce a true output.

normally-closed contact. A contact that passes power if its control is unenergized. The contact blocks power if its control is energized.

normally-open contact. A contact that passes power if its control is energized. The contact blocks power if its control is unenergized.

NOT. A logical operation that yields a false (0, off) output if the input is true (1, on) and a true output if the input is false.

octal number. A number system whose base is 8 and uses the digits 0 - 7. Proceeding from the right-most (least significant) position, the digit weights are 1, 8, 64, 512, and so on.

off-delay timer. A timer that delays the turn-off of a signal and does not delay the turn-on.

off-line programming. Programming the PLC while not connected to the PLC processor through a communication port. Later, the program is downloaded to the processor.

offset. The difference between the *setpoint* and the *process variable* when the system has reached *steady-state.* (ISA, 1979)

on-delay timer. A timer that delays the turn-on of a signal and does not delay the turn-off.

on-line programming. Programming the PLC while connected to the PLC processor through a communication port. Most processors will allow one to make changes while the processor is in the *run mode.*

one-shot contact. See *transitional contact.*

open-loop control. A control strategy where the *manipulated variables* are set to their design values and held constant. (ISA, 1979)

open-loop response. The *process variable* response to a step change in the *manipulated variable* while the controller is in the *manual mode.*

operating point. The normal operating value for the system variables.

operating state. The current condition of the equipment entity, e.g., *process cell* or *unit.* The operating state also defines how the equipment entity will operate and how it will respond to commands.

operator interface. Same as *human-machine interface.*

optical isolation. Isolation provided by optical couplers that consist of a photodiode transferring digital information to a phototransistor. There is no electrical connection between the photodiode and phototransistor.

optical pyrometer. A noncontact temperature sensor that measures temperature by comparing the intensity of the light radiated from the hot target with the brightness of an incandescent lamp filament.

OR. A logical operation that requires at least one input signal to be true (1, on) to produce a true output.

orifice plate. A flat piece of metal with a sharp-edged hole of a certain size bored in it used to measure gas or liquid flow rate.

ORP. Abbreviation for *oxidation-reduction potential.*

output module. Provides the physical interface between the PLC and an *output signal.*

output signal. "A *signal* delivered by a device, element or system." (ISA, 1979)

overdamped. The time response of the system to a step signal input has no *overshoot* and is slower than *critically damped.* (ISA, 1979)

override control. Scheme used to protect process equipment or personnel. See *high-signal selector* and *low-signal selector.*

overshoot. "The maximum excursion beyond the final *steady-state* value of output as the result of an input change." (ISA, 1979)

oxidation-reduction potential. The oxidizing or reducing nature of a chemical.

P&ID. Abbreviation for *Piping and Instrumentation Diagram.*

P-NET. A process automation *local area network* developed by Proces-Data A/S.

parallel circuit. A connection of *contacts, coils,* or *function blocks* where all right ends are connected together and all left ends are connected together.

password. A string of characters chosen by a computer or control system user and used to authenticate the user in order to prevent unauthorized access to the computer or PLC.

peak time. The time from the *setpoint step* change to the time of the first peak of an underdamped *process variable* response.

peer-to-peer. Communication that occurs between similar devices on *a local area network.* In factory automation, generally refers to PLC-to-PLC communication.

percent overshoot. The amount of the *overshoot*, expressed as a percentage of the process variable final value.

permissive. A condition that prevents a device from being started.

PFD. Abbreviation for *Process Flow Diagram.*

pH. A measure of the acidity or alkalinity of a water solution.

photoelectric sensor. A sensor that uses a phototransistor receiver to respond to a modulated light beam to determine proximity or distance. The sensor contains an emitter to generate the light beam or may sense ambient light.

PI control. Abbreviation for Proportional-plus-Integral control. A controller whose output is the sum of *proportional action* and *integral action.*

PID control. Abbreviation for Proportional-plus-Integral-plus-Derivative control. A controller whose output is the sum of *proportional action, integral action*, and *derivative action.*

Piping and Instrumentation Diagram. A symbolic drawing of a process, or portion of a process, showing the piping and instrumentation.

PLC. Abbreviation for *programmable logic controller*.

pneumatic. Refers to a system or component that is moved with air pressure.

pneumatic actuator. A cylinder with a piston that provides the actuation force with air pressure.

POD. Abbreviation for *Process Operation Description.*

process. "Physical or chemical change of matter or conversion of energy; e.g., change in pressure, temperature, speed, electrical potential, etc." (ISA, 1979) For this text, the process is the system to be controlled.

process cell. See *cell.*

Process Flow Diagram. An abstract drawing of a process or plant showing equipment groupings (areas, cells, units, etc.) and the material and/or information flows between them.

process input. When considering the process, an input is generally material moving into the process. From the standpoint of control, the process input is a *manipulated variable.*

Process Operation Description. Design information package that defines the operating strategy and control objectives of the plant systems.

process output. When considering the process, an output is generally material moving out of the process. From the standpoint of control, the process output is a *controlled variable* or a *process variable.*

process unit. See *unit.*

process variable. The measured value of the *controlled variable* which, along with the setpoint, is used by the controller to calculate a value of the *manipulated variable.*

PROFIBUS. Acronym for PROcess FIeld BUS, a process automation *local area network.* There are three parts: *PROFIBUS-DP*, *PROFIBUS-PA*, and *PROFIBUS-FMS.*

PROFIBUS-DP. Acronym for PROcess FIeld BUS - Decentral Periphery, a process automation *local area network* developed for a mix of discrete and analog devices.

PROFIBUS-FMS. Acronym for PROcess FIeld BUS - Fieldbus Messaging Specification, an application layer messaging protocol.

PROFIBUS-PA. Acronym for PROcess FIeld BUS - Process Automation, a process automation *local area network* designed as a substitute for 4-20 mA signal transmission in process control applications.

PROFInet. A protocol developed for distributed automation applications whose lower layers are standard *Ethernet.*

program. In IEC 61131-3, it generally consists of an interconnection of *function blocks*, each of which may be written in any of the IEC languages. In general, a program consists of all of the executable user-written software in the PLC.

program mode. The PLC processor does not scan the program. Depending on the particular PLC processor the physical inputs may be copied into the input image, but the physical outputs are disabled.

programmable electronic system. Any system that implements the control functions. A programmable electronic system encompasses the functions of both a traditional *distributed control system* (DCS) and a traditional *programmable logic controller* (PLC).

programmable logic controller. Developed to provide *discrete control* functions for factory automation. See also *programmable electronic system.*

proportional action. The controller *manipulated variable* is calculated as a constant (called the *proportional gain*) multiplied by the error, the *setpoint* minus the *process variable.* (ISA, 1979)

proportional band. The change in error required to produce a full range, 100%, change in the manipulated variable, due to *proportional action.* It is equal to 100 divided by the *proportional gain.* (ISA, 1979)

proportional gain. The ratio of the change in the *manipulated variable* due to *proportional action* to the change in the error. See also *proportional band.* (ISA, 1979)

protocol. A set of rules that govern how nodes communicate with each other over a *local area network.*

proximity sensor. A noncontact type of *discrete sensor* that senses an object with electromagnetic field, electric field, ultrasonic, or photoelectric technologies.

proximity switch. See *proximity sensor.*

PV. Abbreviation for *process variable.*

rack. For the PLC-5 processor, a rack is defined to be eight *groups.*

radar sensor. A sensor that uses radio waves to measure the distance to an object.

RAM. Abbreviation for *random-access memory.*

random-access memory. Alterable storage for the PLC program and data.

rate action. See *derivative action.*

rated voltage. The voltage range for which a system is designed to operate.

ratio control. Control scheme used in blending or other applications where two streams need to be held in constant ratio to each other.

recipe. "The necessary set of information that uniquely defines the production requirements for a specific product." (ISA, 1995)

register. Storage area equivalent to a word or integer.

regulatory control. The control type used to maintain *process variables* at desired values. It is often referred to as *continuous control* or *discrete-time control.*

relay. An electromechanical device consisting of a coil of wire magnetically coupled to a moveable piece of iron (armature), held in its resting position with a spring. The armature is mechanically connected to electrical contacts. When sufficient current passes through the coil, the armature moves, changing the contact position.

reliability. The ability of a system to perform its function without error, commonly expressed as mean time between failures (MTBF) or the failure probability.

repeatability. The ability of a sensor to produce the same output when the measured value is the same.

reset. A ladder logic output coil that is de-energized when any rung path passes power and remains de-energized when no rung path passes power.

reset action. See *integral action.*

reset windup. See *integral windup.*

resistance temperature device. A temperature sensor that consists of a length of metal (usually platinum) wire. The resistance of the metal wire increases with increasing temperature.

resolution. The smallest change that can be sensed by an analog input channel.

resource. In a *configuration*, it provides the support functions for the execution of *programs*.

retentive timer. A timer that retains its accumulator value when the input signal is false (0, off).

retro-reflective photoelectric sensor. A *photoelectric sensor* where the emitter and receiver are in the same package and a reflector is used to return the light beam to the receiver.

reverse-acting. A process or controller is called reverse-acting if an increase in *the input signal* causes a decrease in the *output signal.*

reverse action. See *reverse-acting.*

rise time. The time required for the process variable to go from 10% to 90% of the *steady state* change. (ISA, 1979)

rotary valve. A solid material feeder that uses wedge-shaped compartments within a cylinder to control material flow from a tank. The flow rate is controlled by the valve rotation speed.

RS-232. A common serial communication standard, it specifies the signal voltages, signal timing, signal function, a protocol, and mechanical connectors.

RTD. Abbreviation for *resistance temperature device.*

run mode. The PLC processor transfers the physical inputs to the input image, scans the program, and transfers the output image to the physical outputs.

rung. The arrangement of contacts, coils, and function blocks to control one of more outputs in a *ladder diagram*.

Safety Instrumented System. The control technology for automatic safety protection.

scan. The process by which a PLC processor reads the physical inputs, executes the user program, and writes the physical outputs.

scan time. The time required to complete the three tasks of a *scan.*

SCR. Abbreviation for *silicon-controlled rectifier.*

seal circuit. A ladder logic circuit that controls a device that must run continuously, but is started and stopped with momentary switches.

sensitivity. See *resolution.*

sensor. A device that monitors a physical phenomenon of the process. Its output is connected to a PLC *input module.*

sequence. The order in which process steps are executed.

sequence control. Enforces the correct operation of process equipment in a step-wise fashion.

sequencer. A type of function block that implements a *sequence.*

sequential function chart. One of the standard PLC languages. A diagram of interconnected *steps*, *actions*, and *transitions* used to for sequential control.

serial communication. A method of communication between two devices whereby the message is sent one bit at a time.

Seriplex. Abbreviation for SERIal multiPLEXed control bus. Originally developed as a low-level bus to interface to discrete components such as panel switches.

servomotor. A specially-designed brushed DC motor or brushless AC motor for precision closed-loop motion control.

set. A ladder logic output coil that is energized when any rung path passes power and remains energized when no rung path passes power.

setpoint. "An input variable which sets the desired value of the *controlled variable.*" (ISA, 1979)

settling time. The time from the *setpoint* change to the time that the process variable response has settled within a certain percentage band of the final value, usually 2% or 5%. (ISA, 1979)

SFC. Abbreviation for *sequential function chart.*

shift register. A set of binary bits arranged so that data can be shifted from one bit to another. A shift register may be the bits in a word, or may be the bits in consecutive words.

signal. "In process instrumentation, physical variable, one or more parameters of which carry information about another variable (which the signal represents)." (ISA, 1979)

silicon-controlled rectifier. A semiconductor device that has the property that when a positive pulse is applied to the gate terminal and there is a positive anode-to-cathode voltage, the rectifier conducts as long as the anode-to-cathode voltage remains positive.

single-acting cylinder. A pneumatic or hydraulic cylinder with one control.

sinking. The designation of a device connection in which the current (power) flows into the device when it is active. An output is called sinking if current flows **in** when the output is active. An input is called sinking if current flows **in** when the input is active.

SIS. Abbreviation for *Safety Instrumented System.*

SISO. Abbreviation for single-input, single-output.

slave. In a *master/slave* type of controlling access to a *local area network*, this node transmits only when polled by the master.

solenoid. (1) An electromechanical device consisting of a coil of wire wrapped around a moveable iron plunger, held in its resting position with a spring. When sufficient current passes through the coil, the plunger moves, effecting some motion. (2) A pneumatic or hydraulic cylinder.

sourcing. The designation of a device connection in which the current (power) flows out of the device when it is active. An output is called sourcing if current flows **out** when the output is active. An input is called sourcing if current flows **out** when the input is active.

SP. Abbreviation for *setpoint.*

speed switch. A special form of a *limit switch* that switch detects the speed or direction of a rotating shaft.

split range control. Control scheme when process has one *process variable* and more than one *manipulated variable.*

ST. Abbreviation for *structured text.*

stable system. A system is considered to be stable if a bounded *input signal* always results in an *output signal* that is also bounded.

state. The current condition of the physical or control entity. The state also defines how the entity will operate and how it will respond to commands. (ISA, 1995)

steady-state. The long-term output response of a system after it has been disturbed. Generally refers to the long-term output due to a *manipulated variable* or *disturbance change.* (ISA, 1979)

step. In a *function chart* or *sequential function chart*, it is an operation spanning a length of time, the state of a process.

stepper motor. A brushless permanent-magnet type motor that makes a fixed angular motion in response to pulsed input signals.

strain gauge. A *sensor* that measures force along an axis based on the principle that the resistance of a conductor changes as it is stretched.

structured text. One of the standard PLC languages. A textual language useful for calculation-intensive functions.

SwiftNet. A *local area network* developed as a very high speed flight data bus.

tagout. The placement of warning tags on energy sources to help ensure the equipment is not restarted until maintenance or repair functions are finished. See also *lockout.*

task. Within a *resource*, it is set up to control one or more programs and/or function blocks to execute periodically or to execute upon the occurrence of a specified trigger.

TBD. Abbreviation for "To be determined".

test mode. The PLC processor transfers the physical inputs to the input image and scans the program (updating the output image), but the physical outputs remain disabled.

thermistor. A temperature sensor most often made from a semiconductor material that has a negative temperature coefficient, that is, its resistance decreases with temperature.

thermocouple. A temperature sensor that consists of a junction of two dissimilar metals. The voltage across the junction changes with the temperature.

thermopile. A series connection of *thermocouples* used to amplify the measured thermocouple voltage.

thermowell. A temperature sensor is mounted inside it to protect the sensor from the process chemicals.

through-beam photoelectric sensor. A *photoelectric sensor* where the emitter and receiver are positioned opposite to each other so that the light beam from the emitter is aimed directly at the receiver.

thumbwheel switch. A switch consisting of a rotary wheel with positions numbered 0 through 9. Each switch has four connections to a *discrete input module*. Thumbwheel switches can be placed adjacent to each other to allow inexpensive operator input of numerical values.

tie-back. For PID control, the operator-supplied *control variable* when in manual mode.

time constant. In an expression for linear system time response, the time constant is the value, τ, in the response term, $Ae^{-s\tau}$. In a *transfer function*, the time constant is the value, τ, in the denominator term, $1+s\tau$. For the output of a first-order system whose input is a step signal, the time constant is the time required to complete 63.2% of the total output change. (ISA, 1979)

toggle switch. A switch consisting of a projecting lever that can assume at least two positions. Each position either opens or closes an electrical circuit.

token passing. A method of controlling access to a *local area network* with bus topology that involves circulating a special message, called the token, among the *nodes*.

topology. The physical structure of a communication network.

tracking mode. The state of a PID controller where its *manipulated variable* tracks another variable, usually the output of another controller. When in this mode, the internal variables of the PID algorithm are modified so that the calculated control variable matches the tracked variable so there is a bumpless transfer when the mode is changed to automatic.

transducer. Same as *sensor*.

transfer function. For a continuous-time system, the transfer function is the ratio of the Laplace transform of the output variable to the Laplace transform of the input variable, with all initial conditions assumed to be zero. (ISA, 1979)

transit-time ultrasonic flowmeter. Uses two ultrasonic (sound) transceivers placed at a 45 degree angle to the flow stream. Both send out ultrasonic pulses that are detected by the other. The difference in transit time between the two beams is proportional to the flow rate.

transition. See *transition condition*.

transition condition. The condition that causes control to pass from one step to the next in a *function chart* or *SFC*.

transitional contact. A contact that passes power for one scan of the rung when its control changes state. The contact may be activated for a positive transition (**off**-to-**on**) or a negative transition (**on**-to-**off**) of the control.

turbine flowmeter. A rotor immersed in the liquid stream that turns as the fluid moves through it. The flow rate is inferred from the rotor speed.

ultrasonic flowmeter. See *transit-time ultrasonic flowmeter* and *Doppler ultrasonic flowmeter*.

ultrasonic sensor. A sensor that uses sound waves to detect the proximity of an object or to measure the distance to an object.

underdamped. The time response of the system to a step signal input has *overshoot*. (ISA, 1979)

unit. A set of equipment modules and control modules usually centered on a major piece of equipment, e.g., a reactor. A unit combines all necessary physical processing and control equipment required to perform one or more major processing activities, e.g., react or separate. (ISA, 1995)

unlatch. A ladder logic output coil that is de-energized when any rung path passes power and remains de-energized when no rung path passes power.

variable-speed AC drive. Converts a constant AC source voltage into a variable frequency three-phase AC voltage. Varying the frequency varies the AC motor speed.

variable-speed DC drive. Converts a constant AC source voltage into a variable DC armature voltage with silicon-controller rectifiers. Varying the armature voltage varies the DC motor speed.

venturi tube. A section of pipe with a conical entrance, a short straight throat, and a conical outlet used to measure gas or liquid flow rate.

vibratory feeder. A solid material feeder that uses a tray with a certain vibrating motion to move the solid particles.

vortex flowmeter. An obstruction, placed in the fluid flow stream, sets up vortices in the flow stream. The frequency of the vortices is proportional to the volumetric flow rate.

weigh belt feeder. A conveyor belt with a weigh scale to control the flow of solid material. The belt speed is controlled in order to maintain the desired flow rate.

word. A group of sixteen binary digits.

WorldFIP. A process automation *local area network* developed by the French.

References

Instrument Society of America, *ISA-S51.1, Process Instrumentation Terminology*, Instrument Society of America, 1979.

Instrument Society of America, *ISA-S88.01, Batch Control, Part 1: Models and Terminology*, Instrument Society of America, 1995.

Index